Gene Therapy Protocols

METHODS IN MOLECULAR MEDICINE™

John M. Walker, SERIES EDITOR

METHODS IN MOLECULAR MEDICINE™

Gene Therapy Protocols

Edited by

Paul D. Robbins

University of Pittsburgh, PA

Humana Press ※ **Totowa, New Jersey**

© 1997 Humana Press Inc.
999 Riverview Drive, Suite 208
Totowa, New Jersey 07512

This publication is printed on acid-free paper. ∞
ANSI Z39.48-1984 (American Standards Institute) Permanence of Paper for Printed Library Materials.

Cover illustration: Fig. 3 from Chapter 19, "Methods for the Use of Genetically Modified Keratinocytes in Gene Therapy" by Sabine A. Eming and Jeffrey R. Morgan.

For additional copies, pricing for bulk purchases, and/or information about other Humana titles, contact Humana at the above address or at any of the following numbers: Tel: 201-256-1699; Fax: 201-256-8341; E-mail: humana@interramp.com

Printed in the United States of America. 10 9 8 7 6 5 4 3 2 1

Library of Congress Cataloging in Publication Data

Main entry under title:

Methods in molecular medicine™.

Gene therapy protocols/edited by Paul D. Robbins.
      p.   cm.—(Methods in molecular medicine™)
    Includes index.
    ISBN 0-89603-307-4 (combbound) (alk. paper); ISBN 0-89603-484-4 (hardcover) (alk. paper)
    1. Gene therapy—methodology. I. Robbins, Paul D. II. Series.
    [DNLM: 1. Gene therapy—methods. 2. Gene transfer.   QZ 50 G3213 1997]
  RB155.8.G465 1997
  616'.042—dc20
  DNLM/DLC
  for Library of Congress   96-42147
                                               CIP

Preface

In the last few years, significant advances have been made in the area of gene therapy for both genetic and acquired diseases. Improvement in gene transfer methods has allowed for development of gene therapy protocols for the treatment of diverse types of diseases, including metabolic, cardiovascular, and autoimmune diseases, as well as cancer. For example, clinical trials for gene therapy of cancer, cystic fibrosis, ADA deficiency, and arthritis, among others, have been initiated in recent years. It is likely that, in the near future, gene therapy will become a common form of treatment for many different types of diseases. Gene therapy takes advantage of recent advances in many areas of molecular and cell biology, including the identification of new therapeutic genes, improvement in both viral and nonviral gene delivery systems, better understanding of gene regulation, and improvement in cell isolation and transplantation. Because of the different and complex techniques involved in achieving successful gene-mediated therapies, it is difficult for scientists to perform all methods required for gene delivery and subsequent in vivo gene expression.

This *Gene Therapy Protocols* volume in the *Methods in Molecular Medicine* series provides scientists with detailed methods for working with gene transfer systems, and methods for gene transfer to specific tissue types either in vivo or ex vivo. The first part of the book is concerned with the methods for working with specific delivery systems, including adenoviruses, retroviruses, herpes viruses, polioviruses, and papilloma viruses, as well as nonviral systems, such as liposomes and DNA conjugates. The latter part of the book is concerned with the application of the gene delivery methods to specific tissues, such as airway epithelium, liver, hematopoietic cells, keratinocytes, tumors, and synovium. In addition, methods for the application of specific therapeutic systems, such as ribozymes and tumor suppressor genes for the treatment of cancer, are presented.

Because of its wide scope, *Gene Therapy Protocols* should be of general interest to undergraduate and postgraduate students and to both basic and clinical researchers.

Paul D. Robbins

v

Contents

Contributors

DAVID C. ANSARDI • *Department of Microbiology, University of Alabama, Birmingham, AL*

ALFRED B. BAHNSON • *Department of Human Genetics, University of Pittsburgh, PA*

EDWARD D. BALL • *Department of Medicine, University of Pittsburgh, PA*

DARLENE BARR • *Division of Transplantation, Department of Surgery, University of Washington, Seattle, WA*

JOHN A. BARRANGER • *Department of Human Genetics, University of Pittsburgh, PA*

JEFFREY S. BARTLETT • *Gene Therapy Center, University of North Carolina, Chapel Hill, NC*

JOHN W. BELMONT • *Department of Molecular and Human Genetics, Baylor College of Medicine, Houston, TX*

RICHARD D. BLAND • *Division of Lung Biology, Childrens Research Center, University of Utah School of Medicine, Salt Lake City, UT*

THOMAS BLANKENSTEIN • *Max-Delbrück-Centrum for Molecular Medicine, Berlin, Germany*

SOPHIE BRANCHEREAU • *Laboratoire Rétrovirus el Transfert Génétique, Institut Pasteur, Paris, France*

JANE C. BURNS • *Department of Pediatrics, School of Medicine, University of California, San Diego, CA*

DIANNE P. CARR • *Departments of Internal Medicine and Biological Chemistry, Howard Hughes Medical Institution, University of Michigan Medical Center, Ann Arbor, MI*

DAVID T. CURIEL • *University of Alabama, Birmingham, AL*

OLIVIER DANOS • *Laboratoire Rétrovirus el Transfert Génétique, Institut Pasteur, Paris, France*

ELAINE M. ELDER • *Immunologic Monitoring and Diagnostic Laboratory, University of Pittsburgh Cancer Institute, Pittsburgh, PA*

SABINE A. EMING • *Research Center, Shriners Burns Institute, Cambridge, MA*

JOHN F. ENGELHARDT • *Institute of Human Gene Therapy, Philadelphia, PA*

xi

CHRIS H. EVANS • *Department of Molecular Genetics and Biochemistry, University of Pittsburgh Medical Center, Pittsburgh, PA*

NICOLAS FERRY • *Centre Regional de Lutte Contre le Cancer Eugene Marquis, Rennes, France*

MARK A. FINDEIS • *Pharmaceutical Peptides, Inc., Cambridge, MA*

XIANG GAO • *Laboratory of Drug Targeting, Department of Pharmacology, University of Pittsburgh School of Medicine, Pittsburgh, PA; Current address: Division of Pulmonary Medicine, Vanderbilt University, Nashville, TN*

JOSEPH C. GLORIOSO • *Department of Molecular Genetics and Biochemistry, University of Pittsburgh Medical School, Pittsburgh, PA*

WILLIAM F. GOINS • *Department of Molecular Genetics and Biochemistry, University of Pittsburgh School of Medicine, Pittsburgh, PA*

JOEL S. GREENBERGER • *University of Pittsburgh Medical Center, Presbyterian Hospital, Pittsburgh, PA*

JEAN-MICHEL HEARD • *Laboratoire Rétrovirus el Transfert Génétique, Institut Pasteur, Paris, France*

LEAF HUANG • *Department of Pharmacology, University of Pittsburgh School of Medicine, Pittsburgh, PA*

ELIZABETH M. JAFFEE • *Department of Oncology, Johns Hopkins University School of Medicine, Baltimore, MD*

LARRY G. JOHNSON • *Cystic Fibrosis/Pulmonary Research and Treatment Center, Department of Medicine, University of North Carolina, Chapel Hill, NC*

ROLAND JURECIC • *Department of Molecular and Human Genetics, Baylor College of Medicine, Houston, TX*

RICHARD KANG • *Orthopedic Surgery, University of Pittsburgh School of Medicine, Pittsburgh, PA*

MARK A. KAY • *Division of Medical Genetics, Department of Medicine, University of Washington, Seattle, WA*

SALEEM A. KHAN • *Department of Molecular Genetics and Biochemistry, University of Pittsburgh School of Medicine, Pittsburgh, PA*

DAVID KRISKY • *Department of Molecular Genetics and Biochemistry, University of Pittsburgh School of Medicine, Pittsburgh, PA*

MICHAEL T. LOTZE • *Cancer Institute, Department of Surgery, Department of Molecular Genetics and Biochemistry, University of Pittsburgh School of Medicine, Pittsburgh, PA*

PEGGY MARCONI • *Department of Molecular Genetics and Biochemistry, University of Pittsburgh School of Medicine, Pittsburgh, PA*

DENNIS E. MCCABE • *Agracetus, Middletown, WI*

JEFFREY R. MORGAN • *Research Center, Shriners Burns Institute, Cambridge, MA*

CASEY D. MORROW • *Department of Microbiology, University of Alabama, Birmingham, AL*

ELIZABETH G. NABEL • *Internal Medicine and Physiology, Cardiovascular Research Center, University of Michigan Medical Center, Ann Arbor, MI*

GARY J. NABEL • *Departments of Internal Medicine and Biological Chemistry, Howard Hughes Medical Institution, University of Michigan Medical Center, Ann Arbor, MI*

MAYA NIMGAONKAR • *Department of Medicine, University of Pittsburgh, PA*

GARRY P. NOLAN • *Department of Pharmacology, Stanford University, Stanford, CA*

JOHN C. OLSEN • *Cystic Fibrosis/Pulmonary Research and Treatment Center, Department of Medicine, University of North Carolina, Chapel Hill, NC*

WARREN S. PEAR • *Department of Biology, Massachusetts Institute of Technology, Cambridge, MA; Current address: Department of Pathology, University of Pennsylvania Medical Center, Philadelphia, PA*

BRUCE R. PITT • *Department of Pharmacology, University of Pittsburgh School of Medicine, Pittsburgh, PA*

DONNA C. PORTER • *Department of Microbiology, University of Alabama, Birmingham, AL*

ZHIHAI QIN • *Max-Delbrück-Centrum for Molecular Medicine, Berlin, Germany*

ISABELLE RIVIÈRE • *New York University Medical Center, New York*

PAUL D. ROBBINS • *Department of Molecular Genetics and Biochemistry, University of Pittsburgh, PA*

BLAKE J. ROESSLER • *Department of Internal Medicine, Division of Rheumatology, University of Michigan Medical Center, Ann Arbor, MI*

JACK A. ROTH • *Department of Tumor Biology, University of Texas M. D. Anderson Science Center, Houston, TX*

MICHEL SADELAIN • *Department of Human Genetics, Memorial Sloan-Kettering Cancer Center, New York*

RICHARD J. SAMULSKI • *Gene Therapy Center, University of North Carolina, Chapel Hill, NC*

HONG SAN • *Departments of Internal Medicine and Biological Chemistry, Howard Hughes Medical Institution, University of Michigan Medical Center, Ann Arbor, MI*

KEVIN J. SCANLON • *City of Hope National Medical Center, Duarte, CA*

MARGARET A. SCHWARZ • *Babies Hospital, Columbia University College of Physicians and Surgeons, New York, NY*

MARTIN L. SCOTT • *Department of Biology, Massachusetts Institute of Technology, Cambridge, MA*

TOSHIYA SHITARA • *Department of Urology, Kitasato University Hospital, Kitasato, Japan*

KYONGHEE SON • *Laboratory of Drug Targeting, Department of Pharmacology, University of Pittsburgh School of Medicine, Pittsburgh, PA; Current address: Department of Pharmaceutics, College of Pharmacy, Rutgers, The State University of New Jersey, Piscataway, NJ*

FRANK SORGI • *Laboratory of Drug Targeting, Department of Pharmacology, University of Pittsburgh School of Medicine, Pittsburgh, PA*

FRANCIS M. SVERDRUP • *Department of Molecular Genetics and Biochemistry, University of Pittsburgh School of Medicine, Pittsburgh, PA*

WILLIAM F. SWAIN • *Agracetus, Middletown, WI*

THERESA L. WHITESIDE • *Cancer Institute, Department of Pathology, and Department of Otolaryngology, University of Pittsburgh School of Medicine, Pittsburgh, PA*

CATHERINE H. WU • *Division of Gastroenterology, University of Connecticut Health Center, Farmington, CT*

GEORGE Y. WU • *Division of Gastroenterology, University of Connecticut Health Center, Farmington, CT*

NING-SUN YANG • *Cancer Gene Therapy, Agracetus, Middletown, WI; Department of Pathology and Laboratory Medicine, University of Wisconsin Medical School, Madison, WI*

ZHI-YONG YANG • *Departments of Internal Medicine and Biological Chemistry, Howard Hughes Medical Institution, University of Michigan Medical Center, Ann Arbor, MI*

JAMES R. YANKASKAS • *Department of Medicine, Cystic Fibrosis/Pulmonary Research and Treatment Center, University of North Carolina, Chapel Hill, NC*

JIING-KUAN YEE • *Department of Pediatrics, City of Hope, Duarte, CA*

ALICE L. YU • *Department of Pediatrics, University of California at San Diego School of Medicine, La Jolla, CA*

WEI-WEI ZHANG • *Section of Thoracic Molecular Oncology, Department of Thoracic and Cardiovascular Surgery, University of Texas M. D. Anderson Science Center, Houston, TX*

1

Methods for Gene Transfer
Using DNA-Adenovirus Conjugates

David T. Curiel

1. Introduction

Strategies have been developed to accomplish gene delivery via the receptor-mediated pathway employing molecular conjugate vectors *(1–13)*. As cells possess endogenous pathways for internalization of macromolecules, the utilization of these pathways for the purpose of DNA delivery represents a strategy that potentially allows certain practical advantages. In this regard, these cellular internalization pathways can be highly efficient. For example, internalization of the iron transport protein transferrin can be on the order of thousands of molecules per minute per cell *(14,15)*. These pathways thus represent a potentially efficient physiologic method to transport DNA across the cell membrane of eukaryotic cells. To accomplish gene transfer via receptor-mediated endocytosis, a vehicle must be derived that allows DNA entry into these cellular pathways. For this purpose, molecular conjugate vectors have been derived. These vector agents consist of two linked functional domains: a DNA-binding domain to transport the DNA as part of the vector complex, and a ligand domain to target a cellular receptor that allows entry of the conjugate-DNA complex into a receptor-mediated endocytosis pathway. For incorporating DNA into the complex for gene delivery, binding must be achieved in a nondamaging, reversible manner. For this linkage, an electrostatic association between the binding domain and the nucleic acid is accomplished. To achieve this, the DNA binding domain is comprised of a polycationic amine, such as poly(L)lysine. This can associate with the negatively charged DNA in an electrostatic, noncovalent manner. To achieve entry of the complex through a receptor-mediated pathway, a ligand for the target cell is utilized. The ligand domain is covalently linked to the polylysine to create the molecular conjugate vector.

From: *Methods in Molecular Medicine, Gene Therapy Protocols*
Edited by: P. Robbins Humana Press Inc., Totowa, NJ

The ligand domain may be a native or synthetic cell surface receptor ligand, an antireceptor antibody, or other agent that allows specific association with target cell membranes.

The interaction of the DNA with its binding domain serves not only to attach it to the molecular conjugate vector, but also to condense it into a compact circular toroid *(5)*. In this configuration, the ligand domain is presented on the exterior of the complex. By virtue of its surface location, the ligand is free to recognize its target receptor on the cell surface membrane. Thus, after binding by means of the ligand domain, the conjugate-DNA complex is internalized by the receptor-mediated pathway. In this schema, the initial localization after internalization is within the cellular endosome. The conjugate-DNA complex may then achieve DNA delivery to the target cell nucleus, where expression of the transported heterologous sequences may occur. Alternatively, the complex may traffic to lysosomal pathways, which would result in degradation of the conjugate-DNA complex. Thus, by exploiting an endogenous cellular entry pathway, the conjugate-DNA complex achieves target cell internalization. After internalization, the complex can be subject to multiple possible fates; however, optimally, DNA delivery to the nucleus permits heterologous gene expression.

The delivery of genes by the receptor-mediated pathway offers certain unique features and potentials *(4,16)*. Because the system is synthetic, the capacity exists to prepare large amounts of the conjugate vector. As delivery is by a physiologic cellular pathway, toxicity associated with membrane perturbation is circumvented. Thus, the potential exists to administer the vector on a repetitive, or continuous basis. Importantly, the marked plasticity of the system allows the potential to derive a vector with the properties of cell-specific targeting. That is, through choice of the ligand domain, it is possible to selectively target cells possessing receptors for that ligand. This would potentially allow employment for those gene therapy applications requiring cell-specific delivery of therapeutic genes. Finally, the molecular conjugate vector system is devoid of viral gene elements. It would thus be devoid of the potential safety hazards deriving from the presence of viral gene sequences and functions.

Gene delivery by the receptor-mediated endocytosis pathway was first described by Wu et al. *(2)*. To selectively target hepatocytes, efforts were directed toward accomplishing cellular internalization through a receptor unique to this cell type. In this regard, hepatocytes possess unique receptors for recognition and clearance of asialoglycoproteins. This receptor is a constituent of a high efficiency internalization pathway specific to hepatocytes. To target through this receptor, asialoorosomucoid, a physiologic ligand for this receptor, was chemically conjugated to poly(L)lysine. The resulting conjugates could form complexes with DNA that could be shown to accomplish gene delivery

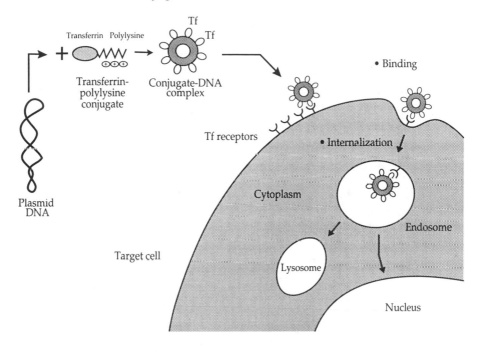

Fig. 1. Gene transfer via the receptor-mediated endocytosis pathway. A bifunctional molecular conjugate is employed to bind DNA and transport it via cellular macromolecular transport mechanisms. The molecular conjugate vector consists of a DNA-binding domain, comprised by a cationic polylysine moiety that is covalently linked to a ligand for a cell surface receptor, in this case transferrin. Plasmid DNA bound to the polylysine moiety of the conjugate undergoes marked condensation to yield an 80- to 100-nm toroid with surface-localized transferrin molecules. When the transferrin ligand domain is bound by its corresponding cell surface receptor, the conjugate is internalized by the receptor-mediated endocytosis pathway, cotransporting bound DNA. Escape from the cell vesicle system is achieved by a fraction of the internalized conjugate-DNA complex to achieve nuclear localization where heterologous gene expression occurs.

specifically through the asiologlycoprotein receptor of hepatocytes. Utilizing this schema, it was shown that selective delivery to hepatocytes could be accomplished both in vitro as well as after in vivo delivery of the conjugates *(1,2,17)*. Utilizing a similar strategy, Birnstiel et al. developed a molecular conjugate system for achieving DNA delivery through the transferrin internalization pathway (Fig. 1; refs. *3,7*). In this context, transferrin is internalized by a receptor-mediated endocytosis mechanism as part of a recycling pathway *(15)*. The transferrin receptor is expressed in a ubiquitous manner but is relatively enriched in proliferative cells and cells of the hematopoietic derivation *(14)*. It was demonstrated that gene transfer could also be accomplished through the transferrin internalization pathway (Fig. 1). In addition to these molecular conjugate vector strategies, gene delivery via the receptor-mediated endocytosis pathway has been described utilizing antibody against the polymerized IgA receptor *(11)* as well as surfactant protein C *(18)* as the ligand domain of the vector. Thus, the receptor-mediated schema of gene delivery has been developed for an increasing number of gene transfer applications to capitalize on the potential to achieve nontoxic cellular entry as well as cell-specific gene delivery.

Despite the many potential advantages of receptor-mediated gene delivery, the efficacy of molecular conjugate vectors, in practice, has been idiosyncratic *(4,8)*. For many target cells, despite the presence of the requisite cell surface receptor, gene transfer via the corresponding internalization pathway has not resulted in efficient expression of transferred DNA. Analysis of the cellular uptake of conjugate-DNA complexes in these instances has frequently demonstrated effective cellular internalization of the conjugate-DNA complex *(3)*. In this regard, the internalized complexes may be demonstrated within cellular endosomes. This finding suggests that the inefficient gene expression is not related to initial binding and internalization steps, but reflects events occurring after cellular entry of the DNA-conjugate complex. Thus, in some instances, the conjugate-DNA complex may be entrapped within cellular endosomes and the DNA thus cannot access the nucleus. Consistent with this concept, it has been reported that treatment of cells with selected lysosomotropic agents can significantly augment gene expression in conjugate-transfected cells *(8)*. This is consistent with the fact that loss of conjugate-DNA complexes through cellular degradative processes may be etiologic of their inability to achieve nuclear localization and thus expression of transferred genes. Taken together, these findings illustrate a fundamental flaw of receptor-mediated gene transfer strategy as initially conceptualized: Despite the fact that the molecular conjugate vector possesses an efficient mechanism to achieve cellular internalization, the fact that it lacks a specific mechanism to escape entrapment within the endosome limits effective gene transfer and expression. This suggests that if the molecular conjugate vector possessed an endosome escape mechanism, the internalized DNA could avoid targeting to cellular pathways eventuating its destruction, with a favorable outcome on gene transfer efficiency.

1.1. Adenovirus Facilitation of Receptor-Mediated Gene Delivery

In developing methods to overcome endosome entrapment of the conjugate-DNA complexes, consideration was given to the entry mechanism of certain viruses. For both enveloped and nonenveloped viruses, the first step to cellular entry involves binding to a specific cellular receptor. For a subset of these viruses, after binding, internalization occurs by virtue of the receptor-mediated endocytosis pathway *(19,20)*. After cellular internalization, these viruses then utilize specific mechanisms to allow endosome escape of their genetic material so that the viral life cycle may be completed in the cell nucleus or cytosol. The viral entry pathway thus possesses certain parallels to the entry pathway of molecular conjugate vectors; like the conjugate vector, viruses may possess specific and efficient receptor-mediated entry mechanisms. However, apart from the conjugate vector, after internalization, viruses possess specific mechanisms to achieve escape from entrapment within the cell vesicle system for completion of their infectious cycle. It was thus hypothesized that the endosome escape property of certain viruses could potentially be exploited to overcome endosome entrapment of the conjugate-DNA complex, and thus facilitate efficient gene transfer. In this regard, previous studies had linked viral entry to enhanced cellular uptake of various macromolecules. Carresco utilized both enveloped and nonenveloped viruses to show augmented cellular internalization of macromolecules *(21)*. These studies did not delineate the mechanistic basis for this phenomenon, or distinguish between membrane-bound or fluid-phase molecules; however, the linkage between viral uptake and enhanced cellular entry of heterologous molecules was clearly established. Specific facilitation of ligands via the receptor-mediated pathway was demonstrated by Pastan et al. *(22)*. This group has developed a system of antitumor therapeutics based on delivery of ligand-toxin chimeras via receptor-mediated endocytosis. In these studies, it was found that entrapment of the chimeric toxin molecule in the cellular endosome limited tumoricidal efficacy. It was noted in this instance that this limitation could be overcome by codelivery of adenovirus with the chimeric toxin. In this schema, the virus colocalized within the same cellular endosome as the conjugate during internalization. Further, it could be shown that it was the adenovirus' ability to disrupt cellular endosomes that allowed ingress of the conjugate into the cytosol, where its activity was thus potentiated. Thus, this work established that adenovirus enters cells via receptor-mediated endocytosis, and during this process, it may colocalize to cellular endosomes with other receptor-bound ligands. The virus exits the endosome via a membrane disruption step that may also allow egress of other endosome contents.

From the standpoint of exploiting this capacity of the adenovirus to achieve endosome escape, it is noteworthy that this effect is mediated by viral capsid proteins and independent of viral gene expression. In this regard, the entry cycle of the adenovirus has been partially elucidated *(19,23,24)*. The virus first achieves target cell attachment through binding to a specific cell surface receptor. Whereas this receptor has not been characterized, its presence has been established by functional studies and it has been shown to be expressed in a rather ubiquitous manner. The adenovirus accomplishes this initial binding step by virtue of a specific capsid protein designed fiber. After binding to the cellular recognition receptor, uptake is facilitated by subsequent binding of specific viral capsid regions to cellular proteins that act as uptake "triggers" *(25)*. After this initial uptake step, the virion is then localized within cellular endosomes. After cellular localization within the endosome, the virus accomplishes endosome disruption to achieve escape from the cell vesicle system. Acidification of the endosome is crucial to the ability of the virus to achieve this vesicle disruption step. In this regard, cellular targets with defective acidification of their endosomes, or alternatively, treatment of normal cells with agents to augment endosomal pH, both have the effect of limiting adenoviral propagation *(26)*. Importantly, replication-defective adenoviral strains deleted in specific gene regions may still, nonetheless, complete the same principal entry steps as wild-type viruses. It is hypothesized that acidification of the endosome induces alterations in the conformation of certain capsid proteins *(19,26)*. This induces changes in their hydrophobicity allowing them to thus interact with the endosome membrane in a manner to achieve vesicle disruption. Thus, it is the capsid proteins that mediate the effect of endosome disruption, viral gene expression is not an essential feature of this process.

Based on this concept, it was hypothesized that the entry process of the adenovirus could be exploited to achieve endosome escape of the internalized conjugate-DNA complex. In this schema, the provision of endosome disruption functions *in trans* would be anticipated to augment the overall gene transfer efficiency mediated by the molecular conjugates (Fig. 2). To test this hypothesis, transferrin-polylysine-DNA complexes containing a firefly luciferase reporter plasmid DNA were codelivered to HeLa cells in conjunction with the replication-defective adenovirus dl312. This use of the replication-defective adenovirus provided a convenient means to separate the possible effects mediated by viral entry and viral gene expression, as this adenovirus strain in defective in its gene expression secondary to genomic deletions in early viral gene regions *(27)*. It could be seen that with increasing input of adenovirus there was a corresponding increase in the level of luciferase gene expression detected *(9)*. This adenoviral augmentation plateaued at a level of luciferase gene expression more than 2000-fold the levels observed when transferrin-polylysine conjugates were utilized without virus. Significantly, the amount of virus required to achieve these plateau levels of augmented gene expression corresponded to the number of receptors for the adenovirus on the target cell *(28)*. Thus, the characteristics of receptor-mediated endocytosis facilitation by this route were saturable, as would be expected in a receptor-limiting context.

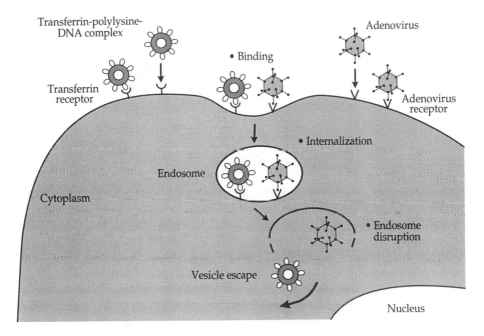

Fig. 2. Mechanism of adenoviral facilitation of molecular conjugate-mediated gene transfer. After binding to their respective cell surface receptors, cointernalization of the transferrin-polylysine conjugate and the adenovirus is within the same endocytotic vesicle. Adenovirus-mediated endosome disruption allows vesicle escape for both the virion and the conjugate-DNA complex.

To determine the mechanistic basis of the virus' ability to augment gene transfer mediated by molecular conjugates, steps were employed to uncouple virus entry and virus-mediated endosome disruption. In this regard, mild heat treatment of the adenovirus will selectively ablate the ability of the adenovirus to accomplish endosome disruption, without impairing its ability to bind to target cells *(28)*. Additionally, this magnitude of heat treatment does not affect the structural integrity of the adenoviral genome. Thus, by selectively ablating the viral endosome disruption capacity, its contribution to adenoviral-mediated augmentation of molecular conjugate gene transfer could be ascertained. In these experiments, heat treatment completely abrogated the ability of the virus to augment the conjugate's gene transfer capacity. This finding establishes that it is specifically the viral property of endosomolysis that contributes to its capacity to augment the conjugate's gene transfer capacity. This underscores the fact that it is the molecular conjugate vector's lack of an endosome escape mechanism that represents its principal limitation to achieving efficient gene transfer to target cells.

The augmented levels of net gene expression accomplished by the adenoviral augmentation of molecular conjugates are consistent with either increased gene expression in a transfected cell subset or an increased number of cells transfected. To distinguish between these possibilities, HeLa cells were transfected with transferrin-polylysine conjugates containing a β-galactosidase reporter gene *(29)*. Cells transduced with the transferrin-polylysine-DNA complexes alone demonstrated a transduction frequency of <1%. When adenovirus was added as a facilitator, however, >90% of the HeLa cells showed expression of the β-galactosidase gene. Thus, the adenoviral augmentation of conjugate-mediated transfer allowed for a significantly enhanced frequency of transfection. To demonstrate further the level to which adenovirus could increase the efficiency of gene transfer mediated by conjugate-DNA complexes, limiting dilutions of transferrin-polylysine-luciferase DNA complexes were delivered to cells with or without adenovirus. It could be demonstrated that, in the presence of adenovirus, the same levels of heterologous gene expression were noted as when two orders of magnitude more DNA were delivered without adenoviral augmentation *(9)*. Thus, the virus appears to confer a high level of efficiency on the process of DNA delivery mediated by molecular conjugates. Importantly, the phenomenon of adenoviral augmentation of conjugate-mediated delivery could be observed in a variety of cell types treated in this manner. In analyzing multiple different cellular targets, the free adenovirus significantly augmented gene expression levels over levels seen with molecular conjugates alone. Additionally, certain cell types that appear refractory to transferrin-polylysine-mediated gene transfer demonstrate susceptibility only in the presence of adenovirus *(9)*. It is likely that, in these instances, there was effective internalization of conjugate-DNA complex, but heterologous gene expression was absent secondary to more complete endosome entrapment of the conjugate-DNA complex. Thus, the susceptibility of these cells to conjugate-mediated gene transfer was only manifest after codelivery of adenovirus.

The selective exploitation of adenoviral entry features is made possible because it is adenoviral capsid proteins that mediate the endosome disruption step of viral entry. In this context, viral gene expression is irrelevant to the ability of the adenovirus to facilitate molecular conjugate entry. Steps may thus be undertaken to ablate viral gene elements and spare the capacity of the capsid to accomplish cell vesicle disruption. In this regard, it has been shown that ultraviolet (UV) light and UV light plus psoralen can be used to ablate viral infectivity and allow retention of the virus' ability to facilitate molecular conjugate-mediated gene transfer *(29)*. Thus, in this context, it is possible to render the adenoviral genome inactive in two complementing manners: genetic deletions of the adenoviral genome and physical inactivation of the adenoviral genome. This is in marked contrast to recombinant viral vectors, whereby the integrity of viral gene elements is crucial, since the heterologous sequences are contained therein. Thus, for recombinant viral vectors, it is not possible to take steps such as UV treatment to more completely inactivate viral gene elements. An additional feature that derives from this strategy is the flexibility allowed in DNA delivery. In this regard, the polylysine component of the molecular conjugate interacts with DNA in a sequence-independent manner. Thus, DNA of any design can be incorporated into the conjugate-DNA complex and delivered for purposes of gene transfer. Furthermore, the fact that the heterologous sequences are not incorporated into a viral genome minimizes the possibility of interactions among the distinct regulatory regions. Of additional practical significance, because the heterologous DNA is not packaged into a virion capsid, the amount of DNA that may thus be delivered is not limited by the corresponding packaging constraints. Using this approach, DNA plasmids of up to 48 kb have been delivered *(29)*. Thus, an enhanced flexibility in terms of size and design of delivered DNA derives from this strategy of gene transfer.

1.2. Adenovirus-Component Molecular Conjugates for Receptor-Mediated Gene Delivery

The utility of the adenovirus in facilitating adenoviral entry *in trans* suggests that it might also be possible to accomplish this with the adenovirus functioning *in cis*. Thus, since molecular conjugates were functionally limited by their lack of an endosome escape mechanism, and since adenovirus possessed such a mechanism, it seemed logical to incorporate the adenovirus into the structure of the molecular conjugate vector. The first technical barrier to achieving this construction was the attachment of the adenovirus to the polylysine-DNA binding moiety. In attaching moieties to the adenoviral capsid, a potential complication undermining this strategy would have been perturbation of the capsid proteins involved in adenoviral binding and entry. In this regard, the adenoviral capsid proteins fiber and penton are thought to be of major importance to these entry steps *(19,26)*. The hexon protein is thought to subserve the function of "scaffolding" of the capsid and is less important in viral entry processes. It was thus determined that the most propitious site to accomplish linkage was via the hexon protein. To achieve this, the strategy delineated in Fig. 3 was carried out. The hexon gene of the adenovirus was first isolated. Specific mutations were introduced into the gene sequence of the hexon gene to create a region coding for a heterologous epitope. The gene sequence altered corresponded to a region of the hexon protein known to be present in the exterior, surface face of the virus. Thus, by genetic techniques, it was possible to generate a chimeric adenovirus with the heterologous epitope

Fig. 3. Construction of chimeric adenovirus containing heterologous epitope in surface region of hexon capsid protein. Since the adenoviral capsid proteins fiber and penton are important mediators of the adenoviral entry mechanism, attachment of capsid-bound DNA was targeted to the hexon protein. A specific attachment site for an immunologic linkage was created by introducing a heterologous epitope into the surface region of the hexon protein by site-directed mutagenesis of the corresponding region of the adenoviral hexon gene. The introduced foreign epitope is a portion of *Mycoplasma pneumoniae* P1 protein.

localized in a manner to permit nonneutralizing interaction with an MAb specific for this epitope. After derivation of the chimeric adenovirus, an attachment schema could be carried out (Fig. 4). The antibody specific for the heterologous epitope served as the site of attachment of the polylysine-DNA-binding moiety. When condensed with DNA, the resulting toroid possessed surface localized immunoglobin capable of recognizing the heterologous epitope on the chimeric virus.

The ability of the adenovirus-polylysine-DNA complexes to mediate gene transfer was evaluated using various components of the complete complex. It could be seen that the specific combination of epitope-marked virus, antibody-polylysine, and DNA resulted in a vector that was capable of achieving high levels of heterologous gene expression *(13)*. In contrast, any other combination of these components did not allow gene transfer to occur. As before, heat inactivation of the virion ablated the capacity of the complexes to accomplish gene transfer, indicating that it was the viral entry features that were responsible for the gene transfer capacity of the complex in this context as for the case of adenovirus functioning *in trans*. As an additional control, complexes were

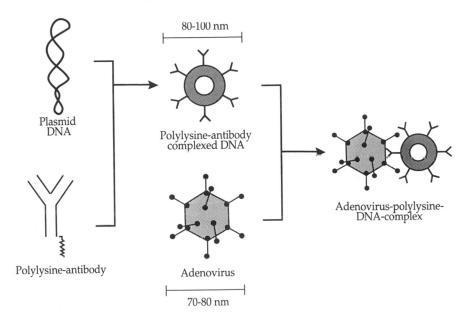

Fig. 4. Schematic of approach to derive adenovirus-polylysine-DNA complexes containing heterologous DNA attached to exterior of adenovirus capsid. To accomplish linkage of adenovirus and a polycationic DNA-binding domain, the chimeric adenovirus containing a heterologous epitope in the exterior domain of its hexon protein was employed in conjunction with an MAb specific for this epitope. Control experiments demonstrated that attachment of the MAb was nonneutralizing for the adenovirus. The MAb was rendered competent to carry foreign DNA sequences by attaching a polylysine moiety. Interaction of the polylysine-antibody complexed DNA with the epitope-tagged adenovirus occurs via the specificity of the conjugated antibody.

constructed with polylysine-condensed DNA that lacked linker antibody. Again, no gene transfer was noted. This emphasizes that the physical linkage between the virus and the DNA is the crucial feature of the complex that allows effective gene transfer to occur. To determine the net efficiency of the complexes in mediating gene transfer, logarithmic dilutions of formed adenovirus-polylysine-DNA complexes were made and applied to target HeLa cells. It could be seen that as few as 10 DNA molecules per cell resulted in levels of reporter gene expression detectable above background levels *(13)*. This compares favorably to gene transfer mediated by other DNA-mediated gene transfer methods, where on the order of 500,000 DNA molecules per cell are required *(30,31)*. Thus, the adenovirus-polylysine-DNA complexes are capable of extremely efficient gene transfer.

For linkage of the polylysine-DNA-binding moiety to the adenoviral exterior, specific steps were undertaken to avoid perturbation of adenoviral capsid proteins relevant to endosome disruption. It has also been shown that these specific steps are not obligatory for functional incorporation of the adenovirus into the configuration of the molecular conjugate vector. Wagner et al. have shown that DNA-polylysine complexes may be attached to the adenoviral capsid by enzymatic means, employing transglutaminase and by exploiting the biotin-streptavidin interaction, using streptavidin-polylysine conjugates in conjunction with biotin-labeled adenovirus *(6)*. It has also been shown by Christiano et al. that direct chemical linkage of adenovirus and polylysine may be achieved utilizing the heterofunctional crosslinking agent EDC *(32)*. Adenovirus-component molecular conjugates derived by these methods possess activity profiles comparable to complexes employing immunologic methods of attachment.

When compared to the maximum levels of gene transfer achieved by free viral facilitation of molecular conjugate-mediated gene transfer, adenovirus in the linked configuration is capable of significantly higher levels of gene expression (data not shown). This likely reflects the different entry pathways of delivered DNA in the two different contexts. In this regard, for free adenovirus facilitation of molecular conjugates, the virus enhances gene transfer by disrupting cell vesicles to allow ingress of the conjugate-DNA complex into the cytosol. In this schema, the complex does not possess any specific mechanism to achieve localization in the nucleus after cell entry. In contrast, in the linked configuration, after endosome disruption, the complex would possess the additional capacity to localize to the nuclear pore, based on the adenoviral moiety's capacity to accomplish this localization *(33)*. In this location, the overall dynamics of gene transfer are likely more favorable for accomplishing expression of the heterologous genes.

In the adenovirus-polylysine-DNA complex configuration, the adenovirus moiety was incorporated to function in the capacity of an endosome disruption agent. In this vector design, however, it also represents the unique ligand domain of the molecular conjugate. Thus, it would be expected that the relative gene transfer efficiency of this vector would be determined by the relative tropism of the adenovirus for a given cellular target. This is indeed the case, as cells with a relatively high number of surface receptors for adenovirus, HeLa, and KB, are highly susceptible to gene transfer by this vector system. In contrast, cells with relatively fewer cell surface receptors for adenovirus, such as HBE1 and MRC-5, have a correspondingly lower susceptibility to gene transfer by the adenovirus-polylysine-DNA complexes *(13)*. To overcome this potential limitation, strategies were developed to determine if the adenovirus could be employed as an endosomolysis agent in conjunction with an alterna-

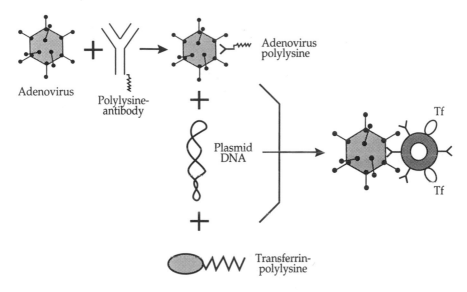

Fig. 5. Strategy for the employment of combination complexes containing adenovirus and transferrin. Complexes were derived that contain transferrin as the ligand domain and adenovirus as an endosomolysis domain. These combination complexes possess the potential to enter cells via the transferrin or adenovirus pathway. In the former instance, after entry via the transferrin pathway, the adenovirus would function in the capacity of an endosomolysis agent. Such conjugates thus possess both specific internalization and endosome escape mechanisms.

tive ligand. This strategy would presumably overcome the limitation of adenoviral receptor targeting of the adenovirus-polylysine-DNA complexes. The derivation of the combination complexes is shown in Fig. 5. This vector construction involves the sequential addition of adenovirus, linker antibody-polylysine, DNA, followed by a second ligand-polylysine. The result would be a complex containing multiple independent functional domains: a ligand domain to target specific cell subsets, an endosomolysis domain to enhance overall gene transfer efficiency by accomplishing cell vesicle escape, and a DNA binding domain.

The combination complexes were delivered to HeLa cells, a cellular target that has receptors for both adenovirus and the alternative ligand, in this case transferrin. It was observed that the combination complexes mediated even further augmentation of gene expression *(13)*. This augmented level of gene expression is clearly of greater magnitude than an additive effect of transferrin-polylysine and adenovirus-polylysine would predict. This suggests that, effectively, there is some element of cooperativity related to the ability of the complexes to enter cells for DNA delivery. This would appear to be because these complexes are capable of entering cells by either the transferrin or adenovirus pathway, and after entry, are capable of achieving cell vesicle escape. To establish this concept, the combination complexes were delivered to target cells relatively lacking adenovirus receptors. The HBE1 cell line was demonstrated to be refractory to transduction with adenovirus-polylysine-DNA complexes based on an absence of adenoviral receptors. When transduced with the combination complexes, however, levels of gene expression comparable to those seen in HeLa cells were noted. In this instance, the complexes achieve entry by nonadenoviral pathways, thus demonstrating the utility of providing a second ligand in the complex design.

With the recognition that high efficiency gene delivery could be achieved by including an endosomolytic domain into the design of the molecular conjugate, alternate strategies were developed to incorporate this functional attribute. In this regard, there are ample rationales for attempting to eliminate intact adenovirus from the conjugate configuration. First, the incorporated virion possesses the capacity to function as an alternate ligand domain, potentially undermining the desired property of cell-specific targeting. In addition, despite the ability to inactivate the viral adenoviral genome, its presence represents a potential safety concern. Thus, attempts have been made to isolate the portion of the adenoviral capsid that mediates cell vesicle disruption for functional inclusion into the molecular conjugate. These attempts, however, have been unsuccessful, likely reflecting the fact that adenovirus-mediated cell vesicle disruption is a complicated process, requiring the coordinated actions of multiple capsid components (personal communication; E. Wagner). This recognition also negatively bears on attempts to utilize recombinant capsid components deriving from adenovirus. As an alternative, Cotten et al. have recently employed a xenotropic adenovirus for this purpose. The adenoviral strain CELO was able to perform as an endosomolysis agent at functional levels comparable to human serotypes *(34)*. The disadvantage of this strategy derives from the relative difficulties encountered in preparing large amounts of this reagent. From the biosafety standpoint, the optimal endosome disruption agent would be a synthetic product to circumvent any issues associated with virus or viral products. Wagner et al. have explored the utility of synthetic viral peptides with fusogenic properties *(35)*. Whereas infusion of these peptides into the molecular conjugate structure augment gene transfer efficiencies, the levels of augmentation observed are far inferior to those observed with adenovirus. Thus, for the present, the adenovirus provides the most efficacious means of conferring on molecular conjugates the capacity to achieve cell vesicle escape and thus accomplish high-efficiency gene delivery.

1.3. Strategies to Enhance Capacity
for Cell-Specific Receptor-Mediated Gene Delivery

In the combination complexes, multiple independent domains provide multiple independent functions. These functions operate in a concerted manner to facilitate overall gene transfer. The incorporation of the adenovirus provides the important functional attribute of cell vesicle escape for the complex. However, by virtue of its binding capacity through its fiber protein, it provides an alternative ligand domain for the complex. This alternative source of binding potentially undermines the capacity to achieve cell-specific targeting, which is one of the theoretical attributes of the molecular conjugate vector system. Thus, it would be desirable to exploit the endosomolytic capacity of the adenovirus without allowing it to behave as an alternative ligand. One strategy to achieve this end is to block adenoviral binding with an antibody specific for the cell receptor binding domain of the fiber protein *(36)*. This type of antibody was derived by immunization with purified adenoviral fiber protein and screening for antibodies with neutralizing capacity. Thus, the capacity of the antibody to block adenoviral binding and internalization was first established. Next, it was determined whether the antibody blockade of adenoviral entry could ablate the ability of free adenovirus to facilitate molecular conjugate-mediated gene transfer. In this analysis, it could be seen that the antifiber antibody ablated the ability of the adenovirus to facilitate molecular conjugate-mediate gene transfer. This confirms that cellular entry of the virus is crucial to its capacity to augment conjugate entry. The next step was to derive combination complexes whereby the adenovirus had been precoated with antibody against the fiber protein to block entry via viral receptor pathways. It was hypothesized that the complex could nonetheless enter via the pathway of the alternative ligand, transferrin, whereby the attachment-blocked virus would mediate endosomolysis. In this analysis, the utilization of binding-incompetent virus as a component of the complex did not decrease the overall levels of gene transfer observed. This indicated that fiber binding was not required for the virus to mediate endosome disruption. Indeed, the process of adenoviral binding and endosome disruption are not functionally linked. Thus, it is possible to construct a molecular conjugate vector whereby the adenovirus is incorporated exclusively in the capacity of an endosomolytic agent and does not function as a competition ligand.

Ablation of the adenovirus moiety as a potential competitor ligand enhances the overall specificity of the conjugate vector for a given target cell. Besides the adenovirus, however, there exist additional sources of nonspecific binding within the conjugate design. For example, it has been shown that certain cells bind to polylysine-DNA-complexes in a nonspecific manner *(16)*. In these instances, when nonligand-polylysine-DNA complexes are codelivered to cells with adenovirus, they may accomplish levels of gene transfer comparable to ligand-polylysine complexes. This is, therefore, another potential confounding factor undermining the potential to achieve a vector system possessing cell-specific binding capacity. Since this nonspecific association between poly-lysine and the target cell surface is on an electrostatic basis, it was hypothesized that steps could be employed to neutralize the charge differential and thus ablate the basis of this nonspecific attachment. To this end, yeast tRNA, a nega-tively charged polynucleotide, was employed to treat polylysine-condensed DNA. It could be seen that the treatment significantly reduced the nonspecific binding mediated by the polylysine-DNA complex *(37)*. To determine whether the tRNA interfered with specific ligand-polylysine internalization, transfer-rin-polylysine-DNA complexes were treated in a similar manner and analyzed for their capacity to achieve binding and internalization when codelivered with adenovirus. In this study it could be seen that the tRNA did not interfere with specific ligand-polylysine gene transfer. Thus, this maneuver is capable of reducing nonspecific cell binding of the polylysine component of the ligand-polylysine complexes without affecting the specific receptor-mediated endocy-tosis uptake of ligand-polylysine complexes. This offers the potential to enhance the cell specificity of the conjugate vector.

Thus, various maneuvers to eliminate potential sources of nonspecificity in the molecular conjugate design may be employed. These strategies may be employed in the various ligand-based strategies to achieve cell-specific gene delivery. In this regard, the specificity of the molecular conjugate is deter-mined by its ligand domain, which dictates the cellular binding of the vector. Employed ligands may be physiologic ligands, as in the case of asialo-glycoprotein and transferrin. In addition, the ligand may represent a synthetic mimic of a physiologic ligand. This has been accomplished for targeting the asialoglycoprotein receptor by Wagner et al. as an asialoglycoprotein mimic *(35)*. Antireceptor antibodies have also been used as in the studies of Curiel et al. where anti-Ig immunoglobulin served as ligand for cell surface immunoglo-bulins for targeting B-lymphocytes *(38)*. The use of viral proteins with specific affinity for cell-type markers has also been demonstrated by targeting CD4 human lymphocytes with HIV gp120-ligand conjugates. In these instances, ligands were employed to direct molecular conjugate vectors into pathways that were known *a priori* to be associated with efficient cellular internaliza-tion. It was hypothesized that it might also be possible to successfully target conjugates employing ligands that do not bind to characterized cellular inter-nalization pathways. In this regard, Batra et al. have developed molecular con-jugates exploiting the utility of cell surface-lectin interactions for vector targeting. It was found that lectins could successfully facilitate effective gene delivery mediated by molecular conjugates *(39)*. Presumably, in this instance, cell surface binding of the lectin-polylysine-DNA complex is sufficient to induce a level of internalization permissive of effective gene delivery. Thus, targeting of molecular conjugate vectors may be designed to exploit characterized cellular receptor-mediated endocytosis pathways. Additionally, in some instances, the employment of ligand moieties possessing cell binding affinity may be sufficient to allow functionally relevant internalization of the conjugate-DNA complex.

The design of adenovirus-component molecular conjugate vectors represents a unique manner of exploiting viral entry features to achieve gene delivery. This strategy is thus distinct from the design of recombinant viral vectors. In the instance of recombinant viral vectors, the overall entry mechanism of the virus is exploited to achieve gene delivery through the incorporation of the foreign gene into the genome of the virus. For the adenovirus-component molecular conjugate vectors, viral entry features are exploited to facilitate gene transfer in a highly selective manner. This possibility arises from the fact that the capacity of the adenovirus to achieve entry is an intrinsic property of its capsid proteins. This mechanism may thus be incorporated into a vector system whereby the viral gene elements are obviated. The vector design that derives from this strategy results in a system with potential advantages related to utility and safety. Furthermore, the development of a vector system with the engineered capacity to achieve cell-specific gene delivery is in conceptual accord with the concept of a "targetable-injectable" vector *(40)*. The further development of the capacities within the present vector design may allow the achievement of a vector system possessing many of the attributes of this proposed vector ideal.

2. Materials

1. Dulbecco's Modified Eagle's Medium (DMEM) supplemented with 10% fetal calf serum (FCS) and penicillin/streptomycin is used for routine cultivation of tissue culture cells. For particular experiments, this is modified as indicated in Section 3.
2. CsCl 1.33: 454.2 mg/mL CsCl in 5 mM HEPES, pH 7.3.
3. CsCl 1.45: 609.0 mg/mL CsCl in 5 mM HEPES, pH 7.3.
4. HBS: HEPES 5 mM, pH 7.3, 150 mM NaCl.
5. Poly-L-lysine: Poly-L-lysine (Sigma, St. Louis, MO) 500-mg bottle dissolved in 50 mL HBS and pH adjusted to 7.3. The final volume is brought up to 84 mL with HBS and reagent aliquoted in 500-µL volumes with storage at –20°C.
6. EDC: (Pierce, Rockford, IL) 1 g EDC is dissolved in 4.0 mL dH$_2$O at time of use and stored at 4°C. This must be discarded immediately after use. Unused EDC powder should be stored under argon at –20°C.
7. Viral preservation medium: Combine the following: 1 mL 1M Tris-HCl (pH 8.0), 2 mL 5M NaCl, and 0.1 g bovine serum albumin (BSA). Bring volume up to 50 mL and mix until BSA in solution. Add 50 mL glycerol, filter sterilize, and store at 4°C.

3. Methods

3.1. Large-Scale Viral Preparation of Adenovirus

1. Grow 293 or HeLa or WI-62 to ~80% confluence in 75-cm flasks (~10^7 cells/flask) × 20 in DMEM/10% FCS/PCN + Strep.
2. Aspirate off media.
3. Dilute viral stock in 100 mL DMEM/2% heat inactivated FCS (2% FCS media) and add 5 mL/flask. Added viral stock should be approx 10^{10}–10^{11} viral particles to achieve MOI ~100–1000/cell.
4. Incubate 37°C, 5% CO_2, 1–2 h.
5. Add 10 mL complete media/flask (DMEM/10% FCS/PCN + Strep).
6. Incubate as above 48–72 h until prominent cytopathic effect is seen in cells.
7. Harvest cells and media from flasks in 50-mL capped centrifuge tubes.
8. Centrifuge 1000 rpm, 10 min, 4°C Beckman GS-GR centrifuge or other table-top centrifuge.
9. Aspirate off supernatant and resuspend combined cell pellets in total volume of 20 mL 2% FCS media.
10. Freeze-thaw 4X (may use 37°C bath alternating with dry ice/ethanol bath).
11. Centrifuge as in step 8 except at 4000 rpm, 20 min, 4°C, and harvest supernatant; save at 4°C while setting up gradients.
12. Set up CsCl gradient tubes as follows:
    a. SW 28 tube: Step 20 mL 1.33 CsCl (discontinuous gradient).
    b. 10 mL 1.45 CsCl (discontinuous gradient).
    c. Overlayer gradient with 5 mL viral cell lysate.
    d. Centrifuge 18,000 rpm, 1.5 h, 20°C.
13. Harvest lowest opalescent band needle puncture in tube with aspiration into syringe (in approx 2 mL).
14. Dilute 1:1 with 5 m*M* HEPES, pH 7.3.
15. SW41 tube:
    a. 4 mL 1.33 CsCl (discontinuous gradient).
    b. 4 mL 1.45 CsCl (discontinuous gradient); overlayer with 4 mL virus diluted from 1st spin.
    c. Centrifuge 25,000 rpm, overnight (>18 h), 20°C.
16. Harvest lower band as before in minimal volume.
17. Use virus directly for chemical coupling to poly-L-lysine or preserve as follows: dilute: 1 part virus to 5 parts viral preservation media.
18. Store in aliquots at –70°C.
19. To measure virus concentration: Mix 100 µL of adenovirus solution with 900 µL 1X TE and determine A260 by spectrophotometry. One A260 equals approx 10^{12} viral particles per mL.

3.2. Chemical Linkage of Adenovirus and Poly-L-Lysine

1. Virus is prepared as in Section 3.1.; after the 2nd spin, resuspend virus in 2.5 mL final volume with 1.33 CsCl.

2. Load onto a PD10 column (Pharmacia, Uppsala, Sweden) pre-equilibrated with HBS.
3. Elute with 2 mL HBS.
4. Resuspend to a final volume of 3.6 mL with HBS.
5. Reaction: Mix 3.6 mL virus, 0.4 mL poly-L-lysine, and 0.04 mL EDC. Leave on ice for 4 h.
6. Mix well with 8 mL of 1.45 CsCl.
7. Centrifuge at 25,000g for 18 h in an SW41 tube.
8. Harvest the opalescent band—dilute with viral preservation medium to achieve concentration of 1×10^{11} particles/mL, and aliquot. Store at $-70°C$.

3.3. Preparation of Adenovirus-Polylysine-DNA Complexes

Recipe for 6.0 µg DNA (transfection of ~1×10^6 cells); may be scaled up or down accordingly.

1. 100 µL Adenovirus-polylysine (EDC-linked AdpL@ 1×10^{11} particles/mL).
2. 6.0 µg plasmid DNA in 200 µL HBS (20 mM HEPES, 150 mM NaCl, pH 7.3), 30 min RT.
3. 4.0 µL poly-L-lysine (pL) in 200 µL HBS, 30 min, RT. Or, 6.0 µL human transferrin-polylysine (Serva; 1 mg/mL) in 200 mL HBS, 30 min, RT.
4. Add to cells that are in 1/2 total vol 2% fetal calf serum media, 60 min., 37°C.
5. Add 1/2 vol of media with fetal calf serum (FCS) to bring final FCS concentration to maintenance level.

4. Notes

For certain applications, adenovirus-component molecular conjugate vectors are ideal in their present form. For example, they have been found to be highly efficient transfection reagents for many in vitro applications. In addition to mediating high-efficiency gene transfer in transformed human cells, they are able to mediate high-efficiency gene transfer in primary cell cultures of various tissue types. This is of significance in ex vivo transduction of cells that are to be retransplanted after transfection with the gene of interest. Another important property of the molecular conjugate design is its ability to deliver large DNA constructs, which is a great limitation in recombinant viral systems. This allows the use of specific promoter elements to enhance overall gene expression. In addition to delivering large genes efficiently, it is also possible to deliver multiple DNA constructs simultaneously.

Despite their efficacy in vitro, use of molecular conjugates in vivo has been idiosyncratic. Gao et al. have shown that molecular conjugate vectors are able to mediate gene transfer in the airway epithelium of cotton rats *(41)*. The observed gene transfer was not, however, as efficient as would be expected from the observed in vitro efficacy. This has been shown to be owing to the instability of molecular conjugates in vivo. It has been shown that the polylysine component of the conjugates is a target of humoral factors after in vivo delivery (E. Wagner, personal communication). Since the basis of conjugate instability is understood, several steps may potentially be taken to address this problem. As the polylysine component is the primary locus of conjugate instability in vivo, it is logical to propose the replacement of the polylysine DNA-binding moiety with some other DNA-binding component to obviate this limitation. An alternate strategy would be to directly link the DNA to the ligand via chemical techniques using crosslinking reagents or with a high affinity biotin-streptavidin linkage. In addition, a conceptually distinct strategy being developed seeks to mask the polycation component of conjugates using stealthing procedures. These are several examples of steps that may be taken to improve the in vivo efficiency of molecular conjugate vectors by mitigating the known basis of conjugate instability. All of these strategies are presently in the development stage.

In their present form, molecular conjugate vectors are able to mediate high efficiency gene transfer via the receptor-mediated endocytosis pathway and thus possess the capacity for targeted delivery. This is largely owing to the plasticity of the conjugate design whereby incorporated ligands determine the vector tropism. It has been shown that viral endosome disruption functions incorporated into the conjugate design dramatically enhance gene transfer efficiency, and that these functions may be exploited selectively in a manner whereby the viral tropism will not undermine conjugate specificity. In addition, since the endosome lysis ability of the adenovirus is not a function of viral gene expression, it is possible to selectively exploit this function without introducing viable viral gene elements, thus taking steps to inactivate the viral genome. This strategy seeks to capitalize on the minimal functional elements of the virus entry pathway that are useful for vector utility. Though not ideal in its present form, this vector design is a developmental step toward the concept of a targetable, injectable gene transfer vector. It is flexible in its tropism and is largely comprised of specifically derived functional components. The next logical step in vector development would be the incorporation of an integration mechanism into the design of the vector. This would enable the delivered DNA to be stably maintained in the host genome leading to long-term gene expression. As it has been demonstrated that distinct functional domains may operate in an independent manner in the context of molecular conjugate vectors, it is not illogical to speculate that a viral integration system could also be incorporated into the design of the present system.

Acknowledgments

The author wishes to express his gratitude to his coworkers Frosty Loechel and Sharon Michael at the University of Alabama at Birmingham; Raj Batra and

Ling Gao at the University of North Carolina, Chapel Hill; and Matt Cotten and Ernst Wagner at the Institute of Molecular Pathology in Vienna, Austria.

References

1. Wu, G. Y., Wilson, J. M., Shalaby, F., Grossman, M., Shafritz, D. A., and Wu, C. H. (1991) Receptor-mediated gene delivery *in vivo*. Partial correction of genetic analbuminemia in nagase rats. *J. Biol. Chem.* **266**, 14,338–14,342.
2. Wu, G. Y. and Wu, C. H. (1988) Receptor-mediated gene delivery and expression *in vivo*. *J. Biol. Chem.* **263**, 14,621–14,624.
3. Zenke, M., Steinlein, P., Wagner, E., Cotten, M., Beug, H., and Birnstiel, M. L. (1990) Receptor-mediated endocytosis of transferrin-polycation conjugates: an efficient way to introduce DNA into hematopoietic cells. *Proc. Natl. Acad. Sci. USA* **87**, 3655–3659.
4. Zatloukal, K., Wagner, E., Cotten, M., et al. (1992) Transferrinfection: a highly efficient way to express gene constructs in eukaryotic cells. *Ann. NY Acad. Sci.* **660**, 136–153.
5. Wagner, E., Cotten, M., Foisner, R., and Birnstiel, M. L. (1991) Transferrin-polycation-DNA complexes: the effect of polycations on the structure of the complex and DNA delivery to cells. *Proc. Natl. Acad. Sci. USA* **88L**, 4255–4259.
6. Wagner, E., Zatloukal, K., Cotten, M., et al. (1992) Coupling of adenovirus to transferrin-polylysine/DNA complexes greatly enhances receptor-mediated gene delivery and expression of transfected genes. *Proc. Natl. Acad. Sci. USA* **89**, 6099–6103.
7. Wagner, E., Zenke, M., Cotten, M., Beug, H., and Birnstiel, M. L. (1990) Transferrin-polycation conjugates as carriers for DNA uptake into cells. *Proc. Natl. Acad. Sci. USA* **87**, 3410–3414.
8. Cotten, M., Lange-Rouault, F., Kirlappos, H., et al. (1990) Transferrin-polycation-mediated introduction of DNA into human leukemic cells: stimulation by agents that affect the survival of transfected DNA or modulate transferrin receptor levels. *Proc. Natl. Acad. Sci. USA* **87**, 4033–4037.
9. Curiel, D. T., Agarwal, S., Wagner, E., and Cotten, M. (1991) Adenovirus enhancement of transferrin-polylysine-mediated gene delivery. *Proc. Natl. Acad. Sci. USA* **88**, 8850–8854.
10. Rosenkranz, A. A., Yachmenev, S. V., Jans, D. A., et al. (1992) Receptor-mediated endocytosis and nuclear transport of a transfecting DNA construct. *Exp. Cell. Res.* **199**, 323–329.
11. Ferkol, T., Kaetzel, C. S., and Davis, P. B. (1993) Gene transfer into respiratory epithelial cells by targeting the polymeric immunoglobulin receptor. *J. Clin. Invest.* **92**, 2394–2400.
12. Citro, G., Perrotti, D., Cucco, C., et al. (1992) Inhibition of leukemia cell proliferation by receptor-mediated uptake of *cmyb* antisense oligodeoxynucleotides. *Proc. Natl. Acad. Sci. USA* **89**, 7031–7035.
13. Curiel, D. T., Wagner, E., Cotten, M., et al. (1992) High efficiency gene transfer mediated by adenovirus coupled to DNA-polylysine complexes. *Hum. Gene. Ther.* **3**, 147–154.

14. Huebers, H. and Finch, C. (1987) The physiology of transferrin receptors. *Physiol. Rev.* **67**, 520–582.

15. Thortesen, K. and Romslo, I. (1990) The role of transferrin in the mechanism of cellular iron uptake. *Biochem. J.* **271**, 1–10.

16. Cotten, M., Wagner, E., and Birnstiel, M. L. (1993) Receptor mediated transport of DNA into eukaryotic cells. *Methods Enzymol.* **217**, 618–644.

17. Wilson, J. M., Grossman, M., Cabrera, J. A., Wu, C. H., and Wu, G. Y. (1992a) A novel mechanism for achieving transgene persistence in vivo after somatic gene transfer into hepatocytes. *J. Biol. Chem.* **267**, 11,483–11,489.

18. Baatz, J. E., Bruno, M. D., Ciraolo, P. J., Glasser, S. W., Stripp, B. R., Smyth, K. L., and Korfhagen, T. R. (1994) Utilization of modified surfactant-associated protein B for delivery of DNA to airway cells in culture. *Proc. Natl. Acad. Sci. USA* **91**, 2547–2551.

19. Pastan, I., Seth, P., FitzGerald, D., and Willingham, M. (1986) Adenovirus entry into cells: Some new observations on an old problem, in *Virus Attachment and Entry into Cells* (Crowell, R. L. and Lonberg-Holm, K., eds.), American Society for Microbiology, Washington, DC, pp. 141–146.

20. Kielian, M. and Jungerwirth, S. (1990) Mechanisms of enveloped virus entry into cells. *Mol. Biol. Med.* **7**, 17–31.

21. Fernandez-Puentes, C. and Carrasco, L. (1980) Viral infection permeabilizes mammalian cells to protein toxins. *Cell* **20**, 769–775.

22. FitzGerald, D. J. P., Padmanabhan, R., Pastan, I., and Willingham, M. C. (1983) Adenovirus-induced release of epidermal growth factor and pseudomonas toxin into the cytosol of KB cells during receptor-mediated endocytosis. *Cell* **32**, 607–617.

23. Chardonnet, Y. and Dales, S. (1970) Early events in the interaction of adenoviruses with HeLa cells. 1. Penetration of Type 5 and intracellular release of the DNA genome. *Virology* **40**, 462–477.

24. Svensson, U. and Persson, R. (1984) Entry of adenovirus 2 into HeLa cells. *J. Virol.* **51**, 687–694.

25. Wickham, T. J., Mathias, P., Cheresh, D. A., and Nemerow, G. R. (1993) Integrins $a_v\beta_3$ and $a_v\beta_5$ promote adenovirus internalization but not virus attachment. *Cell* **73**, 309–319.

26. Seth, P., FitzGerald, D., Ginsberg, H., Willingham, M., and Pastan, I. (1984) Evidence that the penton base of adenovirus is involved in potentiation of toxicity of Pseudomonas exotoxin conjugated to epidermal growth factor. *Mol. Cell. Biol.* **4**, 1528–1533.

27. Jones, N. and Shenk, T. (1979) An adenovirus type 5 early gene function regulates expression of other early viral genes. *Proc. Natl. Acad. Sci. USA* **76**, 3665–3669.

28. Defer, C., Belin, M.-T., Caillet-Boudin, M.-L., and Boulanger, P. (1990) Human adenovirus-host cell interactions: comparative study with members of subgroups B and C. *J. Virol.* **64**, 3661–3673.

29. Cotten, M., Wagner, E., Zatloukal, K., Phillips, S., Curiel, D. T., and Birnstiel, M. L. (1992) High-efficiency receptor-mediated delivery of small and large (48 kilobase) gene constructs using the endosome-disruption activity of defective or chemically inactivated adenovirus particles. *Proc. Natl. Acad. Sci. USA* **89**, 6094–6098.

30. Felgner, P. L., Gadek, T. R., Holm, M., et al. (1987) Lipofection: A highly efficient, lipid-mediated DNA-transfection procedure. *Proc. Natl. Acad. Sci. USA* **84**, 7413–7417.
31. Felgner, P. L., Holm, M., and Chan, H. (1989) Cationic liposome mediated transfection. *Proc. West Pharmacol. Soc.* **32**, 115–121.
32. Cristiano, R. J., Smith, L. C., Kay, M. A., Brinkley, B. R., and Woo, S. L. (1993) Hepatic gene therapy: efficient gene delivery and expression in primary hepatocytes utilizing a conjugated adenovirus-DNA complex. *Proc. Natl. Acad. Sci. USA* **90**, 11,548–11,552.
33. Greber, U. F., Willetts, M., Webster, P., and Helenius, A. (1993) Stepwise dismantling of adenovirus 2 during entry into cells. *Cell* **75**, 477–486.
34. Cotten, M., Wagner, E., Zatloukal, K., and Birnstiel, M. L. (1993) Chicken adenovirus (CELO Virus) particles augment receptor-mediated DNA delivery to mammalian cells and yield exceptional levels of stable transformants. *J. Virol.* **67**, 3777–3785.
35. Wagner, E., Plank, C., Zatloukal, K., Cotten, M., and Birnstiel, M. L. (1992) Influenza virus hemagglutinin HA-2 N-terminal fusogenic peptides augment gene transfer by transferrin-polylysine-DNA complexes: toward a synthetic virus-like gene-transfer vehicle. *Proc. Natl. Acad. Sci. USA* **89**, 7934–7938.
36. Michael, S. I., Huang, C.-H., Romer, M. U., Wagner, E., Hu, P.-C., and Curiel, D. T. (1993) Binding-incompetent adenovirus facilitates molecular conjugate-mediated gene transfer by the receptor-mediated endocytosis pathway. *J. Biol. Chem.* **268**, 6866–6869.
37. Michael, S. I. and Curiel, D. T. (1995) Strategies to achieve targeted gene delivery via the receptor mediated endocytosis pathway. *Gene Ther.* **1**, 223–232.
38. Curiel, T., Cook, D. R., Bogedain, C., Jilg, W., Harrison, G. S., Cotten, M., Curiel, D. T., and Wagner, E. (1994) Efficient foreign gene expression in Epstein-Barr virus-transformed human B-cells. *Virology* **198**, 577–585.
39. Batra, R. K., Johanning, F. W., Wagner, E., Garver, R. I., Jr., and Curiel, D. T. (1994) Receptor-mediated gene delivery employing lectin-binding specificity. *Gene Ther.* **1**, 255–260.
40. Morgan, R. A. and Anderson, W. F. (1993) Human gene therapy. *Ann. Rev. Biochem.* **62**, 191–217.
41. Gao, L., Wagner, E., Cotten, M., Agarwal, S., Harris, C., Romer, M., Miller, L., Hu, P.-C., and Curiel, D. (1993) Direct *in vivo* gene transfer to airway epithelium employing adenovirus-polylysine-DNA complexes. *Hum. Gene Ther.* **4**, 17–24.

2

Methods for the Construction and Propagation of Recombinant Adeno-Associated Virus Vectors

Jeffrey S. Bartlett and Richard J. Samulski

1. Introduction

The development of gene transfer vectors from the human parvovirus, adeno-associated virus (AAV), has provided scientists with an efficient and effective way of delivering genes into mammalian cells. This chapter aims to explore the various practical aspects of the AAV vector system, and in consequence, to highlight particular difficulties that may be encountered by workers new to the field. However, before describing the methodology involved in the generation of recombinant AAV vectors, it is of value to briefly discuss the structure and life cycle of this unique virus. Detailed and more extensive reviews that describe the biology of adeno-associated virus are also available (1–3).

1.1. AAV Structure and Genetics

The AAV genome is encapsidated as a single-stranded DNA molecule of plus or minus polarity (4–7). Strands of both polarities are packaged, but in separate virus particles (4), and both strands are infectious (8). The genome of AAV-2 is 4675 bp in length (9) and is flanked by inverted terminal repeat sequences of 145 bp each (10,11) (Fig. 1). The first 125 nucleotides of these terminal sequences are palindromic and fold back on themselves to form T-shaped hairpin structures that are used to initiate viral DNA replication (for details see reviews by Berns et al. [12,13]). The terminal repeats also contain the sequences necessary to package the viral DNA into virions (14–16). Studies of AAV replication, latent viral chromosomes, and defective interfering particles all point to the viral terminal repeats as the key *cis*-acting elements required for a productive AAV infection.

From: *Methods in Molecular Medicine, Gene Therapy Protocols*
Edited by: P. Robbins Humana Press Inc., Totowa, NJ

Fig. 1. Structure of the AAV-2 genome. Locations of the three AAV promoters are indicated in map units (mμ) (100 mμ = 100% = 4.7 kb). Arrows indicate transcriptional units encoding the replication *(Rep)* proteins and capsid *(Cap)* proteins. A detail of the 145-bp AAV terminal repeat structure is also shown.

1.2. AAV Life-Cycle and the Development of AAV Vectors

Adeno-associated virus is a defective member of the parvovirus family. The AAV can be propagated as a lytic virus or maintained as a provirus that is integrated into the host cell genome *(2)*. In a lytic infection, replication requires coinfection with either adenovirus *(17–19)*, or herpes simplex virus *(20)*; hence the classification of AAV as a defective virus. The requirement of a *helper* virus for a productive infection has made understanding the AAV life cycle more difficult. However, from a vector point of view, it has added a level of control when generating nonreplicative vectors, in that they can be propagated under controlled conditions *(see* Section 3.1.), thereby reducing unwanted spread and providing an important margin of safety. One of the most interesting aspects of the AAV life cycle is the virus' ability to integrate into the host genome. When AAV infects cells in the absence of helper virus, it establishes latency by persisting in the host cell genome as an integrated provirus *(3,21,22)*.

Although AAV establishes a latent infection, if these cells are super-infected with wild-type helper virus, the integrated AAV can be rescued from the chromosome, and re-enter the lytic cycle.

As a prerequisite for vector construction, it was necessary to gain an understanding of the AAV life cycle. This problem was approached by first cloning a double-stranded version of the virus into a plasmid backbone *(23,24)*. Since wild-type AAV could be rescued from an integrated chromosome and enter the lytic cycle following adenovirus infection, it was of interest to determine if such a recombinant AAV plasmid could be used for generating wild-type AAV virus. It was determined that the viral genome could be rescued from the plasmid recombinant backbone by transfection of the plasmid DNA into human cells in conjunction with adenovirus type-5 as helper virus. Similar infectious plasmid clones have been the template for all subsequent vector constructions. The ability to generate large quantities of plasmid DNA that is basically inert until introduced into adenovirus-infected human cells also provides a safe and efficient way of manipulating this system.

The first use of AAV as a vector for the transduction of a foreign gene into the host chromosome was demonstrated by Hermonat and Muzyczka in 1984 *(14)*. A recombinant AAV (rAAV) viral stock was produced using an infectious plasmid vector similar to that described above in which the neomycin resistance gene *(neo^r)* was substituted for the AAV capsid genes. This rAAV was able to transduce neomycin resistance to both murine and human cell lines *(14)*.

Since these first studies, AAV has been used as a viral vector system to express a variety of genes in a number of different eukaryotic cells *(11,25–28)*. All of these experiments have used plasmid vectors in which portions of the AAV genome were substituted with the foreign gene of interest. The size of the inserted non-AAV or foreign DNA is limited to that which permits packaging of the rAAV vector into virions (4.7 kb), and thus depends on the size of the retained AAV sequences.

1.3. Minimal AAV Vectors

Although the early studies described in Section 1.2. demonstrated the potential use of AAV as a vector, several technical problems remained: the need for efficient packaging systems, methods for producing recombinant virus stock free of wild-type AAV, and the identification of minimum AAV sequences required for transduction. This last hurdle would have direct impact on the size of foreign DNA inserts. In attempts to solve these problems, constructs that retained only a limited number of nucleotides from the viral terminal sequences were tested *(8,15,16)*. The remainder of this discussion will focus on the AAV plasmid construct *psub*201 *(8)*, which is a derivative of the original recombinant viral vector described in Section 1.2. *(24)*. This plasmid vector contains

Fig. 2. Plasmid vectors for the generation of recombinant AAV. The present method for producing stocks of rAAV utilizes a two-component plasmid system; AAV plasmid vector, i.e., *psub*201, and AAV helper plasmid, i.e., *pAAV/Ad*. Foreign DNA is inserted between the two *Xba*I sites of *psub*201, removing the *Rep* and *Cap* regions of the AAV genome, are supplied in *trans* by the plasmid *pAAV/Ad*.

two *Xba*I cleavage sites flanking the viral coding domain *(8)*, such that the entire viral coding domain can be excised and foreign DNA sequences can be inserted between the *cis*-acting terminal repeats (Fig. 2). Vectors derived from this plasmid have been shown to transduce genes at frequencies similar to the earlier vectors, suggesting that the minimal *cis*-acting sequences needed in the viral plasmid are only the AAV terminal repeats. Recently, similar vectors have been developed by others. These plasmids are all able to carry foreign gene cassettes of 4.6–5.0 kb in size.

1.4. rAAV Packaging Systems

The present method for producing stocks of recombinant AAV utilizes a two-component plasmid system: AAV plasmid vector, as described in Sections 1.2. and 1.3.; and AAV helper plasmid, which provides the necessary AAV capsid and replication proteins *in trans*. An important consideration is that the vector and helper plasmid DNAs should be sufficiently nonhomologous so as to preclude homologous recombination events between the two, which could generate wild-type AAV. Although there are many variations on this theme, this discussion will focus on the AAV helper plasmid, *pAAV/Ad*, which contains adenovirus type-5 terminal sequences in place of the normal AAV termini. This plasmid has no homology to the AAV vector plasmid and cannot be packaged into AAV virions since it lacks the terminal *cis*-acting domains required for this function. In addition, this hybrid plasmid does not contain adenovirus packaging sequences, thereby eliminating the potential for unwanted adenovirus recombinants.

By cotransfecting the helper plasmid *pAAV/Ad* and the vector *psub201*, containing a foreign gene inserted between the two AAV terminal repeats (in the presence of adenovirus), rescue, replication, and packaging of the foreign gene into AAV particles occurs. The adenovirus genome has been shown to activate the adenovirus terminal repeats on *pAAV/Ad*; this enhances the turning on of the AAV genes. The *rep* gene products recognize the AAV *cis*-acting terminal repeats on the vector *psub201* containing a foreign gene, rescue these recombinant molecules out of the plasmid, and begin to replicate them. The AAV capsids begin to accumulate, and they recognize the AAV *cis*-acting packaging signals located in the AAV terminal repeats and encapsidate the recombinant viral DNA into an AAV virion. The result of such a packaging scheme is an adenovirus helper and AAV particle carrying the recombinant DNA. The adenovirus helper can be removed by a number of physical and genetic techniques. Heating the virus lysate to 56°C for 30 min is one such strategy. In this packaging system, one can generate helper-free stocks of AAV vectors at titers of 10^4–10^5/mL.

1.6. Advantages and Disadvantages of rAAV Vectors for Gene Transfer and Gene Therapy

As mentioned, several AAV vector systems have been developed that consist of a recombinant plasmid capable of being packaged into AAV particles. To date, about 96% of the AAV genome can be replaced with foreign DNA and packaged into an AAV virion. In using this strategy, one starts with an infectious plasmid that effectively removes all of the coding capacity of the AAV genome. The *cis*-acting AAV terminal repeats that are retained do not appear to contain dominant enhancer or promoter activity, and recombinant viruses generated using these elements function as vectors for stable transduction. Expression of the gene or DNA sequence of choice in eukaryotic cells is determined by the control of a transcriptional promoter included with the gene cassette *(29,30)*.

Recombinant AAV is among the newest of the possible genetic transfer vectors. This once obscure virus possesses unique properties that distinguish it from all other vectors. Its advantages include the ability to integrate into the mammalian genome and the lack of any known pathogenicity. Its ability to carry regulatory elements (i.e., tissue-specific enhancers/promoters, splice sites, and so on) without interference from the viral genome allows for greater control of transferred gene expression. In vitro experiments demonstrate that rAAV vectors can transduce primary hematopoietic cells, and they support the development of this vector system for gene transfer *(31,32)*.

Disadvantages currently exist from the inferior packaging systems that yield low numbers of recombinant virions that are contaminated with wild-type adenovirus. The present packaging systems are very inefficient. Yields of wild-type AAV usually exceed 10^{10} virus/mL, whereas recombinant AAV titers are in the 10^4–10^5 virus/mL range. Thus far, two approaches have been reported for removing adenovirus from AAV stocks: heat inactivation and CsCl density centrifugation. The latter method is also an effective way of concentrating AAV virus stocks. Additionally, it may be possible to use an adenovirus with a temperature-sensitive mutation (particularly one in the adenovirus DNA polymerase or structural genes) to produce an AAV vector stock that would be essentially free of adenovirus contamination. Fortunately, these difficulties do not seem to be insurmountable technical problems. Finally, the limitation of the small genome able to be packaged (~5 kb) suggests that genes or cDNAs averaging 3–5 kb will be the most appropriate to be used in this vector.

2. Materials

2.1. Cell Culture—General

1. Human 293 cells. The cells are split 1/6 every 3–4 d. They should not be allowed to overgrow and should be low passage (<p50). The human 293 cells can be obtained from American Type Culture Collection, Rockville, MD (ATCC cat. no. CRL 1573).
2. Phosphate-buffered saline (PBS): 1.0% NaCl, 0.025% KCl, 0.14% Na_2HPO_4, 0.025% KH_2PO_4 (all w/v), pH 7.2; sterile.
3. Dulbecco's Modified Eagle's Medium (DMEM) with glutamine containing 100 U/mL penicillin G and 100 µg/mL streptomycin.
4. Tissue culture dishes (100-mm diameter).
5. Fetal bovine serum (FBS).
6. Phosphate-buffered saline containing 0.5 mM EDTA (PE).

2.2. Recombinant AAV Plasmid Vector

The use of the AAV vector *psub201* requires that the foreign gene cassette be excised with a restriction enzyme that produces *Xba*I sticky ends. Alternatively, the insert and digested vector must be treated with a suitable enzyme to produce flush ends for blunt-end ligation. The inserted gene must have appropriate promoter and maybe enhancer sequences, contain sufficient protein coding regions, have appropriate polyadenylation signals, and should contain an intron for maximal expression with some promoters. Such manipulations and the construction of similar gene cassettes are described elsewhere *(33)*. Once the foreign gene has been inserted into the AAV vector, it may be advisable to sequence across both ends of the gene to ensure against mutation.

It is important to use very pure DNA for transfection. Plasmids should be prepared and purified by double CsCl gradient centrifugation (*see* Note 1).

2.3. Helper Plasmid

The rationale behind the construction of AAV helper plasmids such as *pAAV/Ad* has been discussed in Section 1.4. Very pure DNA should be used for transfection. Therefore, helper plasmid should also be purified by double CsCl gradient centrifugation (*see* Notes 1 and 2).

2.4. Generation of Recombinant Virus

1. Monolayers of 293 cells at approx 80% confluency.
2. Lipofectin reagent (Gibco-BRL), or Transfection-reagent (DOTAP) (Boehringer Mannheim, Mannheim, Germany).
3. Polystyrene tubes (Falcon, Los Angeles, CA): 17 × 100 mm (#2059) or 12 × 175 mm (#2058) (*see* Note 7).
4. Tissue culture dishes (*see* Section 2.1.).
5. DNA samples: CsCl-purified preparations of both recombinant AAV plasmid and helper plasmid (*see* Section 2.1.).
6. Opti-MEM medium (Gibco-BRL).
7. Dulbecco's Modified Eagle's Medium (DMEM) (as described in Section 2.1.), containing 10% FBS.
8. Phosphate-buffered saline (PBS; *see* Section 2.1.).
9. HEPES-buffered saline (HBS): 20 mmol/L HEPES (*N*-2-Hydroxyethyl-pi-perazine-*N'*-2-ethanesulfonic acid), 150 mmol/L NaCl, final pH 7.4. Filter sterilized and stored at 5°C.
10. PE solution (*see* Section 2.1.)
11. Adenovirus stock (type dl309).

2.5. Isolation and Purification of Recombinant Virus

1. Phosphate-buffered saline (PBS; *see* Section 2.1.).
2. Clinical centrifuge for low speed centrifugation.
3. Sonicator (for example, Branson Model 2000, fitted with 0.5-cm microtip).
4. TNE Buffer (10 m*M* Tris-HCl, 100 m*M* NaCl, 1 m*M* EDTA, pH 8.0).
5. Dounce homogenizer.
6. Dialysis tubing.
7. 2% Trypsin solution.
8. 20% Sodium deoxycholate solution.
9. Solid CsCl.
10. CsCl solutions for density gradient centrifugation at 1.7 g/mL, 1.5 g/mL, 1.35 g/mL, and 1.25 g/mL in 0.01*M* Tris-HCl, pH 8.0; 0.001*M* EDTA.
11. Ultracentrifuge capable of 150,000*g*.

2.5. Titration of Recombinant Virus

1. Ninety-six-well tissue culture dishes.
2. DMEM containing 10% FBS, and DMEM containing 2% FBS (*see* Section 2.1.).

3. Adenovirus stock (type dl309) at known titer (*see* Section 2.1.).
4. Wild-type AAV stock at predetermined titer.
5. PE solution (*see* Section 2.1.).
6. Nylon hybridization membranes, 47-mm circular.
7. Phosphate-buffered saline (*see* Section 2.1.).
8. Millipore 47-mm filer holder, or equivalent.
9. 0.5*N* NaOH solution.
10. 1.0*M* Tris-HCl, pH 7.5.
11. Solutions for standard DNA hybridization analysis, including the preparation and purification of radioactively labeled DNA probes.
12. X-ray film (Kodak X-OMAT).

3. Methods

3.1. Generation of Recombinant Virus

This section outlines methods for cotransfecting 293 cells with two plasmids, for rescue of the recombinant AAV genome and packaging into viral particles. The cell line of choice is always 293, because these cells are good recipients of DNA in DNA-mediated gene-transfer procedures, and allow the use of replication-deficient adenovirus as helper virus.

We routinely use one of the transfection procedures outlined below to obtain infectious recombinant virus from recombinant plasmid clones. Although we have investigated a number of other methods (calcium-phosphate precipitation, DEAE-dextran, electroporation, and so on), we have found that the method of choice is most often the one the investigator has the most experience with and is most comfortable with. The reader is encouraged to evaluate other transfection techniques as well.

3.1.1. Transfection of DNA Using Lipofectin Reagent

1. Grow 293 cells on 100-mm tissue culture dishes in DMEM containing 10% fetal bovine serum, until they are 60–80% confluent.
2. Suspend DNAs in 1.0 mL Opti-MEM medium per 100-mm tissue culture dish in a 15-mL polystyrene tube. The amount of DNA used for each transfection is related to the amount of Lipofectin reagent and the number of cells (*see* Note 8). We routinely use 5–25 μg of total DNA; *pAAV/Ad* helper plasmid, and rAAV vector plasmid at a 3:1 ratio, per 100-mm tissue culture dish.
3. Suspend Lipofectin reagent in another 1.0 mL of Opti-MEM medium in a second polystyrene tube. The DNA/Lipofectin ratio should be 1:4 (*see* Note 8).
4. Mix the DNA and Lipofectin together by inverting the tube several times or vortexing gently.
5. Incubate the DNA/Lipofectin mixture for 5 min at room temperature.
6. Aspirate the medium from the cells and wash the monolayer twice with either Opti-MEM medium or PBS.

7. Add the DNA/Lipofectin/Opti-MEM mixture (2 mL) to the cells.
8. Incubate at 37°C under normal 5% CO_2 conditions for 3–6 h.
9. Aspirate the media and replace with DMEM containing 2% FBS and adenovirus at 3–10 IU/cell.
10. Continue incubation for 48 h.

3.1.2. Transfection of DNA Using DOTAP Transfection Reagent

1. Grow cells on 100-mm tissue culture dishes in DMEM containing 10% serum, until they are 60–80% confluent.
2. Dilute DNAs (*see* Section 3.1.1. and Note 8) to 250 μL with HBS in a 15-mL polystyrene tube.
3. Dilute DOTAP transfection reagent to 250 μL with HBS in a second polystyrene tube. The DNA/DOTAP ratio should also be about 1:4 (*see* Note 8).
4. Mix the DNA and DOTAP solutions together and incubate for 10 min at room temperature.
5. Add Opti-MEM medium to bring the total volume to 5 mL and mix gently.
6. Aspirate the medium from the cells and wash the monolayer twice with either Opti-MEM medium or PBS.
7. Add the DNA/DOTAP/Opti-MEM mixture (5 mL) to the cells.
8. Incubate at 37°C under normal 5% CO_2 conditions for 6–24 h.
9. Aspirate the media and replace with DMEM containing 2% FCS and adenovirus at 3–10 IU/cell.
10. Continue incubation for 48 h.

3.2. Isolation and Purification of Recombinant Virus

3.2.1. Rapid Crude Virus Stocks

Concentrated crude virus stocks are prepared from infected 293 cells by scraping the cells infected as described in Section 3.1. into the culture medium and recovering them by pelleting at low speed in a bench-top centrifuge. The cells are then resuspended in a hypotonic buffer, e.g., PBS, and the viruses are released by either three cycles of freeze-thawing or brief sonication. The cell debris can be removed by a second low speed centrifugation if desired, and the lysate stored at −70°C until needed.

Prior to using this crude cell lysate to infect cells, it may be desirable to inactivate the adenovirus by heating the cell lysate at 56°C for 1 h. This treatment will effectively remove the heat-labile adenovirus from the preparation without decreasing the titer of recombinant AAV significantly.

3.2.2. Purified Stocks

Although the rapid, crude viral stocks, prepared as described in Section 3.2.1., are often all that is needed to produce infectious recombinant AAV, in vivo gene transfer necessitates the production of large, high titer, viral stocks.

Since the titer of recombinant AAV from the two-component plasmid system described here is relatively low, the following procedure may be scaled up as needed. Although the volumes described here are per 100-mm tissue culture plate, 150-mm plates or larger vessels may also be used. For larger tissue culture dishes, some amounts may need to be adjusted in proportion to the change in culture dish surface area. This protocol should facilitate the recovery and concentration of rAAV from large volumes of culture media as may be needed.

1. At 48 h postinfection, scrape the cells into the media and collect by low speed centrifugation (500g, 5 min). Remove the media from the cell pellet and resuspend the cells in 10 mL of TNE buffer.
2. Add 1.0 mL 0.2% trypsin solution and 1.0 mL 20% deoxycholate. Mix gently by inverting the tube several times and incubate at 37°C for 1 h.
3. Dounce homogenize the sample 20 times to shear the cellular DNA.
4. Add 5.0 g of solid cesium chloride, mix well to dissolve, and divide the sample between two, 14 × 89 mm, Ultra-Clear (Beckman, Fullerton, CA) ultra centrifuge tubes. Centrifuge at 150,000g in a Beckman SW-41 rotor (or equivalent) for 20 h.
5. After centrifugation, the recombinant viral band may be visible. However, it should not be confused with the slightly less dense adenovirus-helper. If visible, collect the banded virus with a syringe through the side of the tube. If there is no discrete rAAV band, the gradient should be fractionated. Ten 0.5-mL fractions are convenient. Recombinant AAV should band at a density of 1.42–1.45. Determine the density of CsCl in each fraction by either weighing a small amount of each fraction or by using a refractometer. Pool those fractions with densities in the appropriate range. If the rAAV being produced can be easily assayed for biologically (ie., β-galactosidase or luciferase enzyme assay), this activity may also be used to determine which fractions contain recombinant virus.
6. Dialyze the banded virus in boiled dialysis tubing for about 2 h against two changes of 100 vol of PBS to remove the cesium from the preparation.
7. Layer the dialyzed banded virus on the following CsCl step gradient in a Beckman SW-41 centrifuge tube, or equivalent: 0.5 mL CsCl at 1.7 g/mL, 1.5 mL CsCl at 1.5 g/mL, 3.0 mL CsCl at 1.35 g/mL, 1.5 mL CsCl at 1.25 g/mL.
8. Mark the outside of the centrifuge tube at each step interface with a permanent marker.
9. Centrifuge at 150,000g in an SW-41 (Beckman) rotor for 2 h.
10. Recombinant AAV should again band at a density of 1.42–1.45. The band will probably not be visible, but will form at the interface between the 1.35 and 1.5 CsCl steps. Collect the banded virus with a syringe through the side of the tube.
11. Dialyze the banded virus in boiled dialysis tubing for about 2 h against two changes of 100 vol of PBS to remove the cesium from the preparation.
12. Freeze aliquots at –70°C. These virus stocks are stable for many years at –70°C.

3.3. Titration of Recombinant AAV by Replication Center Assay

It is often important to determine the titer of recombinant AAV. Since AAV is a defective virus, direct titration of infectious units by their ability to form plaques on permissive cells is not possible. Therefore, rAAV must be indirectly titered by a replication center assay (as described here), or by its ability to transduce an assayable marker gene. Since the replication center assay will be more applicable to a broader range of rAAV vectors, it is described here.

1. The day prior to performing the assay, plate 293 cells into 96-well tissue culture dishes. The cell density should be approx $2-3 \times 10^4$ cells/well (about 50% of confluence). Set up one row of the plate for determining the recombinant titer (row A), and a second row for wild-type AAV contamination (row H). Up to 11 different preparations of AAV can be titered on a single plate (*see* Fig. 3).
2. The next day, remove the media from the cells, leaving behind just enough to cover the cells. Add 1.0 μL of the rAAV-containing lysate, or purified rAAV preparation, to a well in the first row on the plate (row A), and the same amount to a well in the last row (row H). Other wells can be used to monitor rAAV purification or concentration as described in Section 3.2. Leave the last well in the row A for an "Ad only" control. Rock the plate gently back and forth to mix.
3. In a 15-mL polystyrene tube, add a predetermined amount (*see* step 4) of adenovirus to 2.4 mL of DMEM/2% FBS. Mix well. Dispense 100 μL per each well in row H, and the Ad only control well at the end of row A.
4. To the remaining, approx 1.2 mL of the media/Ad mixture, add a calculated amount of wild-type AAV and dispense 100 μL per each well in row A. The final MOI of adenovirus and AAV should be 20 and 2, respectively.
5. Incubate for 30 h.
6. Remove the media and rinse the cells with a small volume of PBS.
7. Add 250 μL of PE solution to each well and place the dish on ice.
8. Mark each nylon hybridization membrane with pen, prewet with PBS, and mount in the filter holder.
9. Apply 5.0 mL of PBS to each filter.
10. Resuspend the cells from a well of the 96-well plate by pipeting up and down. Apply 50 μL of the cell suspension into the PBS buffer on the top the nylon filter mounted in the filter holder; mix gently. Apply suction.
11. Carefully remove the nylon filter disk from the manifold with flat-tipped forceps. Place the disk with cell side up onto a pool of 0.5*N* NaOH on plastic wrap. Stretch the plastic wrap to ensure that all disks wet evenly. After 2 min, remove disks and place on blotting paper (cell side up).
12. Repeat step 11 with a new sheet of plastic wrap and fresh 0.5*N* NaOH.
13. On a new sheet of plastic wrap, pipet a small amount of 1.0*M* Tris-HCl, pH 7.5. Place the nylon filter disks with cell side up onto the pool of 1.0*M* Tris-HCl, pH 7.5. Stretch the plastic wrap to ensure that all of the disks wet evenly. After 2 min, remove the disk and place on blotting paper (cell side up).
14. Repeat step 13 with a new sheet of plastic wrap and fresh 1.0*M* Tris-HCl, pH 7.5.

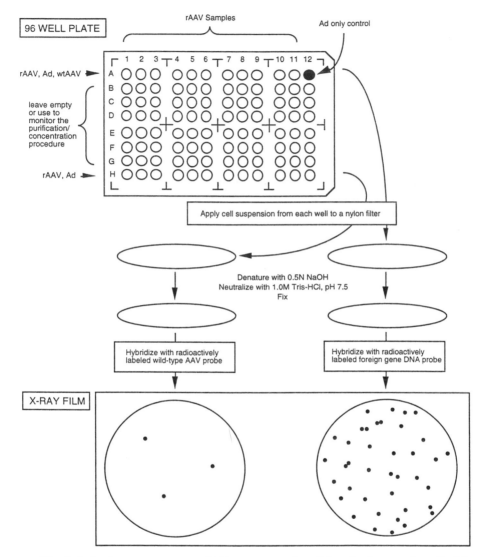

Fig. 3. Infectious center assay. Cells are grown in a 96-well plate, as described in the text, resuspended in PBS and applied to nylon filter membranes. After denaturation, and binding of the replicated AAV DNA to the filters; the filters are probed with radioactively labeled wild-type, or foreign gene, DNA probe to determine the titer of the recombinant AAV preparation (*see text* for details).

15. Allow the disks to dry at room temperature. Fix the DNA to the disks by microwaving for 5 min at full power.
16. Hybridize the filters from row H with a radioactively labeled wild-type AAV probe and from row A with a radioactively labeled foreign gene DNA probe.

Hybridization using probes with a specific activity of 10^7 cpm/μg DNA gives a strong signal on overnight exposure of the filter to X-ray film.

17. The titer of the original rAAV preparation is equal to the number of positive cells per filter multiplied by 5×10^3, expressed as infectious units (IU) per milliliter.

4. Notes

1. All DNA preparations should be pure; double banding through cesium chloride gradients *(34)* or a preparation of equivalent high quality is essential.

2. The AAV terminal repeats may be unstable in plasmids propagated in several commonly used laboratory strains of *E. coli*. Host strains carrying *recA*, as well as *recJ* and *recB* mutations, such as the SURE (Stratagene, La Jolla, CA) strain of cells, are recommended.

3. The small (30-nm diameter) cationic lipid vesicles in the Lipofectin and DOTAP reagents can fuse to form large (>1-μm diameter) multilamellar structures in the presence of polyvalent anions, such as EDTA, citrate, or phosphate *(35)*. Preparations of these large, fused vesicles are less efficacious than the small vesicles. Therefore, tissue culture media containing high concentrations of polyanionic buffers should be avoided.

4. There are components present in serum that can inhibit Lipofectin-mediated transfection. Although a wide variety of serum-free media give good results with lipofection, in a number of cell lines, Opti-MEM 1 (Gibco-BRL) gives the best results with respect to both viability in the presence of Lipofectin and the level of expression obtained. DOTAP transfection reagent is less inhibited by the presence of serum; however, we still recommend the use of serum-free media.

5. The toxicity of the transfection reagent varies among different cell types, and elimination of serum from the transfection media further reduces viability. Screening of serum-free media has identified Opti-MEM as an acceptable serum-free medium, which results in improved viability, relative to DMEM, for human 293 cells.

6. Large nonfunctional DNA/lipid aggregates can form when the DNA concentration during formation of the Lipid/DNA complexes is too high (approx 100 μg/mL or greater). Formation of these large aggregates is exacerbated by increased ionic strength; if it is desirable to prepare a concentrated stock solution of premixed Lipofectin/DNA, or DOTAP/DNA, complexes, they should be prepared at low ionic strength. In an effort to maintain both the DNA and transfection reagent concentrations at the lowest possible concentration, prior to complex formation, the DNA and transfection reagent should be separately diluted into equal volumes of media and then mixed.

7. The concentration-dependent, ionic species and ionic strength-dependent aggregates that can form under different transfection conditions are sticky, and they can be seen to adhere to glassware and to plastic. Polypropylene and glass attract these aggregates more than polystyrene. For this reason, polystyrene mixing containers are preferred for transfection.

8. Optimum transfection activity occurs under conditions in which the net negative charge on the DNA is substantially reduced. Complexes with an excess of positive charge are taken up by cells more effectively than neutral or negatively charged complexes. The optimum transfection activity for DNA seems to occur when the ratio of positively charged molar equivalents (contributed by DOTMA in Lipofectin, or DOTAP in the Transfection-Reagent from Boehringer Mannheim) exceeds by 1.0–2.5 the number of molar equivalents of negative charge contributed by the DNA. The molarity of DOTMA (669.5 mol wt) in a 1 mg/mL Lipofectin solution that contains 50/50 (w/w) of DOPE (neutral lipid) is 0.75 mM; the molarity of DOTAP (774.2 mol wt) in a 1 mg/mL solution is 1.3 mM; and the molar equivalents of negative charge in a 1 mg/mL DNA solution (average mol wt of the nucleotide monomer is 330) is 3 mM. Based on this estimate, the optimum activity occurs when the total mass of lipid (DOTMA + DOPE, or DOTAP) exceeds the mass of DNA by 4–10-fold.

9. Since unsaturated fatty acids are oxidized by airborne oxygen, it is recommended that the DOTAP transfection reagent be removed from the bottle with a sterile cannula and syringe. This will avoid a subsequent reduction of transfection efficiency.

10. As compared to DOTMA, DOTAP has the advantage that it can be decomposed by nonspecific esterases in the cells after fusion and deposition, respectively, although this may have limited relevance to the production of rAAV.

11. Virus yields will be dependent on plasmid transfection efficiency, titer of adenovirus helper, level of AAV gene product expression, the length of time postinfection prior to harvesting, and the ability to remove and concentrate virus from the culture medium. The need to optimize as many variables as possible is apparent.

12. When making virus stocks, it is important not to grow the virus in multiple passages; this will lead to the generation of defective particles that will decrease the efficiency of expression of inserted genes.

References

1. Bartlett, J. S. and Samulski, R. J. (1995) Genetics and biology of adeno-associated virus, in *Viral Vectors: Gene Therapy and Neuroscience Applications* (Kaplitt, M. G. and Loewy, A. D., eds.), Academic, San Diego, pp. 55–73.

2. Cukor, G., Blacklow, N. R., Hoggan, D., and Berns, K. I. (1984) Biology of adeno-associated virus, in *The Parvoviruses* (Berns, K. I., ed.), Plenum, New York, pp. 33–66.

3. Samulski, R. J. (1993) Adeno-associated virus: integration at a specific chromopsomal locus. *Curr. Opin. Gen. Dev.* **3**, 74–80.

4. Berns, K. I. and Adler, S. (1972) Separation of two types of adeno-associated virus particles containing complementary polynucleotide chains. *J. Virol.* **5**, 693–699.

5. Berns, K. I. and Rose, J. A. (1970) Evidence for a single-stranded adeno-associated virus genome: isolation and separation of complementary single strands. *J. Virol.* **5**, 693–699.

6. Blacklow, N. R., Hoggan, M. D., and Rowe, W. P. (1967) Isolation of adenovirus-associated viruses from man. *Proc. Natl. Acad. Sci. USA* **58**, 1410–1415.

7. Mayor, H. D., Torikai, K., Melnick, J., and Mandel, M. (1969) Plus and minus single-stranded DNA separately encapsidated in adeno-associated satellite virions. *Science* **166,** 1280–1282.

8. Samulski, R. J., Chang, L.-S., and Shenk, T. (1987) A recombinant plasmid from which an infectious adeno-associated virus genome can be excised in vitro and its use to study viral replication. *J. Virol.* **61,** 3096–3101.

9. Srivastava, A., Lusby, E. W., and Berns, K. I. (1983) Nucleotide sequence and organization of the adeno-associated virus 2 genome. *J. Virol.* **45,** 555–564.

10. Lusby, E., Fife, K. H., and Berns, K. I. (1980) Nucleotide sequence of the inverted terminal repetition in adeno-associated virus DNA. *J. Virol.* **34,** 402–409.

11. Muzyczka, M. (1992) Use of adeno-associated virus as a general transduction vector for mammalian cells. *Curr. Top. Microbiol. Immunol.* **158,** 97–129.

12. Berns, K. I. (1990) Parvorviridae and their replication, in *Virology*, vol. 2., 2nd ed. (Fields, B. N. and Knipe, D. M., eds.), Raven, New York, pp. 1743–1763.

13. Berns, K. I. and Huaswirth, W. W. (1984) Adeno-associated virus DNA structure and replication, in *The Parvoviruses* (Berns, K. I., ed.), Plenum, New York, p. 1.

14. Hermonat, P. L. and Muzyczka, N. (1984) Use of adeno-associated virus as a mammalian DNA cloning vector: transduction of neomycin resistance into mammalian tissue culture cells. *Proc. Natl. Acad. Sci. USA* **81,** 6466–6470.

15. McLaughlin, S. K., Collis, P., Hermonat, P. L., and Muzyczka, N. (1988) Adeno-associated virus general transduction vectors: analysis of proviral structures. *J. Virol.* **62,** 1963–1973.

16. Samulski, R. J., Chang, L.-S., and Shenk, T. (1989) Helper-free stocks of recombinant adeno-associated viruses: normal integration does not require viral gene expression. *J. Virol.* **63,** 3822–3828.

17. Atchison, R. W., Casto, B. C., and Hammond, W. M. (1965) Adenovirus-associated defective virus particles. *Science* **149,** 754–756.

18. Hoggan, M. D., Blacklow, N. R., and Rowe, W. P. (1966) Studies of small DNA viruses found in various adenovirus preparations: physical, biological, and immunological characteristics. *Proc. Natl. Acad. Sci. USA* **55,** 1457–1471.

19. Parks, W. P., Melnick, J. L., Rongey, R., and Mayor, H. D. (1967) Physical assay and growth cycle studies of a defective adeno-satellite virus. *J. Virol.* **1,** 171–180.

20. Buller, R. M., Janik, J. E., Sebring, E. D., and Rose, J. A. (1981) Herpes simplex virus types 1 and 2 completely help adenovirus-associated virus replication. *J. Virol.* **40,** 241–247.

21. Berns, K. I., Pinkerton, T. C., Thomas, G. F., and Hoggan, M. D. (1975) Detection of adeno-associated virus (AAV)-specific nucleotide sequences in DNA isolated from latently infected Detroit 6 cells. *Virology* **68,** 556–560.

22. Cheung, A. K., Hoggan, M. D., Hauswirth, W. W., and Berns, K. I. (1980) Integration of the adeno-associated virus genome into cellular DNA in latently infected human Detroit 6 cells. *J. Virol.* **33,** 739–748.

23. Laughlin, C. A., Tratschin, J.-D., Coon, H., and Carter, B. J. (1983) Cloning of infectious adeno-associated virus genomes in bacterial plasmids. *Gene* **23,** 65–73.

24. Samulski, R. J., Berns, K. I., Tan, M., and Muzyczka, N. (1982) Cloning of adeno-associated virus into pBR322: rescue of intact virus from the recombinant plasmid in human cells. *Proc. Natl. Acad. Sci. USA* **79,** 2077–2081.
25. Bartlett, J. S., Quattrocchi, K. B., and Samulski, R. J. (1995) The development of adeno-associated virus as a vector for cancer gene therapy, in *The Internet Book of Gene Therapy: Cancer Therapeutics* (Sobol, R. E. and Scanlon, K. J., eds.), Appleton & Lange, Stamford, CT, pp. 27–40.
26. LaFace, D., Hermonat, P., Wakeland, E., and Peck, A. (1988) Gene transfer into hematopoietic progenitor cells mediated by an adeno-associated virus vector. *Virology* **162,** 483–486.
27. Ohi, S., Dixit, M., Tillery, M. K., and Plonk, S. G. (1990) Construction and replication of an adeno-associated virus expression vector that contains human β-globin cDNA. *Gene* **89,** 279–282.
28. Tratschin, J.-D., West, M. H. P., Sandbank, T., and Carter, B. J. (1984) A human parvovirus, adeno-associated virus, as a eukaryotic vector: transient expression and encapsidation of the prokaryotic gene for chloramphenicol acetyltransrerase. *Mol. Cell. Biol.* **4,** 2072–2081.
29. Kumar, S. and Leffak, M. (1991) Conserved chromatin structure in c-myc 5' flanking DNA after viral transduction. *J. Mol. Biol.* **222,** 45–57.
30. Walsh, C. E., Liu, J. M., Xiao, X., Young, N. S., Nienhuis, A. W., and Samulski, R. J. (1992) Regulated high level expression of a human γ-globin gene introduced into erythroid cells by an adeno-associated virus vector. *Proc. Natl. Acad. Sci. USA* **89,** 7257–7261.
31. Goodman, S., Xiao, X., Donahue, R. E., Moulton, A., Miller, J., Walsh, C., Young, N. S., Samulski, R. J., and Nienhuis, A. W. (1994) Recombinant adeno-associated virus-mediated gene transfer into hematopoietic progenitor cells. *Blood* **84,** 1492–1500.
32. Walsh, C. E., Nienhuis, A. W., Samulski, R. J., Brown, M. G., Miller, J. L., Young, N. S., and Liu, J. M. (1994) Phenotypic correction of Fanconi anemia in human hematopoietic cells with a recombinant adeno-associated virus vector. *J. Clin. Invest.* **94,** 1440–1448.
33. Kriegler, M. (1990) *Gene Transfer and Expression: A Laboratory Manual.* Stockton, New York.
34. Maniatis, T., Fritsch, E. F., and Sambrook, J. *(*1982) *Molecular Cloning: A Laboratory Manual.* Cold Spring Harbor Laboratory, Cold Spring Harbor, NY.
35. Felgner, P. L. and Ringold, G. M. (1989) Cationic liposome-mediated transfection. *Nature* **337,** 387,388.

3

Generation of High-Titer, Helper-Free Retroviruses by Transient Transfection

Warren S. Pear, Martin L. Scott, and Garry P. Nolan

1. Introduction

Retroviral gene transfer is presently one of the most powerful techniques for introducing stably heritable genetic material into mammalian cells (reviewed in ref. *1*). One serious drawback of this technique, however, has been the difficulty in readily producing high-titer recombinant retroviruses. For many applications, such as infecting rare target cells or the majority of cells in tissue culture, the recombinant virus titer must be at least 10^6 infectious units/mL. Although one can usually obtain high-titer mixtures of recombinant and replication-competent retroviruses in a relatively short time, many applications such as cell marking studies or studying genes in vivo demand freedom from replication-competent virus.

A milestone in gene transfer technology was the creation of cell lines that could package retroviral RNAs into infectious particles without the concomitant production of replication competent virus *(2,3)* (reviewed in refs. *4* and *5*). In what became the prototype for creating helper-free retrovirus packaging cells, the retroviral structural gene products (*gag, pol*, and *env*) were provided *in trans* by separating them from the elements required for packaging retroviral RNA into virions. The first ecotropic retroviral packaging line, ψ2, was created by stably introducing into NIH3T3 cells an engineered retroviral DNA genome from which the RNA packaging signal, termed ψ, had been removed *(2)*. Production of high-titer, helper-free, infectious virus required the subsequent stable introduction of a retroviral vector containing the ψ retroviral packaging site, transcription and processing elements, and the gene of interest into the ψ2 cells (*see* Chapter 4). Retroviral particles produced in this way could infect target cells and transmit the gene of interest, but not replicate, because

From: *Methods in Molecular Medicine, Gene Therapy Protocols*
Edited by: P. Robbins Humana Press Inc., Totowa, NJ

Fig. 1. Methods used to create high-titer, helper-free retroviral stocks by stable producer lines **(A)** or transient production **(B)**. In both, the first step depicted is introduction of the retroviral DNA by $CaPO_4$-mediated transfection into the packaging cells. Retroviral DNA can be introduced by other methods, including infection. For the production of stable producer clones (A), the next step is cloning of the transfected cells. Although neo selection is depicted, other methods, such as FACS sorting, can be used to identify clones expressing the gene of interest in a much shorter period than drug selection. Following isolation, the individual clones must be expanded, then screened to identify those that produce retrovirus at high titer. Only at this point can the supernatant be harvested for use. In the transient method (B), following transfection, one must wait 48 h in order to obtain adequate expression of the gene(s) of interest. At this time, the supernatant can be harvested and is ready for use.

genomic information encoding the packaging proteins was not carried in the packaged retroviral particles. This original strategy has subsequently been modified by a number of investigators to decrease the risk of producing replication-competent virus and to increase viral titers (*see* reviews in refs. *4* and *5*).

Although infectious retrovirus is produced within 48 h following transfection of these packaging lines, the infectious titer generated by these cells is generally low (10^3–10^4/mL), necessitating identification of those clones that produce retroviruses at higher titer. This is accomplished by selecting single cell clones from the transfected population, then testing each for its ability to produce virus (Fig. 1A). Under optimal circumstances, this requires 1–2 mo and must be repeated for each different construct. During the prolonged selection process, gene(s) encoded by the retroviral vector may inhibit growth of the packaging line, favoring the outgrowth of clones that express low levels of virus, thereby making it difficult to identify clones continuously producing retrovirus at a high titer. Although the biochemical basis for this effect is often unclear, the inability to produce high-titer infectious retroviruses expressing certain genes, such as members of the *abl* and *rel* families, has been experienced by a number of investigators *(7)*.

To minimize potential toxic effects of the introduced gene products on the packaging cell lines, several groups have devised strategies based on transient retroviral production *(6–8)*. This approach has the added benefit of markedly reducing the time and effort required to produce high-titer retroviral stocks. Although the first step in both stable and transient retroviral production is transfection of the retroviral construct into the packaging cell line, at 48 h after transfection, the infectious retroviral titers are several logs higher using the transient production methods (Fig. 1B).

Several factors may account for the ability of the transient retroviral production methods to yield viral supernatants with infectious titers in the range of 10^5–10^7/mL. These include both the properties of the parent cells themselves and changes engineered into them to augment transient production. Unlike previous retroviral packaging cell lines based on either murine or avian cells, the transient approaches utilize cells derived from either primates or humans. These cells offer several potential advantages. First, they are much more transfectable using simple $CaPO_4$-based protocols. Second, they support very high level expression of genes introduced under control of a number of promoters, such as those derived from CMV. Third, they contain fewer endogenous retroviral loci whose products could interfere with infectious virus assembly and release *(9)*. In addition, they have been previously modified to contain viral gene products, such as adenoviral E1A or polyoma large T-antigen, with properties that can be exploited to further enhance expression of new constructs.

The strategy described by Landau and Littman *(6)* uses transient cotransfection of the SV40-transformed African green monkey renal cell line, COS-7, with two modified retroviral plasmids, both containing the SV40 origin of replication. In addition to this viral element, one construct contains the MLV LTR, retroviral packaging site, SV40 origin of replication (*ori*), and DNA element(s) of interest, whereas the second construct encodes retroviral core (*gag*), polymerase (*pol*), and envelope (*env*) proteins but lacks a retroviral packaging site. Virus stocks with titers as high as 10^5 infectious units/mL have been obtained with certain recombinant constructs by using this approach. The ability to obtain titers in this range depends, in part, on large T-antigen-dependent amplification of the plasmids containing the SV40 *ori*, which can enhance infectious recombinant titers by up to 2 logs *(6)*. Although these authors do not report the detection of replication competent virus, the vectors used in this study could produce such genomes after only one recombination event.

Both of the other transient transfection strategies *(7,8)* use the 293 cell line, an adenovirus-transformed human embryonic kidney cell line *(10)* as the basis of their packaging systems. In the approach described by Pear et al. *(7)*, two different plasmids encoding the retroviral structural genes, *in trans*, were stably incorporated into the 293T cell line, a variant of 293 cells into which a temperature-sensitive SV40 large T-antigen had been introduced *(11)*. As the retroviral structural genes are encoded on two different plasmids and contain additional mutations, at least three recombination events are necessary to generate replication-competent retroviruses *(12)*. Stable incorporation of these plasmids is important for preventing helper virus formation since transient introduction of these plasmids together with a Moloney-based retroviral vector yielded replication-competent virus *(7)*. Using this system, all constructs tried by the authors have produced retroviral titers greater than 10^6/mL. This includes not only relatively nontoxic genes such as those encoding β-galactosidase (βgal) and G418 resistance, but also members of the *abl* and *rel* families of proto-oncogenes from which we were unable to identify stable high titer producing clones utilizing the stable production approach *(7)*. These viruses have been used to infect rodent tissue culture cells and murine hematopoietic progenitors with no detectable generation of helper virus *(7)*. Although retroviral vectors containing an extended packaging site *(13)* give approximately a twofold increase in titer, infectious titers greater than 10^6/mL have been obtained with all of the retroviral vectors tried by the authors including pGD *(14)*, pBABE *(15)*, MFG *(16)*, and pBND (D. Turner and C. Cepko, unpublished, described in ref. 7). We have observed no enhancement of titer using retroviral vectors containing an SV40 *ori*, despite the fact that a 293 cell variant (293T) *(11)* was chosen as the starting material for the packaging cell lines.

The system described by Finer et al. *(8)*, termed *kat*, also utilizes 293 cells. However, unlike the cell lines of Pear et al. *(7)*, the *kat* system requires cointroduction of both a plasmid encoding the retroviral structural genes and a plasmid encoding the retroviral vector. The constructs utilized in the *kat* system have been further modified to minimize the creation of replication-competent retroviruses. In general, the titers obtained using *kat*-produced retroviral supernatants are similar to those found by Pear et al. *(7)*. It is unclear whether further advantage would result from the creation of a packaging cell line by stable introduction of the *kat* constructs. Another question is whether all MuLV-based retroviral vectors will function in the *kat* system or whether only the re-engineered *kat* vectors function well in this system.

In summary, both the methods described by Pear et al. *(7)* and Finer et al. *(8)* give rapid production of high-titer, helper-free viruses. These methods are particularly useful in creating retroviral stocks containing genes that are toxic to stable producer lines. Also, the ability to rapidly produce high-titer retroviral stocks offers novel possibilities for using these viruses, for example in the creation of retroviral cDNA libraries.

The remainder of this chapter will focus on the use of the packaging cell lines developed by the authors for rapid production of helper-free retroviruses with ecotropic, amphotropic, and polytropic host ranges. The basic 293 cell transfection protocols are likely to work equally well with the *kat* system plasmids, or other complementation systems that provide the requisite packaging proteins and genomic material to package. Procedures are described for optimizing transfection conditions and performing infections of adherent and nonadherent cell types. The advantages of these transient retroviral production methods should facilitate and extend the use of retroviral gene transfer technology. In addition to producing helper-free ecotropic and amphotropic retroviruses, methods are presented for rapidly pseudotyping retroviral virions with alternative envelope proteins.

1.1. Construction of the Packaging Cell Lines

A detailed description of the 293T/17, Anjou65, and Bosc23 cell lines can be found in ref. *7*. Briefly, a clone termed "293T/17" was isolated from the 293T (293tsa1609neo) population *(11)* that produced retroviral supernatants capable of infecting NIH3T3 cells at titers greater than 10^6/mL following transient transfection with wild-type Moloney virus (pZap) *(17)* and a βgal-expressing retroviral vector (pBND8) (D. Turner and C. Cepko, unpublished, described in ref. *7*). The gag-pol expressing plasmid, pCripEnv- *(12)*, which contains a mutation in the envelope region, lacks the packaging site, and replaces the 3' LTR with the SV40 poly(A) site, was transfected into 293T/17 cells along with a plasmid conferring hygromycin resistance *(18)*. Individual clones were selected and tested for reverse transcriptase activity *(19)*, and one clone, Anjou65, which had the highest reverse transcriptase activity, was used in subsequent experiments. The ecotropic envelope expressing construct, pCripGag-2 *(12)*, which contains mutations in the gag region, lacks the packaging site, and replaces the 3' LTR with the SV40 poly(A) site, was transfected into Anjou65 cells along with a plasmid expressing the gpt-resistance gene *(20)*. Individual clones were isolated and tested for the ability to produce high-titer, βgal-expressing retroviruses. One clone, Bartlett 96, produced βgal retrovirus with a titer in excess of 10^6/mL following transfection with pBND8. Two rounds of limiting dilution subcloning were subsequently performed, giving rise to the Bosc 23 ecotropic packaging line.

We have recently developed an amphotropic counterpart to the Bosc23 cell line, termed Bing (W. Pear, M. Scott, and G. Nolan, unpublished). The construction of this cell line was similar to the Bosc23, except that the amphotropic envelope expressing construct, pCripAMgag *(12)*, was used in place of pCripGag-2. Another difference between the Bing and Bosc cell lines is that the gene encoding hygromycin phosphotransferase resistance was expressed from a retroviral vector in the Bing cell line. As a result, Bing cell supernatants express approximately 100 CFU of hygromycin phosphotransferase resistance per mL of retroviral supernatant. Retroviruses produced by Bing cells are helper-free and able to infect NIH3T3 cells at the same efficiency as supernatants from Bosc cells, as well as infect a wide variety of mammalian cell lines, including human T-cells.

One of the authors has recently developed a second generation packaging system termed ØNX. The major edition is that the *gag-pol* construct has an ires-CD8 surface marker with which one can follow *gag-pol* expression in living cells on a cell-by-cell basis. This facilitates checking of the line for continued high-level *gag-pol* expression using CD8 as proxy. Additionally, non-MMULV-based promoters were used to drive the *gag-pol* and *env* genes, further minimizing the potential for recombination with vector LTRs. Otherwise, construction of these cell lines was similar to Bosc23 and the details of these newer lines will be published in the near future (Achacoso and Nolan, in preparation). Amphotropic and ecotropic versions of these cell lines were prepared and shown to stably express gag-pol and env proteins over several months. These lines are helper-free and produce retroviral supernatants that have titers similar to Bosc23 and Bing. The methods described in this chapter work well with the ØNX cell lines.

1.2. Rapid Pseudotyping of Moloney Retroviral Virions with Vesicular Stomatitus Virus G-Glycoprotein

We have successfully produced high-titer VSV-G-pseudotyped virions for infection of human and nonhuman cell types. The production of VSV-G to pseudotype retroviral virions, demonstrated by Burns et al. *(21)*, is shown here in an adaptation of the transient retrovirus system using the Anjou cell line. A more detailed description of the use of this pseudotyping approach to infect several different human cell lines, mouse cells, fish cells, and insect cells will be published elsewhere (J. Caldwell, J. Lorens, P. Achacoso, and G. Nolan, unpublished results). The method outlined in this chapter for pseudotyping does not require the selection of a stable producer clone, as required by the procedure of Burns *(21)*, and results in the production of recombinant virus 3 d after transfection of the construct. The VSV-G-pseudotyped viruses produced in this fully transient system can be concentrated and used to infect multiple human and nonhuman cell types. It is expected that this approach will also be useful for pseudotyping retroviral virions with designer envelope proteins that confer cell-type specific infection of target cells. Such specificity should be of therapeutic importance in numerous clinical settings.

The main advantage of VSV-G-pseudotyping is the stability imparted on the retroviral virion by the VSV-G envelope. This stability allows for concentration of virion stocks by centrifugation (multiple rounds can be employed for continued concentration) to very high titers. A second advantage is that the VSV-G target epitope is a widely expressed lipid in higher eukaryotes. It is the broad expression of this latter target epitope that expands the potential host range of retrovirus-mediated gene delivery.

2. Materials

All solutions are prepared using double-distilled water. For reagents used in tissue culture, it is recommended that they be prepared in disposable plastic labware. When possible, it is best to order reagents that have been tissue-culture tested by the manufacturer.

1. Growth medium (GM) for 293 cells and derivatives: The following are added directly to DME to give the indicated final concentrations: 10% heat-inactivated fetal bovine serum , 100 U/mL penicillin, 100 U/mL streptomycin, 2 mM L-glutamine.
2. Freezing medium: 90% heat-inactivated fetal calf serum, 10% DMSO.
3. Chloroquine: 25 mM chloroquine stock solution prepared in either PBS or GM and filtered through a 0.2-μM filter and stored at $-20°C$.
4. 2X HBS: 50 mM HEPES, pH 7.05, 10 mM KCl, 12 mM dextrose, 280 mM NaCl, 1.5 mM Na$_2$HPO$_4$. The final pH of the solution should be 7.05 $\pm$ 0.05. Filter through a 0.2-μM filter, aliquot, and store at $-20°C$. Try to avoid multiple freeze/thaw cycles. To thaw, warm to room temperature and invert or vortex the tube to achieve uniform mixing. Although it is unclear why this occurs, the ability of the 2X HBS solution to produce working CaPo$_4$ precipitates deteriorates after 6 mo to 1 yr, even when the 2X HBS solution is stored at $-20°C$.
5. 2M CaCl$_2$: Prepare a 2M solution and filter through a 0.2-μM filter, aliquot, and store at $-20°C$.
6. Standard fibroblast medium (SFM) for growth of NIH3T3 cells: The following are added directly to DME to give the indicated final concentrations: 10% heat-inactivated donor bovine serum, 100 U/mL penicillin, 100 U/mL streptomycin, 2 mM L-glutamine.
7. Polybrene: The stock concentration is 4 mg/mL (dissolved in PBS and subsequently filtered through a 0.2-μM filter and stored at either 4 or $-20°C$).
8. Constructs used in VSV pseudotyping: The cDNA for the VSV-G polypeptide of vesicular stomatitus virus (gift of J. Rose, Yale) was inserted into the vector pME18S (gift of T. Kitamura, DNAX) under the transcriptional control of the SRα promoter element (an SV40/HTLV-1 hybrid promoter). MFG-*lacZ* is a retroviral vector expressing *lacZ* under the control of the MLV LTR (gift of Richard Mulligan, Whitehead Institute).

9. Packaging cell lines: The 293T/17, Anjou65, Bosc23, and Bing cell lines are available for noncommercial use through the American Type Culture Collection (Rockville, MD). In order to obtain the cell line(s), it is first necessary to complete and return a material transfer agreement. The material transfer agreements can be obtained from: Office of the General Counsel, Attn: Teresa L. Solomon, Esq., The Rockefeller University, 1230 York Avenue, New York, NY 10021-6399. Any questions regarding receipt of your transfer agreement should be addressed to this office. The accession numbers for the cell lines are: Bing (CAK8): amphotropic envelope-expressing packaging line: CCRL 11554. Bosc23: ecotropic envelope-expressing packaging line: CCRL 11270. Anjou 65: gag-pol expressing cell line: CCRL 11269. 293T/17: CCRL 11268.

3. Methods (*see* Note 1)

3.1. Growing and Freezing the Cells

The 293 cells and the packaging lines derived from these cells are carried in 293 growth media (GM, *see* Section 2.) and grown in a 37°C degree incubator containing 5% CO_2. To split and passage the cell lines (*see* Note 2):

1. Gently rinse 1X with PBS (without Ca^{2+} or Mg^{2+}).
2. Trypsinize (0.05% trypsin/0.53 m*M* EDTA) until the cells easily detach and can be readily pipeted into a single cell suspension (*see* Note 3).
3. Trypsinization is quenched with GM prior to subculturing in fresh medium.

3.2. Freezing 293 Cells and Derivatives

To assure viability of the cell line, it is recommended that the cells be frozen prior to confluence (*see* Note 4).

1. To freeze: Wash, trypsinize, and quench cells as described in Section 3.1.
2. Centrifuge the cells at 500*g* for 5 min.
3. Remove the media and add 1 mL of freezing solution (*see* Section 2.) per 10^6 cells.
4. Transfer to a 2-mL cryogenic vial.
5. Place the freezing vial at −70°C overnight and transfer to liquid nitrogen on the following day.

3.3. Thawing 293 Cells and Derivatives (see Note 5)

1. Remove one vial from liquid nitrogen and thaw rapidly at 37°C.
2. Immediately add 1 mL GM to the freezing vial and gently transfer this solution to a 15-mL sterile, conical screw-cap tube.
3. Add 2 mL of GM and gently mix the tube to allow for osmotic equilibration.
4. Add 10 mL of GM, close the tube, invert several times, and spin cells at 500*g* for 5 min.
5. Remove the supernatant, resuspend cell pellet in GM, and transfer to a 10-cm tissue-culture dish.

3.4. Transfecting the Packaging Cell Lines (see Notes 1 and 6)

Unless otherwise noted, all conditions are described for 60-mm plates (*see* Note 7).

Fig. 2. Appearance of Bosc 23 cells at the time of transfection. The panels show **(A)** 1.5×10^6 cells, **(B)** 2.2×10^6 cells, and **(C)** 3.0×10^6 cells that had been plated 24 h prior to photography. (B) The optimal density at which the cells are approx 80% confluent and clumping is minimized. The cells in (A) are too sparse. Although the cells in (C) are too dense for routine transfections, in some cases (described in the text), it may be necessary to use this number of cells. Cells were counted and plated in 4 mL GM on 60-mm dishes, 24 h prior to photography. Pictures were taken using a 10X objective lens.

1. Plate 2.5×10^6 cells/60-mm plate in 4 mL of GM 24 h prior to transfection. The dish should be approx 80% confluent prior to transfection (*see* Fig. 2, Note 8).
2. Just prior to transfection, change the medium to 4 mL of GM containing 25 μM chloroquine (*see* Note 9).
3. In an Eppendorf tube, prepare the transfection cocktail by adding 6–10 µg DNA to H_2O such that the final volume is 438 µL. Add 62 µL $2M$ $CaCl_2$ to the

DNA/H$_2$O (*see* Section 2.). Add 500 μL 2X HBS (pH 7.05) by bubbling (*see* Section 2., and Note 10). Immediately (within 1–2 min) add this solution to the cells and gently agitate to ensure uniform mixing. Return the cells to the incubator.

4. Approximately 10 h after adding the chloroquine-containing medium, remove the medium and gently replace with fresh GM. (If chloroquine was not used in step 3, skip to step 5.)

5. Approximately 16–24 h prior to harvesting the retroviral supernatant, remove the medium, and gently add fresh GM (*see* Note 11).

6. Harvest the retroviral supernatant 48 h posttransfection (*see* Note 12, Section 3.5.).

3.5. Harvesting the Retroviral Supernatant

1. When the retroviral supernatant is ready for harvesting, gently remove the supernatant and either filter through a 45-μm filter or centrifuge for 5 min at 500*g* at 4°C to remove living cells. If the retroviral supernatant is to be used within several hours, keep on ice until it is used. Otherwise, the retroviral supernatant may be frozen, resulting in a minimal loss of viral titer (*see* Note 13).

2. To freeze the retroviral supernatant, either snap-freeze the tube in liquid nitrogen or place the tube in dry ice. The frozen samples are stored at –70°C.

To thaw the frozen samples, warm for a minimal period of time at 37°C. The retroviral supernatant is ready for immediate use in subsequent experiments.

3.6. Infection of Adherent Fibroblasts

1. Approximately 12–18 h prior to infection, plate 5×10^5 NIH3T3 cells in SFM (standard fibroblast medium) on a 100-mm plate.

2. Prepare a 3-mL infection cocktail consisting of retrovirus-containing supernatant (either fresh or thawed), polybrene at a final concentration of 4 μg/mL, and SFM.

3. Remove the SFM from the NIH3T3 cells and add the 3-mL infection cocktail to the cells.

4. Return to the incubator for at least 3 h (*see* Note 14).

5. Add 7 mL of SFM to the cells.

6. Harvest (stain, neo select, and so on) the infected cells at 48 h postinfection.

3.7. Infection of Nonadherent Cells
by Addition of Retroviral Supernatant (see Note 15)

The conditions described are for infecting in 60-mm plates.

1. Prepare an infection cocktail consisting of the medium in which the target cells are grown, retroviral supernatant, and polybrene (2 μg/mL) such that the total volume is 3 mL (*see* Note 16).

2. Centrifuge exponentially growing target cells at 500*g* for 5 min. Remove supernatant and resuspend the cells in the infection cocktail at a concentration of 10^5–10^6 cells/mL.

3. Twenty-four hours postinfection, centrifuge the cells (500*g* for 5 min) and resuspend in the appropriate media for normal growth of the target cells (*see* Note 17). Allow the cells to grow for an additional 24–48 h before drug selection or other assays, such as staining for *lacZ* activity.

3.8. Infection of Nonadherent Cells by Cocultivation with Retrovirus-Producing Cells (see Note 15)

Conditions are described for 60-mm plates.

1. Transfect the 293 cells or derivative cell lines as described in Section 3.4., steps 1–4.
2. Twenty-four hours posttransfection, prepare a 3-mL infection cocktail consisting of polybrene at a final concentration of 2 µg/mL, 1 mL fresh or freshly thawed retroviral supernatant, and the nonadherent cells at a density of 10^5–10^6 cells/mL in the appropriate media for normal growth of the target cells (*see* Note 16). Remove the medium from the cells and gently add the infection cocktail to the cells (Add the cocktail to the side of the plate rather than directly to the cells). Return the cells to the incubator.
3. Forty-eight hours posttransfection, gently remove the medium that will contain many nonadherent cells, and transfer to a conical tube. Centrifuge for 5 min at 500g (*see* Note 18). Remove the supernatant and gently resuspend the cell pellet in a *freshly* prepared infection cocktail as described in step 2.
4. With extreme care to avoid disruption of the adherent cells, add the infection cocktail (in which the nonadherent cells have been resuspended) to the wall of the plate (rather than directly to the cells). Return the plate to the incubator.
5. Twenty-four hours later (72 h posttransfection), remove the nonadherent cells from the dish by gently pipeting (*see* Note 19).
6. Centrifuge the cells (5 min at 500g) and resuspend in the appropriate media for normal growth of the target cells. Allow the cells to grow for an additional 24–48 h before drug selection or other assays, such as staining for *lacZ* activity.

3.9. Rapid Pseudotyping of Moloney Retroviral Virions with Vesicular Stomatitus Virus G-Glycoprotein (see Notes 1 and 20)

1. Eight hours prior to transfection, plate the Anjou cells at 3×10^6 cells/60-mm plate in a 1:1 mixture of Anjou cell-conditioned media and fresh GM (*see* Note 21).
2. At eight hours postplating, add chloroquine to 25 µM and mix by gentle agitation of the media in the plate.
3. Cotransfect 5 µg pME-VSV-G and 5 µg MFG-*lacZ* by the calcium phosphate precipitation method described in Section 3.4., step 3.
4. Ten hours later, remove the media and replace with at least 5 mL fresh GM.
5. Seventy-two hours later, remove the retroviral supernatant that can either be used immediately, frozen, or concentrated (*see* step 6, Note 22).
6. The viral supernatant can be concentrated with no apparent loss of titer by centrifugation at 25,000 rpm in an SW41 rotor for 3 h or 50,000g at 5°C for 90 min to 2 h.
7. Infect the target cells using 4 µg/mL polybrene as described in Section 3.6., step 2 (*see* Note 23).

4. Notes

1. The viral supernatants produced by these methods can contain potentially hazardous recombinant constructs. The user of these systems must exercise due caution in the production, use, and storage of recombinant retroviral virions,

especially those with amphotropic and polytropic host ranges. This caution should apply to all genes expressed by the retroviral vectors. Appropriate NIH and other regional guidelines should be followed in the use of these recombinant retrovirus production systems.

2. It is suggested that the cells not be split at densities more dilute than 1:5 in order to maintain the uniformity of the cells in culture and minimize the outgrowth of clonal variants. The cells should not be allowed to become overconfluent, as this leads to the formation of cell clumps in culture that can cause uneven cell distribution after replating and result in less efficient transfection.

   Although it may be possible to carry the cells longer with no loss of efficacy, we generally maintain them for approx 20 passages (2 mo) before establishing a fresh stock by thawing a frozen vial of stock cells (*see* Section 3.3.). Although we initially suggested that the Bosc23 cells should be maintained in gpt selection media *(7)*, we have since found that, by freezing multiple aliquots of the cell lines (*see* Section 3.2.) and following the aforementioned recommendations, it is possible to maintain the cells in GM without selection.

   In the event that the 293-derived packaging cell lines need to be reselected, the following genes have been inserted into the cell lines together with plasmids encoding the antibiotic-resistance genes noted. The suggested antibiotic concentration is given in parentheses next to its name. SV40 large T: G418 (1 mg/mL); gag-pol: hygromycin (400 µg/mL); ecotropic and amphotropic envelopes: mycophenolic acid (50 µg/mL). All antibiotics are added directly to GM except mycophenolic acid, which is added to the gpt selection medium suggested by Mulligan and Berg *(22)*.

3. The 293 cells and their derivatives are much less adherent than NIH3T3 cell lines and easily detach from the tissue culture dishes after approx 30 s of treatment with trypsin at room temperature.

4. It is important to freeze multiple (50–100) vials of each producer cell line after first receiving and expanding them. This will ensure a ready supply of backup vials to allow for uniform virus production over several years.

5. If the cells are to be carried in selective media, this should not be applied until after the first passage.

6. It is recommended that during initial set-up, the user optimize the system by using a retroviral vector expressing an easily assayable marker such as *lacZ* or a cell surface protein. During optimization, one should check for transfection frequency of the producer clone and test infection rate of target cells. Tests for transfection and infection frequencies using a βgal-based system can be readily measured by βgal staining or FACS staining for βgal activity (*see* ref. 7 for methods describing the latter procedures). Only when one is satisfied with the transfection conditions and infection rates should one proceed to using vectors with no readily assayable marker.

7. It should be possible to scale up the protocols.

8. The initial plating of the cells may be the most important step in successfully obtaining high retroviral titers. It is extremely important that the cells are not

overly clumped and are at the correct density. Unlike NIH3T3-derived cell lines, the 293-derived packaging cell lines do not readily form well-spread monolayers. Instead, they tend to clump before confluence, and if the clumping is excessive, the cells will never reach confluence during the 48–72-h period following transfection. In order to prevent clumping, it is essential that the cells be extremely healthy prior to plating. If they are overconfluent, it may be necessary to split them 1:2 or 1:3 for several passages prior to plating for transfection. In addition, the cells are much less adherent than murine fibroblasts and should be handled very gently when washing and changing medium.

For consistency, it is important to count the cells rather than estimating the split. The above cell number is optimized for MFG-*lac*Z. Expression of other inserts may be detrimental to the growth of the cells. This effect may be noted by failure of the packaging cell line to reach confluence by 48–72 h posttransfection. If this occurs, it may be necessary to plate more cells prior to transfection. For example, with constructs expressing either *fas* or P210[bcr/abl], it is necessary to plate 3.0×10^6 cells/60-mm plate 24 h prior to transfection. In general, the cells should be plated at a density so that they are 95–100% confluent at 24 h posttransfection (for an additional discussion of this issue, *see* Notes 10 and 12).

9. The addition of chloroquine to the medium appears to increase retroviral titer by approximately twofold. This effect is presumably owing to the lysosomal neutralizing activity of the chloroquine *(23)*. It is extremely important that the length of chloroquine treatment does not exceed 12 h. Longer periods of chloroquine treatment have a toxic effect on the cells causing a decrease in retroviral titers. The range for chloroquine treatment is 7–12 h, with 9–10 h of treatment giving the best results. For purposes in which achieving maximal retroviral titer is not necessary, such as when comparing the relative titers of different constructs, it may be preferable to omit chloroquine treatment. If chloroquine is not used, it is unnecessary to change the medium prior to transfection. On some occasions, we have obtained slightly improved transfection efficiencies by adding the chloroquine to a 1:1 mixture of 293-conditioned media (obtained from any of the 293-based cell lines) and fresh GM.

10. It is important that the pH of the HEPES be adjusted to 7.05 (within 0.05 U). Although we generally add the HBS to the DNA/$CaCl_2$ solution by bubbling, equivalent results can be obtained by adding the HBS to the DNA/$CaCl_2$ solution and immediately inverting the tube. The HBS/DNA/$CaCl_2$ solution should be added to the cells within 1–2 min of preparation. It is not only unnecessary to wait for the formation of a visible precipitate, but waiting this long (15–30 min) may have a detrimental effect on transfection efficiency and subsequent retroviral titers. In addition, the presence and/or amount of precipitate that one visualizes following transfection is not a reliable indicator of transfection success.

We have used DNA prepared by both cesium chloride gradients and several commercial kits and have not found significant differences among titers between the different preparation methods. It is unnecessary to perform additional phenol or precipitation steps prior to using the DNA (which is stored in TE [8.0] at –20°C).

Up to a point, transfection efficiency and retroviral titers increase with increasing amounts of input DNA. The benefit of increasing the amount of input DNA must be weighed against our findings that this appears to have a direct toxic effect to the cell lines. If it is found that the amount of DNA is toxic to the cell line, it may be necessary to decrease the amount of input DNA or increase the number of plated cells. In some experiments, we have introduced up to 15 μg of DNA to a 60-mm plate during transfection.

Incubator CO_2 concentrations outside the range of 4.5–5.5% may adversely affect transfection efficiency.

11. In order to increase the relative retroviral titer, decrease the volume in this step to 3.0 mL/60-mm dish. Depending on the gene expressed from the introduced construct, the producer cells may be readily dislodged from the culture dish. It is therefore important to add the media to the side of the dish, taking care not to disturb the adherent cells.

12. The packaging cells should be nearly confluent by 24 h posttransfection. Under these circumstances, the retroviral supernatants should be collected at 48 h posttransfection. If the cells are not confluent by this point, it may be necessary to wait until 72 h. With the transient transfection methods, we find that retroviral titers drop if supernatant is harvested after 72 h posttransfection. If the cells are not confluent by 72 h, decrease the amount of input DNA and/or increase the number of initially plated cells with the goal of obtaining a confluent plate by 48 h posttransfection. In some experiments, we have used conditions in which the plate is almost confluent at the time of transfection and have obtained good results.

It is necessary to wait at least 36 h posttransfection to obtain high-titer retroviral supernatants. At this point, it may be possible to harvest the supernatant every 12–72 h without a significant loss in titer.

If a retroviral vector containing an easily assayable marker, such as βgal, is used, it is possible to stain or FACS the cells 48 h posttransfection to test the success of the transfection. When initially optimizing the system, transfection efficiencies should approach at least 50%.

13. Freezing does not appear to cause more than a twofold drop in titer, as long as the cells do not undergo more than one freeze/thaw cycle. If the viral supernates undergo more than one freeze/thaw cycle, there is a significant drop in retroviral titer.

14. No difference in infection efficiency was found between 4 μg/mL polybrene and 8 μg/mL polybrene. If 8 μg/mL polybrene is used, however, it is suggested that the polybrene be left on the cells for 3–5 h since the higher polybrene concentration is toxic to the NIH3T3 cells. At 4 μg/mL polybrene, no toxicity to the fibroblasts is observed; however, a 5-mL infection cocktail is recommended for overnight infections to prevent dehydration. Primary T-cells are sensitive to high concentrations of polybrene; a range of polybrene concentrations should be checked to find a concentration(s) that provides maximal infection efficiency.

15. When working with nonadherent cells, one has the choice of infecting by adding the retroviral supernatant directly to the cells or cocultivating the nonadherent cells with the retroviral producer cells. The advantage of the latter is that there is

ongoing retroviral production; however, this must be weighed against the disadvantage of harvesting producer cells together with the target cells. Although we have not tried, it may be possible to minimize this problem by irradiating or mitomycin C-treating the producer cells prior to cocultivation. In general, we have obtained higher infection frequencies by cocultivation.

16. For many nonadherent cells, achieving an optimal infection requires growth in the appropriate medium. Because 293 cells and their derivatives appear to tolerate many different medium bases and serum types, it is possible to alter the medium at 24 h posttransfection (*see* Section 3.4., step 5) so that the resulting retroviral supernatant will be harvested in the appropriate growth medium. When infecting with supernatants derived from 293 cells or derivatives, it should be remembered that these cells may provide a different cytokine/growth factor milieu than the NIH3T3-derived producer cells. A careful analysis of factor production by these cells has not been performed.

    We use polybrene at a concentration of 2 μg/mL for infection of nonadherent cells, although it may be possible to increase this concentration to 4 μg/mL without significant toxicity.

17. It is possible to increase infectious titers by approximately twofold by centrifuging and resuspending the cells in a *freshly* prepared infection cocktail 24 h after infection. We have not tried repeating this procedure more than once.

18. At this point, it is important that disturbance of the packaging cells is minimized. Use extreme care when removing the nonadherent cells from the packaging cells and do not wash the plate at this step. Also, it is unimportant to remove all of the nonadherent cells at this step. The purpose of this step is to add fresh medium and retroviral supernatant without losing nonadherent cells. Sufficient residual media remains on the plate to maintain the cells during the short centrifugation step described in Section 3.8., step 3. With longer centrifugation times, return the culture plates to the incubator.

19. The plate may be washed at this step; however, extreme care should be used so that the adherent cells do not detach. At this step, one is trying to achieve maximal removal of nonadherent cells. With this procedure, contamination by packaging cells is often less than 10%.

20. The method, described by Burns et al. *(21)*, employs initial selection of a stable producer clone. The transient method described here has possible advantages for retroviral constructs that do not express easily assayable genes, or express genes that might be selected against in prolonged culture conditions while isolating a high-titer clone. The method described below uses a βgal expressing retrovirus, but it is expected that once standardized, the user can employ retroviral vectors with nonselectable markers for infection of human and nonhuman target cells. It is possible to substitute other envelope proteins for the VSV-G polypeptide used here.

21. Conditioned media is defined here as media obtained from a subconfluent culture plate of Anjou cells. Plating in conditioned media results in a more rapid attachment of the cells and a uniform cell distribution at 8 h postplating of cells.

22. Within 36 h after transfection, syncytia can be noted forming in the transfected Anjou cell population. βgal staining of *lacZ* transfected Anjou cells after removal of viral supernatant accentuates visualization of syncytia formation.

23. Coculturing of the target cells with VSV-G transfection producer cells is not recommended owing to syncytia induction. We have also observed syncytia formation following infection of NIH3T3 target cells using concentrated or unconcentrated (base) virus supernatant. This is likely owing to the carryover of membrane fragments bearing VSV-G, which is known to be highly fusogenic. Continued growth of these cells resulted in a population of singly, normally dividing cells. Initial tests detected no helper virus formation (Caldwell et al., unpublished).

Base titers achieved in this system are up to 5×10^5 pseudotyped virions/mL. It has been possible to directly scale the transfections into larger 150-mm plates for transient production of larger volumes of virus (50 mL/150-mm plate) and for subsequent concentration. Our initial attempts at concentration resulted in an infectious titer of 2×10^6 pseudotyped virions/mL. It should be possible to attain higher titers by additional centrifugation.

Acknowledgments

The authors are extremely grateful to David Baltimore for continued encouragement, advice, and support, and in whose laboratory, many of the experiments were conceived and carried out. The authors would also like to thank their colleagues in the Baltimore lab, Nolan lab, and elsewhere for advice and suggestions regarding these protocols. W. S. P. was supported by a Howard Hughes Medical Institute Physician Postdoctoral Fellowship and is a Special Fellow of the Leukemia Society of America. G. P. N. is a Scholar of the Leukemia Society of America and a recipient of the Burrough's Wellcome New Investigator Award in Pharmacology and is supported by NIH R01AI35304, NIH and a gift from Tularik, Inc.

References

1. Mulligan, R. C. (1993) The basic science of gene therapy. *Science* **260,** 926–932.
2. Mann, R., Mulligan, R. C., and Baltimore, D. (1983) Construction of a retrovirus packaging mutant and its use to produce helper-free defective retrovirus. *Cell* **33,** 153–159.
3. Watanabe, S. and Temin, H. M. (1983) Construction of a helper cell line for avian reticuloendotheliosis virus cloning vectors. *Mol. Cell. Biol.* **3,** 2241–2249.
4. Miller, A. D. (1990) Retrovirus packaging cells. *Human Gene Ther.* **1,** 5–14.
5. Danos, O. (1991) Construction of retroviral packaging cell lines, in *Methods in Molecular Biology*, vol. 8 (Collins, M. ed.), Humana, Clifton, NJ, pp. 17–26.
6. Landau, N. R. and Littman, D. R. (1992) Packaging system for rapid generation of murine leukemia virus vectors with variable tropism. *J. Virol.* **66,** 5110–5113.
7. Pear, W., Nolan, G., Scott, M., and Baltimore, D. (1993) Production of high-titer helper-free retroviruses by transient transfection. *Proc. Natl. Acad. Sci. USA* **90,** 8392–8396.
8. Finer, M. H., Dull, T. J., Qin, L., Farson, D., and Roberts, M. R. (1994) *kat*: a high-efficiency retroviral transduction system for primary human T lymphocytes. *Blood* **83,** 43–50.

9. Scadden, D. T., Fuller, B., and Cunningham, J. M. (1990) Human cells infected with retrovirus vectors acquire an endogenous murine provirus. *J. Virol.* **64,** 424–427.

10. Graham, F. L., Smiley, J., Russell, W. C., and Naish, R. (1977) Characteristics of a human cell line transformed by DNA from human adenovirus type 5. *J. Gen. Virol.* **36,** 59–72.

11. DuBridge, R. B., Tang, P., Hsia, H. C., Phaik-Mooi, L., Miller, J. H., and Calos, M. P. (1987) Analysis of mutation in human cells by using an Epstein-Barr virus shuttle system. *Mol. Cell. Biol.* **7,** 379–387.

12. Danos, O. and Mulligan, R. C. (1988) Safe and efficient generation of recombinant retroviruses with amphotropic and ecotropic host ranges. *Proc. Natl. Acad. Sci. USA* **85,** 6460–6464.

13. Bender, M. A., Palmer, T. D., Gelinas, R. E., and Miller, A. D. (1987) Evidence that the packaging signal of Moloney murine leukemia virus extends into the gag region. *J. Virol.* **61,** 1639–1646.

14. Daley, G. and Baltimore, D. (1988) Transformation of an interleukin 3-dependent hematopoietic cell line by the chronic myelogenous leukemia-specific P210 *bcr/abl* protein. *Proc. Natl. Acad. Sci. USA* **85,** 9312–9316.

15. Morgenstern, J. P. and Land, H. (1990) Advanced mammalian gene transfer: high titre retroviral vectors with multiple drug selection markers and a complementary helper-free packaging cell line. *Nucleic Acids Res.* **18,** 3587–3596.

16. Dranoff, G., Jaffee, E., Lazenby, A., Golumbek, P., Levitsky, H., Brose, K., Jackson, V., Hamada, H., Pardoll, D., and Mulligan, R. C. (1993) Vaccination with irradiated tumor cells engineered to secrete murine granulocyte-macrophage colony-stimulating factor stimulates potent, specific, and long-lasting anti-tumor immunity. *Proc. Natl. Acad. Sci. USA* **90,** 3539–3543.

17. Shoemaker, C., Hoffmann, J., Goff, S. P., and Baltimore, D. (1981) Intramolecular integration within moloney murine leukemia virus DNA. *J. Virol.* **40,** 164–172.

18. Bernard, H. U., Krammer, G., and Rowekamp, W. G. (1985) Construction of a fusion gene that confers resistance against hygromycin B to mammalian cells in culture. *Exp. Cell Res.* **158,** 237–243.

19. Goff, S., Traktman, P., and Baltimore, D. (1981) Isolation and properties of Moloney murine leukemia virus mutants: use of a rapid assay for release of virion reverse transcriptase. *J. Virol.* **38,** 239–248.

20. Jasin, M. and Berg, P. (1988) Homologous integration in mammalian cells without target gene selection. *Genes Dev.* **2,** 1353–1363.

21. Burns, J. C., Friedmann, T., Driever, W., Burrascano, M., and Yee, J. K. (1993) Vesicular stomatitis virus G glycoprotein pseudotyped retroviral vectors: concentration to a very high titer and efficient gene transfer into mammalian and nonmammalian cells. *Proc. Natl. Acad. Sci. USA* **90,** 8033–8037.

22. Mulligan, R. C. and Berg, P. (1981) Selection for animal cells that express the *escherichia coli* gene coding for xanthine-guanine phosphoribosyltransferase. *Proc. Natl. Acad. Sci. USA* **78,** 2072–2076.

23. Ausubel, F. M., Brent, R., Kingston, R. E., Moore, D. D., Seidman, J. G., Smith, J. A., and Struhl, K. (1989) *Current Protocols in Molecular Biology*, Wiley, New York.

4

Methods for the Construction of Retroviral Vectors and the Generation of High-Titer Producers

Isabelle Rivière and Michel Sadelain

1. Introduction

1.1. Recombinant Retroviruses as Vectors for Gene Transfer

Retroviral vectors are powerful tools for gene transfer that are useful in the context of experimental as well as clinical applications. Defective recombinant retroviruses allow for efficient gene transfer into a broad range of mammalian cells derived from different species and different tissues. Safe gene transfer can be achieved using helper-free viral stocks, owing to the development of vectors and packaging cell lines that minimize the probability of hazardous recombination events. Retrovirus-mediated gene transfer leads to stable proviral integration in the target-cell genome, a key feature when the foreign genetic material must be faithfully transmitted to the progeny of the transduced parental cell. Murine leukemia virus (MLV)-based vectors accommodate numerous modifications, thus providing a plastic tool that can be tailored for very diverse applications.

There are, nonetheless, limitations to this vector system. Using conventional MLV-based systems, efficient gene transfer is limited to dividing cells expressing the viral receptors. Random proviral integration in the genome, biased toward sites of active chromatin, is prone to causing insertional mutagenesis. The particle packaging constraints limit the size of the inserted sequence to 7–8 kb. Transmission of the vector sequence is subjected to the multiple steps of the retroviral life cycle. In the course of reverse transcription and integration, sequence rearrangements or recombinations that depend on the nature of the juxtaposed retroviral and inserted sequences may occur. Therefore, faithful transmission of the original structure cannot be taken for granted, and every

From: *Methods in Molecular Medicine, Gene Therapy Protocols*
Edited by: P. Robbins Humana Press Inc., Totowa, NJ

new construction must be thoroughly characterized. The construction of one particular vector and the generation of a stable high-titer producer is a rather cumbersome procedure that sometimes demands a significant commitment. Nonetheless, a high-titer producer is a convenient and durable reagent.

1.2. Principles of Retroviral Vector Design

Gene transfer systems based on defective viral vectors typically comprise two components: a replication-defective virus bearing the sequences to be transferred and a helper virus providing *in trans* the replication and packaging functions that allow for propagation of the recombinant genome. In the case of retrovirus-mediated gene transfer, helper-free viral stocks can be generated owing to the availability of recombinant helper genomes that are very inefficiently packaged *(1,2)*. The packaging cell system is described elsewhere in this series *(3)*.

The principles of retroviral vector design are derived from the retroviral life cycle *(see* refs. *4* and *5* for review). Murine leukemia viruses, which provide the constitutive elements of most retroviral vectors and packaging cells, bind to their target cell via a receptor that determines the host range of the infectious particle. Ecotropic particles bind to a receptor present on mouse and rat cells (6,7). Amphotropic and GaLV-coated particles bind to receptors present on numerous mammalian cells, including primate cells *(8)*. The choice of receptor is determined by the sequence of the *env*-encoded glycoprotein. After fusion of the viral and cellular membranes, the core particle enters the cytoplasm where the single-stranded RNA retroviral genome is reverse-transcribed into a double-stranded DNA copy bearing direct, long terminal repeats (LTR) at each end. After transport to the nucleus, the viral DNA integrates into the host cell genome of dividing cells *(9,10)*. This proviral DNA is transcribed by host RNA polymerase and yields two RNA transcripts: one full-length transcript, which bears the packaging signal *(1)*, may serve as either the genomic RNA incorporated into nascent virions or as the template for translation of the *gag-pol*-encoded polypeptides; the second transcript, or subgenomic species, is generated by the splicing of a 5.2-kb intron and serves as the mRNA for the *env*-encoded products. The *gag-pol*-encoded polypeptides and genomic RNA transcript assemble in the cytoplasm to form virions that acquire the retroviral envelope glycoprotein upon budding from the infected cell.

Consequently, the guiding principles of vector design are to retain within the vector the minimal *cis*-acting sequences necessary for genomic transcription, packaging, reverse transcription, and integration, and to avoid recombination between the vector and other viral sequences that could generate a replication-competent genome. The latter stipulation critically depends on the packaging cell design. Recombination events are minimized when the *gag-*, *pol-*, and *env*-encoded polypeptides, coexpressed in the packaging cell, are transcribed from at least two separate plasmids lacking the packaging signal and displaying as little homology as possible with vector sequences *(11–13)*.

The vector itself does not encode any viral product and typically includes the following elements: The LTRs contain essential sequences for reverse transcription and integration in the target cell. The 5' LTR controls vector transcription. Adjacent to the 5' LTR lie three critical elements: the primer-binding site *(14)*, the packaging signal, ψ *(1)*, and additional *gag* sequences (altered within the vector so as to prevent translation of any *gag*-encoded peptide). The latter element enhances the packaging of the vector transcript *(15,16)*, defining an extended packaging region, ψ^+. This fragment usually includes a splice donor site, located 5' to the packaging signal in the Moloney-MLV sequence. The 3' end of the vector includes sequences past the *env* stop codon and the 3' LTR that are necessary for reverse transcription and proviral integration.

The U3 region within the 3' LTR of the vector is reverse-transcribed and incorporated in both LTRs generated in the target cell. This property is exploited in different ways in the design of retroviral vectors. For example, deletions in the 3' U3 region will result in transcriptionally weakened LTRs in the target cell. This deletion is useful for the generation of retroviral enhancer traps or the construction of internal promoter vectors, as shown in Fig. 1, top. New sequences, e.g., an entire transcription unit, can be inserted in the 3' U3 region, which therefore will be duplicated in the target cell, albeit with variable reliability. The 3' U3 region of Moloney-MLV can be replaced with the homologous sequence taken from other viruses to generate novel recombinant LTRs in the target cell, as shown for the LTR-driven vector in Fig. 1, bottom.

1.3. Specific Features of Vector Design

1.3.1. LTR-Driven Expression

The U3 region of the murine leukemia viruses comprises an enhancer and a promoter that together act as a strong transcriptional element. The LTR-driven vectors provide relatively high expression of the transferred gene in a broad range of differentiated or transformed mammalian cells *(18–20)*. Expression levels seem enhanced in vectors that incorporate functional splicing signals including either cryptic *(15)* or engineered *(17,18)* splice acceptor regions. The vectors N2 *(15)* and MFG *(18,20,32,33)* shown in Fig. 2 are representative of this category. However, LTR-driven vectors do not func-

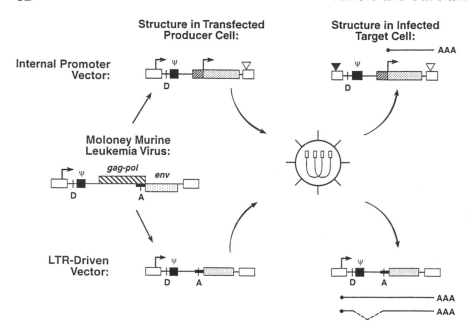

Fig. 1. Schematic representation of the structure of Moloney-MLV (left), internal promoter vectors (top), and LTR-driven vectors (bottom). D, splice donor; A, splice acceptor; ψ, packaging signal; AAA, polyadenylation tract, ▨ internal promoter, ▢ gene of interest.

tion under all circumstances (*see*, e.g., refs. *21* and *25*). Variant LTR-driven vectors have been generated by replacing the Mo-MLV sequences of the 3' LTR with elements from, for example, the Myeloproliferative Sarcoma Virus (MPSV) or Friend Virus *(18,22–24)*. The LTR-driven vectors differ with respect to transmission and expression characteristics, including levels of expression, tissue specificity, and ability to sustain long-term expression in vivo in different cell lineages *(18–21,23,25)*.

1.3.2. Constitutive Internal Promoters

Promoters other than the LTR can be incorporated into retroviral vectors. Viral promoters, such as SV40, CMV, HSV-TK *(15,26,27)*, and mammalian promoters, such as phosphoglucokinase (PGK), histone 4, or β-actin *(28– 30)*, are often used. Transcription from the LTR is minimized by crippling the U3 region of the 3' LTR, most commonly by deletion of the enhancer sequence, as described in Section 1.2. These vectors confer constitutive and nontissue-specific expression, like LTR-driven vectors, but differ with respect to their mean level of expression in different tissues, their ability to be expressed

Fig. 2. Examples of retroviral vector design: N2 *(15)*, MFG *(18)*, HSGneo *(29)*, Mβ6L *(36)*, LXSN *(27)*, and di-cistronic MFG *(41)*. The vector sequences are derived from Moloney-MLV unless otherwise indicated. SD, 5' splice donor; 3' SA*, sequence from *Nde*I to *Nla*III containing the 3' splice acceptor (SA); SA#, cryptic SA; Mo-MuLV, sequences derived from Moloney murine leukemia virus; Mo-MuSV, sequences derived from the Moloney murine sarcoma virus; LCR, locus control region; Enh⁻, deletion in the enhancer sequences; SV40 E/P, SV40 promoter and enhancer sequences; ψ, packaging signal; ψ+, extended packaging signal; IRES, internal ribosome entry site; H4 Pr, histone H4 promoter; β Pr, β-globin promoter; P, *Pst*I; Nr, *Nar*I; Xh, *Xho*I; N, *Nde*I; B, *Bgl*II; X, *Xba*I; Nl, *Nla*III; H, *Hpa*I; C, *Cla*I.

in embryonic cell types, their capacity to sustain long-term expression, and their susceptibility to position effects.

1.3.3. Tissue-Specific Expression

Tissue-specific expression is usually achieved by targeting to a specific cell type a nontissue-specific expression vector, as in the case of hepatocytes *(31)*, myoblasts *(32)*, or synoviocytes *(33)*. When it is not possible to directly target a particular cell type, or when infection has to be directed to a multipotential precursor cell, or if promiscuous promoters fail to sustain expression in the relevant cell population, tissue-specific transcriptional elements must be considered. Several internal promoter/enhancer combinations have been inserted in retroviral vectors, e.g., muscle- or erythroid-specific vectors *(34,35)*. The case of β-globin expression is of particular interest and is probably the most extensively studied tissue-specific vector. In order to treat β-globin disorders by gene addition, it is necessary to incorporate a recombinant β-globin transcription unit that confers high-level, erythroid-specific, stage-specific, and position-independent gene expression, into a vector suitable for efficient transfer into pluripotential hematopoietic stem cells. Moreover, as the β-globin cDNA fails to direct sufficient expression, the β-globin gene, with its two introns, must be incorporated in the vector. Inclusion of the β-globin gene with its promoter, and two proximal enhancers leads to erythroid-specific expression. However, the resulting expression levels are very poor *(35)*, thus establishing that tissue-specific or regulated expression is unlikely to be achieved by merely incorporating a tissue-specific promoter. Over 150 different constructions, varying in their β-globin gene length, transcription regulatory elements, and viral sequences had to be tested before a vector yielding high-titer viral stocks and conferring enhanced erythroid-specific expression was obtained *(see* Section 1.4.2. and ref. *36)*.

1.3.4. Dual Promoter Vectors

There are several ways to achieve dual gene expression from one vector. The most common is to engineer dual promoter vectors *(15,17,27)*. Typically in such a vector the expression of one gene is under LTR transcriptional control and the other, inserted 3' to the stop codon of the first, is under the control of an internal promoter/enhancer combination. One example is LXSN *(27)* in which the gene of interest is driven by the LTR, whereas the gene encoding neomycin phosphotransferase (*neo*[R]) is driven by SV40 transcriptional elements *(see* Fig. 2). Despite the potential for transcriptional interference *(37,38)*, this type of vector, which bears two strong and nontissue-specific promoters, is very widely utilized.

1.3.5. Dicistronic Vectors

The internal ribosomal entry site (IRES) isolated from (+) strand RNA picornaviridae *(39)* can be inserted between two coding sequences to ensure gene coexpression in different cell types (e.g., ref. *40*). Thus, dual gene expression may be achieved using single transcription unit vectors, as shown in Fig. 2. We have found that such vectors are transmitted faithfully, yield high titers, and ensure gene coexpression in different cell types *(41)*. Triple gene transfer may be achieved by building tricistronic vectors *(42)* or dicistronic vectors, including a fusion gene that encodes two functions. Because IRES function depends on cellular factors and may be affected by flanking sequences, it is necessary to establish for every new vector that gene coexpression is faithfully achieved in the tissue of interest.

1.3.6. Future Directions

Today, there are many retroviral vectors available, as illustrated above, yet there is still room for much improvement. Achieving regulated expression in vivo, especially with respect to tissue specificity and inducibility *(55)* of gene expression, and persistent gene expression over the long term in vivo *(18)*, are major objectives. The generation of vectors that express at any proviral integration site, i.e., that overcome position effects, may be achieved by inclusion of chromatin regulators such as locus control regions and insulators *(36)*. Other major ongoing efforts aim to construct new packaging cell lines that yield higher titer virus stocks, or generate particles optimized for human cells *(56)* or specifically targeted to one given tissue. The development of retroviral vector systems that allow for the infection of nondividing cells will vastly extend the use of retrovirus-mediated gene transfer *(54)* when packaging cells are available.

1.4. Generation of High-Titer Retroviral Producers

The titers obtained from producers generated by DNA transfection vary widely on a clonal basis. It is therefore useful to screen several clones to identify the highest titer packaging cell line. Moreover, a clone is a more stable reagent than a pool of producers that is gradually taken over by the fastest growing cells that are not necessarily those with the best titer. Several methods are available for comparing clones for their particle output. These methods range from the determination of viral RNA content in the producer cell supernatant, to proviral copy number determination in generic target cells, to expression studies in generic or specific target cell populations (*see* Section 3.2.). Before undertaking this screening, certain strategies should be considered to increase the likelihood of generating a high-titer producer.

1.4.1. Cross-Infection and Ping-Pong Strategies

As the titer can be limited by the production of the vector transcript within the packaging cell, it may be useful to introduce multiple copies of the template in sites of active chromatin. The introduction of the construct by infection rather than by transfection will favor integration into sites of active chromatin. It will also eliminate the transcriptional interference that may occur in concatameric inserts. This infection can be achieved by repeated infection of the producer cell, if the cells are permissive to superinfection. Viral interference caused by expression of the *env*-encoded glycoprotein can be circumvented by superinfecting an amphotropic producer with recombinant ecotropic viral particles and vice versa *(27,43)*. Cross-infections can be repeated several times, going back and forth between amphotropic and ecotropic packaging cells (ping-pong). However, all crossinfections increase the risk of generating replication competent genomes *(12,44)*. Cocultivation of ecotropic and amphotropic packaging cells is definitely not recommended *(45)*.

1.4.2. Identification of Sequences that Reduce Titers

Some inserts result in vectors consistently yielding low-titer viral stocks, whatever retroviral vector backbone is used. Such is the case for vectors bearing the human β-globin gene *(16,35)*. In contrast, incorporating the human β-globin cDNA sequence in the same vectors yields high titer viral stocks. A panel of vectors bearing recombinant human β-globin genes lacking untranslated sequences was generated (gene lacking intron 1, gene lacking intron 2, and so on) and transfected in the ψ-CRE packaging cell line *(36)*. Transmission of the vector structure to NIH 3T3 fibroblasts was studied by semiquantitative Southern blot analysis as described in Section 3.2.2. The result of this study is shown in Fig. 3. Very low titers are achieved with constructs bearing intron 2 (lanes A–D). The titer is comparable to the titer of the cDNA vector when intron 2 is entirely deleted (lanes E–G) or replaced by the human α1-globin intron 2 (lane J), but only partially increased by subintronic deletions (lane I). This analysis is achieved using pooled producers, analyzed side by side. It therefore reflects the mean transmission achieved by each vector. This systematic study has led to the identification of sequences within intron 2 that dramatically reduce titers, thus leading to the rational design of high titer and genomically stable β-globin vectors that bear a modified β-globin gene *(36)*. The comparison of several clones by this assay, which relies on Southern blot analysis, is also useful to screen for the highest titer producer (*see* Section 3.2.).

1.4.3. Toxic Gene Expression Precluding the Generation of Stable Producers

Expression of certain genes is expected to interfere with the function or proliferation of the packaging cell, e.g., interferons or antiproliferative genes.

A. Whole Gene
B. Lacking Promoter
C. Lacking IVS I
D. Lacking IVS I and Promoter
E. Lacking IVS II
F. Lacking IVS II and Promoter

G. Lacking IVS I and IVS II
H. Lacking IVS I, IVS II and Promoter
I. Only cDNA
J. Containing 89bp IVS II
K. Containing αG IVS II

Fig. 3. Example of vector copy number determination by Southern blot analysis: comparison of vector transmission between β-globin vectors bearing different deletions in the human β-globin gene (*see* text). Genomic DNA (packaging cell, left lane, target cell, right lane) was digested with NheI (LTR to LTR digest) and equal amounts were loaded onto a gel. After transfer, the blots were probed with a human β-globin probe *(36)*.

In this case, the generation of stable producers will require the design of regulated and/or tissue-specific expression vectors that repress gene expression in fibroblasts. Otherwise, it may be necessary to utilize transient producers (*see* Chapter 3).

2. Materials

2.1. Cells

1. Retroviral packaging cell line *(1–3,11–13, 46,47)*.
2. NIH 3T3 fibroblasts.
3. 3T3-116 or 3T3-BAG cells: 3T3-116 cells and 3T3-BAG cells harbor in their genome defective recombinant retroviruses expressing the histidine dehydrogenase (his) and the β-galactosidase gene, respectively *(3)*.

2.2. Cell Culture

1. Selective and nonselective tissue-culture media.
2. DMEM, calf serum (Gibco-BRL, Grand Island, NY).
3. Penicillin, streptomycin, G418 (Gibco-BRL).
4. Methylsulfoxide, DMSO (EM Science, Gibbstown, NJ).
5. 96-, 24-, and 6-well plates, 10-cm diameter plates.

6. Cloning rings placed in a glass Petri dish coated with petroleum jelly or vacuum grease, sterilized by autoclaving.

2.3. Solutions and Materials

2.3.1. Calcium Phosphate Precipitate

1. HBS: 137 mM NaCl, 5 mM KCl, 0.7 mM Na$_2$HPO$_4$, 6 mM dextrose, 21 mM HEPES Na$^+$ (pH 7.05; adjust with 1N NaOH). Filter-sterilize and store at 4°C.
2. 2M CaCl$_2$. Filter-sterilize and store at 4°C.
3. 15% Glycerol in HBS.

2.3.2. Electroporation

1. 0.4-cm Bio-Rad (Hercules, CA) electroporation cuvet 165-2088.
2. Electroporation power device, Bio-Rad Gene Pulser.

2.3.3. Infection

1. Polybrene, stock solution 800 μg/mL (Sigma, St. Louis, MO; cat. no. H9268) in PBS$^-$. Filter-sterilize and store at 4°C.
2. 10-mL Disposable plastic syringes.
3. 0.45-μm Disposable filters (not 0.22-μm).

3. Methods

3.1. Transfection and Selection of Virus-Producing Clones

Producers of recombinant retroviruses are obtained by transfecting any of a variety of retroviral packaging cell lines *(1–3,11–13,46,47)*. There are a number of transfection protocols yielding stable transformants, such as calcium phosphate coprecipitation, electroporation, or lipofection. For constructs lacking a selectable marker, cotransfection with a plasmid such as pSV2neo *(48)* is necessary. Other selectable markers can be used (reviewed in ref. *49*), depending on the markers present in the packaging cell line used *(3)*. A 10-fold molar excess of the retroviral plasmid should be used to ensure that stable selected transfectants have taken up both plasmids. Transfected packaging cells should be transferred into appropriate selective media 24 or 48 h after transfection to allow for integration and expression of the selectable marker gene. After the selection period, individual colonies are isolated. If cloning rings are used, colonies should be sparse enough on the plate to avoid cross-contamination between adjacent colonies. The subcloning can also be performed by limiting dilution in 96-well plates, seeding 0.5–2 cells/well. About 30 colonies are picked and expanded in 24- and 6-well plates, and finally 10-cm plates. At that stage, the viral titer can be assayed and at least one vial per clone should be frozen and stored in liquid nitrogen.

The methods described herein are used to generate high titer producers from the ψ-CRE and ψ-CRIP packaging cells *(12)*.

3.1.1. Calcium Phosphate Transfection: Method A

1. Day 1: Seed the packaging cells (5×10^5 cells) in 10-cm diameter tissue-culture plates in DMEM, 10% calf serum, penicillin-streptomycin medium.
2. Day 2: Mix 10–15 µg of vector DNA and 1 µg of the plasmid DNA carrying the selectable marker (10:1 molar ratio), both at concentrations of 0.5–3 µg/mL, in 0.5 mL HBS. Add 31 µL of $2M$ CaCl$_2$ and flick with finger to mix.
3. Incubate at room temperature for 45 min. A faint precipitate should appear.
4. Remove the medium from the packaging cell line. Add the precipitate and incubate the plates at room temperature for 30–40 min. Rock the plates at 10-min intervals.
5. Add back 10 mL of medium and incubate at 37°C for 4 h.
6. Remove medium and wash once with fresh medium.
7. Optional (*see* Note 1): Add 2.5 mL of 15% glycerol in HBS and incubate at 37°C for 3 min. Remove glycerol and rinse cells once with 10 mL of medium.
8. Add back 10 mL of medium.
9. Incubate at 37°C for 24–48 h.
10. Day 3 or 4: Split cells at 1 to 5, 1 to 10, 1 to 20, 1 to 40 into the appropriate selective media. Re-feed cell cultures with drug-containing media every 3 d. Examine the cultures under a microscope to determine the efficiency of drug selection.
11. Choose the best plates for isolating individual clones, either by picking individual colonies using cloning rings, or by limiting dilution (seeding 0.5–2 cells per well in 96-well plates).

3.1.2. Electroporation: Method B

We provide here the parameters for the packaging cell lines ψ-CRE and ψ-CRIP (also suitable for 3T3 fibroblasts). Although most of the packaging cell lines are derived from 3T3 fibroblasts, it is recommended to optimize parameters for the specific packaging cell line used.

1. Trypsinize the packaging cell line and resuspend the cells at 2×10^7 cells/mL in DMEM, 1% calf serum.
2. Place 250 µL of the cell suspension in 0.4-cm electroporation Bio-Rad cuvet on ice for 10 min.
3. Add to the cell suspension 20–50 µg of mixed vector DNA and plasmid carrying the selective marker (both linearized; *see* Note 2) at a molar ratio of 5:1. Incubate on ice for 10 min.
4. Set up the electroporation apparatus according to the manufacturer's instructions and subject cell/DNA mixture to the electric field (960 µF and 200 V).
5. Return cell/DNA mixture on ice and incubate for 5 min.
6. Plate cells in nonselective medium in 10-cm plates. Proceed to steps 9–11 of Section 3.1.1.

3.1.3. Lipofection: Method C

It is also possible to obtain stable transformants by lipofection. This method is described in details elsewhere *(50)*.

3.1.4. Transient Transfection: Method D

This method is described in detail in Chapter 3.

3.2. Isolation of the Best Producer Clones

The viral titer reflects the rate of release of infectious retroviral particles from the producer cells, but there is no direct method to assess it. Consequently, viral titers are generally derived by estimating the concentration of infectious particles in the producer cell supernatant harvested under defined conditions. This supernatant is typically tested on cells highly susceptible to retroviral infection such as NIH 3T3 fibroblasts. Other indicator cells can be used but the read-out of the viral titer is affected by the susceptibility of the target cells to viral infection (*see* Note 3). There are several ways of estimating titers or assaying for vector transmission. We will emphasize here the quantification of proviral copy number per target cell by Southern blot analysis. After identification of the highest titer clones, two additional tests must be carried out: verification of expression of the transgene and screening for production of helper virus by the clonal producer.

3.2.1. RNA Dot Blot Analysis

The detection of retroviral RNA in the supernatant of the virus-producing cell lines by RNA dot blot *(51)* is not quantitative, nor does it provide information on the structure of the encapsidated vector. However, this method can be used for an initial screening, prior to further characterization of the clones that generate the strongest signals.

3.2.2. Titration on NIH 3T3 Cells Fibroblasts

1. Day 1: Seed the virus-producing cells so that they will almost reach confluence 48 h later. This is done by placing about 5×10^5 cells in a 10-cm plate (the exact seeding density depends on the growth rate of the packaging cell clone and needs to be determined).
2. Day 2: Replace the medium on the producers with 10 mL of fresh medium.
3. Plate NIH 3T3 cells at 5×10^5 cells in 10-cm dishes.
4. Day 3: Harvest the supernatant from almost confluent monolayers of producer cells and filter through 0.45-μm filters (*see* Note 4).
5. Infect NIH3T3 fibroblasts with 5 mL of undiluted and diluted viral supernatant added of 8 μg/mL of polybrene (*see* Note 5). Incubate the plates at 37°C for 4 h. Then replace the supernatant with 10 mL of fresh medium and incubate at 37°C for another 48–72 h.

6. Day 5: Depending on the method chosen to evaluate the virus titer, one can start selection if the retroviral vector carries a selection marker (*see* Section 3.2.2.3.) or prepare the infected NIH 3T3 cells for either FACS analysis or protein expression analysis (*see* Section 3.2.2.2.), or extract high-mol-wt DNA to perform Southern hybridization analysis of integrated proviral genomes (*see* Section 3.2.2.1.).

7. Select 2 or 3 high-titer viral producer cell clones (*see* Note 6). Freeze at least 10 vials of the selected clones and check these for helper-virus (*see* Section 3.3.).

3.2.2.1. TITRATION OF PRODUCER CELL LINES BASED ON PROVIRAL DNA ANALYSIS: METHOD A

Proceed to the extraction of genomic DNA from the target cells *(52)* at 48–72 h after infection. Restriction enzyme digestion and Southern blot analysis are performed using standard procedures *(53)*. The restriction enzyme used should cut in both LTRs of the proviral genome. The probe should not overlap with the retroviral vector sequences.

Load gels with 10 µg of digested genomic DNA per lane. As control for copy number, one can use either plasmid DNA or, ideally, genomic DNA from a cell line carrying one copy per cell of the same retroviral plasmid. All DNA samples are digested with the same restriction enzyme. To determine the number of proviral genome per infected cell using plasmid DNA as control, mix 10 µg of DNA from noninfected NIH 3T3 cells with amounts of plasmid corresponding to 5, 1, 0.5, and 0.2 copies per cell. The amount of plasmid corresponding to 1 copy per cell in 10 µg of genomic DNA is given by the following formula: [plasmid size] × 10/[genome size*]. (*) = 6×10^9 bp for the mouse genome.

In this assay, we consider a clone to be a high titer producer when 0.5 or more integrated copies per cell are detected, using a fivefold dilution of the supernatant to infect NIH 3T3 fibroblasts. We have successfully used such high-titer clones for the efficient infection of murine bone marrow cells as shown in vivo in long-term bone marrow chimeras *(18)*, infection of primary lymphocytes (*see* Chapter 17), embryonic stem cells, and primary murine macrophages (I. Rivière, unpublished observations).

3.2.2.2. IDENTIFICATION OF THE HIGHEST TITER PRODUCER BY EXPRESSION STUDIES IN TARGET CELLS: METHOD B

In some instances, the titer of different clones can be compared by measuring the fraction of target cells expressing the transferred gene. This can be easily done by FACS analysis when the gene encodes a cell surface protein against which specific antibodies are available (*see* Chapter 17). When the protein is detectable using a bioassay, one can compare levels of expression of the transferred gene in target cells infected with different viral stocks. Consequently, the investigator will choose to either directly screen all the clones with the procedure from Section 3.2.2.2., or first proceed to Section 3.2.2.1. and subsequently to Section 3.2.2.2. for a few clones.

3.2.2.3. TITRATION BASED ON THE EXPRESSION
        OF A SELECTABLE MARKER: METHOD C

This method is the most commonly used method, providing that the vector contains a selectable marker. The read out, i.e., the enumeration of drug-resistant colonies, is not a simple measurement of particle formation and gene transfer because it also depends on the expression characteristics of the vector. This method is described in this series *(54)*.

3.3. Detection of Helper Virus

The presence of replication-competent virus generated by recombination events occurring in the producer cell line or in the target tissues must be systematically monitored. There are several ways to assay for helper virus. The mobilization assay consists in challenging a cell line harboring a defective recombinant provirus with the viral stock or the fluid (plasma for example). If helper virus is present, the transcribed defective recombinant provirus will be packaged into retroviral particles (mobilization process) that will appear in the culture media of the challenged cells. The mobilized provirus carries a selectable marker (histidinol dehydrogenase in 3T3-116) or a reporter gene (β-galactosidase in 3T3-BAG) that can be detected by infecting target cells such as NIH 3T3 fibroblasts.

3.3.1. Mobilization Assay (adapted from ref. 3)

1. Day 1–3: Prepare the supernatant of the virus-producing cell lines as described in Section 3.2.2., steps 1, 2, and 4.
2. Day 2: Seed the indicator cell line (3T3-116 or 3T3-BAG, *see* Section 2.) at 5×10^5 cells in 10-cm plates.
3. Day 3: Infect the indicator cell line with 5 mL of each viral stock added with 8 μg/mL polybrene. Incubate the plates at 37°C for 4 h. Replace the infection medium with 10 mL of fresh medium and incubate at 37°C for 48 h.
4. Day 5–7: Split the infected indicator cells and prepare supernatant from these cells as in Section 3.2.2., steps 1, 2, and 4.
5. Day 6: Plate NIH 3T3 cells at 5×10^5 cells/10-cm plate.
6. Day 7: Replace the medium on the NIH 3T3 cells with 5 mL of undiluted and diluted supernatant from the indicator cell line (10-, 100-, and 1000-fold dilutions). Add polybrene to a final concentration of 8 μg/mL and incubate for 4 h. Next, replace the medium with 10 mL of fresh medium and incubate for 48 h at 37°C.
7. Day 9: Split the challenged NIH 3T3 cells at 1 to 10 in selective media, or stain for β-galactosidase activity, according to the indicator cell line used (*see* Section 2.).

3.4. Culturing the Selected Virus-Producer Cell Lines

At least 10 vials of the selected virus-producer cell clones should be frozen in culture medium containing 10% DMSO. If the cells need to be grown for a long period of time, thaw a new vial from the original stock every month.

3.5. Boosting the Titer and Improving the Infection Efficiency

A certain number of approaches can be undertaken if the highest titer producer cell line selected does not allow for infection of the target cells at a sufficient efficiency.

3.5.1. Virus Concentration

The concentration of the virus by centrifugation is sometimes used, but this procedure adversely affects viral infectivity. This method is described in this series *(53)*. VSV-G coated particles are more resistant to virus concentration procedures *(58)*.

3.5.2. Cross-Infection and Ping-Pong

The primary producer cell lines obtained by methods described in Section 3.1. can be used to infect another packaging cell line. This can be achieved by a single cross-infection, which is less likely to generate helper virus than ping-pong (*see* Section 1.4.1.), yet increases this risk relative to that associated with transfection. As ecotropic virus producers are refractory to infection by ecotropic virus but not amphotropic virus, and vice versa, the tropism of the primary producer cell line must be different from that of the packaging cell line to be used.

Use the protocol described in Section 3.2.2. to perform the infection of the secondary packaging cell line (e.g., the ecotropic supernatant is used to infect an amphotropic or GaLV packaging cell line). The highest titer producer is selected as for the primary producers.

The titer can be increased by mixing ecotropic and amphotropic packaging cell lines at a ratio of 1:1. Recombinant retroviruses repeatedly infect the two retroviral packaging cell lines, leading to increased proviral copy integrations, increased virus titer, and generation of replication-competent helper virus *(45)*. We do not recommend this method.

3.5.3. Cocultivation of the Target Cells with the Producer Cell Line

Cocultivation of nonadherent target cells on a monolayer of producers usually results in greater gene transfer efficiency as compared to infection using viral stocks, provided that suitable culture conditions be defined. This method is described in Chapters 16 and 17, dealing with the infection of nonadherent cells (*see also* Note 6).

4. Notes

1. Glycerol shock: This step is optional but improves the transfection efficiency in a twofold range.
2. Linearization of plasmids for electroporation. Linearized DNA is more recombinogenic than supercoiled or nicked circular DNA and increases the number of stable transformants.
3. The susceptibility to infection of the target cells depends itself on various parameters such as viral receptor expression on the cell surface, expression of endogenous retroviral envelope-like products, and the rate of cell division.
4. The titer is determined on a 16–24 h conditioned medium. Do not use 0.22-μm filters to prepare the viral stock. Filtered supernatant can be frozen at –70°C for several months with gradual loss of retroviral particle infectivity.
5. It is suggested to infect the cells with two concentrations of retroviral particles, using for example the harvested viral stock undiluted and diluted 1:5 in the same culture medium.
6. If the target cells are infected by cocultivation (for example with hematopoietic cells), some virus-producing cell clones might be more suitable than others for the survival/cycling status/infection of the target cells. This is related to the intrinsic characteristics of each clone, such as cytokine production, rate of division, and metabolism of the cells, which lead to variability in the content and the pH of the supernatant. Thus, two clones with the same titer as determined on NIH 3T3 fibroblasts may differ with respect to gene transfer efficiency into another target cell type.

Acknowledgments

We thank David A. Sanders for reviewing this manuscript, Richard C. Mulligan for his support, and Vida Petronis for help in the preparation of the manuscript.

References

1. Mann, R., Mulligan, R. C., and Baltimore, D. (1983) Construction of a retrovirus packaging mutant and its use to produce helper-free defective retrovirus. *Cell* **33,** 153–159.
2. Watanabe, S. and Temin, H. M. (1983) Construction of a helper cell line for avian reticuloendotheliosis virus cloning vectors. *Mol. Cell. Biol.* **3,** 2241–2249.
3. Danos, O. (1991) Construction of retroviral packaging cell lines, in *Methods in Molecular Biology, vol. 8: Practical Molecular Virology: Viral Vectors for Gene Expression* (Collins, M., ed.), Humana, Clifton, NJ, pp. 17–27.
4. Coffin, J. M. (1990) Retroviridae and their replication, in *Virology* (Fields, B. N. and Knipe, D. N., eds.), Raven, New York, pp. 1437–1500.
5. Weiss, R., Teich, N., Varmus, H., and Coffin, J., eds. (1994) *RNA Tumor Viruses*, 3rd ed., Cold Spring Harbor Laboratory, Cold Spring Harbor, NY.

6. Kim, J. W., Closs, E. I., Albritton, L. M., and Cunningham, J. M. (1991) Transport of cationic amino acids by the mouse ecotropic retrovirus receptor. *Nature* **352,** 726–728.
7. Wang, H., Kavanaugh, M. P., North, R. A., and Kabat, D. (1991) Cell-surface receptor for ecotropic murine retroviruses is a basic amino-acid transporter. *Nature* **352,** 729–731.
8. Miller, D. G., Edwards, R. H., and Miller, A. D. (1994) Cloning of the cellular receptor for amphotropic murine retroviruses reveals homology to that for gibbon ape leukemia virus. *Proc. Natl. Acad. Sci. USA* **91,** 78–82.
9. Miller, D. G., Adam, M. A., and Miller, A. D. (1990) Gene transfer by retrovirus vectors occurs only in cells that are actively replicating at the time of infection. *Mol. Cell. Biol.* **10,** 4239–4292.
10. Roe, T. Y., Reynolds, T. C., Yu, G., and Brown, P. O. (1993) Integration of murine leukemia virus DNA depends on mitosis. *EMBO J.* **12,** 2099–2108.
11. Miller, A. D. and Buttimore, C. (1986) Redesign of retrovirus packaging cell line to avoid recombination leading to helper virus formation. *Mol. Cell. Biol.* **6,** 2895–2902.
12. Danos, O. and Mulligan, R. C. (1988) Safe and efficient generation of recombinant retroviruses with amphotropic and ecotropic host range. *Proc. Natl. Acad. Sci. USA* **85,** 6460–6464.
13. Markowitz, D., Goff, S. P., and Bank, A. (1988) A safe packaging line for gene transfer: separating viral genes on two different plasmids. *J. Virol.* **62,** 1120–1124.
14. Gilboa, E., Mitra, S. W., Goff, S. P., and Baltimore, D. (1979) A detailed model of reverse transcription and tests of crucial aspects. *Cell* **18,** 93–100.
15. Armentano, D., Yu, S.-F., Kantoff, P. W., von Ruden, T., Anderson, W. F., and Gilboa, E. (1987) Effect of internal viral sequences on the utility of retroviral vectors. *J. Virol.* **61,** 1647–1650.
16. Bender, M. A., Palmer, T. D., Gelinas, R. E., and Miller, A. D. (1987) Evidence that the packaging signal of Moloney murine leukemia virus extends into the gag region. *J. Virol.* **61,** 1639–1646.
17. Cepko, C., Roberts, B. E., and Mulligan, R. C. (1984) Construction and applications of a highly transmissible murine retrovirus shuttle vector. *Cell* **37,** 1053–1062.
18. Rivière, I., Brose, K., and Mulligan, R. C. (1995) Effects of retroviral design on expression of human adenosine deaminase in murine bone marrow transplant recipients engrafted with genetically modified cells. *Proc. Natl. Acad. Sci. USA* **92,** 6733–6737.
19. Keller, G., Paige, C., Gilboa, E., and Wagner, E. F. (1985) Expression of a foreign gene in myeloid and lymphoid cells derived from multipotent haematopoietic precursors. *Nature* **318,** 149–154.
20. Dranoff, G., Jaffee, E., Lazenby, A., Golumbek, P., Levitsky, H., Brose, K., Jackson, V., Hamada, H., Pardoll, D., and Mulligan, R. C. (1993) Vaccination with irradiated tumor cells engineered to secrete murine GM-CSF stimulates potent, specific and long lasting anti-tumor immunity. *Proc. Natl. Acad. Sci. USA* **90,** 3539–3543.

21. Palmer, T. D., Rosman, G. J., Osborne, W. R., and Miller, A. D. (1991) Genetically modified fibroblasts persist long after transplantation but gradually inactivate introduced genes. *Proc. Natl. Acad. Sci. USA* **88,** 1330–1334.

22. Beck-Engeser, G., Stocking, C., Just, U., Albritton, L., Dexter, M., Spooncer, M., and Ostertag, W. (1991) Retroviral vectors related to the Myeloproliferative Sarcoma virus allow efficient expression in hematopoietic stem and precursor cell lines, but retroviral infection is reduced in more primitive cells. *Hum. Gene Ther.* **2,** 61–70.

23. Johnson, G. R., Gonda, T. J., Metcalf, D., Hariharan, I. K., and Cory, S. (1989) A lethal myeloproliferative syndrome in mice transplanted with bone marrow cells infected with a retrovirus expressing GM-CSF. *EMBO J.* **8,** 441–448.

24. Holland, C. A., Ankleseria, P., Sakakeeny, M. A., and Greenberger, J. S. (1987) Enhancer sequences of a retroviral vector determine expression of a gene in multipotent hematopoietic progenitors and committed erythroid cells. *Proc. Natl. Acad. Sci. USA* **84,** 8662–8666.

25. Chalitta, P.-M. and Kohn, D. B. (1994) Lack of expression from a retroviral vector after transduction of murine hematopoietic stem cells is associated with methylation in vivo. *Proc. Natl. Acad. Sci. USA* **91,** 2567–2571.

26. Magli, M.-C., Dick, J. E., Huszar, D., Bernstein, A., and Phillips, R. A. (1987) Modulation of gene expression in multiple hematopoietic cell lineages following retroviral vector gene transfer. *Proc. Natl. Acad. Sci. USA* **84,** 789–793.

27. Miller, A. D. and Rosman, G. J. (1989) Improved retroviral vectors for gene transfer and expression. *BioTechniques* **7,** 980–990.

28. Lim, B., Williams, D. A., and Orkin, S. (1987) Retrovirus-mediated gene transfer of human ADA: expression of functional enzyme in murine hematopoietic stem cells in vivo. *Mol. Cell. Biol.* **7,** 3459–3465.

29. Guild, B. C., Finer, M. H., Housman, D. E., and Mulligan, R. C. (1988) Development of retrovirus vectors useful for expressing genes in cultured murine embryonal cells and hematopoietic cells in vivo. *J. Virol.* **62,** 3795–3801.

30. Wilson, J. M., Danos, O., Grossman, M., Raulet, D. H., and Mulligan, R. C. (1990) Expression of human ADA in mice reconstituted with retrovirus-transduced hematopoietic stem cells. *Proc. Natl. Acad. Sci. USA* **87,** 439–443.

31. Wilson, J. M., Jefferson, D. M., Chowdury, J. R., Novikoff, P. M., Johnston, D. E., and Mulligan, R. C. (1988) Retrovirus-mediated transduction of adult hepatocytes. *Proc. Natl. Acad. Sci. USA* **85,** 3014–3018.

32. Dhawan, J., Pan, L. C., Pavlath, G. K., Travis, M. A., Lanctot, A. M., and Blau, H. M. (1991) Systemic delivery of human growth hormone by injection of genetically engineered myoblasts. *Science* **254,** 1509–1512.

33. Bandara, G., Mueller, G. M., Galea-Lauri, J., Tindal, M. H., Georgescu, H. I., Suchanek, M. K., Hung, G. L., Glorioso, J. C., Robbins, P. D., and Evans, C. H. (1993) Intraarticular expression of biologically active interleukin 1-receptor-antagonist protein by ex vivo gene transfer. *Proc. Natl. Acad. Sci. USA* **90,** 10,764–10,768.

34. Dai, Y., Roman, M., Naviaux, R. K., and Verma, I. M. (1992) Gene therapy via primary myoblasts: long-term expression of factor IX protein following transplantation in vivo. *Proc. Natl. Acad. Sci. USA* **89,** 10,892–10,895.

35. Dzierzak, E., Papayopoulou, T., and Mulligan, R. C. (1988) Lineage-specific expression of a human β-globin gene in murine bone marrow transplant recipients reconstituted with retrovirus-transduced stem cells. *Nature* **331,** 35–41.

36. Sadelain, M., Wang, C.-H. J., Antoniou, M., Grosveld, F., and Mulligan, R. C. (1995) Generation of a high titer retroviral vector capable of expressing high levels of the human β-globin gene. *Proc. Natl. Acad. Sci. USA* **92,** 6728–6732.

37. Cullen, B. R., Lomedico, P. T., and Ju, G. (1984) Transcriptional interference in avian retroviruses: implications for the promoter insertion model of leukemogenesis. *Nature* **307,** 241–245.

38. Bowtell, D. D., Cory, S., Johnson, G. R., and Gonda, T. J. (1988) Comparison of expression in hematopoietic cells by retroviral vectors carrying two genes. *J. Virol.* **62,** 2464–2473.

39. Oh, S.-K. and Sarnow, P. (1993) Gene regulation: translational initiation by internal ribosome binding. *Curr. Opin. Genet. Dev.* **3,** 295–300.

40. Frebourg, T., Sadelain, M. W. J., Ng, Y.-W., Kassel, J., and Friend, S. H. (1994) Equal transcription of wild-type and mutant p53 using bicistronic vectors results in the wild-type phenotype. *Cancer Res.* **54,** 878–881.

41. Sadelain, M. W. J. and Mulligan, R. C. (1992) Efficient retroviral-mediated gene transfer into murine primary lymphocytes. *Ninth International Immunology Congress* (Abstract) 88–34.

42. Morgan, R. A., Couture, L., Elroy-Stein, O., Ragheb, J., Moss, B., and Anderson, W. F. (1992) Retroviral vectors containing putative internal ribosome entry sites: development of a polycistronic gene transfer system and applications to human gene therapy. *Nucleic Acids Res.* **20,** 1292–1299.

43. Bestwick, R. K., Kozak, S. L., and Kabat, D. (1988) Overcoming interference to retroviral superinfection results in amplified expression and transmission of cloned genes. *Proc. Natl. Acad. Sci. USA* **85,** 5404–5408.

44. Muenchau, D. D., Freeman, S. M., Cornetta, K., Zwiebel, J. A., and Anderson, W. F. (1990) Analysis of retroviral packaging lines for generation of replication-competent virus. *Virology* **176,** 262–265.

45. Lynch, C. M. and Miller, A. D. (1991) Production of high titer helper virus-free retroviral vectors by cocultivation of packaging cells with different host ranges. *J. Virol.* **65,** 3887–3890.

46. Markowitz, D., Goff, S. P., and Bank, A. (1988) Construction and use of a safe and efficient amphotropic packaging cell line. *Virology* **167,** 400–406.

47. Miller, A. D., Garcia, J. V., von Suhr, N., Lynch, C. M., Wilson, C., and Eiden, M. V. (1991) Construction and properties of retrovirus packaging cells based on gibbon ape leukemia virus. *J. Virol.* **65,** 2220–2224.

48. Southern, P. and Berg, P. (1982) Transformation of mammalian cells to antibiotic resistance with a bacterial gene under the control of the SV40 early region promoter. *J. Mol. Appl. Gen.* **1,** 327.

49. Kriegler, M. (1990) *Gene Transfer and Expression: A Laboratory Manual.* Freeman, New York.

50. Fairbain, L. J. and Spooncer, E. (1993) Retroviral gene transfer into haemopoietic cells, in *Haemopoiesis: A Practical Approach* (Testa, N. G. and Molineux, G., eds.), Oxford University Press, New York.

51. Huszar, D., Ellis, J., and Bernstein, A. (1989) *Technique* **1,** 28–32.
52. Seif, I., Lauret, E., and Rivière, I. (1991) Isolation of DNA from cells and from enzyme reactions. *Meth. Mol. Cell. Biol.* **2,** 216,217.
53. Sambrook, J., Fritsch, E. F., and Maniatis, T. (1989) *Molecular Cloning: A Laboratory Manual,* vol. 1. Cold Spring Harbor Laboratory, Cold Spring Harbor, New York.
54. Russell, S. J. (1991) Making High Titer Retroviral Producer Cells, in *Methods in Molecular Biology, vol. 8: Practical Molecular Virology: Viral Vectors for Gene Expression* (Collins, M., ed.), Humana, Clifton, NJ, pp. 29–44.
55. Gossen, M., Freundlieb, S., Bender, G., Müller, G., Hillen, W., and Bujard, H. (1995) Transcriptional activation by tetracyclines in mammalian cells. *Science* **268,** 1766–1769.
56. Eglitis, M. A., Schneiderman, R. D., Rice, P. M., and Eiden, M. V. (1995) Evaluation of retroviral vectors based on thie gibbon ape leukemia virus. *Gene Ther.* **2,** 486–492.
57. Naldini, L., Blömer, U., Galley, P., Ory, D., Mulligan, R., Graze, F. H., Verma, I. M., and Trono, D. (1996) In vivo gene delivery and stable transduction of nondividing cells by a lentiviral vector. *Science* **272,** 263–267.
58. Burns, J. C., Friedmann, T., Driever, W., Burrascano, M., and Yee, J.-K. (1993) Vesicular stomatitis virus G glycoprotein pseudotyped retroviral vectors. *Proc. Natl. Acad. Sci. USA* **90,** 8033–8037.

5

Development of Replication-Defective Herpes Simplex Virus Vectors

David Krisky, Peggy Marconi, William F. Goins, and Joseph C. Glorioso

1. Introduction

Numerous diseases of the nervous system result from single gene or multifactorial gene defects such as cancer, immune pathological disorders, metabolic diseases, and common neurodegenerative syndromes (Parkinson's and Alzheimer's diseases). A greater understanding of the molecular, biochemical, and genetic factors involved in the progression of a specific disease state has led to the development of genetic therapies using direct gene transfer to ameliorate the disease condition or correct a genetic defect *in situ*. Standard gene therapeutic approaches employing retroviruses have not proven feasible for treating disorders of the central nervous system (CNS) since these vectors require dividing cells for integration and expression of the transgene, whereas CNS neurons are postmitotic, terminally differentiated cells. Thus, methods for delivery and expression of therapeutic gene products to treat CNS disease will require new delivery strategies and vehicles including the development of novel vectors for direct gene transfer. These vectors should: efficiently deliver the therapeutic gene(s) to a sufficient number of nondividing neurons; persist long-term in a nonintegrated state within the nerve cell nucleus without disturbing host cell functions; and be able to regulate therapeutic gene expression for diseases that may either require high-level transient transgene expression or continuous low level synthesis of the therapeutic product.

Herpes simplex virus type-1 (HSV-1) possesses a number of practical advantages for in vivo gene therapy to brain and other tissues including its ability to infect a wide variety of both dividing and postmitotic cell types; its ability to be propagated to high titers on complementing cell lines; a large

From: *Methods in Molecular Medicine, Gene Therapy Protocols*
Edited by: P. Robbins Humana Press Inc., Totowa, NJ

genome size (152 kb) that enables the virus to accommodate large or numerous therapeutic gene sequences (>35 kb); and the natural biology of HSV-1 infection involves long-term persistence of the viral genome in a latent, nonintegrated state in neuronal cell nuclei *(1–3)* and other postmitotic cell types in the absence of viral protein synthesis, genome integration, or interference with host cell biology. Since the virus does not disrupt normal host cell biology or express viral antigens during latency, cells harboring latent virus will not be attacked by the host's immune system and should allow persistence of the viral genome for the lifetime of the host, obviating the need for repeat dosing of the virus vector. During latency, the viral genome is transcriptionally silent except for the expression of a novel set of viral latency-associated transcripts (LATs) *(4–9)*. Since the LATs are not required for the establishment or maintenance of this latent state *(10–16)*, it should be possible to delete these genes and replace them with the desired therapeutic gene to drive expression of this gene product from an otherwise quiescent genome using the novel latency and neuronal cell-specific promoter complex resident within the vector genome.

1.1. The HSV-1 Life Cycle

The HSV-1 particle (Fig. 1A) is composed of: an envelope containing 12 glycoproteins that allow the virus to attach to and infect cells by fusion of the virus envelope with the cell surface membrane (for review, *see* refs. *17* and *18*); a tegument matrix inside the envelope that is composed of viral structural components involved in shut-off of host protein synthesis *(19–22)*, activation of immediate early viral gene expression, and assembly functions *(23–28)*; a regular icosahedral-shaped nucleocapsid *(29)*; and a linear, double-stranded DNA genome containing approx 78 open reading frames *(30–32)*. The 152-kb viral genome is segmented (Fig. 1B) with each of its long (U_L) and short (U_S) unique segments flanked by inverted repeats (IRs). The viral functions have been categorized as to whether they are essential for virus replication in cell culture or are accessory (nonessential) functions that contribute to virus replication and spread in vivo. The viral genes are arranged in a manner such that many of the essential functions or accessory genes tend to be clustered within the genome. Additionally, since very few HSV-1 genes are spliced and the virus possesses a highly evolved recombination system, it is relatively easy to manipulate and engineer the virus for purposes of gene transfer, deleting individual genes or blocks of genes that may play a role in vector toxicity.

During normal infection, HSV-1 infects the skin following direct contact and undergoes a productive (lytic) infection in skin fibroblasts and epithelial cells (Fig. 2A). The lytic replication cycle of the virus takes place in the nucleus *(17,33)* of the infected cell with the viral genes expressed in a highly regulated cascade *(34)* of coordinated gene expression consisting of three stages; imme-

Fig. 1. Herpes simplex virus type-1 (HSV-1) particle, genome structure, and gene organization. **(A)** HSV-1 virion schematic showing the envelope containing virus-specific glycoproteins surrounding the dense tegument layer that encompasses the icosahedral-shaped nucleocapsid possessing a single copy of linear, double-stranded viral DNA. **(B)** Diagram of the HSV-1 prototype genome depicting the location of essential and accessory (nonessential) viral genes.

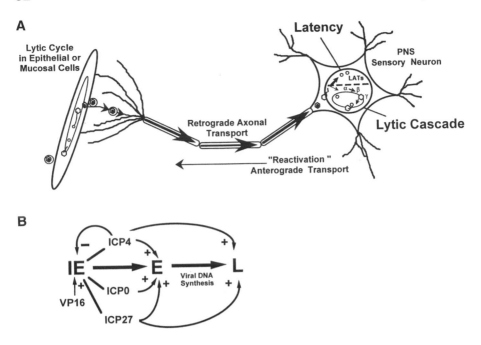

Fig. 2. HSV-1 life cycle. **(A)** Schematic diagram of the HSV-1 lytic replication cycle in vivo. The HSV-1 enters mucosal or epithelial cells and proceeds through the lytic replication pathway. The resulting progeny virus particles can encounter and fuse with the cell surface membrane of peripheral nerve termini that innervate the site of primary infection. The viral nucleocapsid then travels via retrograde axonal transport to the neuronal cell body where the virus can either proceed through the highly regulated cascade of lytic gene expression, or enter latency during which the viral lytic gene program is interrupted and the latency-associated transcripts (LATs) are the sole viral RNAs expressed. In response to a wide variety of stimuli, the virus is capable of reactivating from the latent state, entering the lytic portion of the HSV life cycle at which time progeny virions can either be transported back to the site of the primary infection or the virus may enter the CNS. **(B)** Temporal cascade of HSV-1 gene expression detailing the roles of HSV-1 IE gene transactivators ICP4, ICP27, ICP0, and the IE promoter stimulatory molecule VP16. The immediate early (IE or α) genes are expressed immediately upon infection in the absence of *de novo* protein synthesis. The VP16 (αTIF, Vmw65) virus tegument protein interacts with the cellular factor Oct-1 to positively regulate the expression of the IE genes by binding to their promoters. The IE gene products ICP4, ICP27, and ICP0 are responsible for activating early (E or β) genes. Following viral DNA replication, the ICP4 and ICP27 IE polypeptides regulate the expression of the late (L or γ) genes.

diate early (IE or α), early (E or β), and late (L or γ) (Fig. 2B). Three of the viral IE genes are transcriptional activators that induce expression of E and L genes *(35–42)*. Early gene functions participate in viral DNA replication, which must proceed in order for late gene expression to occur *(43,44)*. The late gene products are largely structural products comprising the nucleocapsid, tegument, and viral envelope glycoproteins. Viral particles are assembled within the nucleus, bud from the nuclear membrane, and particle maturation proceeds during migration through the golgi followed by egress from the cell. Following focal replication of the virus in these permissive cell types, the virus invades the nervous system by directly infecting axon terminals of local sensory neurons of the peripheral nervous system (PNS) *(45,46)*. The virus nucleocapsids are transported in a retrograde manner back to the neuronal cell body where the virus can either replicate or enter latency. During latency, the linear viral genomes circularizes, becomes methylated, and forms a higher order nucleosomal structure *(1–3,47)*. At this point, the lytic genes become inactive and the viral latency transcripts (LATs) are readily detected by *in situ* hybridization using LAT specific riboprobes *(6–9,15)*. The virus can remain within the latent state for the lifetime of the individual, or it can be induced to reactivate from latency by a variety of stimuli resulting in the resumption of the lytic cycle and the subsequent synthesis of progeny virions that may traverse the axon by anterograde transport establishing an active infection at or near the site of primary infection.

1.2. Engineering HSV-1 Vectors

The optimal HSV vector should be: safe and completely devoid of replication-competent virus; noncytotoxic; incapable of affecting normal host cell biology; able to persist in the neuronal cell body in a nonintegrated state; and capable of expressing the therapeutic gene(s) to appropriate levels at the proper time(s). The two major considerations in the design of HSV-1 vectors concern the elimination of the cytotoxic properties of the virus and the development of promoter systems for proper expression of the therapeutic gene. Considerable effort has been put forth into addressing both of these issues of vector design. In this work we will concentrate on the engineering of HSV-1 vectors deleted for essential gene functions that display reduced toxicity following infection.

1.2.1. Solving the Problem of HSV-1 Cytotoxicity

Since UV-irradiated virus displays substantially reduced cytotoxicity in vitro *(48,49)* and disruption of viral IE gene expression by interferon also reduces toxicity, it is presumed that the cytotoxicity of HSV-based vectors results from the expression of HSV-1 gene products. The fundamental approach to designing HSV-1 vectors with reduced toxicity is to remove the essential IE genes (*see* Fig. 1B) of the virus, as well as several nonessential genes, whose products interfere with host cell metabolism and are part of the virion (tegument) structure. Deletion of the two essential IE genes that encode the infected cell proteins 4 (ICP4) and 27 (ICP27), blocks early and late gene expression *(35,39)* (*see* Fig. 2B). These deletions require that the missing functions are supplied *in trans* using a complementing cell line *(35,50)*. In order to ensure that recombination does not occur between the defective virus and the viral sequences present within the complementing cell line during propagation, it is essential that these sequences do not share homology with sequences present within the viral genome, and that the deletion of the IE genes from the virus exceed the limits of the complementing sequences. Since many of these viral IE genes are toxic to cells, expression of the complementing genes must be inducible upon infection with the defective virus. This is achieved through the use of HSV-1 IE promoters to drive expression of these toxic transactivating genes from the cell, since these promoters have been shown to respond to the HSV-1 transactivator VP16 (Vmw65 or α-TIF) *(24–28)*, a virion tegument component that accompanies the viral DNA molecule into the nucleus of the infected cell. VP16 recognizes a consensus sequence (octomer-TAATGARAT) located at various sites in all HSV-1 IE promoters and together with the cellular transcription factors, octomer binding protein one (Oct-1) and HCF (also termed C1, VCAF-1, and CFF) *(51–55)*, transactivates the IE gene promoters *(56–59)*. In the absence of virus infection, the complementing IE genes in the cell chromosome are silent. However, upon infection with the replication-defective mutant, the VP16/Oct-1/HCF complex transactivates the IE promoters upstream of the complementing viral sequences in the cell line, thereby inducing expression of the necessary products for propagation of the deletion virus.

A third IE gene of interest is ICP0, which is both cytotoxic and capable of promiscuous transactivation of a variety of cellular genes *(60–63)* as well as enhancing the level of expression of other viral genes *(64)*. ICP0 appears to cooperatively collaborate with ICP4, for example, to increase the activity of this key viral function *(65,66)*, although ICP0 is not a promoter binding protein and thus appears to stimulate an event prior to direct promoter activation *(67)*. Although ICP0 is a nonessential viral function, deletion of ICP0 results in decreased viral titers *(40,68)*, and propagation of high-titer stocks of virus deleted for ICP0 in conjunction with the essential IE genes will require the production of a cell line capable of complementing ICP0, as well as ICP4 and ICP27. Generation of such a line has been extremely difficult, since even low-level synthesis of ICP0 is toxic to the host cell. The two remaining IE genes, ICP22, which affects the phosphorylation of RNA polymerase II *(69)* and ICP47, which affects the processing of MHC class I antigens *(70,71)*, may also need to be deleted depending on the specific therapeutic application.

In addition to the viral IE gene functions, two additional genes represent targets of interest for removal to reduce toxicity. The infecting virus carries in with the particle a tegument component that has a virion-associated host shut-off (vhs) activity *(19,20)*. The vhs appears to interfere nondiscriminately with mRNA stability *(21)*. Removal of the UL41 (vhs) gene does not affect viral replication *(22)*, but enhances the health of the cell on infection with nonreplicating viral mutants *(72)*. Finally, the virus encodes its own ribonucleotide reductase large (RR1) and small (RR2) subunit gene products. The large subunit (RR1) is expressed both at IE as well as E times during replication owing to its unusual IE-E hybrid promoter *(73)*. Because RR1 also has an associated protein kinase activity *(74)*, it is also prudent to delete this gene.

It is anticipated that deletion of these six genes (ICP4, ICP0, ICP27, ICP22, vhs, and RR1) will essentially shut down viral gene expression upon infection of noncomplementing cells, rendering the virus safe, noncytotoxic, and capable of establishing latency in many if not all nondividing cells. Moreover, the retention of expression of ICP47, recently shown to down-regulate MHC class I antigen expression *(70,71)*, should provide an additional level of protection from immune surveillance at the initiation of infection in vivo.

1.2.2. Construction of Mutant Viruses Deleted for IE and Other Toxic Functions

The first generation of replication-defective mutant viruses consisted of mutants deleted for the essential ICP4 gene. One of these recombinants, designated d120, can be grown on a complementing cell line (E5) that expresses ICP4 *in trans* on infection with the ICP4 deletion mutant virus *(35)*. We have subsequently introduced the β-galactosidase (*lacZ*) reporter gene, under control of the strong human cytomegalovirus (HCMV) immediate early gene promoter, into the thymidine kinase gene locus of the genome of this replication-defective mutant in order to rapidly identify cells and tissues infected with this vector to evaluate the potential uses for such vectors. We have shown that the transgene was transiently expressed in a variety of cell types in culture and in various tissues in vivo. Long-term expression of the transgene both in culture and in some cells in vivo may be affected by the virus-induced toxicity leading to death of the cells in culture and/or immune recognition and clearance in vivo. Therefore, it is clear that additional IE genes must be removed to further reduce viral toxicity.

In order to generate second generation replication-defective viruses deleted for multiple IE essential gene functions, it was necessary to construct a cell line to complement the essential IE gene functions. A cell line was constructed to complement both ICP4 and ICP27 by transfecting Vero cells with a plasmid containing the HSV-1 sequences coding for ICP4 and ICP27 along with a neomycin-expression (SV2-neo) cassette for rapid selection of individual clones. In order to eliminate the chance of homologous recombination and rescue of the mutant viruses during propagation in the complementing line, the plasmid containing the coding regions for ICP4 and ICP27 was engineered to avoid overlap of these sequences with the deletions present within the virus. One clone, designated 7B, was isolated after multiple rounds of drug selection and this clone was able to complement the growth of the IE deletion mutants d120 (ICP4⁻) *(35)* and 5dl1.2 (ICP27⁻) *(75)*.

A second generation, double-mutant virus deleted for both ICP4 and ICP22 was engineered using the 7B cell line (Fig. 3A). This recombinant, d4/22, was engineered by recombining the linearized plasmid PB5, containing the HCMV IE promoter-*lac*Z BGHpA cassette surrounded by ICP22 flanking sequences, into the ICP22 gene locus of the ICP4 replication-defective mutant d120. Positive recombinants were propagated and isolated on the 7B complementing cell line owing to the production of blue plaques following X-gal staining (Fig. 3B). The d4/22 recombinant fails to replicate or produce the blue plaque phenotype on normal noncomplementing (Vero) cells (Fig. 3B).

The cassette combined into the ICP22 locus is unique in that it contains the *lac*Z gene construct flanked by two 8-bp recognition sites for *Pac*I that are not present at any other site in the viral genome. Thus, the expression cassette can be easily removed by digestion with the *Pac*I restriction enzyme followed by religation of the genome yielding a recombinant with a single *Pac*I site that produces clear plaques on the 7B complementing cell line. In order to efficiently introduce a new gene cassette into the ICP22 locus of this recombinant, the recombinant genome is simply cleaved with *Pac*I and used in marker transfer transfection assays with plasmid-containing sequences that span the *Pac*I site in ICP22. The desired recombinant will lack the HCMV-*lac*Z expression cassette, and thus can be easily isolated as a clear plaque on a background of blue plaques produced by the parental virus. The recombination frequency obtained using this approach is tenfold greater than that seen in standard marker rescue experiments.

The d4/22 double mutant was examined for reduced toxicity in cell culture compared to both wild-type (KOS strain) and the d120 (ICP4⁻) parental virus. Myoblasts were infected with the various viruses at a multiplicity of infection (MOI) of 0.5 and the number of viable cells was determined at 2 and 4 d postinfection using trypan blue exclusion. This specific MOI was chosen since d120 uniformly kills cells at an MOI of one or greater. As shown in Fig. 4, this double mutant (d4/22) is less cytotoxic than d120 for myoblasts at an MOI of 0.5, and much less toxic than wild-type virus, although some toxicity still remains. It is believed that the removal of other toxic gene targets from the d4/22 double mutant should further reduce HSV vector toxicity to a point that it should eventually approach that observed with mock-infected cells.

A

d120 (ICP4⁻) (DeLuca *et al.*, 1985)

d4/22 (ICP4⁻/ICP 22⁻)

B

Fig. 3. HSV vector mutation strategies and propagation. (A) Construction of ICP4⁻/ICP22⁻ double deletion mutant. To construct the d4/22 mutant, d120 (ICP4⁻) viral DNA was transfected into the 7B (4/27) line along with the plasmid PB5 in which ICP22 sequences were deleted and replaced with the HCMV IE promoter-*lacZ* BGHpA cassette. (B) The resulting recombinant can be isolated and propagated on the 7B line producing blue plaques because of the presence of the HCMV IEp-*lacZ* cassette in the ICP22 locus. No plaques are detected on noncomplementing Vero cells. In addition, the d4/22 mutant will also produce blue plaques on the E5 ICP4 complementing cell line *(35)*.

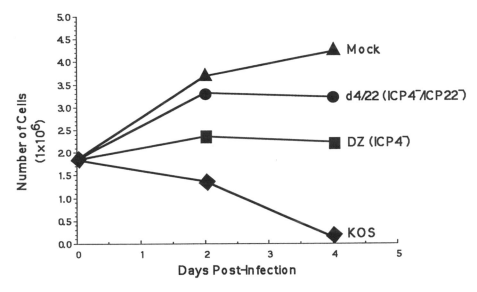

Fig. 4. Cytotoxicity of recombinant viruses. Myoblasts (1.8×10^6) were either mock-infected or infected with wild-type KOS, DZ (ICP4$^-$), or the d4/22 (ICP4$^-$/ICP22$^-$) double deletion mutant (MOI = 0.5). The number of viable cells were counted at 2 and 4 d postinfection. The increase in cell numbers observed in mock and other samples reflects myoblast cell division over the 2–4-d time period. Deletion of ICP22 from the ICP4 backbone reduced toxicity.

2. Materials

1. Vero (African green monkey kidney ATCC#CCL81) cells, other permissive cells such as HELs or BHKs, or complementing cell lines are required to propagate HSV-1 accessory or essential gene deletion viruses.
2. MEM-10%FCS: Eagle's Modified Essential Medium supplemented with nonessential amino acids, 100 U/mL penicillin G, 100 μg/mL streptomycin sulfate, 2 mM glutamine, and 10% fetal calf serum.
3. TBS, pH 7.5: 50 mM Tris-HCl, pH 7.5, 150 mM NaCl, 1 mM EDTA.
4. Lysis buffer: 10 mM Tris-HCl, pH 8.0, 10 mM EDTA.
5. TE: 10 mM Tris-HCl, pH 8.0, 1 mM EDTA.
6. TE equilibrated phenol:chloroform:isoamyl alcohol (25:24:1 v/v).
7. 2X HBS: 20 mM HEPES, 135 mM NaCl, 5 mM KCl, 5.5 mM dextrose, 0.7 mM Na$_2$HPO$_4$, pH 7.05. Accurate pH of this solution is critical.
8. 1X MEM/X-gal/agarose overlay: Add an equal volume of 2X MEM-20% FCS containing 200 U/mL penicillin G, 200 μg/mL streptomycin sulfate, and 4 mM glutamine to an equal volume of 1.5% (w/v) low melting point (LMP) agarose that was autoclaved and cooled to 37°C and contains the chromogenic substrate X-gal at a final concentration of 300 μg/mL. X-gal is highly insoluble and must be dissolved in dimethyl formamide (DMF).

9. 1.0% Methylcellulose overlay: Add 25 g methylcellulose to 100 mL PBS, pH 7.5, in a 500-mL sterile bottle containing a stir bar. Autoclave the bottle on liquids cycle for 45 min. After the solution cools, add 350 mL of MEM supplemented with nonessential amino acids, 100 U/mL penicillin G, 100 μg/mL streptomycin sulfate, and 2 mM glutamine. Mix well and place the bottle on a stir plate at 4°C overnight. Once the methylcellulose has entered solution, add 50 mL of FCS.

10. 1X PBS, pH 7.5: 135 mM NaCl, 2.5 mM KCl, 1.5 mM KH$_2$PO$_4$, 8.0 mM Na$_2$HPO$_4$, pH 7.5.

3. Methods

3.1. Isolation of Viral DNA for Transfection

Engineering a new virus recombinant requires a plasmid containing the particular sequence of interest flanked by sufficient amounts of viral sequences homologous to the desired gene locus within the HSV-1 genome, along with purified, infectious viral DNA. The quality and purity of these two reagents will determine the frequency of generating the desired recombinant virus. It is imperative that the sequence of interest in the plasmid contain at least 500–1000 bp of flanking HSV-1 sequences to achieve a higher frequency of producing and isolating the recombinant. The quality of the viral DNA used in the transfections to synthesize new recombinants can be evaluated by two criteria: whether the DNA is intact and at the proper concentration, as determined by Southern blot analysis *(76)*; or, more importantly, whether the viral DNA is infectious and capable of producing an optimal number of plaques following transfection of 1 μg of viral DNA. We have optimized the protocol for the production of highly infectious viral DNA and routinely obtain preps in which 1 μg of purified viral DNA will yield 100–1000 plaques.

1. Infect a subconfluent to confluent monolayer of cells in a T150 tissue culture flask at an MOI of 3. The cell should have been split at both 1 and 3 d prior to infection.
2. Allow the infection to proceed for approx 18–24 h depending on both the cell type and virus used. All cells should be rounded-up and still adhered to the flask, yet they should be just about ready to detach.
3. Remove the cells by tapping the flask or use a cell scraper to dislodge the cells.
4. Pellet the cells for 5–10 min at 2000–3000 rpm at 4°C in a 15-mL conical polypropylene tube.
5. Wash the cells once with 10 mL of TBS (pH 7.5).
6. Lyse the cells in 5 mL of lysis buffer (10 mM Tris-HCl, pH 8.0, 10 mM EDTA) plus 0.25 mg/mL proteinase K plus 0.6% SDS.
7. Wrap the lid of the tube in parafilm and incubate the tube on a nutator platform at 37°C overnight.
8. Extract the suspension twice with phenol:chloroform:isoamyl alcohol (25:24:1), being careful to not be too vigorous. Yet, it is important to invert the tube enough

to achieve proper mixing of the phases. When removing the aqueous phase, remember to leave the interface behind, as the DNA stays at this point, thus increasing the overall yield.

9. Extract the aqueous phase twice with chloroform, again being careful during mixing.
10. Remove the aqueous phase to a new tube, going as close to the interface as possible. The DNA present at the interface is extremely viscous and will enter the pipet as a visible slurry.
11. Add 2 vol of cold isopropanol to precipitate. Mix well.
12. The DNA can be spooled on a heat-sealed Pasteur pipet or the mixture can be stored at −20°C overnight. If spooling the DNA, remove the spooled DNA and transfer the pipet to a new tube, breaking off the Pasteur pipet. Let dry overnight, then resuspend in 0.5–1.0 mL TE buffer or dH$_2$O using wide-bore pipet tips.

At this point, it is important to determine the quality of the DNA prep. The DNA concentration is determined spectrophotometrically at 260 nm. Southern blot analysis of digests of 1 µg quantities of the DNA prep with several diagnostic restriction enzymes should determine whether the DNA is intact. Transfection of 1 µg quantities of the DNA prep into permissive tissue culture cells will allow the determination of the number of infectious particles per 1 µg of DNA.

3.2. Construction of Recombinant Virus: Transfection of Plasmid/Viral DNA

Once the proper plasmid has been constructed, deleting the HSV-1 gene of interest yet maintaining sufficient HSV-1 flanking sequences to allow efficient recombination into the viral genome, it is possible to marker transfer these sequences into the virus taking advantage of the highly active recombinational machinery of the virus by transfecting both linearized plasmid and purified viral DNA into permissive cells using the calcium phosphate method *(77,78)*. Cloning of a reporter gene cassette at the site of the deleted HSV-1 sequences in the plasmid will allow for a more rapid identification and purification of the desired recombinant virus from the ensuing transfection reaction.

1. Split Vero cells (for deletion of nonessential HSV-1 genes) or the specific complementing cell line (for deletion of essential HSV-1 gene[s]) 1:10 3 d prior to transfection.
2. At 1 d prior to transfecting, split the cells again and plate in 60-mm tissue culture dishes at a cell density of 1 × 10^6 cells/plate in MEM-10% FCS.
3. Linearize the plasmid construct at a restriction enzyme site between the flanking HSV-1 sequence and any *Escherichia coli* DNA present within the bacterial vector.
4. Make up the transfection mixture by adding 1–5 µg from the viral DNA prep (the amount of DNA that yields 200 or more plaques by transfection) to an amount of linearized plasmid DNA (or restriction fragment) equal to 10X and 50X genome equivalents of viral DNA. Viral DNA or plasmid DNA alone is used as controls for the transfection.

5. Add 600 µL of 2X HBS to each tube, mix, and place on ice for 20 min.
6. Add 41 µL of 2*M* CaCl$_2$ dropwise, mixing gently. Set at room temperature for 20 min.
7. Aspirate the media from the plates and rinse with 1 mL of 2X HBS.
8. Pipet transfection mixture up and down to break-up large clumps of precipitate, add carefully to cell monolayers, and place plates at 37°C for 40 min in a CO$_2$ incubator.
9. Add 4 mL MEM-10% FCS per plate and place at 37°C for 4 h in a CO$_2$ incubator.
10. Aspirate media from plates and wash with 1 mL of HBS, being careful not to cause the cell monolayer to lift off the plate.
11. Slowly and carefully add 2 mL of 20% glycerol (dilute 100% glycerol in 2X HBS) per plate and leave on cells at room temperature for *exactly* 4 min.
12. Carefully remove all of the glycerol shock solution by aspiration and wash the monolayer three times with 2 mL of MEM-10% FCS. Be sure that the monolayer remains intact.
13. Carefully add 4 mL of MEM-10% FCS, and incubate the plates at 37°C in a CO$_2$ incubator.
14. Observe the plates twice daily under the microscope for the production of CPE, indicating the presence of infectious foci. This usually takes 3–5 d depending on the virus and cell type used to propagate the recombinant.
15. Once a majority of the cells have rounded up, the media is removed and stored temporarily at 4°C, and virus is isolated from the cell pellet by three cycles of freeze-thawing and sonication followed by centrifugation at 2000 rpm for 5 min at 4°C, and this supernate is then combined with the removed media and stored at –80°C for use as a stock.

This stock of virus can now be analyzed for the presence of recombinants and purified as described in the next section.

3.3. Isolation and Purification of Recombinant Virus

The stock of virus obtained from the transfection can now be used to isolate the desired recombinant. If recombination of the sequences into the viral genome results in deletion of an essential HSV-1 gene product, then it is easy to screen for recombinants by simply replica plating virus on both the complementing cell line and on the noncomplementing line (Vero). The desired recombinant will only be capable of producing plaques on the complementing cell line. However, deletion of nonessential functions cannot be selected for and thus it is necessary to isolate and purify the recombinant through three rounds of limiting dilution. This process can be greatly enhanced by the inclusion of a reporter gene cassette within the sequences to be recombined back into the viral genome. We have optimized the limiting dilution procedure for the detection of recombinants expressing the β-galactosidase (*lacZ*) reporter gene.

3.3.1. Limiting Dilution Procedure
for the Detection of Recombinants Expressing LacZ

The advantage of employing limiting dilution is that it does not require the standard plaque isolation technique in which single well-isolated plaques are picked following agarose or methylcellulose overlay. Contamination of positive recombinants with parental virus represents a considerable problem using the standard plaque isolation procedure since it is difficult to find well-isolated plaques on a plate, and virus from an adjacent plaque can get sucked up along with that from the designated plaque in the act of picking a plaque through the agarose or methylcellulose overlay.

1. Titer the stock of recombinant virus from the transfection.
2. Add 30 PFU of virus to 3 mL of 1×10^6 cells in suspension (MEM-10% FCS) within a 15-mL conical polypropylene tube.
3. Wrap the lid of the tube with parafilm, and place the tube on a nutator rocker platform at 37°C for 1 h.
4. Following the 1-h period for virus adsorption, add 7 mL of fresh media and plate 100 μL of the mixture in each well of a 96-well flat-bottomed plate.
5. Incubate the plates at 37°C in a CO_2 incubator for a period of 2–5 d, until the appearance of plaques.
6. The plates are scored for wells containing only single plaques. Theoretically, by adding 30 PFU, it should be possible to obtain 30 out of 96 wells that contain single plaques.
7. Transfer the media from each well into a new 96-well plate. Store the plate at –80°C for future use as a virus stock.
8. Overlay each well with 100 μL 1X MEM/X-gal/agarose using a multichannel pipetor.
9. Let the agarose overlay solidify at room temperature and then incubate the plates at 37°C in a CO_2 incubator overnight or for several hours until the appearance of readily detectable blue plaques occurs.

Wells containing single blue plaques are scored and the overall frequency of original recombination event is determined. Media from the frozen stock 96-well plate stored at –80°C can now be used in the next round of the limiting dilution procedure. With each subsequent round of limiting dilution, the ratio of desired recombinants within the population should approach 100%. We will routinely proceed through one additional round of limiting dilution after the ratio reaches 100% to ensure purity of the stock. At this point, the virus stock can be used to produce a midi-stock for the eventual preparation of a high titer stock for general experimental use and, at the same time, this stock is used to produce viral DNA to confirm the presence of the insert as well as the absence of the deleted sequences by Southern blot analysis *(76)*.

3.3.2. Limiting Dilution for the Detection
of Recombinants Lacking Reporter Genes

If the recombinant virus lacks a *lacZ* expression cassette, it is still possible to isolate and identify the desired recombinant using the limiting dilution technique in combination with either dot blot *(79)* or Southern blot *(76)* analyses. Steps 1–6 are identical to the above procedure.

1. Titer the stock of recombinant virus from the transfection.
2. Add 30 PFU of virus to 3 mL of 1×10^6 cells in suspension (MEM-10% FCS) within a 15-mL conical polypropylene tube.
3. Wrap the lid of the tube with parafilm, and place the tube on a nutator rocker platform at 37°C for 1 h.
4. Following the 1-h period for virus adsorption, add 7 mL of fresh media and plate 100 μL of the mixture in each well of a 96-well, flat-bottomed plate.
5. Incubate the plates at 37°C in a CO_2 incubator for a period of 2–5 d until the appearance of plaques occurs.
6. The plates are scored for wells containing only single plaques. Theoretically, by adding 30 PFU, it should be possible to obtain 30 out of 96 wells that contain single plaques.
7. Transfer the 80 μL of the media from each well into a new 96-well plate. Store the plate at −80°C for future use as a virus stock.
8. For each of the single plaque wells, use the remaining 20 μL of media to infect one well of a 24-well plate containing subconfluent-to-confluent cell monolayers.
9. Incubate the plates at 37°C in a CO_2 incubator for a period of 2–3 d until the appearance of virus-induced CPE is evidenced by cell rounding.
10. Scrape each well with a pipetman tip to remove the monolayer and transfer to a 1.5-mL microfuge tube.
11. Spin for 10 min in a microfuge at room temperature to pellet cells and virus.
12. Aspirate off the supernate and wash with 500 μL of TBS, pH 7.5.
13. Pellet the cells for 5 min in a microfuge, and aspirate off the supernate.
14. Resuspend the pellet in 200 μL of lysis buffer containing 25 mg/mL proteinase K and 0.6% SDS.
15. Digest overnight at 37°C on a nutator rocking platform or on an orbital shaker.
16. Extract the suspension with phenol:chloroform:isoamyl alcohol (25:24:1), vortexing vigorously to mix the two phases. It is not essential to be careful during mixing since it is not crucial for this prep of viral DNA to be highly infectious. Again, when removing the aqueous phase, remember to leave the interface behind.
17. Extract the aqueous phase with chloroform.
18. Transfer the aqueous phase to a new tube, going as close to the interface as possible. The DNA present at the interface is extremely viscous, and will enter the pipet as a visible slurry.
19. Add 500 μL of cold isopropanol to precipitate. Mix well and store overnight at −20°C.

20. Spin tubes in microfuge for 15 min and remove supernate by aspiration.
21. Wash pellet with 500 µL of 70% ethanol, spin tubes in microfuge for 5 min, remove supernate by aspiration, and air dry.
22. Resuspend pellet in 50 µL of TE or dH$_2$O.

At this point, the viral DNA can be used either in dot blot *(79)* or Southern blot *(76)* hybridization analyses employing probes specific to the inserted sequences. Southern blot analyses are more suited to identifying recombinants containing a deletion of viral sequences owing to the production of an altered restriction pattern with the recombinant.

3.4. Preparation of High-Titer Stocks of Recombinant Virus

Prepare a midi-stock of recombinant virus from a monolayer of cells in a T25 tissue-culture flask and obtain the titer of the stock for preparation of the final stock.

3.4.1. Titration of Virus Stock

This procedure can be used to obtain the titer of any size virus stock.

1. Seed six-well tissue culture plates with 0.5–1.0×10^6 cells per well at 1 d prior to titration of the stock.
2. Prepare a series of tenfold dilutions (10^{-2}–10^{-10}) of the virus stock in 1 mL of cold MEM without serum.
3. Add 100 µL of each dilution to a near confluent monolayer of cells in a single well of a six-well tissue culture plate (in duplicate).
4. Allow the virus to adsorb for a period of 1 h at 37°C in a CO$_2$ incubator. Rock the plates every 15 min to distribute the inoculum.
5. Aspirate off the virus inoculum, add 3 mL of 1.0% methycellulose overlay and reincubate the plates for 3–5 d until well-defined plaques appear.
6. Aspirate off the methycellulose, and stain with 1 mL of 1% crystal violet solution (in 50:50 methanol:dH$_2$O v/v) for 5 min. The stain fixes the cells and virus.
7. Aspirate off stain, rinse gently with tap water too remove excess stain, and air dry.
8. Count the number of plaques per well, determine the average for each dilution, and multiply by a factor of 10 to get the number of plaque forming units/mL (PFU/mL) for each dilution. Multiply this number by 10 to the power of the dilution to achieve the titer in PFU/mL.

3.4.2. Virus Stock Preparation

The following procedure calls for preparing a virus stock from two roller bottles worth of cells; however, it can either be scaled up or down depending on specific needs.

1. Seed two 850-cm^2 roller bottles with 2.0×10^7 cells per roller bottle 1–2 d prior to infection.

2. Decant media from the bottles.
3. Add 1×10^6 PFU of virus (MOI = 0.01) in 10-mL of MEM without serum per roller bottle.
4. Allow the virus to adsorb for a period of 1 h at 37°C.
5. Remove the inoculum and add 100–125 mL MEM-10% FCS.
6. Incubate at 37°C until all the cells have rounded-up and are starting to come off the monolayer (2–3 d). It is important to observe the roller bottles at least twice daily under the microscope, as the exact time of harvest is crucial to obtaining a high-titer stock and depends on the virus and cell type used to propagate the recombinant.
7. Dislodge the cells from the plastic surface either by tapping the roller bottle or through the use of a cell scraper and transfer the suspension to 50-mL conical polypropylene tubes.
8. Pellet the infected cells at 2500 rpm for 5 min at 4°C.
9. Decant the supernate into new tubes and store temporarily at 4°C.
10. Resuspend the pellets into a final vol of 2 mL MEM-10% FCS.
11. Subject the infected cell suspension to three cycles of freeze-thawing (–80°C→37°C).
12. Sonicate the suspension of 5 s.
13. Pellet the cell debris at 3000 rpm for 5 min at 4°C.
14. Resuspend the pellet in 1 mL MEM-10% FCS and combine with the supernate stored at 4°C.
15. Transfer to 50-mL Oakridge polypropylene tubes and pellet the virus at 20,000 rpm for 30 min at 4°C.
16. Carefully aspirate of the supernate and resuspend the pellets into a final volume of 1–2 mL of MEM-10% FCS. Aliquot the virus into 2-mL cryotubes and store at –80°C.

The titer of the stock can be determined by the virus titration procedure detailed above. In order to further purify the virus, the virus pellets can be resuspended in PBS instead of MEM-10% FCS and centrifuged on sucrose, dextran T10, or nycodenz gradients. Following these various separation procedures, it is necessary to add glycerol to a final concentration of 10% to the virus stock in order to properly cryopreserve the virus.

4. Notes

1. The DNA that is produced using the viral DNA isolation technique is not composed exclusively of viral DNA, but also contains cellular DNA. The cellular DNA in this mixture acts as carrier when precipitating the DNA during the isolation, thus increasing the yield of DNA. In addition, the cellular DNA acts as carrier DNA during transfections and increases the overall efficiency of forming a precipitate, thereby increasing the chance of obtaining the desired recombinant. If necessary, pure viral DNA can be prepared from virus harvested solely from the media of infected cells or from virus particles that have been gradient purified. The yield of DNA obtained in this instance is significantly reduced.

2. The use of wide-boar pipetman tips (Bio-Rad) will help prevent shearing of the viral DNA, thereby increasing the infectivity of the viral DNA preparation.

3. The quality of the viral DNA preparation is crucial to the recombination frequency. The quality of the viral DNA can be evaluated by Southern blot or by determining the number of infectious centers following transfection. We have found that some preps will appear to be intact by Southern blot analysis, yet still contain a significant number of viral genomes that are nicked and, thus, are not infectious. It is important that the preparation yields 100–1000 plaques/µg of viral DNA.

4. The quality of the plasmid DNA also plays a factor in the recombination frequency. Between 2 and 500 bp of HSV-1 flanking sequence is sufficient; however, 1 kb or greater will dramatically increase the chance of isolating the desired recombinant. The size of the sequence to be inserted into the HSV-1 vector genome can affect the generation of the desired recombinant. It is possible for the virus to package up to an additional 10% of the genome, 15 kb for wild-type virus and potentially more for single and multiple gene deleted viruses. If the insert is too large or contains sequences that affect the stability of the viral genome, part or all of the insert will be lost over time and it will not be possible to obtain a purified isolate of the desired recombinant. The specific gene locus targeted for insertion/ deletion can affect the recombination event. Recombination into the repeat sequences can yield a mixture of viruses containing insertion into one or both copies of the gene. The recombinational machinery of the virus can convert an isolate with a single copy into a recombinant with inserts in both copies. The same mechanism can also produce virus lacking the insert in both copies (i.e., wild-type virus). Southern blot analysis can confirm whether the insert is present in 0, 1, or 2 copies.

5. It is important to linearize the plasmid construct before transfection to increase the recombination frequency compared to that obtained with uncut supercoiled plasmid. Digestion of the plasmid to release the insert, followed by purification of the restriction fragment does not increase the recombination frequency. Although the frequency is the same, use of purified fragment is superior since no chance exists for the insertion of plasmid vector sequences into the virus by semihomologous recombination.

6. The pH of the HBS transfection buffer (HEPES) is extremely crucial to the transfection efficiency. Depending on the cell type being transfected, other buffers such as BBS (BES) or PiBS (PIPES) may result in higher efficiencies.

7. Other transfection procedures can also be employed, such as lipofectin, that will produce equivalent or greater recombination frequencies.

8. Glycerol or DMSO can be used to shock cells during transfection. The percentage of glycerol or DMSO used depends on the cell type being transfected. We have found that glycerol is less toxic than DMSO for Vero cells and that 20% glycerol produced the highest number of transformants with the lowest level of toxicity.

9. Bluo-gal can be substituted for X-gal in the 1X MEM/agarose overlay. Although Bluo-gal is more costly than X-gal, it is superior to X-gal since it produces a darker blue reaction product with reduced background staining of the cell monolayer and it has a greater solubility in DMF.

10. The viral DNA miniprep procedure routinely yields enough DNA for 3–5 restriction enzyme digestions for Southern blot analysis.
11. Virus stocks should be maintained at a low passage. Use one vial of a newly prepared stock as a stock for preparing all future stocks. In order to reduce the chance of rescuing wild-type virus during the propagation of viruses carrying deletions of essential gene(s), stocks should be routinely prepared from single plaque isolates.

References

1. Dressler, G. R., Rock, D. L., and Fraser, N. W. (1987) Latent herpes simplex virus type 1 DNA is not extensively methylated in vivo. *J. Gen. Virol.* **68,** 1761–1765.
2. Mellerick, D. M. and Fraser, N. (1987) Physical state of the latent herpes simplex virus genome in a mouse model system: evidence suggesting an episomal state. *Virology* **158,** 265–275.
3. Rock, D. L. and Fraser, N. W. (1985) Latent herpes simplex virus type 1 DNA contains two copies of the virion joint region. *J. Virol.* **55,** 849–852.
4. Croen, K. D., Ostrove, J. M., Dragovic, L. J., Smialek, J. E., and Straus, S. E. (1987) Latent herpes simplex virus in human trigeminal ganglia. Detection of an immediate early gene "anti-sense" transcript by in situ hybridization. *N. Engl. J. Med.* **317,** 1427–1432.
5. Deatly, A. M., Spivack, J. G., Lavi, E., and Fraser, N. W. (1987) RNA from an immediate early region of the type 1 herpes simplex virus genome is present in the trigeminal ganglia of latently infected mice. *Proc. Natl. Acad. Sci. USA* **84,** 3204–3208.
6. Gordon, Y. J., Johnson, B., Romanowski, E., and Araullo-Cruz, T. (1988) RNA complementary to herpes virus type 1 ICP0 demonstrated in neurons of human trigeminal ganglia. *J. Virol.* **62,** 1832–1835.
7. Rock, D. L., Nesburn, A. B., Ghiasi, H., Ong, J., Lewis, T. L., Lokensgard, J. R., and Wechsler, S. (1987) Detection of latency-related viral RNAs in trigeminal ganglia of rabbits infect with herpes simplex virus type 1. *J. Virol.* **61,** 3820–3826.
8. Spivack, J. G. and Fraser, N. W. (1987) Detection of herpes simplex virus type 1 transcripts during latent infection in mice. *J. Virol.* **61,** 3841–3847.
9. Stevens, J. G., Wagner, E. K., Devi-Rao, G. B., Cook, M. L., and Feldman, L. T. (1987) RNA complementary to a herpesviruses α gene mRNA is prominent in latently infected neurons. *Science* **255,** 1056–1059.
10. Fareed, M. U. and Spivack, J. G. (1994) Two open reading frames (ORF1 and ORF2) within the 2.0-kilobase latency-associated transcript of herpes simplex virus type 1 are not essential for reactivation from latency. *J. Virol.* **68,** 8071–8081.
11. Hill, J. M., Sedarati, F., Javier, R. T., Wagner, E. K., and Stevens, J. G. (1990) Herpes simplex virus latent phase transcription facilitates *in vivo* reactivation. *Virology* **174,** 117–125.
12. Ho, D. Y. and Mocarski, E. S. (1989) Herpes simplex virus latent RNA (LAT) is not required for latent infection in the mouse. *Proc. Natl. Acad. Sci. USA* **86,** 7596–7600.

13. Javier, R. T., Stevens, J. G., Dissette, V. B., and Wagner, E. K. (1988) A herpes simplex virus transcript abundant in latently infected neurons is dispensable for establishment of the latent state. *Virology* **166**, 254–257.

14. Leib, D. A., Bogard, C. L., Kosz-Vnenchak, M., Hicks, K. A., Coen, D. M., Knipe, D. M., and Schaffer, P. A. (1989) A deletion mutant of the latency-associated transcript of herpes simplex virus type 1 reactivates from the latent infection. *J. Virol.* **63**, 2893–2900.

15. Sedarati, F., Izumi, K. M., Wagner, E. K., and Stevens, J. G. (1989) Herpes simplex virus type 1 latency-associated transcript plays no role in establishment or maintenance of a latent infection in murine sensory neurons. *J. Virol.* **63**, 4455–4458.

16. Steiner, I., Spivack, J. G., Lirette, R. P., Brown, S. M., MacLean, A. R., Subak-Sharpe, J., and Fraser, N. W. (1989) Herpes simplex virus type 1 latency-associated transcripts are evidently not essential for latent infection. *EMBO J.* **8**, 505–511.

17. Roizman, B. and Sears, A. E. (1990) Herpes simplex viruses and their replication, in *Field's Virology*, 2nd ed. (Fields, B. N., Knipe, D. M., Chanock, R. M., Hirsch, M. S., Melnick, J. L., and Roizman, B., eds.), Raven, New York, pp. 1795–1841.

18. Spear, P. G. (1993) Membrane fusion induced by herpes simplex virus, in *Viral Fusion Mechanisms* (Bentz, J., ed.), CRC, Boca Raton, FL, pp. 201–232.

19. Kwong, A. D. and Frenkel, N. (1987) Herpes simplex virus-infected cells contain a function(s) that destabilizes both host and viral mRNAs. *Proc. Natl. Acad. Sci. USA* **84**, 1926–1930.

20. Kwong, A. D., Kruper, J. A., and Frenkel, N. (1988) Herpes simplex virus virion host shutoff function. *J. Virol.* **62**, 912–921.

21. Oroskar, A. A. and Read, G. S. (1989) Control of mRNA stability by the virion host shutoff function of herpes simplex virus. *J. Virol.* **63**, 1897–1906.

22. Read, G. S. and Frenkel, N. (1983) Herpes simplex virus mutants defective in the virion-associated shut off of host polypeptide synthesis and exhibiting abnormal synthesis of α (immediate early) viral polypeptides. *J. Virol.* **46**, 498–512.

23. Ace, C. I., McKee, T. A., Ryan, M., Cameron, J. M., and Preston, C. M. (1989) Construction and characterization of a herpes simplex virus type 1 mutant unable to transinduce immediate-early gene expression. *J. Virol.* **63**, 2260–2269.

24. Batterson, W. and Roizman, B. (1983) Characterization of the herpes simplex virion-associated factor responsible for the induction of α genes. *J. Virol.* **46**, 371–377.

25. Campbell, M. E. M., Palfreyman, J. W., and Preston, C. M. (1984) Identification of herpes simplex virus DNA sequences which encode a trans-acting polypeptide responsible for stimulation of immediate early transcription. *J. Mol. Biol.* **180**, 1–19.

26. Kristie, T. M. and Roizman, B. (1987) Host cell proteins bind to the cis-acting site required for virion-mediated induction of herpes simplex virus type 1 α genes. *Proc. Natl. Acad. Sci. USA* **84**, 71–75.

27. McKnight, J. L. C., Kristie, T. M., and Roizman, B. (1987) Binding of the virion protein mediating α gene induction in herpes simplex virus type 1-infected cells to its cis site requires cellular proteins. *Proc. Natl. Acad. Sci. USA* **84**, 7061–7065.

28. Post, L. E., Mackem, S., and Roizman, B. (1981) Regulation of α genes of herpes simplex virus: expression of chimeric genes produced by fusion of thymidine kinase with α gene promoters. *Cell* **24**, 555–565.

29. Newcomb, W. W. and Brown, J. C. (1994) Induced extrusion of DNA from the capsid of herpes simplex virus type 1. *J. Virol.* **68**, 443–450.

30. McGeoch, D. J., Dolan, A., Donald, S., and Rixon, F. J. (1985) Sequence determination and genetic content of the short unique region in the genome of herpes simplex virus type 1. *J. Mol. Biol.* **181**, 1–13.

31. McGeoch, D. J., Dolan, A., Donald, S., and Brauer, D. H. (1986) Complete DNA sequence of the short repeat region in the genome of herpes simplex virus type 1. *Nucleic Acids Res.* **14**, 1727–1744.

32. McGeoch, D. J., Dalrymple, M. A., Davison, A. J., Dolan, A., Frame, M. C., McNab, D., Perry, L. J., Scott, J. E., and Taylor, P. (1988) The complete DNA sequence of the long unique region in the genome of herpes simplex virus type 1. *J. Gen. Virol.* **69**, 1531–1574.

33. Roizman, B. and Sears, A. E. (1993) Herpes simplex virus and their replication, in *The Human Herpesviruses* (Roizman, B., Whitley, R. J., and Lopez, C., eds.), Raven, New York, pp. 11–68.

34. Honess, R. W. and Roizman, B. (1974) Regulation of herpes virus macromolecular synthesis. I. cascade regulation of the synthesis of three groups of viral proteins. *J. Virol.* **14**, 8–19.

35. DeLuca, N. A., McCarthy, A. M., and Schaffer, P. A. (1985) Isolation and characterization of deletion mutants of herpes simplex virus type 1 in the gene encoding immediate-early regulatory protein ICP4. *J. Virol.* **56**, 558–570.

36. Dixon, R. A. F. and Schaffer, P. A. (1980) Fine-structure mapping and functional analysis of temperature-sensitive mutants in the gene encoding the herpes simplex virus type 1 immediate early protein VP175. *J. Virol.* **36**, 189–203.

37. O'Hare, P. and Hayward, G. S. (1985) Three trans-acting regulatory proteins of herpes simplex virus modulate immediate-early gene expression in a pathway involving positive and negative feedback regulation. *J. Virol.* **56**, 723–733.

38. Preston, C. M. (1979) Abnormal properties of an immediate early polypeptide in cells infected with herpes simplex virus type 1 mutant tsK. *J. Virol.* **32**, 357–369.

39. Sacks, W. R., Greene, C. C., Aschman, D. A., and Schaffer, P. A. (1985) Herpes simplex virus type 1 ICP27 is an essential regulatory protein. *J. Virol.* **55**, 796–805.

40. Sacks, W. R. and Schaffer, P. A. (1987) Deletion mutants in the gene encoding the herpes simplex virus type 1 immediate-early protein ICP0 exhibit impaired growth in cell culture. *J. Virol.* **61**, 829–839.

41. Stow, N. D. and Stow, E. C. (1986) Isolation and characterization of a herpes simplex virus type 1 mutant containing a deletion within the gene encoding the immediate early polypeptide Vmw 110. *J. Gen. Virol.* **67**, 2571–2585.

42. Watson, R. J. and Clements, J. B. (1980) A herpes simplex virus type 1 function continuously required for early and late virus RNA synthesis. *Nature* **285**, 329,330.

43. Holland, L. E., Anderson, K. P., Shipman, C., and Wagner, E. K. (1980) Viral DNA synthesis is required for efficient expression of specific herpes simplex virus type 1 mRNA. *Virology* **101,** 10–24.

44. Mavromara-Nazos, P. and Roizman, B. (1987) Activation of herpes simplex type 1 γ2 genes by viral DNA replication. *Virology* **161,** 593–598.

45. Cook, M. L. and Stevens, J. G. (1973) Pathogenesis of herpetic neuritis and ganglionitis in mice: evidence of intra-axonal transport of infection. *Infect. Immun.* **7,** 272–288.

46. Stevens, J. G. (1989) Human herpesviruses: a consideration of the latent state. *Microbiol. Rev.* **53,** 318–332.

47. Deshmane, S. L. and Fraser, N. W. (1989) During latency, herpes simplex virus type 1 DNA is associated with nucleosomes in a chromatin structure. *J. Virol.* **63,** 943–947.

48. Johnson, P. A., Miyanohara, A., Levine, F., Cahill, T., and Friedmann, T. (1992) Cytotoxicity of a replication-defective mutant of herpes simplex virus type 1. *J. Virol.* **33,** 272–285.

49. Leiden, J. M., Frenkel, N., and Rapp, F. (1980) Identification of herpes simplex virus DNA sequences present in six thymidine kinase-transformed mouse cell lines. *J. Virol.* **33,** 272–285.

50. Samaniego, L., Webb, A., and DeLuca, N. (1995) Functional interaction between herpes simplex virus immediate-early proteins during infection: gene expression as a consequence of ICP27 and different domains of ICP4. *J. Virol.* **69,** 5705–5715.

51. Katan, M., Haigh, A., Verrijizer, C. B., van der Vliet, P. C., and O'Hare, P. (1990) Characterization of a cellular factor which interacts functionally with Oct-1 in the assembly of a multicomponent transcription complex. *Nucleic Acids Res.* **18,** 6871–6880.

52. Kristie, T. M. and Sharp, P. A. (1993) Purification of the cellular C1 factor required for the stable recognition of the Oct-1 homeodomain by herpes simplex virus a-trans-induction factor (VP16). *J. Biol. Chem.* **268,** 6525–6534.

53. Xiao, P. and Capone, J. P. (1990) A cellular factor binds to the herpes simplex virus type 1 transactivator Vmw65 and is required for Vmw65-dependent protein-DNA complex assembly with Oct-1. *Mol. Cell. Biol.* **10,** 4974–4977.

54. Wilson, A. C., LeMarco, K., Peterson, M. G., and Herr, W. (1993) The VP16 accessory protein HCF is a family of polypeptides processed from a large precursor protein. *Cell* **74,** 115–125.

55. Werstuck, G. H. and Capone, J. P. (1993) An unusual cellular factor potentiates protein-DNA complex assembly between Oct-1 and Vmw65. *J. Biol. Chem.* **268,** 1272–1278.

56. Gerster, T. and Roeder, R. G. (1988) A herpesvirus trans-acting protein interacts with the transcription factor OTF-1 and other cellular proteins. *Proc. Natl. Acad. Sci. USA* **85,** 6347–6351.

57. O'Hare, P. and Goding, C. R. (1988) Herpes simplex virus regulatory elements and the immunoglobulin octamer domain bind a common factor and are both targets for virion transactivation. *Cell* **52,** 435–445.

58. Preston, C. M., Frame, M. C., and Campbell, M. E. M. (1988) A complex formed between cell components and an herpes simplex virus type 1 structural polypeptide binds to a viral immediate early gene regulatory DNA sequence. *Cell* **52,** 425–435.
59. Stern, S., Tanaka, M., and Herr, W. (1989) The Oct-1 homeodomain directs formation of a multi-protein-DNA complex with the herpes simplex virus transactivator VP16. *Nature* **341,** 624–630.
60. Cai, W. Z. and Schaffer, P. A. (1989) Herpes simplex virus type 1 ICP0 plays a critical role in the de novo synthesis of infectious virus following transfection of viral DNA. *J. Virol.* **63,** 4579–4589.
61. Everett, R. D. (1987) The regulation of transcription of viral and cellular genes by herpesvirus immediate-early gene products. *Anticancer Res.* **7,** 589–604.
62. Gelman, I. H. and Silverstein, S. (1985) Identification of immediate-early genes from herpes simplex virus that transactivate the virus thymidine kinase gene. *Proc. Natl. Acad. Sci. USA* **82,** 5265–5269.
63. O'Hare, P. and Hayward, G. S. (1985) Evidence for a direct role for both the 175,000 and 110,000-molecular-weight immediate-early protein of herpes simplex virus in transactivation of delayed-early promoters. *J. Virol.* **53,** 751–760.
64. Cai, W. and Schaffer, P. A. (1992) Herpes simplex virus type 1 ICP0 regulates expression of immediate-early, early, and late genes in productively infected cells. *J. Virol.* **66,** 2904–2915.
65. Quinlan, M. P. and Knipe, D. M. (1985) Stimulation of expression of a herpes simplex virus DNA-binding protein by two viral factors. *Mol. Cell. Biol.* **5,** 957–963.
66. Zhu, Z., Cai, W., and Schaffer, P. A. (1994) Cooperativity among herpes simplex virus type 1 immediate-early regulatory proteins: ICP4 and ICP27 affect the intracellular localization of ICP0. *J. Virol.* **68,** 3027–3040.
67. Maul, G. G. and Everett, R. D. (1994) The nuclear localization of PML, a cellular member of the C3HC4 zinc-binding domain protein family, is rearranged during herpes simplex virus infection by the C3HC4 viral protein ICP0. *J. Gen. Virol.* **75,** 1223–1233.
68. Chen, J. and Silverstein, S. (1992) Herpes simplex viruses with mutations in the gene encoding ICP0 are defective in gene expression. *J. Virol.* **66,** 2916–2927.
69. Rice, S. A., Long, M. C., Lam, V., and Spencer, C. A. (1994) RNA polymerase II is aberrantly phosphorylated and localized to viral replication compartments following herpes simplex virus infection. *J. Virol.* **68,** 988–1001.
70. Hill, A., Jugovic, P., and York, I. A. (1995) Herpes simplex virus turns off the TAP to evade host immunity. *Nature* **375,** 411–415.
71. York, I. A., Roo, C., Andrews, D. W., Riddell, S. R., Graham, F. L., and Johnson, D. C. (1994) A cytosolic herpes simplex virus protein inhibits antigen presentation to CD8+ T lymphocytes. *Cell* **77,** 525–535.
72. Johnson, P. A., Wang, M. J., and Friedman, T. (1994) Improved cell survival by the reduction of immediate-early gene expression in replication-defective mutants of herpes simplex virus type 1 but not by mutation of the virion host shutoff function. *J. Virol.* **68,** 6347–6362.

73. Desai, P., Ramakrishnan, R., Lin, Z. W., Osak, B., Glorioso, J. C., and Levine, M. (1993) The RR1 gene of herpes simplex virus type 1 is uniquely transactivated by ICP0 during infection. *J. Virol.* **67,** 6125–6135.

74. Luo, J. H. and Aurelian, L. (1992) The transmembrane helical segment but not the invariant lysine is required for the kinase activity of the large subunit of herpes simplex virus type 2 ribonucleotide reductase. *J. Biol. Chem.* **267,** 9645–9653.

75. McCarthy, A. M., McMahan, L., and Schaffer, P. A. (1989) Herpes simplex virus type 1 ICP27 deletion mutants exhibit altered patterns of transcription and are DNA deficient. *J. Virol.* **63,** 18–27.

76. Southern, E. M. (1975) Detection of specific sequences among DNA fragments separated by gel electrophoresis. *J. Mol. Biol.* **98,** 503–517.

77. Graham, F. L. and van der Eb, A. J. (1973) A new technique for the assay of infectivity of human adenovirus 5 DNA. *Virology* **52,** 456–467.

78. Shapira, M., Homa, F. L., Glorioso, J. C., and Levine, M. (1987) Regulation of the herpes simplex virus type 1 late ($\gamma2$) glycoprotein C gene: sequences between base pairs -34 to $+29$ control transient expression and responsiveness to transactivation by the products of immediate early (α) 4 and 0 genes. *Nucleic Acids Res.* **15,** 3097–3111.

79. White, B. A. and Bancroft, F. C. (1982) Cytoplasmic dot hybridization. *J. Biol. Chem.* **257,** 8569–8572.

6

Methods for the Use of Poliovirus Vectors for Gene Delivery

Casey D. Morrow, David C. Ansardi, and Donna C. Porter

1. Introduction

Poliovirus is a member of the Picornaviridae family of viruses. Characteristic of all members of this family, the poliovirus genome consists of approx 7500 bp of RNA of the plus sense polarity *(1,2)*. Poliovirus is undoubtedly one of the most thoroughly characterized animal viruses. The three-dimensional structure of the entire virion is known *(3)*, an infectious cDNA clone of the poliovirus genome has been generated *(4,5)*, the entire nucleic acid sequence of poliovirus has been determined *(1)*, and the cellular receptor that poliovirus uses to enter cells has been cloned and sequenced *(6)*. The availability of a transgenic mouse expressing the poliovirus receptor has facilitated further description of the pathogenesis of poliovirus *(7,8)*.

The expression of the poliovirus genome occurs by the translation of the entire open reading frame, resulting in a long polyprotein that is subsequently processed by virus-encoded proteinases 2A and 3C *(9)* (Fig. 1). The initial proteolytic processing results in the release of a capsid precursor protein, P1, by the proteinase 2A *(10)*. The subsequent processing of the nonstructural precursor proteins P2 and P3 is accomplished by proteinase 3C *(11)*. The capsid precursor P1 is efficiently processed by 3C^{pro} in the form of a fusion protein between 3C^{pro} and 3D^{pol}, called 3CD *(12)*. Previous studies have established that processing of P1 by 3CD will occur efficiently even when the two proteins are expressed from individual recombinant vaccinia viruses *(12,13)*.

The availability of an infectious clone of poliovirus has provided an opportunity to utilize molecular biologic techniques to investigate various regions of the poliovirus genome that are required for replication. Early studies have demonstrated that the majority of the P1 region of poliovirus could be deleted as

From: *Methods in Molecular Medicine, Gene Therapy Protocols*
Edited by: P. Robbins Humana Press Inc., Totowa, NJ

Fig. 1. Genomic organization of poliovirus: The entire poliovirus genome has been cloned and the 7500 bp nucleic acid sequence determined *(1)*. The viral RNA genome contains a long 5' nontranslated region (approx 750 nucleotides containing an internal ribosome entry site [IRES]). Translation begins at nucleotide 743 and results in the synthesis of a long polyprotein. The amino-terminal glycine of the polyprotein is covalently linked to a single molecule of a 14-carbon fatty acid, myristic acid (a tetradecanoic acid). The processing of the polyprotein occurs by two viral-encoded proteinases, 2A and 3C. Following translation of the 2A proteinase, the autocatalytic activity of this enzyme releases the capsid precursor P1 from the polyprotein *(10)*. The capsid precursor is subsequently processed by the 3C proteinase in the form of a precursor, 3CD, to give the viral capsid proteins VP0, VP3, and VP1. Following encapsidation of the viral genomic RNA, VP0 is further processed by an as yet unknown mechanism, giving VP4 and VP2. Further processing of the P2 and P3 region polyproteins is carried out by the viral 3C proteinase. Processing of the P3 polyprotein results in the release of a viral-genome linked protein, VPg, which is found attached to all 5' poliovirus RNA molecules, and is believed to be involved in replication and encapsidation of genomic RNA. The viral RNA-dependent RNA polymerase, 3D, is released from the polyprotein by the catalytic activity of 3C. Further details regarding the sequential cleavage of the P2 and P3 proteins and the kinetics of this reaction can be found in Lawson and Semler *(29)*. The processing of the P1 polyprotein by the 3CD viral proteinase has been demonstrated to occur in *trans* using both in vitro and in vivo systems *(12,13)*.

Fig. 2. Schematic of a poliovirus replicon: In previous studies, we have described poliovirus replicons that express regions of the HIV-1 genome *(17,19,20)*. We have found that we can substitute foreign gene sequences between nucleotides 949–3359 of the poliovirus genome. This allows us to substitute a sequence of approx 2.5 kb of genetic information to maintain the appropriate size of the poliovirus genome. The plasmid containing the poliovirus replicon is linearized using the *Sal*I restriction endonuclease. Following in vitro transcription using T7 RNA polymerase, the RNA is transfected into cells. The replication of the RNA genome results in the synthesis of a polyprotein containing a VP4-foreign gene fusion protein that can be detected in the transfected cells using appropriate antibodies. Synthetic proteolytic cleavage sites for the 2A proteinase is engineered at the amino and carboxy termini of the foreign gene to express proteins that can be subsequently released from the poliovirus polyprotein *(20)*.

long as the translational reading frame was maintained between the P2 and P3 regions *(14–16)*. Replication of a chimeric genome in which foreign gene sequences were inserted into the poliovirus genome were observed as long as the translational reading frame was maintained between the inserted genes and the remainder of the poliovirus polyprotein *(17,18)*. These chimeric genomes maintain the capacity for replication and are referred to as "replicons." To date, however, there has been no demonstration that genomes that do not have the capacity to replicate (i.e., in which the translational reading frame is disrupted) can be complemented *in trans* by viral proteins. Previous studies from our laboratory have demonstrated that between 800 and 2600 bp of foreign gene sequences can be substituted in the poliovirus genome *(17,19–21)*. A prototype replicon is presented in Fig. 2. In this replicon, the foreign gene is positioned between the VP4 coding sequences and the 2A gene of poliovirus. The foreign gene is positioned such that the translational reading frame is maintained between the VP4-foreign protein 2A protein. We have constructed these replicons such that cleavage sites for the 2A proteinase are positioned at the amino and carboxy termini of the foreign protein. The expression of the foreign protein occurs upon proteolytic processing of the VP4-foreign protein fusion protein from the remainder of the polyprotein, as a result of the autocatalytic activity of the 2A proteinase. A second cleavage occurs by the 2A proteinase *in trans* to release the foreign protein, which contains only minimal changes at the amino terminus (usually only two amino acid changes) and eight additional amino acids at the carboxy terminus *(20)*. We have used this vector to express a number of different proteins, most of which retain their native features.

The poliovirus replicon cDNA is positioned immediately downstream from the phage T7 promoter. The plasmid templates are first linearized at a unique *Sal*I restriction site outside of the viral genome; the DNA templates are then used for in vitro transcription to generate an RNA copy. The transfection of the replicon RNA into tissue culture cells results in the replication of the RNA. The replication features for these genomes are similar to those seen in poliovirus-infected cells in that there is an asymmetric overproduction of the plus strand RNA. Since the poliovirus replicons do not encode a functional P1 capsid precursor protein, the genomes do not have the capacity to spread to other cells. Previous studies from this laboratory have demonstrated that poliovirus genomes containing deletions in the P1 region, or replicons that contain foreign gene insertions in the P1 region, could be encapsidated into poliovirions if transfected into cells previously infected with a vaccinia virus (VV-P1), which expresses the P1 protein of poliovirus *(19–22)*. The features of this complementation system are presented in Fig. 3. Upon transfection of the replicon RNA into cells previously infected with VV-P1, the replicon undergoes RNA replication and expression of viral proteins. Previous studies from this laboratory have demonstrated that transfection of poliovirus replicons into vaccinia virus-infected cells actually results in enhanced replication and expression of viral proteins *(23)*. Expression of the viral proteins from the chimeric genome results in the production of 3CD proteinase, which processes the P1 protein expressed by the recombinant vaccinia virus *in trans*. Upon processing of the P1 protein, assembly of subviral intermediates of poliovirus as well as encapsidation of the chimeric RNA genome occurs. Amplification of the encapsidated RNA genomes is accomplished by reinfection of cells with the encapsidated replicons and VV-P1. Multiple serial passage of the encapsidated replicon in the presence of VV-P1 results in the production of high titer stocks of the encapsidated replicons. Removal of the vaccinia virus is accomplished using a combination of detergents and immunoabsorption with anti-vaccinia virus antibodies. The methods for production of the replicons, transfection into cells, and the generation of stocks of encapsidated replicons are described in the following sections.

2. Materials

All general laboratory chemicals were purchased from Sigma (St. Louis, MO). Restriction enzymes were obtained from New England Biolabs (Beverly, MA). Tissue culture media and supplements were purchased from Gibco-BRL

Fig. 3. Encapsidation of poliovirus replicons using VV-P1: Schematic representation of the encapsidation of the replicons transfected into cells previously infected with a recombinant vaccinia virus VV-P1, which expresses the poliovirus capsid precursor protein. This system is based on the ability of the poliovirus capsid precursor protein, P1, to be processed by the poliovirus protease 3CD, provided in *trans* from the replication of the replicon RNA. Once the P1 protein has been processed, the encapsidation of the replicon RNA ensues, resulting in a polio virion containing the encapsidated replicon.

(Gaithersburg, MD). The [^{35}S] Translabel (methionine/cysteine) and methionine/cysteine-free DMEM were purchased from ICN Biochemicals (Costa Mesa, CA). The T7 RNA polymerase was prepared in this laboratory by the method of Grodberg and Dunn *(24)*; alternatively, the transcription kit Megascript from Ambion (Austin, TX) can be used.

2.1. Tissue Culture Cells and Viruses

Two common cell lines, HeLa and BSC40 (a derivative of CV-1) were grown in Dulbecco's Modified Eagle's Medium (DMEM) supplemented with 10% fetal calf serum (complete medium). The recombinant vaccinia virus VV-P1, which expresses the poliovirus P1 capsid precursor protein, has been previously described *(13)*.

3. Methods
3.1. Overview

The first step in the expression of a foreign protein from a poliovirus replicon is the subcloning of the gene of interest into a modified poliovirus cDNA. We have fused foreign genes between nucleotides 949 and 3359 of the poliovirus genome. The gene is fused such that a synthetic 2A (tyrosine-glycine) cleavage site is positioned at the junction between the VP4 gene (amino terminus) and the foreign protein, which also has a 2A cleavage site at the carboxy terminus. We have found that following the expression of this fusion protein, the viral proteinase 2A^{pro} will process the synthetic 2A positioned between VP4 and the foreign protein, respectively, resulting in the full-length desired protein. The processed protein will then need to be evaluated to determine if it has maintained its native conformation *(20)* (*see* Fig. 2). Standard molecular biology techniques can be used to subclone the foreign gene of interest into the replicon cDNA; to facilitate cloning, we have constructed replicon cDNAs that contain unique *Xho*I or *Sac*I (5') and *Sna*BI (3') restriction sites. In our previous studies, we used DNA oligomers and PCR to create the appropriate restriction sites in the foriegn genes *(20,21)*. Once a suitable replicon has been constructed, the following procedures should be carried out to obtain stocks of encapsidated replicons:

3.2. Preparations of Template and In Vitro Transcription

The preparation of the template replicon DNA required for in vitro transcription is a critical step. Single, well-isolated *E. coli* colonies transformed with replicon DNA are picked from the plate and inoculated directly into 200 mL of LB plus 50 mg/mL of ampicillin. After overnight growth, the *E. coli* are collected by centrifugation and processed using the alkaline lysis procedure *(25)*. The plasmid DNA is purified by ultracentrifugation in CsCl$_2$ gradients *(25)*. After centrifugation, the band containing the DNA is visualized by UV and removed using a syringe. The ethidium is extracted from the DNA with water-saturated butanol and the DNA is dialyzed against TE buffer (10 mM Tris pH 7.8, 5 mM EDTA) overnight. The DNA is then precipitated with 0.3M NaOAC and 3 vol of 100% ethanol at −70°C overnight. The precipitate is collected by centrifugation, washed with 70% ETOH, dried, and resuspended in TE buffer; the DNA is quantitated by UV 260/280.

The DNA (5 μg) is linearized by *Sal*I digestion, followed by successive phenol-chloroform (1:1) and chloroform extractions. The DNA is precipitated with 0.3M NaOAC and 3 vol of 100% ethanol at −70°C for at least 2 h. The precipitate is collected by centrifugation, washed once with 70% ethanol, and dried. The in vitro transcription mixtures (100 μL) contain 5 μg of linearized DNA template, 5X transcription buffer (100 mM Tris pH 7.7, 50 mM MgCl$_2$, 20 mM spermidine, 250 mM NaCl), 10 mM dithiothreitol, 2 mM each of GTP, UTP, ATP, and CTP, 40 U of recombinant RNasin (Promega, Madison, WI), and approx 5 μg of purified T7 RNA polymerase per reaction mixture. After 90 min at 37°C, 5% of the in vitro synthesized RNA was analyzed by native agarose gel electrophoresis. Under these conditions, the full-length RNA transcripts (approx 7.5 kb) comigrate with the 2.0–2.2 kb DNA markers obtained from *Hin*dIII digest of phage λ. We have found that the Megascript kit from Ambion works well for in vitro transcription of the replicon DNAs.

The in vitro transcribed RNAs can be transfected immediately or frozen at −70°C overnight prior to use. The best results are obtained if the in vitro synthesized RNA is transfected without further processing (such as phenol-chloroform extraction).

3.3. Transfection of replicon RNA

The transfection of the replicon RNA into cells can be accomplished using a variety of established methods. In our laboratory, we have utilized DEAE-Dextran as a facilitator (mol wt 500 kDa, obtained from Sigma). For our transfections, HeLa cells were first infected with 10 plaque-forming units (PFU) per cell of VV-P1. The amounts of virus and RNA used have been optimized for a single well of a six-well plate (Falcon, Los Angeles, CA, 3046). After 2 h of infection, the cells were transfected using a protocol adapted from the originally described method of Vaheri and Pagano *(26)*. The cells are washed twice with phosphate buffered saline (PBS; calcium and magnesium-free). The cells are then incubated with approx 10 μg of the in vitro synthesized RNA (approximately one-fifth of the in vitro reaction) with DEAE-Dextran at a concentration of 300 μg/mL in PBS at 37°C for approx 2 h. Although the cells have a tendency to round up from this procedure, they do not detach from the plate. Following two h incubation, cells are washed carefully with DMEM, followed by the addition of complete medium.

3.4. Serial Passage of Encapsidated Replicons

Transfection of the replicon RNA into cells previously infected with VV-P1 results in expression of the appropriate poliovirus proteins (e.g., 3CD) for the proteolytic processing of the P1 protein expressed from VV-P1 (19–22). This results in the assembly of subviral particles and the subsequent encapsidation of the poliovirus replicon RNA. The procedure for passaging the encapsidated replicons is presented in Fig. 4. Twenty-four hours after transfection of the replicon RNA into VV-P1-infected cells, the cells are lysed on ice by the addition of Triton-X-100 at a final concentration of 1%. The lysates are then treated with RNase A for 10 min at room temperature, and the extract is clarified by low-speed centrifugation at 14,000g for 20 min. The supernatants are then adjusted to 0.25% SDS, and overlaid onto a 30% sucrose cushion (30% sucrose, 30 mM Tris pH 8.0, 1% Triton X-100, and 0.1M NaCl). Following centrifugation in a Beckman SW-55 TI rotor at 290,000g for 1.5 h at 4°C, the supernatant is gently decanted and the pelleted virions are washed with a buffer consisting of 30 mM Tris pH 8.0, 0.1M NaCl. To avoid losses during the washing procedure, the pellet is again recentrifuged in the wash buffer for an additional 1.5 h using the Beckman SW 55 TI rotor at 290,000g. The pellets are then resuspended in complete medium and designated as passage one of the replicons. For additional serial passage of the encapsidated replicons, BSC40 cells are first infected with 20 PFU/cell of VV-P1. At 2 h postinfection, the cells are infected with passage one of the encapsidated replicons. At this stage, care is needed to maintain the small volumes during the infection owing to the low titer of the encapsidated replicons. After 24 h, the infection is terminated by three successive freeze-thaws, followed by sonication and clarification by a low-speed centrifugation at 14,000g for 20 min. Previous studies from this laboratory have determined that the low-speed centrifugation results in the removal of approx 90–95% of the vaccinia virus from the cell lysate (19–22). The passage procedure is repeated by first infecting BSC40 cells with VV-P1, followed by reinfection with the cell supernatant. After 5–6 serial passages, the cell monolayer takes on a cytopathic effect consistent with that of a poliovirus infection rather than a vaccinia virus infection. This is easily visualized because poliovirus results in cellular destruction leading to the detachment of the cell monolayer from the culture flask, whereas vaccinia virus-infected cells do not readily detach. Once this type of cytopathic effect is observed, the stock of the encapsidated replicons can be increased by infecting larger amounts of BSC40 cells. Generally, this procedure is initiated by increasing the size from one well of a 24-well plate to two and then four wells of a 24-well plate, followed by one well of a 6-well plate, leading eventually to the serial passage of stock in large tissue culture flasks.

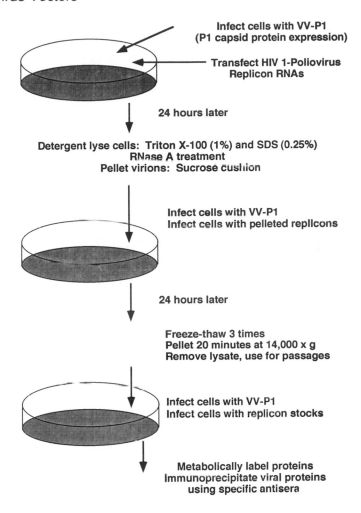

Fig. 4. Replicon encapsidation and passaging protocol: The procedure for the serial passage and development of stocks of the encapsidated replicon is presented. The important feature of this system is that, once the replicon has been successfully encapsidated, it can be passaged in a manner similar to poliovirus as long as coinfecting VV-P1 is present. Once sufficient stocks of the replicon have been obtained, removal of VV-P1 by either detergent treatment or immunoadsorption results in a pure stock of the encapsidated replicons.

3.5. Detection of Encapsidated Replicons

The detection of the encapsidated replicons can be accomplished by several methods. One method is to utilize radioactive probes specific for the inserted foreign gene sequence in the poliovirus genome. A simple dot blot procedure can be used to detect the presence of the replicons (*see* Section 3.7.). A second method is to use metabolic labeling followed by immunoprecipitation to assay for protein expression from the encapsidated replicon. In this case, we use antibodies specific for the foreign protein to be expressed or antibodies to the poliovirus 3D polymerase, if antibodies to the foreign protein are not available. It is important to note that because the poliovirus RNA is translated into a single polyprotein that is then processed, a feature of the expression of foreign proteins using the replicons is that equivalent amounts of the foreign protein and the poliovirus replicative proteins, such as the 3D^{pol} (or 3CD) protein, should be expressed. To metabolically label cells, the cells are infected with the stocks of encapsidated replicons. At 6 h postinfection, the cells are starved for methionine-cysteine by incubation in DMEM minus methionine-cysteine for 30 min. After starvation, 100 µCi of ^{35}S-Translabel is added to these cultures for an additional 1 h. Cultures are then processed for immunoprecipitation of viral proteins by lysing the cells with a buffer consisting of 150 mM NaCl, 10 mM Tris-pH 8.0, 1% Triton X-100, 1% sodium deoxychlate, and 0.2% sodium dodecyl sulfate (SDS, RIPA buffer). Upon lysis of the cells, the extract is centrifuged at 14,000g for 10 min to pellet any residual debris and the designated antibodies are added to the supernatants followed by incubation at 4°C for 24 h rocking. The immunoprecipitates are collected by addition of 100 µL of protein A Sepharose (10% wt/vol in RIPA buffer). After 1 h rocking at room temperature, the protein A Sepharose beads are collected by a brief centrifugation, washed four times with RIPA buffer, and the bound material is diluted by boiling for 5 min in gel sample buffer. The proteins can then be analyzed by SDS-PAGE; after fluorography the proteins can be visualized by autoradiography. In all cases thus far examined, we have found that the expression of the viral proteins correlates with the capacity of the RNA to replicate in the infected cells.

3.6. Isolation of Encapsidated Poliovirus Replicons Devoid of Vaccinia Virus

Once a sufficient stock of the encapsidated replicons is obtained, it is important to concentrate these replicons and remove any residual vaccinia virus. This can be accomplished by adjusting the concentration of the supernatant to 1% Triton X-100 and 0.25% SDS. The virus stock is then overlaid on a 30% sucrose cushion (30% sucrose, 30 mM Tris pH 8.0, 1% Triton X-100, and 0.1M NaCl), and the encapsidated replicons are pelleted through the cushion in an SW 41 rotor at 160,000g for 3 h at 4°C. Although the majority of the vaccinia virus has been inactivated by the detergents, a residual amount of vaccinia virus, generally less than 0.1% of the input amount, is still detectable in the sample. To remove the residual vaccinia virus, the pelleted virions are resuspended in PBS (phosphate-buffered saline) in the presence of antivaccinia antibodies (Lee Biomolecular, San Diego, CA). The sample is incubated at 4°C for 24 h, followed by the addition of protein A Sepharose. The protein A Sepharose is collected by low-speed centrifugation and the supernatant containing the encapsidated replicon is then used for further characterization. We have found that this procedure virtually eliminates any remaining vaccinia virus from the preparations.

3.7. Estimation of the Titer of Encapsidated Poliovirus Replicons

Since these replicons have the capacity to infect a cell but lack capsid proteins, the replicons cannot form plaques, and therefore virus titers cannot be quantitated by traditional assay. To overcome this problem, we have devised a method to estimate the titer of the encapsidated replicons by comparison with wild-type poliovirus of known titer. For these studies, RNA from a titered stock of poliovirus is isolated according to previously described procedures *(27)*. The virion RNA is then precipitated in 2.5 vol of ethanol using $0.2M$ $LiCl_2$. The encapsidated replicon RNA is extracted using the same procedure. Following precipitation, the RNAs are washed consecutively with 80% ethanol and 100% ethanol, dried, resuspended in DEPC-treated H_2O, and serially diluted and spotted onto nitrocellulose paper (dot blot apparatus from Bio-Rad, Hercules, CA).

For detection of poliovirus-specific RNA, a 503-bp riboprobe was generated complementary to nucleotides 671–1174 of the poliovirus genome. The details for the construction of the plasmid to generate this riboprobe can be found in Choi et al. *(17)*. The in vitro transcription of this plasmid results in a complementary RNA that will hybridize to the plus strand RNA of both wild-type poliovirus and the encapsidated chimeric RNA genomes. The in vitro transcriptions are performed under standard conditions using 5X transcription buffer (100 mM Tris pH 7.7, 50 mM $MgCl_2$, 20 mM spermidine, 250 mM NaCl), 10 mM dithiothreitol, 2 mM each of ATP, GTP, and CTP, ^{32}[P]-UTP, 40 U recombinant RNasin (Promega), and approx 5 µg of purified T7 RNA polymerase per reaction. The conditions for hybridization can be found in Choi et al. *(17)*. To determine the relative titer of the encapsidated replicons, the radioactivity associated with each dilution was quantitated using a phosphorimager (or similar radiation scanner). A standard curve was generated in which the radioactive intensity is plotted vs the plaque-forming units of the wild-type poliovirus genome. Extrapolation of the radioactivity of the encapsidated replicon samples to the curve gives an estimation of the approximate titer of the stocks of encapsidated replicons. The resulting titer is expressed in infectious units of replicons, since the infection of cells with the replicons does not lead to plaque formation owing to the absence of the P1 capsid gene. We have determined experimentally that the infectivity of equal amounts of infectious units of the encapsidated replicons correlates with similar amounts of plaque-forming units of wild-type poliovirus.

3.8. Future Directions

We have effectively encapsidated genomes that express a foreign gene of approx 3.0 kb (e.g., β-galactosidase). We have grown such replicons to titers of 10^7 infectious U/mL using standard laboratory conditions. Recent studies from other laboratories have described the use of internal ribosome entry sites (IRES elements) positioned within the poliovirus genome to construct polycistronic replicons *(28)*. This technology could easily be applied to these replicons to produce two different proteins from the same replicon. The design of these constructs would be limited only by the upper limit for the encapsidation of the poliovirus RNA genome, which is probably around 8000 bp (400–500 bp larger than the wild-type genome).

Finally, one of the unique features of these encapsidated replicons is that it is now possible to use these replicons as a means to deliver foreign antigens or biologically active proteins to cells in the absence of an infectious virus. Once suitable stocks of the encapsidated replicons have been generated, the complementing vaccinia virus, VV-P1, can be effectively removed, resulting in a stock of encapsidated replicons that have the capacity to infect a cell and undergo *one* round of replication. Since these replicons do not encode a functional capsid protein, they can be viewed as noninfectious, thus greatly reducing concerns of disease caused by the vector used in delivery of the foreign gene.

4. Notes

One of the critical features for the initiation and maintenance of the encapsidated genomes is to accurately titer the recombinant vaccinia virus expressing the poliovirus capsid precursor protein (VV-P1). It is important to titer on the particular cell type that will be used for the transfection and encapsidation process (i.e., HeLa or BSC40 cells). We have found that it is critical to maintain a multiplicity of infection of approx 20 PFU/cell so that every cell is infected. Great care has to be maintained during the passaging of the encapsidated genomes. In the early stages of passaging, there is a low level of encapsidated genomes and it is imperative that low culture volumes are maintained to increase the multiplicity of infection of the encapsidated genomes. Since the inherent infectivity of poliovirus is somewhat low (approx 40–1000 particles per infectious units), it is important at early stages to optimize the conditions for infectivity. As the number of serial passages increases, the levels of encapsidated replicons increase, allowing for the expansion of the stock of the encapsidated replicons. Again, during the expansion, care has to be taken to avoid overdilution of the encapsidated replicons.

Acknowledgments

We thank Dee Martin for preparation of the manuscript. This work is supported in part by NIH grants AI25005, AI15128, AI28147, DAMD 17-94-J-4403 (US Army), and a grant from the American Foundation for AIDS Research (AmFAR 50449-15-PG) to CDM.

References

1. Kitamura, N., Semler, B. L., Rothberg, P. G., Larsen, G. R., Adler, C. J., Dorner, A. J., Emini, E. A., Hanecak, R., Lee, J. J., van der Werf, S., Anderson, C. W., and Wimmer, E. (1981) Primary structure, gene organization and polypeptide expression of poliovirus RNA. *Nature* **291,** 547–553.
2. Koch, F. and Koch, G. (1985) *The Molecular Biology of Poliovirus.* Springer-Verlag Vienna.
3. Hogle, J. M., Chow, M., and Filman, D. J. (1985) Three-dimensional structure of poliovirus at 2.9 Å resolution. *Science* **229,** 1358–1365.
4. Racaniello, V. and Baltimore, D. (1981) Cloned poliovirus complementary DNA is infectious in mammalian cells. *Science* **214,** 916–919.
5. Semler, B. L., Dorner, A. J., and Wimmer, E. (1984) Production of infectious poliovirus from cloned cDNA is dramatically increased by SV40 transcription and replication signals. *Nucleic Acids Res.* **12,** 5123–5141.
6. Mendelsohn, C. L., Wimmer, E., and Racaniello, V. R. (1989) Cellular receptor for poliovirus: molecular cloning, nucleotide sequence, and expression of a new member of the immunoglobulin superfamily. *Cell* **56,** 855–865.
7. Ren, R., Costantini, F. C., Gorgacz, E. J., Lee, J. J., and Racaniello, V. R. (1990) Transgenic mice expressing a human poliovirus receptor: a new model for poliomyelitis. *Cell* **63,** 353–362.
8. Ren, R. and Racaniello, V. R. (1992) Poliovirus spreads from muscle to the central nervous system by neural pathways. *J. Infect. Dis.* **166,** 747–752.
9. Palmenberg, A. C. (1990) Proteolytic processing of picornaviral polyprotein. *Ann. Rev. Microbiol.* **44,** 603–623.
10. Toyoda, H., Nicklin, M. J. H., Murray, M. G., Anderson, C. W., Dunn, J. J., Studier, F. W., and Wimmer, E. (1986) A second virus-encoded proteinase involved in proteolytic processing of poliovirus polyprotein. *Cell* **45,** 761–770.
11. Hanecak, R., Semler, B. L., Anderson, C. W., and Wimmer, E. (1982) Proteolytic processing of poliovirus polypeptides: antibodies to polypeptide P3-7c inhibit cleavage of glutamine-glycine pairs. *Proc. Natl. Acad. Sci. USA* **79,** 3973–3977.
12. Ypma-Wong, M. F., Dewalt, P. G., Johnson, V. H., Lamb, J. G., and Semler, B. L. (1988) Protein 3CD is the major poliovirus proteinase responsible for cleavage of the P1 capsid precursor. *Virology* **166,** 265–270.
13. Ansardi, D. A., Porter, D. C., and Morrow, C. D. (1991) Coinfection with recombinant vaccinia viruses expressing poliovirus P1 and P3 proteins results in polyprotein processing and formation of empty capsid structures. *J. Virol.* **65,** 2088–2092.

14. Cole, C. N. (1975) Defective interfering (DI) particles of poliovirus. *Prog. Med. Virol.* **20,** 180–207.
15. Hagino-Yamagishi, K. and Nomoto, A. (1989) In vitro construction of poliovirus defective interfering particles. *J. Virol.* **63,** 5386–5392.
16. Kaplan, G. and Racaniello, V. R. (1988) Construction and characterization of poliovirus subgenomic replicons. *J. Virol.* **62,** 1687–1696.
17. Choi, W. S., Pal-Ghosh, R., and Morrow, C. D. (1991) Expression of human immunodeficiency virus type 1 HIV-1 gag, pol and env proteins from chimeric HIV-1-poliovirus minireplicons. *J. Virol.* **65,** 2875–2883.
18. Percy, N., Barclay, W. S., Sullivan, M., and Almond, J. W. (1992) A poliovirus replicon containing the chloramphenicol acetyl-transferase gene can be used to study the replication and encapsidation of poliovirus RNA. *J. Virol.* **66,** 5040–5046.
19. Porter, D. C., Ansardi, D. C., Choi, W. S., and Morrow, C. D. (1993) Encapsidation of genetically engineered poliovirus mini-replicons which express HIV-1 gag and pol proteins upon infection. *J. Virol.* **67,** 3712–3719.
20. Porter, D. C., Ansardi, D. C., and Morrow, C. D. (1995) Encapsidation of poliovirus replicons encoding the complete human immunodeficiency virus type 1 *gag* gene using a complementation system which provides the P1 capsid protein *in trans. J. Virol.* **69,** 1548–1555.
21. Ansardi, D. C., Moldoveanu, Z., Porter, D. C., Walker, D. P., Conry, R. M., LoBuglio, A. F., McPherson, S., and Morrow, C. D. (1994) Characterization of poliovirus replicons encoding carcinoembryonic antigens. *Cancer Res.* **54,** 6359–6363.
22. Ansardi, D. C., Porter, D. C., and Morrow, C. D. (1993) Complementation of a poliovirus defective genome by a recombinant vaccinia virus which provides P1 capsid precursor in trans. *J. Virol.* **67,** 3684–3690.
23. Pal-Ghosh, R. and Morrow, C. D. (1993) A poliovirus mini-replicon containing an inactive 2A proteinase is expressed in vaccinia virus-infected cells. *J. Virol.* **67,** 4621–4629.
24. Grodberg, J. and Dunn, J. J. (1988) OmpT encodes the *Escherichia coli* outer membrane protease that cleaves T7 RNA polymerase during purification. *J. Bacteriol.* **170,** 1245–1253.
25. Sambrook, J., Fritsch, E. F., and Maniatis, T. (1989) *Molecular Cloning: A Laboratory Manual,* 2nd ed. Cold Spring Harbor Laboratory, Cold Spring Harbor, NY.
26. Vaheri, A. and Pagano, J. S. (1965) Infectious poliovirus RNA: a sensitive method of assay. *Virology* **27,** 434–436.
27. Rico-Hesse, R., Pallansch, M. A., Nottay, B. K., and Kew, O. M. (1987) Geographic distribution of wild poliovirus type 1 genotypes. *Virology* **160,** 311–322.
28. Alexander, L., Lu, H. H., and Wimmer, E. (1994) Poliovirus containing picornavirus type 1 and.or type2 internal ribosomal entry site elements: genetic hybrids and the expression of a foreign gene. *Proc. Natl. Acad. Sci. USA* **91,** 1406–1410.
29. Lawson, M. A. and Semler, B. L. (1992) Alternate poliovirus nonstructural protein processing cascades generated by primary sites of 3C proteinase cleavage. *Virology* **191,** 309–320.

7

Methods for the Construction
of Human Papillomavirus Vectors

Saleem A. Khan and Francis M. Sverdrup

1. Introduction

A number of vector systems have been developed for the delivery of therapeutic genes into cells (1). Many viral vectors suffer from the disadvantage of random integration into the chromosome, making the expression of the cloned genes dependent on the chromosomal context of the inserted DNA. Papillomaviruses (PVs) are potentially important vector systems because of their extrachromosomal replication in target cells. The PVs are small DNA viruses that infect humans and a wide range of animals. Human papillomaviruses (HPVs) induce benign proliferative squamous epithelial and fibroepithelial lesions (warts and papillomas) in their natural hosts (2). Some HPVs are also involved in the pathogenesis of anogenital cancer and, in particular, cancer of the cervix (2). Papillomaviruses contain circular, double-stranded DNA of approx 8 kb, and usually replicate extrachromosomally at a copy number estimated to be between 10 and 100 (3). The potential advantages of PV vectors include expression of cloned genes from an extrachromosomal state that may be more amenable to uniform expression and possible elimination of problems associated with integration of DNA into transcriptionally inactive regions of the cellular chromosomes. Since PV DNA is not encapsidated, it may be possible to insert larger DNA sequences into such vectors, provided the DNA can still replicate in a stable manner. Bovine papillomavirus type 1 (BPV-1) vectors have been used to produce stable cell lines expressing foreign proteins (for reviews, *see* refs. 4–7). The BPV-1 vectors used in these studies contained both replication and transforming genes, and in most cases, extrachromosomal replication of these vectors was accompanied by transformation of the target cells (8–12). Recent advances in our understanding of the replication and transforming

From: *Methods in Molecular Medicine, Gene Therapy Protocols*
Edited by: P. Robbins Humana Press Inc., Totowa, NJ

genes of PVs have resulted in renewed efforts to develop vectors that can be established as stable extrachromosomal plasmids and express foreign proteins without oncogenic transformation of the host cell. The current article deals mostly with the potential of HPVs as vectors for gene therapy.

1.1. Organization of the HPV Genome

Most PVs have a similar genomic organization and their genome has been divided into the early and late regions. The early region includes eight ORFs (E1 to E8) involved in viral DNA replication, episomal maintenance, and cellular transformation (5). The late region comprises genes that encode the viral structural proteins, L1 and L2 (5). The E6 and E7 proteins of the high risk HPVs such as types 16 and 18 are involved in cell proliferation and tumor development (2,13). A number of recent studies with PVs have shown the requirement for the viral E1 and E2 proteins in DNA replication (14–19). The long control region (LCR) of PVs contains the promoter and enhancer sequences, including the binding sites for many viral and cellular factors. The LCR also contains the origin of replication (ori) of PVs (3,18,19).

1.2. Replication of Human Papillomaviruses

The keratinocytes of stratified squamous epithelia are the natural hosts for HPVs. In benign papillomas and condylomas, HPV DNA replicates as a multicopy plasmid. The copy number of HPV is influenced by the differentiation state of the cell. In the basal cells of squamous epithelium, HPV DNA replicates at a low but stable copy number, whereas in the upper differentiating cells, vegetative replication occurs resulting in a high copy number. In the final stages of terminal differentiation, the late genes encoding structural proteins L1 and L2 are expressed. HPVs such as type 1a that cause common warts produce large amounts of virion and DNA, whereas types 16 and 18, which are predominantly associated with anogenital cancers, produce extremely low levels of DNA and virions. It is important to note that vegetative replication of HPV DNA is not required for their potential use as vectors for gene therapy. The PVs have been extensively studied in recent years for their replication properties. These studies have shown that the viral E1 and E2 proteins are both necessary and sufficient to support the transient replication of plasmids containing the ori of PVs (14–19). In the case of HPV-1a, the E1 protein alone is sufficient for replication of ori-plasmids (20). The ori of PVs contains an E1 binding site and multiple E2 binding sites. The E2 binding sites appear to act cooperatively to increase the efficiency of replication. We have also found that a region upstream of the HPV-1a origin appears to negatively regulate replication in transient assays (20). The E1 protein of PVs is a nuclear phosphoprotein of approx 600 amino acids that has origin-binding, DNA helicase and ori-specific unwinding activities *(21,22)*. Recently, the overexpression of the BPV-1 E1 protein has been shown to perturb the host cell cycle, resulting in an increase in the duration of the G2 and M phases *(23)*. The viral E2 protein is an activator as well as repressor of viral transcription *(24)*. The E2 ORF encodes several proteins that originate from selective promoter usage and alternative mRNA splicing. The full-length transactivator form of E2 activates transcription by binding to viral promoters located near the E2 binding sites. It also negatively regulates the transcription of the E6 and E7 oncogenes *(24)*. The E2 protein stimulates HPV replication by forming a complex with E1 and enhancing its binding to the origin *(25,26)*. To be useful for gene therapy, it is important to develop PV vectors that replicate extrachromosomally and do not cause oncogenic transformation of the target cells. This may be possible since recent studies have shown that, whereas the E1 and E2 genes are required for PV replication, the E6 and E7 oncogenes are dispensable at least for transient replication. Here we describe our recent efforts to develop HPV-based vectors and their replication in various cell lines.

1.3. Development of HPV Vectors

In order to identify viral sequences required for HPV replication, we have carried out transient replication analysis in various human cell lines. Plasmids containing the HPV-18 origin replicated efficiently in human C-33A, 293, HeLa, and IB-3 cell lines upon cotransfection with plasmids expressing the viral E1 and E2 proteins *(19)*. The copy number of the HPV-18 ori plasmids was ~500–1000/cell. The above information was used to generate vectors in which all the elements required for replication (the E1 and E2 genes, and the origin) were present on a single plasmid (Fig. 1). In these constructs, the E1 and E2 proteins were expressed from various promoters. Although all HPV-based plasmids replicated to various extent in C-33A cells, plasmids pFS101 and pFS106 showed maximal replication. Plasmid pFS101 replicates to much higher levels than pFS102. The E2 gene in these two plasmids is expressed from the RSV 3' LTR and the HPV-18 LCR promoters, respectively. It is possible that high levels of E2 expressed from the stronger RSV promoter in pFS102 may inhibit DNA replication. This is consistent with previous studies in which high levels of E2 appeared to inhibit DNA replication *(19,26)*. The copy number of pFS101 and pFS106 in transiently transfected cells was found to be approx 100/cell. Some of the plasmids shown in Fig. 1 were also found to replicate in IB-3 cells. We are now testing the stable replication of plasmids pFS101 and pFS102 that contain the hygromycin resistance gene in various cell lines. Additional HPV-18 vectors are being developed in which the E1 and E2 proteins are being expressed from various promoters in order to obtain vectors with a range of copy numbers.

Fig. 1. Vectors constructed from HPV-18 DNA. The plasmids are shown in a linearized form and are present on a pUC19 backbone. The E1 gene is indicated by a shaded arrow and its expression is directed by either the RSV 3' LTR (RSV) or the SV40 early promoter (SV40). The E2 gene is indicated by a hatched arrow and its expression is directed by either the HPV-18 p105 promoter (small black arrow), the RSV LTR, or the HSV tk promoter (tk).

We are also developing HPV-1a based vectors for gene delivery. It is well known that during in vivo infections, HPV-1a produces large amounts of virions and DNA compared to HPV-18. Transient replication of HPV-1a usually gives several-fold higher levels of replication than HPV-18. Replication analysis with HPV-1a showed that the E1 protein was sufficient to support replication of plasmids containing the HPV-1a origin *(20)*. We have also found that an E1 binding site is sufficient to function as origin, and multimerization of the E1 binding site greatly stimulates replication. HPV-1a-based vectors are being developed that contain the E1 and E2 genes and the ori, E1 and ori, or E1 and multimerized E1 binding sites. A previous study showed that the presence of a strong heterologous promoter/enhancer sequence inhibited replication of BPV-1 vectors and resulted in its integration into the host genome *(7)*. We have recently seen a similar inhibitory effect of active promoters with HPV-1a vectors in transient replication assays. We are investigating the nature of this inhibition and attempting to overcome it using weaker promoters. However, HPV-18 vectors are clearly able to replicate in the presence of transcriptionally active regions.

So far, a system for HPV virion production using transfected DNA has not been reported, although raft culture systems have been established that allow viral DNA replication and virion production using HPV-infected primary cells or cell lines *(27–29)*. Clearly the development of a tissue culture system for production of virions from transfected HPV DNA would greatly facilitate the use of these vectors for gene therapy. Currently, the use of physical delivery methods such as calcium phosphate precipitation, electroporation, lipofection, and bioballistics *(30)* would appear to provide the best means for the use of HPV vectors for gene delivery into cells.

2. Materials

1. Medium and cell lines: Human epithelial cell lines C-33A, 293, HeLa, and IB-3 are grown as monolayers in Dulbecco's Modified Eagle's Medium supplemented with 10% fetal bovine serum along with penicillin, streptomycin, and glutamine. C-33A and HeLa are human cervical carcinoma cell lines, whereas 293 is an adenovirus type 5 transformed human embryonic kidney cell line. IB-3 is an SV40 T-antigen-transformed human bronchial epithelial cell line derived from a cystic fibrosis patient.
2. 2X BBS: 50 mM BES, 280 mM NaCl, and 1.5M Na$_2$HPO$_4$, pH adjusted to 6.96 with NaOH. Filter sterilize and store at –20°C.
3. Phosphate-buffered saline (PBS): 8 g NaCl, 0.2 g KCl, 1.15 g Na$_2$HPO$_4$ (anhydrous), and 0.2 g KH$_2$PO$_4$ (anhydrous)/L.
4. 0.25M CaCl$_2$.
5. Hirt lysis solution: 0.6% SDS, 10 mM EDTA.
6. Proteinase K.

3. Methods

3.1. DNA Transfections

To test the ability of HPV-based vectors to replicate, replication analysis is carried out in appropriate cell lines using the calcium phosphate transfection method *(31)*.

1. Plate cells at a density of 2–4 × 10^5 cells on a 60-mm plate and incubate overnight in 5% CO$_2$ at 37°C.
2. Mix 5 μg of the HPV vector DNA with 0.25 mL of 0.25M CaCl$_2$ and 0.25 mL of 2X BBS. Let stand at room temperature for 15–20 min.

3. Add the calcium phosphate-DNA solution drop-wise to the cells with constant swirling to mix well.
4. Incubate cells at 37°C overnight in 2% CO_2.
5. Remove medium and rinse cells three times with DMEM (1% serum). Feed cells with normal medium.
6. Incubate cells at 37°C in 5% CO_2 for 3–4 d for transient replication analysis. For stable transfection, start selection an with appropriate concentration of the drug in the medium after 1 d. Stable colonies should be visible after approx 10 d of selection in the medium.

Replication of the HPV DNA is assayed by the isolation of Hirt fraction *(32)* and Southern blot analysis *(33)* as described in Section 3.2..

3.2. Replication Analysis

The ability of the various HPV vectors to replicate extrachromosomally in transfected cells is tested as follows:

1. Wash the cells obtained after transient or stable transfection as described in Section 3.1. with PBS, and treat with 0.5 mL of Hirt lysis solution.
2. Scrape the cell lysate into a microcentrifuge tube and add 150 μL of 5*M* NaCl. Mix and incubate at 4°C for 2 h.
3. Centrifuge for 30 min in a microcentrifuge, collect the supernatant, and treat with 50 μg/mL of proteinase K at 37°C for 4 h.
4. Extract samples twice with phenol/chloroform/isoamylalcohol (25:24:1) and recover the DNA by alcohol precipitation.
5. To distinguish between replicated and unreplicated DNA, treat one-half of each sample with an excess of the restriction endonuclease *Dpn*I. DNA samples can also be linearized with an enzyme to convert the various forms of HPV DNA into a single band.
6. Analyze the DNA samples by agarose gel electrophoresis and Southern blot hybridization using an appropriate probe generated by random primer labeling.

4. Notes

A number of important factors should be considered for the design of HPV vectors. For example, the direction of transcription of the E1 and E2 genes with respect to each other and the origin affects the efficiency of replication. This is evident from the observation that plasmid pFS106 replicates to much higher levels than pFS105. Also the strength of promoters driving the E1 and E2 genes affects replication. Therefore, it is important to use different promoters for the expression of the E1 and E2 genes in HPV vectors to optimize their replication. It may be desirable to use a single transcription unit for the expression of the E1 and E2 genes. This could be accomplished by the placement of an internal ribosome entry site sequence from the encephalomycarditis virus between the E1 and E2 genes, immediately upstream of the initiating ATG codon of the E2 ORF. The use of various origin subregions of HPVs may also provide a means for modulating the copy number of these vectors. We are also testing the cloning capacity of the HPV vectors that are still able to replicate stably in an extrachromosomal form. It is known that BPV-1 and HPVs can attach to a wide range of mammalian cell lines of both fibroblastic and epithelial origin *(34)*. This interaction presumably involves a conserved cell surface receptor. The development of a tissue culture system for the production of viral particles from transfected HPV DNA will clearly provide an impetus for further development of such vectors. Since no packaging system for HPVs is currently available, introduction of such vectors into cells usually involves calcium phosphate precipitation, electroporation, lipofection, and bioballistics. Other potential delivery systems would include packaging of HPV vectors into infectious adenovirus or herpesvirus particles and delivery into target cells. This would involve cloning of recombinogenic sequences surrounding the HPV DNA that would promote the removal and circularization of the vector DNA after delivery into target cells. Such efforts are currently underway in our laboratory.

Recent studies demonstrating the ability of transfected PV DNAs to replicate in a wide range of mammalian cell lines of fibroblastic and epithelial origin have generated a renewed interest in papillomavirus vectors. It may be possible to develop PV vectors that replicate in other types of cells by ensuring the expression of the E1 and E2 genes using promoters that are active in various cell types. Continued development of these vectors may lead to the exciting prospect of their use in gene therapy involving various tissues.

References

1. Mulligan, R. C. (1993) The basic science of gene therapy. *Science* **260**, 926–932.
2. zur Hausen, H. (1991) Human papillomaviruses in the pathogenesis of anogenital cancer. *Virology* **184**, 9–13.
3. Lambert, P. F. (1991) Papillomavirus DNA replication. *J. Virol.* **65**, 3417–3420.
4. DiMaio, D. (1987) Papillomavirus cloning vectors, in *The Papovaviridae 2. The Papillomaviruses* (Salzman, N. P. and Howley, P. M., eds.), Plenum, New York, pp. 293–319.
5. Sarver, N., Gruss, P., Law, M.-F., Khoury, G., and Howley, P. M. (1981) Bovine papillomavirus deoxyribonucleic acid: a novel eukaryotic cloning vector. *Mol. Cell. Biol.* **1**, 486–496.
6. Stephens, P. E. and Hentschel, C. G. (1987) The bovine papillomavirus genome and its uses as a eukaryotic vector. *Biochem. J.* **248**, 1–11.
7. Waldenstrom, M., Schenstrom, K., Sollerbrant, K., and Hansson, L. (1992) Replication of bovine papillomavirus vectors in murine cells. *Gene* **120**, 175–181.
8. Baker, M. D., Murialdo, H., and Shulman, M. J. (1988) Expression of an immunoglobulin light-chain gene in lymphoid cells using a bovine papillomavirus-1 (BPV-1) vector. *Gene* **69**, 349–355.

9. MacGregor, G. R. and Burke, J. F. (1987) Stability of a bacterial gene in a bovine papillomavirus-based shuttle vector maintained extrachromosomally in mammalian cells. *J. Gen. Virol.* **68,** 247–252.

10. Matthias, P., Boeger, U., Danesch, U., Schutz, G., and Bernard, H.-U. (1986) Physical state, expression and regulation of two glucocorticoid-controlled genes on bovine papillomavirus vectors. *J. Mol. Biol.* **187,** 557–568.

11. Meneguzzi, G., Binetruy, B., and Cuzin, F. (1984) Plasmidial maintenance in rodent fibroblasts of a BPV-1-pBR322 shuttle vector without immediately apparent oncogenic transformation of the recipient cells. *EMBO J.* **3,** 365–371.

12. Sarver, N. A., Ricca, G. A., Link, J., Nathan, M. H., Newman, J., and Drohan, W. N. (1987) Stable expression of recombinant factor VIII molecules using a bovine papillomavirus vector. *DNA* **6,** 553–564.

13. Bedell, M. A., Jones, K. H., Grossman, S. R., and Laimins, L. A. (1989) Identification of human papillomavirus type 18 transforming genes in immortalized and primary cells. *J. Virol.* **63,** 1247–1255.

14. Chiang, C.-M., Ustav, M., Stenlund, A., Ho, T. F., Broker, T. R., and Chow, L. T. (1992) Viral E1 and E2 proteins support replication of homologous and heterologous papillomaviral origins. *Proc. Natl. Acad. Sci. USA* **89,** 5799–5803.

15. Del Vecchio, A. M., Romanczuk, H., Howley, P. M., and Baker, C. C. (1992) Transient replication of human papillomavirus DNAs. *J. Virol.* **66,** 5949–5958.

16. Mungal, S., Steinberg, B. M., and Taichman, L. B. (1992) Replication of plasmid-derived human papillomavirus type 11 DNA in cultured keratinocytes. *J. Virol.* **66,** 3220–3224.

17. Ustav, M. and Stenlund, A. (1991) Transient replication of BPV-1 requires two viral polypeptides encoded by the E1 and E2 open reading frames. *EMBO J.* **10,** 449–457.

18. Ustav, E., Ustav, M., Szymanski, P., and Stenlund, A. (1993) The bovine papillomavirus origin of replication requires a binding site for the E2 transcriptional activator. *Proc. Natl. Acad. Sci. USA* **90,** 898–902.

19. Sverdrup, F. and Khan, S. A. (1994) Replication of human papillomavirus DNAs supported by the HPV-18 E1 and E2 proteins. *J. Virol.* **68,** 505–509.

20. Gopalakrishnan, V. and Khan, S. A. (1994) The E1 protein of human papillomavirus type 1a is sufficient for the initiation of viral DNA replication. *Proc. Natl. Acad. Sci. USA* **91,** 9597–9601.

21. Seo, Y.-S., Muller, F., Lusky, M., and Hurwitz, J. (1993) Bovine papillomavirus (BPV)-encoded E1 protein contains multiple activities required for BPV DNA replication. *Proc. Natl. Acad. Sci. USA* **90,** 702–706.

22. Yang, L., Mohr, I., Fouts, E., Lim, D. A., Nohaile, M., and Botchan, M. (1993) The E1 protein of bovine papillomavirus 1 is an ATP-dependent DNA helicase. *Proc. Natl. Acad. Sci. USA* **90,** 5086–5090.

23. Belyavski, M., Miller, J., and Wilson, V. (1994) The bovine papillomavirus E1 protein alters the host cell cycle and growth properties. *Virology* **204,** 132–143.

24. McBride, A. A., Romanczuk, H., and Howley, P. M. (1991) The papillomavirus E2 regulatory proteins. *J. Biol. Chem.* **266,** 18,411–18,414.

25. Mohr, I. J., Clark, R., Sun, S., Androphy, E. J., MacPherson, P., and Botchan, M. R. (1990) Targeting the E1 replication protein to the papillomavirus origin of replication by complex formation with the E2 transactivator. *Science* **250,** 1694–1699.
26. Lusky, M., Hurwitz, J., and Seo, Y-S. (1994) The bovine papillomavirus E2 protein modulates the assembly of but is not stably maintained in a replication-competent multimeric E1-replication origin complex. *Proc. Natl. Acad. Sci. USA* **91,** 8895–8899.
27. Dollard, S. C., Wilson, J. L., Demeter, L. M., Bonnez, W., Reichman, C., Broker, T. R., and Chow, L. T. (1992) Production of human papillomavirus and modulation of the infectious program in epithelial raft cultures. *Genes Dev.* **6,** 1131–1142.
28. Meyers, C., Frattini, M. G., Hudson, J. B., and Laimins, L. A. (1992) Biosynthesis of human papillomavirus from a continuous cell line upon epithelial differentiation. *Science* **257,** 971–973.
29. Sterling, J., Stanley, M., Gatward, G., and Minson, T. (1990) Production of human papillomavirus type 16 virions in a keratinocyte cell line. *J. Virol.* **64,** 6305–6307.
30. Yang, N. S., Burkholder, J., Roberts, B., Martinell, B., and McCabe, D. (1990) In vivo and in vitro gene transfer to mammalian somatic cells by particle bombardment. *Proc. Natl. Acad. Sci. USA* **87,** 9568–9572.
31. Chen, C. and Okayama, H. (1987) High-efficiency transformation of mammalian cells by plasmid DNA. *Mol. Cell. Biol.* **7,** 2745–2752.
32. Hirt, B. (1967) Selective extraction of polyoma DNA from infected mouse cell cultures. *J. Mol. Biol.* **26,** 365–369.
33. Sambrook, J., Fritsch, E. F., and Maniatis, T. (1989) *Molecular Cloning—A Laboratory Manual*, 2nd ed., Cold Spring Harbor Laboratory, Cold Spring Harbor, NY.
34. Roden, R. B. S., Kirnbauer, R., Jenson, A. B., Lowy, D. R., and Schiller, J. T. (1994) Interaction of papillomaviruses with the cell surface. *J. Virol.* **68,** 7260–7266.

8

Methods for Liposome-Mediated Gene Transfer to the Arterial Wall

Elizabeth G. Nabel, Zhi-yong Yang, Hong San, Dianne P. Carr, and Gary J. Nabel

1. Introduction

Cationic liposomes are preparations of positively charged lipids used for transfection of mammalian cells in vitro and in vivo. Although viruses efficiently infect mammalian cells, the potential risks of viral gene delivery spurred research in the development of synthetic chemical vectors that would duplicate viral delivery but have no risk of infectious complications. These nonviral vectors were first developed in the late 1980s. Cationic lipids are attractive vectors for vascular gene transfer studies owing to ease of preparation, reproducibility, and safety (1–3). In this chapter, we describe our experience with vascular gene transfer using four liposome reagents: DOTMA/DOPE, DC-cholesterol, DOSPA/DOPE, and DMRIE/DOPE.

Cationic liposomes interact spontaneously and rapidly with polyanions such as DNA, mRNA, and antisense oligonucleotides to form liposome complexes. One of the first reagents developed is DOTMA (N-[1-{2,3-dioleyloxy}propyl]-N,N,N-trimethylammonium chloride)/DOPE (dioleoyl-phosphatidylethanolamine), mixed in equal molar ratios (4) (Lipofectin, Gibco-BRL, Gaithersburg, MD). Additional cationic liposomes reagents used in vascular gene transfer studies include DC-cholesterol (dioleoyl phosphatidylethanolamine [DOPE]/3b[n-{N',N'-dimethylaminoethane}-carbamoyl]cholesterol); DOSPA/DOPE (2,3-dioleyloxy-N-[2{spermine carboxamido} ethyl]-N,Ndimethyl-1-propan-aminiumtrifluoroacetate [DOSPA]/dioleoyl phosphatidylethanolamine [DOPE]) (Gibco-BRL); and DMRIE/DOPE (1,2dimyristyloxypropyl-3-dimethyl-hydroxyethyl ammonium bromide [DMRIE]/dioleoyl phosphatidylethanolamine [DOPE]) (Vical, San Diego, CA).

From: *Methods in Molecular Medicine, Gene Therapy Protocols*
Edited by: P. Robbins Humana Press Inc., Totowa, NJ

Cationic liposomes were developed, in part, to overcome some of the deficiencies of neutral and anionic liposomes. Problems associated with the use of neutral and anionic liposomes for DNA delivery were low encapsulation efficiency and lysosomal degradation of liposomes and DNA *(5)*. DNA encapsulated by cationic liposomes achieve a much higher concentration in target tissues than the same agent incorporated in neutral or anionic liposomes. Cationic liposomes have geometry and physical properties conducive to stable bilayer formation. The entrapment of DNA into the aqueous compartment of the cationic liposomes is not dependent on or limited by the size of the DNA. The development of this condensation technology with cationic liposomes avoids some of the encapsulation efficiency problems associated with anionic or neutral vesicles. Cationic liposomes are small in size (approx 250 n*M*) and homogeneous, thereby delivering polynucleotide more uniformly over target cells. An important property of cationic liposomes is fusion with cells in a manner that escapes degradation in lysosomes. DNA liposome complexes enter cells by either direct fusion with plasma membrane or by fusion with endosomal membranes after endocytosis. Following release from lysosomes, plasmid DNA is maintained in an extrachromosomal form.

Cationic liposomes have been employed in arterial gene transfer studies in vivo in several animal models including normal and atherosclerotic arteries of rats *(6)*, rabbits *(7,8)*, dogs *(9,10)*, and pigs *(11–15)*. There are several advantages of cationic liposomes for vascular gene transfer studies. An important feature of liposome vectors is the favorable safety profile. Liposome vectors contain no viral sequences. There are no cDNA size constraints in vector construction. Cationic liposomes have been administered intravenously and intraarterially with minimal biochemical, hemodynamic, or cardiac toxicity *(1,2,16)*. In addition, cationic liposome and DNA complexes are straightforward to prepare for experimental use.

In general, approx 5–15% of endothelial cells and smooth muscle cells are transfected in vitro with liposome vectors. The efficiency of transfection in HUVECs is lower, ~1–5% in vitro. In porcine arteries in vivo, the efficiency of gene transfer is 0.1–1%. Following liposomal transfection, gene expression is observed for approx 1 mo. Cell division is not required for liposome transfection, although the efficiency appears to be increased in proliferating cells *(17)*. Further modifications to the chemical formulation of cationic liposomes appear promising in terms of improvement of transfection efficiencies. Complexing a heat-inactivated hemagglutinating virus of Japan (HVJ) with cationic liposomes improves transfection efficiencies in a rat arterial model of gene transfer *(6)*.

2. Materials

1. DOTMA/DOPE: N-[1-(2,3-dioleyloxy)propyl]-N,N,N-trimethyl ammonium chloride (DOTMA) and dioleoyl phosphatidylethanolamine (DOPE) (Lipofectin, Gibco-BRL, Gaithersburg, MD).
2. DC-cholesterol: dioleoyl phosphatidylethanolamine (DOPE)/3b[n(N',N'-dimethyl-aminoethane)-carbamoyl]cholesterol (Dr. L. Huang, University of Pittsburgh, Pittsburgh, PA).
3. DMRIE/DOPE: 1,2-dimyristyloxypropyl-3-dimethyl-hydroxyethyl ammonium bromide (DMRIE)/diolcoyl phosphatidylethanolamine (DOPE) (Vical).
4. DOSPA/DOPE: 2,3-dioleyloxy-N-[2(spermine carboxamido) ethyl]-N,N-dimethyl-1-propanaminiumtrifluoroacetate (DOSPA)/dioleoyl phosphatidyletha-nolamine (DOPE) (Lipofectamine, Gibco-BRL).
5. Opti-MEM.
6. Medium 199.
7. Dulbecco's Modified Eagle's Medium (DMEM).
8. Media supplements: amphotericin B, fetal calf serum, fetal bovine serum, gentamicin, glutamine, heparin, penicillin, streptomycin, endothelial cell growth supplement.
9. Other media additives: collagenase, trypsin, EDTA.
10. Dispersing medium: 2 mg/mL collagenase, 0.1 mg/mL elastase, 0.5 mg/mL soya bean trypsin inhibitor, 1 mg/mL bovine serum albumin (defatted), 20 U/mL penicillin, and 100 µg/mL streptomycin in M199.
11. Ca^{2+} and Mg^{2+}-free Dulbecco's phosphate buffered saline (Pi/NaCl).
12. 0.2% gelatin-coated T25 flask.
13. DMSO.
14. Glutaraldehyde.
15. Alkaline phosphatase substrate solution: PBS containing 5-bromo 4-chloro 3-indolylphosphate-p-toluidine (1 mg/mL) (Gibco-BRL) and nitroblue tetrazolium chloride (1 mg/mL).
16. X-gal substrate: dissolve 2 mg X-gal (5-bromo-4-chloro-3-indolyl-β-D-galactosi-dase) in 0.5 mL dimethylformamide to a final concentration of 20 mg/mL. For 100 mL, 2.5 mL of X-gal solution is added to 5.0 mL $1M$ Tris-HCl pH 7.5, 0.2 mL of $5M$ NaCl, 0.1 mL of $1M$ $MgCl_2$, 5.0 mL of $2.5M$ ferriferrocyanide, and 87.1 mL distilled H_2O.

3. Methods

3.1. Derivation and Culture of Porcine Endothelial Cells

Primary cultures of porcine endothelium are derived from the carotid artery, pulmonary artery, coronary artery, and aorta of Yorkshire pigs. The arteries are placed in HEPES-buffered M199 with gentamicin and amphotericin B and transported to the laboratory on ice. The artery is rinsed in sterile PBS (pH 7.4) until all blood is washed off. Excess tissue is removed from the artery. The artery is placed in 10 mL serum-free M199 containing collagenase, 0.5 µg/µL, and kept at 37°C for 15 min. The artery is laid flat and opened lengthwise. The endothelium is gently scraped with a #10 scalpel blade to remove endothelial cells.

Cells removed by this means are collected by centrifugation (4°C at 800g for 10 min) and resuspended in M199 supplemented with 20% FBS, 2 mM glutamine, 50 U/mL penicillin, 50 µg/mL streptomycin, 150 ng/mL endothelial cell growth supplement and 90 µg/mL heparin. The cells are placed into a 0.2% gelatin-coated T25 flask and incubated overnight. Cells are passaged with trypsin and 0.02 mM EDTA at a passage ratio of 1:2 or 1:3. Cell monolayers are identified as endothelial cells by phase-contrast microscopy. Representative dishes of cells are further characterized by staining for factor VIII-related antigen (vWF).

Aliquots of endothelial or smooth muscle cells are stored in liquid nitrogen by resuspending approx 10^6 cells in 0.5 mL of ice-cold fetal calf serum on ice. An equal volume of ice-cold fetal calf serum containing 10% DMSO is added, and cells are transferred to a prechilled screw-cap Corning (Corning, NY) freezing tube. These cells are transferred to a −70°C freezer for 24 h before transferring to liquid nitrogen for long-term storage.

3.2. Derivation and Culture of Porcine Smooth Muscle Cells

Primary vascular smooth muscle cell cultures are also generated from domestic Yorkshire pigs. Vascular smooth muscle cells are enzymatically derived from a 10-cm segment of artery or vein. The vessel is rinsed in M199 containing 200 U/mL penicillin and 200 mg/mL streptomycin and then incubated without agitation for 30 min at 37°C in 4 mL of dispersing medium: 2 mg/mL collagenase, 0.1 mg/mL elastase, 0.5 mg/mL soybean trypsin inhibitor, 1 mg/mL bovine serum albumin (defatted), 200 U/mL penicillin, and 100 mg/mL streptomycin in M199. The adventitia is removed with the aid of forceps as an intact, everted tube. The remaining media and intima are rinsed with M199, placed in 5 mL of fresh dispersing medium for an additional 30–60 min at 37°C, and rinsed again in M199. The medial tube is minced and incubated for 2–3 h in fresh dispersing medium. The isolated cells are washed twice and resuspended in M199 containing 10% fetal bovine serum. The procedure yields 0.5–1.5 × 10^6 cells, which are transferred to a 75-cm^2 tissue culture flask. Stock cultures are passaged by washing once with 2 mL Ca^{2+} and Mg^{2+}-free Dulbecco's phosphate-buffered saline (Pi/NaCl) and incubating for 5 min at 37°C with 1 mL 0.05% trypsin in Pi/NaCl containing 0.02% Na EDTA. The cultures are passaged twice weekly and are used for experiments between the 4th and 15th passages. The stock cultures are grown in M199 containing 10% fetal calf serum, 100 U/mL penicillin, and 100 mg/mL streptomycin.

3.3. In Vitro Transfection of Porcine Endothelial and Smooth Muscle Cells (see Note 1)

Porcine endothelial and smooth muscle cells are transfected with DNA liposome conjugates at 50–75% confluency. Plasmid DNA is transfected into endothelial and smooth muscle cells by first diluting the cationic liposome in 0.5 mL Opti-MEM (Gibco-BRL, Grand Island, NY) at room temperature. The following concentrations of cationic liposomes are used: 12 µg 1 mg/mL DOTMA/DOPE; 10 µg 1 mg/mL DC-cholesterol; 10 µg 1 mg/mL DMRIE/DOPE; and 10 µg 2 mg/mL DOSPA/DOPE. The DNA (stock concentration >1 mg/mL) is diluted into 0.5 mL Opti-MEM media, and is added to the cationic liposome solution to a final volume of 1.0 mL. The DNA liposome complexes are mixed by gentle tapping, and left at room temperature for 5–10 min. The attached cells are washed twice with OptiMEM. The cells are incubated with the DNA liposome solution at 37°C for 3–5 h. The media is removed, and the cells are maintained in M199 and 10% calf serum for 1–2 d (*see* Note 1).

3.4. In Vivo Transfection of Arteries (see Note 2)

Direct gene transfer in porcine iliofemoral arteries is performed using the following protocol. Domestic Yorkshire pigs are anesthesized and intubated and, using sterile surgical techniques, the iliofemoral arteries are exposed bilaterally. A double balloon catheter (USCI, Billerica, MA) is inserted through a side branch and positioned in the iliofemoral artery. The proximal balloon is positioned just below a side branch, which is an anatomical marker. There are no side branches between the double balloons that would allow for runoff of transfection solution. The proximal balloon is inflated with 1 cc of air (180 mm Hg), and the arterial segment is rinsed with 5 mL saline and 5 mL Opti-MEM to clear the vessel of blood. Approximately 10 min prior to the insertion of the catheter, the DNA liposome conjugates are prepared as described in Section 3.3. The distal balloon is inflated at 180 mm Hg, and the solution is instilled into the arterial space between the balloons at 150 mm Hg, measured by a pressure transducer, and allowed to incubate for 20 min. Following incubation, the catheter is removed, and the arterial circulation is restored. Both the left and right iliac arteries are transfected in each animal. The animals recover for 3 wk.

At the time of sacrifice, tissue samples are prepared in a variety of ways to accommodate the requirements of the specific assay: PCR, *in situ* hybridization, immunohistochemistry, morphometry, light microscopy, and scanning/transmission EM. Tissue samples for DNA and RNA isolation were snap frozen in liquid nitrogen and stored at −70°C until used. Systemic organs are biopsied for analysis by light microscopy. Separate sterile, clean instruments and gloves are used to biopsy each organ in order to avoid contamination of nontransfected tissues. In addition, samples of blood are obtained prior to gene transfer and at the time of sacrifice for biochemical analyses including glucose, electrolytes, and renal and hepatic function.

3.5. Histochemical Detection of Alkaline Phosphatase Activity

We have used two reporter genes in our vascular gene transfer studies: a human placental alkaline phosphatase gene and a nuclear targeted *lacZ* gene.

Human placental alkaline phosphatase is heat stable at temperatures above 65°C and can be differentiated from endogenous forms of alkaline phosphatase protein by heat inactivation. Histochemical staining in transfected cells is performed 2 d following transfection with a human placental alkaline phosphatase gene. Cells are washed once in PBS and lifted off the plate using 2 m*M* EDTA + PBS. Cells are removed from the culture dish, spun down, and fixed in 10% buffered formalin. The fixed cells are washed once with PBS and divided to form two cell pellets. One pellet is embedded in paraffin, and the other is embedded in optimal cutting tissue processing medium (O.C.T., Miles Diagnostic, Elkhart, IN) and stored at –80°C. Tissue specimens from harvested organs are fixed in 10% buffered formalin for 16 h, placed in 70% ethyl alcohol and embedded in paraffin. Paraffin blocks are sectioned at 6 μm thickness onto poly-L-lysine slides. The slides were deparaffinized in three changes of xylene, rehydrated in 100, 95, and 75% ethyl alcohol, and incubated in PBS at 65°C for 60 min to inactivate endogenous alkaline phosphatase. The sections are incubated in substrate solution for 19 h. This substrate yields a dark blue-purple stain. Sections are rinsed with PBS and counterstained with a neutral red stain.

3.6. Histochemical Detection of β-Galactosidase Enzyme Activity

Endothelial or smooth muscle cells are fixed in 1.25% glutaraldehyde in PBS for 5 min. Tissues are fixed in 1.25% glutaraldehyde and 4% paraformaldehyde for 20 min. Cells and tissues are rinsed in PBS three times and are incubated in X-gal substrate at 37°C for 2–6 h. Cells may be stored at 4°C in phosphate-buffered saline, or counter-stained with neutral red. Tissues are embedded in paraffin, sectioned at 6 μm thickness, and counterstained with neutral red. Alternatively, tissues are frozen in O.C.T. embedding compound, sectioned at 10–12 μm thickness, fixed in 1.25% glutaraldehyde, and stained with X-gal solution.

4. Notes

1. The ratio of cationic liposomes to DNA is an important determinant of transfection efficiency. Titration of DNA to liposome concentration should be performed with each cationic liposome preparation and each cell line in vitro. Differences in target cell, plasmid, and cationic lipid will require adjustment to the DNA lipid ratio. In general, we optimize the liposome DNA ratio in vitro on the desired target cell, and use this optimal ratio for in vivo studies.

2. When performing in vivo arterial gene transfer, having serum-free conditions at the site of transfection is important. When using a double catheter, we flush the inner space between the two balloons with Opti-MEM to rid the space of serum components. Cationic liposomes can be inactivated by serum proteins. If it is technically impossible to rid the transfection site of serum, rinsing the tissue with Opti-MEM is preferable.

References

1. Nabel, E. G., Gordon, D., Xang, Z. -Y., et al. (1992) *Hum. Gene Ther.* **3,** 649–656.
2. San, H., Yang, Z. Y., Pompili, V. J., et al. (1993) *Hum. Gene Ther.* **4,** 781–788.
3. Nabel, G. J., Nabel, E. G., Yang, Z., et al. (1993) *Proc. Natl. Acad. Sci. USA* **90,** 11,307–11,311.
4. Feigner, P. L., Gadek, T. R., Holm, M., et al. (1987) *Proc. Natl. Acad. Sci. USA* **84,** 7413–7417.
5. Feigner, P. L. (1990) *Adv. Drug Del. Rev.* **5,** 163–187.
6. Morishita, R., Gibbons, G. H., Kaneda, Y., Ogihara, T., and Dzau, V. J. J. (1993) *Clin. Invest.* **91,** 2580–2585.
7. Leclerc, G., Gal, D., Takeshita, S., Nikol, S., Weir, L., and Isner, J. M. J. (1992) *Clin. Invest.* **90,** 936–944.
8. Losordo, D. W., Pickering, G., Takeshita, S., et al. (1994) *Circulation* **89,** 785–792.
9. Lim, C. S., Chapman, G. D., Gammon, R. S., et al. (1991) *Circulation* **83,** 2007–2011.
10. Chapman, G. D., Lim, C. S., Gammon, R. S., et al. (1992) *Circ. Res.* **71,** 27–33.
11. Nabel, E. G., Plautz, G., and Nabel, G. J. (1990) *Science* **249,** 1285–1288.
12. Nabel, E. G., Plautz, G., and Nabel, G. J. (1992) *Proc. Natl. Acad. Sci. USA* **89,** 5157–5161.
13. Nabel, E. G., Yang, Z., Liptay, S., et al. (1993) *J. Clin. Invest.* **91,** 1822–1829.
14. Nabel, E. G., Yang, Z., Plautz, G., et al. (1993) *Nature* **362,** 844–846.
15. Nabel, E. G., Shum, L., Pompili, V J., et al. (1993) *Proc. Natl. Acad. Sci. USA* **90,** 10,759–10,763.
16. Stewart, M. J., Plautz, G. E., Del Buono, L., et al. (1992) *Hum. Gene Ther.* **3,** 267–275.
17. Takeshita, S., Gal, D., Leclerc, G., et al. (1994) *J. Clin. Invest.* **93,** 652–661.

9

Methods for Targeted Gene Transfer to Liver Using DNA-Protein Complexes

Mark A. Findeis, Catherine H. Wu, and George Y. Wu

1. Introduction

The potential of therapeutic gene transfer to treat human disease has prompted a diverse and growing range of basic and applied research efforts to explore and develop gene therapy strategies *(1–5)*. Reported approaches to gene therapy include the uses of retroviruses *(6,7)*, adenovirus *(8,9)*, receptor-mediated endocytosis *(10,11)*, direct injection *(12)*, and liposomes *(13,14)*, among others. Targeted delivery of DNA via receptors has been successfully applied using protein ligands to the hepatic asialoglycoprotein receptor (ASGr) *(10,15–18)*, and, subsequently, the transferrin receptor *(11)*. The ASGr is a cell-surface receptor that is highly represented on hepatocytes. Thus, genes targeted to this receptor can be delivered in a highly selective manner to the liver.

The practicality of receptor-mediated targeted delivery via the hepatic ASGr was demonstrated over a decade ago for the delivery of agents covalently bound to carriers such as asialofetuin *(19–21)* and asialoorosomucoid *(22)* or galactose-terminated neoglycoproteins *(23,24)*. This strategy was then extended to the use of asialoorosomucoid-polylysine (ASOR-PL) conjugates to carry DNA into hepatocytes *(15–18)*. Targeted delivery by this technique has been used successfully in vitro *(10,25–27)* and in vivo *(28–32)* for the delivery of DNAs coding for a variety of genes.

In a refinement of receptor-mediated gene delivery, we have used adenovirus as an additional component of ASGr-targeted DNA complexes to achieve enhanced gene delivery and expression *(33)*. Adenoviruses are common pathogens in man and animals *(34,35)* and have broad tissue specificity *(36)*. The

From: *Methods in Molecular Medicine, Gene Therapy Protocols*
Edited by: P. Robbins Humana Press Inc., Totowa, NJ

virus normally enters cells by binding to plasma membrane of the host cell through adenoviral fibers that project from the capsid *(37)*. Binding triggers internalization of viral particles within endosomal vesicles *(38)*. Acidification of endosomes results in a conformational change of the capsid proteins that disrupts the endosomal membrane *(39)*. This event permits the viral nucleic acid to enter the cytosol of the host cell prior to exposure to lysosomal enzymes that would occur normally during endocytosis. The endosomolytic property of adenoviruses has been used previously to enhance the delivery of polypeptides *(39)* and more recently plasmid DNA *(40)*. However, in the latter instance, the DNA complex retained the original infection specificity of the virus in addition to that of the ligand.

Because the viral fibers govern the infection specificity of adenovirus, chemical coupling of an asialoglycoprotein to these structures was expected to result in a new ability to enter cells by the ASGr while simultaneously blocking recognition of the cells' endogenous receptors for the virus. Our strategy (Fig. 1) was to take advantage of the fact that the adenovirus contains carbohydrate groups that are exclusively located on the fibers *(41)*. Mild oxidation of the carbohydrate residues allows covalent linkage of an asialoglycoprotein-polylysine conjugate to the surface of the virus. Addition of foreign DNA results in electrostatic binding to the polylysine of the conjugate and coating of the modified virus by the DNA to form a targetable complex. Internalization of the complex is achieved in a cell-specific fashion mediated by receptor recognition of the asialoglycoprotein component of the complex and enhanced by the endosomolytic properties of the virus.

ASOR is readily available by isolation of orosomucoid (also referred to as α_1-acid glycoprotein) from human plasma *(42)* followed by desialylation to expose penultimate galactose groups. Although orosomucoid is commercially available, it is readily isolable from plasma in good yield *(42)*. Orosomucoid can be desialylated by a simple acid treatment with heating, thus avoiding the expense of using neuraminidase to cleave sialic acid residues *(43)*. Conjugates formed by crosslinking polylysine (PL) with proteins have been reported using carbodiimide-mediated amide bond formation *(26,27)* and thiol reagents *(10,11,25)*. The product mixtures obtained in the formation of conjugates of this type are heterogeneous and highly charged. Previously described methods for the preparation of ASOR-PL targeted to the ASGr have used dialysis *(22)*, gel-filtration *(22,25)*, and ion-exchange HPLC *(11,26)* for purification of the conjugate from reaction byproducts and residual starting materials. We describe here techniques for the preparation of ASOR-PL conjugates and of adenovirus-ASOR-PL conjugates that effectively bind DNA in an electrostatic complex for targeted delivery of DNA to ASGr-bearing cells *(44)*.

Fig. 1. Formation of adenovirus-ASOR-PL-DNA complexes. Step 1: Mild oxidation is used to modify carbohydrate on viral fibers. Step 2: ASOR-PL conjugate is chemically coupled to the modified carbohydrate. Step 3: Adenovirus-ASOR-PL conjugate is combined with DNA to form a complex targeted to the asialoglycoprotein receptor. Reprinted with permission from ref. *33*.

2. Materials
2.1. Isolation of Orosomucoid

1. Pooled human plasma (American Red Cross, Farmington, CT).
2. DEAE and CM Sepharose beads (Millipore, Milford, CT).
3. Spectra/Por2 dialysis tubing (12–14 kDa mol-wt cut-off) (Spectrum Industries, Los Angeles, CA).

2.2. Chemical Coupling of Asialooromucoid to Polylysine

1-(3-Dimethylaminopropyl)-3-ethylcarbodiimide (EDC) (Sigma, St. Louis, MO).

2.3. Adenovirus

Type 5 adenovirus (from Dr. Hamish Young, Columbia University, New York).

2.4. Cell Lines

1. HeLa S_3 cells (American Type Culture Collection/NIH, Rockville, MD).
2. SK Hep1 cells (from Dr. David Shafritz, Albert Einstein College of Medicine, Bronx, NY).
3. Huh7 cells (from Dr. T. Jake Liang, Massachusetts General Hospital, Boston, MA).

2.5. Assay for Hepatitis B Surface Antigen

Hepatitis B surface antigen ELISA kits (Abbott Laboratories, North Chicago, IL).

2.6. β-Galactosidase Marker Gene

1. Plasmid βact nls *lac*Z A1 (from Dr. Claire Bonnerot, Pasteur Institute, Paris, France).
2. X-gal (Life Technologies, Gaithersburg, MD).

3. Methods
3.1. Preparation of Human Orosomucoid (α_1-Acid Glycoprotein)

Buffers used in this isolation contain the stated concentration of sodium acetate (NaOAc) and added glacial acetic acid to obtain the desired pH: Buffer 1, $0.05M$

NaOAc, pH 4.5; Buffer 2, $0.10M$ NaOAc, $0.05M$ NaCl, pH 4.0; Buffer 3, $0.1M$ NaOAc, $1.0M$ NaCl, pH 4.0. These buffers are slightly different from those used with DEAE cellulose anion-exchange media *(42)*. Buffer 2 ($0.10M$ NaOAc, pH 4.0) without $0.05M$ NaCl added was used as an additional wash step prior to the elution of orosomucoid (OR). The OR-rich fraction was eluted with $0.10M$ NaOAc, $0.10M$ NaCl, pH 4.0, then purified by ammonium sulfate precipitation.

DEAE Sepharose Fast Flow and CM Sepharose Fast Flow media were packed in 5-cm diameter by 30-cm height Waters AP-5 columns (Millipore) according to the manufacturer's instructions. The DEAE Sepharose column was equilibrated with Buffer 1, and the CM sepharose column was equilibrated with Buffer 2. Buffer was pumped through the column with a Rainin Rabbit-Plus peristaltic pump (Rainin, Woburn, MA) equipped with a high-flow pump head fitted with 5.0-mm diameter silicone tubing at a flow rate of 45 mL/min.

Pooled human plasma (4 U, ~1.2 L, outdated human plasma from the American Red Cross) was transferred to Spectra/Por 2 dialysis tubing (12–14 kDa mol wt cutoff from Spectrum) and dialyzed overnight at 4°C against 20 L of Buffer 1. The dialyzed plasma was then centrifuged in a Beckman JA-14 rotor (Beckman Instruments, Fullerton, CA) at $30,100g$ for 15 min at 4°C. The supernatant was then filtered through Whatman #2 paper (Whatman, Clifton, NJ), followed by an additional filtration through a 0.45-μm nylon Zapcap filter (Schleicher & Schuell, Keene, NH). The precipitate was discarded. The dialyzed and filtered plasma was applied to the DEAE sepharose column at a flow rate of 25 mL/min (a lower flow rate is required owing to the high viscosity of plasma). The column was then washed with Buffer 1 until the eluate had an absorbance at 280 nm of <0.10 cm^{-1}. The column was then washed with Buffer 2. The OR-rich eluate was collected starting when the A_{280} began to increase and ending after the A_{280} had peaked and was <0.10 cm^{-1}.

The OR-rich Buffer 2 eluate was then applied to the CM sepharose column (previously equilibrated with Buffer 2), which was then washed with Buffer 2. The eluate was collected starting when the A_{280} began to increase and ending after the A_{280} had peaked and was <0.10 cm^{-1}. After this purified OR fraction was collected, the CM Sepharose column was washed with Buffer 3 (1 L).

The purified OR was concentrated tenfold and then diafiltered with 10 vol of water in an Amicon CH2 Hollow Fiber Concentrator fitted with an Amicon S1Y10 Spiral Membrane Ultrafiltration Cartridge (Amicon, Beverly, MA). The desalted OR fraction was then lyophilized and stored at −20°C. A sample of the OR was run on SDS-PAGE *(45,46)* and showed a single band at the expected apparent mol wt of 44 kDa by staining with Coomassie blue. The actual mol wt of OR has been reported in the range of 41,000 kDa *(47,48)*, and more recently was determined by mass spectrometry to be 36,800 *(49)*. Although there is some variability in the amount of OR in human plasma samples, the typical yield of lyophilized salt-free OR using this procedure is ~600 mg.

3.2. Preparation of Asialoorosomucoid

Asialoorosomucoid (ASOR) is prepared by cleavage of terminal sialic acid residues from the branched carbohydrates on the surface of OR *(43)*. The OR (10 mg/mL) isolated as above is dissolved in water. An equal volume of $0.1N$ sulfuric acid (2.78 mL/L of concentrated H_2SO_4 in water) is added to the OR solution, and the resulting mixture is heated at 80°C for 1 h in a water bath to hydrolyze sialic acids from the protein. The acidolysis mixture is removed from the water bath, neutralized with NaOH solution, dialyzed against water for 2 d, and then lyophilized. The thiobarbituric acid assay of Warren *(50)*, or Uchida *(51)*, is then used to verify desialylation of the OR. Targetability of ASOR samples is verified by labeling with ^{125}I and measuring liver uptake in rats or mice *(28)*.

3.3. Synthesis of Asialoorosomucoid-Polylysine Conjugates

3.3.1. Method A

The ASOR (166 mg) is dissolved in water (5 mL), and the solution is filtered through a 0.45-μm syringe filter. The filter is washed with water (5 mL), the filtrates combined, and the pH is adjusted to 7.4 with $0.1N$ NaOH. Poly-L-lysine (PL, as the HBr salt, 37 mg) of average 25 kDa mol wt is dissolved in water (5 mL), and the pH of the solution is adjusted to 7.4 (*see* Note 1). 1-(3-Dimethylaminopropyl)-3-ethylcarbodiimide (EDC, 25 mg) is dissolved in water (0.33 mL) and added directly to the ASOR solution. The PL solution is added to the ASOR-EDC solution and the pH is readjusted to 7.4. Additional EDC (25 mg in 0.33 mL of water) is added after 2 h and 3 h. The reaction mixture is covered and maintained at 37°C for 72 h total. The reaction mixture is then transferred to 12–14 kDa mol wt cut dialysis tubing and dialyzed at 4°C against water (20 L) for 2 d with one change of water. The dialysate is lyophilized (169 mg) prior to further purification (Method A).

3.3.2. Method B

The ASOR and PL (mol wt = 41,000) in a 1:1 weight ratio in 5 mL of deionized water at pH 7.4 were coupled by the addition of EDC in a 140-fold molar excess over ASOR and stirred for 16 h at 25°C. The reaction mixture was then dialyzed against deionized water at 4°C for 72 h, lyophilized, and purified (Method B).

Table 1
Recipe for the Preparation of Analytical Gels

Solutions to prepare for use in casting acid-urea gels[a]

8 M Urea	48 g plus H_2O to 100 mL
Running gel buffer (RGB)	48 mL 1M potassium hydroxide
	17.2 mL glacial acetic acid
	water to 100 mL
4X Sample buffer (4X SB)	1.34 g potassium hydroxide
	2 mL glacial acetic acid
	water to 100 mL
10X Running buffer (10X RB)	311.8 g β-alanine
	80.4 mL acetic acid
	water to 1 L
30% Bis/acrylamide	30 g acrylamide
	0.8 g bisacrylamide
	100 mL H_2O
10% ammonium persulfate	100 mg in 1 mL H_2O
Methyl green stock	0.1% methyl green in 1:3 (4X SB in 8M urea)
Coomassie stain	1 g/L in 40% ethanol, 10% acetic acid in H_2O
Destaining solution	10% ethanol, 7.5% acetic acid in H_2O

Gel recipe (for 10% running gel, 4% stacking gel)[b]

	Running Gel	Stacking Gel
30% Bis/acrylamide	13.3 mL	1.3 mL
Buffer	5 mL RGB	2.5 mL 4X SB
8M urea	20 mL	5 mL
H_2O	1.2 mL	1.3 mL
10% Ammonium persulfate	0.3 mL	0.1 mL
TEMED[c]	0.2 mL	0.012 mL

[a]Ref. *46*, p. 68.
[b]Proportions of solutions in (A) to use for casting running gels and stacking gels, respectively.
[c]*N,N,N',N'*-Tetramethylethylenediamine.

3.4. Analytical Acid-Urea Gel Electrophoresis

Analytical gels are prepared using the recipe in Table 1 adapted from the method of Panyim and Chalkley *(52)*. Prior to the addition of TEMED, acrylamide solutions are degassed under vacuum (~20 mmHg) for 10 min. After samples are loaded on cast gels, electrophoresis is run from anode to cathode (electrodes connected in *reverse* polarity from the usual). Voltage is at 90–150 V. Methyl green can be used as a tracking dye in these gels, although we usually omit it. Gels are stained with 0.1% Coomassie brilliant blue R250 in ethanol-acetic acid-water (40:10:50 v/v).

Fig. 2. Elution profile from preparative acid-urea elution electrophoresis. The sample was a crude product mixture (169 mg) from the cross-linking of ASOR with 25 kDa average mol wt PL as described in Method A. Fractions (10 mL) were collected starting between peaks 1 (the ion front and unbound PL) and 2. Peaks 2 (fractions 5–17, 27 mg) and 3 (fractions 19–43, 43 mg) were pooled, dialyzed against water, and lyophilized before further fractionation by cation-exchange HPLC. Reprinted with permission of the American Chemical Society *(44)*.

3.5. Purification of ASOR-PL Conjugates

3.5.1. Method A

3.5.1.1. PREPARATIVE ACID-UREA GEL ELUTION ELECTROPHORESIS

Preparative gels are cast and run in the Bio-Rad (Hercules, CA) Model 491 Prep Cell apparatus (recipe, Table 1) in a manner similar to that used for analytical gels and according to the instructions for the use of the apparatus. Running gel solutions are degassed under vacuum, poured into the gel holder, and allowed to stand overnight to ensure full polymerization. Stacking gel solutions are degassed with nitrogen gas bubbling prior to the addition of TEMED and allowed to polymerize for 30 min. After assembly of the elution electrophoresis apparatus (with the electrodes connected in *reverse* polarity), the elution chamber is eluted with a peristaltic pump at 1 mL/min, the sample is loaded, and electrophoresis is conducted at 11 W for small gels and 22 W for large gels. The eluate is passed through a UV detector operating at 280 nm. Fractions (5 mL) are collected starting after the ion front (first sharp peak) is eluted from the gel (Fig. 2) *(44)*.

Table 2
Conditions for HPLC Purification
of ASOR-PL Conjugates

Time, min	%A	HPLC Gradient[a] %B	%C	%D
0	25	0	75	0
8	25	0	75	0
9	0	25	75	0
20	0	25	75	0
21	0	25	70	5
35	0	25	70	5
36	0	25	65	10
50	0	25	65	10
51	0	25	60	15
65	0	25	60	15
66	0	25	55	20
80	0	25	55	20
81	0	25	25	50
95	0	25	25	50

[a]For cation-exchange chromatography on Waters CM 15HR packing in a 10-mm diameter × 100-mm length column. Flow rate = 1.8 mL/min. Buffers: (A) $0.4M$ sodium acetate, pH 5.0; (B) $0.4M$ sodium acetate, pH 2.3; (C) water; (D) $2M$ NaCl. Buffers are made up to the stated concentration in sodium acetate; pH is adjusted by adding HCl.

3.5.1.2. CATION-EXCHANGE HPLC FRACTIONATION OF ASOR-PL

Cation-exchange HPLC is performed using a 1 × 10 cm Waters AP-1 column packed with CM 15HR packing material. The gradient described in Table 2 is used to chromatograph ASOR-PL mixtures that had been freed of unreacted PL by preparative electrophoresis. Fractions of interest elute after the buffer pH is lowered to 2.3 and the salt concentration begins to increase. Typically, the first major peak observed under these conditions will have the best properties for DNA binding resulting in ASOR-PL-DNA complexes with increased solubility (Fig. 3A) *(44)*. Figure 3B shows an analytic acid–urea gel comparing crude prep gel peak 2, in lane 2, with HPLC peaks 1–3, in lanes 2–4, respectively. Lanes 5–8 show the contents of prep gel peak 3.

Fig. 3. *(Opposite page)* **(A)** High-performance liquid chromatography ion-exchange chromatogram of ASOR-PL (peak 2 from Fig. 2) and associated analytical acid-urea electrophoresis gel (*see* Table 2 for HPLC gradient conditions). **(B)** The acid urea gel shows that after both preparative electrophoresis and HPLC cation-exchange, the

(Continued) fractions isolated are free of unbound polylysine (*see* lane A). Lane 1 corresponds to the crude sample applied to the HPLC column (peak 2, Fig. 2) and lanes 2, 3, and 4 correspond to HPLC peaks 1, 2, and 3 in Fig. 3A. The ASOR-PL isolated from peak 1 (lane 2) produces DNA complexes with greater solubility than the ASOR-PL isolated from peaks 2 and 3. Lanes 5–8 are the corresponding fractions to prep gel fraction 3 (*see* Fig. 2). Whereas the fraction in lane 6 elutes at a similar position to the fraction in lane 2 (chromatogram not shown), it forms DNA complexes with lower solubility. Reprinted with permission of the American Chemical Society *(44)*.

3.5.2. Method B

3.5.2.1. Cation-Exchange HPLC Fractionation of ASOR-PL

The purification sequence was reversed with equivalent results. Chromatography was performed using an Aquapore CX-300 1.0×25 cm cation exchange column (Rainin) with step-wise elution at a flow rate of 4.0 mL/min with $0.1M$ sodium acetate, pH 5.0, 12 min; pH 2.5, 24 min; pH 2.25, 12 min; and pH 2.0, 14 min. The second peak eluted from the column, as detected by UV absorption at 230 nm, was collected. This fraction was further purified by preparative electrophoresis essentially as described in Method A. The purified conjugate was dialyzed against $0.025M$ Tris-$0.001M$ EDTA (T-E) buffer through membranes with 12–14 kDa exclusion limits *(44)* *(see* Note 2).

3.6. Propagation and Preparation of Adenovirus

Type 5 adenovirus, kindly provided by Dr. Hamish Young, Columbia University, New York, was propagated and amplified in HeLa S_3 cells as described previously *(53)*. To avoid potential cytotoxic effects of wild-type virus in studies on targeted gene expression, replication defective dl312 adenoviruses were also studied after propagation in 293 cells as described previously *(54)*.

3.7. Coupling of Adenovirus to ASOR-PL Conjugates *(33)*

Adenovirus samples, 1.0×10^{12} particles, each in a total volume of 100 µL of $0.01M$ Tris, 135 mM NaCl, 5 mM KCl, 1 mM MgCl$_2$, were reacted with 100 µL of $0.02M$ NaIO$_4$ for 30 min at 25°C in the dark. Then, 100 µL of $0.20M$ NaAsO$_2$ in T-E buffer were added for an additional 60 min. To quantitate the amount of conjugate coupled to adenovirus, ASOR-PL conjugate was radiolabeled with Na^{125}I by a chloramine-T method *(55)* to a specific activity of 215 cpm/ng protein. Increasing amounts of [^{125}I]-ASOR-PL from 20 µg to 1 mg (in terms of ASOR content) in 140 µL of the adenoviral sample buffer and 100 µL of $0.02M$ NaBH$_3$CN were added to adenoviral samples and incubated for 15 h at 4°C. Samples were then applied on a discontinuous CsCl gradient *(56)* (2.5 mL of CsCl at densities of 1.4, 1.3, and 1.2 g/mL). Samples were ultracentrifuged at 100,000g for 4 h at 4°C. Fractions (350 mL each) were collected beginning at the top of the tubes, the radioactivity determined in each sample, and the fractions dialyzed against 150 mM NaCl, 10 mM EDTA, 10 mM Tris, pH 8.0. The radioactive peak found at the interface between 1.4 and 1.3 g/mL, where the virus usually bands *(56)*, was recovered and recentrifuged through another CsCl gradient to further purify the modified virus. Unbound conjugate remained at the top of the gradient tubes. For infectivity and gene transfection studies, virus was modified in an identical procedure using unlabeled virus in the coupling reaction.

The number of modified viral particles in each fraction was determined by quantitation of DNA by UV absorption *(57)* after proteinase K-phenol-chloroform extraction *(58)*. In brief, purified modified virus was treated with SDS and proteinase K to make final concentrations of 0.1% and 100 µg/mL, respectively. The samples were incubated at 37°C for 1 h followed by phenol-chloroform extraction, chloroform extraction, and precipitation with 2.5 vol of ethanol at −20°C overnight. The nucleic acid was collected by centrifugation at 8000g for 20 min at 4°C and the DNA concentration determined by measurement of the UV absorption at 260 nm. The maximum amount of ASOR-PL bound to virus was obtained with starting ratios of 20 µg of conjugate to 1×10^{11} viral particles. At this ratio, it was calculated that approx 24 molecules of conjugate were bound to each viral particle. Total protein content of the modified virus was determined by the Bio-Rad assay as instructed by the manufacturer. Purified modified virus was filtered through 0.45-µm membranes (Millipore) and remained stable in T-E buffer at 4°C for at least 2 wk without loss of activity.

3.8. Gel Retardation Assay (10)

Concentrations of DNA are based on an extinction coefficient of 20 $(mg/mL)^{-1}$ cm^{-1} at 260 nm, and agarose gel electrophoresis of DNA is performed as described by Sambrook *(45)*. A series of samples is prepared by adding 20-µL aliquots of ASOR-PL solutions in 0.15*M* NaCl to 20-µL samples of plasmid DNA at 200 ng/µL and 0.15*M* NaCl to give ASOR-PL:DNA mass ratios of 4.0:1, 3.5:1, 3.0:1, 2.5:1, 2.0:1, 1.5:1, and 1.0:1. After a 15-min incubation at room temperature, the test samples and a sample of DNA alone are electrophoresed on a 1% agarose gel eluted with 1X TPE *(45)* at 50 V for 45 min. The optimum ASOR-PL:DNA ratio for complex formation is determined from the migration of the samples as the lowest ratio that gave 80–90% complete DNA retardation (Fig. 4A).

3.9. DNA-Conjugate Complex Formation

To form targetable complexes, two methods may be used:

1. Plasmid DNA, 0.5 mg in 1 mL of 2*M* NaCl, is added to ASOR-PL conjugate, 0.15 mg (with respect to ASOR content), in 600 µL of 2*M* NaCl at 25°C. The mixture is then placed in 1.0-cm (flat width) dialysis tubing with an exclusion limit of 12–14 kDa, and dialyzed step-wise successively at 4°C for 0.5 h against 1.0 L of NaCl in each of the following concentrations: 1.5*M*, 1.0*M*, 0.5*M*, 0.25*M*, and 0.15*M*. If the size of the plasmid is larger than 8 kb, it is advisable to dialyze more slowly, taking 24 h for each change. After the final dialysis, the complex is filtered through 0.45-µm membranes. Complete complexation is determined by testing samples for retardation by agarose gel electrophoresis. No free DNA should be present.

Fig. 4. (A) Gel retardation assay of the binding of ASOR-PL synthesized and purified as described in the text in complex with plasmid DNA (plasmid pSVHBV, provided by Dr. H. C. Chiou, TargeTech). Lane 1 is plasmid in the absence of conjugate. Lanes 2–8 contain weight ratios of ASOR-PL to DNA of 1.0, 1.5, 2.0, 2.5, 3.0, 3.5, and 4.0, respectively. **(B)** Gel of an ASOR-PL-DNA complex prepared at a ratio of 3:1 as described in the text. Reprinted with permission of the American Chemical Society *(44)*.

2. An ASOR-PL-DNA complex is formed at a 2:1 ASOR/PL:DNA ratio by adding 2.5 mL of an ASOR-PL solution at 1.5 mg/mL and $0.15M$ NaCl to a 2.5-mL stirred solution of DNA at 1.0 mg/mL and $0.15M$ NaCl at 25 µL/min via a peristaltic pump. After complete addition, the complex is filtered through a 0.45-µm filter and the concentration of soluble, complexed DNA is measured by UV absorbance at 260 nm (final concentration of complexed DNA: 374 µg/mL, 75% recovery). Complexation of the DNA is then confirmed by agarose gel electrophoresis (Fig. 4B). Complexes in $0.15M$ NaCl are usually stable at 4°C for at least 2–3 d.

3.10. Formation of Complexed DNA and Modified Virus (33)

To form targetable complexes, plasmid DNA, 0.5 mg in 1 mL of $2M$ NaCl was added in a ratio of 2 µg DNA to 0.4 µg modified virus, with respect to total protein. This ratio was determined as optimal using an agarose gel retardation assay as described previously *(25)*. The sample was then placed in dialysis tubing with an exclusion limit of 12–14 kDa (Spectrapore), and dialyzed stepwise successively at 4°C for 0.5 h against 1 L of NaCl solution in each of the following concentrations: $1.5M$, $1.0M$, $0.5M$, $0.25M$, and $0.15M$. After the final dialysis, the complex was filtered through 0.45-µm membranes prior to use in subsequent studies.

3.11. Cells and Cell Culture

To assess viral infectivity, three cell lines were used: human cervical carcinoma, HeLa S_3 [asialoglycoprotein receptor (–)], human hepatoma, SK Hep1 [asialoglycoprotein receptor (–)] cells, and human hepatoma Huh 7 [asialoglycoprotein receptor (+)] cells *(59)* were cultured in plastic dishes. Cells were seeded at densities of 5×10^5 cells in 35-mm plastic dishes containing minimal essential medium (MEM) (Gibco-BRL, Gaithersburg, MD) and 5% fetal calf serum (Gibco-BRL) under 5% CO_2 at 37°C.

3.12. Assays of Viral Infectivity

To assess residual infectivity of modified viruses, cells were allowed to attach for 24 h, after which time medium was removed and virus, modified or unmodified in medium, was added at concentrations of 100 viral particles/cell. Virus samples were incubated with cells at 37°C for 48 h. Cells were then stained with Trypan blue and counted microscopically. Infection assays were performed in triplicate and the results expressed as mean $\pm$ SD of viable cells.

3.13. Assays for Targeted Gene Expression (33)

To assay for gene transfection, a plasmid, pHBVsurf, containing the gene for human hepatitis B surface antigen driven by the SV-40 promoter (kindly provided by Dr. T. Jake Liang, Massachusetts General Hospital, Boston, MA) was used *(59)*. The plasmid was grown in *E. coli*, isolated and purified as described previously *(60)*. Cells, seeded at 5.0×10^5/35-mm dish, were treated 24 h later with 2 mL of medium containing 2 µg DNA in the form of DNA complex alone, DNA complexed to modified wild-type virus, DNA complex plus wild-type virus, DNA complex plus modified dl312 virus, DNA complexed to modified dl312 virus, and DNA complexed to modified dl312 virus plus 1000-fold excess of ASOR by weight with respect to the ASOR content of the complex. In samples containing virus, approx 2000 viruses/cell were present and in competition studies, a 1000-fold excess of viral particles/cell was used. All transfections were performed in triplicate and parallel dishes were prepared for cell counting. Medium, 200 µL from each dish, was removed at 24 h and assayed for HBV surface antigen concentration by ELISA (Abbott, North Chicago, IL) and expressed as pg/10^6 cells/24 h $\pm$ SD.

To determine the number of cells that express targeted genes, a plasmid pTZ βact nls lacZ A1 (a kind gift of Dr. Claire Bonnerot, Pasteur Institute, Paris, France) *(61)* containing the gene for β-galactosidase driven by a retroviral promoter with an SV-40 nuclear localizing sequence was employed. Asialoglycoprotein receptor (+) and (–) cells, all seeded at 5.0×10^5 cells/dish, were transfected separately, 24 h later, with 2 µg DNA in 2 mL of medium as DNA complex alone, DNA complexed to modified dl312 adenovirus at 2000 particles/cell, DNA complexed to modified dl312 adenovirus plus a 1000-fold excess of ASOR. After 24 h of incubation, cells were fixed and washed *(62)*, and then stained with X-gal *(63)* (Life Technologies, Gaithersburg, MD); the number of cells with blue-stained nuclei was determined by counting microscopically. The fraction of positive cells was calculated and expressed as mean ± SD of 10 high power fields.

4. Notes

1. The procedures described here represent a general guide that accommodates considerable flexibility. In our laboratories, we have prepared conjugates using PLs over a wide range of average molecular weights (4–60 kDa) with some variation in DNA binding and delivery.
2. Care must be taken to properly purify ASOR-PL to allow the formation of a soluble DNA complex. For applications in vivo, in particular, the ASOR-PL should be free of both unbound PL and the highly cross-linked ASOR-PL species that migrate more slowly in the acid-urea gels. ASOR-PL purified in this manner allows the formation of DNA complexes at a concentration suitable for iv injection into experimental animals (up to 1 mg/mL DNA). For in vitro experimentation, for which complexes can be made up at lower concentrations, it is possible (though not preferable) to use less rigorously purified ASOR-PL to prepare soluble targetable complexes. Complexes of oligonucleotides *(26,64)* are more soluble than those of plasmid DNAs and also may be prepared with less highly purified ASOR-PL.

Acknowledgments

Supported in part by grants from NIH: DK42182 (George Y. Wu), March of Dimes 1-0786 (George Y. Wu); and TargeTech (Catherine H. Wu). George Y. Wu, and Catherine H. Wu hold equity in Immune Response Corp. The technical assistance of Pei-Li Zhan is gratefully acknowledged. The data presented in Figs. 2–4 were collected by Timothy D. McKee and Mary E. DeRome (TargeTech, Meriden, CT). The purification of orosomucoid described was developed by Todd Mockler, Chris Coffin, Timothy McKee, and Mary E. DeRome (TargeTech).

References

1. Wolff, J . A. (ed.) (1994) *Gene Therapeutics: Methods and Applications of Direct Gene Transfer*, Birkhäuser, Boston.
2. Findeis, M. A. (1994, April issue) Genes to the rescue, *Technol. Rev.* **97,** 46–53.
3. Mulligan, R. C. (1993) The basic science of gene therapy. *Science* **260,** 926–932.
4. Anderson, W. F. (1992) Human gene therapy. *Science* **256,** 808–813.
5. Miller, A. D. (1992) Human gene therapy comes of age. *Nature* **357,** 455–460.
6. Mulligan, R. C. (1991) Gene transfer and gene therapy: principles, prospects, and perspective, in *Etiology of Human Disease at the DNA Level* (Lindsten, J. and Pettersson, U., eds.), Raven, New York, pp. 143–189.
7. Jolly, D. J., Yee, J.-K., and Friedmann, T. (1987) High-efficiency gene transfer into cells. *Methods Enzymol.* **149,** 10–25.
8. Rosenfeld, M. A., Yoshimura, K., Trapnell, B. C., Yoneyama, K., Rosenthal, E. R., Dalemans, W., Fukayama, M., Bargon, J., Stier, L. E., Stratford-Perricaudet,

L., Perricaudet, M., Guggino,W. B., Pavirani, A., Lecocq, J.-P., and Crystal, R. G. (1992) *In vivo* transfer of the human cystic fibrosis transmembrane conductance regulator gene to the airway epithelium. *Cell* **68**, 143–155.

9. Herz, J. and Gerard, R. D. (1993) Adenovirus-mediated transfer of low density lipoprotein receptor gene acutely accelerates cholesterol clearance in normal mice. *Proc. Natl. Acad. Sci. USA* **90**, 2812–2816.

10. Wu, G. Y. and Wu, C. H. (1987) Receptor-mediated in vitro gene transformation by a soluble DNA carrier system. *J. Biol. Chem.* **262**, 4429–4432.

11. Wagner, E., Zenke, M., Cotten, M., Beug, H., and Birnstiel, M. L. (1990) Transferrin-polycation conjugates as carriers for DNA uptake into cells. *Proc. Natl. Acad. Sci. USA* **87**, 3410–3414.

12. Nabel, G. J. and Felgner, P. L. (1993) Direct gene transfer for immunotherapy and immunization. *Trends Biotechnol.* **11**, 211–215.

13. Zhu, N., Liggitt, D., Liu, Y., and Debs, R. (1993) Systemic gene expression after intravenous DNA delivery into adult mice. *Science* **261**, 209–211.

14. Stribling, R., Brunette, E., Liggitt, D., Gaensler, K., and Debs, R. (1992) Aerosol gene delivery *in vivo*. *Proc. Natl. Acad. Sci. USA* **89**, 11,277–11,281.

15. Findeis, M. A., Merwin, J. R., Spitalny, G. L., and Chiou, H. C. (1993) Targeted delivery of DNA for gene therapy via receptors. *Trends Biotechnol.* **11**, 202–205.

16. Chiou, H. C., Spitalny, G. L., Merwin, J. R., and Findeis, M. A. (1994) In vivo gene therapy via receptor-mediated DNA delivery, in *Gene Therapeutics: Methods and Applications of Direct Gene Transfer* (Wolff, J. A., ed.), Birkhäuser, Boston, pp. 143–156.

17. Findeis, M. A., Wu, C. H., and Wu, G. Y. (1994) Ligand-based carrier systems for delivery of DNA to hepatocytes, in *Neoglycoconjugates, Methods in Enzymology* (Lee, Y. C., and Lee, R. T., eds.), pp. 341–350.

18. Wu, G. Y. and Wu, C. H. (1991) Targeted delivery and expression of foreign genes in hepatocytes, in *Liver Diseases, Targeted Diagnosis and Therapy Using Specific Receptors and Ligands* (Wu, G. Y. and Wu, C. H., eds.), Marcel Dekker, New York, pp. 127–149.

19. Wu, G. Y., Wu, C. H., and Stockert, R. J. (1983) Model for specific rescue of normal hepatocytes during methotrexate treatment of hepatic malignancy. *Proc. Natl. Acad. Sci. USA* **80**, 3078–3080.

20. Wu, G. Y., Wu, C. H., and Rubin, M. I. (1985) Acetaminophen hepatotoxicity and targeted rescue: a model for specific chemotherapy of hepatocellular carcinoma. *Hepatology* **5**, 709–713.

21. Keegan-Rogers, V. and Wu, G. Y. (1990) Targeted protection of hepatocytes from galactosamine toxicity in vivo. *Cancer Chemother. Pharmacol.* **26**, 93–96.

22. Wu, G. Y., Keegan-Rogers, V., Franklin, S., Midford, S., and Wu, C. H. (1988) Targeted antagonism of galactosamine toxicity in normal rat hepatocytes in vitro. *J. Biol. Chem.* **263**, 4719–4723.

23. Ponzetto, A., Fiume, L., Forzani, B., Song, S. H., Busi, C., Mattioli, A., Spinelli, C., Marinelli, M., Smedile, A., Chiaberge, E., Bonino, F., Gervasi, G. B., Rapicetta, M., and Verme, G. (1991) Adenine arabinoside monophosphate and acyclovir monophosphate coupled to lactosaminated albumin reduce woodchuck

hepatitis virus viremia at lower doses than do the unconjugated drugs. *Hepatology* **14**, 16–24.

24. Fiume, L., Busi, C., Mattioli, A., Balboni, P. G., and Barbanti-Brodano, G. (1981) Hepatocyte targeting of adenine-9-β-D-arabinofuranoside 5'-monophosphate (ara-AMP) coupled to lactosaminated albumin. *FEBS Lett.* **129**, 261–264.

25. Wu, G. Y. and Wu, C. H. (1987) Receptor-mediated *in vitro* gene transformation by a soluble DNA carrier system. *J. Biol. Chem.* **262**, 4129–4432.

26. Wu, G. Y. and Wu, C. H. (1992) Specific inhibition of hepatitis B viral gene expression *in vitro* by targeted antisense oligonucleotides. *J. Biol. Chem.* **267**, 12,436–12,439.

27. Cristiano, R. J., Smith, L. C., and Woo, S. L. C. (1993) Hepatic gene therapy: adenovirus enhancement of receptor-mediated gene delivery and expression in primary heaptocytes. *Proc. Natl. Acad. Sci. USA* **90**, 2122–2126.

28. Wu, G. Y. and Wu, C. H. (1988) Receptor-mediated gene delivery and expression *in vivo*. *J. Biol. Chem.* **263**, 14,621–14,624.

29. Wu, G. Y., Wilson, J. M., and Wu, C. H. (1989) Targeting genes: delivery and persistent expression of a foreign gene driven by mammalian regulatory elements *in vivo*. *J. Biol. Chem.* **264**, 16,985–16,987.

30. Wu, G. Y., Wilson, J. M., Shalaby, F., Grossman, M., Shafritz, D. A., and Wu, C. H. (1991) Receptor-mediated gene delivery *in vivo*: partial correction of genetic analbuminemia in Nagase rats. *J. Biol. Chem.* **266**, 14,338–14,342.

31. Wilson, J. M., Grossman, M., Cabrera, J. A., Wu, C. H., Chowdhury, N. R., Wu, G. Y., and Chowdhury, J. R. (1992) Hepatocyte-directed gene transfer *in vivo* leads to transient improvement of hypercholesterolemia in low density lipoprotein receptor-deficient rabbits. *J. Biol. Chem.* **267**, 963–967.

32. Wilson, J. M., Grossman, M., Cabrera, J. A., Wu, C. H., and Wu, G. Y. (1992) A novel mechanism for achieving transgene persisitence *in vivo* after somatic gene transfer into hepatocytes. *J. Biol. Chem.* **267**, 11,483–11,489.

33. Wu, G. Y., Zhan, P.-L., Sze, L. L., Rosenberg, A. R., and Wu, C. H. (1994) Incorporation of adenovirus into a ligand-based DNA carrier system results in retention of the original receptor specificity and enhances targeted gene expression. *J. Biol. Chem.* **269**, 11,542–11,546.

34. Huebner, R. J., Rowe, W. P., Ward, T. G., Parrott, R. H., and Bell, J. A. (1954) Adenoidal-pharyngeal-conjunctival agents: a newly recognized group of common viruses of the respiratory system. *N. Engl. J. Med.* **251**, 1077–1086.

35. Pereira, H. G., Huebner, R. J., Ginsberg, H. S., and Van der Veen, J. (1963) A short description of the adenovirus group. *Virology* **20**, 613–620.

36. Grayston, J. T., McCarthy, M. A., Smith, M., and Loosli, C. G. (1958) Adenoviruses. II. The sensitivity of different tissue culture strains of cells to adenoviruses. *J. Infect. Dis.* **103**, 86–92.

37. Hennache, B. and Boulanger, P. (1977) Biochemical study of KB-cell receptor for adenovirus. *Biochem. J.* **166**, 237–247.

38. Chardonnet, Y. and Dales, S. (1970) Early events in the interaction of adenoviruses with HeLA cells. I. Penetration of type 5 and intracellular release of the DNA gnome. *Virology* **40**, 462–477.

39. Seth, P., FitzGerald, D., Ginsberg, H., Willingham, M., and Pastan, I. (1984) Evidence that the penton base of adenovirus is involved in potentiation of toxicity of pseudomonas exotoxin conjugated to epidermal growth factor. *Mol. Cell Biol.* **4,** 1528–1533.

40. Curiel, D. T., Agarwal, S., Wagner, E., and Cotten, M. (1991) Adenovirus enhancement of transferrin-polylysine-mediated gene delivery. *Proc. Natl. Acad. Sci. USA* **88,** 8850–8854.

41. Ishibashi, M., and Maizel, J. V., Jr. (1974) The polypeptides of adenoviruses. IV. Early and late glycopolypeptides. *Virology* **58,** 345–361.

42. Whitehead, P. H. and Sammons, H. G. (1966) A simple technique for the isolation of orosomucoid from normal and pathological sera. *Biochim. Biophys. Acta* **124,** 209–211.

43. Schmid, K., Polis, A., Hunziker, K., Fricke, R., and Yayoshi, M. (1967) Partial characterization of the sialic acid-free forms of α_1-acid glycoprotein from human plasma. *Biochem. J.* **104,** 361–368.

44. McKee, T. D., DeRome, M. E., Wu, G. Y., and Findeis, M. A. (1994) Preparation of asialoorosomucoid-polylysine conjugates for targeted delivery of DNA. *Bioconjugate Chem.* **5,** 306–311.

45. Sambrook, J., Fritsch, E. F., and Maniatis, T. (1989) *Molecular Cloning,* 2nd ed, Cold Spring Harbor Laboratory, Cold Spring Harbor, Chapter 6, pp. 6.2–6.13.

46. Hames, B. D. (1981) An introduction to polyacrylamide gel electrophoresis, in *Gel Electrophoresis of Proteins* (Hames, B. D. and Rickwood, D., eds.), IRL, Oxford, UK, Chapter 1.

47. Schmid, K. (1976) α_1-Acid glycoprotein, in *The Plasma Proteins,* 2nd ed., vol. 1. (Putnam, F. W., ed.), Academic, New York, pp. 183–228.

48. Schmid, K. (1989) Human plasma α_1-acid glycoprotein—biochemical properties, the amino acid sequence and the structure of the carbohydrate moiety, variants and polymorphism, in *Alpha$_1$-Acid Glycoprotein: Genetics, Biochemistry, Physiological Functions, and Pharmacology, Progress in Clinical and Biological Research,* vol. 300 (Baumann, P., Eap, C. B., Müller, W. E., and Tillement, J.-P., eds.), Liss, New York, pp. 7–22.

49. Chait, B. T. and Kent, S. B. H. (1992) Weighing naked proteins: practical, high accuracy mass measurement of peptides and proteins. *Science* **257,** 1885–1894.

50. Warren, L. (1959) The thiobarbituric acid assay of sialic acids. *J. Biol. Chem.* **234,** 1971–1975.

51. Uchida, Y., Tsukuda, Y., and Sugimori, T. (1977) Distribution of neuraminidase in *Arthrobacter* and its purification by affinity chromatography. *J. Biochem.* **82,** 1425–1433.

52. Panyim, S. and Chalkley, R. (1969) High resolution acrylamide gel electrophoresis of histones. *Arch. Biochem. Biophys.* **130,** 337–346.

53. Green, M. and Piña, M. (1963) Biochemical studies on adenovirus multiplication. IV. Isolation, purification and chemical analysis of adenovirus. *Virology* **20,** 199–207.

54. Jones, N. and Schenk, T. (1979) An adenovirus type 5 early gene function regulates expression of other early viral genes. *Proc. Natl. Acad. Sci. USA* **76,** 3665–3669.

55. Greenwood, F., Hunter, C. W. M., and Glover, J. S. (1963) The preparation of ^{131}I-labelled human growth hormone of high specific radioactivity. *Biochem. J.* **89,** 114–123.
56. Lawrence, W. C., and Ginsburg, H. S. (1967) Intracellular uncoating of type 5 adenovirus deoxyribonucleic acid. *J. Virology* **1,** 851–867.
57. Precious, B., and Russell, W. C. (1985) Growth, purification, and titration of adenoviruses, in *Virology: A Practical Approach* (Mahy, B. W. J., ed.), IRL, Oxford, UK, pp. 193–205.
58. Rowe, D. W., Moen, R. C., Davidson, J. M., Byers, P. H., Bornstein, P., and Palmiter, R. D. (1978) Correlation of procollagen mRNA levels in normal and transformed chick embryo fibroblasts with different rates of procollagen synthesis. *Biochemistry* **17,** 1581–1590.
59. Liang, T. J., Makdisi, W. J., Sun, S., Hasegawa, K., Zhang, Y., Wands, J. R., Wu, C. H., and Wu, G. Y. (1993) Targeted transfection and expression of hepatitis B viral DNA in human hepatoma cells. *J. Clin. Invest.* **91,** 1241–1246.
60. Birnboim, H. C. and Doly, J. (1979) A rapid alkaline extraction procedure for screening recombinant plasmid DNA. *Nucleic Acids Res.* **7,** 1513–1518.
61. Bonnerot, C., Rocancourt, D., Briand, P., Grimber, G., and Nicolas, J.-F. (1987) A β-galactosidase hybrid protein targeted to nuclei as a marker for developmental studies. *Proc. Natl. Acad. Sci. USA* **84,** 6795–6799.
62. Beddington, R. S. P., Morgernstern, J., Land, H., and Hogan, A. (1989) *In situ* transgenic enzyme marker for the midgestational mouse embryo and the visualization of inner cell mass clones during early organogenesis. *Development* **106,** 37–46.
63. Sanes, J. R., Rubenstein, J. L. R., and Nicolas, J. F. (1986) Use of recombinant retrovirus to study post-implantation cell lineage in mouse embryos. *EMBO J.* **5,** 3133–3142.
64. Carmichael, E. P., Chiou, H. C., Findeis, M. A., Spitalny, G. L., and Merwin, J. R. (1995) Targeted delivery of anti-hepatitis B antisense oligonucleotides, in *Delivery Systems for Antisense Oligonucleotide Therapeutics* (Akhtar, S., ed.), CRC, Boca Raton, FL, pp. 267–282.

10

Methods for the Use of Retroviral Vectors for Transfer of the CFTR Gene to Airway Epithelium

John C. Olsen, Larry G. Johnson, and James R. Yankaskas

1. Introduction

Cystic fibrosis (CF) is a recessive genetic disease that affects the regulation of ion transport in the epithelia of various organs in the body including the lungs, pancreas, intestine, salivary glands, and urogenital tract. The protein encoded by the CF gene is an integral plasma membrane protein called the cystic fibrosis transmembrane conductance regulator (CFTR) and has been shown to function as a chloride channel *(1)*. In the lungs, CFTR dysfunction affects electrolyte and fluid transport across the apical membrane of airway epithelial cells. There, sodium hyperabsorption and defective chloride secretion lead to dehydration of the fluids on the airway surface and, in turn, this leads to chronic infections and severe damage. The severity of CF lung disease and the potential accessibility of the airways to gene transfer vectors has led to proposals that gene therapy be applied for the treatment of CF lung disease *(2)*.

Heterozygotes with mutations in the CFTR gene show no phenotypic abnormalities. Thus, gene transfer of a normal CFTR cDNA to CF airway epithelial cells grown in culture corrects the chloride transport defect. Although current gene therapy trials use adenoviral vectors and liposomes to deliver CFTR cDNA to CF patients in vivo, it is possible that retroviral vectors may be used in the future. Potential advantages of using retroviruses include stable integration, which could lead to long-term therapy and the unlikelihood of vector rescue by other viruses that commonly infect the respiratory tract. Disadvantages of using retroviruses include the relatively low titers that are produced by commonly used packaging cell lines and the fact that retroviruses require dividing cells for integration and the proliferation rate of epithelial cells lining the airway of normal individuals is low. However, a recent study showing that the

From: *Methods in Molecular Medicine, Gene Therapy Protocols*
Edited by: P. Robbins Humana Press Inc., Totowa, NJ

proliferation rate of the airway epithelium of CF patients may be quite high suggests that retrovirus vectors might indeed be useful in transferring genes directly to injured lungs *(3)*. Alternatively, retroviral vectors may prove useful for transferring genes to fetal lungs in which the cellular proliferation rate is known to be relatively high.

In this chapter, procedures to effect and evaluate retroviral gene transfer into human airway epithelial cells are described in three sections. First, procedures are described for the preparation of primary airway epithelial cell cultures that can then be used to evaluate the gene transfer capabilities of various gene transfer vectors. Second, methods used to increase the titers of CFTR cDNA-containing retroviral vectors are described. Finally, methods are outlined for evaluating the phenotypic correction of the chloride transport defect.

1.1. Principles of Ion Transport in CF

The airway epithelium is a semipermeable barrier composed of surface epithelial cells together with the tight junctions that join them at their apical borders, and submucosal glands that secrete liquid and mucins into the airway lumen. These components play an important role in lung defense through secretion of airway surface liquid and active mucociliary clearance that acts to entrap and clear inhaled foreign substances. The regulation of the volume and composition of airway surface liquids is achieved by active ion transport.

In human airway epithelia under resting conditions, Na^+-is the major ion flux across the airway epithelium. Sodium is absorbed across the epithelium in a two-step process that involves passive entry into the cell down an electrochemical gradient through conductive pathways or channels in the apical membrane followed by extrusion across the basolateral membrane by the activity of the Na^+-K^+-ATPase. The entry of Na^+ into the airways is inhibited by the Na^+ channel blocker, amiloride. Airway epithelia also possess the potential to add salt and water to the airway surface liquid through the secretion of Cl^-. Chloride transport across the airway epithelium is complex and involves Cl^- entry across the basolateral membrane, electrochemical forces for Cl^- flow across the apical cell membrane, and apical membrane Cl^- permeabilities. Chloride may enter the cell from the submucosal compartment through the Na^+-K^+-$2Cl^-$ cotransporter. When an electrochemical driving force exists, Cl^- may exit the apical surface of the cell and enter the airway surface liquid through either a cAMP-mediated Cl^- channel (CFTR) or, alternatively, through an alternative Cl^- conductive pathway that appears to be regulated by Ca^{2+}-mediated agonists. Experimentally, a driving force for apical Cl^- exit can be created by blocking Na^+ absorption with amiloride, which hyperpolarizes the apical membrane, and by removing Cl^- from the luminal surface of cells, which produces a chemical gradient.

In CF, Na^+ absorption is raised two- to threefold over that measured in normal airway epithelia *(4)*. This appears to be caused by an increased open probability of the apical Na^+ channels *(5)* and is accompanied by an increase in the Na^+-K^+-ATPase number and/or activity *(6)*. Moreover, CF is characterized by the absence of a cAMP-activated apical membrane Cl^- channel (i.e., CFTR). The localization of rate-limiting Na^+ and Cl^- conductances and of normal CFTR in the apical cell membrane is probably important physiologically, and suggests that polarized epithelia may be essential to evaluate the cellular physiology that causes CF.

Because regulation of airway surface liquid composition involves the regulation of the movement of ions across the airways, polarized airway epithelial tissues generate a transepithelial resistance (R_t), a transepithelial potential difference (V_t), and a transepithelial current called the short circuit current (I_{sc}) that can be monitored electrically. These measurements can be used to assess the phenotypic correction of the ion transport defect in polarized CF epithelial cells following gene transfer of a normal CFTR cDNA.

2. Materials

2.1. Primary Culture of Human Airway Epithelial Cells

1. F12 + 7X growth medium for primary airway epithelial cells (*see* Note 1): Medium F12 with glutamine and HCO_3^- (Life Technologies, Gaithersburg, MD) supplemented with 7 hormones and growth factors (Table 1). Penicillin (50 U/mL), streptomycin (50 μg/mL), and gentamicin (40 μg/mL) are added as antibiotics.
2. Joklik's Calcium-free and Magnesium-free Minimum Essential Medium (JMEM) (Life Technologies).
3. Phosphate-buffered saline (PBS): 8 g NaCl, 0.2 g KCl, 2.16 g $Na_2HPO_4 \cdot 7H_2O$, and 0.2 g KH_2PO_4/L.
4. 3T3 fibroblast-conditioned medium: Grow 3T3 mouse embryo fibroblasts (American Type Culture Collection, Rockville, MD) in Dulbecco's Modified Eagle's Medium (DMEM, Life Technologies) containing 10% fetal bovine serum (FBS). When cells become 90% confluent, change the medium to DMEM containing 2% FBS (0.64 mL/cm^2). After 3 d, collect conditioned medium, filter sterilize, and store at 4°C. The conditioned medium may be used within 3 wk, or stored at $-20°C$ for up to 6 mo.
5. 1.0 mg/mL protease Type XIV (Sigma, St. Louis, MO) plus 0.1 mg/mL deoxyribonuclease I (Sigma) in JMEM (0.2-μm filter sterilized).
6. 0.4% trypan blue in PBS (Sigma).
7. Collagen-coated matrix supports (CMS) (*see* Note 2): These matrices are cast on a beveled orifice (4.5-mm diameter) in the bottom of a 2.5-cm diameter polycarbonate cup and can be made by the following previously published protocol that has been modified slightly *(7)*:
   a. Dissolve type III calfskin collagen (Sigma) in 0.2% acetic acid at 15 mg/mL.
   b. Add 0.5 vol of 2.5% glutaraldehyde and cool in an ice bath until jelling begins.

Table 1
Hormone and Growth Factor Preparation for F12 + 7X Airway Epithelial Cell Growth Medium

Additive[a,b]	Stock preparation[c]	Stock concentration	Stock storage temperature	Stock expires	Final concentration in growth medium
Insulin	20 mg/4 mL H_2O	5 mg/mL	–20°C	3 mo	10 µg/mL
Hydrocortisone	(1) 50 mg/13.8 mL ethanol	$10^{-2}M$	–20°C	1 yr	
	(2) dilute 1:10 with PBS	$10^{-3}M$	–20°C	3 mo	$10^{-6}M$
ECGS	15.0 mg/4 mL H_2O	3.75 mg/mL	–20°C	1 mo	3.75 µg/mL
EGF	100 µg/4 mL H_2O	25 µg/mL	–20°C	3 mo	25/ng/mL
Triiodothyronine	(1) 20 mg/5 mL 0.2M NaOH				
	(2) add 5 mL H_2O	3 mM	–20°C	1 yr	
	(3) dilute 1:100 in H_2O	$3 \times 10^{-5}M$	–20°C	3 mo	$3 \times 10^{-8}M$
Transferrin	10 mg/4 mL H_2O	2.5 mg/mL	–20°C	3 mo	5 µg/mL
Cholera toxin	0.5 mg/5 mL H_2O	100 µg/mL	–4°C	1 yr	10 ng/mL

[a]Abbreviations: ECGS, endothelial cell growth supplement; EGF, epidermal growth factor.
[b]All additives can be obtained from Collaborative Research (Lexington, MA) except cholera toxin, which can be obtained from Sigma (St. Louis, MO).
[c]Stocks do not need filtering if handled with sterile technique.

    c. Apply a bead of collagen/glutaraldehyde around the orifice of the inverted polycarbonate, and drag mixture across the orifice with a Pasteur pipet, forming a thin sheet.

    d. Dry in air (3–4 h).

    e. Apply a second coat of collagen (with glutaraldehyde) over the bottom surface of the matrix. Dry overnight.

    f. Apply a third coat of collagen (without glutaraldehyde) to the inside surface of the matrix. Dry overnight.

    g. Rinse four times with 20 mM NaHCO$_3$ in 130 mM NaCl. Dry overnight.

    h. Coat inside surface with 30 μL calfskin collagen (3 mg/mL, Vitrogen, Celtrix Labs, Palo Alto, CA). Dry overnight.

    i. Sterilize unit in 70% ethanol for 30 min. Rinse in sterile culture medium. Incubate overnight at 37°C in F12 + 7X growth medium to test for sterility.

    j. CMS dishes can be stored in PBS at 4°C for up to 1 mo.

2.2. Gene Transfer Using Retroviral Vectors

1. Retroviral vector producing cells, produced according to the protocols as described previously *(8,9)*.
2. Polybrene (Sigma) stock of 4 mg/mL and sterilized by passing through a 0.2-μm syringe filter.
3. Sodium butyrate (Sigma) stock of 500 mM and sterilized by passing through a 0.2-μm syringe filter.
4. Centrifugal concentrators: Either 300K Macrosep (Filtron Technology Corporation, Northborough, MA) or Centriprep-100 (Amicon, Danvers, MA) concentrator devices have been used successfully for concentrating retroviral vectors.
5. Ultracentrifuge tubes: We use conical-shaped polyallomer centrifuge tubes for the SW 28 rotor (Konical, Beckman Instruments, Palo Alto, CA) that are ideal for pelleting virus to a small area. Conical-shaped tubes must be used with adapters (Beckman Instruments) that are placed in the bottom of the rotor and support the conical bottom of the tubes during centrifugation.
6. Disposable syringe filters: Syringe filters combining a prefiltration and final filtration in one step (e.g., Uniflo Plus 0.2 μm, Schleicher & Schuell, Keene, NH) allow the filtration of ~30 mL of virus-containing medium before it is necessary to change filters.
7. Hank's Balanced Salt Solution (HBSS): 0.4 g KCl, 0.06 g KH$_2$PO$_4$, 8 g NaCl, 0.048 g Na$_2$HPO$_4$, and 1 g D-glucose/L.

2.3. Measurement of CFTR Function

1. Krebs bicarbonate Ringer's (KBR) solution, pH 7.4, with the following constituents in mmol/L: Na$^+$ 140, K$^+$ 5.2, Cl$^-$ 120, Ca^{2+} 1.25, HCO$_3^-$ 25, Mg^{2+} 1.25, HPO$_4^{2-}$ 2.4, H$_2$PO$_4^-$ 0.4, and D-glucose 5.0. Stock solutions of reagents in distilled water are prepared as follows: K$_2$HPO$_4$ 8.36 g/L, KH$_2$PO$_4$ 1.09 g/L, NaCl 134.41 g/L, NaHCO$_3$ 42.01 g/L. Fifty milliliters of each stock are added to a flask and brought up to 800 mL with distilled H$_2$O. The solution is gassed by bubbling 95% O$_2$/5% CO$_2$ into the solution for 10–15 min to adjust the pH from

8.5–7.4. Fifty milliliters of a stock solution of 4.88 g/L $MgCl_2 \cdot 6H_2O$ and 2.66 g/L $CaCl_2$ (anhydrous) is then added followed by 0.9 g D-glucose dissolved in 10 mL water. (The presence of an insoluble precipitate after addition of the $MgCl_2$ and $CaCl_2$ means that the pH was too alkaline owing to insufficient gassing.) The solution is then brought up to 1 L with distilled water.

2. Cl^--free Ringer's solution, pH 7.4, with the following constituents in mmol/L: Na^+ 140, K^+ 5.2, gluconate 120, Ca^{2+} 2.5, HCO_3^- 25, Mg^{2+} 1.2, HPO_4^{2-} 2.4, $H_2PO_4^-$ 0.4, SO_4^{2-} 1.2, and D-glucose 5.0. To prepare 1 L, add 50 mL each of the K_2HPO_4, KH_2PO_4, and $NaHCO_3$ stocks from above plus 200 mL of a 125.4 g/L Na gluconate stock to a flask. Bring to 800 mL with distilled water and gas with 95% O_2/5% CO_2 for 10–15 min. Add 50 mL of 10.66 g/L calcium gluconate with 5.92 g/L $MgSO_4 \cdot 7H_2O$ and 0.9 g D-glucose dissolved in 10 mL water. Bring up to 1 L with distilled water.

3. Forskolin (Sigma), a $10^{-2}M$ stock of 4.1 mg/mL in 70% ethanol.

4. Amiloride (Sigma), a $10^{-2}M$ stock of 2.66 mg/mL in water.

5. Current voltage clamps, Model VCC600, Physiologic Instruments, San Diego, CA.

6. Epithelial V/Ω meter (EVOM), World Precision Instruments, Sarasota, FL.

7. Lucite Ussing chambers: These are available from a variety of sources, including World Precision Instruments, or they can be made in your local physics shop.

8. Twin perfusion columns, glass: These are available from World Precision Instruments, a variety of other companies, and can also be made in your local glass shop.

3. Methods

3.1. Isolation and Primary Culture of Human Airway Epithelial Cells

3.1.1. Tissue Procurement and Transport

1. Obtain excess excised nasal or bronchial tissues from fresh surgical specimens (e.g., nasal polyps; *see* Notes 3–5).

2. Transport to laboratory in chilled (4°C) JMEM solution.

3. Remove and discard loose connective tissue by blunt and sharp dissection.

4. Incubate in excess volume (30–60 mL/5 g tissue) of chilled (4°C) JMEM containing penicillin (50 U/mL), streptomycin (50 mg/mL), and gentamicin (40 mg/mL) for 2–24 h.

3.1.2. Cell Isolation

1. Rinse tissue with fresh JMEM plus antibiotics, and incubate in 5 mL 1.0 mg/mL protease Type XIV plus 0.1 mg/mL deoxyribonuclease I in JMEM at 4°C for 16–48 h, agitating gently 4–6 times (*see* Note 6).

2. Add fetal bovine serum to 10% to neutralize the protease.

3. Remove tissue pieces, pellet cell suspension (500g for 5 min).

4. Wash cells with JMEM containing 10% FBS and pellet at 500g for 5 min.

5. Stain aliquot of cells with trypan blue solution, and count viable and dead cells in a hemacytometer.

6. Resuspend cells in growth medium to desired volume (*see* Section 3.1.3.).

3.1.3. Primary Culture

The decision to grow primary airway epithelial cells on plastic or on collagen supports will be influenced by the purpose of the experiment. For testing the efficiencies of gene transfer vectors or for using an anion efflux assay to measure CFTR function, culturing cells in plastic tissue culture dishes will suffice. For experiments requiring polarized sheets for measuring the vectorial transport of ions, it will be necessary to culture cells on collagen supports.

1. Plastic: Plate cells in F12 + 7X growth medium in 35-mm dishes (or six-well plates) at 2.5×10^5 viable cells/dish. After 24 h, wash cells with growth medium, and replace medium every 2–3 d. The plating efficiency should be 20–40%.
2. Collagen supports: Plate cells at $1–5 \times 10^6$ cells/cm^2 (*see* Note 7). Rinse gently after 24–48 h, then replace medium every 2–3 d. The plating efficiency should be about 50–80%.

3.2. Gene Transfer Using Retroviral Vectors

Primary human airway epithelial cells are a good host for retroviral vectors containing either the amphotropic envelope or pseudotyped with the gibbon ape leukemia virus (GALV) envelope. We have observed the highest gene transfer efficiencies (60–80% of primary cells transduced after a single infection) with retrovirus vectors containing the GALV envelope *(10)*; however, it is not uncommon to transduce 20–40% of primary cells with amphotropic vectors *(10,11)*.

1. Plate cells in plastic tissue culture dishes or on collagen supports as described in Section 3.1.3.
2. At 72 h after plating, infect cells by replacing medium with 0.5–1 mL retroviral vector. Add polybrene to 8 µg/mL and return cells to incubator.
3. After 2 h, remove virus and replace with fresh growth medium. Analyze cells for expression 48 h after infection.

3.3. Boosting Titers
of Retroviral Vectors Containing CFTR cDNA

A problem often encountered by investigators is that the titer of recombinant retroviruses is inadequate for gene transfer applications. For retrovirus vectors containing a normal CFTR cDNA, the preparation of high-titer packaging cell lines is further confounded by the observation that high level expression of CFTR affects the growth rate and viability of many cell types including NIH 3T3 fibroblasts *(12)*, the parental cell type of many widely used packaging cell lines. Here we describe methods for inducing the increased production of retrovirus vectors by treating producer cell lines with sodium butyrate and concentrating retrovirus vectors using centrifugal filtration or by pelleting in the ultracentrifuge. By using these two approaches in tandem, it is possible to increase viral titers 100-fold to 1000-fold.

3.3.1. Boosting Titer
by Sodium Butyrate Treatment

We have used this method to increase titers of amphotropic retrovirus vectors produced by PA317 cells (13) and to increase the production of GALV-pseudotyped vectors produced by PG13 cells (14). For a given clonal packaging cell line, preliminary titration of sodium butyrate (from 0.5–30 mM) should be done to find the concentration giving the optimum enhancement of vector production. Depending on the vector and the particular producer clone (see Note 8), sodium butyrate treatment may enhance vector production from twofold to >1000-fold (15).

1. Plate the virus producer cells in tissue culture dishes and allow the cells to grow until they have just reached confluence.
2. Remove the medium from the cells and replace with fresh growth medium containing sodium butyrate. Place cells back into CO_2 incubator.
3. After 20–24 h of sodium butyrate treatment at 37°C, or after 48 h of treatment at 32°C (see Note 9), remove the supernatant containing the virus and pass through a 0.2-μm syringe filter to remove cells and cell debris. Alternatively, cells can be selectively pelleted from medium by centrifugation at 5000g for 10 min.
4. The virus can be stored indefinitely in aliquots at –70°C, or it can be concentrated immediately by the methods described in Sections 3.3.2. or 3.3.3.

3.3.2. Concentrating Retroviral Vectors
by Centrifugal Filtration

This procedure is a relatively gentle method for concentrating retroviral vectors approx 30- to 50-fold without significant loss of infectivity.

1. Prerinse filters (100- to 300-μm pore size) before use by centrifuging 15 mL deionized, sterile H_2O through filtration device for 20 min. Discard filtrate and any remaining retentate. If filtration device is not going to be used immediately, keep filter membrane wet with H_2O. Decant H_2O just prior to use. If desired, the filtration unit can be presterilized prior to use by following the manufacturer's instructions.
2. Add 15 mL virus (0.2-μm filtered) to the appropriate chamber of the filtration device. If virus has been frozen after harvesting from the producer cells, it is necessary to pass through a 0.2-μm filter to remove any serum protein denatured by the freeze-thaw process.
3. Centrifuge in a fixed angle rotor at 500g at 4°C. Every 30 min, stop the centrifugation and remove the filtrate until the volume of the retentate containing the virus reaches the desired reduction in volume.
4. Remove particulate matter from the virus by passing the retentate through a 0.2-μm syringe filter (prewetted with H_2O). Store virus in aliquots at –70°C.

3.3.3. Concentrating Retroviral Vectors by Pelleting in an Ultracentrifuge

The successful application of this method appears to be dependent on the stability of the viral envelope glycoproteins. Murine retroviral vectors with the ecotropic envelope surface glycoprotein or pseudotyped with the GALV or vesicular stomatitis virus G *(16)* envelope glycoproteins can be pelleted with significant (>25–90%) recovery of total infectivity. In contrast, pelleting vectors with the amphotropic envelope results in poor recovery (<15%). The following method has been used with the Beckman SW 28 rotor using the conically shaped Konical tubes (30-mL capacity) to pellet virus, but should be adaptable for use with other rotors and tubes.

1. Prerinse polyallomer ultracentrifuge tubes successively with ~20-mL aliquots of acetone (three times), 95% ethanol (twice), and endotoxin-free, double-distilled H_2O (three times). Allow tubes to drain in tissue culture hood.
2. Fill centrifuge tubes with virus (0.2-μm filtered) collected from the vector producer cells. If the virus has been frozen, denatured protein can be removed from the thawed virus by filtering using a syringe filter. If relatively large volumes (>50 mL) of virus are to be processed, it is advisable to use a syringe filter with a prefilter (e.g., Uniflo Plus).
3. Carefully place tubes into rotor buckets. (If the Beckman Konical tubes are used, be sure to use special adapters to prevent tube collapse.)
4. Pellet the virus using a swinging bucket rotor (e.g., SW 28) in an ultracentrifuge at 100,000g for 2 h at 4°C.
5. Decant supernatant and allow tubes to drain. Remove excess liquid from sides of tube above the pellet with Kimwipes or other lintless laboratory wipers.
6. Suspend virus in a small volume of HBSS and store in aliquots at −70°C. Alternatively, suspend virus in growth medium and use for immediate gene transfer as described in Section 3.2.

3.4. Measurement of CFTR Function

A variety of methods are available for measuring the function of CFTR. Most of these assay systems focus on the measurement of a cAMP-mediated Cl^- secretory response. Some of the assays also permit the evaluation of basal Na^+ transport and Cl^- secretory function.

3.4.1. Efflux Assays

The advantages of efflux assays are that they do not require an intact epithelium and they can be easily performed on cells grown in plastic dishes. These assays measure the rate of loss of Cl^- from corrected and/or normal cells as compared to CF epithelial cells. The cAMP-mediated agonists such as forskolin or other β-agonists may be added to more critically evaluate the cAMP-mediated Cl⁻ secretory response. Corrected or normal airway epithelial cells should exhibit a significantly increased rate of Cl⁻ efflux compared to CF cells.

Two different kinds of anion efflux assays are currently being employed: those based on radioactive isotopes, and those involving the use of ion-selective electrodes *(17)*. The radioisotopic assays use either ^{36}Cl⁻ or ^{125}I⁻. Published methods for efflux assays have generally been used with nonairway epithelia, and may require adaptations for airway epithelia. The ^{36}Cl⁻ efflux assay is described here (*see* Note 10):

1. Grow cells in 35-mm plastic tissue culture dishes to about 70–90% confluence. For cells infected with retroviral vectors, analyze cells 48 h after infection.
2. Load cells with radioactive chloride by replacing the growth medium with 1 mL KBR, pH 7.4, containing 5.0 µCi ^{36}Cl⁻ (specific activity > 3 mCi/g Cl⁻). Incubate in tissue culture incubator for 2 h at 37°C.
3. Wash cells four times rapidly (30–45 s/wash) with 1.0 mL KBR at room temperature.
4. After last wash, add and remove sequentially at 1 min intervals 1-mL aliquots of isotope-free Cl⁻-free Ringer's solution with $10^{-4}M$ amiloride at room temperature. Carry out assay for 10 min. Save each sample in a 20-mL liquid scintillation vial.
5. To assess cAMP-mediated Cl⁻ permeability, add 10 µL $10^{-3}M$ forskolin to the 1-mL aliquots of sampling buffer (Cl⁻-free Ringer's solution with $10^{-4}M$ amiloride) at the 3-min time point.
6. At the end of the sampling period, extract the radioisotope in the cell layer with 2 × 500 µL washes of 0.1% sodium dodecyl sulfate. Combine these washes in a 20-mL liquid scintillation vial.
7. Add 10 mL of an appropriate liquid scintillation counting fluid to each sample. Determine the amount of ^{36}Cl⁻ in the efflux aliquots and cells by liquid-scintillation counting. Calculate the total radioactivity loaded into cells from the sum of the counts of each individual efflux time interval plus the counts remaining in the cells at the end of the sampling period.
8. Plot efflux curves as the percent of counts remaining in the cells vs time. Rate constants, if desired, may be determined by fitting efflux curves to exponential functions using a standard statistics computer program.

3.4.2. Bioelectric Characterization of Ion Transport in Epithelial Sheets

The ion transport properties that characterize cystic fibrosis are dependent on polarized epithelial cells. Thus, the advantage of using assays to measure ion transport across epithelial sheets grown on permeable collagen matrix supports (CMS) is that many in vivo properties of an intact epithelium are preserved. The CMS cultures develop tight junctions and form a polarized monolayer with the basolateral surface of the plasma membrane towards the filter and the apical surface toward the culture medium. Ion channels often show specificity in localizing to the apical membrane (e.g., CFTR) or basolateral membrane and this property is retained in CMS cultures *(9,18)*. Application of electrophysiological techniques to CMS cultures provides an opportunity for detailed studies of the role of apical and basolateral membrane channels in transepithelial ion movement. Ussing chambers allow separation of the apical solution from the basolateral solution. Therefore, the movement of ions from one bath to the other must involve either transcellular flow or flow through the paracellular path of the epithelial sheet. The current required to clamp the V_t to zero, the short circuit current (I_{sc}), is monitored continuously except for measurements of the spontaneous V_t across the epithelial sheet at about 5-min intervals. The transepithelial resistance of cultured airway epithelial preparations is dominated by the paracellular path such that changes in apical membrane Cl^- permeability have minimal effect on transepithelial resistance. We describe here methodology that can be used to differentiate between normal and CF airway epithelia, and to assess the ion transport properties of phenotypically "corrected" CF cells following gene transfer of a normal CFTR cDNA.

1. Cultures growing on CMS are transduced with the gene transfer vector on d 3 as described in Section 3.2.
2. On d 4 of culture, the culture medium is changed to a mixture of 50% F12 + 7X and 50% 3T3 conditioned medium. This growth medium formulation helps in the formation of epithelial sheets with tight junctions *(see* Note 11).
3. Measure V_t and R_t beginning on d 3–4 in cultures using an epithelial V/Ω meter (EVOM). The EVOM electrodes should be sterilized before use by soaking in 70% ethanol and equilibrated in growth medium prior to use. All measurements should be made in a tissue culture hood at room temperature. R_t should also be measured across a blank CMS and subtracted from R_t to yield the tissue resistance to be used for calculation of current. When the culture has fully differentiated into an epithelial sheet with tight junctions (d 6–7 in culture), the V_t and R_t measurements will reach plateau values corresponding to a $V_t \cong 10$ mV for normal cells and ~20–30 mV for CF cells with $R_t = 300$–400 $\Omega \cdot cm^2$. If cell lines are used instead of primary cells, the V_t is generally lower, although R_t tends to be similar to that of primary cultures.
4. Mount cultures in Ussing chambers containing bilateral KBR (pH 7.4) and interface to electrometers. During the experiment, the buffer in each chamber is continuously gassed by bubbling with a mixture of 95% O_2/5% CO_2.
5. Place current-voltage clamp in voltage clamp mode to monitor the basal short circuit current (I_{sc}) and begin recording data continuously on chart recorder. Using the pulse circuit modulator, pass a 2–5 mV pulse every 10–15 s. This allows determination of the change in R_t and can be used to calculate V_t using Ohm's law. Alternatively, switch to open circuit momentarily to read V_t directly. Continue monitoring the basal I_{sc} until it stabilizes (5–10 min).

6. Add 10 µL/mL $10^{-2}M$ amiloride to the luminal bath (the solution bathing the apical side of the epithelial sheet away from the filter). Continue to take measurements until the response stabilizes (about 5 min).

7. Drain the luminal bath and replace with a solution of Cl^--free Ringer's solution, pH 7.4, containing $10^{-4}M$ amiloride. When the I_{sc} stabilizes (about 10–30 min), add 1 µL/mL of $10^{-2}M$ forskolin. Continue taking measurements until a steady state level is reached (about 3–5 min).

3.4.3. Interpretation of Transepithelial Bioelectric Data

3.4.3.1. BASAL Na^+ TRANSPORT

The I_{sc} when the epithelial sheets are mounted in KBR solution represents basal Na^+ absorption. This has been shown with both cultured and excised human airway epithelia preparations *(4,19)*. In CF, the I_{sc} is increased two- to threefold over that measured in normal airway epithelia.

3.4.3.2. BASAL Cl^- PERMEABILITY

In normal or corrected airway epithelia, the Na^+-channel blocker amiloride abolishes the basal Na^+ absorption and induces Cl^- secretion at a rate that is proportional, in part, to the apical membrane Cl^- conductance. However, because the apical membrane Cl^- conductance is absent in CF, no significant Cl^- secretion is induced by amiloride. Replacement of the solution in the luminal bath with a Cl^--free solution causes a change in V_t, which reflects, in part, the Cl^- permselectivity of the apical membrane. In CF, this change tends to be small, whereas in normal or corrected CF airway epithelium, the change in V_t with Cl^--free substitutions is markedly increased *(9,20–23)*. The small change that does occur in CF reflects movement of Cl^- through the paracellular path, whereas the change that occurs in normal or corrected tissues reflects both paracellular movement flow and the movement of Cl^- through CFTR Cl^- channels in the apical membrane *(20,21,24)*.

3.4.3.3. cAMP-MEDIATED Cl^- PERMEABILITY

The change in I_{sc} in response to cAMP-agonists is used to assess regulation of the apical membrane Cl^- conductance by CFTR. This response tends to be negligible in CF, whereas it tends to be significantly greater in normal or corrected airway epithelial cells *(9,20–23)*.

4. Notes

1. Growth factor supplements: Insulin and ECGS are essential for proliferation. The other factors have smaller effects on proliferation rates, and may be titrated to meet individual needs.

2. Permeable tissue culture substrates: Commercially prepared substrates made of polycarbonate or polyester, and with various coatings are available from Costar (Cambridge, MA), Millipore (Bedford, MA), and other manufacturers.

3. Research use of human tissues: Research involving human subjects must be reviewed and approved by the local Institutional Review Board (IRB). The University of North Carolina at Chapel Hill IRB has determined that the research use of *excess excised tissues* that were removed for standard clinical indications is authorized by the consent obtained in the IRB approved Consent for Operation Form, and that additional consent is not required.

4. Application to other species: These techniques can be applied, with minor variations, to nasal and airway tissues from mice, dogs, and other laboratory animals *(23,25,26)*.

5. Airway epithelial cell lines: Immortalized airway epithelial cell lines have been generated from primary cultures with simian virus 40 and human papilloma virus genes *(18,27–32)*. These cell lines have increased growth capability and variable retention of differentiated phenotypic properties.

6. Cell yield and viability: Epithelial cell yield increases and viability decreases by increasing protease exposure times to 72 h. The percentage of ciliated cells decreases with longer incubation times.

7. Plating on permeable supports: Epithelial cell attachment to collagen-coated supports can be maximized by plating epithelial cells in a minimal volume of medium, and adjusting the volume of medium in the outer well to maintain a small hydrostatic gradient opposing the cells to the surface of the support. Hydration is maintained by a humidified incubator and by adding medium to adjacent wells in a multiwell culture dish.

8. Sodium butyrate: The effect of sodium butyrate on increasing vector production appears to be by increasing steady-state levels of RNA transcribed from the retroviral LTR sequence *(15)*. We have not detected the induction of replication-competent retroviruses in vector-producing cultures after sodium butyrate treatment. For reasons incompletely understood, there is a vector construct dependency on the extent of induction by sodium butyrate. For example, production of the CFTR-containing LCFSN vector *(9)* is increased 20-fold to 1000-fold, whereas production of vectors containing other inserts is increased only up to about tenfold *(15)*.

9. Temperature of retroviral vector production: A previous report suggests that increased titers can be achieved by incubating packaging cells at 32°C and collecting virus after 48 h *(33)*. We have confirmed this result for many but not all producer cell lines. In addition, at least for CFTR-containing vectors, the combination of lowered temperature and sodium butyrate treatment often results in a synergistic enhancement of retroviral vector production *(15)*.

10. Alternate efflux assay: Another method of performing anion efflux assays is to use an iodide-sensitive electrode. The technique is similar to that described in Section 3.4.1., but instead of using a radioisotope, the cells are loaded with nonradioactive NaI and the rate of loss of iodide from the cells is measured with an iodide-sensitive electrode at 1-min intervals.

11. Differentiation inducing conditions: Polarized morphology, ion transport, and other differentiation functions can be induced by combinations of the following

conditions: plating at high density ($1–5 \times 10^6$ cells/cm^2, depending on cell type); adding a hydrated collagen gel (0.8 mL of 3 mg/mL acid solubilized collagen, 0.2 mL of 5X concentrated F12 medium, and sufficient NaOH to alkalinize to pH 8.0) to the filter followed by incubation at 37°C for 30 min before plating cells; exposing the apical surface of cells to humidified air/CO$_2$ (rather than medium) after attachment; and addition of retinoic acid, $10^{-7}–10^{-6} M$ to the culture medium.

12. Quality of CMS tissue preparations: Cultures that are not confluent or fail to develop a resistance (e.g., cultures that contain a significant proportion of cell types other than epithelial cells) are excluded from study. Cultures that have V_t <–0.5 mV or R_t <50 Ω · cm^2 generally tolerate mounting in Ussing chambers poorly and may have to be excluded. Exclusion criteria should be established before initiating the experiment to prevent bias in data analysis.

References

1. Welsh, M. J. and Smith, A. E. (1993) Molecular mechanisms of CFTR chloride channel dysfunction in cystic fibrosis. *Cell* **73,** 1251–1254.

2. Wilson, J. M. (1993) Vehicles for gene therapy. *Nature* **365,** 691,692.

3. Leigh, M. W., Kylander, J. E., Yankaskas, J. R., and Boucher, R. C. (1995) Cell proliferation in bronchial epithelium and submucosal glands of cystic fibrosis patients. *Am. J. Respir. Cell Mol. Biol.* **12,** 605–612.

4. Boucher, R. C., Stutts, M. J., Knowles, M. R., Cantley, L., and Gatzy, J. T. (1986) Na$^+$ transport in cystic fibrosis respiratory epithelia. Abnormal basal rate and response to adenylate cyclase activation. *J. Clin. Invest.* **78,** 1245–1252.

5. Gabriel, S. E., Clarke, L. L., Boucher, R. C., and Stutts, M. J. (1993) CFTR and outward rectifying chloride channels are distinct proteins with a regulatory relationship. *Nature* **363,** 263–268.

6. Stutts, M. J., Knowles, M. R., Gatzy, J. T., and Boucher, R. C. (1986) Oxygen consumption and ouabain binding sites in cystic fibrosis nasal epithelium. *Ped. Res.* **20,** 1316–1320.

7. Yankaskas, J. R. and Boucher, R. C. (1990) Transformation of airway epithelial cells with persistence of cystic fibrosis or normal ion transport phenotypes. *Methods Enzymol.* **192,** 565–571.

8. Miller, A. D. and Rosman, G. J. (1989) Improved retroviral vectors for gene transfer and expression. *BioTechniques* **7,** 980–990.

9. Olsen, J. C., Johnson, L. G., Stutts, M. J., Sarkadi, B., Yankaskas, J. R., Swanstrom, R., and Boucher, R. C. (1992) Correction of the apical membrane chloride permeability defect in polarized cystic fibrosis airway epithelia following retroviral-mediated gene transfer. *Hum. Gene Ther.* **3,** 253–266.

10. Bayle, J.-Y., Johnson, L. G., George, J. A. S., Boucher, R. C., and Olsen, J. C. (1993) High efficiency gene transfer to primary monkey airway epithelial cells with retrovirus vectors using the GALV receptor. *Hum. Gene Ther.* **4,** 161–170.

11. Engelhardt, J. F., Yankaskas, J. R., and Wilson, J. M. (1992) In vivo retroviral gene transfer into human bronchial epithelia of xenografts. *J. Clin. Invest.* **90,** 2598–2607.

12. Stutts, M. J., Gabriel, S. E., Olsen, J. C., Gatzy, J. T., O'Connell, T. L., Price, E. M., and Boucher, R. C. (1993) Functional consequences of heterologous expression of the cystic fibrosis transmembrane conductance regulator in fibroblasts. *J. Biol. Chem.* **268**, 20,653–20,658.

13. Miller, A. D., and Buttimore, C. (1986) Redesign of retrovirus packaging cell lines to avoid recombination leading to helper virus production. *Mol. Cell. Biol.* **6**, 2895–2902.

14. Miller, A. D., Garcia, J. V., von Suhr, N., Lynch, C. M., Wilson, C., and Eiden, M. V. (1991) Construction and properties of retrovirus packaging cells based on gibbon ape leukemia virus. *J. Virol.* **65**, 2220–2224.

15. Olsen, J. C., and Sechelski, J. (1995) Use of sodium butyrate to enhance production of retroviral vectors expressing CFTR cDNA. *Hum. Gene Ther.* **6**, 1195–1202.

16. Yee, J. K., Miyanohara, A., LaPorte, P., Bouic, K., Burns, J. C., and Friedmann, T. (1994) A general method for the generation of high-titer, pantropic retroviral vectors: highly efficient infection of primary hepatocytes. *Proc. Natl. Acad. Sci. USA* **91**, 9564–9568.

17. Venglarik, C. J., Bridges, R. J., and Frizzell, R. A. (1990) A simple assay for agonist-regulated Cl and K conductances in salt-secreting epithelial cells. *Am. J. Physiol.* **28**, C358–C364.

18. Yankaskas, J. R., Haizlip, J. E., Conrad, M., Koval, D., Lazarowski, E., Paradiso, A. M., Schlegel, R., Sarkadi, B., and Boucher, R. C. (1993) Cystic fibrosis tracheal epithelial cells immortalized by HPV-18 oncogenes retain a well-differentiated phenotype. *Am. J. Physiol.* **264**, C1219–C1230.

19. Willumsen, N. J. and Boucher, R. C. (1991) Transcellular sodium transport in cultured cystic fibrosis human nasal epithelium. *Am. J. Physiol.* **261**, C332–C341.

20. Willumsen, N. J., Davis, C. W., and Boucher, R. C. (1989) Intracellular Cl⁻ activity and cellular Cl⁻ pathways in cultured human airway epithelium. *Am. J. Physiol.* **256**, C1033–C1044.

21. Willumsen, N. J. and Boucher, R. C. (1989) Shunt resistance and ion permeabilities in normal and cystic fibrosis airway epithelium. *Am. J. Physiol.* **256**, C1054–C1063.

22. Johnson, L. G., Olsen, J. C., Sarkadi, B., Moore, K. L., Swanstrom, R., and Boucher, R. C. (1992) Efficiency of gene transfer for restoration of normal airway epithelial function in cystic fibrosis. *Nature Genet.* **2**, 21–25.

23. Clarke, L. L., Grubb, B. R., Gabriel, S. E., Smithies, O., Koller, B. H., and Boucher, R. C. (1992) Defective epithelial chloride transport in a gene-targeted mouse model of cystic fibrosis. *Science* **257**, 1125–1128.

24. Willumsen, N. J., Davis, C. W., and Boucher, R. C. (1989) Cellular Cl⁻ transport in cultured cystic fibrosis airway epithelium. *Am. J. Physiol.* **256**, C1045–C1053.

25. Clarke, L. L., Burns, K. A., Bayle, J.-Y., Boucher, R. C., and Van Scott, M. R. (1992) Sodium- and chloride-conductive pathways in cultured mouse tracheal epithelium. *Am. J. Physiol.* **263**, L519–L525.

26. Van Scott, M. R., Lee, N. P., Yankaskas, J. R., and Boucher, R. C. (1988) Effect of hormones on growth and function of cultured canine tracheal epithelial cells. *Am. J. Physiol.* **24**, C237–C245.

27. Gruenert, D. C., Basbaum, C. B., Welsh, M. J., Li, M., Finkbeiner, W. E., and Nadel, J. A. (1988) Characterization of human tracheal epithelial cells transformed by an origin-defective simian virus 40. *Proc. Natl. Acad. Sci. USA* **85,** 5951–5955.

28. Jetten, A. M., Yankaskas, J. R., Stutts, M. J., Willumsen, N. J., and Boucher, R. C. (1989) Persistence of abnormal chloride conductance regulation in transformed cystic fibrosis airway epithelia. *Science* **244,** 1472–1475.

29. Scholte, R. J., Kansen, M., Hoogeveen, A. T., Willemse, R., Rhim, J. S., van der Kamp, A. W. M., and Bijman, J. (1989) Immortalization of nasal polyp epithelial cells from cystic fibrosis patients. *Exp. Cell Res.* **182,** 559–571.

30. Buchanan, J. A., Yeger, H., Tabcharani, J. A., Jensen, T. J., Auerbach, W., Hanrahan, J. W., Riordan, J. R., and Buchwald, M. (1990) Transformed sweat gland and nasal epithelial cell lines from control and cystic fibrosis individuals. *J. Cell Sci.* **95,** 109–123.

31. Jefferson, D. M., Valentich, J. D., Marini, F. C., Grubman, S. A., Iannuzzi, M. C., Dorkin, H. L., Li, M., Klinger, K. W., and Welsh, M. J. (1990) Expression of normal and cystic fibrosis phenotypes by continuous airway epithelial cell lines. *Am. J. Physiol.* **259,** L496–L505.

32. Cozens, A. L., Yezzi, M. J., Kunzelmann, K., Ohrui, T., Chin, L., Eng, K., Finkbeiner, W. E., Widdicombe, J. H., and Gruenert, D. C. (1994) CFTR expression and chloride excretion in polarized immortal human bronchial epithelial cells. *Am. J. Respir. Cell Mol. Biol.* **10,** 38–47.

33. Kotani, H., Newton, P. B., III, Zhang, S., Chiang, Y. L., Otto, E., Weaver, L., Blaese, R. M., Anderson, W. F., and McGarrity, G. J. (1994) Improved methods of retroviral vector transduction and production for gene therapy. *Hum. Gene Ther.* **5,** 19–28.

11

Methods for Adenovirus-Mediated Gene Transfer to Airway Epithelium

John F. Engelhardt

1. Introduction

Recombinant adenoviral vectors have proven to be extremely efficient tools for transferring genes into multiple organ systems including the lung *(1–5)*, liver *(6–10)*, muscle *(11,12)*, joint *(13)*, vasculature *(14,15)*, and central nervous system *(16–18)*. The lung presents unique advantages as a target organ for the evaluation of these vectors as tools for in vivo gene therapy owing to the accessibility of target cells by direct instillation or inhalation of recombinant virus in the airway. Multiple therapeutic applications of gene therapy to the lung include both inherited disorders such as cystic fibrosis (CF) and α_1-antitrypsin deficiency, as well as acquired disorders such as bronchitis, asthma, emphysema, and respiratory malignancies. The most widely studied application to date has involved the analysis of recombinant adenoviruses for gene therapy of CF lung disease *(1–5)*. To this end, multiple phase I clinical trails are now underway evaluating the safety of recombinant adenoviral vectors for gene therapy of cystic fibrosis lung disease *(19)*. This clinical application of these vectors in CF lung disease presents the largest comprehensive effort of in vivo gene therapy to date. Such a substantial effort has offered the advantage of multiple preclinical studies evaluating delivery of adenoviral vectors to the lung in numerous animal models such as the cotton rat *(4,5,20)*, human bronchial xenografts *(1)*, mouse *(21)*, and nonhuman primates *(2,3,22,23)*.

Cystic fibrosis is the most common autosomal recessive disease in the Caucasian population, affecting 1 in 2500 births each year *(24)*. Although multiple organs are affected in this disease, the most severe and life-threatening pathology occurs in the lung and results in production of abnormally viscous mucus, poor mucocilliary clearance, chronic bacterial infections, bronchiectasis, and

From: *Methods in Molecular Medicine, Gene Therapy Protocols*
Edited by: P. Robbins Humana Press Inc., Totowa, NJ

eventually pulmonary failure and death. The cloning of the gene defective in CF (CFTR, the cystic fibrosis transmembrane conductance regulator) has allowed for the identification of the cellular defect and has made possible the application of gene replacement as a potential therapy for lung disease *(25–27)*. The cellular targets for gene therapy of CF lung disease have traditionally been thought to reside in the small airways, as inferred by the fact that this region is most severely affected *(24)*. Recent studies localizing CFTR mRNA and protein have demonstrated that multiple cellular targets throughout the lung exist, including a subpopulation of cells in the submucosal glands, bronchioles, and alveolar regions *(28a,28b)*. The pathophysiologic significance of each of these cellular and anatomical target regions based on expression studies is unknown. However, current therapeutic approaches delivering recombinant virus directly to the airway will most likely exclude gene transfer to submucosal gland regions.

The airways of the lung can be grossly divided into two regions, the conducting and respiratory epithelium. The cell types that compose the conducting airway epithelium within the cartilaginous bronchi and large bronchioles include a heterogeneous combination of cell types including basal, goblet, intermediate, and ciliated cells *(29)*. Although it is generally accepted that both goblet and basal cells have the capacity for self renewal, the pleuripotent characteristics of these cell types to give rise to ciliated and intermediate cells is currently debated *(30–32)*. More distal regions of the conducting airway epithelium include the smaller bronchioles that are composed of at least two cell types, Clara and ciliated cells *(33)*. Studies localizing CFTR to a subset of nonciliated cells in this region have suggested that the target cell in the distal conducting airways may in fact be a subset of Clara cells *(28a)*. The progenitor cell of this region has traditionally been thought to be the Clara cell *(33)*. The most distal regions of the lung that are composed of the respiratory epithelium may also be an important target for gene therapy of CF as suggested by recent studies localizing CFTR mRNA and protein *(28a)*. This region is composed of type I and II alveolar cells as well as alveolar macrophages *(33)*. The progenitor cell of this region is generally accepted to be type II alveolar cells *(33)*. Strategies for prolonged gene therapy to the lung in CF will likely need to target progenitor cells in the airways that give rise to CFTR-expressing cellular targets. Because the turnover of airway epithelial cells in the airway is relatively long in the nondisease state *(31)*, alternative efficient strategies targeting differentiated CFTR-expressing cells directly, may also provide substantial lengths of correction.

Current recombinant adenoviral constructs have been based on the Ad5 and Ad2 serotypes in which transgenes are inserted into the E1 deleted region. Deletion of E1 sequences serves two functions in the construction of recombinant adenoviral vectors, including the crippling of adenoviral replication and the creation of space for transgene insertions. Because of the limited packaging size of adenoviral DNA *(34)*, the application of recombinant adenoviral vectors for gene therapy of CF in which the CFTR cDNA is 4.7 kb, has created the need for further deletion of within non-E1 regions of the adenovirus. Two approaches including the deletion of E3 sequences or E4 sequences not needed for replication of the virus have been used to circumvent problems associated with this large cDNA insert.

Multiple animal models including the cotton rat *(4,5,20,23)*, mouse, human bronchial xenografts *(1)*, and nonhuman primates *(2,3,23)* have been used for evaluating the efficiency of recombinant adenoviral gene transfer to the lung epithelium. Each animal model possesses several advantages in the analysis of host–vector interactions and efficiency of gene transfer. The most commonly used model includes the cotton rat, which has been shown to be permissive for adenoviral infection and provides a pathophysiologically relevant correlation to human adenoviral infections in the lung *(35)*. In contrast, the mouse, traditionally thought to be less permissive for adenoviral infection, provides the added advantage of genetically defined mouse strains for the evaluation of host–vector inflammatory responses in the generation of more therapeutic viral vectors with increased persistence and decreased host inflammatory responses *(21,36)*. The human bronchial xenograft, although immune incompetent with respect to T-cells, provides the ideal system for the analysis of cellular interactions between human epithelium and these vectors. This system has been useful in addressing the capacity of these vectors to replicate and express viral genes within the relevant target human airway epithelium *(1)*. Lastly, nonhuman primates have proven to be useful animals in the safety and efficacy evaluation of recombinant adenoviral vectors within an animal model that is evolutionarily close to humans. In addition, this model has allowed for the evaluation of alternative delivery systems (i.e., delivery to a subsegment of the lung via bronchoscopy) that are not feasible in rodent models *(2)*.

Several delivery methods have been used in the analyses of recombinant adenoviral vectors in animal models targeting airway epithelium, including: transtracheal instillation of virus by midline incision *(4,5,20,23)*, selective administration of virus to subsegments of the lung by bronchoscopy *(2)*, and nasal administration of virus *(37,38)*. Analysis of in vivo delivery of these vectors to the airways of immune competent animal models has demonstrated efficient recombinant adenovirus-mediated gene transfer, which is transient (<21 d) and associated with mononuclear-predominant inflammatory infiltrates *(20,21)*. Alternatively, immune incompetent (T-cell deficient athymic mice) animal models, including human bronchial xenografts grafted into nu/nu mice and nu/nu mouse lung, have demonstrated that extended persistence of transgene expression (>100 d) can be achieved in the absence of inflammatory responses *(21)*. These studies have set the stage for the improvement of these vectors for gene therapy applications by alteration of the adenoviral genomic components that are responsible for eliciting host cellular immune responses and the decline of transgene expressing cell in vivo *(20,21)*. Hence, although the current applications of these vectors for gene therapy will require frequent repetitive doses, the future construction of second generation vectors has provided a renewed enthusiasm for the use of these vectors with prolonged transgene expression and minimal host inflammatory responses *(20,21)*.

Critical to the evaluation of recombinant in vivo models of gene transfer are sensitive methods for the analysis of transgene expression. Hence, this review will also discuss the applications and methodologies of histochemical, immunocytochemical, and *in situ* hybridization localization techniques for the analysis of transgene-expressed proteins and mRNA *(1,2)*. Such methodologies provide the foundation for the therapeutic assessment of efficacious gene transfer to the lung.

2. Materials

2.1. Solutions

1. Glycerol-BSA viral storage buffer: 10 mM Tris-HCl, pH 8.0, 100 mM NaCl, 0.1% BSA, 50% glycerol. Filter sterilize through a 0.2-μm filter and store at −20°C.
2. Heavy CsCl: Add 42.23 g CsCl to 57.8 mL 10 mM Tris-HCl, pH 8.0 (final density of 1.45 g/mL).
3. Light CsCl: Add 22.39 g CsCl to 77.6 mL 10 mM Tris-HCl, pH 8.0 (final density of 1.20 g/mL).
4. X-gal staining solution: 1 mg/mL X-gal (5-bromo-4-chloro-3-indolyl-β-D-galacto-pyranoside), 5 mM K$_3$Fe(CN)$_6$, 5 mM K$_4$Fe(CN)$_6$, 1 mM MgCl$_2$, in PBS, pH 7.4.
5. DepC treatment of water and plastic wear: 1 mL depC is mixed with 1 L of H$_2$O and allowed to inactivate RNase for 20 h followed by autoclaving for 1 h.
6. Proteinase-K *in situ* solution: 50 mM Tris-HCl, pH 8.0, 50 mM EDTA, 10 μg/mL proteinase-K.
7. *In situ* prehybridization solution: 10 mM Tris-HCl, pH 8.0, 50% formamide, 2.5X Denhardts, 0.6M NaCl, 1 mM EDTA, 0.1% SDS, 500 μg/mL *Escherichia coli* tRNA, and 10 mM DTT.
8. *In situ* RNase A pretreatment buffer: 200 μg/mL RNase A in 10 mM Tris-HCl, pH 8.0, 150 mM NaCl, 1 mM EDTA.
9. *In situ* hybridization buffer: 1 × 10^7 cpm/mL of sense or antisense radiolabeled probe in 10 mM Tris-HCl, pH 8.0, 50% formamide, 2.5X Denhardts, 25% Dextran sulfate, 0.6M NaCl, 1 mM EDTA, 0.1% SDS, 500 μg/mL *E. coli* tRNA, and 10 mM DTT.
10. *In situ* RNase A posthybridization wash buffer: 20 μg/mL RNase A in 10 mM Tris-HCl, pH 8.0, 100 mM NaCl, 1 mM EDTA.

2.2. Antibodies

1. Goat anti-Ad3-FITC antibody: Chemicon (El Segundo, CA) #1056.
2. Rabbit anti-β-galactosidase antibody: 5'→3' Inc. (West Chester, PA) #5307-063100.
3. Goat antirabbit-FITC antibody: Boehringer Mannheim (Indianapolis, IN) #100825.
4. Citifluor antifadent: Citiflour (London, UK) #AF1.

3. Methods

3.1. General Propagation and Purification of Adenovirus

The propagation of recombinant adenoviral vectors, in which transgenes are inserted into the E1 deleted region of the adenoviral genome, are performed in the complementing 293 cell line, which provides deleted E1 functions *in trans* by stably integrated E1a and E1b viral genes within the cellular genome. Because the purity and functional integrity of recombinant viral preparation are extremely crucial for applications of in vivo gene transfer, this review will briefly summarize methods used for the propagation and analysis of recombinant adenoviral stocks for application to the lung.

1. Seed 40 × 150 mm tissue culture dished with 293 cells in Dulbecco's Modified Eagle's Medium (DMEM) containing 10% fetal calf serum (FCS) and 1% penicillin/streptomycin (PS).
2. Eighty percent confluent, 150-mm dishes of 293 cells are infected with purified stocks of virus at an MOI = 10 in DMEM/1%PS in the absence of FCS for 2 h, total volume of 10 mL. Since, on average, an 80% confluent, 150-mm dish of 293 cell consists of 5×10^7 cells, we routinely infect with 5×10^8 PFU/plate (*see* Note 1).
3. Two hours postinfection, 10 mL of 20% FCS/DMEM/1%PS are added to each plate and the infection is allowed to progress for 30–48 h. Plates should be considered ready to harvest when infected cells can be easily dislodged by tapping (*see* Note 2).
4. Infected cell suspensions are harvested and combined in 1000-mL centrifuge bottles, cooled to 4°C on ice, and pelleted by centrifugation at 3500g in a Beckman J6 centrifuge for 25 min at 4°C.
5. Supernatants are discarded and cell pellets resuspended in 20 mL of 10 mM Tris-HCl, pH 8.0, for hypotonic lysis followed by three rounds of freeze thawing in an ethanol dry ice and 37°C baths. Care should be taken to avoid extended periods at 37°C.
6. Crude lysates are then pelleted to remove cellular debris by centrifugation at 1500g for 25 min in a table-top centrifuge at 4°C.
7. The supernatants that contain crude viral lysates are carefully removed so as not to disturb the loose cellular pellet. To increase yields, the cellular pellet is resuspended in an additional 6 mL of cold 10 mM Tris-HCl, pH 8.0, and the centrifugation is repeated. At no time should the cellular/viral suspensions be vortexed, as this results in shearing of genomic DNA and complications in the CsCl purification.

8. Combined viral supernatants (18 mL) are loaded onto a double-stack CsCl step gradient consisting of a 10-mL heavy solution (solution 2) and a light (solution 3) CsCl cushion and centrifuged at 50,000g for 2 h in a Beckman SW28 rotor at 5°C.

9. The lower band of intact virus is removed, combined with an equal volume of 10 mM Tris-HCl, pH 8.0, loaded onto a second step gradient consisting of a 4-mL heavy solution (solution 2) and a light solution (solution 3) CsCl cushion, and centrifugated overnight for 16–18 h at 75,000g in an SW41 rotor at 5°C.

10. The lower band of virus is removed for preparation of desalting. Typical preparations starting with 40 150-mm plates of 293 cells should end with approx 0.5 mL of concentrated CsCl purified virus.

3.2. Desalting of Concentrated Viral Stocks for In Vivo Use

Desalting of concentrated viral stocks for preparation of in vivo delivery is a critical step in which the most concentrated stocks (>2 × 10^{13} particles/mL) may precipitate depending on the method used. Precipitation of adenovirus will drastically lower the functional titer several logs. We have found that traditional methods of dialysis into PBS or buffered saline solutions increases the likelihood of precipitation of high titer stocks and, hence, we have adopted a method of gel-filtration desalting that is more rapid and avoids problems of variable precipitation encountered with dialysis.

1. 10-mL gel-filtration columns are constructed using typical 10-mL laboratory plastic pipets plugged with sterile glass wool and fitted with tubing to regulate flow. These columns are filled with a 50:50 slurry of autoclaved Sephadex G50 (medium grade) hydrated in PBS.

2. 0.5 mL of concentrated CsCl-banded virus is loaded onto gel-filtration columns, eluted in PBS, and the effluent virus (which is clearly visible as it migrates through the column as an opaque band) is collected in 250-µL aliquots.

3. The fractions composing the predominant visual peak are assessed for concentration of virus particles by OD$_{260}$ and the most concentrated fractions combined.

4. Typical recoveries by this purification scheme are 70–90% with less than a twofold dilution from the original sample.

Once virus has been purified, it should be used immediately for in vivo gene transfer experiments. A small sample should be diluted 1:5 with glycerol-BSA viral storage buffer (solution 1) and stored at –20°C for titering on 293 cells. Storage by this method for up to several weeks does not result in any detectable loss of viral titer.

3.3. Titering of Viral Stocks by Gene Expression

Crucial to the interpretation of in vivo gene transfer efficiency are accurate methods for titering of viral stocks for experimentation. Such titering should assess the relative fraction of virus capable of expressing transgene in reference to the total number of viral particles present in the sample as detected by OD_{260} (where an OD_{260} of 1 is equal to 10^{12} particles). The resultant ratio (conc. total particles)/(conc. functional particles), gives the necessary information for assessing the infectability of stocks used. Three methods of titering have traditionally been used for assessing the infectability of recombinant viral stocks including: PFU (plaque forming units), LFU (*lacZ* forming units), and FFU (fluorescent foci forming units). Since the readout of the PFU assay typically takes 7–9 d, we have attempted to develop assays based on the presence of viral protein or transgene expression in 293 indicator cells that can give titers within 20 h.

1. Subconfluent monolayers of 293 cells grown in 60-mm, six-well tissue culture dishes are infected with serial dilution of viral stocks made in DMEM/1%PS (ranging from 10^{-4}–10^{-9}).
2. 1 mL of each dilution is placed in each well for 2 h.
3. Add 100 µL FCS to each well and incubate for an additional 18 h. Since the replication time of E1-deleted recombinant virus is approx 24 h, it is critical that the timing of infections not exceed 20 h (*see* Note 3).
4. For LFU assays, media from each well are aspirated and 0.5% glutaraldehyde in PBS are added gently to each well for 10 min.
5. Cells are then washed two times for 15 min in PBS containing 1 mM MgCl$_2$.
6. *LacZ* transgene expression is then detected in the presence of X-gal staining solution (solution 4) at 37°C for 6–10 h.
7. Five 20X fields are quantitated for the total number of *lacZ* expressing cells and the total number of *lacZ* expressing cells in each well determined by the fractional area of a 20X field. Typically, dilutions that give 30–50 cells per field are chosen for quantification. Comparison of viral titers performed by LFU to that obtained by PFU assays reveals identical results when infections are performed as described in Section 3.3. prior to agar overlaying.

An alternatively useful method of titering viral stocks by FFU is based on similar principles as described above with the exception of detecting either transgene expression or viral protein expression using immunofluorescent techniques.

1. Subconfluent monolayers of 293 cells grown in 24-well tissue culture dishes are infected with serial dilution of viral stocks made in DMEM/1%PS (ranging from 10^{-4}–10^{-9}).
2. 100 µL of each dilution is placed in each well for 2 h.
3. Add 10 µL FCS to each well and incubate for an additional 18 h.
4. Following infection, the media is aspirated and cell monolayers are fixed in –20°C methanol for 10 min followed by air drying.
5. Methanol-fixed cells are blocked in 20% goat serum/PBS (0.45-µm filtered) for 30 min followed by incubation in a 1:10 dilution of FITC-labeled goat anti-Ad3 antibody in 1.5%GS/PBS for 90 min.

6. Cells are washed three times in 1.5%GS/PBS and covered with 100 μL Citifluor antifadent (University of Kent at Canterbury, England).
7. Fluorescent cells are visualized using an inverted fluorescent microscope and quantitated as described in Section 3.3., step 1 for the LFU assay (*see* Note 4).

3.4. In Vivo Delivery of Recombinant Viruses to the Lung

Multiple model systems have been used to study recombinant adenoviral gene delivery to the lung, including transtracheal instillation, selective bronchoscopy of lung subsegments followed by instillation of virus, and nasal inhalation. We will review the most widely used method of transtracheal administration as applied to small rodent animal models such as the mouse and cotton rat.

1. 80–120 g cotton rats are anesthetized with isoflourane.
2. The neck is cleaned with an isopropyl alcohol swab and a 1-cm midline incision is made with a sharp scalpel.
3. The trachea is exposed by blunt dissection and a small, 3-mm incision is made through the muscle surrounding the trachea.
4. $1–5 \times 10^{10}$ infectious particles (as measured by PFU, LFU, or FFU) in a total volume of 100–150 μL in PBS is instilled through a tuberculin syringe followed by 300 μL of air.
5. The incision is closed with two staples and the animals are returned to their cages.

Similar procedures can be performed on mice by reducing the total dose and volume of virus according to the total weight (kg) of the animal. Typically a 25-g mouse tolerates a dose of 2×10^9 PFU of recombinant virus instilled in a total volume of 25–35 μL.

3.5. Harvesting of Lungs for Histologic Analysis

The lungs from animals infected with E1-deleted recombinant *lacZ* adenovirus typically express highest levels of transgene activity between 3 and 7 d. Several methods of tissue preparation have been employed in an attempt to analyze multiple experimental endpoints, including histopathology, using formalin inflation fixed lungs; localization of *lacZ* transgene activity, by *in situ* histochemical staining of lungs by inflation; and multiple histologic endpoints such as immunocytochemistry, histochemistry, and *in situ* hybridization, in lungs inflated with OCT for frozen sectioning. In this review we will summarize the most flexible of these techniques used for frozen sectioning.

1. Animals are euthanized by an overdose of 200 mg/kg pentobarbital.
2. The thorax is opened and the proximal end of the trachea is exposed and canulated with an 18-gage angiocath 3-mL syringe filled with 37°C 1:1 mixture of OCT embedding medium in PBS. We have adopted this method of *in situ* inflation to avoid accidental nicking of the lungs upon removal, which will result in insufficient inflation pressures.

3. Gentle pressure is applied until the lungs are visually inflated within the thorax. Typically, inflation of a cotton rat lung requires 2 mL of OCT.
4. Once inflated, the heart–lung cassette is removed and quickly cooled in ice-cold PBS for 10 min.
5. The hardened lung cassette is removed and trimmed of nonlung tissue on an ice-cooled surface.
6. The lung is cut into large (approx 1-cm) wedges and placed in plastic embedding blocks filled with 100% OCT embedding medium such that the cut face is in contact with the bottom of the block.
7. Blocks are frozen in a pulverized dry ice/isopentane slurry. Since some air may be retained within the lung tissue, care should be taken to manipulate tissue samples during freezing to retain placement on the bottom of the block.
8. 6-μm frozen sections are cut using a cryostat and processed for multiple histologic analyses such as immunocytochemistry, histochemistry, and *in situ* hybridization.

Similar methods of lung inflation can be used to retain better morphology, which is useful in histopathologic evaluation by inflation with buffered formalin followed by embedding in paraffin for sectioning. Alternatively, lungs can also be stained *in situ* with X-gal by inflation fixation in 0.5% glutaraldehyde/PBS for 10 min, followed by two sequential 15-min lavages with 1 m*M* MgCl/PBS and staining in X-gal staining solution for 1 h at 37°C. Following staining in X-gal, lungs should be washed with PBS twice by lavage, instilled with buffered formalin/1% glutaraldehyde, and postfixed overnight before processing in paraffin for sectioning.

3.6. Histochemical Detection of LacZ Transgene Activity

1. 6-μm frozen sections are fixed in 0.5% glutaraldehyde in PBS for 10 min. Care should be taken to avoid repeated freeze thawing of freshly cut sections before processing for histochemical staining. Hence, slides are precooled and sections only thawed once for placement onto slides. Once sections are placed on slides they should be kept within the cryostat (–18°C) until staining and not air dried. Alternatively, slides can be stored at –80°C for several weeks without substantial loss of β-galactosidase activity.
2. Sections are washed twice for 15 min with 1 m*M* MgCl$_2$/PBS, placed in X-gal staining solution (solution 4) for 4–6 h, followed by washing two times in PBS and postfixed in buffered formalin containing 1% glutaraldehyde for 15 min (*see* Note 5).
3. Sections are counterstained briefly in hematoxylin (without blueing). Alternatively, sections stained in neutral red also provide good contrast of blue X-gal precipitate.

3.7. Immunocytochemical Detection of LacZ Transgene Activity

1. Frozen sections (6-μm) are postfixed in –20°C methanol for 10 min followed by air drying.
2. Sections are blocked with (0.45-μm filtered) 20% goat-serum in PBS for 30 min.

3. Blocking solution is replaced with 60 μg/mL of rabbit anti-β-galactosidase (5'→3') in the presence of 1.5% goat serum/PBS for 90 min.
4. Sections are washed three times for 8 min in 1.5% goat serum/PBS.
5. Sections are incubated with 5 μg/mL of a goat antirabbit-FITC antibody in 1.5% goat serum/PBS for 30 min.
6. Sections are washed three times for 8 min in 1.5% goat serum/PBS.
7. Coverslip sections in antifadent (Citifluor) and visualize by fluorescent microscopy.

3.8. In Situ *Hybridization Detection* of *Transgene-Expressed mRNA*

In situ hybridization of transgene-expressed mRNA has proven to be an extremely powerful tool in the assessment of gene transfer efficiencies from non-*lacZ* recombinant vectors. Because analysis of therapeutic transgene expression is most often assessed within a setting of endogenous gene expression, we have developed two approaches to circumvent this problem: the use of probe sequences from the transgene that are not conserved across species, and transgene-specific probes based on unique sequences inserted in the 3' untranslated region of the expressed transgene mRNA. These two methods have been extensively used in several animal models analyzing recombinant adenoviral expression of CFTR in the lung *(2,4)*.

1. Frozen sections (6-μm) are mounted on positively charged slides (Probe-On Plus, Fisher, Pittsburgh, PA) and fixed with 4% paraformaldehyde in phosphate-buffered saline (PBS) for 3 h. Care should be taken to keep sections at −18°C while sectioning and to fix sections as soon as possible.
2. Following fixation, sections are dehydrated through graded concentrations of ethanol consisting of mixtures of depC-treated water and ethanol at 30, 50, 70, 95, and 100%. After this fixation step, care should be taken to use RNase-free precautions for all of the subsequent steps *(see* Note 6).
3. Sections are then desiccated overnight under vacuum and stored at −20°C until *in situ* analysis is performed.
4. Before prehybridization, sections are treated with 10 μg/mL proteinase-K (solution 6) for 30 min at 30°C, rinsed twice in 0.2X SSC for 30 s each and fixed in 4% paraformaldehyde/PBS for 20 min.
5. Following fixation to inactivate proteinase-K, sections are rinsed twice for 4 min in 0.1M triethanolamine [TEA] (pH 8.0), incubated in 0.25% acetic anhydride/0.1M TEA (pH 8.0) for 10 min at room temperature (RT), rinsed in 0.2X SSC twice for 2 min, and followed by dehydration in graded concentrations of ethanol as described in Section 3.8., step 2. Sections are again dried under vacuum for 3 h to overnight.
6. Sections are submerged in prehybridization buffer (solution 8) for 4 h at 54°C. Alternatively, RNase control sections are treated with 200 μg/mL RNase A pretreatment buffer (solution 7) for 1 h at 37°C followed by fixation in 4% paraformaldehyde/PBS for 20 min to inactivate RNase. Following fixation, slides are

    rinsed twice for 2 min in 0.2X SSC before the prehybridization step (RNase-pretreated slides serve as a negative control for mRNA specific hybridization).

7. Slides are removed from the prehybridization solution and coverslipped with 25 µL of hybridization buffer (solution 9) containing 1×10^7 cpm/mL ^{35}S antisense or sense probes. The edge of each coverslip is then sealed with DPX mounting media. Slides are incubated flat in a 54°C oven for 16–18 h. Probes were synthesized with the Promega (Madison, WI) in vitro transcription system using 0.25 mCi of ^{35}S UTP and ^{35}S CTP as the sole source of these nucleotides for transcription from the T7 and SP6 RNA polymerase promoters. A detailed method of in vitro transcription reaction is outlined in Section 3.9.

8. Following hybridization, slides are washed in 4X SSC for 20 min at room temperature (four 5-min changes), treated with RNase (20 µg/mL) posthybridization wash buffer (solution 10) for 30 min at 37°C, rinsed in 2X SSC/1 mM DTT at room temperature for 20 min (four 5-min changes), and finally washed for three 15-min changes of 0.5X SSC/1 mM DTT at 54°C.

9. Slides are dehydrated through graded concentrations of ethanol (30% ethanol/0.1X SSC/1 mM DTT; 70% ethanol/0.1X SSC/1 mM DTT; 95% ethanol, 2X 100% ethanol) and air dried prior to dipping in undiluted photoemulsion (Kodak, Rochester, NY).

10. Slides were developed at 1 and 2 wk and analyzed by bright- and dark-field microscopy.

3.9. Generation of In Situ-Radiolabeled Probes

The generation of radiolabeled RNA probes with high specific activity is critical to the success of sensitive *in situ* mRNA detection protocols. To this end, we have developed a technique utilizing PCR-generated template DNA for in vitro transcription reactions. Using this methodology, highly specific probes can be generated with 50 ng of template DNA. Additionally, this methodology allows for the flexible generation of multiple probes to different portions of the cDNA without the need for subcloning into riboprobe plasmids. Ideally, PCR templates should be 500–600 bp in length. This probe length allows for the greatest sensitivity without encountering barriers of probe penetration. Typically, we will generate our PCR riboprobe templates by using cDNA template primers in which SP6 and T7 RNA polymerase binding sites have been added to the 5' end of the oligonucleotide (Fig. 1). Additionally, we have incorporated a not1 cloning site into our primers for use in generating probes for which plasmid templates are not readily available and genomic DNA is used as template. These additional sequences also assure adequate secondary structure of PCR fragment DNA for RNA polymerase binding by avoiding terminal DNA binding sites that may be less favorable for transcription initiation. The PCR-amplified template DNA is purified by low melting point agarose gel electrophoresis followed by organic extraction in 2X phenol, 1X phenol:CHCl$_3$ once, and 2X CHCl$_3$, followed by ethanol precipitation.

Fig. 1. The PCR primer sequences for generation of template DNA for *in situ* riboprobes. Additional sequences homologous to the cDNA of interest are added to the 3'-end of primer sequences shown. Typically, these cDNA homologous sequences are 24 bp long with a 50% GC content. Such primers will have a melting temperature of 72°C and provide minimal background in PCR reactions with annealing temperatures of 68°C.

1. 0.25 mCi of both $S^{35}CTP$ and $S^{35}UTP$ are combined into a 0.5-mL Eppendorf tube, frozen on dry ice, and lyophilized within a Speed-vac.
2. To the radioactive pellets, the following components of the Promega in vitro transcription kit are added: 4 µL of 5X buffer, 2 µL 100 mM DTT, 1 µL of ATP, 1 µL of GTP, 1 µL of template DNA (50–100 ng of PCR template), 0.5 µL RNasin, 9.5 µL depC H_2O, and 1 µL of T7 or SP6 RNA polymerase.
3. Reactions are incubated for 1 h at 37°C, followed by the addition of 0.5 µL RNasin, 1 µL RQ1 DNase, and incubation for 15 min at 37°C.
4. 80 µL of depC H_2O are added and the resultant mixture extracted with 100 µL of phenol:chloroform (1:1) and chloroform, followed by the addition of 25 µg *E. coli* tRNA and precipitation twice with ammonium acetate (final concentration 0.7M) and 2.5 vol of –20°C ethanol to remove unincorporated nucleotides.
5. Probe pellets are resuspended in 10 mM Tris-HCl, pH 8.0, 10 mM DDT, 1 mM ETDA, 0.3% SDS, and frozen on dry ice in 10-µL aliquots. Probes can be stored at –134°C for 1–2 wk without substantial increases in background. However, best results are usually obtained with fresh probe. The specific activity of probes generated by this methodology is generally $1–2 \times 10^7$ cpm/ng template DNA.

4. Notes

1. We have found that increased yields of recombinant adenovirus are obtained from infection with purified stocks rather than crude lysates owing to nonspecific cytopathic effects caused by cell debris within the crude lysates.
2. The time necessary to achieve cytopathic effect (CPE) varies for different recombinant vectors. Hence, plates should be monitored closely following infection within the 30–48 h window to determine the optimal time for harvesting based on

generation of CPE. Appropriate harvesting based on optimal CPE will affect yields in the production of virus.

3. It is important to note that the length of viral infection will significantly effect the accuracy of LFU and FFU titering if infections are longer than 21 h. This results from the amplification of viral replication within 293 cells and artifactual elevation of the apparent titer.

4. In all fluorescent antibody assays, the addition of antifadeñt is critical to avoid photobleaching that will make quantification and photography difficult.

5. Postfixation in formalin/1% glutaraldehyde helps to minimize leaching of X-gal precipitate in organics used for dehydration of tissue sections before coverslipping in xylene-soluble permount.

6. Care should be taken to avoid RNase contamination during the *in situ* hybridization procedure. To this end, all solutions are made with depC-treated water and dedicated reagents. Most reagents cannot be treated directly with depC. Hence all solutions should be made in depC-treated glassware or RNase-free plasticware with depC-treated autoclaved H_2O. When it is necessary to pH an RNase free solution, this should be performed by aliquoting a small amount into a secondary vessel to avoid direct contact of contaminated electrodes with *in situ* solutions. Gloves should be worn at all times. In addition, all glass wear is baked at 250°C for 20 h and plasticware is treated by submerging in water containing depC for 16–20 h, followed by autoclaving to inactivate depC.

Acknowledgments

I gratefully acknowledge the support and advice of James Wilson in the preparation of this review and the research that has gone into the development of these technologies. Much of the technology cited in this review is the result of research supported by the NIDDK grant ROI DK47967 (J.F.E.).

References

1. Engelhardt, J. F., Yang, Y., Stratford-Perricaudet, L. D., Allen, E. D., Kozarsky, K., Perricaudet, M., Yankaskas, J. R., and Wilson, J. M. (1993) Direct gene transfer of human CFTR into human bronchial epithelia of xenografts with E1 deleted adenoviruses. *Nature Genet.* **4,** 27–34.

2. Engelhardt, J. F., Simon, R. H., Yang, Y., Zepeda, M., Weber-Pendleton, S., Doranz, B., Grossman, M., and Wilson, J. M. (1993) Adenovirus-Mediated transfer of the CFTR gene to lung of nonhuman primates: biological efficacy study. *Hum. Gene Ther.* **4,** 759–769.

3. Bout, A., Perricaudet, M., Baskin, G., Imler, J.-L., Scholte, B. J., Pavirani, A., and Valerio, D. (1994) Lung gene therapy: *in vivo* adenovirus-mediated gene transfer to Rhesus monkey airway epithelium. *Hum. Gene Ther.* **5,** 3–10.

4. Rosenfeld, M. A., Yoshimura, K., Trapnell, B. C., Yoneyama, K., Rosenthal, E. R., Daleman, W., Fukayama, M., Bargon, J., Stier, L. E., Stratford-Perricaudet, L., Perricaudet, M., Guggino, W. B., Pavirani, A., Lecocq, J.-P., and Crystal, R. G. (1992) In vivo transfer of the human cystic fibrosis transmembrane conductance regulator gene to the airway epithelium. *Cell* **68,** 143–155.

5. Mastrangeli, A., Danel, C., Rosenfeld, M. A., Stratford-Perricaudet, L., Perricaudet, M., Pavirani, A., Lecocq, J. P., and Crystal, R. G. (1993) Diversity of airway epithelial cell targets for *in vivo* recombinant adenovirus-mediated gene transfer. *J. Clin. Invest.* **91,** 225–234.

6. Yang, Y., Raper, S. E., Cohn, J. A., Engelhardt, J. F., and Wilson, J. M. (1993) An approach for treating the hepatobiliary disease of cystic fibrosis by somatic gene transfer. *Proc. Natl. Acad. Sci. USA* **90,** 4601–4605.

7. Ishibashi, S., Brown, M. S., Goldstein, J. L., Gerard, R. D., Hammer, R. E., and Herz, J. (1993) Hypercholesterolemia in low density lipoprotein receptor knockout mice and its reversal by adenovirus-mediated gene delivery. *J. Clin. Invest.* **92,** 883–893.

8. Li, Q., Kay, M. A., Finegold, M., Stratford-Perricaudet, L. D., and Woo, S. L. (1993) Assessment of recombinant adenoviral vectors for hepatic gene therapy. *Hum. Gene Ther.* **4,** 403–409.

9. Kozarsky, K. F., McKinley, Dr., Austin, L. L., Raper, S. E., Stratford-Perricaudet, L., and Wilson, J. M. (1994) In vivo correction of LDL receptor deficiency in the Watanabe heritable hyperlipidemic rabbit with recombinant adenoviruses. *J. Biol. Chem.* **269,** 13,695–13,702.

10. Engelhardt, J. F., Ye, X., Doranz, B., and Wilson, J. M. (1994) Ablation of E2a in recombinant adenoviruses improves transgene persistence and decreases immune response in mouse liver. *Proc. Natl. Acad. Sci. USA* **91,** 6196–6200.

11. Quantin, B., Perricaudet, L. D., Tajbakhsh, S., and Mandel, J. L. (1992) Adenovirus as an expression vector in muscle cells in vivo. *Proc. Natl. Acad. Sci. USA* **89,** 2581–2584.

12. Ragot, T., Vincent, N., Chafey, P., Vigne, E., Gilgenkrantz, H., Couton, D., Cartaud, J., Briand, P., Kaplan, J. C., Perricaudet, M., and Kahn, A. (1993) Efficient adenovirus-mediated transfer of a human minidystrophin gene to skeletal muscle of mdx mice. *Nature* **361,** 647–650.

13. Roessler, B. J., Allen, E. D, Wilson, J. M., Hartman, J. W., and Davidson, B. L. (1993) Adenoviral-mediated gene transfer to rabbit synovium *in vivo. J. Clin. Invest.* **92,** 1085–1092.

14. Lee, S. W., Trapnell, B. C., Rade, J. J., Virmani, R., and Dichek, D. A. (1993) In vivo adenoviral vector-mediated gee transfer into balloon-injured rat carotid arteries. *Circ. Res.* **73,** 797–807.

15. Lemarchand, P., Jones, M., Yamada, I., and Crystal, R. G. (1993) In vivo gene transfer and expression in normal uninjured blood vessels using replication deficient recombinant adenovirus vectors. *Circ. Res.* **72,** 1132–1138.

16. Davidson, B. L., Allen, E. D., Kozarsky, K. F., Wilson, J. M., and Roessler, B. J. (1993) A model system for *in vivo* gene transfer into the central nervous system using an adenoviral vector. *Nature Genet.* **3,** 219–223.

17. Davidson, B. L., Doran, S. E., Shewach, D. S., Latta, J. M., Hartman, J. W., and Roessler, B. J. (1994) Expression of *Escherichia coli* beta-galactosidase and rat HPRT in the CNS of *Macaca mulatta* following adenoviral mediated gene transfer. *Exp. Neurol.* **125,** 258–267.

18. Bajocchi, G., Geldman, S. H., Crystal, R. G., and Mastrangeli, A. (1993) Direct *in vivo* gene transfer to ependymal cells in the central nervous system using recombinant adenovirus vectors. *Nature Genet.* **3,** 229–234.

19. O'Neal, W. K. and Beaudet, A. L. (1994) Somatic gene therapy for cystic fibrosis. *Hum. Mol. Genet.* **3,** 1497–1502.

20. Engelhardt, J. F., Litzky, L., and Wilson, J. M. (1994) Prolonged transgene expression in cotton rat lung with recombinant adenoviruses defective in E2a. *Hum. Gene Ther.* **5,** 1217–1229.

21. Yang, Y., Nunes, F. A., Berencsi, K., Gonczol, E., Engelhardt, J. F., and Wilson, J. M. (1994) Inactivation of E2a in recombinant adenoviruses limits cellular immunity and improves the prospect for gene therapy of cystic fibrosis. *Nature Genet.* **7,** 362–369.

22. Simon, R. H., Engelhardt, J. F., Yang, Y., Zepeda, M., Pendleton, S. W., Grossman, M., and Wilson, J. M. (1993) Adenovirus-mediated transfer of the CFTR gene to lung of non-human primates: toxicity study. *Hum. Gene Ther.* **4,** 771–780.

23. Zabner, J., Petersen, D. M., Puga, A. P., Graham, S. M., Couture, L. A., Keyes, L. D., Lukason, M. J., St. George, J. A., Gregory, R. J., Smith, A. E., and Welsh, M. J. (1994) Safety and efficacy of repetitive adenovirus-mediated transfer of CFTR cDNA to airway epithelia of primates and cotton rats. *Nature Genet.* **6,** 75–83.

24. Boat, T. F., Welsh, M. J., and Beaudet, A. L. (1989) Cystic fibrosis, in *The Metabolic Basis of Inherited Disease* (Scriver, C. R., Beaudet, A. L., Sly, W. S., and Valle, D., eds.), McGraw Hill, New York, pp. 2649–2680.

25. Rommens, J. M., Ianuzzi, M. C., Kerem, B.-S., Drumm, M. L., Melmer, G., Dean, M., Rozmahel, R., Cole, J. L., Kennedy, D., Hidaka, N., Zsiga, M., Buchwald, M., Riordan, J. R., Tsui, L.-C., and Collins, F. S. (1989) Identification of the cystic fibrosis gene: chromosome walking and jumping. *Science* **245,** 1059–1065.

26. Riordan, J. R., Rommens, J. M., Kerem, B.-S., Alon, N., Rozmahel, R., Grzeiczak, Z., Zielenski, J., Lok, S., Plavsic, N., Chou, J.-L., et al. (1989) Identification of the cystic fibrosis gene: cloning and characterization of complementary DNA. *Science* **245,** 1066–1072.

27. Kerem, B.-S., Rommens, J. M., Buchanan, J. A., Markiewicz, D., Cox, T. K., Chakravarti, A., Buchwald, M., and Tsui, L.-C. (1989) Identification of the cystic fibrosis gene: genetic analysis. *Science* **245,** 1073–1080.

28a.Engelhardt, J. F., Zepeda, M., Cohn, J. A., Yankaskas, J. R., and Wilson, J. M. (1994) Expression of the cystic fibrosis gene in adult human lung. *J. Clin. Invest.* **93,** 737–749.

28b.Engelhardt, J. F., Yankaskas, J. R., Ernst, S. A., Yang, Y., Marino, C. R., Boucher, R. C., Cohn, J. A., and Wilson, J. M. (1992) Submucosal glands are the predominant site of CFTR expression in the human bronchus. *Nature Genet.* **2,** 240–248.

29. Breeze, R. G. and Wheeldon, E. B. (1977) The cells of the pulmonary airways. *Am. Rev. Respir. Dis.* **116,** 705–777.

30. Breuer, R., Zajicek, G., Christensen, T. G., Lucey, E. C., and Snider, G. L. (1990) Cell kinetics of normal adult hamster bronchial epithelium in the steady state. *Am. J. Resp. Cell. Mol. Biol.* **2,** 51–58.

31. Donnelly, G. M., Haack, D. G., and Heird, C. S. (1982) Tracheal epithelium: cell kinetics and differentiation in normal rat tissue. *Cell Tissue Kinet.* **15,** 119–130.

32. Johnson, N. F. and Hubbs, A. F. (1990) Epithelial progenitor cells in the rat trachea. *Am. J. Respir. Cell. Mol. Biol.* **3,** 579–585.

33. Kauffman, S. L. (1980) Cell proliferation in the mammalian lung. *Int. Rev. Exp. Pathol.* **22,** 131–191.

34. Bett, A. J., Prevec, L., and Graham, F. L. (1993) Packaging capacity and stability of human adenovirus type 5 vectors. *J. Virol.* **67,** 5911–5921.

35. Ginsberg, H. S., Horswood, R. L., Chanock, R. M., Prince, G. A. (1991) Role of early genes in pathogenesis of adenovirus pneumonia. *Proc. Natl. Acad. Sci. USA* **87,** 6191–6195.

36. Ginsberg, H. S., Moldawer, L. L., Sehgal, P. B., Redington, M., Kilian, P. L., Chanock, R. M., and Prince, G. A. (1991) A mouse model for investigating the molecular pathogenesis of adenovirus pneumonia. *Proc. Natl. Acad. Sci. USA* **88,** 1651–1655.

37. Prince, G. A., Porter, D. D., Jenson, A. B., Horswood, R. L., Chanock, R. M., and Ginsberg, H. S. (1993) Pathogenesis of adenovirus type 5 pneumonia in cotton rats (*Sigmodon hispidus*). *J. Virol.* **67,** 101–111.

38. Trapnell, B. C., Yei, S., Wert, S., Mitterder, N., and Whitsett, J. A. (1993) Evaluation of the host response to *in vivo* adenovirus-mediated gene transfer. *Ped. Pul.* **S145(Suppl. 9),** 241.

12

Methods for Retrovirus-Mediated Gene Transfer to Fetal Lung

Bruce R. Pitt, Margaret A. Schwarz, and Richard D. Bland

1. Introduction

With the advent of improved vectors for DNA delivery, somatic gene therapeutic approaches have expanded rapidly in the last few years. The vast majority of applications include ex vivo and in vivo protocols in patients postnatally. Nonetheless there is increasing interest and compelling reasons to consider prenatal application of somatic gene therapy *(1,2)*. In the current chapter, we will review theoretical, ethical, and experimental support for in utero gene therapy and then outline the methodology and large animal model we are currently using to consider retrovirus-mediated gene transfer to fetal lung. In this latter regard, the candidate inherited disorder is cystic fibrosis and the reader is referred to Chapters 1 and 12 in this volume.

1.1. Human Fetal Gene Therapy

The potential for human fetal gene therapy coincides with advances in molecular medicine and recent developments in fetal medicine including advances in prenatal human genetics, ultrasonography and surgical, anesthetic, and tocolytic techniques *(3)*. The most compelling reason to consider fetal gene therapy is that the disorder may result in irreversible and life threatening morbidity in the postnatal period (including adolescence and maturity) that may be prevented by corrective gene therapy *in utero*, at a time when pathophysiology of the disorder is minimal. Advantages for fetal gene therapy relate to our current understanding of available DNA delivery systems and thus the immunologically primitive fetus with rapidly dividing and proliferating tissues may provide a more permissive environment for gene-transfer protocols. For ethical considerations, fetal gene therapy is limited to somatic and not germ cell

From: *Methods in Molecular Medicine, Gene Therapy Protocols*
Edited by: P. Robbins Humana Press Inc., Totowa, NJ

transfer *(4,5)*. Thus, in spite of enormous technical advances in embryonic stem cell manipulations and/or homologous recombination, ethical and logistic issues suggest that genetic manipulation of early embryonic human stem cells is not likely to be a part of fetal gene transfer in the foreseeable future.

1.2. Gene Delivery to Extrapulmonary Tissue in Postimplantation Embryonic Experimental Animals

Original observations on fetal gene transfer involved the use of retroviruses (*see also* Chapters 1,9,15,17,20,27 in this volume). Jaenisch first reported widespread expression of Moloney murine leukemia virus (M-MuLV) specific sequences in mouse tissue after injection of replication-competent virus into 8–9 d gestational age (g.a.) mice *(6)*. Subsequently, Jaenisch and colleagues *(7)* used a replication-defective retrovirus to express human c-ha-*ras*-1 oncogene in mouse tissue after direct microinjection of viral supernatant into the 8.5 d g.a. conceptus. Others have reported expression of transgenes in the central nervous system of fetal rat pups after plasmid *(8)* and replication-defective retroviral *(9)* DNA transfer.

Many of the current preclinical approaches to rational fetal gene therapy relate to transduction of fetal hematopoietic tissue. Many laboratories have been able to transfect bone marrow cells in culture. Concerns about longevity of expression, problems with obtaining and transducing totipotent stem cells, and potential requirements for bone marrow ablation to facilitate the graft, however, have prompted alternative strategies. Depending on gestational age, fetal blood, and/or liver are important sources of hematopoietic precursors, and at this stage, potential stem cells proliferate more rapidly to facilitate fetal bone marrow development. Kantoff et al. *(10)* obtained fetal blood cells from 93–105 d g.a. sheep (term: 147 d), infected them ex vivo with a replication-defective M-MuLV-based vector containing cDNA to neomycin-resistance gene, and returned the transduced fetal hematopoietic cells to the lamb via an indwelling catheter. Neomycin-resistance gene sequences were detected in progenitor cells for up to 2 yr. Alternatively, Clapp et al. *(11)* directly injected replication-defective retrovirus into fetal liver of rat pups (11–18 d g.a.; term: 22 d) and noted transgene expression and proviral integration in bone marrow, thymus, and spleen for 6–7 mo postnatally. More recently, transduced cells obtained from human cord blood have been used in a clinical trial for treatment of adenosine deaminase deficiency in neonates *(12)*.

In a parallel vein, gene transfer to mature liver, in experimental animals *(13)* and patients *(14)*, has been accomplished by infection of cultured hepatocytes followed by hepatocellular transplantation of transduced cells into the portal vein. A similar ex vivo approach for hepatocellular transplantation *in utero* has recently been described *(15,16)* and the potential for enhanced graft survival in the immunologically incompetent fetal liver seems favorable. Direct in vivo retrovirus-mediated gene transfer to liver has also been accomplished *(17)* in partially hepatectomized mature rats and after ip injection in utero in rat pups (14 d g.a.).

1.3. Gene Transfer to Fetal Lung

Gene therapy to mature lung has advanced to the stage of several important clinical trials for cystic fibrosis *(18)*. Although the target tissue for complementation with normal cystic fibrosis transmembrane conductance regulator (CFTR) gene remains somewhat obscure, the respiratory epithelium appears to be one useful site. The peculiarities of the anatomy of lung preclude ex vivo approaches, and, accordingly, somatic gene transfer to lung has been vigorously pursued *(19,20)*. Adenoviral *(18)* and cationic liposomal *(21)* vectors have been employed, as they may transfer DNA to nonreplicating cells that are representative of the normally quiescent respiratory epithelium. Intrinsic to the current nature of these vectors is that expression of transgene is transient, and in the case of adenoviral vectors, potential local inflammatory responses are possible. Several investigators have noted potential advantages to somatic fetal gene therapy for CF (and other pulmonary disorders) including:

1. Potential limited immune response of the fetus, thereby minimizing inflammation and perhaps prolonging adenovirus-mediated transgene expression *(22)*;
2. Increased number of accessible dividing cells (and perhaps stem cells), thereby allowing use of retroviral vectors *(23)*;
3. Greater expression of CFTR in fetal than adult lungs suggesting an important, but yet undetermined, role for fetal alveolar CFTR *(24,25)*;
4. Interestingly, in light of point 3, above, the impression that fetal lungs of patients with CF are structurally normal (26); and
5. Minimal numbers of macrophages and protein as well as less complex surface lining material than the mature lung, thereby facilitating delivery of macromolecules including DNA in the fluid-filled future airspaces.

Some principles of this approach that may support human applications have been outlined in experiments in vitro *(27,28)*. Currently, the most efficient vector for somatic lung gene transfer, e.g., adenovirus, has shown some promise after introduction into amniotic fluid of fetal sheep and mice *(29)* and rats *(30)*. It is, however, associated with surprisingly significant inflammatory response when directly instilled in fetal sheep airways *(22,31)*.

In addition to CF, other diseases that are candidates for fetal gene therapy include inherited disorders such as alpha-1 antitrypsin deficiency and surfactant apoprotein-B deficiency as well as chronic lung injury of early infancy, an iatrogenic disorder often called bronchopulmonary dysplasia.

This chapter outlines our initial approaches with a large animal model of retrovirus-mediated gene transfer to fetal sheep lung. As noted, reports from other investigators *(22,31)* have outlined a similar approach using adenoviral vectors.

2. Materials

2.1. Retroviral Supernatant Production

We used MFG retroviral vectors in which *LacZ* or secreted (human interleukin receptor antagonist protein or growth hormone) cDNAs were inserted, as recently described *(32–34)*. The MFG vector is a simplified retroviral vector derived from M-MuLV in which the polymerase and envelope gene sequences are deleted to render the virus replication defective. Partial *gag* sequences were retained to increase packaging efficiency of the unspliced transcript. The inserted cDNAs were transcribed from promoter/enhancer sequences from the retroviral long terminal repeat. High titer amphotrophic producer of recombinant retrovirus was obtained by cotransfection of plasmid (pSV2neo) into packaging (CRIP) cells. NIH3T3 cells were cultivated in DMEM and supplemented with glucose (4.5 g/L) and 10% v/v heat inactivated calf or sheep serum, penicillin (100 U/mL), and glutamine (200 mg/mL), and were infected with the virus. Conditioned medium containing viral supernatants were tested for their titer and presence of helper virus, concentrated 3X, and stored at −70°C.

2.2. Fetal Surgery

Twin fetal lambs (104–117 d g.a.) were surgically prepared with chronic catheters as previously described *(31,32)*. The ewe was sedated with ketamine (15 mg/kg, im) and then underwent a hysterotomy with halothane and nitrous oxide anesthesia. The uterus was opened with a small incision and polyvinyl catheters were placed directly into the fetal carotid artery, jugular vein, and trachea. A fluid-filled catheter was also placed in the amniotic sac. Catheters were sutured to the ewe's uterus and abdomen. Wounds were closed with silk sutures and catheters were exteriorized and placed in a pouch sewn on the ewe's flank. Antibiotics were injected into the amniotic sac (penicillin [1,000,000 U] and kanamycin [400 mg]) and fetal vein (penicillin [300,000 U] and gentamicin [10 mg]) at the time of surgery and daily thereafter. The ewes also received 5 mL of a mixture of penicillin and dihydrostreptomycin (Combiotic, 200,000 U/mL procaine of penicillin G and 250 mg/mL dihydrostreptomycin, Pfizer, New York) and 600 mg kanamycin, im each day. Hematocrit, arterial pH, and blood gas tension were measured every other day.

3. Methods

3.1. Administration of Retrovirus to Fetal Lambs

1. 1–2 d after surgery, blood was withdrawn from the carotid artery catheter for determination of hematocrit, pH, and blood gas tension.
2. We then withdrew 30–60 mL of tracheal fluid into a sterile syringe.
3. A 10-mL solution of MFG-viral supernatant (3×10^6 particles/mL) was brought to room temperature immediately before use and polybrene (*see* Note 4) was added to a final concentration of 2 µg/mL. Viral supernatant was delivered directly into the tracheal catheter (over 1–2 min) and was flushed into the lungs with 30–60 mL of previously withdrawn lung liquid.
4. The identical procedure was performed on the other twin with the other MFG-vector.
5. All catheters were flushed with heparinized saline and antibiotics were given.
6. The same procedure was repeated on three consecutive days.

3.2. Histochemical Techniques

1. The ewe and her fetuses were killed with an overdose of sodium pentobarbital (50 mg/kg, iv). In some cases, the fetuses were aborted spontaneously after 1–3 wk.
2. Lungs were removed and inflated, ex vivo, to 30 cm H_2O transpulmonary pressure by injecting a phosphate-buffered solution containing 4% paraformaldehyde and 0.1% glutaraldehyde (pH 7.4) into the trachea. Lungs were immersed in PBS containing 30% sucrose and stored at 4°C.
3. Small blocks of tissue were obtained from proximal and distal sections of each lobe and snap frozen in liquid nitrogen. Frozen sections were cut on a Reichart-Jung 2800E Cryostat (Cambridge Instruments, Boston, MA) and mounted on poly-L-lysine-coated glass slides.
4. For histochemical localization of β-galactosidase activity, small blocks of fixed tissue were rinsed in PBS and incubated in a solution containing 1 mg/mL 5-bromo-4-chloro-3-indoyl-D-galactopyanoside (X-gal; Sigma, St. Louis, MO) in Tris phosphate-buffered saline (pH 8.0) with 5 mM potassium ferricyanide and potassium ferrocyanide.
5. Tissue was incubated for 4–24 h (optimal time was 8 h) and washed in PBS.
6. Tissue was then frozen and sectioned as in step 3. Sections were counterstained with eosin and hematoxylin and observed with a light microscope.
7. Alternatively, standard immunocytochemical techniques can be performed on the same fixed tissue (*see* steps 2 and 3).

4. Notes

1. We have performed experiments outlined above using MFG-based replication-defective retroviral vectors to express β-galactosidase and human interleukin receptor antagonist protein in the lungs of developing sheep *(37)*. We have noted detectable levels of β-galactosidase via histochemistry in the upper and lower airways of some of these animals as long as 3 wk after infection. Localization of β-galactosidase was most prominent in epithelial cells of proximal airways with

additional histochemical appearance associated with fibroblasts and macrophages in the submucosa. In addition, relevant developments from other laboratories *(22,30,31)* as well as new and novel retroviral constructs *(38)* highlight some of the concerns and potential future directions of *in utero* retrovirus-mediated gene transfer to lung. The approach may be most applicable to inherited disorders such as cystic fibrosis or surfactant apoprotein B deficiency, in which a potential lifetime therapy may ultimately be exacted after a limited therapeutic application *in utero*. Obviously, such a theoretical goal requires lifetime expression of the therapeutic gene with minimal toxicity to the patient (both fetus and mother). Thus, issues of efficiency, longevity of expression (including retroviral shutdown), progenitor cell expression, and potential germ cell contamination will have to be considered along with developments in fetal surgery and *in utero* genetic diagnosis to bring these issues to clinical consideration.

2. Sheep are the animal of choice for long-term *in utero* physiological studies. The uterine muscle is thinner and does not contract as vigorously as the primate, thereby minimizing surgery-induced abortion. Since the sheep is polycotyledenous, there is less likelihood of separating the placenta during surgery *(36)*. The fetus is relatively large (3–5 kg at term) and facilitates intrapulmonary maneuvers as well as greatly simplifying chronic catheterization and sample withdrawal. A significant portion of lung development occurs prenatally, and thus a large portion of the replicating cells is likely to be accessible, especially during early gestation *(39)*. Unlike primates, twin pregnancies are common in sheep, thus providing a useful control. Unfortunately, sheep are less than ideal with respect to serving as a model for human disease. There are no known spontaneous cystic fibrosis lesions in sheep, nor is there the likelihood that transgenic knockout models will be created for this disorder in this expensive, large, mammal that takes approx 5 mo to develop *in utero*. In this regard, progress with *in utero* mouse surgery and micromanipulation will be of great value.

3. We have focused on applications of retroviral vector-mediated gene transfer to fetal lung. Alternative vectors may (or may not) be as useful. For instance, adenoviral vectors, although extraordinarily efficient in mature, nondividing airway cells, are intrinsically transient, and current generation vectors have produced significant intrapulmonary inflammatory response in the fetus *(22,31)*. Adeno-associated viral vectors also work well in nondividing cells and appear ideal for gene transfer for CF in mature lung *(40)*. Their application for *in utero* transfer has not been reported as of this date although they appear to be useful candidates *(41)*. In our initial experience *(37)*, we instilled almost 10^8 viral particles over 3 d to produce a modest level of expression that lasted at least 3 wk in the fetal lung. Limitations of overall pattern and level of expression may have included:

   a. The absolute number of cells undergoing mitosis at the time of infection;
   b. Number of cells with appropriate surface receptors for the amphotrophic receptor required to recognize recombinant MFG-based vectors;
   c. *In situ* shutdown of retroviral transgene; and
   d. Retroviral titer.

It is possible that infection of an earlier age fetus may be useful since the number of proliferating cells is likely to be greater, and cell types with different sensitivities to retroviral infection may be apparent *(42)*. Alterations in the envelope protein may also be useful since it has been shown that switching from a murine-based vector to Gibbons Ape Leukemia virus backbone enhanced gene transfer to respiratory epithelium in vitro *(43)*. Reports of extraordinarily high titer pseudotyped retrovirus are also likely to enhance efficiency of *in utero* retrovirus-mediated gene transfer *(38)*.

4. Several problems occurred in our initial experiments. We noted significant pulmonary toxicity that led to early fetal demise in most of the animals studied. The toxicity was most likely owing to the presence of polybrene, a cation used to enhance viral entry into cells, that may have been pneumotoxic *(44)*. Initial attempts at using a secreted reporter gene (e.g., human IRAP) for prospective assessment of gene transfer revealed that expression was not sufficient to readily detect measurable levels in either fetal or maternal plasma or amniotic fluid. Furthermore, the presence of transgenic protein in the retroviral supernatant made determinations 1 wk after infection ambiguous.

We used a relatively invasive surgical procedure to introduce viral supernatant. Advances in fetal medicine and surgery make the likelihood of more acceptable procedures such as video fetoscopy, potentially useful for gene therapy. Issues of germ-line transmission remain speculative.

Acknowledgments

This work was supported in part by the Cystic Fibrosis Foundation (BRP), NIH HL32154 (BRP), and NIH HL49098 (RDB). MAS is a clinician-scientist of the American Heart Association.

References

1. Ledley, F. D. (1993) Prenatal application of somatic gene therapy. *Obstet. Gynecol. Clin. North Am.* **20,** 611–620.
2. Coutelle, C., Douar, A.-M., Colledge, W. H., and Froster, U. (1995) The challenge of fetal gene therapy. *Nature Med.* **1,** 864–866.
3. Adzick, N. S. and Harrison, M. R. (1994) Fetal surgical therapy. *Lancet* **343,** 897–902.
4. Wivel, N. A. and Walters, L. (1993) Germ-line gene modification and disease prevention: some medical and ethical perspectives. *Science* **262,** 533–538.
5. Garan, H. (1994) Fetal gene therapy under the microscope. *Nature* **372,** 852.
6. Jaenisch, R. (1980) Retroviruses and embryogenesis: microinjection of moloney leukemia virus into midgestation mouse embryos. *Cell* **19,** 181–188.
7. Compere, S. J., Baldacci, P. A., Sharpe, A. H., and Jaenisch, R. (1989) Retroviral transduction of the human c-Ha-*ras*-1 oncogene into midgestation mouse embryos promotes rapid epithelial hyperplasia. *Mol. Cell. Biol.* **9,** 6–14.
8. Jiao, S., Acsadi, G., Jani, A., Felgner, P. L., and Wolff, J. A. (1992) Persistence of plasmid and DNA expression in rat brain cells in vivo. *Exp. Neur.* **115,** 400–413.

9. Price, J. (1991) Cell lineage studies using retroviruses, in *Methods in Molecular Biology 8. Practical Molecular Virology, Viral Vectors and Gene Expression.* (Collins, M. K. L., ed.), Humana, Totowa, NJ, pp. 103–110.

10. Kantoff, P. W., Flake, A. W., Eglitis, M. A., Scharf, S., Bond, S., Gilboa, E., Erlich, H., Harrison, M. R., Zanjani, E. D., and Anderson, W. F. (1989) In utero gene transfer and expression: a sheep transplantation model. *Blood* **73,** 1066–1073.

11. Clapp, D. W., Dumenco, L. L., Hatzoglou, M., and Gerson, S. L. (1991) Fetal liver hematopoietic stem cells as a target for in utero retroviral gene transfer. *Blood* **78,** 1132–1139.

12. Jenks, S. (1993) Infants gene therapy gains easy RAC approval. *J. Natl. Canc. Instit.* **85,** 1108,1109.

13. Chowdhury, J. R., Grossman, M., Gupta, S. J., Chowdhury, N. R., Baker, J. R., Jr., and Wilson, J. M. (1991) Long-term improvement after ex vivo gene therapy in LDLR-deficient rabbits. *Science* **254,** 1802–1805.

14. Grossman, M., Raper, S. E., Kozarsky, K., Stein, E. A., Engelhardt, J. F., Muller, D., Lupien, P. J., and Wilson, J. M. (1994) Successful ex vivo gene therapy directed to liver in a patient with familial hypercholesterolaemia. *Nat. Genet.* **6,** 335–341.

15. Zanjani, E. D., Flake, A. W., Rice, H., Hedrick, M., and Tavassoli, M. (1994) Long-term repopulating ability of xenogeneic transplanted human fetal liver hematopoietic stem cells in sheep. *J. Clin. Invest.* **93,** 1051–1055.

16. Soriano, H. E., Gest, A. L., Bain, D. K., Vander Straten, M., Lewis, D. E., Darlington, G. J., Finegold, M. J., and Ledley, F. D. (1994) Feasibility of hepato-cellular transplantation via the umbilical vein in prenatal and perinatal lambs. *Fetal Diag. Ther.* **8,** 293–304.

17. Hatzoglou, M., Lamers, W., Bosch, F., Wynshaw-Boris, A., Clapp, D. W., and Hanson, R. W. (1991) Hepatic gene transfer in animals using retroviruses containing the promoter from the gene for phophoenolpyruvate carboxykinase. *J. Biol. Chem.* **265,** 17,285–17,293.

18. Crystal, R. G., McElvaney, N. G., Rosenfeld, M. A., Chu, C.-S., Mastrangeli, A., Hay, J. G., Brody, S. L., Jaffe, H. A., Eissa, N. T., and Danel, C. (1994) Administration of an adenovirus containing the human CFTR cDNA to the respiratory tract of individuals with cystic fibrosis. *Nat. Genet.* **8,** 42–51.

19. Rosenfeld, M. A., Siegfried, W., Yoshimura, K., Yoneyama, K., Fukayama, M., Stier, L. E., Paakko, P. K., Gilardi, P., Stratford-Perricaudet, L. D., Perricaudet, M., Jallat, S., Pavirani, A., Lecocq, J.-P., and Crystal, R. G. (1991) Adenovirus-mediated transfer of a recombinant a1-antitrypsin gene to the lung epithelium. *Science* **252,** 431–434.

20. Rosenfeld, M. A., Yoshimura, Y., Trapnell, B. C., Yoneyama, K., Rosenthal, E. R., Dalemans, W., Fukayma, M., Bargon, J., Stier, L. E., Stratford-Perricaudet, L., Perricaudet, M., Guggino, W. B., Pavirani, A., Lecocq, J.-P., and Crystal, R. G. (1992) In vivo transfer of the human cystic fibrosis transmembrane conductance regulator gene in the airway epithelium. *Cell* **68,** 143–155.

21. Caplen, N. J., Gao, X., Hayes, P., Elaswarapu, R., Fisher, G., Kinrade, E., Chakera, A., Schorr, J., Hughes, B., Dorin, J. R., Alton, E. W. F. W., Geddes, D. M., Coutelle, C., Williamson, R., Huang, L., and Gilchrist, C. (1994) Gene therapy for cystic fibrosis in humans by liposome-mediated DNA transfer: the production of resources and the regulatory process. *Gene Ther.* **1,** 139–147.

22. Vincent, M. C., Trapnell, B. C., Baughman, R. P., Wert, S. E., Whitsett, J. A., and Iwamoto, H. S. (1995) Adenovirus-mediated gene transfer to the respiratory tract of fetal sheep in utero. *Hum. Gene Ther.* **6,** 1019–1028.

23. Engelhardt, J. F., Yankaskas, J. R., and Wilson, J. M. (1992) In vivo retroviral gene transfer into human bronchial epithelia of xenografts. *J. Clin. Invest.* **90,** 2598–2607.

24. Trezise, A. E. O., Chambers, J. A., Wardle, C. J., Gould, S., and Harris, A. (1993) Expression of the cystic fibrosis gene in human foetal tissues. *Hum. Mol. Genet.* **2,** 213–218.

25. Tizzano, E. F., Chitayat, D., and Buchwald, M. (1993) Cell-specific localization of CFTR mRNA shows developmentally regulated expression in human fetal tissues. *Hum. Mol. Genet.* **2,** 219–224.

26. Oppenheimer, E. (1981) Similarity of the tracheobronchial mucous gland and epithelium in infants with and without cystic fibrosis. *Hum. Pathol.* **12,** 36–48.

27. Peault, B., Tirouvanziam, R., Sombardier, M.-N., Chen, S., Perricaudet, M., and Gaillard, D. (1994) Gene transfer to human fetal pulmonary tissue developed in immunodeficient SCID mice. *Hum. Gene Ther.* **5,** 1131–1137.

28. Ballard, P. L., Zepeda, M. L., Schwartz, M., Lopez, N., and Wilson, J. M. (1995) Adenovirus-mediated gene transfer to human fetal lung ex vivo. *Am. J. Physiol.* **268** *(Lung Cell. Mol. Physiol. 12)*, L839–L845.

29. Holzinger, A., Trapnell, B. C., Weaver, T. E., Whitsett, J. A., and Iwamoto, H. S. (1995) Intraamniotic administration of an adenoviral vector for gene transfer to fetal sheep and mouse tissues. *Ped. Res.* **38,** 844–850.

30. Sekhon, H. S. and Larson, J. E. (1995) In utero gene transfer into the pulmonary epithelium. *Nature Med.* **1,** 1201–1203.

31. McCray, P. B., Jr., Armstrong, K., Zabner, J., Miller, D. W., Koretzky, G. A., Couture, L., Robillard, J. E., Smith, A. E., and Welsh, M. J. (1995) Adenoviral-mediated gene transfer to fetal pulmonary epithelia in vitro and in vivo. *J. Clin. Invest.* **95,** 2620–2632.

32. Dranoff, G., Jaffee, E., Lazenby, A., Golumbek, P., Levitsky, H., Brose, K., Jackson, V., Hamada, H., Pardoll, D., and Mulligan, R. C. (1993) Vaccination with irradiated tumor cells engineered to secrete murine granulocyte-macrophage colony stimulating factor stimulates potent, specific and long-lasting anti-tumor immunity. *Proc. Natl. Acad. Sci. USA* **90,** 3539–3543.

33. Bandara, G., Mueller, G. M., Lauri-Galea, J., Tindal, M. H., Georgescu, H. I., Suchanek, M. K., Hung, G. L., Glorioso, J. C., Robbins, P. D., and Evans, C. H. (1993) Intraauricular expression of biologically active interleukin 1-receptor antagonist protein by ex vivo gene transfer. *Proc. Natl. Acad. Sci. USA* **90,** 10,764–10,768.

34. Ohashi, T., Boggs, S., Robbins, P. D., Bahnson, A., Patrene, K., Wei, F.-S., Wei, J.-F., Li, J., Lucht, L., Fei, Y., Clark, S., Kimak, M., He, H., Mowery-Rushton, P., and Barranger, J. A. (1992) Efficient transfer and sustained high expression of human glucocerebrosidase gene in mice and their functional macrophages following transplantation of bone marrow transduced by a retroviral vector. *Proc. Natl. Acad. Sci. USA* **89,** 11,332–11,336.

35. Chapman, D. L., Carlton, D. P., Nielson, D. W., Cummings, J. J., Poulain, F. R., and Bland, R. D. (1994) Changes in lung liquid during spontaneous labor in fetal sheep. *J. Appl. Physiol.* **76,** 523–530.

36. Rudolph, A. and Heyman, M. A. (1980) Methods for studying the circulation of the fetus in utero, in *Animal Models in Fetal Medicine* (Nathanielsz, P. W., ed.), Elsevier-North Holland Biomedical, Amsterdam, pp. 1–57.

37. Pitt, B. R., Schwarz, M. A., Pilewski, J. M., Nakayma, D. K., Mueller, G. M., Robbins, P. A., Watkins, S. A., Albertine, K. A., and Bland, R. D. (1995) Retroviral-mediated gene transfer in lungs of living fetal sheep. *Gene Ther.* **2,** 344–350.

38. Burns, J. C., Friedmann, T., Driever, W., Burrascano, M., and Yee, J. K. (1993) Vesicular stomatitis virus G glycoprotein pseudotyped retroviral vectors: concentration to very high titer and efficient gene transfer into mammalian and nonmammalian cells. *Proc. Natl. Acad. Sci. USA* **90,** 8033–8037.

39. Hu, L.-H., Davies, P., Adzick, N. S., Harrison, M. R., and Reid, L. M. (1987) The effects of intrauterine pneumonectomy in lambs. *Am. Rev. Res. Dis.* **135,** 607–612.

40. Flottee, T. R., Afione, S. A., Conrad, C., McGrath, S. A., Solow, R., Oka, H., Zeitlin, P. L., Guggino, W. B., and Carter, B. J. (1993) Stable in vivo expression of the cystic fibrosis transmembrane conductance regulator with an adeno-associated virus vector. *Proc. Natl. Acad. Sci. USA* **90,** 10,613–10,617.

41. Zeitlin, P. L., Chu, S., McVeigh, U., Ferguson, K., Flotte, T. R., and Guggino, W. B. (1995) Alveolar stem cell transduction by an adeno-associated viral vector. *Gene Ther.* **2,** 623–631.

42. John, H. A. (1994) Variable efficiency of retroviral-mediated gene transfer into early-passage cultures of fetal lamb epithelial, mesenchymal, and neuroectodermal tissues. *Hum. Gene Ther.* **5,** 283–293.

43. Bayle, J.-Y., Johnson, L. G., St. George, J. A., Boucher, R. C., and Olsen, J. C. (1993) High-efficiency gene transfer to primary monkey airway epithelial cells with retrovirus vectors using the gibbon ape leukemia virus receptor. *Hum. Gene Ther.* **4,** 161–170.

44. Yu, X.-Y., Schofield, B. H., Croxton, T., Takahashi, N., Gabrielson, E. W., and Spannhake, E. W. (1994) Physiologic modulation of bronchial epithelial cell barrier function by polycationic exposure. *Am. J. Resp. Cell Mol. Biol.* **11,** 188–198.

13

In Situ Retrovirus-Mediated Gene Transfer into the Liver

Nicolas Ferry, Sophie Branchereau, Jean-Michel Heard, and Olivier Danos

1. Introduction

Gene transfer into hepatocytes is a promising approach for the treatment of genetic liver diseases. Candidate diseases for human trials are life-threatening disorders resulting from a single genetic defect that do not compromise other liver functions and the organization of the hepatic tissue. Orthotopic liver transplantation has been successfully performed in patients with genetic liver disease, but their use is limited by the high mortality risk, the need for chronic immunosuppression, and the availability of organs. Gene therapy would provide an alternative to transplantation by restoring the expression of the defective gene in an organ that is otherwise structurally and functionally normal.

Hepatocytes can be isolated from a liver biopsy, grown in vitro, genetically modified with retroviral vectors, and reimplanted by injection into the portal vein or in the spleen. This ex vivo approach has been successfully used in animal models and in human patients *(7–9,12,20)*, but the in vitro step is highly labor intensive and introduces contamination risks.

Alternative techniques have taken advantage of the fenestrated nature of the vascular endothelium in the liver, that allows direct contact between the hepatocytes and substances carried by the blood stream. A simple portal injection of recombinant retroviruses *(2,13,14)* or adenoviruses *(11,16)* results in the uptake and expression of the foreign genetic material by the hepatocytes. A more thorough perfusion of the whole organ, which requires a temporary isolation from the circulation, increases gene transfer efficiency *(3,5,18)*.

In this chapter, we describe the procedures that we have developed in mice, rats, and dogs for retrovirus-mediated gene transfer into hepatocytes in vivo,

From: *Methods in Molecular Medicine, Gene Therapy Protocols*
Edited by: P. Robbins Humana Press Inc., Totowa, NJ

by selective perfusion of the regenerating liver *(2,5,3)*. The technique includes a partial hepatectomy that triggers hepatocyte division, making them susceptible to retroviral infection. Liver perfusion is performed at the time of maximal mitotic activity in the regenerating liver. The organ is isolated from the circulation by clamping efferent and afferent vessels, and perfused for 10–15 min with a retroviral vector preparation. The asanguinous perfusion ensures a complete and blood-free irrigation of the parenchyme with the retroviral vector, without spreading to other tissues.

The proportion of dividing cells at a given time after hepatectomy varies between species. In rats, where this has been thoroughly studied, the peak of mitotic activity is observed around 24 h, with around 15% dividing hepatocytes at this time *(4)*. This sets the upper limit of expected gene transfer efficiency with the current retroviral vectors. Using an amphotropic retrovirus vector encoding an *nls-lac* Z reporter gene, we routinely obtain around 1% of hepatocytes expressing the nucleus-targeted β-galactosidase for periods of time longer than 1 yr *(2,5)*. These procedures can be performed by investigators with basic surgical skills. Following the recommendations detailed here, a survival rate above 90% is expected.

2. Materials

2.1. Production of Recombinant Retroviruses

1. Retroviral vector supernatant is prepared according to procedures described in Chapter 3. We use supernatant from ΨCRIP or ΨCRE packaging cell lines freshly harvested or from a stock frozen at –80°C.
2. Polybrene: 0.8 mg/mL solution in PBS (100X stock solution, stable at 4°C).
3. Cellulose acetate 0.45-μm sterile filters.
4. Concentration can be obtained by ultrafiltration on Amicon cells or Filtron macrosep tubes. For large volumes (>100 mL), tangential filtration on a Sartorius device is used (Sartocon Mini SM 17521 with a Polysulfon membrane, porosity 100,000).

2.2. Surgery

1. Sterile surgical tools are required to perform hepatectomy and liver perfusion. Microsurgery tools are used for mice and rats.
2. Retractors adapted to rats and mice.
3. Ackland clamp C1.
4. Mosquito forceps: curved, 4.5 cm.
5. Bulldog clamps: straight and curved, 4.5 cm.
6. Microclamp: angulated, pressure 15 Gms.
7. Scissors: straight, heavy, and blunt, blades 12 cm.
8. Scissors: straight, 10 cm.
9. Scissors: Castroviejo-Gilbert.
10. Forceps: Halsted-Kocher, delicate, curved, nontraumatic.

11. Iris forceps: delicate, straight, 1-mm jaws.
12. Dissection forceps: curved and straight with 12-cm teeth.
13. Microvascular forceps 3 and 5.
14. Needle holder: Finochieto 13 cm.
15. Needle holder: O'Brien, curved, extra delicate with 0.8-mm jaws.
16. Silicone irrigator with irrigating canula olive tip.
17. Electrocoagulator.
18. Sterile cheese cloths and sterile physiologic serum.
19. 4/0 vicryl suture, 8/0 monobrin suture, 4/0 and 2/0 ethicrin suture, 10/0 silk suture.
20. Intraflon 22-gage catheter.
21. Butterfly 25 gage.
22. Silastic tubing 0.012 in. id × 0.025 in. od.
23. Peristaltic pump with connecting tubing (Masterflex digistaltic pump, Cole Parmer, Niles, IL).
24. Surgical microscope.

3. Methods

3.1. Production of Recombinant Retroviruses

Amphotropic retroviral vector is produced according to usual procedures and harvested from the supernatant of confluent packaging cells. Optimal conditions for virus production including cell density, type of support, media, and temperature may vary from one producer to the other *(15)*.

Small-scale production of under 100 mL of viral supernatant is usually sufficient for experiments in rats and mice. Liver perfusion in large mammals requires the production of more than 500 mL, which has to be conducted in roller bottles or in large-scale tissue culture devices such as Nunc's "cell factories." Production of large batches is also required before concentration. The best results are obtained with freshly concentrated virus. However, it is convenient to use aliquots of a calibrated concentrated stock kept at –80°C. A procedure for 10–30-fold concentration of large batches by tangential flow filtration has been described *(17)*. If needed, small volumes can also be concentrated 10-fold using 300-kDa cutoff membranes on an Amicon ultrafiltration cell (2–3 h at 4°C) or a Macrosep centrifugal concentrator (3500*g* for 1 h).

3.2. Anesthesia

3.2.1. Rats

Rats are readily anesthetized using ether. Anesthesia is induced by placing animals in a tightly covered glass recipient containing a piece of surgical cotton presoaked in ether. After placing the animal on the surgical table, anesthesia is maintained by securing the body of a 50 mL-syringe containing an ether-wetted piece of cotton in front of its nose.

3.2.2. Mice

Ether is not recommended in mice and we use ip injections of ketamine or Avertin at 150 mg/kg. Pentobarbital, which is mainly metabolized by the liver, induces very long anesthesia in partially hepatectomized mice.

3.2.3. Dogs

General anesthesia is induced with pentobarbital (20 mg/kg of body wt) and maintained with 0.5% fluothane administered through endotracheal tube. Antibiotictherapy (amoxicilline, 100 mg/kg/d) is given preoperatively and for 3 d postoperatively. Feeding is stopped 12 h before surgery and restarted progressively after 24 h.

3.3. Partial Hepatectomy

In rats and mice, two-thirds partial hepatectomy is essentially carried out as described by Higgins and Anderson *(10)*.

3.3.1. Rats

1. After opening the abdominal cavity by midline incision, the liver is exposed by retracting the abdominal walls with small retractors. The liver ligaments are then carefully sectioned with fine scissors. Care must be taken at this step to avoid any injury of the liver pedicule vessels.
2. The basis of the median and left lateral lobe is then surrounded with a 4/0 vicryl suture. After controlling the correct position of the suture, it is tightened carefully and secured by two or three knots. Both lobes should rapidly turn dark red, indicating that the blood flow has been stopped. They are then sectioned and the stump is replaced in the abdominal cavity.
3. The right adrenal vein is usually sutured at the time of partial hepatectomy. For doing this, the caudate lobe is retracted to expose the right adrenal pedicule. The right adrenal vein is then carefully dissected and sutured with a 4/0 vicryl suture. The abdominal wall is closed in two steps (muscle and skin) using a 2/0 ethicrin suture with a straight triangular needle.

3.3.2. Mice

The procedure is essentially the same as for rats. However, better results are obtained when the two large lobes are removed successively. The gallbladder has to be left intact. The hepatectomy in mice is more conveniently carried out under a surgical microscope. Care must be taken to avoid compression of the hepatic pedicule by suture knots. This would compromise the inward blood flow through the remnant liver lobes. The right adrenal vein is usually electrocoagulated rather than sutured. The abdominal wall is closed as for rats, using a 4/0 ethicrin suture.

3.3.3. Dogs

1. The far left lobes, corresponding to 44% of the liver mass, are removed *(6)*.
2. The abdomen is opened via a long midline incision and the falciform and the left triangular ligaments are divided.
3. The hilar structure (bile ducts, hepatic arteries, and portal veins) is ligated first and the liver transection is perfomed by carefully crushing the tissue with a Kelly forceps (Kellyclasie).
4. The two hepatic veins are suture-ligated.
5. The abdominal wall is closed without drains. The resected lobes must be weighed to estimate the remnant liver mass.

3.4. Asanguineous Perfusion

After a lag period allowing the regenerating liver to reach the time of maximal mitotic activity (24 h in mice and rats; 72 h in dogs) *(see* Note 1), animals are again anesthetized and the abdominal cavity is opened by removing the sutures placed at the time of hepatectomy.

3.4.1. Rats

1. The abdominal cavity is largely exposed using two, or preferably four, retractors. The intestinal mass is moved to the left side of the animal and maintained in a sterile cheese cloth, wetted with physiologic serum. It is very important to check that the intestine remains wetted during the whole surgical procedure.
2. The portal vein and the hepatic artery are localized and carefully dissected. The gastroduodenal vein is also dissected at its junction with the portal vein. Two sutures (4/0 vicryl) are placed on the gastroduodenal vein, which is then sectioned between them to free the portal vein from any attachment.
3. The infrahepatic vena cava is also dissected in its upper renal portion. The suprahepatic vena cava is carefully freed from any adherence. This can be difficult if the hepatectomy stump is too large and hides this portion of the vena cava. After all dissections are completed, the liver is ready to be isolated from the blood circulation.
4. For this, an angulated microclamp is placed on the hepatic artery and bulldog clamps are successively placed on the portal vein, the infrahepatic vena cava, and the suprahepatic vena cava under the diaphragm. Under microscopic viewing, the wall of the portal vein is carefully opened, and a silastic tube is introduced into the opening. This tube is connected to a larger tube placed in a peristaltic pump that ensures a constant flow through the liver. A 22-gage catether is placed in the infrahepatic vena cava and connected to a tube in order to direct the flow to a waste recipient placed below the level of the animal. The perfusion is started by turning on the peristaltic pump, with an inward flow of 4–5 mL/min.
5. At the end of the perfusion, the portal vein is carefully sutured under the microscope using 10/0 silk suture. Another clamp is placed on the infrahepatic vena cava just upstream of the 22G catether to isolate the opening of the vena cava.

The portal, hepatic artery, and suprahepatic clamps are then released to restore a normal portal flow. This leaves a few minutes to suture the infrahepatic vena cava using a 10/0 silk suture.

6. It is essential that the clamping of the portal vein in rats does not exceed 20 min, to avoid irreversible ischemic lesion of the intestine.

3.4.2. Mice

In mice, the protocol is essentially the same except that:

1. We usually place only one suture with no section of the gastroduodenal vein. The hepatic artery is electrocoagulated to avoid traumatic injury of the hepatic pedicule during dissection.
2. The portal vein and infrahepatic vena cava are clamped with Ackland clamps.
3. The perfusion usually requires lower volumes of retrovirus-containing medium and can therefore be performed using a hand-controlled syringe instead of a peristaltic pump.
4. After clamping the vena cava, we frequently observe a respiratory arrest in mice. This requires a mechanical ventilation system during the clamping period. A simple tube connected to a bulb, in which the nose of the animal is placed, is sufficient to ensure ventilation. The frequency and volume of air can be directly monitored by the obsevation of the amplitude of the diaphragm movements at each insuflation.
5. The outward catether placed in the infrahepatic vena cava is smaller in mice (30G). Because of rapid clotting, the suture of the vena cava is not necessary if the opening of the vein wall has been kept small. It is sufficient to apply a piece of cheese cloth to ensure correct clotting. The whole procedure is usually carried out in less than 10 min.

3.4.3. Dogs

In dogs, the perfusion is performed 72 h after partial hepatectomy.

1. The inferior vena cava is mobilized above and below the liver to allow the placement of the vascular clamps.
2. The right adrenal vein is ligated to avoid bleeding during the perfusion, since the clamp cannot be applied above its insertion. The blood inflow is occluded by placing a vascular clamp on the hepatic pedicle (in mass or selectively on the portal vein and the hepatic artery). The vena cava is then clamped, first below and then above the liver *(1)*.
3. The portal vein is canulated with a 14-gage catheter (Vialon, Becton Dickinson, Rutherford, NJ).
4. A suction cannula used for collecting the perfusion outflow is placed into the infrahepatic vena cava through a 4-mm incision of the anterior wall, made above the clamp.
5. The single pass perfusion is started via the portal catheter at 1 mL/min/g of estimated remnant liver. The flow rate can be moderately and transiently increased

to ensure a satisfactory perfusion of all segments. The average duration of the perfusion is under 20 min. The liver is then rinsed with PBS and the perfusion is stopped.

6. The portal vein and the vena cava incisions are then sutured with a 5/0 nylon monofilament, and the liver is revascularized by declamping first the portal vein, then the vena cava below, and finally, above the liver.
7. The abdominal wall is closed in two layers, without drainage.

3.5. Analysis

3.5.1. Histology

In order to prepare histological sections on which the activity of the introduced gene can be revealed, the liver is fixed *in situ* by perfusion.

1. The anesthetized animal is placed on the surgical table and the abdominal wall is opened. The portal vein is carefully dissected and a butterfly 27-gage needle is secured into the vein. The thorax is opened and the lower vena cava is sectioned. Immediatly afterward, the liver is first rinsed by perfusing physiologic serum (20–40 mL in rats; 5–10 mL in mice; 200 mL in dogs).
2. After washing, the organ is perfused with a 4% paraformaldehyde solution freshly prepared in PBS.
3. Once the liver has hardened, it can be easily removed from the animal and minced with a razor blade in 5-mm thick fragments. These fragments are rinsed in PBS and immersed overnight at 4°C in a 30% sucrose solution freshly prepared in PBS.
4. The fragments are then ready to be snap-frozen in dry ice or liquid nitrogen-refrigerated isopentane, and cryostat sections can be prepared.

3.5.2. DNA Analysis

Detection of the transgene after retroviral mediated transfer can be performed by PCR or Southern blot analysis on total liver DNA.

1. Liver fragments are immediately frozen by immersion in liquid nitrogen. The tissue is then finely powdered in liquid nitrogen.
2. The powder is incubated for 3 h at 50°C in 5 mL of a mixture containing 10 mM Tris-HCl (pH 7.5), 1 mM EDTA, 100 mM NaCl, 1% SDS, and 500 µg/mL proteinase K.
3. At the end of the incubation, 5 mL of phenol is added and mixed gently by rotational agitation for 1 h. After centrifugation (2000g for 2 min), the aqueous phase is collected and phenol is extracted once.
4. The high-mol-wt DNA is then extracted twice for 10 min with chloroform: isoamylalcohol (24/1, v/v).
5. DNA is then precipitated with 1 vol of isopropanol and the high-mol-wt DNA precipitate is collected using the tip of a Pasteur pipet and dissolved in 500 µL of sodium acetate (300 mM). DNA is then precipitated again with 2 vol of ethanol at −20°C for 30–60 min and centrifuged for 30 min. The pellet is washed with 1 mL of 70% ethanol, centrifuged, and air dried.

6. The final pellet is then resuspended in 0.5–1 mL of water and stored at 4°C until used. PCR is run on 0.5–1 μg of high-mol-wt DNA using two synthetic oligonucleotides as primers, one of which is complementary to the vector sequence and the other one to the transgene *(5)*. We usually performed 40 cycles of amplification at 95°C for denaturation, 55°C for hybridization, and 72°C for elongation under conditions recommended by the Taq polymerase supplier. The PCR assay allows the detection of 1 positive cell in 10^4, and is therefore not much more sensitive than direct staining for a histochemical marker or *in situ* hybridization *(7)*.

4. Notes

1. Retroviral vectors derived from murine leukemia viruses will integrate in dividing cells only *(19)*. Therefore the perfusion procedure should be carried out at the time of maximal hepatocytes division *(2)*. In rats and mice, the peak of DNA synthesis in hepatocytes occurs 24–30 h following partial hepatectomy. In dogs, the regeneration process is somewhat slower and the perfusion is carried out 3 d after partial hepatectomy. When working on a specific animal model, one has to first delineate the kinetics of liver regeneration to ensure an optimal gene transfer by perfusing during the peak of DNA synthesis.
2. Different animal strains may react differently to our surgical procedure. Examples are renal ischemia after vena cava clamping in Fischer rats or the exquisite sensitivity to hepatectomy resulting in high level of mortality in the C3H mice strain. We recommend, whenever possible, to use Wistar or Lewis rat strains or C57B16 mice to carry out liver perfusions.
3. Simplified methods for retrovirus-mediated gene transfer into the regenerating liver have been described. In these procedures, there is no complete vascular exclusion of the liver at the time of infection, and the viral supernatants are either slowly injected into the portal stream *(13)* or bolus-injected in the portal vein after single clamping of the portal vein *(2,18)*. In our hands, the complete vascular exclusion procedure results in a 10-fold increase in gene transfer efficiency when compared to portal bolus injection technique *(2)*. This may be owing in part to the smaller volumes of vector-containing supernatant that can be infused during a single bolus injection. In addition, the organ is not washed free of blood during the bolus injection. This may decrease efficiency since retroviral particles can bind to blood cells still in the liver sinusoids or, depending on the animal species, be inactivated by the complement.
4. The titer of the viral supernatant perfused into the liver is a critical parameter. We have observed that most viral particles originally present in the perfusion fluid were able to escape the liver. This was evidenced by a minimal (<10%) decrease in the viral titer measured in the outflow. Better results are always obtained with freshly collected, high titer viral preparations. A titer of 10^5 viral particles/mL (assayed on NIH 3T3 cells) is the minimum required to achieve easily detectable gene transfer into the liver of rodents.

References

1. Adam, R., Poggi, L., Capron, M., Morin, J., Gigou, M., Miramand, J. C., Szekely, A. M., and Houssin, D. (1987) Asanguineous isolated hyperthermic *in vivo* perfusion of the liver in the rat. *Eur. Surg. Res.* **19,** 366–374.
2. Branchereau, S., Calise, D., and Ferry, N. (1994) Factors influencing retroviral-mediated gene transfer into hepatocytes in vivo. *Hum. Gene Ther.* **5,** 803–808.
3. Cardoso, J. E., Branchereau, S., Prema Roy, J., Houssin, D., Danos, O., and Heard, J. M. (1993) In situ retrovirus-mediated gene transfer into dog liver. *Hum. Gene Ther.* **4,** 411–418.
4. Fabrikant, J. I. (1968) The kinetics of cellular proliferation in regenerating liver. *J. Cell. Biol.* **36,** 551–565.
5. Ferry, N., Duplessis, O., Houssin, D., Danos, O., and Heard, J. M. (1991) Retroviral-mediated gene transfer into hepatocytes *in vivo*. *Proc. Natl. Acad. Sci. USA* **88,** 8377–8381.
6. Francavilla, A., Porter, K., Benichou, J., Jones, J., and Starzl, T. (1978) Liver regeneration in dogs: morphologic and chemical changes. *J. Surg. Res.* **25,** 409–419.
7. Grossman, M., Raper, S. E., Kozarsky, K., Stein, E. A., Engelhardt, J. F., Muller, D., Lupien, P. J., and Wilson, J. M. (1994) Successful ex vivo gene therapy directed to liver in a patient with familial hypercholesterolaemia. *Nature Genet.* **6,** 335–341.
8. Grossman, M., Raper, S. E., and Wilson, J. M. (1992) Transplantation of genetically modified autologous hepatocytes into nonhuman primates: feasibility and short-term toxicity. *Hum. Gene Ther.* **3,** 501–510.
9. Grossman, M., Wilson, J., and Raper, S. (1993) A novel approach for introducing genetically-modified hepatocytes into the portal circulation. *J. Lab. Clin. Med.* **121,** 472–478.
10. Higgins, G. M. and Anderson, R. M. (1931) Experimental pathology of the liver I. Restoration of the liver of the white rat following partial surgical removal. *Arch. Pathol.* **12,** 186–202.
11. Jaffe, H. A., Danel, C., Longenecker, G., Metzger, M., Setoguchi, Y., Rosenfeld, M. A., Gant, T. W., Thorgeirsson, S. S., Stratford-Perricaudet, L. D., Perricaudet, M., Pavirani, A., Lecocq, J. P., and Crystal, R. G. (1992) Adenovirus-mediated in vivo gene transfer and expression in normal rat liver. *Nature Genet.* **1,** 372–378.
12. Kay, M. A., Baley, P., Rothenberg, S., Leland, F., Fleming, L., Ponder, K. P., Liu, T., Finegold, M., Darlington, G., Pokorny, W., and Woo, S. L. C. (1992) Expression of human $\alpha 1$-antitrypsin in dogs after autologous transplantation of retroviral transduced hepatocytes. *Proc. Natl. Acad. Sci. USA* **89,** 89–93.
13. Kay, M. A., Li, Q., Liu, T. J., Leland, F., Toman, C., Finegold, M., and Woo, S. (1992) Hepatic gene therapy: persistent expression of Human alpha1-antitrypsin in mice after direct gene delivery in vivo. *Hum. Gene Ther.* **3,** 641–647.
14. Kay, M. A., Rothenberg, S., Landen, C. N., Bellinger, D. A., Leland, F., Toman, C., Finegold, M., Thompson, A. R., Read, M. S., Brinkhous, K. M., and Woo, S. L. C. (1993) In vivo gene therapy of hemophilia B: sustained partial correction in factor IX-deficient dogs. *Science* **262,** 117–119.

15. Kotani, H., Newton, P. B., Zhang, S., Chiang, Y. L., Otto, E., Weaver, L., Blaese, R. M., Anderson, W. F., and McGarrity, G. J. (1994) Improved methods of retroviral transduction and production for gene therapy. *Hum. Gene Ther.* **5,** 19–28.

16. Li, Q., Kay, M. A., Finegold, M., Stratford-Perricaudet, L. D., and Woo, S. L. C. (1993) Assessment of recombinant adenoviral vectors for hepatic gene therapy. *Hum. Gene Ther.* **4,** 403–409.

17. Paul, R. W., Morris, D., Hess, B., Dunn, J., and Overell, R. W. (1993) Increased viral titer through concentration of viral harvests from retroviral packaging lines. *Hum. Gene Ther.* **4,** 609–615.

18. Rettinger, S. D., Ponder, K. P., Saylors, R. L., Kennedy, S. C., Hafenrichter, D. G., and Flye, M. W. (1993) In vivo hepatocyte transduction with retrovirus during in-flow occlusion. *J. Surg. Res.* **54,** 418–425.

19. Roe, T. Y., Reynolds, T. C., Yu, G., and Brown, P. O. (1993) Integration of murine leukemia virus DNA depends on mitosis. *EMBO J.* **12,** 2099–2108.

20. Roy Chowdhury, J. R., Grossman, M., Gupta, S., Roy Chowdhury, N. R., Baker, J. R., and Wilson, J. M. (1991) Long-term improvement of hypercholesterolemia after ex vivo gene therapy in LDLR-deficient rabbits. *Science* **254,** 1802–1805.

14

Methods for Delivery of Genes to Hepatocytes In Vivo Using Recombinant Adenovirus Vectors

Darlene Barr and Mark A. Kay

1. Introduction
1.1. The Liver as a Target Organ

In many ways, the liver represents an ideal target organ for gene delivery. Anatomically, the sheer bulk of its tissue mass and its dual blood supply are advantageous for intravascular injection of virus into either portal or systemic circulation. The portal vein provides a direct iv route into the liver. It also theoretically provides an indirect route by oral administration since the portal system drains the gut.

The liver is the site of production of a large number of proteins functioning in a wide variety of physiologic functions including metabolism, coagulation, cholesterol packaging, detoxification, and other enzymatic activities. Hepatic deficiencies result in human diseases that are potentially correctable by introduction of the cDNA or gene expressing the missing protein. Examples of these diseases include inborn errors of metabolism, such as tyrosinemia (type 1), phenylketonuria, ornithine transcarbamylase deficiency, and alpha 1-antitrypsin deficiency. Other hepatic protein deficiencies include lipoprotein receptor deficiencies that result in considerable cardiovascular mortality. In theory, exogenous proteins can be produced since hepatocytes are well equipped for secretion into plasma. Erythropoietin is one example of a protein that may be heterotopically produced in the liver with potential benefit to thousands with anemia secondary to chronic renal failure.

1.2. Gene Transfer into Hepatocytes

A number of different vectors and procedures have been developed for hepatic gene transfer. Both ex vivo and in vivo methods have been used. These

From: *Methods in Molecular Medicine, Gene Therapy Protocols*
Edited by: P. Robbins Humana Press Inc., Totowa, NJ

approaches have been reviewed *(1,2)*. The widely used retroviral vectors require dividing hepatocytes for gene transfer, resulting in low transduction rates (1–2%), but long-term gene expression.

1.3. Advantages of Adenoviral Vectors for Hepatocyte Transduction

Adenoviruses are linear, double-stranded DNA viruses that are unencapsulated and icosahedral. They are pathogenic in humans but infection generally results in a mild upper respiratory disease. Most adults have been exposed to a type of adenovirus. Of the more than 43 serotypes identified in humans, serotypes 2 and 5 are the most widely used as vectors. None have been associated with malignancy in humans and their safety has been demonstrated by use of live viral vaccines in the 1970s *(3,4)*. In addition to its safety, adenovirus (Ad) is an attractive vector from the viewpoint of the molecular biologist. The Ad life cycle has been extensively studied and its genome mapped *(3)*. The Ad genome is divided into early (E1–E4) and late (L1–L5) transcription regions. The virus can be rendered replication defective by deleting the E1 region. After E1 deletion, the virus can still be grown and manipulated in vitro in a permissive cell line, such as 293, Ad 5-transformed human embryonic kidney cells that supply E1 in *trans*. Additional deletions in the E3 region can be utilized to accommodate a fairly large amount of foreign DNA, up to 8.5 kb *(3,5,6)*. Advanced generation vectors deleted for various portions of the viral genome are being developed by a number of different laboratories. Adenovirus is easily concentrated and purified to titers in the range of 10^{11}–10^{12} viral plaque forming units (PFU)/mL.

The adenovirus exhibits a natural tropism for the respiratory tract but is also capable of transducing many other tissues, including the liver. A major advantage of using adenovirus is the ability to transduce nondividing cells in direct contrast to retroviruses. Efficient transduction of hepatocytes has been demonstrated both in culture and in mouse models. Approximately 95–100% of hepatocytes can be transduced in vivo by injecting 1×10^{10} viral PFU systemically *(7)*. Recombinant adenovirus has been used for hepatic gene transfer to express therapeutic gene products in mice *(8–10)*, rats *(11)*, rabbits *(12)*, and dogs *(13)*.

1.4. Disadvantages of Adenoviral Vectors

Despite the advantage of high levels of transgene protein production, the expression is transient, disappearing over a period of weeks to months. The mechanism for shutdown is related to cell-mediated immunity against infected cells *(14)*. Furthermore, secondary transduction of heptaocytes using adenoviral vectors has been unsuccessful, likely owing to the generation of neutralizing antibodies after the first infusion *(9,15)*.

In this chapter, we describe the details of intraportal and systemic iv methods of delivering adenoviral vectors in a mouse model. The principles are the same in other animal models as briefly described at the end.

2. Materials

1. Dialysis Buffer: 10 mM Tris-HCl pH 8.0, 1 mM MgCl$_2$, 10% glycerol.
2. Human 293 cells grown in HgDMEM with 10% fetal calf serum, and 1 mM glutamine, penicillin/streptomycin is optional.
3. Mice: 12–30 g.
4. Ear tags or ear punch device for animal identification.
5. Avertin (tribromoethanol). Stock Solution: Mix 25 g of 2,2,2-tribromoethanol in 25 mL tert-Amyl alcohol. Store at room temperature. Protect from light. Keeps for 2 mo. Working solution: Mix 1.2 mL stock solution in 98.8 mL PBS (12 mg/mL). Store at 4°C in foil wrapped bottle. Keeps 2–3 wk.
6. Buprenorphine.
7. Mouse restraining device.
8. For portal vein injection: cork board; cotton tipped swabs. Surgical instruments: iris scissors, Adson forceps with teeth, nontoothed forceps, needle holder, 3-0 Vicryl or silk suture on a tapered needle, Gelfoam (absorbable gelatin sponge, Upjohn, Kalamazoo, MI) in 0.5 × 0.5-cm squares. Warming lights (40-watt incandescent desk lamp), tuberculin or insulin syringes with 27- or 30-gage needles, and microcentrifuge.

3. Methods

Instructions for preparation of the adenovirus for infusion into mice will be detailed. These techniques may be modified for use in other large and small animal models. General instruction in the care and handling of rodents is available in ref. *16*. Mice should be housed in accordance with standards of the institutional animal care board. Decontaminate equipment with 5% SDS or bleach prior to autoclaving.

The viral stock can be diluted in PBS or basal media without serum. Generally, we dilute virus to 0.1 mL per injection dose. Methods for both intraportal and iv injection via lateral tail veins will be described. Generally, most of the virus is taken up by the liver by either injection method *(17)*. We inject about 1 × 10^{10} PFU per animal to achieve close to 100% hepatocyte gene transduction. After portal vein infusion, up to 50 copies of adenoviral genomes are present per diploid host DNA *(7,17)*. Lesser amounts of adenovirus can be infused for lower rates of gene transfer *(7,17)*. Portal vein injection requires a laparotomy. Both techniques are performed with a general anesthetic. We suggest intraperitoneal Avertin (tribromoethanol). Tail vein injections can be performed without an anesthetic when one becomes facile with the technique.

3.1. Adenovirus Preparation

1. The methods used are modified from Graham and Prevec *(4)*.
2. Grow a human cell line such as 293 to 70% confluence. Remove media from cells.
3. Add the thawed adenovirus at a multiplicity of infection (MOI) of 10 viral. Incubate at room temperature for 1 h, occasionally swirling the plate.
4. Replace with 10 mL fresh media per 10-cm dish. Incubate until full cytopathic effect is noted, usually 36–48 h later.
5. Harvest cells by pipeting media until they lift off the plate and centrifuge gently to pellet cells. Add small volume of PBS. Total volume about 36 mL/125–10-cm dish or 50–15-cm dish.
6. Lyse cells: Thaw cells/PBS at 37°C. Repeat freeze and thaw two more times.
7. Spin out cellular debris on a table-top centrifuge before layering lysate on step gradient.
8. Step gradient: Form gradient by carefully layering CsCl solutions of the following densities in an ultraclear SW 40 Ti tube: 6 mL cell layer, 3 mL 1.25 g/cm^3, 3 mL 1.35 g/cm^3, 0.5 mL 1.5 g/cm^3.
   Spin for 1 h at 35,000 rpm, 12°C, acceleration profile 1, deceleration profile 1.
9. Adenovirus will appear as a bluish-white band at the interface between the 1.25 and 1.35 g/cm^3 layers. Collect virus. Spin virus in a second continuous 1.35 g/mL CsCl gradient. Spin in an SW 40 Ti rotor at 35,000 rpm for 16 h. Remove adenovirus (blue white band).
10. Dialyze virus overnight (50,000 mol wt cutoff) in dialysis buffer.
11. Quantitate Ad viral DNA at OD_{260}, 25-µL aliquot in 475 µL of 0.1% SDS, 10 mM Tris. One OD unit equals about 10^{12} particles/mL. Generally, the particle titer is 20–100-fold higher than the number of plaque-forming units. Plaque titer can be performed as described in ref. *4*.
12. Store in aliquots at –80°C.

3.2. Preparation

For survival experiments, mark the animal in some manner. Tail marking will be removed with normal grooming in 2–3 d. For long-term experiments, numbered ear clips work well. Patterns of triangular and circular ear punches can also be used, but the pattern must be clearly identifiable and checked periodically for distortion from chewing or healing over.

3.3. Anesthetic Management

1. Grasp the mouse tail at the base with the dominant hand. Allow the mouse to catch an edge of the cage with his forefeet. Firmly grasp posterior aspect of neck and shoulders with the nondominant hand to prevent head mobility and biting. Cradle the animal in the palm and turn abdominal side forward. Turn the animal head down to displace abdominal viscera from the lower abdomen. Inject 0.5–1.0 mL Avertin in the right lower quadrant (0.5 mL for a small 10–20 g mouse and 0.8–1.0 mL for larger mice). This dose provides approx 30 min of anesthesia of suitable depth for laparotomy.

2. Gage the depth of anesthesia by first observing for motion and breathing. The animal should be motionless except for steady respiratory effort. Second, test the response to pain by pinch or pin prick to the web space of the foot. If withdrawal of the limb is noted, an abdominal incision will not be tolerated and 25% of the dose should be repeated. If no respirations are noted and the eyes are white and glassy, the mouse is overanesthetized.

3.3. Laparotomy (for Portal Vein Injection)

1. Place the mouse supine on a cork surgical board or other flat surface. Secure extremities with tape or pins in the web spaces of feet.
2. Shave the abdomen in the midline using a small electric shaver or with light scraping using a scalpel. Swab with skin antiseptic.
3. Make a vertical midline incision using iris scissors. Tent up the skin of the abdominal wall fascia by grasping just lateral to midline with an Adson-toothed forceps to prevent injury to bowel.
4. With two fingers, gently rotate the intestines in the right lower quadrant to the left exposing the superior mesenteric vein. (The portal vein is formed by the confluence of splenic and superior mesenteric veins.) The bowels will stay in this position if covered by a moistened gauze.
5. Retract the liver lobes cephalad with a cotton tipped swab. The superior mesenteric and portal veins should be clearly visible. Confirm the identity of the portal vein by tracing its entry into the hepatic hilum.
6. Retract the small bowel mesentery inferolaterally with the nondominant hand to hold the portal vein taunt.
7. Inject the viral preparation in the portal vein (as close to the confluence of splenic and superior mesenteric veins as possible) with the dominant hand. The total volume of the infusate should not exceed 0.5 mL (we generally use 0.1 mL) and should be room temperature.
8. Withdraw the needle carefully and place a small piece of Gelfoam over the puncture site. Gelfoam, combined with gentle digital pressure, should result in hemostasis in 3–5 min. Too much pressure will cut off portal flow and will injure the liver if held for long periods of time.
9. Lift the Gelfoam off slowly with a forceps to check hemostasis. If the Gelfoam does not peel easily, add a drop or two of saline to soak it off. If still bleeding, reapply Gelfoam and pressure. If hemostasis is satisfactory but bleeding recurs after several attempts to remove the Gelfoam, it can be left in place; there is, however, an increased risk of infection.
10. Replace the intestines and liver lobes to their anatomic positions.
11. Close the skin and abdominal wall *en bloc* with a continuous suture of 3-0 silk or Vicryl. Warm saline placed in the peritoneal cavity prior to closure will help prevent dehydration.
12. Recover the animal under warming lights and examine every 15–20 min until ambulating. Provide free access to food and water. When fully recovered, animals can be observed grooming, ambulating, and feeding. If the animal exhibits signs of pain, i.e., listlessness, administer butrenorphine 2.0 mg/kg sc every 12 h.

3.4. Tail Vein Injection

1. Anesthetize mice as described.
2. Place prone on a flat surface.
3. Warm mouse tails under a lamp to induce vasodilation.
4. Lay the tail flat on the table and stroke with the thumb for further venodilation.
5. Identify the paired lateral tail veins on both sides of midline of the dorsum of the tail. They are dark blue structures that may be better appreciated in lower levels of light and by rotating the tail from side to side.
6. Steady the tail proximally with the index finger and distally with the thumb (nondominant hand).
7. With the dominant hand, insert the needle into the vein at a 45° angle from the horizontal plane of the table. (A slight bend in the needle is sometimes helpful, but take care not to lacerate the vein.) Start at the midportion of the tail so that one may move more proximally if the first attempt fails.
8. Inject with slow gentle pressure. If the needle is correctly positioned in the lumen of the vein, the injection will go in easily. If any force is required, the needle has become displaced and the injection will be sc if one is able to inject at all. (With too much force, the syringe will pop off, splashing virus in your face.) Occasionally one may observe a successful injection flowing downstream by noting the color change from the dilute infusate.
9. Withdraw the needle and apply firm digital pressure until hemostasis is assured. Recover the mice as described in Section 3.3., step 12. No postoperative analgesics should be required.

3.5. Large Animal Models

For larger animals, the scale-up in concentration of virus is roughly proportional to their size. For transduction of rat hepatocytes, we infuse 1×10^{11} PFU in 100 g animals. In dogs weighing 12–17 kg, we have perfused the portal vein with about 1.5×10^{11} PFU/kg and have obtained more than 1 adenovirus genome/copy per diploid copy of host DNA *(13)*. Kozarsky and Wilson used 1.5×10^{13} viral particles (about 1.5×10^{11} PFU) in 2–4 kg rabbits to achieve approx 100% hepatocyte transduction and 4×10^{12} particles to achieve 50–75% transduction *(12)*.

4. Notes

Most of the adenovirus is taken up by the liver by the injection routes described; however, a significant amount is taken up to lesser degrees by other tissues. (*See* Kay et al. *[13]*, Smith et al. *[9]*, and Vrancken-Peeters et al. *[17]* for tissue distribution.) The relative distribution of adenovirus is the same if the virus is administered by peripheral or portal vein infusion. More recently, a method of transducing hepatocytes by infusion via the biliary tract has been described in the rat *(18)* and mouse *(14)*. The method leads to similar hepatocyte transduction. Additionally, biliary epithelial cells are transduced at greater frequencies than by the vascular infusion methods. The persistence of gene expression varies among different mouse strains *(15)*.

5. Summary

Adenoviral vectors provide an efficient vehicle for hepatic gene delivery. Their use has been complicated by the immunologic response directed against transduced hepatocytes and the inability to retransduce cells because of humoral immunity. It is of interest that between different inbred mouse strains there can be a wide variation in the persistence of gene expression *(15)*. There is cautious optimism that less antigenic vectors *(19–21)*, possibly in combination with immunomodulatory agents *(22)*, may allow for improved adenovirus-mediated gene transfer in animals and ultimately in humans.

References

1. Strauss, M. (1994) Liver directed gene therapy: prospects and problems. *Gene Ther.* **1,** 156–164.
2. Kay, M. A. and Woo, S. L. C. Gene therapy for metabolic disorders. *Trends Genet.* **10,** 253–257.
3. Gooding, L. R. and Wold, W. S. M. Molecular mechanisms by which adenoviruses counteract antiviral immune defenses. *Crit. Rev. Immunol.* **10,** 53–71.
4. Graham, F. L. and Prevec, L. (1991) Manipulation of adenovirus vectors. *Meth. Mol. Biol.* **7,** 109–128.
5. Berkner, K. L. (1988) Development of adenovirus vectors for the expression of heterologous genes. *Biotechniques* **6,** 616–629.
6. Bett, A. J., Haddara, W., Prevec, L., and Graham, F. L. (1994) An efficient and flexible system for construction of adenovirus vectors with insertions and deletions in early regions 1 and 3. *Proc. Natl. Acad. Sci. USA* **91,** 8802–8806.
7. Li, Q., Kay, M. A., Finegold, M., Stratford-Perricaudet, and Woo, S. L. C. (1993) Assessment of recombinant adenoviral vectors for hepatic gene therapy. *Hum. Gene Ther.* **4,** 403–409.
8. Stratford-Perricaudet, L. D., Levrero, M., Chasse, J. F., Perricaudet, M., and Briand, D. (1990) Evaluation of the transfer and expression in mice of an enzyme-encoding gene using a human adenovirus vector. *Hum. Gene Ther.* **1,** 241–256.
9. Smith, T. A. G., Mehaffey, M., Kayda, D. B., Saunders, J. M., Yei, S., Trapnell, B. C., McClelland, A., and Kaleko, M. (1993) Adenovirus mediated expression of therapeutic plasma levels of human factor IX in mice. *Nature Genet.* **5,** 392–402.
10. Kay, M. A., Li, Q., Liu, T. J., Leland, F., Toman, C., Finegold, M., and Woo, S. L. C. (1992) Hepatic gene therapy: persistent expression of human alpha 1 antitrypsin in mice after direct gene delivery in vivo. *Hum. Gene. Ther.* **3,** 641–647.
11. Jaffe, H. A., Danel, C., Longenecker, G., Metzger, M., Setoguchi, Y., Rosenfeld, M. A., Grant, T. W., Thorgelrsson, S. S., Stratford-Perricaudet, L. D., Perricaudet, M., Parirani, A., Lecocq, J. P., and Crystal, R. G. (1992) Adenovirus mediated in vivo gene transfer and expression in normal rat liver. *Nature Genet.* **I,** 372–378.

12. Kozarsky, K. F., McKinley, D. R., Austin, L. L., Ruper, S. E., Stratford-Perricaudet, L. D., and Wilson, J. M. (1994) In vivo correction of low density lipoprotein receptor deficiency in the watanabe heritable hyperlipidemic rabbit with recombinant adenoviruses. *J. Biol. Chem.* **269**, 13,695–13,702.

13. Kay, M. A., Lauden, C. N., Rothenberg, S. R., Taylor, L. A., Leland, F., Wiehle, S., Fang, B., Bellinger, D., Finegold, M., Thompson, A. R., Read, M., Brinkhous, K., and Woo, S. L. C. (1994) In vivo hepatic gene therapy: complete albert transient correction of factor IX deficiency in hemophilia B dogs. *Proc. Natl. Acad. Sci. USA* **91**, 2353–2357.

14. Yang, Y., Nunes, F. A., Berencsi, K., Furth, E. E., Gönczöl, E., and Wilson, J. M. (1994) Cellular immunity to viral antigens limits E-1 deleted adenoviruses for gene therapy. *Proc. Natl. Acad. Sci. USA* **91**, 4407–4411.

15. Barr, D., Tubb, J., Ferguson, D., Scaria, A., Lieber, A., Wilson, C., Perkins, J., and Kay, M. A. (1995) Strain related variations in adenoviral-mediated transgene expression from mouse hepatocytes in vivo: comparisons between immunocompetent and immunodeficient inbred strains. *Gene Ther.* **2**, 151–155.

16. Williams, C. S. F. (1976) *Practical guide to laboratory animals.* Mosby, St. Louis, MO.

17. Vrancken Peeters, M. J. T. F. D., Lieber, A., Perkins, J., and Kay, M. A. (1996) A method for multiple portal vein infusions in mice: quantitation of adenovirus-mediated hepatic gene transfer. *Biotechniques* **20**, 278–285.

18. Yang, Y., Raper, S. E., Cohn, J. A., Engelhardt, J. F., and Wilson, J. M. (1993) An approach for treating the hepatobiliary disease of cystic fibrosis by somatic gene transfer. *Proc. Natl. Acad. Sci. USA* **90**, 4601–4615.

19. Engelhardt, J. F., Ye, X., Doranz, B., and Wilson, J. M. (1994) Ablation of E2A in recombinant adenoviruses improves transgene persistence and decreases inflammatory response in mouse liver. *Proc. Natl. Acad. Sci. USA* **91**, 6196–6200.

20. Scaria, A., Curiel, D. T., and Kay, M. A. (1995) Complementation of a human adenovirus early region 4 deletion mutant in 293 cells using adenovirus-polylysine-DNA complexes. *Gene Ther.* **2**, 295–298.

21. Wang, W., Jia Xiao-Chi, and Finer, M. H. (1995) A packaging cell line for propagation of recombinant adenovirus vectors containing two lethal gene-region deletions. *Gene Ther.* **2**, 775–783.

22. Kay, M. A., Holterman, A.-X., Meuse, L., Gown, A., Ochs, H., Linsley, P. S., and Wilson, C. B. (1995) Long-term hepatic adenovirus mediated gene expression in mice following CTLA4Ig administration. *Nature Genet.* **11**, 191–197.

15

Methods for Producing High-Titer, Pantropic Retroviral Vectors for Gene Transfer into Leukemic T-Cells

Jane C. Burns, Jiing-Kuan Yee, and Alice L. Yu

1. Introduction

Current limitations to the use of Moloney murine leukemia virus (MoMLV)-derived retroviral vectors as a tool for gene transfer include the inability to obtain high-titer vector stocks and the narrow host cell range of these vectors. To overcome these disadvantages, we developed a new class of pantropic retroviral vector that has a broadened host cell range and can be concentrated to very high titers (>10^9 colony forming units [CFU]/mL) (1).

1.1. Pantropic Retroviral Vectors

Pseudotyped pantropic vectors contain the vesicular stomatitis virus G glycoprotein (VSV-G) substituted for the retroviral envelope protein (Fig. 1). The host range of the amphotropic and ecotropic retroviral vectors is limited to cells that express a specific protein receptor on the cell surface that acts as a ligand for the envelope protein. The human amphotropic virus receptor encoded on chromosome 8 has recently been cloned and sequenced (2). The VSV-G envelope protein, in contrast, binds to phospholipid components in the cell membrane, thus permitting these VSV-G pseudotyped particles to enter virtually every cell with a plasma membrane (3). The extremely broad host cell range of these vectors has been demonstrated by infection of a wide variety of organisms including cows, goats, fish, newts, and insects (4,5 and JCB, unpublished observations).

An additional consequence of the substitution of VSV-G for the retroviral envelope protein is increased stability of the virus particle. Pantropic vectors

From: *Methods in Molecular Medicine, Gene Therapy Protocols*
Edited by: P. Robbins Humana Press Inc., Totowa, NJ

Fig. 1. Comparison of amphotropic retroviral and VSV-G envelope proteins. The figure is not drawn to scale. The placement of the disulfide bond between the subunits of the amphotropic envelope protein is arbitrary since the exact location is unknown.

can be concentrated by simple physical methods such as ultracentrifugation to high titer (10^8–10^9 CFU/mL) with greater than 75% recovery of the total number of infectious particles *(1)*. This method allows generation of vector stocks at titers sufficient for microinjection of nanoliter volumes into small cavities. Such approaches have permitted the creation of transgenic fish by microinjection of concentrated vector into the developing fish embryo *(5)*. Future human gene therapy applications may include direct injection into tumors or into discrete vascular beds for which small volume, high titer vector stocks are essential.

1.2. Application of Pantropic Vectors to Gene Therapy of Leukemia

The goal of gene therapy in leukemia is, simply stated, to convert cells with the malignant phenotype into normal cells. This can most easily be conceptualized as a treatment of cells in the bone marrow that would reconstitute normal gene function and restore the normal phenotype. To make such an approach successful, the following conditions should be met:

1. Identification of a discrete gene or genes whose mutation has resulted in the altered phenotype or whose reconstitution will result in a normal phenotype.

2. Availability of a method for therapeutic gene delivery that will allow every malignant cell to be treated.

Retroviral vector treatment could be administered either in vivo by direct iv injection of retroviral vectors or ex vivo by treatment of residual leukemic cells harvested from the bone marrow followed by reinfusion of these treated cells into the host.

Acute leukemia in childhood is an appropriate target for this type of therapeutic approach. Bone marrow transplantation (BMT) is considered the treatment of choice for acute myeloblastic leukemia (AML) in first remission and for acute lymphoblastic leukemia (ALL) in second remission. Since the majority (75%) of BMT candidates do not have an HLA-matched sibling, autologous BMT provides an important alternative, if the residual leukemic cells in the marrow can be eliminated. Current strategies to immunologically purge the bone marrow of residual leukemic cells often fail to eliminate all malignant cells. Gene therapy strategies to restore normal tumor suppressor gene function (e.g., p53) in the leukemic cells may be a useful adjunct to eliminate residual malignant cells. The easy accessibility of leukemic cells for preclinical studies make leukemia an ideal model for gene therapy. In addition, evidence is now mounting for the presence of cancer cells in the bone marrow and circulation in a variety of other malignancies, such as breast cancer, lung cancer, and neuroblastoma. Thus, gene therapy treatment of the bone marrow may have broader application to a number of solid tumors as well as hematologic malignancies.

We describe here a method to generate helper virus-free, high titer pantropic vector stocks for infection of primary human leukemic T-cells. This approach has been successfully used to infect leukemic cells harvested from the bone marrow and peripheral blood of pediatric patients with newly diagnosed or relapsed T-cell acute lymphoblastic leukemia (T-ALL). The pantropic vector was more efficient than the corresponding amphotropic retroviral vector with the identical genome in infecting human leukemic T-cells.

2. Materials

2.1. Cell Lines and Media

1. PA317 mouse fibroblasts *(6)*, 293 gag-pol human kidney epithelial cells *(1)*, and 208F rat fibroblasts *(7)* are grown in Dulbecco's Modified Eagle's Medium (DMEM) with 4.5 gm/L glucose and supplemented with 10% fetal calf serum, penicillin (100 U/mL), streptomycin (100 μg/mL), and L-glutamine (2 mM).
2. Human T-cells are grown in RPMI-1640 supplemented with 10% fetal calf serum, antibiotics, and L-glutamine as in item 1.
3. Syringe-tip filters (0.45- and 0.2-μm).

2.2. Reagents and Solutions for Cell Culture,
Infection of T-Cells, and Concentration of Pantropic Vector

1. Polybrene stock solution (4 mg/mL): Dissolve 0.4 g of hexadimethrine bromide in 100 mL of sterile water and store at 4°C.
2. Protamine sulfate stock solution (2.5 mg/mL): dissolve 250 mg protamine sulfate (tissue culture grade, Sigma, St. Louis, MO) in 100 mL PBS. Filter sterilize and store at 4°C.
3. G418 stock solution (40 mg/mL): Dissolve 4 g active Geneticin (Gibco-BRL, Gaithersburgh, MD) in 100 mL 0.1M HEPES, pH 7.9, filter sterilize, and store at 4°C.
4. Phosphate-buffered saline (PBS): 137 mM NaCl, 2.6 mM KCl, 8.1 mM Na$_2$HPO$_4$, 1.5 mM KH$_2$PO$_4$. Autoclave and store at room temperature.
5. 0.1X Hank's Balanced Salt Solution (HBSS): Dilute 1 mL HBSS in 9 mL sterile ddH$_2$O and store at 4°C.
6. Auszyme EIA kit, Abbot Laboratories, North Chicago, IL.
7. Giemsa stain.
8. Phorbol 12-myristate 13-acetate (PMA) stock solution: Reconstitute the contents of the vial containing PMA with DMSO to make a final concentration of 20 μg/mL. Store at –20°C.
9. Calcium ionophore stock solution: Dissolve 5.2 mg in DMSO to give a final concentration of 2 mM. Store at –20°C.
10. rIL-2 stock solution: 1 × 10^5 U/mL in RPMI. Store at 4°C.

2.3. Reagents for Detection
of Retroviral Genome in Infected Cells

1. Cell lysis buffer: 100 mM NaCl, 10 mM Tris-HCl, pH 7.4, 25 mM EDTA, 0.5% SDS, and 200 μg/mL proteinase K. Store buffer at 4°C and add proteinase K (frozen stock) just before use.
2. 10X Taq buffer: 500 mM KCl, 100 mM Tris-HCl, pH 8.4, 15 mM MgCl$_2$. Store at 4°C.
3. PCR primers for S gene: Dilute to a final concentration of 6.25 μM. Use 1 μL each primer/reaction.
   a. Upstream primer sequence for S gene: 5' GGC TAT CGC TGG ATG TGT CT 3'.
   b. Downstream primer sequence for S gene: 5' ACT GAA CAA ATG GCA CTA GT 3'.
4. 10X dNTP stock solution: dilute dCTP, dUTP, dATP, and dGTP with ddH$_2$O to a final concentration of 2 mM. Store at 4°C.

3. Methods
3.1. Production of Pantropic Vector

Pantropic vectors can be produced with a wide variety of genes and internal promoters. Described here is the production of the pantropic vector LSRNL *(8)* in which the Hepatitis B surface antigen gene (S) is expressed from the 5'

LSRNL

Fig. 2. Genetic organization of vector, LSRNL. LTR or L, Moloney murine leukemia virus long terminal repeat; HBsAg or S, Hepatitis B surface antigen; RSV or R, Rous sarcoma virus long terminal repeat; neo or N, neomycin phosphotransferase.

Moloncy murine leukemia virus LTR (L) and the neomycin phosphotransferase gene (N) is expressed from the Rous sarcoma virus LTR (R) (Fig. 2). This retroviral construct has the advantage that clones may be screened for S antigen production by simply sampling the culture media from each clone and using the Auszyme EIA kit to easily and quickly determine the relative amounts of S antigen in the supernatant. This process identifies the clone that is most likely to produce high titers of pantropic vector when the cells are subsequently transfected with the VSV-G plasmid.

The general method for production of pantropic virus is illustrated in Fig. 3. In the first step, amphotropic virus is produced in PA317 cells. In the second step, this virus is used to infect 293 cells stably expressing the MoMLV *gag* and *pol* genes. Pantropic virus particles are produced when the 293 gag-pol/LSRNL cells are transfected with a plasmid expressing the VSV-G protein under the control of a strong promoter (hCMV).

All work with pantropic retroviral vectors is performed according to Biosafety Level-2 (BSL-2) practices. It should be remembered that, although pantropic vectors are replication incompetent, they readily infect a broad range of cells including all dividing human cells. Care must be taken to avoid creating aerosols of the virus except inside a tissue culture hood equipped with a HEPA filter.

3.1.1. Generation of Stable 293 gag-pol Producer Cell Line

1. Day 1: Seed approx $1-5 \times 10^5$ PA317 cells in a 10-cm tissue culture plate.
2. Day 2: Transfect by standard calcium phosphate coprecipitation *(9)* with 20 μg pLSRNL.
3. Day 3: Seed approx 1×10^5 293 gag-pol cells in a 10-cm tissue culture plate for infection on d 4.
4. Day 4: Aspirate and filter (0.45-μm) supernatant from PA317 cells transfected on d 2. Use 1–2 mL to infect 293 gag-pol cells in the presence of 8 μg/mL polybrene.
5. Day 5: At least 16 h after infection, aspirate culture medium from infected 293 gag-pol cells and replace with fresh medium containing 400 μg/mL of G418. Continue to refeed culture with fresh medium containing G418 until resistant colonies appear in 12–14 d. Because 293 gag-pol cells adhere only loosely to the

PRODUCTION OF VSV-G PSEUDOTYPED VECTORS

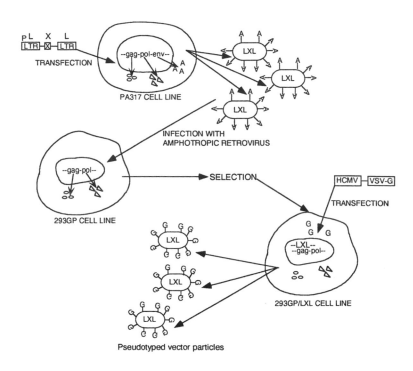

Fig. 3. Method for production of pantropic retroviral vectors.

tissue culture plate, care must be taken to avoid disturbing the colonies when changing the medium.

6. Week 2: Aspirate all medium from the plate of colonies. Pick individual G418-resistant colonies by placing 3 µL of media directly over colony with a micropipetor. Aspirate up and down to dislodge the cells and transfer to G418-containing medium in a 24-well plate. Repeat the procedure until 10–20 colonies have been selected.

7. To screen colonies for S gene production, aspirate 200 µL of culture media per clone *(8)*. Use the manufacturer's instructions for Procedure B to test supernatants for the amount of S antigen secreted into the medium.

3.1.2. Generation of Pantropic Vector

1. Day 1: To generate pantropic vector, choose the clone with the highest production of S antigen and seed a 10-cm plate with $1–5 \times 10^5$ cells.

2. Day 2: Transfect these cells by calcium phosphate coprecipitation with 20 µg of the plasmid hCMV-VSV-G. Remove the calcium phosphate-DNA precipitate

after 6–8 h and gently replace medium. Care must be taken not to disturb the monolayer, as the cells are fragile and poorly adherent after transfection. Longer incubation with the precipitate will kill the cells.

3. Day 3: Seed a 10-cm plate with 1×10^5 208F rat fibroblasts for titering virus.
4. Days 4–6: Collect virus-containing culture supernatant once a day beginning 48 h after transfection. The highest titer virus is produced at 48–96 h post-transfection. Culture supernatant should be filtered (0.45-μm) and an aliquot removed to determine virus titer. Remaining supernatant may be frozen at –70°C until needed.
5. To titer virus, dilute appropriately with DMEM (e.g., anticipate 1×10^6 cfu/mL, use 20 μL of 1:1000 dilution of virus per 10-cm plate) and add diluted virus to 208F cells in the presence of polybrene (8 μg/mL).
6. After overnight incubation with virus and polybrene, replace medium with DMEM complete medium containing G418 (400 μg/mL). Replace medium every 3–4 d until colonies are visible (usually 10–14 d).
7. Fix colonies in methanol and stain with Giemsa stain to facilitate counting colonies. Calculate titer of virus. Assume that each colony represents one infectious unit of virus.

3.2. Concentration of Pantropic Vector

1. UV sterilize swinging buckets, caps, and ultracentrifuge tubes for an SW41 or other suitable swinging bucket rotor.
2. Under sterile conditions, transfer viral culture supernatant to the centrifuge tubes, and tighten caps.
3. To pellet virus particles, centrifuge at 50,000g (25K in an SW41 rotor) for 90 min at 4°C. Decant supernatant and wipe inside walls of tube with a tissue (nonsterile Kimwipe works well) to remove excess medium. Place tube upright in ice and add 30 μL 0.1X HBSS/tube. Allow invisible pellet to resuspend overnight at 4°C.
4. Resuspend pellet by pipeting vigorously up and down but avoid foaming the solution. Concentrated vectors stocks may be frozen at –70°C for at least 3 mo without loss of titer (*see* Note 3).

3.3. Infection of T-Cells

1. Separate leukemic cells from bone marrow by Ficoll-Hypaque centrifugation.
2. Pre-incubate mononuclear cells with PMA (20 ng/mL) and 2 μ*M* calcium ionophore for 3 h at 37°C.
3. Suspend cells in RPMI-1640 supplemented with 10% fetal calf serum and 200 U/mL IL-2.
4. Aliquot 1×10^7 cells/tube and incubate overnight at 37°C with 5 μg/mL protamine sulfate and virus stock (MOI 0.5–2.0) added to culture medium (*see* Note 2).
5. Wash cells and resuspend in RPMI with additives. Analyze at 48 h after infection for presence of provirus in cells (*see* Note 1).

3.4. Detection of Provirus in Infected T-Cells

A polymerase chain reaction (PCR) assay can be used to detect provirus in infected T-cells. A positive PCR signal documents that attachment, uncoating, and reverse transcription of the RNA genome into the DNA provirus have successfully occurred. It should be noted that the following assay detects infected cells containing proviral DNA but does not provide information about integration of the provirus into the host cell genome (*see* Note 4).

1. Lyse approx 1×10^5 cells infected 48–72 h previously with the pantropic vector, LSRNL, in 500 μL cell lysis buffer at 37°C overnight.
2. Isolate the DNA following phenol extraction and isopropanol precipitation and resuspend in 25–100 μL sterile ddH$_2$O.
3. Quantitate the concentration of DNA spectrophotometrically and use 0.5–1 μg DNA per PCR reaction.
4. Add the DNA to a 500-μL Eppendorf tube containing 50 μL of mineral oil. Centrifuge briefly and heat at 100°C for 2 min. Quickly chill on ice.
5. Prepare the PCR reaction mix (25 μL final volume) by mixing 0.5 μ*M* each primer, 200 μ*M* dNTP's, 2 U *Taq* DNA polymerase, 2.5 μL 10X *Taq* buffer, and sufficient water to equal 25 μL when mixed with the DNA. Chill reaction mix on ice and add to DNA by centrifuging briefly so that reaction components are below mineral oil overlay.
6. Place the reaction tube in a thermal cycling device and proceed with the following thermal profile: 94°C for 3 min, followed by 40 cycles of 94°C for 1 min, 58°C for 40 s, and 72°C for 40 s. End with a final extension step at 72°C for 5 min.
7. Analyze 10 μL of PCR reaction mixture on a 2% agarose gel stained with ethidium bromide. If additional sensitivity is required, the resolved DNA can be transferred to a nylon membrane and hybridized with a labeled S PCR product probe to visualize the predicted 334 bp amplification product.

4. Notes

1. In addition to the virus particles with their RNA genome, culture supernatants also contain contaminating S protein as well as DNA fragments from the producer cells containing provirus. It is not possible, therefore, to reliably measure S antigen in the T-cell culture supernatants with the Auszyme kit, as one cannot distinguish between preformed S antigen from the 293 gag-pol/LSRNL cells and newly synthesized S antigen from the LSRNL-infected T-cells. Similarly, cells must be washed extensively to remove contaminating provirus derived from the 293 gag-pol/LSRNL cells before DNA is extracted for PCR analysis to confirm T-cell infection. Alternatively, a method of DNA extraction in which nuclei are separated from membranes before lysis may be used.
2. Protamine sulfate must be used as the polycation during infection of T-cells as polybrene is toxic to primary T-cells, even at low concentrations (>4 μg/mL). Poly-L-lysine (5 μg/mL) may also be used.

3. With one round of centrifugation, vector stocks can easily be concentrated 100-fold with >90% recovery of infectious particles *(1)*. If further concentration of vector is required, a second round of centrifugation achieves an additional 10-fold concentration of vector with approx 75 % recovery of infectious particles.

4. The S PCR assay presented here can detect 100 copies of target sequence in a background of 1 µg of genomic DNA by ethidium bromide stained gel and 1 copy of target sequence by Southern hybridization.

References

1. Burns, J. C., Friedmann, T., Dreiver, W., Burrascano, M., and Yee, J.-K. (1993) Vesicular stomatitis virus G glycoprotein pseudotyped retroviral vectors: concentration to very high titer and efficient gene transfer into mammalian and nonmammalian cells. *Proc. Natl. Acad. Sci. USA* **90,** 8033–8037.

2. van Zeijl, M., Johann, S. V., Closs, E., Cummingham, J., Eddy, R., Shows, T. B., and O'Hara, B. (1994) A human amphotropic retrovirus receptor is a second member of the gibbon ape leukemia virus receptor family. *Proc. Natl. Acad. Sci. USA* **91,** 1168–1172.

3. Mastromarino, P., Conti, C., Goldoni, P., Hauttecoeur, B., and Orsi, N. (1987) Characterization of membrane components of the erythrocyte involved in vesicular stomatitis virus attachment and fusion at acidic pH. *J. Gen. Virol.* **68,** 2359–2369.

4. Burns, J. C., Matsubara, T., Lozinski, G., Yee, J.-K., Friedmann, T., Washabaugh, C. H., and Tsonis, P. A. (1994) Pantropic retroviral vector-mediated gene transfer, integration, and expression in cultured newt limb cells. *Develop. Biol.* **165,** 285–289.

5. Lin, S., Gaiano, N., Culp, P., Burns, J. C., Friedmann, T., Yee, J.-K., and Hopkins, N. (1994) Integration and germ-line transmission of a pseudotyped retroviral vector in zebrafish. *Science* **265,** 666–668.

6. Miller, A. D. and Buttimore, C. (1986) Redesign of retrovirus packaging lines to avoid recombination leading to helper virus production. *Mol. Cell. Biol.* **6,** 2895–2902.

7. Quade, K. (1979) Transformation of mammalian cells by avian myelocytomatosis virus and avian erythroblastosis virus. *Virology* **98,** 416–465.

8. Miyanohara, A., Elam, R. L., Witztum, J. L., and Friedmann, T. (1992) Long-term transgene expression for genetically modified hepatocytes grafted to the rat liver. *New Biologist* **4,** 261–267.

9. Graham, F. L. and van der Eb, A. J. (1973). A new technique for the assay of infectivity of human adenovirus 5 DNA. *Virology* **52,** 456–467.

16

Methods for Efficient Retrovirus-Mediated Gene Transfer to Mouse Hematopoietic Stem Cells

John W. Belmont and Roland Jurecic

1. Introduction

A variety of genetic and acquired diseases could conceivably be treated by gene therapy targeted to hematopoietic stem cells (HSC). Inevitably, the effort to develop reliable methods of gene transfer into stem cells has raised many questions about their biology and role in the development and maintenance of hematopoiesis. As a result, we currently have a convergence of research goals in the areas of stem cell biology and gene therapy. Murine models for stem cell transduction have played a useful role in establishing two basic principles: retroviral vectors can transduce pluripotent self-renewing hematopoietic stem cells and retroviral vectors can express foreign gene products in the differentiated progeny of stem cells. Murine models also have allowed the identification of several key factors that allow efficient transduction of stem cells and each of these is dealt with here. However, methods for stem cell transduction that are effective with mouse cells have only been partially successful in dog, nonhuman primate, and human models. Whereas scale-up of stem cell transduction procedures for human applications will present unique technical problems, mouse models may yet provide further insight into the mechanisms of efficient stem cell gene transfer that can then be used to design enhanced and reproducible protocols.

1.1. Developmental Hierarchy of Murine Hematopoietic System

Hematopoiesis is an ongoing developmental process by which large numbers of mature blood cells with very specific functions and limited life-spans are continually replenished. Experiments using retroviral integration markers

From: *Methods in Molecular Medicine, Gene Therapy Protocols*
Edited by: P. Robbins Humana Press Inc., Totowa, NJ

have demonstrated that all blood cell types in mice originate from a common cell termed pluripotent hematopoietic stem cell (HSC) and provided some of the most rigorous evidence available for the existence of a transplantable stem cell *(1–5)*. The HSC are defined functionally by their potential to regenerate and maintain all lineages upon transplantation into lethally irradiated or immunodeficient mice and are thus also called long-term repopulating (LTR) cells. Stem cells arise during embryonic development from the extraembryonic mesoderm as the yolk sac blood islands form. They then migrate to the fetal liver (where hematopoiesis takes place later during *in utero* development) and finally, take up residence in the bone marrow (BM), where they continue to survive in adulthood. The hematopoietic system is maintained by self-renewal and differentiation of HSC into uncommitted and committed progenitor cells, which in turn give rise to mature blood cells. Hematopoiesis is regulated by an intricate network of interactions between hematopoietic cells, cells of the hematopoietic microenvironment (stromal cells), and various growth factors. Proliferation, differentiation, and functional maturation of all hematopoietic cell types seem to be regulated by various hematopoietic growth factors (HGFs), which include interleukins (ILs), colony stimulating factors (CSFs), stem cell factors (SCF), leukemia inhibitory factors (LIF), erythropoietin (Epo), and other factors (interferons, transforming growth factors, tumor necrosis factors) *(6–10)*. The establishment of efficient protocols for gene transfer into murine hematopoietic cells as well as the assessment of gene transfer efficiency have depended on various in vitro and in vivo assays for hematopoietic progenitors and LTR cells.

1.2. In Vitro Models for Murine Hematopoiesis

1.2.1. Colony Assays for Mouse Progenitors

In the mid 1960s, semisolid culture techniques that allow the clonal growth of murine BM cells with added growth factors were developed *(11)*. These assays for colony forming cells (CFC) provided evidence for the presence of myeloid and lymphoid progenitor cells that are able to produce single and multilineage colonies of differentiated cells. Lineage-committed progenitors that can be demonstrated by CFC assays include progenitors for granulocytes (CFU-G), macrophages (CFU-M), erythrocytes (CFU-E), granulocytes and macrophages (CFU-GM), B-lymphocytes (CFU-B), and multilineage progenitors for granulocytes, erythrocytes, macrophages, and megakaryocytes (CFU-GEMM or CFU-Mix) *(10,11)*. Further modifications of the basic CFC assay have been developed that allow assessment of more primitive or noncommitted progenitor cell populations. Blast cell colony assays (CFU-Bl) detect colonies consisting of cells that are morphologically immature and, when replated, give rise to secondary colonies of various lineages including more blast cell colonies *(12)*. The high proliferative potential colony forming cell (HPP-CFC) assay detects very large colonies (>0.5-mm diameter) at 10–12 d of culture, formed by rare cells from normal or 5-fluorouracil-treated bone marrow. Recent studies indicate that HPP-CFC cells share many of the features of HSC *(13)*. All these CFC assays have allowed the identification, purification, and cloning of numerous cytokine regulatory proteins, specific for growth of these colonies. They have also proven useful in analysis of gene transfer efficiency into murine committed and primitive progenitors. Individual colonies, derived from transduced BM cells, can be analyzed by PCR for proviral integration and for expression by other means to reflect retrovirus infection efficiency. For example, cells transduced with a *neo*-containing retrovirus can be selected in G418 for expression of the provirus. Other assays applicable to study of provirus expression in individual colonies include: analysis of isolated mRNA by reverse-transcription to cDNA and subsequent PCR (RT-PCR), microenzyme analysis, and immunocytochemistry on cytospin slides.

1.2.2. Long-Term Culture of Murine Bone Marrow

Long-term bone marrow cultures (LTBMC) have been particularly useful in the study of hematopoiesis, as the complex microenvironment of mammalian bone marrow precludes accurate and intensive analysis of this process in vivo. When cultured together, hemopoietic cells and marrow stromal cells can support hematopoiesis in vitro in the absence of added growth factors *(14–19)*. Stromal cells sustain hematopoiesis by cell–cell interactions, cell–matrix interactions, and secreted growth factors *(7–10)*. In LTBMC, cellular kinetics is in a dynamic equilibrium. For several months the loss of committed progenitors and mature cells through differentiation and cell death is balanced by constant differentiation of more primitive uncommitted progenitors. Thus, LTBMC share many characteristics with in vivo hematopoiesis and may be considered as an in vitro counterpart of the bone marrow. Simple manipulation of the culture conditions can be used to influence the type of hematopoiesis that is supported (e.g., myelopoiesis vs lymphopoiesis). The myeloid LTBMC selectively supports growth and differentiation of myeloerythroid pluripotent and committed progenitors (CFU-S, CFU-GEMM, CFU-GM cells) as evidenced by their transplantation into irradiated animals and by CFC assays. Although myeloid cultures do not contain cells with lymphoid surface markers, they do contain lymphoid precursor cells, as evidenced by their ability to reconstitute B- and T-lymphocytes in irradiated animals or B-cell progenitors (CFU-B) in immunodeficient CBA/N and SCID mice *(14–16)*. The lymphoid LTBMC selectively supports growth and differentiation of B-lineage cells from very early precursors to membrane IgM-bearing B-cells. All available evidence indicates that lymphoid LTBMC are restricted to B-lymphoid differentiative pathway, since T-cells and cells of the myeloid lineage are undetectable as assessed by immunofluorescence and in vivo reconstitution experiments in immunodeficient or lethally irradiated mice. Furthermore, lymphopoiesis ceases and myelopoiesis does not establish upon transfer of established lymphoid cultures to myeloid culture conditions *(17–19)*. In both LTBMC systems, the establishment and maintenance of active hematopoiesis depends on clonal proliferation and differentiation of primitive hemopoietic cells called long-term culture-initiating cells (LTC-IC) *(20,21)*. The kinetics of lymphoid LTBMC establishment have indicated that cells initiating hematopoiesis in lymphoid cultures are primitive lymphoid precursors, which are closely related to pluripotent stem cells *(22)*. Long-term bone marrow cultures have played an important role in the establishment of protocols for cell-free retroviral vector transduction of LTC-IC cells and HSC, which included autologous or heterologous stromal support.

1.3. In Vivo Models for Murine Hematopoiesis

Although in vitro systems have proven useful in the analysis of committed and primitive progenitors, it has been difficult to correlate the growth of cells in culture with the maintenance and differentiation of the most primitive progenitors and stem cells. Analysis of these cells has depended on BM transplantation into lethally irradiated recipients. Three in vivo assays have been established and widely applied in the study of primitive progenitors and HSC *(6)*. The first assay detects the myeloerythroid-restricted precursors, termed colony forming unit-spleen (CFU-S) cells, that home to the spleen of recipient animals after injection *(23)*. The quantitative nature of this assay is based on a direct linear relationship between splenic nodules or colonies present 8–12 d after transplantation and the number of cells injected and the clonal origin of colonies. The second assay, termed marrow repopulation assay (MRA), detects the population of pre-CFU-S cells or marrow repopulating CFU-S d 12 cells (MRA-CFU-S$_{12}$) *(24)*. These cells are present in the marrow 12–14 d after initial transplant and are defined by their ability to generate CFU-S$_{12}$ in a secondary recipient. The MRA assay provides semiquantitative results that can be used to compare different populations for hematopoietic repopulating ability. These two assays have found broad application in retroviral vector-mediated gene transfer studies. They have been used extensively to identify conditions that enhance transduction of primitive hematopoietic progenitors by causing their proliferation or expanding their pool *(25,26)*.

The hematopoietic stem cell activity, defined by long-term repopulation of all hematopoietic lineages in irradiated animals, has been analyzed with long-term reconstitution (LTR) and competitive repopulation assays (CRA) *(27,28)*.

In these assays, the test population is transplanted into lethally irradiated animals without (LTR assay) or with (CRA assay) an excess of syngeneic BM cells whose LTR capacity has been markedly reduced by two previous cycles of serial transplantation. The latter compromised population contains a normal frequency of mature clonogenic progenitors; they provide short-term support for recovering transplant recipients, but, in the later stage of engraftment, exert very little competitive pressure on test population. Genetically marked cells (isolated from transgenic mice) or congenic marker systems (Ly-5) are used to detect progeny of test population. Three to six months after transplant, peripheral blood of reconstituted animals is periodically analyzed for lineage-specific markers and donor vs host cells. As a final test for stem cell activity, bone marrow of reconstituted primary recipients can be transplanted into secondary recipients and ability of test population to generate all hematopoietic lineages in secondary hosts is analyzed. However, since the above assays are not quantitative, it is unclear whether reconstitution originates from individual pluripotent cells or various primitive progenitors (6). In comparison, stem cell marking by retroviral vector insertion offers the unique advantage of allowing determination of clonal relatedness among groups of repopulating cells. To quantitate LTR cells in BM populations enriched for HSC, limited numbers of genetically marked cells (1–20 cells) are coinjected with syngeneic BM cells into lethally irradiated animals and level of repopulation by marked cells is analyzed as described (6).

To study reconstitution in murine transplantation models, various properties unique to the repopulating cells have been exploited. In addition to using a Y-chromosome marker to study repopulation in sex-mismatched transplants, various polymorphic loci on congenic backgrounds (hemoglobin, glucose-phosphate-isomerase, Thy-1, and Ly-5 antigens) have proven useful for analyzing the differentiation of repopulating cells into mature hematopoietic lineages. Along with CFU-S and LTR assays, these markers have been particularly informative in the development of stem cell enrichment protocols and functional analysis of enriched populations.

1.4. Enrichment of Murine Hematopoietic Stem Cells

Enrichment of murine HSC has depended on development of fluorescence-activated cell sorter (FACS) separation techniques, based on cell surface antigen expression, lectin binding, and uptake of fluorescent vital dyes. A rare population of mouse BM cells (0.05%) was isolated by FACS, which expresses low levels of Thy-1 antigen (Thy-1^{lo}), high levels of Sca-1 antigen (stem cell antigen-1, a member of the Ly-6A/E antigen family) and is lineage-negative (Lin$^-$), i.e., it does not express markers characteristic of B-cells, T-cells, granulocytes, and myelomonocytic cells. Small numbers of Thy-1^{lo}Lin$^-$Sca-1$^+$ and

Lin⁻Sca-1⁺ cells can generate long-term repopulation of both lymphoid and myeloid lineages, protect mice from lethal irradiation, and further repopulate secondary recipients *(29–33)*.

Further fractionation of Thy-1^{lo}Lin⁻Sca-1⁺ and Lin⁻Sca-1⁺ cells on the basis of *c-kit* proto-oncogene (receptor for stem cell factor—SCF) expression has shown that long-term repopulating ability is essentially restricted to cells expressing the Sca-1 antigen and *c-kit*, but has also underlined functional heterogeneity of both enriched populations *(34)*. Studies of long-term repopulation by Thy-1^{lo}Lin⁻Sca-1⁺ cells have confirmed that this population contains in vitro colony-forming cells (CFC), d-12 CFU-S, long-term repopulating (LTR) cells for both the myeloid and lymphoid lineages and cells capable of long-term repopulation of only the lymphoid lineage *(33)*. Cell cycle analysis of Thy-1^{lo}Lin⁻ Sca-1⁺ cells has shown that a significant proportion (18–22%) of these cells are actively proliferating during steady-state hematopoiesis and that this subpopulation exhibits reduced stem cell activity *(35)*. Recent purification and functional analysis of Lin⁻Sca-1⁺ cells that express carbohydrate binding sites for the lectin wheat-germ agglutinin (WGA) have demonstrated that this population (Lin⁻Sca-1⁺WGA⁺ cells), although highly enriched for LTR and CFU-S cells, is still functionally heterogenous *(36,37)*. In spite of substantial progress in purification of cell populations highly enriched for stem cell activity, novel markers are needed to more precisely define the phenotype of LTR cells and separate them from the rest of the primitive hematopoietic cells. However, purification of rare BM populations has enabled retroviral transduction and assessment of gene transfer efficiency into highly enriched primitive hematopoietic progenitors and stem cells.

1.5. Ex Vivo Maintenance
of Murine Primitive Hematopoietic Cells

The CFC assays and procedures for enrichment of progenitor and stem cells have enabled the study of growth factor requirements of these rare cells that might lead to culture conditions for their propagation without differentiation—a key goal in gene therapy research. The analysis of in vitro response of phenotypically and functionally defined murine progenitor and stem cell populations to various growth factors has shown that Thy-1^{lo}Lin⁻Sca-1⁺ and Lin⁻Sca-1⁺ cells are generally not responsive to any single factor tested but require a combination of factors (IL-1, IL-3, IL-6, G-CSF, M-CSF, GM-CSF, SCF) for maximal colony formation in CFC assays *(32,34,38–40)*. These studies have revealed a synergistic pattern of action of multiple growth factors and suggested that primitive murine hematopoietic cells need multiple GF signaling for entering the cell cycle and initiation of differentiation. Furthermore, culture of Thy-1^{lo}Lin⁻Sca-1⁺ and Thy-1^{lo}Lin⁻Sca-1⁻ cells at limiting dilution in Dexter's myeloid LTC has demonstrated that only this rare population contains cells with LTC-IC activity *(41)*.

Further efforts, directed toward determining the combination of factors that support survival and cycling of primitive progenitors and stem cells without differentiation have demonstrated that SCF in synergy with IL-3 and IL-6 induces expansion of CFC and CFU-S cells in vitro and in vivo *(42–44)*. Recently it was shown that SCF, IL-6, and Epo induce amplification of Sca-1$^+$Lin$^-$WGA$^+$ cells in serum-free cultures with maintenance of long-term reconstituting cells *(37)*. Furthermore, the analysis of mice deficient for LIF has generated evidence that LIF is required for the survival of HSC, but not their terminal differentiation *(45)*.

1.6. Efficient Gene Transfer to Mouse Hematopoietic Stem Cells

The low frequency of HSC in the bone marrow (one in 10^4–10^5 nucleated cells) presents a difficult problem for gene transfer, making efficient transduction of such a rare subpopulation dependent on near quantitative gene transfer. The first demonstration that hematopoietic progenitors could be transduced with a retroviral vector was provided by Joyner et al. *(46)*. In those experiments, a vector carrying the bacterial Tn5, neomycin phosphotransferase (*neo*) gene was shown to confer G418 resistance to murine hematopoietic colonies. Williams et al. *(47)* and Dick et al. *(48)* extended these studies by demonstrating that very primitive precursors could also be transduced by similar vectors. After some early problems with the design of vectors that were permissive for expression of foreign genes, numerous publications have demonstrated conclusively that retroviral vectors can express genes at physiologically relevant levels in the differentiated progeny of stem cells (49–51).

Gene transfer to murine hematopoietic cells has been achieved using retroviral vectors containing a variety of genes, including the bacterial neomycin-resistance gene (neo^r), human dihydrofolate reductase (DHFR), and multidrug resistance-1 (MDR1) genes, human β-globin, human adenosine deaminase (ADA), CD18, and glucocerebrosidase (GC) *(49–51)*. Several groups have demonstrated retrovirus-mediated gene transfer of human ADA into mouse HSC in the absence of replication-competent retrovirus. Stable and potentially therapeutic levels of in vivo expression of the human ADA were achieved in all hematopoietic tissues of recipient mice *(52,53)*. Although some early studies suggested that expression in stem cells was limited by regulation of the retroviral long terminal repeat promoters, multiple examples have subsequently shown that such simple vectors do express introduced genes. These studies have demonstrated that the single most important factor limiting long-term expression is the efficiency with which stem cells are transduced.

A number of variables appear to be important for efficient transduction of murine primitive progenitors and stem cells, such as: use of very high titer viruses (>10^6 infectious particles/mL), 5-fluorouracil pretreatment of the donor animals prior to BM harvest, gradient separation of BM cells for enrichment of stem cells, coculture of the target BM cells with the retrovirus-producing cells or viral supernatant infection of BM cells on stromal cell layers, and inclusion of hematopoietic growth factors (recombinant IL-1, IL-3, IL-6, SCF, LIF) in the culture media before and/or during transduction *(54–61)*. The presence of growth factors, which increases survival and number of cycling progenitors and stem cells, appears to be critical for efficient transduction and expression of the transgene in the progeny of transduced progenitors and stem cells. However, the optimal set of growth factors that would induce cycling of primitive hematopoietic cells without their differentiation in vitro has not been determined yet. Recent reports on efficient transduction of highly enriched murine long-term repopulating cells and spleen-colony forming cells (CFU-S) were the first to demonstrate the feasibility of introducing heterologous genes into purified HSC, an approach that could represent a major advance in the field of gene therapy *(62,63)*.

2. Materials

1. Methylcellulose mix (final concentration): MC stock (0.8–0.9%)—*see* Section 3.1.2. procedure below for method of preparation, fetal calf or calf serum (30%), deionized bovine serum albumin (1%), 2-mercaptoethanol, tissue culture grade ($10^{-4}M$), L-glutamine (0.29 mg/mL) (*see* Note 1).
2. Colony stimulating factors (CSF): 3 U/mL Epo with 100 U/mL rIL-3 or 10% (v/v) WEHI-3B cell-conditioned medium (CM).
3. Myeloid long-term culture media: Alpha medium supplemented with 400mg/L L-glutamine, 40 mg/L i-inositol, 10 mg/L folic acid, 12.5% horse serum*, 12.5% FCS* (each serum should be used without heat inactivation), $10^{-4}M$ 2-mercaptoethanol, $10^{-6}M$ hydrocortisone sodium succinate in alpha medium, added immediately prior to use. Do not use after 7 d (*see* Notes 2 and 3).
4. Bone marrow/retrovirus transduction culture medium (BMM): IMDM (base media), 10% BCS, 10 mg/mL BSA, 0.0017% α-thioglycerol (Sigma, St. Louis, MO; tissue culture grade), 4 μg/mL polybrene, 100 U/mL penicillin, 100 μg/mL streptomycin (Gibco-BRL, Gaithersburg, MD), 10 U/mL recombinant murine LIF (commercial source).
5. Percoll discontinous density gradient: Prepare Percoll solutions with densities of 1.10, 1.09, 1.07, and 1.06 gcm^{-3} according to the protocol recommended by the manufacturer (Pharmacia, Uppsala, Sweden). Adjust the pH of solutions to pH 7.0 and osmolarity to 300 ± 5 mOsm/kg. Keep all solutions sterile and at 4°C.

---

*Standardize by pretesting selected lots for the ability to sustain clonogenic output from a single inoculum of normal marrow for 8–12 wk in culture as an appropriate endpoint.

6. Monoclonal antibodies (MAb) specific for murine T-lymphocytes (CD4, clone GK1.5; CD8, clone 53.6.7.), B-lymphocytes (B220, clone RA3-6B2), macrophages (Mac-1, clone MI/70), granulocytes (Gr-1, clone RB6-8C5), Thy-1.1 (clone 19XE5), and Thy-1.2 antigen (clone 53.2.1) are widely available from commercial sources. Monoclonal anti-Ly-6A.2 (Sca-1, clone E13-161-7) could now be obtained from commercial sources or by inquiries to Dr. I. L. Weissman (Stanford University, Palo Alto, CA).

7. Equipment:
   a. Microisolator system (Lab Products Inc., Maywood, NJ): Microisolator cages, laminar flow cage changing hood, and laminar flow cage racks.
   b. Small animal irradiator: Many investigators prefer the Gammacell 40 ^{137}Cs source because of dose rate and field homogeneity (Nordion, Ontario, Canada).

8. Mice can be purchased SPF from reliable vendors. Recent screening information should be enclosed with each shipment or be available on request. Mice can be maintained SPF in a monitored-barrier facility or in a conventional facility with adequate precautions. Mice to be rendered immunodeficient by lethal total body irradiation (TBI) should be housed in autoclaved microisolator cages with autoclaved bedding, food, and water. Hepa-filtered ventilated cage racks and special changing hoods provide a necessary, additional level of safety in a conventional facility with endemic mouse viruses. The colony should be monitored quarterly for mouse viral pathogens (mouse level II complete antibody profile, Microbiological Associates, Rockville, MD), bacterial pathogens, and endo- and ectoparasites.

3. Methods

3.1. Committed Progenitor Colony Assays

3.1.1. Bone Marrow Cell Preparation

1. Sacrifice mice by cervical dislocation and secure to dissection board.
2. Flood the hind limbs with 70% ethanol and reflect the skin.
3. Reflect muscles at their attachments; cut away as much as possible with scissors.
4. Separate femur and tibia from the body at the hip joint and at the base of the feet.
5. Remove muscles with paper tissue, then place in a dish with IMDM and antibiotics on ice.
6. Once all bones have been collected, transfer to fresh IMDM in the culture hood.
7. Remove bone epiphyses with scissors and using a syringe (25–27-gage needle) filled with IMDM plus 10% fetal or bovine calf serum; expel the marrow.
8. Prepare single-cell suspension by gentle repeated pipeting. Perform viable cell count by Trypan blue exclusion. Wash 2X in IMDM at 1000g for 10 min. From one mouse, 4–5 × 10^7 bone marrow cells can be obtained.

3.1.2. Preparation of 2% Stock Methylcellulose

1. Prepare 2X IMDM by dissolving a 1-L packet plus 3.25 g NaHCO$_3$ in a total volume of 500 mL with water. Sterilize by filtration through a 0.22-μm filter.

2. Add 20 g methylcellulose (Methocel MC 4000 mPa.s, Fluka, Ronkonkoma, NY) to 500 mL boiling ddH$_2$O in weighed, sterile 2-L Erlenmeyer flask. Reheat just to the boiling point and remove immediately from heat.

3. Cool to 40–50°C under running water and add the 500 mL of double-strength IMDM. Hold overnight at 4°C with continuous stirring. Check weight and adjust to 1000 g with sterile water if necessary.

4. Dispense in 40-mL aliquots in 50-mL conical tubes. These can be stored at –20°C indefinitely. Avoid frost free freezer. Thaw at room temperature.

3.1.3. Culture Preparation

1. Dilute cells in IMDM plus CSF mixture to 5 × 10^4/1-mL culture.

2. Prepare cultures in triplicate. Mix cells, supplements, and methylcellulose in a 3-mL syringe fitted with an 18-gage needle. Avoid bubbles.

3. Dispense 1 mL in the middle of a 35-mm culture dish, rock gently, or rotate to spread.

4. Place two dishes of cells plus one dish of sterile water in 10-cm Petri or tissue culture dish. Transfer to incubator, fully humidified, 5% CO$_2$, 37°C.

5. Examine at 7, 14, and 21 d with an inverted microscope.

3.1.4. Colony Identification

Colonies are defined as >50 cells, although their size varies widely (an average-sized colony has 200–500 cells). Size is dependent on the proliferative status of the marrow and the combination of growth factors added. With practice, individual colony types can usually be determined by microscopic inspection. Confirmation can be accomplished by individual colony picking and microscopic inspection of cytospin slide preparations stained with Wright-Giemsa stain. The following is a list of common colony types and suggested stains for positive identification.

1. BFU-E: Erythroid burst-forming unit, erythropoietic progenitors more primitive than CFU-E, which generates colonies containing multiple erythroblast clusters in culture (mature BFU-E: 3–8 clusters, primitive BFU-E: >8). Positive staining with benzidine.

2. CFU-G: Granulocyte, multishaped nuclei representing the varying stages of differentiation from myelocyte (ring-shaped nuclei in mice) to the characteristic polymorph. Positive myeloperoxidase staining.

3. CFU-M: Macrophages, round eccentric nucleus, often with cytoplasmic evidence of phagocytosis. Positive with nonspecific esterase staining.

4. CFU-GM: Contains both granulocytes and macrophages.

5. CFU-Mix: More primitive precursor that gives rise to three or more of the following cell types: granulocytes, erythroid cells, macrophages, mast cells, eosinophils, and megakaryocytes. Mast cells contain metachromatic granules that stain positive with Astra Blue, whereas eosinophils stain bright green with Luxol Fast Blue.

3.1.5. Gene Transfer Analysis for Murine CFC Cells

1. Select G418 or hygromycin B-resistant colonies if the vector encodes *neo* or hygromycin phosphotransferase. Without selection, pick well-isolated individual colonies, transfer into sterile Eppendorf tubes, wash with PBS (2X).
2. Resuspend in 10 μL of sterile ddH$_2$O, boil for 2 min, and briefly centrifuge. Use the supernatant as a source of DNA for PCR analysis.

3.2. Myeloid Long-Term Culture of Mouse Bone Marrow

3.2.1. Establishment of Dexter's Myeloid LTBMC

1. Seed 2–3 × 10^7 BM cells in 10 mL of myeloid-LTC media in T-25 flask (Costar, Cambridge, MA; 0.2-μm vented filter flask).
2. Maintain at 37°C, 5% CO$_2$ in air for 3 d, then transfer to 33°C, 5% CO$_2$ in air.
3. After 7 d and then at weekly intervals, remove half of the media and nonadherent cells and replenish the cultures with fresh media to 10 mL. Confluent hematopoietically active stromal layers should be established after 2–3 wk.
4. Cultures should maintain active hematopoiesis for at least 2–3 mo. Hematopoietic activity can be monitored by output cell number and CFC assays.

3.2.2. Preparation of Stromal Feeder Layers for Culture of Enriched or Transduced BM Cells

1. Establish LTBMC in T-25 flasks or for limiting-dilution analysis in 96-well plates as described in Section 3.2.1.
2. After the adherent monolayer has become established, irradiate cultures with a total dose of 20 Gy in order to remove all endogenous hematopoietic activity. Maintain in LTC medium with weekly half-media change.
3. Seed sorted cells enriched for HSC activity at several graded concentrations and maintain the culture as described. For whole BM infected with recombinant retrovirus, seed 3 × 10^6 cells/flask and maintain as described in Section 3.2.1.

3.3. In Vivo Assays for Progenitor and Stem Cells

3.3.1. Primary CFU-S, d 12 (CFU-S-12)

1. Irradiate recipient animals with total dose of 9.0–12 Gy, dependent on the strain of mice used. Lower dose rates (0.3–1.0 Gy/min) are preferred. Nontransplanted radiation control mice should live for 14–21 d if housing and radiation standards are adequate. The mice should be transplanted within 6–12 h of lethal TBI. Transplant lethally irradiated mice with 10^5 whole marrow cells or 100–500 sorted BM cells enriched for stem cell activity.
2. Inject cells (resuspended in phosphate-buffered saline, PBS) iv into the retro-orbital venous plexus with a blunt needle (in 50–100 μL vol) or into the lateral tail vein using a 25-gage needle (in a volume of up to 0.5 mL). Anesthesia is required for retro-orbital injection. Use a 50-mL conical tube containing a gauze dampened with methoxyflurane (Metofane) for the anesthetic chamber.

   a. Mice anesthetize and recover quickly (<1–2 min).
   b. Monitor anesthesia by toe pinch (withdrawal of limb) and respiration (rate and depth).
3. After 12 d, dissect the spleens.
   a. Fix in Bouin's solution, consisting of: 75 mL saturated picric acid, 25 mL 37% formalin, and 5 mL concentrated acetic acid.
   b. Enumerate colonies with the aid of a dissecting scope.
   c. If interested in assessing gene transfer efficiency; carefully dissect large, discrete colonies (approx 10^6 cells) without fixation. Protein extracts for expression studies of the transferred gene and DNA for provirus analysis can be prepared. Whole marrow recovered after retroviral transduction will yield approx 10–20 CFU-S-12/10^5 cells transplanted.
   d. Spleens can also be fixed in neutral-buffered formalin, followed by sectioning and H&E staining to identify microscopic colonies and determine the cellular composition of all colonies.

3.3.2. Marrow Repopulating Ability-CFU-S, d 12 (MRA-CFU-S-12)

1. Transplant lethally irradiated mice with 10^6 whole marrow cells. If using enriched cell populations, cell dose is dependent on the enrichment achieved. Quantitation of MRA can be approached by limiting dilution of the marrow inoculum in the primary recipients.
2. After 13 d, isolate the marrow from one femur.
3. Perform viable cell count and inject secondary lethally irradiated recipients with 10^5 cells.
4. Maintain 12 d, then harvest spleens and count colonies or dissect as in Section 3.3.1.

3.3.3. Long-Term Reconstitution and Competitive Repopulation Assay

1. Transplant lethally irradiated mice with 10^5–10^6 whole marrow cells or 200–500 sorted cells of unknown stem cell content (test population). For competitive repopulation assay, transplant the equal number of "competitor" fresh bone marrow cells with known repopulating ability or compromised bone marrow cells. Quantitation of repopulating cells in "test" population can be further enhanced by transplanting graded numbers of cells while using the competitor population at a constant cell dose.
2. Allow mice to reconstitute for at least 6 mo.
3. Engraftment can be studied by measuring the percentage of mature cells in various lineages bearing the genetic marker of "test" population by flow cytometry. Alternatively, colony assays and/or CFU-S assays can be used, starting with marrow cells of the primary recipients. This is particularly helpful since it allows precise quantitation within the precursor pools.

3.4. Retroviral Vector Transduction of Murine HSC

1. Establish monolayer of irradiated virus-producing cells.
   a. Trypsinize from logarithmic growth phase (~70% confluent flasks). Wash cells and resuspend in growth media.
   b. Irradiate (20 Gy) in suspension ($1-5 \times 10^6$/mL).
   c. Plate irradiated cells at 3×10^6 cells in 100-mm tissue culture dishes. Allow cells to adhere at least 4 h prior to addition of BM cells.
2. Remove media and add 3×10^6 BMC in 10 mL BMM to established virus-producing monolayers. Cocultivate for 72 h at 37°C, 5% CO_2.
3. Harvest marrow cells from dishes.
   a. Remove nonadherent cells and save.
   b. With fresh media, vigorously wash the fibroblast layers to dislodge adherent marrow cells.
   c. Allow fibroblast clumps to settle by gravity for 10 min.
   d. Repeat gravity sedimentation if necessary to remove clumps.
   e. Combine fractions, wash 2X in IMDM, prepare single cell suspension, and perform viable cell count.
4. Inject marrow cells into lethally irradiated syngeneic recipients.
   a. Cell number injected is dependent on assay conducted.
   b. For long-term transplant controls include: mice injected with the mock-infected marrow (cells incubated over packaging cells without vector) and radiation control mice.
5. Although transduction is vector-dependent, you may expect transduction efficiencies of 50–100% under these conditions, using a vector with a titer of $\geq 10^6$ U/mL.

3.5. Enrichment of Murine Hematopoietic Stem Cells

The protocol described herein is a modification of the method for enrichment of mouse Lin⁻Sca-1⁺ cells *(36)*. It includes two steps. The first is a selection of low density marrow cells using a discontinuous Percoll gradient. This step removes the majority of granulocytic cells and thus reduces the sorting time. The second step is sorting of cells on the basis of size, cellular heterogeneity, and fluorescence intensity.

1. Prepare bone marrow cells from 5–10 mice (8–12 wk old) as described. Form the Percoll gradient by layering sequentially 2 mL of 1.10, 1.09, and 1.07 gcm⁻³ solution.
2. Resuspend up to 5×10^7 cells in 2 mL of low density (1.06 gcm⁻³) Percoll solution and load on top of a three-layer discontinuous Percoll gradient in round-bottomed polystyrene tubes. Centrifuge at 1000g, 4°C for 25 min.
3. Harvest the low density cells at the 1.06/1.07 gcm⁻³ interface and wash twice in cold 0.15M NaCl. Count the viable cells (yield should be ~13% of the starting number of cells) and resuspend in PBS with 5% FCS and antibiotics (10^7 cells/mL).
4. Incubate the cells with a cocktail of lineage-specific rat MAb, directly conjugated with FITC. After 35-min incubation on ice, wash the cells twice (800g for 10 min) and resuspend at the same density.

5. Incubate the cells with rat anti-Ly6.2A (Sca-1) for 35 min on ice. Wash the cells twice with PBS and incubate for another 30 min with phycoerythrin (PE)-conjugated F(ab')2 goat antirat IgG and repeat the wash. Count the viable cells and resuspend at 3×10^6/mL in PBS with 5% FCS and antibiotics.

6. Analyze the cells on a presterilized dual laser FACStarPlus or FACS-Vantage instrument (Becton Dickinson Immunocytometry Systems, Rutherford, NJ) and set the gates for four-parameter sorting. Select the cells for sorting on the basis of intermediate forward scatter (to exclude small lymphocytes and debris), low side scatter (to exclude highly granular cells), low levels of FITC fluorescence (lineage negative cells, Lin⁻), and high levels of PE fluorescence (Sca-1⁺ cells). Keep the cells at 4°C.

7. Sort the cells at a rate of 1000–2000 cells/s and collect them in cold PBS containing 10% FCS and antibiotics. After completion of the sort (yield is approx 0.05–0.1% of starting cell number; the purity and viability of sorted cells should be about 90% or more), wash the cells twice ($800g$ for 10 min), count, and resuspend as required for assays (*see* Note 4).

4. Notes

1. Methylcellulose (MC) as the semisolid support medium for colony assays has several advantages. Foremost is the relative ease of picking colonies for replating, DNA prep, or microscopic examination. Methylcellulose is less viscous at room temperature than at 37°C but requires volume displacement pipeting for accuracy. Methylcellulose preparations for mouse progenitor assays are available from StemCell Technologies, Vancouver, BC.

2. Different lots of serum and BSA should be pretested and selected for the best growth of colonies in MC and establishment and maintenance of LTBMC.

3. Only deionized-distilled water (ddH₂O) should be used to prepare cell culture media and other solutions. Plasticware is preferred for pipets and other supplies. All glassware should be thoroughly rinsed with ddH₂O prior to sterilization. Low level contamination with organic solvents or soaps will cause poor cell growth.

4. Several parameters that affect sorting should be mentioned. The purity, yield, and viability of sorted cells are the most important parameters to control. The purity of the sort is usually assessed by reanalyzing the sample of sorted cells and determining the percentages of all events that pass through the sorting windows. The yield of cells is determined practically, as losses often occur during sorting, thus making the number of sorted cells reported by instrument inaccurate. By knowing the starting concentration of cells and the percentage of cells gated, the theoretical yield can be calculated. The number of sorted cells can then be measured and the actual yield calculated. The ultimate goal of sorting is to obtain a highly purified and viable (~95%) cell population. Among the many factors that will affect viability of sorted cells, the most important are the temperature and the collecting medium. During the entire procedure, cells should be kept at 4°C in IMDM or PBS supplemented with 5–10% FCS and antibiotics.

References

1. Lemischka, I. R., Raulet, D. H., and Mulligan, R. C. (1986) Developmental potential and dynamic behaviour of hematopoietic stem cells. *Cell* **45,** 917–927.
2. Snodgrass, R. and Keller, G. (1987) Clonal fluctuation within the hematopoietic system of mice reconstituted with retrovirus-infected stem cells. *EMBO J.* **6,** 3955–3960.
3. Capel, B., Hawley, R., Covarrubias, L., Hawley, T., and Mintz, B. (1989) Clonal contribution of small numbers of retrovirally marked hematopoietic stem cells engrafted in unirradiated neonatal W/W^v mice. *Proc. Natl. Acad. Sci. USA* **86,** 4564–4568.
4. Keller, G. and Snodgrass, R. (1990) Life span of multipotential hematopoietic stem cells in vivo. *J. Exp. Med.* **171,** 1407–1418.
5. Jordan, C. T. and Lemischka, I. R. (1990) Clonal and systemic analysis of long term hematopoiesis in the mouse. *Genes Dev.* **4,** 220–232.
6. Spangrude, G. J. (1992) Characteristics of the hematopoietic stem cell compartment in adult mice. *Int. J. Cell Cloning* **10,** 277–285.
7. Dorshkind, K. (1990) Regulation of hemopoiesis by bone marrow stromal cells and their products. *Ann. Rev. Immunol.* **8,** 111–137.
8. Ogawa, M. (1993) Differentiation and proliferation of hematopoietic stem cells. *Blood* **81,** 2844–2853.
9. Metcalf, D. (1989) The molecular control of cell division, differentiation commitment and maturation in haemopoietic cells. *Nature* **339,** 27–30.
10. Metcalf, D. (1993) Hematopoietic regulators: redundancy or subtlety. *Blood* **82,** 3515–3523.
11. Metcalf, D. (1984) *Clonal Culture of Hemopoietic Cells: Techniques and Applications.* Elsevier, Amsterdam.
12. Suda, T., Suda, J., and Ogawa, M. (1983) Single-cell origin of mouse hematopoietic colonies expressing multiple lineages in variable combinations. *Proc. Natl. Acad. Sci. USA* **80,** 6689–6693.
13. McNiece, I. K., Bertoncello, I., Kriegler, A. B., and Quesenberry, P. J. (1990) Colony-forming cells with high proliferative potential (HPP-CFC). *Int. J. Cell Cloning* **8,** 146–160.
14. Dexter, T. M., Allen, T. D., and Lajtha, L. G. (1977) Conditions controlling the proliferation of hematopoietic stem cells in vitro. *J. Cell Physiol.* **91,** 335–344.
15. Spooncer, E. and Dexter, T. M. (1984) Long-term bone marrow cultures, in *Current Methodology in Experimental Hematology,* vol. 48 (Baum, S. J., ed.), Bibliotheca Haematologica, Springer Verlag, Berlin, pp. 366–383.
16. Fulop, G. M. and Philips, R. A. (1989) Use of scid mice to identify and quantitate lymphoid-restricted stem cells in long-term bone marrow cultures. *Blood* **74,** 1537–1544.
17. Whitlock, C. A. and Witte, O. N. (1982) Long term culture of B lymphocytes and their precursors from murine bone marrow. *Proc. Natl. Acad. Sci. USA* **79,** 3608–3612.
18. Dorshkind, K. and Witte, O. N. (1987) Long-term murine hemopoietic cultures as model systems for analysis of B-lymphocyte differentiation, in *Differentiation of B Lymphocytes,* vol. 135 (Paige, C. J. and Gisler, R. H., eds.), *Current Topics in Microbiology and Immunology,* Springer Verlag, Berlin, pp. 23–42.

19. Denis, K. A. and Witte, O. N. (1989) Long-term lymphoid cultures in the study of B-cell differentiation, in *Immunoglobulin Genes* (Honjo, T., Dorshkind, K., and Leder, P., eds.), Academic, San Diego, pp. 45–59.

20. Sutherland, H. J., Eaves, C. J., Eaves, A. C., Dragowska, W., and Lansdorp, P. M. (1989) Characterization and partial purification of human marrow cells capable of initiating long-term hematopoiesis in vitro. *Blood* **74,** 1563–1570.

21. Sutherland, H. J., Lansdorp, P. M., Henkelman, D. H., Eaves, A. C., and Eaves, C. J. (1990) Functional characterization of individual human hematopoietic stem cells cultured at limiting dilution on supportive marrow stromal layers. *Proc. Natl. Acad. Sci. USA* **87,** 3584–3588.

22. Muller-Sieburg, C. E., Whitlock, C. A., and Weissman, I. L. (1986) Isolation of two early B lymphocyte progenitors from mouse marrow: a committed pre-pre-B cell and a clonogenic Thy-1^{lo} hematopoietic stem cell. *Cell* **44,** 653–662.

23. Till, J. E. and McCullogh, E. A. (1961) A direct measure of the radiation sensitivity of normal mouse marrow cells. *Radiat. Res.* **14,** 213–222.

24. Ploemacher, R. E. and Brons, N. H. C. (1988) Isolation of hematopoietic stem cell subsets from murine bone marrow. II. Evidence for an early precursor of day-12 CFU-S and cells associated with radioprotective ability. *Exp. Hematol.* **16,** 27–32.

25. Ploemacher, R. E. and Brons, N. H. C. (1989) Separation of CFU-S from primitive cells responsible for reconstitution of the bone marrow hemopoietic stem cell compartment following irradiation: Evidence for a pre-CFU-S cell. *Exp. Hematol.* **17,** 263–266.

26. Fletcher, F. A., Williams, D. E., Maliszewski, C., Anderson, D., Rives, M., and Belmont, J. W. (1990) Murine leukemia inhibitory factor (LIF) enhances retroviral-vector infection efficiency of hematopoietic progenitors. *Blood* **76,** 1098–1103.

27. Harrison, D. E. (1980) Competitive repopulation: a new assay for long-term stem cells functional capacity. *Blood* **55,** 77–81.

28. Szilvassy, S. J., Humphries, R. K., Lansdorp, P. M., Eaves, A. C., and Eaves, C. J. (1990) Quantiative assay for totipotent reconstituting hematopoietic stem cells by a competitive repopulation strategy. *Proc. Natl. Acad. Sci. USA* **87,** 8736–8740.

29. Spangrude, G. J., Heimfeld, S., and Weissman, I. L. (1988) Purification and characterization of mouse hematopoietic stem cells. *Science* **241,** 58–62.

30. Spangrude, G. J. and Scollay, R. (1990) A simplified method for enrichment of mouse hematopoietic stem cells. *Exp. Hematol.* **18,** 920–926.

31. Smith, L. G., Weissman, I. L., and Heimfeld, S. (1991) Clonal analysis of hematopoietic stem-cell differentiation in vivo. *Proc. Natl. Acad. Sci. USA* **88,** 2788–2792.

32. Heimfeld, S. and Weissman, I. L. (1991) Development of mouse hematopoietic lineages. *Curr. Top. Dev. Biol.* **25,** 155–175.

33. Chung, L. L. and Johnson, G. R. (1992) Long–term hemopoietic repopulation by Thy-1^{lo}, Lin$^-$, Ly6A/E$^+$ cells. *Exp. Hematol.* **20,** 1309–1315.

34. Okada, S., Nakauchi, H., Nagayoshi, K., Nishikawa, S., Miura, Y., and Suda, T. (1992) In vivo and in vitro stem cell function of c-kit and Sca-1-positive murine hematopoietic cells. *Blood* **80,** 3044–3050.

35. Fleming, W. H., Alpern, E. J., Uchida, N., Ikuta, K., Spangrude, G. J., and Weissman, I. L. (1993) Functional heterogeneity is associated with the cell cycle status of murine hematopoietic stem cells. *J. Cell Biol.* **122,** 897–902.

36. Jurecic, R., Van, N. T., and Belmont, J. W. (1993) Enrichment and functional characterization of Sca-1+WGA+, Lin−WGA+, Lin−Sca-1+ and Lin−Sca-1+WGA+ bone marrow cells from mice with an Ly-6ᵃ haplotype. *Blood* **82**, 2673–2683.

37. Rebel, V. I., Dragowska, W., Eaves, C. J., Humphries, R. K., and Lansdorp, P. M. (1994) Amplification of Sca-1+Lin−WGA+ cells in serum-free cultures containing steel factor, interleukin-6, and erythropoietin with maintenance of cells with long-term in vivo reconstituting potential. *Blood* **83**, 128–136.

38. Heimfeld, S., Hudak, S., Weissman, I., and Rennick, D. (1991) The *in vitro* response of phenotypically defined mouse stem cells and myeloerythroid progenitors to single or multiple growth factors. *Proc. Natl. Acad. Sci. USA* **88**, 9902–9906.

39. Li, C. L. and Johnson, G. R. (1992) Rhodamine123 reveals heterogeneity within murine Lin−, Sca-1+ hemopoietic stem cells. *J. Exp. Med.* **175**, 1443–1447.

40. Muench, M. O., Schneider, J. G., and Moore, M. A. S. (1992) Interactions among colony-stimulating factors, IL-1β, IL-6, and *kit*-ligand in the regulation of primitive murine hematopoietic cells. *Exp. Hematol.* **20**, 339–349.

41. Weilbaecher, K., Weissman, I., Blume, K., and Heimfeld, S. (1991) Culture of phenotypically defined hematopoietic stem cells and other progenitors at limiting dilution on Dexter monolayers. *Blood* **78**, 945–952.

42. Vries de, P., Brasel, K. A., Eisenman, J. R., Alpert, A. R., and Williams, D. E. (1991) The effect of recombinant mast cell growth factor on purified murine hematopoietic stem cells. *J. Exp. Med.* **173**, 1205–1211.

43. Bodine, D. M., Orlic, D., Birkett, N. C., Seidel, N. E., and Zsebo, K. M. (1992) Stem cell factor increases colony-forming unit-spleen number in nitro in synergy with interleukin-6, and in vivo in *Sl/Sl*ᵈ mice as a single factor. *Blood* **79**, 913–919.

44. Miura, N., Okada, S., Zsebo, K. M., Miura, Y., and Suda, T. (1993) Rat stem cell factor and IL-6 preferentially support the proliferation of *c-kit*-positive murine hemopoietic cells rather than their differentiation. *Exp. Hematol.* **21**, 143–149.

45. Escary, J., Perreau, J., Dumenul, D., Ezine, S., and Brulet, P. (1993) Leukaemia inhibitory factor is necessary for maintenance of haematopoietic stem cells and thymocyte stimulation. *Nature* **363**, 361–364.

46. Joyner, A., Keller, G., Phillips, R. A., and Bernstein, A. (1983) Retrovirus transfer of a bacterial gene into mouse hematopoietic progenitor cells. *Nature* **305**, 556–558.

47. Williams, D. A., Lemischka, I. R., Nathan, D. G., and Mulligan, R. C. (1984) Introduction of new genetic material into pluripotent haematopoietic stem cells of the mouse. *Nature* **310**, 476–480.

48. Dick, J. E., Magli, M. C., Huszar, D., Phillips, R. A., and Bernstein, A. (1985) Introduction of a selectable gene into primitive stem cells capable of long-term reconstitution of the hemopoietic system of W/Wᵛ mice. *Cell* **42**, 71–79.

49. Kantoff, P. W., Freeman, S. M., and Anderson, W. F. (1988) Prospects for gene therapy for immunodeficiency diseases. *Ann. Rev. Immunol.* **6**, 581–594.

50. Cournoyer, D., Scarpa, M., Moore, K. A., Fletcher, F. A., MacGregor, G. R., Belmont, J. W., and Caskey, C. T. (1991) Gene replacement therapy: human and animal model progress, in *Etiology of Human Disease at the DNA Level* (Lindsten, J. and Pettersson, U., eds.), Raven, New York, pp. 199–203.

51. Cournoyer, D. and Caskey, C. T. (1993) Gene therapy of the immune system. *Ann. Rev. Immunol.* **11**, 297–329.

52. Moore, K. A., Fletcher, F. A., Villalon, D. K., Utter, A. E., and Belmont, J. W. (1990) Human adenosine deaminase expression in mice. *Blood* **75**, 2085–2092.

53. van Beusechem, V. W., Kuklerm, A., Einerhand, M. P. W., Bakx, T. A., van der Eb, A. J., van Bekkum, D. W., and Valerio, D. (1990) Expression of human adenosine deaminase in mice transplanted with hemopoietic stem cells infected with amphotropic retroviruses. *J. Exp. Med.* **172**, 729–736.

54. Einerhand, M. P. W., Bakx, T. A., Kukler, A., and Valerio, D. (1993) Factors affecting the transduction of pluripotent hematopoietic stem cells: long-term expression of a human adenosine deaminase gene in mice. *Blood* **81**, 254–263.

55. Bodine, D. M., McDonagh, K. T., Seidel, N. E., and Nienhuis, A. W. (1991) Survival and retrovirus infection of murine hematopoietic stem cells in vitro: effects of 5-FU and method of infection. *Exp. Hematol.* **19**, 206–212.

56. Barker, J. E., Wolfe, J. H., Rowe, L. B., and Birkenmeier, E. H. (1993) Advantages of gradient vs. 5-fluorouracil enrichment of stem cells for retroviral-mediated gene transfer. *Exp. Hematol.* **21**, 47–54.

57. Chertkov, J. L., Jiang, S., Lutton, J. D., Harrison, J., Levere, R. D., Tiefenthaler, M., and Abraham, N. G. (1993) The hematopoietic stromal microenvironment promotes retrovirus-mediated gene transfer into hematopoietic stem cells. *Stem Cells* **11**, 218–227.

58. Bodine, D. M., Karlsson, S., and Nienhuis, A. W. (1989) Combination of interleukins 3 and 6 preserves stem cell function in culture and enhances retrovirus-mediated gene transfer into hematopoietic stem cells. *Proc. Natl. Acad. Sci. USA* **86**, 8897–8901.

59. Fletcher, F. A., Williams, D. E., Maliszewski, C., Anderson, D., Rives, M., and Belmont, J. W. (1990) Murine leukemia inhibitory factor (LIF) enhances retroviral-vector infection efficiency of hematopoietic progenitors. *Blood* **76**, 1098–1103.

60. Fletcher, F. A., Moore, K. A., Ashkenazi, M., De Vries, P., Overbeek, P. A., Williams, D. E., and Belmont, J. W. (1991) Leukemia inhibitory factor improves survival of retroviral vector-infected hematopoietic stem cells in vitro, allowing efficient long-term expression of vector-encoded human adenosine deaminase in vivo. *J. Exp. Med.* **174**, 837–845.

61. Luskey, B. D., Rosenblatt, M., Zsebo, K., and Williams, D. A. (1992) Stem cell factor, interleukin-3, and interleukin-6 promote retroviral-mediated gene transfer into murine hematopoietic stem cells. *Blood* **80**, 396–402.

62. Szilvassy, S. J., Fraser, C. C., Eaves, C. J., Lansdorp, P. M., Eaves, A. C., and Humphries, R. K. (1989) Retrovirus-mediated gene transfer to purified hemopoietic stem cells with long-term lympho-myelopoietic repopulating ability. *Proc. Natl. Acad. Sci. USA* **86**, 8798–8802.

63. Spain, L. M. and Mulligan, R. C. (1992) Purification and characterization of retrovirally transduced hematopoietic stem cells. *Proc. Natl. Acad. Sci. USA* **89**, 3790–3794.

17

Methods for Retrovirus-Mediated Gene Transfer into Primary T-Lymphocytes

Michel Sadelain

1. Introduction

Recombinant retroviruses are efficient vectors for introducing genes into many mammalian cell types. They are useful in the context of clinical as well as experimental applications, owing to their ability to generate high-titer and helper-free viral stocks. Retroviral vectors are especially appropriate for the transduction of primary lymphocytes, because gene transfer is mediated by nonimmunogenic vectors and stable vector integration in the target genome is achieved. Stable integration in cells undergoing clonal expansion ensures that the foreign genetic material will be faithfully transmitted to the cells' progeny.

1.1. Factors Controlling Retrovirus-Mediated Gene Transfer

Gene transfer mediated by viral vectors follows the molecular pathway of the natural infectious process. Therefore, the factors enhancing or restricting natural infection will influence retrovirus-mediated gene transfer efficiency. The basis for the design of retroviral vectors and packaging cells are briefly reviewed in Chapters 3 and 4. The critical factors relevant to retroviral infection include:

1. Cell division: Cell division is required for efficient retrovirus-mediated gene transfer *(1,2)*. Therefore, postthymic T-lymphocytes must be activated and cycling in order to be transduced using current Moloney-murine leukemia virus (MLV)–based vectors.
2. Viral receptor expression: The receptors for MLV particles *(3–6)* are expressed by T-lymphocytes. However, the receptor distribution is poorly characterized with respect to T-cell subset, cell cycle, and activation status.

From: *Methods in Molecular Medicine, Gene Therapy Protocols*
Edited by: P. Robbins Humana Press Inc., Totowa, NJ

3. External factors: Several factors outside the target cell are able to interfere with retroviral infection. The presence in the extracellular compartment of nonspecific mediators, such as complement *(7)* and interferons *(8)*, or specific factors, such as neutralizing antibodies *(9)* and soluble receptor-like moieties *(10)*, will adversely affect the infectious process. These factors can act on a number of the steps necessary for the efficient generation of a provirus, from the binding of the viral particle to the target cell receptor to the chromosomal integration of the reverse-transcribed viral genome. Virally induced resistance to infection, or viral interference, can operate on the receptor itself, the cytoplasmic membrane, or inside the cell. All of these mechanisms can contribute to reducing the efficiency of retrovirus-mediated gene transfer.

Thus, ex vivo retrovirus-mediated gene transfer is only possible in cycling T-lymphocytes expressing the viral receptor and under conditions that elude extracellular and intracellular mechanisms of resistance to infection.

1.2. Considerations for the Culture and Retroviral Infection of Primary T-Cells

Lymphocyte division can be elicited by numerous stimuli, either by engaging the T-cell receptor with superantigen or processed antigen and MHC, in conjunction with adequate costimulatory signals, or by various cross-linking agents, which include lectins and antibodies. However, it is difficult to greatly expand primary lymphocytes and maintain them in culture for sustained periods of time, whatever the initial mitogenic signal(s) *(11)*. Optimal conditions for the expansion of antigen-reactive clones require periodic antigen pulsing and the addition of lymphokine and adequate antigen-presenting cells. Otherwise, prolonged culture of polyclonal lymphocytes will typically lead to T-cell subset imbalance, uncontrolled repertoire bias, phenotypic alterations, and postactivation apoptotic cell death.

The addition of high-titer retroviral stocks to freshly harvested lymphocytes results in very low infection efficiency. Mitogenic stimulation of the lymphocytes before exposure to the viral particles, as well as the addition of a polycation such as polybrene or protamine sulfate, is an absolute prerequisite for achieving significant gene transfer *(12–17)*. Whereas retroviral supernatants are sufficient for achieving significant gene transfer in human T-lymphocytes (>10% gene transfer efficiency), supernatants only yield marginal gene transfer (<1%) in primary murine T-lymphocytes. Several factors affect the infection efficiency:

1. T-cell activation: Numerous stimuli can trigger mitosis in lymphocytes. The timing of the exposure to the virus relative to the initiation of T-cell activation is a critical variable that varies with the activation conditions. In the procedure described below, a 48-h interval between the two events is optimal for human lymphocytes.

2. Culture conditions: Cell densities must be optimized for lymphocyte survival in vitro. Cocultivation of preactivated lymphocytes with high-titer producers under well-defined conditions is more efficient than supernatant-mediated infection (*see* Note 1). Cocultivation is essential to achieve substantial gene transfer in murine primary lymphocytes (>10% gene transfer efficiency; *see* Note 2).

3. Medium composition: Certain elements must be present throughout the infection procedure: a suitable, prescreened serum, interleukin-2, and an enhancer of infection, such as polybrene, protamine sulfate, or polycationic liposomes. Polybrene increases infection efficiency but its toxicity reduces lymphocyte recovery. Thus, the lymphocytes should be grown in their preferred medium before and after exposure in the infection step. The level of receptor expression can be affected by the medium composition, at least in some circumstances *(18)*.

4. Retroviral particles: Amphotropic particles may be used for both murine and human target cells. Ecotropic particles can only be used to infect the former. Some recent data suggest that particles coated with the GaLV retroviral envelope might be more effective than particles bearing the amphotropic envelope for the infection of human T-lymphocytes (M. Sadelain, unpublished observations, and R. A. Morgan, Bethesda, MD, personal communication).

1.3. Gene Transfer, Gene Expression, and Vector Design

Gene transfer can be quantified directly by analyzing the target-cell genomic DNA or indirectly by assaying for gene expression. Genomic DNA analysis based on a careful vector copy number determination is an accurate way to quantify gene transfer (*see* Chapter 4). Gene transfer efficiency can also be estimated using gene expression assays, provided that gene expression can be readily determined on a per cell basis (*see* Note 3). This quantification may be achieved by either subcloning the infected population by limiting dilution and scoring the fraction of positive wells (by DNA, RNA, or protein analysis), or more directly by immunofluorescence when a marker is amenable to fluorescent detection, e.g., a cell-surface marker or *Escherichia coli* β-galactosidase. An ideal marker is biologically inactive or neutral in lymphocytes, nonimmunogenic, and easily detectable by fluorescence-activated cell-sorting (FACS). An example of gene transfer analysis by cell-surface phenotyping is shown in Fig. 1.

When the gene of interest must be expressed in every lymphocyte with a high degree of certainty, it is necessary to introduce a selectable marker or a screening marker into the vectors. Selectable markers, such as neomycin phosphotransferase, are effective but lead to all the caveats mentioned above. As we and others reported earlier *(19,20)*, the use of cell-surface markers as screening markers is superior for purifying lymphocytes and hematopoietic cells

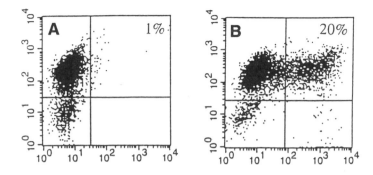

Fig. 1. Retrovirus-mediated gene transfer in human primary T-lymphocytes: analysis of transgene expression by cell-surface phenotyping. On the Y axis, CD3 signal; on the X axis, cell-surface marker signal. **(A)** T-cells infected with a control vector; **(B)** T-cells infected with a vector encoding a modified low-affinity human nerve growth factor receptor (LNGFR*) as the reporter molecule. LNGFR is mutated in the extracellular domain to complement a large cytoplasmic domain deletion that alone fails to abrogate receptor function (*25*, Grallardo, M., et al., manuscript in preparation). The percentage indicated in the upper-right quadrant is the percent of LNGFR*-positive cells among all cultured T-lymphocytes. The infection procedure is described in the text. The viral supernatant is harvested from a PG13 *(24)* producer cell line that was generated as described in Chapter 4.

because the transduced cells can be sorted by panning, column or magnetic separation, or FACS. Thus, dual-expression vectors coexpressing the gene of interest and a cell-surface marker are necessary. Dual promoter vectors are often used, but they are prone to transcriptional interference *(21,22)*. In the event of such interference, the assumption that the gene of interest is expressed in a cell identified as expressing the marker gene is tenuous. The average frequency of uncoupled expression must be experimentally determined for any vector. The internal ribosomal entry site (IRES) from Picornaviridae, which allows for the generation of bicistronic mRNA, can be used to resolve this problem (*see* Chapter 4), if it is established that the IRES element is functional in T-lymphocytes.

Ideally, the retroviral vector should provide for a predictable and controlled level of transgene expression, one that is independent of the site of integration, constant over time, and eventually inducible or regulated. A discussion of these issues, however, is beyond the scope of this chapter. The Moloney MLV transcriptional control elements *(12–14)*, which control gene expression in many retroviral vectors (*see* Chapter 4), as well as other constitutive promoters *(15–17)*, have been shown to function in T-lymphocytes.

2. Materials
2.1. Reagents

1. RPMI-1640 (Gibco-BRL, Grand Island, NY).
2. Phosphate-buffered solution, PBS⁻ (Gibco-BRL).
3. Lymphoprep, Nycomed Pharma (Gibco-BRL).
4. Fetal bovine serum (FBS).
5. Penicillin, streptomycin (Gibco-BRL).
6. Phytohaemagglutinin (Murex Diagnostics, Norcross, GA). Stock in culture medium is stored at –20°C.
7. Polybrene (Sigma, St. Louis, MO). Stock in phosphate-buffered saline is stored at 4°C.
8. Interleukin-2, human, step1–purified, or recombinant.
9. hT medium: 10% (v/v) FBS, penicillin 100 U/mL, streptomycin 100 µg/mL in RPMI-1640.

3. Methods

The methods described here are established for freshly harvested human peripheral blood lymphocytes (*see* Note 4). High-titer (>10^6 infectious particles/mL) producer cell lines are generated from the packaging cells ψ-CRIP and PG13 *(23,24)* as described in Chapter 4. All cell culture is carried out in humidified incubators at 37°C in a 5% CO_2 atmosphere.

The procedure described here is used in an experimental setting. It provides a conceptual framework and practical reference for methods specifically designed for gene transfer in antigen-specific T-cell clones or T-cell lines used in a clinical setting.

3.1. Infection of Primary Human T-Lymphocytes

1. Day 1: Freshly harvested peripheral blood cells are washed once in PBS⁻, separated over a monolayer of Ficoll (2500 rpm for 20 min at 25°C), and washed twice. The cells are cultured at a density of 1–2 × 10^6 cells/mL in hT medium containing PHA at 0.5 µg/mL.
2. Day 3: The nonadherent cells are harvested, washed once, and resuspended at a density of 10^6 cells/mL in hT medium containing human IL-2 at 10 U/mL. An equal volume of high-titer viral supernatant is admixed along with polybrene (4 µg/mL final concentration). The lymphocytes are cultured for 24 h.
3. Day 4: The cell cultures are harvested, washed once, and resuspended at a density of 10^6 cells/mL in hT medium containing human IL-2 at 10 U/mL.
4. Day 7: 90% or more of the live cells are CD3-positive. The cells are ready for further manipulation: cell sorting, direct use in vitro, genomic DNA extraction, or infusion in vivo. Alternatively, when using selection strategies, drug-resistance selection can start on d 5.

3.2. Determination of Gene Transfer Efficiency

Direct methods are based on the accurate quantification of vector copy number integrated in the target cell genomic DNA. This result may be achieved through a reliable and quantitative PCR-based assay or by quantitative Southern blot analysis (*see* Chapter 4).

Indirect methods are based on expression assays in single cells (*see* Section 1.3.). The most immediate assays are those in which the fraction of positive cells can be determined by screening or sorting based on marker detection: panning, column or magnetic separation, or FACS analysis. An example of such an analysis is shown in Fig. 1.

Absence of helper virus in viral stocks and in transduced target cell populations must always be verified (*see* Chapter 4).

4. Notes

1. When comparing infection efficiency achieved under different conditions, it is important to measure the infection efficiency at the same time-point after initiation of T-cell activation. Indeed, the percentage of positive cells may increase over time without necessarily reflecting an increased level of infection (e.g., if the noninfected cells have a shorter survival span than the infected cells).
2. The infection efficiency achieved by cocultivation of nonadherent target cells with the producers is often superior to infection using filtered viral stocks. Murine primary lymphocytes stringently require cocultivation with the packaging cell line. It is unknown whether cocultivation increases infection or survival of the target cells.
3. Gene transfer efficiency can be accurately assessed from expression studies if the following three conditions are met: all intact integrated vectors are expressed, all cells expressing the transgene are detected, and all positive cells bear one copy of the vector (the latter is a reasonable assumption when all cells are equally susceptible to infection and <50% of the cells are positive). After the prolonged culture necessary for drug-resistance selection, it is very difficult to estimate the fraction of cells that were originally transduced.
4. The procedures described herein result in infection rates of >10% in both $CD4^+$ and $CD8^+$ subsets, as determined by FACS analysis and confirmed by Southern blot analysis (Grallardo et al., manuscript in preparation). It is important to use high-titer viral stocks (>10^6 particles/mL).

Acknowledgment

The author thanks V. Petronis for excellent assistance in the preparation of the manuscript.

References

1. Miller, D. G., Adam, M. A., and Miller, A. D. (1990) Gene transfer by retrovirus vectors occurs only in cells that are actively replicating at the time of infection. *Mol. Cell. Biol.* **10,** 4239–4292.
2. Roe, T. Y., Reynolds, T. C., Yu, G., and Brown, P. O. (1993) Integration of murine leukemia virus DNA depends on mitosis. *EMBO J.* **12,** 2099–2108.

3. Kim, J. W., Closs, E. I., Albritton, L. M., and Cunningham, J. M. (1991) Transport of cationic amino acids by the mouse ecotropic retrovirus receptor. *Nature* **352,** 726–728.

4. Wang, H., Kavanaugh, M. P., North, R. A., and Kabat, D. (1991) Cell-surface receptor for ecotropic murine retroviruses is a basic amino-acid transporter. *Nature* **352,** 729–731.

5. Miller, D. G., Edwards, R. H., and Miller, A. D. (1994) Cloning of the cellular receptor for amphotropic murine retroviruses reveals homology to that for the gibbon ape leukemia virus. *Proc. Natl. Acad. Sci. USA* **91,** 78–82.

6. van Zeijl, M., Johann, S. V., Closs, E., Cunningham, J., Eddy, R., Shows, T. B., and O'Hara, B. (1994) A human amphotropic retrovirus receptor is a second member of the gibbon ape leukemia virus receptor family. *Proc. Natl. Acad. Sci. USA* **91,** 1168–1172.

7. Cooper, N. R., Jensen, F. C., Welsh, R. M., Jr., and Oldstone, M. B. A. (1976) Lysis of RNA tumor viruses by human serum: direct antibody-independent triggering of the classical complement pathway. *J. Exp. Med.* **144,** 970–982.

8. Vieillard, V., Lauret, E., Rousseau, V., and De Maeyer, E. (1994) Blocking of retroviral infection at a step prior to reverse transcription in cells transformed to constitutively express interferon β. *Proc. Natl. Acad. Sci. USA* **91,** 2689–2693.

9. Zinkernagel, R. M. (1993) Immunity to viruses, in *Fundamental Immunology*, 3rd ed., Raven, New York, pp. 1211–1250.

10. Traunecker, A., Luke, W., and Karjalainen, K. (1988) Soluble CD4 molecules neutralize human immunodeficiency virus type 1. *Nature* **331,** 84–86.

11. Fathman, C. G., Fitch, F. W., Denis, K. A., and Witte, O. N. (1989) Long term culture of immunocompetent cells, in *Fundamental Immunology*, 2nd ed., Raven, New York, pp. 803–815.

12. Yamada, G., Kitamura, Y., Sonoda, H., Harada, H., Taki, S., Mulligan, R. C., Osawa, H., Diamantstein, T., Yokoyama, S., and Taniguchi, T. (1987) Retroviral expression of the human IL-2 gene in a murine T cell line results in cell growth autonomy and tumorigenicity. *EMBO J.* **6,** 2705–2709.

13. Rosenberg, S. A., Aegersold, P., Cornetta, K., Kasid, A., Morgan, R., Moen, R., Karson, E. M., Lotze, M. T., Yang, J. C., Topalian, S. L., Merino, M. J., Culver, K., Miller, A. D., Blaese, R. M., and Anderson, W. F. (1990) Gene transfer into humans: immunotherapy of patients with advanced melanoma using tumor infiltrating lymphocytes modified by retroviral gene transduction. *N. Engl. J. Med.* **323,** 570–578.

14. Rivière, I., Brose, K., and Mulligan, R. C. (1995) Effects of retroviral design on expression of human adenosine deaminase in murine bone marrow transplant recipients engrafted with genetically modified cells. *Proc. Natl. Acad. Sci. USA* **92,** 6733–6737.

15. Strair, R. K., Towle, M., Heald, P. W., and Smith, B. R. (1990) Retroviral-mediated transfer and expression of exogenous genes in primary lymphoid cells: assaying for a viral transactivator activity in normal and malignant cells. *Blood* **76,** 1201–1208.

16. Ferrari, G., Rossini, S., Giavazzi, R., Maggioni, D., Nobili, N., Soldati, M., Ungers, G., Mavilio, F., Gilboa, E., and Bordignon, C. (1991) An in vivo model of somatic cell gene therapy for human severe combined immunodeficiency. *Science* **251,** 1363–1366.

17. Culver, K., Cornetta, K., Morgan, R., Morecki, S., Aebersold, P., Kasid, A., Lotze, M., Rosenberg, S. A., Anderson, W. F., and Blaese, R. M. (1991) Lymphocytes as cellular vehicles for gene therapy in mouse and man. *Proc. Natl. Acad. Sci. USA* **88,** 3155–3159.

18. Kavanaugh, M. P., Miller, D. G., Zhang, W., Law, W., Kozak, S. L., Kabat, D., and Miller, A. D. (1994) Cell-surface receptors for gibbon ape leukemia virus and amphotropic murine retrovirus are inducible sodium-dependent phosphate symporters. *Proc. Natl. Acad. Sci. USA* **91,** 7071–7075.

19. Sadelain, M. and Mulligan, R. C. (1992) Efficient retroviral-mediated gene transfer into murine primary lymphocytes. Ninth International Immunology Congress, Budapest.

20. Mavilio, F., Ferrari, G., Rossini, S., Nobili, N., Bonini, C., Casorati, G., Traversari, C., and Bordignon, C. (1994) Peripheral blood lymphocytes as target cells of retroviral vector-mediated gene transfer. *Blood* **83,** 1988–1997.

21. Cullen, B. R., Lomedico, P. T., and Ju, G. (1984) Transcriptional interference in avian retroviruses: implications for the promoter insertion model of leukemogenesis. *Nature* **307,** 241–245.

22. Bowtell, D. D., Cory, S., Johnson, G. R., and Gonda, T. J. (1988) Comparison of expression in hematopoietic cells by retroviral vectors carrying two genes. *J. Virol.* **62,** 2464–2473.

23. Danos, O. and Mulligan, R. C. (1988) Safe and efficient generation of recombinant retroviruses with amphotropic and ecotropic host range. *Proc. Natl. Acad. Sci. USA* **85,** 6460–6464.

24. Miller, A. D., Garcia, J. V., von Suhr, N., Lynch, C. M., Wilson, C., and Eiden, M. V. (1991) Construction and properties of retrovirus packaging cells based on gibbon ape leukemia virus. *J. Virol.* **65,** 2220–2224.

25. Hantzopoulos, P. A., Suri, C., Glass, D. J., Goldfarb, M. P., and Yancopoulos, G. D. (1994) The low affinity NGF receptor, p75, can collaborate with each of the TRKs to potentiate functional responses to the neurotrophins. *Neuron* **13,** 187–201.

18

Methods for Retrovirus-Mediated Gene Transfer to CD34⁺-Enriched Cells

Alfred B. Bahnson, Maya Nimgaonkar, Edward D. Ball, and John A. Barranger

1. Introduction

Hematopoietic stem cells (HSC) provide for continuous replenishment of the entire immune and hematopoietic systems, and also replenish themselves in a process termed self-renewal *(1)*. The HSCs can be enriched from hematopoietic tissues using MAbs that bind to the CD34 antigen, a universally recognized marker for hematopoietic progenitors *(2–4)*. Enriched HSC populations are being widely investigated for use in transplantation and gene therapy because they appear to provide rapid hematopoietic reconstitution in myeloablated patients *(5–11)*, and they offer good targets for gene transfer *(12–17)*.

A major impediment to retroviral transduction of HSC has been their paucity in hematopoietic tissues. The CD34⁺ cells account for only 1–4% of mononuclear cells in the bone marrow (BM), <1% in peripheral blood (PB), and <1% in cord blood (CB) *(18,19)*. CD34⁺ enrichment provides an important advantage for gene therapy protocols because it greatly reduces the quantities of viral supernatants needed to achieve a useful multiplicity of infection (MOI) compared with requirements for nonenriched cells from these sources. For example, with a titer of 10^6 cfu/mL, full strength supernatant will achieve an MOI of 10:1 when cells are suspended at 10^5 cells/mL. An average marrow infusion of 2×10^8 nucleated cells/kg recipient body wt for a 70-kg patient would require suspension of the cells in 140 L of supernatant to achieve this MOI. Enrichment reduces these requirements by a factor of 100, making the procedure practical. By reducing associated quantities of cytokines and DMSO, costs and discomfort are also reduced.

From: *Methods in Molecular Medicine, Gene Therapy Protocols*
Edited by: P. Robbins Humana Press Inc., Totowa, NJ

Cytokines are required for in vitro survival and expansion of CD34+-enriched cells, but no known combination of cytokines can prevent the process of differentiation that accompanies in vitro handling *(20–22)*. Cocultivation of CD34+ cells on adherent stromal cell layers appears to enable relatively long-term maintenance and, in some cases, low-level expansion of very early progenitors *(23)*. Cycling among HSC is sought as a part of the transduction process with retroviral vectors, since cell division appears to be a requirement for retroviral transduction *(24)*. Cycling may be brought about with cytokines applied in vitro *(25,26)* or with in vivo mobilization of cycling cells using cytokines and/or chemotherapy *(27,28)*. An ideal prestimulation procedure would encourage the self-renewal of HSC without induction of differentiation.

Studies aimed at better defining factors and culture conditions for expansion of HSC may be crucial for successful application of gene therapy to hematopoietic disease. These efforts rely on assays for precursors and progenitor cells at various stages of differentiation. The colony forming methylcellulose assay provides an estimate of myeloid progenitor cells (CFU) *(29)*, and may be combined with the assay for long-term culture initiating cells (LTC-IC) to measure more primitive hematopoietic progenitors *(30)*. The severe combined immune deficient (SCID) mouse model permits assay of both myeloid and lymphoid cells, and is thus an assay for *pluri*potent stem cells *(31)*.

Characterization of surface markers by flow cytometry provides more immediate information regarding quantities and phenotypes of subpopulations of hematopoietic cells. The CD34 antigen is highly expressed in early multipotential progenitors and colony forming cells (e.g., CFU-blast, pre-CFU, CFU-GEMM), whereas lower levels of CD34 expression are associated with more committed progenitors (e.g., BFU-E, CFU-GM, CFU-Meg, CFU-Eo, CFU-Osteoclast) *(32)*. The CD34+ cells that are negative for CD38 and HLA-DR are considered to be among the earliest stem cells; they give rise to both hematopoietic and stromal elements *(33)*. As these cells mature, they acquire a variety of surface antigens specific for their lineage of differentiation. For example, expression of the CD33, CD45, CD15, and CD11 antigens are associated differentially with myeloid and lymphoid differentiation. Differences in the proportions of the various subpopulations of CD34+ cells in BM compared with PB and G-CSF-mobilized PB may relate to the relative effectiveness of each of these sources for long-term engraftment and reconstitution in the patient *(34,35)*. Ongoing studies of correlation between the assays and patient outcomes should eventually provide a useful definition of the stem cell phenotype.

Specific conditions for optimal retroviral transduction of CD34+-enriched cells are not conclusively determined. Reports and protocols differ with respect to many variables, e.g., the concentrations and combinations of cytokines used, timing of prestimulation and virus exposures, and the presence or absence of stromal cells. The effectiveness of IL-3, IL-6, and SCF for promoting retroviral transduction and stem cell preservation has been demonstrated in murine *(36–38)* and human *(14,39,40)* cells. Cytotoxic prestimulation of stem cells in vivo with 5-fluorouracil (5-FU) is effective for enhancement of transduction efficiency in mice *(36)*. Using an optimized protocol based on coculture with the murine producer cells, we and others have demonstrated transduction of cells capable of long-term reconstitution of lethally irradiated primary recipients, which yield progeny (self-renewal of stem cells) capable of reconstitution of secondary lethally irradiated recipient mice *(41,42)*. Using an MFG-based vector, we have demonstrated expression in secondary recipients up to 12 mo posttransplant *(41)*. These studies provide ample encouragement for the future potential of a well-optimized clinical protocol.

The effectiveness of 5-FU for enhancement of transduction of primate stem cells is less clear cut, however *(43)*. Studies in nonhuman primates have yielded less efficient retroviral transduction and engraftment using protocols based on supernatant infection or coculture in comparison to the murine studies *(44,45)*.

Early results of human clinical trials using retroviral transduction of CD34+ or mononuclear hematopoietic cells are just beginning to be evaluated. The technique has been useful for demonstrating a contribution to relapse from the autologous bone marrow transplant (ABMT) in CML *(46)* and neuroblastoma *(47)*. Low detection of transduced cells following gene therapy experiments in children with adenosine deaminase deficiency *(48,49)* and for marking ABMT cells in multiple myeloma and breast cancer patients *(50)*, emphasizes a need for further optimization of protocols.

The comparison of results between the different studies using CD34+ cells is confounded by differing assay systems, differing vectors, differing supernatant titers, and many other variables. Estimates of transduction efficiency therefore range widely within and between different studies (Table 1).

Of the three protocols that have been approved by the Recombinant DNA Advisory Committee (RAC) for gene therapy of Gaucher disease, one *(53)* employs direct suspension of CD34+ cells into full strength vector-containing supernatant without prestimulation. The cytokines IL-3, IL-6, and SCF (concentrations were unspecified in the RAC proposal) and 4 mg/mL protamine sulfate are present, and the mixtures are completely changed daily for 3 d. Another *(54)* employs a 5-d incubation on a 14-d-old autologous long-term marrow stromal layer in a system containing 50% long-term culture medium (LTCM) and 50% vector-containing supernatant with IL-1, IL-3, IL-6, and SCF at 50 ng/mL and 5 mg/mL protamine sulfate. From the latter protocol, both nonadherent and adherent cells are harvested for assay and patient infusion. Problems may appear in evaluating the efficiency of gene transfer to HSCs because of transduction of adherent cells in this system. We reported an

Table 1
Transduction Efficiency in Human CD34⁺ Cells

Source	Cytokines	Prestimulation	Infection	Assay	Efficiency, %	Ref.
BM, PB	IL-3, IL-6, SCF, and combination	None; chemo	1 and 3 d	CFU-PCR	8, 25–33	14
BM	None	Chemo	1X	CFU-G418^R	1–4	46
BM, PB	IL-3, IL-6, SCF	Chemo	3 d	CFU-G418^R	2.5–40	50
CB	IL-3, IL-6, SCF	None	3 d	CFU-G418^R	12–20	49
BM, PB	IL-3, IL-6, IL-11, SCF	None	4 d	CFU-PC$_R$	25–42	51
Gaucher	IL-3, IL-6, IL-11, SCF	None	4 d	LTC-IC	30–50	51
BM, PB	?	None	5 d	CFU-PCR	15–40	52
BM, PB	?	None	5 d	LTC-IC	14	52
BM (ADA)	?	None	Coculture	CFU-Xyl-A	5–10	48
PB	Varies	1–3 d	Varies	Southern	10–30	17
BM, CB	IL-3, IL-6, SCF	1 d	1–4X	Southern	30–80	16

experiment in which stromal Gaucher cells were transduced and nonadherent cells were not *(16)*. In our clinical study *(55)*, we propose to use a 1-d prestimulation of CD34⁺-enriched cells in LTMC media containing IL-3, IL-6, and SCF at 10 ng/mL followed by three, 12-h exposures to 50% fresh supernatant while maintaining cytokine concentrations at 10 ng/mL and protamine sulfate at 4 mg/mL.

It is clear that many problems remain to be solved in the use of CD34⁺ cells for gene therapy. Nevertheless, it is also clear from the numerous preclinical studies with human cells and with animal models that the potential for success is high. It is hoped that the methods described here will encourage others to contribute to this field.

2. Materials

2.1. Medium

1. Human long-term bone marrow culture medium (LTCM) is used for prestimulation and expansion of CD34⁺ cells and for long-term cultures. It consists of Iscove-Modified Dulbecco's Medium (IMDM) (Gibco-BRL, Gaithersburg, MD) containing 12.5% fetal bovine serum (FBS) (Hyclone, Logan, VT), 12.5% horse serum (HS) (Hyclone), 2 mM L-glutamine, $1 \times 10^{-6}M$ 2-mercaptoethanol, $1 \times 10^{-6}M$ alpha-thioglycerol, 1 µg/mL hydrocortisone, and penicillin/streptomycin.
2. Packaging cells and producers are grown in 10% calf serum (CS) (Gibco-BRL) in Dulbecco's Modified Eagle medium (DMEM) (Gibco-BRL) containing 50 U/mL penicillin, 50 µg/mL streptomycin, and 2 mM L-glutamine.

2.2. Additional Reagents

1. Cytokines, IL-3, IL-6, and stem cell factor (SCF) are prepared as concentrated stock solutions in LTCM. The 1000X contains 10 µg/mL of each cytokine, and a combination 100X stock solution containing all three cytokines at 1 µg/mL each is used for addition of factors to small volumes of medium or supernatant. Aliquots are stored at −80°C until needed.
2. Protamine sulfate is prepared as a concentrated stock solution in phosphate buffered saline (PBS); 1000X contains 4 mg/mL.
3. Methylcellulose medium (without erythropoietin) is obtained ready-to-use from Stem Cell Technologies, Vancouver, BC.
4. CFU-GM colony DNA extraction mixture consists of 1.5 parts glycogen, 10 parts 2M sodium acetate at pH 4.5, 100 parts phenol, and 20 parts chloroform. Homogenize immediately before use by vigorous shaking.

2.3. Immunoaffinity Column and Anti-CD34 Antibody

The biotinylated anti-CD34 antibody, the avidin column, and necessary reagents (CEPRATE LC [CD34] Cell Separation System) are supplied by CellPro, Bothell, WA.

3. Methods

3.1. Generation of Amphotropic Vector-Containing Supernatants

Amphotropic producer cell lines containing nonselectable markers may be generated by infection with filtered supernatants from ecotropic producers, stably or transiently transfected with the vectors in plasmid form. The amphotropic packaging cells are infected multiple times if necessary to obtain clones which, on the average, carry several copies of the vector of interest. The highest titer clones are used to produce stock supernatants.

1. Obtain ecotropic supernatant from stably or transiently transfected ecotropic producer cells.
2. Split freshly confluent amphotropic producer cells 1:40 one day prior to infection.
3. The next day, remove the medium from the amphotropic packaging cells and apply a 1:2 dilution of ecotropic supernatant in fresh medium containing polybrene (8 μg/mL final concentration), and incubate for 12 h or overnight.
4. Repeat step 3 one or more times.
5. Clone infected cells by limiting dilution in a 96-well plate or by seeding at low density in a tissue culture dish.
6. Transfer clones to 24-well plates and harvest supernatants as cells reach confluence.
7. Screen supernatants for virus activity by infecting appropriate targets cells, e.g., 3T3, and assay for expression of the vector of interest.
8. Select highest titer clone and expand into 15-cm tissue culture dishes.
9. Replace the medium daily as the cells become confluent. Filter the supernatants and store at −70°C.
10. After the cells become fully confluent, do not split them but continue to feed once or twice daily as long as desired (*see* Note 1), filtering and freezing each collection. With each collection, aliquot a small volume into a cryotube.
11. Following a series of collections, assay and compare the small aliquots to evaluate conditions for, and collections having, the highest titer.

3.2. Enrichment of CD34⁺ Cells

Bone marrow cells from normal patients are obtained from allogeneic transplant donors, cord blood cells are obtained from discarded placentas following normal delivery, and G-CSF-primed peripheral blood cells are obtained from patients undergoing autologous bone marrow transplant combined with high-dose chemotherapy. The CD34$^+$ enrichment is performed using an MAb and an avidin-biotin immunoaffinity system according to the manufacturer's instructions.

1. Hematopoietic cells are applied to a Ficoll-hypaque gradient, and the light density cells are washed and resuspended at $1-2 \times 10^8$/mL in phosphate-buffered saline (PBS) containing 1% bovine serum albumin (BSA).

2. Biotinylated anti-CD34 MAb (80 µL/mL) is added and cells are incubated at room temperature for 25 min.
3. The antibody-labeled cells are applied to the prepared avidin column, followed by a wash with PBS containing 1% BSA.
4. Adsorbed CD34⁺ cells are released by mechanical manipulation.
5. Samples may be analyzed with a direct staining method on a FACScan flow cytometer (Becton Dickinson, Rutherford, NJ) as described elsewhere *(17)*.

3.3. Prestimulation and Transduction of Human CD34⁺ Cells

The transduction protocol consists of two phases: a 24 h prestimulation step in LTCM containing IL-3, IL-6, and SCF (10 ng/mL each) followed by repeated additions of vector-containing supernatants over a period of 2–3 d. A multiplicity of infection (MOI = infectious vector copy:3T3 target cell ratio) of 10–20, and a cell concentration of ≤5 × 10⁵/mL are maintained (*see* Note 2). In each experiment, nontransduced control cells are subjected to mock transduction or transduction with a different vector in parallel with cells receiving the vector of interest.

1. Count the CD34⁺-enriched cells and suspend them at 2.5 × 10⁵/mL in LTCM containing IL-3, IL-6, and SCF at 10 ng/mL. The total number of cells obtained will determine the volume and type of vessel needed to accommodate them. We sometimes begin with as few as 2.5 × 10⁵ cells in 1 mL in a 24-well plate. Incubate the cells for 24 h.
2. The following day, add an equal volume of virus-containing supernatant to which has been added 8 µg/mL of protamine sulfate and 10 ng/mL of IL-3, IL-6, and SCF. Incubate 12–24 h.
3. For the next infection, reduce the volume by drawing off half the medium or transfer the cells to a larger plate if necessary and add an equal volume of freshly thawed virus-containing supernatant containing 4 µg/mL protamine sulfate and 10 ng/mL of the three cytokines. Incubate for 12–24 h.
4. Repeat step 3 with another aliquot of freshly thawed virus-containing supernatant.
5. After the final infection, thoroughly resuspend the samples and determine the cell concentrations.
6. Plate 10⁴/mL or fewer cells in methylcellulose cultures according to the instructions of the supplier (Stem Cell Technologies, Vancouver, Canada). These are assayed after 12–14 d by PCR amplification (*see* Section 3.4.1.) of individual colonies to yield an estimate of the efficiency of transduction of CFU-GM.
7. Cells may be plated into irradiated long-term bone marrow cultures at this time (*see* Section 3.4.3.).
8. Expand the remaining cells by addition of LTCM containing IL-3, IL-6, and SCF or other cytokine combinations, if desired. Maintain cell concentrations below 10⁶/mL. The CD34⁺-enriched cells will continue to differentiate and expand between 2–3 logs for approx 3 wk. Harvest cells for assay of gene product or for Southern blot hybridization analysis, as appropriate (*see* Note 3).

3.4. Determination of Transduction Efficiency

3.4.1. Extraction of DNA from CFU-GM Colonies for PCR Analysis

The polymerase chain reaction is performed on individual methocel colonies following phenol/chloroform microextraction of the DNA as described by Deiserroth et al. *(46, see* Note 4).

1. Select isolated colonies using a micropipet and a steady hand while observing on an inverted microscope. Transfer the colonies to Eppendorf tubes.
2. Add 100 µL of homogenized extraction mixture, vortex, and allow to sit on ice for 15 min.
3. Centrifuge the samples for 10 min at 10,000*g*.
4. Transfer the top aqueous layer to a new Eppendorf tube and add 100 µL of isopropanol.
5. Store the samples at –20°C for 1 h or overnight, then centrifuge for 10 min at 10,000*g*.
6. Remove the supernatant, wash the pellet with 70% ethanol, centrifuge, remove the wash, and allow the pellet to air dry.
7. Redissolve the pellet in 20 µL water for use in a standard PCR reaction.

3.4.2. Determination of Copy Number by Southern Blot

For determination of copy number by Southern blot hybridization, infected and control sample bands on autoradiographs are compared with bands produced using spiked amounts of DNA from cell lines carrying known vector copy numbers per cell.

1. Infect a human or mouse cell line with vector-containing supernatants. If the titer is high (e.g., 10^7 or greater) a single infection may transduce the majority of the target cells with one or more copies per cell. For lower titer supernatants, multiple infections may be necessary to permit isolation of a number of infected clones.
2. Clone the infected cells by limiting dilution, and expand the clones to obtain at least 100 µg of DNA. Usually, 10^7 cells is sufficient. Be sure to cryogenically preserve viable samples of each clone.
3. Digest the DNA from each clone with an enzyme that cuts only once within the vector, outside of the region used for the probe. By this means, each different integration site will yield a differently sized DNA fragment, depending on the distance from the recognition sequence within the vector through the probed region to the nearest recognition site in the flanking genomic DNA.
4. Also, digest another portion of DNA with an enzyme that cuts only within the LTRs, thereby yielding a single band of defined mol wt, independently of the number of different integration sites.
5. Run the digests on an agarose gel, blot, and probe the blot by standard methods (e.g., *see* ref. *56*).
6. Select several clones that reveal one or more copies of the vector. Confirm the clonality by subcloning and reanalysis of each subclone. Confirm the copy num-

ber by using a second unique enzyme to give the same number of bands that were obtained from step 3.

7. Use the DNA obtained from the clones to spike into noninfected control DNA in order to generate standard mixtures that are equivalent to the desired copy numbers or fractions of copies per cell (*see* Note 5).

8. Digest these standard mixtures along with unknown samples using an enzyme that recognizes a site within the LTRs.

9. Run the samples and standards together in an agarose gel, blot, and probe.

10. Using a beta scanner, densitometer, or visual estimation, compare vector band intensities of the known copy number standards with the samples. Ideally, prepare a standard curve that encompasses the sample band intensities.

11. Use the standard curve or extrapolate to determine sample copy numbers based on the standard mixtures.

3.4.3. Long-Term Bone Marrow Culture (LTC) Initiating Cells

Southern analysis of in vitro expanded cells and PCR analysis of CFU-GM provide estimates for transduction efficiency, but neither of these methods yields conclusive evidence for transduction of primitive stem cells. Initiation of hematopoiesis in irradiated long-term cultures, and subsequent demonstration of transduced CFU-GM from such cultures after 5 wk, is indication that progenitors more primitive than CFU-GM have been transduced.

1. At least 2 wk prior to transduction of CD34⁺-enriched samples, establish LTC stromal layers by charging T25 tissue culture flasks with 2.5×10^7 mononuclear cells from human bone marrow in 10 mL of LTCM.

2. Incubate the flasks at 37°C for 3 d and then at 33°C thereafter. Feed the flasks weekly by replacement of half the medium with fresh LTCM.

3. Prior to seeding of cells, expose the stroma to 2000 rad. Change the medium and incubate overnight.

4. Seed transduced and control CD34⁺-enriched cells at a concentration of 5×10^5 cells per flask.

5. Continue to incubate the flasks at 33°C with weekly replacement of half the medium.

6. After 6 wk, plate the adherent and nonadherent cells in methocel cultures for generation of colonies from CFU-GM, and analyze for presence of the vector sequence by PCR.

4. Notes

1. Optimum conditions for collection of supernatant may vary between different packaging lines. With ΨCRIP producer lines, we have found that the highest titer supernatants are obtained after the cells reach confluence. As the dishes become confluent, feed the cells fresh medium daily to maintain a healthy monolayer, but do not split the cells. Instead, collect overnight supernatants from dishes (15 cm) fed with 30 mL of medium the previous afternoon, and collect 8-h supernatants during the afternoon from dishes fed with 10 mL of fresh medium in the morning.

2. The transduction process is under continuing investigation and is complicated by many variables. It is often difficult to obtain the quantity of cells needed to make multiparameter comparisons in a single experiment, and unknown variables between experiments further complicate this objective. Unexpected loss of titer is sometimes observed. Variables that we have investigated include the requirement for cytokine-prestimulation (24 h seems to be a requirement), specific requirement for SCF in addition to IL-3 and IL-6 (SCF adds an increment of improvement), the presence of fibroblasts (not apparently helpful), use of centrifugation to enhance transduction (can definitely help, *see* ref. *57*), multiple infections (definitely additive up to 3–4X, *see* ref. *16*), and effect of cryogenic preservation of cells (does not prevent subsequent transduction after thawing).

   The protocol we use maintains a constant virus concentration at the initiation of each infection cycle, i.e., a 1:1 mixture of fresh supernatant in medium is applied. We find virus concentration (dilution ratio) to be a reproducibly important variable for infection of 3T3 targets; although the effect is not linear, higher transduction occurs at higher supernatant concentrations. Supernatant titer appears to be of crucial importance, and every effort should be put into obtaining and preserving high titer supernatant stocks.

3. Since these cells undergo 2–3 log expansions during this time, the copy number measurement represents an overall average for the progeny of transduced progenitors, and should theoretically be comparable to transduction efficiency as measured by PCR of CFU-GM. It is as if all of the colonies and any background cells were pooled and assayed as an average. It should be kept in mind that background cells, i.e., cells that do not proliferate into colonies but which survive or may otherwise contaminate CFU-GM colonies with DNA, may contribute to positive PCR results. Controls for highly transduced samples should therefore include analyses of random samples of methocel taken from areas between visible colonies. Positive results for such control samples indicate a likelihood for overestimation of transduction efficiency based on CFU-GM.

4. Protocols for direct PCR analysis of boiled, proteinase K-treated methocel colonies were attempted prior to the use of the more involved phenol/chloroform extraction procedure. The improvement in signal sensitivity with the procedure reported by Deisseroth et al. *(46)* has been well worth the effort.

5. In spiking human DNA with infected control DNA, correction is made for the difference between the mouse and human genome size, i.e., 2.9 and 3.7×10^9 bp per haploid genome, respectively. Thus, 78% as much mouse DNA is added to spike a given quantity of human DNA in comparison to the amount that would be added to spike the same quantity of mouse DNA at the same copy number. For example, if a characterized murine clone contains 5 copies per cell, then 2 µg should be spiked into 8 µg of control mouse DNA for a 1 copy standard, but only 1.6 µg should be spiked into 10 µg of control human DNA for a 1 copy standard. In each case, the total DNA for the species is 10 µg, and quantitation of the vector copy number is dependent on the precision of this loading in each lane for unknown samples as well as on the precision of the standard DNA spike loading.

If endogenous sequences are present that hybridize to the probe or to a second probe without interference with the vector sequence, then these bands may be used as reference bands to normalize each lane for variations in the quantity of DNA loaded. In this case, the precision of the loading of control noninfected DNA in the spiked samples is also important. The latter potential source of error could be avoided in the ideal case in which several clones were available carrying a range of copy numbers per cell for the species of interest. Consideration should also be given to the karyotype of the infected cell lines being used for copy number standards. If a cross-hybridizing reference band is used to normalize DNA quantity in each lane, then it is important that the chromosomes that carry the relevant cross-hybridizing sequence(s) are present in normal diploid amount or that the sex be ascertained if the sequence is sex-linked. It is also advantageous to use euploid lines, if possible, since significant aneuploidy requires complicated adjustments to be made in comparing control DNA to infected primary cells from chromosomally normal individuals. All of these factors contribute to the uncertainty of the Southern technique for quantitation, but to the extent to which they may be controlled, it seems proper to do so.

References

1. Golde, D. W. (1991) The stem cell. *Sci. Am.* **265(6),** 86–93.
2. Civin, C. and Gore, S. (1993) Antigenic analysis of hematopoiesis: a review. *J. Hematotherapy* **2,** 137–144.
3. Civin, C., Strauss, L., Brovall, C., Fackler, M., Schwartz, J., and Shaper, J. (1984) Antigenic analysis of hematopoiesis. III. A hematopoietic progenitor cell surface antigen defined by a monoclonal antibody raised against KG-1a cells. *J. Immunol.* **133,** 157–165.
4. Andrews, R., Singer, J., and Bernstein, I. (1986) Monoclonal antibody 12-8 recognizes a 115-kd molecule present on both unipotent and multipotent hematopoietic colony-forming cells and their precursors. *Blood* **67,** 842–845.
5. Molineux, G., Pojda, Z., Hampson, I., Lord, B., and Dexter, T. (1990) Transplantation potential of peripheral blood stem cells induced by granulocyte colony-stimulating factor. *Blood* **76,** 2153–2158.
6. Gianni, A., Tarella, C., Siena, S., Bregni, M., Boccadoro, M., Lombardi, F., Bengala, C., Bonadonna, G., and Pileri, A. (1990) Durable and complete hematopoietic reconstitution after autografting of rhGM-CSF exposed peripheral blood progenitor cells. *Bone Marrow Transplantation* **6,** 143–145.
7. Bensinger, W. and Berenson, R. (1990) Peripheral blood and positive selection of marrow as a source of stem cells for transplantation. *Prog. Clin. Biol. Res.* **337,** 93–98.
8. Hillyer, C. D., Comenzo, R. L., Miller, K. B., Schenkein, D. P., Tiegerman, K. O., Fogaren, T. A., Wazer, D. E., Parker, L., Abrams, R. A., Desforges, J. F., Rudders, R. A., and Berkman, E. M. (1991) Prompt engraftment using autologous peripheral blood stem cells for double autologous bone marrow rescue. *Am. J. Hematol.* **36,** 152,153.

9. Berenson, R. J. (1992) Transplantation of CD34⁺ hematopoietic precursors: clinical rationale. *Transplant. Proc.* **24**, 3032–3034.

10. Schwartzberg, L., Birch, R., Blanco, R., Wittlin, F., Muscato, J., Tauer, K., and Hazelton, B. (1993) Rapid and sustained hematopoietic reconstitution by peripheral blood stem cell infusion alone following high-dose chemotherapy. *Bone Marrow Transplantation* **11**, 369–374.

11. Shpall, E., Ball, E., Champlin, R., LeMaistre, C., Holland, H., Saral, R., Hoffman, E., and Berenson, R. (1993) A prospective, randomized phase III study using the CEPRATE SC stem cell concentrator to isolate CD34⁺ hematopoietic progenitors for autologous marrow transplantation after high dose chemotherapy. *Blood* **82 (suppl 1),** 321,83a.

12. Bregni, M., Magni, M., Siena, S., Di Nicola, M., Bonadonna, G., and Gianni, A. M. (1992) Human peripheral blood hematopoietic progenitors are optimal targets of retroviral-mediated gene transfer. *Blood* **80,** 1418–1422.

13. Bahnson, A., Nimgaonkar, M. T., Boggs, S. S., Robbins, P. D., Patrene, K., Fei, Y., Li, J., Ball, E. D., and Barranger, J. A. (1993) Transduction and expression of the human glucocerebrosidase gene in the long term murine model and in the Rhesus monkey bone marrow and human CD34⁺ cells. *Sixth International Symposium on Autologous BMT* (Dicke, K. A. and Keating, A., eds.), Baylor College of Medicine Press, Baylor, TX, pp. 138–144.

14. Cassel, A., Cottler-Fox, M., Doren, S., and Dunbar, C. E. (1993) Retroviral-mediated gene transfer into CD34-enriched human peripheral blood stem cells. *Exp. Hematol.* **21,** 585–591.

15. Moore, M. (1993) Ex vivo expansion and gene therapy using cord blood CD34⁺ cells. *J. Hematotherapy* **2,** 221–224.

16. Bahnson, A., Nimgaonkar, M., Fei, Y., Boggs, S., Robbins, P., Ohashi, T., Dunigan, J., Li, J., Ball, E. D., and Barranger, J. B. K. (1994) Transduction of CD34⁺ enriched cord blood and Gaucher bone marrow cells by a retroviral vector carrying the glucocerebrosidase gene. *Gene Therapy* **1,** 176–184.

17. Nimgaonkar, M., Bahnson, A., Boggs, S., Ball, E. D., and Barranger, J. A. (1994) Transduction of mobilized peripheral blood CD34⁺ cells with the glucocerebrosidase gene. *Gene Ther.* **1,** 201–207.

18. Bender, J., Unverzagt, K., Walker, D., Lee, W., Van Epps, D., Smith, D., Stewart, C. C., and To, L. B. (1991) Identification and comparison of CD34-positive cells and their subpopulations from normal peripheral blood and bone marrow using multicolor flow cytometry. *Blood* **77,** 2591–2596.

19. Nagler, A., Peacock, M., Tantoco, M., Lamons, D., Okarma, T. B., and Lamons, D. (1993) Separation of human progenitors from human umbilical cord blood. *J. Hematotherapy* **2,** 243–245.

20. Bodine, D., Crosier, P., and Clark, S. (1991) Effects of hematopoietic growth factors on the survival of primitive stem cells in liquid suspension culture. *Blood* **78,** 914–920.

21. Lansdorp, P. M. and Dragowska, W. (1992) Long-term erythropoiesis from constant numbers of CD34⁺ cells in serum-free cultures initiated with highly purified progenitor cells from human bone marrow. *J. Exp. Med.* **175,** 1501–1509.

22. Haylock, D. N., To, L. B., Dowse, T. L., Juttner, C. A., and Simmons, P. J. (1992) Ex vivo expansion and maturation of peripheral blood CD34⁺ cells into the myeloid lineage. *Blood* **80,** 1405–1412.

23. Koller, M. R., Emerson, S. G., and Palsson, B. O. (1993) Large-scale expansion of human stem and progenitor cells from bone marrow mononuclear cells in continuous perfusion cultures. *Blood* **82,** 378–384.
24. Miller, D., Adam, M., and Miller, A. (1990) Gene transfer by retrovirus vectors occurs only in cells that are actively replicating at the time of infection. *Mol. Cell. Biol.* **10,** 4239–4242.
25. Bodine, D., Karlsson, S., and Nienhuis, A. (1989) Combination of interleukins 3 and 6 preserves stem cell function in culture and enhances retrovirus-mediated gene transfer into hematopoietic stem cells. *Proc. Natl. Acad. Sci. USA* **86,** 8897–8901.
26. Luskey, B. D., Rosenblatt, M., Zsebo, K., and Williams, D. A. (1992) Stem cell factor, Interleukin-3, and Interleukin-6 promote retroviral-mediated gene transfer into murine hematopoietic stem cells. *Blood* **80,** 396–402.
27. Tarella, C., Ferrero, D., Bregni, M., Siena, S., Gallo, E., Pileri, A., and Gianni, A. (1991) Peripheral blood expansion of early progenitor cells after high-dose cyclophosphamide and rhGM-CSF. *Eur. J. Cancer* **27,** 22–27.
28. Siena, S., Bregni, M., Brando, B., Ravagnani, F., Bonadonna, G., and Gianni, A. (1989) Circulation of CD34⁺ hematopoietic stem cells in the peripheral blood of high-dose cyclophosphamide-treated patients: enhancement by intravenous recombinant human granulocyte-macrophage colony-stimulating factor. *Blood* **74,** 1905–1914.
29. Pluznik, D. H. and Sachs, L. (1966) The induction of clones of normal mast cells by a substance from conditioned medium. *Exp. Cell. Res.* **43,** 553–563.
30. Eaves, C. J., Cashman, J. D., and Eaves, A. C. (1991) Methodology of long-term culture of human hematopoietic cells. *J. Tissue Culture Meth.* **13,** 55–62.
31. Lapidot, T., Pflumio, F., Doedens, M., Murdoch, B., Williams, D., and Dick, J. (1992) Cytokine stimulation of multilineage hematopoiesis from immature cells engrafted in SCID mice. *Science* **255,** 1137–1141.
32. Civin, C., Trishman, T., Fackler, M., Bernstein, I., Buhring, H., Campos, L., Grteaves, M., Kamoun, M., Katz, D., Lansdorp, P., Look, A., Seed, B., Sutherland, D., Tindle, R., and Uchanska-Ziegler, B. (1989) Report on the CD34 cluster workshop, *in Leucocyte Typing IV, White Cell Differentiation Antigens.* (Knapp, Dorken, Gilks, Rieber, Schmidt, Stein and von dem Borne, eds.), Oxford University Press, New York. pp. 818–829.
33. Terstappen, L., Huang, S., Safford, M., Lansdorp, P., and Loken, M. (1991) Sequential generations of hematopoietic colonies derived from single nonlineage-committed CD34⁺CD38-progenitor cells. *Blood* **77,** 1218–1228.
34. Pincus, S., Nimgaonkar, M., Roscoe, R., Patel, A., Ball, E. D., and Winkelstein, A. (1993) A comparative study of blood and marrow derived CD34⁺ cells: subset analysis reveals differences in the frequencies of primitive hematopoietic stem cells. *Blood* **82 (suppl 1),** 12a.
35. Bender, J., Unverzagt, K., Walker, D., Lee ,W., Van Epps, D., Smith, D., Stewart, C. C., and To, L. B. (1991) Identification and comparison of CD34-positive cells and their subpopulations from normal peripheral blood and bone marrow using multicolor flow cytometry. *Blood* **77,** 2591–2596.
36. Bodine, D., Karlsson, S., and Nienhuis, A. (1989) Combination of interleukins 3 and 6 preserves stem cell function in culture and enhances retrovirus-mediated gene transfer into hematopoietic stem cells. *Proc. Natl. Acad. Sci. USA* **86,** 8897–8901.

37. Bodine, D., Crosier, P., and Clark, S. (1991) Effects of hematopoietic growth factors on the survival of primitive stem cells in liquid suspension culture. *Blood* **78,** 914–920.

38. Luskey, B. D., Rosenblatt, M., Zsebo, K., and Williams, D. A. (1992) Stem cell factor, Interleukin-3, and Interleukin-6 promote retroviral-mediated gene transfer into murine hematopoietic stem cells. *Blood* **80,** 396–402.

39. Nolta, J. A. and Kohn, D. B. (1990) Comparison of the effects of growth factors on retroviral vector-mediated gene transfer and the proliferative status of human hematopoietic progenitor cells. *Hum. Gene Ther.* **1,** 257–268.

40. Nolta, J. A., Crooks, G. M., Overell, R. W., Williams, D. E., and Kohn, D. B. (1992) Retroviral vector-mediated gene transfer into primitive human hematopoietic progenitor cells: effects of mast cell growth factor (MGF) combined with other cytokines. *Exp. Hematol.* **20,** 1065–1071.

41. Ohashi, T., Boggs, S., Robbins, P., Bahnson, A., Patrene, K., Wei, F. S., Wei, J. F., Li, J., Lucht, L., Fei, Y., Clark, S., Kimak, M., Ho, H., Mowery-Rushton, P., and Barranger, J. A. (1992) Efficient transfer and sustained high expression of the human glucocerebrosidase gene in mice and their functional macrophages following transplantation of bone marrow transduced by a retroviral vector. *Proc. Natl. Acad. Sci. USA* **89,** 11,332–11,336.

42. Lemishka, I. R., Raulet, D. H., and Mulligan, R. C. (1986) Developmental potential and dynamic behavior of hematopoietic stem cells. *Cell* **45,** 917–927.

43. Weider, R., Cornetta, K., Kessler, S. W., and Anderson, W. F. (1991) Increased efficiency of retroviral-mediated gene transfer and expression in primate bone marrow progenitors after 5-Fluorouracil-induced hematopoietic suppression and recovery. *Blood* **77,** 448–455.

44. van Beusechem, V. W., Kukler, A., Heidt, P. J., and Valerio, D. (1992) Long-term expression of human adenosine deaminase in Rhesus monkeys transplanted with retrovirus-infected bone marrow cells. *Proc. Natl. Acad. Sci. USA* **89,** 7640–7644.

45. van Beusechem, V. W., Bakx, T. A., Kaptern, L. C. M., Bart-Baumeister, J. A. K., Kukler, A., Braakman, E., and Valerio, D. (1993) Retrovirus-mediated gene transfer in Rhesus monkey hematopoietic stem cells: effect of viral titers on transduction efficiency. *Hum. Gene Ther.* **4,** 239–247.

46. Deisseroth, A. B., Zu, A., Claxton, D., Hanania, E. G., Fu, S., Ellerson, D., Goldberg, L., Thomas, M., Janicek, K., Anderson, W. F., Hester, J., Korbling, M., Durett, A., Moen, R., Berenson, R., Heimfeld, S., Hamer, J., Calvert, L., Tibbits, P., Talpaz, M., Kentarjian, H., Champlin, R., and Reading, C. (1994) Genetic marking shows that PH+ cells present in autologous transplants of chronic myelogenous leukemia contribute to relapse after autologous bone marrow in CML. *Blood* **83,** 3068–3076.

47. Rill, D. R., Santana, V. M., Roberts, W. M., Nilson, T., Bowman, L. C., Krance, R. A., Heslop, H. E., Moen, R. C., Ihle, J. N., and Brenner, M. K. (1994) Direct demonstration that autologous bone marrow transplantation for solid tumors can return a multiplicity of tumorigenic cells. *Blood* **84,** 380–383.

48. Hoogerbrugge, P. M., v Beusechem, V., Valerio, D., Moseley, A., Harvey, M., Fischer, A., Debree, M., Gaspar, B., Morgan, G., and Levinsky, R. (1993) Gene transfer in 3 children with adenosine deaminase deficiency. *Blood* **82(Suppl 1),** 315a.

49. Kohn, D. B., Weinberg, K. I., Parkman, R., Lenarsky, C., Crooks, G. M., Shaw, K., Hanley, M. E., Lawrence, K., Annett, G., Brooks, J. S., Wara, D., Elder, M., Bowen, T., Hershfield, M. S., Berenson, R. I., Moen, R. C., Mullen, C. A., and Blaese, R. M. (1993) Gene therapy for neonates with ADA-deficient SCID by retroviral-mediated transfer of the human ADA cDNA into umbilical cord CD34⁺ cells. *Blood* **82(Suppl 1),** 315a.

50. Dunbar, C. E., O'Shaughnessy, J. A., Cottler-Fox, M., Carter, C. S., Doren, S., Cowan, K. H., Leitman, S. F., Wilson, W., Young, N. S., and Nienhuis, A. W. (1993) Transplantation of retrovirally-marked CD34⁺ bone marrow and peripheral blood cells in patients with multiple myeloma or breast cancer. *Blood* **82(Suppl 1),** 217a.

51. Xu, L. C., Blanco, M., Stahl, S. K., Kessler, S., Dunbar, C., and Karlsson, S. (1993) Correction of the enzyme deficiency in hematopoietic cells of Gaucher patients using a clinically acceptable retroviral supernatant transduction protocol. *Blood* **82(Suppl 1),** 217a.

52. v Kalle, C., Keim, H. P., Zaboikin, N. M., Darovsky, B., Goehle, S., Berenson, R., Miller, A. D., Storb, R., and Scheuning, F. G. (1993) Retrovirus-mediated transfer of human glucocerebrosidase cDNA into canine and human repopulating hematopoietic cells. *Blood* **82(Suppl 1),** 216a.

53. Karlsson, S., Dunbar, C., and Kohn, D. (1993) Retroviral mediated transfer of the cDNA for human glucocerebrosidase into hematopoietic stem cells of patients with Gaucher's disease. *Fed. Reg.* **58,** 47,907–47,909.

54. Schuening, F., Sanders, J., and Scott, C. R. (1993) Retrovirus-mediated transfer of the cDNA for human glucocerebrosidase into peripheral blood repopulating cells of patients with Gaucher's disease. Recombinant DNA Advisory Committee approval 12/2/93. Human Gene Transfer Protocol #9312-061, Office of Recombinant DNA Activities, NIH, Bethesda, MD.

55. Barranger, J. A., Ball, E., Boggs, S., Robbins, P. D., Bahnson, A., Nimgaonkar, M., and Rice, E. O. (1993) Recombinant DNA research action under the guidelines; proposals entitled: gene therapy for Gaucher disease: ex vivo gene transfer and autologous transplantation of CD34(+) cells. *Fed. Reg.* **58,** 47,907–47,909.

56. Brown, T. (1993) Analysis of DNA sequences by blotting and hybridization, in *Current Protocols In Molecular Biology (Suppl 21)*, (Ausabel, F. M., Brent, R., Kingston, R. E., Moore, D. D., Seidmen, J. G., Smith, S. A., and Struhl, K., eds.), Greene Publishing, Wiley, New York, Section 2.9.1–2.10.16.

57. Bahnson, A. B., Dunigan, J. T., Baysal, B. E., Mohney, T., Atchison, R. W., Nimgaonkar, M. T., Ball, E. D., and Barranger, J. A. (1995) Centrifugal enhancement of retroviral-mediated gene transfer. *J. Virol. Meth.* **54,** 131–143.

19

Methods for the Use of Genetically Modified Keratinocytes in Gene Therapy

Sabine A. Eming and Jeffrey R. Morgan

1. Introduction

Recent advances in molecular genetics have resulted in the development of new technologies for the introduction and expression of genes in human somatic cells. Recombinant retroviral vectors have become a popular method for introducing such genes, primarily because the frequency of gene transfer is usually high and the introduced genes are stably integrated into the host genome. Gene therapy and gene transfer technology, although typically thought of as a means to correct genetic disease, have other potential clinical applications in the areas of protein delivery and tissue engineering. Numerous types of cells/tissues have been successfully genetically modified and are potential targets for retroviral mediated gene therapy *(1)*. The successful use of these tissues in gene therapy relies on methods to cultivate and transplant the cells after genetic modification.

In this chapter, we describe the use of retrovirus-mediated gene transfer to genetically modify human keratinocytes, the principal cell type of the epidermis. Epidermal keratinocytes are an attractive target for gene therapy because they are easy to obtain, grow rapidly under appropriate culture conditions, and can be transplanted. Using appropriate culture conditions, the lifetime of diploid human keratinocytes in vitro has been reported to be 50–140 population doublings *(2)*. In fact, the keratinocytes from the epidermis of a 1-cm^2 biopsy can be expanded to an area of 1 m^2 in approx 30 d in vitro *(3)*. When grown to confluence, cultured keratinocytes form a coherent multicell, layered epithelial sheet, that organizes itself into a differentiated epidermis when grafted to animals or humans *(4–6)*. The successful use of cultured epidermal sheet grafts

From: *Methods in Molecular Medicine, Gene Therapy Protocols*
Edited by: P. Robbins Humana Press Inc., Totowa, NJ

as long-term wound coverage indicates that the epidermal stem cell survives in culture and can reconstitute a differentiated and renewable epidermis.

Although the primary role of the mammalian epidermis is the formation of a protective barrier between the individual and the external environment, recent work has shown that keratinocytes synthesize and secrete numerous proteins that are involved in a variety of metabolic activities; e.g., keratinocytes are a source of many cytokines *(7)*. It has been shown that at least two proteins (apolipoprotein E, type VII collagen of dermal anchoring fibrils) endogenously secreted by keratinocytes can cross the basement membrane separating the epidermis from the dermis *(8,9)*. This observation suggests that epidermal-derived proteins, in addition to acting at local sites, may affect distant cells, tissues, and organs.

Cultured primary keratinocytes have been successfully genetically modified with retroviral vectors encoding several different genes, including human growth hormone (hGH) *(10)*, neomycin (neo) *(11)*, the β-subunit of human chorionic gonadotrophin (β-hCG) *(12)*, clotting factor IX *(13)*, and platelet-derived growth factor (PDGF-A) *(14)*. When grafted as an epithelial sheet onto athymic mice, modified keratinocytes reconstituted a stratified epithelium with well-defined stratum basale, spinosum, granulosum, and corneum.

In addition to the delivery of therapeutic proteins, genetically modified skin grafts potentially can be used toward the correction of inherited diseases of the skin. Much progress has been made in identifying the molecular defects in several inherited diseases of the skin, including xeroderma pigmentosum and various forms of epidermolysis bullosa, a family of skin-blistering diseases *(15,16)*. Grafting of autologous keratinocytes, modified to express a functional copy of the defective gene, could potentially restore normal epidermal function at those sites of the body most severely affected by disease.

In this chapter, we describe methods for the culture of diploid human keratinocytes, the genetic modification of these cells by retrovirus-mediated gene transfer, and the transplantation of modified keratinocytes to the athymic mouse.

2. Materials

2.1. Cell Culture and Genetic Modification

2.1.1. Fibroblast Feeder Layer/Virus-Producing Cell Line

1. Fibroblast feeder layer: 3T3-J2 mouse fibroblast cell line (originally provided by H. Green, Department of Physiology and Biophysics, Harvard Medical School, Boston, MA).
2. Virus-producing cell line: Ψ-CRIP amphotropic packaging cell line, a derivative of NIH 3T3 fibroblasts that expresses retroviral gag, pol, and env gene products (originally obtained from R. Mulligan, Whitehead Institute of Biomedical Research, Cambridge, MA).

3. Fibroblast tissue-culture medium: Dulbecco's Modified Eagle's Medium (DMEM, high glucose, L-glutamine, 110 mg/L sodium pyruvate, Gibco-BRL, Gaithersburg, MD), bovine calf serum 10% (HyClone, Logan, UT), penicillin-streptomycin (Boehringer, Indianapolis, IN) 100 IU/mL–100 μg/mL.
4. Mitomycin C (Boehringer): 15 μg/mL in serum-free DMEM.

2.1.2. Keratinocytes

1. Source for human keratinocytes: newborn foreskins (average size: 1–2 cm^2).
2. KCM (keratinocyte tissue-culture medium):
   a. DMEM/Ham's F12 medium (Gibco-BRL) (3:1).
   b. Fetal bovine serum 10% (JRH Bioscience, Lenexa, KS).
   c. Penicillin-streptomycin 100 IU/mL-100 μg/mL.
   d. Adenine (6-aminopurine hydrochlolide, Sigma, St. Louis, MO); make up fresh at time medium is prepared; prepare stock (50X) of 1.2 mg/mL in DMEM/F12 (3:1), adjust pH to 7.5 with 1N NaOH, sterilize by filtration using a 0.45-μm filter; add 2 mL of stock to 100 mL of KCM; final concentration: $1.8 \times 10^{-4}M$.
   e. Cholera toxin (Vibrio cholerae, Type Inaba 569 B, Calbiochem, La Jolla, CA); prepare concentrated stock of $10^{-5}M$ in distilled water, store at 4°C; take 0.1 mL of concentrated stock and make up to 10 mL with DMEM (10% fetal calf serum), sterilize by filtration using a 0.45-μm filter and aliquot in 1-mL portions ($10^{-7}M$), store at –20°C; add 0.1 mL to 100 mL of KCM; final concentration: $10^{-10}M$.
   f. Epidermal growth factor (mouse, Collaborative Biomedical Products, Bedford, MA); resuspend lyophilized material in distilled water to prepare stock of 10 μg/mL; sterilize by filtration using a 0.45-μm filter and aliquot in 1-mL portions, store at –20°C; add 0.1 mL to 100 mL KCM with first medium change; final concentration: 10 ng/mL.
   g. Hydrocortisone (chromatographic standard, Calbiochem); prepare stock of 5 mg/mL in 95% ethanol, store at 4°C; take 0.4 mL of stock and make up to 10 mL with serum-free DMEM, sterilize by filtration using a 0.45-μm filter, and aliquot in 1-mL portions; add 0.2 mL to 100 mL of KCM; final concentration: 0.4 μg/mL.
   h. Insulin (pork, 100 U/mL [3.8 mg/mL], Novo Nordisk, Danbury, CT); add 0.13 mL of stock to 100 mL of KCM; final concentration: 5 μg/mL.
   i. T/T3 stock (transferrin/triiodo-L-thyronine stock); T stock (transferrin, human, partially iron saturated, Boehringer) 5 mg/mL in PBS; T3 stock (3,3',5 triiodo-L-thyronine, sodium salt, Sigma) dissolve 13.6 mg in the minimum amount of 0.02N NaOH and make volume up to 100 mL with distilled water, sterilize by filtration using a 0.45-μm filter and store at –20°C ($2 \times 10^{-4}M$); add 0.1 mL T3 stock to 9.9 mL of T stock, sterilize by filtration using a 0.45-μm filter and aliquot in 1-mL portions, store at –20°C; add 0.1 mL of T/T3 stock to 100 mL of KCM; final concentration transferrin: 5 μg/mL, triiodo-L-thyronine: $2 \times 10^{-9}M$.

3. KCM selective growth medium: If KCM is used as selective growth medium for cells carrying the drug resistance gene *neo* (neomycin phosphotransferase), add 0.6 mg/mL G418.

4. PBS (phosphate-buffered saline): 138 mM NaCl, 2.7M KCl, 8.1 mM Na$_2$HPO$_4$, 1.5 mM KH$_2$PO$_4$; sterilize by filtration using a 0.45-μm filter.

5. EDTA solution ([ethylenedinitriolo]tetraacetic acid disodium salt, Boehringer): 5 mM in PBS; sterilize by filtration using a 0.45-μm filter.

6. Trypsin solution (trypsin 1-300, ICN Biochemicals, High Wycombe, UK): D-dextrose 0.1% (w/v), trypsin 0.1% (w/v) in PBS, pH 7.5; sterilize by filtration using a 0.45-μm filter, store at –20°C, avoid repeated thawing/freezing.

7. Trypsinizing flask (25 mL, Wheaton Scientific, Millville, NJ).

8. Rhodamine B (Sigma): 1% (w/v) in distilled water.

9. Formaldehyde (Sigma, 37%): dilute stock 1:10 (v/v) in PBS.

2.2. Grafting of Modified Cells

1. Dispase II (Boehringer): 2.4 mg/mL in serum-free DMEM; prepare fresh before use.

2. Ethanol: 70% in distilled water.

3. Anesthesia (2,2,2,-tribromoethanol, Aldrich, Milwaukee, WI): prepare concentrated stock of 1.6 g/mL in 2-methyl-2-butanol alcohol; store at 4°C. Before use, prepare working solution by diluting 12-μL (concentrated stock)/mL 0.9% NaCl at 40°C, sterilize by filtration using a 0.45-μm filter.

4. Surgical instruments: straight, sharp scissors, curved scissors, forceps.

5. Ligaclips (LC-100, small, Ethicon, Somerville, NJ).

6. Ligaclip Cartridge Base (Ethicon).

7. Ligaclip applier (LC-105, small, Ethicon).

8. Athymic nude mice, NIH Swiss *nu/nu*, 6–8 wk, average weight: 20–30 g (outbread, TAC:N:NIFS-nufDF, Taconic, Germantown, NY).

9. Silastic-sheeting (0.005 × 6 × 8 in., Dow Corning, Midland, MI): Wash off powder as recommended by the manufacturer, prepare rectangular sheets 1.8 × 1.8 cm (slightly larger than graft) and sterilize by autoclaving.

10. Dental wax, byte ryte, (Mizzy, Cherry Hill, NJ).

11. Tris-buffer: 25 mM Tris-HCl, 1 mM EDTA, pH 7.5.

3. Methods

3.1. Keratinocyte Cell Culture

Although there are several methods for the culture of human keratinocytes, the method developed by Rheinwald and Green is preferred for two reasons: the cells have great growth potential and the epithelia produced from these cultures have had the most clinical application. In addition to media containing fetal calf serum and added factors (i.e., EGF, cholera toxin, transferrin, insulin, hydrocortisone), this method uses a fibroblast feeder layer that is crucial to the clonal growth of keratinocytes *(17)*. The fibroblast feeder layer also conditions the media and inhibits the growth of contaminating dermal fibroblasts present in the biopsy used to initiate primary cultures. As the cells reach confluence, they stratify and form multicell, layered sheets that can be detached from the dish as an intact sheet and grafted. We have modified the Rheinwald and Green method to maintain these conditions for optimal cell growth and also for the genetic modification of the cells by retrovirus-mediated gene transfer.

3.1.1. Fibroblast Feeder Layer

Cocultivation of the epidermal cells with a feeder layer is critical for the clonal growth of keratinocytes and optimal growth is important for retrovirus-mediated gene transfer.

1. Grow 3T3-J2 cells in 75-cm^2 flasks or other suitable dishes.
2. Before the primary keratinocytes from the processed biopsy can be added, the feeder layer must be prepared by treating the fibroblasts with mitomycin C, which limits the further proliferation of the fibroblasts. Moreover, as shown by Rheinwald and Green, the density of the feeder cells is important for optimal keratinocyte growth. Prepare feeder layer by growing the cells to 50% confluence and incubating cells for 2 h at 37°C with 15 mL of DMEM supplemented with mitomycin C; remove mitomycin C medium and wash cells twice with DMEM. Alternatively, grow the 3T3-J2 cells to near confluence, treat the cells with mitomycin C, trypsinize, and inoculate 2×10^6 cells /75-cm^2 flask (use comparable densities for other size dishes) in fibroblast culture media. Let the cells attach overnight (37°C, 10% CO$_2$) before adding keratinocytes.
3. Two hours prior to adding keratinocytes, replace fibroblast media with 12 mL KCM (without EGF) and equilibrate flasks in humidified incubator (37°C, 10% CO$_2$).

3.1.2. Preparation of Primary Cultures of Keratinocytes from Biopsy Material

1. Place each biopsy in individual 15-mL sterile culture tubes containing KCM (without EGF) at 4°C. Keep biopsies on ice until processed.
2. Biopsies should be processed no later than 6–8 h after they were obtained. Place the biopsy in a 10-cm dish containing 10 mL PBS. If necessary, dissect to flatten the tissue. Trim off as much connective tissue as possible using the curved scissors.
3. Transfer the biopsy to a 50-mL culture tube containing 10 mL PBS; wash the biopsy by vigorously shaking the tube for approx 60 s. Repeat this washing step 10 times by transferring the biopsy to a new culture tube containing fresh PBS.
4. Place the tissue into a 10-cm dish and, with curved scissors, carefully remove any remaining connective tissue from the dermis. Transfer the epithelium into a 60-mm dish, add 3 mL trypsin solution, and mince very finely (tissue fragments of approx 0.5 mm^3) with sharp scissors. Transfer the minced tissue suspension into a trypsinizing flask. Prewet the spout of the flask with EDTA solution to avoid sticking of the tissue to the glass. Rinse culture dish by adding 3 mL EDTA solution and transfer to the flask. Add 3 mL of trypsin and 3 mL of EDTA solutions (prewarmed) to the flask. Gently stir the tissue fragments at 37°C.

5. After 60 min, remove the flask from the incubator, allow the large tissue fragments to settle, and pour off the cell suspension into a 15-mL culture tube. Add fresh trypsin/EDTA solution (12 mL of trypsin/ EDTA solution 1:1 at 37°C) and repeat trypsinization step for one more harvest. Pellet the cells obtained from the first harvest by centrifugation at 70*g* for 5 min. Resuspend cell pellet in 3 mL KCM (without EGF) and add the cells from one harvest (1–2 × 10⁶ cells) to a 75-cm² flask containing mitomycin C treated 3T3-J2 cells and 12 mL KCM. Each harvest should be plated into a separate flask. To get even seeding of the cells, the incubator shelf should be leveled and the flasks should not be stacked for the first 24 h.

6. Refeed cultures with 15 mL KCM every 4 d, adding EGF at the first medium change after inoculation. When the culture becomes dense, use 18 mL/75-cm² flask.

7. Primary cultures inoculated with epidermal cells from one harvest should approach confluence within 12–14 d and will contain 12–15 × 10⁶ keratinocytes/75-cm² flask. The cultures can now be trypsinized and subcultured. As keratinocytes grow into a confluent epithelium, most of the feeder layer is displaced. Prior to trypsinization, remove residual fibroblasts with a brief wash with EDTA solution as follows: Add 10 mL EDTA solution/75-cm² flask, incubate for 1 min at 37°C, shake the flask to remove fibroblasts, and aspirate off the EDTA solution; repeat washing step if needed. Next, trypsinize the keratinocytes by incubation with 5 mL trypsin solution and 5 mL EDTA solution/75-cm² flask for 15–20 min at 37°C. Neutralize the trypsin/EDTA solution by adding 10 mL KCM/75-cm² flask; pipet the cell suspension repeatedly to dissociate residual cell aggregates. Inspect under the microscope to be sure that trypsinization is complete. Pellet the cells by centrifugation at 70*g* for 5 min, resuspend cell pellet in the appropriate volume of KCM (without EGF) to obtain the desired cell density and pass cells to a mitomycin C-treated feeder layer.

3.1.3. Colony Forming Efficiency

The colony forming efficiency of normal and genetically modified keratinocytes is a good measure of the growth performance of the cells and should be performed at each subculture.

1. At each subculture, inoculate 100 keratinocytes (modified or unmodified cells) in triplicate 60-mm dishes containing 5 × 10⁵ mitomycin C-treated 3T3-J2 cells.

2. After 12 d, fix the colonies with buffered formaldehyde (10 min), then stain with rhodamine B (30 min). Vigorously growing colonies should form uniform, circular colonies with a plating efficiency of 20–30%. Irregular-shaped colonies are more differentiated and have diminished growth potential.

3.2. Retroviral Mediated Gene Transfer into Keratinocytes

Recombinant retroviruses provide an effective means for the efficient and stable introduction of a gene into a dividing cell population. The details of the molecular biology of retrovirus-mediated gene transfer is beyond the scope of this chapter and the reader is referred to several review articles *(18–20)*. Nevertheless, all recombinant retroviruses are produced by specialized packaging cell lines that are a derivative of 3T3 fibroblasts. Several groups have made comparable packaging cell lines and these packaging cell lines express the viral gag, pol, and env genes necessary to package recombinant retroviruses *(21)*. Moreover, packaging cell lines can be easily cultured and they continuously shed recombinant retrovirus into the media. The recombinant retroviruses produced by these packaging cell lines are free of wild-type replication virus but are able to integrate and express the gene(s) of interest in a target cell.

3.2.1. Use of Virus-Producing Cell Line as Feeder Layer

1. To genetically modify human keratinocytes, the 3T3-J2 fibroblasts feeder layer is replaced with a packaging cell line that produces the recombinant retrovirus of interest. The keratinocytes are cocultivated with the virus-producing cell line that sheds recombinant virus into the media that infects the growing keratinocytes.
2. To prepare the virus-producing cell line for keratinocyte cocultivation, handle the cells as the 3T3-J2 cell line described in Section 3.1.1. One day prior to inoculation with keratinocytes, treat virus-producing cells with mitomycin C, trypsinize, and plate 2×10^6 cells/75-cm^2 flask. For control cultures (unmodified keratinocytes), prepare parallel flasks with 3T3-J2 fibroblasts.

The cocultivation of keratinocytes with the virus-producing cell line provides not only a feeder layer for proper growth of keratinocytes but also the continuous production of recombinant retrovirus that integrates into the dividing keratinocytes.

3.2.2. Infection of Keratinocytes

1. After about 12 d, the primary cultures of keratinocytes are ready to be passed. Dissociate the cells by trypsin treatment and inoculate 10^6 keratinocytes/75-cm^2 flask containing 2×10^6 virus-producing cells (for unmodified controls, use 3T3-J2 cells).
2. After 4–6 d of cocultivation with the virus-producing cells, the cells have been genetically modified and the keratinocytes are ready to be subcultured. Prepare parallel cultures for grafting, protein analysis, DNA/RNA isolation, and plating efficiency analysis. An overview for the preparation of tertiary cultures is given in Table 1 and will vary depending on the experiments needs.

3.2.2.1. TIME-COURSE OF PROTEIN SECRETION BY GENETICALLY MODIFIED KERATINOCYTES

If the transferred gene encodes a secreted protein, its synthesis can be monitored by analyzing conditioned culture media for the presence of the protein.

1. Inoculate 10^6 modified or unmodified keratinocytes/10-cm dish, containing 10^6 mitomycin C-treated 3T3-J2 cells; prepare two dishes for each condition.

Table 1
Preparation of Tertiary Cultures

Culture (dish size)	Number of dishes per condition[a]	3T3-J2 (cells/dish)	Keratinocytes (cells/dish)
Protein analysis (10 cm)	2	10^6	10^6
Plating efficiency (60 cm)	3	5×10^5	100
Graft (35 mm)	as needed[b]	2×10^5	10^5

[a]Condition: modified or unmodified keratinocytes.
[b]35-mm dish = 1 graft, 1 graft/mouse.

2. After cells reach confluence (6–7 d), wash cells once with DMEM and add 30 mL of KCM (with EGF)/10-cm dish. Over a 4-d period, take two time points (AM/PM, 1 mL each) per day. Pellet the cell debris by brief centrifugation at 15,000g; store aliquots at –20°C.
3. At the end of the time-course, trypsinize and count keratinocytes. Normalize protein production to cell number.

3.2.2.2. EFFICIENCY OF GENE TRANSFER

Several methods can be used to determine the efficiency of gene transfer. If the vector contains a drug resistance gene, infected cells can be selectively grown in culture medium containing the corresponding drug. However, the feeder layer used to grow the keratinocytes in selective media must be resistant to the drug. The following example is for vectors encoding the drug resistance gene *neo*.

1. Trypsinize modified keratinocytes as before.
2. Pass cells onto dishes containing a modified 3T3-J2 feeder layer. These modified 3T3-J2 feeder cells have been previously genetically modified to express the *neo* gene and are resistant to the antibiotic, G418.
3. Culture keratinocytes on the modified feeder layer in KCM containing G418. After about 6 d, drug-resistant keratinocyte colonies will form and can be expanded in number.

Alternatively, the efficiency of gene transfer can be assayed by estimating the number of gene copies of the virus integrated into the cellular DNA of the epidermal cells. Total genomic DNA can be isolated from modified keratinocytes at the end of the time-course (described in Section 3.2.2.1.).

1. After trypsinization and counting, wash cells with PBS.
2. Centrifuge cells at 120g for 10 min, discard supernatant, and store cells at –80°C until processing for DNA.

3. Prepare genomic DNA using any of the standard protocols to prepare high-mol-wt DNA from mammalian cells.
4. DNA is digested with a restriction enzyme that cuts once in each LTR of the retroviral genome. After fractionation by agarose gel electrophoresis, the DNA is transferred to a membrane and the number of retrovirus gene copies is estimated by Southern blot hybridization with a labeled probe specific for the transferred gene.

3.2.2.3. PREPARATION OF MODIFIED GRAFTS

1. Inoculate 10^5 modified or unmodified keratinocytes into 35-mm dishes, containing 2×10^5 mitomycin C-treated 3T3-J2 cells.
2. Within 6–7 d, these cultures reach confluence. Graft cultures no more than 2 d later. Overconfluent cultures form blisters and should not be grafted.

3.3. Grafting of Modified Epithelial Sheets

3.3.1. Dispase Treatment

1. When the epithelium reaches confluence, wash cultures twice with serum-free DMEM and add 4 mL of dispase solution. After 30 min at 37°C, the edges of the epithelium will loosen and half of the medium should be removed to minimize folding and curling of the graft. Within 1 h at 37°C, the epithelium should completely detach from the plastic dish and float in the medium.
2. Wash epithelium several times with DMEM. With a gentle stream from a 1-mL pipet, straighten out the curled edges of the graft. Be careful to maintain the original orientation of the graft (*see* Note 3b).
3. After dispase treatment, grafting should be performed within 30 min. While preparing the animals for grafting, keep the graft moist in DMEM (1–2 mL/35-mm dish) at 37°C (10% CO_2).

3.3.2. Grafting Modified Epithelia

Several methods have been described for the transplantation of cultured human keratinocytes onto athymic mice. We prefer a model described by Barrandon et al. in which the cultured epithelium is grafted onto the inner side of a full thickness skin flap on the back of the mouse *(22)*. By placing the epithelial sheet under the skin, the graft is protected from desiccation and wound contraction and the boundaries of the genetically modified graft are easy to identify. The grafting of genetically modified epithelia described in this section is a modified form of the model described by Barrandon et al. The entire surgical procedure must be performed on anesthetized animals using sterile conditions in a laminar flow hood. The grafting procedure requires about 30–40 min/mouse.

1. Anesthetize mice by intraperitoneal injection of 2,2,2-tribromoethanol (23 G 3/4-in. needle, 30 µL working solution per gram of mouse).
2. Disinfect the entire back of the mouse with ethanol (70%).

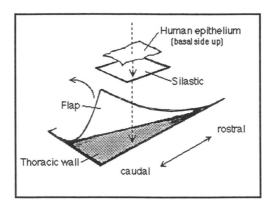

Fig. 1. Preparation of graft site and insertion of silastic sheet with graft.

3. To prepare a skin flap on the back of the mouse, make a 2 × 2 cm L-shaped, full thickness incision (through the panniculus carnosus) starting at the lower back of the mouse. Grasp the free corner of the skin flap with forceps and retract the flap while dissecting it carefully from the thoracic wall. Loosen the internal connective tissue membranes and be careful not to damage the well-vascularized inner part of the flap.

4. Close the flap and remove the dispase-treated graft from the incubator. Carefully aspirate the medium off the graft, keeping the epithelium flat. Place a sheet of silastic over the graft so that the upper surface of the epithelium adheres to it. With fine forceps, grasp one corner of the silastic together with an edge of the epithelium and invert. The epithelium is now sitting on the silastic membrane with its basal side facing upward. If necessary, straighten out the edges of the epithelium with the blunt end of the forceps.

5. Peel back the skin flap and slide the silastic with epithelium onto the thoracic wall. The basal surface of the epithelium is facing upward. The preparation of the graft site and the insertion of the silastic with the graft is illustrated in Fig. 1.

6. Grasp the free corner of the skin flap with forceps and, in one continuous motion, gently place the skin flap over the epithelium. After the skin flap is placed over the epithelium, avoid any further manipulation of the flap to ensure proper contact of the epithelium to the inner side of the mouse skin (*see* Note 3c).

7. Close the incision with surgical clips. With forceps, pinch the edges of the incision to form lips and apply clips over the incision. When positioning the wound edges, minimize manipulation of the skin flap.

8. Lift the animal by grasping the neck and tail (maintain horizontal position) and place gently in the recovery cage. House animals one to a cage.

9. As early as 7 d, grafts form a well-stratified epithelium. After 10 d, grafts become macroscopically visible as a slightly raised area under the mouse skin. Clips detach spontaneously after 3–4 d.

Fig. 2. Human epithelium 7 d after grafting onto the athymic mouse. The human epithelium is easily discriminated from the underlying mouse dermis by its opaque appearance and defined circular shape (arrows indicate margin of human epithelium).

10. To harvest the graft, sacrifice the animal by CO_2 asphyxiation. Make a U-shaped incision, starting at the lower back of the animal. With forceps, grasp the caudal edge of the skin flap plus the silastic, and carefully raise the flap by dissection.

11. As a result of a foreign body reaction, a thin fibrous membrane has formed over the silastic sheeting. Before taking off the silastic sheeting that covers the epithelium, completely remove this fibrous membrane by dissection. After the membrane is removed, grasp one edge of the silastic and gently peel it off the human epithelium, which will remain on the mouse skin. After removal of the silastic sheet, the engrafted human epithelium appears as a circular, well-defined, opaque area at the inner surface of the skin flap. Trace the area of the graft as a measure of the take of the genetically modified graft (Fig. 2).

12. The human epithelium and subjacent mouse tissue can now be prepared either for histology analysis or the epithelium can he processed for tissue extraction. For histological processing, place the biopsy *in toto* (human epithelium adherent to underlying mouse tissue) into fixative. Pin the mouse tissue (human epithelium facing upward) onto a thin wax plate to prevent curling of the edges. Figure 3 shows the histology of a section through a graft harvested 7 d after transplantation. At low magnification, the various layers of the sandwich graft are recognizable. Starting from the top layer, the sandwich is composed of mouse epitheliums mouse dermis, mouse subcutaneous fat, panniculus carnosus, mouse hypodermic, and human epithelium.

13. To detect proteins expressed in the genetically modified epithelium, a tissue extract of the grafted epithelium can be prepared. Harvest the epithelium as described in step 8 and remove the silastic sheet. Grasp one edge of the human epithelium with fine forceps and dissect the human epithelium from the underlying mouse tissue using sharp scissors. Snap-freeze the epithelium in liquid nitrogen and keep at −80°C until used. In a 4°C cold room, grind the frozen tissue

Mouse
Epidermis

Dermis

Subcutaneous
Fat

Panniculus
Carnosus

Hypodermis

Human
Epithelium

Fig. 3. (A) Human and mouse tissue in sandwich configuration 7 d after grafting at low magnification (H&E, ×100). **(B)** Human epithelium at high magnification. Stratification of the epithelium is well defined. Since the human epithelium is covered by the silastic membrane, the cornified layer does not exfoliate and is therefore thicker than normal (H&E, ×200).

to powder in a chilled mortar (–80°C overnight). Transfer the powder to an Eppendorf tube and resuspend in 300–400 µL of Tris buffer (25 mM). Sonicate the solution for 10 s at 50 W. Pellet the cell debris by centrifugation for 5 min at 15,000g and transfer the supernatant into a new vial. Levels of the expressed protein can be detected in tissue extract by ELISA or other protein analysis.

4. Notes

1. Cells must be actively dividing in order to be genetically modified with recombinant retroviruses. It is imperative that optimal cell proliferation be maintained throughout the entire experiment. Moreover, keratinocytes lose their growth potential after they reach confluence. Therefore, we recommend that the primary cultures of keratinocytes be passed onto the virus-producing feeder layer prior to reaching confluence.

   The effectiveness of genetic modification is also a function of the amount (titer) of recombinant retrovirus produced by the packaging cell line. The titers of different packaging cell lines, as well as different retroviral vectors, can vary significantly. It is important to use virus-producing cell lines with titers >10⁵/mL.

2. Poor clonal growth of primary keratinocytes and the overgrowth of primary cultures by human dermal fibroblasts might indicate problems with the feeder layer. To ensure optimal growth conditions for keratinocytes, 3T3-J2 cells or virus-producing cells should not be prepared more than 24 h prior to inoculation with keratinocytes. During the experiment, do not allow the feeder layer to deterio-

rate. Additional mitomycin C-treated feeder cells can be added if necessary. Fresh stocks of 3T3-J2 cells should be prepared on a regular basis (every 3–4 mo).

3. Common problems encountered with the grafting technique are opening of the incision after surgery, absence of the graft, and impaired graft take.

   a. Premature opening of the wound within the first 24 h after surgery is caused by inaccurate closure of the incision with liga clips. Be sure that the edges of the wound are brought together in parallel and the liga clips are applied with enough force. Open wounds should be closed with sutures on anesthetized animals.

   b. Absence of the graft after transplantation is most likely caused by grafting the epithelium in the inverted orientation (basal side of the human epithelium not facing the inner side of the mouse skin flap). Cultured epithelium has a polarity with basal proliferative cells on the side that was attached to the dish before dispase treatment. It is imperative that this side of the epithelium be applied to the inner side of the mouse skin flap. The graft will not take if the epithelium is inverted. Therefore, when washing the detached epithelium, be mindful at all times of the proper orientation of the graft.

   c. Impaired graft take (adherence) of the transplanted epithelium is evident as poor differentiation of the epithelium or decreased graft size. Graft take is the function of many factors. It is important that the cells used to prepare the graft are healthy. Poor cultures (i.e., low plating efficiencies) will produce poor grafts. If the cultures are confluent for too long and form blisters, the grafts will be poor. The best grafts have been prepared from primary, secondary, or tertiary cultures. Problems during surgery can also contribute to poor grafts. Vigorous manipulation of the detached epithelium during the grafting procedure can traumatize this extremely thin and fragile structure. Although the detached epithelium contracts to approximately one-third of its original size, do not try to stretch the tissue and minimize manipulation of the epithelium during the grafting procedure. Dislocation of the graft by subgraft fluid collection or increased motion of the animal after grafting are additional reasons for impaired graft take. Allow some of the excess medium covering the graft to evaporate (30–40 s) before covering the epithelium with the mouse skin flap. This helps promote adherence of the graft to the flap.

References

1. Mulligan, R. C. (1993) The basic science of gene therapy. *Science* **260,** 926–932.
2. Rheinwald, J. G. and Green, H. (1977) Epidermal growth factor and the multiplication of cultured human epidermal keratinocytes. *Nature* **265,** 421–424.
3. Green, H., Kehinde, O., and Thomas, J. (1979) Growth of cultured human epidermal cells into multiple epithelia suitable for grafting. *Proc. Natl. Acad. Sci. USA* **76,** 5665–5668.
4. Banks-Schlegel, S. and Green, H. (1980) Formation of epidermis by serial cultivated human epidermal cells transplanted as an epithelium to athymic mice. *Transplantation* **29,** 308–313.

5. Gallico, G. G., O'Connor, N. E., Compton, C. C., Kehinde, O., and Green, H. (1984) Permanent coverage of large burn wounds with autologous cultured human epithelium. *N. Engl. J. Med.* **311,** 448–451.

6. Arons, J. A., Wainwright, D. J., and Jordon, R. E. (1992) The surgical applications and implications of cultured human epidelmis: a comprehensive review. *Surgery* **111,** 4–11.

7. Mackay, I. A. and Leigh, I. M. (1991) Epidermal cytokines and their roles in cutaneous wound healing. *Br. J. Dermatol.* **124,** 513–518.

8. Barra, R. M., Fenjves, E. S., and Taichman, L. B. (1994) Secretion of apolipoprotein E by basal cells in cultures of epidermal keratinocytes. *J. Invest. Dermatol.* **102,** 61–66.

9. Ryynanen, J., Sollberg, S., Parente, M. G., Chung, L. C., Christiano, A. M., and Uitto, J. (1992) Type VII collagen gene expression by cultured human cells and in fetal skin. Abundant mRNA and protein levels in epidermal keratinocytes. *J. Clin. Invest.* **89,** 163–168.

10. Morgan, J. R., Barrandon, Y., Green, H., and Mulligan, R. C. (1987) Expression of an exogenous growth hormone gene by transplantable human epidermal cells. *Science* **237,** 1476–1479.

11. Flowers, M. E. D., Stockschlaeder, M. A. R., Schuening, F. G., Niederwieser, D., Hackman, R., Miller, D., and Storb, R. (1990) Long-term transplantation of canine keratinocytes made resistant to G418 through retrovirus-mediated gene transfer. *Proc. Natl. Acad. Sci. USA* **87,** 2349–2353.

12. Morgan, J. R. and Eden, C. A. (1991) Retroviral-mediated gene transfer into transplantable human epidermal cells, in *Clinical and Experimental Approaches to Dermal and Epidermal Repair: Normal and Chronic Wounds*, vol. 365 (Barbul, A., Eaglstein, W. H., Marshall, D., Caldwell, M. D., Hunt, T. K., Pines, E., and Skover, G., eds.), Wiley-Liss, New York, pp. 417–428.

13. Gerrard, A. J., Hudson, D. J., Brownlee, G. G., and Watt, F. M. (1993) Towards gene therapy for haemophilia B using primary human keratinocytes. *Nature Genet.* **3,** 180–183.

14. Eming, S. A., Lee, J., Snow, R. G., Tompkins, R. G., Yarmush, M. L., and Morgan, J. R. (1995) Genetically modified human epidermis overexpressing PDGF-A directs the formation of a cellular and vascular connective tissue stroma when transplanted to athymic mice-implications for the use of genetically modified keratinocytes to modulate dermal regeneration. *J. Invest. Dermatol.* **105,** 756–763.

15. Coulombe, P. A., Hutton, M. E., Letai, A., Hebert, A., Paller, A. S., and Fuchs, E. (1991) Point mutations in human keratin 14 genes of epidermolysis bullosa simplex patients: genetic and functional analyses. *Cell* **66,** 1301–1311.

16. Arrand, J. E., Bone, N. M., and Johnson, R. T. (1989) Molecular cloning and characterization of a mammalian excision repair gene that partially restores UV resistance to xeroderma pigmentosum complementation group D cells. *Proc. Natl. Acad. Sci. USA* **86,** 6997–7001.

17. Rheinwald, J. G. and Green, H. (1975) Serial cultivation of strains of human epidermal keratinocytes: the formation of keratinizing colonies from single cells. *Cell* **6,** 331–344.

18. Morgan, J. R., Tompkins, R. G., and Yarmush, M. L. (1993) Advances in recombinant retroviruses for gene delivery. *Adv. Drug Deliv. Rev.* **12,** 143–158.

19. Cornetta, K., Morgan, R. A., and Anderson, W. F. (1991) Safety issues related to retroviral-mediated gene transfer in humans. *Hum. Gene Ther.* **2,** 5–14.

20. Roemer, K. and Friedmann, T. (1992) Concepts and strategies for human gene therapy. *Eur. J. Biochem.* **208,** 211–225.

21. Danos, O. (1991) Construction of retroviral packaging cell lines, in *Methods in Molecular Biology*, vol. 8, *Practical Molecular Virology: Viral vectors for Gene Expression* (Collins, M., ed.), Humana, pp. 17–27.

22. Barrandon, Y., Li, V., and Green, H. (1988) Two techniques for grafting of cultured human epidermal cells onto athymic animals. *J. Invest. Dermatol.* **91,** 315–318.

20

Methods for Particle-Mediated Gene Transfer into Skin

Ning-Sun Yang, Dennis E. McCabe, and William F. Swain

1. Introduction

During the past 5 yr, particle-mediated delivery techniques have been developed as a physical means for gene transfer into various eukaryotic systems, including plants, insects, fish, and mammals *(1–7)*. For mammalian somatic tissues, this technology, popularly known as the gene gun method, has been shown effective in transfection of skin, liver, pancreas, muscle, spleen, and other organs in vivo *(3,4)*; brain, mammary, and leukocyte primary cultures or explants ex vivo *(2,5–7)*; and a wide range of different mammalian cell lines in vitro *(3,6,7)*.

Among the applications of gene gun technology, transfection of skin tissues of live animals has resulted in the most interesting findings, enabling a series of transgenic studies with both basic research and gene therapy applications. Briefly, high levels of transgene expression have been demonstrated by in vivo particle-mediated gene transfer of skin epidermal tissues. This result was shown to be highly reproducible for virtually all animal species tested, including mouse, rat, hamster, rabbit, pig, dog, and rhesus monkey *(2–4,8,9,11)*. The adaptability of skin gene transfer across a whole range of experimental animal systems illustrates the power and versatility of the gene gun transfection method. Efficient delivery and expression of transgenes in skin tissues has been extended to a variety of reporter genes (e.g., luc, CAT, β-gal, and so on *[2,4]*) and candidate therapeutic genes (TH, hGH, hAAT *[5,8,9]*, a number of cytokines *[10]*, and viral antigens *[11]*), demonstrating the wide ranging applicability of this gene transfer strategy.

In vivo gene transfer to skin tissues has been used to develop genetic immunization technology *(9,11)*, for gene therapy of subcutaneous tumors *(10)* and wound healing *(8)*, for delivery of RNA as transgenes *(12)*, and for in vivo

From: *Methods in Molecular Medicine, Gene Therapy Protocols*
Edited by: P. Robbins Humana Press Inc., Totowa, NJ

analysis of transcriptional promoters and other regulatory sequences in recombinant gene constructs (4,13).

Histological studies show that genes can be introduced into and expressed in different cell layers of epidermal or dermal tissues by adjusting the ballistic variables. These include the motive force for particle acceleration, gold particle size, pretreatment and manipulation of epidermal and dermal tissues prior to blasting, and DNA formulations for coating gold particles. In general, topical skin gene delivery results in high-level transient expression almost exclusively in the superficial epidermal cell layers (3,4). Treatment of dermal tissues via exposure of the underside of a skin flap can result in long-term transgene expression, though at a much reduced level (4). Since the epidermis is exquisitely competent for eliciting both humoral and cell-mediated immune responses (9,11) and highly efficient in synthesis and secretion of transgenic proteins as well as easily accessible, it appears to be an attractive target for gene transfer; particularly for vaccine and cancer immunotherapy approaches. Mechanisms involving different cell types in transgene expression, secretion, and genetic immunization may now be effectively studied using the gene gun approach for transgenic studies of skin.

Several gene gun designs were developed for particle-mediated gene transfer in eukaryotic systems (1,2). For in vivo DNA delivery into mammalian somatic tissues, virtually all the reported studies have employed one of two hand-held device models: an electric discharge/Accell design or a helium-discharge/Biolistics design. More recently, a new hand-held device has been developed (the Accell pulse gun) that uses a helium jet for particle acceleration. These three types of gene gun have all been shown to efficiently deliver DNA to the epidermis.

In this chapter, we will describe the general principles, mechanisms, protocols, and uses of the particle-mediated gene transfer technology for gene transfer into skin tissues in vivo. Specific applications of this technology to basic molecular biology as well as gene therapy and genetic immunization will be discussed.

1.1. Hardware Designs

Particle-mediated gene transfer is a physical means for gene transfer and was originally developed for gene transfer to plant cells (1,14–16). It is also known as the microprojectile, biolistic, or gene gun method. With particle-mediated gene transfer, microscopic gold particles are coated with transgenes of interest and accelerated by a motive force to sufficient velocities to penetrate the target cells, resulting in intracellular delivery of the DNA molecules. The motive force can be generated by a high-voltage electric discharge (Accell), a helium pressure wave (Biolistics), or by other means (17). The

Accell high voltage-discharge device requires a large capacitor and switching capable of quickly transferring a 10 μF, 5–25 kV charge to arc points. The Accell device is a relatively large instrument (3 × 2 × 2 ft), mainly housing the necessary electrical components. A highly valuable feature of the Accell electric device is that the shockwave for particle acceleration can be fine-tuned by adjusting the discharge voltage *(2–4)*. This device was designed and has been continuously modified by D. McCabe (Agracetus, Middleton, WI) and has been used effectively by a number of researchers working on particle-mediated gene transfer *(1–8,10–13)*.

The Bio-Rad (Hercules, CA) Biolistics device employs a small cylinder and a rupture membrane (~2 in. in diameter and 10 in. in length) to generate and regulate a shockwave from compressed helium *(9,19)*. More recently, a new helium pulse gun has been developed (Accell User's Manual, Auragen), and its improved features for particle-mediated gene transfer to skin will be described (Fig. 3A; Notes 3–5). For transgenic studies involving most experimental animals, all three types of hand-held gene guns apparently can perform similarly well for skin tissues in vivo. Specific advantages may exist for one type over another, depending on the special need for certain experimental conditions.

1.2. Mechanics of the Particle-Mediated Gene Transfer Devices

The particle acceleration mechanism of the original Accell gene gun device is diagrammed in Fig. 1. In principle, microscopic gold particles are coated with DNA in a precipitated, dry form in an ethanol suspension, and evenly deposited onto a carrier sheet. A strong shockwave, generated by the high voltage electric discharge, then accelerates the mylar sheet carrying the DNA/gold particles to a very high velocity, resulting in controlled penetration of target tissues (e.g., skin) placed in the pathway of particles, effecting efficient intracellular delivery of DNA. Other technical details for gene gun operation are described in the legend of Fig. 1. Whereas the energy source for generating a shockwave using the Biolistics helium pressure gun (PDS 2000) is different from Accell's energy source, the mode and mechanism of accelerating a kapton membrane sheet carrying predeposited, DNA-coated gold particles for transfecting target cells *(9,19)* is somewhat similar to that described in Fig. 1.

1.2.1. Hand-Held Gene Gun Device

An improved design of the hand-held Accell gene gun device is shown in Fig. 2. A cassette mode gene tab (containing DNA/gold particles on the mylar sheet) and a retainer tab are designed to facilitate efficiency in gene transfer experiments.

1.2.2. Mechanism and Design of an Accell Helium Pulse Gun

More recently, D. McCabe (at Auragen) has developed a helium pulse gun that establishes a new mechanism of particle acceleration, and is diagrammed in

Fig. 1. The motive force is generated in a spark discharge chamber containing two electrodes. A 10-µL water droplet is placed in between the electrodes, and a high-voltage capacitor is discharged through the water droplet that vaporizes instantly, creating a shock wave. We have found that a polyvinyl chloride pipe with an internal diameter of 13 mm is adequate for use at the spark discharge chamber. The electrodes are located opposite each other, project into the interior of the chamber approx 5 mm below the top, and are protected at the tips with an arc-resistant alloy. The gap between the two electrodes can be adjusted by appropriately threading them into or out of the spark chamber. A spacer ring is placed above the spark chamber that, in a fixed apparatus for transformations of a single crop species, can be a vertical extension of the spark discharge chamber. However, a removable spacer ring allows the distance from the spark discharge to the carrier sheet to be varied so that the force of the shock wave can be adjusted. The motive force can also be adjusted by varying the voltage of the discharge. The carrier sheet on which the DNA-coated gold particles are precipitated is placed on top of the spacer; the function of this sheet is to transfer the force of the shock wave from the spark discharge into acceleration of the carrier particles. Located above the carrier sheet is a 100-mesh stainless steel screen that retains the sheet so that it does not proceed to the target tissue. The target tissue can be placed on Petri plate in such a way that when the plate is inverted over the retaining screen, the tissue is in the direct path of the gold particles. The whole assembly is under a partial vacuum in order to minimize aerodynamic drag. (Reprinted from ref. *16*.)

Fig. 2. Hand-held device for the Accell electric-discharge gene gun.

Fig. 3A. This device was found to be a convenient means for gene transfer to both small and large animals (Fig. 3B–D). Using DNA/gold particles loaded within a small teflon tube as a cartridge, this new gene gun design can hold 12 cartridges in a revolving cylinder. Each gene transfer can be performed in less than 5 s, thus being a highly efficient device for repeated, multiple gene deliveries. This design may be especially desirable in clinical applications for gene therapy and immunization.

1.2.3. Operational Parameters for Gene Transfer

Functional parameters that can be modified to optimize particle-mediated gene transfer to skin include the following: physical acceleration rate for particle penetration; shape, form, and size of particles; particle loading rate per target area; and DNA loading rate per particle. For transfecting appropriately treated skin tissues, a discharge voltage of 15–22 kV for the Accell device *(4)* and a pressure of 300–500 psi for the helium pulse gun (McCabe, D., Burkholder, J., and Yang, N.-S., unpublished results) have been found to confer high levels of transgene expression in mouse skin. Particles made from dense materials, including gold, tungsten, iridium, and platinum are all capable of effective coating and delivery of DNA via gene gun gene transfer. However, gold particles are most commonly chosen for two reasons: elemental gold is chemically inert with no cytotoxic effects, and owing to its use in the electronics industry, uniform sized μm-scale gold particles are commercially available.

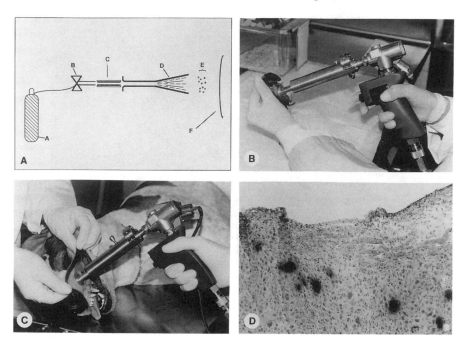

Fig. 3. Design, operation, and function of the Accell helium-discharge pulse gun.
(A) Diagram of the Accell helium pulse particle-mediated gene delivery mechanism
(Courtesy of D. McCabe); A, helium reservoir; B, release valve; C, DNA/gold cartridge; D, exit nozzle; E, accelerating gold particles coated with DNA; F, target
tissue. **(B)** Accell helium pulse gun gene transfer to mouse skin tissue. Epidermal transfections can be conveniently performed at a rate of 5 s per mouse. **(C)** Particle-mediated
gene transfer to canine oral mucosal tissue. **(D)** Transgene expression of pCMV
Lac-Z DNA delivered using the helium pulse gene gun into surgically exposed subcutaneous mouse tumor tissues. Histological data shown here demonstrates that the
1–3-μm DNA-coated microscopic gold particles can effectively penetrate 20–30 cell
layers and deliver transgenic DNA into targeted tumor cells. The transfection was
performed into the dermal side of the skin flap, which was reflected surgically before
gene delivery.

A wide range of gold particle sizes have been evaluated for gene transfer via
particle-mediated gene transfer. These include 0.95-, 1–3-, 5–7-, and ≥15-μm
diameter gold particles. For mammalian skin tissues, the 0.95- and 1–3-μm
gold particles are recommended *(3,4,11)*. Some gold particles are commercially available in different forms (e.g., as round particles, crystals, or even aggregates). For gene transfer to skin epidermal cells, crystal and spherical gold
particles were found to be similarly useful in gene delivery.

1.2.4. Molecular and Cell Biology Considerations

A major advantage of the particle-mediated gene delivery method for gene transfer is its capacity for in vivo intracellular delivery of high copy numbers of DNA into target tissues. Onto a single 1–3-μm gold particle, more than 10,000 copies of 5–10 kb plasmid DNA (but usually only 1000–5000) can be effectively coated with Ca^{2+}/ spermidine or PEG formulation precipitated form *(7,14,19,20)*. With a predetermined gold particle loading rate of 0.1 mg/cm$^{2'}$ approx 1–2 gold particles (1–3 μm) per cell can be delivered via random distribution into the epidermis containing stratified epithelial cells on the order of ~15 μm in diameter. Excessive particle loading rates (e.g., ≥5 particles/cell) can often cause trauma to transfected tissues. On the other hand, too low a particle load (e.g., 1 particle/3 cells) often results in low gene transfer efficiency. A preliminary gene transfer to any tissues using reporter genes can effectively determine the optimal particle loading rate and DNA dosage for specific skin gene transfer systems. Use of a reporter gene capable of histological assay greatly facilitates optimization of transfection efficiency.

Another important feature of particle-mediated gene delivery is the absence of restriction on the size of the DNA vectors. We and others *(2,18)* have shown that plasmid DNA, genomic DNA (≥23 kb), and reporter genes cloned in lambda phage genomic libraries (~44 kb) can all be effectively delivered by gene gun techniques for transgene expression in transfected mammalian cells. This capability offers new opportunities for transferring multiple genes, large size genomic DNA gene(s), or multiple tandem genes into mammalian somatic tissues. In addition, cotransfection of multiple genes on different plasmids has also been shown to be efficiently achieved by using the particle-mediated gene transfer method *(21)*. Furthermore, we have recently shown that RNA molecules can be similarly delivered as DNA vectors via gene gun technology *(12)*.

2. Materials

2.1. Instrumentation

The Accell electric-discharge gene gun is available through collaborations with Agracetus (Middleton, WI). The PDS 2000 Biolistics helium pressure device is commercially available from Bio-Rad *(9,19,22)*. The newly developed Accell helium pulse gun will likely become commercially available (from Bio-Rad) in the future. Mechanical operation and/or manipulation of the gene gun devices are relatively straightforward, as detailed by the manufacturer's manuals.

2.2. Elemental Gold Particle Preparations

Microscopic gold particles of different sizes (e.g., 0.95, 1–3, 5–7 μm, and so on) and in different shapes (e.g., spherical particles, crystals, aggregates, and so on) can be purchased from Degussa Corporation (South Plainfield, NJ). It is important that these gold particles be obtained as elemental gold, not as gold salt or colloidal gold. If necessary, the gold particles can be washed and cleaned by rinsing them in distilled water, 70% ethanol, and 100% ethanol in sequence prior to use. The particles can also be sterilized in phenol or $CHCl_3$ if necessary. It is important to microscopically examine each newly purchased gold particle preparation, making sure that the lot, particle size, and form are correct and appropriate as desired for the test systems. It is also useful to test each new lot of gold particles in a gene transfer and expression assay as some lots do not perform satisfactorily for reasons that are currently unknown.

2.3. DNA Vectors

A clean plasmid DNA preparation purified from CsCl gradient or Qiagen (Chatsworth, CA) columns, ethanol precipitated, and redissolved in TE buffer (10 mM Tris-HCl, pH 7.0, 1 mM EDTA), dilute EDTA (0.1 mM), or distilled water should be used for coating particles. We have not observed significant differences in transfection efficiencies between supercoiled plasmids and linear DNA in contrast to published reports using other methods. Genomic DNA preparations, genomic DNA clones in lambda phage or cosmid libraries, or cocktails of different DNA vector systems or preparations can be mixed in desired molar ratios in aqueous solution, and then loaded onto gold particles.

For exploratory gene transfer experiments, convenient reporter gene systems that have low endogenous background, have a sensitive assay, and are inexpensive are recommended for verification of transient gene expression systems. A vital assay is a distinct plus.

2.4. Reagents for Coating DNA onto Gold Particles and Gene Transfer

1. 0.1M spermidine in H_2O. Use only fresh spermidine made weekly from a free base solution (Sigma).
2. 2.5M $CaCl_2$ in H_2O.
3. 50% PEG (mol wt 3000–4000) in H_2O.
4. 100% EtOH at –20°C.

2.5. Materials for Loading Carrier Sheet

1. 0.5-mL mylar sheets (1.8 cm^2).
2. Coated particle preparation suspended in EtOH.
3. Desiccant.
4. Vacuum desiccator.
5. Vacuum pump.

2.6. Reagents for Treatment and Care of Skin

1. Electric hair clippers.
2. Depilatory (i.e., Nair).

3. RPMI-1640 with 1 μg/mL gentamicin solution.
4. Tegaderm adhesive (3M).
5. PBS.
6. Anesthesia: ketamine 70 mg/kg and xylazine 17 mg/kg.

2.7. Tissue Extraction Buffers and Enzyme Assay Systems

2.7.1. Luciferase Assay

1. Extraction buffer: 34 mL H_2O, 10 mL $0.5M$ potassium phosphate buffer (pH 7.5), 5 mg BSA, 6 mg Pefabloc SC, 5 mL 10% TX-100.
2. 5X reaction buffer: 0.46 gm glycylglycine, 0.7 gm $MgCl_2 \cdot 6H_2O$, add to 20 mL H_2O while stirring; 0.540 gm ATP; 0.225 mL $2M$ Tris-HCl pH 7.5. Adjust pH to 7.8, bring up to 30 mL, then add 15 mg BSA.
3. Luciferin solution: dissolve 14 mg luciferin in one drop of $1M$ NaOH. Immediately add to 50 mL H_2O with 566 μL 7.5% $NaHCO_3$. Adjust pH to 6.0. Protect from light.
4. Luminometer (Lumat LB 9501, Berthold Systems, Pittsburgh, PA).

2.7.2. CAT Assay

1. CAT buffer: 4.275 gm sucrose, 3.125 mL $2M$ Tris-HCl (pH 7.5), 0.25 gm ascorbate (Na salt), 0.25 gm cysteine (free base), 6.2 mg leupeptin, 0.5 mL $0.5M$ EDTA. Bring up to 25 mL with distilled H_2O and pH to 7.5.
2. Hot mix: 50 μL ^{14}C-chloramphenicol, 200 μL 50 μM acetyl CoA, 150 μL distilled H_2O.
3. Ethyl acetate.

2.7.3. X-Gal Assay

1. X-gal substrate (5-bromo-4-chloro-3-indolyl-β-D-galactoside): Dissolve X-gal into dimethyl formamide at a concentration of 40 mg/mL.
2. Buffer solution: 44 mM HEPES buffer, 3 mM K^+ ferricyanide, 3 mM K^+ ferrocyanide, 15 mM NaCl, 1.3 mM $MgCl_2$, pH 7.4.
3. X-gal buffer: Add X-gal substrate to buffer solution to make a final 1 mg/mL solution.

2.7.4. Cytokine Assay and Other Assays

General extraction buffer: 9.5 mL PBS (0.2 gm potassium chloride, 0.2 gm potassium phosphate monobasic, 8.0 gm NaCl, 1.15 gm sodium phosphate dibasic to 1 L distilled H_2O), 2.4 mg Pefabloc, 0.5% Triton X-100.

3. Methods

3.1. Coating DNA onto Gold Particles

1. Purified plasmid DNA or other DNA vectors via CsCl gradient centrifugation or Qiagen columns followed by ethanol precipitation and redissolved in TE buffer.

2. Prepare DNA solution at a concentration of 1 µg/µL, and store at 4°C.
3. Precipitate the DNA onto the gold particles: Weigh approx 10 mg of gold particles into an Eppendorf tube. Add DNA at the desired DNA/gold ratio and bring volume up to 100 µL with distilled H_2O. Add 100 µL 0.1M Spermidine and mix gently. Add 100 µL of 2.5M CaCl quickly while vortexing. Continue vortexing for 15 s. Incubate at room temperature for 10 min, then centrifuge briefly. Remove supernatant and wash particles with 100% EtOH by gently vortexing and again centrifuge briefly. Resuspend particles at the desired suspension ratio in 100% EtOH. Sonicate briefly to disperse particles. Particle suspensions can be used immediately or stored at 4 or –25°C if precautions are taken to exclude moisture. As an alternative, the DNA can be precipitated using 50% PEG and 1.0M $CaCl_2$ *(7)*.
4. DNA dosage: For transfecting mammalian skin tissues, DNA dosages at 0.1, 0.5, 1, and 2.5 µg plasmid DNA/mg particle have been found to exhibit a linear relationship with transgene expression levels.

3.2. Deposit DNA/Gold Particles onto Carrier Sheet

1. Carefully cut clean mylar sheets into a uniform size (1.8 cm^2) for the Accell device using a sharp razor blade.
2. Place a single mylar sheet into a 60-mm dish.
3. Vigorously shake DNA particle suspension and pipet 324 µL onto the mylar sheet, being careful not to break the meniscus.
4. Shake the particle preparation again and repeat dispension onto a different sheet.
5. Load less than 8 sheets at a set.
6. Allow the particles to settle out for 1–3 min and adhere to the sheet.
7. Break the meniscus and place the sheet onto a larger plastic dish with the rest of the set and immediately place them in a desiccator and pull a vacuum until the sheets are completely dry (~2 min).
8. The DNA-coated sheets are ready to use or can be stored at 4°C under desiccation.

3.3. Preparation of the Particle-Mediated Gene Transfer Device

1. Place mylar sheets loaded with DNA-coated particles onto the propulsion platform.
2. Turn on the capacitor and dial to the desired discharge voltage.
3. Appropriately place the targeted skin over the particle pathway.
4. Simultaneously press the safety release and discharge trigger to transfect the skin.
5. Other information on manipulating the Accell electric-discharge device is described in Fig. 1.

3.3. Animal Care and Skin Treatment

1. Small experimental animals (including mouse, rat, hamster, rabbit, and so on) are anesthetized using a mixture of ketamine and xylazine as appropriate for species. Large animals including dogs, pigs, and rhesus monkeys are anesthetized under the guidance of the consulting veterinarian as required by the Animal Welfare Act and administered by the institution's IACUC.

2. Animal hair in the target area is removed with clippers. A depilatory such as Nair can be used to remove residual stubble, but this treatment is not necessary. If using a depilatory, care should be taken not to allow prolonged treatment, as this may damage the target tissue.

3.4. Epidermis and Dermis Gene Transfer

1. Exposed epidermal cell layers can be effectively transfected at a gold particle loading rate of 0.2-, 0.1-, 0.05-, or 0.01-mg particles (1–3-μm or 0.95-μm diameter) per cm^2 of skin tissue, the exact rate being determined experimentally. In general, a 0.1-mg particle/cm^2 is highly effective for most animal species.
2. With the Accell device, apply a set of discharge voltages (15, 18, 22, and 24 kV) for optimization of epidermis gene transfer. Eighteen kilovolts is often found to be optimal for rodent epidermal systems, but a matrix of voltage and particle rates should be run since these interact.
3. To transfect dermal tissues, make an incision and dissociate the full thickness skin tissue of the target size (~3.2 cm^2) from the facia and muscle tissue using standard surgical procedures and tools. Flip the skin flap over, exposing the dermal tissue and transfect the fibroblasts, muscle cells, and other stromal cell types at 15–24 kV. Moisten dermal tissues with sterile saline before closing. Close incision with sutures or wound clips.
4. If desired, apply semiocclusive skin dressings such as Tegaderm (3M, St. Paul, MN) or Opsite (Smith and Nephew, Hull, UK) to transfected epidermis. This application often results in higher transient gene expression.
5. Sacrifice the animals at designed time points after gene transfer. Excise the skin target and assay for transgene activities or sequences as described in Section 3.5.

3.5. Reporter Gene Expression Assays

3.5.1. Tissue Extraction

1. Collect transfected skin tissues from test animals by excising a small uniform portion of the 3.24 cm^2 targeted surface area. A piece as small as (1–2 mm^2) can be enough for Luc, β-gal or CAT reporter gene expression assays.
2. Drop the freshly excised skin piece into the appropriate buffer (1:1, wt:vol) and freeze in liquid nitrogen.
3. Immediately before performing the assay, grind, scissor mince, or homogenize the frozen skin, keeping it as cold as possible. Avoid foaming the tissue.
4. Centrifuge the sample at high speed to separate the tissue from the lysate. Soluble crude tissue extracts are used in microliter quantities for various reporter gene assays.

3.5.2. Luciferase Assay

1. After lysate has been collected, prepare dilutions in PBS if necessary.
2. Add 80 μL reaction buffer, 1–10 μL lysate, and 310 μL distilled H_2O into a reaction tube and vortex.

3. Read relative light units in a luminometer (e.g., Lumat LB 9501, Wallac, Gaithersburg, MD) and run a standard curve to quantify results.

3.5.3. X-Gal Staining

1. Perform a whole mount tissue staining by simply placing the excised skin target into X-gal buffer. For best results, we suggest gluing the skin to a 35-mm dish to keep the skin stretched out for better examination. The tissue can also be fixed in methanol:acetone (1:1) for 10 min and then stained with X-gal buffer as described by MacGregor et al. *(23)*.
2. For microscopic examination at the cellular level, make tissue sections using a cryostat microtome or paraffin sectioning. After the tissue has been sectioned into ~10-μm-sections, place the slide in ice-cold 1.5% glutaraldehyde solution for 10 min, and wash in ice-cold PBS 5 times for 5 min each. The tissue slides are then stained with X-gal buffer for 1 h. Avoid prolonged staining because a blue background can develop in hair follicles of certain skin tissues.

3.5.4. ELISAs and RIA

Enzyme-linked immunosorbent assay (ELISA) tests are most commonly used for cytokine quantification. They may be purchased as a kit or antibody pairs may be purchased, and used in a sandwich-style assay (i.e., capture Ab-cytokine-detecting Ab-conjugate-substrate). The ELISAs may be run on serum, plasma, skin extract (using general extraction buffer), or tegaderm-stripped cell extract. Some transgenes such as hGH can be detected using a radioimmunoassay (RIA). This assay can also be used with serum, plasma, skin extract, or tegaderm extract.

4. Notes

1. Particle-mediated gene transfer provides a physical means of delivering biologically active molecules, including DNA, RNA, and proteins intracellularly. Because of its physical nature, this method displays properties distinct from those characteristic of chemical and biological gene transfer agents, and it may prove advantageous in many cases. The method is readily adaptable to a wide range of tissue and cell types, from walled fungal cells and plant cells in organized meristematic tissues *(1,14)* to various mammalian cells and organs *(2,18)*. A major advantage of particle-mediated gene transfer is its applicability to cells in vivo. Its effectiveness has also been demonstrated in several animal species including natural populations that are genetically heterogeneous, which is especially significant in extrapolation of experimental results in laboratory animals to human populations.
2. No restrictions on the size or form of the DNA transferred have been encountered thus far, other than those inherent in the need to prepare the DNA and perform routine manipulations, like pipeting. The amount of DNA required for particle-mediated gene transfer is relatively low; for example, nanogram amounts of DNA per cm^2 of target area have been shown effective for vaccine applica-

tions *(24)*. This amount corresponds to 100–1000 plasmid molecules per particle, on average, assuming a uniform distribution of DNA on the particles. In other studies, an amount of 5000 copies of cDNA delivered per cell was found to be optimal for commonly used reporter genes *(3,4,18)*.

3. The current disadvantages of particle-mediated gene transfer in vivo are the limited transfection efficiency for certain tissue systems (particularly if permanent gene transfer to the target cells is necessary) and the depth of tissue that can be accessed. Although transient transfection efficiencies from 5–15% can frequently be obtained in vivo, and efficiencies approaching 30–50% are possible in vitro, efficiencies for stable (i.e., integrative) gene transfer in vivo are apparently low, and have not been clearly established in various transfected somatic tissues. Long-term transgene expression following particle-mediated gene transfer has been observed in muscle and dermis, but these tissues seem to be the exception rather than the rule. More general long-term gene expression may be possible through a combination of particle-mediated gene transfer and replicating or actively integrating vector systems, but for the present it appears that the technique is most suitable in applications where short- to medium-term transgene expression is sufficient or desirable.

4. The current devices for particle delivery can achieve penetration depths up to a few hundred micrometers depending on the target tissue, corresponding to a depth of 20–30 cell layers in a stratified tissue like the epidermis. This depth of penetration, though not sufficient to reach internal organs, is greater than that typically achieved with viral vectors or chemical gene transfer agents where penetration is often limited to only one or two cell layers. The gene gun method at present also cannot deliver gene systematically to cell fractions scattered in large, three-dimensional tissues like liver or brain as can certain other gene transfer agents that can be administered through the circulatory system *(26)*.

   Skin is an attractive target tissue for gene therapy applications, and appears particularly amenable to particle-mediated gene transfer. One striking advantage of skin is its accessibility. One can conduct gene transfer to skin without resorting to invasive procedures. The organization and dimensions of the epidermis are also a good fit with the penetration capabilities of the current particle acceleration devices.

   A second advantage of skin derives from its continuous turnover. A vast majority of epidermal keratinocytes are differentiated nondividing cells destined to eventually exfoliate from the body. Gene transfer to these cells is thus temporary and self-reversing, unless the gene transfer itself disrupts their normal differentiative process. Gene transfer to the basal cells that repopulate the epidermis, although conceptually possible, is currently unlikely owing to the scarcity of these cells and their position in the deepest regions of the epidermis. We have not yet observed sectors of permanent transgenic epidermal cells as a result of epidermal gene transfer. Approaches seeking to transfect these generative cells to produce stable transgenic skin will thus probably require special targeting strategies to be successful.

5. Particle-mediated gene transfer to skin tissues of various animal species results in high level expression of reporter genes *(4)*. Epidermal gene delivery using cytokine genes resulted in reduction or prevention of growth of subcutaneously transplanted tumors in mouse models *(10)*. In this study, high levels of cytokines were detected in transfected tumor and neighboring normal skin tissues, and much lower but significant levels were also detected in serum of test animals. In addition, gene transfer to keratinocytes has been employed to produce therapeutic proteins locally, e.g., to produce growth factors to promote healing in wounds *(8)*. Systemic distribution of endogenous proteins produced in skin has been reported *(25)*. Future augmentation of transgene expression may extend this observation more effectively to transgenic systems.

6. The epidermis plays a key role in providing first-line immunological responses. The immune and inflammatory processes now clearly demonstrated in cutaneous tissue make it a suitable target for gene transfer-based vaccines. In addition to keratinocytes, the epidermis contains Langerhans cells and dendritic epidermal T-lymphocytes, both of which serve as professional antigen presenting cells. Particle-mediated gene transfer to skin has been shown to result in induction of high level and durable humoral and cytotoxic immune responses *(9,11,24)*. These immune responses were shown to be fully protective in immunized mice subjected to a lethal challenge with influenza virus *(11)*. These studies demonstrate the usefulness of particle-mediated gene transfer to skin in the context of a prophylactic vaccine, and suggest the potential of a similar immunotherapeutic approach to infectious disease and cancer.

7. The use of mRNA, ribozymes, or oligoribonucleotides to transfer genetic or biochemical information into somatic cells in vivo or in vitro may be advantageous in certain gene therapy protocols because RNA molecules do not integrate into nuclear DNA under normal cellular physiology, hence eliminating the possibility of insertional mutagenesis in transgenic cells. Qiu et al. *(12)* showed recently that the particle-mediated gene transfer technology offers good opportunities for these gene transfer/gene therapy approaches. The particle-mediated gene transfer method for gene delivery to skin tissue may also provide an efficient and convenient system for basic research in posttranscriptional, translational, and ribozyme regulations in mammalian somatic cells in vivo.

References

1. Christou, P. (1994) Application to plants, in *Particle Bombardment Technology for Gene Transfer* (Yang, N.-S. and Christou, P., eds.), Oxford University Press, New York, pp. 71–99.
2. Yang, N.-S. and Ziegelhoffer, P. (1994) The particle bombardment system for mammalian gene transfer, in *Particle Bombardment Technology for Gene Transfer* (Yang, N.-S. and Christou, P., eds.), Oxford University Press, New York, pp. 117–141.
3. Yang, N.-S., Burkholder, J., Roberts, B., Martinell, B., and McCabe, D. (1990) In vivo and in vitro gene transfer to mammalian somatic cells by particle bombardment. *Proc. Natl. Acad. Sci. USA* **87,** 9568–9572.

4. Cheng, L., Ziegelhoffer, P., and Yang, N.-S. (1993) In vivo promoter activity and transgenic expression in mammalian somatic tissues evaluated by using particle bombardment. *Proc. Natl. Acad. Sci. USA* **90,** 4455–4459.

5. Jiao, S., Cheng, L., Wolff, J., and Yang, N.-S. (1993) Particle bombardment-mediated gene transfer and expression in rat brain tissues. *Bio/Technology* **11,** 497–502.

6. Thompson, T. A., Gould, M. N., Burkholder, J. K., and Yang, N.-S. (1993) Transient promoter activity in primary rat mammary epithelial cells evaluated using particle bombardment gene transfer. *In Vitro Cell Dev. Biol.* **29A,** 165–170.

7. Burkholder, J. K., Decker, J., and Yang, N.-S. (1993) Transgene expression in lymphocyte and macrophage primary cultures after particle bombardment. *J. Immunol. Methods* **165,** 149–156.

8. Andree, C., Swain, W. F., Page, C. P., Macklin, M. D., Slama, J., Hatzis, D., and Eriksson, E. (1994) In vivo transfer and expression of an EGF gene accelerates wound repair. *Proc. Natl. Acad. Sci. USA* **91,** 12,188–12,192.

9. Tang, D. C., DeVit, M., and Johnston, S. A. (1992) Genetic immunization is a simple method for eliciting an immune response. *Nature* **356,** 152–154.

10. Sun, W. H., Burkholder, J. K., Sun, J., Culp., J., Turner, J., Lu, X. G., Pugh, T. D., Ershler, W. B., and Yang, N.-S. (1995) In vivo cytokine gene transfer by gene gun suppresses tumor growth in mice. *Proc. Natl. Acad. Sci. USA.* **92,** 2889–2893.

11. Fynan, E. F., Webster, R. G., Fuller, D. H., Haynes, J. R., Santoro, J. C., and Robinson, H. L. (1993) DNA vaccines: protective immunizations by parenteral, mucosal, and gene gun inoculations. *Proc. Natl. Acad. Sci. USA* **90,** 11,478–11,482.

12. Qiu, P., Ziegelhoffer, P., Sun, J., and Yang, N.-S. (1996) Gene gun delivery of mRNA in situ results in efficient transgene expression and immunization. *Gene Therapy* **3,** 262–268.

13. Rajagopalan, L. E., Burkholder, J. K., Turner, J., Culp, J., Yang, N.-S., and Malter, J. S. (1995) Targeted mutagenesis of GM-CSF cDNA increases transgenic mRNA stability and protein expression in normal cells. *Blood* **86,** 2551–2558.

14. Sanford, J. (1988) The biolistic process. *Trends Biotechnol.* **6,** 299–302.

15. McCabe, D., Swain, W., Martinell, B., and Christou, P. (1988) Stable transformation of soybean (glycine max) by particle acceleration. *Bio/Technology* **6,** 923–926.

16. Christou, P., McCabe, D., Martinell, B., and Swain, W. (1990) Soybean genetic engineering-commercial production of transgenic plants. *Trends Biotechnol.* **8,** 145–151.

17. Sautter, C., Waldner, H., Neuhaus-Url, G., Galli, A., Neuhaus, G., and Potrykus, I. (1991) Micro-targeting: high efficiency gene transfer using a novel approach for the acceleration of microprojectiles. *Bio/Technology* **9,** 1080–1085.

18. Yang, N.-S. (1992) Gene transfer into mammalian somatic cells in vivo. *CRC Crit. Rev. Biotechnol.* **12,** 335–356.

19. Williams, R. S., Johnston, S. A., Riedy, M., DeVit, M. J., McElligot, S. G., and Sanford, J. C. (1991) Introduction of foreign genes into tissues of living mice by DNA-coated microprojectiles. *Proc. Natl. Acad. Sci. USA* **88,** 2726–2730.

20. Klein, T., Wolf E., Wu, R., and Sanford, J. (1987) High-velocity microprojectiles for delivering nucleic acids into living cells. *Nature* **327,** 70–73.

21. Li, C.-C. H., Ruscetti, F. W., Rice, N. R., Chen, E., Yang N.-S., Mikovits, J., and Longo, D. L. (1993) Differential expression of Rel family members in HTLV-1 infected cells: transcriptional activation of c-rel by Tax protein. *J. Virol.* **67,** 4205–4213.
22. Fitzpatrick-McElligot, S. (1992) Gene transfer to tumor-infiltrating lymphocytes and other mammalian somatic cells by microprojectile bombardment. *Bio/Technology* **10,** 1036–1040.
23. Price, J., Turner, D., and Cepko, C. (1987) Lineage analysis in the vertebrate nervous system by retrovirus-mediated gene transfer. *Proc. Natl. Acad. Sci. USA* **84,** 156–160.
24. Eisenbraun, M. D., Fuller, D. H., and Haynes, J. R. (1993) Examination parameters affecting the elicitation of humoral immune responses by particle bombardment mediated genetic immunization. *DNA Cell Biol.* **12,** 791–797.
25. Fenjves, E. S., Gordon, D. A., Pershing, L. K., Williams, D. L., and Taichman, L. B. (1989) Systemic distribution of apolipoprotein E secreted by grafts of epidermal keratinocytes: implications for epidermal function and gene therapy. *Proc. Natl. Acad. Sci. USA* **86,** 8803–8807.
26. Perales, J. C., Perkol, T., Beegen, H., Ratnoff, O., and Hanson, R. W. (1994) Gene transfer in vivo: sustained expression and regulation of genes introduced into the liver by receptor-targeted uptake. *Proc. Natl. Acad. Sci. USA* **91,** 4086–4090.

21

Methods for Liposome-Mediated Gene Transfer to Tumor Cells In Vivo

Gary J. Nabel, Zhi-yong Yang, and Elizabeth G. Nabel

1. Introduction

Despite considerable progress in the understanding of the molecular basis of cancer, many malignancies remain resistant to traditional forms of treatment. Certain cancers, such as melanoma or renal cell carcinoma, respond to modulation of immune function, presumably because the immune system is induced to recognize mutant proteins in tumor cells. The advent of cationic liposomes as safe and increasingly efficient vectors for gene transfer in vivo has allowed the development of new approaches to immunotherapy that offer alternative therapies for cancer in the future.

Cationic liposomes represent synthetic genetic delivery systems that avoid the potential infectious complications of viral vectors. Liposomal delivery of nucleic acids to the cytoplasm to cells allows them to overcome lysosomal degradation with subsequent delivery to the nucleus. The efficiency of DNA encapsulation into conventional anionic liposomes is low since the volume of conventional liposomes is small relative to plasmids. Transfection efficiencies are also poor for this reason, and because conventional liposomes do not efficiently bypass lysosomal degradation. In contrast, cationic liposomes, also called cytofectins, were developed to overcome these encapsulation and transfection deficiencies. Studies employing cationic liposomes encapsulating DNA have shown site-specific transfection in humans in vivo. In vivo gene transfer with DNA-cationic liposome complexes is proving to be safe to the host, lower in cost because of the relative ease of preparation, and applicable to the treatment of cancer. Cationic liposomes are now finding clinical application in several human gene therapy protocols for the treatment of malignant

From: *Methods in Molecular Medicine, Gene Therapy Protocols*
Edited by: P. Robbins Humana Press Inc., Totowa, NJ

melanoma, colon, and other cancers. Development of new liposomes offers potentially more effective gene delivery than originally described compounds.

Positively charged lipids form complexes with DNA by interacting with the negatively charged phosphodiester backbone. This electrostatic interaction is highly dependent on the molar ratio between the DNA and the liposome, and occurs spontaneously. Ideally, the complex incorporates the DNA completely, regardless of its size. DNA liposome complexes assemble spontaneously in aqueous solutions without extensive preparation, making it possible to analyze different vectors in vitro or in animal models.

The ratio of cationic and neutral lipids to DNA is the most important determinant of transfection efficiency. When the amount of positive charges contributed by the liposome equals the number of negative charges on the DNA, the DNA liposome complex will be neutral. Titration of DNA to liposome therefore determines its overall charge and thus its uptake by cells. Differences in the type of target cell, plasmid, and mixture making up the liposome complex require individual adjustments to the DNA-to-lipid ratio. With all methods of cell transfection, expression levels and transfection efficiencies depend on the plasmid expression vector, cell line, and host cell. Cationic liposomes are also often inactivated by polyvalent, negatively charged serum components, and serum-free conditions at the transfection site are important for the successful use of catheter-based delivery. Direct gene transfer of cationic liposomes with either catheter-based delivery or direct injection has shown gene expression limited to the site of gene introduction. Plasmid DNA in liposome complexes is unlikely to integrate or propagate in animal cells. Cationic liposomes have also been well-tolerated in vivo, and biochemical, hemodynamic, or cardiac toxicities have not been observed.

The prototype cationic lipid for gene transfer was DOTMA (N[1-{2,3-dioleyloxy}propyl]-N,N,N-tri-methylammonium chloride), which was mixed with an equimolar amount of DOPE (dioleoyl phosphatidylethanolamine). The lipid DOTMA/DOPE comprised the cationic liposome commercially known as Lipofectin (Bethesda Research Laboratories, Gaithersburg, MD). Lipofectin was used in a number of laboratory studies, but has not been utilized in human gene transfer clinical protocols. For human studies, two different cationic liposome formulations have been used. The first includes DC-cholesterol (3b[N-(N'N'-dimethylaminoethane)-carbamoyl] cholesterol) mixed with DOPE. DC-cholesterol/DOPE in low concentrations has proven to reduce toxicity to cells in vitro, is metabolized in vivo, and has provided successful gene transfer into malignant tumors in humans. At high absolute concentrations of DNA, however, these liposome complexes have led to aggregation and in vivo toxicity following iv injection in mice, which limited the doses that could be delivered.

More recently, a cationic liposome comprised of dimyristyloxypropyl-3-dimethyl-hydroxyethyl ammonium (DMRIE) with DOPE has allowed up to 100-fold higher concentrations of lipid and DNA to be administered in vivo with minimal toxicity. In vitro studies of the comparative efficiency of transfection with DC-Chol/DOPE and DMRIE/DOPE in different cell lines showed improved transfection efficiencies of two- to seven-fold with DMRIE/DOPE, with the greatest improvement in cell lines which are difficult to transfect, such as the MCA 205 fibrosarcoma.

This improvement may be owing to the higher concentration of plasmid DNA used with the cationic liposome. In previous studies, the higher concentration of plasmid was toxic to cells when used with DC-Chol/DOPE. Analyses of the biochemical and pathologic changes in pigs and mice after administration of DMRIE/DOPE with DNA concentrations up to 1000-fold proposed for human trials showed no adverse effects. Thus, although DMRIE/DOPE may not necessarily be more potent than DC-Chol/DOPE, DMRIE/DOPE showed a lack of toxicity that allowed larger quantities of DNA to be used. Additional improvements in lipid chemistry and, possibly, in cell targeting will facilitate the development of specific and efficient gene transfer in vivo.

Because of its greater ease of preparation and administration, direct gene transfer, rather than cell-mediated or ex vivo gene delivery, represents a promising technique for clinical applications. Cationic liposomes have several desirable features for direct gene transfer. Because there are fewer constraints on packaging, different enhancer/promoter elements or various sized plasmids can be used. In contrast to retroviral vectors, division of the target cell is not necessary, allowing recombinant gene expression in nondividing cells. Expression is site-specific, minimizing concerns about widespread dissemination of the vector. Thus, DNA liposome complexes are applicable for delivery to focal sites of disease. Target cells include vascular endothelial and smooth muscle cells of the tumor microcirculation or tumor cells themselves.

A characteristic feature of the pathologic lesions of many human diseases is the abnormal expression of genes focally. In cardiovascular disease, for example, growth factors, cellular adhesion, procoagulant, and other gene products stimulate formation of atherosclerotic plaques that can ultimately have profound effects on myocardial perfusion. The focal lesions of cancer are tumors, against which the immune system can potentially provide protection. The immune system can contribute to the surveillance and destruction of neoplastic cells, as shown in a number of studies in which cellular and humoral immune effectors inhibit tumor cell growth. Studies have shown that the expression of highly immunogenic class I major histocompatibility complex (MHC) antigen is often lacking or decreased in freshly isolated cells from naturally occurring tumors. Deficient expression of class I MHC molecules may limit the present action of tumor antigens to cytotoxic T-cells, thus facilitating tumor cell growth. Several tumor cell lines exhibiting low levels of class I MHC proteins have been shown to become less oncogenic when expression vectors encoding the relevant class I MHC antigen were introduced into them. Direct in vivo transfection of this antigen into tumors via DNA/liposome complexes may provide an effective immunotherapy against cancer. In particular, the introduction of foreign histocompatibility antigens may induce an allogenic response locally, which can enhance local immunity and lead to improved immune recognition of tumors. The additional delivery of cytokine or other genes, including growth inhibitors, antiangiogenic factors, or prodrug converting enzymes, may further enhance this process and provide additional approaches to utilize direct gene transfer to enhance antitumor responses.

2. Materials

2.1. Vector Production and Analysis

A eukaryotic expression vector plasmid, pHLA-B7, is prepared by insertion of an HLA-B7 gene cDNA into the Rous sarcoma virus (RSV) RSV β-globin plasmid *(1,2)*. The β-globin gene is removed by digestion with *Hind*III and *Bgl*II, treated with calf intestinal alkaline phosphatase, phenol and chloroform extracted, ethanol precipitated, and treated with the Klenow fragment of *Escherichia coli* DNA polymerase to generate the plasmid backbone. An insert is prepared as a *Bam*HI to *Sal*I fragment of pLJ-HLA-B7 *(3)*, kindly provided by Dr. Alan Korman, which is treated with Klenow enzyme and ligated to the fragment from RSV-β-globin. The resultant plasmid contains pBR322, the RSV enhancer, and the SV40 polyadenylation sequence, similar to RSV-β-globin *(1)*. Plasmids are grown and purified in the absence of the ethidium bromide or penicillin derivatives, using a commercially available column chromatography method (Promega, Madison, WI).

2.2. HLA-B7/β-2 Microglobulin Plasmid Expression Vector

The expression vector for the class I MHC gene is prepared as follows: the HLA-B7 gene is inserted into a simplified eukaryotic expression vector that utilizes the RSV enhancer to stimulate expression of the HLA-B7 gene. A second open reading frame is included using an internal ribosome initiation site derived from encephalomyocarditis virus (ECMV). This plasmid uses a bovine growth hormone poly A site, eliminating all viral processing and polyadenylkation sequences. The plasmid DNA is grown in a standard *E. coli* host strain (DH5a or XL1-blue). This vector has been constructed by insertion of the HLA-B7 gene cDNA into the RSV β-globin plasmid. Briefly, the β-globin gene has been removed from this plasmid by digestion with *Hind*III and *Bgl*II treated with Klenow fragment of DNA polymerase and used as the backbone to insert the *Bam*HI to *Sal*I fragment of HLA-B7 treated with Klenow enzyme. This plasmid contains pBR322, a kanamycin resistance gene, the RSV enhancer, HLA-B7, ECMV ribosome entry site, β-2 microglobulin, and the bovine growth hormone polyadenylation sequence.

2.3. Cationic Liposomes

We have used two cationic liposomal preparations for our in vivo human gene therapy trial. In the first trial *(4)*, dimethylaminoethane-carbamoyl cholesterol (DC-Chol)/dioleoyl phosphatidylethanolamine (DOPE) was mixed in an optimal concentration (15 nmol DC-Chol/Dope) and combined with 1 µg DNA in 0.7 mL *(5,6)*. In the second trial, the DNA/liposome formulation is prepared by incubation of DNA (5 µg) and dimyristyloxy-propyl-3-dimethy-hydroxyethyl ammonium (DMRIE)/DOPE (15 nmol) in a final volume of 1 mL in lactated Ringers solution *(7)*.

3. Methods

3.1. Study Design for DC-Cholesterol/DOPE Gene Transfer (Clinical Protocol I)

Patients with stage IV melanoma who met guidelines of the clinical protocol *(8)* are treated in the Clinical Research Center. Informed written consent is obtained according to The Committee to Review Grants for Clinical Research and Investigation Involving Human Beings, the Recombinant DNA Advisory Committee of the National Institutes of Health, and the Food and Drug Administration.

A cutaneous tumor nodule is identified for treatment, and its borders measured. Other control (untreated) nodules are quantitated by computerized tomography immediately prior to the procedure. For our first clinical protocol, the DC-Chol/DOPE liposome preparation was used with the indicated DNA dose escalation. At each treatment, Group I ($n = 3$) received 1 injection of ~0.2 mL of DNA liposome (0.29 µg DNA) complex into the tumor (0.86 µg cumulative dose). Group II ($n = 3$) received 3 injections (0.2 mL each) at one session within the same nodule (2.58 µg cumulative dose). All patients receive a total of three treatments with a 2-wk interval between treatments.

3.2. Preparation and Administration of DNA Liposome Complex

DNA liposome complexes are mixed immediately prior to injection by adding 0.1 mL of lactated Ringer's solution into a sterile vial of HLA-B7 plasmid DNA (20 µg/mL; 0.1 mL). An aliquot of this solution (0.1 mL) is added at room temperature to 0.1 mL of 150 µ*M* (dioleoyl phosphatidylethanolamine/3b [N-(N',N'-dimethylaminoethane)-carbamoyl] cholesterol) liposome *(5)* in lactated Ringer's solution in a separate sterile vial. The DNA and liposome vials are prepared in accordance with Food and Drug Administration guidelines and quality control procedures. After incubation for 15 min at room temperature, an additional 0.5 mL of sterile lactated Ringer's solution is added to the vial and mixed. The DNA liposome solution (0.2 mL) is injected into the patient's melanoma nodule under sterile conditions at the bedside after administration of local anesthesia (1% lidocaine), using a 22-gage needle. The injection is performed once per treatment session (Group I, patients 1, 2, 3A) or three times per treatment session (Group II, patients 3B, 4, 5). For catheter delivery, the DNA liposome solution (0.6 mL) is delivered into the artery using percutaneous delivery.

For pulmonary artery gene transfer, percutaneous right heart catheterization is performed from the right femoral vein using sterile techniques. An 8-French sheath was inserted into a right femoral vein, and a 7-French Van Aman pigtail catheter is advanced into a pulmonary artery under fluoroscopic guidance. After pressure measurement, selective catheterization of an artery is performed, and the catheter is exchanged for a 5-French occlusion balloon catheter (Medi-Tech, Watertown, MA) over a 0.025-in. exchange guidewire. After balloon inflation, digital subtraction angiography is performed to confirm catheter position and arrest of blood flow. Confirmation that blood flow is arrested is performed by inflation of the balloon injection of iv contrast dye into the vascular space. No diffusion of the contrast material should be noted over a 5-min period, thus ensuring that delivery of DNA and liposomes proceeds antegrade in the vasculature and is not immediately admixed with blood to inactivate the DNA liposome complex. The artery is rinsed with 30 mL of sterile saline, and the HLA-B7 DNA liposome solution, 1.43 µg of DNA in a volume of 0.6 mL, is instilled, followed by an additional 1.0 mL of sterile saline. This solution is injected through the end hole of the catheter into the artery. An additional 3.0 mL of sterile saline is instilled through the catheter, and the HLA-B7 DNA liposome solution incubated for 20 min to achieve transduction of the local microcirculation. The balloon is deflated, and the catheter and femoral sheath are removed. To determine the effects of DNA liposome delivery to the pulmonary vasculature, hemodynamic and biochemical monitoring is performed. The patient's electrocardiogram (ECG) (six-lead) is continuously recorded prior to, during, and after injection of the DNA liposome solution. Pulmonary artery, pulmonary capillary wedge pressure, and systemic blood pressure are measured 5 min prior to gene transfer and 20 min after delivery of DNA and liposomes.

Biochemical parameters are also measured one day before and one day after each treatment. During each treatment, 0.6 mL of DNA liposome solution are administered followed by an additional total of 4 mL of sterile saline to distribute it to the local microcirculation.

3.3. Analysis of HLA-B7 Gene Expression

To confirm recombinant HLA-B7 gene expression within treated tumor nodules, core needle biopsy samples of the injected tumor are performed 3–7 d after gene transfer. Genomic DNA is isolated from biopsy material *(3)*, and PCR for HLA-B7 gene is performed with primers: (sense) 5' AGT GCC CAG GGC TCT GAT GTG TCT CTC ACA 3' (HLA-B7) and (antisense) 5' ACC ACA GAA GTA AGG TTC CTT CAC AAA GAT 3' (SV40 poly A), yielding a 301-bp fragment. For the RNA analysis, the same primers are amplified after reverse transcription with an oligo dT primer. Analysis of plasmid in blood is performed with the same primers or a different set: (sense), 5' CTA CGT GGA CGA CAC CCA GTT CGT C 3' and (antisense) 5' AGG GTG GCC TCA TGG TCA GAG ATG G 3', yielding a 525-bp fragment. RNA in analyzed by PCR after DNase digestion and incubation with reverse transcriptase as described *(9)*. Southern blot hybridization of PCR products from the DNA and RNA analysis in performed with an internal probe from pHLA-B7 derived by digestion with *Pvu*II and *Bgl*II by standard methods *(10)*. A control using 293 cells transfected with plasmids in vitro is used to define conditions to establish the conditions for DNase digestion. Typically, DNase (225 U/reaction) is used to digest DNA in a total volume of 20 μL. Under these conditions, no PCR signal should be detected in the absence of reverse transcription.

3.4. Study Design for DMRIE/DOPE Gene Transfer (Clinical Protocol II)

In patients undergoing this gene transfer protocol, the tumor nodule and its borders are measured prior to injection. A needle biopsy is performed when possible to confirm the diagnosis and for analysis as a pretreatment sample. Alternately, a separate untreated nodule is used. Tissue is stored as frozen sections for further immunohistochemical analysis and PCR. In addition, this nodule and other control (untreated) nodules are imaged by CT immediately prior to the procedure, and its size quantitated. The skin overlying the tumor nodule is sterilized and anesthetized using 0.01% lidocaine. For gene transfer, a 22-gage needle is used to inject the DNA liposome complex. The complex is prepared as follows: 10 min prior to delivery, 0.1 mL of plasmid DNA (0.05–50 mg/mL) in lactated Ringer's solution is added to 0.1 mL of DMRIE/DOPE liposome solution (0.15–15 μM). Each component is stored separately in sterile vials and certified as acceptable by the FDA. The solution is left at room temperature for 5–10 min and 0.8 mL of sterile lactated Ringer's is added to the liposome DNA solution. The optimal composition of the DNA/liposome complex has been established for each batch by titration of DNA concentration and liposome concentration independently on human melanoma and renal cell carcinoma in vitro, and confirmed by direct injection into melanoma or other tumors in vivo prior to use. Each component, the liposome preparation and the DNA, is tested for contaminants and toxicity and used according to previously established guidelines. The liposome solution and DNA is aliquoted in individual sterile vials mixed under sterile conditions.

For direct injections of the HLA-B7 plasmids, escalating doses are studied. Four groups (three patients each) are studied sequentially with at least 1 mo of observation prior to evaluation of the next group. Patients in each group receive intratumor injections. Group I receives 3 injections of 0.2 mL within the same nodule (3 µg of DNA plus 4.5 nM DMRIE/DOPE). Group II receives the same treatment with a 10-fold higher concentration of DNA liposome complex. Group III receives 100-fold higher dose, and Group IV receives 1000-fold higher amount.

For catheter-based gene delivery, the same dose escalation is used, except a single 0.6-mL injection into the end artery that perfused an isolated nodule is used with an occlusion balloon catheter. Doses are repeated within each subject for whom the toxicity treatment is with grade II. Dose escalation begins if three patients show toxicities < grade III from the treatment. If one patient displays toxicity > grade II, the treatment is repeated on three additional patients. If two patients develop toxicity > grade II, the dosage is reduced. The maximal tolerated dose is defined as the dose at which two or more patients out of six develop grade III or IV toxicity. Once the treatment dose is defined, an additional 4–6 patients are entered at that dose to ascertain the safety of this dose for wider application.

Prior to the injection with the needle in place, gentle aspiration is applied to the syringe to ensure that no material is injected iv. Immediately after the injection procedure, a blood sample is obtained to check serum enzymes, chemistries, and blood counts, and to analyze for the presence of plasmid DNA in the peripheral blood by PCR. The patient is observed in the Clinical Research Center for an additional 24–48 h, and another blood collection is performed after this time. If there are no complications, the patient is discharged after 24–48 h.

3.5. Confirmation of Gene Transfer and Expression

Needle biopsy of the injected nodule is performed after administration of local anesthesia prior to injection and subsequently to treatment (preferably at d 3). If sufficient material can be obtained, RNA PCR analysis is performed. A portion of this tissue is processed to obtain DNA for PCR analysis. The remaining tissue is processed for pathologic analysis and immunohistochemical and/or immunofluorescent staining. For internal organs, CT- or ultrasound-guided thin needle biopsies will be obtained when possible.

3.6. Analysis of Immune Response

Evidence of gene transfer is obtained indirectly by examination of the specific immune response to HLA-B7. The analysis is performed as follows: two weeks prior to the initial treatment, a blood sample is obtained to derive lymphocytes that will be immortalized using the Epstein–Barr virus. An aliquot of these cells is further infected with an amphotropic HLA-B7 retroviral vector, and expression is confirmed on the cell surface. These cells are subsequently used in the laboratory as target cells for the cytolytic T-cell assay.

References

1. Hyde, S. C., Gill, D. R., Higgins, C. F., et al. (1993) *Nature* **362,** 250–255.
2. Gorman, C., Padmanabhan, R., and Howard, B. H. (1983) *Science* **221,** 551–553.
3. Nabel, E. G., Plautz, G., and Nabel, G. J. (1992) *Proc. Natl. Acad. Sci. USA* **89,** 5157–5161.
4. Nabel, G. J., Nabel, E. G., Yang, Z., et al. (1993) *Proc. Natl. Acad. Sci. USA* **90,** 11,307–11,311.
5. Gao, X. and Huang, L. (1991) *Biochem. Biophys. Res. Commun.* **179,** 280–285.
6. Stewart, M. J., Plautz, G. E., Del Buono, L., et al. (1992) *Hum. Gene Ther.* **3,** 267–275.
7. Feigner, J. H., Kumar, R., Sridhar, C. N., et al. (1994) *J. Biol. Chem.* **269,** 2550–2561.
8. Nabel, G. J., Chang, A., Nabel, E. G., et al. (1992) *Hum. Gene Ther.* **3,** 399–410.
9. Nabel, E. G., Yang, Z., Liptay, S., et al. (1993) *J. Clin. Invest.* **91,** 1822–1829.
10. Sambrook, J., Fritch, E. F., and Maniatis, T. (1989) in *A Laboratory Manual,* Anonymous, Cold Spring Harbor Laboratory, Cold Spring Harbor, NY, pp. 31–57.

22

Methods for Retrovirus-Mediated Gene Transfer to Tumor Cells

Elizabeth M. Jaffee

1. Introduction

The past several years have seen a renewed interest in active immunotherapy approaches for the treatment of human tumors because of the exciting findings learned from preclinical studies employing genetically altered tumor vaccines. Many clinical protocols are currently being conducted using several different genetic approaches for augmenting antitumor immune responses. These include:

1. Ex vivo gene transfer of cytokine genes into tumor cells.
2. Ex vivo gene transfer of suicide genes into tumor cells with subsequent activation of the suicide mechanism in vivo.
3. Ex vivo cytokine gene transfer to cultured tumor-infiltrating lymphocytes (TIL) to generate more potent T-cells for adoptive transfer.
4. In vivo gene transfer of major histocompatibility complex (MHC) class I molecules by direct injection of the gene into an accessible tumor mass.

Whereas the recent preclinical studies performed in mouse tumor models are indeed paving the way for clinical trials with genetically engineered tumor vaccines, a number of critical technical considerations remain that will have significant impact on whether or not this new immunotherapy approach will translate into true clinical benefit for human cancer patients. First, most human tumors are difficult to establish as cell lines, even in the short-term. Yet, until cellular tumor antigens are identified, autologous cell lines will need to be established from each patient to be treated, as a means of providing tumor antigens at the site of activation of the immune system. Even in cases where subselection of continuously growing tumor lines can be achieved, there is a high likelihood that, after extended passage, the antigenic composition will change significantly, relative to the original primary tumor from which the

From: *Methods in Molecular Medicine, Gene Therapy Protocols*
Edited by: P. Robbins Humana Press Inc., Totowa, NJ

tumor line originated. Second, high efficiency gene transfer systems are needed to genetically alter these primary tumor lines. Ideally, high-efficiency gene transfer would obviate the need for cointroduction of a selection marker, thereby minimizing the level of in vitro passage and maximally preserving the original antigenic composition of the explanted primary tumor.

Defective retroviral vector systems are unquestionably the gold standard for high-efficiency gene transfer in the initial stages of human gene therapy. These vectors have the potential for being free of helper virus, and are therefore extremely safe. Nonetheless, they require at least one cell cycle in order for integration and gene expression to occur. Early generations of retroviral vectors have been notoriously inconsistent in their gene transfer efficiency as well as in consistency of gene expression. Recently, newer generations of retroviral vectors that have taken advantage of modifications in the intronic gag sequences as well as positioning of the start sites of the inserted gene, appear to have successfully circumvented a number of these problems and allowed efficient gene transfer into primary human tumor explants in the absence of selection (1). Other gene-transfer systems such as adenovirus-based systems as well as nonviral gene transfer systems including liposomes, are currently under evaluation, though their ultimate usefulness in clinical cancer settings remains to be determined. These alternative systems are discussed in other chapters.

This chapter will provide an overview of retrovirus-mediated gene transfer as it relates to cancer therapy, and a detailed discussion of the methods required for ex vivo, retrovirus-mediated gene transfer to tumor cells.

1.1. Rationale for the Use of Genetically Altered Tumor Cells for the Treatment of Cancer

1.1.1. The Role of the Immune System in the Treatment of Cancer

The rationale for genetically altered, tumor vaccine-based immunotherapy of established cancer depends on the existence of antigens within tumors that can be recognized as foreign by the host immune response. It is the tremendous diversity of the T- and B-cell receptors that endows the immune system with the ability to distinguish fine antigenic differences among cells. For the generation of an antitumor immune response, two criteria must be fulfilled. First, the tumor must present novel antigens or neoepitopes not found on normal cells. Second, the immune system must be appropriately activated to respond to these novel antigens. The classic studies of Boon and colleagues (2–3) have demonstrated that tumor antigens recognized by T-cells fall into one of three categories:

1. Novel peptide sequences generated by point mutations in genes encoding various cellular proteins.

2. Examples in which the gene encoding the tumor antigen is identical to the germ-line sequence, but is not expressed in any normal tissues.
3. Examples in which the gene encoding the tumor antigen is a highly specific differentiation antigen.

As a consequence, the immune system need not be tolerized to the gene during development, and peptides derived from the nonmutated form can serve as tumor-specific antigens. The MAGE-1 gene encodes a human melanoma antigen that was the first human antigen identified. The MAGE-1 antigen falls into the second category of tumor antigens, and is expressed in as many as 50–60% of human melanomas *(3)*. The tyrosinase protein is an example of a differentiation antigen that encodes for another human melanoma antigen *(4)*. This antigen was found to be expressed by 39 of 39 fresh melanoma samples tested, and was also overexpressed relative to normal skin samples. These antigens, plus an additional set of differentiation antigens more recently identified in human melanomas *(5)*, have indeed renewed faith in the concept of common sets of tumor-specific antigens, thereby allowing for the possibility of specific antigen or peptide-based vaccination strategies. But until more common tumor antigens have been identified at the genetic level, and the prevalence and biorelevance of these antigens has been assessed, an individual's tumor is the only source of tumor antigens for vaccination at this time. An intensified search by many groups of investigators to identify other tumor antigens expressed by tumors other than melanoma is currently underway.

1.1.2. History of the Development of Gene-Altered Tumor Vaccines

The first studies demonstrating enhanced immunogenicity of genetically altered tumors were performed 25 yr ago, starting with Lindenmann and Klein *(6)*, who showed that vaccination with influenza virus-infected tumor cell lysates generated enhanced systemic immune responses against a challenge with the original wild-type tumor cells. Furthermore, these early studies showed that nonvirally infected tumor cell lysates, or tumor cell lysates mixed with the same virus, are not immunogenic, and cannot elicit a systemic immune response against challenge with the parental tumor cells. Because adequate immunization against the tumor required that the tumor cells be infected with the virus, Lindenman and his colleagues hypothesized that weak antigens derived from the tumor cells might become associated with or incorporated into the virus, and subsequently become potent immunogens. However, based on what we have learned since then about immune responses, the enhanced immune response generated by the virally-infected tumor cells was probably the result of high viral protein expression and subsequent availability of both MHC class I and II antigenic epitopes required for priming the CD4[+] and

CD8$^+$ T-cell arms of the immune system. The antitumor response that was generated in addition to the antiviral response, probably occurred as a consequence of the expression of tumor antigens at the same site as the viral antigens. It is important to point out that the studies of Lindenmann and his colleagues provide the first evidence that employing immune modulators in a paracrine fashion, may be a critical first step for generating effective, specific, antitumor immune responses. As newer techniques of gene transfer have been developed, infection with infectious virus has been replaced with specific gene transfer in an attempt to more carefully regulate the nature of the genetic alteration in the tumor.

This and other studies have encouraged an increased effort in murine tumor models aimed at directly altering the tumor cell's genetic material to enhance immune responses generated against them. The enhancement of immune responses in the vaccine setting can be divided mechanistically into two categories. First is enhancement of the presentation of antigens to T-cells. This mechanism implies an increase in peptide-MHC density at the site of activation of T-cells. Second is enhancement of costimulation. This mechanism takes into account the fact that T-cells require extra costimulatory signals in addition to engagement of the T-cell receptor in order to become efficiently activated. Costimulatory signals may either be membrane-bound ligands such as B7 that are critical for T-cell activation, or soluble mediators such as cytokines. Because so many of the molecules necessary for antigen presentation and costimulation have been identified and cloned, it was natural to utilize gene transfer strategies to alter the expression of these molecules locally.

1.1.3. Murine Studies Employing Genetically Altered Tumor Vaccines

Introduction of MHC genes into tumors was among the first approaches for enhancing the immunogenicity of tumors. Increasing MHC class I expression by gene transfection typically results in decreased tumorigenic capacity in murine tumor models (7). The decreased tumorigenicity is felt to be owing to enhanced presentation of tumor-specific antigens to CD8$^+$ CTLs in vivo. However, enhanced expression of self MHC class I molecules does not always increase immunological potency of a tumor and, in certain circumstances, has been shown to inhibit natural killer (NK) cells, thereby resulting in paradoxically increased tumorigenicity (8). Tumor immunogenicity has also been enhanced by the transfer of allogeneic MHC class I genes (9,10). In certain cases, the rejection of tumors expressing allogeneic MHC class I molecules may result in enhanced systemic immune responses against subsequent challenge with the unmodified parental tumor. This represents an example of the general phenomenon of enhancing tumor vaccine potency by introducing genes encoding any foreign antigen (referred to as xenogenization). The mechanism by which xenogenized tumors enhance systemic immune responses against challenge with the parental tumor is still not clear, although the mechanism has been postulated to be the result of nonspecific effects owing to increased local cytokine induction.

There has been more interest in the study of immune responses generated by tumor cells genetically engineered to secrete various cytokines. This strategy does not involve inducing the expression of any foreign genes in tumor cells, but rather seeks to locally alter the immunological environment of the tumor cell so as to either enhance antigen presentation of tumor-specific antigens to the immune system or to enhance the activation of tumor-specific lymphocytes. As mentioned, one of the most important concepts underlying the use of cytokine gene-transduced tumor cells is that the cytokine is produced at very high concentrations local to the tumor. Systemic concentrations are generally quite low. This paracrine physiology much more closely mimics the natural biology of cytokine action than does the systemic (iv) administration of recombinant cytokines. Many cytokine genes have been introduced into tumor cells with varying effects on both tumorigenicity and immunogenicity. Some of these cytokines, when produced by tumors, induce a local inflammatory response that results in elimination of the injected tumor. This local inflammatory response is most often predominately dependent on leukocytes other than classical T-cells. These systems have been used to uncover in vivo effects of cytokines that result in activation of tumoricidal potential by various types of leukocytes.

This new tumor vaccine approach, using genetically-altered autologous tumor cells to secrete local concentrations of cytokines, has been best developed in murine models *(11–19)*. In some of these models, lymphokine gene-transduced tumor cells have been shown to generate a local, tumor-specific, immune response when administered as a subcutaneous vaccination *(11–13,15–19)*. In addition to rejecting the genetically modified tumor cells, vaccinated animals may develop a T-cell-dependent systemic immunity that, in some cases, can cure micro metastases established prior to treatment with the genetically altered tumor cells *(11–13,17,18)*. In all cases in which systemic immunity against wild-type tumor challenge has been analyzed, it is mediated by T-cells. However, given the number of studies done to date with cytokine-transduced tumor cells, it is not surprising that variable results have been seen when different tumor systems are analyzed. Additional variables to the cytokines employed include: cell dose, level of cytokine expression, location of immunization and challenge sites, and vaccination schedule.

Given the large number of potential cytokine genes in the armamentarium, and the technical difficulties in transducing human tumor cells to make vaccines, it is critical that they be compared for efficacy. Also, given that most mouse tumors show significant immunogenicity when simply irradiated, identification of genes that truly enhance a tumor's immunogenicity above that of irradiated wild-type cells is important. The first study that directly compared multiple cytokine and other genes in murine tumor models used a highly transmissible, defective retroviral vector. This study demonstrated that, in a number of poorly and moderately immunogenic tumors, including a murine renal cell carcinoma, immunization with granulocyte-macrophage colony-stimulating factor (GM-CSF)-transduced tumors produced the greatest degree of systemic immunity, which was enhanced relative to irradiated nontransduced tumors *(17)*. Immunity was dependent on both CD4$^+$ and CD8$^+$ T-cells, despite the fact that the tumors were MHC class II$^-$. The potency of GM-CSF's effect locally may relate to its unique ability in promoting the differentiation of hematopoietic precursors to dendritic cells, which are the most potent antigen-presenting cells for helper T-cells *(20,21)*.

1.2. Features of Retroviral Vectors

1.2.1. Rationale for Choosing a Retroviral Vector for Gene Transfer into Tumor Cells

Gene transfer into tumor cells can be accomplished by a variety of methods involving either naked DNA or the use of viral vectors. There are many methods for transferring naked DNA into cells, including:

1. Coprecipitation with calcium phosphate *(22)*.
2. The use of electroporation that exposes cells to rapid pulses of high voltage current, thereby providing a physically induced opening in the cell membrane for entry of DNA *(23)*.
3. Direct introduction of DNA into cells by microinjection *(24)*.
4. Encapsidation of DNA into liposomes *(25)*.

Use of any of these methods will often result in the introduction of multiple copies of the cytokine gene randomly into the host cell's genome. Several of these methods can result in transient expression of the gene (for 24–72 h) by as many as 50% of the cells in the transfected population, because the transfected DNA can exist free in the cell nucleus for a short time *(26)*. However, stable gene expression that requires integration of the transfected DNA into the host's genome usually occurs in <1% of the cells within the population undergoing transfection. To achieve stable integration and expression of the DNA into a high proportion of the cell population, it is often necessary to select for the minority of cells in the transfected population that have successfully retained the foreign DNA. This can be accomplished by cotransfecting DNA that encodes for a selectable marker, that will allow cells expressing its product to survive in growth media that contains a substrate for the gene's product, that is normally toxic to most mammalian cells. In this way, in vitro selection of those cells that have successfully incorporated the transferred DNA can be accomplished. However, although in vitro selection will enhance the number of gene-transduced tumor cells in the cell population to nearly 100%, it is at the theoretical expense of antigen expression loss among that tumor cell population. In theory, loss of particular antigenic populations of tumor cells will decrease the effectiveness of the vaccine.

Currently, the most efficient method of stable gene delivery into mammalian cells is through the use of viral vectors, which infect their target cell by binding specific cell surface receptors. Most viral vectors are constructed so that they contain the sequences encoding for the expression of the gene and all of the genetic signals including the promoters, enhancers, splicing signals, and signals for polyadenylation of RNA transcripts, all of which are necessary for the transcription and ultimate translation of the inserted cytokine gene sequences. Often, the vectors will also contain selectable markers *(27)*. Potential adverse consequences following viral infection can include:

1. Damage or death to the host cell.
2. The activation of other latent viruses integrated into the host's genome.
3. The activation of silent host genes such as proto-oncogenes.
4. Transformation of the defective viral vector from replication-incompetent to replication-competent by recombination with host gene sequences (which results in the production of helper virus).

All of these possibilities should be considered in choosing a viral vector system for gene transfer.

Retroviruses have been the most commonly employed vectors for the preparation of cytokine-secreting tumor vaccines, for study in murine models, and in human vaccine therapy trials. There are at least two reasons for this. First, as mentioned above, retroviruses usually do not enter into a lytic cycle of viral replication and therefore, do not kill their host cell soon after viral infection. Second, retroviruses can infect most mammalian cells and integrate into the host genome, which is a critical requirement for efficient gene transfer and expression in a stable and heritable fashion. Most of the retroviral vectors employed in cytokine-secreting tumor vaccine studies have been developed from either avian or murine retroviruses. A key feature of these retroviral vectors is their incompetence to replicate following transduction into the host cell. Details of the mechanisms of infection, replication, integration, and gene expression of these viral vectors have already been described in significant detail in the literature *(28–33)*. However, it is important to note that host cell replication and DNA synthesis are required for provirus integration, and thus, efficient gene transfer is restricted to replicating cells.

1.2.2. Structure of the Retroviral Vector

The transduction procedures that will be described employ the MFG retroviral vector system. However, several other retroviral vectors are also available for this use *(34,35)*. The structure of MFG has recently been described *(20,33)*. Briefly, in this vector, Moloney murine leukemia virus (Mo-MuLV) long-terminal repeat (LTR) sequences are used to generate both a full-length viral RNA (for encapsidation into virus particles) and a subgenomic mRNA (analogous to the Mo-MuLV env mRNA) that is responsible for the expression of inserted sequences. The vector retains both sequences in the viral gag region shown to improve the encapsidation of viral RNA *(20)* and the normal 5' and 3' splice sites necessary for the generation of the env mRNA. Protein coding sequences are inserted between the *Nco*I and *Bam*HI sites in such a way that the cDNA sequences encoding the gene of interest are cloned into the downstream site such that the cDNA inserts AUG at the exact position relative to the 3' splice acceptor site where the *env* gene starts in the original virus. It is therefore expressed as a subgenomic transcript off of the 5' LTR. No selectable marker exists in the vector. This feature, together with deletion of sequences in the 5' portion of the gag-region intron, results in high titer production of viral particles by the packaging line as well as uniformly high levels of expression regardless of the particular gene cloned into the vector.

The use of these high efficiency retroviral vectors to carry cytokine genes into tumor cells has a number of specific advantages:

1. The transduction is rapid and selection is unnecessary. Subcloning experiments documented that nearly 100% efficiency is achieved in a 4-h infection followed by 48 h culture to allow for integration of the viral vector into the host cell's genome.
2. The absence of selection avoids the potential problem that selected subclones may display different immunologic and biologic properties from the original tumor cell population.
3. Using retroviral supernatants from different cytokine producer cell lines, combinations of cytokines can easily be simultaneously introduced into the same cell.

However, there are also several potential disadvantages to the use of this vector system. First, entry into the cell is dependent on the expression of specific viral receptors on the host's cell surface. Because the identity of most retroviral receptors is still unknown, it is difficult to determine whether or not a particular host cell expresses these receptors, and, to what extent these receptors are expressed. As will be discussed, the retroviral packaging lines do have the ability to produce virus particles that can infect a wide host range. Second, as mentioned earlier, efficient retroviral gene transfer requires that the host cell proliferate for integration of the viral genes into the host cell's genome, and for expression of the transferred gene. Third, retroviruses are difficult to purify, concentrate, or store for long periods of time, because of their fragility. Their fragility is probably manifested by the loss of their *env* gene product, which ultimately translates into decreased infectivity. Fourth, there is the theoretical concern that retroviral integration may lead to insertional mutagenesis because the virus integrates into random sites in the host's genome, and may interrupt vital cellular genes or insert retroviral regulatory sequences that modify the expression of nearby cellular genes. Finally, as will be discussed in Section 1.2.3., helper virus production by the retroviral packaging line has occurred when employing some of the earlier generations of these packaging lines. This potential problem is the major concern when choosing a viral vector to employ for the production of genetically altered tumor vaccines for clinical trials. Helper virus detection has not been reported to have occurred in any of the clinical trials employing retroviral vectors thus far, nor in most of the animal studies designed to test the safety of these vectors. However, in one study in which immunosuppressed monkeys purposefully received high concentrations of replication-competent retroviruses, lymphomas developed *(36)*, illustrating the potential seriousness of helper virus contamination.

1.2.3. Construction of the Packaging and the Producer Lines

The other critical component of the retroviral vector system is a cell line that produces the viral proteins that are required for encapsidation of the viral RNA. This cell line, referred to as the retrovirus packaging line, is produced by transfection of proviral DNA containing the retroviral genes necessary for the synthesis of the viral proteins, into a fibroblast cell line. The most commonly employed fibroblast cell line is the murine NIH 3T3 cell line. After transfection of the proviral DNA vector into the packaging cell line, this line is then referred to as the retrovirus producer cell line. The first generation of packaging lines contained the stable introduction of a mutant Moloney murine leukemia virus proviral genome that contained a deletion of the encapsidation sequence (psi sequence) *(30,37)*. However, these packaging cell lines have been shown to produce low levels of replication competent virus, both psi negative, and wild-type virus, through recombinational events involving a copackaged recombinant genome carrying the psi sequence, at low efficiency *(38)*. Newer constructs of packaging lines have not been shown to produce helper virus *(29,31,39,40)*. Most of the producer cell line clones derived from these packaging cell lines have been shown to produce retroviral titers in the range of 10^6 cfu/mL, levels that allow for high efficiency gene transfer *(29)*. These titers are comparable to low normal titers obtained for replication-competent retroviruses.

2. Materials

1. Retroviral vector producer lines: The MFG retroviral producer cell lines were obtained from R. C. Mulligan (Whitehead Institute for Biomedical Research, Cambridge, MA). Both the amphotropic and ecotropic retroviral producer cell lines, CRIP and CRE, respectively, are grown in Dulbecco's Modified Eagle's Medium (DMEM) with high glucose (4500 g/L), supplemented with 10% bovine calf serum, penicillin (100 U/mL final concentration), streptomycin (100 μg/mL final concentration), L-glutamine (2 mM final concentration), and gentamycin (50 μg/mL final concentration), at 37°C, and 10% CO_2. trypsin (0.25%)-EDTA (0.1%) for passaging the cell lines.

2. Tumor cell lines: All tumor cell lines to be transduced should be maintained in their optimal growth media before and after performing the transduction procedure to enhance the proliferation capacity of the cell population.

3. Retroviral gene transfer to tumor cells: Tumor cells and retroviral supernatant that has been prepared as described in Methods. In addition, DEAE-dextran 10 mg/mL stock solution prepared by dissolving 1 g into 100 mL of the producer line growth media (DMEM + 10% calf serum), and filtered through a 0.45-μm filter. Store in sterile 5-mL aliquots at 4°C for up to 6 mo. Sterile tumor growth media and sterile 1X PBS.

3. Methods

3.1. Maintenance of Retroviral Vector Producer Lines

1. Grow the retroviral producer cell line in culture to confluency in large flasks (162-cm^2 or greater). These cells grow in an adherent monolayer.

2. When the cells have reached confluency, remove the supernatant, and incubate the cells with enough trypsin-EDTA to cover the bottom of the flask (usually 2–3 mL) at room temperature until the cells become nonadherent (usually 1–2 min).

3. Quench the trypsin with at least 3–4 vol of the growth media containing the calf serum.

4. Centrifuge for 10 min at 1500 rpm, at 4°C.

5. Remove the supernatant and count the cells.

6. Replate the cells at about a 1:10 dilution of the number of cells in the confluent flask (about 2 × 10^6 cells per 162-cm^2 flask).

7. Split the cell lines 1:10 every 3–4 d, or when each flask reaches confluency.

3.2. Preparation of Retroviral Supernatants

1. Two days prior to transduction, trypsinize the producer cells, wash them once, and replate them at a density of 2 × 10^6 cells per 100-mm culture dish.

2. One day prior to transduction, remove the media, and add 10 cc of fresh media to the cells.

3. On the day of transduction, collect a 24-h retroviral supernatant and filter through a 0.45-μm filter to remove contaminating retroviral producer cells.

3.3. Maintenance of Tumor Cell Lines

1. Grow the tumor cells in culture in optimal tumor growth media to confluency.
2. On the day prior to transduction, replate the cells at a density of $2–5 \times 10^5$ cells per 75-cm^2 culture dish.

3.4. Performing Retroviral Gene Transfer to Tumor Cells

1. Incubate the freshly collected retroviral supernatant with the 10 μg/mL final concentration of the transduction enhancer DEAE-dextran (*see* Section 4.4.) for approx 10 min at room temperature, so that the retrovirus will bind to the enhancer prior to exposure to the tumor cells.
2. Remove the growth media from the tumor cells and replace it with 10 cc of retroviral supernatant containing the enhancer.
3. Incubate the cells at 37°C for 24 h (*see* Section 4.4.).
4. Following incubation of the tumor cells with the retroviral supernatant, remove the supernatant, and wash the cells twice with sterile PBS to rinse away residual retroviral supernatant.
5. Add 10 cc of tumor growth media and allow the cells to grow for 48 h.

3.5. Testing for Cytokine Gene Product

1. At 48 h following transduction, remove the growth media, and add 10 cc of fresh tumor growth media.
2. Collect a 24-h supernatant for evaluation of cytokine secretion. To do this, remove the supernatant, centrifuge or filter through a 0.45-μm filter to remove the cells, and aliquot the supernatant into three 1-mL, sterile aliquots that can be stored frozen at −70°C until the time of testing for cytokine secretion. Three separate aliquots should be stored so that repeat testing can be performed without multiple freeze/thaws (which might reduce the concentration of the gene product).
3. Following collection of the cell supernatant, take up the cells and count them. Record the total number of cells that contributed to the production of the cytokine over 24 h. This number will be used to calculate the concentration of cytokine secretion per given number of tumor cells after the concentration of cytokine in the supernatant is determined.

4. Notes

4.1. Maintenance of Retroviral Vector Producer Lines

1. Producer lines derived from the NIH 3T3 fibroblast cell line grow in an adherent monolayer. They do best when they are plated at a threshold density of about 1/10 the flask's total cell capacity. Plating the cells at a lower density may result in loss of the cell line.
2. Exposure to trypsin results in the rapid release of the producer cells from the tissue culture flask. Be aware that overexposure to trypsin will result in significant cell death.

3. The MFG producer line grows in media supplemented with bovine calf serum. Substitution of fetal bovine serum may result in a change in growth kinetics and viral particle production. The growth requirements recommended by the laboratory in which the producer line originated should always be used to culture the producer line being employed.

4. It is advantageous to initially expand enough of the producer cells to allow for freezing down of a large stock of aliquots for two reasons. First, prolonged passage in culture may increase the possibility of recombination events within the producer cells that may result in the production of helper virus. Second, there is the theoretical concern that prolonged passage in culture may result in a decrease in the population of producer cells capable of efficiently producing the viral particles.

5. The MFG producer cell lines freeze well in 90% calf serum plus 10% DMSO. Recovery of viable producer cells will be severely compromised if these cells are frozen in other types of serum. Each producer line should be frozen in the same type of serum that is used for in vitro growth. These cells can be stored long-term in liquid nitrogen.

4.2. Preparation of Retroviral Supernatants

6. Retroviruses are difficult to titer because they do not form plaques. It is therefore recommended that every retroviral producer line be titered for transduction efficiency using an easily transducible cell line. NIH 3T3 cells are a good choice for comparison with other murine cell lines. For the transduction of human primary cultures, a human cell line may be a more appropriate cell line for comparison. Titering can be accomplished by using the transduction procedure described in Sections 3.1.–3.5., and by performing serial two- to five-fold dilutions of the retroviral supernatant prior to exposure of retrovirus to the cell line. Dilutions of the retroviral supernatant should be made with the cell line's growth media for best results. Most supernatants are optimal either undiluted, or between a 1:2 and 1:10 dilution.

7. Before assuming that insufficient transduction rates are owing to low titer supernatants as a result of a poor supernatant collection, it is important to first determine if the producer cells themselves are still capable of producing high quantities of retroviral particles. Because the producer cells themselves also express the gene encoded by the retroviral vector, an easy way to evaluate the producer line for production of the vector is to assay the cells for expression of the gene product. However, in vitro loss of high titer producer lines owing to long-term culture can easily be avoided by routinely thawing a new aliquot of producer cells every 3–4 wk.

8. If expression is at the expected level, then the problem is more likely to be owing to a low titer retroviral supernatant resulting from suboptimal supernatant collection. There are two major causes of low titer retroviral supernatants: inadequate retroviral supernatant collection resulting from insufficient numbers of producer cells or overgrowth of producer cells; and suboptimal growth conditions for retroviral supernatant collection, in particular, a bad lot of calf serum, use of the wrong media and supplements, inadequate CO_2 concentration during incubation, and so on.

9. A recent study performed to evaluate the improvement of retroviral vector production observed that the growth of 21/22 producer cell lines at 32°C for up to 2 wk after the cells reached 100% confluence increased vector titers *(42)*. Growth of the producer lines at 32°C is thought to increase the stability of the viral particles. In addition, improved vector production may be a result of the decreased metabolism of the producer cells at this lower temperature.

10. For optimal transduction efficiencies, freshly collected retroviral supernatants should be used. Although it is possible to store the supernatants at 4°C for several days, and to freeze these supernatants at −70°C for several weeks, the efficiency of transduction may decrease by as much as 50% following thaw of the supernatant.

11. Producer lines must be frozen in the same type of serum used for in vitro growth unless otherwise advised. The substitution of other serum may not support the growth of these cells well, and may result in significant cell death during freezing and storage.

4.3. Maintenance of Tumor Cell Lines

12. Most proliferating cell lines can be transduced with a retroviral vector. However, the efficiency of transduction will depend on the percentage of cells that are actively proliferating at the time of exposure to the retrovirus, since integration into the host genome is required for stable expression of the transferred gene. Therefore, the growth conditions for each cell line being transduced should be optimized before attempting this transduction procedure. Most long-term cell lines already have defined growth conditions that support optimal growth. However, it is now possible to transduce many primary, short-term cancer cell lines, and conditions for optimizing their growth may already have been described.

13. The actual density of cells in the flask should be optimized for every tumor cell type, keeping in mind that the cells will need to be able to proliferate maximally for at least 48 h following transduction to allow for optimal integration and expression of the gene. For cells with a 48–72 h doubling time, adequate transduction can be achieved by plating the cells at a density that will result in approx 1/3 confluency of the flask on the day of transduction.

4.4. Performing Retroviral Gene Transfer to Tumor Cells

14. Both a negative and a positive control group should be included in each transduction experiment to confirm that gene expression is the result of gene transfer. A good negative control group is to incubate a flask of each cell type to be transduced with retroviral producer cell growth media containing the enhancing polymer alone. An adequate positive control group would include the transduction of any easily transducible cell line with the same lot of retroviral supernatant used to transduce the test tumor cells.

15. Transduction efficiency can be enhanced by the addition of polymers to the retroviral supernatant just prior to exposure of the target cells to the retroviral vector. Enhanced gene transfer is thought to occur via a charge-mediated mechanism that affects virus binding to or penetration of the target cell. The polycations

protamine, polybrene, and DEAE-dextran are routinely used for this purpose *(1,33,43)*. In addition, liposome-forming compounds such as DOTAP (Boehringer Mannheim, Indianapolis, IN) have also been successfully used to enhance retroviral gene transfer and may be less toxic to the host cell than other enhancers *(1)*. Liposome-forming agents probably enhance gene transfer into the host cell by first forming stable interactions with the virus, then adhering to the cell surface, followed by fusing with the cell membrane and releasing the virus into the cell cytoplasm *(44)*. Because most enhancers are toxic to the cell lines at high concentrations, yet higher concentrations of polymers may be required for enhanced transduction efficiency to some cell lines, it is recommended that a titer of the enhancer be performed on each new batch of enhancers used, to determine the least toxic, most enhancing concentration of the polycation or lipid compound. Table 1 illustrates recommended ranges of polycation and lipid reagent concentrations for the commonly employed transduction enhancers.

16. Longer incubation times will increase the number of proliferating cells that are exposed to the retroviral vector, and therefore, may increase the efficiency of transduction. Hardy tumor cell lines may tolerate the retroviral supernatant containing low concentrations of enhancer for 24–48 h without significant cell death. However, primary human tumor cultures may not tolerate a change in the growth media for more than several hours. Therefore, it is best to perform a pilot study evaluating the rate of tumor cell death over time when exposed to the retroviral supernatant containing the enhancer, to optimize the transduction procedure.

17. There is recent evidence to suggest that the efficiency of retroviral transduction can be improved by a 90-min centrifugation at 2500 rpm, and 32°C, prior to an overnight incubation (at 32°C) of the tumor cells with the retroviral supernatant *(42)*. However, some tumor cells may not tolerate an overnight incubation at 32°C.

18. It is often useful to perform the initial transduction studies on new tumor cell lines using the retroviral vector containing a marker gene (for example, the *lacZ* gene that expresses the cytoplasmic enzyme beta-galactosidase that will turn the transduced cell's cytoplasm blue when exposed to the substrate bluogal or X-gal). Marker genes can be used quantitatively to determine the number of tumor cells in the transduced population that are capable of expressing the transferred gene (the transduction efficiency of the vector for a particular tumor cell line).

19. It is not uncommon to have a high titer retroviral supernatant. If this is the case, the supernatant can be diluted 1:5 or 1:10 (depending on titer) with target cell growth media, prior to the transduction procedure, to decrease target cell toxicity from the retroviral supernatant. In fact, be aware that a dilution of a high titer retroviral supernatant may be necessary because higher titer supernatants may contain inhibitors against successful retroviral transduction.

20. The procedure described in Sections 3.1.–3.5. can be used for transduction of adherent and nonadherent tumor cell lines, and does not require any special modifications. For nonadherent cell lines, media changes require that the tumor cells be taken up with the supernatants and centrifuged to remove the supernatant. The cells are then resuspended in the fresh media and replated.

Table 1
Commonly Employed Transduction Enhancing Reagents

Transduction enhancer	Target cell type	Concentration range (final concentration in retroviral supernatant)
DEAE-dextran	Murine tumor cell lines	5–10 μg/mL
(Sigma, St. Louis, MO)	Human tumor cell lines	10–100 μg/mL
Polybrene	Murine tumor cell lines	5–10 μg/mL
(Sigma, St. Louis, MO or Aldrich Milwaukee, WI)	Human tumor cell lines	10–100 μg/mL
Protamine sulfate	Murine tumor cell lines	5–10 μg/mL
(Lilly, Indianapolis, IN)	Human tumor cell lines	5–100 μg/mL
DOTAP	Murine tumor cell lines	5–10 μg/mL
(Boehringer Mannheim, Indianapolis, IN)	Human tumor cell lines	10–100 μg/mL

21. Freezing of large stocks of the transduced tumor cells is recommended to prevent loss of gene expression, as well as to prevent in vitro selection with loss of antigen expression. Transduced tumor cell lines can be frozen down and stored in liquid nitrogen long-term without loss of gene expression. Controlled-rate freezing is recommended to prevent a significant decrease in viability following thawing. A cheap and efficient way of control-rate freezing is to immerse the freezing vial of cells in a propanol bath (Nalgene Cryo 1°C Freezing Container), and to place the apparatus into a −70°C freezer overnight. This will freeze the cells at approx 1°C per min. The cells can then be placed into liquid nitrogen for long-term storage.

22. Primary human tumor lines are more difficult to transduce than long-term established lines. However, with the increasing applications of gene therapy to the clinics, there is an increasing need for improved methods of gene transfer to these cells. The most important criteria for efficient gene transfer to primary human tumor cultures is to optimize the growth conditions for maximal proliferation capacity. In addition, increasing the concentration of transduction enhancing polymer may result in improved transduction efficiency (1). It is often beneficial to initially screen the different enhancing polymers for the upper limits of concentration of polymer, and incubation time, that each primary tumor cell line can tolerate, before significant cell death is observed.

4.5. Testing for Gene Product Expression

23. Following transduction of tumor cells with the cytokine gene, the transduced cells should be evaluated for the total quantity of cytokine produced and for the quantity of cytokine that is bioactive. The total quantity of cytokine produced is best determined by ELISA. The ELISA kits are now commercially available for

Table 2
Common Bioassays Used
to Quantitate Cytokine Production

Cytokine	Cell Line for Bioassay (ref.)
Human IL-2	CTLL-2 *(45)*
Murine IL-2	CTLL *(46)*
Human IL-3	TF-1 cells *(47)*
Murine IL-3	NFS 60 *(48)*
Human IL-4	PHA-activated Peripheral *(49)* blood mononuclear cells
Murine IL-4	CT4S or HT-2 cells *(46,50)*
Human IL-5	TF-1 cells *(47)*
Murine IL-5	Same
Human IL-6	T 1165.85.2.1 cells *(51)*
Murine IL-6	Same
Human IL-7	PHA-activated peripheral *(49)* blood mononuclear cells
Murine IL-7	Same
Human GM-CSF	TF-1 cells *(47)*
Murine GM-CSF	NFS-60 cells *(48)*
Human Interferon-gamma	Antiviral assay *(52)*
Murine interferon-gamma	Antiviral assay *(46)*
Human TNF-alpha	Cytotoxic assay *(53)*
Murine TNF-alpha	Cytotoxic assay *(53)*

quantitation of most murine and human cytokines (Genzyme, Boston, MA, Endogen, R&D systems). Although these kits are expensive, they usually have a sensitivity of 1–4 pg/mL, and are specific for the cytokine being tested. Bioassays are also available for many murine and human cytokines. Although they are often not as sensitive or specific as ELISA, they provide important information concerning the function of the cytokine being secreted by the tumor cells. Cell lines for bioassay of common murine and human cytokines are listed in Table 2. For all of these assays, serial dilutions are made of the tumor cell supernatants collected as described in Section 3.5. Most of the bioassays rely on cell lines that are growth factor-dependent. In these assays, the degree of proliferation of the cell lines in the presence of the serially diluted cytokines is determined by ^{3}H-thymidine incorporation. A recombinant standard is also run along with the test samples to accurately quantitate the cytokine in the test samples. Because several cytokines may stimulate the same cell line, duplicate curves are often run for each sample, one curve in the presence of cytokine-blocking antibody, to evaluate the percent of proliferation that is specifically the result of that cytokine. The exceptions are: the TNF-alpha assay (which is a cytotoxic assay) and the interferon-gamma assay (which is an antiviral assay). The exact procedures for performing these assays can be found in the references listed in Table 2.

24. Genes encoding cytokines are currently one of the most commonly employed genetically altered tumor vaccine strategies in preclinical models and in clinical trials. However, other gene-modified vaccine strategies, including tumor cell surface expression of MHC class I and II molecules, and costimulatory cell surface molecules (for example B7), are also under investigation. Successful gene transfer of these gene products can be assayed using cell surface staining with MAb specific for the gene product and analyzed by standard flow cytometric methods.

25. Evaluation of vector copy number should be considered, particularly in cases of suboptimal gene product expression, to determine if the problem is at the level of transcription, or owing to inadequate transduction. Vector copy number can be evaluated by Southern blot hybridization using standard procedures.

26. If the problem is owing to inadequate transduction and all of the transduction conditions have been optimized, it is possible to significantly improve on the transduction efficiency by subjecting the transduced cells to one or two more rounds of transduction.

References

1. Jaffee, E. M., Dranoff, G., Cohen, L. K., Hauda, K. M., Clift, S., Marshall, F. F., Mulligan, R. C., and Pardoll, D. M. (1993) High efficiency gene transfer into primary human tumor explants without cell selection. *Cancer Res.* **53,** 2221–2226.
2. Lurquin, C., Van Pel, A., Mariame, B., De Plaen, E., Szikora, J.-P., Janssens, C., Reddehase, M., LeJeune, J., and Boon, T. (1989) Structure for the gene coding for tum⁻ antigen P91A: a peptide encoded by the mutated exon is recognized with L^d by cytolytic T cells. *Cell* **58,** 293–303.
3. Van Der Bruggen, P., Traversari, C., Chomez, P., Lurquin, C., De Plaen, E., Van Den Eynde, B., Knuth, A., and Boon, T. (1991) A gene encoding an antigen recognized cytotoxic T lymphocytes on a human melanoma. *Science* **254,** 1643–1648.
4. Brichard, V., Van Pel, A., Wolfel, T., Wolfel, C., De Plaen, E., Lethe, B., Coulie, P., and Boon, T. (1993) The tyrosinase gene codes for an antigen recognized by autologous cytolytic T lymphocytes on HLA-A2 melanomas. *J. Exp. Med.* **178,** 489–495.
5. Kawakami, Y., Eliyahu, S., Delgado, C. H., Robbins, P. F., Rivoltini, L., Topalian, S. L., Miki, T., and Rosenberg, S. A. (1994) Cloning of the gene coding for a shared human melanoma antigen recognized by autologous T cells infiltrating into tumor. *Proc. Natl. Acad. Sci. USA*, in press.
6. Lindenmann, J. and Klein, P. (1967) Viral oncolysis: increased immunogenicity of host cell antigen associated with influenza virus. *J. Exp. Med.* **126,** 93–108.
7. Wallich, R., Bulbuc, N., Hammerling, G., Katzav, S., Segal, S., and Feldman, M. (1985) Abrogation of metastatic properties of tumor cells by de novo expression of H-2K antigens following H-2 gene transfection. *Nature* **315,** 301–305.
8. Karre, K., Ljunggren, H., Piontek, G., and Kiessling, R. (1986) Selective rejection of H-2 deficient lymphoma variants suggests alternative immune defense strategy. *Nature* **319,** 675–686.

9. Itaya, T., Yamagiwa, S., Okada, F., Oikawa, T., Kurumaki, N., Takeichi, N., Hosokawa, M., and Kobayashi, H. (1987) Xenogenization of a mouse lung carcinoma (3LL) by transfection with an allogeneic class I major histocompatibility complex gene (H-2Ld). *Cancer Res.* **47,** 3136–3140.

10. Plautz, G., Yang, Z.-Y., Wu, B.-Y., Gao, X., Huang, L., and Nabel, G. (1993) Immunotherapy of malignancy by in vivo gene transfer into tumors. *Proc Natl. Acad. Sci. USA* **90,** 4645–4649.

11. Fearon, E. R., Pardoll, D. M., Itaya, T., Golumbek, P., Levitsky, H. I., Simons, J. W., Karasuyama, H., Vogelstein, B., and Frost, P. (1990) Interleukin-2 production by tumor cells bypasses T helper function in the generation of an antitumor response. *Cell* **60,** 397–403.

12. Golumbek, P. T., Lazenby, A. J., Levitsky, H. I., Jaffee, E. M., Karasuyama, H., Baker, M., and Pardoll, D. M. (1991) Treatment of established renal cancer by tumor cells engineered to secrete interleukin-4. *Science* **254,** 713–716.

13. Gansbacher, B., Zier, K., Daniels, B., Cronin, K., Bannerji, R., and Gilboa, E. (1990) Interleukin 2 gene Transfer into tumor cells abrogates tumorigenicity and induces protective immunity. *J. Exp. Med.* **172,** 1217–1224.

14. Tepper, R. I., Pattengale, P. K., and Leder, P. (1989) Murine interleukin-4 displays potent anti-tumor activity in vivo. *Cell* **57,** 503–512.

15. Hock, H., Dorsch, M., Diamantstein, T., and Blankenstein, T. (1991) Interleukin 7 induces CD4+ T cell-dependent tumor rejection. *J. Exp. Med.* **174,** 1291–1298.

16. Asher, A. L., Mule, J. J., Kasid, A., Restifo, N. P., Salo, J. C., Reichert, C. M., Jaffe, G., Fendly, B., Kriegler, M., and Rosenberg, S. A. (1991) Murine tumor cells transduced with the gene for tumor necrosis factor-alpha. *J. Immunol.* **146,** 3227–3234.

17. Dranoff, G., Jaffee, E. M., Lazenby, A., Golumbek, P., Levitsky, H., Brose, K., Jackson, V., Hamada, H., Pardoll, D. M., and Mulligan, R. C. (1993) Vaccination with irradiated tumor cells engineered to secrete murine GM-CSF stimulates potent, specific and long lasting anti-tumor immunity. *Proc. Natl. Acad. Sci. USA* **90,** 3539–3543.

18. Porgador, A., Tzehoval, E., Katz, A., Vadai, E., Revel, M., Feldman, M., and Eisenback, L. (1992) Interleukin-6 gene transfection into lewis lung carcinoma tumor cells suppresses the malignant phenotype and confers immunotherapeutic competence against parental metastatic cells. *Cancer Res.* **52,** 3679–3686.

19. Colombo, M. P., Ferrari, G., Stoppacciaro, A., Parenza, M., Rodolfo, M., Mavilio, F., and Parmiani, G. (1991) Granulocyte colony-stimulating factor gene transfer suppresses tumorigenicity of a murine adenocarcinoma in vivo. *J. Exp. Med.* **173,** 889–897.

20. Inaba, K., Steinman, R. M., Pack, M. W., Aya, H., Inaba, M., Sudo, T., Wolpe, S., and Schuler, G. (1992) Identification of proliferating dendritic cell precursors in mouse blood. *J. Exp. Med.* **175,** 1157–1167.

21. Inaba, K., Inaba, M., Romani, N., Aya, H., Deguchi, M., Ikehara, S., Muramatsu, S., and Steinman, R. M. (1992) Generation of large numbers of dendritic cells from mouse bone marrow cultures supplemented with granulocyte/macrophage colony-stimulating factor. *J. Exp. Med.* **176,** 1693–1702.

22. Graham, F. L. and Van Der Eb, A. J. (1973) A new technique for the assay of infectivity of human adenovirus 5 DNA. *Virology* **52**, 456–467.

23. Potter, H., Weir, L., and Leder, P. (1984) Enhancer-dependent expression of human kappa immunoglobulin genes introduced into mouse pre-B lymphocytes by electroporation. *Proc. Natl. Acad. Sci. USA* **81**, 7161–7165.

24. Capecchi, M. R. (1980) High efficiency transformation by direct microinjection of DNA into cultured mammalian cells. *Cell* **22**, 479–488.

25. Felgner, P. L., Gadek, T. R., Holm, M., Roman, R., Chan, H. W., Wenz, M., Northrop, J. P., Ringold, G. M., and Danielsen, M. (1987) Lipofection: a highly efficient, lipid-mediated DNA transfection procedure. *Proc. Natl. Acad. Sci. USA* **84**, 7413–7417.

26. Banerji, J., Rusconi, S., and Schaffner, W. (1981) Expression of a beta-globin gene is enhanced by remote SV40 DNA sequences. *Cell* **27**, 299–308.

27. Kingston, R. E. (1993) Introduction of DNA into mammalian cells, in *Current Protocols in Molecular Biology*, vol. 1 (Ausubel, F. M., Brent, R., Kingston, R. E., Moore, D. D., Seidman, J. G., Smith, J. A., and Struhl, K., eds.), Wiley, pp. 9.0.1.–9.17.2.

28. Mulligan, R. C. (1991) Gene transfer and gene therapy. Principles, prospects, and perspective, in *Etiology of Human Diseases at the DNA Level* (Lindsten, J. and Pettersson, U., eds.), Raven, New York, pp. 143–181.

29. Danos, O. and Mulligan, R. C. (1988) Safe and efficient generation of recombinant retroviruses with amphotropic and ecotropic host ranges. *Proc. Natl. Acad. Sci. USA* **85**, 6460–6464.

30. Mann, R., Mulligan, R. C., and Baltimore, D. (1983) Construction of a retrovirus packaging mutant and its use to produce helper-free defective retrovirus. *Cell* **33**, 153–159.

31. Miller, D. A. and Buttimore, C. (1986) Redesign of retrovirus packaging cell lines to avoid recombination leading to helper virus production. *Mol. Cell. Biol.* **6**, 2895–2902.

32. Armentano, D., Sheau-Fung, Y., Kantoff, P., von Ruden, T., Anderson, W. F., and Gilboa, E. (1987) Effect of internal viral sequences on the utility of retroviral vectors. *J. Virol.* **61**, 1647–1650.

33. Wilson, J. M., Jefferson, D. M., Chowdhury, J. R., Novikoff, P. M., Johnston, D. E., and Mulligan, R. C. (1988) Retrovirus-mediated transduction of adult hepatocytes. *Proc. Natl. Acad. Sci. USA* **85**, 3014–3018.

34. Muenchaw, D. D., Freeman, S. M., Cornetta, K., Zweibel, J. A., and Anderson, W. F. (1990) Analysis of retroviral packaging lines for the generation of replication competent virus. *Virology* **176**, 262–265.

35. Miller, D. A., Miller, D. G., Garcia, V. J., and Lynch, C. M. (1993) Use of retroviral vectors for gene transfer and expression. *Meth. Enzymol.* **217**, 581–599.

36. Donahue, R. E., Kessler, S. W., Bodine, D., McDonagh, K., Dunbar, C., Goodman, S., Agricola, B., Byrne, E., Raffeld, M., Moen, R. C., Bacher, J., Zsebo, K. M., and Neinhuis, A. W. (1992) Helper virus induced T-cell lymphoma in nonhuman primates after retroviral mediated gene transfer. *J. Exp. Med.* **176**, 1125–1135.

37. Miller, A. D., Law, M. F., and Verma, I. M. (1985) Generation of helper-free amphotropic retroviruses that transduce a dominant acting, methotrexate-resistant dihydrofolate reductase gene. *Mol. Cell Biol.* **5**, 431–437.

38. Mann, R. and Baltimore, D. (1985) Varying the position of a retrovirus packaging sequence results in the encapsidation of both unspliced and spliced RNAs. *J. Virology* **54**, 401–407.

39. Bosselman, R. A., Hsu, R. Y., Bruszewski, J., Hu, F., Martin, F., and Nicholson, M. (1987) Replication-defective chimeric helper proviruses and factors affecting generation of competent virus: expression of Muloney murine leukemia virus structural genes via the metallothionein promoter. *Mol. Cell. Biol.* **7**, 1797–1806.

40. Markowitz, D., Goff, S., and Bank, A. (1988) A safe packaging line for gene transfer: Separating viral genes on two different plasmids. *J. Virol.* **62**, 1120–1124.

41. Small, J. and Scangos, G. (1983) Recombination during gene transfer into mouse cells can restore the function of deleted genes. *Science* **219**, 174–176.

42. Kotani, H., Newton, P. B., Zhang, S., Chiang, Y. L., Otto, E., Weaver, L., Balese, M. R., Anderson, F. W., and McGarrity, G. J. (1994) Improved methods of retroviral vector transduction and production for gene therapy. *Hum. Gene Ther.* **5**, 19–28.

43. Cornetta, K. and Anderson, F. (1989) Protamine sulfate as an effective alternative to polybrene in retroviral-mediated gene transfer: implications for human gene therapy. *J. Virol. Meth.* **23**, 187–194.

44. Leventis, R. and Silvius, J. R. (1990) Interactions of mammalian cells with lipid dispersions containing novel metabolizable cationic amphiphiles. *Biochem. Biophys. Acta* **1023**, 124–132.

45. Gearing, A. J. H. and Bird, C. B. (1987) Production and assay of IL-2, in *Lymphokines and Interferons, A Practical Approach* (Clemens, M. J., Morris, A. G., and Gearing, A. J. H., eds.), IRL, Washington, DC, pp. 291–301.

46. Coligan, J. E., Kruisbeck, A. M., Margulies, D. H., Shevach, E. M., and Strober, W. (1991) *Current Protocols in Immunology*, Greene and Wiley-Interscience, NY.

47. Kitamura, T., Tojo, A., Kuwaki, T., Chiba, S., Miyazono, K., Urabe, A., and Takaku, F. (1989) Identification and analysis of human erythropoietin receptors on a factor-dependent cell line, TF-1. *Blood* **73**, 375–380.

48. Holmes, K. L., Palaszynski, E., Fredrikson, T. N. (1985) Correlation of cell-surface phenotype with the establishment of interleukin3-dependent cell lines from wild-mouse murine leukemia virus-induced neoplasms. *Proc. Natl. Acad. Sci. USA* **82 (19)**, 6687–6691.

49. Yokota, T., Otsuka, T., Mosmann, T., banchereau, J., DeFrance, T., Blanchard, D., De Vries, J. E., Lee, F., and Arai, K. (1986) Isolation and characterization of a human interleukin cDNA clone, homologous to mouse B-cell stimulatory factor 1, that expresses B-cell stimulatory factor 1, that expresses B-cell- and T-cell-stimulating activities. *Proc. Natl. Acad. Sci. USA* **83**, 5894–5898.

50. Fernandez-Botran, R., Krammer, P. H., Diamanttein, T., Uhr, W., and Vitetta, E. S. (1986) B cell-stimulatory factor 1 (BSF-1) promotes growth of helper T cell lines. *J. Exp. Med.* **164**, 580–593.

51. Nordan, R. P., Pumphrey, J. G., and Rudikoff, S. (1987) Purification andNH2-terminal sequence of a plasmacytoma growth factor derived from the murine macrophage cell line P388D1. *J. Immunol.* **139**, 813–817.
52. Meager, A. (1987) *Lymphokines and Interferons, A Practical Approach* (Clemens, M. J., Morris, A. G., and Gearing, A. J. H., eds.), IRL, Washington, DC, p. 129.
53. Mathews, N. and Neale, M. L. (1987) Cytotoxicity assays for tumor necrosis factor and lymphotoxin, in *Lymphokines and Interferons, A Practical Approach* (Clemens, M. J., Morris, A. G., and Gearing, A. J. H., eds.), IRL, Washington, DC, pp. 221–225.

23

Cationic Liposome-Mediated Gene Transfer to Tumor Cells In Vitro and In Vivo

Kyonghee Son, Frank Sorgi, Xiang Gao, and Leaf Huang

1. Introduction

Development of safe and effective technology for delivering functional DNA into cells in an intact organism is crucial to broad applications of gene therapy to human disease. Both viral and nonviral vectors have been developed. Of the technologies currently being studied, liposomal delivery system is particularly attractive. Cationic liposome-mediated gene transfection (lipofection), a relatively new technique pioneered by Felgner and coworkers (1), was highly efficient for transfecting cells in culture. The liposomes were composed of an equimolar mixture of a synthetic cationic lipid N-[1-(2,3,-dioleyloxy)propyl]-N,N,N,-trimethylammonium chloride (DOTMA) and a helper lipid dioleoyl-phosphatidylethanolamine (DOPE) (Fig. 1). The DOTMA/DOPE mixture (Lipofectin) forms complexes with DNA by charge interaction upon mixing at room temperature. Other cationic lipids are DOTAP, LipofectAMINE, Lipofectam, and DC-chol. The DOTAP is a diester analog of DOTMA and commercially available. LipofectAMINE and Lipofectam are polycationic lipids with a spermine head group that show increased frequency and activity of eukaryotic cell transfection (2,3). 3β-[N-(N',N'-dimethyaminoaminoethane) carbamoyl] cholesterol (DC-chol) (Fig. 1), a cationic cholesterol derivative, was introduced by Gao and Huang (4) and is routinely used in our laboratory. The DC-chol is now commercially available but can be easily synthesized with a single-step reaction from N,N-dimethylethylenediamine and cholesterol chloroformate (4), and improves the efficiency of transfection with minimal toxicity. Liposomes prepared with DC-chol and DOPE (3:2 molar ratio) are stable at 4°C for at least 1 yr (unpublished data).

From: *Methods in Molecular Medicine, Gene Therapy Protocols*
Edited by: P. Robbins Humana Press Inc., Totowa, NJ

DOPE
(Dioleoylphosphatidylethanolamine)

DC-chol
(3β [N-(N',N'-dimethylaminoethane)-carbamoyl] cholesterol)

Fig. 1. Chemical structures of DOPE and DC-chol.

Complexes of plasmid DNA and DC-chol/DOPE liposomes can be easily prepared by simple mixing. A plasmid containing a reporter gene such as *Escherichia coli* chloramphenicol acetyltransferase (CAT) *(5)*, β-galactosidase *(6)*, or luciferase *(7)*, under the control of a promoter of interest, is introduced into eukaryotic cells. Within a few days after transfection, the cells are harvested and the amount of reporter gene protein in the lysate is measured. This is usually done with a simple enzymatic assay. The transfection activity of the complex tested with many cell lines and primary cells depends on the cell type. Transformed epithelial cells such as epidermal carcinoma A431 cells, lung epithelial carcinoma A549 cells, embryonic kidney epithelium 293 cells, and airway epithelium IB3-1 cells are readily transfected, but fibroblast and endothelial cells are less efficiently transfected *(8;* unpublished data). Suspension cells including lymphoid cells are difficult to transfect using cationic liposomes, in general. Human ovarian carcinoma cells grown as subcutaneous solid tumors in SCID mice can be transfected by directly injecting plasmid DNA/liposome complex into the tumor. The level of reporter gene expression in the tumor cells was significantly elevated if the animal received a single ip injection of cisplatin 1 wk before the intratumor lipofection *(9)*. This observation may have a profound clinical implication as it suggests a sequential, combination therapy.

Because of the apparent safety and the versatility offered by liposomal delivery system, this technology has proven important in delivering DNA for therapeutic purposes in humans. The DC-chol/DOPE liposomes have been used in clinical trials for cancer *(10)* and cystic fibrosis transmembrane conductance regulator (CFTR) *(11)* gene therapy.

2. Materials

1. DC-chol/ DOPE (Avanti Polar Lipids, Alabaster, AL) liposomes (2 nmol/μL).
2. Plasmids pSV2CAT (constructed by Dr. Mark Magnuson, Vanderbilt University) or pCMVCAT (constructed by Dr. Hassan Farhood, University of Pittsburgh), pCMVβgal, and pRSVLuc at 1 μg/μL in TE buffer (10 mM Tris-HCl, pH 7.4, 0.1 mM EDTA) was amplified in *E. coli* and purified by CsCl gradient ultracentrifugation method *(12)*.
3. Sterile tissue-culture flasks and tubes, plates, and pipets.
4. Autoclaved Pasteur pipets, microcentrifuge tubes (1.5-mL), yellow and blue tips, phosphate-buffered saline (PBS).
5. Tissue-culture medium supplemented with penicillin (100 U/mL)/ streptomycin (100 mg/mL) (Gibco-BRL, Gaithersburg, MD) with or without 10% fetal bovine serum (FBS) (Hyclone, Logan, UT).
6. 0.05% Trypsin plus 0.53 mM EDTA in Ca^{2+} or Mg^{2+}-free sterile saline (Gibco-BRL).
7. Lysis buffer: 0.1% Triton X-100 in 0.25M Tris-HCl, pH 7.8.
8. 25-gage needle.
9. Tissue-Tearor Homogenizer (Biospec Product Corp., Bartlesville, OK).
10. Tumor extraction buffer: 40 mM Tris-HCl, pH 7.5, 10 mM EDTA, and 150 mM NaCl.
11. Mice of interest (animal care in accordance with the AAALAC guidelines).

3. Methods
3.1. Purification of Plasmid DNA

Growth of the bacterial culture, harvesting, and lysis of the bacteria, and purification of plasmid DNA were as described by Sambrook et al. *(12)*.

3.2. Tissue Culture Cells and in Vitro Transfection

1. Culture cells of interest in defined medium supplemented with 10% fetal bovine serum (FBS) at 37°C with 5% CO_2.
2. Trypsinize cells and plate them into 12-well plates the day before transfection such that the culture is 60–80% confluent.
3. Add appropriate quantity of cationic liposomes (10–20 nmol) to the bottom of a 1.5-mL microcentrifuge tube.
4. Add 1 mL plasmid DNA (0.5–2.0 μg) diluted with serum-free culture medium to the liposomes.
5. Incubate for 10 min at room temperature to form liposome/DNA complex.
6. Remove serum-containing medium from each well and wash the cells once with serum-free medium.
7. Add the liposome/DNA mixture to each well and incubate cells for 5 h at 37°C in 5% CO_2 (transfection).

8. Remove the serum-free medium and add 1 mL of serum-containing medium to each well.
9. Incubate the cells in 5% CO_2 for 1–2 d (posttransfection).
10. Remove serum-containing medium and wash once with PBS.
11. Add 200 μL of lysis buffer to each well and incubate 10–15 min at room temperature.
12. Collect the lysed cells in microcentrifuge tubes (ready for CAT, β-galactosidase, and luciferase assay as well as for protein assay).

3.3. Tumor Inoculation on Mice and Intratumor Transfection

1. Seed human ovarian adenocarcinoma 2008 cells *(9)* in 150-mm tissue culture plates and grow to confluency in complete medium.
2. Treat cells with trypsin-EDTA (Gibco-BRL), harvest, and wash with complete medium, and resuspend in sterile PBS at 2×10^7 cells/mL.
3. Inject 0.1-mL aliquots sc to the flanks and back of mice using a 25-gage needle.
4. Let solid tumors grow to about 8 mm in diameter.
5. Dilute 30 μg of pUCCMVCAT in 1X TE buffer with 100 μL of 5% dextrose and mix with 30 nmol of DC-chol/DOPE liposomes (3:2, mol/mol) in 20 m*M* HEPES buffer, pH 7.8. Total volume equals to 145 μL.
6. Incubate the mixture for 10 min.
7. Directly inject the DNA/liposome complex into the tumor in three different sites.
8. After 48 h, sacrifice the animal and excise the tumor.
9. Homogenize the tumor in extraction buffer.
10. Lyse cells by three freeze/thaw cycles.
11. Heat the lysate at 65°C for 10 min and centrifuge at 16,000*g* for 10 min.
12. The supernatant is ready for protein and CAT assay, or it can be frozen at –80°C for at least 7 d.

4. Notes

Different cell lines require different optimal liposome/DNA ratio and different total amounts of complex. Defining and optimizing transfection conditions are important. In vitro transfection protocol of DC-chol/DOPE liposomes should be optimized with respect to the ratio of liposome/DNA, dose of the complex, the incubation time with cells for transfection, and posttransfection, and serum concentration *(13)*. In vivo transfection of DC-chol/DOPE liposomes on tumor directly *(9)* should be optimized with respect to tumor size, number of injections on tumor, and injection volume and the ratio of liposome/DNA.

1. Effects of DC-chol and DNA on in vitro transfection activity are shown in Figs. 2 and 3, respectively. Both curves are bell-shaped, indicating that it is important to define the optimal concentrations of liposomes and DNA. The transfection efficiencies are different in two figures owing to different cell density at transfection *(see* ref. *3)*. The optimal ratio of DC-chol (nmol)/DNA (μg) is between 10 and 20 for a variety of transformed epithelial cells.

Fig. 2. The effect of DC-chol liposomes concentration on transfection activity. The CHO cells were transfected with 1 µg pRSVLuc DNA complexed with various concentrations of DC-chol liposomes (0–20 nmol) for 7 h and cells were harvested after 37 h for luciferase assay.

Fig. 3. The effect of DNA concentration on transfection activity. The CHO cells were transfected with 10 nmol of DC-chol liposomes complexed with various concentrations of pRSVLuc DNA (0–2.5 µg). Transfection and posttransfection conditions were the same as Fig. 2.

Fig. 4. The effect of DNA/liposome complex dose on transfection activity. The CHO cells were transfected with various doses of DNA/liposome complex (1:1, μg/nmol). Transfection and posttransfection conditions were the same as Fig. 2.

2. The in vitro transfection activity increases with the amount of liposome/DNA complex added to the cells. The effect of the complex dose on transfection activity is shown in Fig. 4 for a complex of liposome/DNA ratio of 1 μg/nmol. Note that this is a suboptimal ratio that allows transfections with high complex doses and minimal toxicity.

3. Cell density (the status of the cultured cells that are seeded on plate) is another factor for a successful transfection and high level expression of foreign DNA in vitro. The efficiency reduces greatly if transfection is performed on the confluent cells (*see* Fig. 5).

4. The toxicity varies among cell types, and is dependent on the confluency of the cell culture. Confluent cells are more resistant to the toxicity of the liposome/DNA complex. As a compromise between high transfection activity and low toxicity, cells with 60–80% confluency are the optimum.

5. Supercoiled DNA gives higher transfection efficiency compared to nicked, covalently closed, or linear DNA.

6. pCMVCAT (an expression plasmid of CAT gene under the control of CMV early promoter) is more efficient for high level of expression than pSV2CAT (an expression plasmid of CAT gene under the control of SV40 early promoter).

7. Use serum-free medium, or very low concentration of serum if cells are not stable for at least 4–5 h in the absence of serum since the in vitro transfection activity is strongly inhibited by the presence of high concentrations of serum component. The

Fig. 5. The effect of cell density on transfection activity. A431 cells $(0.1–10 \times 10^5$ cells/well) were seeded in six-well plate and incubated for 24 h. Cells were transfected for 4 h with 4 μg pUCSV2CAT and 40 nmol of DC-chol/DOPE liposomes in 2 mL of McCoy's medium without serum and then incubated for 36 h in complete medium. Cells seeded at $5–10 \times 10^5$/well reached 100% confluency at the time of transfection.

DC-chol liposomes can tolerate up to 2% FBS without significantly reducing activity *(4)*.

8. The DC-chol/DOPE liposomes and plasmid DNA should be sterile for in vitro tissue culture work.

9. Liposome/DNA complex should not be incubated for more than 15–20 min since prolonged incubation results in the formation of large complexes and reduced transfection efficiency.

10. Transfection on different-sized culture wells gives similar results when volumes were adjusted in proportion to surface area of the wells.

11. Transfectability decreases with increase in tumor size.

12. There is dose limitation of liposome/DNA complex: high dose (>complex of 300 μg DNA and 300 nmol DC-chol/DOPE liposomes) could result in tumor disruption.

13. More injection sites on a single tumor increases the transfection efficiency.

14. Best in vivo transfection is obtained when the ratio of liposome/DNA complex is 1 nmol/μg.

15. Tumors (size of 8–10 mm) have difficulty to take injection volumes of liposome/DNA complex greater than 200 μL.

16. Preinjection of cisplatin to mice 1 wk before lipofection greatly increases the transfection efficiency of solid tumors (*in situ* lipofection) *(9)*. Tumor cells taken from animals injected with cisplatin are also more transfectable in vitro as compared to cells taken from animals injected with PBS (Fig. 6).

Fig. 6. The effect of cisplatin on transfection activity of tumor cells. SCID mice bearing human ovarian 2008 tumor cells (sc solid tumor) were ip injected with cisplatin (5 mg/kg) or PBS (control). One week later, the tumors were excised and tumor cells were cultured and transfected in vitro with pUCCMVCAT DNA/DC-chol liposome complex according to the method described in the text.

Acknowledgments

This work is supported by NIH grants HL 50256, CA 59327, and DK 44935.

References

1. Felgner, P. L., Gadek, T. R., Holm, M., Roman, R., Chan, H. W., Weinz, M., Northrop, J. P., Ringold, G. M., and Danielsen, M. (1987) Lipofectin: a highly efficient, lipid-mediated DNA-transfection procedure. *Proc. Natl. Acad. Sci. USA* **84,** 7413–7417.
2. Hawley-Nelson, P., Ciccarone, V., Gebeyehu, G., Jesee, J., and Felgner, P. (1993) LipofectAMINE™ reagent: a new, higher efficiency polycationic liposome trans-fection reagent. *Focus* **15,** 73–79.
3. Behr, J. P., Demeneix, B., Loeffler, J.-P., and Perez-Mutul, J. (1989) Efficient gene transfer into mammalian primary endocrine cells with lipopolyamine-coated DNA. *Proc. Natl. Acad. Sci. USA.* **86,** 6982–6986.
4. Gao, X. and Huang, L. (1991) A novel cationic liposome reagent for efficient transfection of mammalian cells. *Biochem. Biophys. Res. Commun.* **179,** 280–285.
5. Sankaran, L. (1992) A simple quantitative assay for chloramphenicol acetyl-transferase by direct extraction of the labeled product into scintillation cocktail. *Anal. Biochem.* **200,** 180–186.
6. Lim, K. and Chae, C.-B. (1989) A simple assay for DNA transfection by incubation of the cells in culture dishes with substrates for β-galactosidase. *BioTechniques* **7,** 576–579.
7. DeWet, J. R., Wood, K. V., DeLuca, M., Helinski, D. R., and Subramani, S. (1987) Firefly luciferase gene: Structure and expression in mammalian cells. *Mol. Cell. Biol.* **7,** 725–737.

8. Gao, X. and Huang, L. (1993) Cationic liposomes and polymers for gene transfer. *J. Liposome Res.* **3,** 17–30.

9. Son, K. and Huang, L. (1994) Exposure of human ovarian carcinoma to cisplatin transiently sensitize the tumor for liposome mediated gene transfer. *Proc. Natl. Acad. Sci. USA* **91,** 12,669–12,672.

10. Nabel, G. J., Chang, A., Nabel, E. G., Plautz, G., Fox, B. A., Huang, L., and Shu, S. (1992) Clinical Protocol: immunotherapy of malignancy by *in vivo* gene transfer into tumors. *Hum. Gene Ther.* **3,** 399–410.

11. Middleton, P. G., Caplen, N. J., Gao, X., Huang, L., Gaya, H., Geddes, D. M., and Alton, E. W. (1994) Nasal application of the cationic liposome DC-Chol:DOPE does not alter ion transport, lung function or bacterial growth. *Eur. Respir. J.* **7,** 442–445.

12. Sambrook, J., Fritsh, E. F., and Maniatis, T. (1989) Plasmid vectors, in *Molecular Cloning: A Laboratory Manual,* vol. 1, Cold Spring Harbor Laboratory, Cold Spring Harbor, NY, pp. 1.33–1.52.

13. Farhood, H., Bottega, R., Epand, R. M., and Huang, L. (1992) Effect of cationic cholesterol derivatives on gene transfer and protein kinase C activity. *Biochim. Biophys. Acta* **1111,** 239–246.

24

Methods for the Use of Cytokine Gene-Modified Tumor Cells in Immunotherapy of Cancer

Zhihai Qin and Thomas Blankenstein

1. Introduction

The development over the past few years has shown that gene therapy has become a true perspective. By January 1994, 63 clinical gene therapy protocols (gene therapy or marker studies) have been reviewed and most approved by U.S. control committees. Of these, 13 aim at inserting and expressing cytokine genes in tumor cells in order to use such gene-modified cells as vaccines in cancer patients. This idea is based on mouse experimental models that showed that tumor cells transfected with a variety of cytokine genes were rejected in immunocompetent animals. Tumor rejection induced by the locally produced cytokine results from an inflammatory response at the tumor site. Several observations are remarkable: the high efficacy of local cytokines to induce an antitumor response in the absence of systemic toxicity; a surprisingly large number of cytokines possess antitumor activity in this assay (IL-1, IL-2, IL-4, IL-6, IL-7, TNF, LT, IFN-γ, MCAF, G-CSF, GM-CSF, IP-10); and in several models, cytokine-producing tumors were heavily infiltrated by T-lymphocytes that contributed to tumor destruction (for review *see* ref. *1*). The latter observation is interesting because T-cells can most specifically recognize and destroy tumor cells and are critically involved in tumor immunity. Consistently, in several tumor models, mice that were immunized by cytokine-gene transfected tumors also rejected the nontransduced parental tumor and occasionally were able to eliminate small preexisting tumor loads. Tumor immunity was dependent on T-cells. Thus, cytokine gene-modified tumor cell vaccines are thought to trigger a local immune response in cancer patients, which is directed against putative, so far unknown tumor antigens and which are effective against residual (presumably small) tumor loads (e.g., micro-

From: *Methods in Molecular Medicine, Gene Therapy Protocols*
Edited by: P. Robbins Humana Press Inc., Totowa, NJ

metastasis). It is important to note that these genetic approaches to cancer immunotherapy are the beginning of a developing field and still have to address some unresolved problems such as inappropriate presentation of tumor antigens by the tumor cells, tumor-induced immune suppression, tumor heterogeneity, or the question as to whether they are more effective than the previous attempts of immunotherapy. Currently, three cytokine gene therapy variations with IL-2, IL-4, TNF, IFN-γ, or GM-CSF genes are tested: transfected autologous tumor cells; transfected allogeneic tumor cells; and transfected autologous fibroblasts mixed with tumor cells as vaccine. In most cases, the cells are irradiated before injection. Results from these initial clinical trials do not exist yet.

The experimental procedure that has led to the aforementioned clinical trials is illustrated in Fig. 1. It includes rapid isolation of cytokine genes by PCR; cloning into eukaryotic expression vectors, either conventional or retroviral plasmids; gene transfer and expression of cytokine genes in tumor cells; and analysis of the tumorigenicity of the gene-modified cells in mice. Such an approach has been pursued with as many different cytokines and tumor cells as listed in Table 1 (*see* Note 1). In most experiments, retrovirus infection or electroporation was used for cytokine gene transfer. Here, protocols are given for detection of cytokines in the culture supernatant of transduced tumor cells, test of antitumor activity in vivo, and analysis of vaccine effects of cytokine producing tumor cells.

2. Materials

2.1. Animals

Mouse inbred strains syngeneic to most tumors used for gene transfection (e.g., BALB/c, C3H, C57BL/6, CBA, DBA/2) as well as immunodeficient BALB/c nu/nu (T-cell deficient) mice can be obtained from several breeding farms (e.g., Bomholtgard, Ry, Denmark). Usually, we use 6–8-wk-old female mice.

2.2. Cell Lines

The culture condition for the cytokine indicator cell lines is shown in Table 2. The culture media should be changed every 2–3 d. Cells grow best at concentrations between 1×10^4 and 5×10^5/mL. Suboptimal cytokine supply may lead to loss of factor-dependency.

2.3. Cell Proliferation Assay

1. D-PBS: Dulbecco's phosphate buffered saline.
2. RPMI containing 10% FCS.
3. 11.30 Ci/mmol ^{3}H Thymidine.
4. 96-Well U-bottomed plates.
5. β Counter.

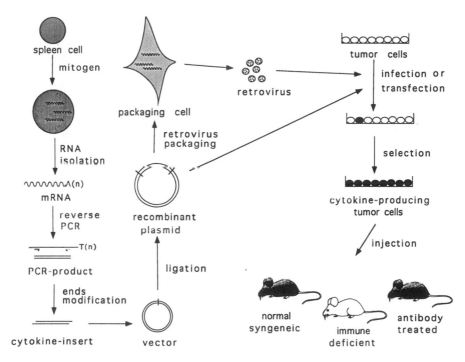

Fig. 1. Scheme for analysis of antitumor activity of local cytokines. Most cytokine cDNAs can easily be obtained by reverse PCR with RNA of mitogen-activated spleen cells and cloned into appropriate expression vectors. Gene transfer into tumor cells is done by either electroporation or retrovirus infection. In this chapter, protocols are given for the right lower part of the flow diagram: measuring biological activity of the transfected cytokine and analysis of local and systemic antitumor effects induced by the transfected cytokine in mice.

2.4. Cytotoxic Assay

1. RPMI/5% FCS.
2. Actinomycin D: 20 µg/mL.
3. Crystal violet solution: 0.5% crystal violet, 3% formaldehyde, 0.17% NaCl, 22.3% ethanol in water.
4. 33% Acetic acid, 1% Triton X-100.

3. Methods
3.1. Cytokine Detection

Cytokine production by gene-modified tumor cells is determined by cell lines in which proliferation is dependent on the exogenous cytokine or which are sensitive to the cytotoxic activity of a cytokine or whose phenotype changes

Table 1
Murine Tumor Cell Lines Used for Cytokine Gene Transfer *(1,2)*

Strain	Cell line	Type	Gene transfected
BALB/c	CMS-5	Fibrosarcoma	hIL-2, mIFN-γ, mGM-CSF
	C-26	Colon carcinoma	hG-CSF
	CT-26	Colon carcinoma	mIL-2, mIFN-γ, mGM-CSF
	J558L	Plasmacytoma	mIL-2, mIL-4, mIL-5[a], mIL-6[a], mIL-7, hIL-8[a,b], mTNF, hTNF[b], hLT[b], mIFN-γ, mMCAF[a,b], hM-CSF[a], mIP-10
	K485	Mammary adenocarcinoma	mIL-4, mIP-10
	RENCA	Renal cell carcinoma	mIL-4, mGM-CSF
	TS/A	Mammary adenocarcinoma	mIL-2, mIL-5[a], mIL-7, mIFN-γ, mIL-10[ab]
	X63	Plasmacytoma	mIL-2, mIL-4
C3H	MBT-2	Bladder carcinoma	hIL-2, mIFN-γ
	FSA	Fibrosarcoma	mIL-7
	1591-RE	Skin tumor, UV-induced	hTNF
BALB/c × C3H	4TO7	Mammary tumor	hIL-2
C57BL/6	203-glioma	Glioblastoma	mIL-7
	3LL	Lung carcinoma	m/hIL-2, mIL-4, hIL-6, mIFN-γ
	B16(-F10)	Melanoma	m/hIL-2, mIL-4, mIL-5[a], mIL-6, mIFN-γ, hTNF, mGM-CSF, hMCAF[a]
	EL4	T-lymphoma	mIL-2
	MCA-101	Fibrosarcoma	mIFN-γ [a]
	MCA-102	Fibrosarcoma	hIL-2, hTNF[a]
	MCA-205	Fibrosarcoma	hTNF, mIL-6
	MCA-207	Fibrosarcoma	mIL-6
CBA	Sp1	Adenocarcinoma	mIFN-γ
DBA/2	EB	T-lymphoma	mTNF
	ESB	T-lymphoma	mTNF[a]
	P815	Mastocytoma	mIL-2
	FLC	Friend leukemia	mIFN-γ
NFS/N	NIH3T3	Oncogene transformed	mIL-1
A/J	C1300	Neuroblastoma	mIFN-γ

[a]Indicates those cytokines whose expression in tumor cells did not reduce tumorigenicity; for all others antitumor activity was defined by either delayed tumor growth or tumor rejection of transfected tumor cells or by vaccine effects of modified cells.

[b]Unpublished observation. The letters h and m indicate human or mouse cytokine gene.

Table 2
Indicator Cells for Detection of Several Cytokines

Detected cytokine	Indicator cell line	Culture condition				Ref.
		Medium	FCS, %	2-ME	Cytokine[a]	
IL-2	CTLL-2[b]	RPMI-1640	10	50 μM	IL-2	3
IL-3	BA/F3[b]	RPMI-1640	10	No	IL-3	4
IL-4	CT.4S[b]	RPMI-1640	10	50 μM	IL-4	5
IL-5	B13[b]	RPMI-1640	10	50 μM	IL-5	6
IL-6	TEPC1033[b]	RPMI-1640	10	50 μM	IL-6	7
IL-7	IXN-2B[b]	RPMI-1640	10	50 μM	IL-7	8
GM-CSF	FDCP-1[b]	RPMI-1640	10	50 μM	IL-3	9
TNF	L929[c]	RPMI-1640	5	No	No	10
LT	L929[c]	RPMI-1640	5	No	No	10
IFN	WEHI3[d]	RPMI-1640	10		No	11

[a]50–100 U/mL (1 U is defined as the amount of cytokine required for half maximal proliferation of the indicator cells) are needed to ensure proliferation of the cells for a 3-d period at concentration of 1×10^4–5×10^5 cells/mL.

[b]Proliferation of cells is dependent on the growth factor. [^{3}H] incorporation is proportional to the amount of cytokine in the culture.

[c]Cells are sensitive to the cytotoxic activity of the cytokine. Cell death is proportional to the amount of cytokine in the culture.

[d]Cytokine induces MHC class II expression.

upon exposure to the cytokine to be tested. Alternatively, ELISAs for most cytokines are commercially available. Table 2 lists some indicator cell lines that can be used for detection of most immunotherapeutically relevant cytokines. A proliferation assay for IL-6, which is similar for other cytokines with the respective cells, and a cytotoxic assay for TNF/LT is given in Sections 3.1.1. and 3.1.2.

3.1.1. Protocol 1: Cell Proliferation Assay

1. Harvest exponentially growing TEPC1033 cells and wash three times with D-PBS.
2. Distribute 4×10^3 cells/well in 100 μL RPMI/10% FCS in 96-well U-bottomed plates (Costar, Cambridge, MA). Add 100 μL/well of serial dilutions of culture supernatant to be tested or IL-6 standard in triplicates.
3. For specificity control, incubate the test supernatant with an anti-IL-6 neutralizing antibody for 30 min at 37°C (most anticytokine antibodies are sold by several suppliers and should be used according to the instructions).
4. Incubate cells for 48 h at 37°C. Then, add 0.5–1 μCi/well of a [^{3}H]thymidine solution (NEN).
5. After 4 h incubation at 37°C, harvest the cells with a semiautomated apparatus and determine incorporated [^{3}H]thymidine in a β counter.

3.1.2. Protocol 2: L929 Cytotoxicity Assay for TNF/LT

1. Distribute 3×10^4 cells/well in 100 µL RPMI/5% FCS medium in 96-well, flat-bottomed plates and grow cells for 24 h.
2. Replace culture supernatant with 10 µL/well of a 20 µg/mL Actinomycin D solution and add 100 µL/well of dilutions of test samples, TNF standard, and controls in triplicates.
3. After 20 h incubation at 37°C, discard test supernatants and stain cells with 50 µL/well of crystal violet solution.
4. Wash plates with tap water thoroughly and dry for 30 min at room temperature.
5. Dissolve crystal violet bounded to surviving cells with 100 µL/well of a solution containing 33% acetic acid and 1% Triton X-100.
6. Measure $OD_{595\ nm}$ absorption against blank by an ELISA reader. To confirm specificity of cytotoxicity, incubate the test supernatants first with cytokine antibodies for 30 min at 37°C, and then determine the activity.

3.2. Analysis of In Vivo Antitumor Effect of Cytokines Produced by Transduced Tumor Cells (see Note 2)

1. Harvest exponentially growing cells (*see* Note 3) and wash two times with D-PBS.
2. Resuspend cells in D-PBS at concentrations that 0.2 mL contain one-, five-, and 10-fold the minimal tumorigenic dose.
3. Inject tumor cells in a 0.2-mL volume subcutaneously into mice at a shaved region that allows easy monitoring of the growing tumors. The following groups should be included and each group should consist of at least five animals:
   a. Syngeneic mice injected with increasing numbers of parental cells.
   b. Syngeneic mice injected with increasing numbers of mock-transfected cells.
   c. Syngeneic mice injected with increasing numbers of transduced cells producing different amounts of cytokine.
   d. Nude mice injected with parental cells and cytokine-producing cells.
   e. Syngeneic mice coinjected with a mixture of cytokine-producing and parental cells at different ratios (e.g., 1:1 and 1:10).
4. Monitor tumor size two times per week and record it as the mean value of the largest diameter and the diameter of the right angle (*see* Notes 4 and 5).

3.3. Analysis of Vaccine Effect of Cytokine Gene Modified Tumor Cells

This is the most critical step as it relates to gene therapy. The question is whether cytokine gene-modified tumor cells in some general form are able to serve as a vaccine that can protect mice from either a subsequent challenge with parental cells or even lead to elimination of small pre-existing tumor loads. One should keep in mind that some mouse tumor cells that have been used for vaccine experiments are inherently immunogenic before the genetic modification *(12)*. Thus, the protocol should be designed to conclusively attribute the vaccine effect to the transfected cytokine rather than to the immunogenicity of the tumor and to compare the strength of the vaccine effect to previous approaches of immunotherapy that have been already extensively tested in cancer patients (*see* Note 6).

1. Harvest exponentially growing cells (parental and cytokine-producing) and wash twice with D-PBS.
2. Resuspend cells in D-PBS in which 0.2 mL of cell suspension contain 5–10 times the minimal tumorigenic dose.
3. Inject tumor cells in a volume of 0.2 mL sc into the neck region of syngeneic mice (*see* Note 7). Include the following groups:
   a. Leave one group of mice untreated, as control.
   b. Parental tumor cells, irradiated (5000–10,000 rad, the dose that is required for prevention of in vivo growth may depend on the tumor cells).
   c. Parental tumor cells, irradiated, admixed with 100 µg formaline-fixed *Coryuebacterium parvum* (we have obtained it from R. North, Trudeau Institute).
   d. Parental tumor cells, viable, admixed with 100 µg formaline-fixed *C. parvum*. This group may be larger since we observed that part of the mice did not reject the tumor *(13)*.
   e. Cytokine-producing cells, irradiated.
   f. Cytokine-producing cells, viable (tumor rejection can be complete; however, it is influenced by the choice of cytokine, level of cytokine secretion, and the particular tumor) (*see* Note 8).
4. After 2–4 wk, challenge each five mice per group with one-, five-, and 10-fold the minimal tumorigenic dose of parental tumor cells sc at the belly region. Monitor tumor growth as described in Section 3.2.

4. Notes

1. It is important to note that several cytokines transfected into different tumor cells reliably acted tumor-suppressively (e.g., IL-2, IL-4, IL-7), whereas others succeeded in some but failed in other models to suppress tumor growth (e.g., IL-6) or even stimulated tumor growth/metastasis (e.g., TNF). Furthermore, the cellular mechanisms responsible for tumor rejection can differ for the same cytokine in different tumor models *(1)* and different cytokines may partly activate common cellular pathways in the same tumor model *(14)*. Tumor suppression was generally defined by host immune response and not by direct effects of the transfected cytokine on the tumor cells whose contribution, however, cannot be excluded (e.g., upregulation of MHC class I molecules by IFN-γ). Finally, antitumor activity was variously defined by partial or complete loss of tumorigenicity of transfected tumors or by the ability of transfected tumors to induce tumor immunity against challenge with the parental tumor. Often, the antitumor effect was proportional to the amount of cytokine secreted by the tumor.
2. Before gene transfer, inject tumor cells in increasing numbers into syngeneic mice (at least five per group) in order to determine the minimal dose for 100% tumor

take. A long period of in vitro culture of tumor cells may lead to change of tumor-igenicity. Passaging of tumor cells in vivo may prevent such phenotypic changes.

3. Prepare in parallel parental tumor cells, mock-transfected cells (vector without cytokine gene), and several clones producing varying amounts of the transfected cytokine in order to determine the dose dependency of the antitumor effect. Make sure that the gene transfer procedure or cytokine secretion has not changed the growth rate of the cells in vitro.

4. This relatively simple readout system for antitumor activity of cytokines is possible only for subcutaneously growing tumors. Some tumor cells are highly metastatic and require additional analysis of the respective organs *(15)*. Observation of mice over a longer period (up to 5 mo) is recommended because, under certain experimental conditions (e.g., in nude mice), tumors may grow out after a long latency period *(14,16)*.

5. Evidence that can clearly attribute an antitumor effect to the secreted cytokine: Tumor growth of mock-transfected cells has to be similar to that of parental cells. Tumor suppression should be proportional to the level of cytokine secreted by the different clones. Tumor growth of cytokine producing cells can be restored by parallel application to mice of cytokine-neutralizing antibodies *(17,18)*. Tumor growth of parental cells coinjected with cytokine transfectants is at least partially suppressed. Cytokine producing cells that grow as tumor after a certain latency period may have stopped cytokine production although the cells stably express the cytokine in vitro over that period *(14)*. Tumor suppression is more obvious in syngeneic compared to immunodeficient mice. For example, cytokine-producing tumors are completely rejected in syngeneic mice; in nude mice, however, they are initially suppressed but lately grow out in most cases. This, additionally, would indicate T-cell-dependent and -independent effector mechanisms responsible for tumor suppression *(14)*. Several investigators analyzed tumor growth in mice depleted for defined cell populations, like CD4, CD8, MAC-1, or asialo GM1 positive cells. In combination with immunohistochemical analysis of tumor tissues, this may give valid information of involved effector cells *(14,17,18)*.

6. Tumor cell vaccines have been tested in cancer patients for quite a long time. One frequently employed approach consisted in irradiated tumor cells admixed with adjuvants Bacille Calmette-Guerin or *C. parvum*. In animal models, such vaccines showed results comparable to those obtained by cytokine gene-modified tumor cells *(19)*; in cancer patients it was difficult to obtain reproducible therapeutic effects *(20)*.

7. Alternatively, vaccine cells were injected intraperitoneally. Whether the injection site influences the vaccine effect is not known.

8. The vaccine effect of viable seems to be superior to that of irradiated tumor cells *(13)*.

Acknowledgment

This work was supported by the Deutsche Krebshilfe, Mildred-Scheel Stiftung e.V. and the BMBF.

References

1. Blankenstein, T. (1994) Increasing tumor immunogenicity by genetic modification. *Eur. J. Cancer* **30A,** 1182–1187.
2. Colombo, M. P. and Forni, G. (1994) Cytokine gene transfer in tumor inhibition and tumor therapy: where are we now? *Immunol. Today* **15,** 48–51.
3. Gillis, S., Ferm, M. M., Ou, W., and Smith, K. A. (1978) T cell growth factor: parameters of production and a quantitative microassay for activity. *J. Immunol.* **120,** 2027–2032.
4. Palacios, R. and Steinmetz, M. (1985) IL-3-dependent mouse clones that express B-220 surface antigen, contain Ig genes in germ-line configuration, and generate B lymphocytes *in vivo. Cell* **41,** 727–734.
5. Hu-Li, J., Ohara, J., Watson, C., Tsang, W., and Paul, W. E. (1989) Derivation of a T cell line that is highly responsive to IL-4 and IL-2 (CT.4R) and of an IL-2 hyporesponsive mutant of that line (CT.4S). *J. Immunol.* **142,** 800–807.
6. Rolink, A. G., Melchers, F., and Palacios, R. (1989) Monoclonal antibodies reactive with the mouse interleukin 5 receptor. *J. Exp. Med.* **169,** 1693–1701.
7. Van Snick, J., Vink, A., Cayphas, S., and Uyttenhove, C. (1987) Interleukin-HP1, a T cell derived hybridoma growth factor that supports the *in vitro* growth of murine plasmacytomas. *J. Exp. Med.* **165,** 641–649.
8. Park, L. S., Friend, D. J., Schmierer, A. E., Dower, S. K., and Namen, A. E. (1990) Murine interleukin 7 (IL-7) receptor. Characterization on an IL-7-dependent cell line. *J. Exp. Med.* **171,** 1073–1089.
9. Dexter, T. M., Garland, J., Scott, D., Scolnick, E., and Metcalf, D. (1980) Growth of factor-dependent hemopoietic precursor cell lines. *J. Exp. Med.* **152,** 1036–1047.
10. Flick, D. A. and Gifford, G. E. (1984) Comparison of in vitro cell cytotoxic assays for tumor necrosis factor. *J. Immunol. Meth.* **68,** 167.
11. Coligan, J. E., et al. (1992) *Current Protocols in Immunology* (Coligan, J. E., Kruisbeek, A. M., Margulies, D. H., Sherach, E. M., and Strober, W., eds.), Greene and Wiley, New York, pp. 6.8.3.
12. Dranoff, G., Jaffee, E., Lazenby, A., Golumbek, P., Levitsky, H., Brose, K., Jackson, V., Hamada, H., Pardoll, D., and Mulligan, R. C. (1993) Vaccination with irradiated tumor cells engineered to secrete murine granulocyte-macrophage colony-stimulating factor stimulates potent, specific, and long-lasting anti-tumor immunity. *Proc. Natl. Acad. Sci. USA* **90,** 3539–3543.
13. Hock, H., Dorsch, M., Kunzendorf, U., Überla, K., Qin, Z., Diamantstein, T., and Blankenstein, T. (1993) Vaccination with tumor cells genetically engineered to produce different cytokines: effectivity not superior to a classical adjuvant. *Cancer Res.* **53,** 714–716.
14. Hock, H., Dorsch, M., Kunzendorf, U., Qin, Z., Diamantstein, T., Blankenstein, T. (1993) Mechanisms of rejection induced by tumor cell targeted gene transfer of interleukin-2, interleukin-4, interleukin-7, tumor necrosis factor or interferon-. *Proc. Natl. Acad. Sci. USA* **90,** 2774-2778.
15. Qin, Z., Krüger-Krasagakes, S., Kunzendorf, U., Hock, H., Diamantstein, T., and Blankenstein, T. (1993) Expression of tumor necrosis factor by different tumor

cell lines results either in tumor suppression or augmented metastasis. _J. Exp. Med._ **178,** 355–360.

16. Li, W., Diamantstein, T., and Blankenstein, T. (1990) Lack of tumorigenicity of interleukin 4 autocrine growing cells seems related to the anti-tumor function of interleukin 4. _Mol. Immunol._ **27,** 1331–1337.

17. Blankenstein, T., Qin, Z., Überla, K., Müller, W., Rosen, H., Volk, H.-D., and Diamantstein, T. (1991) Tumor suppression after tumor cell targeted tumor necrosis factor alpha gene transfer. _J. Exp. Med._ **173,** 1047–1052.

18. Hock, H., Dorsch, M., Diamantstein, T., and Blankenstein, T. (1991) Interleukin 7 induces CD4+ T cell-dependent tumor rejection. _J. Exp. Med._ **174,** 1291–1298.

19. Dye, E. S., North, R. J., and Mills, C. D. (1981) Mechanisms of anti-tumor action of corynebacterium parvum. I. Potential tumor-specific immunity and its therapeutic limitations. _J. Exp. Med._ **154,** 609–620.

20. Oettgen, H. F. and Old, L. J. (1991) _The History of Cancer Immunotherapy_ (DeVita, V. T., Helman, S., Rosenberg, S. A., eds.), Lippincott, New York, pp. 87–199.

25

Methods for Generation of Genetically Modified Fibroblasts for Immunotherapy of Cancer

Elaine M. Elder, Michael T. Lotze, and Theresa L. Whiteside

1. Introduction

Considerable evidence has accumulated indicating that cultured human or rodent tumor cells can be successfully transduced with cytokine genes and selected in the appropriate antibiotic–containing culture media. The selected transductants are generally able to secrete the cytokine coded for by the transduced gene, and in many cases, substantial levels (e.g., ng quantities) of the cytokine are produced. Using retroviral vectors, it has been possible to obtain stably transduced tumor cells with a variety of cytokine genes (1–4). These tumor cells have been used for immunotherapy of cancer in numerous animal models of tumor growth or metastasis, and more recently, in vaccination protocols in patients with cancer. One possible criticism that can be leveled at this type of vaccination approach is that cultured, genetically modified, and selected tumor cells might have phenotypic characteristics that are substantially different from those of unmodified tumor cells. Since retroviral vectors are often used for transduction, it is also possible that viral antigens expressed on transduced tumor cells contribute to the immune response generated as a result of vaccination. Also, primary cultures of human tumor cells are often difficult to establish and maintain.

To circumvent this criticism, an alternative approach to vaccination has been proposed, in which autologous fibroblasts are established and transduced with a given cytokine gene and serve as a source of the cytokine. Such transduced fibroblasts, when admixed with autologous irradiated tumor cells in a vaccine provide the cytokine needed for the effective generation of the specific immune response, one that is presumably directed at the tumor-associated antigens being presented on the tumor cells. The advantages of this proce-

From: *Methods in Molecular Medicine, Gene Therapy Protocols*
Edited by: P. Robbins Humana Press Inc., Totowa, NJ

dure are that autologous fibroblasts can be easily obtained and successfully cultured from nearly all patients, that autologous tumor cells need not be cultured prior to vaccination, and that gene transfer using retroviral supernatants is perfectly feasible using cultured human fibroblasts. In addition, tumor vaccines can be customized as desired by mixing a variable number of cytokine–producing fibroblasts with tumor cells, without a concern about adequate supplies of the former.

In this chapter, we describe the procedure for generation of human genetically–modified fibroblasts for clinical use in vaccination protocols. The procedure, which has been developed in our laboratory as a part of the ongoing IL-4 and IL-12 autologous fibroblast vaccination trials *(5–7)*, is broadly applicable, allowing for gene transfer of a variety of vectors, and it is feasible for utilization in any well-established cellular laboratory.

2. Materials

All reagents and materials used in the biopsy tissue processing, culture, and harvest of fibroblasts are sterile. All culture medium supplemented with growth factors is made fresh and used within 5 wk of preparation.

1. 0.25% (w/v) Trypsin + 0.02% (w/v) ethylenediamine tetraacetic acid (EDTA) in phosphate buffered saline (PBS). Store at –20°C. Thaw just prior to use.
2. Antimicrobial wash medium (Minimal Essential Medium + 5 µg/mL fungizone + 250 µg/mL gentamicin) Store at 4°C.
3. Minimal Essential Medium (MEM).
4. Human AB Serum pretested for adventitious agents (HABS).
5. Fibroblast culture medium (Fibroblast Basal Medium + 10% HABS + 250 ng/mL fungizone + 50 µg/mL gentamicin + 1 ng/mL human fibroblast growth factor-Beta + 5 µg/mL insulin). Store at 4°C. Use within 5 wk of supplementation.
6. 1% (w/v) Type 1 collagenase in MEM. Store at –20°C.
7. Retroviral vector supernatant, certified for clinical use to be free of replication-competent retroviruses. Store at –70°C. Thaw immediately prior to use. Do not refreeze.
8. Protamine sulfate.
9. 0.9% (w/v) saline for injection.
10. Geneticin (G418).
11. Sterile dissecting tools (scalpels, forceps, and scissors); sterile trypsininizing flasks and Petri dishes; T25, T75, and T150 sterile, plastic culture flasks; microplate carriers with T25 flask adaptors; sterile 2-, 5-, 10-, and 25-mL pipets; and sterile 1.8-mL cryovials.

3. Method

3.1. Outgrowth of Fibroblasts from Human Skin Specimens

To establish autologous dermal fibroblasts in primary cultures, human skin is first aseptically collected at surgical resection or biopsy. Approximately 10–

20 cm^2 of tissue are necessary to establish a fibroblast culture. Immediately after surgical resection, the skin is placed in antimicrobial wash medium in sterile containers. These should be prepared ahead of the resection and be available to the surgeon at the time the skin is obtained. It is necessary to label the containers with the patient's name, date of collection, and specimen type, including body site from which the skin was excised.

The tissue should be transported to the laboratory by hand, immediately after resection. A zippered specimen transport bag is used to transport the specimen, which is maintained at room temperature (24°C).

The skin is processed immediately after it arrives at the laboratory as follows:

1. If the skin was not transported in antimicrobial wash medium, transfer it to a container of antimicrobial wash medium and incubate the entire piece of skin for 30 min at room temperature.
2. Fibroblasts can be obtained by either outgrowth from small pieces of skin in explant culture or by enzymatic digestion of skin to yield a single cell suspension. To prepare skin for either explant culture or digestion, it is necessary to:
   a. Place the piece of skin in a sterile Petri dish. Cut off the outer edges of the skin with a scalpel and discard. Remove any attached fat with scissors and discard.
   b. Slice the trimmed piece of skin into small strips with scalpel and forceps, and carefully slice off the epidermis as well as connective tissue and discard. Place trimmed pieces in a separate dish. The best source of fibroblasts is the papillary region of the dermis.
   c. Mince into 2–3-mm pieces working quickly, so that the tissue does not dry out.
3. To establish explant culture, proceed as follows:
   a. Using dissecting tools, place 15–20 small pieces of trimmed skin 1–2 cm apart on the flat surface of T25 or T75 culture flasks. To improve adherence of tissue to the flask, pretreat the flat surface of the flask with HABS as follows: Add 1–2 mL of HABS to completely cover the plating surface of the flasks and incubate for 20–30 min in an atmosphere of 5% CO_2 in air at 37°C. Aspirate off any residual HABS and place the pieces of tissue on the flat surface of the flask.
   b. Stand the flasks on end in the incubator for 30 min in order to allow the pieces of skin to adhere to the surface of the flask.
   c. Remove the flasks from the incubator and carefully pipet 5–10 mL of fibroblast culture medium into the bottom of the upright flasks. Do not dislodge the tissue pieces as the culture medium is added.
   d. Return the flasks to the incubator with the flat surface down. This allows the culture medium to come into contact with the tissue pieces. Culture medium must completely cover the bottom surface of the flask, but not cover the tissue.
4. For preparation of a single cell suspension by enzymatic digestion, proceed as follows:
   a. Place pieces of skin into 125-mL trypsinizing flasks with 20 mL of 1% Type I collagenase.

b. Stir in a water bath at 37°C on a magnetic stirrer until the skin pieces are partially digested. Pour off the partial digest and add fresh enzyme solution as required. The digestion may be continued overnight.

c. Centrifuge the cell digest and wash the cell pellet once with MEM. Count the number of cells in a hemacytometer using a trypan blue dye solution and record the total number of viable cells and the viability as the percent of unstained cells.

d. Centrifuge the cell suspension and resuspend the pelleted cells in fibroblast culture medium. Plate the cells at $0.5-1.0 \times 10^6$ cells/mL in T25 or T75 flasks. Incubate at 37°C in an atmosphere of 5% CO_2 in air.

3.2. Culture of Fibroblasts

Once a fibroblast culture is established from explant or single-cell digest, the culture should be maintained continuously. Cryopreservation of fibroblasts at the early stage of culture (prior to second passage) is not recommended. When the cells are in the log phase of growth, they can be cryopreserved. When there are at least 1×10^6 cells in the log phase of growth, transduction with a retroviral vector is performed in order to introduce the gene of choice into the fibroblasts. The vector should contain a selectable marker gene, such as the neomycin phosphotransferase gene. Successfully transduced fibroblasts are selected in culture by exposure to G418, a neomycin analog, which is toxic to cells that have not integrated the vector containing the neomycin-resistance gene along with the gene of choice. As the culture proliferates, aliquots of the cells are cryopreserved at passage two or three (i.e., in the log phase of growth).

The fibroblast cultures are handled as follows:

1. Do not disturb explants for 5–7 d, and then observe under the microscope for the outgrowth of fibroblasts. Replace medium on d 7 and continue to monitor the culture.

2. Observe cultures initiated with enzymatically digested skin microscopically on the day after plating. Change the medium and continue to monitor the cultures.

3. When outgrowth is approx 80–100% confluent in the digest-derived cultures or when outgrowth is extensive and dense around explants, trypsinize and split the cultures as follows:

   a. Decant or aspirate (by pipet) the medium from the explant cultures, dislodge the explant tissue pieces, and discard.

   b. Add the trypsin-EDTA solution to the culture flasks so that the monolayers are covered. Use the following volumes as a guide: 2–3 mL/T75 flask; 3–3.5 mL/T150 flask.

   c. Let the flasks stand at room temperature for 3 min. Tapping the side of the flask against the palm of the hand will help to detach the fibroblasts. Extend the time of incubation in the presence of trypsin if the fibroblasts are not detached. Incubation at 37°C can be used to hasten the process of the fibroblast detachment.

   d. Remove the detached cells from the flask and place in a conical centrifuge tube. Rinse the flasks with MEM containing 10% HABS and add to the centrifuge tube. Serum is required to inhibit the action of trypsin.

   e. Centrifuge the cell suspension at 460g for 10 min. Resuspend the cell pellet in 10 mL of fibroblast growth medium. Count viable cells and record their number and viability.

   f. Adjust the concentration of cells in suspension as required for culture or cryopreservation.

   g. To split the cultures, add approx 5000 cells/cm^2 to the culture flasks. Add a total volume of 5, 10, 20, or 30 mL of cell suspension in fibroblast growth medium to a T25, T75, T150, or T225 flask, respectively. For example, 7.5 × 10^5 cells would be plated in a T150 flask.

4. Fibroblast cultures should be examined in an inverted tissue culture microscope every other day to monitor the rate of expansion and to detect any signs of poor growth or contamination.

3.3. Transduction and Selection of Fibroblasts

Cultured human fibroblasts in the log phase of growth are transduced with a retroviral vector containing a cytokine gene, such as IL-4, and a gene for selection, such as neomycin phosphotransferase. The successfully transduced fibroblasts are selected for resistance to neomycin by culture in the presence of G418, a neomycin analog.

1. When 2 × 10^6 primary human fibroblasts have been established in culture and are in the log phase of growth, they are prepared for transduction. At least 1 × 10^6 cells, representing approximately one–half of the total culture, are incubated in the presence of retroviral vector supernatant. A control (mock–transduced) culture is also established and treated exactly the same as the transduced cell culture except that medium instead of the retroviral supernatant is used.

2. To prepare fibroblast monolayers for transduction, trypsinize the cells and resuspend them in fibroblast culture medium. Plate the cells in T25 or larger flasks at 7500 cells/cm^2. Incubate at least 1–2 d to allow the fibroblasts to adhere to the plastic flasks and re-enter the log phase of growth.

3. When cultures are actively proliferating and are between 50 and 80% confluent, proceed with transductions as follows:

   a. Aspirate the culture medium and add a volume of the retroviral vector supernatant that will give a multiplicity of infection (MOI) of at least 1. The MOI is calculated according to the following formula:

titer of supernatant × volume of supernatant/number of fibroblasts

The titer of the viral supernatant is generally provided by the supplier. Add a total of 5 µg/mL protamine sulfate to the supernate used for transduction. The protamine sulfate is diluted 1:20 in 0.9% saline to prepare a working stock solution. A volume of the working stock of protamine sulfate is then added at a 1:100 dilution to the volume of viral vector supernate used for the transduction. This will produce a final 1:2000 dilution of protamine sulfate, which will give the required concentration of 5 µg/mL. For the mock transduced control culture, use an equal volume of 10% HABS in MEM with the protamine sulfate.

    b. Incubate the flasks for 2–3 h at 37°C in 5% CO_2 in air. Aspirate the viral supernatant and wash 3 times with MEM. Add fresh fibroblast culture medium and continue to incubate the cultures.

4. Selection of transduced fibroblasts in 0.05–0.1 mg/mL G418 should begin no earlier than 3 d after the completion of the transduction procedure. There should be evidence of proliferation of the fibroblasts after the transduction procedure before the cells are put under selective pressure. Alternatively, selection may begin following the first passage of the transduced culture.

5. Observe the selected fibroblasts daily. Within 1 wk of exposure to the G418, there should be evidence of cell loss owing to elimination of nontransduced fibroblasts in the flasks. The G418-sensitive fibroblasts will die and become detached from the plastic surface, leaving plaques or holes in the monolayer. These dead cells will be removed when culture medium is replaced or when the cultures are passaged.

    The selected cells must be monitored carefully. If there are any signs of widespread toxicity, recover the cells by removing the medium containing G418, wash the monolayers twice with fresh medium, and replace with fresh fibroblast growth medium.

    Continue to culture the cells in G418. The concentration of G418 in the culture may be gradually increased depending on the degree of toxicity in the culture.

6. Transduced and transduced-selected fibroblasts are now ready to be tested for the ability to produce the relevant cytokine, e.g., IL-4. Collect culture supernatant, centrifuge to clarify, aliquot in 1-mL volumes, and store in 2-mL microvials at –70°C.

7. The ability of the fibroblasts to produce the relevant cytokine is generally determined by an ELISA assay. Using the results of the ELISA assay, calculate the units or micrograms of the cytokine being produced by 1×10^6 fibroblasts in a 24-h period.

3.4. Harvest and Characterization of Fibroblasts for Adoptive Transfer

The preparation of gene-modified fibroblasts for use in adoptive therapy is generally adapted to the specific treatment protocol. The dose of cytokine delivered by the fibroblasts and the number of fibroblasts to be administered are the most important criteria to be considered in the harvest of the fibroblasts for adoptive transfer. The production of cytokine, for example, is measured by ELISA, and the quantity produced by the cultured cells is used to calculate the dose to be administered to the patient.

Prior to harvest and administration, several criteria for safety should be met. Safety testing is performed to document that the gene-modified fibroblasts in culture are free of replication-competent retroviruses as well as bacterial and/

or fungal contaminants. Cultures for aerobic and anaerobic bacteria, fungi, and mycoplasma are performed at least 2–3 d prior to fibroblast administration. Only the cultures that are negative for adventitious agents and free of endotoxin are accepted for adoptive transfer. S+/L– assays should be performed to document that the cells are free of helper virus.

On the day of fibroblast harvest for treatment, the cultures are tested by the Gram stain for the presence of bacteria. Fibroblasts that are free of bacteria by the Gram stain, are at least 90% viable, and produce adequate quantities of the specific gene product, are acceptable for transfer.

A general procedure for preparation of fibroblasts to be used in a vaccine protocol with autologous tumor cells includes the following steps:

1. Trypsinize the fibroblast monolayers, wash, count, and determine viability of the cells.
2. Save the supernatant from the transduced cultures and use it for the following assays:
   a. Quantification of a gene product by ELISA.
   b. Safety testing for bacterial and fungal sterility, endotoxin assay, and mycoplasma testing.
   c. Safety testing for detection of replication-competent retrovirus in S+/L– assays.
3. Save $2–4 \times 10^6$ gene-modified fibroblasts for detection by PCR of the envelope gene of the helper virus and for the marker gene, i.e., neomycin phosphotransferase.
4. Irradiate the cells with a total of 5000 rads to prevent proliferation in vivo. Wash the fibroblast preparation and resuspend in 0.9% sterile saline.
5. Remove a sample of the harvested fibroblasts for a STAT Gram stain test.
6. Reserve a small number of transduced fibroblasts (both irradiated and non-irradiated) and put into culture to demonstrate:
   a. Failure to proliferate after irradiation to rule out unrestricted proliferation.
   b. Quantification of the gene product after irradiation.
   The cultures are set-up in T25 flasks at 2.5×10^5 cells/flask in 5 mL of complete fibroblast growth medium.
7. The fibroblasts may be mixed with irradiated autologous tumor for vaccine preparation. The mixture is centrifuged and the pellet is resuspended in 0.1 mL of sterile saline for intradermal injections.
8. Aspirate the resuspended fibroblasts, with or without tumor cells, into a 1-cc syringe with a 27-gage needle. Label the syringe and deliver it to the clinic site for administration to a patient.

4. Notes

1. In our experience, enzymatic digests of skin yield better fibroblast cultures than those established from explants. Suspensions obtained by digestion of skin are easier to handle and easily yield rapidly expanding fibroblasts. Digest-derived cultures can be established within 10 d compared to 21 d for explant-derived cultures.

2. The success rate for establishment of fibroblast cultures is 96% in our experience. Samples obtained from some patient samples may not generate cultures at all or may not generate cultures with a logarithmic rate of growth. These cultures are not useful for viral transduction.
3. Selection in G418 should be done with care. Concentrations of 0.05–0.1 mg/mL should be used initially for selection. Once the fibroblasts have been under selective pressure for 1 wk, the concentration of the selective agent may be gradually increased to 0.2 or 0.3 mg/mL.
4. The production of a cytokine by fibroblasts will vary depending on the percentage of transduced cells in culture that express the gene. The selection process is critical for providing a culture enriched in successfully transduced fibroblasts.

References

1. Gansbacher, B., Zier, K., Daniels, B., Cronin, K., Bannerji, R., and Gilboa, E. (1990) Interleukin 2 gene transfer into tumor cells abrogates tumorigenicity and induces protective immunity. *J. Exp. Med.* **172,** 1217–1224.
2. Golumbek, P. T., Lazenby, A. J., Levitzky, H. I., Jaffee, L. M., Karasuyama, H., Baker, M., and Pardoll, D. M. (1990) Treatment of established renal cancer by tumor cells engineered to secrete interleukin-4. *Science* **254,** 713–716.
3. Gansbacher, B., Rosenthal, F. M., and Zier, K. (1993) Retroviral vector-mediated cytokine-gene transfer into tumor cells. *Cancer Invest.* **11,** 345–354.
4. Jaffee, E. M., Dranoff, G., Cohen, L. K., Hauda, K. M., Clift, S., Marshall, F. F., Mulligan, R. C., and Pardoll, D. M. (1993) High efficiency gene transfer into primary human tumor explants without cell selection. *Cancer Res.* **53,** 2221–2226.
5. Lotze, M. T. and Rubin, J. T. (1994) Gene therapy of cancer: a pilot dtudy of IL-4-gene-modified fibroblasts admixed with autologous tumor to elicit an immune response. *Hum. Gene Ther.* **5,** 41–55.
6. Tahara, H. and Lotze, M. T. (1995) IL-12 Gene therapy using direct injection of tumors with genetically engineered autologous fibroblasts. *Hum. Gene Ther.* **6,** 1607–1624.
7. Elder, E. M., Lotze, M. T., and Whiteside, T. L. (1996) Successful culture and selection of cytokine gene-modified human dermal fibroblasts for the biologic therapy of patients with cancer. *Hum. Gene Ther.* **7,** 479–487.

26

Methods for Gene Transfer to Synovium

Richard Kang, Paul D. Robbins, and Christopher H. Evans

1. Introduction
1.1. Rationale

Development of methods for gene transfer to synoviocytes was borne from the idea that gene therapy could be used to more effectively treat rheumatoid arthritis (RA) and other joint disorders *(1)*. Current pharmaceutical modalities in use against RA have limited effectiveness because of problems related to inefficient targeting of drugs to the joint, as well as inefficacies of the drugs themselves. Drug delivery to the joint by traditional oral, iv, and intramuscular routes, depends on passive diffusion of the drug from the synovial vasculature into the joint space *(2)*. Thus, high systemic concentrations of the drug are necessary to achieve therapeutic intra-articular drug levels; in chronic RA, perfusion of the synovium may be compromised *(3)*, driving required systemic drug levels even higher. This is of major concern, as the pharmaceuticals used to treat this disease are associated with serious side effects. Further compounding these problems is the chronic nature of RA, which requires lifelong treatment with high dosages of these drugs.

As understanding of the pathophysiology of RA has unfolded, many proteins have emerged as possible antiarthritic agents *(4)*. However, the use of such proteins is, as yet, impractical for several reasons. The biological activities of proteins do not survive oral administration. Many proteins have short half-lives in the circulation following injection, and, in any case, are not efficiently delivered to the joint for reasons alluded to above. For large molecules such as proteins, diffusion from the joint vasculature to the joint space is further compromised by the sieving effect of the synovium, through which passage falls as a function of molecular size *(5,6)*. Although the possibility of direct intra-articular injection could overcome these problems, new difficulties

From: *Methods in Molecular Medicine, Gene Therapy Protocols*
Edited by: P. Robbins Humana Press Inc., Totowa, NJ

would arise. Delivery by this method is unpleasant, not suitable for chronic administration, and the rapid clearance of proteins from the joint space *(7)* would require frequent administration to achieve a lasting therapeutic effect. Because of the risk of intra-articular infection, as well as the prohibitive expense of large-scale protein manufacture, intra-articular use of potentially antiarthritic proteins is not feasible.

The use of gene therapy to treat RA could overcome all of these problems *(1,4,7)*. In this method, synoviocytes, the cells that line the joint space, are transduced with a gene (or genes) that encodes a therapeutic protein (or proteins). In so doing, the joint becomes the site of synthesis of its own drug, thus eliminating the problems associated with targeting. The highest concentration of the drug is now found in the joint space, thereby markedly reducing the possibility of side effects caused by systemic administration. By its very nature, the use of gene transfer techniques taps the great potential of proteins as antiarthritic agents, and, with stable insertion and prolonged, regulated expression of the therapeutic transgene product(s), there is the potential for a constant and long-lasting therapeutic action that would, in essence, effect a cure.

1.2. Stategies for Gene Transfer to Synovium

There are two basic strategies for transfer of genes to synovium: the direct or in vivo approach, and the indirect or ex vivo approach *(1)*. The in vivo approach involves intra-articular injection of a vector to effect synoviocyte transduction *in situ*. Although this approach is more straightforward and less technically demanding, it is limited by presently available vectors. Retroviral vectors such as the Moloney murine leukemia virus derivatives are well characterized, and are by far the most commonly used vectors in human gene therapy trials *(7)*. However, they have not been effective when injected into joints, as these vectors require cell division for infection and integration, whereas synoviocytes *in situ* are generally mitotically quiescent *(1)*. Other vectors, such as adenovirus, adeno-associated virus, herpes simplex virus, and liposomes, which do not require cell division for transduction, have been limited in this approach by poor transduction efficiency, low levels of expression, transient expression, cytotoxicity, and immunogenicity *(8)*.

The ex vivo approach involves harvest of synovium, isolation and culture of synoviocytes, transduction in vitro, and reintroduction of transduced synoviocytes into the joint via intra-articular injection. As synoviocytes divide readily in vitro, retroviral vectors are effective in transducing these cells *(9)*. One major advantage to this approach lies in the ability to select for cells cotransduced with a selectable marker, such as *neo*[r] (neomycin resistance), thereby allowing reintroduction into the joint of a relatively pure population of transduced cells. Using the rabbit knee model, we have developed a method for gene transfer to synovial fibroblasts based on retroviral vectors and the ex vivo approach.

1.3. Synovium and Synovial Fibroblasts

Within the diarthrodial joint is a closed space defined by two tissues: synovium and articular cartilage. Synovium lines all the inta-articular surfaces of diarthrodial joint spaces except for those over the articulating ends of the bones that are covered by cartilage. It is a thin membrane, two-thirds of which, in normal rabbits, is covered by synoviocytes 1–3 cell layers thick overlying a relatively acellular subsynovial connective tissue that may be fibrous, adipose, or areolar depending on the anatomic location *(2,10)*. Unlike all other tissues that line body cavities, synovium lacks a basement membrane *(2,10)*.

Synoviocytes are a heterogeneous group of cells that consist of at least two distinct types. Type A synoviocytes resemble macrophages in their morphologic, physiologic, phagocytic, and antigenic characteristics *(10,11)*. Type B synoviocytes are fibroblastic *(2,10)*. The degree to which synovial fibroblasts differ from fibroblasts found elsewhere is unclear. However, human type B synoviocytes stain strongly for uridine diphosphoglucose dehydrogenase (a key enzyme in the synthesis of hyaluronan) *(12)* and are specifically labeled by a MAb 67 *(13)*. The existence of other distinct cell types in the synovium is the subject of controversy, although reference to a type C synoviocyte, which is of a morphology intermediate to that of type A and type B synoviocytes, has been made *(14)*. Of the different synovial cell types, however, only type B synoviocytes are found to grow in vitro after isolation and passage of cells from synovium *(10)*. Thus, our ex vivo method for the retrovirus-mediated transfer of genes to synoviocytes is based on the type B synoviocyte.

1.4. Synovial Cell Transplantation

Essential to the technique of gene transfer to the synovium by the ex vivo approach is a reliable means of synovial cell transplantation. We have found intra-articular injection of synoviocytes to be an effective method *(15)*.

As noted, the diathrodial joint is a closed space. Thus it is expected that intra-articularly injected particulate materials, such as synoviocytes, will engage the synovium. Cartilage, the other exposed surface within the joint, is impermeable to molecules larger than 80 kDa, and cells are unable to adhere to it *(10)*. Numerous studies have shown that particles of cartilage, dacron, carbon, gortex, metals, polymethylmethacylate, and mineral crystals injected intra-articularly are indeed captured by the synovium *(16,17)*. Particles smaller than approx 20 μm in diameter were phagocytosed, whereas larger particles were found lodged in the synovial interstitium. Further evidence to suggest that transplanted synoviocytes would be retained by the synovium is the expression on synoviocytes of cell surface adhesion molecules such as integrins, CD44, and intercellular adhesion molecule-1, by which synoviocytes normally associate with their extracellular environment *(2,18,19)*. Immunohistochemical studies using bromodeoxyuridine-labeled synoviocytes have confirmed that these intra-articularly injected cells are indeed captured by the synovium *(9)*. Whether transplanted synoviocytes migrate out of the joint is the subject of current study in our laboratory.

1.5. Gene Transfer to Synovium: The Ex Vivo Approach

We have developed an ex vivo approach for gene transfer to the synovium using the rabbit knee model. Through this technique, we have been able to transfer the gene encoding interleukin-1 (IL-1) receptor antagonist protein (IRAP) into rabbit knee synovium and study the effects of its in vivo expression on arthropathies resulting from intra-articular injections of interleukin-1β (IL-1β) *(9,20,21)*, a key mediator in the pathophysiology of arthritis, and on antigen-induced arthritis *(22)*. Additionally, we are developing a model for arthritis in the rabbit knee based on transfer of a gene encoding IL-1β to the synovium.

The first step in the ex vivo approach is the harvest of synovial tissue from one knee joint of the New Zealand White rabbit. A partial synovectomy is performed on an anesthetized rabbit by sharp dissection via the medial parapatellar approach. Synoviocytes are isolated from the harvested tissue by digestion in 0.2% (w/v) clostridial collagenase. This initial isolate contains a heterogeneous population of cells including type A and type B synoviocytes, macrophages, mast cells, and red and white blood cells. Subculture of this isolate in Ham's F12 medium supplemented by 10% fetal bovine serum and 100 U/mL penicillin and 100 μg/mL streptomycin eliminates postmitotic and nonadherent cells, leaving a homogeneous population of type B synoviocytes. These synovial fibroblasts are allowed to reach confluence and then are trypsinized and split at a 1:2 ratio. The subsequent split is at a 1:6 ratio in preparation for transduction. After this second split, cells are allowed to reach approx 60% confluency, at which time they are transduced by a retroviral vector. We have used the replication-defective retroviruses MFG and BAG, which are both derivatives of the Moloney murine leukemia virus *(23–25)*. If the vector contains a selectable transgene, such as *neo*[r], which codes for neomycin phosphotransferase, transduced cells can be selected by culture in media containing G418 (a synthetic neomycin analog). This step is performed by increasing the concentration of G418 incrementally, as our experience has shown that immediate placement of these primary synoviocytes in the final concentration of G418 (0.5 mg/mL) results in excessive cell death. At concentrations higher than 0.5 mg/mL, G418 is toxic to all of the synoviocytes regardless of successful transduction.

In preparation for autologous transplantation, the transduced, selected cells are trypsinized, washed three times in Gey's balanced salt solution (GBSS), and approx 10^7 cells are resuspended in 1 mL of GBSS. This cell suspension is injected intra-articularly into the rabbit knee through the patellar tendon. Experiments using radiopaque dye have confirmed the success of this technique and have established 1 mL to be a useful and safe volume for delivery of cells to the synovium *(10,15)*. Use of higher volumes entails risk of capsular rupture.

After the transplantation of transduced synoviocytes, synovial lavage fluid can be harvested to test for expression of secreted transgene products. Lavage is necessary because the rabbit knee joint contains insufficient synovial fluid for direct aspiration. The rabbit knee is lavaged with 1 mL of GBSS using the same approach for intra-articular injection of cell suspension. In our studies of transfer of the IRAP and IL-1β genes to the synovium, commercially available enzyme-linked immunosorbent assay (ELISA) kits were used to analyze the lavage fluid. Lavage fluid can also be analyzed for inflammatory cell counts (hemocytometry) and differentials (Wright's stain), glycosaminoglycan content (dimethylmethylene blue assay), and so on, by methods described elsewhere *(20,26)*.

Further analysis of the synovial tissue can be made after sacrificing the rabbit. Transgene expression can be checked in vitro by harvesting the synovial tissue, isolating and culturing the synoviocytes as outlined earlier in this section, and analyzing the supernatant for secreted transgene products. If marker transgenes, such as *neo*^{r} or *lacZ*, have been used for transduction, these cultured synoviocytes can be selected and/or stained, respectively. The *lacZ* gene codes for β-galactosidase, which allows cells that express this transgene to turn blue when stained using the X-gal technique *(27)*. This staining technique can also be applied to synoviocytes *in situ* although high background staining sometimes makes results of this analysis ambiguous *(9)*.

Presence of transgene and transgene mRNA can be assessed by isolating DNA and mRNA from synovial tissue using established methods with analysis by Southern or Northern blotting, by PCR or reverse transcriptase-PCR, or by *in situ* hybridization techniques.

2. Materials

1. Antibiotic: Cefazolin sodium (Ancef or Kefzol) 150 mg im.
2. Anesthetic: Pentobarital (Nembutal) 30 mg/kg iv and Isoflurane, 1 L/min inhalational.
3. Suture: Polyglycolic acid (Vicryl or Dexon) 4.0 with a cutting needle.

4. Gey's balanced salt solution (GBSS) (Gibco-BRL, Gaithersburg, MD) with 1% penicillin (stock 10,000 U/mL) and 1% streptomycin (stock 10,000 μg/mL) (P/S) (Gibco-BRL).
5. Phosphate-buffered saline (PBS) (Gibco-BRL).
6. Clostridial collagenase grade CLS (Worthington, Freehold, NJ) 0.2% in GBSS.
7. Trypsin grade TRL (Worthington) 0.2% in GBSS.
8. Polybrene (Sigma, St. Louis, MO): 8 mg/mL stock.
9. Glutaraldehyde (Sigma): 0.5% in PBS. Make fresh each use.
10. 1 mM MgCl$_2$ in PBS.
11. 5-bromo-4-chloroindolyl-β-D-galactosidase (X-gal) solution (Sigma): 750 μL X-gal (stock 40 mg/mL in dimethylformamide), 1500 μL/mL KC solution (stock 0.82 g K$_3$Fe [CN$_6$], 1.05 g K$_4$Fe[CN]$_6$ · 3H$_2$O), 30 μL MgCl$_2$ (stock 1M), 32.45 mL PBS (store at 4°C in the dark).
12. G418 (Geneticin) (Gibco-BRL).
13. Ham's F12 (Gibco-BRL) with 10% fetal bovine serum (grade: certified, does not require heat inactivation) (Gibco-BRL) and 1% P/S (Gibco-BRL).
14. Nylon monofilament mesh/45-μm pore size (Nytex).

3. Methods

3.1. Harvest of Synovium from the New Zealand White Rabbit

1. Administer preoperative prophylactic antibiotics to the rabbit.
2. Anesthetize the rabbit.
3. Shave, prep, and drape the knee using sterile technique.
4. Make a 3-cm medial parapatellar incision through the skin extending 1 cm below the joint line.
5. Continue the incision through the outer joint capsule, centering the incision between the patellar tendon and the medial collateral ligament.
6. Dissect the outer capsule from the subsynovial inner capsule superiorly as far as possible, inferiorly to the medial meniscus, medially to the infrapatellar fat pad, and laterally to the medial collateral ligament.
7. Lift the exposed subsynovial inner capsule and the attached synovium with fine-toothed forceps and excise (*see* Note 1).
8. Place the harvested tissue into GBSS.
9. Close the outer capsule over the exposed joint space with a running suture.
10. Close the skin with interrupted sutures.

3.2. Isolation and Culture of Synoviocytes

1. Place tissue into the inner compartment of a two-compartment digestion chamber (*see* Note 2) containing 10 mL of 0.2% (w/v) clostridial collagenase with constant stirring at 37°C for 2 h.
2. Use a 10-mL syringe with a 21-gage needle to aspirate the cell suspension from the outer compartment of the digestion chamber.
3. Centrifuge the cell suspension at 600g.

4. Decant the supernatant.
5. Resupend the cells in 4 mL of medium (*see* Note 3).
6. Incubate the cells in a T-25 tissue culture flask at 37°C in 5% CO_2 (*see* Note 4).
7. Replace media every 4 d.

3.3. Passage of Synoviocytes

Passage of the cultured synoviocytes should be performed when the cells reach confluence. The first split is 1–2. The second split is 1–6 in preparation for transduction.

1. Decant medium from the T-25 tissue culture flask.
2. Add 2.5 mL of 0.25% trypsin solution.
3. Swirl the trypsin solution over the cells 10 times.
4. Discard the trypsin solution.
5. Repeat steps 2–4.
6. Incubate the cells in the residual trypsin solution for 15 min at 37°C, monitoring the cells for detachment (*see* Note 5).
7. Add a volume of medium appropriate to the split ratio (e.g., if splitting cells of one T-25 flask 1–2, add 8 mL media).
8. Incubate the synoviocytes in T-25 tissue culture flasks at 37°C in 5% CO_2.
9. Replace media every 4 d.

3.4. Transduction of Synoviocytes

The synoviocytes are ready for viral transduction when they reach approx 60% confluence after the second split (*see* Note 6).

1. Decant medium from the flasks.
2. Add 1 mL medium containing 1×10^6 viral particles and 8 µg polybrene to each flask.
3. Incubate the cells with viral particles at 37°C in 5% CO_2 for 2 h, swirling culture every 20 min.
4. Add 3 mL medium.
5. Incubate the synoviocytes in T-25 tissue culture flasks at 37°C in 5% CO_2.
6. Replace media every 4 d.

3.5. Selection and Testing of Synoviocytes for Expression of Transgene

The following three procedures can be performed on synoviocytes isolated, cultured, and transduced prior to transplantation as well as cells isolated and cultured from synovium harvested after sacrifice.

3.5.1. Neomycin Resistance Selection

This procedure should be performed starting no sooner than 48 h after transduction of synoviocytes with a vector containing transgene coding for *neo*[r].

1. Replace medium with medium containing 0.25% G418.
2. Monitor daily for cell death and replace media as necessary.
3. Increase the concentration of G418 to 0.5% once cells have resumed growth (approx 2–4 d).
4. Monitor daily for cell death and replace media as necessary.
5. Repeat steps 3 and 4 once.

3.5.2. LacZ Expression

1. Aliquot 0.2 mL of cell solution into a 30-mm tissue culture grade Petri dish.
2. Add 0.8 mL medium.
3. Incubate cells at 37°C in 5% CO_2 for 48 h.
4. Rinse cells with PBS.
5. Fix cells with 0.5% glutaraldehyde at room temperature for 10 min.
6. Wash cells with 1 mM $MgCl_2$ at room temperature for 10 min.
7. Repeat step 6.
8. Stain cells with X-gal solution at 37°C overnight (min. 2 h).
9. Replace X-gal solution with PBS.
10. Plates may be stored at 4°C for at least 2 wk.

3.5.3. Testing for Cytokine Production

This testing may be performed 3 d after transduction of synoviocytes.

1. Harvest an aliquot of supernatant from the cell culture.
2. Perform ELISA and/or bioassay.

3.6. Preparation of Synoviocytes for Transplantation

1. Trypsinize the cells once they reach confluence as outlined in Section 3.3.
2. Wash the cells 3X in GBSS.
3. Resuspend cells at 10^7 cells/mL in GBSS.

3.7. Transplantation of Cultured Transduced Synoviocytes

In an autograft procedure, the cultured transduced synoviocytes should be reimplanted into the contralateral (unoperated) knee.

1. Hold the rabbit firmly in a supine position with the knees in approx 30° of flexion.
2. Slowly inject 10^7 synoviocytes in 1 mL GBSS through the patellar tendon into the joint space of the knee using a 1-mL tuberculin syringe with a 26.5-gage needle (*see* Notes 7 and 8).

3.8. Post-Transplantation Testing

3.8.1. Joint Lavage

1. Hold rabbit firmly in supine position with knees in approx 30° of flexion.
2. Slowly nject 1 mL GBSS through the patellar tendon into the joint space of the knee using a 1 mL tuberculin syringe with a 26.5-gage needle.

3. Flex and extend the knee several times through its full range of motion.
4. Aspirate the knee using the same approach, syringe, and needle as in the injection (*see* Note 9).

3.8.2. Harvesting and Testing of Synovium

1. Sacrifice the rabbit.
2. Reflect skin from the knee.
3. Separate the knee from the rabbit at the level of the midfemur proximally and the midtibia distally.
4. Transect the patellar tendon at its insertion into the tibial tubercle.
5. Reflect the patellar tendon superiorly to expose the joint capsule.
6. Incise the capsule transversely at its inferior aspect.
7. Continue this incision longitudinally on the medial and lateral aspects of the capsule while maintaining tension superiorly on the patellar tendon to expose the synovium.
8. Sharply excise the exposed synovium.
9. Isolate and culture synoviocytes as outlined in Section 3.2.
10. Select and test as outlined in Section 3.5.
11. Additional analyses of synovium can be made. These include Southern and Northern blotting, PCR, and reverse transcriptase-PCR on DNA and mRNA isolated from synovium to check for presence of transgene and transgene mRNA, respectively. Sections of synovium can be analyzed by *in situ* hybridization and immunohistochemistry, as well as by more traditional histological methods.

4. Notes

1. If the yield of synoviocytes from the harvested synovial tissue is poor, the surgical technique may be at fault. The synovium has a strong tendency to retract when cut. Therefore, it is important to grasp securely the inner capsule, and with it the synovium, while excising this tissue. A useful trick is to make a small (2 mm) transverse incision inferiorly, then slide one point of the forceps into the joint space so that the synovium and inner capsule are sandwiched between the points of the forceps. The tissue is then excised without releasing the tissue, thus preventing retraction of the synovium.
2. The two-compartment digestion chamber is described in detail by Green *(28)*. The purpose of its use is to separate the cells from extracellular debris. In lieu of this technique, synovial tissue may be digested in a single chamber vessel under the same conditions as described in Section 3.2. and filtered through a nylon monofilament mesh of 45-μm pore size.
3. When resuspending cells, use only the smallest amount of medium possible initially to prevent formation of clumps of cells, which are difficult to separate once formed.
4. Given the relatively low number of synoviocytes isolated from the small synovial harvest and the relative "fragility" of these cells after isolation by collagenase digestion, it is best to leave the cells undisturbed for 48 h to allow maximal adherence to the tissue culture flask.

5. During trypsinization, synoviocytes will lose the stellate/dendritic morphology that they possess in adherence, and assume a rounded shape. The cells initially will detach in clumps of rounded cells; allow the majority of cells to separate from each other before stopping trypsinization.

6. Synoviocytes are transduced with multiple transgenes by use of retroviral vectors containing multiple transgenes or by sequential transduction by multiple retroviral vectors. In sequential transduction, the second transduction should be made following selection, when applicable, and passage after the first transduction.

7. The depth of the needle stick should not exceed 1 cm during intra-articular injection, and depression of the syringe plunger should meet with little or no resistance. Resistance to advancement of the syringe plunger indicates that the tip of the needle is not in the joint space.

8. As the synovium is a well-innervated structure, intra-articular injection can be painful, especially if done rapidly. Intra-articular injection of a 1-mL vol should take 10–15 s.

9. It often requires considerable practice to retrieve a useful volume of the injected GBSS during joint lavage. The needle should not be inserted too deeply, otherwise it will penetrate the posterior capsule and may lacerate the popliteal artery. Firm massage of the suprapatellar, infrapatellar, and lateral aspects of the knee during aspiration helps to increase the amount of fluid recovered; in general, it should be possible to recover ≥ 0.5 mL of fluid. When knees are badly inflamed, lavage is often difficult because of the presence of large numbers of leukocytes, fibrin, and other debris in the joint. Under such conditions, the only recourse is to sacrifice the animal and recover the GBSS surgically.

References

1. Bandara, G., Robbins, P. D., Georgescu, H. I., Mueller, G. M., Glorioso, J. C., and Evans, C. H. (1992) Gene transfer to synoviocytes: prospects for gene treatment of arthritis. *DNA Cell Biol.* **11,** 227–231.

2. Hung, G. L. and Evans, C. H. (1994) Synovium, in *Knee Surgery* (Fu, F. H., Harner, C. D., and Vince, K. G., eds.), Williams and Wilkins, Baltimore, MD, pp. 141–154.

3. Stevens, C. R., Blake, D. R., Merry, P., Revell, P. A., and Levick, J. R. (1991) A comparative study by morphometry of the microvasculature in normal and rheumatoid synovium. *Arthritis Rheum.* **36,** 1508–1513.

4. Evans, C. H. and Robbins, P. D. (1994) Prospects for treating arthritis by gene therapy. *J. Rheum.* **21,** 779–782.

5. Levick, J. R. (1981) Permeability of rheumatoid and normal human synovium to specific plasma proteins. *Arthritis Rheum.* **24,** 1550–1560.

6. Wallis, W. J., Simkin, P. A., and Nelp, W. B. (1987) Protein traffic in human synovial effusions. *Arthritis Rheum.* **30,** 57–63.

7. Evans, C. H. and Robbins, P. D. (1994) Gene therapy for arthritis, in *Gene Therapeutics: Methods and Applications of Direct Gene Transfer* (Wolff, J. A., ed.), Birkhäuser, Boston, pp. 320–343.

8. Nita, I., Galea-Lauri, J., Georgescu, H. I., Mueller, G., Gao, X., Huang, L., Glorioso, J. C., Robbins, P. D., and Evans, C. H. (1994) Direct gene transfer to synovium. *Transactions of the 40th Annual Meeting of the Orthopaedic Research Society* **19**, 479.

9. Bandara, G., Mueller, G. M., Galea-Lauri, J., Tindal, M. H., Georgescu, H. I., Suchanek, M. K., Hung, G. L., Glorioso, J. C., Robbins, P. D., and Evans, C. H. (1993) Intraarticular expression of biologically active interleukin 1-receptor-antagonist protein by *ex vivo* gene transfer. *Proc. Natl. Acad. Sci. USA* **90**, 10,764–10,768.

10. Hung, G. L., Robbins, P. D., and Evans, C. H. (1994) Synovial Cell Transplantation, in *Methods in Cell Transplantation* (Ricordi, C., ed.), R. G. Landes, pp. 227–234.

11. Revell, P. A. (1989) Synovial lining cells. *Rheumatol. Int.* **9**, 49–51.

12. Wilkinson, L. S., Pitsillides, A. A., Worrall, J. J., and Edwards, J. C. W. (1992) Light microscopic characterization of the fibroblast-like synovial intimal cell (synoviocyte). *Arthritis Rheum.* **35**, 1179–1184.

13. Stevens, C. R., Mapp, P. I., and Revell, P. A. (1988) A monoclonal antibody (MAb 67) marks type B synoviocytes. *Rheumatol. Int.* **10**, 103–106.

14. Kinsella, T. D., Baum, J., and Ziff, M. (1970) Studies of isolated synovial lining cells of rheumatoid and non-rheumatoid synovial membranes. *Arthritis Rheum.* **13**, 734–742.

15. Evans, C. H., Bandara, G., Mueller, G., Robbins, P. D., Glorioso, J. C., and Georgescu, H. I. (1992) Synovial cell transplants for gene transfer to joints. *Transplantation Proc.* **24**, 2966.

16. Evans, C. H., Mazzocchi, R. A., Nelson, D. D., and Rubash, H. E. (1984) Experimental arthritis induced by intraarticular injection of allogeneic cartilaginous particles into rabbit knees. *Arthritis Rheum.* **27**, 200–207.

17. Olson, E. J., Kang, J. D., Fu, F. H., Georgescu, H. I., Mason, C. G., and Evans, C. H. (1988) The biochemical and histological effects of artificial ligament wear particles: *in vitro* and *in vivo* studies. *Am. J. Sports Med.* **16**, 558–570.

18. Haynes, B. F., Hale, L. P., Patton, K. L., Martin, M. E., and McCallum, R. M. (1991) Measurement of an adhesion molecule as an indicator of inflammatory disease activity: up-regulation of the receptor for hyaluronan (CD44) in rheumatoid arthritis. *Arthritis Rheum.* **34**, 1436–1443.

19. Galea-Lauri, J., Wilkinson, J. M., and Evans, C. H. (1993) Characterization of monoclonal antibodies against CD44: evidence of a role for CD44 in modulating synovial metabolism. *Mol. Immunol.* **30**, 1383–1392.

20. Hung, G. L., Galea-Lauri, J., Mueller, G. M., Georgescu, H. I., Larkin, L. A., Suchanek, M. K., Tindal, M. H., Robbins, P. D., and Evans, C. H. (1994) Suppression of intra-articular responses to inerleukin-1 by transfer of the interleukin-1 receptor antagonist gene to synovium. *Gene Ther.* **1**, 64–69.

21. Evans, C. H. and Robbins, P. D. (1994) The interleukin-1 receptor antagonist and its delivery by gene transfer. *Receptor* **4**, 9–15.

22. Ohtani, K. and Evans, C. H. Manuscript in preparation.

23. Ohashi, T., Boggs, S., Robbins, P. D., Bahnson, A., Patrene, K., Wei, F. S., Wei, J. F., Li, J., Lucht, L., Fei, Y., Clark, S., Kimak, M., He, H., Mowery-Rushton, P., and Barranger, J. A. (1992) Efficient transfer and sustained high expression of the human glucocerebrosidase gene in mice and their functional macrophages following transplantation of bone marrow transduced by a retroviral vector. *Proc. Natl. Acad. Sci. USA* **89,** 11,332–11,336.

24. Dranoff, G., Jaffee, E., Lazenby, A., Golumbek, P., Levitsky, H., Brose, K., Jackson, V., Hamada, H., Pardoll, D., and Mulligan, R. C. (1993) Vaccination with irradiated tumor cells engineered to secrete murine granulocyte-macrophage colony-stimulating factor stimulates potent, specific, and long-lasting anti-tumor immunity. *Proc. Natl. Acad. Sci. USA* **90,** 3539–3543.

25. Price, J., Turner, D., and Cepko, C. (1987) Lineage analysis in the vertebrate nervous system by retrovirus-mediated gene transfer. *Proc. Natl. Acad. Sci. USA* **84,** 156–160.

26. Farndale, R. W., Buttle, D. J., and Barrett A. J. (1986) Improved quantitation and discrimination of sulfated glycosaminoglycans by use of methylene blue. *Biochem. Biophys. Acta* **883,** 173–177.

27. Sanes, J. R., Rubenstein, J. L. R., and Nicolas, J. F. (1986) Use of a recombinant retrovirus to study post-implantation cell lineage in mouse embryos. *EMBO J.* **5,** 3133–3142.

28. Green, W. T., Jr. (1971) Behavior of articular chondrocytes. *Clin. Orthop.* **75,** 248–260.

27

Methods for Adenovirus-Mediated Gene Transfer to Synovium In Vivo

Blake J. Roessler

1. Introduction

The synovial membrane that lines diarthrodial joints is composed of a loose layer of cells (1–4 cells in depth) that overlie the surface of articular and periarticular subsynovial tissues including connective tissue, adipose tissue, tendon, bone, and articular cartilage. Using light microscopy, the synovial lining tissue appears discontinuous and lacks a clearly defined basement membrane, although the cells appear to be retained by a reticulum. Cells present below this membrane include mast cells and endothelial cells (up to 10% of the total cell population; refs. *1,2*). Ultrastructural studies of the synovium have indicated that at least two major types of cells are present within the synovial membrane. Type A cells are monocytoid in appearance and contain abundant endoplasmic reticulum with fewer vesicles, vacuoles, and mitochondria. Type B cells are fibroblastoid in appearance and contain large granules, numerous filopodia, mitochondria, and intracellular vesicles. The percentage of Type A and B cells present within adult synovium varies between species (*3–5*). In addition, cells with an intermediate ultrastructural appearance and morphology may exist within adult synovium (*6*).

The synovial membrane is a multifunctional mesothelium that participates in multiple aspects of joint physiology and host immunity in both normal and disease states. Synoviocytes produce and secrete a variety of high-mol-wt glycosaminoglycans, principally hyaluronate, that provide joint fluid with its appropriate mechanical properties of lubrication and force distribution (*7,8*). Synoviocytes also can express an extensive panel of proinflammatory cytokines (*9–12*). It has also been established that the expression of a series of cell adhesion molecules by synoviocytes is important in the recruitment and activation

From: *Methods in Molecular Medicine, Gene Therapy Protocols*
Edited by: P. Robbins Humana Press Inc., Totowa, NJ

of circulating lymphocytes into the synovium in diseases such as rheumatoid arthritis (*13*). Synoviocytes can also function as antigen-presenting cells in the context of both MHC I- and MHC-II-type receptors (*6*).

Thus it can be seen that the alteration of synoviocyte biology using gene transfer has potential applications for the pathophysiological analysis, and perhaps treatment, of a wide variety of articular diseases. Similar to many other organ systems, gene transfer to synovium can be accomplished using either ex vivo or in vivo techniques. In specific applications, the use of intra-articular injection techniques to access the joint space for the direct transduction of the complex epithelium that we refer to as synovium may have potential advantages over the use of isolation of synovial cells in culture for ex vivo transduction. Therefore, we have chosen to focus our efforts on the development of specific techniques that will improve our ability to target synoviocytes for gene transfer in vivo using recombinant adenoviral vectors (*14*).

Because of its relatively large size, the knee joint represents a convenient model system for the analysis of gene transfer to the synovial membrane. In addition, well-described animal models of synovitis can be induced within the knee joint and provide the investigator with an in vivo model that can be defined in both time and space and be applied to the analysis of transduced synovial cell biology. Among these are models of adjuvant-induced arthritis in both rats and rabbits (*15–17*). The reader is referred to cited references for a more comprehensive description of these animal models. The advantages of these adjuvant models are that the severity of synovitis in a specific knee joint can be modulated, and that one knee can be used as an internal control that allows for comparative analysis of biological effect within a given animal.

Although best applied to the analysis of transduced synovium within the knee joint, the methods described herein can be applied to the study of the synovial membrane present in any joint space that can be accessed using an open-bore needle that will allow the introduction of recombinant adenoviral suspension into the joint cavity.

2. Materials

2.1. Animal Strains

Male or female New Zealand White Rabbits 2.0–2.5 kg in weight are used for these experiments. Female Lewis rats 100 g in weight are also used for these experiments.

2.2. Solutions

1. Phosphate-buffered saline (PBS) is used to dilute recombinant adenovirus immediately before intra-articular injection and is used for intra-articular lavage. (12.2 g NaCl, 0.27 g KCl, 1.92 g $Na_2HPO_4 \cdot 2H_2O$, 0.34 g KH_2PO_4, double distilled water to 2 L, autoclave prior to use.)

2. A Sephadex G50 (Pharmacia, Uppsala, Sweden) column in PBS buffer is used to desalt the recombinant adenoviral suspension after purification by CsCl gradient ultracentrifugation.
3. Providone/iodine is used to disinfect the periarticular skin surface.
4. 10% neutral-buffered formalin v/v, pH 7.0 (Richard-Allan Medical, Richland, MI) is used to fix representative samples of synovial tissue.
5. OCT (Sigma, St. Louis, MO) is used to embed representative samples of synovial tissue by quick freezing in dry ice/ethanol.
6. Cal-rite (Richard-Allan Medical) is used to decalcify representative samples of bone and cartilage.

2.3. Equipment

Twenty-seven-gage sterile disposable hypodermic needles 0.5 inch in length (Becton Dickinson, Rutherford, NJ) are used for intra-articular injections in rabbits; 30-gage multiuse needles 0.25 in. in length (Becton Dickinson) are used for intra-articular injections in rats and are autoclaved prior to use.

3. Methods

3.1. Determination of Viral Particle Number

Freshly prepared suspensions of recombinant adenoviral particles are spectrophotometrically analyzed at 260 nm in order to determine the number of viral particles/mL. Absorbance times dilution $\times 10^2$ approximates the number of adenoviral particles/mL. Additional plaque assays must be performed on fresh aliquots of these preparations in order to verify the number of plaque forming units (PFU) per mL (*18*). A range of doses based on particles/mL or total number of particles/joint can be used for these experiments. Generally, we have used doses in the range of 10^9–10^{12} particles/mL (*4*). However, the optimal dose for any particular series of experiments must be determined empirically, and is dependent on both the properties of the recombinant adenoviral genomic backbone being used and the biology of the transgene being expressed.

3.2. Intra-articular Injections

3.2.1. Rabbits

Rabbits are anesthetized using a single intramuscular dose of ketamine/xylazine (40 mg/kg ketamine, 7.5 mg/kg xylazine). The area surrounding the knees is shaved and cleaned with a providone/iodine solution. Freshly prepared recombinant adenoviral suspension is then placed into a 1-cc syringe and a 27-gage needle is attached to the syringe. The inferior margin of the patella is identified by palpation and the joint space is entered in an anterior-posterior plane. The needle is advanced until the hub contacts the overlying skin and the suspension (total volume of 0.5 cc/knee) is then slowly introduced into the joint space over a period of 30 s.

3.2.2. Rats

Rats are anesthetized using a single intramuscular dose of ketamine/ xylazine. The area surrounding the knees is shaved and cleaned with a providone/iodine solution. Fresh recombinant adenoviral suspension is then placed into a 1-cc syringe and a 30-gage needle is attached to the syringe. The knee is held in 30° of flexion and the inferior margin of the patella is identified by palpation; the joint space is entered in an anterior-posterior plane. The needle is advanced until the hub contacts the overlying skin and the suspension (total volume of 0.1 cc/knee) is then slowly introduced into the joint space.

3.3. Analysis of Transduced Synovium

3.3.1. Rabbits

Rabbits are euthanized using approved techniques and the skin surrounding the knee is sharply dissected away from underlying fascia.

3.3.1.1. INTRA-ARTICULAR LAVAGE

Using a scalpel, an incision is made along the medial aspect of the patellofemoral ligament from the tibial plateau to the superior margin of the patella. The patellofemoral ligament is reflected laterally and the joint space is exposed. The joint space is lavaged with 1–2 cc of PBS in 0.5-mL aliquots and the lavage fluid is aspirated from the joint cavity using a disposable transfer pipet. Cellular debris are removed by centrifugation and the recovered lavage fluid is frozen at –70°C until use.

3.3.1.2. ISOLATION OF ARTICULAR TISSUE AND SYNOVIUM

In order to provide a method to ensure that comparable samples of synovium are recovered from each experimental animal, a section of the patellofemoral ligament is removed *en bloc*. After intra-articular lavage has been completed, the patellofemoral ligament is transected along its insertion onto the tibial plateau and then incised along the lateral aspect of the ligament. The entire patellofemoral ligament is then transected 1 cm above the superior margin of the patella. Using sharp dissection, this rectangular section of tissue can be subdivided into smaller samples that are frozen in O.C.T. compound embedding medium (Tissue-Tek, Miles Inc., Elkhart, NJ) or placed directly into 10% buffered formalin. Sections obtained from these tissue blocks can then be analyzed using standard histologic and immunohistologic techniques.

3.3.2. Rats

Rats are euthanized using approved techniques and the skin surrounding the knee is sharply dissected away from the underlying tissue.

3.3.2.1. ISOLATION OF ARTICULAR TISSUE AND SYNOVIUM

Using sharp dissection, the entire knee joint, including periarticular muscle and fascia, is removed *en bloc*. A circumferential incision to the level of periosteum is made approx 1.5 cm above and below the superior and inferior margins of the knee joint. Using heavy scissors or a saw blade, the femur is transected 1 cm above the superior margin of the patella and the tibia/fibula are transected 1 cm below the tibial plateau. The entire block of tissue can then be immersed in 10% buffered formalin. Following decalcification using conventional methods, the sample can be divided into representative tissue blocks that can then be analyzed using standard histologic and immunohistologic techniques.

4. Notes

1. Suspensions of recombinant adenovirus should be kept on ice until immediately before use.
2. Transgene expression in vivo can be detected within 24 h postinfection; with the use of first generation E1A, E1B-deleted recombinant adenoviruses probably peak at 4–7 d postinfection.
3. Alternatively, samples of transduced synovium can be dissected free of underlying subsynovial tissue using needle-nosed forceps and iridectomy shears. These strips of synovial membrane can be further cut into smaller fragments, which can then be frozen or fixed as described in Section 3.3.1.2.

References

1. Castor, C. W. (1960) The microscopic structure of the normal human synovial tissue. *Arthritis Rheum.* **3,** 140–151.
2. Castor, C. W. (1971) Connective tissue activation. I. The nature, specificity, measurement and distribution of connective tissue activating peptide. *Arthritis Rheum.* **14,** 41–54.
3. Steinberg, P. J. and Hodde, K. C. (1990) The morphology of synovial lining of various structures in several species as observed with scanning electron microscopy. *Scanning Microsc.* **4,** 987–1019.
4. Barland, P., Novikoff, A. B., and Hamerman, D. (1962) Electron microscopy of the human synovial membrane. *J. Cell Biol.* **14,** 207–220.
5. Ghadially, F. N. (1983) *Fine Structure of Synovial Joints: A Text and Atlas of the Ultrastructure of Normal and Pathological Articular Tissues.* Butterworths, London.
6. Burmester, G. R., Jahn, B., Rohwer, P., Zacher, J., Winchester, R. J., and Kalden, J. R. (1987) Differential expression of Ia antigens by rheumatoid synovial lining cells. *J. Clin. Invest.* **80,** 595–604.
7. Castor, C. W., Bignall, M. C., Hossler, P. A., and Roberts, D. J. (1981) Connective tissue activation. XXI. Regulation of glycosaminoglycan metabolism by lymphocyte (CTAP-I) and platelet (CTAP-III) growth factors. *In Vitro* **17,** 777–785.

8. Pitsillides, A. A. and Blake, S. M. (1992) Uridine diphosphoglucose dehydroge-
    nase activity in synovial lining cells in the experimental antigen induced model of
    rheumatoid arthritis: an indication of synovial lining cell function. *Ann. Rheum.
    Dis.* **51,** 992–995.
9. Redini, F., Lafuma, C., Pujol, J. P., Robert, L., and Hornebeck, W. (1988) Effect
    of cytokines and growth factors on the expression of elastase activity by human
    synoviocytes, dermal fibroblasts and rabbit articular chondrocytes. *Biochem.
    Biophys. Res. Commun.* **155,** 786–793.
10. Remmers, E. F., Lafyatis, R., Kumkumian, G. K., Case, J. P., Roberts, A. B.,
    Sporn, M. B., and Wilder, R. L. (1990) Cytokines and growth regulation of
    synoviocytes from patients with rheumatoid arthritis and rats with streptococcal
    cell wall arthritis. *Growth Factors* **2,** 179–188.
11. Case, J. P., Lafyatis, R., Remmers, E. F., Kumkumian, G. K., and Wilder, R. L.
    (1989) Transin/stromelysin expression in rheumatoid synovium. A transformation-
    associated metalloproteinase secreted by phenotypically invasive synoviocytes.
    Am. J. Pathol. **135,** 1055–1064.
12. Brinckerhoff, C. E. and Harris, E. D. (1981) Survival of rheumatoid synovium
    implanted into nude mice. *Am. J. Pathol.* **103,** 411–419.
13. Lindsley, H. B., Smith, D. D., Davis, L. S., Koch, A. E., and Lipsky, P. E. (1992)
    Regulation of the expression of adhesion molecules by human synoviocytes.
    Semin. Arthritis Rheum. **21,** 330–334.
14. Roessler, B. J., Allen, E. D., Wilson, J. M., Hartman, J. W., and Davidson, B. L.
    (1993) Adenoviral mediated gene transfer of rabbit synovium *in vivo. J. Clin.
    Invest.* **92,** 1085–1092.
15. Consden, R., Doble, A., Glynn, L. E., and Nind, A. P. (1971) Production of chronic
    arthritis with ovalbumin. *Ann. Rheum. Dis.* **30,** 307–315.
16. Henderson, B. and Glynn, L. E. (1981) Metabolic alterations in the synoviocytes
    in chronically inflamed knee joints in immune arthritis in the rabbit: comparison
    with rheumatoid arthritis. *Br. J. Exp. Pathol.* **62,** 27–33.
17. Crofford, L. J. and Wilder, R. L. (1993) Arthritis and autoimmunity in animals, in
    Arthritis and Allied Conditions (Koopman, W. and McCarty, D., eds.), Lea &
    Febiger, Malvern, PA, pp. 525–539.
18. Graham, F. L. and van der Eb, A. J. (1973) A new technique for the assay of
    infectivity of human adenovirus 5 DNA. *Virology* **52,** 456–467.

28

Methods for the Use of Stromal Cells
for Therapeutic Gene Therapy

Joel S. Greenberger

1. Introduction

The logic behind the use of bone marrow stromal cells in gene therapy relies heavily on data that indicate the uniqueness of the bone marrow stromal cell as a differentiated cell phenotype distinct from the embryo fibroblast, adult connective tissue fibroblast, and cells derived from other sites such as the skin, or connective tissue in muscle (Table 1) (1–15). Bone marrow stromal cells comprise the slowly proliferating supportive tissue of the hematopoietic microenvironment. The anatomic localization, biology, physiology, and growth of these cells in tissue culture have been the subject of intense investigation by experimental and clinical hematologists for several years (16–28). A major controversy in basic hematology has been the question of whether bone marrow stromal cells of the hematopoietic microenvironment are transplantable. Classic bone marrow transplantation biology (30–38) has provided significant data to indicate that the hematopoietic stem cell and committed progeny are transplantable in vivo (for review, see refs. 29,39). Techniques to transplant bone marrow stem cells have gained common acceptance in both experimental and clinical hematology. In contrast, transplantation of slowly proliferating stromal cells of the hematopoietic microenvironment has only recently been demonstrated (29,33,40–51), and confirmed by others (52). The use of bone marrow stromal cells in somatic cell gene therapy has recently become a realistic option for clinical therapeutic management.

Data to support the uniqueness of the bone marrow stromal cell phenotype has come from several sources. The physiologic function of the marrow stromal cell as a regulatory supportive structure for the hematopoietic stem cell has been shown to be a unique property, distinct from cells of other tissues

From: *Methods in Molecular Medicine, Gene Therapy Protocols*
Edited by: P. Robbins Humana Press Inc., Totowa, NJ

Table 1
Biologic Property Unique to Bone Marrow Stomal Cells

Property	Refs.
Differentiation to osteoblasts in DCS or in bFGF	*9,53*
SM actin isoform detected similar to vascular smooth muscle cell	*13*
GAP junction connexins detected between cells	*12*
Stimulate proliferation of CD34^{++}/CD38$^-$ cells	*11*
Produce and respond to PDGF	*10*
Adipocyte phenotype stimulated by corticosteroid adipocyte phenotype, inhibited by IL-11	*8,16*
Release of novel factors increase proliferation induced by SCF, IL-3, LIF, G-CSF using human lin$^-$/CD34$^+$/HLADr$^-$ cells	*7*
Interferon induces apoptosis	*6*
Produce novel 37-kDa membrane adhesive protein	*5*
Fibronectin variant detected unique to stromal cells EDa domain, lacks EDb domain	*4*
Support primary plasmacytoma growth	*3*
Human stromal cells include adventitial-reticular cells with NGF receptor	*15*
Mouse stromal cells show H513E3 antibody positivity	*2*
Barrier cell function with contractile actin microfilaments	*1*

(1,3,11,15,16,18,44–46). Bone marrow stromal cells have been shown to be unique with respect to production of specific cell surface and extracellular matrix molecules *(4,5,7,11,12,38)*; their response is unique to the addition of extracellular cytokines in response patterns biologically distinct from the response of skin fibroblastic cells, macrophages, and endothelial cells derived from other sources *(2,6,8,9,14,21,32,40,45)*; Table 1); and the bone marrow stromal cell phenotype has been shown to be uniquely altered in genetic mutant mouse strains *(27,33,42)*. These data add further support to the notion that there is expression of specific phenotypic characteristics in bone marrow stromal cells.

The mechanism by which bone marrow stromal cells uniquely support hematopoietic stem cells, another unique property of this cell type *(44–46)*, has been one focus of intense investigation. The response of cells of the hematopoietic microenvironment to toxic agents that are commonly administered to cancer patients, including radiation therapy and chemotherapy, have been shown to produce biologic alteration in these cells that can be related to abnormalities of the bone marrow organ function *(19,20,22–25,28,30,31,34,35,39,41,43)*. Thus, the first central theory behind the use of bone marrow stromal cells in somatic cell gene therapy is the *uniqueness of the cell phenotype*. A second theoretical requirement for the use of bone marrow stromal cells in gene therapy involves demonstration of the biological stability of these cells once transplanted, their capacity for expansion in vitro, and their capacity for expression of transgenes. Basic research in tissue culture expansion of bone marrow stromal cells led not only to the demonstration of transplantability of the expanded clonal lines *(29,33)*, but also to transplantation of the noncloned, expanded fresh cultures *(47–50)*. Lack of detectable malignant transformation of expanded stromal cells in culture following reinoculation into experimental animals was also a critical finding that led to the potential therapeutic use of this cell phenotype *(47–50)*.

2. Materials

1. To expand bone marrow stromal cells in vitro for transgene insertion and preparation for reinfusion, several sources of tissue culture medium as well as conventional laboratory tissue culture facilities are required. Experiments have been carried out using mouse, dog, and human bone marrow. Since no clinical protocols have been initiated to date using transgene expressing human marrow stromal cells, the methods for this technique of expansion of human stromal cells rely on reference to those previously published methods for mouse cell culture *(44)*.

2. Bone marrow stromal cell lines such as the GBL-neo[r] line containing the neo[r] marker gene *(29)* or those mouse cell lines obtained by fresh explant and expansion of uncloned lines *(33)*, are grown in a 37°C, 7% CO_2, high humidity incubator using conventional tissue culture methods. Cells are grown in Dulbecco's Modified Eagle's Medium supplemented with 10% fetal calf serum, and then passaged in 25-cm^2 flasks (Corning, Corning, NY), 100-cm^2 or 190-cm^2 flasks. Of particular note has been the observation over many years that plastic preparations from some biological supply companies do not support bone marrow stromal cells *(16,17)*.

3. Materials for introduction of transgenes include equipment necessary to provide for niche irradiation of long-bone sites to 1000–1200 cGy, usually to one long-bone (Fig. 1). In previous experiments, we have irradiated mice to 2 Gy or 10 Gy to either one or both hind limbs, using total body irradiation and a previously published shielding technique *(33)*. The irradiation of one bone site to one dose in a single fraction has been shown to facilitate iv homing of stromal cells to the cleared (irradiated) site *(29)*. This has been carried out routinely in laboratory animals by a cesium 137 gamma cell 40 irradiator. In experiments with larger animals, a Co^{60} teletherapy machine, or linear accelerator, has been used. This requires the collaboration and participation of a radiation oncologist, as well as close supervision by an institutional therapy physicist and radiation safety program officer. Our most recent experiments have suggested that irradiation may not be necessary for stromal cell homing in all cases. However, at the present time, our central working hypothesis is that the enhanced homing and stability of iv injected stromal cells to the high-dose irradiated site is a requisite for the research procedure; thus, a program should include the availability of an ionizing irradiation source for focused irradiation of one marrow site.

Bone Marrow Stromal Cell Line Engraftment *In Vivo*

Fig. 1. Schematic of the steps involved in development of bone marrow stromal cell line transplantation: Long-term bone marrow cultures set up according to published methods *(16)* are subdivided into a stromal adherent cell compartment and clonal lines are established. A reporter gene, in this case GPIA-1-neo^r *(29)*, is inserted, and selection is carried out by growing the cells in G418. These cells are then engrafted into an irradiated animal (in this case, a 30–33-g mouse) with a boost irradiation dose given to one hind limb. Mouse strains used in this have included GP1/b as recipients for GP1/a marked cells, and Sl^d/Sl^d and mi/mi mice for various experiments looking at mutations that lead to alterations of the hematopoietic microenvironment. Following transplantation of stromal cell lines, in vivo measurements have included hematocrit, WBC, and platelet count, and bones are then explanted following sacrifice of the animal for study of these cells at a later time. As shown in the diagram, long-term bone marrow cultures established from such transplanted mice can be tested for the number of colonies of neo^r-positive stromal cells *(29)*. This is a measure of transgene expression relative to the total number of adherent cells. The long-term bone marrow cultures themselves are then tested for colony-forming unit-spleen and colony-forming unit (granulocyte/erythroid/megakaryocyte/macrophage[CFU-GEMM], and colony-forming unit-culture composed of granulocyte/macrophage cells [CFU-GM]).

3. Method

3.1. Mouse Stromal Cell Transgene Experiments

Mouse bone marrow cells are explanted to tissue culture by procedures identical to the initial steps in the step-up of long-term bone marrow cultures *(16)*. Detailed methods describing the technique and optimization of long-term bone marrow cultures for mouse and human cells have previously been published *(16,18)*.

1. Briefly, the cells are flushed into 25-cm^2 Corning plastic flasks via a 25-gage needle inscrted into the transverse section of the femur and tibia of excised bones from 30–33 g adult mice. The cells are initially cultured in prescreened lots of 25% horse serum *(18)*, then switched to medium supplemented with fetal calf serum at weeks 3–4 *(17)*. This is done to decrease lipid accumulation in the bone marrow stromal cells (this technique should be noted and emphasized). Horse serum is used initially to maximize adherence; however, the high lipid content and high corticosteroid content in those hemopoiesis/supportive lots of horse serum also increase fat accumulation in stromal cells *(18)*. The lipid accumulation causes the stromal cells to round up and dctach. Thus, the available number of stromal cells for further expansion and transgene insertion is decreased if horse serum is continually used. The switch to fetal calf serum maintains the adherence of those cells that have already attached, but it minimizes fat uptake.
2. The addition of hydrocortisone, or other 17-hydroxycorticosteroid to the medium during the first four weeks of establishment of stromal cell cultures in the mouse, is critical *(16)*. Whereas the mcchanism of adipogenesis in marrow stromal cells is not yet completely elucidated, recent data suggest that one or more growth factors in the bone marrow microenvironment may contribute to the corticosteroid-dependent lipogenesis *(8)*. Recent information also suggests that tenascin expression in stromal cells is down-regulated by glucocorticoids in several cell types, and this may contribute to the initial adherence of these cells *(14)*.
3. Cells are expanded in the above conditions and then switched to fetal calf serum. At this point, several different commercially available tissue culture medias have been used to promote expansion of stromal cell lines including; Dulbecco's Modified Eagle's Medium, RPMI-1640, and McCoy's Modified Medium *(25)*. We have found that with most mouse strains and stocks, including those from mutant mouse strains, the Dulbecco's Modified Eagle's Medium is adequate *(31,42)*. When bone marrow stromal cells are used in cocultivation experiments with hematopoietic cells, different tissue culture media may be required, including those supplemented by specific hematopoietic growth factors *(46)*.

   Transgene insertion is accomplished by a variety of techniques. We have found that retroviral vector transfer using a packaging-defective virus works extremely well *(51)*.
4. Animals are prepared for reinoculation of the gene transduced cells that are selected by neo^r (G418) resistance in vitro, or selection for another selectable marker transgene *(29)*, and then injected iv with a single cell suspension of the harvested cells. We have used 1 Gy or 10 Gy total body irradiation to the right hind limb in mice, depending on the sensitivity of specific strains of mice to

irradiation *(33*, Fig. 1). For transgene-expressing stromal cell transplant in most normal mouse strains, a dose of 10 Gy to the right hind limb is ideal.

5. Mice are irradiated and then immediately transplanted with 5×10^5 individually suspended stromal cells of either clonal lines or freshly expanded noncloned cell explants. We have found that this cell number is ideal for adult 30–33 g mice based on the dose–response curves of cells injected *(29)*. Depending on the growth factor transgene, or other secreted product transgenes being used *(47–50)*, larger cell numbers may be required. A dose–response curve experiment similar to that previously published by us is recommended *(29)*. In some experiments, we have injected a single cell suspension of transduced stromal cells 48 h after irradiation *(33)*; however, the immediate injection on the same day as irradiation produces comparable results.

6. Measurement of stromal cell engraftment is carried out by use of the CFU-F assay, or colony-forming unit-fibroblast assay *(19*, Fig. 2). This is carried out by flushing cells from the irradiated or nonirradiated limb at various times after transplant, then preparing serial dilutions of single cells, and then placing these cell lines into Plastic Petri dishes. Individual colonies are scored at limiting dilution at 7 and 14 d after incubation at 37°C Gy, 7% CO_2. Plating efficiency may vary after irradiation; however, it is important not to explant cells from the irradiated limb before 6 mo to allow for repair of potentially lethal irradiation damage in the irradiated site (Fig. 3). Six months ensures that repair is reasonably complete *(19)*. One might think that the engrafted cells would home to the irradiated site and still be recoverable immediately following explant. However, we have found that damage *in situ* of nontransduced stromal cells that are repairing sublethal damage in vivo, contributes to increased cell death in culture and actually prevents the survival of viable, nonirradiated, transduced cells that have homed to that site *(19)*. Thus, we recommend a 6-mo delay before explant of marrow from the irradiated site. Experiments have been carried out to demonstrate that transduced cells will survive if explanted earlier; however, recovery is suboptimal *(29)*.

3.2. Gene Transfer to Human Bone Marrow Stromal Cells

The methods for growing human stromal cells in tissue culture have been published by a number of laboratories. In the method we have used, bone marrow stromal cells are explanted in tissue culture in 25-cm square flasks for 3 wk with media changes every week. The medium used has been Dulbecco's Modified Eagle's Medium supplemented with 10% fetal calf serum and $10^{-5}M$ hydrocortisone sodium hemisuccinate *(44)*. To generate homogeneous stromal cell monolayers, the adherent cells from human marrow were treated differently depending on the source.

1. With human marrow, total hip or rib bone marrow fragments were obtained, and single cells were prepared from a suspension after the fragments of tissue were minced in culture with scissors and forceps. If human aspirate or needle biopsy material was obtained, the cells could be immediately trypsinized, passaged for

Measurable Parameters of Engraftment *In Vitro* of Hematopoietic Cells to Bone Marrow Stromal Cells

Fig. 2. Schematic diagram of the technique of studying bone marrow stromal cell support of hematopoiesis in vitro: Irradiated stromal cells are used as a feeder layer for assays that have been described as the long-term culture initiating cell assay, CFU-Dexter, or CFU "cobblestone" (for review, *see* ref. *56*). Hematopoietic cells, either nonadherent cells from long-term bone marrow culture or sorted populations, are engrafted onto stromal cell cultures and cobblestone islands *(36)*, representative of attachment sites quantitated. Nonadherent cells from these cocultures have been tested for the colony-forming assay as described in the legend to Fig. 1, or passaged in vitro to develop factor-independent cell lines *(55)*, and then assayed for tumor formation in vivo. The final step often requires expression of an oncogene, transgene, or factor-independent phenotype induced by another experimental protocol, such as treatment with chemical carcinogen *(55)*.

Fig. 3. Morphologic appearance of mouse long-term bone marrow cultures developed from bones removed 8 wk after transplantation of the GBl-neo^r cell line to the irradiated hind limb of a C57Bl/6J (GP1/b) adult mouse using the experimental protocols described in the legend to Fig. 1: **(A)** Transplanted, right hind limb. **(B)** Control, right hind limb. (A) A culture derived from an animal transplanted with the clonal cell line. (B) An irradiated animal not given the clonal cell line. (A) Shows an active hematopoietic culture indicating stable engraftment of the stromal cells that support hemopoiesis following explant. (B) Shows residual recipient cells of macrophage or fibroblast morphology that survived the irradiation. No active hematopoiesis is seen.

at least four passages, and then either frozen in liquid nitrogen, or used immediately for gene transfer. The morphology of these cultures varies between marrow specimens; the reason for this variation is not yet known. In prior studies, a homogenesis population of large fibroblast-like cells has been seen and is usually devoid of nonspecific esterase, or macrophage-like cells *(44)*. Stromal cell cultures prepared by these techniques have been shown to express collagen type I, fibronectin, or adhesion molecules by indirect immunostaining techniques *(44)*.

2. Transgene insertion is carried out by tissue culture of the cells in 2 μg/mL of dextran, or polybrene, for 24 h before the addition of a packaging-defective retrovirus containing the transgene. These techniques have previously been published in detail *(51)*. We have found, as have others, that use of the neomycin-resistance gene and subsequent selection of the cells in G418 is greatly enhanced if the cells are cultured in medium without G418 for 2–3 d before the selection begins. We have found this is attributable to the toxicity of polybrene for the cells and the requirement of the cells to recover for several days before G418 selection begins. Electroporation and lipofection techniques have also been used for stromal cells along with other vector transfer systems that have been tested. For the stromal cell gene transfer experiments reported by us, use of retroviral vector transfer to the stromal cells is highly reproducible and, in many ways, the optimal technique *(36*, Fig. 4).

3.3. Injection of Gene-Transduced Stromal Cells into Mice

This technique requires tail-vein injections very similar to that for the CFU-S assay (colony cloning in its spleen) and requires iv injection of 0.1–0.2 mL single-cell suspension (for review, *see* ref. *33*). Clumping of stromal cells can be minimized by proper trypsinization, washing, and resuspension prior to injection. Cells can be prevented from adhering by placing the syringes containing the cells in ice prior to injection. To minimize trauma to the animal, the cells should be warmed to body temperature immediately before injection.

4. Notes

1. The most common source of problems in laboratories working with bone marrow stromal cells is failure to appreciate the uniqueness of the phenotype. The cells should not be assumed to be similar to permanent embryo fibroblast cell lines such as NIH/3T3 or Balb/3T3 just because of similarities in morphology *(33)*. Thus, respect for the uniqueness of the cell phenotype is required before initiating this type of gene therapy using bone marrow stromal cell lines.

   Our laboratory has been very successful at establishing permanent stromal lines from a variety of different mouse strain marrows, including mutant mouse strains *(27,42)*, because of the attention to detail during the first 4 wk after explant.

2. The preparation of a single-cell suspension for explant of stroma is *not* recommended. Although we have had success in prior experiments with single cell suspensions, the original technique of flushing clumped marrow stroma and placing it in an incubator immediately after flushing is still optimal *(17)*. The clumped

Fig. 4. Expression of the β-Gal culture transgene following retroviral infection of a freshly explanted bone marrow stromal cell culture using a retroviral vector *(57)*. **(A)** Initial transfection results with one cell positive in a field of around 50 cells. **(B)** Selection of positive cells by cell sorting and amplification of a higher percentage of positive cells. Such amplification in vitro is used to select for a uniform population of transgene expressing cells to make quantitation by *Lac*-Z as precise as is the quantitation using the G418 resistance genes described in the legend to Fig. 1.

cells initially represent several different morphologic types, including cells that look like fibroblasts, reticular adventitial cells, endothelial cells, adipocytes, and macrophages. There is significant controversy as to whether these different morphologic types represent in vivo differentiation of a common stromal cell progenitor that is still recognizable after explant or if they represent multiple, different cell phenotypes. Biological differences in cell phenotypes have been more important than morphologic differences *(33)*. Therefore, it is emphasized that the cultures should be flushed, placed in the incubator, and media-changed weekly with no further manipulation of the cultures for 4 wk.

Another problem frequently encountered by investigators setting up this technique is a desire to manipulate the cultures or alter them too much during the first 4 wk.

3. Observation under an inverted microscope (not to exceed 15 min/d) is recommended, however, prolonged maintenance of cultures outside the incubator is to be avoided. The media change should be carried out by initially removing 50–75% of the tissue culture volume in a 25-cm² flask (7–8 mL); the flask should then be media-changed individually.

4. The flask should not be up-ended and left with the adherent surface exposed to air. This is very important because the cells will desiccate rapidly. Technicians are always instructed to do an initial media change one flask at a time, to replace medium by using prewarmed bottles of medium and serum in a water bath before taking them into the hood, and then pippeting the medium onto the upper surface of the flask where no cells are adherent. Flushing medium onto a surface where stromal cell colonies are growing is an excellent way to dislodge these colonies and destroy the culture. After four media changes over 4 wk, the cells are ready for passage.

5. Passaging the cells should be accomplished with careful attention to detail by using the same technique of passaging one flask at a time. Initially, 1–2 passages are recommended rather than immediate serial dilution. This is different from the CFU-F assay, described previously *(19)*, that was done to quantitate the recovery of cells rather than to establish permanent lines.

The stromal cells are passaged when they reach confluence. The stromal cells should not be permitted to pile up and overgrow culture medium. Upon reaching confluence when the cells are touching (Fig. 4B), they should be trypsinized or scrapped with a rubber policeman and passaged again. Passages, and the technique for establishing lines, are well-described in one of our most recent papers *(42)*.

Cloning of permanent stromal cell lines for therapeutic gene transfer requires a selection of individual colonies by the technique of penicylinder, or limiting dilution cloning by Poissen statistics, both of which are identical to that previously described for embryo fibroblast lines. Once the cells have reached a stage suitable for cell line cloning (usually 12–16 wk after explant) they have adapted to tissue culture and are quite viable.

Despite their similarity to embryo fibroblasts, or other connective tissue fibroblasts, these cells have distinct phenotypic properties (previously described in Table 1). Clonal lines should be expanded and then frozen down in liquid nitrogen in 1.0 mL vol containing not less than 1×10^7 cells/vial. Various techniques of liquid nitrogen freezing and thawing have been published and we have detected no significant difference in technique provided the cells are healthy at the time of freeze-down. The use of retroviral vector transfer to insert transgenes is a technique that has been previously published, and has been used successfully on stromal cell lines, as well as uncloned stromal cultures *(29,51)*.

References

1. Weiss, L. and Geduldig, U. (1991) Barrier cells: stromal regulation of hemato-poiesis and blood cell release in normal and stressed murine bone marrow. *Blood* **78,** 975–990.
2. Hasthorpe, S., Bogdanovski, M., Rogerson, J., and Radley, J. M. (1992) Charac-terization of endothelial cells in murine long-term marrow culture. Implication for hemopoietic regulation. *Exp. Hematol.* **20,** 476–481.
3. Degrassi, A., Hilbert, D. M., Rudikoff, S., Anderson, A. O., Potter, M., and Coon, H. G. (1993) *In vitro* culture of primary plasmacytomas requires stromal cell feeder layers. *PNAS USA* **90,** 2060–2064.
4. Lerat, H., Lesitsky, J.-C, Singer, J. W., Keating, A., Herve, P., and Charbord, P. (1993) Role of stromal cells and macrophages in fibronectin biosynthesis and matrix assembly in human long-term marrow cultures. *Blood* **82,** 1480–1492.
5. Shiota, Y., Wilson, J. G., Harjes, K., Zanjani, E. D., and Tavassoli, M. (1993) A novel 37-Kd adhesive membrane protein from cloned murine bone marrow stro-mal cells and cloned murine hematopoietic progenitor cells. *Blood* **82,** 1436–1444.
6. Nakano, T., Otsuka, T., Ogo, T., Niiro, H., Kuga, S., Zipori, D., Furukawa, Y., and Niho, Y. (1993) Transfection of interferon-gene in a mouse bone marrow stromal preadipocyte cell line causes apoptotic cell death. *Exp. Hematol.* **21,** 1498–1503.
7. Verfaillie, C. M. (1993) Soluble factor(s) produced by human bone marrow stroma increase cytokine-induced proliferation and maturation of primitive hematopoietic progenitors while preventing their terminal differentiation. *Blood* **82,** 2045–2053.
8. Keller, D. C., Du, X. X., Srour, E. F., Hoffman, R., and Williams, D. A. (1993) Interleukin-11 inhibits adipogenesis and stimulates myelopoiesis in human long-term marrow cultures. *Blood* **82,** 1428–1435.
9. Pitaru, S., Kotev-Emeth, S., Noff, D., Kaffuler, S., and Savion, N. (1993) Effect of basic fibroblast growth factor on the growth and differentiation of adult stro-mal bone marrow cells: enhanced development of mineralized bone-like tissue in culture. *J. Bone Min. Res.* **8,** 919–929.
10. Abboud, S. L. (1993) A bone marrow stromal cell line is a source and target for platelet-derived growth factor. *Blood* **81,** 2547–2553.
11. Issaad, C., Croisille, L., Katz, A., Vainchenker, W., and Coulombel, L. (1993) A murine stromal cell line allows the proliferation of very primitive human CD34++/CD38- progenitor cells in long-term cultures and semisolid assays. *Blood* **81,** 2916–2924.
12. Dorshkind, K., Green, L., Godwin, A., and Fletcher, W. H. (1993) Connexin-43-type gap junctions mediate communications between bone marrow stromal cells. *Blood* **82,** 38–45.
13. Galmiche, M. C., Koteliansky, V. E., Briere, J., Herve, P., and Charbord, P. (1993) Stromal cells from human long-term marrow cultures are mesenchymal cells that differentiate following a vascular, smooth muscle differentiation pathway. *Blood* **82,** 66–76.

14. Ekblom, M., Fassler, R., Tomasini-Johansson, B., Nilsson, K., and Ekblom, P. (1993) Down-regulation of tenascin expression by glucocorticoids in bone marrow stromal cells and in fibroblasts. *J. Cell Biol.* **123,** 1037–1045.

15. Cattoretti, G., Schiro, R., Orazi, A., Soligo, D., and Colombo, M. P. (1993) Bone marrow stroma in humans: anti-nerve growth factor receptor antibodies selectively stain reticular cells *in vivo* and *in vitro*. *Blood* **81,** 1726–1738.

16. Greenberger, J. S. (1978) Sensitivity of corticosteroid-dependent, insulin-resistant lipogenesis in marrow preadipocytes of mutation diabetic-obese mice. *Nature* **275,** 752–754.

17. Greenberger, J. S., Davisson, P. B., and Gans, P. J. (1979) Murine sarcoma viruses block corticosteroid-dependent differentiation of bone marrow preadipocytes associated with long-term *in vitro* hemopoiesis. *Virology* **95,** 317–333.

18. Greenberger, J. S. (1979) Corticosteriod-dependent differentiation of human bone marrow preadipocytes. *In Vitro* **15,** 823–828.

19. Greenberger, J. S., Otten, J. A., Eckner, R. J., and Tennant, R. W. (1982) *In vitro* quantitation of lethal and leukemogenic effects of gamma irradiation on stromal and hematopoietic stem cells in continuous mouse bone marrow culture. *Int. J. Rad. Oncol. Biol. Phys.* **8,** 1155–1165.

20. Greenberger, J. S., Klassen, V., Kase, K., and Sakakeeny, M. A. (1984) Effects of low dose rate irradiation on plateau phase bone marrow stromal cells *in vitro*: demonstration of a new form of nonlethal physiologic alteration of support of hematopoietic stem cells. *Int. J. Rad. Oncol. Biol. Phys.* **10,** 1027–1037.

21. Rothstein, L., Pierce, J. H., Aaronson, S. A., and Greenberger, J. S. (1985) Amphotropic retrovirus vector transfer of the v-*ras* oncogene into human hematopoietic and stromal cells in continuous bone marrow culture. *Blood* **65,** 744–752.

22. Naparstek, E., Donnelly, T., Kase, K., and Greenberger, J. S. (1985) Biologic effects of *in vitro* x-irradiation of murine long-term bone marrow cultures on the production of granulocyte-macrophage colony stimulating factors. *Exp. Hematol.* **13,** 701–708.

23. FitzGerald, T. J., Rothstein, L., Kase, K., and Greenberger, J. S. (1986) Radiosensitivity of human bone marrow granulocyte-macrophage progenitor cells: effect of dose rate on purified target cell populations. *Radiation Res.* **107,** 205–215.

24. Naparstek, E., Donnelly, T., Shadduck, R., Wagner, K., Kase, K. R., and Greenberger, J. S. (1986) Persistent production of granulocyte-macrophage colony-stimulating factor (CSF-1) by cloned bone marrow stromal cell line D2XRII after x-irradiation. *J. Cellular Physiol.* **126,** 407–417.

25. Naparstek, E., Pierce, J., Metcalf, D., Shadduck, R., Ihle, J., Leder, A., Sakakeeny, M. A., Wagner, K., Falco, J., FitzGerald, T. J., and Greenberger, J. S. (1986) Induction of growth alterations in factor-dependent hematopoietic progenitor cell lines by cocultivation with irradiated bone marrow stromal cell lines. *Blood* **67,** 1395–1403.

26. Greenberger, J. S. (1986) Future directions in clinical bone marrow transplantation: interests coverage on the bone marrow microenvironment. *Br. J. Hematol.* **62,** 603–605.

27. Anklesaria, P., Klassen, V., Sakakeeny, M. A., FitzGerald, T. J., Rybak, M. E., and Greenberger, J. S. (1987) Biological characterization of cloned permanent stromal cell lines from anemic *Sl/Sld* and +/+ littermates. *Exp. Hematol.* **15,** 636–644.

28. Greenberger, J. S., FitzGerald, T. J., Klassen, V., Anklesaria, P., Bushnell, D., Kase, K., and Sakakeeny, M. A. (1988) Alteration in hematopoietic stem cell seeding and proliferation by low dose rate irradiation of bone marrow stromal cells *in vitro. Int. J. Rad. Oncol. Biol. Phys.* **14,** 85–94.

29. Anklesaria, P., Kase, K. R., Glowacki, J., Holland, C. H., Sakakeeny, M. A., Wright, J. H., FitzGerald, T. J., Lee, C-YL, and Greenberger, J. S. (1987) Engraftment of a clonal bone marrow stromal cell line *in vivo* stimulates hematopoietic recovery from total body irradiation. *PNAS USA* **84,** 7681–7685.

30. FitzGerald, T. J., Santucci, M. A., Harigaya, K., Woda, B., McKenna, M., Sakakeeny, M. A., Pierce, J. H., Kase, K., Holland, C. A., and Greenberger, J. S. (1988) Radiosensitivity of permanent human bone marrow stromal cell lines: effect of dose rate. *Int. J. Rad. Oncol. Biol. Phys.* **15,** 1153–1159.

31. FitzGerald, T. J., Anklesaria, P., Le, D., Sakakeeny, M. A., Kase, K., and Greenberger, J. S. (1988) Radiosensitivity of cloned permanent murine bone marrow stromal cell lines: non-uniform effect of low dose rate. *Exp. Hematol.* **16,** 820–827.

32. Greenberger, J. S. and Anklesaria, P. (1989) Recent studies of the hematopoietic microenvironment in long-term bone marrow cultures. *Immunologic Res.* **8,** 226–235.

33. Anklesaria, P., FitzGerald, T. J., Kase, K., Ohara, A., Bentley, S., and Greenberger, J. S. (1989) Improved hematopoiesis in anemic *Sl/Sl^d* mice by therapeutic transplantation of a hematopoietic microenvironment. *Blood* **74,** 1144–1152.

34. Greenberger, J. S., Wright, E., Henault, S., Sakakeeny, M. A., Anklesaria, P., FitzGerald, T. J., Wheaton, M., Kase, K., and Kuzawa, D. (1990) Hematopoietic stem cell and marrow stromal cell specific requirements for gamma-irradiation leukemogenesis *in vitro. Exp. Hematol.* **18,** 408–416.

35. Santucci, M. A., FitzGerald, T. J., Harigaya, K., Woda, B., Sakakeeny, M. A., Anklesaria, P., Kase, K., Holland, C. A., and Greenberger, J. S. (1990) Gamma-irradiation response of cocultivated bone marrow stromal cell lines of differing intrinsic radiosensitivity. *Int. J. Rad. Oncol. Biol. Phys.* **18,** 1083–1092.

36. Anklesaria, P., Teixido, J., Laiho, M., Pierce, J., Greenberger, J. S., and Massague, J. (1990) Cell homing and proliferation mediated by membrane TGF-binding to EGF receptor. *PNAS USA* **87,** 3289–3293.

37. Bentley, S. A., Kirby, S. L., Anklesaria, P. A., and Greenberger, J. S. (1990) Biochemical and functional characterization of proteoglycans produced by *Sl/Sl^d* murine bone marrow stromal cell lines. *J. Cell Physiol.* **145,** 53–59.

38. Anklesaria, P., Greenberger, J. S., FitzGerald, T. J., Wicha, M., and Campbell, A. (1991) Reduced expression of haemonectin may contribute to the defective hematopoiesis of Steel mutant mice. *Blood* **77,** 1691–1698.

39. Greenberger, J. S. (1991) Toxic effects on the hematopoietic microenvironment. *Exp. Hematol.* **19,** 1101–1109.

40. Bleiberg, I., Greenberger, J., Anklesaria, P., and Glowacki, J. (1992) Origin of stromal cells associated with osteoclast recruitment in subcutaneous implants of bone particles in chimeric mice. *Exp. Hematol.* **20,** 957–962.

41. Greenberger, J. S., Leif, J., Crawford, D., Anklesaria, P., English, D., Sakakeeny, M. A., Rubin, J. R., Pierce, P. H., Shadduck, R. K., and FitzGerald, T. J. (1992) Humoral and cell surface interactions during gamma-irradiation leukemogenesis *in vitro*. *Exp. Hematol.* **20,** 92–102.

42. Ohara, A., Anklesaria, P., Schultz, L., and Greenberger, J. S. (1992) Biological characterization of permanent clonal bone marrow stromal cell lines derived from "moth-eaten" Me^v/Me^v and *SCID* mice. *J. Cell Cloning* **10,** 33–47.

43. Greenberger, J. S. (1992) Is the marrow stroma of AML patients a "leukemic" stroma? *Exp. Hematol.* **20,** 1041,1042.

44. Teixido, J., Hemler, M. E., Greenberger, J. S., and Anklesaria, P. (1992) Role of β1 and β2 integrins in the adhesion of human CD34+^{hi} stem cells to bone marrow stroma. *J. Clin. Invest.* **90,** 358–367.

45. Gimble, J., Youkhana, K., Hua, X., Wang, C.-S., Bass, H., Medina, K., and Greenberger, J. S. (1992) Adipogenesis in a myeloid supporting bone marrow stromal cell line. *J. Cell Biochem.* **50,** 73–82.

46. Neben, S., Anklesaria, P., Greenberger, J. S., and Mauch, P. (1993) Quantitation of murine hematopoietic stem cells *in vitro* by limiting dilution analysis of cobblestone area formation on a clonal stromal cell line. *Exp. Hematol.* **21,** 438–444.

47. Anklesaria, P., Glowacki, J., Pierce, J., Kase, K., Ohara, A., FitzGerald, T. J., Bentley, S., and Greenberger, J. S. (1989) Therapy of hematopoietic disorders by clonal bone marrow stromal cell line transplant. ISEH Meeting, Paris, France. *Exp. Hematol.* **17,** 661A.

48. Anklesaria, P., Brody, R., Brettler, D., Ricca, G., Levine, P., and Greenberger, J. S. (1990) Expression of biologically active human recombinant factor VIII-C by a transplantable clonal bone marrow stromal cell line: an alternate model for somatic gene therapy. ASH Meeting, Boston, MA., 12/90. *Blood* **76(Suppl. 1),** 526A.

49. Greenberger, J. S., Anklesaria, P., Hurwitz, D. R., Nathan, M., Sarver, S., Ricca, G., Catalfamo, J., Brody, R., Brettler, D., Levine, P., Merrill, W., Leif, J., Pratt, D., and Buckley, C. (1992) Expression of human factor VIII:C in bone marrow stromal cells. Proceedings of Workshop On Gene Therapy For Hemophilia Meeting, Bethesda, MD 3/18/92–3/19/92. *Proc. N.H.L.B.I./NIH* **8,** 72,73.

50. Greenberger, J. S., Anklesaria, P., Catalfamo, J., Brody, B., Merrill, W., Leif, J., Emami, S., Brooks, M., Nathan, N., Hurwitz, D. R., Ricca, G., Sarver, N., Brettler, D., and Levine, P. (1992) Gene therapy for hemophilia using bone marrow stromal cell transplantation. XX International Congress of the World Federation Of Hemophilia, Athens, Greece, 10/12/92–10/17/92, vol. 17, 82,83.

51. Anklesaria, P., Holland, C., Klassen, V., Sakakeeny, M. A., FitzGerald, T. J., and Greenberger, J. S. (1987) Expression of a selectable gene transferred by retroviral vector to hematopoietic stem cells and stromal cells in murine continuous bone marrow cultures. *Exp. Hematol.* **15,** 195–202.

52. Brazolot Millan, C. L. and Carter, R. F. (1993) Apparent engraftment of trans-
    duced long-term culture adherent cells into the canine bone marrow compartment
    following intravenous or direct intra-marrow infusion. *Blood* **82(Suppl. 1),** 428A.
53. Bab, I., Ashton, B. A., Gazit, D., Marx, G., Williamson, M. C., and Owen, M. E.
    (1986) Kinetics and differentiation of marrow stromal cells in diffusion chambers
    in vivo. J. Cell Sci. **84,** 139–151.
54. Nolta, J. A., Hanley, M. A., and Kohn, D. B. (1993) *In vivo* system to assess the
    efficiency of retroviral-mediated transduction of primitive human hematopoietic
    progenitors. *Blood* **82(Suppl. 1),** 1371.
55. Crawford, D. R. and Greenberger, J. S. (1991) Active oxygen transforms murine
    myeloid progenitor cells at cytotoxic concentrations. *Int. J. Cancer* **49,** 744–749.
56. Teixido, J., Hemler, M. E., Greenberger, J. S., and Anklesaria, P. (1992) Role of
    β1 and β2 integrins in the adhesion of human CD34+[hi] stem cells to bone marrow
    stroma. *J. Clin. Invest.* **90,** 358–367.
57. Anklesaria, P., Holland, C., Klassen, V., Sakakeeny, M. A., FitzGerald, T. J., and
    Greenberger, J. S. (1987) Expression of a selectable gene transferred by retroviral
    vector to hematopoietic stem cells and stromal cells in murine continuous bone
    marrow cultures. *Exp. Hematol.* **15,** 195–202.

29

Suppression of the Human Carcinoma Phenotype by an Antioncogene Ribozyme

Toshiya Shitara and Kevin J. Scanlon

1. Introduction

A spectrum of oncogenes have been identified and are thought to be associated with the progression of neoplasia. These oncogenes include the following: growth factors/receptors, kinases, nuclear proteins (i.e., Fos/Jun), and tumor suppressor genes. Perturbation of one or more of these genes can transform normal cells into invasive/metastatic cancer cells. Understanding the role of these oncogenes for specific types of cancer may lead to a more rational basis for tissue-specific targets in cancer gene therapy.

Fos is one of the immediate early response genes to extracellular mitogenic stimuli *(1)*, growth factors *(2)*, phorbol esters *(3)*, chemotherapy agents *(4,5)*, and other oncogenes *(6)*. The nuclear proteins Fos and Jun form a complex that modulates transcriptional activation of a variety of genes possessing AP-1 (activator protein 1) sites, and these genes are important in the control of cell growth *(7,8)*. The Jun protein can form both homo- and heterodimers that bind to the AP-1 site *(9,10)*. In contrast, Fos does not form a dimer and therefore cannot bind to DNA by itself. However, Fos can associate with Jun to generate stable heterodimers that have higher DNA-binding activity than the Jun dimers *(11)*. AP-1 activity is elevated in neoplastic transformation along with other transforming oncogenes such as activated H-*ras (12,13)*. The effect of H-*ras* on AP-1 is perceived to act through the enhanced transcriptional activity of c-*jun* by specific changes in the phosphorylation state of Jun *(14)*. The inductions of c-*fos* and c-*jun* are transient; however, their effect through the signal transduction pathway can establish long-term changes in the cell growth and differentiation *(15–18)*. Thus, targeting the *fos* oncogene may be a primary target for cancer gene therapy.

From: *Methods in Molecular Medicine, Gene Therapy Protocols*
Edited by: P. Robbins Humana Press Inc., Totowa, NJ

Several strategies have been utilized to inhibit c-*fos* oncogene expression: microinjection of Fos MAbs *(19)*, *fos* antisense RNA *(6,20,21)*, and *fos* ribozyme RNA *(22,23)*. Antibody and antisense studies have only been able to effect partial and/or transient reversion of the *fos* transformed phenotype *(6,19–21)*. In EJ (patient's initials) human bladder carcinoma cells, the activated H-*ras* is thought to play an important role in tumorgenesis, invasion, and metastasis *(24,25)*. Our previous work showed the reversal of the malignant phenotype with H-*ras* ribozyme in EJ cells *(26,27)*. The c-*fos* ribozyme has been chosen to determine its efficacy against human tumor growth. Also, the importance of c-*fos* has been identified as an appropriate target for cancer gene therapy.

The designing of an effective ribozyme is complex and requires not only an understanding of nucleic acid biochemistry but also the role of the target gene in maintaining the cell phenotype. Perhaps one of the weaknesses of the early antisense studies was a limited understanding of the role of the target gene in the specific cell type. The ability to demonstrate ribozyme efficacy in vivo requires choosing the correct gene that plays a critical role in maintaining the unique cell phenotype. Two examples of this strategy are that the drug-resistant human ovarian carcinoma cells were able to maintain their phenotype by an overexpression of the c-*fos* oncogene *(23)*, and that a human bladder carcinoma cell line was able to maintain an aggressive, metastatic phenotype owing to a homozygous H-*ras* codon 12 mutation *(25–27)*. Down-regulation of these two oncogenes by antioncogene ribozymes produced profound phenotypic changes in the human carcinomas. However, not all genes have such a dramatic effect on maintaining unique phenotypes. Additional factors that can influence the efficacy of ribozymes are: the mRNA half-life, nuclease activity in the cell, and the stability of the protein in the cell. The cell also has the capacity to be dynamic and overcome the effects of the ribozymes by altering its cellular metabolism. The length of the ribozyme flanking sequences as well as its accessibility to the target site of the RNA are also critical for ribozyme activity. The higher the GC content of the flanking sequence, the slower the on/off rate of the ribozyme to bind to RNA and the shorter the turn-over rate. Finally, the stability of the ribozyme RNA in the cell will play a role in the ribozyme efficacy.

Ribozymes can enter the cell by two methods: diffusion (endocytosis) or a vector-mediated process. If transient expression of ribozyme is required, then modifying the RNA to be more resistant to nucleases is critical, and enhancing the uptake of ribozyme can be achieved with lipofection and/or receptor-mediated carriers. If long-term expression is required, then vector-mediated uptake with a strong promoter system is critical for the stable long-term expression of ribozyme RNA. Viral vector systems have unique delivery problems and are currently limited in their usefulness in cancer gene therapy.

Ultimately, the utility of ribozymes in cancer gene therapy will be realized when we understand the following criteria: identifying critical cancer gene(s) that maintains the neoplastic phenotype; developing a tissue-specific delivery system, with a high rate of infection; and a tissue specific promoter/enhancer with long-term stable expression of the ribozyme. These problems are not technically impossible to achieve, but they must be successfully addressed before gene therapy will become a routine treatment strategy in patients.

2. Materials and Methods

1. Reagents: T4 polynucleotide kinase was obtained from New England Biolabs, Beverly, MA. *Taq* DNA polymerase was obtained from Perkin-Elmer/Cetus, Norwalk, CT. The (alpha ^{32}P)UTP, (alpha ^{32}P)dCTP, and (gamma ^{32}p)ATP were obtained from New England Nuclear, Boston, MA. The RPMI-1640 media and fetal calf serum were obtained from Gibco-BRL (Gaithersburg, MD).
2. Synthetic nucleotides: Synthetic oligodeoxyribonucleotides were prepared on an Applied Biosystems (Foster City, CA) Model 380B DNA synthesizer and the sequences for the primers used in this study were previously described *(23)*.
3. Cells: Human bladder carcinoma EJ cells were obtained from ATCC (Rockville, MD). The EJ cells were plated in triplicate at 10^4 cells/35-mm^2 dish onto 0.3% agar and supplemented with 1–20% fetal bovine serum. Colonies were counted 13 d later with Giemsa dye stain. Linear regression analysis was performed on the resulting log growth curve data (6–9 d) and used to determine the slope and intercept on the log axis for cell number. Thymidine nuclear uptake studies were used to determine the rate of (^{3}H)dThd incorporation in acid-insoluble material. The EJ cells (2.5×10^3 cells/35-mm^2 dish) were grown for 48 h, then incubated for 2 h with (^{3}H)dThd (10^6 dpm/dish), washed, acid precipitated, and counted. The EJ cell control (100%) represented 1.6 ($\pm$0.3) fmol/mg DNA/h *(28)*.
4. Plasmid: The plasmid pMAMneo contains a 1.45-kb LTR sequence of MMTV and RSV-LTR (Clontech Lab, Palo Alto, CA). The *fos* ribozyme and the sequence and orientation of the ribozyme were confirmed by dideoxynucleotide sequencing of the construct as previously described *(23)*.
5. Transfection by electroporation: Subconfluently growing EJ cells were transfected by electroporation according to a protocol provided by IBI (New Haven, CT) and previously described methods *(23)*. Individual G418-resistant colonies were picked up, grown, and screened for expression of the *fos* ribozyme by the polymerase chain reaction (PCR) assay described below. The cells were challenged 8–12 wk later with G418 (1 mg/mL) to test for the presence of the neomycin gene.
6. PCR: The procedure follows that of Saiki et al. *(29)* as modified by Scanlon et al. *(23)* and a commercially available protocol (GeneAmp, Perkin-Elmer/Cetus). To detect transfected EJ with *fos*R, the RNA PCR assay was used as previously described *(23)*.
7. Northern blot analysis: Messenger RNA (mRNA) isolation using the guanidium isothiocyanate and oligo(dT)-cellulose method, electrophoresis on horizontal agarose gels, hybridization, and densitometric analysis (Ambis, San Diego, CA) were performed as previously described *(23,30)*.

8. Western blot analysis: For immunoblotting, the MiniProtean II gel electrophoresis apparatus (Bio-Rad, Hercules, CA) and the ImmunoBlot Assay kit (Bio-Rad) were used according to the specifications of the manufacturer and a previously described method *(22)*. The Fos MAb (Ab-1) was obtained from Oncogene Science (Manhasset, NY). α-Tubulin antibody (Oncogene Science) was used as a control.

3. Results

The criteria for successfully treating cancer cells with ribozymes requires analysis by several parameters. We have used the strategy of transfecting tumor cells and using neomycin (G418) selection pressure to preselect clones for analysis. This approach does not evaluate the efficiency of transduction but it does allow for demonstration of the utility of ribozymes to target and down-regulate a specific gene expression. The criteria used to select clones for analysis are the following: morphological changes, ribozyme RNA expression (RNA-PCR assay), and Northern and Western blotting of the target gene. After this selection process, an analysis of several ribozyme-containing clones was undertaken to demonstrate the ribozyme effects on the EJ cell phenotype.

A *fos* ribozyme was cloned into a dexamethasone-inducible plasmid (pMAMneo) to study the transient expression of *fos* ribozyme RNA and its effect on EJ cells. The cells were transfected with the pMAMneo *fos* ribozyme plasmid by electroporation. Colonies were selected on the basis of G418-resistance and changes in the cellular morphology. Twenty of the ribozyme-expressing colonies were found to have a stable resistance to G418 when they were rechallenged with G418 (1 mg/mL).

A time-course of ribozyme RNA induction by dexamethasone was characterized (data not shown). There was some leakage of the *fos* ribozyme RNA in the absence of dexamethasone treatment. The *fos* ribozyme RNA induction increases within 2 h after dexamethasone administration, and peaks 12 h after treatment. Ribozyme RNA can be detected for 72–96 h by RNA-PCR assay. The ribozyme clones are responsive to dexamethasone for 3–9 mo. The *fos* ribozyme RNA expression was detected in transfected clones Rz1, Rz3, and Rz6 by the RNA-PCR assay (Fig. 1). Dexamethasone administration dramatically increased the expression of the *fos* ribozyme RNA in the transfected clones (Fig. 1). Expression of c-*fos* was correspondingly decreased by activation of the *fos* ribozyme (Fig. 1). Northern blot analysis indicated that the level of endogenous c-*fos* mRNA was decreased in ribozyme-containing clones at the 24-h time-point, whereas the phosphoglycerate kinase (PGK) mRNA remained unchanged. Western blot analysis confirmed the reduction of Fos levels while the α-tubulin levels remained unchanged (Fig. 1).

Fig. 1. EJ cells and EJ ribozyme-transfected cells: Morphology of EJ cells (EJ), dexamethasone-treated EJ cells transfected with pMMV-*fos* Rz (Rz1, Rz3, Rz6) are shown. Expression of ribozyme is demonstrated by RNA–PCR. c-*fos* and PGK RNA was analyzed by Northern blots. Fos and α-tubulin proteins were characterized by Western blot analysis. EJ represents EJ cells, C1 represents EJ Rz1, C3 represents EJ Rz3, C6 represents EJ Rz6, and Dex represents dexamethasone (5 μ*M*) treatment for 12 h.

In two ribozyme clones (Rz1, Rz3), both the generation time and the rate of DNA synthesis were substantially lower than in parental EJ cells. The ribozyme clones were 26 and 29%, respectively of the control as evidenced by the (^{3}H) thymidine incorporation assay (Table 1). The EJ cells exhibited long, spindly cells that rapidly spread to cover the growth surface, whereas the clone transfected with the ribozyme under optimal concentrations of dexamethasone were round and tended to grow in patches (Fig. 1). These effects were maintained in EJ cells for 6–8 wk and then the cells reverted back to the untreated phenotype.

Table 1
(^{3}H) Thymidine Incorporation Assay for EJ Ribozyme-Transfected Cells

Cell lines	Dex, 5 μM	Generation time, h	(^{3}H)dThd Incorporation[a]	Colonies[b] 1%/20% serum
EJ	−	14.4	100	45/82
	+	15.6	91	38/65
EJ V[c]	−	14.4	78	42/93
	+	15.4	84	32/58
EJ Rz1	−	16.8	67	28/51
	+	21.6	26	3/3
EJ Rz3	−	19.2	73	34/59
	+	21.6	29	1/2
EJ Rz6	−	19.2	—	31/49
	+	25.2	—	2/4

[a]To determine the rate of (^{3}H)dThd incorporation in acid-soluble material, EJ cells (2.5×10^3/ 35 mm^2 dish) were grown for 48 h, then incubated for 2 h with (^{3}H)dThd (10^6 dpm/dish), washed, acid precipitated, and counted as previously described *(27)*.

[b]EJ cell lines (10^4 cells/35 mm^2 dish) were grown in 0.3% agar with 1% or 20% fetal bovine serum. Colonies were counted 15 d later. The control cells (EJ) equaled 82 colonies in 20% serum and 45 colonies in 1% serum.

[c]EJ V indicates that the pMAMneo vector without *fos* ribozyme was transfected into EJ parent cells and used as a control.

The effects of *fos* ribozyme action were examined on mRNA levels and genes whose overexpression was associated with AP-1 binding sites. Genes with the signal transduction pathway for cellular transformation and cell growth were examined. Gene expression for dTMP synthase, DNA polymerase β, and topoisomerase I were decreased with that in c-*fos*. Gene expression for the transforming growth factor β-1 (TGFβ-1) and platelet-derived growth factor receptor (PDGFR) was also decreased (data not shown), which was associated with a decrease in cell growth characteristics as seen in Table 1.

There are several criteria that we use for vector-mediated transfection of ribozymes. As seen in Fig. 1, the effect of the ribozyme on EJ cells is reflected in morphological changes from spindly EJ cells to short, round cells in the ribozyme-containing clones. Thus it is easier to choose ribozyme expressing clones by choosing clones with the significantly altered morphology. Alternatively, a back-up system for analysis was the semiquantitative RNA-PCR assay to determine the highest level of *fos* ribozyme RNA (Fig. 1). However, the ultimate test for ribozyme efficacy was to determine the level of *fos* gene expression by Northern analysis and Fos protein expression by Western analysis. In all the ribozyme-containing clones tested, there was a direct correlation between the level of ribozyme expression and the down-regulation of the target gene by Northern blot analysis.

4. Discussion

Ribozymes are RNAs that have site-specific RNA cleavage or ligation activities that may have therapeutic applications in human diseases *(31–33)*. The hammerhead ribozyme was derived from the plus strand of tobacco ringspot virus satellite RNA, and site-specifically cleaves RNA substrates *in trans (34,35)*. Antioncogene hammerhead ribozymes have been designed and transfected into several human carcinoma cell lines *(22,23,26,27,36–38)*. Because the ribozymes down-regulated only the target gene, ribozymes may be used to clarify the role of the oncogenes in the human carcinoma cells. In the previous study, we showed the efficacy of anti-H-*ras* ribozyme in the human bladder carcinoma EJ cells that have homozygous point mutation of H-*ras* codon 12 *(26,27)*. In this study, we have demonstrated efficiency of anti-*fos* ribozyme and the role of fos in maintaining the EJ human bladder carcinoma phenotype.

For long-term expression, we have used the mammalian expression vector systems such as the pHβ Apr-1 vector containing the β-actin promoter. This vector stably expressed the anti-H-*ras* ribozyme for 6–24 mo *(26,27)*. The H-*ras* ribozymes showed continuous expression in the EJ cells, and markedly decreased tumorigenecity of EJ cells in nude mice; this means that the pHβ Apr-1 vector system is stable at least for a couple of months. In the present study, we used a dexamethasone-inducible mammalian expression vector, pMAMneo. The anti-*fos* ribozyme expression was induced by dexamethasone, and dramatically down-regulated the *fos* oncogene expression, whereas this was barely suppressed by the ribozyme without dexamethasone. The results suggest that the dexamethasone-inducible vector system is useful for the regulation of ribozyme expression (i.e., modulation of the target gene expression).

The induction of c-*fos* gene expression is one of the earliest nuclear responses to a wide variety of growth and differentiation factors *(1–6)* and suggests modulation of the cell growth through the AP-1 sites *(7,8)*. In this study, we used the anti-*fos* ribozyme (*fos* Rz) driven by the pMAMneo vector plasmid, which limit the growth of the EJ bladder carcinoma cells.

The anti-*fos* ribozyme transformants (Rz1, Rz3, and Rz6) showed completely down-regulation of c-*fos* RNA expression with dexamethasone (Fig. 1), as well as TGF-β1 and PDGF (data not shown). Moreover, the transformants were characterized by altered cell growth, as shown by generation time, [^{3}H]dThd incorporation, soft agar cloning assay (Table 1), and morphological changes (Fig. 1) as compared to EJ parent cells. These results suggested that the c-*fos* oncogene plays an important role for tumorigenicity in EJ cells. The expression of H-*ras* ribozyme can also inhibit growth of the EJ transformants *(25–27)*.

In addition, the *fos* ribozyme also led to down-regulation of the gene expression of TGF-β1 and PDGF that was associated with cell growth *(39)*. This may be explained by the fact that these two genes contain AP-1 binding sequences in their 5' regulatory sequence, and Fos/Jun complex can stimulate AP-1 site *(40,41)*.

The previous data suggest the possibility of designing site-specific hammerhead ribozymes against various substrate sequences in order to modulate target gene expression.

5. Notes

1. It appears that understanding the biology of the cells and the role of the target gene in the cell's phenotype is critical for selecting targets of ribozymes. Conversely, ribozymes can be used to determine the role of the specific gene in a metabolic pathway or cellular phenotype.
2. The ribozyme design will depend on selectivity of the target, whether the gene is overexpressed (i.e., *fos*; *see* ref. *23*) or mutated, such as the H-*ras* codon 12 *(26)*. The effect of the ribozymes may also be rate limiting if the mutation is homozygous *(26)* or heterozygous *(37)* in the target gene.
3. One of the most powerful aspects of the ribozyme is its selectivity in discriminating oncogenes from proto-oncogenes *(25–28,37,38)*.
4. Ribozyme activity has been shown to be enhanced for the H-*ras* ribozyme by reducing the flanking sequences from 20 to 12 bases. The shorter flanking sequences reduce specificity but enhance the turnover rate.
5. Alternatively, ribozymes can be used with conventional therapy or biological response modifiers to achieve more dramatic effects on tumors *(37)*.
6. Cellular uptake of ribozymes is limited by two problems: permeability and nucleases. Lipofection can enhance cellular uptake of ribozymes. Nuclease-resistant RNA bases or DNA bases can be incorporated into the ribozymes to enhance stability. If a transient effect on the target gene is required, this system will work well. If long-term, stable expression is required, then a vector system with a promoter/enhancer system is required.
7. Electroporation is an effective method for the introduction of DNA into the cell, but the efficiency is poor. Viral-mediated transfer of ribozymes has a higher efficacy but the tumor cells do not have a high rate of transduction. Modification of the viral surface protein *(42)* or receptor-mediated strategies is currently being used to improve the transduction efficacy of viral vector systems for gene therapy.
8. Promoter/enhancer systems could allow for tissue-specific gene expression; however, only a few tissue-specific promoters have been identified.
9. Site-specific chromosome integration and long-term stable expression would be critical for a useful gene therapy vector.

Acknowledgments

This work was supported by the National Institutes of Health, CA 50618. We would like thank Drs. Y. Ohta, H. Ishida, and H. Kijima for their comments on the manuscript. We would also like to thank Ms. Carol Polchow for preparing the manuscript.

References

1. Curran, T. and Franza, B. R., Jr. (1988) Fos and Jun: the AP-1 connection. *Cell* **55,** 395–397.
2. Greenberg, M. E. and Ziff, E. B. (1984) Stimulation of 3T3 cells induces transcription or the c-*fos* proto-oncogene. *Nature* **311,** 433–438.
3. Angel, P., Imagawa, M., Kain, M., Chiu, R., Stein, B., Imbra, R. J., Rahmsdorf, H. J., Jonat, C., Herrlich, P., and Kain, M. (1987) Phorbol ester-inducible genes contain a common *cis* element recognized by at TPA-modulated trans-acting factor. *Cell* **49,** 1687–1692.
4. Hollander, M. C. and Fornace, A. J., Jr. (1989) Induction of fos RNA by DNA-damaging agents. *Cancer Res.* **49,** 1687–1692.
5. Kashani-Sabet, M., Wang, W., and Scanlon, K. J. (1990) Cyclosporin A suppresses cisplatin-induced c-*fos* gene expression in ovarian carcinoma cells. *J. Biol. Chem.* **265,** 11,285–11,288.
6. Ledwith, B. J., Manam, S., Kraynak, A. R., Nichols, W. W., and Bradley, M. O. (1990) Antisense-*fos* RNA causes partial reversion of the transformed phenotype induced by the c-Ha-*ras* oncogene. *Mol. Cell. Biol.* **10,** 1545–1555.
7. Curran, T., Beveren, C. V., Ling, N., and Verma, I. M. (1985) Viral and cellular proteins are complexed with a 39,000 Dalton cellular protein. *Mol. Cell. Biol.* **5,** 167–172.
8. Rauscher, F. J., III., Cohen, D. R., Curran, T., Bos, T. J., Vogt, P. K., Bohmann, D., Tjian, R., and Franza, B., Jr. (1988) Fos-associated protein p39 is the product of the *jun* proto-oncogene. *Science* **240,** 1010–1016.
9. Vogt, P. K. and Bos, T. J. (1990) *jun*: oncogene and transcription factor. *Adv. Cancer Res.* **55,** 1–35.
10. Cantley, L. C., Auger, K. R., Carpenter, C., Duckworth, B., Graziani, A., Kapeller, R., and Soltoff, S. (1991) Oncogenes and signal transduction. *Cell* **64,** 281–302.
11. Rauscher, F. J., III., Voulalas, P. J., Franza, B. R., Jr., and Curran, T. (1988) Fos and Jun bind cooperatively to the AP-1 site: reconstitution *in vitro*. *Genes Dev.* **2,** 1687–1699.
12. Zmeler, J. L., Schatz, C., Wasylyk, C., Chatton, B., and Wasylyk, B. (1988) A Harvey-*ras* responsive transcription element is also responsive to a tumor-promoter and to serum. *Nature* **332,** 275–278.
13. Wasylyk, C., Zmeler, J. L., and Wasylyk, B. (1988) Transforming but not immortalizing oncogenes activate the transcription factor PEA2. *EMBO J.* **7,** 2475–2483.
14. Mizel, S. B. (1991) Ha–*ras* augments c–Jun activity and stimulates phosphorylation of its activation domain. *Chemtracts-Biochem. Mol. Biol.* **2,** 294–296.
15. Muller, R., Bravo, R., and Burckhardt, J. (1984) Induction of c-*fos* gene and protein by growth factor precedes activation of c-*myc*. *Nature* **312,** 616–620.
16. Angel, P., Hattori, K., Smeal, T., and Karin, M. (1988) The jun proto-oncogene is positively autoregulated by its product, Jun/AP-1. *Cell* **55,** 875–885.
17. Rahmsdorf, H. J., Schonthal, A., Angel, P., Litfin, M., Ruther, U., and Herrlich, P. (1987) Posttranscriptional regulation of c-*fos* mRNA expression. *Nucleic Acids Res.* **15,** 1643–1659.

18. Huang, J. S., Huang, S. S., and Deuel, T. F. (1984) Transforming protein of simian sarcoma virus stimulates autocrine growth of SSV-transformed cells through PDGF cell-surface receptors. *Cell* **39,** 79–87.

19. Riabowol, K. T., Vosatka, R. J., Ziff, E. B., Lamb, N. J., and Feramisco, J. F. (1988) Microinjection of *fos*-specific antibodies blocks DNA synthesis in fibroblastic cells. *Mol. Cell. Biol.* **8,**1670–1676.

20. Holt, J. T., Gopal, T. V., Moulton, A. D., and Nienhuis, A. W. (1986) Inducible production of c-*fos* antisense RNA inhibits 3T3 cell proliferation. *Proc. Natl. Acad. Sci. USA* **83,** 4794–4798.

21. Nishikura, K. and Murray, J. M. (1987) Antisense RNA of proto-oncogene c-*fos* blocks renewed growth of quiescent 3T3 cells. *Mol. Cell. Biol.* **7,** 639–649.

22. Funato, T., Yoshida, E., Jiao, L., Tone, T., Kashani-Sabet, M., and Scanlon, K. J. (1992) The utility of an anti-*fos* ribozyme in reversing cisplatin resistance in human carcinoma. *Adv. Enzyme Reg.* **32,** 195–209.

23. Scanlon, K. J., Jiao, L., Funato, T., Wang, W., Tone, T., Rossi, J. J., and Kashani-Sabet, M. (1991) Ribozyme-mediated cleavage of c-*fos* mRNA reduces gene expression of DNA synthesis enzymes and metallothionein. *Proc. Natl. Acad. Sci. USA* **88,** 10,591–10,595.

24. Tabin, C. J., Bradley, S. M., Bargmann, C. I., and Weinberg, R. A. (1982) Mechanism of activation of a human oncogene. *Nature* **300,** 143–149.

25. Kashani-Sabet, M., Funato, T., Florenes, V. A., Fodstad, O., and Scanlon, K. J. (1994) Suppression of the neoplastic phenotype *in vivo* by an anti-*ras* ribozyme. *Cancer Res.* **54,** 900–902.

26. Kashani-Sabet, M., Funato, T., Tone, T., Jiao, L., Wang, W., Kashfian, B. I., Yoshida, E., Wu, A. M., Moreno, J. G., Traweek, S. T., Ahlering, T. E., and Scanlon, K. J. (1992) Reversal of human bladder malignant phenotype by an anti-*ras* ribozyme. *Antisense Res. Dev.* **2,** 3–15.

27. Tone, T., Kashani-Sabet, M., Funato, T., Jiao, L., Shitara, T., Fodstad, O., and Scanlon, K. J. (1993) H-*ras* ribozyme-mediated suppression of the neoplastic phenotype of EJ cells. *In Vivo* **7,** 471–476.

28. Scanlon, K. J., Kashani-Sabet, M., and Sowers, L. C. (1989) Overexpression of DNA replication and repair enzymes in cisplatin-resistant human colon carcinoma HCT8 cells and circumvention by azidothymidine. *Cancer Commun.* **1,** 269–273.

29. Saiki, R. K., Scharf, S., Faloona, F., Mullis, K. B., Horn, G. T., Erlich, A., and Arnheim, N. (1985) Enzymatic amplification of β-globin genomic sequences and restriction site analysis for diagnosis of sickle cell anemia. *Science* **230,** 1350–1354.

30. Scanlon, K. J. and Kashani-Sabet, M. (1988) Elevated expression of thymidylate synthase cycle genes in cisplatin-resistant human ovarian carcinoma A2780 cells. *Proc. Natl. Acad. Sci. USA* **85,** 650–653.

31. Cech, T. R. (1990) Self-splicing of group I introns. *Ann. Rev. Biochem.* **59,** 543–568.

32. Aitman, S. (1987) Ribonuclease P: an enzyme with a catalytic RNA subunit. *Adv. Enzymol.* **62,** 1–36.

33. Symons, R. S. (1992) Small catalytic RNAs. *Ann. Rev. Biochem.* **61,** 641–671.

34. Uhlenbeck, O. C. (1987) A small catalytic oligonucleotide. *Nature* **328,** 596–600.
35. Haseliff, J. and Gerlach, W. L. (1988) Simple RNA enzymes with new and highly specific endoribonuclease activity. *Nature* **334,** 271–280.
36. Holm, P. S., Scanlon, K. J., and Dietel, M. (1994) Reversion of multidrug resistance in a MDR mediated drug resistant cell line by introduction of a hammerhead ribozyme. *Br. J. Cancer* **70,** 239–243.
37. Ohta, Y., Tone, T., Shitara, T., Funato, T., Jiao, L., Kashfian, B. I., Yoshida, E., Horng, M., Tsai, P., Lauterbach, K., Kashani-Sabet, M., Florenes, V. A., Fodstad, O., and Scanlon, K. J. (1994) H-*ras* ribozyme-mediated alteration of the human melanoma phenotype. *Ann. New York Acad. Sci.* **716,** 242–253.
38. Funato, T., Shitara, T., Tone, T., Jiao, L., Kashani-Sabet, M., and Scanlon, K. J. (1994) Suppression of H-*ras*-mediated transformation in NIH3T3 cells by a *ras* ribozyme. *Biochem. Pharm.* **48,** 1471–1475.
39. Cross, M. and Dexter, T. M. (1991) Growth factors in development, transformation, and tumorigenesis. *Cell* **64,** 271–280.
40. Kim, S. J., Angel, P., Lafyatis, R., Hattori, K., Kim, K. Y., Sporn, M. B., Karin, M., and Roberts, A. B. (1990) Autoinduction of transforming growth factor 131 is mediated by the AP-1 complex. *Mol. Cell. Biol.* **10,** 1492–1497.
41. Mercola, D. (1992) Platelet-derived growth factor, transformation, and antisense, in *Gene Regulation: Biology of Antisense RNA and DNA* (Erickson, R. P. and Izant, J. G., eds.), Raven, New York, pp. 329–353.
42. Yang, Y. Nunes, F. A., Berencsi, K., Furth, E. E., Gönczöl, E, and Wilson, J. E. (1994) Cellular immunity to viral antigens limits E1-deleted adenoviruses for gene therapy. *Proc. Natl. Acad. Sci. USA* **91,** 4407–4411.

30

Methods for Cancer Gene Therapy Using Tumor Suppressor Genes

Wei-Wei Zhang and Jack A. Roth

1. Introduction

Under experimental conditions, fusion of normal and malignant cells in many different combinations most often results in the suppression of the tumorigenic phenotype of tumor cells *(1)*. This phenomenon led to a hypothesis that the normal genome might contain "recessive cancer genes" that, when expressed, would suppress the growth of tumors *(2)*. Since the identification and cloning of the retinoblastoma (*Rb*) and *p53* genes, the study of what are now called tumor suppressor genes has progressed rapidly. Although tumors generally develop through multiple changes in several genes, the malignant phenotype can be reversed by the introduction of a single chromosome derived from a normal cell, suggesting that single suppressor genes may be able to overcome the effects of multiple changes related to tumor progression *(3)*.

Among the tumor suppressor genes thus far characterized, the *p53* gene is the most extensively studied *(4,5)*. Mutations of the *p53* gene and allele loss on chromosome 17p, on which this gene is located, are among the most frequent alterations identified in human malignancies. The *p53* protein is highly conserved through evolution and is expressed in most normal tissues. Wild-type *p53* has been shown to be involved in control of the cell cycle, transcriptional regulation, DNA replication, and induction of apoptosis. The wild-type *p53* gene can suppress cell transformation and neoplastic cell growth *(6–8)*. Recently, it was demonstrated that the growth of human lung cancer cells was suppressed by wild-type *p53* that was stably expressed in the cells after retrovirus-mediated gene transfer *(9)*.

From: *Methods in Molecular Medicine, Gene Therapy Protocols*
Edited by: P. Robbins Humana Press Inc., Totowa, NJ

The strategy for tumor suppressor gene therapy for cancer is to suppress the malignant phenotype of tumor cells by replacing the inactivated gene with a normal (wild-type) one to restore control of cell growth and differentiation. To effectively carry out this strategy, the therapeutic genes must be delivered efficiently and expressed at a high level in the tumor. Adenoviral vectors have many advantages over other viral vector systems and other in vitro techniques for introducing DNA into eukaryotic cells *(10–12)*. Adenoviruses are easy to manipulate and can be obtained in high titers, 10^9–10^{12} plaque-forming units (PFU)/mL. They have a broad range of hosts and high rates of infectivity. Several recent animal studies have demonstrated that the use of recombinant adenoviruses for gene therapy is possible *(13)*. Recombinant adenoviruses have been successfully administered to a variety of tissues through different routes, including intratracheal instillation *(14)*, muscle injection *(15)*, peripheral iv injection *(16)*, and stereotactic inoculation to the brain *(17)*.

We used recombinant adenovirus as a vector and wild-type *p53* as a therapeutic gene to construct a *p53* adenovirus and studied its efficacy as an anticancer agent in vitro and in vivo. The virus, Ad5CMV-*p53*, carries an expression cassette that contains human cytomegalovirus E1 promoter, human wild-type *p53* cDNA, and SV40 early polyadenylation signal *(18)* (Fig. 1). The Ad5CMV-*p53* virus mediated an efficient transfer and high-level expression of the *p53* gene in human lung cancer cells *(19)*. Growth of the lung cancer cells in which *p53* was deleted or mutated was greatly inhibited by Ad5CMV-*p53*, whereas growth of the cell line containing wild-type *p53* was less affected. Tumorigenicity tests in nude mice demonstrated that Ad5CMV-*p53* prevented tumor formation. When animal tumors were treated locally with Ad5CMV-*p53* and systemically with the chemotherapeutic agent cisplatin, a strong tumoricidal effect through apoptosis of tumor cells was detected *(20)*.

The methods described in this chapter are based on our experimental designs for studying the Ad5CMV-*p53* virus. These methods, as examples for research on tumor suppressor gene therapy of cancer, can be adapted and further developed for study of a specific gene in transfer and its therapeutic efficacy.

2. Materials

2.1. Determination of Gene Transfer and Expression

2.1.1. Determination of Infectivity

1. Phosphate-buffered saline (PBS): 10 mM sodium phosphate, pH 7.4, 150 mM NaCl.
2. 3.8% formalin in PBS.
3. H_2O_2/methanol: 1.0% H_2O_2 in methanol.
4. Blocking solution: 0.15% horse serum and 0.1% bovine serum albumin (BSA) in PBS.

Primer 1: 5'-GGCCCACCCCCTTGGCTTC-3'

Primer 2: 5'-TTGTAACCATTATAAGCTGC-3'

Primer 3: 5'-TCGTTTCTCAGCAGCTGTTG-3'

Primer 4: 5'-CATCTGAACTCAAAGCGTGG-3'

Fig. 1. Ad5CMV-*p53* genome structure, PCR primer locations, and their sequences. The Ad5CMV-*p53* genome is about 35.4 kb divided into 100 map units (1 m.u. = 0.35 kb). The *p53* expression cassette replaced the E1 region (1.3–9.2 m.u.) of the Ad5 genome. Primer 1 is located in the first intron downstream of the human cytomegalovirus major IE gene promoter. Primer 2 is located in the SV40 early polyadenylation signal. The two primers are located 15–20 bp from either end of the *p53* cDNA and define a 1.40-kb PCR product. Primers 3 and 4 are located at 11 and 13.4 m.u., respectively, on the Ad5 genome, defining a 0.86-kb viral genome-specific PCR product.

5. Primary antibodies: Anti-*p53* monoclonal antibody (MAb) (pAb1801; Oncogene Science, Uniondale, NY) and antiactin antibody (Amersham, Arlington Heights, IL).
6. Biotinylated secondary antibody and avidin/biotinylated-peroxidase complex (ABC) reagents (Vector Laboratories, Burlingame, CA).
7. Diaminobenzidine tetrahydrochloride (DAB) stock solution: 100 mg DAB to 16.6 mL PBS (6 mg/mL final). Make 0.5-mL aliquots and store at –20°C.
8. DAB/H_2O_2 solution: Mix 0.5 mL DAB stock solution with 4.5 mL PBS with 0.1% BSA, add 100 mL of 3% H_2O_2, and let stand for 30 min. The solution must be freshly made and the tube should be wrapped with foil to protect from light.
9. Harris hematoxylin.
10. 4% Acetic acid: 8 mL acetic acid in 192 mL H_2O.
11. Saturated Li_2CO_3 solution: 6.6 g Li_2CO_3 in 500 mL H_2O.
12. 70 and 100% Ethanol solutions.
13. Xylene.
14. Cytoseal 60 (Stephens Scientific, Riverdale, NJ).

2.1.2. Detection of Intracellular Vector DNA

1. PBS: 10 mM sodium phosphate, pH 7.4, 150 mM NaCl.
2. Lysing buffer: 0.6% sodium dodecyl sulfate (SDS); 50 mM Tris-HCl, pH 7.4, 10 mM EDTA.
3. 4M NaCl solution.
4. Phenol/chloroform/isoamyl alcohol (24/24/1), pH 8.0.
5. Isoprapanol.
6. 70% Enthanol.
7. 10X dNTP mix: 2 mM each of dATP, dCTP, dGTP, and dTTP in deionized H$_2$O.
8. 10X Polymerase chain reaction (PCR) buffer: 100 mM Tris-HCl, pH 9.0 at 25°C, 15 mM MgCl$_2$, 500 mM KCl, 1% Triton X-100.
9. Primers: The following two pairs of primers were designed for specific detections of the *p53* insert (primers 1 and 2) and adenoviral vector (primers 3 and 4) (Fig. 1).
   a. Primer 1: 5'-GGCCCACCCCCTTGGCTTC-3'
   b. Primer 2: 5'-TTGTAACCATTATAAGCTGC-3'
   c. Primer 3: 5'-TCGTTTCTCAGCAGCTGTTG-3'
   d. Primer 4: 5'-CATCTGAACTCAAAGCGTGG-3'
10. *Taq* DNA polymerase: 5 U/mL (Promega, Madison, WI).

2.1.3. Analysis of Gene Expression

1. SDS-polyacrylamide gel electrophoresis (PAGE) sample buffer: 125 mM Tris-HCl, pH 6.8, 1% SDS, 1% 2-mercaptoethanol, 10% glycerol, 0.5% bromophenol blue.
2. 30% Acrylamide/0.8% bisacrylamide solution.
3. 4X Tris-HCl/SDS gel buffer: 1.5M Tris-HCl, pH 8.8, 0.4% SDS for separating gel; 1.5M Tris-HCl, pH 6.8, 0.4% SDS for stacking gel. Store solutions at 4°C.
4. Electrophoresis and transfer apparatus: mini-gel system (Bio-Rad, Hercules, CA) or equivalent.
5. Butanol for overlay in preparation of separating gel.
6. Prestained protein molecular weight markers.
7. 5X SDS-PAGE running buffer: 15.1 g Tris base, 72.0 g glycine, 5.0 g SDS; add deionized H$_2$O to 1 L. Do not adjust pH of the stock solution. The pH is 8.3 when the solution is diluted to 1X for use in the protocol.
8. Transfer buffer: 20 mM Tris/150 mM glycine, pH 8.0, 20% methanol. Store at 4°C.
9. Whatman 3 MM filter paper.
10. Hybond-ECL membrane: 0.45-mm, 20 × 20 cm (Amersham).
11. 5% Blotto solution: 5% nonfat dry milk (Carnation; Nestlé, Glendale, CA) in PBS with 0.3% Tween-20.
12. Primary antibodies: Anti-*p53* MAb (pAb1801; Oncogene Science) and antiactin MAb (Amersham).
13. Secondary antibody: Horseradish peroxidase-anti-IgG conjugate (Amersham).
14. Heat-sealable plastic bag.
15. Hyperfilm-ECL (Amersham).
16. ECL detection reagents A and B (Amersham).

2.2. Examination of the Cancer-Inhibitory Effect

2.2.1. Determination of Cell Growth

1. Trypsin-EDTA solution.
2. 0.4% Trypan blue solution: 0.4% trypan blue in 0.85% saline.
3. Hemocytometer.

2.2.2. Assay of Bystander Effect

1. Microconcentrator: Centriprep-30 and -100 (Amicon).
2. Trypsin-EDTA solution.
3. 0.4% Trypan blue solution: 0.4% trypan blue in 0.85% saline.
4. Hemocytometer.

2.3. Analyses of the Cancer-Inhibitory Mechanism

2.3.1. Analysis of Cell Cycle

1. 100% Ethanol stored at −20°C.
2. 0.5% Tween-20 in PBS.
3. DNase-free RNase A stock solution: 10 mg/mL in 10 mM Tris-HCl, pH 7.5, 15 mM NaCl.
4. Propidium iodide (PI) 20 mg/mL in PBS.
5. "Cell Fit" program (Becton Dickinson, Rutherford, NJ).

2.3.2. Examination of Apoptosis

1. 0.01% NP-40 in PBS.
2. Proteinase K solution: 20 mg/mL (Boehringer-Mannheim, Mannheim, Germany).
3. 2% H_2O_2 in methanol, freshly made.
4. Terminal deoxynucleotidyl transferase (TDT) buffer: 30 mM Tris-HCl, pH 7.2, 140 mM sodium cacodylate, 1 mM cobalt chloride.
5. TDT enzyme: 17 U/mL (U.S. Biochemicals, Cleveland, OH).
6. Biotin-dUTP (Boehringer-Mannheim).
7. TB buffer: 300 mM NaCl and 30 mM sodium citrate.
8. ABC reagents (Vector Laboratories).
9. Peroxidase substrate: DAB stock and working solution (as in Section 2.1.1.).
10. Harris hematoxylin.
11. 4% Acetic acid: 8 mL acetic acid in 192 mL H_2O.
12. Saturated Li_2CO_3 solution: 6.6 g Li_2CO_3 in 500 mL H_2O.
13. 70 and 100% Ethanol solutions.
14. Xylene.
15. Cytoseal 60 (Stephens Scientific).
16. DNase I solution (for positive control): 50 mg/mL DNase I in 10 mM Tris-HCl, 140 mM sodium cacodylate, 4 mM $MgCl_2$, and 10 mM dithiothreitol (DTT).

2.4. Evaluation of Tumor Suppressor Gene Therapy in Animal Models

2.4.1. Orthotopic Lung Cancer Model

1. Nude mice: BALB/c female *nu/nu* mice at age of 5 wk.
2. 100% Ethanol.
3. Disinfectant: Bacdown (Decon Laboratories, Bryn Mawr, PA) or 10% bleach.
4. Inhalation anesthetic agent: Metofane (methoxyflurane).
5. Surgical scalpel (#10) (Bard-Parker; Becton Dickinson, Franklin Lakes, NJ).
6. Forceps, hemostats, and scissors.
7. 1-cc Syringes with 25-gage needles (Bard-Parker).
8. Freshly prepared cell suspension in PBS at $1–5 \times 10^7$ cell/mL, stored on ice.
9. Viruses in PBS at $1–5 \times 10^{10}$ PFU/mL and PBS as vehicle control.
10. Stainless steel wound clip tools (Clay Adams; Becton Dickinson, Sparks, MD): Autoclips (9 mm), Autoclip Applier, and Autoclip Remover.
11. Vernier calipers.
12. O.C.T. compound (embedding medium for frozen tissue specimens, Miles, New Haven, CT).
13. Liquid N_2 and portable container.
14. 10% neutral-buffered formalin.

2.4.2. Combination Therapy Model

1. Nude mice: BALB/c female *nu/nu* mice at age of 5 wk.
2. 100% Ethanol.
3. Disinfectant: Bacdown (Decon Laboratories) or 10% bleach.
4. Inhalation anesthetic agent: Metofane (methoxyflurane).
5. 1-cc Syringes with 25-gage needles (Bard-Parker).
6. Freshly prepared cell suspension in PBS at $1–5 \times 10^7$ cell/mL, stored on ice.
7. Vernier calipers.
8. Chemotherapeutic agent: cisplatin (CDDP) at 0.5 mg/mL in PBS.
9. O.C.T. compound
10. Liquid N_2 and portable container.
11. 10% Neutral buffered formalin.

3. Methods

3.1. Determination of Gene Transfer and Expression

3.1.1. Determination of Infectivity

1. Infection: To cell monolayers in 60-mm dishes at 80% confluence, add 0.5 mL viral solution at different multiplicities of infection (MOI) for 30 min at room temperature. Appropriate controls of vector and mock-infection should be applied. Add 6 mL medium and return dishes to cell incubator (37°C, 5% CO_2).
2. Twenty hours after infection, rinse cells with PBS and air dry.

3. Fix cells with 3.8% formalin for 5 min.
4. Treat cells with 1.0% H_2O_2 in methanol for 5 min.
5. Wash cells with PBS for 5 min.
6. Block cells with 0.15% horse serum and 0.1% BSA in PBS for 15 min.
7. Wash cells with PBS for 5 min.
8. Incubate cells with primary antibodies (1:500) in PBS with 0.1% BSA for 1 h.
9. Wash cells with PBS for 5 min with 2–3 changes.
10. Incubate cells with secondary antibody (1:1000) in PBS with 0.1% BSA for 30 min.
11. Wash cells with PBS for 5 min with 2–3 changes.
12. Incubate cells with ABC reagents at 37°C for 30 min.
13. Wash cells with PBS for 5 min with 2–3 changes.
14. Incubate cells with DAB/H_2O_2 solution at 37°C for 20–30 min. Monitor development of reddish brown color under microscope.
15. Stop color reaction by washing cells with PBS for 5 min with 2–3 changes.
16. Counterstain cells with Harris hematoxylin for 1 min.
17. Wash cells with deionized H_2O for 3 min with 3 changes.
18. Treat cells with 4% acetic acid for 3 min.
19. Wash cells with deionized H_2O for 3 min.
20. Treat cells with saturated Li_2CO_3 for 3 min.
21. Wash cells with deionized H_2O for 3 min.
22. Dehydrate cells with 70% ethanol for 2 min and 100% ethanol for 5 min.
23. Treat cells with xylene for 5 min.
24. Mount cells with cover slides using Cytoseal 60.

3.1.2. Detection of Intracellular Vector DNA

1. Infect cells in 60-mm dishes at appropriate MOI of virus and vector control. Use medium alone as mock-infection.
2. At different times after infection, rinse cells with PBS and quickly with deionized H_2O.
3. Add 0.75 mL lysing buffer to cell monolayers, followed by 0.25 mL 4M NaCl.
4. Mix by scraping and collect cell lysate.
5. Leave cell lysate at 4°C overnight.
6. Pellet precipitated genomic DNA at 4°C for 15 min.
7. Collect supernatant, extract with one vol of phenol/chloroform.
8. Precipitate DNA with 0.6 vol of isopropanol at –80°C for 30 min.
9. Rinse pellets with 70% ethanol, air dry pellets, and resuspend pellets with 20 mL H_2O.
10. Make multiple 31-mL PCR mixture with a ratio of 5 mL each of 10X buffer, 10X 2 mM-dNTP mix, primers (total four), and 1 mL *Taq* polymerase.
11. Distribute 31 mL of mixture to each PCR tube and add 19 mL DNA sample to each tube.
12. Run a 30-cycle PCR at 94°C, 0.5 min; 58°C, 1 min; and 72°C, 2 min.
13. Analyze 5 mL each of PCR products in 1.2% agarose gel (*see* example in Fig. 2).

Fig. 2. Agarose gel analysis of PCR products. Human lung cancer H358 cells (homozygously deleted *p53*) were infected with Ad5CMV-*p53* and a control virus (vector only, carrying no *p53* gene) at an MOI of 50 PFU/cell. Medium was used for mock infection. At 24 h postinfection, vector DNA was extracted and analyzed by PCR as described in Section 3.1.2. Five microliters of each PCR reaction were analyzed on 1.2% agarose gel. The bands from the 1.4-kb *p53* insert, the 0.86-kb viral genome fragment, and the primers are indicated. Lanes 1 and 2 show the positive and negative controls, where the purified viral DNA and the DNA extracted from mock-infected cells, respectively, were used as templates. Lanes 3 and 4 show the DNA templates prepared from the cells infected with control virus and Ad5CMV-*p53*, respectively.

3.1.3. Analysis of Gene Expression

1. Infect cells in 60-mm dishes at appropriate MOI of virus and vector control. Use medium alone as mock-infection.
2. At different times after infection, rinse cells with PBS and quickly with deion-ized H_2O.
3. Add SDS-PAGE sample buffer to cell monolayers at 0.2–0.5 mL/dish.
4. Collect cell lysate by scraping and boil lysate for 3 min.
5. Run 8% SDS-PAGE with 10–20 mL sample per lane in Bio-Rad mini-gel apparatus.
6. Transfer proteins from gel to Hybond-ECL membrane at 100 V for 1 h.
7. Block membrane with 5% Blotto for 20 min at room temperature or overnight at 4°C.
8. Primary antibody reaction: Anti-*p53* 1:2000 and anti-actin 1:4000 in Blotto for 1 h.
9. Wash membrane in Blotto for 15 min with three changes.
10. Secondary antibody reaction: Horseradish peroxidase-conjugated IgG 1:5000 in Blotto for 30 min.

1 2 3 4 5 6 7

-p53
-Actin

D1   D3   D5   C

Fig. 3. Western analysis of *p53* expression mediated by Ad5CMV-*p53*. Human lung cancer H358 cells (homozygously deleted *p53*) were infected with Ad5CMV-*p53* or a control virus (vector only, carrying no *p53* gene) at an MOI of 50 PFU/cell. On postinfection days 1, 3, and 5, as indicated, cellular lysates were prepared and analyzed by Western blotting as described in Section 3.1.3. Twenty microliters of each protein sample were fractionated by SDS-PAGE. After transfer to ECL-membrane, proteins were first probed with anti-*p53* and antiactin MAb in the same binding reaction, followed by probing with horseradish peroxidase-conjugated secondary antibody; they were then detected with ECL regents. An optimal exposure of developed ECL membrane is shown. Lanes 1, 3, and 5 represent samples prepared from the control-virus-infected cells. Lanes 2, 4, and 6 represent samples from cells infected with Ad5CMV-*p53*. Lane 7, indicated as C (control), represents the sample of mock-infected cells.

11. Wash membrane in Blotto for 10 min with three changes.
12. Add ECL detection agents (A and B) for 1 min.
13. Quickly dry membrane with paper towel. Put membrane in plastic bag.
14. Expose X-ray film against membrane briefly in darkroom and develop the exposed film (*see* example in Fig. 3).

3.2. Examination of the Cancer-Inhibitory Effect

3.2.1. Determination of Cell Growth

1. Inoculate cells at 10^5 cells/60-mm dish and incubate overnight.
2. On d 0, infect cells at 10–50 MOI of virus and vector control, with triplicate dishes for each treatment, including medium alone as mock-infection.
3. From d 1–6, count cells daily (triplicate dishes for each time point).
4. Cell counts: Rinse cells with PBS, harvest cells with trypsin-EDTA, resuspend cells in 1–5 mL medium, dilute cell suspension with 0.4% trypan blue in 0.85% saline, and count cells in hemocytometer.
5. Average cell counts for each time point and plot cell growth curves.

3.2.2. Assays of Bystander Effect

Two types of methods can be used for bystander-effect assays: cell mix and cell-free medium assays.

3.2.2.1. Cell Mix Assay (Batch A)

1. Inoculate multiple dishes of cells at 10^6 cells/60-mm dish and incubate overnight.
2. Divide cell dishes into two batches. Infect one batch of cells at 10–50 MOI of virus and vector control. Use medium alone as mock-infection. Leave the other batch untreated.
3. Twenty hours after infection, wash cells with PBS.
4. Harvest both batches of cells separately with trypsin-EDTA and suspend cells in medium.
5. Count cells in hemocytometer.
6. Mix treated cells with equal number of untreated cells and inoculate 2×10^5 cells/dish with triplicate dishes for each treatment.
7. Count cells daily for 6 d (triplicate dishes for each time point).
8. Average cell counts for each time point and plot cell growth curves.

3.2.2.2. Cell-Free Medium Assay (Batch B)

1. Inoculate batch A cells at 2×10^7 cells/100-mm dish and incubate overnight.
2. On d 0, infect cells at 10–50 MOI of virus and vector control with one dish for each treatment, including medium alone as mock-infection.
3. On d 1, wash treated cells with PBS twice and culture the cells with new medium (12 mL/dish).
4. On d 2, inoculate batch B cells at 1×10^5 cells/60-mm dish and incubate overnight.
5. On d 3, collect culture media from each treatment of the batch A cells.
6. Centrifuge the culture media by $10,000g$ at 4°C for 15 min.
7. Collect supernatants (about 11 mL from each dish).
8. Fractionate each of the supernatants with Centriprep-100.
9. Dilute the concentrated supernatants (about 2 mL/fraction) with fresh medium up to 18 mL, designate as fraction >100 kDa.
10. Further fractionate the through-fractions with Centriprep-30.
11. Dilute the concentrated fractions (about 2 mL/fraction) and the through-fractions with fresh medium up to 18 mL, designate as fractions 30–100 kDa and <30 kDa, respectively.
12. Wash batch B cells with PBS.
13. Treat batch B cells with the fractions: 6 mL of each fraction for each of triplicate dishes of cells.
14. From d 4–9, count cells daily (triplicate dishes for each time point).
15. Average cell counts for each time point and plot cell growth curves.

3.3. Analyses of the Cancer-Inhibitory Mechanism

3.3.1. Analysis of Cell Cycle

1. Inoculate cells at 2×10^6 cells/60-mm dish and incubate overnight.
2. Infect cells at appropriate MOI of virus and vector control for different time points. Use medium alone as mock-infection.

3. Harvest cells with trypsinization and wash cells with PBS.
4. Resuspend cell pellet in 300 mL PBS.
5. Fix cells with 700 mL prechilled 100% ethanol at –20°C for 20 min.
6. Pelletize cells and wash with PBS.
7. Treat cells with 0.5% Tween-20 in PBS.
8. Wash cells with PBS.
9. Incubate cells with DNase-free RNase A (1 mg/mL) in PBS at 37°C for 15 min.
10. Pelletize cells and wash with PBS.
11. Resuspend cell pellets with 500 mL of PI/PBS solution.
12. Run cell samples in flow cytometer using "Cell Fit" program and analyze data with SOBR mathematical model *(21)*.

3.3.2. Examination of Apoptosis

1. Infect cells in 60-mm dishes at appropriate MOI of virus and vector control. Use medium alone as mock-infection.
2. At different times after infection, rinse cells with PBS.
3. Fix cells with 4% paraformaldehyde in PBS for 5 min.
4. Incubate cells with 0.01% NP-40/PBS for 5 min.
5. Treat cells with 20 mg proteinase K/mL in PBS for 15 min.
6. Wash cells with PBS for 3 min with three changes.
7. Treat cells with 2% H_2O_2/methanol for 5 min.
8. Wash cells with PBS for 3 min with three changes.
9. Wash cells with TDT buffer for 2 min.
10. Incubate cells with TDT enzyme (1:400 dilution of 17 U/mL) and biotin-dUTP (1:100 dilution of 50 nmol) in TDT buffer at 37°C for 45 min.
11. Treat cells with TB buffer for 5 min with two changes.
12. Wash cells deionized H_2O for 1 min.
13. Block cells with 2% BSA.
14. Rinse cells with PBS.
15. Incubate cells with ABC reagents at 37°C for 30 min.
16. Wash cells with PBS for 5 min with 2–3 changes.
17. Incubate cells with DAB/H_2O_2 solution at 37°C for 20–30 min. Monitor development of reddish brown color under microscope.
18. Stop color reaction by washing cells with PBS for 5 min with 2–3 changes.
19. Counterstain cells with Harris hematoxylin for 1 min.
20. Wash cells with deionized H_2O for 3 min with three changes.
21. Treat cells with 4% acetic acid for 3 min.
22. Wash cells with deionized H_2O for 3 min.
23. Treat cells with saturated Li_2CO_3 for 3 min.
24. Wash cells with deionized H_2O for 3 min.
25. Dehydrate cells with 70% ethanol for 2 min and 100% ethanol for 5 min.
26. Treat cells with xylene for 5 min.
27. Mount cells with cover slides using Cytoseal 60.

3.4. Evaluation of Tumor Suppressor Gene Therapy in Animal Models

3.4.1. Orthotopic Lung Cancer Model

1. Harvest tumor cells at exponential growth phase and suspend cells in PBS at a concentration of $1-5 \times 10^7$ cells/mL. Store on ice.
2. Irradiate nude mice at 350 cGy of ^{137}Cs.
3. Anesthetize mice with inhalation of methoxyflurane.
4. Position mice on operating board.
5. Sterilize anterior neck area with 100% ethanol.
6. Open skin with scalpel and carefully separate muscle layers with hemostat to expose trachea.
7. Advance needle (25-gage) through tracheal wall toward bronchi and inject 0.1 mL of cells slowly.
8. Apply Autoclips to close surgical wound.
9. Return mice to cage.
10. On the third and fourth days, repeat the intratracheal injections (*see* step 7) with 0.1 mL/mouse of viral solutions (1×10^{10} PFU/mL) or equal volume of vehicle only (PBS).
11. Observe general condition of the treated mice weekly for 6–8 wk.
12. Kill mice by cervical dislocation.
13. Dissect mice to harvest mediastinal block (including lungs, heart, bronchi, and trachea).
14. Grossly examine tumor formation. Tumors usually grow along the lower part of the trachea near the bifurcation, with a solid tumor mass protruding from the surface of the tracheal wall.
15. Measure tumor cross-sectional diameters with Vernier calipers. Determine tumor volume by calculating a spherical body ($4/3pr^3$) with the average tumor diameter determined from the square root of the product of the cross-sectional diameters.
16. Tumor samples with adjacent tracheal tissue may be immediately embedded in O.C.T. compound and snap-frozen in liquid N_2 for frozen-section preparations for enzymatic staining or immunostaining. Alternatively, the samples can be fixed in 10% formalin for histologic sectioning and analyzed with H&E staining.

3.4.2. Combination Therapy Model

1. Harvest cells at exponential growth phase and suspend cells in PBS at a concentration of $1-5 \times 10^7$ cells/mL. Store on ice.
2. Irradiate nude mice at 350 cGy of ^{137}Cs.
3. Subcutaneously inject 0.1 mL of cell suspension into the right flank of mice.
4. Allow tumors to grow for 30–40 d or until the average diameter of tumor reaches 5 mm. (The average diameter is a square root of the product of two perpendicular diameters of tumor measured with calipers.)
5. Inject into each tumor 100 mL of PBS alone or viral solutions ($1-5 \times 10^{10}$ PFU/mL).
6. Intraperitoneally inject cisplatin solution (3 mg/kg) or equal volume of PBS.

7. Measure tumor size with calipers daily for 2 wk.
8. To examine the histologic characteristic of the tumor after treatment, a tumor sample should be collected 3–5 d after treatment. Tumor samples can be immediately embedded in O.C.T. compound and snap-frozen in liquid N_2 for frozen section preparations (3–5 mm) for enzymatic staining or immunostaining. Alternatively, the samples may be fixed in 10% formalin for histologic sectioning and analyzed with HE staining.

4. Notes
4.1. Determination of Gene Transfer and Expression

1. Generation, propagation, and titer determination of recombinant viruses for experiments should be referred to the appropriate chapters in this book or other references. Adenoviruses need to be purified through CsCl-banding, dialyzed in PBS, and stored in aliquots at –80°C. Retroviruses may be harvested in serum-free medium, filtrated, and stored in aliquots at –80°C.
2. Cell culture medium and conditions should be prepared according to the requirement of the particular cell lines chosen for experiments.
3. For each experiment appropriate controls such as vector and vehicle (mock-infection) controls should be set up.
4. Infectivity of viral vector can also be assessed by using reporter genes such as *LacZ*.
5. For vector DNA extraction or Western blot sampling, if cell monolayers need to be harvested or cells are in suspension, pelletize cells by centrifugation. Rinse cells with PBS. Resuspend cell pellets in 100–200 mL of H_2O. Add an equal volume of 2X lysing buffer or 2X SDS-PAGE sample buffer.
6. To semiquantitatively detect the transferred gene and its product in cells, vector-control PCR primers or cellular-protein (b-actin) antibodies can be applied in the same reactions for PCR analysis of the transferred gene or Western analysis of the expressed protein. Two pairs of the PCR primers that detect *p53* gene and adenoviral vector DNA in a single PCR analysis or the anti-*p53* and antiactin antibodies used in the Western blotting have been successfully used in studies of the *p53* adenovirus, as shown in Figs. 2 and 3.
7. To obtain an optimal exposure, the membrane can be exposed serially to X-ray film. In the darkroom, place one side of the X-ray film against the membrane, expose for 1 min, move film toward the other side and expose membrane for 3 min, and so on for 5 min. Develop the exposed film.

4.2. Studies of the Cancer-Inhibitory Effect of the Tumor Suppressor Gene

8. Two types of simple experiments for examining tumor cell growth after transfer of a tumor suppressor gene are described. For further studies, more complicated assays, such as [H^3] thymidine uptake, growth in soft agar or spheroids, or those that detect specific effects caused by transferred genes, need to be applied.

9. Dosages of viral vectors for study of the inhibitory effect should be based on the data obtained from infectivity experiments. The MOI that enables 85–95% efficiency of gene transfer should be used.
10. Trypsinization is one of the key steps that affect the accuracy of cell counts. Condition should be set up to avoid under- or over-trypsinization for harvesting monolayer cells. Alternatively, assays similar to conventional cell counts but that do not acquire trypsin to harvest cells may be applied.

4.3. Analyses of the Cancer-Inhibitory Mechanisms of Tumor Suppressor Genes

11. Cell cycle and apoptosis assays are examples of experiments designed to study the function of the *p53* protein. Studies of the mechanisms of cancer inhibition by a given tumor suppressor gene after gene transfer may be specifically designed to meet the needs of the investigators.
12. Pi iodide is used to stain cellular DNA. This is a simple and quick method, but it is less accurate than BrdU labeling, which is much more complicated and relatively cumbersome. If more accurate data are needed, BrdU labeling should be used.
13. Data generated by the Cell Fit program should be analyzed by using the SOBR mathematical model; alternately S-FIT or R-FIT *(22)* can be used.
14. For analysis of apoptosis, conventional DNA extraction and gel analysis can be used. Analysis by flow cytometry of cells labeled with fluorescence by TDT reaction is another approach.
15. If paraffin-embedded tissue sections are used for TDT staining, deparaffinize the tissue sections by treating them with xylene for 5 min twice, 100% ethanol for 5 min twice, 95 and 70% ethanol for 3 min each. Finally, wash slides with PBS for 5 min.

4.4. Evaluation of Tumor Suppressor Gene Therapy— An Animal Model

16. Different tumor cell lines or different tumor suppressor gene vectors need different types of animal models. The two models described in this chapter are for applying recombinant *p53* adenovirus in the study of lung cancer treatment in vivo.
17. Safety procedures should be observed in infecting animals with the viral solutions in the animal room. Use 10% bleach or Bacdown solution to clean the laminar flow hood before and after the operation.
18. Operations on animals should be handled carefully and delicately to avoid extensive tissue damages and bleeding, particularly when operating on the exposed trachea. To avoid pneumothorax, do not dissect into the upper chest. Since operation on animals by inexperienced personnel often results in animal death, extra animals for each treatment group should be prepared.
19. In our experiments, a single-pass intratumoral injection of viral solution (100 mL of $1–5 \times 10^9$ PFU/tumor of a 5-mm average diameter) resulted in 60–70% infection of the tumor mass. The infection rate can be improved by using single-pass injection each day for 3 d.

References

1. Klein, G. (1987) The approaching era of the tumor suppressor genes. *Science* 238, 1539–1545.
2. Harris, H., Miller, O. J., Klein, G., Worst, P., and Tachebana, T. (1969) Suppression of malignancy by cell fusion. *Nature* 223, 363–368.
3. Anderson, M. J. and Stanbridge, E. J. (1993) Tumor suppressor genes studied by cell hybridization and chromosome transfer. *FASEB J.* 7, 826–833.
4. Montenarh, M. (1992) Biochemical, immunological, and functional aspects of the growth-suppressor/oncoprotein *p53*. *Crit. Rev. Oncogen.* 3, 233–256.
5. Tominaga, O., Hamelin, R., Remvikos, Y., Saimon, R. J., and Thomas, G. (1992) *p53* from basic research to clinical applications. *Crit. Rev. Oncogen.* 3, 257–282.
6. Finlay, C. A., Hinds, P. W., and Levine, A. J. (1989) The *p53* proto-oncogene can act as a suppressor of transformation. *Cell* 57, 1083–1093.
7. Cheng, J., Yee, J.-K., Yeargin, J., Friedmann, T., and Haas, M. (1992) Suppression of acute lymphoblastic leukemia by the human wild-type *p53* gene. *Cancer Res.* 52, 222–226.
8. Takahashi, T., Carbone, D., Takahashi, T., Nau, M. M., Hida, T., Linnoila, I., Ueda, R., and Minna, J. D. (1992) Wild-type but not mutant *p53* suppresses the growth of human lung cancer cells bearing multiple genetic lesions. *Cancer Res.* 52, 2340–2343.
9. Cai, D. W., Mukhopadhyay, T., Liu, Y., Fujiwara, T., and Roth, J. A. (1993) Stable expression of the wild-type *p53* gene in human lung cancer cells after retrovirus-mediated gene transfer. *Human Gene Ther.* 4, 617–624.
10. Strafford-Perricaudet, L. and Perricaudet, M. (1991) Gene transfer into animals: the promise of adenovirus, in *Human Gene Transfer* (Cohen-Haguenauer, O. and Boiron, M, eds.), John Libbey Eurotext, France, pp. 51–61.
11. Graham, F. L. and Prevec, L. (1991) Manipulation of adenovirus vectors, in *Methods in Molecular Biology*, vol. 7, *Gene Transfer and Expression Protocols* (Murray, E. J., ed.), Humana, Clifton, NJ, pp. 109–128.
12. Grunhaus, A. and Horwitz, M. S. (1992) Adenoviruses as cloning vectors. *Semin. Virol.* 3, 237–252.
13. Strafford-Perricaudet, L., Levrero, M., Chasse, J. F., Perricaudet, M., and Briand, C. B. (1991) Evaluation of the transfer and expression in mice of an enzyme-encoding gene using a human adenovirus vector. *Human Gene Ther.* 1, 241–256.
14. Rosenfeld, M. A., Siegfried, W., Yoshimura, K., Yoneyama, K., Fukayama, M., Stier, L. E., Paakko, P. K., Gilardi, P., Stratford-Perricaudet, L., Perricaudet, M., Jallat, S., Pavirani, A., Lecocq, L.-P., and Crystal, R. G. (1991) Adenovirus-mediated transfer of a recombinant a1-antitrypsin gene to the lung epithelium in vivo. *Science* 252, 431–434.
15. Ragot, T., Vincent, N., Chafey, P., Vigne, E., Gilgenkrantz, H., Couton, D., Cartaud, J., Briand, P., Kaplan, J.-C., Perricaudet, M., and Kahn, A. (1993) Efficient adenovirus-mediated transfer of a human minidystrophin gene to skeletal muscle of *mdx* mice. *Nature* 361, 647–650.

16. Herz, J. and Gerard, R. D. (1993) Adenovirus-mediated transfer of low-density lipoprotein receptor gene acutely accelerates cholesterol clearance in normal mice. *Proc. Natl. Acad. Sci. USA* **90,** 2812–2816.
17. Le Gal La Salle, G., Robert, J. J., Bernard, S., Ridoux, V., Stratford-Perricaudet, L. D., and Perricaudet, M. (1993) An adenovirus vector for gene transfer into neurons and glia in the brain. *Science* **259,** 988–990.
18. Zhang, W.-W., Fang, X., Branch, C. D., Mazur, W., French, B. A., and Roth, J. A. (1993) Generation and identification of recombinant adenovirus by liposome-mediated transfection and PCR analysis. *BioTechniques* **15,** 868–872.
19. Zhang, W.-W., Fang, X., Mazur, W., French, B. A., Georges, R. N., and Roth, J. A. (1994) High-efficiency gene transfer and high-level expression of wild-type *p53* in human lung cancer cells mediated by recombinant adenovirus. *Cancer Gene Ther.* **1,** 5–13.
20. Fujiwara, T., Grimm, E. A., Mukhopadhyay, T., Zhang, W.-W., Owen-Schaub, L. B., and Roth, J. A. (1994) Induction of chemosensitivity in human lung cancer cells in vivo by adenovirus-mediated transfer of the wild-type *p53* gene. *Cancer Res.* **54,** 2287–2291.
21. Baisch, H., Beck, H.-P., Christensen, I. J., Hartmann, N. R., Fried, J., Dean, P. N., Gray, J. W., Jett, J. H., Johnston, D. A., White, R. A., Nicolini, C., Zeitz, S., and Watson, J. V. (1982) A comparison of mathematical methods for the analysis of DNA histograms obtained by flow cytometry. *Cell Tissue Kinetics* **15,** 235–249.
22. Baisch, H., Gohde, W., and Linden, W. (1975) Analysis of PCP data to determine the fraction of cells in the various phases of the cell cycle. *Rad. Environ. Biophys.* **12,** 31–39.

Index

P9-AGD-650

THE UNITED STATES: POLITICAL

— International boundaries
— State boundaries
⊛ National capital
✴ State capitals

| 0 | 100 | 200 Miles |
| 0 | 100 | 200 Kilometers |

ATLANTIC OCEAN

GULF OF MEXICO

ATLANTIC OCEAN

PUERTO RICO   VIRGIN ISLANDS

GULF OF MEXICO

0   80 Miles
0   80 Kilometers

CUBA

THE AMERICAN PAST
A Survey of American History

THE AMERICAN PAST
A Survey of American History
FOURTH EDITION

Joseph R. Conlin
California State University, Chico

THE HARCOURT PRESS

Harcourt Brace College Publishers

Fort Worth   Philadelphia   San Diego   New York   Orlando   Austin   San Antonio
Toronto   Montreal   London   Sydney   Tokyo

To J.R.C. and L.V.C.

Publisher	Ted Buchholz
Acquisitions Editor	Drake Bush
Developmental Editor	Phoebe Culp
Project Editor	Mark Hobbs
Production Manager	Cindy Young
Book Designer	Sue Hart
Photo Research/Permissions	Lili Weiner

Address for Editorial Correspondence: Harcourt Brace College
Publishers, 301 Commerce Street , Suite 3700, Fort Worth, TX
76102.

Address for Orders: Harcourt Brace & Company, 6277 Sea Harbor
Drive, Orlando, Florida 32887. 1-800-782-4479, or 1-800-433-0001
(in Florida).

ISBN: 0-15-500613-4

Library of Congress Catalog Card Number: 92-75287

Printed in the United States of America

3 4 5 6 7 8 9 0 1   069   9 8 7 6 5 4 3 2

CONTENTS IN BRIEF

PREFACE TO THE FOURTH EDITION

History, like other humanities and social sciences, is not in good health as the twentieth century eases into its twilight years. The afflictions are several. On the one hand, scholar's newsletters and journals regularly lament the fact that the reading public has next to no interest in the work of professional historians. Critics purporting to speak for the reading public shrug their shoulders and complain that professional historians have become so specialized in their interests and so technical in their methodologies that their writings could possibly be of interest to only a tiny number of like-minded colleagues.

At the same time, the profession itself seems increasingly bipolarized between those who still cling to "that noble dream" of recapturing in their writings and lectures what happened in the past as close an approximation of what actually happened as possible, and those who, having long given up on that goal as a chimera, or as an excuse for advocating one ideology or another, unapologetically employ the past to advocate their own causes.

The publication of no textbook is going to cure these ills. I should, however, indicate where I mean *The American Past* to stand in reference to them.

First, I believe that educated people should be interested in history, and that the burden for ensuring that this is so lies on the shoulders of professional historians. Toward that end, I have tried to make *The American Past* a teacher's textbook. It is aimed not primarily at students training to be professional historians—they will find their own way—but at budding accountants, architects, engineers, nurses, psychologists, and zoo-keepers who find themselves facing a historian's lectern under duress or by default because they were required to "take history" or because they were unable to "find something else" to round out their fifteen units.

Our colleges and universities offer and require survey courses in United States history because of the belief of most of us that the knowledge and analytical skills to be gained in such courses are beneficial to all educated men and women and to the society of which they are members. But as self-evident as that assumption may be to historians, it is one in which many of our survey course students do not share.

The task facing the survey course instructor is to prove to their captives that the authorities were quite right to require their satisfactory completion of a course in American history. There are a good many classroom manners by which students are successfully wooed to such an appreciation of knowing their nation's past. If, in twenty-five years of teaching the survey course, I have learned one thing about doing it, it is not to disdain a method that works simply because it is not mine.

However, it seems that there is only one way to perform the part of the job that faces the textbook author—the seduction of students to a love of the *reading* of history. That is by presenting them with a book that, however massive and forbidding it appears to be in September, proves over the semester to be attractive, vivid, colorful, alive, enjoyable to read. Many a colleague has sent me utterly justified criticisms of something about *The American Past*. It has eased my mortification when the letter-writer has added, "the students really like this book."

Next to writing a narrative that is engaging, I have strived to be comprehensive. *The American Past* is a political history in structure. But I have tried to integrate into this most obvious and forthright of organizations a balanced treatment of the economic, social, cultural, intellectual, constitutional, diplomatic, and military sub-disciplines.

Writing attractively for non-historians demands painting in broad strokes, avoiding the hyper-specialized bureaucratization of professional history that so troubles historians today. Individual lecturers will focus on the subject and methods of analysis that they find most exciting and rewarding. A textbook, I think, should provide a general framework in which to understand these emphases, not try to sell the author's interests to the exclusion of others. Nor should a textbook be an instrument of political advocacy. However flawed my attempt to be an unprejudiced judge, I have to the best of my abilities preached no gospel here.

Every chapter of this edition has been rewritten to some extent. The early chapters, and the final group of chapters, dealing with the post-World War II era, have been completely overhauled to reflect the bonanza discoveries in early American history over the past several years, and my own ever-changing reconceptualizatons of recent developments. A number of the special features—the boxed inserts and the essays titled "How They Lived" and "Notable People"—are new with this edition.

Finally, those who have previously assigned *The American Past* will immediately observe that illustrations are fewer in this edition, and the decorative second color is gone. These changes were made in response to an ever-increasing chorus of student complaints, forwarded by their teachers, that textbooks have become unacceptably expensive. I miss the elegant appearance of past editions, but the cause is compelling. By abandoning frills, bells, and whistles, Harcourt Brace Jovanovich has sharply cut the retail price of the book.

I am in debt to a number of colleagues, who have used the book and, even after three editions, found slips and a few full-blown errors to be corrected: Anthony M. Brescia of Nassau Community College, Allen Dennis of Delta State College, William F. Mugleston of Mountain View College, William Fagan of Eastern Wyoming College, W J. Trunkes of the Embry-Riddle Aeronautical University.

Two colleagues at California State University, Professors Lisa Emmerich and Carl H. Peterson, have read, respectively, sections dealing with American Indian history and the *ante bellum* period. I have been able to respond to some of their criticisms and will explain to them personally why I am still pondering others.

Drake Bush, history editor at Harcourt Brace Jovanovich College Publishers, and one of my oldest friends after all these years, put up with my aches and pains as only an old friend will. Mark Hobbs oversaw the conversion of typescript into printed page; Phoebe Culp assisted in the development of this edition. Sue Hart designed this edition, and Cindy Young was the Production Manager.

CONTENTS

MAPS

THE AMERICAN PAST
A Survey of American History

Jacques Cartier claiming Labrador, now part of Canada, for King Francis I of France, 1534.

A COLLISION OF WORLDS

AMERICA AND EUROPE
25,000 B.C.(?) - A.D. 1550

When did human beings first set foot on American soil? No one knows. Or, to put it more accurately,

the many experts who claim they know cannot prove their knowledge to the satisfaction of many

other experts. And they quarrel like squirrels. Is a fossilized footprint 10,000 years old, or 30,000? Is

a curious pebble the handiwork of a primeval tool-maker, or just wind-tossed and stream-shaped? The

date human beings discovered and settled America is controversial.

THE FIRST AMERICANS

History and Prehistory

It is generally agreed, however, that the first Americans were Asian nomads who trundled across a bridge of land that, during the last Ice Age, 10,000 to 40,000 years ago, connected Siberia to Alaska. These first discoverers of America, and the many colonists who followed them, fanned out to populate two continents in just a few thousand years, a most remarkable migration. They were, of course, the ancestors of the people customarily called "Indians."

Historians, who study the past through the written word, can tell us nothing of these people, or about anyone else who lived, loved, hated, and died before the invention of writing. For our knowledge of humankind before writing, we must look to folklorists and archaeologists, who sift particles of information, like flecks of gold, from the gravel of ancient tales and artifacts.

The portraits these scholars sketch are fuzzier than pictures drawn from documents. But without archaeologists and folklorists, the story of most of the Americas could not begin until 1492, just 500 years ago, when Europeans, who scribbled endlessly of their achievements, follies, and sins, discovered the New World for themselves. Thanks to archaeologists and folklorists, we can pencil in the outlines of a more ancient heritage.

A Diverse People

Presumably, the Ice Age ancestors of the Indians shared a very similar hunting and gathering culture. But their ways of living multiplied rapidly. The Americas were uncrowded to say the least, and many parts of the two continents were inviting as homes. Wandering tribes found it easy to split up when their numbers grew too heavy for their technology. Different bands went different ways. Soon enough, isolation from distant cousins and the great variety of American climates and landforms produced a multiplicity of cultures.

Native American languages, for example, once just a handful, multiplied until there were more than 500. Some tribes lived precariously into the modern era, surviving day to day on the food they could hunt, gather, and grub. Others coped with harsh deserts by devising ingenious techniques of farming and irrigation. Indeed, the people of Meso-America, meaning *between* the Americas (Mexico and Central America), invented agriculture. They unlocked the profound secret of how to produce food rather than depend on nature to provide it. This achievement was duplicated elsewhere only in the hills of ancient Iraq. All other peoples of the world—

This watercolor of an American Indian of the Atlantic coast was painted by John White, an artist and mapmaker who accompanied the first English colonists to Roanoke in 1585.

or so the evidence seems to say—learned how to farm by imitating these inventors and those who learned from them.

Some Indian peoples had mastered only primitive tool making when they were dazzled by European technology. Others perfected handicrafts to a level of refinement unmatched anywhere in Africa, Asia, or Europe. Some of the first Americans were brutal with the weak among them, cruel toward enemies. Others were meek and peaceable, threatening no one.

The closeness of the Indians to nature meant that

many were canny in lore based on observation and experimentation. Of the drugs and medicines in use in the United States today, more than 200 were known to prehistoric Americans. Given the isolation of the first Americans from the rest of humanity after 10,000 B.C., when a rising sea level drowned the Siberian-Alaskan land-bridge, preventing significant cultural contact, their achievements are astonishing.

MESO-AMERICAN CIVILIZATION

Only in Meso-America, however, where intensive agriculture allowed the growth of a large, dense, and highly organized population, did Native Americans make the breakthrough that signals the birth of civilization and history. The Olmecs of Central America, and the Mayans who succeeded them, developed a system of writing with which they carved records in stone and composed books on processed strips of cactus fiber.

In the 1500s, a zealous Spanish bishop concluded that these writings were full of "superstition and lies of the devil." He ordered them burned so that only three Mayan literary works survive to this day. But inscribed rock proved too much for righteous censors. Carvings are abundant in Meso-America and, in recent decades, experts have begun to decipher them. They provide us with a chapter of American history that had once been given up as forever lost.

City States

The Olmecs and Mayans built at least 40 cities in Meso-America with populations of perhaps 20,000 each. Twice that many people lived in Dziblichltun. Individually, these cities could be grand places, divided into neighborhoods dedicated to specific crafts, surrounded by farmland strung out along canals or perched on terraces carved from hillsides. At the center of each stood at least one stone pyramid, a temple. One such structure at Chichen Itzá rose 18 stories.

The Mayans were superb mathematicians and astronomers as well as builders. They discovered the concept of zero—another breakthrough achieved in only one other world culture—making higher mathematics possible. They measured the earth's tour around the sun at just over 365 days.

Cultural Cul de Sac

The government of each city, an oligarchy of noble-priests, was efficient enough to have overseen the building of many monumental structures. But the Mayans were not a united people. Each city state was quite in-dependent of every other. In fact, the Mayans were chronically at war. Their religious beliefs compelled it, for the Mayan gods—jaguar-like beings, eagles, serpents, the sun—demanded sacrifices of human blood.

In solemn public rituals, Mayan noblewomen drew strings of thorns through wounds in their tongues, men through the foreskins of their penises. Their falling blood was absorbed into strips of fiber which were burned, dispatching it to the heavens. But symbolic blood sacrifice did not satisfy the Mayan deities. They also demanded that priests drag victims to the tops of the great pyramids where their hearts, still beating, were torn from their breasts.

Divine blood-lust meant that the Mayans had to make war constantly, not to dominate and exploit their neighbors, thus increasing a city's wealth, but just to seize captives. The Mayans expended vast resources in a direction that, in material and intellectual terms, led nowhere. Their culture did not, in that word so central to the story of western civilization, *progress*, or move forward. Their genius and energy, not to mention untold thousands of lives, were devoted merely to staying on the right side of the gods, to standing still.

Endless warfare may explain why, by 1500, virtually every Mayan city had been abandoned, the people scattering to live in small villages in the jungle. Archaeologists have found massive stone idols that were deliberately buried, as if being hidden from enemies, to be unearthed at a time that was never to come. Or, the Mayan cities may have been rendered useless by soil depletion. (The earth below tropical jungle is easily exhausted by intense cultivation.) Whatever the explanation, by 1500, Meso-American civilization was being preserved only to the north, in the fertile temperate valley of Mexico, by the Aztecs.

The Aztecs

The Aztecs were comparative newcomers to Meso-America. They arrived in Mexico from the north during the 1200s. They were a poor and barbaric folk by comparison with the peoples who had brought Mayan civilization to central Mexico. However, like the German barbarians who invaded the Roman Empire, and the Turks who conquered the more sophisticated Arabs, the Aztecs knew a better way of living when they saw it. Carving out an enclave on the shores of Lake Texcoco, they shook off their old ways (except for their great god, Huitzilopochtli) and embraced Meso-American culture.

Gradually, Aztec power grew. By 1500, they dominated almost every other Mexican people, collecting tribute from the shores of the Gulf of Mexico to the Pacific. They put this wealth to work building one of the world's most splendid cities, Tenochtitlán. By 1500, it covered six square miles and was home to some 200,000 people, five times as many as lived in London in that year.

Tenochtitlán was easily defended for it was surrounded by Lake Texcoco. Only three causeways connected the city to the mainland homes of restive subject peoples. Within the capital, however, canals and broad thoroughfares made internal movement easy. One plaza, site of a major market, could host 50,000 people exchanging goods that had been borne as far as 800 miles.

Like the Mayans, the Aztecs practiced human sacrifice. Indeed, Huitzilopochtli, the war god, demanded 10,000 hearts in ordinary years. In 1478, a year he was angry, his priests sent 20,000 volunteers and captives to their doom.

Bad years seemed to come frequently during the late 1400s and early 1500s. Omens of all sorts, from natural calamities to rumors of female spirits wandering the streets in the night lamenting what was to come of their children, had many Aztecs on edge, including the emperor Moctezuma II, whose reign began in 1502. The Aztec calendar, inherited from the Mayans, also hinted impending disaster. Some scholars have suggested that, psychologically, the Aztecs were easy prey for a people who devoted their resources not just to staying on the right side of the Gods, but to the exploitation of the new and the strange, wherever they found it.

EUROPE: AN EXPANSIVE CULTURE

On October 12, 1492, on an island beach in the Bahamas, more than a thousand miles east of the Aztec realm, a group of rough young men, mostly Spaniards, waded ashore from three small ships to name their landfall San Salvador, or Holy Savior. Their leader was a red-haired Italian about forty years of age, Cristobal Colón to his Spanish crew, Christopher Columbus to us.

Falling to his knees, for Columbus was as pious as any Aztec priest, he thanked his God for deliverance from the sea. He then proclaimed that the land on which he stood was the possession of the queen who had financed his voyage, Isabella, and her husband, Ferdinand, the rulers of Spain. He observed that the native Arawaks who greeted them "are very gentle, and do not know what it is to be wicked, or to kill others, or to steal." Then he set about looking for the emperor of China and goods that he might sell back home at a profit, and gold that he would take any way he could. He mused that the gentle Arawaks could easily be enslaved, forced to work for the Spanish.

The historical development of the America we know began on that day. Its cultural origins lay not on the pyramids of Mexico, but in the churches, state chambers, and counting houses of Western Europe, that continent

MANY DISCOVERERS

Columbus was not the first individual to link the Americas and the rest of the world since the Ice Age. Eskimos and Aleuts, seafaring hunters of the Arctic, regularly touched land in both Asia and North America. It is possible that hapless Japanese fishermen survived being blown off course to land in the Americas. Certain themes in American Indian art tantalize some archaeologists as "Asian."

Then there is legend—lots of it. The Olmecs told of black peoples in Central America between 1000 B.C. and 500 B.C. Some have seen African features in the buried Olmec heads. A Chinese document of 200 B.C. tells of Hee Li, who visited a land to the East he called Fu-Sang. Irish bards sang of St. Brendan, an intrepid monk said to have lived in a country far to the west of the Emerald Isle.

According to Icelandic sagas, Norsemen led by Thorfinn Karlsefni, Leif Erickson, and a sword-swinging woman warrior named Freydis, founded a colony in North America, "Vinland," probably at L'Anse aux Meadows, Newfoundland, around 1000 A.D. A pronounced lack of hospitality on the part of the *skraelings*, as the sagas called the native inhabitants, forced their withdrawal to Greenland.

that was to extend the lineaments of its culture throughout the entire world.

The Motives

Columbus believed he had reached an outlying island of the Indies, the name Europeans gave to the countries of Asia: Cipango (Japan), Cathay (China), the Spice Islands (Indonesia), and India itself. It was for this reason that he gave the people who greeted him the name that has stuck to all Native Americans to this day—*indios*, Indians, *indiens*.

Columbus was looking for a feasible route to the Indies. He wanted to discover—to reveal what was then unknown—a sea route between Europe and Asia. In part, religion motivated him. Columbus was decidedly medieval in his belief that the Christian God had selected him to bring the gospel ("good news") of Jesus Christ to the peoples of the East. And he spoke of finding gold with which his sovereigns could wage war against the Muslim Arabs and Turks, winning the holy places of Christianity back from them.

Columbus was more modern in his desire for glory and individual recognition. He was not unaffected by the culture of the Renaissance, which honored (and enriched) artists, architects, scholars, writers, and discoverers of the new as individuals.

Columbus also wanted to do business. He wanted to find rubies and pearls, porcelains, fine silk cloth, tapestries and carpets beyond the craft of European weavers, exotic drugs, dyes, perfumes, and spices—cinnamon, nutmeg, allspice, cloves, peppercorns. Such Asian luxuries made life more pleasant and more interesting, something more than a struggle for survival on earth and salvation after death.

These things were extremely expensive in Europe, and only the rich could afford them. But, in the age of Columbus, the rich made the big decisions such as whether or not to bet money on seafarers who proposed risky ventures into unknown waters.

News from Afar

The goods of the Indies had trickled into Europe since the days of the Roman Empire. At first, they were simply wonders of utterly mysterious origin. In the thirteenth century, however, a merchant of Venice, Marco Polo, traveled overland to China, lived there a dozen years, and returned to write an account of his adventures, commonly known as *The Voyages of Ser Marco Polo*. The book circulated in manuscript among the great houses and monasteries of Europe and reached lesser places in the garbled accounts of traveling monks and ballad singers. It told of the Great Khan and the mandarins of China, who luxuriated amidst gold and porcelain and fine silks and tapestries that were precious beyond price in Europe. Thanks to a plentitude of exotic spices, they enjoyed meals that were exquisite pleasures rather than mere exercises to stave off weakness or induce a stupor.

Some of Polo's tales must have given skeptical readers pause. (He told of snakes wearing eye-glasses too.) But informed Europeans had more reliable knowledge of the Arabs' and Turks' earthly garden of delights. Between the eleventh and the thirteenth centuries, thousands of European knights had invaded the world of Islam on the Crusades, wars fought to win the holy places of Christianity from the followers of Mohammed.

The Crusades failed. The Middle East remained largely Muslim. In the meantime, however, Europeans who lived in the Middle East were introduced to a quality of life far more attractive than that they left at home and to which they returned. When the last Crusaders limped back to Europe, their wants helped to create a lucrative and ever-increasing market for merchants who could deliver the desirable goods of the East.

What Asia Offered

Oriental carpets and tapestries brightened castle walls and insulated cold stone floors. Although they did not improve the barbaric medical practices of the time, drugs from the East relieved some of the pain that injury, disease, and doctors inflicted.

Rich Europeans also coveted what we call "status symbols." The knight and lady who sported gems not found in Europe announced wordlessly to one and all that they could pay high prices for baubles at no great inconvenience. When they donned expensive silks and cottons imported from the East and dyed in rare oriental hues, they announced by their sartorial splendor that they were of a higher order than the louts in the next castle over in their itchy linen and wool—until the louts next door bought their own.

Roman Catholicism, then the religion of all Western Europeans but a small minority of Jews (and Muslims in Spain), taught that it honored God to adorn cathedrals and chapels with beautiful and valuable objects such as pearls and rubies. Incense, imported from northeastern Africa, played a prominent part in religious ritual. Burning the processed resin was thought to be as pleasing to the Lord as it surely was to his unwashed worshippers.

Of all the goods that aroused European interest in the Asian trade, none was to be more important in the long run than spices. They enhanced the pleasure of eating. Their flavors shattered the monotony of a diet restricted to a few basic ingredients. Their preservative qualities made it possible to keep, through the winter, meat that would otherwise spoil.

A Business with a High Overhead

The goods of the Indies were borne by ship through the Indian Ocean and Persian Gulf. Or they were carried overland in caravans to Constantinople or the Levant at the eastern end of the Mediterranean Sea (present-day Syria, Lebanon, and Israel). From there, they found Europe in the fleets of powerful Italian city-states, particularly Venice and Genoa. Functioning as middlemen—as wholesale distributors—Italian merchants sold the spices and the rest to smaller fry all over the continent.

By the time the goods of the Indies reached consumers, they were expensive indeed. The costs of transport alone were prodigious. The pepper that enlivened a French stew may have traveled as far as eight thousand miles on a donkey's back. Raising costs yet higher, the trade routes passed through the lands of warlike Central Asian tribes or, if they came by sea, through the haunts of East African pirates. Merchants had either to pay such bandits for safe passage, a kind of "protection money," or hire tough armed men to battle villains off. Either way, another cost was added to the selling price.

Nobody Likes a Middleman

The Levantine traders took a handsome profit, and the Italians added their immodest commission, shrugging off pious condemnations of price-gouging. Today, the splendid Renaissance cathedrals and palaces the Italian merchant princes built with their loot are an inspiration to the world. In the time of Columbus, the glories of

Italy were just as likely to cause resentment and envy among those customers whose purchases made them possible.

Envy of Italian wealth fathered the dream of finding a new route to the Indies. The prince whose sailors bypassed the Italian middlemen would stop the flow of his country's wealth to Italy. Indeed, such a prince could imagine his subjects displacing the Italians as Europe's wholesalers of Asian products. Thus the navigator who found a workable route to the Indies could expect princely rewards for his services.

PORTUGAL AND SPAIN: THE VAN OF EXPLORATION

Portugal and Spain led the quest for new trade routes. A glance at a map reveals one reason why these two countries should have been in the van. Both face westward toward the Atlantic, Portugal entirely so.

But location is not enough in itself to explain why a country becomes expansive, outgoing. The Portugese and Spanish were first to challenge the Italian monopoly of Asian imports because they were Europe's first truly unified nation states. They were the first European countries to shake off the dead hand of medieval feudalism and create centralized governments sufficiently powerful to direct the use of national resources toward the end of national enrichment abroad.

National Monarchies

The rest of Europe was politically fragmented in the 1400s. Italy was a collage of independent city-states, not a nation. Middle Europe was a patchwork of hundreds of virtually independent domains ruled by barons and knights and bishops and abbots of the Roman Catholic Church. Some of these princes were powerful and fearsome. Most were petty landlords with mentalities as narrow as their fields of barley. They looked inward, thought small. Their ambition was to bleed what they could from their wretched peasants, seize real estate from a neighbor fallen on bad times, and extort silver from wandering merchants.

In most of Western Europe, however, powerful kings and queens—monarchs, or sole rulers—methodically schemed, toiled, and battled to increase and expand their power at the expense of the nobility. Enriched by taxes collected on land and by loans from the merchants of the cities and market towns, the national monarchs hired professional armies capable of destroying the castles of troublesome barons. They confronted or negotiated with the Church over its great powers. They created

cadres of royal officials to enforce their laws and to concentrate power and control of resources in their hands. As masters of vast realms, they could rise above the petty visions of petty lords. They could and did look forward and outward to greater national accomplishments, rather than fret about next fall's harvest or the disappointing contents of a peddler's pack.

Iberian Nationalism

France and England were well along in the process of national unification at the end of the fifteenth century. Both were to be major players in the overseas expansion of European power and culture. Portugal was already a unified nation in 1400. Its kings had come to the fore by leading centuries-long wars of national liberation against the Moors—Muslim Arabs, and Berbers—having North African (Moroccan) roots. Indeed, the Portugese transformed a struggle for independence into a war of expansion, seizing Ceuta in Morocco as early as 1415.

Prince Henry, a son of King John I who fought at Ceuta, helped turn Portugal's attention even farther abroad. Later dubbed Henry the Navigator, this remarkable man was fascinated by the sea and far-off lands, both known and imagined. He sent more than 30 expeditions down the coast of Africa to buy gold and slaves from black kingdoms south of the Sahara. Under his aegis, the Portugese colonized Madeira, 350 miles off the coast of Africa, and the Azores, Atlantic islands 800 miles west of Portugal.

Perhaps most important, Henry endowed a kind of think-tank of exploration at Sagres. There, mariners returning from the deep shared their experiences with mapmakers, scholars expert in ancient travel accounts, and ship builders.

Together they speculated, often brilliantly, concerning world geography. Confronted with contrary winds off Cape Bojador in West Africa, the Portugese developed a vessel that was to make long ocean voyages possible, the caravel. Caravels could be rigged with the triangular sails of the Mediterranean, which made it possible to beat against the wind, or with the large square sail of northern European vessels, which pushed a ship at high speed when the wind was favorable. "The best ships in the world and able to sail anywhere," said Luigi da Cadamosto, an Italian in Prince Henry's service.

Portugal's Route to Asia

Prince Henry died in 1460 but the explorations he inspired went on. Most notably, in 1488, a ship commanded by Bartholomeu Diaz returned to Portugal after reaching the Cape of Good Hope at the foot of the African continent. The corner had been turned—there

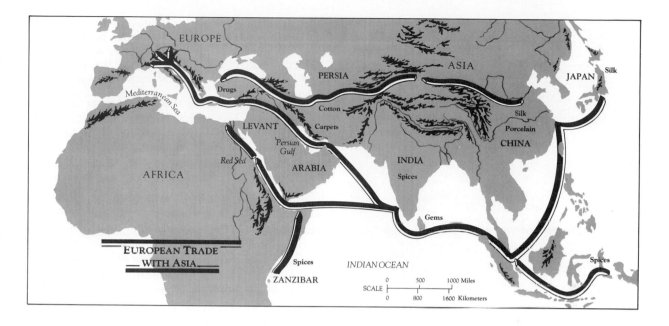

would be clear sailing to the Indies by way of coasting Africa.

Not for ten years would another Portugese, Vasco Da Gama, actually reach East Africa and the Indian port of Calicut. The Portugese would then build a commercial empire consisting of small trading posts stretching from West Africa to the Persian Gulf and Macau in China. The single Portugese outpost in the Americas was the consequence of a mishap befalling a navigator bound for Asia by Da Gama's route. In 1500, Pedro Cabral was blown far off the coast of Africa and landed on the bulge of the South American continent. His landfall established Portugal's claim to Brazil.

In the meantime, Portugal's progressive successes tracing the African coast had the effect of killing any interest King John II might otherwise have had in "the Enterprise of the Indies," a plan presented to him by Christopher Columbus. In Portugal since 1476, Columbus argued that the best way to East Asia lay not to the south via Africa, but due west across the Atlantic. John II entertained his scheme for several years, but eventually dismissed him. The King called Columbus "a big talker, full of fancy and imagination."

Spain Looks West

In 1484, Columbus took his Enterprise of the Indies to neighboring Spain. He found plenty of ridicule there too. Scholars at the University of Salamanca described his project as "vain, impracticable, and resting on grounds too weak to merit the support of the government." But he had influential backers too, and the rulers of Spain, Isabella of Castille and Ferdinand of Aragon, were jealous of the Portugese discoveries. They paid Columbus a modest annuity to keep him around.

Until 1492, however, Isabella and Ferdinand were preoccupied with more compelling business. They were on the verge of concluding Spain's centuries-long *reconquista* of the country from the Moors. Until the last Moorish stronghold in Spain, the city of Granada, sur-

PRESTER JOHN

In fifteenth century Europe, fear of the powerful Moslem Arabs and Turks led to a widespread belief in the existence of Prester John—Priest John—a powerful Christian king who was said to dwell somewhere beyond the realm of Islam. If only Europeans could make contact with him, they could together destroy the dread infidel, as they called Moslems. Indeed, a "letter" from John that reached Europe in the twelfth century read, "We have made a vow to visit the sepulchre of our Lord, as befits the glory of our Majesty, to wage war against and chastise the enemies of the cross of Christ."

Prester John seemed to be wherever he would be most useful to troubled Europeans. To Germans, he lived in central Asia. To the Portugese, Prester John was a black African king who lived to the south of their ancestral enemies, the Moors. Some scholars suggest that the existence of a black Christian kingdom in Ethiopia provides the kernel of truth at the core of the legend. Be that as it may, the search for John was a part of the exploration movement of the fifteenth century.

Christopher Columbus (1451–1506) as depicted in a portrait by DeBry. The portrait is fanciful. No likeness of Columbus, done during his lifetime, has survived.

rendered, which it did in January 1492, Columbus met only frustration.

Then, events moved with remarkable dispatch. Columbus was commissioned Admiral of the Ocean Sea, an exalted hereditary title. He was granted extensive authority over any lands he discovered, and a generous share of any profits he made. Investors outfitted him with three small ships, two caravels, the *Nina* and the *Pinta*, and a less useful larger carrack, the *Santa Maria*. The total cost of the expedition was but $14,000, a pittance if Columbus made good on the boast he would reach the Indies.

Dreams Die Hard

He did not make good on his boast, of course, but Columbus never admitted that, instead of one of the 7,448 islands Marco Polo said lay off Asia, he had found a world new to Europe. Four times he crossed the Atlantic bearing letters of introduction addressed to the emperor of China (and other documents with blanks in which he could fill in names). Four times he returned after conversations with Indians who had not heard of such grand persons. Four times he told Isabella and Ferdinand that, after the next voyage,

I will give them as much gold as they need, . . . and I will also give them all the spices and cotton they need, and as for resin which until now has been found only in Greece, and which the traders of Genoa sell at the price they choose, I will bring back as much of it as their Majesties may order.

To the day of his death in 1506, Christopher Columbus insisted that he had reached Asia on that October day. Sustained for a lifetime by a glorious dream, he could not admit that his discovery pointed toward quite another conclusion.

As for the Spaniards that stayed on Cuba and Hispaniola (present-day Haiti and the Dominican Republic), most of them soldiers, when they recognized that they were living in a "New World," they grew despondent and increasingly vicious toward the native *indios*. Instead of reaping rewards, as the Portuguese were doing on their African route, they were masters of steamy, tropical, mosquito-plagued islands. Far from being a prize, America was an obstacle in the way to Asia, a chain across what was to have been a river of commerce. Columbus himself seized slaves by the hundred and ordered the mutilation of Indians who failed to bring in a quota of gold every three months. His successors on Hispaniola

FLUNKING GEOGRAPHY

An old story has it that Columbus had to struggle to convince Isabella and her advisors that the earth was a sphere. A celebrated painting shows him holding an orange and lecturing thick-skulled Spaniards about orbs. In fact, the shape of the earth was never an issue in Columbus's campaign to win financial backing. Only the uneducated and superstitious believed that the world was flat, that a ship would fall off the edge into a void. Isabella and the scholars of the University of Salamanca knew better. The ancients said the world was round. During a lunar eclipse, the shadow of the earth on the moon was round. In the early 1400s, Pierre d'Ailly had written, "Although the earth is carved into mountains and valleys, which are the cause of its imperfect roundness, it may be considered round, and this explains why lunar eclipses caused by the earth's projected shadow appear round."

The ironic fact of the matter is Columbus's hopes of reaching the Indies by sailing west were based on a major geographical error: he seriously underestimated the *size* of the globe. Columbus thought that Japan lay about 2,500 nautical miles west of the Canary Islands (where he said his farewell to the known world). In fact, it is about 9,000 miles. Had Columbus's geography been better, he would have abandoned his enterprise, for no ship of the time could have been provisioned for so long a voyage. The most seaworthy of Columbus's vessels, the *Pinta*, could hold about as much in the way of supplies as a modern two-car garage.

Why "America?" Why Not "Columbia?"

Columbus is largely to blame for the fact that his great discovery was not named for him. He never admitted that he had found a "New World."

The man for whom the Americas were named was another Italian, Amerigo Vespucci, who accompanied several Spanish expeditions to the coast of South America, the first in 1499. Without claiming to have discovered anything, Vespucci wrote several descriptive letters in which he stated that the lands he saw were previously unknown. In 1507, a German cartographer, Martin Waldseemüller, the first mapmaker to show the Americas separate from Asia, misconstrued Vespucci's claims and named the New World for him in the Latin form of his name.

and Cuba and everywhere the Spanish went acted in ways that made him took like a saint.

Frustrating Explorations

In 1513, Vasco Nuñez de Balboa discovered the weakest link in the chain when he led a party across the Isthmus of Panama. At its narrowest point, the Isthmus was only 40 miles wide. But Balboa's trail was not very useful as a trade route. Tropical diseases were so virulent that crossing Panama was as risky as a throw of the dice. Moreover, from a peak called Darien, Balboa discovered another great ocean, the Pacific. The implication was obvious: Asia might be very far indeed from where he stood.

In 1519, Ferdinand Magellan confirmed the suspicion. A Portuguese sailing for Spain with five ships and 265 men, Magellan found a way to the Pacific around the southern tip of South America. His life was lost in the Philippines, but one of his vessels, commanded by Juan Sebastian del Caño and carrying only eighteen men, limped back to Europe.

It was a magnificent achievement—the first voyage around the world. As a way to Asia, however, the Magellan-del Caño route was unworkable. Due to powerful adverse winds and currents in the Strait of Magellan, it sometimes took a month (and more) just to reach the Pacific. (Columbus crossed the Atlantic in just four weeks.) So long as ships were powered by sail, masters on a tight schedule avoided sailing westward around South America.

A Poor Bargain

International politics also served to pen the Spanish up in the Western Hemisphere. In 1493, in order to avoid conflict between Spain and Portugal, the Pope drew a line on the map of the world that divided all lands not "in the actual possession of any Christian king or prince" between the two nations. The papal bull, *Inter Caetera*, set this boundary a hundred leagues west of the Azores. The next year, in the Treaty of Tordesillas, the Portuguese persuaded Isabella and Ferdinand to move the line farther to the west (thus laying the grounds for Portugese settlement of Brazil after 1500). Wherever the line was drawn, Spain was shut out of all Asia except the Philippines.

Until 1521, the Spanish in the New World thought of Tordesillas as a bad bargain indeed. Their share of the world's non-Christian wealth was profoundly disappointing. On the Caribbean island of Hispaniola, site of the largest Spanish colony, soldiers writhed in discomfort and frustration, brutalized the native people, and fought viciously among themselves. The few who, like Balboa, ventured to the mainland returned with bad news. Or, like Juan Ponce de Leon, who in 1513 scoured Florida looking for a "fountain of youth," they made fools of themselves.

THE SPANISH EMPIRE

Then, in 1519, pretty much the worst of times in Spanish America, an extraordinary soldier, acting on a rumor little more substantial than the nonsense that excited Ponce de Leon, landed on the coast of Mexico with 508 soldiers, 200 Indians, some Africans, seven small cannons, and 16 horses. What this motley party found and did in Mexico brought an end to Spanish grumblings that the Portuguese alone had benefited from the age of discovery.

Cortez in Mexico

Hernán Cortez had heard of Tenochtitlán and of Aztec riches. He landed at what is now Vera Cruz and was attacked by the Tabascans, whom the Spaniards devastated with their cannons at the loss of only two of their own men. Cortez then made peace with the Tabascans, offering them an alliance against the Aztecs. It was a procedure—victory in battle, peace, anti-Aztec alliance—that Cortez would repeat with every native people he confronted on his march to Tenochtitlán. Totomacs, Tlaxcalans, Cholulans—all joined the Tabascans in following him. Before marching, however, with the no-nonsense boldness that centuries of war against the Moors had instilled in the Spanish soldier, Cortez

The fleet of Ferdinand Magellan, in the straits bearing his name, during the first voyage to circumnavigate the globe, 1519–1522.

burned the ships that had brought him to Mexico. It would be conquer or die for his Spanish troops. There was no third option.

Reaching Tenochtitlán on November 8, 1519, Cortez was disgusted by Aztec polytheism and human sacrifice. But Meso-American religion served the wily Spaniard well. A legend taught that a fair-skinned deity named Quetzalcoatl would come one day to rule Mexico. The Aztec emperor, Moctezuma II (Montezuma), feared Cortez to be this god. According to an Aztec close to him, Moctezuma "enjoyed no sleep, no food. . . . Whatsoever he did, it was as if he were in torment." Cortez was actually welcomed into the city where he soon made the emperor his prisoner.

Aztec nobles soon realized that the Spaniards were less than divine. They tried to stop human sacrifice and when they stumbled on a huge store of "jewels, precious stones, silver, and an astonishing amount of gold," according to an Aztec account, "as if they were monkeys, the Spanish lifted up the gold banners and gold necklaces . . . . Like hungry pigs they craved that gold." Cortez even told Moctezuma that he suffered from an illness that could be cured only by gold.

The Conquest

The Aztecs rebelled and the Spaniards barely managed to fight their way out of Tenochtitlán. Their greed nearly destroyed them. With their lives in the balance, the Spaniards insisted on carrying eight tons of treasure on their retreat.

But it was the Aztecs who were doomed by the gold. Cortez gathered new Indian allies and Spanish reinforcements from Cuba. He returned to Tenochtitlán, and conquered the great city brick by brick. About 15,000 people were killed on the final day of the battle, August 13, 1521.

Hernán Cortez not only won a battle; he gained a ready-made empire for Spain. He and his lieutenants simply inserted themselves at the top of Aztec society in place of the nobles they had wiped out. They lived off the labor of the lower classes as the Aztec nobility had done. Rarely has one people been able to set itself up over another with such ease. The already centralized political structure and oppression of the people of Mexico made it possible for the Spaniards to rule with minimal resistance.

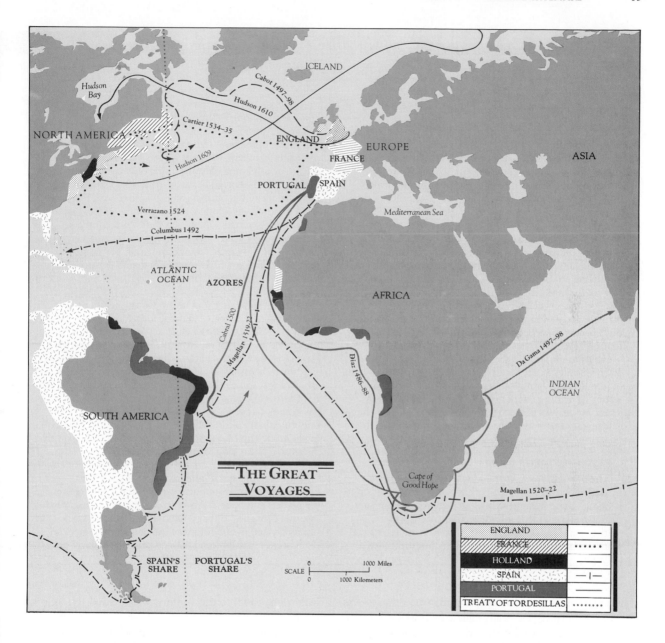

The Conquistadores

The conquest of Mexico breathed fire into Spain's interest in the New World. There was a rush to the Americas as thousands of people of all classes packed into ships to search for their own Mexicos. The young (and some not so young) men called themselves *conquistadores* (conquerors) and in little more than a generation they subdued an area several times the size of Europe.

Rarely has history shaped a people for conquest as Spanish history shaped the conquistadors. Because much of Spain is naturally poor—dry or mountainous or both—agriculture never attracted the ambitious. Be-

cause the Christian Spanish associated trade with despised Moors and Jews, the upper classes shunned commerce. The sole worldly role of the *hidalgo*, the aristocratic Spanish male, was to fight. He was a soldier, a knight. The bravery and fortitude of the conquistadores under hopeless conditions awes us to this day. The other side of their military character, their ruthlessness and cruelty, has also been noted.

The Spanish nation's zealous devotion to Roman Catholicism factored in the extraordinary achievement. Because the national enemy had been of another faith, Spanish nationalism and Roman Catholicism were of a piece. Like their Muslim foes, the Spaniards believed

HOW THEY LIVED

LOCKED IN A CIRCLE OF TIME

In no part of the world have archaeologists made more exciting finds in our time than in Meso-America. Not long ago, and perhaps in elementary school textbooks to this day, the ancient Mayans of Mexico and Guatemala were thought to have been as the Spanish *conquistadores* of the sixteenth century found them: docile and primitive villagers, eking out a simple existence by farming in clearings in the jungle. The great pyramids of the Yucatán peninsula, such as at Chichén Itzá were well-known—as high as 18 stories, they were hard to miss—but most had been abandoned to the jungle before the Spanish conquest. It was assumed until recently that they were religious centers to which the scattered Mayan peasants came on special occasions.

Today, thanks to "high-tech" archaeological digs and the deciphering of Mayan hieroglyphics after 400 years of puzzlement, we know that between 250 B.C. and 900 A.D., the Mayans created a true and grand civilization, no matter how rigorously that problematic term is defined.

Far from simple villagers, they lived in cities as large as 6 square miles in size (at El Mirado) with a hinterland not of jungle but of farmland "well-cleared and free from weeds" as vast in extent as 50 square miles (at Tikal). These cities were fortified with moats and walls, for the Mayan city-states were chronically at war with one another, and the people built dams and long canals, the purpose of which is not yet understood: there is no need to irrigate in the rainy tropics.

The population of several Mayan city-states rose to 20,000 and at Dzîbilchltún perhaps 40,000. In addition to peasants, there were artisans of all sorts; far-ranging merchants dealing in jade, obsidian, salt, cacao, pottery, feathers, and jaguar pelts; priests who were superb mathematicians and astronomers; and a hereditary nobility, a warrior class as in other early civilizations. One palace at Uxmal was as long as a football field.

The Mayans had stadiums in which spectators watched ball games of religious significance. In one version reminiscent of handball, teams of players kept a rubber ball in the air, or careening off walls, using only their hips and buttocks to strike it. (They wore pads.) In pok-a-tok, perhaps the most difficult ball game ever invented, the court was a hundred yards long with stone walls 30 feet high on either side. Near the top of each wall was mounted a stone ring—vertically, not horizontally like a basketball hoop. Using only hips, elbows, and arms, players attempted to knock a ball 6 inches in diameter through a barely-larger hole in the ring.

Not surprisingly, few goals were scored, but Mayanologists are not sure what that meant for the competitors. Some evidence indicates that the individual who scored a goal was entitled to all the clothing worn by the spectators, riches indeed. Some experts think that pok-a-tok was played by captives and the losing team was sacrificed.

Human sacrifice was central to the religion of the Mayans, just as it was to the Aztecs. Indeed, the most revolutionary recent discovery by Mayanologists is the fact that the Aztecs, rather savage invaders from the North, did not bring their culture with them. They adopted Mayan civilization. The Meso-American civilization the Spanish discovered had a long, continuous history, dating back as much as 2,500 years when it originated with the Olmecs.

When the Olmecs dominated Meso-America, the Greeks, the founders of European civilization, were simple herders and raiders. And yet, while Europe progressed over the centuries so that a handful of Spaniards could run roughshod over millions of Indians, Meso-American civilization virtually stood still after the classical era of

---

that a war for the purpose of spreading true religion was *ipso facto* sanctified. Death in such a war was a guarantee of salvation. It was a value that made for soldiers unafraid to die and, for that, very formidable.

Such cultural baggage would curse Spain in later centuries. Disdain for agriculture, trade, and other productive work contributed to the nation's eventual impoverishment. In the sixteenth century, however, reckless bravery and religious fanaticism were superbly calculated to conquer a New World.

Exploration North and South

After news of his Mexican treasure reached him, the Spanish king, Charles I, encouraged additional conquests by promising conquistadores the lion's share of the gold and silver they won. (Charles got one-fifth.) He also granted land to his subjects, and *encomiendas*, the legal right to force the Indians who owned the land to work for them.

Only one conquistador's find rivaled that of Cortez. In 1531, an aging pig farmer named Francisco Pizarro led 106 foot soldiers and 62 horses high into the Andes mountains of South America. There he found the empire of the Incas, another advanced culture with rich sources of gold and silver. As bold as Cortez, Pizarro was far greater a villain, an artist of deceit and treachery. But he too conquered an empire and inserted himself and his lieutenants (those who were not murdered by their own comrades) at the top of Inca society.

Few other expeditions brought back much gold and silver, particularly those that ventured north into what is now the United States. Between 1539 and 1542, Hernando De Soto explored our Southeast in a fruitless search for riches. He was buried by his soldiers in the

the Mayans. For some 600 years before Hernando Cortéz landed at Vera Cruz, there was little resembling cultural "progress" in Meso-America.

The bloodlust of the Meso-American deities was responsible in part for the stagnation. The Meso-American city-states devoted vast resources to wars fought for no purpose other than to seize captives for gory mutilation by, in the words of Bernal Díaz, priests "clad in long white cotton cloaks, . . . their long hair reeking with blood, and so matted together, that it could never be parted or even combed out again."

However, the unique character of one of the Mayans' greatest achievements, their complex and ingenious system for marking the passing of time, also provides an insight into why Meso-American civilization was trapped in a cul-de-sac.

The Mayan priests were excellent astronomers. They traced the route of Venus more precisely than contemporaries elsewhere in the world. (The pyramid at Chichén Itzá is in part a "Venus observatory.") Their solar calendar was near perfect, counting 365 days in a year. But because there are virtually no seasons in the tropics, and even the "rainy season" in Yucatán was wildly erratic, the solar year was of comparatively less interest to the Mayans than to makers of calendars elsewhere in the world. One solar cycle did not lead to another, always into the future, as in other civilizations.

Instead, the Mayans invented a variety of other calendars, some still not completely understood. The two most important of these meshed with the solar year, and with one another as the chief means of dating and chronicling events. One was a 13-day cycle, the other, called *tzolkin*, of 260 days. (20 × 13 = 260; the basis of Mayan mathematics was 20 rather than ten; they invented the zero, a

breakthrough accomplished in only one other civilization, ancient India.) If one imagines the three cycles as wheels meshing with one another, a 13-cog wheel within a 260-cog wheel within a 365-cog wheel, no single alignment of cogs would be repeated for 18,980 days, or 52 years on the button.

The complexity of the calculation (and there were others yet more complex) demonstrates the sophistication of Mayan mathematics. However, the beauty of their cycles within cycles also locked the Mayan mind into a rigidly circular view of time. The Mayans believed that each day was identical in every way to the day 52 years earlier, and 104 years and 156 years earlier, and so on. Each 5,200 years, they believed, the universe was destroyed and created anew. (After 13 of these cycles, the universe would be destroyed for good.) Time passed but mankind did not progress; what might seem to be change was only bringing things back to where they had already been and would be again.

As sophisticated as the Meso-Americans were, their worldview was as ill-adapted to cope with the unexpected, with what did not fit in. Hurricanes worried the Mayans more because of their unpredictability than because of their destructiveness. Because their solar year was divided into 18 months of 20 days each, leaving 5 days without a tidy place at the end of the year, the Mayans regarded the 5 leftovers as evil.

How much more paralyzing must it have been for their legatees, the Aztecs, to learn of the arrival of huge seagoing canoes, white-skinned men with hairy faces, suits of iron, horses, and cannons that had thunder within them? There was nothing in the annals of the priests about such an event 52 years past.

Mississippi River. Only half of the mourners returned alive.

During the same years, Francisco Coronado trekked extraordinary distances in our Southwest. His quest was for the Seven Cities of Cibola among which, according to an imaginative priest, Fray Marcos de Niza, was "the greatest city in the world, . . . larger than the city of Mexico." Coronado's 1,500 men found only dusty villages of adobe brick. "Such were our curses that some hurled at Fray Marcos," wrote one, "that I pray God may protect him from them."

Spanish America

For a century, Mexican and Peruvian gold and silver made Spain the richest and most powerful nation of Europe. American wealth financed the cultural blossoming of Spain as well as huge armies to do the kings'

bidding. By the end of the 1600s, Spain's empire stretched from Tierra del Fuego at the foot of South America to Mexico.

Over so vast an area, economy and society varied immensely. For the most part, however, the ownership of land in Spanish America was concentrated in the hands of a small group of privileged *encomenderos* who lived off the labor of Indians in peonage or black Africans in slavery. Government was centralized in the hands of viceroys (vice kings). The Roman Catholic Church exercised great power, sometimes protecting those on the bottom from the greed and cruelty of the upper classes.

The empire flourished. Before more than a handful of other Europeans had slept overnight in the New World, Spain boasted two hundred towns and cities, and two universities in the Western Hemisphere.

Cortéz and his Indian interpreter, Malinche, lead a group of conquistadores in this drawing from an Aztec manuscript.

The majority of Spain's American subjects were Indians but their fate was not a happy one. It has been estimated that there were at least 5 million inhabitants of Mexico in 1500, and perhaps many more. In 1600, there were a million Mexican Indians.

The Black Legend

It can seem almost wonderful that any Native Americans survived in Spanish America. Indeed, the possibility of their extinction was a main point put in the hard-hitting words of Bartolome De Las Casas, a Dominican priest who devoted his life to lobbying the Spanish king for laws protecting the Indians. Most scholars today believe that his scorching descriptions of the conquistadores, *A Brief Relation of the Destruction of the Indians*, are exaggerated. The Spaniards treated the Indians, De Las Casas said, "not as beasts, for beasts are treated properly at times, but like the excrement in a plaza." Nevertheless, his words served as the basis of the *leyenda negra*, the "Black Legend" of Spanish barbarity that remained an article of faith in the English-speaking world for three centuries and is once again in fashion.

The savage behavior of many *encomenderos* should be viewed in the context of Europe in the sixteenth century. It was an era of chilling indifference to human suffering. Nor was the callousness only European, it was Asian, African, Native American, and it was directed not only toward those of different race. Warfare in Eu-

AND THE MEEK SHALL INHERIT HISPANIOLA

Columbus wrote of the Arawaks to Isabella and Ferdinand, "So loving, so tractable, so peaceable are these people, that I swear to your Majesties, there is not in the world a better nation, nor a better land. They love their neighbors as themselves, and their discourse is ever sweet and gentle, and accompanied with a smile; and though it is true they are naked, yet their manners are decorous and praiseworthy."

The Arawak population of Hispaniola in 1492 was at least 200,000, in 1508 60,000, in 1514 14,000. By 1570, only two small Arawak villages survived on the island.

rope during the period and into the seventeenth century meant unmitigated horror for any poor devil caught in the paths of marauding armies. The Turks massacred the population of Constantinople in 1453. The horrors of Meso-American religion have already been noted. Africans devised devilishly ingenious tortures without any tutoring from outside.

Many more Indians died of pick and shovel than at sword point. The Arawaks of the Caribbean, for example, were a physically delicate people who seem to have died off within a generation under the hard labor into which they were forced. An even more devastating scourge of the native peoples was a weapon Europeans did not even know they possessed: disease.

THE COLUMBIAN EXCHANGE

The collision of worlds occasioned by Columbus's voyage established a biological pipeline between land masses that had drifted apart about 150 million years before human beings appeared on the earth. Some species had flourished in both worlds: oaks, dogs, deer, mosquitoes, and the virus that causes the common cold. Some species had been well developed by the time of the separation of the continents. Others, such as sea birds and plants producing air and water-borne seeds, navigated the ocean sea long before the *Santa Maria*. There were, however, a large number of animals and plants in the Americas that were new to the first Europeans to arrive. And they brought with them species of flora and fauna that were unknown to the Indians.

The Impact on America

Because mammals in Spanish America were generally smaller and less suited for meat and draft than Old World livestock, the Spaniards immediately imported hogs, cattle, and sheep along with European grasses to feed them (plus about 70 percent of what we know as weeds). The arrival of these beasts not only altered the ecology of the New World, the Indians introduced to them soon came to depend on them for survival.

Even those native peoples which escaped Spanish political domination were glad to raid the strangers' flocks and herds as a step toward better living. The magnificent wool-weaving art that is closely identified with the Navajo of the American Southwest was developed when the Navajo domesticated sheep.

The impact of the horse was more dramatic. The people of Mexico were initially terrified by the sight of a mounted man. It reinforced their belief that the Spaniards were gods. Even after the Indians recognized that horses were ordinary beasts, the Spanish equestrian monopoly gave the conquistadores an immense advantage in battle.

Two centuries later, herds of wild horses had migrated north to the Great Plains of North America. There they became the basis of several cultures. The Sioux, Commanche, Pawnee, Apache, Nez Percé, Blackfoot, Crow, and other tribes of the plains, previously an agricultural people, captured the mustangs and became peerless horsemen independent of European example. Their semi-nomadic way of life was built around the horse and the herds of bison they hunted long before they had any contact with the "white eyes."

Other valuable "green immigrants" from Europe were grains such as wheat and barley, citrus fruits, and—possibly the most valuable crop—sugar cane. (It is difficult to imagine a Caribbean island without cane.)

Feeding the World

The American continents contributed few food animals to the world larder. (The woodlands turkey and other game birds are noble exceptions.) The plant foods of the New World, by way of contrast, revolutionized European, African, and Asian diets. Maize (Indian corn), an American native, astonished Europeans by the height of its stalks and size of its grains. Cultivation of the crop spread to every continent, increasing the food supply and contributing to the rapid increase in population that has characterized the last five hundred years of human history.

Florida Indians, who traded extensively with other Native Americans, bringing crops to a tribal granary; an engraving by Theodore DeBry (ca. 1590).

The white potato and the sweet potato, two more Americans, were scarcely less important. The white potato became a major staple in temperate countries from Ireland to northern China. The sweet potato flourished in warmer areas and became a staple in West Africa, where it was introduced by slave traders. Beans, squash and pumpkins, manioc, peppers, and tomatoes are other foods that were unknown in Europe, Africa, and Asia before Columbus sailed the ocean blue.

Many national cuisines depend on foods of American origin, particularly the tomato and the extraordinary variety of chili peppers that have been developed from a Mexican forebear. It has been estimated that of 640 food crops grown in Africa today, all but 50 originated in the Americas. The Indians also contributed tobacco to Old World civilization.

New Diseases for Old

The sixteenth century understood the exchange of animals and plants. But people of that day were merely conscious of the most tragic of the inter-continental transactions in microscopic forms of life. Many diseases for which Europeans, Africans, and Asians had developed immunities were unknown to American Indians before 1492. They had been insulated from them by 3,000 miles of open sea. Biologically, the Indians had not "learned to live with" measles, smallpox, whooping cough, chicken pox, and even mild influenzas.

The effect of these diseases on the Indians was catastrophic. While Europeans and Africans suffered badly enough from the epidemics that swept through the colonies, the Indians died in heart-rending numbers. Invisible bacteria and viruses killed far more Native Americans than did Spanish swords or English muskets. Like wild horses out of Mexico, Old World diseases preceded the white advance, brought to isolated Indian villages by individuals who had made contact with the newcomers.

In return, the Indians probably made a gift of venereal disease to Europe and then to Africa and Asia. Medical historians disagree on the origins of syphilis, but we know that it was first identified by physicians in 1493— in Cadiz, Spain, the port to which Columbus returned after his first voyage. From Spain, syphilis traveled to Naples, where several of Columbus's crewmen are known to have gone. Then it spread like wildfire throughout the world, following the trade routes, exactly where sailors, a notoriously promiscuous lot, would be expected to take it.

Europeans, Africans, and Asians reacted to syphilis as Indians reacted to measles and chicken pox. Symptoms were severe and death came quickly. About 10 million people died of syphilis within 15 years of Columbus's voyage. Only later did the disease take on the slower-acting form in which we know it today.

For Further Reading

On American Indians (whom we shall look at in more detail in subsequent chapters), see Alvin M. Josephy, Jr., *The Indian Heritage of America* (1968); Harold E. Driver, *Indians of North America* (1970); Wilcomb E. Washburn, *The Indian in America* (1975); Robert F. Spencer and Jesse D. Jennings et al., *The Native Americans: Ethnology and Backgrounds of the North American Indians* (1977).

There is as yet no single book bringing together exciting recent research on the Meso-Americans in the pre-Columbian period, but, on Mayan art and religion, have a look at Linda Sechele and Mary Ellen Miller, *The Blood of Kings* (1986). Carroll L. Riley et al., *Man Across the Sea: Problems of Pre-Columbian Contact* (1971) deals with Pre-Columbian America from the other sides of the Atlantic and Pacific. Also see David B. Quinn, *North America from Earliest Discovery to First Settlements: The Norse Voyages to 1612* (1977).

For Europe during the age of discovery, see J. H. Parry, *The Age of Reconnaissance* (1963); J. H. Elliott, *The Old World and the New* (1970); Fernand Braudel, *Capitalism and Medieval Life* (1973). Charles R. Boxer, *The Portuguese Seaborne Empire* (1969) is the standard work on Portugal overseas. On the many explorations in the Americas, two works by Samuel Eliot Morison are both classics and still well worth a read, his biography of Columbus, *Admiral of the Ocean Sea* (1942) and *The European Discovery of America*, 2 vol. (1971, 1974). Kirkpatrick Sale, *The Conquest of Paradise* (1990) depicts Columbus as an ass when he is not a fiend: silly; a shame from so fine a writer.

Students interested in Spanish conquests cannot do better than with a history in the grand old literary tradition, William H. Prescott, *History of the Conquest of Mexico* (1873). See also the biographical study, William W. Johnson, *Cortes* (1975). Miguel Leon-Portilla, *The*

Broken Spears (1962) tells of the conquest of Mexico from the Aztec point of view.

Standard works in English on early Spanish America are Clarence H. Haring, *The Spanish Empire in America* (1947); Charles Gibson, *Spain in America* (1966); Carl Sauer, *The Early Spanish Main* (1966); and especially James Lockhart and Stuart B. Schwartz, *Early Latin America* (1983). The book that revealed the significance of the distinct biotic systems of Old World and New is Alfred E. Crosby, *The Columbian Exchange: Biological and Cultural Consequences of 1492* (1972). See also William Cronon, *Changes on the Land* (1983).

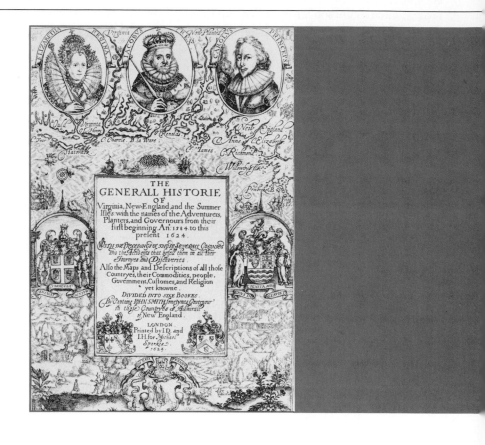

The frontispiece of Captain John Smith's General History of Virginia, *1624, written in part to encourage English men and women to settle in Virginia.*

ENGLAND GOES TO AMERICA

THE STRUGGLE TO PLANT A COLONY 1550 - 1624

The English King Henry VII passed up a chance to have Chistopher Columbus plant his flag on an

American beach. Henry failed to act when Columbus, momentarily discouraged in Spain, wrote to

him proposing that he sail westward to the Indies in Henry's employ. Nevertheless, England's claim

to a piece of the Americas was almost as old as Spain's. In 1497, Henry VII sent another Italian sailor,

John Cabot, across the North Atlantic in search of a route to Asia. Cabot discovered Newfoundland

and Nova Scotia, which he claimed for England. Cabot actually touched on continental America a year earlier than Columbus did.

The French showed little interest in overseas exploration until 1523, when a French privateer captured a Spanish ship bringing Aztec gold home. His curiosity aroused by so pretty a cargo, King Francis I sent his Italian navigator, Giovanni Verrazano, across the ocean. Verrazano claimed much of what is now the east coast of North America for France. When the pope scolded Francis, reminding him that all the world's non-Christian lands had already been divided between Portugal and Spain, the king dipped his pen in sarcasm. He asked to examine the section of Adam's will that gave the pope the right to bestow so pretty a gift.

ENGLAND'S PROBLEMS

Adam's will or no, Cabot and Verrazano notwithstanding, Spain enjoyed a near monopoly in the Americas for a century. It was not that England, France, and other European nations were indifferent to American riches. It was, simply, that through most of the 1500s—Spain's *siglo de oro* or "golden century"—no European nation was quite up to challenging Spanish might. During the second half of the 1500s, France was convulsed by vicious civil wars to determine which great duke would be king. Henry VII resolved a similar dispute in England in 1485. But the Tudor dynasty he founded was vexed by the miscarriages of a queen, a royal divorce, short reigns, and religious tensions. Only toward the end of the sixteenth century under Elizabeth I, the last of the Tudor monarchs, did the English challenge Spain in America.

The Protestant Reformation

The sixteenth century was a time of religious turmoil in much of Europe. It was the era of the Protestant Reformation. During the same years that Cortez was shattering Aztec civilization, the German monk Luther was shattering the unity of European Christendom. While Francisco Coronado was exploring the deserts of western North America, and Hernán DeSoto the Mississippi Valley, a French lawyer named John Calvin was laying the foundations of a dynamic religious faith that would profoundly influence American as well as European history.

In 1517, in the German city of Wittenberg, Martin Luther posted a paper bearing 95 "theses," or subjects for debate, to a church door. He attacked several doctrines and practices of the Roman Catholic Church as corrupt or false. Called to account by the Holy Roman Emperor Charles V (who was also king of Spain as Charles I), Luther denied the authority of the pope to determine true religion. The only infallible source of God's word, Luther declared, was the Holy Bible.

In a remarkably short time, large parts of Germany, Scandinavia, and the Netherlands fell in behind the passionate monk. Many ordinary folk had long been disgusted by a moral laxity that was too common among the priests of the Roman Catholic Church. Many princes and princelings were attracted to Luther's Protestantism for less admirable reasons. They could seize the Church's domains—between one fourth and one third of the land in Europe—if they broke with Rome.

Thus was much of northern and central Europe permanently lost to Roman Catholicism. A large minority of the French also embraced Protestant doctrines, as did most Scots. In Spain, however, the powerful monarchy stood by Rome and used the Spanish Inquisition, a religious court designed to root out Muslims and Jews, to persecute suspected Protestants. In England, Henry VIII, crowned king in 1509, also remained loyal to Catholicism. When he condemned Lutheranism in a scholarly book, *Defense of the Seven Sacraments*, the pope honored Henry as "Defender of the Faith."

The Church of England

The title proved to be high irony for, in 1527, Henry himself broke with the papacy. He had little quarrel with Catholic doctrine and ritual. Henry just wanted the pope to annul his marriage to a Spanish princess, Catherine of Aragon, who was nearing the end of her child-bearing years after a history of babies dead in womb or cradle. Catherine had a daughter, Mary. But these were days when monarchs still rode the battlefield. Henry believed that, for his young dynasty to survive a foreign or domestic threat, he must have a son. And then, there was Cupid. Henry was infatuated with a comely young lady of the court, Anne Boleyn, who wanted a wedding ring, not a mistress's pillow.

Popes were inclined to be sympathetic to royal problems of this sort. However, Pope Clement VII feared the mighty Emperor Charles V, who happened to be the nephew of Catherine of Aragon, more than he wanted to oblige Henry. He refused the annulment whence Henry VIII had Parliament declare papal authority invalid in England. The king, according to the Act of Supremacy, was head of the Christian Church in England. Most of Henry's bishops promptly sanctioned the annulment and blessed his marriage to Anne Boleyn.

Like the German princes he had attacked, Henry confiscated the rich lands owned by monasteries and nunneries in England. The monks and nuns were sent packing; the estates that had supported them were sold to ambitious subjects. Thus did Henry fill his treasury, scatter potential enemies, and create a class of well-to-do landowners who had good reason to support him.

A Changing Church

Henry VIII made few changes in religious doctrine and church structure. His "reformation" had few consequences for the daily lives and Sunday worship of the English people. But, as so many people in power have discovered before and since, tinkering with an established order often liberates a spirit of debate and an impulse to innovate. This is what happened in England. A true Protestantism germinated at all levels of the English Church during the reign of Edward VI (r. 1547–53), Henry VIII's son by Jane Seymour, the third of his six wives. In the boy king's name, religious reformers turned the Church of England in a Protestant direction.

Alas for them, Edward was a sickly lad who died in 1553, just sixteen years of age. Worse, his rightful successor was his older half-sister, Catherine of Aragon's daughter, Mary. Mary Tudor was a zealous Catholic who had seethed for two decades over her mother's humiliation. Now queen, she married her cousin, Prince Philip of Spain, soon to be known as "His Most Catholic Majesty" because of his zeal on behalf of the Roman Church. Then Mary shocked even him by the zeal with which she rooted out Protestants in her Court. Mary also persecuted, as best sixteenth century methods allowed, Protestants among the common people. Three hundred were executed, earning the queen the unflattering nickname of "Bloody Mary."

Had Mary lived a long life and borne a child, England might have been brought back to Catholicism. But like her half-brother, Edward, Mary sat the throne for only a short time. She died in 1558, childless.

In the meantime, many English Protestants had fled her axes and stakes to live in exile in Geneva. There they honed their religious views under the most radical of the Protestant reformers, John Calvin. They were to become known as Puritans for their determination to "purify" the Church of England of the vestiges of Catholicism: statues, incense, mystical services, and the authority of bishops, for which they found no justification in the Geneva Bible, which they translated into English.

THE ELIZABETHAN AGE

England's ruler after Bloody Mary was one of the shrewdest politicians ever to wear a crown. Elizabeth I, Henry VIII's daughter by Anne Boleyn, was a survivor. To have been alive and kicking in 1558, she had to have been. Her mother was beheaded by her father when she was three. When Elizabeth was fourteen, the English Church embraced Protestantism and English foreign policy took an anti-Spanish turn. She went along. When Elizabeth was twenty, England returned to Rome under Mary and became an ally of Spain. Elizabeth went along. Now queen at twenty-five, she was well practiced in the arts of concealing her sympathies and cajoling influential schemers with wildly differing views of religious truth and foreign policy. She also knew how to bide time.

Philip II rushed to England to propose to the new monarch. Elizabeth waffled. To marry his Most Catholic Majesty, the king of Spain, would surely set English Protestants to plotting against her. But to reject Philip abruptly would risk a war with Spain for which England was unprepared. Coyly flirtatious when circumstances demanded, regal when it served her purposes, Elizabeth seemed to say yes to Philip's suit, then no, then maybe. In fact, she said nothing at all. She wore Philip down (he found a wife in France), and had her way. She won time to determine in which direction lay the most auspicious prospects.

The Sea Dogs

Elizabeth's policy toward the New World was also devious. During the first two decades of her reign, an official state of peace with Spain meant that she recognized Spain's claim to all the Americas except Brazil (which, in 1580, Philip also took over). Beginning about 1577, however, Elizabeth first tolerated, then quietly encouraged a restless, swashbuckling fraternity of Spaniard-hating sea captains who were determined to chip away at Philip's empire.

The most daring of these "sea dogs" (the name comes from a shark native to English waters) was a slave-trader aspiring to better things, Francis Drake. In 1577, this remarkable sailor set sail in the Golden Hind, rounded South America by the Strait of Magellan, and swooped down on undefended Spanish ports on the Pacific. No ship of any nation save Spain had ever plied these waters. Ports like Valparaiso in Chile and Callao in Peru were hardly fortified.

The pickings were easy but, Drake reckoned correctly, Spanish warships would await him in the Atlantic. Therefore, he sailed north to California—some say he discovered San Francisco Bay—scraped the barnacles from the hull of the Golden Hind, and struck west across the Pacific. Drake's expedition was only the second, after that of Magellan and Del Caño, to circumnavigate the globe.

At about the same time, another Sea Dog, Martin

Sir Francis Drake (ca. 1540–1596), English privateer, commanded only the second expedition to circumnavigate the globe.

Bad Weather, Worse Luck

In the meantime, in 1578, Gilbert and Raleigh had tried to plant a colony in North America. Foul weather forced them to return to England. In 1583, Gilbert returned and built an outpost in Newfoundland. However, the descent of the northern winter persuaded him to turn south whence his two ships were caught in a storm. Bold sea dog to the end, Gilbert's last recorded words, called across the waves to his second vessel, were "We are as near to heaven by sea as by land." He was never seen again.

The next year, Raleigh sent out an exploration party which recommended the shores of Chesapeake Bay as the best site for an English colony. The climate was mild, the soil good, and the Chesapeake seemed quite far enough from St. Augustine to be safe from Spanish assault. Raleigh named the country Virginia after Elizabeth, the "Virgin Queen." In 1587, he shipped 91 men, 17 women, and 9 children to settle it.

The Mysterious Lost Colony

Strong winds blew the expedition south to Roanoke Island in what is now North Carolina. The sandy, wooded island was not nearly so good a site as on the Chesapeake. Still, Roanoke might have been England's first successful American colony had it not been three

Frobisher, scouted Newfoundland for a likely site at which to plant a colony. In 1578, quietly, Elizabeth licensed two half-brothers, Humphrey Gilbert and Walter Raleigh, to establish an English settlement in any land "not in the actual possession of any Christian prince."

Elizabeth was up to her usual game. While appearing to acquiesce in Spain's monopoly in the New World, she was in fact challenging it. Although Philip II claimed all of North America for Spain, the northernmost outpost in his "actual possession" was a lonely fort at St. Augustine in Florida, founded in 1565.

But Elizabeth's game with Philip was nearly up. The "Spanish party" at her court had withered away. Those who wanted to singe Philip II's beard were ascendant. Then, in 1580, Drake returned to England, his ship so stuffed with Spanish treasure that it listed dangerously, sorely at risk of capsizing. The profit on the voyage was 4700 percent. Coveting her share of the loot and knowing full well that Philip's patience was exhausted anyway, Elizabeth boarded the *Golden Hind* and knighted Drake.

Sir Walter Raleigh (ca. 1552–1618), unsuccessful colonizer.

long years before the settlers were resupplied. When Raleigh's agents finally returned to the Carolina coast in 1590, they found only abandoned buildings, already in decay. The word CROATOAN, and nothing else, was carved on one of them in "fayre Capitall letters."

This was a good sign. Governor John White—whose granddaughter, Virginia Dare, the first English child born in North America, was among the missing—had instructed the colonists that, if they left, they were to leave the name of their destination. If they were forced to leave, they were to punctuate their message with a cross. There was no cross at Roanoke so White concluded the colony had voluntarily removed to Croatoan Island near Cape Hatteras. Sailing there, White's entourage wandered about, discharging muskets and singing English songs to assure any who were hiding in the woods that they were not Spaniards. To no avail: there was no trace of the Roanokers on Croatoan.

The most plausible explanation of their fate is that the colonists, finding themselves unable to survive on their own resources, joined with the friendly Lumbee Indians of Croatoan. Late in the 1600s, after the Lumbees had moved to the interior of North Carolina, some members of the tribe were observed to be fair-skinned and blue-eyed, with a number of English words in their language.

BEGINNINGS OF AN EMPIRE

Why was Raleigh delayed in resupplying Roanoke? In part it was because of financial problems for which he had a positive genius. More important, in 1588 and 1589, he and other Englishmen of wealth and power were preoccupied with a mortal threat to the nation. Philip II of Spain, quietly enraged by Drake and other Sea Dogs, had mobilized his riches to assemble a fleet of 130 ships with which to invade England.

The Spanish Armada

The Spanish (or "Invincible") Armada of 1588 was a disaster. Designed to transport 30,000 troops that would conquer England, its large, clumsy galleons, galleasses, and galleys were outmaneuvered in the English Channel and harassed by small, quick English pinnaces. In the port of Calais in France to pick up reinforcements, the Armada was savaged by "fireships," old vessels the English smeared with tar and stuffed with gunpowder and sailed aflame and unmanned, rudders lashed, to amidst the anchored Spanish fleet.

The next year, trying to return home by rounding the British Isles to the north, the Armada was beset by Arctic storms. Only half of the ships made it back to Spain—only a third of the soldiers. The Elizabethans may be excused for suggesting that God had lined up on their side: they called the storms that finished off the Armada "the Protestant Wind."

Spanish power did not collapse. Far from it. Philip II's income from the Americas continued to top $12 million a year. (Spanish gold and silver imports peaked during the 1590s!) Nevertheless, the sea dogs had demonstrated that Spain was less than invincible. As the century drew to a close, England, France, and the Netherlands (a former Spanish province) were ready to chance creating their own American empires.

Promoters

If the sea dogs showed the English that they could challenge mighty Spain, some less-traveled Elizabethans promoted the idea that England should establish American colonies. The most important of them was Richard Hakluyt, a bookish but by no means parochial minister of the Church of England. Hakluyt spent much of his life rummaging through the libraries of Oxford and London, collecting and publishing explorers' accounts of the geography, resources, and recommendations of the Americas. His first collection was published in 1582, not long after Drake's return on the *Golden Hind*. His masterwork, *The Principal Navigations, Voyages, Traffiques, and Discoveries of the English Nation*, was published in three volumes between 1598 and 1600, after the danger of Spanish invasions had passed.

In these books and in innumerable earnest discussions with men of capital, Hakluyt argued for investing in American colonies that would "infallibly" produce a profit, add to England's glory, and "enlarge the glory of the gospel."

Hakluyt lived until 1616, long enough to be a shareholder in the first successful English settlement in America. Sir Walter Raleigh survived until 1618, but he was not so lucky. After a lifetime sinking his (and others') money in failed attempts to colonize North America, the dashing soldier, poet, and personal favorite of Elizabeth ran afoul of her successor, James I. Imprisoned by the king, Raleigh spent the last thirteen years of his life in the Tower of London, harmlessly writing books of history.

Other writers contributed to the promotional campaign. Like advertisers of every era, they played down the dangers and risks, inflated the prospects, and simply lied through their teeth. Virginia rivaled:

Tyrus for colours, Balsam for woods, Persia for oils, Arabia for spices, Spain for silks, Narcis for shipping, the Netherlands for fish, Pomona for fruit and by tillage, Babylon for corn, besides the abundance of mulberries, minerals, rubies, pearls, gems, grapes, deer.

Playwrights Francis Beaumont and John Fletcher wrote of the place:

> Where every wind that rises blows perfume,
> And every breath of air is like an incense.

Hard Economic Facts

Naturally, the boosters held out the possibility that England too might fall into gold and silver mines as the Spanish had, or find the passage to Asia that the Spanish had not. Some of them imagined outposts in America from which sea dogs would sally forth to seize Spanish ships and raid Spanish ports. As Hakluyt showed, the North American continent provided dozens of likely harbors and coves for such enterprises. Even in the Caribbean, the overextended Spaniards had already abandoned islands which the English, Dutch, and French would later make their own.

But an economy could not be built on a foundation of piracy. Moreover, expensive as the Spanish found it to be—twenty warships to defend a treasure fleet of twenty merchantmen—it was possible to protect valuable cargoes against high seas raiders. Rather more persuasive to sober investors in London and English ports like Bristol and Plymouth, there were signs by 1600 that Spain's American gold and silver mines were as much a curse as a blessing upon that country.

It was true that Spain's fabulous American wealth enabled grandees at home to purchase whatever they desired, from a grand style of life that was the envy of Europe to huge armies that terrorized the continent. It was also true, however, that the men of the Spanish ruling class assumed that their matchless bravery and sense of honor were quite enough on which to base a national economy.

Philip II was not fooled. Taciturn, hard-working, ascetic in his personal habits, invariably dressed in black, ever thinking in the longest of terms—eternity—Philip knew that the mines of Mexico and Peru had bottoms. The gold and silver would run out. Therefore, he proclaimed and tried to enforce measures that would provide for his beloved Spain when it did. But he was not successful. His subjects spent and spent on their luxuries. Philip himself spent and spent on his wars and invasion fleets, all together ensuring that one day their country would be one of the poorest in Europe.

Easy Come, Easy Go

Instead of putting American gold and silver to work to improve Spanish agriculture, Spain purchased much food abroad, impoverishing its own farmers. Fisheries were neglected in favor of buying from others. Philip II's attempts to encourage manufacture of textiles and leather and iron goods were thwarted by the cheaper costs of imports. Even the bulk of the vaunted Spanish army swore in German or Italian. Spain paid to have its warships built abroad. Thanks to the neglect of shipbuilding, many of Spain's cargoes were carried by foreign vessels.

The result was that gold and silver dribbled out of Spain as steadily as they poured in. American riches ended up in countries with no mines but with lively merchant marines and enterprising manufacturers. Other nations did the final count of the Spanish doubloons. They included enemies of Spain quite glad to make whatever the Spanish would buy and to transport whatever the Spanish would ship.

Every transaction made Spain poorer and its enemies richer. England and Holland, Spain's bitterest foes, actually fought wars with each other to determine which would have the edge in bleeding the Spanish of their loot. In the Treaty of Utrecht in 1713, England would take as spoils of victory not an island but the *asiento de negros*, the right to sell 4,000 African slaves in the Spanish colonies annually for a period of 30 years.

Mercantilism

The recognition that trading nations like England were getting richer at the expense of Spain led to the formulation of an economic policy known as mercantilism, which may be awkwardly translated as "merchant-ism." Although the mercantilist philosophy was not systematized until Thomas Mun published *England's Treasure by Foreign Trade* in 1664 (and the word *mercantilism* was not coined for another century), the English, French, and Dutch were acting on mercantilistic notions in the early 1600s.

The object of mercantilism was to increase a nation's wealth in gold and silver—the wealth of all the realm's subjects, not merely the royal treasury. The key to doing this was a favorable balance of trade. That is, the people of the nation must sell more goods abroad, or more costly goods, than they bought from other countries.

Thus, overseas merchants became of peculiar value to the nation. If a ship's master from Bristol or Plymouth carried a cargo of Dutch cloth to the Spanish colony of Cuba and sugar back to France, the gold and silver coin that he charged the shippers enriched England at the expense of three rival nations. Mercantilist policy was, therefore, to encourage England's merchant marine in every way possible.

Manufacturing was another activity dear to mercantilist hearts. Long before 1600, the English had learned that it was economic lunacy to ship raw wool abroad and to buy it back in the form of woven cloth. The manufactured cloth cost more than the wool that went into it. The difference represented coin drained out of the realm. The Crown, therefore, had forbidden the export of raw wool and, through subsidies and favors, encouraged the carders, spinners, dyers, and weavers whose skills added value to the sheep's lost fleece. Mercantilists urged the Crown to favor all such manufacturers.

The Colonial Connection

In the best of all possible mercantilistic worlds, England would be completely self-sufficient. The isle would produce everything its people needed and buy nothing abroad. Were that ideal achieved, the gold and silver from trade and sales abroad would roll in, while none would leave.

In the real world, such self-sufficiency was out of the question. An island nation in a northerly latitude, England imported any number of tropical products. The English people drank a good deal of wine but produced little; it had to be imported from France and Portugal. England consumed large quantities of furs in the manufacture of clothing and felt. These were imported from Muscovy (Russia) and Scandinavia. As a maritime nation, England consumed timber and naval stores (tar, pitch, fiber for rope) in quantities far beyond the capacity of the country's depleted forests. Forest products, too, had to be imported from Scandinavia.

In practice, then, the object of mercantilism was to minimize imports that cost money and maximize exports and the trade that brought money in. It was at this point that mercantilists became promoters of colonies.

First of all, colonies were a means of reducing England's dependence on foreign countries. By gaining control of the forests of North America, which teemed with fur-bearing animals and seemingly limitless timber and naval stores, England could stop the flow of gold and silver to Scandinavians and Russians. By occupying islands in the tropics, the English could produce their own sugar and stop paying money to the Spanish for it. And by settling loyal subjects overseas, the Crown would create exclusive and dependable markets for English manufactures. The colonists themselves would have to scare up the coin with which they purchased these goods.

Surplus Population

Another circumstance that encouraged the founding of colonies was the widespread anxiety that there were just too many Englishmen and women. Indeed, the population of the island had boomed during the 1500s, probably because of a decline in the incidence of mortal disease.

But food production and opportunities for employment had not kept pace with this population explosion.

Some believed that the "enclosure movement" was at fault. That is, raising sheep was more profitable than farming the land in small family plots. Therefore, wealthy landowners and villagers who owned land in common converted their fields into pasture which they "enclosed" with hedges that served as fences. Tending sheep called for a fraction of the labor force that tilling the land did. Consequently, villagers who lost their rights to farm the land were sent packing.

This surplus population wandered the countryside where their struggle to survive worried villagers and gentry alike. They begged, they stole, they waylaid travelers on lonely stretches of road. The refugees also congregated in cities where they formed a large, half-starved, and seemingly permanent underclass that, like the poor of many ages, was a source of disease, crime, and disorder. "Yea many thousands of idle persons," Richard Hakluyt wrote, "having no way to be set on work, . . . often fall to pilfering and thieving and other lewdness, whereby all the prisons of the land are daily pestered and stuffed full of them."

One response to England's population problem was a chilling criminal code. In the seventeenth and eighteenth centuries, a wretch could be hanged for the pettiest thefts, of as little as a rabbit from a gentleman's hutch. When there seemed to be too many people for the country to support, it was not easy to mount an argument against hanging that was likely to appeal to hardheaded realists. When the poor were so numerous as to worry the ruling class, it was easy to believe that only the constant threat of the gallows kept them from running completely amok.

Or, the pestering poor could be sent abroad. To Hakluyt and his fellows, colonies were safety valves. People who were economically superfluous and socially dangerous at home could, by the alchemy of a sea voyage, become valuable, happy consumers of English goods and the gatherers of the raw materials that England needed. "The fry of the wandering beggars of England," he wrote, "that grow up idly, and hurtful and burdenous to this realm, may there be unladen, better bred up, and may people waste countries to the home and foreign benefit, and to their own more happy state."

Indeed, the desperation of the poor rendered many Englishmen and women glad to go overseas. As for those who found the idea unattractive, the "bloody code" served nicely as an inducement. North America was better than the noose. During the first century and a half of English settlement in the New World, it has been estimated that about one colonist in ten (about 50,000 total) was a convict.

HOW THEY LIVED

COMMON SEAMEN IN THE AGE OF DISCOVERY

They were little people by today's standards. Few of the seamen who sailed the seas of the world were taller than five and a half feet. But they were as tough as the oak planks they walked, for they could not have otherwise survived to adulthood in the fifteenth and sixteenth centuries. Diseases that are now merely a nuisance carried off those children who were weak and sickly in the Age of Discovery.

Common seamen were often little more than children themselves: young teenagers or men in their early twenties. Reaching adulthood did not guarantee a long life, however. The odds were that a person who survived the childhood diseases of the sixteenth century would die before the age of thirty-five. The odds were even worse for the men who went to sea.

Ships were frequently wrecked when their wooden hulls faced the might and fury of the Atlantic. The rules governing ships meeting at sea were those of the jungle: do what you are strong enough to do. The men on a Spanish vessel were prepared to battle every Portuguese, Dutch, French, English, or freebooting pirate ship they encountered. Spanish ships sailing from the Americas were especially attractive prey—who knew what treasures might be stored in their leaky hulls?—and defeat in battle meant death, or enslavement. Vasco da Gama once poured boiling oil on the belly of a prisoner in order to extract information from him.

If the sixteenth-century sailor survived the assaults from other ships, he then faced hazards on his own vessel. He might be killed by one of his own crewmates in a fight over a trivial matter. Or he might be executed for a petty offense as an object lesson to his fellows. Discipline on the high seas consisted of quick, harsh punishment for the slightest transgressions. These were usually flogging, keel-hauling (dragging a man under water the length of the hull where, if he was not drowned, his body was shredded and broken by barnacles), or hanging from the yardarm. After a mutiny against him, Magellan decapitated one ringleader, quartered another alive, and marooned a third on a desert island. When he pardoned the rest, they were so grateful that they became Magellan's most loyal followers.

Finally, the common seaman not only continued to risk the diseases that plagued people on land, but he also ran a higher risk of scurvy. Scurvy is a vitamin C deficiency and was a very common disease in the centuries before our own. The disease can be completely reversed by a few days crash diet of fresh fruits and vegetables. The island of Curaçao in the Caribbean got its name—*curaçao* is the Portuguese word for "cure"—when Columbus left several men nearly dead from scurvy there, later returning to find them fit and strong. They had fed on fresh fruits in his absence.

At sea, however, the men's daily diet did not contain fresh fruit and consisted of about one pound of salt beef, one and a half pounds of biscuit, two and a half pints of water, and one and a quarter pints of wine. The captain's larder served him and his officers scarcely better, although there might be onions, garlic, and dried fruits in it.

Sixteenth-century sailors worked with their muscles as few people do today. They loaded cargoes of a hundred tons with only the help of a winch or a windlass. At sea they hauled only with the aid of ropes heavy canvas fifty feet up and down the masts. Merely holding the ship on course in peaceful seas was heavy work. The crude tiller pitted the seaman's strength directly against the forces of wind and ocean currents. Every ship leaked and had to be pumped by hand regularly, and constantly during storms.

On long voyages the ship had to be serviced and refitted regularly. When this was wanted, the ship was sailed onto a beach where it was "careened," turned on its side, and the barnacles covering its hull were scraped off. Then the hull was recaulked with pitch and tar. If the captain decided that the sails needed to be rearranged, the seamen virtually rebuilt the ship above deck. Even when such special tasks were not needed, the crew was kept hopping every moment, repairing sails and lines, and scrubbing the decks with vinegar and salt water. Boredom was far more dangerous than overwork.

Why did someone choose such a life? The first answer is that *choose* is the wrong word. Most sailors were born and raised in seaports. They were literally bred to the life. Occupation, like social status, was not something about which a person of the sixteenth century had much choice. What else could a young man of Cádiz or Seville (or Le Havre or Bristol) do to make his way through life?

Then too, some portion of the crews of the sixteenth century were forced onto the ships. The crew for Columbus's momentous voyage, for example, was put together in part by drafting convicts. For several centuries to come, short-handed captains made up their crews by waylaying ("shanghaiing") young men.

Finally, for all its dangers and discomforts, the sea offered a remote but alluring chance for social and economic advancement. While some of the great captains of the era were, like Magellan, born into the upper classes, others, like Columbus, worked their way up. Columbus first shipped out as a boy, perhaps only ten years old, and was illiterate until he was thirty. Yet he became the adviser of royalty and, for what the title was worth, Admiral of the Ocean Sea. Quite a number of the *conquistadores*, who first came to the New World as common seamen, lived to become wealthy landowners.

Of course, such success stories tell us of only a tiny fraction of the whole. For most sailors, life was brutal and short. But, in the sixteenth century, these seamen, brutal or not, were the agents of the great adventure that revolutionized the world.

Private Enterprise

While king and Parliament were persuaded to favor colonization, the financing and organizing of colonies were carried out by private companies that were forerunners of the modern corporation. These Merchants-Adventurers companies ("adventurer" refers to the adventuring or risking of capital) had developed in response to the expense and risks involved in overseas trading expeditions.

That is, it was not cheap, nor a sure thing, to send a ship packed with trade goods out to sea where pirates, warships of hostile nations, and nature's storms and shoals were waiting. Instead of gambling an entire fortune on a single ship's luck, investors preferred to join with others and divide both the risks and the anticipated profits into shares. If a ship owned by such a company went down, individual shareholders lost money, but they were not totally ruined. Adventurers of capital covered themselves at home, too. Typically, they secured charters from the Crown granting them a monopoly of the importation and sale of the goods they intended to buy.

The Muscovy Company, founded in 1555, was such a chartered monopoly. Its shareholders had government sanction to import furs and forest products from Russia—which no other English merchant might legally do. The most famous and longest lasting of the trading companies was the East India Company, founded in 1600. It would rule much of India for a century and a half.

Companies Founding Colonies

When King James I was persuaded to establish English outposts in North America, therefore, he quite naturally chartered private companies to do the job. In 1606, he authorized the Virginia Company of Plymouth to establish a settlement on the coast of North America between 38° and 45° north latitude. The Virginia Company of London had the same rights between 34° and 41°. These tracts overlapped, but the two groups were forbidden to set up within a hundred miles of one another. The buffer zone was designed to avoid rivalries that, in the Spanish colonies, had sometimes turned violent. It also hurried the two companies along by setting a premium on being first. The first to succeed had the pick of site.

NOVA BRITANNIA.

OFFERING MOST

Excellent fruites by Planting in
VIRGINIA.

Exciting all such as be well affected
to further the same.

LONDON
Printed for SAMVEL MACHAM, and are to be sold at
his Shop in Pauls Church-yard, at the
Signe of the Bul-head.
1609.

Advertisement to encourage emigration to the New World.

JAMESTOWN, VIRGINIA

The Plymouth Company was the first at sea. Soon after winning its charter, the Plymouth group sent an expedition to the mouth of Maine's Kennebec River. Like Humphrey Gilbert in Newfoundland, however, the settlers found the northerly climate uncongenial. They scurried home within a few months.

The First Families of Virginia

The London Company had better luck in Raleigh's Virginia, if fifteen years of suffering and wholesale death may be called "better luck." In May 1607, Captain Christopher Newport brought three ships into Chesapeake Bay and landed his passengers on a peninsula on the James River (named for the king). Newport had Roanoke on his mind. He would select no island that could be surrounded by ships, but he made sure to pick a peninsula site that could be defended from the natives almost as easily as an island. Captain John Smith, a soldier assigned to remain in Virginia, called Newport's choice "a verie fit place for the erecting of a great citie." This was nonsense. Jamestown (as the village was called) sat on low-lying land. All around was brackish, malarial swamp poorly suited to crops.

Jamestown's dim agricultural prospects were not overly important to Newport or Smith. The first English settlers of Virginia were not expected to be self-supporting, growing their own food. Their assignment was to

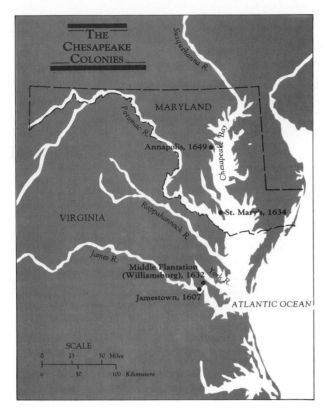

look for gold and to buy goods from the local Indians that would turn a profit back in England. And, preposterously, several Polish glassmakers among them—Protestant refugees from persecution—were to set up a workshop in which to practice their trade. The first Virginians arrived in their new home with some illusions.

The Problem of Survival

They found mere survival to be a struggle. Raw wilderness proved to be too demanding a host for the English. They had no experience as foragers. They could not compete as hunters and gatherers with the native Indians for whom hunting and gathering was a way of life, providing perhaps two-thirds of their food. Hunger, as John Smith would write, "forced many to flee for reliefe to the Savage Enemy."

In fact, there is some evidence to indicate that, at about 40,000 in 1607, the Native American population of the Chesapeake region had reached a level at which the Indians were suffering shortages in winter. (The Indians called the area Tsenahkommaka in their Algonkian language, "densely-populated land.") The sudden introduction of 200 new residents may have been just too much for Virginia. Once the Jamestowners' numbers declined to a few dozen, they did hang on. If they survived on such as oysters and snakes and toadstools, that is what foraging is all about.

There were soldiers like John Smith among them. The Virginians could have lived by raiding Indian farms, and they did raid some. But the Indians, loosely allied in what the English called the Powhatan Confederacy, held the preponderance of power in the region and would continue to hold it for more than a decade. Had the Powhatans been determined to wipe out the newcomers, they could easily have done so. Jamestown may have survived destruction in war largely because, along with food, annual relief ships brought trade goods coveted by the Indians.

Finally, there was disease: malaria, dysentery, typhoid fever, scurvy, and simple enervating apathy took a devastating toll. In 1607, 144 Englishmen landed at Jamestown. The next year, 38 were still alive. In 1608 and 1609, 500 new colonists arrived. By 1610, only 60 survived.

Then a new governor arrived, Lord De la Warr. He is credited with saving Jamestown by instituting a rigorous discipline aimed at making the colony self-sufficient in food. The settlers were marched to work in the fields as if they were soldiers. Troublemakers and the merely idle were dealt with swiftly and harshly. De la Warr and his successors, Sir Thomas Dale and Sir Thomas Gates, prescribed the death penalty for dozens of offenses, including individually trading with the Indians. They actually executed people for little more than laziness and whipped them for throwing wash water into the streets or carrying out "the necessities of nature" within a quarter-mile of the fort. Under their authoritarian rule, fields were expanded, better shelters built, and the settlement expanded along the James River.

Still mortality remained high. Between 1610 and 1618, 3,000 new settlers arrived. In 1619, the population of Virginia was but 1,000. Between 1619 and 1623, 4,000 settlers arrived. In 1624 the population of Virginia was 1,300.

The "Stinking Custom"

If the Virginians had not found a way to make money, their backers would surely have given up on them, leaving them to assimilate into the Powhatan tribes. But they did find profit growing tobacco, a native American plant that Columbus had brought back to Europe on his first voyage to the New World.

Slowly but inexorably, the habit of "drinking" tobacco smoke had spread throughout Europe during the 1500s. Some powerful people found smoking loathsome. In 1604, King James I wrote A Counterblaste to Tobacco, which described the habit as "beastly" and "vile." He forbade smoking it in his presence. (An Ottoman sultan went further. He threatened to execute smokers!)

THE INCONVENIENCIES
THAT HAVE HAPPENED TO SOME PERSONS WHICH HAVE TRANSPORTED THEMSELVES

from *England* to *Virginia*, vvithout prouisions necessary to sustaine themselues, hath greatly hindred the *Progresse* of that noble *Plantation*: For preuention of the like disorders heereafter, that no man suffer, either through ignorance or misinformation; it is thought requisite to publish this short declaration: wherein is contained a particular of such necessaries, as either priuate families or single persons shall haue cause to furnish themselues with, for their better support at their first landing in Virginia; whereby also greater numbers may receiue in part, directions how to prouide themselues.

Apparrell.

Apparrell for one man, and so after the rate for more.

	li.	s.	d.
One Monmouth Cap	00	01	10
Three falling bands		01	03
Three shirts		07	06
One waste-coate		02	02
One suite of Canuase		07	06
One suite of Frize		10	00
One suite of Cloth		15	00
Three paire of Irish stockins		04	
Foure paire of shooes		08	08
One paire of garters		00	10
One doozen of points		00	03
One paire of Canuase sheets		08	00
Seuen ells of Canuase, to make a bed and boulster, to be filled in *Virginia* 8.s. One Rug for a bed 8.s. which with the bed seruing for two men, halfe is		08	00
Fiue ells coorse Canuase, to make a bed at Sea for two men, to be filled with straw, iiij.s. One coorse Rug at Sea for two men, will cost vj.s. is for one		05	00
	04	00	00

Victuall.

For a whole yeere for one man, and so for more after the rate.

	li.	s.	d.
Eight bushels of Meale	02	00	00
Two bushels of pease at 3.s.		06	00
Two bushels of Oatemeale 4.s. 6.d.		09	00
One gallon of *Aquauitæ*		02	06
One gallon of Oyle		03	06
Two gallons of Vineger 1.s.		02	00
	03	03	00

Armes.

For one man, but if halfe of your men haue armour it is sufficient so that all haue Peeces and swords.

	li.	s.	d.
One Armour compleat, light		17	00
One long Peece, fiue foot or fiue and a halfe, neere Musket bore	01	02	00
One sword		05	
One belt		01	
One bandaleere		01	06
Twenty pound of powder		18	00
Sixty pound of shot or lead, Pistoll and Goose shot		05	00
	03	09	06

Tooles.

For a family of 6. persons and so after the rate for more.

	li.	s.	d.
Fiue broad howes at 2.s. a piece		10	00
Fiue narrow howes at 16.d. a piece		06	08
Two broad Axes at 3.s. 8.d. a piece		07	04
Fiue felling Axes at 18.d. a piece		07	06
Two steele hand sawes at 16.d. a piece		02	08
Two two-hand-sawes at 5.s. a piece		10	00
One whip-saw, set and filed with box, file, and wrest		10	—
Two hammers 12.d. a piece		02	00
Three shouels 18.d. a piece		04	06
Two spades at 18.d. a piece		03	—
Two augers 6.d. a piece		01	00
Sixe chisels 6.d. a piece		03	00
Two percers stocked 4.d. a piece		00	08
Three gimlets 2.d. a piece		00	06
Two hatchets 21.d. a piece		03	06
Two froues to cleaue pale 18.d.		03	00
Two hand bills 20. a piece		03	04
One grindlestone 4.s.		04	00
Nailes of all sorts to the value of	02	00	00
Two Pickaxes		03	—
	06	02	08

Houshold Implements.

For a family of 6. persons, and so for more or lesse after the rate.

	li.	s.	d.
One Iron Pot		07	00
One kettle		06	—
One large frying pan		02	06
One gridiron		01	06
Two skillets		05	—
One spit		02	—
Platters, dishes, spoones of wood		04	—
	01	08	00

For Suger, Spice, and fruit, and at Sea for 6 men — 00 | 12 | 06

So the full charge of Apparrell, Victuall, Armes, Tooles, and houshold stuffe, and after this rate for each person, will amount vnto about the summe of — 12 | 10 | 00

The passage of each man is — 06 | 00 | 00

The fraight of these prouisions for a man, will bee about halfe a Tun, which is — 01 | 10 | 00

So the whole charge will amount to about — 20 | 00 | 00

Nets, hookes, lines, and a tent must be added, if the number of people be greater, as also some kine. And this is the vsuall proportion that the Virginia Company doe bestow vpon their Tenants which they send.

Whosoeuer transports himselfe or any other at his owne charge vnto *Virginia*, shall for each person so transported before Midsummer 1625. haue to him and his heires for euer fifty Acres of Land vpon a first, and fifty Acres vpon a second diuision.

Imprinted at London by FELIX KYNGSTON. 1622.

Recommended provisions for would-be emigrants to Virginia in 1622.

But some physicians seized on tobacco as a miracle drug, prescribing it for any number of ailments. (It was not the worst nostrum physicians of the era prescribed.) Many other people were addicted to "recreational use" and the Spanish supplied them from their West Indian plantations. One of them was John Rolfe, a Virginian usually remembered for his marriage to the Powhatan "princess" Pocahontas, an alliance that helped ensure peace in Virginia for several years.

Importing tobacco seed from the Spanish West Indies, Rolfe began to experiment in his garden in 1612. When he had more than enough for his own pipe, he shipped a few hogsheads (barrels) packed with the leaf back to England. The reception was sensational, for tobacco had a large market. In 1617, Virginia exported 10 tons of the stuff, in 1618 25 tons.

The Tobacco Boom

Immigrants with the sweet scent of smoke in their nostrils hurried across the Atlantic. The very streets of

Jamestown were planted in the weed. A colony recently in trouble for its incapability of producing food now neglected food production for the cultivation of a weed to be burned. Authorities feared losing control, one lamenting that the settlers' "greediness after great quantities of tobacco causeth them after five or six years continually to remove and therefore neither build good homes, fence their grounds, or plant any orchards."

In 1632, the Virginia Assembly feared that other basic tasks would not be performed for the lure of blue smoke. In "An Acte for Tradesmen to Worke on Theire Trades," the Assembly declared:

> The necessitie of the present state of the country requiringe, It is thought fitt, that all gunsmiths and naylers, brickmakers, carpenters, joyners, sawyers and turners, be compelled to worke at theire trades and not suffered to plant tobacco or corne or doe any other worke in the grounde.

Who Shall Till the Fields?

An industrious individual could tend a thousand tobacco plants and four acres of maize, beans, and squash—enough to support a household of five people. It did not require a mastery of higher mathematics to calculate what the income from 10,000 or 50,000 tobacco plants would buy.

The land for growing tobacco was rich, seemingly endless, and for sale at a pittance. The problem was labor. Who would work for another in a land offering such an extraordinary opportunity to get rich? The Jamestowners enslaved Indians with some success. However, unlike the Indians of Mexico, the natives of Virginia were unfamiliar with intensive, disciplined labor, and resisted it. Moreover, they had the bad habit of disappearing in a

An early tobacco label, from the Imperial Tobacco Company in Briston.

forest which, to them, was not forbidding wilderness but a congenial home.

In 1619, a Dutch ship tied up at Jamestown and paid for their tobacco with about twenty black African captives, probably seized as a prize from a slave trader bound for the West Indies. Soon, human cargos from Africa would arrive regularly in Virginia (see Chapter 5). Not until after 1700, however, would enslaved blacks comprise a majority of the work force. During the seventeenth century, ambitious Virginians made the transition from toiling farmer to comfortable planter by importing white servants from England.

The Headright System

Under the "headright system," introduced by the London Company to encourage settlement in Virginia in 1618, each head of a household who came to the colony received 50 acres of land for every person whose Atlantic passage he paid. Thus, a family of five could secure 250 acres upon disembarking.

People with cash to spare could amass even larger estates instantly by recruiting servants from among the destitute masses of England. In return for their transportation to Virginia, these people signed contracts binding themselves to labor for their master without pay for a number of years, usually seven. Thus was Virginia peopled, thus the tobacco grown.

The Massacre of 1622

For fifteen years, the English coexisted reasonably well with the native peoples of the Powhatan Confederacy. Red and white skirmished often enough, but few battles

---

ROYAL DECREES

Both James I (r. 1603–1625) and his son, Charles I (r. 1625–1649) disapproved of tobacco. James called it "a custom loathesome to the eye, harmful to the brain, dangerous to the lungs, and in the black stinking fume thereof, nearest resembling the Stygian smoke of the pit that is bottomless." That was in 1604, before there was an English colony, let alone a colony flourishing by growing tobacco.

However, as late as 1631, when Virginia was booming because of the leaf, Charles I ordered the Earl of Carlisle to limit tobacco cultivation on his estate because of "the great abuse of tobacco to the enervation of the body and of courage." Several years later, the governor of Virginia was chided because "the King has long expected some better fruit from the colony than smoke and tobacco."

were serious. The aged head of the several tribes, whom the English also called Powhatan, did not view the tiny enclave of foreigners as much of a threat, and he was fascinated by the goods that the newcomers offered him in trade, from firearms to woven cloth, pots, pans, mirrors. In 1614, when John Rolfe married Powhatan's daughter, Pocahontas, something of a detente was inaugurated.

Then Pocahontas died while visiting England, and shortly thereafter, Powhatan joined her in death. He was succeeded as chief by his brother Opechancanough, an altogether different sort of fellow. Opechancanough recognized what many Indians after him were to learn: the once little, once half-starved white enclave with interesting things to sell was growing in size and strength, pushing into ancestral lands.

In March 1622, Opechancanough tried to turn back the tide. He entered Jamestown with warriors as if to talk or trade. Suddenly, the band attacked, killing the founder of the tobacco business, John Rolfe, and 346 others, about a third of Virginia's white population.

One of three was not enough. The survivors regrouped, bandaged their wounds and retaliated with their superior weapons, sorely punishing the Powhatans. Indeed, they called for a kind of genocide, "a perpetuall

warre without peace or truce [to] roote out from being any longer a people, so cursed a nation, ungratefull to all benefitte, and incapable of all goodnesse." By 1625, it is estimated that the Powhatan tribes were reduced from 40,000 to 5,000.

After one last Indian offensive in 1644, the Powhatans were reduced yet further and driven far into the interior. In 1669, 2000 were counted. By 1685, the culture was apparently extinct. The pattern of white-Indian relations that would be repeated for over two and a half centuries had been drawn in the mud of Jamestown.

A Royal Colony

The massacre of 1622 wrote an end to the London Company. Although some planters and merchants were getting rich from tobacco, the company itself never recorded a profit. Citing this failure and the massacre as excuses, James I revoked the company's charter in 1624 and placed Virginia under his direct control. The House of Burgesses, a legislative assembly of 22 members elected by landowners and established in 1619, continued to function. But the king appointed a governor with the power to veto their actions. Virginia thus became the first royal colony, under the direct rule of the Crown.

For Further Reading

The English leapt into the van of European civilization and expansion during the sixteenth century. The literature tracing these portentous developments is too vast for more than skimming here. G. R. Elton, *England Under the Tudors* (1974) is a good introduction to the era. On the English religious context, see Charles H. and Katherine George, *The Protestant Mind of the English Reformation* (1961). For social and "mental" background, we have Peter Laslett, *The World We Have Lost* (1965). Specifically related to interest in North America is Carl Bridenbaugh, *Vexed and Troubled Englishmen* (1968) and A. L. Rowse, *Elizabethans and America* (1959). Dealing with important incidents are Garrett Mattingly, *The Armada* (1959) and Thomas E. Roche, *The Golden Hind* (1973). See also these biographies: Paul Johnson, *Elizabeth I* (1974); P. L. Barbour, *The Three Worlds of Captain John Smith* (1964); Stephen J. Greenblatt, *Sir Walter Raleigh* (1973); and James A. Williamson, *Sir Francis Drake* (1975).

On Virginia, see Carl Bridenbaugh, *Jamestown, 1544–1699* (1980); Alden Vaughan, *Captain John Smith and the Founding of Virginia* (1975); Edmund S. Morgan, *American Slavery, American Freedom* (1975). On the dis-

placed Indians of the country, see Gary Nash, *Red, White, and Black* (1974); Thad W. Tate and David W. Ammerman, eds., *The Chesapeake in the Seventeenth Century* (1979); the relevant chapters of James Axtell, *The Invasion Within: The Contest of Cultures in Colonial America* (1985); and Peter Wood et al., *Powhatan's Mantle: Indians in the Colonial Southeast* (1989). See also James Merrell, *The Indians's New World: Catawbas and their Neighbors from European Contact through the Era of Removal* (1989).

General works that will also be of use in connection with subsequent chapters are Charles M. Andrews, *The Colonial Period of American History* (1934–38), an old chestnut much corrected but still valuable; Daniel Boorstin, *The Americans: The Colonial Experience* (1958); Wesley F. Craven, *The Southern Colonies in the Seventeenth Century* (1949); Jack P. Greene and J. R. Pole, eds., *Colonial British America* (1984); Curtis E. Nettels, *The Roots of American Civilization* (1938); John E. Pomfret with Floyd Shumway, *Founding of the American Colonies* (1970); Clarence Ver Steeg, *The Formative Years* (1964).

William Penn's promises to the Delaware Indians in return for their permission to establish the Pennsylvania colony.

3

PURITANS AND PROPRIETORS

THE GROWTH OF COLONIAL AMERICA 1620 - 1732

In 1608, a year after Jamestown was founded, about 125 villagers from England's Midlands set out on a voyage of their own. From the hamlet of Scrooby in Nottinghamshire, they made their way to the coast and took ship to Holland, where they settled in the city of Leiden.

These simple and mostly poor villagers were breaking the law. Like other nations of that time, England forbade subjects to travel abroad without permission. The Scrooby group broke the law because they had been persecuted for their religious beliefs at home. They were members of a small sect sometimes called "Separatists" because they believed that Christians who were "saved"—who had been elected by God for salvation—should worship only in the company of other "Saints," separate from the majority of people who were damned. This tenet earned them the hostility of the Church of England, to which all subjects of the king were required to adhere, and of the Crown, which was closely allied with the Church.

The Separatists are better known to us as the Pilgrims. Their leader for a generation, William Bradford, called them that because they did a good deal of wandering, a pilgrimage, in search of a home.

THE NEW ENGLAND COLONIES

Leiden was not to be their home. Not that the Pilgrims were persecuted in Holland: the Dutch were a tolerant folk. Indeed, the atmosphere of Leiden was a bit too free and easy for the Pilgrims. They fretted that their children were absorbing a casual attitude toward parental authority, "getting the reins off their necks." At the very least, they were, like the children of immigrants before and since, becoming as much Dutch as English. The Pilgrims might have yearned for a refuge where their religious beliefs were unfettered. They were also stolidly English, as ethnocentric as any Chinese, Ghanian, or Powhatan Indian. Many Dutch customs offended them.

Plymouth Plantation

The success of Virginia, such as it was by 1620, helped provide a solution to the Pilgrim dilemma. Profits gained from growing tobacco on the Chesapeake rekindled the enthusiasm of the Plymouth branch of the Virginia Company for investing in a trans-Atlantic settlement.

The trouble was, Jamestown's newfound prosperity meant that most English emigrants headed in that direction. The Plymouth Company had difficulty finding settlers for an entirely new colonial venture far to the north of Virginia. Then, Sir Edwin Sandys, a major shareholder in the company, hit on a solution. He won the agreement of the king not to molest the unhappy Separatists if they moved to North America.

In 1620, some of the exiles returned to England just long enough to board two small ships, the *Mayflower* and the *Speedwell*. The *Speedwell* leaked all too well and hastened back to port. The *Mayflower* was itself none too seaworthy, but it survived a rough passage longer than that of Christopher Columbus a century earlier.

Just over 100 colonists disembarked at the southern end of Massachusetts Bay. They built the Plymouth col-

ony on the site of Pawtuxet, an Indian village that had been wiped out in an epidemic several years earlier. This ready-made settlement, fields ready to plant, the Pilgrims regarded as a sign of God's approval. He had "cleared" the land of others so that his Saints might dwell there. Nevertheless, the first winter in America was as terrible as Virginia's starving times. Half the Pilgrims died of malnutrition or disease before spring.

Then another sign, "a special instrument sent of God": an English-speaking Indian, Squanto, wandered into the village. A native of Pawtuxet, Squanto had been kidnapped in 1615 and taken to England. When he finally managed to return to North America, he discovered ragged Plymouth where his native village had stood. Squanto adopted the Pilgrims as his tribe and proved an invaluable friend indeed. He guided the newcomers about the country, taught them native methods of fishing and cultivation, and, according to Governor William Bradford, asked for prayers so that "he might goe to the Englishmens God in Heaven."

Self-Government

Squanto was a better citizen than some of the people who arrived on the *Mayflower*. Even before landing, Separatist elders such as Bradford and William Brewster, and the colony's military officer, Captain Miles Standish, grew anxious that, once ashore, the "strangers" among them—non-Separatists—would defy their authority. Several had said as much. What was worse, they could claim legal grounds for going their own way. Plymouth lay outside the expanse of land assigned to the Pilgrims in their royal charter. Therefore, the legal authority the charter vested in the leaders of the expedition was uncertain.

In order to establish it firmly, 41 of the settlers signed the Mayflower Compact. This document began by as-

---

INCREASING AND MULTIPLYING

Nearly half the settlers of Plymouth died during the first winter on Massachusetts Bay. Just two of the survivors, however, more than made up for the loss within their own lifetimes. John Alden and Priscilla Mullins arrived on the *Mayflower* and married soon thereafter. (The wedding was immortalized and romanticized two centuries later by Henry Wadsworth Longfellow).

The Aldens both lived into their eighties. They had 12 children of whom 10 survived to adulthood. Eight of the Aldens married and, together, had at least 68 children, more than died in Plymouth in 1620–21. Alden's and Mullins's great-grandchildren, a few of whom they lived to know, numbered 400, four times the original population of the colony.

serting the party's enduring loyalty to "our dread Sovereign Lord King James," a standard opening for documents of all kinds. Then, the signers bound the settlers together in a "Civil Body Politik" for the purpose of enacting and enforcing laws.

What is memorable in the Mayflower Compact is the implicit principle that the authority of government rests on the consent of those who are governed. King James got his ceremonial due. But, concerned about the legal validity of the king's charter in the place they settled, the signers—a majority of the adult males—based their authority to make laws for their colony on their *consent* to be subject to those laws.

Plymouth was a rather democratic place during its first years. Almost every male head of household was a shareholder in the company and could, therefore, vote to elect the governor. (Bradford held the post for 30 years.) Important questions were resolved by majority vote.

A Subsistence Economy

There was little outside interference in the affairs of Plymouth. This was a consequence of the fact that the Pilgrims never came up with a commodity that was as big a money-maker as John Rolfe's tobacco plants. Furs purchased from the Indians provided some cash with which to buy goods from England. Fishing for cod off the coast of New England helped. Still, Plymouth remained largely a community of subsistence farmers. The Pilgrims raised enough food to live. Indeed, after the first terrible winter, they thrived. But none got rich tilling New England's rocky soil.

The dearth of profits discouraged the investors back home, and by 1627 they were ready to cut their losses. They agreed to sell their shares in the company to the settlers. Although it took 15 years to complete the transaction, the sale had the effect of transfering control of Plymouth Plantation to those who lived there. Plymouth remained a self-governing commonwealth until 1691, when it was absorbed into its younger but larger neighbor, Massachusetts Bay.

Massachusetts Bay

Self-government was half accidental in Plymouth. If a weary Pilgrim plowman had turned up a gold mine in his corn field—or just a saleable staple such as tobacco or sugar—the English investors and king would have seized on the colony with a greedy grip. Plymouth's very lack of rich resources assured its autonomy. In the most important colony of New England, by way of contrast, self-government was the consequence of well-laid plans.

There were no "starving times" in Massachusetts Bay, established in 1630 some forty miles up the coast from Plymouth. The founders of the Bay Colony planned the finest details of their Great Migration before they weighed anchor in England. Provisions were abundant, and more than a thousand people formed the first wave of settlement. By design, they formed a cross section of

THE FORGOTTEN COLONY

Many English settlements in North America are rarely remembered because they were abandoned or absorbed by those that survived. For example, hundreds of English fishermen set up base camps on the shores of Newfoundland, Nova Scotia, and New England to which they returned year after year. Some evolved into villages that survive today. One of the most interesting forgotten colonies was "Merrymount," located near what is now Quincy, Massachusetts, a few miles from Plymouth.

In 1623, a curious character named Thomas Morton arrived at Plymouth in a servant ship commanded by Captain Wollaston. The captain disliked the area and left for Virginia with most of his servants. He apparently intended to send for the rest, but Morton led a peaceful rebellion among them, persuading those who remained (in the words of Plymouth Governor Bradford) to join in a colony where they would be "free from service, and . . . trade, plante, & live togeather as equalls."

Morton presided over a riotous style of life that infuriated the austere Puritans. Like many pioneers after them, the Merrymounters were frequently drunk, and they "set up a May-pole, drinking and dancing aboute it many days togeather, inviting the Indean women, for their consorts, dancing and frisking togither, (like so many fairies, or furies rather,) and worse practices."

Worst of all, Morton seems to have stolen the Indian trade from Plymouth—firearms for furs and hides. This worried Governor Bradford because the Indians were better hunters than the whites "by reason of ther swiftnes of foote, & nimblnes of body" and because the firearms could be turned against his own people.

He resolved to break up the colony and sent Captain Miles Standish and a few other men to arrest Morton. There was no battle because, according to Bradford, Morton and his friends were too drunk to shoot. The only casualty was a Merrymounter who staggered into a sword and split his nose.

Morton was put on an uninhabited island to await the next ship bound for England. There, the Indians brought him food and liquor. He managed to slip away, returning on his own to England, where he denounced the Pilgrims in words as impassioned as Bradford's. Neither he nor Plymouth was punished, however, and Morton later returned to America to lead a quieter life. It is interesting to reflect on how differently New England might have developed had Morton's taste for the "high life" and anarchic attitude toward government and social class taken hold, as it might well have done. Morton seems to have been prospering, and Bradford tells us that when "the scume of the countrie, or any discontents" heard that Morton forbade the holding of servants, they "would flock to him from all places."

The seal of the colony of Massachusetts Bay (1676).

depraved, that men and women bore the guilt and burden of Adam and Eve's original sin within their breasts. In the words of the Massachusetts poet Anne Bradstreet, man was a "lump of wretchedness, of sin and sorrow."

If God were just, and nothing more, every such lump would be damned to hell for eternity. Since God was all good, there was nothing that sin-stained men and women could do to earn salvation. No act of charity, no act of faith, no ritual sacrifice from so corrupt a source could possibly merit divine approval.

Was there then no hope? In fact there was, and in the Puritans' hope for the next world lies the key to understanding the kind of society they built in this one. God in his infinite love for his creatures granted the gift of grace to some. The "elect" did not deserve this amazing gift. They were as sinful and corrupt as the damned souls who surrounded them. God alone predestined them to join him in paradise.

In return for this gift, the elect were bound by a covenant (or contract) with God to enforce divine law in the community in which they lived. If they failed to keep their part of the bargain, if they tolerated sin within the community, God would punish them as severely as he had punished his chosen people of an earlier epoch, the ancient Hebrews.

An Errand in the Wilderness

It is not quite correct, therefore, to say as many books once did, that the Puritans came to America in order "to worship as they pleased." They were, first of all, a powerful minority in England. They worshiped pretty much as they pleased on the fens of Lincolnshire and the moors of Yorkshire. One of their most respected preachers, John Cotton, had been the pastor of St. Bo-

English society. They were of both sexes, more or less balanced in numbers, of all ages and social classes up to the rank of lady and gentleman. There were skilled artisans and professionals among them, most notably well-educated ministers of God.

The founders of Massachusetts Bay intended to create, quite literally, a *New* England that would duplicate the society they knew at home. In only one particular did the settlers of Massachusetts reject English ways. Although they considered themselves communicants of the Church of England, they abhorred its practices in *Anno Domini* 1630. Their New England would be a truly godly commonwealth such as the world had not known since the days of the Apostles.

In order to ensure that they had the autonomy to create and control such a Zion, the settlers brought with them the charter of the Massachusetts Bay Company, the legal justification of their right to self-government. Shareholders who would not leave England sold out to actual settlers. There were no company directors back home to question decisions made in Massachusetts.

Puritan Religious Beliefs

These cautious, prudent people—calculating every contingency—were the Puritans. Their religion was Calvinistic, like that of the Separatists. They were disciples of the French lawyer and Protestant theologian John Calvin, who believed that human nature was inherently

---

HYPOCRITES?

"We are decendid," wrote the humorist Artemus Ward in 1872, "from the Puritans, who nobly fled from a land of despitism to a land of freedim, where they could not only enjoy their own religion, but prevent everybody else from enjoyin' his."

Witty, yes, but it is wrong to imply that the Puritans were hypocrites because they persecuted religious practices other than their own in Massachusetts. They came to America because they disapproved of the religious practices of the dominant Church of England. They never claimed that, in Massachusetts, they would tolerate those or other forms of worship they regarded as sinful. Intolerant, yes, but not hypocritical.

tolph's in old Boston, which is said to be the largest parish church in England.

It is more accurate to say that the Puritans came to America because they were not at all pleased with the way the majority of English men and women were worshiping. Their "errand in the wilderness" of Massachusetts was to purify the Church of England of the many Roman Catholic practices to which the Anglican establishment clung—the authority of bishops, statues in churches, sacramental services patterned on the Catholic mass, and so on; hence, the name "Puritans."

To Puritans, the English Church was guilty of blasphemy, a most grievous violation of God's covenant with the nation and deserving of severe punishment. "I am verily persuaded," wrote John Winthrop, the civil leader of the Massachusetts Puritans, "God will bring some heavy affliction upon this land."

In Massachusetts, Winthrop and the Puritans believed, they would be safe from God's wrath because they would observe his covenant. For years, some Puritan leaders harbored the gratifying illusion that Old England would look across the Atlantic, see by shining example the errors of its ways, and invite the Puritan fathers back home in triumph to usher England back to God. "We shall be as a citty on a hill," Winthrop wrote hopefully, a beacon inspiring to the godly everywhere.

A Commonwealth

The Puritans believed in community, that individuals should support one another in life's spiritual quest—and in its material concerns, too. In the godly commonwealth, in Winthrop's words, "every man might have need of [every] other, and from hence they might be knit more nearly together in the bond of brotherly affection."

There was little room for individualism in such a community. The Puritans enforced a strict code of moral and social behavior on everyone. The Puritan belief that God punished the community that left sinners unpunished, as well as the sinners themselves, explains why the Puritans were swift and harsh with what are today called "victimless crimes," or acts not regarded as crimes at all. As a girl named Tryal Pore confessed to a Massachusetts court when she was found guilty of fornication in 1656, "by this my sinn I have not only done what I can to Poull Judgement from the Lord on my selve but allso upon the place where I live."

The same sense of community moved Puritans to point out to their neighbors that they might be committing sins. Judge Samuel Sewall of Massachusetts was not thought to be a busybody—in the disagreeable connotation which we fix to the word—when he visited a wig-wearing relative to tell him that his hairpiece was sinful. Sewall was looking after his kinsman's soul and the well-being of the community alike. The man liked his wig too well to give it up; however, he did not tell Sewall to mind his own business. He argued only as to whether wearing a wig really was a sin.

Blue Laws

The lawbooks of Massachusetts and other New England colonies were filled with regulations that, in the late twentieth century, would be considered outrageous or ridiculous. God commanded that the sabbath be devoted to him. Therefore, the Puritans forbade on Sunday activities that on another day might be perfectly in order: working; playing games, such as was the custom in England; "idle chatter"; singing; whistling; breaking into a run; and "walking in a garden." Some things were permitted in private but not in public: married couples were forbidden to embrace or kiss in public. A sea captain, returning home after a long voyage, kissed his wife on the threshold of their cottage and was fined for his impatience.

Other minor offenders—a woman who was a "scold," for example, given to nagging in public—spent a few hours in the stocks or pillory on market day. This intriguing mode of punishment humiliated the offender by subjecting him or her to the ridicule by passers-by. More serious crimes, such as wife beating, were punished with a public flogging.

Lest the Puritans be thought unduly harsh, almost all the colonies had similar laws. Indeed, in one particular, Massachusetts was far more benevolent than other English communities. Because the Bible was their guide in these, as in other matters, the Puritans reserved capital punishment for those offenses that merited the death penalty in the Good Book: murder, treason, witchcraft, and several sexual offenses (incest, homosexuality, and bestiality).

Adultery was also a capital crime, but few of the myriad offenders seem to have hanged for it. In 1695, a law of Salem, Massachusetts, punished adulterers by requiring them to sew an A cut from cloth on their everyday garment. Although the psychological implications of this sentence provided the inspiration for Nathaniel Hawthorne's great novel The Scarlet Letter, written a century and a half later, the punishment was actually a liberalization of the traditional practice. Earlier offenders had been branded with a hot iron: T for thief, A for adulterer, etc.

The Puritans believed that social class and social distinctions were divinely decreed. "Some must be rich, some poore," said John Winthrop, not some are rich, some poor. It was therefore a crime for people of lesser class to ape the fashions of their betters. In Connecticut in 1675, 38 women were arrested for dressing in silk.

A brank—a device made of iron used for the punishment of scolds, gossips, and liars in early Massachusetts.

Obviously, the offenders could afford their finery, but their social standing in the community did not warrant their wearing it. Other laws forbade people of modest station to wear silver buckles on their shoes. Such adornments were fit only for magistrates and ministers.

A Well-Ordered Society

Between 1630 and 1640, 21,000 people settled in New England. Most were farmers who depended largely on the labor of the family. Indentured servants were few in Massachusetts compared to Virginia and other colonies. Africans were few throughout the colonial period.

By retaining close control over settlement, the Puritans were able to construct a village society more like the one they knew in the old country than took root elsewhere in English America. Arriving groups were allotted land for towns. There was a church at the center, of course, with the congregation itself governing most of its affairs. Each family was granted fields for tillage, a woodlot for fuel, the right to keep animals on the village common. Social status in old England determined just how much a family received.

When newcomers settled too far from the town center to find church and common convenient, the town's lands were divided into communities quite independent of one another. When towns lacking new land grew crowded, people moved west and north, not as individuals but as members of a new community given authority to establish a new village.

Such firm social control enabled the Puritans to found schools and create one of the most literate populations in the world. So well-planned and organized was their colony that Boston was building ships two years after it was a "howling wilderness." So quickly was New England populated that the Puritans had a college for training ministers, Harvard in Cambridge, Massachusetts, as early as 1636.

THE EXPANSION OF NEW ENGLAND

Not everyone stayed within the boundaries of Massachusetts. Puritan insistence that everyone in the community conform to God's law, as they defined it, played a large part in the expansion of New England beyond the Bay Colony. Religion was a major factor in the founding of Rhode Island, Connecticut, New Haven, and New Hampshire.

Troublesome Roger Williams

Rhode Island and Providence Plantations, still the long official name of the smallest state, was founded by a brilliant, zealous, and rather cranky Puritan divine named Roger Williams. Arriving in Massachusetts in 1631, he quarreled with John Winthrop and the colony's other overseers almost before he made his bed. Williams was the strictest sort of Puritan. His demanding conscience, as rigorous with himself as with others, led to his banishment from Massachusetts Bay.

That is, Williams agreed with the mainstream Massachusetts Puritans that the vast majority of people were damned, that only a few were saved. But just who were they? Who were the elect? The Massachusetts Puritans had highly refined procedures for identifying "Visible Saints" and, therefore, who was eligible for church membership and the right to vote. Williams said that no one

---

JOHN COTTON ON DEMOCRACY

The Puritans did not believe in democracy. John Cotton (1584–1652), the most influential minister in the early years of Massachusetts Bay, put it this way in a letter to England: "Democracy I do not conceyve that ever God it ordeyne as a fitt government eyther for church or for commonwealth. If the people be governors, who shall be governed?"

Roger Williams, who founded Rhode Island after being banished from Masschusetts Bay in 1635, believed in separation of church and state.

Williams pointed out, and the Indians' right to the land was as good as anyone's. The king of England had no right to give it away. Only by purchasing land from the natives could newcomers justly take possession of it.

In fact, the Massachusetts Puritans usually paid the Indians for the land they settled. (Bought, that is, with a hefty dollop of swindle thrown in; no one, including Williams, believed that there was anything ungodly in a bargain.) Nevertheless, when Williams attacked the charter with which the Puritans assured their control of Massachusetts, he touched the same tender nerve he had bruised in calling for the separation of church and state.

By 1635, Winthrop and his party had enough. Williams was ordered to return to England. Instead, he escaped into the forest, wintered with the Narragansett Indians, and in 1636, established a farm and township, Providence, on land purchased from those people.

Roger Williams may have believed that the King had no right to give away Indian land, but he was also a prudent man. In 1644, he sailed to London where he secured a charter for his colony. He may have denied the right of king or Parliament to give away what did not belong to them, but he also knew how to play the game. The Puritans of Massachusetts, staking so much

could be sure of anyone's election but his own. To underscore his point, he said that although he prayed with his wife, he did not even know if she was truly saved. Only she and God did.

Williams was, in a word, the ultimate Separatist. He concluded from his beliefs that religion and government—"church and state"—should be entirely separate. If no one could determine who was saved, there must be no religious test, such as Massachusetts enforced, to determine the right to vote and otherwise participate in civil affairs.

Because church members were a minority in Massachusetts, this preachment threatened Puritan control of the Commonwealth, the very reason the Puritans had come to America. If the damned majority were to make laws to suit their unregenerate selves, the Lord's covenant would soon lay in tatters and God would "surely break out in wrath" against them.

Rhode Island: The Sewer of New England

Roger Williams also made enemies in Massachusetts by challenging the validity of the royal charter on which Puritan control of the colony was legally based. New England had been occupied when the English arrived,

In Adam's fall,
We sinned all.

on their own royal charter, would not dare to violate another.

Before 1644, the Puritans could have rooted out Williams and his followers with little difficulty. But, with Williams beyond the boundaries of Massachusetts, the worst Puritan fears were allayed. The Bay Colony would not suffer for the blasphemous doctrines he preached. In an odd way, Rhode Island was invaluable to Massachusetts. It was a place to which they could banish all their troublesome dissenters. It was the "sewer of New England."

Anne Hutchinson

In 1638, another Massachusetts dissenter was banished to the shores of Narragansett Bay. Like Williams, Anne Hutchinson was a devout Puritan. Taking seriously the admonition that Saints should study the word of God, she invited people to her home after services to discuss the sermon they had just heard. Hutchinson's own observations were often critical and sometimes acidic. When her informal meetings grew in popularity, they raised the hackles of preachers who were wounded by her sharp intelligence and formidable wit.

They shook their heads that a woman should dabble in subtle theology. "You have stept out of your place," Winthrop told Hutchinson, "you have rather bine a Husband than a Wife and a Preacher than a Hearer." The governor expressed his fears that women jeopardized their mental balance by pondering theological questions too deeply.

Still, had Hutchinson's offense been no greater than crowing, she might have gotten off with a scolding. She had influential supporters as well as powerful critics. But Hutchinson believed that the Holy Spirit directly instructed some persons, such as herself, to speak out. This tenet, like those of Williams, challenged the Puritan order. For if the Holy Spirit directly tutored some people, what right had the authorities to regulate preaching?

Known as "Antinomianism," Hutchinson's doctrine pointed logically, like Williams' separatism, to the separation of church and state. Like Williams, she was banished to Rhode Island. Later, she emigrated to New York where, in 1643, she was killed in an Indian raid.

New Hampshire and Connecticut

New Hampshire's first settlers were followers of Anne Hutchinson who moved north from Massachusetts with a minister, John Wheelright. Wheelright was, in some ways, more of a trouble-maker than Hutchinson. However, New Hampshire never developed Rhode Island's reputation for eccentricity. New Hampshire was peopled largely by orthodox Puritans looking for better lands than they could find in Massachusetts.

The rich bottomlands of the Connecticut river valley also played a major part in the populating of that colony. However, religious bickering of a less portentous sort led the Reverend Thomas Hooker and his followers there in 1636 to found Hartford. In England, Hooker had been more prominent than even John Cotton. In Massachusetts, he was unwilling to play second fiddle to anyone.

The migration to Connecticut caused a conflict with the Pequots, the most powerful Indian tribe of lower New England. In May 1637, after a Pequot raid on the Connecticut village of Wethersfield, Massachusetts and Plymouth sent a combined force that, by night, surrounded and set fire to the largest of the tribe's villages. As the Pequots fled the flames, the New Englanders shot and killed more than 400 of them, women and children as well as men. After a few more smaller actions, the Pequots were for all practical purposes exterminated.

During the Pequot War, Theophilus Eaton and John Davenport, ministers who worried that Massachusetts was too soft on moral offenders, settled at New Haven on Long Island Sound. New Haven was the strictest of the Puritan commonwealths and its strictures influenced Connecticut, into which it was incorporated in 1662.

NOTABLE PEOPLE

TWO WOMEN OF NEW ENGLAND

In the seventeenth century, a woman was superior in authority to every member of her household but her husband. Children and servants were expected to defer to her; she was obligated to obey her husband. Woman's world was centered around the hearth and the cradle. It was her husband's right and responsibility to deal with the world, to instruct children, servants, and wife in religion, and to represent the household in civil matters.

In a subsistence economy, of course, women were called on to work as hard as men and as grown children, and the records are full of widows operating town businesses efficiently and profitably. In the professions, in public life, and in matters of the soul and the intellect, however, women's names are hardly to be found. This, the people of the seventeenth century believed, was as it should be. John Winthrop liked to tell the story of a woman who tried to wrestle with difficult religious questions instead of just listening to what was told her. Her mind, Winthrop concluded, snapped under the strain.

That woman could not have been Anne Marbury Hutchinson (1591–1643) or Anne Dudley Bradstreet (1612–72), both of whom Winthrop knew. Hutchinson nearly toppled the Massachusetts theocracy within a decade of its founding, and Bradstreet became, anonymously in her lifetime, the first American poet of distinction.

Anne Marbury was born in Lincolnshire in 1591. At the age of 21, she married a Puritan merchant named William Hutchinson. Little is known of her life in England. But she must have turned heads there, for shortly after she emigrated to Massachusetts in 1634 she began to turn the colony upside down.

Hutchinson was fascinated by the intricacies of theology, and she organized discussion groups at her home to meet after Sunday sermons. In principle, there was nothing amiss in this. Puritans were encouraged to discuss religion at every pass, and the meetings at the Hutchinson home attracted some of the colony's most distinguished leaders, including Henry Vane, the twenty-three-year-old governor of Massachusetts.

However, when Anne Hutchinson began to dominate the discussions—to deliver sermons of her own, in effect—she was approaching the brink of what the Puritans (and the times generally) considered improper. When she sharply criticized several of the colony's most respected ministers, she stood at the brink. When she challenged the principles on which the government of Massachusetts was based, she fell.

In claiming that God moves some people to preach without reference to education and election of ministers, and civil authority generally, she was attacking covenant theology itself—the belief that a pact existed between God and those who governed the community. This was intolerable, and at a trial in which she debated very deftly with her accusers and judges, she was found guilty of "transducing the ministers." One judge pronounced sentence with the words, "I do deliver you up to Satan."

Instead of going to hell, Hutchinson, her family, and several loyal disciples went to Portsmouth, Rhode Island. Still tendentious, Hutchinson quarreled with other disciples. After the death of her husband in 1642, she moved to New Netherland to a farm in what is now the borough of the Bronx in New York City. The Bronx was frontier at that time, and, the next year, Hutchinson and all her children but one were killed by Indians.

Anne Bradstreet never challenged the authorities. On the contrary, she was a part of the Massachusetts Establishment. She emigrated to Massachusetts from her native Northampton in the Winthrop expedition of 1630. Both her father, Thomas Dudley, and her husband, Simon Bradstreet, later served as governors of the colony, always choosing the right side in political disputes.

Bradstreet made her mark above the crowd with her pen. In 1650, a book of her poems was published in London as *The Tenth Muse Lately Sprung Up in America*. It was remarkable enough for a book written by a woman to be published in the seventeenth century. It would have been unacceptable to sign it with the author's name. Instead, Anne was identified on the title page as "A Gentlewoman in Those Parts."

The book was little noticed. While craftsmanlike, the poems in *The Tenth Muse* did not stand out in a literary age dominated in England by John Milton. Bradstreet was no revolutionary in literature as well as in politics. She imitated the forms of others and clung to standard classical and religious themes. Nevertheless, if unextraordinary when measured against the finest English poetry of the seventeenth century, Bradstreet's love lyrics, descriptions of the Massachusetts landscape, and variations on Puritan religious beliefs raise her far above any American contemporary.

One Connecticut law provided that "If any Childe or Children above fifteen years old, and of sufficient understanding, shall Curse or Smite their natural Father or Mother, he or they shall be put to death, unless it can be sufficiently testified, that the Parents have been unchristianly negligent in the education of such Children."

THE PROPRIETARY COLONIES

Except for New Hampshire, the New England colonies were corporate colonies. Their governments, derived from commercial charters of incorporation, were broadly

DOUBLE DUTCH

The Dutch of New Netherland coined the word, "Yankee," or, rather "Jan Kies." It was a collective personification of a none too admired group. The New Netherlanders, called New Englanders Jan Kies, just as World War II soldiers called their German enemies "Jerry" and our soldiers in Vietnam called the Viet Cong "Charlies."

The English retaliated with a host of insulting uses of the word "Dutch." A one-sided deal was a "Dutch bargain," a potluck dinner a "Dutch lunch." (Young men and women still speak of "going Dutch" if each is to pay his share of the costs of a date.) "Dutch courage" was strong liquor; a "Dutch Nightingale" was a frog; and a "Dutch widow" was a prostitute.

One of the few more-or-less cordial uses of the adjective is in "Dutch Uncle," which means a firm but kindly disciplinarian, but it dates from a later era. In the seventeenth century, the English and Dutch were fierce rivals and not likely to speak fondly of one another.

they were called because they trembled with emotion at their religious services, "Quakers."

The Quakers were figures of scorn, amusement, and some worry in England. George Fox, the founder of the society, wandered about preaching in village squares. Conventional people thought of him and his followers much as later generations would think of "Holy Rollers" or "Hare Krishnas."

The Quakers worried some people in authority because they preached an absolute Christian pacifism. Members were forbidden to take up arms, even in self-defense. Seventeenth-century armies were not made up of draftees, but pacifism was still a challenging doctrine in a time when war was considered a normal state of affairs.

The Quakers also disturbed the establishment because they taught that every individual had the light of God within. Consequently, Christians had no need of priests, ministers, and bishops. In their early years, the Quakers also challenged the legitimacy of civil authority and social class. When they were haled before magistrates, Quakers refused to remove their hats and to take oaths. Telling the truth was the individual's responsibility to God, they said, and none of the civil authority's business.

The Quakers dramatized their belief in the equality of all people before God by addressing everyone, including nobles and the king himself, in the familiar *thee, thy,* and *thou* form of the second-person pronoun. This seems merely quaint today, but in the seventeenth century it was highly insulting to address a social superior or even a stranger in that way.

Finally, believing that all people were equal before God, Quaker women were as active as the men in preaching and testifying. This affronted the popular feeling that women should not play a role in public life, least of all in religious matters.

William Penn's Holy Experiment

William Penn was the Quakers' savior. Whereas almost all Quakers were of the lower classes, he was a gentleman of wealth and education. Penn used his prestige to moderate some of the Quakers' more extravagant habits, and he gave them a refuge. Like other proprietors, he saw his Pennsylvania ("Penn's Woods") as a means of making money. But he also envisioned it as a Holy Experiment. All people who believed in "One Almighty and Eternal God" were welcome. Because the Quakers believed in an Inner Light, they would not impose their faith on any person.

Pennsylvania thrived from the start. Pietists from the German Rhineland and from Switzerland, whose ideas resembled those of the Quakers, settled there in great numbers. They developed the fertile rolling land of southeastern Pennsylvania into model farms. Their descendants survive, many still observing seventeenth-

This charcoal sketch by Francis Place is the only known authentic likeness of William Penn.

century customs, as the Pennsylvania Dutch of Lancaster and York counties.

Along with Charleston, South Carolina, Philadelphia was the colonies' first "planned city." The streets of the "greene countrie towne" were laid out on a gridiron, making possible a tidiness that even the well-ordered Puritans had been unable to demand of Boston. Philadelphia became the largest and most prosperous city in English North America, at least in part because of the Quakers' enlightened policies. At the time of the American Revolution, it was "the second city of the British empire," smaller only than London in the English-speaking world.

The Quakers maintained control of the Pennsylvania assembly until after the age of religious fanaticism had passed. Unlike Maryland, therefore, Pennsylvania remained a refuge for persecuted sects. It was the most cosmopolitan of the English colonies. New Jersey and Delaware developed as separate proprietary colonies; however, they too were heavily populated by Quakers and practiced much the same policies as Pennsylvania.

The Carolinas: Another Feudal Experiment

The proprietors of the Carolina Grant of 1663 (named after Charles II, *Carolus* in Latin) were a consortium of eight powerful gentlemen and nobles. In 1669, they attempted to fasten on their grant a social structure that was more fantastic than the patroonship plan for New Netherland. Their scheme was outlined in The Fundamental Constitutions of Carolina, the brainchild of Anthony Ashley Cooper, one of the most active of the proprietors. Its 120 detailed articles were actually written by his secretary, the political philosopher John Locke, whose primary place in history is as a defender of principles of political liberty. It is difficult to imagine that in the Fundamental Constitutions he created a blueprint for a society that was as rigidly structured as the feudal patroonship system of New York.

The Carolina grant was divided into square counties, in each of which the proprietors ("seigneurs") owned 96,000 acres. Other contrived ranks of nobility called "caciques" (an Indian title) and "landgraves" would have smaller but still vast tracts. The work would be done by humble "leetmen" and even humbler African slaves, over whom their owners were guaranteed "absolute power and authority."

Some historians think that this fantastic system was simply a promotional device designed to excite English land buyers with the promise of puffed-up titles. Certainly, it was unworkable. A city might be laid out in squares, but not a country shaped by rivers, creeks, hills, swamps, and mountains. The abundance of land meant that development would be free and open, not a subject of strict regulation. Although the Fundamental Constitutions remained technically in effect for several decades, the document had little to do with the actual development of the Carolinas.

One Carolina Becomes Two

Geography shaped the colony. The vastly different environments of the northern and southern parts of the Carolina grant dictated that settlements there would develop in significantly different ways.

In the north, most settlers were small farmers who drifted down from Virginia and planted tobacco, as they had done at home. Centered on Albemarle Sound, northern Carolina was poor, rather democratic of mood, and independent. It was quite isolated even from Virginia by the Great Dismal Swamp. In 1677, a Virginian named John Culpeper led a rebellion in northern Carolina that briefly defied all outside authority.

In the southern part of the grant, the proprietors and early settlers from Barbados (an English sugar-growing island) founded Charleston on the coast where the Ashley and Cooper rivers flowed into the Atlantic. At first, southern Carolina was a trading colony, tapping the interior as far as present-day Alabama for furs and hides and converting the vast pine forests into timber and naval stores. By 1700, however, the outline of a plantation system similar to that of tidewater Virginia took shape.

Possibly from their African slaves, the planters learned how to grow rice, a lucrative export crop. The easily flooded lowlands along the rivers were ideally suited to its cultivation. Long-staple cotton, used in manufacturing fine textiles, found favorable conditions on the sandy sea islands that fringed the coast.

Rice nicely lent itself to being worked by large gangs of laborers, and by 1700, half of the 5,000 people in southern Carolina were slaves. This was by far the highest proportion of Africans in any mainland colony.

Their owners dominated south Carolina society to an extent that even the tobacco grandees of Virginia and Maryland might have envied. Because the low country that produced their wealth was so unhealthy, however, this small elite took to keeping town houses in Charleston. There they spent at least the malarial summer months and, in some cases, the better part of the year.

The result was an urban, cultured, and cosmopolitan society that was quite obnoxious to the small farmers of northern Carolina. In 1712, recognizing the different social bases of the northern and southern settlements, the proprietors granted the two Carolinas separate assemblies and governors. When they sold their holdings to the king in 1729, he wisely confirmed them as separate royal colonies: North Carolina and South Carolina.

Georgia: A Philanthropic Experiment

Georgia was the last of the thirteen colonies to be founded. It was chartered in 1732, with Savannah actually established the next year. The Crown's interest in this afterthought of a settlement was as a military buffer state protecting valuable South Carolina against the Spanish in Florida. Although Spain had recognized England's right to its colonies in 1676, ten years later an armed force destroyed a small English settlement on the Florida side of the boundary. During an English-Spanish war between 1702 and 1713, Charleston was threatened.

In Colonel James Oglethorpe, Parliament found the perfect man to develop a fortress colony. Oglethorpe was an experienced and successful soldier. He was also a philanthropist who was troubled by the misery of the English poor. At that time, a person could be imprisoned for debt and not released until his obligation was paid—a somewhat self-defeating provision since a man in jail could hardly earn money for his creditors.

Oglethorpe and others conceived of Georgia (named for the king) as a place to which such unfortunates might go to begin anew. They received the colony as a "trust." That is, they were to make no profit from it. Landholdings were to be small, only 50 acres, both to discourage land speculators and to encourage the formation of a compact, easily mobilized defense force. Slavery was forbidden. Oglethorpe did not want to see the development of an elite such as dominated South Carolina. He also prohibited alcohol, believing that drunkenness was a major source of crime and poverty in England.

In all, the trustees sent about 1,800 debtors and paupers to Georgia, and about 1,000 people came on their own. Unfortunately, among the latter were some slaveowners from South Carolina. Oglethorpe, although inclined to be a tyrant, was unable either to keep them out or to keep the other Georgians independent of the bottle. He returned to England disgusted, and in 1752 the trustees returned control of the colony to the king, one year earlier than their charter required.

The experiment in social engineering was a failure, as others had been. The natural character of the region determined how it developed. Although sparsely populated at the time of independence, Georgia became a slavery-based agricultural colony much like South Carolina.

Other English Colonies

With the founding of Georgia, the thirteen colonies that were to become the original United States were marked on the maps of North America, and recorded in the books of the Board of Trade, the agency that administered the colonies for the Crown. It is well to note, however, that England was active elsewhere in the Western Hemisphere. In fact, several English possessions still loosely tied to Great Britain are older than most of the settlements strung out on the mainland from New Hampshire to Georgia, and their history was intertwined with our own.

English-speaking Belize (formerly British Honduras), in Central America, dates from the early 1600s, although, as a haven of pirates, it was hardly an official colony. Bermuda, east of Georgia, was settled in 1609 when Sir George Somers, bound for Virginia, was shipwrecked there. (This incident was the inspiration of William Shakespeare's play *The Tempest*.) Tobago, a tiny island off the coast of Venezuela, was seized by English adventurers in 1616, four years before Plymouth was founded. Nearby, Barbados, from which many South Carolinians came, dates from 1627. (Local tradition insists that English settlement in Barbados dates from 1605, two years before Jamestown.)

In 1621, Sir William Alexander received a charter to found English colonies in Acadia, present-day Nova Scotia. However, the French controled most of that rugged land until 1713. In 1655, an English fleet under Admiral William Penn, the father of the founder of Pennsylvania, seized Jamaica from Spain. Several continuously occupied trading posts on Hudson Bay, which was discovered for England by a Dutch navigator, Henry Hudson, were planted in the 1670s. The Bahamas, where Columbus first saw the New World, have been British since about the same time.

Tropical islands where sugar cane grew were the most lucrative colonies from the Crown's point of view. To ordinary folk interested in actually settling in the New World, the thirteen mainland colonies beckoned more seductively. There society was remarkably free, and the economy offered the greatest opportunities in the world.

For Further Reading

The books cited in the final paragraph of "For Further Reading" following Chapter Two are also all relevant in part to this chapter. On Plymouth, students should surely begin with the history written by the colony's great governor, William Bradford, *History of Plimmoth Plantation* (numerous editions), enhancing understanding with George Langdon, *Pilgrim Colony: A History of New Plymouth 1620–1691* (1966). On Massachusetts

Bay, see (with some wariness) James Truslow Adams, *The Founding of New England* (1930) and the less literary but also less tendentious George L. Haskin, *Law and Authority in Early Massachusetts* (1960); Mary J. Jones, *Congregational Commonwealth* (1968); Darrett Rutman, *Winthrop's Boston: Portrait of a Puritan Town 1630–1649* (1965); and James Axtell, *The Invasion Within: The Contest of Cultures in Colonial North America* (1985) and Axtell's *The European and the Indian* (1981).

Our appreciation of the Puritans owes largely to the work of two unambivalently great American historians, Perry Miller and the profession's reigning dean, Edmund S. Morgan. Students interested in the subject should read all their works, beginning with Miller's *The New England Mind* (1939, 1953) and *Errand into the Wilderness* (1964) and Morgan's *Visible Saints* (1963); *The Puritan Dilemma: The Story of John Winthrop* (1958); *The Puritan Family* (1966); and *Roger Williams: The Church and the State* (1967). On Ann Hutchinson, see Emery Battis, *Saints and Sectarians: Anne Hutchinson and the Antinomian Controversy in Massachusetts* (1962).

In recent decades, special studies of Puritan society and culture by other scholars have been numerous and many worthy of the inspirers. The briefest of samplings would include: John Demos, *A Little Commonwealth: Family Life in Plymouth Colony* (1970); Philip Greven, Jr., *Four Generations: Population, Land, and Family in Colonial Andover* (1970); Kenneth Lockridge, *A New England Town* (1971); Samuel Powell, *Puritan Village* (1963); David Stannard, *The Puritan Way of Death* (1977); Michael Walzer, *The Revolution of the Saints* (1965); and Larzer Ziff, *Puritanism in Old and New England* (1973).

On the Middle Colonies, see Thomas J. Wertenbaker, *The Founding of American Civilization: The Middle Colonies* (1938); Edwin B. Bronner, *William Penn's "Holy Experiment"* (1962); Gary Nash, *Quakers and Politics: Pennsylvania 1681–1726* (1971); Thomas J. Condon, *New York Beginnings: The Commercial Origins of New Netherland* (1968); Michael Kammen, *Colonial New York* (1975); and Robert C. Ritchie, *The Duke's Province* (1977).

For the later southern colonies, see William S. Powell, *Colonial North Carolina* (1973); Eugene Sirman, *Colonial South Carolina* (1966); and Phinizy Spalding, *Oglethorpe in America* (1977).

An early map of Massachusetts Bay, Rhode Island, and Connecticut, looking westward—inland—rather than to the north.

COLONIAL SOCIETY

ENGLISH LEGACIES AND LAWS, AMERICAN FACTS OF LIFE

There is a nod of truth in the old adage that the British Empire was created in a fit of absent-mindedness. The approval of the Crown, in the form of a charter, was the essential first step in founding a colony. But, quite unlike the case in Spanish America, neither king nor parliament played an active role in setting up any of them. From the frontier farms outside Portsmouth in New Hampshire to the stockade around Savannah in Georgia, every English settlement in North America was funded and promoted in what today would be called "the private sector."

The creators of the American colonies were enterprising investors, religious groups looking for a sanctuary, courtiers making the most of the king's friendship, or, in the belated case of Georgia, philanthropists who believed the world might be made a better place.

So casual were England's kings toward their American real estate—in law, it all started out as royal property—that the boundaries drawn for colonies were often vague and overlapping, breezy strokes of a quill pen on maps in London that caused endless bickering on the actual ground.

And yet, the empire grew. By 1702, when Queen Anne ascended the throne, 300,000 of her subjects made their homes in a North American empire that stretched a thousand miles north to south.

TRADE LAWS AND GEOGRAPHY

Parliament first took an interest in formulating a coherent colonial policy during the 1650s, shortly after Puritan revolutionaries had executed King Charles I. His son, Charles II returned to reign in 1660 and confirmed most of these enactments. Charles II also created a Committee for Trade and Plantations, usually known as the Lords of Trade, to advise him.

The Lords of Trade were negligent or simply ineffective. Not until 1696, when the Committee was reorganized as the fifteen-member Board of Trade, was the Crown provided a body of advisors dedicated to studying colonial questions.

The Navigation Acts

As the names of Britain's "colonial office"—Lords of Trade, Board of Trade—indicate, commerce between colonies and mother country was the question in which the Crown was most interested. Indeed, said Charles II in 1668, "the thing that is nearest the heart of the nation is trade."

Basic colonial policy was stated in the Navigation Acts of 1660–1663. These laws were mercantilistic, and defined the purpose of the American colonies as to enrich the mother country relative to other nations. The prosperity of the colonies was a consideration; however, when the economic interests of colonials clashed with those of Britons, the latter were what counted.

Thus, the Navigation Acts stipulated that all colonial trade be carried in vessels built and owned by English or colonial merchants. These ships were to be manned by crews in which at least three seamen in four were English or colonials. Not even niggardly seamen's wages were to be paid to foreigners.

Next, the Navigation Acts required that European goods to be sold in the colonies be carried first to certain English ports called *entrepôts* (places from which goods are distributed). There they were to be monitored and only then shipped to America. The purpose was to ensure a precise record of colonial trade, to collect taxes on trade goods, and to see to it that English merchants and port laborers benefited from every colonial transaction.

Quite important trade goods were covered by this provision. For example, wealthy colonists had a taste for claret, a French wine. But they could not import it directly from France. First the bottles and casks had to pass through the entrepôts. This raised the cost, of course—that was the idea. The premium that colonial bibbers paid for their wines went into English purses.

The Navigation Acts also dealt with colonial exports, designating some "enumerated articles." These could be shipped only to an English port, even if they were destined for sale on the continent of Europe. Once again, the object was to guarantee that part of the profit on colonial transactions went to English merchants. Moreover, taxes on the enumerated articles were an important source of revenue. Charles II collected £100,000 a year from the tax on tobacco alone.

The enumerated articles included most colonial prod-

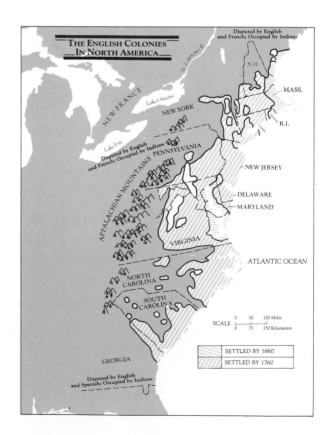

THE ENGLISH COLONIES IN NORTH AMERICA

ucts that could be sold for cash on the world market: molasses, furs and hides, naval stores, rice, cotton, and tobacco. Foodstuffs—grain, livestock, salted fish—and lumber not suited to ship building were not enumerated. They could be shipped directly to foreign ports and were.

THE SOUTHERN COLONIES

Imperial trade law was uniform; the Navigation Acts applied to every colony from Massachusetts to Barbados. However, the disparate topography, climate, and social structure of England's far-flung provinces meant that the Acts affected colonials in sharply different ways.

Already by 1700, North Americans thought in terms of New England colonies, middle colonies, and the South. New England was made up of New Hampshire, Massachusetts, Rhode Island, Connecticut. To the south and west lay the Middle Colonies: New York, New Jersey, Pennsylvania, Delaware. The South included Maryland, Virginia, North Carolina, South Carolina (and, after 1732, Georgia).

With good reason, English merchants smiled contentedly when they thought of the southern colonies. They produced, next to sugar, the most profitable of the enumerated articles. Like the sugar islands of the West Indies, the southern colonies were home to a large, bonded labor force of white servants and black slaves for whom cheap clothing, shoes, and tools had to be purchased in England. And living off the labor of these workers by 1700 was an increasingly rich and extravagant master class that coveted every luxury that ever merchant thought to load on sailing ship.

Tobacco: Blessing and Curse

The tobacco plant grew in England; it is almost as adaptable to climates and soils as maize. But English farmers were not permitted to plant the weed. So long as all Virginia and Maryland leaf was brought into the country to pass through customs, merchants and the Crown profited directly from every pipe that was lit in country home and hovel.

By the 1660s, however, Maryland's and Virginia's monopoly on England's smoking habit was not enough to ensure prosperity in those colonies. The wholesale price of tobacco (the price at which the planters sold) collapsed from two pence halfpenny a pound to a halfpenny. The Chesapeake planters had expanded their acreage so quickly that their markets were no longer able to absorb production.

From the planter's point of view, the solution to the

Workers at a Virginia wharf load tobacco into ships for export.

problem of falling prices was obvious. The Dutch tapped markets that the English could not, and they lacked an adequate source of tobacco. However, the Navigation Acts prohibited the planters from selling to England's chief commercial rivals. Planters complained in memorials to the Crown. "If the Hollanders must not trade to Virginia, how shall the planters dispose of their tobacco ? . . . The tobacco will not vend in England, the Hollanders will not fetch it from England." (The Dutch, who were also mercantilists, refused to enrich English merchants by buying from them.) "What must become thereof?"

Smuggling

One thing that became thereof was a rather cavalier attitude toward English trade laws. Planters and shippers evaded the Navigation Acts, or they simply ignored them.

Thus, merchantmen collected cargos of tobacco at the plantations, then called at a colonial port. Although having no business there, simply by dropping anchor they fulfilled the letter of the law that all enumerated articles be shipped to an imperial port before it was carried elsewhere. The Crown acted to end this practice in 1673 by providing for the collection of a "plantation duty" on tobacco in colonial as well as British ports.

Outright smuggling was a common colonial vocation. Dutch traders arriving at Virginia and Maryland wharves had little difficulty persuading distressed planters to sell them their leaf. Such brazen defiance of imperial law was not difficult thanks to the topography of the Chesapeake region.

The Tidewater

The Chesapeake is a huge estuary made up of uncountable smaller ones. Among hundreds of briny creeks and inlets, the larger rivers that empty into the great bay—the Potomac, the Rappahannock, the James—are broad, slow-moving streams. They were quite deep enough for the small sea-going vessels of the seventeenth and eighteenth centuries to sail for as many miles inland as high tide pushed salt water. Ships and even large schooners might careen nervously in the river mire when the tide ebbed, but the sea dependably returned to float them and their profitable cargoes back to Europe.

The land washed by this salt water, a series of peninsulas called capes or necks, was known as "the tidewater." It was the first part of the tobacco colonies to be settled, and it became home to an elite that dominated Virginia and Maryland society.

Although their descendants did not like to admit it, few tidewater aristocrats had been well-to-do when they settled in America. Few Britons of high station and

---

THE OYSTER WAR

In 1632, when King Charles I drew the boundary between Virginia and Maryland, he did not, as was customary, set it at the *thalweg*, or deepest part of the Chesapeake Bay, but at the high-water mark on the Virginia side. This gave Maryland oystermen the right to harvest oysters up to the very shores of the Old Dominion. Virginia oystermen were not delighted with this state of affairs, and they periodically engaged in a shooting war that killed at least 50 men. Disputes between Virginia and Maryland watermen were to play a part in the writing of the American Constitution in 1787. The war raged off and on throughout the nineteenth century with boats sunk and blood spilled. The last known fatality was in 1959. Today, oystermen on the Chesapeake are forbidden to carry firearms.

---

wealth emigrated to a land where the life expectancy was 40 years of age. Most of the men and women of the "First Families of Virginia" were from families of artisans, petty merchants, or yeomen—the middling sort. They brought enough capital with them to develop plantations, sometimes of considerable size, but their social pretensions were possible only because of the boom in tobacco.

Indeed, some Virginians of quite modest origins profited richly from the tobacco boom. In 1629, seven members of the Virginia assembly—by definition the colony's elite—had been indentured servants only five years earlier. This was social mobility pushed by gale force winds, but it did not last.

Depression at the End of the World

The odds of getting rich dwindled in the tobacco colonies in the later 1600s. Indeed, making a merely decent living became difficult for all but the best-off planters. The collapse in the price of tobacco bankrupted hundreds of small farmers so that larger planters, who were less vulnerable to the downturn, picked up small holdings and became even more powerful.

After 1660, even comparatively well-off immigrants to Virginia were forced to trek into the backcountry if they wished to build estates. There in the piedmont, or foothills of the Appalachians, they found hundreds of hard-scrabble frontiersmen. Some had been recently dispossessed in the tidewater. Others were freed servants without land—unmarried, boisterous young men who survived by doing casual work for wages. In 1676, differences between these westerners and the tidewater planters burst into a miniature civil war, rag-tag and improvised but plenty nasty.

HOW THEY LIVED

A PURITAN FAMILY GOES TO MEETING

Early in the morning on Sunday, Thursday, and on special days of feasting and Thanksgiving, even before the sun rose in winter, the Puritan family bundled up in heavy woolen clothing and furs and walked to the meeting house. Few people skipped worship services, even during a blizzard. There was a fine for absenteeism, and if the weather could be withering, the distance to be traveled was short. Most New Englanders lived in villages, their houses clustered together with the meeting house near the center.

They went to a a *meeting house*, not to a church. To call the simple, unpainted clapboard structure a church would have been "popish," and the Puritans shunned every emblem that hinted of the Church of Rome. In the meeting house, there were no statues or other decoration, such as adorned Catholic and Anglican churches. The building was a place of preaching and worship, not an object for beautification. A weathercock rather than a cross sat atop the steeple, and was a good Calvinist symbol. It reminded the congregation that even St. Peter had sinned by denying that he knew Christ before the cock crowed three times after the Romans had seized the Lord. The sinfulness of humanity was a theme on which the Puritans constantly dwelled. In their churchyards, the tombstones were carved with death's heads—skulls.

Inside the meeting house in winter, it was little warmer than the snow-swept fields that surrounded the village. There may have been a fireplace, but the heat had little effect on those sitting more than ten feet from the flames. The congregation bundled in envelopes made of fur—*not* sleeping bags; there was a fine for nodding off!—and people rested their feet on brass or iron footwarmers that contained coals brought from home. In towns that prohibited the use of footwarmers—since they were a fire hazard—worshipers brought to meeting a large, well-trained dog to lie at their feet.

The women sat on the left side of the meeting house with their daughters. The men sat on the right side, but boys who were apt to be mischievous were placed around the pulpit where a churchwarden could lash out at fidgety ones with a switch. He probably had his work cut out often enough, for the service went on and on, sermons alone running at least an hour and a half and sometimes three hours. If a sermon was shorter, there might well be gossip about the preacher's lack of zeal. And lest anyone wonder how long the sermon was lasting, an hourglass sat conspicuously on the preacher's pulpit; when the sand ran down, the hourglass was turned by the man who kept watch over the boys. Many people took notes—some out of piety; some, no doubt, to keep themselves awake.

Although the Puritans forbade organs in their meeting houses (organs were not mentioned in the scriptures), they loved to sing psalms, at home as well as at service. The *Bay Psalm Book*, from which they sang, was written with accuracy rather than poetry in mind.

The psalms, which are so beautiful in the King James Version of the Bible, sounded awkward and strained in Puritan voices. For example, in the Puritans' translation, the magnificent and touching Psalm 100 is barely comprehensible.

The rivers on of Babylon, there when we did sit downe;
Yes even then we mourned, when we remembered Sion.
Our harp we did hang it amid upon the willow tree,
Because there they thus away led in captivitie,
Required of us a song, thus asks mirth; us waste who laid
Sing us among a Sion's song unto us then they said.

Morning services ended around noon, and the family returned home for a meal that had been prepared the previous day. Like observant Jews, the Puritans took the sabbath very seriously. There would be no work and certainly no play or sports, as in the Anglican England they had fled. Even conversation was spare on Sunday. It was no more proper to talk about workaday matters and tasks than to perform them. At most, a pious family discussed the morning's sermon and other religious topics. In the afternoon, the family returned to the meeting house to hear secular announcements and another sermon and to sing psalms. Sunday was a day of rest only in one sense of the word!

The solemnity of the Puritan sabbath and the earnestness with which the pious approached life did not mean that family life was without affection, laughter, and homely enjoyment. It was partly because of their love for their children that, in the Half-way Covenant of 1657, the Massachusetts Puritans eased the requirements of church membership and, according to some historians, fatally diluted the vitality of that remarkable people's religion.

East-West Conflict

The royal governor of Virginia in 1676 was Sir William Berkeley. In the colony for more than 30 years—a long time for an English gentleman—he had done quite well for himself. Berkeley was a major landowner (he was one of the proprietors of the Carolinas) and the social doyen as well as the political leader of the tidewater planters.

He and his friends supplemented their earnings from tobacco by carrying on a prosperous trade with the Indians. In return for furs and deerskins, they provided manufactured goods, especially woven cloth blankets, iron products ranging from pots to traps, and rum. When the bottom dropped out of tobacco prices in the 1660s, this business loomed larger in their accounts. It also provided the Berkeley group with good reason to cultivate a working relationship with the tribes that supplied them.

Settlers in the Piedmont, by way of contrast, looked on Indians as obstacle and enemy. As they expanded their fields, they encroached on the hunting grounds of the Susquehannocks and other Algonkian and Iroquoian-speaking peoples, including some tribes that had already been forced off ancient lands in the tidewater. Inevitably, there were bloody clashes. The Indians complained to Berkeley of white marauders. The settlers of the Piedmont complained of hit-and-run raids on their farms. Berkeley and his associates, caught in the middle, tried to resolve the conflict by building a system of defensive stockades along the line of white settlement.

His plan did not win over the Piedmont whites. The forts were so far apart that Indian raiders, especially the aggressive Susquehannocks, could easily slip between them, wreak havoc, and retreat. More important, like frontier settlers for two centuries to come, Virginia's backcountry pioneers did not think in terms of holding a line. Ever increasing in numbers, they were an expansive people. They meant to clear the land of the natives, not to share it with them.

Bacon's Rebellion

But Berkeley and his friends opposed wars for the purpose of extirpating or even pushing back the Indians. The fur and hide trade was too vital to them. Tempers flamed in the backcountry. When the death toll of whites climbed to more than a hundred, and kidnappings of women and children increased, the piedmont planters took matters into their own hands. Nathaniel Bacon, an immigrant of some means, set himself up as the commander of a force that decimated the Oconeechee tribe. The Oconeechees had not been involved in attacks on whites and had even expressed some interest in an alliance with the white Virginians against the Susquehannocks. No matter; they were Indians. Bacon crushed them and then turned his "army" toward the colonial capital of Jamestown.

Angry words with Berkeley led to shove in what passed for streets in the capital. The governor arrested Bacon as a rebel but was forced to release him when his supporters demonstrated that they were quite capable of taking over the little town. After a period of uneasy stalemate between tidewater and piedmont, Bacon returned to Jamestown and blustered that he would hang the governor. Berkeley took him seriously enough to flee across the Chesapeake to the Eastern shore. For several months, Nathaniel Bacon and his frontier rebels governed Virginia.

Legacy of Suspicion

It will never be known how the English authorities would have dealt with this first American rebellion. In October 1676, Nathaniel Bacon fell ill and, like so many Virginians, died before his time. (He was 29.) Bacon must have been a compelling figure. Without his leadership, the rebels quickly lost heart and scattered into the forests. Berkeley returned, rounded up several dozen, and hanged them.

The governor never regained his preeminence. Charles II was disgusted by his ruthlessness, remarking that "the old fool has hanged more men in that naked country than I have done for the murder of my father." Berkeley was recalled to England where he died within a few months.

The suspicion and ill feeling between tidewater and piedmont endured for more than a century. The tidewater aristocracy continued to dominate Virginia's economy, government, and culture. The people of the backcountry continued to resent them.

A Land Without Cities

The great planters could dominate Virginia and Maryland so thoroughly because, short of rebellion, no other social group able to compete with them existed. There was no urban middle class of merchants, bankers, and manufacturers in Virginia or Maryland because no centers of commerce developed in the tobacco colonies. The broad, deep rivers emptying into the Chesapeake allowed ships from Europe to tie up at the private wharves of the great tidewater plantations. The planters sold their tobacco and received the goods that they had ordered the previous year in their own backyards. Small farmers whose lands did not front on tidewater depended on the great planters' facilities for their trade. Such people were unlikely to mount a resistance to planter power.

They were exhilarating days in the naked land when the merchantmen arrived. Servants and slaves rolled great hogsheads of tobacco to the dock, enjoying the expansive hospitality of the master. Farmers, backcountry planters and their families, and Indians gathered to dance, drink, race on foot and horseback, and shoot targets. For women, who lived a far more isolated life than their menfolk, the arrival of a tobacco factor (agent) was a rare opportunity to enjoy company. Everyone discussed the news that the shipmasters brought with them about European battles and the machinations of the kings they had left behind. Some received letters from old-country associates. The sailors enlivened the carnival with their giddiness at being ashore after weeks at sea, and they spent their wages on games and drink and the favors of women.

This eighteenth-century tidewater plantation was a complete community in itself.

A People Who Lived on Imports

Most important was the receipt of the manufactured goods on which the isolated colonists depended in order to live in something like a European style. A single ship might be loaded with spades, shovels, axes, and saws; household items such as kettles, pots, pans, sieves, funnels, pewter tankards, and tableware. There were oddments such as buttons, needles, thread, pins, and ribbons. There were textiles for both the planter families' fine clothing and rough wraps for servants and slaves; shoes and boots; bricks, nails, and paint; goods to trade with the Indians (which would include all of the above plus trinkets, mirrors, and the like); firearms, shot, and gunpowder. And for the very wealthy few there were luxuries: silver candlesticks, chests and other fine furniture, wine, brandy, spices, books, and perhaps even violins and harpsichords with which to grace a parlor and enliven an evening.

All the business affairs that were carried out in cities elsewhere were transacted at the great plantations for a week or two each year. When the ships departed for London, Plymouth, Bristol, or perhaps Amsterdam, they took not only tobacco but also Virginia's and Maryland's banks, factories, and commercial apparatus. The middle class of the tobacco colonies lived across the Atlantic. Virginia's and Maryland's shops were afloat.

Even the capitals of the tobacco colonies, Jamestown (Williamsburg after 1699) and Annapolis, were ghost towns when the legislative assemblies were not in session. County seats were clusters of buildings at the crossings of trails. Small farmers lived isolated from one another by forests. There were churches, but no public houses—inns and taverns—worth mentioning.

A Life of Elegance

By the end of the seventeenth century, the great planters of Virginia and Maryland were creating a gracious style of life patterned after that of the country gentry back home. They copied as best they could the manners, fashions, and quirks of English squires and their wives. When tobacco was returning a good price, they built fine houses in the style of English manors and furnished them with good furniture. They stocked their cellars with port and Madeira wine, hock from the Rhineland,

and claret from France, which they generously poured for one another at dinners, parties, balls, and simple visits that marked the origins of "Southern hospitality."

Some tidewater families educated their sons at Oxford, Cambridge, or the Inns of Court (the law schools of Great Britain). Or, if they feared the effects of English miasmas on innocent American bodies (smallpox, a deadly scourge in Europe, did not spread so easily in rural America), they schooled their heirs at the College of William and Mary. The college was founded at Williamsburg in 1693 and staffed by Oxford and Cambridge graduates.

And yet, the grandeur of the great planters' social and cultural life must not be over stated. William Byrd of Westover was one of the richest of them (he owned 179,000 acres when he died in 1744), very well-educated, and he preferred living in London. When his first wife, Lucy Park, died, Byrd returned to England to find the daughter of a wealthy nobleman to replace her. However, when he pressed his suit, he learned that his would-be bride was to have an annual income equal to Byrd's whole fortune. Her father rather scornfully rejected Byrd as too poor. William Byrd looks like a duke in his portraits, but the fact remains that even the richest tobacco planters were poor relations of the English upper classes.

The earliest known view of the busy Charleston, South Carolina, harbor.

A Habit of Debt

Like many poor relations with pretensions, the planters were almost constantly in debt. When the profits from tobacco dropped, or even disappeared, the Virginians and Marylanders found it difficult to break the pleasant habits of consumption. They continued to order the luxuries from England that enhanced their lives. To pay for them, they mortgaged future crops—at a discount, of course—to the merchants who delivered the goods. It was not unusual that, by the time the tobacco went into the ground in spring, the imported products it was to pay for had already been purchased and, in the case of wine, had already been consumed.

Planter debt gratified mercantilists. It meant more money in the form of interest and discounts flowing from colony to mother country. In time, chronic indebtedness would make anti-British rebels of almost the entire tidewater aristocracy. During the lifetimes of first-generation gentlemen like William Byrd, however, England stood not as an enemy but as a mother country—loved, admired, and imitated.

The Carolinas

The social structure of South Carolina was similar to that of Virginia and Maryland but the rhythms of life quite different. The cash crops there were rice and, by the mid-1700s, indigo, a plant that produced a precious blue pigment for dying cloth. Indigo was developed as a crop by Eliza Lucas Pinckney on her father's Wappoo plantation.

Rice and indigo nicely complemented one another. They required intensive labor at different times of the year. Thus, South Carolina slaves were productive twelve months a year.

However, the low-lying rice plantations were extremely unhealthy. Flooded for much of the growing season, rice fields were breeding grounds for mosquitoes and mosquito-borne diseases—malaria and the dreaded yellow fever. Consequently, while the slaves were left to fend as best they might, the South Carolina planters spent much of the year in airy Charleston, open to the sea, leaving the management of their plantations to hired overseers.

By congregating in a real city, South Carolina's elite was all the more conscious of its privileged position, all the more united in its determination to preserve it. No colony (or state) was dominated by so small an aristocracy as that which ran South Carolina for over 200 years.

North Carolina was an exception within the South. Although tobacco was grown there, the colony was largely a society of small farmers with very few servants and slaves. Quite unlike its neighbor to the south, North Carolina was never the province of a tiny elite.

THE NEW ENGLAND COLONIES

New England was peopled by immigrants similar in background to those English men and women who went South. However, the Puritan heritage continued to shape New England society long after the generation of Winthrop and Cotton died out and their zeal faded. Just as important in explaining New England's way of life was geography. The land and the climate decreed an economy for Connecticut, Rhode Island, Massachusetts, and New Hampshire that was quite different from that in the Chesapeake colonies and the Carolinas.

Geography and Society

The preeminent facts of life in New England were the cold climate, short growing season, and the demanding rocky character of the soil.

Winter and summer, temperatures in New England were 20° to 30° F colder than in Virginia. The subtropical diseases of the South were unknown in Massachusetts and the other New England colonies. On average, New Englanders lived ten years longer than southerners. Rather more striking, twice as many children survived infancy in Massachusetts than in Virginia.

The result was a large number of extended families—in fact, the world's first society in which men and women could expect to know their grandparents. The Puritan emphasis on "well-ordered households" was reinforced by the climate with which the Puritans' Lord presented them.

In its soil, New England was less blessed. Geologically, New England is a huge glacial moraine. It was there that the continental glaciers of the last ice age halted their advance. When they receded, they left behind the boulders and gravel that they had scooped from the earth on their trip from the Arctic.

Before the farmers of New England could plow, they had to clear thousands of rocks from every acre, breaking up the big boulders and piling the lot in the endless stone fences of the region that are so picturesque to those of us who did not have to build them. This back-breaking toil went on for decades, for each year's sub-zero winter heaved more boulders to the surface of the earth.

The intensive labor required to clear and plant the land reinforced the Puritans' ideological commitment to a society of small family farms. The demanding New England countryside could and did produce food for a fairly dense population. But there were no plantations, no big commercial farms. Families grew their own sustenance and, at most, a small surplus for sale in the towns and cities.

The Need for Coin

Few products of New England's soil could be sold in old England. The crops that New Englanders produced in no plenitude were much the same as those that flourished in the mother country: grain (mostly Indian corn in New England), squash, beans, orchard nuts and fruits (particularly apples), livestock of all sorts, and perishable vegetables.

Consequently, English mercantilists took less interest in New England than in the South and the West Indies. Indeed, English shipbuilders, merchants, and fishermen resented the competition of the New Englanders. Boston was sending ships down the ways before 1640. The shipwright's craft flourished in every town with a protected harbor.

Whaling, a calling that New Englanders would eventually dominate, began as early as 1649. Fishermen sailed out of Portsmouth, Marblehead, New London, and dozens of towns to harvest more than their fair share of the codfish of the North Atlantic. In every port of the world open to commerce, the nickname "Yankee Trader" came to signify shrewdness at business with a hint that the Yankee was a thief. Newport, Rhode Island, was a center of the African slave trade, another pursuit that English shippers would have preferred to reserve for themselves.

The New Englanders had no choice but to compete. It took money—gold and silver coin—to purchase English manufactures, and the country produced no cash crop. Only through fishing and trade could the Yankees solve their "balance of payments" problem.

Yankee Traders

Some New England traders plied three-legged routes to accumulate coin. For example, a ship might call in West Africa, purchase captives, and transport them to the West Indies where they were exchanged for molasses made from sugar cane. The molasses was returned to New England, where it was distilled into rum. Resuming the cycle, the rum went to West Africa as one of the goods exchanged for slaves. Not only did shippers in this "triangular trade" profit from each exchange of cargoes, but the colonies improved their balance of payments by manufacturing cheap molasses into higher priced rum. It was home-grown mercantilism!

There were other "triangles." New Englanders carried provisions from the Middle Colonies to the West Indies; sugar and molasses from there to England; and English manufactures back home. Or, reversing direction, they might carry tobacco from Maryland and Virginia to England; manufactures to the West Indies; and molasses back home or slaves to the southern colonies. Only a

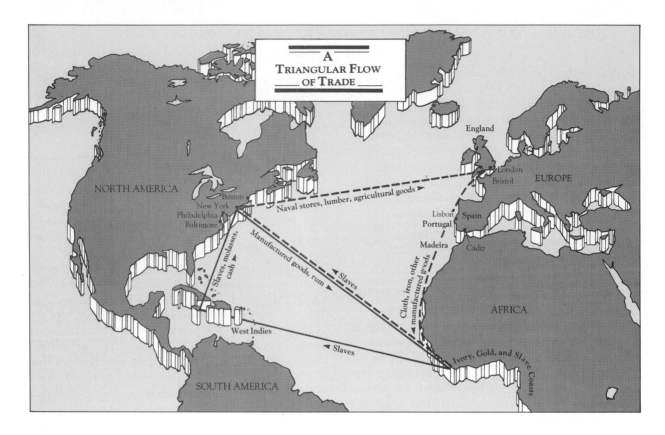

A TRIANGULAR FLOW OF TRADE

very few ships were involved in triangular trading at one time. Many more plied a leg or two of these routes when opportunity offered or necessity required. Many more merchantmen were involved in the coastal trade, transporting a variety of goods from one colonial port to another. The facts of economic life in New England demanded ingenuity, improvisation, and opportunism.

An Independent Spirit

To many English mercantilists, the Yankees were no better than common smugglers. Indeed, the most pious Puritan and Quaker shipmasters saw no sin in dodging British trade laws. Because their charters gave them such extensive powers of self-government, the corporate colonies of Massachusetts, Plymouth, Rhode Island, and Connecticut functioned much like independent commonwealths. They acknowledged the king. Technically, the Puritans claimed that they were members of the Church of England. But these proved to be but polite formalities in a century when two English kings were dethroned, one of them decapitated, and when it took a month for a ship to cross the Atlantic carrying new laws.

During the years when Oliver Cromwell ruled England as virtual dictator (1649–58), the New England colonies disregarded almost every directive that he and

Parliament issued. In 1652, Massachusetts even minted its own money, the "Pine Tree Shilling," thus assuming a right reserved to sovereign rulers since antiquity.

Nor did Massachusetts retreat when Charles II became king in 1660. The colony continued to strike the shilling, to evade royal instructions, and to protect smugglers and even pirates. Charles was forced to sue to have the Massachusetts charter revoked. In 1684, he won his case.

The Dominion of New England

The next year, a new king, James II, combined all the New England colonies into a single "Dominion of New England." (New York and New Jersey were later added.) He abolished all local assemblies within the Dominion and gave what amounted to a viceroy's power to his appointed governor, Sir Edmund Andros.

Andros never had a chance. Not only was he detested in New England, but James II's reign was short-lived. In 1688, the king was forced to flee the country in the "Glorious Revolution." The news was the signal for popular uprisings in several colonies. In Maryland, John Coode seized power from the Catholic proprietors whom he assumed had fled England with the Catholic James II. In New York, a German named Jacob Leisler gained effective control, claiming that he acted in the name of the new English sovereigns, William and Mary. In New

The "Pine Tree Shilling," the first colonial coin, and quite illegal, was minted in Massachusetts between 1652 and 1684, a symbol of New England's independence of mind.

England, the merchant elite so briefly out of power simply resumed acting as it always had—independently—while Andros prudently put to sea.

However, the Calverts of Maryland had not supported James II, and they and the Penn family in Pennsylvania regained their proprietary rights under William and Mary. In New York, Leisler became overconfident by the ease with which he had taken control. Rashly, he ordered a volley fired at arriving troops who really did act in the name of the new king and queen. He was hanged.

As for New England, William and Mary knew better than to revive the hated Dominion, but they had no intention of allowing Massachusetts to return to its semi-independent status. They restored the charters of Connecticut and Rhode Island (where there had been little tumult), but they made Massachusetts, with Plymouth incorporated into it, a royal colony. After 1691, the governor of the Bay Colony was no longer elected but was appointed by the Crown.

This was no easy pill for latter-day Puritans to swallow. They had regarded their mission in America as divinely mandated. They expected to be at odds with the Crown. But for God to allow the Crown to take control of the "citty on a hill" from his chosen people, permanently to all appearances, that was a mighty blow to their morale.

The Devil in Massachusetts

It has been suggested that the loss of the charter, and with it self-government, helps account for the remarkable hysteria that convulsed parts of Massachusetts beginning in January 1692—the Salem witchcraft scare. That is, covenant theology taught that when the Saints committed or tolerated sin within their community, God punished the community as well as the guilty individuals. The loss of the charter was harsh punishment indeed. Only some very terrible sin could account for God's toleration of such a disaster. In January 1692, some lat-

ter-day Puritans believed they had discovered what that sin was.

Several young girls of Salem, a village north of Boston, fell ill with fits of screaming and crawling about while making odd throaty sounds. Their physician found no earthly affliction. He reckoned that the girls had been bewitched by Satan or by Satan's sworn servants, witches.

Few were shocked and fewer laughed at the mention of witchcraft. Most seventeenth-century Europeans and Americans believed that people could strike a bargain with Satan by which they traded their souls for the power of black magic. Witchcraft was mentioned in the Bible along with the admonition "thou shalt not suffer a witch to live." Since the Middle Ages, thousands of people had been executed for worshiping Satan, or for having sexual intercourse with imps called *incubi* and *succubi*. Others had suffered lesser penalties for practicing minor magic—a fine for causing a neighbor's cow to go dry, for example. Just the year before the outbreak of sorcery in Salem, a witch had been hanged in Boston. No doubt the incident weighed on the minds of the unstable young ladies who found themselves the center of attention in Salem.

Hysteria

They were also agitated by the spooky tales of a slave in the home of the Reverend Samuel Parish, Tituba, who had come from the West Indies where the occult practices we know as voodoo were well developed. In any case, once the word *witch* was spoken, the girls began to accuse easy targets of enchanting them, misfits and unpleasant people, the kind of people who had few friends to defend them. Tituba, of course, was black, an outcast.

"Accusation of a Witch" at Salem, a painting by Elias C. Larrabee.

Senile Sarah Good smoked a pipe and muttered to herself. Bridget Bishop dressed eccentrically and kept a bawdy tavern. Sarah Osborne lived with a man who was not her husband. There was an 88-year-old man notorious as a crank.

Soon, better established people were named as witches. Most of them had been on the "wrong side" of a political battle. They had opposed the appointment of the Reverend Parish to the Salem pulpit and, no doubt, had had unpleasant things said about them in the Parish household. Parish's supporters were prominent among the persecutors.

Such petty animosities cannot account for the fact that some of Massachusetts' most distinguished men, including the great preachers Increase and Cotton Mather and respected judge Samuel Sewall, participated in the witch-hunt. Nevertheless, after the accused turned from the weak and the eccentric to the prominent and powerful, the authorities brought the hysteria to an end. In the meantime, 139 people had been accused, 114 were charged, and 19 were hanged. One man was pressed to death—a plank was laid on him and stones heaped on it—because he refused to plead either innocent or guilty. (To plead not guilty and then to be convicted meant that the accused forfeited his property.) His final words were, "Put on more weight." A nine-year-old girl was kept chained for nine months.

Aftermath

Although a witch would be executed in Scotland as late as the era of the American Revolution, the Salem hysteria was the last mass witchcraft scare in the Western world. It should be added, however, that many people involved in the accusations and persecutions later admitted that they had been wrong and publicly asked forgiveness of God and their community. They did not admit that they had been wrong in believing in witchcraft, but they did take responsibility for having falsely accused innocent people or, in the case of Judge Samuel Sewall, for having accepted inadequate evidence in reaching his decisions. His example of rectitude has not had overwhelming influence on public officials since his time.

THE MIDDLE COLONIES

Not every person of the period believed in witchcraft. At the height of the Salem hysteria, when William Penn was asked if there might not also be witches in Pennsylvania, he replied sarcastically that people were quite free to fly about on broomsticks within the boundaries of his colony.

The liberality of the laws of the Middle Colonies, particularly those guaranteeing religious toleration and easy access to land, ensured that New York and the Quaker colonies of Pennsylvania, New Jersey, and Delaware would be contented, placid provinces. Between the time of Leisler's Rebellion in New York in 1689, and a dispute between Quakers and non-Quakers in Pennsylvania in the mid-1700s, the Middle Colonies grew faster than either New England or the South.

Balanced Economies

Except for the Hudson Valley of New York, where a few Dutch patroonships survived into the eighteenth century, great estates were rare in the Middle Colonies. As in New England, the agricultural pattern was a patchwork of small, family farms tilled by the landowners themselves with comparatively few servants and slaves. Unlike that of New England, the climate of the Middle Colonies provided a long growing season, and the soil in the alluvial valleys of the Hudson, Delaware, Schuylkill, and Susquehanna rivers was deep and rich. The farmers of the Middle Colonies were also blessed in that they could grow the same crops they grew in Europe, using much the same methods. They did not have to develop new economic strategies as in New England and the South.

The Middle Colonies produced a large surplus of grain and livestock. Pennsylvania earned the nickname "bread-basket of the colonies," and Delaware, New Jersey, and New York were scarcely less productive.

Because foodstuffs (with the exception of rice) were not enumerated under the Navigation Acts, the products of the Middle Colonies could be sold wherever the sellers could find a market. A canny merchant class in the cities of Philadelphia and New York soon found one. They shipped grain and meat animals on the hoof to the sugar islands of the West Indies, where a small master class forced huge gangs of black slaves to grow cane and little else. The Middle Colonies found a comfortable niche for themselves within the imperial system. They were neither over dependent on the mother country, nor constantly in competition and at odds with British policies.

The merchants of Philadelphia and New York governed those cities as though they were personal property. However, because landowning farmers (who were, therefore, voters) were so numerous in the Middle Colonies, merchants were not able to dominate the elected assemblies as planters dominated them in the South. Neither agricultural nor commercial interests were completely in charge. Instead, they cooperated to counterbalance the power of the proprietor's appointed governor in Pennsylvania and of the royal governors in Delaware, New Jersey, and New York.

Liberal Institutions

New Jersey and Delaware practiced toleration on the same Quaker grounds as did Pennsylvania. In New York, the Church of England was established but laws proscribing other forms of worship were rarely enforced. For a time, a Roman Catholic, Thomas Dongan, served as governor of New York. A Jewish synagogue established under Dutch rule in 1654 continued to flourish unimpeded.

Indeed, once the Puritan grip on Massachusetts was broken, religious toleration was the rule in all the colonies. America was a young country in need of people. Whatever the law said, there were few serious attempts to discourage immigration. Few questions were asked about an individual's personal beliefs.

Until about 1700, most colonists either had been born in England or had English-born parents. There were a few third-generation families in Virginia and Maryland,

more in New England. And there were representatives of other backgrounds: a handful of Jews in Rhode Island, New York, and South Carolina; a contingent of French Protestants in South Carolina who had fled persecution at home.

Among Europeans, however, the most important non-English group was made up of Germans who congregated in Lancaster and York counties, Pennsylvania, just to the west of Philadelphia. Many of these refugees from persecution and chronic warfare were members of pietistic religious sects with beliefs much like those of the Quakers. William Penn and his heirs actively recruited the Amish and Mennonite sectarians for his Holy Experiment. They were hard-working, productive, utterly untroublesome, and they loyally supported the English brethren who had provided them a refuge.

Non-English minorities suffered little discrimination because of their origins, religion, and language. By no means, however, was America the land of opportunity for everyone. Equality and liberty were not extended to the two large groups of colonial people not of the Caucasian race.

For Further Reading

Once again, see the final paragraph of the bibliography following Chapter 2 for general works dealing with colonial America and, concerning the development of the colonies, the titles listed under "For Further Reading" for Chapter 3. See, in addition: Lewis C. Gray, *History of Agriculture in the United States to 1860* (1933) and, as a corrective in some particulars, Howard S. Russell, *A Long, Deep Furrow: Three Centuries of Farming in New England* (1976).

On social and cultural developments, see James A. Henretta, *The Evolution of American Society, 1700-1815* (1973); Thomas J. Wertenbaker, *The Planters of Colonial Virginia* (1927); and Louis B. Wright, *Cultural Life of the American Colonies 1607-1763* (1957) and *The First Gen-*tlemen of Virginia* (1940); and Carl Bridenbaugh, *Myths and Realities: Societies of the Colonial South* (1963). The standard work on Bacon's rebellion is Wilcomb E. Washburn, *The Governor and the Rebel* (1957).

Witchcraft in Salem and elsewhere in colonial America is the subject of enduring controversy. Once the standard explanation and still provocative is Marion G. Starkey, *The Devil in Massachusetts* (1969). Books adding new dimensions to the topic include Paul Boyer and Stephen Nissenbaum, *Salem Possessed* (1974); John Demos, *Entertaining Satan: Witchcraft and the Culture of Early New England* (1982); and Carl Karlsen, *The Devil in the Shape of a Woman* (1987).

*The trustees of the Georgia colony receive a delegation of
native Georgians in London, 1734.*

THE OTHER AMERICANS

THE INDIANS, FRENCH, AND AFRICANS OF COLONIAL NORTH AMERICA

When the North American colonies were mentioned to a British gentleman of the age of Queen Anne, he might speak of precious national possessions, daily enriching the mother country and adding to her glory. Or he might speak of ragged little gaggles of his countrymen gone too far from home for their own good. At a time when London was becoming a sophisticated metropolis, rustic colonials were easy targets of ridicule.

But not, perhaps, for Britons of the poor and middling sort. Their steady emigration to America tells us that a good many of them thought America a land of opportunity, even a fount of wealth far preferable to what the old country provided.

There were other perspectives from which to envision the colonies. To many West Africans, North America was one of the dread places to which people were taken in chains, never to return. To the French, the British in America were rivals, in hot competition for primacy in the wilderness of the North American interior.

And then there was the perspective of those for whom North America was neither new nor a wilderness nor—they had thought—a place to compete for, but an ancestral home, the people most of us know as Indians.

THE INDIANS OF NORTH AMERICA

The most striking characteristic of the Native American world was diversity. Indeed, American prehistory is a stunning lesson in just how rapidly cultures diversify when population is small and scattered, and when people of differing beliefs and practices do not constantly interact with one another. Although all Indians were descended from culturally similar bands of Asians, they had divided and divided again into a kaleidoscope of linguistic and cultural groups, and even of distinct physical types. American Indians differed more in appearance among themselves than did the East Asians who were their closest relations.

An Extraordinary Diversity

Native American political systems ran the gamut from would-be totalitarianism (the Incas in Peru) to the absence of the idea of government among some peoples of the North American high desert (especially in what is now Nevada). Socially, there were caste systems so complicated that tribes supported genealogical specialists as the only means to keep track of them (in the southeastern United States). Other tribes were egalitarian and democratic.

There were tribes in which a man virtually ignored the existence of every woman but his wife, others that required women to speak in a different language from men. Yet others traced descent through the female line and relied on councils of women to make important tribal decisions (the Iroquois). The variety of social relationships among the Indians at the time the whites arrived was more diverse than it was in Europe.

Some Indians were warlike and aggressive, renowned for their cruelty toward enemies. Every tribe in the Northeast (and Europeans, too) feared the Mohawks because they scalped their victims, sometimes alive. Other Indians were gentle folk, principled pacifists who had survived by finding secluded nooks of the continent in which to live. Many of the California tribes, with whom whites became acquainted only later, did not resist violent interlopers, but submitted, bewildered at the turn fate had taken. Many Indians were genuine monotheists who worshiped a single Manitou, or "Great Spirit." Others were superstitious fetishists. They worried about the supernatural powers in stones, trees, bugs, birds, and depended on magicians to cope with other-worldly powers.

There was intense cultivation and a quasi-urban way of life among the Pueblo Indians of New Mexico and Arizona. In California, whole peoples grubbed out a subsistence on little but acorns, a few roots and berries, and the odd small animal they snared. In the Pacific Northwest, food was so abundant that the potlatch tribes expressed a disdain for material goods such as we associate with only very rich and wasteful economies. Some Florida tribes had so sophisticated and far-reaching a trading network, they lived abundantly without farming.

Language and Culture

The diversity of Native American cultures may best be illustrated by the Indian languages. There are only the obscurest relationships between any North American tongue and the contemporary language of any Asian people. Among the Indians themselves, the linguistic differences were greater than they were in Europe. During the colonial period, the Indians of the Americas spoke about 500 mutually unintelligible tongues. In one corner of North Carolina, several small tribes living within ten miles of one another for at least a century could not communicate except by sign language.

Fragmentation was the natural tendency of language before the modern era. Until language is written down and rules of expression devised, and when there is no pressing need to communicate with more than a few daily associates, language changes very rapidly. This may be observed today in the almost constant emergence of new slang words and expressions in American English. Today, however, new phrases are made immediately familiar to almost everyone through the newspapers, magazines, television, and cinema. They are then either adopted into the language of all or discarded into wastebaskets in which future antiquarians will rummage.

In worlds that grow smaller culturally, like the Roman, Arabic, or Chinese empires, or our own technologically shrunken earth, a common means of communication can develop. In the vast, thinly populated world of the North American Indians, with bands constantly breaking up into smaller bands, distinct tongues developed and multiplied at an astonishing rate. Tribal views of "foreigners" reflected linguistic fragmentation. The word of many a tribe for itself translated as "the people" or "the human beings." Those outside the tribe were called "the beasts" or "the other things."

THE INDIANS OF THE EASTERN WOODLANDS

It is possible that the process of political and cultural fragmentation was being reversed on the Atlantic coast at the time the English first settled there. About 1570, five previously hostile Iroquois nations bound together in a confederation that successfully prevented conflict among them and coordinated some inter-tribal activities. Powhatan, the most powerful sachem of the Chesapeake region, dominated six tribes and asserted some authority over some twenty others when Jamestown was founded. While there were 50 language families in North America as a whole, there were only three significant linguistic groups in the territory staked out by the people of the thirteen English colonies.

Major Groups

Algonkians (or Algonquins) occupied the coast from New England through the Chesapeake Bay and parts of interior New York and Pennsylvania. Tribes in this group included the Mohegans (or Mohicans), Narragansett, Abnaki, Lenni Lenape (Delawares), Pequots, Chippewas, and Powhatans. Algonkian speakers were the peoples with whom the English first made contact in both Virginia and Massachusetts and whom, by taking their lands, they made their enemies.

The second major linguistic group of the Eastern Woodlands was the Iroquoian. The Iroquois occupied a large wedge-shaped territory, running from the eastern Great Lakes through New York and into Pennsylvania. The Conestogas and Eries were Iroquoian-speaking as were the powerful Hurons who lived along the St. Lawrence river in New France, what is now Canada. But the most important Iroquois so far as the English were concerned were five tribes that had joined together in a confederation under the legendary figure Hiawatha a century before the founding of New England.

The Five Nations of the Iroquois Confederacy were the Cayugas, Mohawks, Oneidas, Onandagas, and Senecas. Farther south, separated from the main group by Algonkian territory, were the Tuscarora of inland Vir-

The Iroquois, allied to the English, were savages to the French. In fact, the Iroquois were a politically sophisticated people who survived while other tribes of the Eastern Woodlands disappeared.

senger pigeons, deer, moose, bear, and beaver, and they tended tobacco plants. The women did all the other farming, cultivating corn, beans, and pumpkins, using the "slash and burn" method. This is an easy form of clearing land that suited the eastern peoples—who were primarily hunters and gatherers—and was to prove indispensable to each wave of white pioneers in a densely forested country.

Slash and burn involved, in this case, stripping a ring of bark from around the trunks of trees, thus killing them. When the last foliage fell, admitting sunlight to the forest floor, the women burned the underbrush and built small mounds a few feet apart. In each mound they planted a few seeds of corn, three or four beans, and some squash. These "three sisters" of the Indian diet nicely complemented one another. The cornstalks served as support for the beans. The squash helped to keep down competitive weeds.

As John Winthrop, Jr., observed, the Indians loaded "the Ground with as much as it will bear." A single woman tending two acres could grow fully half the food needed by a family of five. Because English women were less likely to work in the fields, some New England Indians said that the white men were fools "for spoiling good working creatures, meaning women: And when they see any of our *English* women sewing with their

ginia and North Carolina. During the 1710s, they were defeated by colonial forces from South Carolina and trekked north to become the sixth nation of the Iroquois League.

The earliest Southern colonists had less contact with the third major linguistic group of the Eastern Woodlands, the Muskohegan. These tribes included the Apalachee, Chickasaw, Choctaw, Creek, Natchez, and Seminole. These socially sophisticated tribes lived in what are now the southeastern states of Florida, Georgia, Alabama, Mississippi, and Tennessee. Few English settlers penetrated this country until late in the seventeenth century, when South Carolinians developed a slave, hide, and skin trade there.

A Mixed Economy

The economy of all Eastern Woodlands Indians was much the same. In the proper season, they gathered eggs, berries, and fruits. The men hunted migratory birds, pas-

Clearing land by the "slash and burn" method was copied from the Indians by white pioneers in the Eastern Woodlands.

needles, or working coifes, or such things, they will cry out, Lazie squaes."

Different Values

So primitive a method of cultivation did not in itself provide sufficient food. Every tribe looked more to the forests than to the fields for its survival, depending primarily on hunting, fishing, trapping, and gathering edible plants. Thus, each tribe competed with its neighbors for hunting grounds.

Hunting and foraging provided half a community's sustenance. In order to survive, however, summer villages of 500 or more were forced to break up into wandering family groups during the depths of winter so as not to put too much of a strain on a single sector of a tribe's hunting grounds. Even then, life was a cycle of feast and famine. Samuel Lee of Massachusetts observed that the Indians were "very patient in fasting, & will gird in their bellies till they meet with food; but then none more gluttons. . . . They eat 10 times in 24 hours, when they have a beare or a deere."

The Eastern Indians valued their weapons, tools, and household goods. They thought of them as their exclusive property, much as Europeans did. But, hunting and gathering did not require constant occupation or exclusive control of a specific tract of land. Consequently, the European concept of private property in land was alien to the Eastern tribes. The land was God's. Tribes used it and competed to use it, often violently. But no one "owned" it.

CONFRONTATION

To the Eastern Woodlands Indians, the earliest English colonies were curious enclaves on the edge of the universe. The continent was the Indians' world; the Atlantic was a barrier, an abyss. The people who came across it were seen as members of new tribes—soon more numerous than any other tribe, to be sure, and peculiar in more ways than in the color of their skin. Nevertheless, for many decades, the whites were just another people with whom to fight, to trade, to compete for the means of living. England and Europe? They were just words, the names of the places from which the whites received the goods that the Indians so desired.

Two Different Worlds

The experience of the Native Americans who first confronted English settlers was rather different than that of Indians who knew the Spanish. First of all, there were not too many of them—possibly as few as 150,000 Indians lived in those parts of the continent the English penetrated during their first century in America. By comparison, 100,000 Aztecs lived in Tenochtitlán alone when Cortez first laid eyes on the great city.

And yet, despite the loose political organization of the Indians of the Eastern Woodlands, the English had a much harder time of dominating the natives than the Spanish did in Mexico and Peru. In large part, this was due to the fact that the English took little interest in conquering, living among, governing, and "europeanizing" the Native Americans, as the Spaniards did in their part of the New World.

Some Indians were enslaved to work on plantations. In 1708, Indians captured or purchased from southern tribes in South Carolina numbered 1400, 14 percent of the colony's population. But Indians escaped too easily in a land that was, after all, their own. White servants and black slaves (for whom masters paid twice the price of an Indian) were more dependable laborers.

The character of the English emigration also served to keep Indians and Europeans in different worlds. Unlike New Spain, which was conquered by soldiers, New England was settled by families with men and women coming in roughly equal numbers. Even in the South by the time of Queen Anne, the English population was approaching sexual parity. Men found little need to look among the native peoples for wives or casual consorts. With marriage within the race easy, it was feasible in English America to define miscegenation as disreputable, and to consign "half-breeds" to the Indians. Indeed, whites who married Indians generally chose to live with their spouse's people where acceptance by the tribe determined status, not skin color. So did many whites (usually women and children) who were kidnapped by Indians specifically for the purpose of replacing tribe members who had died or been killed.

Land Hunger

The goal of English colonization was to replicate, as closely as possible, the way of life the settlers knew back home. Indians had no place in Little Englands. The object was to get land from them, pushing them peacefully or forcefully outside the pale of white settlement.

Like the Spanish, conscientious colonials devised moral and legal justifications for taking Indian land. The Pilgrims justified their occupation of Plymouth on the grounds that no one was there when they arrived. John Cotton of Massachusetts elaborated on this rationale, adding "just war" as a means of securing title to land.

Roger Williams, the Dutch, and the Pennsylvania Quakers bought the land they wanted. Their view of these transactions, however, differed sharply from that of the Indians. To Europeans, purchase meant exclusive use of the land as, indeed, intensive agriculture required. The Indian sellers often believed they were agreeing to share their slice of the Manitou's earth with the newcomers. "Sell the land?" said the nineteenth-century chief Tecumseh, echoing many before him. "Why not sell the air, the clouds, the great sea?" Thus could Staten Island be "sold" to the Dutch three times over: three different tribes were accepting the Hollanders.

Moreover, "chiefs" with whom the Europeans dealt did not possess the sovereign power to dispose of land that the newcomers assumed they had. And many Indians must have been simply bewildered by European dealings. Jasper Danckhaerts wrote of a transaction in New York in 1679: "the Indians hate the precipitancy of comprehension and judgement [of the whites], the excited chatterings, . . . the haste and rashness to do something, whereby a mess is often made of one's good intentions."

Other colonials lacked both patience and good intentions. They shrugged, shot, and took. Possession by right of conquest was not a universally approved principle in the seventeenth century, but it had a long pedigree and some compelling recommendations.

Bringers of Baubles

The Indians' first reaction to the English was curiosity. Few in the Eastern Woodlands were as flabbergasted by the sight of whites as the Arawaks had been. From the visits of European explorers and fishermen, and from gossip among tribes, they knew of the existence of white-skinned strangers before they confronted them face to face.

The earliest English settlements posed no threat, and the colonists did offer goods that were highly desirable to a Stone Age people. There were the famous baubles: glass beads, ribbons, trinkets, mirrors. New to Indians, they were accorded the high price of any rarity. It was

ENGLISH LEGALISM

The English colonists—in New England at least—were as legalistic as the Spanish in justifying the taking of land from the Indians. However, the Puritans based the legality of their seizures not on a royal proclamation like the *requerimiento*, but on the Bible. In 1630, John Cotton spelled out the three ways in which "God makes room for a people." First, in a just, unprovoked war, which God would bless (Psalms 44:2 "Thou didst drive out the heathen before them"), the victors had the right to the land they conquered. Second, newcomers had the right to purchase land or accept it as a gift "as *Abraham* did obtaine the field of *Machpelah*" or as the Pharoah gave the land of Goshen "unto the sons of Jacob." Third—and here was legalistic loophole-making at its best, "when hee makes a Countrey though not altogether void of inhabitants, yet voyd in that place where they [the newcomers] reside . . . there is liberty for the sonne of *Adam* or *Noah* to come and inhabite, though they neither buy it, not aske their leaves." In other words, given the fact that most of North America was uncultivated forest, it was fair game.

with $24 worth of such goods that Peter Minuit purchased Manhattan Island in 1626. Woven blankets were highly prized. As a New Englander observed, the Indians' fire had served for warmth "instead of our bed cloathe." A novelty brimming with tragedy, but coveted nonetheless, was liquor, usually rum. Some Eastern tribes made a weak corn beer, but nothing so potent as distilled alcohol. From the first, the Indians took with tragic zest to "firewater." It devastated many tribes physically and morally.

Much more important to a people who smelted no metals were the European commodities that improved their standard of living: brass and iron vessels; tools (spades, hatchets); woven blankets (which were much warmer than hides) and other textiles; and firearms, which allowed the Indians to hunt more efficiently and get a leg up on old tribal enemies.

In return for such goods, the Indians provided foodstuffs to the earliest settlers. When the English became agriculturally self-sufficient, they supplied furs and hides for the European market.

The Fur and Hide Trade

In the decline and destruction of the Eastern Woodlands tribes, furs and hides played a far greater role than liquor, or even the military superiority of the English. The English (and Dutch and French) appetite for animal skins resulted in the destruction of the ecology of which the Eastern Indians had been a part for centuries.

REAL ESTATE SWINDLE

In most land deals between Indians and whites, by our standards the Indians were swindled. Manhattan Island was purchased for $24. Even the Quakers set boundaries for purchases at how far a man could walk during a set period of time and then set off relays of fast runners to enlarge the tract. In at least one case, however, the Indians did the swindling. The Raritan Indians sold Staten Island, one of the five boroughs of New York City, to various Dutch and English groups a total of six times.

Before the whites arrived, the Woodlands tribes killed only those deer, beaver, and other animals that they needed for food and clothing. Why do otherwise? Because the Indians were so few, their needs had little impact on the wildlife population. Probably, their harvests had a healthy effect on wildlife by preventing overpopulation and disease.

But Europeans could not get enough American skins and pelts. The upper classes back home coveted the lush furs of the beaver, otter, and weasel. Both furs and deerskin were made into felt, which was pressed into hats and dozens of other useful goods. In order to increase production, and buy more European goods, the tribes rapidly exterminated the valuable creatures in their ancestral hunting grounds.

It does not take very long to destroy a species when hunting is relentless and systematic. In only a couple of generations, nineteenth-century Americans would annihilate a population of passenger pigeons that previously had darkened the skies. The nearly total destruction of the North American bison after the construction of the transcontinental railroad took only ten years! Thus it happened in the Eastern Woodlands, as Indians and the odd white hunter and trapper set out after deer and beaver.

Unlike the case of the passenger pigeon, very much like the case of the bison, the destruction of the animals of the eastern forests meant the destruction of a way of life.

A New Kind of Warfare

The demands of the fur traders also introduced a new kind of warfare to the world of the Indians. Not that war was new to them; on the contrary, enmity toward other tribes was an integral part of Iroquois and Algonkian culture.

But traditional Indian warfare was largely a ritualistic demonstration of individual bravery. A young man gained as much glory in "counting coup," giving an enemy a sound rap, as in taking his life. Women and children were rarely killed, and rape seems to have been unusual. Men on the warpath were sworn to continence, and rape was the only capital crime among the Indians of New England.

Once part of an intercontinental economy, however, the Indians embraced a different concept of warfare. No longer was the main object glory, retribution, or thievery, but the exploitation of other tribes' hunting grounds and, if necessary, the total elimination of the competition.

The colonists tacitly encouraged this localized genocide by providing the weapons that made it possible. They also helped spread the practice of scalping, which

had been peculiar to the Mohawks, as a means of measuring a tribe's efficiency. In 1721, Quaker Pennsylvania paid $140 for an Algonkian warrior's scalp and $50 for a squaw's. And to make the purpose of the bounty unmistakable, a live prisoner was worth a paltry $30.

The gory practice of scalping eventually spread over much of the continent. Because tribes involved in the fur trade penetrated the West long before the whites dared to do so, Indians in the interior were introduced to European trade goods, European diseases, and the report of English and French muskets long before they saw their first paleface.

THE FRENCH IN NORTH AMERICA

Anglo-Indian relations were complicated by the presence of another European people in North America. In 1608, just a year after Jamestown was settled, Samuel de Champlain planted the white banner of the French Bourbons on the banks of the St. Lawrence River. He built one fort at Quebec and another at Port Royal in Nova Scotia. Montreal was not founded until 1642, on the site of an Indian stockade.

Grand Empire, Few People

Driven by the same impulses as the English Crown, determined to keep pace with their rivals in North America, the Bourbon kings of France were disappointed by the reluctance of their subjects to cross the Atlantic. For farmers, which most French men and women were, the problem was the climate and soil of New France. The soil of Nova Scotia and the St. Lawrence basin was even less inviting than New England's and the winters were worse. Censuses of the immigrant population of Canada showed a high proportion of people who had been urban tradesmen or laborers in the old country, not peasants.

Bourbon religious intolerance served to defeat the object of populating New France. Louis XIV (r. 1643–1715) forced the Hugenots, Protestants much like the English Puritans, to leave France. But they were forbidden to emigrate to New France where they might well have chosen to go.

Instead, the French kings used their absolute power to force emigration by people they deemed expendable at home. Entire villages of poor and rugged Brittany were uprooted and shipped to Quebec. Soldiers stationed in North American forts were ordered to remain when their term of service was complete. Prostitutes from the streets of Paris and French seaports were rounded up and dispatched to be their wives—as were the respectable daughters of peasants who got into tax trouble.

But New France would not grow. By 1713, after a century of settlement, the French population in North America was 25,000, about the same number of people as lived in the single English colony of Pennsylvania, which was less than 40 years old. As the great nineteenth century historian, Francis Parkman wrote, "France built its best colony on a principle of exclusion and failed; England reversed the principle, and succeeded."

French Expansion

Still, the boldness of the French Canadians almost made up for the poverty of their numbers. French traders, trappers, and priests fanned out in the north woods surrounding the Great Lakes while the English huddled within a few miles of ocean breakers. These *coureurs de bois* (which translates as "runners of the woods") reverted more than halfway to savagery, as Europeans defined the Indians' way of life.

In traveling through the Indians' forests, consorting with and marrying native women, and adopting Indian dress (with a few of their own affectations), the *coureurs de bois* renounced their European heritage in a way that was incomprehensible to the English. When a governor of Virginia reached the crest of the Appalachians, he celebrated by setting a table with pressed linen, fine china, and silver, and by pouring three kinds of wine into crystal glasses. When a Frenchman broke new

ground much deeper in the interior, he roasted a slab of meat and ate it with his hands while hunkering in the dust.

Spurred on by the tales of the *coureurs de bois*, intrepid French explorers charted what is now the central third of the United States. In 1673, Louis Joliet and Jacques Marquette, a Jesuit priest, descended the Mississippi to the mouth of the Arkansas River. In 1682, Robert Cavelier, the Sieur de La Salle, reached the mouth of the Father of Waters. (The Mississippi had never been discovered from the Gulf of Mexico because, at the end of its journey, the great river divides into hundreds of muddy channels lazing their way through forbidding swamps.) In 1699, Pierre le Moyne, the Sieur d'Iberville, began the series of settlements on the Gulf that became New Orleans and the hub of the second French province in North America, Louisiana.

It was a flimsy empire by English standards, a string of lonely log forts and trading posts in the wilderness: Kaskaskia and Cahokia in the Illinois country; St. Louis where the Missouri flows into the Mississippi; dots on a map connected by lakes, rivers, creeks, and portages (a word that Americans learned from the Canadians meaning a place canoes had to be *carried* from one waterway to another).

But the French had one big edge on their English rivals. Most of the Algonkian-speaking people, plus the

New Biloxi, in the French province of Louisiana, was established by John Law, a Scottish promoter (ca. 1720).

Hurons, an Iroquoian tribe independent of the confederation—a large majority of the Indians of the northeastern forests—were friendlier to the French than to the English.

Contrasting Ways of Life

The French were able to maintain better relations with these tribes for several reasons, none more important than the fewness of their numbers that King Louis so regretted. In remaining so few, the French did not threaten the natives with inundation as the growing English settlements did.

Second in importance, while the English way of life clashed head-on with Indian use of the land, French economic interests in North America seemed only to benefit the tribes. Both English and French wanted to trade European goods for furs and hides. But whereas New France was little more than trading posts and trappers, the English colonies were primarily agricultural settlements. The French glided quietly through the forests, like the Indians and the deer themselves. The English chopped the forests down. Each acre of land put under cultivation meant one acre less in the hunting and gathering economy.

The Role of Religion

The difference in religion between the Roman Catholic French and the Protestant English, particularly the Puritans of New England, also affected their respective relations with the tribes. Like every Christian people in the Americas, both English and French partly justified their presence in terms of winning the Indians over to true faith. The intention to do so was mentioned more or less sincerely in every colonial charter. A few pious Englishmen, such as Roger Williams and John Eliot, the "Apostle of the Indians" who devoted his life to preaching among the tribes of the upper Connecticut Valley, took the mission seriously. Dartmouth College in Hanover, New Hampshire originated as a school for Indians. When the College of William and Mary was established in Virginia in 1693, provision was made for Indian education. (Not one Indian showed up to register.)

It was not difficult, however, for the English colonists to lose interest in saving the souls of savage redskins. The Anglican and Puritan religions were both highly nationalistic; that is, the colonists' religious beliefs were intimately wrapped up with their English customs, prejudices, language, moral codes, manners, and even the kind of clothes they wore. The Puritans, moreover, looked upon salvation, and, therefore, church membership, as a gift given to very few of their own culture. Foreigners were scorned not only because, in the case of

---

THANKS BUT NO THANKS

In 1744, Virginia signed a treaty with the Iroquois Confederacy. To seal their friendship, colonial officials invited each of the six associated tribes to send a young man to be educated at the College of William and Mary. According to Benjamin Franklin, the Iroquois replied:

We are convinced . . . that you mean to do us good . . . and we thank you heartily. But you, who are wise, must know that different nations have different conceptions of things; and you will therefore not take it amiss, if our ideas of this kind of education happen not to be the same with yours. We have had some experience of it; several of our young people were formerly brought up at the colleges of the northern provinces; they were instructed in all your sciences; but, when they came back to us, they were bad runners, ignorant of every means of living in the woods, unable to bear either cold or hunger, knew neither how to build a cabin, take a deer, or kill an enemy, spoke our language imperfectly, were therefore neither fit for hunters, warriors, nor counselors; they were totally good for nothing. We are, however, not the less obliged by your kind offer . . . and to show our grateful sense of it, if the gentlemen of Virginia will send us a dozen of their sons, we will take great care of their education, instruct them in all we know, and make men of them.

---

the Spanish and French, they were Roman Catholic, but because their customs were different. Indians, with their even more unusual ways of doing things, were infinitely farther beyond the pale.

The French had their fair share of cultural prejudices, too. However, their Roman Catholic Church held that everyone should belong to it. (The word *catholic* means "universal.") The Church had been built on accommodating religious beliefs to a welter of cultures as far distant and as exotic as those in Japan and China. When French priests preached to Indians, therefore, they emphasized the similarities between Indian tradition and Catholic practice. By way of contrast, English Protestant preachers seemed always to be talking about practices the Indians had to give up.

The priests of New France had another advantage over the Protestants in the competition for native American loyalties. The ornate Roman Catholic ritual—the mystery of the Mass and other ceremonies, the vividly decorated statues—appealed to the Indians' aesthetic sense. The Puritans remained a people of the word. Bible study and long, learned sermons were the foundations of Protestant worship services. Both were foreign to Indian culture.

The Five Nations

Despite these handicaps, the English won Indian allies, and very valuable ones at that. Ancient hatreds among the native peoples, dating back to long before the arrival of Europeans, put the Iroquois Confederation, the Five Nations, squarely on the side of the English.

It is not clear how long the Cayugas, Mohawks, Oneidas, Onandagas, and Senecas had been warring with the Algonkians and their fellow Iroquois, the Hurons. In 1609, however, when Samuel de Champlain, in company with a group of Hurons, opened fire on a party of Mohawks, the balanced match-up tipped decisively in favor of the friends of the French. Over the next several decades, the Algonkians and the Hurons exploited their French friends and gunpowder to wear down the Five Nations. The hardships and fears of this period guaranteed that when the Iroquois themselves made contacts with Europeans—first the Dutch in Fort Orange and then the English, who replaced them in New York—they had a generation's worth of scores to settle.

And settle them they did. With their own firearms and white allies, the Iroquois took the offensive against the Algonkians, Hurons, and French with a frightening vengeance. The *coureurs de bois* so feared the Five Nations that they added as many as a thousand miles to their trek to the trapping grounds in the Illinois country rather than take the chance of running into a party of Cayugas, Oneidas, or Senecas.

AMERICANS FROM AFRICA

To Europeans who came to the colonies to farm, the Indians were as much an impediment to progress as the massive oaks and maples of the forests were. The land had to be cleared of both trees and people before agriculture could thrive. Colonists came to view the people of the third race of North America, by way of contrast, as valuable and eventually essential to economic development. These were black people, mostly from around the Gulf of Guinea in West Africa, who were imported against their wills to America in order to solve the commercial farmer's problem of getting things done in a country where land was limitless, but backs to bend over it were few.

Slavery in the Western Hemisphere

There may have been crewmen of African origin with Columbus. Estéban the Moor, who explored around the Gulf of Mexico, could have been of African descent. (The Spanish did not always distinguish between Ber-bers and Arabs of the Mediterranean and black Africans from below the Sahara.) In any case, blacks had resided in the Americas for a century before any English men and women did. By the mid-1500s, they were the backbone of the labor force in the West Indies, on the Spanish Main, and in Portuguese Brazil. Some of these people, particularly those of mixed race, were free subjects of the Spanish kings. A few exceptional individuals rose from slavery to prosper as craftsmen, sailors, landowners, and even as priests of the Church. The vast majority, however, were slaves—the personal property of other people in accordance with laws that had their origins in Roman times.

The English also needed cheap, dependable labor, particularly in the tobacco colonies. But they did not turn immediately to slavery to solve their problem. Unlike the Spanish and Portuguese, the English lacked a tradition of holding people in bondage for life. English society had developed relatively uninfluenced by the Roman imperial heritage in which slavery was accepted as a fact of life. Even the medieval institution of serfdom, which bound families to a piece of land—if the land were sold, the right to the serf's services went with it—had died out in England centuries before North America was colonized.

Nor did the English, like the Spanish and Portuguese, have a history of trade and war with the peoples of Africa, which resulted in large numbers of enslaved black captives in Spain and Portugal. The institution of slavery was, simply, unfamiliar to them. As late as 1620, when a Gambian merchant offered slaves to an English shipmaster as payment for his trade goods, the captain replied indignantly that "we were a people who did not deal in any such commodities, neither did wee buy or sell one another, or any that had our owne shapes." The African was amazed and said that the other white men who came to his country wanted nothing but slaves. The English captain answered that "they were another kinde of people different from us."

Had this goodly sailor's principles prevailed among his compatriots, North America would have been spared its greatest historical tragedy, the enslavement of millions of Africans and their descendants on the basis of their race. However, just a year before the curious incident on the Gambia River—and a year before the Mayflower anchored at Plymouth, Massachusetts—the history of black Americans had begun as part of an institution with which the English were familiar—indentured servitude.

New Uses for an Old Institution

During the first century of colonization, the English settlers solved their labor problem by adapting to America

HOW THEY LIVED

BECOMING A SLAVE

There must have been many girls named Akueke and Matefi among the Africans who were brought to the tobacco colonies as slaves. Akueke and Matefi were common Ibo names, and the Ibo people of what is now Nigeria were favorite targets of the slave traders. The Hausas and Yorubas raided their villages up the Niger River. So did the Ashantis, who built an empire on making slaves of other tribes, and white men from Europe and the American colonies.

Akueke and Matefi were probably captured at night. Slave traders wrote of calling peacefully on the mud walled compounds by day, trading openly, and then swooping down on the same village under cover of darkness. The brutal clamor of the raid heightened the nightmare of enslavement. Mostly the traders took men, but teenage girls—healthy and young enough to have a long life of childbearing ahead of them—were also desirable merchandise. Older men and women, however, could not withstand the rigors of the "middle passage" across the Atlantic and were either left behind or clubbed to death by rough men in an ugly business.

The captives were marched quickly toward the sea in "coffles," tied or chained together to prevent daring or desperate individuals from making a break for the bush or mangrove swamps of coastal West Africa. If the raiders feared an attack in retaliation, there was no delay on behalf of people ill, injured, or exhausted. They were cut out of the coffles and, as likely as not, killed on the spot.

At one of the many mouths of the Niger, the Volta, the Sassandra, or any of the dozens of southward flowing rivers of the region, the girls were put into a stockade called a "factory." There they might stay for weeks, fed on yams, millet, and possibly some meat and fish if her captors worried about the health of their slaves. If there had not been whites in the party that captured her, they soon made their appearance. At the African end, the trade took place at or near the mouths of rivers where Portuguese, Spanish, Dutch, French, English, or American ships could anchor close to shore.

Akueke and Matefi would only half understand the transactions that took place after the buyers felt their muscles and looked at their teeth, as if they were horses. They were sold for (in 1700) about £5 in iron bars, cloth, rum, guns, and other tools such as kettles and axes. To the captives, the experience was terrifying. They had been wrenched out of familiar surroundings and a static, reassuring life in which their fate was prescribed by laws and traditions, into a world of dizzying uncertainty. They probably knew of people who had been kidnapped like them, but had little idea what happened to them. They simply disappeared.

Some historians have compared the experience of enslavement to the treatment of Jews in Nazi Germany: a midnight call by the Gestapo, weeks of being shunted about like livestock, every moment living in fear of death and at the constant cruel mercies of all-powerful captors, all leading to a bewildered sense of unreality and helplessness. In one sense, the African's lot was better than that of the Jews. Their masters wanted to keep them alive; the Jews in Germany were scheduled for deliberate extermination.

The ship on which new slaves were shipped across the Atlantic was probably, by the eighteenth century, specially constructed for the purpose. "Shipped" is the appropriate word. Akueke and Matefi and their unlucky companions were packed side by side on their backs on decks like shelves, one deck only two feet above the other. They were chained, wrist to wrist and ankle to ankle. Instead of providing reasonable conditions under which the whole cargo might survive, most slave traders packed their holds tightly with the maximum number of people that would fit, absorbing the losses of the high mortality that resulted. If a ship made the crossing with only 5 percent or 10 percent breakage, that is, one of ten or one in twenty dead, it was considered a grand success. But the traders could absorb as much as a one in three loss and still make a profit. The girls who cost £5 in West Africa sold for £25 or £30 in Virginia.

A contagious disease or simple bad luck with weather—calm or storm—could send scurvy or dysentery sweeping through the holds. Every morning, the crew's first task was to check through the slaves in order to cut out the dead and dump their bodies overboard. If the weather was especially bad or the captain or crew merely nervous about mutiny, the Africans would rarely be allowed on deck (and then only in small groups). The stench and filth in the hold—from sweat, vomit, urine, and feces—can hardly be imagined. Numerous people simply cracked, killing themselves or others in fits of insanity.

Young girls were liable to the sexual abuse of the sailors. It depended largely on the character of the captain. He might be so hardened by the trade that he allowed his men (and perhaps himself) full rein. Many did. However—rather more difficult to understand—many English and New Englander slave traders were pious, morally strict Calvinists or Quakers who would punish such sins with a lashing, or worse, while positive that their business was entirely honorable. The unholy and horrible business of shipping humans as if they were cattle was not recognized as morally wrong. They were "captives" and enslavement was justified on that basis.

Arrival in Virginia or South Carolina (or New York or Massachusetts) was practically a deliverance for the Africans. There were horrors yet to be undergone—the sale at market, the less dramatic but emotionally devastating experience of settling into a new, altogether foreign way of life, and the hard forced labor for which they had been seized. But anything was for the better after the nightmarish Middle Passage across the ocean. This—the fact that any life was to be preferred to the horrors of enslavement and shipment—may explain why rebellion was so rare among "first generation" American slaves. In a pathetic sense, they were glad to have arrived.

an institution by which, back home, skills involving long training and practice were passed from generation to generation, and by which communities provided for the raising of orphans and illegitimate children.

In England, boys were trained to be blacksmiths, coopers (barrelmakers), bakers, wheelwrights, clerks, printers, or whatever by binding them to a master of the craft. For a period of seven years—customarily from age fourteen to age twenty-one—the master was entitled to the apprentice's complete obedience and to the use of the boy's labor in return for housing, board, clothing, and teaching the lad the "mysteries" of the master's trade. Ideally, master, apprentice, and society benefited.

Similarly, communities provided for orphans, girls as well as boys, by binding them to householders as servants. In return for the labor of the child (no craft was involved in this kind of arrangement), the family that took in an orphan assumed the community's financial responsibility to care for the helpless waif.

Apprentices and servants were not "free." The law gave their masters the same broad authority over them that parents legally held over their children. This included the right to administer pretty harsh corporal punishment for wrongdoing. At the same time, apprentices and servants were not slaves. Their persons were not the property of their masters. They retained certain individual rights their masters were bound to respect. The term of their servitude was spelled out in a legal document. The day came when the apprentice and the maid servant walked off as free as anyone of their class. In theory, once again, everyone benefited: the householder got a servant; the orphan was raised to adulthood; the community was spared the cost of caring for a child.

Colonial Servants

Colonial planters and farmers who needed laborers adapted this familiar institution in the form of indentured servitude. For an outlay of from £6 to £30, which paid the cost of transatlantic passage, and the fee of a contractor who signed up servants in England, a colonist secured the services of a legally bound worker for between four and seven years. (The price of a servant, and the length of time served, depended upon just how badly American masters needed hands, and how many English men and women were willing to sign an indenture, as the document was called.)

The system worked. Well into the 1700s, indentured servants brought in the bulk of America's cash crops, particularly in the plantation regions of the southern colonies. During the colonial period, about 350,000 of 500,000 immigrants to America stepped from the ship as bound servants. The proportion was undoubtedly higher in the South where, because more than 80 per-

---

INDENTURED SERVANTS

The word *indenture* refers to a notch, literally an indentation in the paper on which the contract between a master and a person being bound into servitude was written. Most servants were illiterate and could understand the contract terms only if a third party read it to them. To protect them against fraud, one copy of the contract was placed atop its duplicate before signing and then snipped with a few notches, or "indentures." In any contract dispute, the indentures had to match.

The following contract of 1659 between "Richard Smyth of Virginia, planter, and Margaret Williams of Bristol, spinster" (an unmarried woman), was typical:

Witnesseth that the said Margaret doth hereby covenant, promise, and grant to and with the said Richard, his executors and assigns [the master could sell her services to another], from the day of the date hereof, until her first and next arrival at Virginia, and after, for and during the term of four years, to serve in such service and employment as the said Richard or his assigns shall there employ her, according to the custom of the country in the like kind. In consideration whereof the said master doth hereby covenant and grant to and with the said servant to pay for her passing [her transportation to Virginia], and to find and allow her meat, drink, apparel, and lodging, with other necessaries during the said term; and at the end of the said term to pay unto her one axe, one hoe, double apparel [two suits of clothes], fifty acres of land, one year's provision, according to the custom of the country.

---

cent of the servants were men—by custom, English women did not work in the fields—there was little natural increase of population among the lower classes. (Not until black slaves replaced white indentured servants would Virginia's population stabilize.)

A majority of servants signed their indentures voluntarily. They were more than willing to trade several years of their wretched lives for the chance of a fresh start. However, the practice of filling the hold of a servant ship by kidnapping boys or careless adults in English seaports was common enough. It was not wise to drink too heavily in a tavern near the harbor on the night a servant ship was scheduled to weigh anchor. In addition, English courts sentenced criminals—guilty of petty or vicious crimes—to "transportation" to the colonies where they joined the ranks of indentured servants.

Before the Mayflower

Most indentured servants were British: English, Scottish, Welsh, Irish. As early as 1619, however, a Dutch vessel sailed up the Chesapeake Bay and displayed to the settlers a dozen black Africans whom the Dutch had probably captured from a slave ship bound for the Spanish West Indies. The Virginians bought them, and continued to buy blacks throughout the 1600s.

The members of at least one generation of African-Americans were servants rather than slaves. As early as 1650, colonial records reveal that there was a small, free black population in the Chesapeake colonies. The only plausible deduction is that, like white indentured servants, the first blacks in English America were freed after a number of years in bondage. However, also by 1650, the assemblies of the plantation colonies were passing laws stating that black servants would, in the future, serve *durante vita*, during life. This fatal, tragic turn in law and custom was due to changing economic and social circumstances in the colonies, to problems inherent in the institution of indentured servitude, and to the peculiar vulnerability of the first black Americans.

Declining Prices, Declining Death Rate

As long as the price of tobacco was high, Chesapeake planters were willing to pay the substantial price of a servant's four to seven years of labor, which was the equivalent of several thousand pounds of the golden weed. It did not even matter much that, because of malaria, typhoid fever, and contagious diseases ranging from smallpox to influenza, servants were likely to die before their term of service was over. (The mortality rate

Charlestown, July 24th, 1769.

TO BE SOLD,

On THURSDAY the third Day of AUGUST next,

A CARGO

OF

NINETY-FOUR

PRIME, HEALTHY

NEGROES,

CONSISTING OF

Thirty-nine MEN, Fifteen BOYS, Twenty-four WOMEN, and Sixteen GIRLS.

JUST ARRIVED,

In the Brigantine DEMBIA, *Francis Bare*, Master, from SIERRA-LEON, by

DAVID & JOHN DEAS.

Poster announcing the sale of black slaves, 1769.

in the southern colonies was terrible: Governor Berkeley of Virginia estimated that, during the 1660s, four out of five indentured servants in that colony died within a few years of arriving.) However, in only a couple of seasons of labor, a servant could repay the master's investment. Certainly it made no sense to lay out the higher price of a black slave serving *durante vita*. The slave's "vita" was not likely to last very long.

Also during the 1660s, the profits in tobacco declined, and toward the end of the century the death rate took a dive. The planters were presented with a pressing incentive to save on the annual cost of labor and encouraged to buy workers who would, now that they were surviving, serve for as long as possible. Blacks seemed immune to some of the diseases that toppled whites in the South's semitropical climate. Moreover, as Bacon's Rebellion illustrated so dramatically, white servants and former servants could be troublesome people.

SEVEN YEARS IN SERVICE

The standard term of service for an indentured servant was seven years. This was based on the traditional term of an apprentice's service. This number, in turn, was based on the practice of dividing a person's minority, which ended at age twenty-one, into three equal parts: seven years of infancy, or more or less complete dependence; seven years of childhood, by the seventeenth century regarded as critical education years; and seven years of preadulthood, *not* then known as adolescence. The belief that a term of service should be seven years was also based on the Biblical story (Genesis 29) in which Jacob labors seven years for Laban in order to win the hand of Laban's daughter, Rachel. The seven years "seemed unto him but a few days, for the love he had for her," which was surely not the way the indentured servants in Virginia looked upon their terms. They would have found much more relevant the fact that Laban betrays Jacob, gives him his elder daughter Leah at the end of his term, and forces Jacob to labor another seven years to win Rachel.

The Servant Problem

The violence of the Bacon episode was exceptional. At the best of times, however, the court records of the colonies are filled with cases of masters complaining about their servants' insolence, negligence, and laziness; about stolen food and drink, rowdy parties, and pregnancies among the women, which exempted them from work for as long as a year.

More serious was the runaway problem. Throughout the colonies, including the most settled parts of the tidewater, America was densely forested. Farms and plantations were mere gaps in a wilderness. In Virginia and Maryland, the grandest plantations were separated from one another by belts of virgin hardwood or second-growth "pineys" (old fields gone to scrub). There were few towns. "Roads" were narrow tracks; most of them were not wide enough for two horsemen to pass without bumping.

Thus a servant could easily run away, hide, and elude capture. Planters' letters were filled with complaints of missing workers and lost investments. The recapture and return of runaways seems to have been the major activity of county sheriffs, the only law-enforcement officials in rural areas. Officials in cities like Baltimore and Philadelphia were flooded with descriptions of runaways, although, with hundreds of recent immigrants walking the streets of coastal cities, they probably caught very few. Punishment was harsh—a whipping and extra time in service. But the opportunities of freedom and the odds of success tempted many.

The most famous runaway was Benjamin Franklin. In 1723, at the age of 17, he walked out on his brother, to whom he was bound, and traveled from Boston to Philadelphia. Any number of people suspected him for what he was, a runaway, but no one tried to stop him.

The Badge of Race

In the ease with which a white runaway could blend into a crowd, and in the reluctance of many colonials to turn in people they suspected of being runaway servants, lies another reason planters turned from white indentured servants to black slaves as their work force. A black's color was a badge. An escaped slave could not blend into the crowds milling in the seaport towns. If it was assumed that a black person was a slave unless he or she could prove otherwise, the work force was that much more controllable. Sheriffs and bailiffs (who were rewarded for the service) routinely detained blacks who were unknown to them without waiting for masters to announce a runaway. By 1670, there were 2,000 blacks in Virginia, more than half of them slaves under a law passed in that year. After 1700, when the institution was universally accepted, the slave population grew rapidly until, by the time of the Revolution, there were about 500,000 slaves in the thirteen colonies, all but 50,000 in the South. A British officer observed, "They sell the servants here as they do their horses, and advertise them as they do their beef and oatmeal."

THE SLAVE TRADE

This demand for black laborers completely changed the English and colonial attitude toward trading in "any that had our owne shapes." Not only did ships from England and New England, especially Newport, Rhode Island, sail annually to West Africa to capture or purchase slaves, but the British actually pursued a policy of expanding their share of the trade. In 1713, British diplomats demanded of and won from Spain the *asiento de negros*, or right to supply blacks to the Spanish colonies. Trade in human beings became an integral part of the mercantilist system and a profitable leg of colonial trading tours.

Although dating from 1860, this engraving of a slaver depicts the inhuman conditions suffered by Africans on the "Middle Passage" since 1619.

Collaboration in Atrocity

The African slave trade was a sordid business in which African kings collaborated with European and American merchants. At first, African chiefs seem to have sold only their criminals and members of enemy tribes to the white-skinned strangers. As the European demand grew and the profits soared, some aggressive tribes began to build their economies on raids inland in search of fresh sources of supply. The economy of the Ashanti Confederation of West Africa rested more than casually on the commerce in slaves.

For the most part, the whites anchored their ships off the coast, or fortified themselves in stockades on islands like Gores off Dakar or at the mouths of rivers with the iron bars, brass, kettles, cloth, guns, powder, liquor, and tobacco that they traded for their human merchandise. Occasionally, however, some joined their African partners or ventured inland themselves. A trader of 1787 explained how the business worked: "In the daytime we called at the villages we passed, and purchased our slaves fairly; but in the night we . . . broke into the villages and, rushing into the huts of the inhabitants, seized men, women, and children promiscuously."

The cruelest part of the trade was the sea crossing, which was called the "middle passage" because it was flanked by overland marches at either end. Rather than providing the most healthful circumstances possible for their valuable cargo and keeping mortality low, the traders crammed the slaves in layers of low decks "like herrings in a barrel."

If only one in twenty captives died, the voyage was considered an extraordinary success. If one in five died, by no means unusual, the profits were still considerable. A slave who cost £5–10 in Africa in 1700 sold in the New World for a minimum of £25. The Portuguese, who were said to be more humane than the English and New England traders, called their slave ships *tumbeiros*, or "coffins." Only as the eighteenth century progressed did mortality decline. By the late 1700s, ship's masters reported that proportionally more slaves survived than crewmen, of whom one in five in the Guinea trade would not complete a voyage. (By way of contrast, deaths at sea on the North Atlantic routes was one in every hundred.)

West African Roots

The Portuguese took their slaves in the southern part of Africa (Angola) and even on the east coast. English and

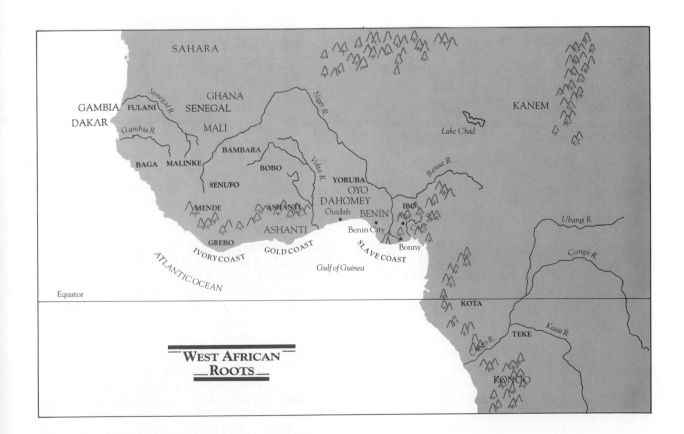

WEST AFRICAN ROOTS

American traders concentrated on the lands bordering the Gulf of Guinea, present-day Gambia, Senegal, Liberia, Ivory Coast, Ghana, Togo, Benin, and Nigeria.

Much of the coastline was mangrove swamp, but approximately a hundred miles inland the country pitched upward and provided a living that was rich enough to support a large population and a sophisticated culture. Until profits from the slave trade enabled the Ashanti Empire to extend its sway over a vast area in the late seventeenth century, there were few large domains in West Africa, but rather a great number of tribes speaking many languages and following a variety of customs. Most West Africans were polytheists who worshiped a complicated hierarchy of gods and spirits. Many tribes venerated the spirits of dead ancestors, and sacrifice was central to most religions. Islam and Christianity had made some headway, but since they were the faiths of the slavers, not very much.

West Africa was no Eden. The people who lived there were skillful agriculturists. Once the sweet potato was introduced in the sixteenth century, probably by Spanish or Portuguese slave traders, its cultivation spread so rapidly that it became the staple crop of much of the region. The West Africans' experience with intensive farming, as well as their sturdy physique, made them all the more appealing to American planters. In addition to rice cultivation, which Africans probably introduced to the Carolinas, the heavy hoe, which was the mainstay of chopping weeds in the fertile southern soil, was of African origin.

The Vulnerability of a Disunited People

There was no such person as a typical captive. Males might have been princes, priests, or criminals. Most likely, however, they were ordinary farmers who had the bad luck to cross the path of a raiding party. Most female slaves also came from the ordinary classes. Their status in Africa depended on the tribe to which they belonged. In most, women did a major part of the heavy labor. In other tribes, such as the Ashanti, descent was traced in the maternal line, and women were accorded high status.

Like the American Indians, the Africans were no technological match for Europeans. Superior weaponry and attractive trade goods made it easy for most slave traders to have their way. Also, as among the Indians, ancestral hatreds among African tribes made it easy for outsiders to manipulate the superior numbers of the natives. Not only was one tribe more than happy to sell its neighbors to the white men, but the divisions among the blacks were exploited to make them more manageable. "The safest way," wrote William Smith, who took part in an expedition of 1748, "is to trade with the different Nations, on either side of the River, and having some of every sort on board, there will be no more likelihood of their succeeding in a Plot, than of finishing the tower of Babel."

Once in the colonies, these diverse peoples adopted English as the only feasible means of communication among themselves. In time, they also found in their masters' Protestant religion a solace to their misery, albeit with a great deal of emphasis on the stories of the ancient Hebrews' captivities and deliverance. For the most part, however, they were shut out of the mainstream of American development for more than three centuries after the first African stepped nervously from the gangplank of the Dutch ship to the soil of Virginia.

For Further Reading

On the Indians of North America, see Alvin M. Josephy, Jr., *The Indian Heritage of America* (1968); Harold E. Driver, *Indians of North America* (1970); Wilcomb E. Washburn, *The Indian in America* (1975); Robert F. Spencer and Jesse D. Jennings et al., *The Native Americans: Ethnology and Backgrounds of the North American Indians* (1977). Of special interest are James Axtell, *The European and the Indian* (1981); Douglas Leach, *Flintlock and Tomahawk* (1958); Gary Nash, *Red, White, and Black: The Peoples of Early America* (1974); Neal Salisbury, *Manitou and Providence: Indians, Europeans, and the Making of New England* (1982); Richard Slotkin, *Regeneration Through Violence* (1973); Alden Vaughan, *New England Frontier: Puritans and Indians, 1620–1675* (1965); A. F. C. Wallace, *The Death and Rebirth of the Seneca* (1970).

A series of books by Francis Parkman more than a century old remain the finest works on French America: *The Pioneers of France in the New World* (1865); *The Jesuits in North America* (1867); *The Old Regime in Canada* (1874); *Count Frontenac and New France Under Louis XIV* (1877); and *LaSalle and the Discovery of the Great West* (1879). A fine single volume history of the subject is William J. Eccles, *France in America* (1972). Also valuable are Eccles, *The Canadian Frontier 1534–1760* (1969); Raphael N. Hamilton, *Marquette's Explorations*

(1970); Joseph P. Donnelly, *Jacques Marquette, S.J.* (1968); and Samuel Eliot Morison, *Samuel B. Champlain: Father of New France* (1972).

On indentured servitude and the evolution of African slavery in English America, see David W. Galenson, *White Servitude in Colonial America* (1981) and Edmund S. Morgan, *American Slavery, American Freedom* (1975). Winthrop D. Jordan, *White Over Black* (1968) presents a widely respected thesis concerning the background of white racism. Philip D. Curtin, *The Atlantic Slave Trade* (1969) has displaced all earlier studies of the subject. An invaluable overview is David B. Davis, *The Problem of Slavery in Western Culture* (1966). The early pages of Kenneth Stampp, *The Peculiar Institution* (1956) provide important information on the early days of slavery in Anglo-America. Among the best special studies are G. W. Mullin, *Flight and Rebellion* (1972) and T. H. Breen and Stephen Innes, *"Myne Owne Ground," Race and Freedom on Virginia's Eastern Shore* (1980).

General James Wolfe, informed of his victory at Quebec as he lay dying on the battlefield, 1759.

BRITISH AMERICA IN BLOOM
THE COLONIES IN THE EIGHTEENTH CENTURY

In 1706, a male child was born into the household of a Boston tallowmaker—that is, a craftsman who manufactured candles and soap from the fat of cattle and sheep. But there would not have been much excitement about the arrival of Benjamin Franklin. He was the tenth child in the family.

Large families were common in the colonies. The typical wife, who married in her early twenties, bore six to eight children, and a majority survived. Big families were economic assets rather than, as today, a luxury. Children consumed little and the necessities of life—food, clothing, and shelter—

were abundant and cheap. There was plenty of work to be done in the households of farmers, artisans, and shopkeepers and it began at a tender age. A child of five or six could feed chickens, gather eggs, fetch firewood. Adolescents, costly to a modern American family, contributed far more to a household's accounts than they took.

Benjamin Franklin went to work for his father at ten. At twelve, he was bound as an apprentice to his half-brother, a printer. They did not get along and Ben ran away to Philadelphia, but only after he had learned the mysteries of the trade.

In the eighteenth century, a printer was as much a writer as a setter of type, and Franklin's pen was nimble, imitating the elegant style of the popular English essayists Joseph Addison and Richard Steele. None faulted him for lack of originality. Colonials did not believe that Americans should write or paint or sculpt in a distinctively American way. Bostonians (and New Yorkers and Baltimoreans) were happy to be colonials. They were pleased to be the overseas subjects of a realm that they believed the most beneficent on earth. They gladly took their social customs and culture, as well as the manufactured goods they consumed, from the mother country.

During Ben Franklin's long life (he lived until 1790), British North America flowered, eventually outgrowing its dependent status and mentality. Franklin did not miss a turn on that long road. Was there a population explosion in the colonies? Franklin capitalized on it, financing his own apprentices in print shops. Was the population growing less English? Franklin knew what it meant (and did not like it); he lived in the colony with the most heterogeneous population. Did the wars of Europe transform the colonies into a force in international affairs? Franklin espoused an aggressive foreign policy and several times went to Europe as a lobbyist on behalf of American interests.

He was the best-known American of his time, respected at home, lionized in Europe. He founded libraries, learned societies, the first American hospital, and the first trained fire department. Devoted to social improvement, he was a scientist, a wit, and a celebrity who charmed countesses and ragamuffins alike. There was scarcely a major event or trend in the eighteenth century in which Franklin did not figure. He devised a scheme to unite the colonies as early as 1754, the Albany Plan of Union. He signed the Declaration of Independence and the Constitution. Slavery, which during his lifetime evolved from a minor aspect of colonial life into a matter of grave concern, did not escape Franklin's notice. The last public act of his life was to petition the American government to abolish the institution.

Benjamin Franklin (1706–1790) was as comfortable with princes as with artisans. He could discuss Enlightment science, politics, or the price of moveable type. He wrote banalities but also keen satire. There was no American— or European—quite like him in the eighteenth century.

SOCIETY AND ECONOMY

Between 1700 and 1776, colonial population increased tenfold, from about 250,000 people to about 2.5 million. Natural increase accounted for much of this astonishing growth. Both family size and life expectancy at birth were greater in North America than on any other continent. In rural New England, setting aside infants and women dying in first childbirth, life expectancy could be as high as it is today with all our precautions and medicine. The New England male who survived his first five years, and the female who bore children easily or never married, stood a good chance of surviving into their sixties and seventies. Colonials also married younger than their English cousins. Wives were newly pregnant every two or three years.

The colonies were also flooded with immigrants— perhaps 350,000 newcomers between 1700 and the War for Independence. The majority, but by no means all, were English.

Immigration from Germany

Germans and German-speaking Swiss and Austrians responded enthusiastically to William Penn's invitation that they take up farms in Pennsylvania. By the 1750s they were so numerous in Philadelphia, Lancaster, and York counties that Benjamin Franklin, who called the settlers "the most stupid of their nation," was alarmed. They will "Germanize us instead of Anglifying them," he wrote, "and will never adopt our Language or Customs." Indeed, Germans represented a third of Pennsylvania's population and, in 1776, it was proposed that German, not English, should be the official language of the newly independent state. The Declaration of Independence was first set into type in a German-American newspaper, *Wöchenliche Philadelphische Staatsnote*.

Many of the German immigrants were members of the plain-living Moravian, Amish, Mennonite, and Hutterite sects. Like the Quakers, they were pacifists and, having little interest in politics, they passively supported their benefactors. No doubt, their bloc voting annoyed Franklin, a member of Pennsylvania's anti-Quaker faction, as much as the sounds of German on the streets of Philadelphia.

The Scotch-Irish

Even more numerous than the Germans were the Scotch-Irish. These people were descendants of Protestant Scots whom James I had settled in northern Ireland to counter-balance the Catholic Irish. By the early 1700s, they had lost favor with the Crown and suffered from steep increases in rent and from parliamentary acts that undercut the weaving industry, on which many depended for their livelihood. About 4,000 Scotch-Irish

a year gave up on the Emerald Isle and emigrated to the colonies.

They were a combative people back home, ready with cudgels and pikes to combat papists, and they did not mellow in American air. James Logan, a Quaker and the agent of the Penn family in Philadelphia, wrote to England in consternation: "I must own, from my experience in the land office, that the settlement of five families from Ireland gives me more trouble than fifty of any other people."

The Scotch-Irish wanted land. To acquire it, they moved to the backcountry in Virginia and the Carolinas, as well as to western Pennsylvania. There they confronted potent Indian tribes, with which Quakers like Logan tried to have amicable relations. On this issue, these obstreperous frontiersmen helped drive the Quakers from public life.

The Retirement of the Quakers

Scotch-Irish frontiersmen often took Indian policy into their own hands. Far from the capital of Philadelphia, they attacked the Native Americans for good reason and bad. Franklin's anti-Quaker party generally supported them in the colonial assembly. When Britain and France

A view of a Moravian settlement in Bethlehem, Pennsylvania, 1757. Pennsylvania was home to a number of religious sects in the eighteenth century.

were at war, so did the Crown, for the tribes to the west of British America were allies of the French in Canada.

The dominant Quakers were sincere in their pacifism. But they were not immune to the advantages of political power nor oblivious to the conditions of retaining it during wartime. When the Crown requested money to fight the French, the Quakers accommodated by such contrivances as voting money "for the king's use." They preserved their pacifist consciences while not running afoul of a government at war.

But the aggressiveness of the Scotch-Irish frontiersmen presented the Quakers with a more difficult problem. If they clung to their principle that government should be responsive to popular wishes, they would be parties to carnage on the Pennsylvania frontier, a mockery of their pacifism. But if they insisted on peace and fair dealings with the Indians, they would deny the demands of the majority of Pennsylvanians, thus mocking their democratic notions.

By the end of the 1750s, most Quaker officeholders gave up wrestling with their consciences and retired from public life. Thus, they preserved their personal scruples while the backcountry settlers, Franklin's party, and the Crown got the aggressive policies that they desired.

Family

Whatever their national origin or religion, colonials assumed that the family was the basic social and economic institution. Early Puritan laws requiring all people, including bachelors, spinsters (unmarried women), infants, and the elderly to live within a household were long gone. But the practice survived: the "loner" was looked upon with suspicion.

The family, not the individual, was vested with political identity. Only the head of a property-owning household voted, no matter that there might be several adults living in the home. Property laws, inherited from England, were designed to maintain the family as the basic economic unit. Virginia, Maryland, and South Carolina enacted laws of primogeniture and entail. Primogeniture required that a landed estate be bequeathed as a unit to the eldest son of the deceased, or if there was no male heir, to his first daughter. Entail meant that a property could not be subdivided. A person who wanted to sell an estate had to sell it in one piece.

The purpose of these laws was to preserve the economic power and privileges of the wealthy. If a tobacco planter with a thousand acres and thirty slaves, enough to support a household in grand style, were free to divide his estate among four or five children, the result would be four or five households of middling size. If each of these properties were subdivided in the next generation, the result would be a community of struggling subsistence farmers where once there had been a grandee.

A class of people conscious of their social position wanted no such leveling. And the colonial rich, especially in the cities, grew richer during the eighteenth century. In 1700, the richest tenth of Philadelphia's population owned about 40 percent of the city's wealth. By 1774, the richest tenth owned 55 percent.

Social Mobility

Primogeniture did not mean that propertied people were insensitive to the fortunes of their daughters and younger sons. They provided for them by bequeathing them money (personal as opposed to real property) or land that was not part of an entailed estate. As in England, "second sons" might be educated to the ministry or another profession, which maintained their social standing without breaking up the family estate. Or, they might serve in the military.

For example, George Washington's older brother, Lawrence, inherited the family lands. He assisted George in training as a soldier and as a surveyor (which meant land speculator) in the hope he would found his own landed family. Washington also kept an eye peeled for an heiress or wealthy widow to marry, which he found in Martha Custis.

Daughters of the middle and upper classes were provided with dowries in order to attract husbands of means, or, at least, of the same social class. The woman who came into property as a daughter without brothers or as the widow of a man who had no direct male descendants—as did Martha Custis Washington—was likely to be deluged with proposals not many days after she buried her benefactor. The woman who wished to control her property required a strong will indeed to resist such pressure.

Women's Rights

Unmarried women could own property in their own right, thus enjoying the status of head of the household. (In law, such persons could vote, although the few instances when a lady tried to do so excited a good deal of comment.) Married women, however, lost control of the property they brought to marriage. The legal principle of coverture held that, in law, "husband and wife are one and that one the husband." A husband had the "use" of his wife's land and money. The married woman's economic welfare was guaranteed by laws reserving for her at least a third of her husband's property when he died.

Although the colonial woman's status was inferior to that of a man, she enjoyed a far more favorable situation than her cousins in Europe. In most colonies, husbands were not permitted to beat their wives. At least one man in Massachusetts was fined because he referred to his wife as "a servant"; that is, he demeaned her. Visitors from Europe frequently commented on the respect and deference colonial men paid women, and the protections women were provided by custom and law. In the old Puritan colonies, a woman could sue for divorce on the grounds of adultery, bigamy, desertion, impotence, incest, or absence of over seven years.

The Lower Orders

Laws pertaining to property and customs restraining behavior toward women had meaning only to the middle and upper classes. To people of the lower orders, scraping out an existence took precedence over such niceties.

In the countryside, poor farmers and propertyless wage workers were a potential source of disorder as in the days of Bacon's Rebellion. In the seaports, a marginal class of unskilled workers, roustabouts, ex-servants, sailors on leave, and plain derelicts congregated in disreputable quarters of the towns.

There was enough casual work to be done to keep them alive, but not enough compensation to generate a sense of belonging to the community or respect for conventional morals. Illegitimate births were common. Perhaps as many as a third of all births occurred outside marriage or in less than nine months after the wedding.

The colonial poor often mixed racially, and thereby earned the further contempt of their betters. "The crowd" they formed was kept under control by strict laws and erratic but no-nonsense law enforcement. Nevertheless, the crowd made its presence and wishes known

INDIGO

Indigofera tinctoria was the source of a brilliant, coveted, and expensive blue dye. By the eighteenth century, it was grown on a small scale in Montserrat and other islands of the West Indies. During the early 1740s, the plant was introduced into South Carolina by a remarkable woman, Eliza Lucas, the daughter of a West Indian planter who also owned land in South Carolina. Eliza was educated in England, almost unheard of for a woman of any social class, and her extraordinary father then entrusted her with the management of a South Carolina plantation.

In 1745, she married another rich planter, Charles Pinckney, but, in the meantime, she had imported West Indian slaves who knew how to grow and process *Indigofera tinctoria,* thus creating another cash crop that was invaluable in South Carolina.

Indigo brought a high price and a subsidy from Britain. It grew on high ground which rice growers had theretofore considered wasteland. Moreover, its growing season was precisely the opposite of that of rice, allowing planters owning huge work forces to keep their slaves busy the year around.

Thus, Eliza Lucas Pinckney's experiments made slaves doubly valuable in South Carolina, contributing to the fact that, a generation later, while Virginia's tobacco growers seriously considered abandoning slavery, South Carolina's slaveholders were hard-liners on the question. The South Carolina delegation to the Second Continental Congress insisted that a backhanded slap at slavery in the Declaration of Independence be deleted before they would sign.

in occasional "bread riots." The lower classes were to play a major part in the tumult that preceded the American Revolution. As with submerged peoples before and since, riot was their most accessible means of political expression, for they could not vote. Only about 20 percent of colonial adult males had that right.

Slave Rebellions

The lowliest of the lowly were the slaves. They were not numerous north of the Mason-Dixon line, the boundary between Pennsylvania and Maryland that was surveyed in 1769. Slaves represented only 8 percent of the population in Pennsylvania, 3 percent in Massachusetts. As early as the 1750s, Quakers John Woolman of New Jersey and Anthony Benezet of Pennsylvania condemned slavery as intrinsically immoral. (Benezet also wrote pamphlets on behalf of women and Indians.)

In the southern colonies, by way of contrast, slavery grew in importance. The number of blacks in Virginia, most of whom were slaves, increased from about 4,000 in 1700 to 42,000 in 1743, and to more than 200,000 at the time of the American Revolution. In some Virginia counties and over much of South Carolina, blacks outnumbered whites.

Now and then, slaves rebelled. In 1739, about twenty blacks from the Stono plantation near Charleston seized guns, killed several planter familes, and put out a call for an uprising. About 150 slaves joined them and "with Colours displayed, and two Drums beating," they began to march toward Florida where, they had learned, the Spanish would grant them freedom.

Most were captured within a week, but some managed to reach St. Augustine and settled to the north of the town in the fortified black village of Santa Teresa de Mose. They swore to "shed their last drop of blood in defense of the Great Crown of Spain, and to be the most cruel enemies of the English." The threat—or at least the attraction to other slaves—was great enough that, the next year, General Oglethorpe of Georgia attacked Santa Teresa.

The reverberations of the Stono rising reached as far north as New York. In the summer of 1741, with virtually no justification, 31 blacks and 4 whites were executed for plotting a rebellion.

WORLD WARS, COLONIAL WARS

The fabulous growth of the thirteen mainland colonies during the eighteenth century, coupled with the physical isolation from the mother country, ensured that so expansive and ever more confident a people as the Americans could not remain the tail on the British imperial lion. This is not to say that American independence was inevitable; however, some independence of interests and action was.

The colonists demonstrated this clearly between 1689 and 1763 when the mother country was involved in a series of worldwide wars. The Americans participated, or withheld participation, according to what they perceived to be their interests, as opposed to those of Great Britain.

Another Kind of War

By the beginning of the eighteenth century, Britain and France were possessed of far-flung and growing empires. Therefore, the European wars of 1689–1763 were also world wars. They were fought not only in Europe and North America, but also in the Caribbean, in South America, in India, and wherever ships flying belligerent flags met on the high seas.

There the resemblance to twentieth century wars ends. In the late seventeenth and the eighteenth centuries, war was considered an extension of diplomacy, the concern of rulers rather than of ordinary people. Wars were fought frankly to win or to defend territory or trade from rivals, or to avenge what one prince regarded as the insult of another. There was no clash of ideologies, no claim that one social, economic, or political system was engaged in a life-or-death struggle.

Armies were made up of professional soldiers, rough men for whom fighting was a means of making a living. Soldiers did not think at all that they were defending or furthering an abstract ideal. If they were attached to anything, it was to their comrades.

What did ordinary farmers, artisans, and shopkeepers have to do with such a business? As little as they could help. At best, war meant heavier taxation. At worst, people were unlucky enough to make their homes where armies fought or marched. Then they suffered, no matter whose flag the fighting men were waving.

Otherwise, ordinary people went on as in peacetime. Because princes neither expected, sought, nor won popular support for their wars, it was not a matter of treason in the modern sense of the word when, as in the world wars of 1689 to 1763, many Americans simply sat out the conflict or even continued trading with the French enemy.

King William's War, 1689–1697

The wars began when William of Orange, the ill-tempered ruler of the Netherlands, became king of England in 1689. To William, the colonies and even English domestic affairs mattered only to the extent that they affected his animosity toward the King of France, Louis XIV. William's life had been dedicated to preventing the expansion of France to the River Rhine.

William was a superb soldier. He had wrestled Louis

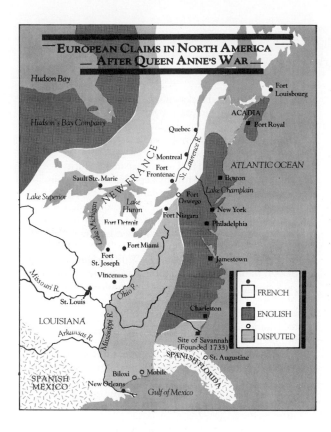

EUROPEAN CLAIMS IN NORTH AMERICA
AFTER QUEEN ANNE'S WAR

was traditional warfare, warning the colonials out of their traditional hunting grounds.

Petite guerre worked. Each successful raid moved the unmarked boundary between New France and New England deeper into lands that the colonials considered their own. More aggravating to the New England commercial elite were assaults on their merchant and fishing vessels by French ships out of Port Royal in Acadia (Nova Scotia). In 1690, an expedition from Massachusetts captured the French base, but in vain. By the terms of the Peace of Ryswick in 1697, the fortress was returned to France. The English armies had not fared well in the European theater, and the peacemakers gave up Port Royal in order to limit concessions to France at home. The New Englanders were reminded that their interests were subordinate to those of England in Europe, as interpreted, in this case, by a Dutchman.

Queen Anne's War, 1702–1713

In part because of pressures by their Indian allies, the French took North America more seriously. While King William's War was still in progress, they began to build a chain of forts in the backcountry. During the brief peace of 1697 to 1702, the Gulf of Mexico and Illinois country settlements were sketched in on French maps. Then, in 1700, the king of Spain died without an heir, and Louis XIV moved to place his grandson on the throne of the declining but still rich empire. Austria, where a dynasty related to the dead Spanish king still ruled, joined England to support another claimant.

Again, the colonists named the war after the reigning British sovereign, Queen Anne, but this time European dynastic squabbles were of more than casual interest to colonials in the far North and South. The same dynasty ruling both Spain and France meant the union of neighbors who previously had sniped at each other. This time around, Southerners, who had taken no part in King William's War, were in the thick of things.

Like the New Englanders, South Carolinians competed with the Spanish and French in the fur and hide trade. Beaver pelts were not so lush in the warm southern climate, but there were deer and bison, important sources of leather. The South Carolinian network of Indian contacts extended beyond the Mississippi River, well into territory that the French thought of as their own. However, the Carolinians had some formidable Indian enemies in what is now Georgia, Alabama, and Mississippi. Slave-catching expeditions among the Creek and Cherokee peoples kept the southwestern frontier in a state of chronic *petite guerre*.

In the North, the French and their Indian allies were more audacious than before, wiping out the substantial town of Deerfield, Massachusetts in 1704. Once again, however, the New Englanders captured Port Royal. This time, at the Peace of Utrecht in 1713, the British kept

XIV to the mat with the limited resources of the Dutch and a few German princelings. He could not wait to turn the greater wealth and power of England on the hated foe. In 1689, he got his chance. Louis XIV claimed the right to take possession of a small but valuable province on the River Rhine.

Few Americans (let alone Indians) cared who ruled there, or who became archbishop of Cologne (another matter over which Louis and William squabbled). Unconsciously, but with a certain elegance, they proclaimed their disdain for the war that the dispute caused by ignoring Europe's name for the conflict, the War of the League of Augsburg. In America, the war was called King William's War, as though it had been foisted on the colonies by an outsider.

In North America, French, Algonkians, and Hurons struck the first blow in the winter of 1689–1690 with a series of raids on frontier settlements in New York, New Hampshire, and Maine (then part of Massachusetts). These were not great battles on the European pattern. Although often led by French officers, they were Indian-style attacks in which a few dozen warriors hit without warning at isolated farms in the forest, killing or capturing the settlers and burning houses and fields. The French called it *petite guerre*, "little war," and viewed the raids as harassment and as a warning. To the Indians, it

NOTABLE PEOPLE

WILLIAM BYRD (1674–1744)

William Byrd of Westover was born in Virginia in 1674. He had the good luck to come into his maturity just as the plantation aristocracy was entering its golden age. Indeed, the historian Louis B. Wright called Byrd "the Great American Gentleman" because his life epitomized the elegance and culture of his class. In his famous portrait, Byrd looks more like a duke than a rude colonial.

Byrd loved the social whirl of London. He was educated in Holland and in England, at the Inns of Court, and, rather remarkable for the time, made several trips back to the mother country as a lobbyist for the Virginia colony. He appears to have been a bit bored by the quiet life of the New World.

Like most planters, Byrd chased after riches. During one long sojourn in London, he tried unsuccessfully to find a wealthy wife. One nobleman rejected his request to marry his daughter by sneering that her annual income was more than the Virginian's entire fortune. There was a big difference between being rich in England and rich in America.

And yet, few English owned the empire in land that Byrd amassed. He inherited 26,321 acres in 1704 and possessed 179,000 acres when he died in 1744. Most of this was wilderness, a speculation on the future, but huge tracts were planted in tobacco and food crops. William Byrd presided over a small kingdom of servants and slaves.

How did such a grandee spend his day? He awakened with the sun but stayed in bed to eat a small breakfast brought by a servant. Much more bookish than most planters, Byrd read for an hour or two in one of the six languages he knew (Hebrew, Greek, Latin, French, Dutch, and English). When he rose, he did some calisthenics ("I danced my dance"). Then his day varied according to circumstances and the season.

Byrd would often have guests to entertain. In a country with few towns and fewer inns, a gentleman like Byrd provided hospitality for travelers. Ordinary people were treated as such; they were provided some sort of roof and simple food for a day or two. Gentlemen and ladies, however, stayed in the plantation house and were feted at banquet-sized meals for as long as they chose. Living in isolation, cultured and sociable people like Byrd craved company. On a plantation that produced more than enough food for master and servant, the expense of wholesale entertainment was hardly noticed.

When there were no guests (and Byrd was not visiting someone else), there was plenty of work to be done. Although a grand gentleman did not labor in the fields, he was no idler. Managing thousands of acres and hundreds of people required nearly constant attention. A plantation was a delicately integrated community that was involved in the cultivating, processing, and storing of food,

some manufacturing, blacksmith work, and barrelmaking, for example. Other planters of Byrd's class took greater interest than he did in account books and the mechanics of agriculture. But no one responsible for such an operation could escape endless duties.

Indeed, William Byrd had to oversee many of the household functions that usually kept the planter's wife busy from daybreak to long after dark. His first wife, Lucy Park, was a poor housekeeper. She and Byrd frequently quarreled about her management of the kitchen and larder, and he complained to his diary when he had to supervise the bottling of wine.

Byrd regularly rode and boated to Williamsburg. A gentleman in his position had interests to protect, and he was, at various times, a member of the House of Burgesses and the Governor's Council. In the capital, he roomed at a tavern. During the afternoon and early evening he conducted business, after which he and his cronies regularly got drunk. Every morning he vowed to break out of the cycle but only occasionally kept his word. There were few diversions in the sleepy town but dining, drinking, and chatting.

Byrd was something of a roué, but, oddly, otherwise practiced strict moderation. Virginia's abundance produced such a variety of fine foods that meals were huge, delicious, and long. Through most of his life, however, Byrd shunned gluttony. He practiced a strict regimen designed by a fashionable Scottish physician, George Cheyne, who made a handsome living by prescribing "fad diets" to the wealthy of London and of the resort city of Bath. Byrd adopted two of these regimens: the "milk diet" and the recommendation that a person eat only one dish at a meal. Thus, while his dinner companions were stuffing themselves with as many as seven or eight kinds of meat (the typical fare at a wealthy house), Byrd ate only one. Like a contemporary "Weight Watcher," he kept a written record of every morsel he consumed.

Life in London, in Williamsburg, and at Westover was comfortable, but no Virginian was ever far from the outdoors. In 1728, Byrd helped command an expedition that surveyed the "dividing line" between Virginia and North Carolina, a route which took him into the Great Dismal Swamp. There, without complaint, he slept on the sodden ground and lived off game like any pioneer. He described the expedition and the way of life of the occasional settler the surveyors met. He told of people ailing with malaria and other diseases, drinking themselves to death with cheap, sometimes poisonous rum, and scraping hour by hour for their food. It is difficult to imagine a more striking contrast with his own lot in life, but, while witty in depicting these early-day "poor whites," Byrd was never surprised. The grandest of the great American gentlemen were not insulated from the harsher realities of life.

it and the whole of Acadia. The war had gone well for England in Europe and the French were forced to retire to Cape Breton Island and build a new and stronger Atlantic fortress, Louisbourg.

In the South, the treaty resolved few difficulties for the simple reason that no European nation held the trump card there. The Creek and Cherokee nations were large, confident, and proud. They were far less dependent on Europeans than were the Algonkians and Hurons of the North, in part because they had selectively adopted the ways of the whites. The southern tribes took easily to European agricultural techniques and even to the use of slave labor (although many Africans became full members of the nations). They would not finally fall before white expansion for more than a century after Queen Anne's War.

In the Middle Colonies, there were no difficulties to be resolved by the negotiators of the Peace of Utrecht. Virginia, Maryland, Delaware, New Jersey, and Pennsylvania had not taken part in Queen Anne's War. New York actually issued a formal declaration of neutrality and continued to trade with French Canada during the years in which the New England colonists were the victims of bloody raids.

THE LONG PEACE, 1713–1739

For 26 years after 1713, North America was at peace, and they were generally prosperous years for the colonies. While tobacco never sold for the bonanza prices of the mid-1600s, the weed returned handsome enough profits to large planters. Rice, naval stores, and hides and furs were lucrative. And ships' masters of the New England and Middle Colonies plied both old and new sea routes. In troubled times to come, colonists with historical memories would look back on "the long peace" as a kind of golden age.

Salutary Neglect

The vision of a golden age was wrapped up in a parcel with the colonial policy of the first British prime minister, Robert Walpole. By disposition a lazy, easygoing fellow who fancied his daily outsized bottle of port wine and idle gossip with other comfortable gentlemen, Walpole believed that the best way to govern a country or an empire during good times was to govern as little as

A French and Indian raid wiped out the town of Deerfield, Massachusetts, in 1704.

possible. Action only disturbed what was working quite well on its own.

Walpole's policy came to be called "salutary neglect." If the colonists were content, bustling, and prosperous, he believed, thus enriching the English merchant class as it was their role on earth to do, it was salutary—healthful—not to disturb things.

For the most part, therefore, Walpole winked at colonial violations of the Navigation Acts. Only when interest groups that suffered from his inaction complained did he appear to take notice. Even then, Walpole's strategy was splendidly neglectful. He would ask Parliament to satisfy complaints and immediately forget about its enactment. For example, in 1732, London hat makers complained that the growth of hat-making in the northern colonies was hurting their business in North America. Walpole obliged the British hatters by saddling colonial hat makers with various restrictions. They were not to sell their wares outside the boundaries of their own colonies, nor to train blacks in the craft. London's hatters were happy. American hat makers ignored the law, and colonial officials enforced it only now and then.

The Molasses Act

The Molasses Act of 1733 was enacted in response to the complaints of the sugar planters of the British West Indies that Americans were buying molasses from French islands, where it was cheaper. They pointed out that the principles of mercantilism entitled them to a monopoly of the huge molasses market in New England, just as the tobacco growers of Virginia and Maryland had a monopoly in the sale of that product within the Empire. Therefore, they demanded that Walpole place a tax on foreign molasses.

Such a law was bound to rile the New Englanders. Rum, distilled from blackstrap molasses, was the common man's liquor in the colonies and was also valuable in the slave trade. New England traders were accustomed to filling the holds of their ships with the cheaper French molasses. Walpole solved the problem by approving the Molasses Act of 1733 and promptly forgetting about it. The West Indian planters were placated, if not particularly helped. New England shipmasters were as content to buy French molasses illegally as legally. The bootleg product was either smuggled into Boston and other ports or provided with false invoices stating that the cargo came from British Jamaica or Barbados. Colonial customs officers were not fooled by the phoney documents, but they could be bribed; and if a penny or so on each barrel made them happy too, that was the idea of salutary neglect.

Another law that was ignored in the interests of prosperity and calm was passed in 1750 at the behest of English ironmakers, who wanted a monopoly of the co-

ESTIMATED POPULATIONS OF FIVE LEADING PORT CITIES: 1630–1775					
Year	New York	Philadelphia	Boston	Charleston	Newport
1630	300	—	—	—	—
1640	400	—	1,200	—	96
1650	1,000	—	2,000	—	300
1660	2,400	—	3,000	—	700
1680	3,200	—	4,500	700	2,500
1690	3,900	4,000	7,000	1,100	2,600
1700	5,000	5,000	6,700	2,000	2,600
1710	5,700	6,500	9,000	3,000	2,800
1720	7,000	10,000	12,000	3,500	3,800
1730	8,622[a]	11,500	13,000	4,500	4,640[a]
1743	11,000	13,000	16,382[a]	6,800	6,200
1760	18,000	23,750	15,631[a]	8,000	7,500
1775	25,000	40,000	16,000	12,000	11,000
[a] Actual census.					

lonial market in iron goods. The act forbade colonists to engage in most forms of iron manufacture. But not only did colonial forges continue to operate with impunity, several colonial governments actually subsidized the iron industry within their borders. Salutary neglect was a wonderful way to run an empire—so long as there was no war and times were good.

Political Autonomy

An unintended consequence of Walpole's easygoing colonial policy was the steady erosion of the mother country's political control over her American daughters. In part, the seizure of the governors' powers by colonial assemblies merely reflected what was going on in England at the same time. During the eighteenth century, Parliament assumed governmental functions formerly exercised by the kings and queens. In the colonies, elected assemblies took powers from the governors, who were appointed by either the monarch or proprietors.

The key to this important shift in the structure of government was the English political principle that the people, through their elected representatives, must consent to all tax laws. In England, Parliament held the power of the purse; all money bills had to be approved by the House of Commons. In the colonies, the elected assemblies—whether called the House of Burgesses or the House of Delegates or whatever—owned this important prerogative.

Theoretically, the governor of a colony could veto any budget bill that he did not like. But to do so was risky. An assembly that was determined to have its way could retaliate by denying the governor the funds that he needed in order to operate his office and even his personal household, "starve him into compliance" as a hungry royal governor of New York phrased it in 1741.

Men on the Move, Men in the Middle

The power of the purse was a formidable weapon. Few men who served as governors in America were particularly wealthy before they took the job. Englishmen who were rich enough to maintain themselves opulently in London did not choose to live in Boston, Williamsburg, or Savannah. Most of the royal and proprietary governors were men on the make and, to make money in the colonies, they had to get along with powerful colonials, the men who were elected to seats in the assemblies.

Of course, it was possible to get along too well with influential Americans, to yield too much, and to earn the displeasure of the Crown or proprietor. But during the era of salutary neglect, it came easily for governors to cooperate. As long as the quitrents flowed back to England, a governor was doing the important part of his job.

Religious Developments

Religious developments also reflected Britain's policy of neglect. While toleration had been the rule in the colonies after the collapse of Puritan power in New England in the 1690s, religious regimentation virtually disappeared during the Walpole era.

Except in Rhode Island and Pennsylvania, every colonial was required to contribute to the support of the legally established church. In some colonies, members of other denominations were not allowed to vote, serve on juries, or exercise other civil rights. For example, Catholics were penalized in Maryland and North Carolina.

But rarely did authorities interfere with worship. In this atmosphere, one of the peculiarities of American society to this day took root: the bewildering multiplicity of religious denominations. Already by mid-century, it was not uncommon for modest villages to support two or three meeting houses close enough to one another that the congregations might have harmonized their hymns. During the 1740s, religions divided along yet finer lines, and another distinctively American institution, the revival, was born.

The Great Awakening

The first American revival, the Great Awakening, broke out almost simultaneously in several colonies. The towering figure of the movement was the Reverend Jonathan Edwards of Northampton, Massachusetts. In 1734, Edwards began to preach sermons emphasizing the sinfulness of humanity, the torment everyone deserved to suffer in hell, and the doctrine of salvation only through the grace of God. "The God who holds you over the pit of hell," Edwards preached in his most famous sermon, "much as one holds a spider or some loathsome insect over the fire, abhors you, and is dreadfully provoked."

SINNERS

In the Hands of an

Angry GOD.

A SERMON

Preached at *Enfield*, *July* 8th 1 7 4 1.

At a Time of great Awakenings ; and attended with remarkable Impreſſions on many of the Hearers.

By *Jonathan Edwards*, A.M.

Paſtor of the Church of CHRIST in *Northampton*.

Amos ix. 2, 3. *Though they dig into Hell, thence ſhall mine Hand take them ; though they climb up to Heaven, thence will I bring them down. And though they hide themſelves in the Top of Carmel, I will ſearch and take them out thence ; and though they be hid from my Sight in the Bottom of the Sea, thence I will command the Serpent, and he ſhall bite them.*

B O S T O N : Printed and Sold by S. KNEELAND and T. GREEN. in Queen-Street over againſt the Priſon. 1 7 4 1.

The sermons of Jonathan Edwards helped fuel the Great Awakening.

This was good Calvinist doctrine. In one sense, Edwards was simply preaching the old time religion of early Massachusetts. However, whereas the Puritans closely scrutinized the claims of every man and woman who said they had been saved, Edwards was inclined to admit to the fold everyone who displayed the physical, highly emotional signs of being visited by the Holy Spirit.

Revivals were aimed at stimulating this trauma of salvation. People broke down weeping, fainting, frothing at the mouth, shrieking, and rolling about the floors. Many had to be restrained lest they injure themselves. Edwards himself took care not to inspire false conversions by refraining from theatrical arm waving and dancing about. It was said that he stared at the bellpull at the entrance to his church rather than incite ungodly hysteria.

But other revivalists had less integrity—or less good sense. Demagogic preachers tore their clothes and rolled their eyes like lunatics, pranced and danced about pulpit or platform, and whooped and hollered. They devised a large bag of psychological tricks to arouse their audiences to a state of high excitement, which virtually became the purpose of the revival.

A Groping for Equality

The Great Awakening affected all social classes, but revivalism appealed most to the poorest, least privileged people. The intense emotion of the revival meeting offered a moment's release from the struggle to survive on the margins of society. The assurance of happiness in the hereafter compensated for deprivation in the here and now. The emphasis on the equality of all men and women before God rendered society's disdain for the unsuccessful more bearable.

Equality was the message of the farthest ranging of the Awakening's ministers, English-born George White-field. Traveling tirelessly throughout the colonies, Whitefield often preached for 60 hours a week. During one 78-day period, he delivered more than a hundred *lengthy* sermons reeking of hell's sulphur and exhortations to accept God.

The teachings of the Great Awakening about salvation bore some resemblance to those of Anne Hutchinson a hundred years earlier. The college education of traditional ministers counted for nothing compared to the man who preached with the hand of God on his shoulder. But while the civil authority was ready and able to clamp down on Hutchinson, the freer atmosphere of the eighteenth century permitted the revivalist message to burn over the colonies.

Oddly, given the anti-intellectual bias of revivalism, the Great Awakening led to the foundation of a number of "New Light" colleges. On the grounds that the established institutions of learning, such as Harvard and Yale, were dominated by "dry husks," the College of New Jersey (Princeton) was founded in 1746—Jonathan Edwards was its third president—and Dartmouth in New Hampshire in 1769. Other new colleges, such as Brown in Rhode Island, King's College (Columbia) in New York, and Queen's College (Rutgers) in New Jersey, were founded by the "Old Lights" to defend against the new preaching, which they regarded as ignorant and a threat to the established order.

Of all the colonial-era colleges and universities, only the University of Pennsylvania, chartered at Benjamin Franklin's urging in 1751, was without a religious affiliation.

The Age of Enlightenment

Franklin was a member of no church. Indeed, while Americans of modest means were turning to emotional religion, Franklin and much of the educated upper class were adopting the world view of the European Enlight-enment, the belief that human reason by itself, without any revelation from the heavens, could unlock the secrets of the universe and guide the improvement, even the perfection, of humanity and society.

The origins of eighteenth-century rationalism lay in the discoveries of the English scientist Sir Isaac Newton, especially those published in his *Principia Mathematica* (1687) and *Opticks* (1704). In these highly technical and difficult books, Newton showed that forces as mysterious as those that determined the paths of the planets and the properties of light and color worked according to laws that could be reduced to mathematical equations.

Although Newton was a physicist and mathematician (and his personal religion was rather mystical), the impact of the rationalism he taught was felt in practically every field of human knowledge and art— the pure sciences, economics, music, politics, religion, and even war.

The order and symmetry that Newton found in the universe were translated into architecture by strict laws of proportion and in literature into inflexible "classical" rules of style and structure. Baroque music explored the multitudinous variations that could be played on simple combinations of notes.

Philosophers likened the universe to a clock—intricate, but understandable when dismantled and its parts examined rationally. God, according to deism, as the rationalists called their religious belief, did not intervene in the world of nature. Rather, like a clockmaker, he had set the natural world in motion according to laws that human beings could discover and understand, whence he retired to allow his creatures to exercise their precious reason. The educated members of the last generation of colonial Americans were to some degree partisans of this rationalism.

THE WARS RESUME

In 1739, Great Britain went to war with Spain. For a year, the conflict was known as the War of Jenkins' Ear because Parliament was said to have become enraged when a shipmaster named Robert Jenkins arrived in London with his ear in a box. It had, Jenkins said, showing the souvenir to anyone who asked and many who did not, been savagely separated from his head by Spanish customs officials.

Georgians, South Carolinians, and Virginians were involved in the earliest fighting, and not because of any sympathy for the disfigured Jenkins. As they expanded into the interior, they had increasingly clashed with the Spanish. Colonial Southerners were the majority of the force that assaulted the black fortress village of Santa Teresa de Mose in 1740 and, the next year, a disastrous

THE WARS RESUME 95

attack on the port of Cartagena in Colombia. Of the 1,500 who set out, only 600 escaped the cutlasses of the Spanish, the incompetence of the British commanders, and the tropical diseases of the Spanish Main.

One survivor was Lawrence Washington, the brother of then nine-year-old George Washington. Not as bitter as many of his fellows, Lawrence named his estate Mount Vernon, after his British commander, Admiral Edward Vernon.

King George's War, 1740–1748

By the time Lawrence returned to Virginia, the great powers of Europe were again on the march. The eight-year conflict that began in 1740 is known in world history as the War of the Austrian Succession. For the colonists once again, it did not matter much who wore the crown of the remote Austrian Empire. They called their theater of the conflict King George's War.

Petite guerre flickered once more on the frontiers of New England, this time extending into New York. But there was no repetition of the Deerfield disaster. Much better prepared than previously, a force of 4,000 men, mostly from Massachusetts, besieged the great French fortress at Louisbourg. On June 17, 1745, the French commander surrendered.

This was a glorious victory. Louisbourg was considered impregnable, "the Gibraltar of North America." As the base from which French privateers operated, the fortress was an ominous presence looming over New England merchants and fishermen. But, again, the American celebration was short-lived. Under the terms of the Treaty of Aix-la-Chapelle, Louisbourg was returned to the French. The British had lost Madras in India to a French-led army and traded Louisbourg for its return.

Parliament reimbursed Massachusetts for the expense of the campaign. But this could not make up for the 500 men who lost their lives on Cape Breton Island, nor for the fact that the French raiders were restored to their sanctuary. The protest was mild. The colonists were loyal British subjects. Still, British nullification of the greatest military victory that Americans had ever won rankled in many breasts.

The Struggle for a Continent

The world war that broke out in 1756 was somewhat different from those that preceded it. There was a diplomatic revolution in Europe, with Austria, previously England's ally, joining forces with France. England then formed an alliance with its old enemy Prussia. To the colonists, it made no difference who killed whom in the Old World, or which European prince got money from Great Britain to fight. In North America, it was still the English and the colonists versus the French and their Indian allies.

For the first time, the Middle Colonies participated in the struggle. (It was during this war that the Quakers turned over the government of Pennsylvania to the pro-war party.) And once again, the colonists had their own name for the conflict. What became known as the Seven Years' War in Europe was called the French and Indian War in America.

This time, Britain would not return North American fortresses for territory on the other side of the globe. From the beginning, the Crown made it clear that a major object of the war was to drive France out of North America for all time.

Despite their usual success at petite guerre, the French were in a perilous situation. There were only about 50,000 whites in all of French-claimed territory, compared with 1.2 million in the thirteen English colonies plus Nova Scotia. The French still claimed the goodwill of the majority of Indians in the region, but even this advantage was partially nullified by the efficiency and fierceness of the pro-British Iroquois.

For the first time since the long series of wars began, the largest English colony, Virginia, took a serious interest in the fighting. The Virginians were beginning to look beyond the Appalachian Mountains and north of the Ohio River to lands that were dominated by Algonkian Indians. This country was particularly attractive to the wealthy tobacco planters who dominated the Old Dominion because a combination of exhausted soil and a glut in the international tobacco market was undercutting their income. They saw speculation in Ohio Valley real estate as the likeliest means of restoring their fortunes.

Humiliations on the Frontier

With the heart of New France thinly populated, the French had little interest in cultivating the Ohio Valley. But the country was of vital interest to French trappers and France's Indian allies. As early as 1753, in order to placate them, the French began to lay out a string of forts in what is now western Pennsylvania.

Robert Dinwiddie, the governor of Virginia, responded by sending 22-year-old George Washington to inform the French that they were trespassing on Virginian soil. Accompanied by 150 men, Washington was also instructed to construct a fort where the Allegheny and Monongahela rivers join to form the Ohio (the site of present-day Pittsburgh). Washington never got that far. He was handily defeated by the French in an almost bloodless battle. The French seized the strategic site, calling the stockade they built Fort Duquesne.

Washington was released, and he returned to Virginia to accept a commission under the command of General Edward Braddock. From the first, things went poorly. Braddock, an arrogant, stubborn, and unimaginative soldier, was roundly defeated and killed in 1755 in the

George Washington in a uniform of the French and Indian War, 1772.

Pennsylvania forests. The rout of Braddock's forces left the American frontier vulnerable to raiding fiercer than any since the destruction of Deerfield. The French were also winning in Europe and India. For the British, it was a dismal hour.

Germ Warfare and Refugees

For those at the mercy of the British, it was even worse. Both General Braddock and the supreme commander of British forces in North America, Sir Jeffrey Amherst, employed a primitive form of germ warfare against the Indians. They saw to it that blankets used by smallpox victims fell into the natives' hands. The results were catastrophic.

In Nova Scotia, the British feared that the French farmers and fishermen who were the majority in the province would rise in rebellion against the stronghold at Halifax. To forestall such a revolt, they launched a mass deportation. Thousands of Acadians—*Acadie* was the French name for Nova Scotia—were forced aboard ship and dispersed throughout the other English colonies from Massachusetts to Georgia and the West Indies. A few managed to make their way back home overland. Others found a haven in the French territory of Louisiana where their descendants still form a distinct ethnic and cultural group in the state of Louisiana, the Cajuns (a corruption of *Acadiens*).

Pitt and Wolfe

When it appeared the French would win the war, perhaps regaining all of Nova Scotia, two men appeared on

the scene to change the course of North American history. William Pitt became prime minister of Great Britain in 1757, and he selected the young General James Wolfe to join Sir Jeffrey Amherst's army in North America. Pitt turned the war around by leaving the fighting in Europe to Prussia while concentrating Britain's power across the Atlantic. Wolfe engineered one of the most daring attacks on a city in military history.

A nervous, frail-looking young man, so intense that his colleagues thought him insane, Wolfe looked at French Canada as a woodsman eyes a tree. He saw Quebec City as the root structure that supported the whole. The St. Lawrence and Ohio-Mississippi Rivers were but trunks and branches. It was all very well to snip and hack at leaves here and there, as Wolfe conceived of *petite guerre* and even the capture of Louisbourg. The secret to a total victory over French Canada was to strike at the source of its life.

The theory was easier than its practical application. Quebec stood atop a steep, rocky cliff. On September 12, 1759, after leading several futile frontal attacks on this natural fortress (his failures lulled the French commander, Louis de Montcalm, into overconfidence), Wolfe quietly led 4,000 troops up a steep, narrow trail under cover of night. When the sun rose over the Plains of Abraham, a broad prairie on the undefended landward side of Quebec, Montcalm saw a scarlet-coated army in full battle formation.

The Glorious Victory

It was a risky as well as a daring gambit. Wolfe had no avenue of retreat—a violation of the military canon. If the battle did not end in total triumph (and few military victories were total in the eighteenth century), Wolfe's whole army would be destroyed. Perhaps James Wolfe was crazy? If so, Louis de Montcalm was so unnerved by his madness that, despite his superior position and artillery, he joined in battle with little preparation. After a single close-range exchange of musket fire, Montcalm lost his life and with it the French empire in America. Wolfe did not live to savor his triumph—he, too, died on the battlefield.

The war in Europe dragged on until 1763, but, as far as the colonists were concerned, it was over at Quebec. In the Peace of Paris, the British redrew the map of North America. Great Britain took Florida from Spain as well as Canada from France. In order to compensate Spain for the loss of Florida, France handed over Louisiana (the central third of what is now the United States) to the Spanish.

The year 1763 saw the first British Empire in full bloom. Britain had elected to find its future outside the European continent and had succeeded on every front. Or so it seemed.

The Granger Collection

William Pitt, the British prime minister, assigned General James Wolfe the task of capturing the French city of Quebec. Wolfe launched a bold surprise attack, and his troops captured the city. However, Wolfe died in the battle.

For Further Reading

On relations with the mother country, see two old chestnuts by George L. Beer, still valuable, *The British Colonial System* (1908) and *The Old Colonial System* (1912); Daniel Boorstin, *The Americans: The Colonial Experience* (1958); Eli Hecksher, *Mercantilism* (1935); Richard Hofstadter, *America at 1750* (1971); Leonard W. Labaree, *Royal Government in America* (1930); James Henretta, *Salutary Neglect* (1972); and Stephen Webb, *The Governors-General* (1979). Absolutely essential is Bernard Bailyn, *The Origins of American Politics* (1968).

On the Anglo-French wars, the great Francis Parkman is again the historian of first resort in his *A Half Century of Conflict* (1892) and *Montcalm and Wolfe* (1884). Then move on to Howard H. Peckham, *The Colonial Wars, 1689-1762* (1964); Douglas E. Leach, *Arms for Empire: A Military History of the British Colonies in North America* (1973); and Fred Anderson, *A People's Army: Massachusetts Soldiers and Society in the Seven Years' War* (1984).

On the Indian role in the conflicts, see Francis Jennings, *Empire of Fortune* (1990) and James Merrell, *Beyond the Covenant Chain: The Iroquois and Their Neighbors* (1987).

On cultural developments, see Louis B. Wright, *Cultural Life of the American Colonies* (1957); Alan Heimert and Perry Miller, eds., *The Great Awakening* (1967); Perry Miller, *Jonathan Edwards* (1958); Edwin S. Gaustad, *The Great Awakening in New England* (1957); Henry F. May, *The Enlightenment in America* (1976); Benjamin Franklin's autobiography (various editions); and Carl Van Doren, *Benjamin Franklin* (1938).

Colonial social history has been a field of busy endeavor in recent years. Most of this work is to be found in scholarly journals, but see James Axtell, *The School Upon a Hill* (1974); James T. Lemon, *The Best Poor Man's Country* (1972); James G. Leyburn, *The Scotch-Irish* (1962); and Robert W. Wells, *The Population of the British Colonies in America Before 1776* (1975).

"The Bloody Massacre," an engraving by the agitator Paul Revere, designed to enflame anti-British feelings in the colonies

7

YEARS OF TUMULT

THE QUARREL WITH THE MOTHER COUNTRY
1763 - 1770

In 1763, church bells pealed throughout the thirteen colonies to celebrate Britain's triumph in the

Seven Years War. Muskets were fired, barrels of cider tapped. Surely, there had never been a moment

when to be a British subject was sweeter. In 1776, however, a scant thirteen years later, the thirteen

colonies declared their independence and took up arms against the mother country. Contemplating

this remarkable turn of events, Oliver Wolcott of Connecticut wondered rhetorically what had gone

wrong. "So strong had been the Attachment" of Americans to Great Britain in 1763, Wolcott wrote, that "the Abilities of a Child might have governed this Country."

Wolcott blamed the rupture on British folly, incompetence, and tyranny. He had a point about folly and incompetence. Blunder after stupidity atop miscalculation characterized British colonial policy between 1763 and 1776. But it would be a mistake, given the education in tyranny that the twentieth century has provided us, to accept Wolcott's third explanation of the American Revolution. Far from tyrannized, colonial Americans may have been the world's freest people between 1763 and 1776.

What worried men like Wolcott was a shift in British imperial administration that departed from the salutory neglect of the Walpole era. What made it possible for colonials to translate their worry into anger and rebellion was the self-confidence born of the colonies' extraordinary growth during the eighteenth century.

THE PROBLEMS OF EMPIRE

General Wolfe's capture of Quebec City put Canada in British hands. However, before the peace negotiators sat down in Paris in 1763, there was a question as to whether or not the British would keep Wolfe's prize. Some diplomats proposed that, like Port Royal and Louisbourg after earlier wars, Quebec and Canada be returned to France. Instead, Britain would take as the fruits of her victory the French sugar islands of Martinique and Guadaloupe.

One Side of the Story

A land of endless mosquito-infested forests was not so grand an imperial prize, so one argument went. Moreover, the native peoples of Canada and the trans-Appalachian West—former French allies—were numerous, powerful, and suspicious of Great Britain. As for the *habitants* of the St. Lawrence valley, Britain had recently expelled French peasants from Nova Scotia for fear of rebellion. What sense did it make, a few years after that scare, to take 50,000 French Canadians into the empire?

The sugar islands, by way of contrast, could be managed by small military garrisons. The handful of planters that dominated Guadaloupe and Martinique cared less about the color of the flag that flew over the harbor than about the price of their crop. And that crop could be sold profitably throughout the world. Sugar was the crude oil of the eighteenth century.

There was yet another consideration. By 1763, the thirteen colonies constituted a substantial country in themselves. Was it not possible that the colonials had remained loyal Britons only out of fear of French and Indian attack? Remove that threat from their back yard, as the acquisition of Canada would do, and the Americans would no longer need British naval and military protection, nor be grateful for it. They might unite, in the words of a Swedish observer, Peter Kalm, and "shake off the yoke of the English monarchy."

All That Red on the Map!

These arguments did not carry the day. British taxpayers were weary of war, and if Canada remained French, another North American conflict was inevitable. Influential colonials like Governor William Shirley of Massachusetts and Benjamin Franklin, then in England as an agent of Pennsylvania, spoke lyrically of the potential of the vast Canadian land mass.

Such lobbyists found unexpected allies in the sugar planters of the British West Indies. This small but influential group feared that raising the Union Jack over Martinique and Guadaloupe would glut the imperial sugar market, driving down the price of their commodity. The British planters also relished the idea of adding 50,000 sweet-toothed Canadians to their list of customers.

And, in the end, few Britons seriously doubted the loyalty of the Americans. In 1763, it was difficult to imagine that anyone who had the choice would choose to be anything but British.

Les Canadiens

The French Canadians could imagine otherwise. For one thing, they were Roman Catholics, pious communicants of a faith that was disliked and discriminated against in eighteenth-century Britain. Catholics were generally unmolested in the thirteen colonies. But there was a big difference between tolerating a small, quiet, and largely genteel Roman Catholic minority in Maryland, and coming to terms with a universally Catholic province. To Protestants, particularly the descendants of the Puritans, who were Quebec's closest neighbors, Catholicism meant superstition, blasphemy, and oppression.

Nor was the precedent of Britons governing foreigners encouraging. For two centuries, Catholic Ireland had been an English province. Avaricious conquerors (including several men who had been interested in American land) had resorted to unspeakable atrocities in order to create estates and reduce the Irish to submission. Their descendants, the Anglo-Irish gentry, looked on the Irish peasantry as lazy, superstitious, and barbaric, not to mention prone to intermittent rebellion.

As in Ireland, however, the British held the military trump card in Canada. Moreover, the *Canadiens* had no experience with representative government, no inclination to pelt the Crown with protests and supplications as the assemblies of the thirteen colonies did. The Estates General, the French equivalent of Parliament, had not met since 1614. At home, the Bourbon king was an absolute monarch and his appointee, a military man, had commanded New France as though the colony were a regiment. To the *habitants*, taking orders from officers in red uniforms was not much different in day-to-day terms from command by Frenchmen in blue and buff. Their country had been defeated in war and they knew it. The British had time to devise a formula by which to govern the new province.

Pontiac's Conspiracy

The Indians who had been allied to the French presented a more urgent problem. Unlike the French army, the warriors of the St. Lawrence and Ohio river valleys had not been decisively defeated in battle. The Treaty of Paris might proclaim them subjects of George III but, in reality, they were securely in possession of the forests west of the Appalachians, their ancestral home. And, almost immediately, the British blundered in dealing with them.

The Indians of the trans-Appalachian West customarily exchanged "gifts"—really a form of trade—with other peoples, including Europeans, as a sign they were on friendly terms. Traditionally, the now vanquished French had annually presented the Shawnee, Chippewa, Wyandot, Ottawa, and other tribes with blankets, iron tools and vessels, firearms, liquor. So, when the British commander, General Sir Jeffrey Amherst informed the Indians in the summer of 1763 that he would not be providing this tribute, several tribes united behind a resourceful Ottawa named Pontiac.

Pontiac's warriors besieged Detroit and Pittsburgh (Fort Duquesne), overran other frontier forts, and drove deep into Virginia and Pennsylvania, killing more than 2,000 people—a larger number than was lost in any battle of the French and Indian War. British regulars and some colonial forces regrouped and defeated Pontiac at Bushy Run near Pittsburgh. But they had only stung the trans-Appalachian Indians, not destroyed their power.

The Proclamation of 1763

Amherst restored the gift-giving and informed the Crown of the problem. In October 1763, in order to let tempers cool, an imaginary line was drawn on the Appalachian divide, between the sources of the rivers that emptied into the Atlantic and those that flowed into the Ohio-Mississippi river system. The Crown proclaimed, "we do strictly forbid, on pain of our displeasure, all our loving subjects from making any purchases or settlements whatever" west of the line. A few plucky

frontiersmen who had already pushed into the closed zone were forced to return east, and there was a freeze on land sales in the trans-Appalachian region.

Many Indians believed that their problem with the colonials was solved forever. Pontiac's uprising, which was concluded only in 1764, after the Proclamation, has been called the Indians' War for Independence. But few colonials regarded the Proclamation Line as anything more than what one young land speculator, George Washington, called "a temporary expedient to quiet the minds of the Indians." Too many Virginia planters and influential British politicos dreamed of riches from Ohio Valley real estate to consider the freeze permanent. Indeed, two newly appointed superintendents of Indian affairs immediately began to purchase territory from the western tribes. The southern part of the line of 1763 was redrawn within a few months, and, regularly over the next decade, trans-Appalachian lands were opened to speculation and settlement.

But Americans were already an impatient people, and the West was the place to which many looked for their fortunes. By interfering even temporarily with expansion, the British touched a tender nerve. Protest was quiet. Few colonials were so foolish as to belittle the power of the western Indians after the devastation Pontiac wreaked. Later, however, Americans would remember the Proclamation of 1763 as an early example of King George III's campaign to throttle their "liberties."

The Redcoats

In the wake of Pontiac's rebellion, General Amherst asked Parliament for a permanent American garrison of 5,000 to 6,000 troops. The soldiers would be stationed in Canada and in a string of frontier forts along the Great Lakes and the Ohio River. Parliament responded by voting Amherst 10,000 soldiers, thereby sending more than twice as many troops to North America as had been stationed there during the years of the French menace.

A few years later, when many of these soldiers were billeted in coastal cities in order to police riotous colonial crowds, they became the "hated redcoats" and the "lobsters." When the force first began to arrive, however, the Americans' biggest concern was the expense of maintaining them—£200,000 a year. The Quartering Act of 1765 charged the cost of the troops' shelter, food, and drink to the colony in which they were posted. Indeed, one of Parliament's motives in doubling Amherst's request was to pension off the aging veterans of the French and Indian War at colonial expense. The men had some reward coming to them, and the English have never liked to keep large standing armies at home during peacetime. Unhappily, Parliament ignored the fact that Britain's loyal colonial subjects might also have

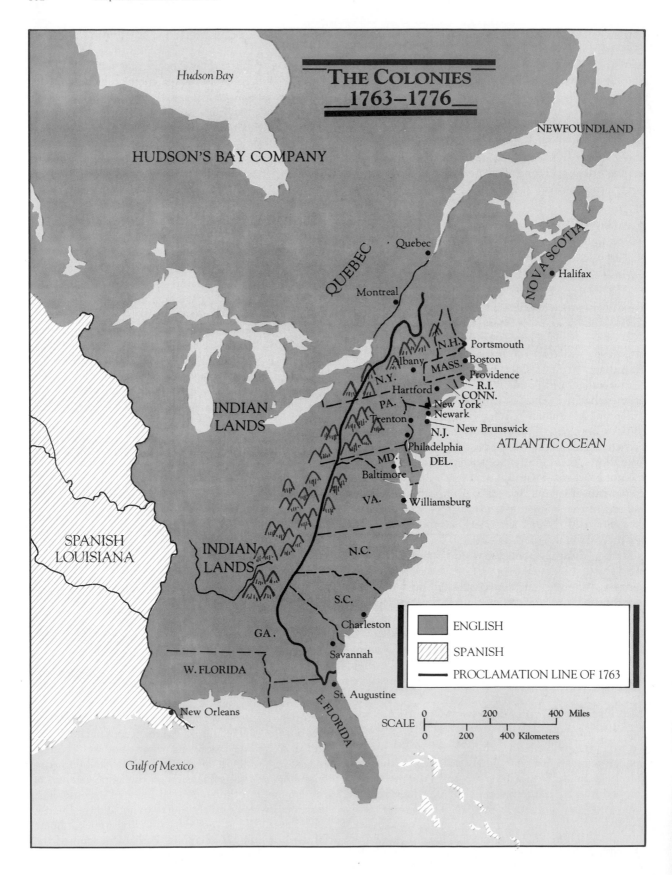

Hudson Bay

THE COLONIES
1763–1776

NEWFOUNDLAND

HUDSON'S BAY COMPANY

QUEBEC

· Quebec

NOVA SCOTIA

· Halifax

Montreal

N.H. · Portsmouth

Albany · MASS. · Boston

N.Y. · Providence

Hartford · R.I.

CONN.

PA. · New York

Trenton · Newark

N.J. · New Brunswick

Philadelphia

DEL.

MD.

ATLANTIC OCEAN

INDIAN
LANDS

Baltimore

VA. · Williamsburg

INDIAN
LANDS

SPANISH
LOUISIANA

N.C.

S.C.

GA. · Charleston

Savannah

W. FLORIDA

St. Augustine

E. FLORIDA

· New Orleans

Gulf of Mexico

	ENGLISH
	SPANISH
	PROCLAMATION LINE OF 1763

SCALE

| 0 | 200 | 400 Miles |
| 0 | 200 | 400 Kilometers |

inherited this tradition. Another point of friction had, imperceptibly, been created.

Reorganizing the Empire

The flurry of activity in the wake of the war was a signal that the men who governed Great Britain were taking a keen interest in colonial affairs. Some sort of change was sorely needed. Counting Canada, the West Indies, and British Honduras, twenty colonies in the Western Hemisphere now flew the British flag. If each were to go merrily its own way, as the thirteen "ancient provinces" of North America had been accustomed to do, the result would be chaos.

During and immediately after the French and Indian War, Parliament methodically scrapped the policy of salutary neglect and tried to create in its stead a centrally administered empire that was to be self-supporting.

Money

Before the war, Parliament had been content that the colonies were profitable to British land speculators, manufacturers, and merchants. Prewar governments had not been overly concerned that the administration of the colonies had been a net cost to the Exchequer. Until the French and Indian War, the cost of colonial government had run an average of £70,000 a year, while colonial trade annually pumped as much as £2 million into British counting houses and manorial treasuries. That was not a bad bargain.

By 1764, however, the costs of colonial government had risen to £350,000. In addition, Parliament had serious financial difficulties. William Pitt had borrowed wherever and whatever he could to win the war. A national debt of £130 million had Britain teetering on the edge of bankruptcy.

Higher taxes at home were out of the question. Each year, British landowners paid 20 percent of their income into the Exchequer, a crushing burden in an agricultural society. Other taxes were also high. When Parliament tried to increase a small tax on cider, the daily drink of southwestern England, villagers rioted.

Cutting costs was a possibility. The British government was shot through with graft and top-heavy with officials who slopped at the public trough without doing anything in particular. But they were the people whose job it was to solve the financial problem. They were no more inclined to do so at their own expense than politicians of any era are to cut their expense accounts and pensions. Then as now, the British officials preferred to find more money to pay the bills.

The Villain Grenville

The task of finding revenue fell to George Grenville, who became prime minister in 1763. Grenville was a

George Grenville was an estimable figure in British politics and government. Unfortunately, his plans for the empire took colonial sensibilities into too little consideration.

talented individual and an expert on money matters. If the reforms he introduced had succeeded, history might well record him as the architect of the British Empire. Instead, he is a fleeting figure in the British history books and, to Americans, a villain.

Among his abilities, Grenville brought a fatal limitation to his task. Like too many English politicians of the era, he knew little about Americans and did not see much sense in learning more. He had a vision of worldwide British power, but he contemplated it through the half-closed eyes of the complacent upper class. To Grenville, Americans were half-civilized louts whose opinions were not worthy of consideration. He would have smiled at Samuel Johnson's famous quip, "I am willing to love all mankind, except an American."

And Grenville knew that Americans paid few taxes. Using somewhat distorted figures, he calculated that the average English taxpayer paid an annual tax of 26 shillings, while a British subject living in Massachusetts paid one shilling a year and the average Virginian only five pence (less than half a shilling). And yet, the colonials had gained the most from the French and Indian War, the cause of the crushing debt that hung over England. Colonials should, therefore, Grenville concluded, do their part in paying off the debt and meeting their own current expenses.

Few Americans openly denied the justice of this deduction. Unfortunately, even if the thirteen assemblies had been willing to vote Grenville enough money to satisfy him, they did not get the chance to do so. Instead of requesting grants of funds, as Walpole and Pitt had done, Grenville treated the financial crisis as part and parcel of his administrative reforms.

The Sugar Act of 1764

Grenville's first move was to overhaul the ineffective Molasses Act of 1733. Its sixpence-a-gallon tax on molasses imported into the colonies from non-British sources was so high that American merchants felt morally justified in ignoring it. Instead, they paid a bribe of a penny or so per gallon to customs collectors. If they were arrested as smugglers, they could usually count on juries of their neighbors to acquit them regardless of the evidence—and then join them at the nearest inn for a dram of cheap rum, the principal product made from molasses.

Grenville's Sugar Act of 1764 struck at both the revenue problem and the problem of enforcement. It enlarged the customs service, increasing its efficiency. The law also transferred responsibility for enforcing trade laws from local courts to a new system of vice-admiralty courts that would try violators without juries. Finally, the Sugar Act cut the molasses duty to threepence-a-gallon. Grenville calculated that merchants would pay the lower rate rather than run the risk of conviction in courts they could not control. Also in 1764, Grenville levied duties on imported wines, silks, tropical foods, and other luxury goods.

The First Protest

In New England, where molasses was a major item of trade, protest was loud and fierce. The Boston Town Meeting declared that the city would import no British goods of any kind until Parliament repealed the obnoxious tax. Other cities, including New York, followed suit. Even "the young Gentlemen of Yale College" announced that they would not "make use of any foreign spirituous liquors" until Grenville backed down from his importunity. Their painful sacrifice was eased by the fact that the supply of beer, cider, and fiery New England rum was limitless in New Haven.

Grenville was not moved. He assumed that the Americans simply did not want to pay any taxes, that they wanted to enjoy the benefits of being a part of the British Empire at no cost to themselves. Importers of molasses, sippers of Madeira, and wearers of silk wanted the best bargains they could get. To this extent, the Sugar Act protest was sheer self-interest.

The Rights of British Subjects

Nonetheless, as thoughtful protesters pointed out, there were two worthy principles at stake. As a tax designed to keep French molasses out of the empire, the old Molasses Act of 1733 had regulated trade. According to colonists like Daniel Dulany of Maryland, who wrote a widely distributed pamphlet on the Sugar Act, this was perfectly legitimate. Parliament had the right and the obligation to regulate trade for the good of the empire.

But the Sugar Act of 1764 was not designed to keep foreign molasses out of the empire. New England distillers could make a profit on rum after paying the threepence duty. Indeed, so far as Grenville was concerned, the more foreign molasses they imported legally, the better. His goal was to raise money. The official title of the Sugar Act was the American Revenue Act.

It was Grenville's announced goal—revenue—that raised a ticklish constitutional question. It was a "sacred right" of British subjects that they consented to the taxes levied on them. To many Britons, the meaning of English history was the struggle that won such rights. By 1764, Parliament had almost total control of money matters in Great Britain. But Americans were not directly represented in Parliament. They had their own "little parliaments," their elected assemblies. According to the Sugar Act protesters, only these bodies could tax them. This arrangement had, in fact, been the unofficial custom for 150 years.

Trial by Jury

Just as important was the right of a British subject to be tried for a crime before a jury of his or her peers, or social equals. This right, dating back to Magna Carta of 1215, Britons and colonials believed, set them apart from, and made them superior to, the French, Spanish, Poles, Chinese, and Hottentots. By denying colonials this ancient right, as Grenville did in setting up juryless vice-admiralty courts, he was tampering with the essence of British liberties.

It is impossible to say what would have happened if Grenville's program had ended with the Sugar Act. The Americans were noisy, and some of their language was bitter, but there was no violence. The Sugar Act protest began and ended with an annoying but perfectly legal boycott of imports. To the extent that colonial resentment was a matter of greed, the protest might well have died out. The duties of 1764 seriously affected only wealthy consumers and a small number of shippers and distillers. When, in 1766, the molasses duty was reduced to a penny (the level of the traditional bribe), protest ceased, although "the principle of the thing" remained quite intact.

But Grenville did not stop with the Sugar Act. In 1765, he announced a new bill to raise money in Amer-

Tempers flash and canes are brandished at a town meeting. The scene could be mocked, but the right to participate actively in government was one New Englanders valued and meant to keep.

STAMPS

What we call a stamp is, by eighteenth century standards, a misnomer. The adhesive-backed evidence that postage has been paid on a letter was invented only in 1834 (the perforations in 1854) and, when it was, the speakers of no other European language chose "stamp" to name the ingenious device. To them, and to colonial Americans, a stamp was something impressed *on* or stamped *into* paper, not something attached to it. Eighteenth-century stamping was what we would call embossing.

Thus, the stamp that caused all the excitement in 1765 was an embossment, pressed into the paper to be used for licenses, newspapers, and so on by a press. Few Americans ever saw the Stamp Act stamps. Save for a little in Georgia, none of the embossed paper was ever sold.

Few Americans ever laid eyes on this stamp, embossed into the paper with which Parliament hoped to tax the colonies in 1795.

ica by means of a tax that could not easily be ducked. Those who did not pay it suffered directly from the very act of non-compliance.

· THE STAMP ACT CRISIS

The English people had been paying a stamp tax since 1694. In order to be legal, documents such as wills, bills of sale, various licenses, deeds, insurance policies, and other contracts had to be inscribed on paper that was embossed with a government stamp. Purchase of the paper constituted payment of a tax and evasion was not possible. A contract, deed, or other legal document that was not written on the stamped paper could not be legally enforced.

The Stamp Act of 1765

Grenville's Stamp Act of 1765 went somewhat further than the English law. It required that in addition to colonial legal documents, all newspapers, pamphlets, handbills, and even playing cards were to be printed on the embossed government paper. The cost varied from a halfpenny on a handbill to £1 for a liquor license, quite a sum in both cases.

Enforcement of the law was entrusted to the unpopular vice-admiralty courts. However, Grenville tried to court colonial favor by providing that all money raised under the Stamp Act would be used solely in "defending, protecting, and securing the colonies." None of it would go back to England to retire the debt or for any other purpose.

This provision did not soothe American sensibilities. On the contrary, the stipulation that the revenues from the Stamp Act were to be raised and spent entirely within the colonies led individuals like the Pennsylvania Quaker, John Dickinson, to devise a detailed constitutional distinction between "external taxes," duties on trade between the colonies and other places, which Dickinson said were legitimate, and "internal taxes," duties collected within the colonies, which he said were unacceptable. The Stamp Act was plainly internal, Dickinson argued. It was a direct tax on the people by a body in which they were not represented—Parliament. Clearly, only a colonial assembly could enact such a tax within its boundaries. (Indeed, Massachusetts had experimented with a stamp act in 1755.)

Grenville had no ear for this argument. In his administrative scheme, Parliament was the supreme governing authority for the entire empire. Most members of Parliament agreed with him. After a dull debate, addressing few of the issues, they voted 204 to 49 to enact the tax. Many prominent Americans also failed to see any problem with the Stamp Act. Richard Henry Lee of Virginia, who would introduce the independence resolution in 1776, applied for a job as a stamp tax collector in 1765.

A Stupid Law

Constitutional questions aside, the Stamp Act was politically stupid. Its burden fell most heavily on just those people who were best able to stir up a fuss. Newspaper editors, with their influence on public opinion, were hard hit. Advertisements, a newspaper's bread and butter, were taxed two shillings, and every edition had to be printed on stamped paper. Printers, who depended to a large extent on putting out broadsides (posters used for announcing goods for sale and public meetings—including protest meetings!), saw their business taxed at every turn of the press.

Lawyers, the single largest group in colonial public office and persuaders by profession, had to pay a tax on every document with which they dealt. Tavernkeepers, saddled with more expensive licenses by the new law, were key figures in every town and neighborhood. Their inns were the gathering places where, over rum, brandy, coffee, or tea, locals read newspapers and discussed politics.

What was worse for Grenville, most of these groups were concentrated in cities, where they could easily meet with one another, cooperate, and have an impact out of proportion to their numbers. It was one thing to upset such groups one at a time, as the Sugar Act had riled shippers and distillers. The Stamp Act hit all of these key elements at once, and, possibly to everyone's surprise, they won the support of large numbers of ordinary working people.

Riot

Parliament approved the Stamp Act at the end of February 1765, scheduling it to go into effect in November. As soon as the news reached the colonies, they erupted in anger. Local organizations called Sons of Liberty (a phrase used to describe Americans by one of their friends in Parliament, Isaac Barré) condemned the law and called for a boycott of British goods.

Some of the Sons took violent action. When the stamped paper was delivered to warehouses in port cities, mobs broke in and lit bonfires. Men who had accepted jobs as stamp masters were shunned, hanged in effigy, or roughed up. A popular if brutal method of punishing tax collectors was to daub them, sometimes naked, with hot tar, roll them in chicken feathers, and carry them, straddling a fence rail, about town.

One official in Maryland was forced to flee for his life to New York. That was a mistake. The New York Sons of Liberty were the rowdiest of all. They located the Marylander and forced him to write a letter of resignation. Led by Isaac Sears, the captain of a merchant vessel, the New Yorkers frightened their own lieutenant governor (another future revolutionary named Cadwallader Colden) so that he went into hiding. When they could not find Colden, they burned his carriages. In Boston, the crowd looted and burned the homes of several officials of the Crown.

Rowdies are seldom popular, but the Stamp Act rioters were. When one governor was asked why he did not call out the militia to restore order, he pointed out that it would mean arming the very people who were wreaking havoc. The British had expected protests. Isaac Barré had warned of resistance. But everyone was caught short by what seemed the whole American people on a rampage.

The Stamp Act Congress

Among those surprised were prominent and wealthy colonials who hated the Stamp Act but shuddered to hear the shouts of angry crowds in the streets. Mobs are beasts, moving easily from one target to another, and the colonial crowd had as many grievances against its social betters in the colonies as against Parliament. In October 1765, in an attempt to channel and control the protest, 37 delegates from nine colonies assembled in New York City in the Stamp Act Congress.

Although the Congress was the brainchild of one of the more volatile agitators, James Otis of Massachusetts, the fourteen resolutions and the "Declaration of Rights and Grievances" the delegates adopted were largely the

The burden of the stamp tax caused the Pennsylvania Journal *to announce on October 31, 1765, that it was ceasing publication.*

work of conservative men like John Dickinson. The Stamp Act Congress criticized the Stamp Act, Sugar Act, and other parliamentary policies while the delegates prominently and tactfully made it clear they acknowledged "all due subordination" to the Crown.

THE BRITISH CONSTITUTION

What did "all due subordination" mean? Loyalty to the king? Unquestionably. All agreed on the importance of the monarch as the symbol which unified the British people wherever they dwelled. *Lèse majesté*—"injuring the king"—was the gravest of political crimes, punishable by hanging, often followed by disembowelment and quartering (harnessing four horses to each of the traitor's limbs and cracking the whip).

On other rather basic questions of governance, however, Britons and colonials disagreed. Fundamental dis-

agreement was possible because, while the British constitution included a few hallowed written documents, like Magna Carta of 1215 and the Bill of Rights of 1689, it was largely unwritten. Most of the principles and practices of British government had evolved over the centuries through tradition, actual usage, and acceptance over time.

What Is Representation? The Colonial Case

Colonial protesters said that Parliament had no right to tax them because they were not represented in Parliament. Their own assemblies, which they elected, were their little parliaments, alone empowered with the power to tax them. Colonials did not vote for members of the British Parliament.

The colonial case is easy for us to understand, for it is the governing principle of representation in the United States today. In order for an individual to be represented in government, he or she must be entitled to vote for a city council member, county supervisor, state legislator,

HOW THEY LIVED

AT HOME AMONG THE IROQUOIS

By the middle of the eighteenth century, the Iroquois Confederacy, consisting of the Cayuga, Seneca, Onondaga, Oneida, and Mohawk tribes, numbered about 15,000 people and securely controlled most of what is now New York State and much of western Pennsylvania. Iroquois hunters and war parties ranged even farther, over 1 million square miles, as far west as the Mississippi River and as far north as Hudson's Bay.

The hunters and warriors were men, of course. Men also traveled to carry out the intricate and constant diplomatic negotiations that the confederacy depended on for its stability and to deal with non-Iroquois peoples, including the English and French. "It is not an exaggeration," Anthony F. C. Wallace wrote in the standard history of the Senecas, "to say that the full-time business of an Iroquois man was travel."

Iroquois women stayed home in more or less fixed towns. They raised the corn that was the staple of the Iroquois diet. They cared for the children in the secure village, instilling Iroquois values into them. They kept the long houses in repair and maintained order in the towns, governing by social pressure—reputation was extremely important to the Iroquois—rather than by force. Finally, with their husbands absent much of the time, the women effectively decided whose children they would bear.

Descent, therefore, had to be traced through the maternal line. A typical Iroquois town consisted of about 12 to 40 long houses in each of which dwelt 50 or 60 members of a clan. The clan (whose animal symbol was carved above the door of the long house and painted red) included its eldest female member and her daughters, immature male children, and sons-in-law. Because of a strict incest taboo, an Iroquois male left the clan into which he had been born and became a member of his wife's clan. Indeed, because marital relationships were fragile and transitory, an Iroquois man might drift from clan to clan throughout his life. At any given time, however, he was obligated to defend the honor of his wife's clan. For example, if a member of her clan was killed and the matriarch insisted that revenge be taken, a warrior was required to do so, even if it was against the clan into which he had been born.

In addition to the authority to declare war between clans (which was not frequent and was governed by a complex set of rules), the elder women of the Iroquois selected each of the 49 delegates of the confederacy when

death created a vacancy. They also participated, albeit more quietly than the orating men, in community decision making.

The system worked extremely well. Iroquois lands remained secure because the mobile men were such effective warriors and home life was placid and orderly. A Quaker wrote that the Senecas

appear to be naturally as well calculated for social and rational enjoyment, as any people. They frequently visit each other in their houses, and spend much of their time in friendly intercourse. They are also mild and hospitable, not only among themselves, but to strangers, and good-natured in the extreme, except when their natures are perverted by the inflammatory influence of spirituous liquors.

Alcohol was a serious problem. A good sale of pelts and hides to the whites inevitably led to the purchase of rum and wholesale drunkenness among men, women, and children. Although this was the most tragic element introduced into Iroquois life by the arrival of whites, it was not the only one. Contact with Europeans, into its fifth generation by the middle of the eighteenth century, also meant guns and metal tools ranging from scissors, knives, awls, kettles, and other household goods, to hatchets and axes. The latter influenced Iroquois building methods: by the mid-1700s long houses were made less often in the traditional way—sheets of elm bark lashed to bent saplings—and increasingly of logs.

Another interesting consequence of the mixing of cultures was the increased tendency of Iroquois to abandon living by clan in the long houses and to cluster in single-family log cabins. The white presence probably made for a more intensive agriculture by the end of the colonial era. Not only was game scarcer because of overtrapping, but European tools made it possible for the Seneca alone to produce as many as a million bushels of corn a year by 1750. It is difficult to imagine such a crop resulting from traditional slash and burn cultivation.

The appearance of the Iroquois also changed. European calico shirts, linen breechcloths, and woolen blankets characterized the Indians whom the Americans of the eighteenth century knew. Nevertheless, the Iroquois continued to shun Christian missionaries, and they "made obscene gestures" when anyone suggested that the white settlers' way of life was superior to their own.

---

representative, or senator. The Senators from Kentucky are not held to represent Iowa farmers. Only those legislators for whom those farmers are eligible to vote do so. Reforms of voting laws throughout United States history—extending the vote to people who did not own

property, to blacks, and to women—have been based on this concept of representation: One must be able to vote in order to be represented.

James Otis spoke for this way of thinking at the Stamp Act Congress of 1765 when he suggested that Parliament

A *1770 broadside announcing a boycott of merchants importing British goods.*

constituents in the city of Bristol during the dispute with the colonies, "you choose a member . . . but when you have chosen him, he is not a member of Bristol, but he is a member of Parliament."

The colonials practiced virtual representation in their own elections. George Washington and other Virginians were elected to the House of Burgesses from counties in which they did not reside. Often, would-be burgesses stood for seats in more than one county at a time so that they were covered in the event they were defeated in one. Few objected to this practice. It was assumed (in theory) that those who were elected would act with the interests of all Virginians in mind.

The colonists also practiced virtual representation when they restricted the suffrage to free, white, adult male heads of household who possessed a certain minimum of property in land or money. The number of actual voters in colonial elections amounted to a small proportion of the inhabitants of any colony. Nevertheless, the colonists considered the interests of the poor, women, children, and in a queer way, black slaves, to be virtually represented. The assumption was that elected assembly members acted on behalf of all, not just on behalf of the few freeholders who voted for them. This position was precisely the position that Parliament took when the colonials complained that they were not represented in Parliament: the colonists were virtually represented in that ancient body.

BRITISH POLICIES AND POLICY-MAKERS

The Stamp Act crisis was not resolved by adding up debaters' points. Few political battles are. If the protesters' constitutional argument was flimsy, they were a powerful and articulate group in every colony with support among all social classes. None of them spoke of independence or, after the riots, of rebellion. But they were adamant that Americans were not subjects of Parliament. They took their "rights as British subjects," as they interpreted them, quite seriously.

Poor Leadership

Some members of Parliament appreciated the colonial position and supported the Americans. William Pitt, now the Earl of Chatham, rejoiced "that America has resisted. Three millions of people so dead to all the feelings of liberty," he said, "so voluntarily to submit to be slaves, would have been fit instruments to make slaves of the rest." Americans returned the compliment and idolized Pitt. They also honored Colonel Isaac Barré, who had done military service in New England and (rare

end the dispute by allowing the colonists to elect members of Parliament. His colleagues ignored him. They did not want to send representatives to Parliament; they wanted Parliament to recognize the authority of their own assemblies over them, at least in matters of taxation. Grenville might well have confounded the colonial protesters by acting favorably on the Otis proposal. He did not do so because he and other members of Parliament, including many who were sympathetic to the colonials, believed that the Americans were already represented in Parliament.

Virtual Representation: The British Case

Indeed, by the lights of the eighteenth century, the British were quite correct. The British concept of representation differed (and differs) from our own. For example, it was (and is) not necessary that a member of the British Parliament reside in the electoral district that sends him or her to the House of Commons. While it is unlikely to happen in our own time, a member of Parliament may never set foot in the district from which he or she is elected. Districts are for the sake of convenience in balloting, but each member of Parliament is regarded as virtually representing the entire nation. As Edmund Burke, a friend of the Americans, put it to his own for a British officer) was personally fond of Americans. Edmund Burke, the father of traditional conservatism, saw the colonists as the defenders of British tradition and the Grenville group as dangerous innovators. At the other extreme, English radicals like John Wilkes egged on the colonial protesters because he saw them as natural allies in his agitations on behalf of a free press, and in opposition to George III.

Unfortunately, except for a brief spell in 1766 and 1767 when the Marquis of Rockingham and Lord Chatham headed ministries, such men did not make colonial policy. For the most part, the leader of Parliament was unable to see beyond constitutional fine points and their snobbish disdain for colonial rustics. This narrow-mindedness was one consequence of the way English politics functioned during the reign of King George III.

Politics as Usual

Members of Parliament used party names like Whig and Tory, but there were no political parties in any meaningful sense of the word. Parliament was a collection of at least half a dozen shifting factions. Some, such as Edmund Burke's "Old Whigs," ever on the watch for violations of traditional liberties, were drawn together by agreement on a principle. Most of Parliament's cliques, however, were alliances of convenience, groups of men who supported one another because they were related by blood or marriage or for the purpose of serving their own immediate and none too lofty interests.

There was money to be made in politics, not only through outright graft (which was not rare), but also through the distribution of public offices and government favors—the colonials played this game. One way for an American speculative venture to gain parliamentary approval was to cut in a parliamentary clique as stockholders. Benjamin Franklin named one land company after Robert Walpole, and may be said to have profited when he was named Postmaster-General for the colonies, the highest imperial post to which any American rose.

King George III

A new wrinkle was added to British politics after 1760, when George III ascended the throne at the age of 22. George's predecessors had used the royal favors at their disposal to reward military heroes, to support musicians and artists, or simply to keep congenial companions lolling about the palace. The first two Georges were German. George I could not even speak English, and George II, who could a little, preferred French. Coming from the small state of Hanover, they were delighted merely to have the rich royal income of Britain at their disposal. Neither took much interest in domestic matters.

George III, by way of contrast, had been raised an Englishman. His mother had urged him to "be a king," and he meant to have a hand in government. The days when the English monarch could issue decrees were long gone. But George could and did use the patronage he controlled to build his own parliamentary faction, the "king's friends."

The "king's friends" were no more venal than the other parliamentary factions. Nor was George III evil, as the Americans would come to depict him. He could not have been a tyrant had he wished to be. Indeed, several times during his first ten years as king and politician, George III used his faction to support conciliation with the colonies, and he won American favor by doing so. (There would be plenty of statues of him to be toppled when American opinion changed.)

But George III was not intelligent. And he was vain and stubborn. The king was uneasy with political cronies whose abilities exceeded his own, and with those who failed or refused to flatter him. By keeping such men out of office and raising up mediocrities and sycophants, he denied power to those who best understood the American situation. What was worse, the King was erratic. (Eventually he went insane.) He dismissed even lackeys on the slightest pretext.

Colonial policy was inconsistent. The effect was to worsen relations between Britain and its colonies and to embolden the more radical American agitators.

Mixed Victory

Thus, George Grenville, a hard-liner who always insisted that he could have solved the colonial problem in 1765 with the use of the army, was dismissed in July 1765 over an unrelated matter. Early the next year, during the short ministry of Lord Rockingham, Chatham moved to repeal the Stamp Act, and it was done. The colonial

A teapot—made in England for export—commemorating the repeal of the Stamp Act of 1766.

celebrations were so noisy that few paid much attention to the fact that king and Parliament had not yielded an inch on principle. Parliament had also passed a Declaratory Act which stated that Parliament "had, hath, and of right ought to have, full power and authority to make laws and statutes of sufficient force and validity to bind the colonies and people of America, subjects of the crown of Great Britain, in all cases whatsoever."

Not only did this Declaratory Act deny the Americans' claims for their own assemblies, the wording was lifted from a law of 1719 that had made Ireland completely subject to Great Britain. The colonials might well have wondered if their rights as British subjects were being restored, or if they had been reduced to the unenviable status of the Irish. But they did not. Chatham became prime minister a short time later, and he ignored the Declaratory Act with the panache of Robert Walpole. In November, he eliminated another aggravation when he reduced the duty on molasses from threepence to a penny a gallon. The colonial protesters were Georgian politicians, too. What mattered a piece of paper when a good friend held power?

Then, in one of those accidents that change the course of events, Chatham was taken ill, and he ceased to play an active part in the government. From the perspective of the colonists, the man who stepped into the vacuum was as unfortunate a personality as George Grenville.

Champagne Charley and the Townshend Duties

Charles Townshend was no more evil a man than Grenville or King George. In fact, he was rather too convivial and charming—a hail fellow well-met who won the nickname "Champagne Charley" because of his penchant for arriving at the House of Commons giggling and unsteady on his feet. (In fairness to Townshend, Parliament met in the evening and, on a given night, any number of members were at less than their best.)

Townshend was Chancellor of the Exchequer, a post equivalent to our Secretary of the Treasury, and he hoped to become prime minister. To win such favor, Townshend planned to cut taxes and make up for the loss of revenues that would result in the colonies. He studied the Americans' distinctions between external taxes for regulating trade and internal taxes for raising money, and designed duties that were undeniably external in form. The Townshend Duties were imposed on paper, paint, lead, glass, and tea imported into the colonies.

It was an odd combination of goods. Although none of the taxed goods were produced in the colonies in any quantity, all of them except tea could be made there. In failing to appreciate that the controversy was not an academic debate, Townshend invited a boycott, which he got. Trade between England and America fell off by 25 percent, then 50 percent. Townshend had predicted that his duties would bring in £40,000 annually. The actual take was £13,000 in 1768 and under £3,000 the next year, hardly enough to operate a few frontier forts.

There was little violence. The boycott was organized by merchants, wealthy men who were still nervous about the Stamp Act riots. But it worked. English merchants felt the pinch and flooded Parliament with petitions for repeal. They pointed out that if Townshend had answered the colonial distinction between internal and external taxes, he had also penalized goods that English manufacturers and merchants shipped abroad! In 1770, with the exception of the threepence-per-pound tax on tea, Parliament repealed the Townshend duties. The tea tax was kept in the spirit of the Declaratory Act. It was Parliament's statement that Parliament retained the right to tax the colonies.

For Further Reading

Among a vast number of general histories of the events leading up to the American Revolution, and differing radically in their explanations and focus, are: J. R. Alden, *A History of the American Revolution* (1969); Bernard Bailyn, *The Ideological Origins of the American Revolution* (1967); "The Political Role of Bernard Donoghue," *British Politics and the American Revolution* (1965); Lawrence H. Gipson, *The Coming of the Revolution* (1954); Jack P. Greene, *The Reinterpretation of the American Revolution* (1968); Merrill Jensen, *The Founding of a Nation* (1968); Robert Middlekauff, *The Glorious Cause: The American Revolution, 1763–1789* (1982); John C. Miller, *Origins of the American Revolution* (1943); and Edmund S. Morgan, *The Birth of the Republic* (1956); and Alfred T. Young, *The American Revolution: A Radical Interpretation* (1976).

Valuable special studies include Carl Bridenbaugh, *Seat of Empire: Eighteenth Century Williamsburg* (1950); John Brook, *King George III* (1972); Edmund S. and Helen Morgan, *Prologue to Revolution: The Stamp Act Crisis* (1953); Lewis B. Namier, *England in the Age of the American Revolution* (1930); Arthur M. Schlesinger, *The Colonial Merchants and the American Revolution, 1763–1776* (1951); Charles S. Sydnor, *Gentleman Freeholders* (1952). On Pontiac's uprising, see Wilbur R. Jacobs, *Wilderness Politics and Indian Gifts* (1966) and, edited by the same historian, *Dispossessing the American Indian: Indians and Whites on the Colonial Frontier* (1985).

Rebellious colonials raise a "Liberty Pole," a symbol of resistance to British rule.

FROM RIOT TO REBELLION

THE ROAD TO INDEPENDENCE
1770 - 1776

Nothing was settled by the repeal of the Townshend duties. Neither the leaders of Parliament nor

colonial protesters had yielded an inch on the principle at stake: Did Parliament have the right to

tax the colonies? The Declaratory Act remained on the books. Americans ignored it so long as it

gathered dust, but they conceded not a word of its claim. "Ridiculous!," snorted George Mason, a

Virginia planter who would later become a revolutionary.

Nevertheless, almost everyone involved in the dispute was relieved to see an end to confrontation.

For three years after 1770, Parliament avoided provoking the colonials. In the colonies, anti-British protests were few and muted.

In fact, tensions began to ease before March 1770 when the Townshend Acts were scrapped. A door-to-door survey of New Yorkers revealed that a majority of households was willing to buy all the taxed items except tea—which they could get more cheaply from Dutch smugglers. Beginning in early 1770, imports into the New England colonies, the most obstreperous of the provinces, increased from a low of £330,000 to £1.2 million, more than ever before. Total colonial exports rose from £1.7 million in 1770 to £4.5 million in 1772. As, perhaps, most people always do, Americans wanted calm—business as usual—a resumption of daily life unaggravated by the folderol of politics.

STORMS WITHIN THE LULL

Still, several incidents between 1770 and 1773 indicated that not all was harmony in British North America. On the streets of Boston, a bloody brawl between workingmen and British soldiers dramatized a simmering hostility toward the large numbers of redcoats stationed in the colonies. In North Carolina, frontier settlers took up arms against the elite of the eastern counties who governed the colony. And in Rhode Island, farmers protected smugglers who burned a British patrol boat.

The Boston Massacre

On March 5, 1770, the day the Townshend Duties were repealed, the weather in Boston was frigid. The streets were icy, and heaps of shoveled snow blocked the cobbled gutters. No doubt aggravated by the severity of the winter, which brought unemployment as well as discomfort, some men and boys exchanged words with British soldiers who were patrolling the streets. A handful of hecklers grew into a crowd, cursing and throwing snowballs at the redcoats. Some bravos dared them to use their muskets.

When the mob pressed closer on King Street, backing the soldiers against a wall, they fired. Five in the crowd, including a boy and a black seaman named Crispus Attucks, fell dead.

Boston was more stunned than angry. When men who had been active in the Stamp Act crisis tried to revive anti-British feelings, they made little headway. Silversmith Paul Revere prepared (some say plagiarized) an engraving that depicted soldiers aggressively attacking innocent people. Samuel Adams, a former brewer, circulated prints of the "Boston Massacre." Joseph Warren,

a physician, embroidered passionately on the same theme. "Take heed, ye orphan babes," he told a public meeting, "lest, whilst your streaming eyes are fixed upon the ghastly corpse, your feet slide on the stones bespattered with your father's brains."

But the agitation failed to bear fruit. Most people seemed to blame the incident on the mob. John Adams, cousin of Samuel and a friend of Warren, agreed to represent the accused soldiers in court. He was nobody's stooge, least of all of the British. John Adams was strongheaded to the point of self-righteousness and a strident critic of British policies. In arguing the redcoats' case, Adams roundly criticized the practice of stationing professional soldiers in cities like Boston. "Soldiers quartered in a populous town will always occasion two mobs where they prevent one," he said. "They are wretched conservators of the peace." Nevertheless, Adams argued that British policy and an unsavory mob, not the indicted redcoats, bore the blame for the tragedy of March 5. The jury agreed, acquitting all the defendants save two and sentencing them only to branding on the thumb, a slap on the wrist by eighteenth-century standards.

The Hated Redcoats

The significance of the Boston Massacre, and of the "Battle of Golden Hill" in New York in January—in which soldiers and citizens drew blood in a major riot—was that the vast majority of colonials let them pass. Still, such incidents and a hundred less notable exposed a sore spot in colonial city life. As John Adams allowed in his address to the Boston jury, colonials simply did not like the scarlet-uniformed soldiers in their midst. Taxpayers resented paying for their keep. Ordinary working people disliked rubbing shoulders with men who commanded little respect in the eighteenth century.

The soldier of the era was not, like the soldier of today, the boy next door in uniform defending the nation and its ideals. Eighteenth-century soldiers were rough and lusty young men sieved from the dregs of an unjust society. Some were convicted criminals who were in the army because it was offered to them as an alternative to prison. Others, guilty of no crime, had been pressed into service simply because they were unable to support themselves.

"Civilians" feared and despised them. The soldiers' own officers, drawn from the gentry, looked down on them. "Scum" was the word that leapt first to mind when an eighteenth-century officer described his men. Soldiers had few rights and were regularly and brutally punished. If not slaves, they suffered a kind of bondage. There was no feeling among them of selfless service to king and country or of commitment to some abstract national ideal. In America, they were further alienated by the fact that few colonials signed up. The "lobsters" were almost all from Great Britain.

A Dangerous Relationship

So long as the soldiers lived in frontier forts or in isolated bases such as Castle Island in Boston harbor, conflict was minimal. However, after the Stamp Act riots, the Crown stationed large detachments within coastal cities and towns. Some 4,000 redcoats were camping on Boston Common—"center city"—at the time of the Massacre. Others, under the terms of the Quartering Act of 1765, were billeted in vacant buildings and taverns.

Such quartering brought the tightly knit redcoats into intimate daily contact with working-class colonials. They were young men and some found girlfriends, stirring up resentment on that primeval count. Others coarsely accosted young women. When off duty, they competed with local men and boys for casual work. There had been a fist fight over jobs in Boston just a few days before the Massacre. Redcoats also passed idle hours in inns and taverns where colonials gathered.

Inns and taverns were not merely hostels in which travelers supped and bedded down. They were a focal point of urban social life. The colonial tavern was the neighborhood meeting place, more like a contemporary English pub, perhaps, than a modern American bar. Local workingmen popped in throughout the day for a cup of tea or coffee and, in the evening, for a shot of rum, a mug of mulled cider, a pipe of tobacco, and a chat about friends, work, and politics. With time on their hands, unemployed men, and those between jobs such as seamen, spent even more time at "the ordinary." The intrusion of uniformed foreigners, laughing loudly and carrying on by themselves, kept resentments up even when, as between 1770 and 1773, relations with Great Britain were generally good.

Street People

The redcoats had more to do with the anti-British feelings of lower-class colonials than Parliamentary taxation had. Poor people worried about the next day's meal, not about the price of a jeroboam of the best Madeira wine or the fine points of the British constitution. And such people were central to the protest that boiled over into rebellion and revolution. Workingmen, the unemployed, boisterous street boys and apprentices, and the disreputable fringe elements of colonial society did the dirty work in the Stamp Act crisis. They were the ones who fought the soldiers in the streets and who were killed in the Boston Massacre.

They had little to lose as a consequence of rash action. The "street people" were themselves often social outcasts by virtue of class, occupation, or race. Seamen,

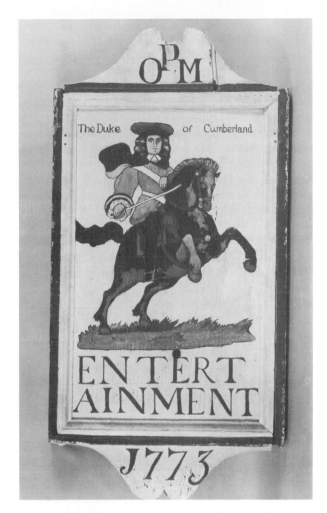

Inns and taverns were places where colonists could socialize and exchange news.

suspect because they came and went, belonging to no community, were prominent in the riotous crowds. (Crispus Attucks was a sailor out of work.) John Adams described the mob on King Street as "Negroes and mulattoes, Irish teagues, and outlandish jack-tars." And yet, the revolution he was to join with enthusiasm owed much to the boldness of the motley crowd.

Demon Rum

It is worth noting the curious role of alcohol in the agitation. The soldiers were a bibulous lot. It was standard military practice to pass around strong drink before battle, and the royal governor of New York dissolved the colonial assembly in 1766 when its members refused to provide the redcoats their accustomed ration of five pints of beer or four ounces of rum a day.

Americans were a hard-drinking folk too, and the lower classes, with more to forget, were the thirstiest of all. Many a signal episode on the road to independence seems to have been carried out by men in their cups. "The minds of the freeholders were inflamed," wrote an observer of the Stamp Act protest in South Carolina, "by many a hearty damn . . . over bottles, bowls, and glasses." The crowd that precipitated the Boston Massacre had come out of the taverns. The Sons of Liberty, who ignited the last phase of the revolutionary movement with the Boston Tea Party of 1773, assembled over a barrel of rum.

Upper-class protest leaders had mixed feelings about this kind of support. They were willing to exploit an angry, perhaps inebriated crowd, by stirring up resentment of British policies and by winking at abuses of the law. John Adams, so scornful of the Massacre mob, called the men at the Boston Tea party "so bold, so daring, so intrepid." But they also worried about "the rabble." They expected the crowd to fade away after having played its historic role.

But the masses did not disappear. British concessions did nothing to remedy their grievances. The redcoats continued to jostle them in the streets and to intrude on their lives. Their elemental economic problems were untouched by lighter taxation and parliamentary expressions of good will. They remained anonymous, producing few individual leaders. But they continued to be fertile ground for agitation.

The Regulators

Conflict between colonial classes was clearer in the countryside. In western South Carolina, between 1767 and 1769, frontiersmen rebelled against the refusal of the colonial assembly, which was dominated by Charleston planters, to set up county governments in the west. They proclaimed their own counties to which they paid taxes that, legally, should have gone to Charleston. The rebels called themselves Regulators because they said they would regulate their own affairs.

In North Carolina, a similar dispute led to actual battle. A band of westerners rode east to demonstrate their resentment of the colony's penny-pinching policies. They were met and defeated by a smaller but better-trained militia at the Battle of Alamance. Only nine men were killed and six later hanged for rebellion, but the modesty of the clash did not sweeten the bitterness in the Carolina backcountry.

Shared Prejudice

Some historians have suggested that the British missed a splendid opportunity to win colonial support when they failed to exploit the hostility between western farmers and the eastern elites. To some extent, British imperial interests coincided with the demands of the frontiersmen: the Regulators wanted more government, not less, and their chief complaint was that not enough tax money was spent on maintaining law and order in their foothills homeland.

By wooing the backcountry farmers with policies that favored them, the British might have gained powerful allies in their disputes with the wealthy Southern planters. Indeed, during the Revolution, many Regulators fought on the British side, while others pushed beyond the Appalachians in order to remain neutral.

The British did not win more backwoods support than they did because their contempt for the lower classes was as ripe as that of the colonial elite. It was difficult for a British gentleman to regard the poor people of the frontier and the city streets as anything other than a rabble.

The Gaspée

In June 1772, a British schooner patrolling the Narragansett Bay in Rhode Island, the Gaspée, spied a vessel believed to be involved in smuggling and sailed after it toward Providence. About seven miles from the port, the Gaspée ran aground. That night, men from eight boats boarded the schooner, set the crew ashore, and burned it to the waterline.

Because the Gaspée was a royal vessel, this was an act of rebellion and authorities believed they knew who the ringleader of the gang was—a merchant named John Brown, who regularly had run-ins with customs collectors. However, neither a £500 reward, nor the fact that Rhode Island's elected governor took part in the inquest, persuaded anyone to provide evidence. The Commission of Inquiry finally disbanded angrily only in June 1773. By that time, the three-year lull in British-American relations was drawing to a close.

THE MARCH TOWARD WAR

The quiet years ended in the spring of 1773, when Parliament once again enacted a law that angered the Americans. This time, however, instead of spontaneous protests under the control of no one in particular, resistance to British policy was aroused and organized by a number of able, deliberate men.

They might best be described as professional agitators. Some of them were orators who articulated anti-British resentments in ringing phrase. Others were organizers, people willing to devote their time to shaping anger into rebellion. There can be no revolutions without such revolutionaries. Men like James Otis of Massachusetts, and Patrick Henry of Virginia, made the difference between spontaneous incidents like the burning of the Gaspée and calculated provocations like the Boston Tea Party.

Rebellious Rhode Islanders burn the British patrol boat Gaspee in Narragansett Bay, 1772.

James Otis

James Otis was a hot-tempered Boston lawyer who could whip up passions to the fighting point like few of his era. In 1761, he led a popular protest in Boston against "writs of assistance." These were general search warrants that empowered customs collectors to enter any property to search for smuggled goods. Arguing against such broad powers, Otis appealed to the cause of the rights of British subjects. Apparently, he coined the phrase so important to the rebels of the 1770s: "Taxation without representation is tyranny." John Adams later said that "then and there," when Otis delivered his address, "the Child Independence was born."

Curiously, Otis grew more moderate while men like John Adams grew more militant. By the time the spirit of revolution matured, Otis was no longer among its leaders. Tragically, he lived out his final years intermittently insane as the result of a brawl with a British official. In a horrible moment that seemed to symbolize his career, he was killed by a bolt of lightning in 1783.

Patrick Henry

Patrick Henry was the counterpart of Otis in the South. Not a deep thinker, Henry was a sharp-tongued Scotch-Irish shopkeeper who educated himself to become one of Virginia's most successful trial lawyers. He caused a furor in 1767 when, only 27 years old, he denounced George III as a tyrant because the king reversed a law that had been passed by the Virginia House of Burgesses.

Two years later, Henry gained attention throughout North America during the Stamp Act crisis. Although only the more moderate of the resolutions he introduced were actually passed by the House of Burgesses, all of them were published throughout the colonies under his name. Henry became even more famous for a speech he delivered to the burgesses. "Caesar had his Brutus," he was quoted as shouting, "Charles I his Cromwell, and George III may profit by their example." Referring offhandedly to the execution of rulers was heady stuff, and Henry was shouted down with cries of "Treason!" Legend has him replying, "If this be treason, make the most of it." (Another account has Henry later apologizing.)

Relentless in his attacks on the Crown (and on the tidewater planters), Patrick Henry spearheaded the final drive toward independence by calling for the establishment of an army in May 1775 with the famous words, "Give me liberty or give me death."

Samuel Adams

More thoughtful and deliberate than Otis and Henry was Samuel Adams of Massachusetts. A brewer as a

Patrick Henry declaiming "Give me liberty or give me death" in a patriotic painting done long after the event. An eyewitness to the speech reported a somewhat less heroic scene.

young man, a tax collector between 1756 and 1764, Adams thereafter devoted himself to the dual career of moral censor and professional anti-British agitator. Indeed, to Samuel Adams, morality and virtue were fundamental to his dislike of British rule. He was obsessed with the concept of republican virtue such as educated people of the eighteenth century attributed to the ancient Greeks and Romans. (He once said that Boston should be a "Christian Sparta.") Political power, he believed, was legitimate only when exercised by men who lived austerely and were ever vigilant to preserve liberty.

Adams' scorn for luxury and fear of tyranny put him at the forefront of every major protest in Boston. He led the battle against the Sugar Act, the Stamp Act, and the Townshend Duties. Unlike other agitators, however, Samuel Adams was no orator. He was nervous at the podium, trembling and stumbling over his words. Nor was he so impetuous as Otis and Henry. Adams was an organizer, the man who handled the undramatic but essential work that transforms anger into protest, and protest into politics. He also served as a link between wealthy critics of British policy, such as the merchant John Hancock, and the Sons of Liberty, drawn from the artisan class, whom he neither feared nor disdained, just so they were virtuous.

Samuel Adams may have been thinking in terms of

independence as early as the mid-1760s. However, perhaps because of his failure to create a fuss over the Boston Massacre, he was generally quiet until the winter of 1773. Then, Parliament presented him with a revolutionary opportunity.

Fatal Turn: The Tea Act

In May 1773, Parliament enacted the legislation that led directly to the American Revolution—the Tea Act. Ironically, the law was not framed with the colonies much in mind, and not really designed to tax Americans. The primary purpose of the Tea Act of 1773 was to bail out the East India Company, a private commercial concern involved in trade with Asia.

The East India Company was invaluable to the Crown. In return for a monopoly of trade with India, the company carried out many governmental and military functions on parts of the subcontinent the British ruled. (The Hudson's Bay Company did much the same in the wilderness north of Canada.) In 1773, however, the Company was teetering on the edge of bankruptcy as a result of mismanagement and bad luck. Among other problems, its capital was tied up in some 17 million pounds of tea in London warehouses for which no buyers could be found. Early in 1773, shares in the East India company plummeted in value from £280 to £160.

To prevent disaster, in which many members of Parliament would have shared, company officials proposed that they be allowed to sell their tea directly to the American colonies. Because the tea was, in effect, being dumped, it would actually be cheaper than the smuggled Dutch tea that had become fashionable in America since the enactment of the Townshend duties. To sweeten the cup further for the colonials, the Company's directors asked that all taxes on the tea be repealed.

The prime minister, Frederick, Lord North, met the Company nine-tenths of the way. His Tea Act eliminated all taxes except the Townshend levy of 3d on the pound. North, a favorite of George III (who uncannily resembled the king), saw a chance to succeed where Grenville and Townshend had failed. Even with the tax, Tea Act tea was a bargain, the cheapest thing going

LONGING FOR THE GOOD OLD DAYS

Not until 1776 did more than a few colonials think of Great Britain's actions as meriting a fight for independence. On the contrary, most of them thought that the solution to the crisis was to go backward—to relations as they had existed before 1763. Benjamin Franklin's advice was to "*repeal* the laws, *renounce* the right, *recall* the troops, *refund* the money, and *return* to the old method of requisition."

across the Atlantic. It would cost Americans money to uphold their principle of "no taxation without representation." Like his predecessors, Lord North believed that colonial protest was built on a bed of simple greed.

The Tea Parties

North was wrong. When a dozen East India Company ships carrying 1,700 chests of tea sailed into American ports, they were greeted by the angriest defiance of British authority since 1765. The Americans would not be bought. Tea Act tea may have been cheap, but the precedent of granting a monopoly on sales in the colonies to a private company was dangerous. If the Tea Act succeeded, any number of parliamentary regulations might follow.

The Company managed to land its tea in Charleston, where it was hastily locked up in a warehouse so that an angry crowd could not get to it. In New York and Philadelphia, authorities ordered the ships to return to England for fear of a riot. In Annapolis, Maryland, a tea ship was burned. But it was a milder action in Boston that triggered the crisis.

The American-born governor of Massachusetts, Thomas Hutchinson, would not permit the tea ships to depart Boston. Instead, while sparks flew at public meetings throughout the town, he hatched a plan to seize the tea for non-payment of a port tax. This would enable him to get the tea ashore and under the authority, not of a vulnerable private company, but of the royal governor.

The ploy was clever, but Samuel Adams was cleverer. On December 16, 1773, the day before Hutchinson could legally seize the tea, Adams presided over a protest meeting attended by a third of the population of Boston. With such immense support, some 60 Sons of Liberty slipped out of the meeting house, dressed up as Mohawk Indians, and boarded the East India Company ships. To the cheers of the crowd, they dumped 342 chests of tea worth £10,000 into Boston harbor.

The Indian costumes were a stroke of political genius. In addition to disguising the perpetrators, they lent an act of gross vandalism the air of a prank, the "Boston Tea Party." Samuel Adams and other protest leaders knew that Britain could not let the incident pass, and they probably gambled that Parliament would overreact. Parliament did. Instead of trying to root out the individual vandals and treat the incident as a criminal matter, Lord North decided to punish Boston and the whole colony of Massachusetts.

The Intolerable Acts

With Lord North's party, the "king's friends," in control of Parliament, the Coercive Acts of 1774—which the Americans called the Intolerable Acts—sailed through both Commons and Lords. The first closed the port of Boston until such time as the city (not the individual culprits) paid for the spoiled tea. Second, the new governor (an army general, Thomas Gage) was empowered to transfer out of the colony the trials of soldiers or other British officials accused of killing protesters. To Bostonians, this seemed to be an open invitation to the redcoats to shoot. Third, the entire structure of government in Massachusetts was overhauled, with elected bodies losing powers to the king's appointed officials. Fourth, a new Quartering Act further aggravated civilian-soldier relations to the breaking point. It authorized the army to house redcoats in occupied private homes!

Lord North hoped that by coming down hard on Massachusetts, he would isolate the Bay Colony, which had never been popular elsewhere in North America, and issue a warning to protesters elsewhere. Instead, the Coercive Acts proved to be intolerable everywhere. Several cities shipped food to paralyzed Boston. More ominous than charity, when Massachusetts called for a "continental congress" to meet in Philadelphia in order to discuss a united response, every colony except Georgia sent delegates.

Salt in the Wound: The Quebec Act

Although it was not designed as one of the Coercive Acts, the Quebec Act of 1774 also angered colonists. This law officially recognized the French language and Catholic religion in the province of Quebec, and extended the boundaries of the province into the Ohio River Valley. Equally important, the Quebec Act failed to provide for an elective assembly for the French Canadians.

There were a number of good reasons for the Quebec Act. Many historians have regarded it as a rare example of enlightened imperial government. Instead of oppressing its French subjects, the Crown respected and pro-

---

THE BOSTON TEA PARTY: THE MORNING AFTER

If the men of Boston who dumped the tea into Boston harbor were in their cups, a few at least suffered no hangovers. One participant remembered what he did on the morning after:

The next morning, after we had cleared the ships of the tea, it was discovered that very considerable quantities of it were floating upon the surface of the water, and to prevent the possibility of any of its being saved for use, a number of small boats were manned by sailors and citizens, who rowed them into those parts of the harbor wherever the tea was visible, and by beating it with oars and paddles so thoroughly drenched it as to render its entire destruction inevitable.

tected their institutions. As for the absence of an elected assembly, there never had been one in New France. Nevertheless, to English-speaking colonial Protestants whose own elected assemblies were under attack, the religious and political provisions of the Quebec Act were alarming. Nor were land-hungry farmers and speculators pleased to hear that western reserves they regarded as their own—in present-day Ohio, Indiana, and Illinois— had been assigned to the French province.

THE REVOLUTION BEGINS

The Intolerable Acts and the Quebec Act mark an important turning point on the road to revolution. Before 1774, confrontations between Americans and the mother country had been scattered, episodic, and local. Except for the Committees of Correspondence, which several colonies had set up to exchange news and opinions via the mails, almost every effort to get the thirteen colonies to act in concert had been initiated by the British and scuttled by the resistance of one colony or another. Now, while most of the delegates to the Continental Congress who trickled into Philadelphia during the summer of 1774 continued to speak of their affection for, and loyalty to, George III, the fact that they were meeting together pointed unmistakably to the possibility of a serious break.

The Delegates

The delegates to the Congress arrived in Philadelphia in early September and began their discussions on the fifth of the month. Some of them, such as Benjamin Franklin, were quite well-known; others, such as Samuel Adams and Patrick Henry, had recently become notorious. Most were gentlemen of only local renown, and, since each of the colonies had closer relations with England than with any other American province, few of the 56 delegates had ever met. The delegates themselves were different in many ways—in temperament, in their sentiments toward Great Britain, in their opinions as to what should and could be done.

But they got along remarkably well. Ironically, the heritage they were soon to rebel against gave them something in common. They were all "gentlemen" in the English mold—merchants, planters, and professionals, particularly lawyers. They prized education and civility. They knew how to keep debates decorous and impersonal. In the evening, they recessed to a round of festive dinners and parties with Philadelphia high society. George Washington rarely dined in his own rooms. John Adams gushed in letters to his wife, Abigail, about the lavishness of Philadelphia cuisine. Only his cousin Samuel, nurturing his ideals of Roman republican frugality,

shunned the social whirl. He quickly won the reputation of being a gradgrind.

Defining the Issues

The delegates worked together smoothly also because most of them were uncertain about what to do. All were angry, even those who would later remain loyal to Britain, and they were determined to settle their squabble with Parliament. The Congress adopted a defiant set of declarations called the Suffolk Resolves, which had been rushed to Philadelphia from Boston (Suffolk County, Massachusetts), by the tumultuous silversmith who had publicized the Boston massacre, Paul Revere. The resolutions stated that the Intolerable Acts were completely invalid, and called for a boycott of trade with Britain if the obnoxious laws were not repealed.

But the Congress also insisted on loyalty to the Crown. The delegates agreed to British regulation of colonial trade, and they almost adopted a conciliatory plan de-

These watercolors of Revolutionary soldiers are crude but frankly grant the place of blacks in eighteenth-century America. Later, when slavery was reinvigorated, the participation of blacks in major historical events was usually forgotten.

signed by Joseph Galloway of Pennsylvania just a few days before they voted for the hard-line Suffolk resolutions. At their parties they self-consciously lifted their glasses to the health of the King and Queen. The idea of rebellion was still quite repugnant.

Unhappily, George III did not share their mood. He, too, was determined to stand firm, and, assuming that he wielded overwhelming power, he was more than willing to use force. "Blows must decide whether they are to be subject to the Country or independent," George told Lord North at a time when no colonial leader had publicly mentioned the possibility of independence.

Learning of the king's intransigence, the delegates to the Congress could no longer ignore the likely consequence of their convention. One of their last actions before adjourning was to call on Americans to organize and train local military units.

Colonial Soldiers

Little encouragement was needed. In the Massachusetts countryside, tempers were already aflame. When a British spy, sent out from Boston to get a feel for the mood of the people, asked an old farmer why, at his age, he was cleaning his gun, the old man replied that "there was a flock of redcoats in Boston, which he expected would be here soon; he meant to try and hit some of them." Did his neighbors feel the way he did? Yes, most of them. "There was one Tory house in sight," the old man said, "and he wished it was in flames."

Younger men oiled their guns and met on village greens to elect officers and drill. Practically every adult male in rural America was armed, for guns were as much tools as were axes. Farm families still hunted for some of their food, and the day when they had to protect themselves from the Indians and the French was not long gone.

The Americans were said to be excellent marksmen. Their rifles were generally more accurate than the redcoats' muskets, and powder and shot were too expensive to waste. But the colonists were not soldiers. They had shunned British attempts to recruit them, and General Wolfe had called his American militia "the dirtiest, most contemptible cowardly dogs you can conceive." Considering the nature of eighteenth-century warfare, however, this was almost a compliment.

How Wars Were Fought

Like so many endeavors of educated people in the Age of Enlightenment, eighteenth-century warfare was highly structured. In battle, two armies in close formation maneuvered to face one another from the best possible position, preferably high ground. After an exchange of artillery, soon to be, but not yet the key to battle, the attacking army closed the gap to the oddly cheerful music of fife and drum (or bagpipes if the soldiers were Scots). The armies exchanged musket fire in volleys. The men pointed rather than aimed their weapons, and the army that stood its ground amidst the horror of smoke, noise, and companions dropping to the sod—in other words, the army that maintained good order and clockwork discipline—defeated the one that panicked, broke ranks, and fled.

The key to winning such battles was long, hard, and tedious training according to manuals written by French and Prussian tacticians. These drills (and a dram of rum or gin before battle) were designed to make a machine of thousands of individual human beings. Marksmanship counted for little. Individual initiative was a curse, to be exorcised by often brutal discipline. The goal was nothing less than unnatural behavior on a grand scale: not fleeing from a terrifying experience.

Lexington and Concord

And so, when General Gage decided to seize rebel supplies at Concord, Massachusetts, 21 miles from Boston, he did not worry about the Minutemen (plain farmers pledged to be ready to fight at a minute's notice). How could such play-soldiers stand up to one of Europe's finest armies? On April 19, 1775, he sent 700 troops to seize the munitions and, if possible, arrest Samuel Adams and John Hancock, who were thought to be hiding in the area.

The Americans were warned by "the midnight ride of Paul Revere," and by William Dawes, and Samuel Prescott of Lexington, who actually got farther than Revere, bringing the news to crossroads and village commons that "the British are coming." When Major John Pitcairn arrived at Lexington, he discovered 70 nervous farmers drawn up in a semblance of battle formation. Their fate seemed to confirm British confidence.

The Americans were frightened and confused at the sight of the solid ranks of tough, grim men who outnumbered them ten to one. They stood around uncertainly, murmuring among themselves. Pitcairn twice ordered them to disperse. Then a shot was fired.

No one knew who started the "battle," a colonial hothead who was determined to force the issue or a British soldier blundering as George III and Lord North had blundered. In the end it did not matter. In London, on the same day as the Battle of Lexington, Parliament was passing another Intolerable Act, which banned Massachusetts fishermen from the Grand Banks of Newfoundland. When Americans heard of that law, which was designed to finish off the already crippled New England economy, it would surely have set off armed rebellion.

Major Pitcairn's men easily cleared Lexington Green and marched on to Concord, where a larger group of Americans met them at a bridge. Surprised and alarmed by the extent of resistance, Major Pitcairn ordered a

Samuel Johnson, who was recognized during his own lifetime as one of the greatest figures of English literature, did not like Americans. Among their own unpleasant traits, Dr. Johnson said, they were shameless hypocrites. "Why is it," he wrote in 1775, "that we hear the loudest yelps for liberty among the drivers of negroes?" His point, of course, was painfully apparent to many of the people who subscribed to the phrase "all men are created equal," and then held one American in five in bondage for life.

Proslavery whites simply ignored the sentiments of the Declaration of Independence. Others, who disliked slavery, lived with the contradiction by consoling themselves that blacks were intellectually and morally inferior to whites, and so could not fulfill the duties of a citizen in a republic. In order to hold to this rationalization, however, they had to ignore the example of two remarkable individuals.

Phillis Wheatley (1755?–84) was born in West Africa, probably in what is now Senegal. She was kidnapped when eight years of age by slavers bound for Boston. There, despite the girl's frail appearance, a successful tailor and merchant, John Wheatley, purchased her as a personal maid for his wife.

Phillis, as the Wheatleys named her, was lucky in her master and mistress. Had she been sold to work on a farm or plantation, her intelligence and charm would have gone unnoticed, as the abilities of other blacks were ignored. The Wheatleys recognized the girl's brilliance and treated her as they did their own children, providing her an education as well as decent food, clothing, and lodging. Wheatley was a prodigy, mastering the English lan-

guage within sixteen months and astonishing visitors by reading and explaining the meaning of the most difficult sections of the Bible, Greek myths, and the poetry of Alexander Pope and Thomas Gray, then the most admired of the English poets.

At the age of thirteen, Phillis wrote her first poem, an ode "To the University of Cambridge in New England" (Harvard), and in the next years a salute to King George III (still immensely popular in America) and a eulogy to George Whitefield, the founder of American Methodism, a faith Phillis adopted.

In 1772 or 1773, John Wheatley freed the young woman, not an uncommon practice in Massachusetts during the decade of the Revolution, and helped pay her passage to England, where she hoped to recover her health and to meet the countess of Huntingdon, a Methodist noblewoman with whom she had corresponded. With the countess's help, Phillis published a book of her *Poems on Various Subjects, Religious and Moral*, but she soon returned to Boston when she heard that Mrs. Wheatley was dying.

In 1775, with the Revolution about to explode, Phillis wrote a letter to George Washington, who responded, expressing his interest in meeting her (they never met). Like many Virginia slaveowners, Washington worried about the wisdom and morality of slavery, and he might have looked on Wheatley as evidence that blacks were indeed capable of great attainments.

In 1778, Phillis alienated the Wheatley heirs by marrying John Peters, a free black who apparently was quite intelligent and was a writer of some ability. Peters, however, was a ne'er-do-well and a deserter. He stole a manu-

retreat to Boston. All the way, Minutemen sniped at the British soldiers from behind trees and stone fences, inflicting serious casualties. When the redcoats reached the city, more than 250 of the expedition were dead or wounded. The Minutemen, elated by their success, set up camp outside Boston.

Bunker Hill

Soon 16,000 Americans surrounded the city. In England, Edmund Burke pleaded with Parliament to evacuate Boston and allow tempers to cool. As usual, the most thoughtful politician of the age was ignored. Lord North dispatched another 1,000 troops to Boston along with three more generals—Henry Clinton, John "Gentleman Johnny" Burgoyne, and William Howe.

They argued Gage out of his reluctance to take provocative action, and Howe agreed to occupy high ground on a peninsula across the Charles River. The day before he moved, the Americans took the peninsula, including

Bunker Hill and, nearer to Boston, Breed's Hill. When Howe's men took to their boats, 1,600 armed colonials were dug in on the summit of Breed's Hill.

Howe sent 2,000 crack troops up the slopes but, at first, no one returned their shots. Then, when the Americans could "see the whites of their eyes" (in other words, when they could aim), they let loose a murderous volley. The redcoats staggered and retreated. Again Howe advanced his troops, and again they were thrown back. Now, however, the British correctly calculated that the Americans were short of ammunition. Reinforcing his badly mauled front line with fresh men, Howe took Breed's Hill with bayonets.

The British had won, or had they? Hearing that 200 men had been killed, and 1,000 wounded, General Clinton remarked that too many such "victories" would destroy the British ability to fight. Clinton was right. The misnamed Battle of Bunker Hill was an American triumph. The British gained nothing, for the colonial script that Phillis was preparing for publication, lost it, and was jailed for bad debts. After bearing three children, all of whom were stillborn or died in infancy, Phillis Wheatley died in poverty in 1784.

Benjamin Banneker (1731–1806), who is known as the black Benjamin Franklin because of the breadth of his interests and the fact that he published a popular almanac, was the son of a free black mother and a slave father who, when Benjamin was still a child, prospered as a planter in Maryland. The elder Banneker educated his son at a Quaker school near Baltimore, one of very few in the colonies that accepted blacks as students.

As a young man, Benjamin farmed his father's lands, which he inherited, but his heart was not in the life. Neighbors remembered him as detached and dreamy, given to eccentric dress and habits. On clear nights, Banneker lay outside on a blanket, studying the stars. In free moments during the day, he studied bees, on which he wrote a treatise, and worked difficult mathematical problems, at which he was a genius. Banneker constructed a wooden clock (said by some to be the first clock made wholly in North America) and was locally famed as an astronomer. His reputation spread in 1789, when he accurately predicted a solar eclipse. This led to the publication of *Banneker's Almanac* (1792–1802), a successor to *Poor Richard's* in popularity, and to a correspondence with Thomas Jefferson, who secured from President Washington a position for Banneker on the commission that surveyed the District of Columbia.

Banneker was a natural scientist; politics were of no great interest to him. As a Quaker, he was a pacifist during the Revolutionary War. In 1791, he wrote a letter to Jefferson, which has since become famous, in which he offered his own example of proof that blacks were capable of citizenship and should be granted it:

> *I apprehend that you will embrace every opportunity to eradicate that train of absurd and false ideas and opinions, which so generally prevail with respect to us [black people]; and that your sentiments are concurrent with mine which are: that one universal Father hath given being to us all; that He not only made us all of one flesh, but that He hath also without partisanship afforded us all with the same faculties and that, however variable we may be in society or religion, however diversified in situation or color, we are all the same family and stand in the same relation to Him.*

Banneker knew that only the most extraordinary individuals, such as Wheatley and himself, could hope to break through the prejudice against blacks. He hoped that political leaders like Jefferson would see in their accomplishments evidence that, given the opportunities of freedom, all blacks could earn places in society commensurate with their abilities. The existence of a Banneker did trouble Jefferson, who wanted to believe that blacks were not the intellectual and moral equals of whites and therefore were not entitled to the rights stated in his Declaration of Independence. Habit, self-interest (Jefferson's social position was built on slave ownership), and the death of the astronomer in 1806, when Jefferson was president, allowed him to suppress his doubts.

militia simply fell back, maintaining their circle around Boston while revolutionaries secured their control of the New England countryside.

Ticonderoga

Rebel morale had another boost in the spring of 1775. Soon after Lexington and Concord, a would-be revolutionary government, the Massachusetts Committee of Safety, instructed Benedict Arnold, scion of a wealthy Connecticut family and a proven soldier, to raise an army and attack Fort Ticonderoga, a small former French outpost on Lake Champlain in New York. Before he started, Arnold learned that a group of backwoodsmen from what is now Vermont, a kind of guerrilla group calling themselves the Green Mountain Boys, were preparing to march on the same fort behind an eccentric land speculator named Ethan Allen.

Arnold caught up with the Green Mountain Boys, but he was unable to get the headstrong Allen to recognize his authority. Quarreling all the way to the remote fort, the two shut up just long enough to capture Ticonderoga on May 10. When the British detachment, having heard nothing of Lexington and Concord, asked in whose name they were supposed to surrender, Allen allegedly replied, "in the name of the great Jehovah and the Continental Congress." Striking and memorable as the words are, since Allen was an aggressive atheist, he was unlikely to have spoken them.

Over the next days, the Arnold-Allen group captured several other small forts. They were not big battles. They were hardly battles at all by European standards. The British garrisons were caught entirely by surprise. But along with Bunker Hill, these triumphs established that a war had begun, forcing Americans to take sides. Nowhere was the psychological impact greater than in Philadelphia, where the Second Continental Congress was already in session.

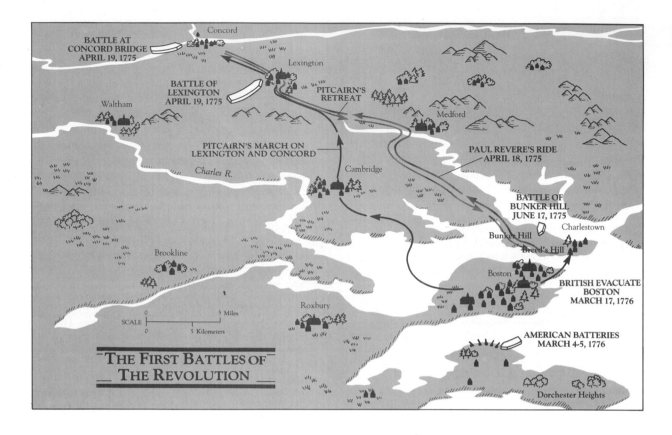

THE FIRST BATTLES OF THE REVOLUTION

The Second Continental Congress

The delegates to the Second Continental Congress were less cautious than those to the First. Some conservatives, such as Joseph Galloway, were no longer present. Their places were taken by militants such as young Thomas Jefferson, a Virginian who had written several scorching anti-British polemics.

Even if the men who gathered in Philadelphia in May 1775 had been more cautious, events would have forced them to take drastic steps. Open-armed rebellion was now a reality, and if the Congress was to retain the authority that Ethan Allen had ostensibly bestowed on it, the delegates had to catch up with the New Englanders. In order to do so, they sent George Washington, silently eloquent in military uniform, to take command of the troops around Boston. The delegates mulled over the news of Bunker Hill, Ticonderoga, an unsuccessful attack on Canada led by Arnold, and the defeat of Governor Dinsmore of Virginia by Virginians and North Carolinians at the end of 1775.

Even where there was no bloodshed, royal authority was disintegrating as governors fled to the safety of British warships, and self-appointed rebel committees took over government functions. Only in isolated Georgia did a decisive royal governor hold fast to real authority. Even he could not prevent three Georgia delegates from making their way to Philadelphia.

Congress still shied away from independence. Its "Declaration of the Cause and Necessity of Taking up Arms" of July 1775 insisted that the rebels sought only their rights as British subjects. But the inconsistency of shooting at George III's soldiers while swearing undying love for the king was preying on the minds of all. Throughout the autumn of 1775, more and more voices were raised for independence. With Lord North refusing to propose any kind of compromise, Congress held back only because of a thread of sentiment—the commitment of virtually all of western civilization to the principle of monarchy, and lingering affection for the person of George III.

ROUSING REVOLUTION IN COMMON SENSE

"O! ye that love mankind! Ye that dare oppose not only the tyranny but the tyrant, stand forth! Every spot of the Old World is overrun with oppression. Freedom hath been hunted around the globe. Asia and Africa have long expelled her. Europe regards her as a stranger and England hath given her warning to depart. O! receive the fugitive and prepare in time an asylum for mankind."

Thomas Paine

BREAKING THE TIE

The man who snipped the thread was not an American, but an Englishman, 38 years of age in 1775, and only recently arrived in the colonies. Benjamin Franklin sponsored Thomas Paine's immigration. Perhaps because both men were of the artisan class—Paine was a corsetmaker—Franklin saw beyond Paine's history of failures in business, "loathesome" personal appearance, and vainglorious opinion of his own talents.

Common Sense

Paine was an insufferable egotist, but his talents as a rouser of protest merited considerable self-esteem. In January 1776, he published a pamphlet that ranks with Luther's 95 theses and the *Communist Manifesto* as works of few words that changed the course of history. In *Common Sense*, Paine argued that it was foolish to risk everything for the purpose of British approval, and he shredded the Americans' sentimental attachment to King George III and to the very idea of monarchy. George was a tyrant, Paine said, a "Royal Brute." All kings were vile.

With a genius for propaganda that would produce many stirring calls on behalf of democracy and liberty over the next 20 years, Paine made converts by the thousands. Within a year, a land with a population of 2.5 million bought 150,000 copies of the pamphlet. (Within a decade, 500,000 copies were printed.) Every American who could read must have at least skimmed it. Paine boasted that it was "the greatest sale that any performance ever had since the use of letters."

Paine's depiction of the king seemed to come to life with every new dispatch from London. George III refused even to listen to American suggestions for peace, and he backed Lord North's plan to hire German mercenaries to crush the rebellion. As the spring of 1776 wore on, colony after colony formally nullified the king's authority within its boundaries. Others, borrowing phrases from Tom Paine, instructed their delegates in Philadelphia to vote for independence.

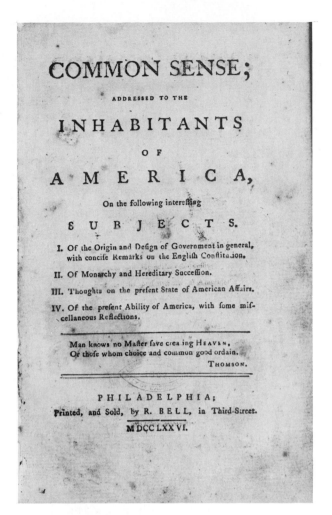

The title page of Thomas Paine's Common Sense. *His pamphlet was so widely distributed that almost every "inhabitant of North America" must have at least skimmed a copy.*

Independence

On June 7, Richard Henry Lee of Virginia introduced the resolution that "these United Colonies are, and of right ought to be free and independent states." For three weeks the delegates debated and privately argued the issue. New England and the Southern Colonies were solidly for the resolution; the Middle Colonies were reluctant and divided. New York never did vote for independence, but Pennsylvania, the large, prosperous, strategically located "keystone" of the colonies, gave in. The pacifistic John Dickinson, a Quaker, and the conservative Robert Morris agreed to absent themselves so that the deadlock in the delegation could be broken in favor of the resolution. (Both men later supported the patriot cause.)

Delaware swung to the side of independence when Caesar Rodney galloped full tilt from Dover to Philadelphia casting the deciding vote in his delegation. On

---

BEST SELLER

In one year, Thomas Paine's *Common Sense* sold 150,000 copies. The population of the thirteen colonies, soon to be independent states, was then 2.5 million; therefore, one copy of Paine's pamphlet rolled off the presses for every 17 Americans. If a book had sold proportionately in the United States in 1987, sales would have been 14.4 million. The actual nonfiction best seller of 1987 was Bill Cosby's *Time Flies*, at 1.7 million copies. The best-selling work of fiction in 1987 was Stephen King's *The Tommyknockers*, at 1.4 million.

July 2, these maneuvers concluded, the Congress broke America's legal ties with England. "The second day of July 1776," an excited John Adams wrote home, "will be the most memorable epoch in the history of America." He was two days off. The "Glorious Fourth" became the national holiday when, on that day, the Congress gathered to adopt its official statement to Americans, and to the world, why it chose "to dissolve the political bands" that tied America to Great Britain.

The Declaration of Independence

Officially, the Declaration of Independence was the work of a committee consisting of Thomas Jefferson, Roger Sherman of Connecticut, John Adams, Benjamin Franklin, and Robert Livingston of New York. In fact, appreciating better than we do today that a committee cannot write anything readable, the actual work was assigned to Jefferson because of his "peculiar felicity of style." The young Virginian holed up in his room near Philadelphia's waterfront, and in two weeks emerged with a masterpiece. Franklin and Adams changed a few words, and the Congress made some alterations, the most important of which was to delete an attack on the institution of slavery.

Then, on July 4, the signing began. John Hancock, the president of the Congress, wrote his name in flamboyant outsized script so that King George would not need his spectacles in order to read it. Hancock was risking little. Along with Samuel Adams, he already had a price on his head. Many of the others who affixed their names, some only months later, were taking a bolder step for they were unknown to the king and his advisers.

King George bore the brunt of Jefferson's attack. He was blamed for practically everything that was wrong in the colonies but the weather and the worms in the corn. The personalization of the attack was quite improper on one level, of course. King George was beholden to Parliament for every colonial policy he tried to enforce. He needed Parliamentary support to raise an army. But the

---

WRITING THE DECLARATION

Thomas Jefferson did not try to be original in writing the Declaration of Independence, but to call on ideas that were in the air so that the American cause would be immediately accepted. His famous statement of the natural rights of man, for example, was taken from a speech that Samuel Adams had made in Boston in November 1772: "Among the natural rights of the colonists are these: first, a right to life; secondly, a right to liberty; thirdly, to property; together with the right to support and defend them in the best manner they can." Beyond that, he drew from philosophical ideas well known to educated people in the colonies, Great Britain, and elsewhere in Europe.

THE FUNNY "S"

In documents of the Revolutionary era, including early printings of the Declaration of Independence, the letter *s* is often written *f*. It is not an *f*; note that the character has only half a crossbar, if that; and it is pronounced with a hiss as surely as the esses in sassy.

The "funny" *f* originated in German handwriting and was adopted by printers in the old German printed alphabet known as Gothic. Its use was reinforced in England because the moveable type used by early English printers was imported from Germany, the home of printing.

Use of *f* was governed by strict rules. It was a lowercase letter, never a capital at the beginning of a proper noun or sentence; the familiar S served that purpose then as now. The *f* appeared only at the beginning or in the middle of a word, never at the end. Thus, *business* was *bufinefs* and *sassiness* was *faffinefs*. The use of this form of *s* died out in the United States during the early nineteenth century.

---

propaganda worked. Like *Common Sense*, Jefferson's essay focused American anger on a visible and vulnerable scapegoat.

Universal Human Rights

The Declaration is not remembered for its catalog of George III's high crimes and misdemeanors. It is one of the great political documents in history because, in his introductory sentences, Jefferson penned one of the most stirring statements of the rights of human beings that has been written to this day. He did not speak only of the rights of American colonials. He put the case for independence in terms of the rights of all human beings: "We hold these truths to be self-evident, that all men are created equal, that they are endowed by their Creator with certain unalienable Rights, that among these are Life, Liberty and the pursuit of Happiness." And he codified the principles that government drew its authority only from the consent of the people to be governed, and that when the people withdrew that consent, they had the right to rebel.

Wording would be borrowed from the Declaration of Independence over the two centuries that have elapsed since its signing by many peoples asserting their right to independence from others, from the republics of Central and South America early in the 1800s, to the Vietnamese on September 2, 1945. In the United States, groups demanding their human rights—from African-Americans to women to labor unions—have based their demands on their "inalienable rights." In the summer of 1776, however, Americans thought less of the Declaration's remote future than the necessity of confirming its pretensions on the battlefield.

The signing of the Declaration of Independence, July 4, 1776, as portrayed by John Trumbull.

For Further Reading

Most of the books listed in the first paragraph of the bibliography for Chapter 7 also deal with events following 1770. In addition, see David Ammerman, *In the Common Cause* (1974); Carl Becker, *The Declaration of Independence* (1922); Robert A. Gross, *The Minutemen and Their World* (1976); Don Higginbotham, *The War for American Independence* (1971); Benjamin W. Labaree, *The Boston Tea Party* (1964); Pauline Maier, *From Resistance to Rebellion* (1972); John Shy, *Toward Lexington: The Role of the British Army on the Coming of the Revolution* (1965); Morton White, *The Philosophy of the American Revolution* (1978); Gary Wills, *Inventing Amer-*

ica: Jefferson's Declaration of Independence (1978); Gordon S. Wood, *The Creation of the American Republic, 1776-1787* (1969); and Hiller B. Zobel, *The Boston Massacre* (1970).

Valuable biographies include Bernard Bailyn, *The Ordeal of Thomas Hutchinson* (1974); Richard R. Beeman, *Patrick Henry: A Biography* (1974); Eric Foner, *Tom Paine and Revolutionary America* (1976); Noel B. Gerson, *The Grand Incendiary: A Biography of Samuel Adams* (1973); and Pauline Maier, *The Old Revolutionaries: Political Lives in the Age of Samuel Adams* (1980).

British General John Burgoyne surrenders to Horatio Gates at Saratoga, New York, in 1777. It was the most important American victory of the war until the climactic fight at Yorktown.

THE WAR FOR INDEPENDENCE

WINNING THE REVOLUTION 1776 - 1781

The signers of the Declaration pledged their lives, their fortunes, and their sacred honor to the cause

of independence. This was no empty vow. Had George III won the quick victory he expected to win,

the delegates to the Second Continental Congress would have been punished severely, perhaps even

hanged. They called themselves Patriots, but from where the king sat, they were traitors. The noose

had been the fate of rebels in Ireland and would be again.

THE IMBALANCE OF POWER

L ooked at without benefit of hindsight, Patriot chances of success in 1776 were not very bright. Despite the military and moral victories of the preceding year, the Patriots had challenged Europe's premier imperial power and one of its finest armies. And they did not even have a majority of Americans behind them.

The Numbers

After the fighting around Boston in 1775, Lord North's military advisor, Lord George Germain, assembled an army of 32,000 men which was dispatched to join the redcoats already in America in a flotilla of more than 400 ships. The campaign to suppress the American Revolution was the largest military endeavor in British history to that date. In addition to British regulars, Germain contracted in January 1776 to hire 18,000 (later 30,000) mercenaries from the petty German princes of Hesse who supported themselves by training and renting out crack soldiers to the highest bidder. By calling on these Hessians, Britain internationalized the civil conflict before Thomas Jefferson made his appeal to "the opinions of mankind." In any case, during much of the war, the British had 50,000 troops ready for battle.

Against this massive force, the Americans could field only hastily organized state militias made up of farmboys, restless apprentices, city laborers, and roustabouts. "To place any dependence on them," George Washington lamented, "is assuredly resting on a broken staff." Terms of enlistment in the militias were short, often geared to the demands of agriculture. At harvest time—and with winter coming on—whole armies evaporated. Nevertheless, state militiamen played a key role in the Revolution. They maintained Patriot authority in those areas the British did not occupy.

Congress also created its own Continental Army. Some 230,000 men were to enlist in it (including repeaters) inspired by patriotism, bounties in money and land, or resentment of British actions. Unfortunately, the enlistees passed out as well as into the army. Washington

himself was never to have more than 18,500 of these continental soldiers ready at one time. On several occasions, his command numbered a mere 5,000. In the South late in the war, General Nathanael Greene had fewer than 2,000 men with whom to fend off a major British army. Still, those that did serve impressed foreign observers by their committment to the cause of independence and their willingness to endure repeated setbacks and terrible hardship. In that sense, they were better soldiers than Britain's professionals. Large numbers of the Hessians, after getting a look at America's abundant and cheap land, were to desert King George.

The Loyalists

The Patriots could not always rely on the support of the civilian population. John Adams overshot the mark when he estimated that a third of the white population was Tory, loyal to the king. Nevertheless, in March 1776, when General William Howe evacuated Boston, a city of just 15,000 people and notorious for its anti-British sentiment, a thousand Americans went with him. When Howe moved his headquarters to New York in September, he was received more as a liberator than as a conqueror. At the end of the war, as many as 100,000 Americans (1 in 30) left their native land for England, the West Indies, and Canada, especially Nova Scotia.

Most northern Anglicans were Loyalists. So were some rich merchants with close commercial ties to England and, in the South, back-country farmers who had been Regulators. Imperial officials naturally supported the Crown as did some very rich South Carolina and Georgia planters who feared that the social disruptions that inevitably accompany war would lead to slave uprisings. Indeed, fear of slave revolt prevented the sugar planters of Jamaica and other West Indian islands from supporting the Revolution. Many were sympathetic to the mainland Patriots; however, outnumbered by their slaves by as much as 6 to 1, they needed a British military presence.

The British did win some support among slaves by promising freedom in return for military service. Black Bostonians asked for such a bargain as soon as Major Pitcairn limped back to the city from Concord. When Lord Dunsmore, governor of Virginia, called for slaves to desert their Patriot masters and serve the British, hundreds did so. Like other Loyalists, and with an even greater fear of retribution, most of the black redcoats left the country after the war, many going to Nova Scotia.

About 5,000 blacks served in the American forces. Native Americans were also divided in their choice of sides. After first declaring neutrality, the Iroquois Confederacy split wide open on the issue of the war, ending a peace of 200 years. The Oneidas and Tuscaroras supported the Patriots (as did the southern Catawbas). The

THE FEARS OF A LOYALIST

The Reverend Mather Byles (1706–88) was an oddity, a Massachusetts Congregational minister who opposed the Revolution. In a sermon of 1776 he expressed his fears of democracy: "Which is better, to be ruled by one tyrant three thousand miles away, or by three thousand tyrants not a mile away?"

General William Howe.

Senecas, Cayugas, and Mohawks were persuaded by a high-ranking brother and sister, Joseph and Mary Brant—she was the widow of a British Indian Commissioner—that their lands would be safer if their old friends, the British, prevailed. In the South, the Creeks sided with the British while the Choctaws were pro-Patriot. Ancient suspicions prevented the Indians from forming a united front and playing a perhaps decisive political role in the conflict.

Neither Bird nor Beast

Far more numerous than active Tories were people who were simply indifferent to the dispute. Adams said they comprised a third of the population and Francis Hopkinson of New Jersey, a Patriot, vilifed them as cynical opportunists willing to hop either way, depending on which side was winning in the neighborhood. In a poem about a metaphorical war between "birds" and "beasts," Hopkinson wrote that there were:

> 'Mongst us to many, like the Bat,
> Inclin'd to do this side or that
> As int'rest leads—or wait to see
> Which party will the stronger be.

He was too harsh, as zealots usually are. As in every era, many Americans wished only to be left alone. Most "Bats" were neither heroes nor villains, just ordinary folk who failed to see what all the high-flown palaver about loyalty and liberty had to do with them. The same might well apply to those Indian tribes that tried to sit the war out.

Patriot Chances

Despite the handicaps, the Patriot cause was far from futile. The rebels were fighting a defensive war in their homeland. As many twentieth-century "wars of liberation" have shown, such conflicts bestow immense advantages on the insurrectionists. Militarily, the Patriots did not have to destroy or even decisively defeat the British. Rebels on their own ground need only to hold on and hold out until war-weariness, demoralization, and dissent take their toll on the enemy.

The army of suppression, by way of contrast, must wipe out the rebel army and occupy the entire country. This the British were never able to do—could not possibly do. The redcoats occupied many port cities through most of the war. As late as 1780, they captured Charleston. But only one American in 20 lived in the seaports. Most of the countryside remained under Patriot control or, at least, beyond the grasp of the British. As a result, the huge British garrison had to be provisioned largely from abroad. Even some grain for horses was carried by ship from England and Ireland. At one point, British com-

WAR CRIMES

Soldiers and Native Americans on both sides were guilty of acts that, today, we would call atrocities. Colonel Henry Hamilton, the British commander of the fort at Detroit, was nicknamed the "hair-buyer" because he paid Indian allies for Patriot scalps, whether of men, women, or children. In 1776, Cherokees devastated the Virginia and Carolina frontiers, leading to a reprisal by South Carolina militiamen who destroyed Cherokee towns and the year's entire crop.

In July 1778, a British-led force of Loyalists and Indians scourged Pennsylvania's Wyoming Valley and, in November, a similar group swept through Cherry Valley, just 50 miles from Albany, New York. On November 11, 40 Patriots were massacred after they had surrendered.

At King's Mountain in 1780, American troops did the same thing, firing on British soldiers trying to surrender. In the same year, Virginia and North Carolina militia burned 1,000 Cherokee villages and destroyed 50,000 bushels of corn, not bothering to count the fatalities. In March 1782, Pennsylvania militia murdered 96 Indians of the Delaware nation who were trying to stay out of the conflict.

Most, but not all, of the baldest atrocities were the work of militia, guerrillas, or Indians. Many probably had less to do with Empire and Independence than with that ageless opportunity of wartime: it is an excellent time to settle old scores.

manders in New York thought they would have to import hay!

Pro-American sentiment was strong in England. Influential members of Parliament such as Edmund Burke and the Marquis of Rockingham sniped at the North ministry throughout the war. These men believed that the Americans were more right than wrong. They hoped to keep North America in the empire, but they regarded the conflict as the fault of King George and Lord North, and were willing to let the Americans go.

The Americans also had reason to hope for foreign intervention. Since 1763, the other major powers of Europe had been uneasy with Great Britain's preeminence. In Spanish Louisiana, Governor Bernardo de Galvez provided arms to the Americans from the start. France, so recently humiliated in North America, India, and Europe, was even more helpful. In May 1776, the French government began to funnel money and arms to the rebels through a secret agent, Pierre de Beaumarchais (who was, incidentally, a scathing satirist of aristocratic foibles in *The Barber of Seville*). Over the next two years, the Americans depended on France for 80 percent of their gunpowder.

Business and Pleasure in Paris

In September 1776, the Continental Congress sent Benjamin Franklin, 70 years old but far from creaky, to join other American diplomats in Paris to work for a French alliance. Franklin was a social sensation in France. Aristocrats, in the final years of their glitter, were enamored of him. The bewigged and powdered ladies and lords of Louis XVI's court were in the throes of a "noble savage" craze. The gist of the fad, based on the writings of Jean-Jacques Rousseau, was that primitives, like their own peasants and the rustic Americans, led happy, wholesome lives because of their closeness to nature.

Queen Marie Antoinette built a model "peasant village" at Versailles, where she and her ladies-in-waiting dressed like shepherdesses, milked well-scrubbed cows, and giggled along behind flocks of perfumed geese. Aware of this silliness, Franklin (who preferred the high life) made a point of appearing at court wearing homespun wool clothing, no wig on his bald head, and rimless bifocal spectacles (which he had invented) on his unpowdered nose.

French high society loved the show, but the foreign minister, Charles, Count Vergennes was more deliberate. Secret shipments of arms were one thing. Before Vergennes would commit the French army and navy to open war, he wanted evidence that the rebels were more than rioters who would disperse after a good snort of gunpowder. In 1776 and the first half of 1777, Franklin was unable to provide Vergennes much encouragement.

Benjamin Franklin donned no powdered wig or silk finery when he mixed with the French aristocracy. He knew perfectly how to exploit their infatuation with the notion that Americans were "noble savages."

"THE TIMES THAT TRY MEN'S SOULS"

General Sir William Howe, who took command of British forces in North America after the Battle of Bunker Hill, was a meticulous planner. No rash acts for him: he moved only when sure of the consequences, preferring to err on the side of caution.

Early in 1776, caution dictated that he evacuate Boston. A Massachusetts general, Henry Knox, had arrived outside the city with 43 cannon and 16 big mortars which Washington positioned on Dorchester Heights, high ground to the south of Boston. Howe decided to reorganize his army in Halifax, Nova Scotia, then to relocate it and his headquarters by sea to New York, where Loyalists were numerous. Washington would have no choice but to follow him and fight on ground more favorable to the British.

The Battle for New York

On July 2, 1776, the same day that Congress voted for independence, Howe landed 10,000 men on Staten Island, just south of New York City. Within seven weeks, he tripled his numbers and moved by ship to Long Island, where Washington's smaller force had hurriedly dug in. The American position was untenable. Washington had to fight on ground laced by navigable waterways that gave the edge to the force with naval power. Washington had a few fishermen from Massachusetts to ferry his soldiers about. Howe could call on a fleet of more than 200 ships, commanded by his brother, Admiral Lord Richard Howe.

On August 27, the two Howes almost surrounded Washington at the Battle of Long Island, but the Americans slipped away to fortifications at Brooklyn Heights, across the East River from Manhattan. Again, Howe's redcoats and Hessians punished the 5,000 rebels; but, in one night, Washington managed to sneak the bulk of his army to Manhattan. Howe pursued him, capturing 3,000 American troops at Fort Washington and forcing General Nathaniel Greene to abandon Fort Lee, across the Hudson River in New Jersey. Once again, Washington and his bedraggled army escaped within hours of capture. They marched north to White Plains and, when nearly surrounded there, crossed the Hudson River into New Jersey.

The Fox and the Hounds

General Howe was having a jolly good time. The New York campaign reminded him of the British gentry's favorite sport, the fox hunt. When the Americans were on the run north of New York City, he infuriated the dignified and self-conscious Washington by sounding the traditional bugle call of the chase.

In truth, Washington's army was as desperate as a fox dodging hounds. Washington had to flee across New Jersey without a fight. When he crossed the Delaware River into Pennsylvania, his men were demoralized and ready to desert. In Philadelphia, one day's march to the south, Congress panicked and fled to Baltimore, effectively leaving the Virginian in command of what was left of the Revolution.

"These are the times that try men's souls," Thomas Paine wrote, "The summer soldier and the sunshine patriot will, in this crisis, shrink from the service of his country." About 3,000 rebels in British-occupied New York and New Jersey took an oath of allegiance to the Crown. The Revolution was in danger of being snuffed out not six months after the signatures on the Declaration of Independence were blotted dry.

But William Howe soldiered by the book, and the book said that an army went into winter quarters when the snow fell. Howe settled into New York City, where his mistress and a lively round of dinners and parties beckoned. He recalled the hounds from Washington's

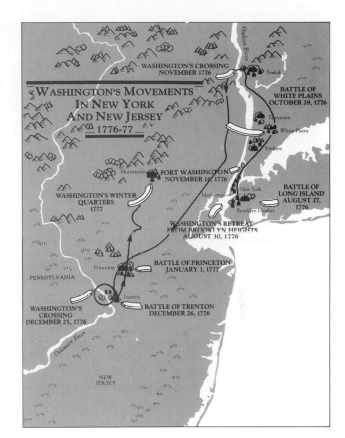

heels, leaving small garrisons of Hessians to guard Trenton and Princeton.

Crossing the Delaware

George Washington was no more an innovator than Howe. Had his army not been near disintegration, he also might have followed the book into winter quarters. Instead, on Christmas night, his New England fishermen rowed the army across the Delaware into New Jersey, the boats dodging ice floes and, in the fog, one another. The troops marched nine miles to Trenton, the most isolated British outpost. At dawn, they caught the Hessians in their bedrolls and, no doubt, none the better for their holiday celebrations. Washington captured almost the entire garrison of 900 men, while his men sustained only five casualties.

An annoyed Howe sent two forces to confront Washington before the Americans could press close enough to New York to ruin the festivities. Washington wisely avoided a fight with General Charles Cornwallis and, on January 3, 1777, defeated another small garrison at Princeton. Cornwallis had no choice but to withdraw to New Brunswick, within range of reinforcement from New York. Washington, satisfied he had done what was needed, set up his winter quarters at Morristown.

The Battle of Princeton, *by William Mercer. The surprised British forces had the upper hand until George Washington arrived with his main force and routed them.*

Washington had indeed done what was needed. He had saved the cause. His offensive across the Delaware provided an indispensable boost to Patriot morale. Still, the victories at Trenton and Princeton did not significantly affect Howe's position or strategy. His army was intact and snug in New York, while another force massed in Canada. The British had the initiative.

The Northern Strategy

Howe's initial plan to win the war, conveyed by letter to Lord Germain in London, was to march north up the Hudson River and join forces with another British army sent south out of Montreal. This pincers movement would isolate New England from the rest of the colonies. With the support of the Royal Navy, the British could subdue Boston and Massachusetts from the west. If the occupation of New England did not discourage the rebels south of New York, the army could then turn in that direction.

Germain was persuaded, but not so much by Howe as by General John Burgoyne, who had returned to England. Burgoyne, a playwright and charming *bon vivant* popular in London society, saw the northern strategy as a way to add glory to his credits. He convinced Germain to put the 8,000 troops and 100 cannons in Canada

under his command. Howe, getting the news in New York, was annoyed, seeing that "Gentleman Johnny," and not himself, would get credit for the campaign.

His pique made him receptive to the pleas of American Loyalists such as Joseph Galloway to move south rather than north. Galloway, a Pennsylvanian, persuaded the general that Loyalists were a majority in Pennsylvania. By taking Philadelphia, Howe would knock the Middle Colonies out of the war, a victory that would exceed in esteem anything Burgoyne managed.

The Watershed Campaign of 1777

In the summer of 1777, leaving 3,000 men in New York under General Henry Clinton, Howe moved by sea into Pennsylvania. Washington followed once again and, on September 11, was defeated at Brandywine Creek, southwest of Philadelphia. On September 26, after another victory at Paoli, Howe occupied Philadelphia. On October 4, Washington counterattacked at the suburb of Germantown but, while close to victory, was finally repulsed. The Americans had to fall back to winter quarters at Valley Forge. Howe was comfortably ensconced in the largest city in the colonies, which was also, in theory, the capital of the independent United States.

Howe had his glory but it was soon tarnished by news

from upper New York. In June, while Howe was putting to sea, General Burgoyne had left Montreal. The first part of the long trek went well. The old Indian trail to Lake Champlain was broad and secure. The lake itself provided a fast highway 125 miles into New York. Fort Ticonderoga, at the foot of the lake, fell without a fight.

Then, however, the wilderness began to take its toll. Burgoyne's heavy artillery and the provisions needed to supply 8,000 troops (and 2,000 camp followers) could be moved only slowly on a trail meant for moccasins. Burgoyne's personal baggage alone was immense, filling 30 carts with a living and dining suite fit for the toast of London, heavy beds and tables, linens, fine china, crystal, silverware, wine, and brandy. Small groups of Patriots felled large trees across the road, creating a far more difficult job for British axemen. During one three-week spell, Burgoyne's army moved less than a mile a day.

Then Gentleman Johnny learned that reinforcements coming east via the Mohawk River had been turned back by Benedict Arnold. Soon, thousands of Iroquois abandoned the British cause. Finally, a Hessian raiding party sent east to seize supplies in Bennington, Vermont was wiped out by local militia. In a series of skirmishes around Saratoga, another fort, Burgoyne lost hundreds more men.

Knowing by now that Howe was en route to Philadelphia, Burgoyne should have given up the expedition

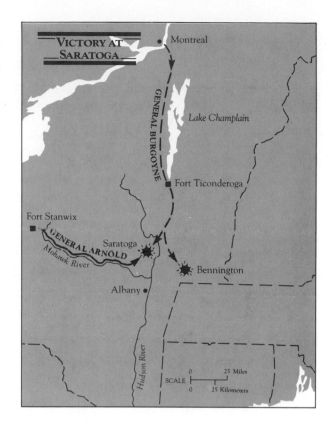

and backtracked to the safety of Canada. Attacking New England was out of the question. Even if he reached New York, he would accomplish little. Instead, Burgoyne sat tight, ordered his wines and sauces, and waited for help from General Clinton in New York.

Burgoyne's blunder was a godsend to the Americans under General Horatio Gates. On October 17, after yet another damaging battle, they accepted the surrender of some 5,700 soldiers. The Battle of Saratoga was the most important event of the year, perhaps of the war. With it, New England was lost to the British. Except for Newport, Rhode Island, which they held only by tying down an army and fleet, the British never again secured a foothold north of New York City.

THE TIDE TURNS

In Paris, Saratoga was exactly the news for which Benjamin Franklin and his colleagues had been waiting. The victory allayed Vergennes's doubts about Patriot chances. The rout and capture of an army of 8,000 crack redcoats and German mercenaries was no skirmish, even by French military standards.

Nor by British standards. When Lord North heard of

George Washington at Verplanck's Point, *by John Trumbull (1790).*

the battle, he wrote to Franklin that King George was willing to end the war on the basis of the terms demanded by Americans up to July 1776. That is, the Intolerable Acts and every other obnoxious law enacted between 1763 and 1775 would be repealed. Great Britain would concede colonial control of internal affairs in return for loyalty to the king.

This attractive offer amounted to an American victory. Essentially, Lord North had proposed to reorganize the empire as a commonwealth of autonomous dominions, the status Britain was to accord to Canada, Australia, and New Zealand in the nineteenth century. But the French offer of a formal alliance was more attractive. By the end of 1777, American animosity toward the mother country had intensified. In New Jersey, British troops had been brutal, bullying farmers, raping women and girls. The old rallying cry, the "rights of British subjects," had lost its magic.

Foreign Friends

On December 17, 1777, Vergennes formally recognized the United States as an independent nation. In February 1778, he concluded a formal treaty of alliance, to go into effect if France and Britain went to war (which they did in June 1778). The agreement provided for close commercial ties between France and the United States and stated that if the United States conquered Canada, France would assert no claims to its former colony. France's reward at the peace table would be the British West Indies.

The Revolutionary War could not have been won without the French alliance. Not only did "America's oldest friend" pour money and some 12,000 men into the fray (2,000 died), but France also provided some 63 warships to make up for the Americans' nearly total lack of sea power. Although Americans relished the one-on-one victories over British warships by such privateering rogues as Scottish-born John Paul Jones ("I have not yet begun to fight") and Irishman John Barry, the American coastline was, without French help, at the mercy of the Royal Navy.

France's diplomatic influence was also critical to the American cause. Spain sent Bernardo de Galvez into British Florida, where he quickly occupied every fort. Vergennes averted a war that was brewing between Prussia and Austria that would have tied down French troops in Europe (a traditional British objective). He persuaded both of those countries, as well as Russia, to declare their neutrality in the American conflict. Vergennes's diplomatic maneuvers denied England an ally against the Americans and paved the way for informal assistance to the Patriots from all over Europe. Next to France, the

DESPAIR AT VALLEY FORGE

The winter of 1777/78 was extremely difficult for Washington's army. Inadequately fed, clothed, and sheltered at Valley Forge, while the British enjoyed comfortable quarters in Philadelphia, many fell to the depths of despair. Albigence Waldo, a surgeon with Connecticut troops, wrote this entry in his journal on December 14, 1777:

Poor food—hard lodging—cold weather—fatigue—nasty cloathes—nasty cookery—vomit half my time—smoked out of my senses—the Devil's in't—I can't endure it—Why are we sent here to starve and freeze?—What sweet felicities have I left at home: A charming wife—pretty children—good beds—good food—good cookery—all agreeable—all harmonious! Here all confusion—smoke and cold—hunger and filthyness—a pox on my bad luck!

Netherlands was the most valuable ally, lending money liberally to Congress.

Mercenaries for Liberty

In addition, the chronic warfare of eighteenth-century Europe had created a class of military professionals who, during times of peace, were unhappily unemployed. Gentlemen and aristocrats of this stripe, hungry for a commission with a salary attached, poured into the infant United States. There was plenty of deadwood in the bunch. But others were able men who were motivated by more than money. Some sympathized with the principles of liberty expressed in the Declaration of Independence.

Such a figure was Marie Joseph, the Marquis de Lafayette, a 19-year-old aristocrat (the British called him "the boy"). He proved an excellent field commander and a

A VISION OF THE FUTURE

John Adams understood that circumstances made him a politician and a revolutonary. But he envisioned another kind of future for his country:

I must study politics and war, that my sons may have liberty to study mathematics and philosophy, geography, natural history and naval architecture, navigation, commerce, and agriculture, in order to give their children a right to study painting, poetry, music, architecture, statuary, tapestry and porcelain.

close personal friend to Washington. Lafayette was no dilettante, dabbling in fashionable notions. After returning to France, he worked for social and political liberalization until his death in 1834.

Equally idealistic was Casimir Pulaski, a Polish noble who had fought for his country's independence from Russia. Recruited in Paris by Benjamin Franklin, Pulaski was a romantic figure, a cavalry commander in gaudy uniform and waxed mustache. He was killed leading a charge at the Battle of Savannah late in the war. Johann Kalb, a Bavarian who took the title Baron de Kalb when he went to America (then as now, titles wore well in the United States), also lost his life during the war, at the Battle of Camden.

Jean Baptiste, the Comte de Rochambeau, who had secured arms for the Americans, arrived in Newport, Rhode Island in 1780 and was to play a major role in the final victorious American battle at Yorktown, Virginia, the next year. Possibly more valuable to the Revolutionary cause than combat officers were support specialists like Tadeusz Kosciusko, an engineer who was expert in building fortifications, a military field in which few Americans were trained. Kosciusko returned to Europe to fight for the independence of Poland, where he became a national hero.

Friedrich Wilhelm von Steuben, a Prussian who also dubbed himself a baron, was an expert in drill. He is credited with supervising the training program that turned Washington's soldiers from a ragtag crowd into a well-disciplined army at Valley Forge during the winter of 1777–78.

The War Drags On

Steuben worked his wonders just in time. Washington lost 2,500 men to disease and exposure during the winter at Valley Forge and, by the spring of 1778, it was obvious that the war would go on for years. The Americans could not hope to force the issue against the British. Their

strategy was to hold on, fighting battles only when conditions were auspicious. Lord Germain and General Clinton (who took over command from a bitter Howe in May 1778) planned to strangle the American economy through a naval blockade and to concentrate British military effort in the South.

Beginning with the occupation of Savannah, Georgia, in December 1778, the redcoats won a series of victories in the South, but they could not break the stalemate. For each British victory, the Americans won another, or, in losing ground, the rebels cost the British so heavily that they had to return to the coast, in easy reach of supply ships flying the Union Jack.

The war wore heavily on the American side too. Prices of necessities soared. Imports were available only at exorbitant cost. On the frontier, British-backed Indians ravaged newly settled areas in Pennsylvania's Wyoming Valley and Cherry Valley in New York. When Congress failed to pay and provision troops during 1780 and 1781, mutinies erupted on the Connecticut, Pennsylvania, and New Jersey lines.

Then, in September 1780, Washington learned that Benedict Arnold, commander of the fortress at West Point, had agreed to sell the fort and his services to the British for £20,000. Disgruntled at what he considered shabby treatment, Arnold was also deeply in debt. He calculated that the British would eventually win, and so accepted a commission along with pensions for his wife and children. It was an expensive proposition, but the British believed that the defection of one of the Revolution's few heroes would demoralize the rebels.

It helped. The campaign of 1781 opened with American hopes lower than they had been since the Battle of Trenton. Washington was idle outside New York. The most active British army, led by Lord Cornwallis, lost a battle at Cowpens, South Carolina, but then repeatedly pummeled Nathaniel Greene the width of North Carolina. Cornwallis then joined with several other commanders (including Benedict Arnold) to mass 7,500 men in Virginia.

Washington Seizes an Opportunity

But Charles Cornwallis had problems. Anywhere away from navigable water was dangerous ground for the British troops. So, on August 1, 1781, Cornwallis set up what he regarded as a routine encampment at Yorktown, Virginia, a little town on the same neck of land where the first permanent English settlement in America had been founded. Cornwallis then requested supplies and further orders from General Clinton in New York. When Clinton dawdled, Washington sensed an opportunity for a decisive blow.

In mid-August, Washington learned that a French

DANIEL BOONE (1734–1820)

Stephen Vincent Benét's poetry celebrated America. In *John Brown's Body* and *Western Star*, his homages ran to more than a hundred pages of often moving verse. And yet, his finest poem about America may be his shortest:

When Daniel Boone goes by, at night,
The phantom deer arise
And all lost, wild America
Is burning in their eyes.

The name of Daniel Boone is probably known to as many schoolchildren as any figure in American history. It evokes an image more vivid than the Gilbert Stuart portrait of Washington: a long, lank woodlands frontiersman in fringed buckskin and coonskin cap, striped tail dangling languidly on "Dan'l's" neck as he crouches behind a hickory with his Kentucky Long Rifle, poised to "cill a b'ar"—or a skulking Shawnee.

The Boone of legend is an *American* hero, simultaneously delving into the mystery of the wilderness and devoted to it, moving on when he needed more "elbow room"—when he could see the smoke rising from his nearest neighbor's fire.

The kernel of truth is there—Boone was superb in the woods and doubtless happiest there—but the rest of the grain is bogus or, at best, very dubious. If Boone ever wore a coonskin cap, it was *in extremis*, when Indians had stolen his wilderness gear, including the broad-brimmed beaver felt hat he preferred. Theft, not murder (as both leg-

end-makers and sentimentalists would have it), was his and the Shawnees' chief crime against one another.

"D. Boon" was not particularly long, just five feet, eight inches tall by his son's recounting. Far from fleeing those who followed him west, his most notable accomplishment was to build a road to encourage others to come. The idea was to have buyers for land he thought he owned.

If Boone was an American type, his patriotism was less than hysterical. He thought seriously of locating in Spanish Florida as a young man, was court-martialed as a Tory during the Revolution (he was acquitted, but the facts remain not quite conclusive), and left the United States for Spanish Missouri in 1799, not because he craved solitude, but because he was embittered with his treatment under the Stars and Stripes. One thinks more of Stephen Austin and Brigham Young than of James K. Polk.

Daniel Boone was born in 1734 near Reading, Pennsylvania, to a family of Quaker inclinations but casual commitments. The family was neither rich nor destitute, and emigrated to "the West" of the era, western North Carolina.

In 1755, at 21 years of age, Boone was a teamster with the disastrous Braddock campaign in western Pennsylvania. He may have made the acquaintance of young George Washington, but comrades much more important to his future were Thomas Walker, who had discovered the Cumberland Gap through the Appalachians in 1750, and a frontier roustabout, John Finley, who had hunted in the trans-Appalachian forests and canebrakes the Iroquois called Kentucky.

admiral, Count François de Grasse, was sailing from the West Indies to the Chesapeake Bay with 3,000 French troops aboard 24 warships carrying 1,700 guns. It was a formidable armada. Although he had just completed plans for an assault on New York, Washington recognized the better prospect in Virginia. Maneuvering around New York City so that Clinton would sit tight, he raced across New Jersey. In September, he joined his troops to those of Lafayette, Rochambeau, Steuben, and de Grasse. This combined army of 17,000 outnumbered Cornwallis's 8,000, almost the first time in the war that the rebels enjoyed numerical superiority.

Yorktown

Cornwallis did not panic. His men were well dug in, and he expected to move them out by sea and resume the war of attrition elsewhere. But between September 5 and 10, de Grasse sent the British evacuation fleet sailing off empty to New York. Cornwallis fought a futile de-

fense. On October 17, he asked for terms, and on October 19, he faced the inevitable and surrendered.

He gave up but without grace. As if to provide one last symbol of the British arrogance that had helped drive the Americans to rebellion, Cornwallis tried to surrender to the French rather than the upstart colonial, Washington. In truth, Yorktown was as much a French as an American victory. About as many Frenchmen as colonials fought there and more French were killed or wounded in action.

But Rochambeau, the ranking French officer at the battle, refused to play Cornwallis's game, directing him to Washington. Then, at the surrender ceremonies, Cornwallis refused to hand his sword personally to Washington, as military etiquette required. Instead, he sent an inferior officer to the American camp with his blade. Washington refused to receive him, nodding that the symbol of capitulation should be given to General Benjamin Lincoln, whom the British had humiliated at

Hardly obsessed with Kentucky, Boone was not to re-discover the Cumberland Gap for himself for twelve years, and then only because Finley showed up on his doorstep with the idea. He was by no means, as legend-maker Timothy Flint would call him in 1847, "the first white man of the West."

In 1769, Boone finally traced the Gap. He really was the first white man to locate the "Warrior's Path," which Shawnee and Cherokee hunters used to move through Kentucky. Ironically, few Indians actually lived on "the dark and bloody ground." The Cherokee and Shawnee uneasily shared Kentucky as a hunting ground. The land's lack of a native population was a major reason that men like Boone found it attractive for settlement. Boone's employer in 1775, Richard Henderson of the Transylvania Company, scrupulously paid the Cherokee for their rights to it.

In 1775, with 30 skilled axmen, Boone supervised the construction of the Wilderness Road, which was, in fact, a trace. Only in 1796 was it widened to accommodate wagons. It was over this trail that he led the first permanent settlers into Kentucky. George Caleb Bingham was right to pick the moment Boone's party emerged into the sun of Kentucky to immortalize him in oils.

Boone was a major in the Virginia militia during the Revolution, but he was also accused of collaboration with the British and their Shawnee allies. Still, as early as 1784, when Boone was 50, the legend was building. A book promoting Kentucky by John Filson included an "autobiographical" sketch allegedly by Boone.

During the Confederation years, Boone supported himself by hunting and hoped to make a bigger killing as a land speculator. Unfortunately, just as he lost thousands of buckskins to Indians, he lost just about every title dispute in which he was involved to another kind of pilferer. By the 1790s, he was virtually landless in the country, now a state, which he had done so much to develop.

It is tempting to remember Boone for his morality as a land speculator, a rarer distinction than being a pioneer. What he did not lose in court he sold in order to compensate associates for whose losses he felt responsible. But he was bitter, too. When he went to Spanish Missouri in 1799, it was in part to get out of the United States.

The flag followed him four years later and, again, men sharper at finagling before the bar separated most of his land from him. Again, he sold to pay off debts, claiming that, in 1815, his assets totaled 50 cents. A creditor from Kentucky who descended upon him at his son's farmstead near Defiance, Missouri, was told, "You have come a great distance to suck a bull and, I reckon, you will have to go home dry."

Boone died in 1820, not sitting up facing west, as the mythmakers told it, but in bed. Three years later, his fame was such that Byron devoted a few stanzas of *Don Juan* to him.

Of the great names which in our faces stare,
The General Boone, back-woodsman of Kentucky,
Was happiest amongst mortals anywhere.

Charleston at the beginning of the southern campaign. It may also have been designed as a jibe that, during the ceremony, a British band played the hymn, "The World Turn'd Upside Down." No doubt, however, many American soldiers hummed along merrily to the tune.

The Treaty of Paris

The British could have fought on. They still had 44,000 troops in North America. But no one had the stomach for it. In February 1782, the House of Commons voted against continuing the war, and Lord North resigned. He was succeeded by the Marquis of Rockingham, the Whig peer who had moved to repeal the Stamp Act in 1766.

The Treaty of Paris was not finally signed until September 1783. The delay was due in part to the fact that, once the war was won, the Americans and the French grew increasingly suspicious of one another. Fearing betrayal, each ally tried to betray the other first. The American

icans won the game. They agreed with the British on independence, a boundary between the United States and Canada, American fishing rights off Newfoundland and Nova Scotia, and a promise that Congress would urge the states not to molest Loyalists or seize Loyalist property.

George III was as unsporting about independence as Lord Cornwallis had been at Yorktown. He wrote of his former colonies that "knavery seems to be so much the striking feature of its inhabitants that it may not in the end be an evil that they become aliens to this Kingdom."

The Father of His Country

George Washington was no knave. But he was in many ways an unlikely candidate to be accorded the honor, "father of his country," and to be heaped with adulation throughout Europe. In every particular by which greatness is usually measured, Washington comes up short. He lacked originality and boldness. He was no thinker,

THE CINCINNATI

Lucius Quinctius Cincinnatus was an early Roman who was twice appointed dictator of the Republic in order to defeat invaders. Each time Cincinnatus was victorious but, instead of using his vast powers to entrench himself as a tyrant, he returned to his farm, a private citizen. It is not surprising that educated Americans of the Revolutionary era, who were steeped in classical lore, thought of George Washington as their Cincinnatus.

In 1784, veteran officers of the Continental Army formed the Society of the Cincinnati. The organization was controversial from the start. It was semisecret and membership was hereditary, passed down by officers to their first-born sons, who passed it to their first-born sons. In other words, the Society preserved the aristocratic principle of primogeniture that was then being abolished in American legal codes. Thomas Jefferson thought the Society represented a "nascent nobility" and most of its members seem indeed to have favored electing a president for life. During the troubled 1790s, rumors of a military coup led by the Cincinnati periodically worried the Jeffersonians.

However, the charter members grew long in the teeth without biting, the principle of primogeniture was abandoned so that all male descendants of Revolutionary officers might belong, and the Society evolved into an organization "devoted to the principles of the Revolution, the preservation of history and the diffusion of historical knowledge." As such it exists today.

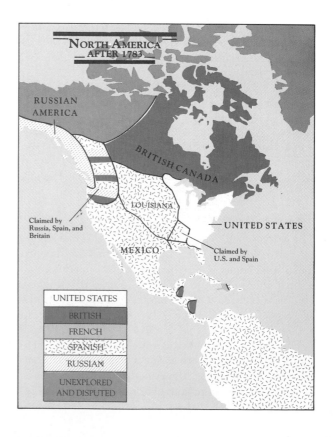

and seems to have read few books. He contributed nothing to the rich literature of colonial protest. His personality was subdued, quiet, dull. He excited no one.

Nor was Washington a successful field commander. His expeditions during the French and Indian War were fiascos. He killed a French emissary with whom he was supposed to negotiate. He built a fort too small for the men he commanded that was under water after one rainstorm. In the early years of the Revolution, he won a few small battles while his defeats were legion. Most of his seven years in command were spent in retreat or wary watchfulness, a step ahead of annihilation. Any number of American generals—Gates, Greene, Arnold!—excelled him as a field commander. His strategy until Yorktown amounted to responding to British actions.

And yet, it would be difficult to overstate Washington's contribution to the establishment of the American republic. It was in successful retreat that his military contribution to independence lay. He kept an army in the field against overwhelming odds. Washington survived in the face of repeated defeats, superior British forces, inadequate provisions, disease, poor shelter for his men during two severe winters, poor support from the Continental Congress, and even a cabal against him.

The British army surrenders to American troops in Yorktown, Virginia, October 19, 1781.

In order to explain his achievement, it is necessary to fall back on the intangibles that transfixed most of his contemporaries. Radicals like Samuel Adams, instinctive conservatives like Alexander Hamilton, intellectuals like Jefferson, warriors like Israel Putnam, cultivated European aristocrats like the Marquis de Lafayette and Rochambeau—all idolized and deferred to the Virginian. Washington's aristocratic bearing, integrity, sense of dignity, and aloofness from petty squabbles set him a head taller than the best of his contemporaries, just as his height (6′2″) made him a physical giant of the time. Despite his setbacks and lack of flash, he held the revolutionary cause together by that vague, undefinable quality known as "character." If the very notion rings a little sappy today, the dishonor is not to the era of the American Revolution.

For Further Reading

Again, students are referred to the bibliography for Chapter 7. Other important general works dealing with the Revolutionary War are Samuel E. Bemis, *The Diplomacy of the American Revolution* (1935); Don Higginbotham, *The War of American Independence: Military Attitudes, Policies, and Practice* (1971); J. Franklin Jameson, *The American Revolution Considered as a Social Movement* (1926); Howard Peckham, *The War for Independence* (1952); and Christopher Ward, *The War of the Revolution* (1952).

Also see Robert M. Calhoon, *The Loyalists in Revolutionary America* (1973); H. J. Henderson, *Party Politics in the Continental Congress* (1974); Merrill Jensen, *The War Within America* (1974); Richard B. Morris, *The Peacemakers* (1965); Mary Beth Norton, *Liberty's Daughters* (1980); Charles Royster, *A Revolutionary People at War* (1979); John Shy, *A People Numerous and Armed* (1976); and Paul H. Smith, *Loyalists and Redcoats* (1964).

Two classic biographies of Washington are James T. Flexner, *George Washington in the American Revolution* (1968) and Douglas S. Freeman, *George Washington* (1948–1957).

The elegantly handwritten Constitution of the United States was signed by the Constitutional Convention on September 17, 1787, and ratified by the required number of states (nine) by June 21, 1788.

INVENTING A COUNTRY

AMERICAN CONSTITUTIONS 1781 - 1789

The American Revolution was not the first war for independence. Peoples subject to others have

risen in rebellion since the dawn of civilization. The history of empires is also a history of uprisings

against imperial domination.

The American Revolution was singular in the fact that Americans had to invent their country and

their sense of nationhood from scratch. They had not been conquered and ruled by foreigners as, for example, the Aztecs had. Most Americans were British, ethnically and culturally. They were rebeling against their own.

Moreover, the thirteen colonies—now states—had had no institutional links with one another before the Revolution. Their only political links had bound them to the mother country.

Consequently, a sense of American nationhood—a sense of shared culture, history, and identity—was slow to take shape. The frame of government the Patriots forged during the Revolution, the Articles of Confederation, was little more than an alliance of independent states with a common problem: 50,000 redcoats determined to subjugate them. Only in 1787, more than a decade after the Declaration of Independence and six years after Yorktown, did "We the people of the United States"—something of an invention even at that date—venture to ordain "a more perfect union" in the Constitution that remains the basic law of the nation today.

THE REVOLUTION ON PAPER

The constitutions of eleven of the thirteen states were drawn up in the midst of the war against Britain. Not surprisingly, these frames of government consciously and specifically reflected the anti-British resentments of the rebels.

Black and White and Read All Over

The most obvious break with the British past was the fact that the first American constitutions were written down and comprehensive, covering every contingency that the authors of the documents could foresee. The unwritten British constitution had served that nation well enough, and it does so to this day. But the lack of a definition of Parliament's powers in black and white had been at the heart of American grievances with the mother country. The Patriots believed that Parliament had violated unwritten tradition in trying to tax them, but they could not prove it and ended up in arms. Written constitutions could be violated too, of course; however, as Thomas Jefferson wrote, "they furnish a text to which those who are watchful may again rally and recall the people."

Notably, the two states that still had written corporate charters at the time of the Revolution, Connecticut and Rhode Island, merely changed the wording of these old documents to suit their independent status. Their colonial charters continued to serve as their state constitutions until 1818 in Connecticut, and 1842 in Rhode Island.

Limiting Power, Striking Down Privilege

The new state constitutions were written not by legislative assemblies but by conventions elected specifically for that purpose. They were then ratified by a popular election and could be altered only by a similar procedure—not by the legislature. The American tradition that "sovereignty" (ultimate governmental power) rested with the people was thereby institutionalized at the time of the Revolution.

Reaction to British rule took other constitutional forms. Because the Patriots had resented the old office-holding elite, they guarded against creating their own by requiring that most officials stand for election annually. Many state constitutions (and the Articles of Confederation) limited the number of years a person elected to office might serve in that office.

The authors of the state constitutions disliked executive power most of all. The royal governors had been George III's representatives in the colonies. They remained staunch Tories when the war broke out. In order to preclude the development of centers of power independent of elected assemblies, the new state governors were allowed little real power. They were largely administrative or ceremonial figures, symbolic heads of state. In Pennsylvania, which in 1776 adopted the most radical constitution of all the new states, there was no governor at all. Nor was there a single executive in the government created by the Articles.

Other old resentments surfaced in the movement to separate church and state. Except in New England, the Anglican church had been the established church, supported by taxes and endowed with other privileges. For that reason among others, the Anglican clergy had been pro-British. Everywhere, Patriots dis-established the Church of England, transforming it into a private denomination like all others. Thomas Jefferson wrote the Virginia ordinance that struck down the privileges of the Anglican church. He regarded this act as one of the major accomplishments of his life.

A Democratic Drift

In every new state, the right to vote was extended to more people than had enjoyed it under the Crown. In Georgia, Pennsylvania, and Vermont (a "state" in fact if not in name), every adult male taxpayer could vote. In most of the other states, the property qualification was lowered so that few free white males were excluded. Women who met other qualifications could vote in New Jersey. In North Carolina, free blacks who met other tests were enfranchised.

There were limits to this democratic trend. Roman Catholics were not allowed to vote in North Carolina until 1835, and Pennsylvania required officeholders to be Christian. John Adams staunchly opposed allowing men without property to vote in Massachusetts. In a majority of states, a voter could not necessarily stand for office. Stricter property qualifications for office-holding were common, and the higher the office, the greater the wealth that was required of a candidate. The Patriots may have been radical by European standards, but they clung to the eighteenth century's belief that property gave a person a greater stake in society and therefore better qualified him to govern it.

Bills of Rights

Eight states included a list of guaranteed individual rights in their constitutions, beginning with Virginia's in 1776. After the vice-admiralty courts, the quartering acts, and arbitrary actions by the British army, the Patriots were determined that there be no vagueness on the question of a person's liberties. Most of the rights later listed in the first ten amendments to the United States Constitution were defined in one or another of the state bills of rights that were written during the 1770s: freedom from cruel punishment; the right of counsel and trial by jury; the right to remain silent during one's own trial; and so on.

Liberty's Limits: Sex and Race

In 1777, when the air was thick with talk of expanding personal liberties, Abigail Adams wrote to her husband, John, who was engaged in writing the Articles of Confederation, to be sure to "remember the ladies and be more generous and favorable to them." But the time was not ripe for redefining women's inferior civil status. Indeed, New Jersey was to rescind its enfranchisement of women in 1807 because an increasing number of women were taking advantage of their right to vote.

By way of contrast, blacks in the northern states, where slavery was of little economic value, won some victories because of the Revolution's expansion of liberties. Quasi-independent Vermont abolished slavery in 1777. Pennsylvania followed suit in 1780. A few years later, Elizabeth Freeman of Massachusetts, whose slave name was Mumber, sued for her freedom on the basis of the Massachusetts constitution, which stated that "all men are born free and equal." The courts agreed and forbade slavery in the Bay State. Rhode Island and Connecticut gradually phased out the institution by prohibiting the enslavement of any person after a date set by law.

In the South, however, as the British Tory, Samuel Johnson trenchantly remarked, "the loudest yelps for liberty [were heard] among the drivers of negroes." Many Southern Patriots were troubled by the hypocrisy inherent in their practices, but economic necessity and the racism a century of slavery fostered were more powerful than libertarian ideals.

The belief that race was an elemental condition of humanity extended even to those who hoped to transcend it. In Virginia, Patrick Henry tried to extend the state's liberties to Native Americans by means of racial assimilation. In 1784, he proposed that the House of Burgesses pay a bounty of £10 to each free white person who married an Indian and £5 for each child born of such unions. Another distinguished Virginian, John Marshall, later commented that the bill "would have been advantageous to this country." He added: "Our prejudices, however, opposed themselves to our interests, and operated too powerfully for them," a timeless commentary on the costs of racism.

AMERICA UNDER THE ARTICLES OF CONFEDERATION

The constitution the Patriots wrote to coordinate the affairs of all thirteen states—the Articles of Confederation—reflected the same fears and ideals as the constitutions of the new states.

Basic Principles

Drafted during the heady years 1776 and 1777, the Articles of Confederation provided for no president, nor any other independent executive. Congress was the only organ of government.

Members of Congress were elected annually and could serve only three years out of every six. That is, if a man were elected to Congress three years in a row, he was ineligible for election again until he had sat out three years. Or, a delegate could serve every other year indef-

---

FOMENTING REBELLION

Abigail and John Adams were touchingly affectionate with each other, and, much rarer, they discussed the momentous issues of the Revolutionary era. Abigail was twitting John when she made her famous appeal for the rights of women in 1777, but it would be a mistake to think that her challenge was nothing more than a joke:

In the new code of laws . . . I desire you would remember the ladies and be more generous and more favorable to them than your ancestors. Do not put such unlimited power into the hands of husbands. Remember, all men would be tyrants if they could. If particular care and attention is not paid to the ladies, we are determined to foment a rebellion, and will not hold ourselves bound to any laws in which we have no choice or representation.

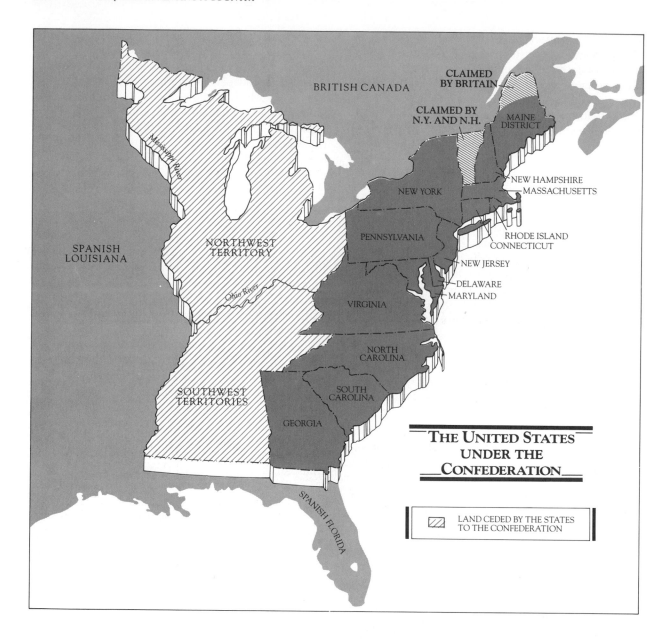

BRITISH CANADA

CLAIMED BY BRITAIN

CLAIMED BY N.Y. AND N.H.

MAINE DISTRICT

NEW HAMPSHIRE

MASSACHUSETTS

NEW YORK

PENNSYLVANIA

RHODE ISLAND
CONNECTICUT

NEW JERSEY

DELAWARE
MARYLAND

SPANISH LOUISIANA

NORTHWEST TERRITORY

Mississippi River

Ohio River

VIRGINIA

NORTH CAROLINA

SOUTHWEST TERRITORIES

SOUTH CAROLINA

GEORGIA

SPANISH FLORIDA

THE UNITED STATES UNDER THE CONFEDERATION

LAND CEDED BY THE STATES TO THE CONFEDERATION

initely. The object of this provision was to prevent the emergence of a class of professional officeholders who regarded public office and its prerogatives as their personal property.

Under the Articles, the United States of America was explicitly not a nation. It was "a firm league of friendship," nothing more. New Hampshire, New Jersey, North Carolina, and the rest explicitly retained their "sovereignty, freedom, and independence." It was a confederation of equals. In Congress, for example, delegates did not vote as individuals. They voted as members of their state Delegation; the state then cast a single vote. The state, not members of Congress, was representative.

Divided Authority

Congress was authorized to wage war and make peace, to maintain an army and a navy, and to supervise diplomatic relations with foreign countries and the Indian nations. Congress was entrusted with maintaining a post office and setting uniform weights and measures. It had the power to coin money, to issue paper money, and to borrow money at home or abroad.

Having granted these powers to Congress, however, the Articles of Confederation also permitted the states to coin money, to ignore the standards of measurement Congress might establish, and individually—as states— to make trade treaties with other countries. Under the

Articles, the states might even, "with the consent of Congress," declare war on a foreign power.

Nor was Congress empowered to regulate trade among the various states. It was "constitutional," in other words, for Delaware to be at war with a foreign power that had a trade agreement with neighboring New Jersey. In fact, New York actually did take military action against Connecticut smugglers.

Successes Against All Odds

The weakness of the ties that bound the states under the Articles was not the consequence of incompetence, indecision, or awkward compromise. Weakness was deliberately written into the Articles because of the revolutionary generation's aversion to strong central government. It was a strong, central government against which the Patriots were in rebellion when they penned the document.

Nor was the Confederation government a disaster. On the contrary, it was under the Articles that the Americans fought and defeated Europe's premier military power. For eleven years of war and peace, a far-flung country of (by 1787) more than 3.5 million souls survived as thirteen "sovereign, free, and independent" states.

By the end of the Confederation era, Congress had created an efficient bureaucracy to administer the day-to-day affairs of the government. States did contribute, albeit reluctantly sometimes, to the Confederation treasury. And Congress solved a problem that could easily have plunged the North Americans into an ugly interstate conflict.

NEW HAMPSHIRE'S SLAVES PETITION FOR FREEDOM

On November 12, 1779, 19 of New Hampshire's 150 black slaves petitioned the state House of Representatives for freedom on the basis of the ideals of liberty that the patriots were asserting. The petition concluded:

Your humble slaves most devoutly pray for the sake of injured liberty, for the sake of justice, humanity and the rights of mankind, for the honor of religion and by all that is dear, that your honors would graciously interpose in our behalf, and enact such laws and regulations, as you in your wisdom think proper, whereby we may regain our liberty and be ranked in the class of free agents, and that the name of slave may not more be heard in a land gloriously contending for the sweets of freedom.

The petition was firmly within the spirit of the Declaration of Independence, but it was rejected by the New Hampshire legislature.

The Western Lands

The treasure that threatened to divide the states was the one that attracted most immigrants to America—land, specifically the land beyond the Appalachians that Great Britain had closed to settlement in 1763. The question was who held title to the vast acreage between the mountains and the Mississippi River?

Colonial charters were the source of the uncertainty. They had been drawn with so little knowledge of North American geography that the boundaries of the individual colonies overlapped, creating a snarl of conflicts thicker than forest underbrush. Virginia insisted that its boundaries fanned out like a funnel at the mountains, encompassing almost the whole trans-Appalachian region. Because its charter was the most ancient, Virginia insisted it held precedence over all others.

Connecticut granted that New York's and Pennsylvania's charters (written later) modified its own western claims. Nevertheless, Connecticut claimed a "western reserve" beyond those states in what is now Ohio. Massachusetts, New York, North Carolina, South Carolina, and Georgia also had claims overlapping those of others.

These disputes were complicated by the fears of the six states with no claims to western lands in their charters: New Hampshire, Rhode Island, New Jersey, Pennsylvania, Delaware, and Maryland. Leaders of those states worried that the landed states would be able to finance their needs indefinitely without taxation by the sale of trans-Appalachian farms. By way of contrast, the landless states would drive their citizens out with high property taxes. On these grounds, Maryland refused to sign the Articles of Confederation until 1781.

The solution was obvious. John Dickinson suggested it as early as 1776. The landed states would have to grant their western territories to the Confederation government, so that all states could share in the wealth.

Fortunately, Virginians—with the most to give up— had good reasons to cede their state's lands to Congress. Virginians played a prominent role in the Confederation government, and they did not want to see it fall apart. Moreover, many Virginians believed that free republican institutions could not survive in large countries. For the sake of hard-won freedoms, such men preferred to see new states carved out of the West.

The Northwest Ordinances

In January 1781, Virginia ceded the northern part of its western claims to the Confederation government. Within a few years, one by one, all the states except Georgia followed suit, with Virginia adding its southern territories to the national domain in 1792. Georgia, with the flimsiest claims, held out until 1802.

This remarkable act—European nations went to war

WESTERN LAND CLAIMS

Claimed by Massachusetts

Claimed by Connecticut

Claimed by New York

Claimed by Virginia

Claimed by North Carolina

Claimed by South Carolina

Claimed by Georgia

over far lesser tracts of real estate—was followed by two congressional acts that were equally wise. The Northwest Ordinances of 1784 and 1787 provided for the creation of equal, self-governing states in the Northwest Territory, the national domain north of the Ohio River that would eventually become the states of Ohio, Indiana, Michigan, Illinois, and Wisconsin. The Northwest Ordinances meant that the United States would hold no colonies. As soon as the population in a designated district equaled that of the smallest state within the Confederation, that territory would be eligible for admission to the Union as an equal partner.

The Rectangular Survey

In 1785, Congress provided for a system of survey to prepare land in the western territories for public sale. Townships six miles square were divided into 36 "sections" of one square mile (640 acres) each. Initially, a section was the smallest plot that could be purchased (at a dollar an acre). $640 was far beyond the means of an ordinary farm family just as 640 acres was far beyond a family's needs. In time, the minimum plot was reduced to a half-section, and then a quarter-section (160 acres). Eventually, a quarter-quarter-section could be purchased, the classic Midwestern American farm of 40 acres.

The thinking behind the rectangular survey system was wise and fruitful. Had purchasers been able to enter public lands and map their own property, they would carve out oddly shaped tracts of prime land, making the most of their dollar per acre. Hills, marshes, rocky ground, and the like would technically belong to the government. However, while no one would pay taxes on these scattered plots or easily be held accountable for their exploitation, settlers would inevitably use them for grazing livestock, cutting wood, digging gravel and stone, and extracting minerals. The rectangular survey forced land buyers to take the poor land along with the good.

The consequences of the rectangular system of land survey can be observed by anyone who travels through rural America. In the East, in the former French parts of Louisiana, and in some areas of the Southwest settled by the Spanish and Mexicans, farms are oddly shaped and roads trace the lay of the land. In the Midwest and much of the Far West, a somewhat irregular checkerboard pattern holds. Roads, on the boundaries of individual properties, are as straight as a surveyor's gaze.

Thomas Jefferson was the chief designer of the Northwest Ordinances. He included in it the slap at slavery he had been denied in the Declaration of Independence. In the act of 1787, slavery was forbidden in the territories north of the Ohio River.

DIFFICULTIES AND FAILINGS

The Northwest Ordinance was an extraordinary achievement. The rectangular survey system was a triumph of statesmanship. The Confederation Congress also succeeded in creating the corps of bureaucrats without which no modern state can function.

At the decision-making level, however, the Confederation was often frustrated and sometimes paralyzed by petty bickering. The sovereignty of the states made diplomacy difficult and threatened to tear the Confederation apart. When a rebellion broke out in Massachusetts in 1787, men who believed that a strong central government was necessary to fulfill the promise of independence stepped forward and effected a bloodless coup d'etat.

Money Problems

The most tenacious of the Confederation's problems were financial. During the war, George Washington had to write dozens of letters to Congress begging for money. Despite the gravity of the peril, the delegates bickered and connived, taking advantage of every limitation on power that the Articles provided. Congress was capable of debating for long hours as to whether a man who claimed $222.60 for ferrying troops across a river should get it.

In 1781, Rhode Island nearly nullified the victory at Yorktown when, alone of the thirteen states, it refused to approve a tariff of a mere 5 percent on imports. This was government by peeve. On another occasion, New York vetoed a tax bill. Because the Articles of Confederation required unanimous state approval to raise money, the government frequently teetered on the brink of bankruptcy.

To meet its obligations, Congress resorted to a device that inevitably frightens people of wealth: It authorized the printing of increasingly larger amounts of paper money—notes popularly known as Continentals. From $6 million in paper money in 1775, Congress printed $63 million in 1778 and $90 million in 1779. Because the value of this currency depended on the people's faith in the ability of Congress to redeem it, the Continentals depreciated rapidly. By 1781, it took almost 150 paper dollars to purchase what one dollar in silver or gold would buy. "Not worth a Continental" was a disdainful catch-phrase that survived the Articles of Confederation.

The assembly of Rhode Island, which was controlled by farmers in debt, also printed paper money, $100,000 worth in 1786. Rhode Island notes were worth even less than Continentals, but the state assembly declared them

BORDER DISPUTES

The states' success in resolving the problem of the western lands was not reflected in other far more petty conflicting claims. For example, when Virginia's Surveyor-General Edmund Scarburgh laid out the boundary between Virginia and Maryland in 1663, he grabbed Cape Charles on what we call the Delmarva Peninsula for Virginia. The two states argued about the curious line until 1894.

Just a mile off the coast of Connecticut is Fisher's Island. It is 30 miles to any point in New York State but Fisher's Island is a part of New York due to the truculent determination of New Yorkers to yield nothing to Con-

necticut during the Confederation era when, indeed, the two states threatened each other with war.

Even more curious is Massachusetts' "Southwick Jog." It is a notch of Massachusetts jutting down into Connecticut through an otherwise geometrical east-west line dividing the two states. Whereas some people from Connecticut still grumble about Fisher's Island, the state willingly granted the Southwick Jog to Massachusetts in 1804 as compensation for land granted elsewhere to Connecticut. The local joke is that the Jog is a handle to keep Connecticut from falling off the map.

---

legal tender for payment of debts at face value. Tales were told of creditors fleeing Rhode Island to avoid being paid back in the useless paper, with debtors, gleefully waving handfuls of the stuff, in hot pursuit. Men of property shuddered. They yearned for a reliable currency that would be valid in every state. Only a strong central government could guarantee such a currency.

Diplomatic Vulnerability

Squabbles among the states made it difficult for Confederation diplomats to negotiate with other nations. France, the indispensable ally in war, would lend no money in peace because the Americans failed to make good on earlier loans. Nor was credit the only problem. Virtually every European country regarded the United States as a collection of weak principalities, like Indian

tribes or the petty states of Germany. They occasionally formed "a firm league of friendship" but, more often, could be played off against one another.

In 1784, a shrewd Spanish diplomat, Diego de Gardoqui, attempted to split the United States in two by playing on the commercial interests of the northern states. He offered to open Spanish trade to American ships (which meant northern ships) if Congress would give up its insistence on the right to navigate on the Mississippi River for 25 years.

Northeasterners cared little about the Mississippi and their representatives tried to ram the treaty through Congress. Had they succeeded, the southern states would have had to go their own way, fulfilling the predictions of even friendly Europeans that the former English colonies would remain weak and divided. The Mis-

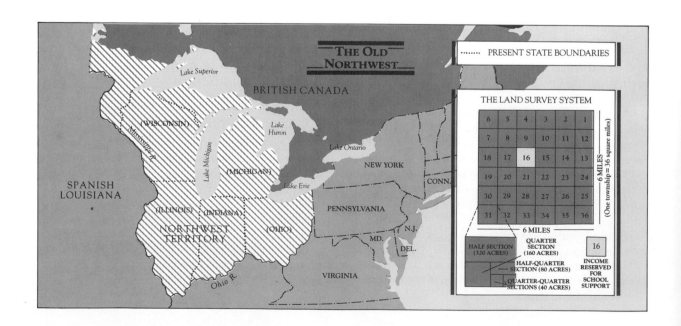

NOTABLE PEOPLE

JAMES MADISON (1751–1836)

"Every person seems to acknowledge his greatness," a delegate to the Constitutional Convention wrote of James Madison of Montpelier Plantation, Virginia. "He blends together the profound politician, with the Scholar. In the management of every great question he evidently took the lead in the Convention, and tho' he cannot be called an Ortor, he is a most agreeable, eloquent, and convincing Speaker."

Students of political science since Madison's time have been even more generous. They have called his *Federalist Papers* one of the masterpieces of political theory. Certainly Madison is America's most impressive political thinker. Alexander Hamilton, his collaborator on the *Federalist Papers*, was not so thoughtful. Thomas Jefferson, Madison's political idol and patron, was a sloganeer by comparison. John C. Calhoun, Madison's illegitimate heir, conceived during a lapse of discretion, was more ingenious, but carping and contrived next to the master.

James Madison was the eldest of ten children born into a comfortable family of planters that had, perhaps, declined from better days. He was tutored at home and then well educated at the College of New Jersey, as Princeton was then known. He probably planned to become a minister. He spent an extra year at Princeton to study languages, theology, and ethics.

The Revolution changed any such plans. Only 25 years of age in 1776, Madison was caught up in the ferment in Virginia and took the lead in fighting for the disestablishment of his own Anglican church in the new state. Whether because he felt himself too weak and sickly for the soldier's life—Madison was tiny in stature and a lifelong hypochondriac who did not "expect a long or healthy life"—or, like Jefferson, because he disdained the military, he spent the war years in civil office. He was a member of the Virginia governor's council and, after 1780, a member of Congress.

His projects in Congress were unexceptionable and, except perhaps in private discourse, he displayed little of the profundity that was to impress the Convention of 1787. It appears that only during the era of the Confederation, which Madison feared would disintegrate at any moment—like his health—did he take up the historical and philosophical study of government. At his frequent request, Thomas Jefferson, serving as minister to France, bought and sent him books about government.

At the Convention of 1787, Madison seems to have spoken even less than implied in the quotation above. The voluminous notes he took on the proceedings (in violation of Convention rules) must have consumed much of his time. But he lobbied assiduously on behalf of the dominance of the large states in the new republic and for a centralized, powerful national government.

Madison accepted the compromises that were necessary to win the support of the small states, but he was not happy about them. Morose, as he often was, he was convinced that the new government was too weak and that "local mischiefs" would split the thirteen states into three countries, New England, a Middle States confederacy, and the South.

A streak of melancholy and misgivings about his abilities run through Madison's life, reflecting his hypochondria. But if he suffered from depression, the attacks were sporadic. He was as often self-confident as trembling. His private conversation was witty and animated. He wooed and won as his wife a vivacious Philadelphia beauty who, like Dolly Madison, brought elegance and flair to Washington's fusty, masculine, whiskey-and-playing-cards society. And despite his chronic groaning, he lived to be 85 years of age.

Although he was a nationalist, Madison was also a devout Virginian. He continued to serve the interests of his state even when Virginia's House of Delegates neglected to pay his salary. (Madison was one of the penurious patriots Haym Salomon bailed out during the war years.)

His devotion to Virginia and to that less-steady nationalist, Jefferson, also helps to account for the great aberration in a career dedicated to strengthening the United States government, Madison's Virginia Resolutions of 1798. This proclamation and Jefferson's Kentucky Resolutions stopped just shy of saying that if an individual state judged an act of Congress in conflict with the Constitution, that state could declare that act null and void within its borders.

Surely Madison, who dissected the most delicate of political organisms in the *Federalist Papers*, understood what "local mischiefs" so ham-handed a doctrine could loose. He lived to see it done in 1828 when John C. Calhoun explicitly formulated the implications of the Kentucky and Virginia Resolutions in his *South Carolina Exposition and Protest*. Calhoun's doctrine of Nullification provided the justification and procedure for the secession of the southern states in 1860 and 1861. Secession from Madison's Union was a state's final recourse when the other states overruled one state's nullification.

Madison referred to Calhoun only indirectly when he wrote, "Let the open enemy of [Union] be regarded as a Pandora with her box opened, and the disguised one as the serpent creeping with his deadly wiles into paradise."

He was also troubled by the positive enthusiasm with which, in his old age, the South defended slavery. Like other Virginians of his generation, Madison regarded slavery as a "dreadful calamity." He took up the study of law during the 1780s so as to have a profession in which he had to "depend as little as possible on the labor of slaves." He supported the work of societies that encouraged the freeing of slaves by transporting free blacks to West Africa. Not long before his death, he told Mrs. Harriet Martineau, the English author of a book about American society, that everything negative ever written about slavery was valid. His was the tragedy of a founder of the Union lived too long into the era of sectional division.

sissippi was a vital artery to the tens of thousands of Virginians and North Carolinians who had moved to what is now Kentucky and Tennessee.

In the far north, England schemed to detach Vermont from the United States. Traditionally a part of New York and claimed by New Hampshire, the isolated Green Mountain country actually functioned as an independent commonwealth under the leadership of Ethan and Levi Allen, two Revolutionary veterans who trusted no one but each other, and kept their backs to the wall even then. The Allens attempted to make a treaty with the British that would have tied the area more closely to Canada than to the Confederation. Congress was powerless to stop them. Only because the British failed to act quickly did the project fall through.

Easily Wounded Pride

Britain's condescension was insulting and infuriating. The former mother country refused to turn over a string of Great Lakes forts that were American under the terms of the Treaty of Paris. Nor did the British send a minister (ambassador) to America. A British diplomat joked that it would be too expensive to outfit thirteen men with embassies and other accoutrements of office. In London, the American minister to Great Britain, John Adams, was ridiculed when he attempted to act with the dignity of a national legate.

It was the same elsewhere. A world-traveling American sea captain said that the United States was regarded "in the same light, by foreign nations, as a well-behaved negro is in a gentleman's family," that is, as an inferior, scarcely to be noticed. Even the venal Barbary States of northern Africa looked down on Americans. These little principalities lived by piracy, collecting tribute from nations whose ships traded in the Mediterranean. When American ships lost the protection that the British annually purchased for vessels flying the Union Jack, they were sunk or captured. The bey of Algiers sold American crews into slavery, and Congress was unable either to ransom them or to launch a punitive expedition. It was a sorry state of affairs for the young men of the Revolution who dreamed of national greatness.

Calls for Change

It was a minor problem in domestic waters that actually launched the movement to overhaul American government. In March 1785, a small group of men from Maryland and Virginia gathered at Mount Vernon, George Washington's home on the Potomac River, to discuss the conflicting claims of Maryland and Virginia fishermen over rights to fish in the Chesapeake Bay. They were unable to draw a boundary between the two states' fisheries. They did, however, conclude that the Chesapeake problem was only one in a tangle of disputes among the states, and between the states and the Confederation government. They invited all thirteen states to send delegates to a meeting the next year in Annapolis, Maryland to discuss what might be done.

Only five states responded, so decisive action was out of the question. Undiscouraged, Washington's former aide-de-camp, Alexander Hamilton of New York, persuaded the small group to assemble once again, this time in more centrally located Philadelphia. They should prepare, Hamilton told them, to discuss all the "defects in the System of the Federal Government."

Hamilton and some other delegates, such as James Madison of Virginia, had more than an academic debate in mind. They intended to plump for replacing the Articles of Confederation with a completely new frame of government. Rumors about their plan spread quickly and met less than resounding approval. Patrick Henry, Madison's rival in Virginia politics, said that he "smelled a rat" and refused to attend. Rhode Island sent no delegates at all. Since the days of Roger Williams, Rhode Islanders had smelled a rat in any hint that their independence of action, which the Articles of Confederation nicely guaranteed, might be harnessed.

Elsewhere, discontent with the Confederation was rife, particularly when, in the winter of 1786–87, a wave of protest among farmers in western and central Massachusetts turned into armed rebellion.

Shays's Rebellion

Massachusetts farmers resented the fact that the state's tax laws, enacted by the merchants of Boston and other seaports, favored trade at the expense of agriculture. In 1786, many farmers assembled in conventions at which they demanded that their property taxes be reduced. To make up for the loss of revenue, they called for the abolition of "aristocratic" branches of the government in Boston.

In several towns, angry crowds surrounded courthouses, harassed lawyers and judges—whom they considered to be unproductive parasites, and forcibly prevented the collection of debts. Then, in September, a Revolutionary War veteran named Daniel Shays led as many as 2,000 armed men against the Springfield arsenal. Shays's Rebellion collapsed in December, but the bitterness of the Shaysites did not sweeten.

Shays and his followers did not regard themselves as a dangerous social force. They believed that they were carrying on the spirit and struggle of the Revolution against a privileged elite. Then minister to France, Thomas Jefferson agreed with them. "A little rebellion now and then is a good thing," he wrote home to a friend. "The tree of liberty must be refreshed from time to time with the blood of patriots and tyrants."

The men who were preparing to gather in Philadel-

By HIS EXCELLENCY

George Clinton, Esq.

Governor of the STATE of NEW-YORK, General and Commander in Chief of all the Militia, and Admiral of the Navy of the fame.

A Proclamation.

WHEREAS His Excellency JAMES BOWDOIN, Esq. Governor of the Commonwealth of Maffachufetts, did iffue his proclamation, bearing date the ninth day of February, fetting forth, that the General Court of the faid Commonwealth had, on the fourth day of the faid month declared, that a horrid and unnatural rebellion had been openly and traiteroufly, raifed and levied againft the faid Commonwealth, with defign to fubvert and overthrow the conftitution and form of government thereof, and further fetting forth, that it appeared that Daniel Shays, of Pelham, and Luke Day, of Weft Spring-

New York Governor George Clinton issued this denunciation of Shays' Rebellion in 1787.

phia in 1787 had another opinion: it was not the pine tree of liberty that needed attention; it was the ailing oak of social peace, stability, and order. George Washington, for one, was deeply troubled by the news of Shays's Rebellion. Society could not tolerate its members taking up arms whenever they felt aggrieved. Washington and many others blamed disorders such as Shays's uprising on excessive democracy.

THE AMERICAN CONSTITUTION

For two hundred years the American Constitution has been hailed with a reverence that can only be described as religious. Patriots, politicians, moralists, and historians—Americans and foreigners alike—have genuflected before a frame of government that could survive for two centuries during which technology, ideology, revolu-

tion, imperialism, and war turned the world upside down and shook it like a terrier with a rat. William E. Gladstone, prime minister of Great Britain in the midst of this tumultuous historical period, was neither alone nor excessive when he called the American Constitution "the most wonderful work ever struck off at a given time by the brain and purpose of man."

"Demigods"

The men who struck it off in the summer of 1787—the "Founding Fathers"—have been heaped with praise, depicted as wise, selfless individuals who peered into their nation's future and designed for it a timeless gift. The Constitution was "intended to endure for ages to come," Chief Justice John Marshall proclaimed in 1819. On the floor of the Senate in 1850, a critical year for the union of states that the Constitution had created, he was echoed by Henry Clay of Kentucky. "The Constitution of the United States," Clay said, "was not made merely for the generation that then existed but for posterity—unlimited, undefined, and endless, perpetual posterity."

In truth, the Constitution has been an astonishingly workable basic law, and the generation of political leaders who wrote and debated it was enviously rich in talent and wisdom. It may be that the nation has not seen their like since. But the Founding Fathers were not "demigods," as Thomas Jefferson feared Americans would make them out to be. They were decidedly human, with prosaic faults and, among their ideals, very immediate purposes to serve.

The Constitutional Convention

The convention in Philadelphia at which the document was actually written began on May 25, 1787. After only a few days, the 55 delegates from twelve states agreed that revision of the Articles of Confederation was not enough. In fact, they had little choice but to start from scratch. It was easier to effect a coup d'etat, to create a new government without regard to the procedures of the one that existed, than to amend the Articles of Confederation. Amendment required that every state agree to the change and Rhode Island had made it quite clear that the state opposed any revision.

The Constitutional Convention met in secret. For four months the delegates bolted the doors and sealed the windows of the Pennsylvania State House (Independence Hall), a demi-heroic sacrifice in the humid Philadelphia summer. In addition, every member swore not to discuss the proceedings with outsiders. George Washington, who presided, was furious when a delegate misplaced a sheet of notes.

There was nothing sinister in the secrecy. The purpose of the convention was common knowledge. The delegates sequestered themselves because they knew they

The "Founding Fathers" at the Constitutional Convention in Philadelphia, 1787.

were performing a historic act, and should proceed with the utmost caution and calm. As James Wilson, a Pennsylvania delegate, said, "America now presents the first instance of a people assembled to weigh deliberately and calmly, and to decide leisurely and peaceably, upon the form of government by which they will bind themselves, and their posterity." No small business that: never had a nation been founded so methodically—invented. The delegates wished to voice their frankest opinions without fear of affecting their political careers back home.

Moreover, they knew there would be opposition to their constitution. Wilson said that "the people" were assembled in Independence Hall. The document that the convention produced begins with the words "We the People of the United States." In fact, the men who drew up the Constitution represented just one political tendency in North America: they wanted their "platform" to be complete before they had to defend it against their critics.

The Delegates

The job was finished in September 1787. After a celebration at City Tavern, the delegates scattered north and south, most to lobby for their states' approval of their document. They were a formidable lot. By virtue of wealth and education they were influential people back home. Of the 55, only Roger Sherman of Connecticut, who had been a cobbler as a young man, and Alexander Hamilton, the bastard child of a feckless Scottish merchant, could be said to have been weaned on anything less glittering than a silver spoon.

Lifetimes spent in justifying independence and creating state governments made most of the delegates keen students of political philosophy. During the years preceding the convention, James Madison augmented his own library with 200 books ordered from Europe. Just as important was the delegates' practical experience. Seven had been state governors; 39 had sat in the Continental Congress.

The Founding Fathers were young. Only nine signers of the Declaration of Independence were among them (and three of them refused to sign the Constitution). Only Benjamin Franklin, 81 years old in 1787, was antique. The other Founding Fathers averaged just over 40 years of age, and the two leading spirits of the meeting were only 36 (James Madison) and 32 (Alexander Hamilton). Another was just 26. Such men had been just old enough in 1776 to play a minor role in the war. They had been children at the time of the Stamp Act crisis. They were heirs of the Revolution, not makers of it.

The comparative youth of the Founding Fathers is of some importance in understanding the nature of the Constitution they wrote. Most delegates had not had the habit of thinking as colonials impressed in their minds. They had not grown to full maturity thinking of themselves as Virginians or New Yorkers before they decided to become Americans. Their vision of the United States was forged in the crucible of a national struggle, "these United States" versus a foreign power.

Unlike their more provincial forebears, these young men moved freely and often from one state to another. In the Continental Army (a third of the delegates had been soldiers, mostly junior officers) and in the Confederation Congress, they had met and mixed easily with men from other states and from Europe. They thought in terms of a continent rather than of coastal enclaves that looked back to a mother country for an identity. They wanted the United States to take its place in the world as an equal among nations. Thus were they chagrined at the weakness of the Confederation government.

A Conservative Movement

Youth does not, as we are accustomed to think, equate with radicalism. The men who drew up the Constitution were conservatives in the classic meaning of the word. They did not believe with Jefferson (then in France) that human nature was essentially good and eternally malleable, that people and human society were perfectible if left free. The Founding Fathers feared the darker side of human nature. If free of institutional restraints,

ALEXANDER HAMILTON ON DEMOCRACY

"All communities divide themselves into the few and the many. The first are the rich and the wellborn, the other the mass of the people. . . . The people are turbulent and changing; they seldom judge or determine right. Give therefore to the first class a distinct, permanent share in the government. They will check the unsteadiness of the second, and as they cannot receive any advantage by change, they therefore will ever maintain good government."

such traditional conservatives believed, selfish individuals would be quick to trample on the rights of others. To conservatives, democracy and liberty did not go hand in hand. On the contrary, people left to their own devices would destroy liberty.

The most pessimistic, and therefore the most conservative, of the lot was Alexander Hamilton. Sent to King's College in New York by friends who recognized his talents, Hamilton never returned to the West Indies, where he was born. He served George Washington as aide-de-camp during the Revolutionary War and impressed his superior with his intelligence and perhaps also with his conservatism, for Hamilton had no sympathy with democratic ideas. A few years after the adoption of the Constitution, he would listen to Thomas Jefferson expound on the wisdom and virtue inherent in the people and snap back angrily, "Your people, sir, are a great beast."

Had Hamilton been an Englishman, he would have defended those institutions that conservatives believed helped to control the passions of the people: the ceremonial monarchy, the privileged aristocracy, the established church, education in tradition, the centuries-old accretion of law and custom that is the British constitution. In fact, Hamilton was an unabashed admirer of English culture and government. Like Edmund Burke, he thought of the American Revolution as a conservative movement. In rebelling, the Americans had defended tradition against a reckless Parliament.

In the Constitution, Hamilton wanted to recapture as much of tradition as he could. He suggested that president and senators be elected for life, thus creating a kind of monarch and aristocracy. He was unable to sway his fellow delegates. As much as many of them may have harbored similar sentiments, they also understood that the "common run" of people would not accept such backsliding toward the old order. What the majority of delegates did approve, and Hamilton accepted, was a system of government that expressed democratic yearnings but placed effective checks on them. The government they created was a "mixed government." It

CONSERVATIVES

In identifying men such as Washington, Hamilton, and Adams as conservatives, it is important not to confuse their political philosophy with that of the "conservatives" of the late twentieth century. Classical conservatives like these three Founding Fathers were suspicious of human nature and therefore inclined to cling to tried and true institutions rather than to experiment. Unlike conservatives of today, they believed that a strong central government that was active in the economic life of the nation was desirable and essential. They had no more tolerance for unbridled economic freedom than for excess of political freedom.

Present-day conservatives, by way of contrast, want a minimum of government interference in the economy. Implicitly, they say that in economic life human nature should not be closely supervised.

Alexander Hamilton (1755–1804), advocate of a strong central government.

was a balance of the three principles: the "democratical" (power in the hands of the many); the "aristocratical" (power in the hands of a few); and the "monocratical" (power in the hands of one).

Mixed Government

The chief exponent of mixed government, John Adams, did not attend the Constitutional Convention. In 1787, Adams was serving unhappily as minister to Great Britain. Before going abroad, however, Adams had stamped his ideas about government on the Massachusetts state constitution against which the Shaysites had rebelled. It provided for a strong governor, a voice for the wealthy in the state senate, and a voice for the people in the state assembly.

James Madison pushed for a similar structure for the new national government. He had his way. The basic principle of the American Constitution is a complex network of checks and balances.

Checks, Limits, and Balances

The House of Representatives was "democratical." Representatives were elected frequently (every two years) by a broad electorate—all free, white, adult males in many states. The Senate and the Supreme Court reflected Adams "aristocratical" principle. Senators were elected infrequently (every six years) by state legislatures. Senators were insulated from the democratic crowd by both the length of their terms and a buffer of state legislators. However, because state legislatures were elected by the same broad electorate that chose the House of Representatives, senators were not completely independent of the popular will.

The Supreme Court was. Justices were appointed by the president, but, once confirmed by the Senate and seated, they were immune to his influence. Justices served for life and could be removed only by a difficult impeachment process.

The "monocratical" principle was established in the presidency, the most dramatic break with the government of the Confederation. The president alone represented the whole nation, but he owed his power neither to the people nor to Congress. He was put into office by an electoral college that played no other role than selecting the president.

An intricate system of checks and balances tied together the three branches of government. Only Congress could make laws, and both democratic House and aristocratic Senate had to agree to the last syllable. The president could veto an act of Congress if he judged it adverse to the national interest. However, Congress could override his veto by a two-thirds majority of both houses.

Judging according to these laws was the job of the judiciary, with the Supreme Court the final court of appeal. In time (it was not written into the Constitution), the Supreme Court claimed a legislative role of its own in the principle of "judicial review." That is, in judging according to the law, the Supreme Court also interpreted the law. Implicit in this process was the power to declare a law unconstitutional. This proved to be a mighty power because, while there are checks on the Court, they are indirect and difficult to exercise.

Finally, the Constitution can be amended, although the process for doing so was designed to be difficult. An amendment may be proposed in one of two ways: two-thirds of the states' legislatures can petition Congress to summon a national constitutional convention for that purpose. Or, and this is the only method by which the Constitution has in fact been amended, Congress can submit proposals to the states. If three-fourths of the states ratify a proposed amendment, it becomes part of the Constitution.

The Federal Relationship

Another network of checks and balances defined the relationship between the central government and the states. Under the Articles of Confederation, the United States was not a nation. The Articles created a confederation of independent states that retained virtually all the powers possessed by sovereign nations. The powers of the Confederation government itself were severely limited.

Under the Constitution, the balance shifted, with preponderant and decisive powers going to the federal government at the expense of the states. The states were not reduced to mere administrative divisions, like the counties of England or the provinces of France. Nationalistic sentiments may have been riding high in 1787, but local interests and jealousies were far from dead. If the Constitution were to win popular support, the states had to be accommodated.

Small states like New Jersey and Connecticut were particularly sensitive. If they were not to be bullied and even absorbed by their larger, wealthier neighbors, delegates from the small states insisted they must be accorded fundamental protections. These they received in the decision that states, rather than population, would be represented in the Senate. That is, each state elected two senators, no matter what its population. Virginia, the largest, was ten times as populous as Rhode Island, but had the same number of senators. Without this "Great Compromise," which was accomplished after a tense debate in July 1787, the Constitution would not have been completed and union not achieved without coercion.

The Constitution and Slavery

The difference between North and South also was recognized in convention compromises, particularly in the matter of America's 700,000 slaves. By 1787, the institution of slavery was dying in all the states north of Maryland and Delaware. Indeed, with the exception of the delegates from South Carolina, few of the Founding Fathers looked favorably on slavery. Tellingly, the unpleasant word "slave" does not appear in the Constitution, as if the framers were embarassed that such an institution existed in a country consecrated to liberty.

Rather, in a provision that prohibited Congress from abolishing the African slave trade for 20 years (Article I, Section 9), slaves are referred to obliquely as "such Persons as any of the States now existing find proper to admit." Elsewhere in the document, slaves are designated "all other persons." This euphemism was also used in the "three-fifths compromise" by which slaves and indentured servants were counted as three-fifths of a person for purposes of taxation and representation in the House of Representatives.

RATIFYING THE CONSTITUTION

The Constitution provided that it would go into effect when nine of the thirteen states ratified it. Three did so almost immediately—Delaware and Connecticut almost unanimously, Pennsylvania in a manner that dramatized the widespread opposition to the new government and the determination of the supporters of the Constitution to have their way.

Federalist Shenanigans

People who favored the Constitution called themselves Federalists. This was something of a misnomer, since the Federalists sought to replace a federated government with a highly centralized one. In Pennsylvania, the Federalists managed ratification only by physically forcing two anti-Federalist members of the state convention to remain in their seats when they tried to leave. This rather irregular maneuver guaranteed a quorum so that the Federalists could cast a legal pro-Constitution vote.

It was only the first of a series of manipulations that later led some historians to speculate that a majority of Americans preferred the old Articles to the Constitution. In Massachusetts, ratification was voted in February 1788 by the narrow margin of 187–168, and then only because several anti-Federalist delegates voted against their announced position. Anti-Federalists also claimed that the midwinter date prevented many anti-Federalist western farmers from getting to the polls.

In June 1788, Edmund Randolph of Virginia, an anti-Federalist, changed his vote and took a coterie of followers with him. Even so, the Federalist victory in Virginia was by a vote of only 89 to 79. A switch of five or six people would have reversed the verdict of the largest state, and that, in turn, would have kept New York in the anti-Federalist camp.

In New York, a large anti-Federalist majority was elected to the ratifying convention. After voting at first to reject the Constitution, they reversed their decision when news of Virginia's approval reached them. Even then, the vote was a razor-thin 30–27 and the New Yorkers saddled ratification with the proviso that a convention be called to amend the Constitution. It never was. Technically, New York's vote was no.

The Anti-Federalists

North Carolina was decisively anti-Federalist. The state ratified the Constitution reluctantly and not until November 1789, eight months after the new government began to function. Rhode Island held out even longer, until May 1790. Rhode Island became the thirteenth state to accept the Constitution only when Congress threatened to pass a tariff that would have kept its goods out of the other twelve states.

Today, now that the Constitution has worked successfully for 200 years, it would be easy to ignore the anti-Federalists of 1787 and 1788 as an unimportant historical force or as a collection of non-constructive reactionaries and cranks. In fact, the reasons why many anti-Federalists preferred the old Articles of Confederation were firmly within the tradition of the Revolution.

Debate gives way to a battle in Congress, as portrayed in this 1798 cartoon.

Among the anti-Federalists were fiery old patriots who feared that centralized power was an invitation to tyranny. Samuel Adams, still padding about Boston shaking his head at moral decadence, opposed the new government until Massachusetts Federalists, needing the old lion's support, agreed to press for a national bill of rights.

In Virginia, legendary Patrick Henry battled James Madison around the state. Some of Henry's arguments against the Constitution were rather bizarre. At one point, he concluded that the Constitution was an invitation to the Pope to set up court in the United States, a most extraordinary bit of textual exegesis.

But Henry and other anti-Federalists also argued that free republican institutions could survive only in small countries such as Switzerland and ancient Greece, and they had the weight of historical evidence on their side. Their favorite example was the Roman republic which, when it grew into an empire, also grew despotic. Would the same thing happen to a unitary, centrally-governed United States? Many anti-Federalists sincerely believed that it would.

Answering such objections was the Federalists' most difficult task. Madison, Hamilton, and John Jay of New York took it upon themselves to do so in 85 essays under the name *The Federalist Papers*, still a basic textbook of political philosophy. They argued that a powerful United States would guarantee liberty. These ingenious essays, however, were less important to the triumph of the Federalists than their agreement to add a bill of rights to their Constitution.

The Bill of Rights

The Constitutional Convention dedicated little time to debating the rights of citizens under the new government. The concern of the delegates was strengthening government, not putting limits on the powers that it was to exercise over individuals. The delegates, including even Hamilton, were not necessarily opposed to guaranteeing the civil liberties of citizens. They assumed that these were accounted for in the lists of rights most states included in their basic law.

Because the Constitution made the national government superior to those of the states, however, anti-Federalists such as Samuel Adams and Edmund Randolph agreed to drop their opposition to the new government only when the various rights that had been adopted by the states since 1776 were guaranteed on a national level.

The first ten amendments to the Constitution were ratified in 1791. The First Amendment guaranteed the freedoms of religion, speech, the press, and peaceable assembly. The Second Amendment guaranteed the right to bear arms. The Third and Fourth Amendments guaranteed security against the quartering of troops in private homes (then still a sore issue among Americans) and against unreasonable search and seizure.

The famous Fifth Amendment is a guarantee against being tried twice for the same crime and, in effect, against torture; it is the basis of the citizen's right to refuse to testify in a trial in which he or she is a defendant. The Sixth Amendment also pertains to trials, ensuring the right to a speedy trial and the right to face accusers (no secret witnesses). The Seventh and Eighth Amendments likewise protect the rights of a person who is accused of committing a crime.

The Ninth and Tenth Amendments are catch-alls. They state that the omission of a right from the Constitution does not mean that the right does not exist, and that any powers not explicitly granted to the federal government are reserved to the states.

For Further Reading

The era of the Confederation and the writing of the American Constitution are, unsurprisingly, a field of controversy among historians as tumultuous as the interpretation of the American Revolution. The cause of much of the dispute is Charles A. Beard, *An Economic Interpretation of the Constitution of the United States* (1913). Discredited as much of Beard's explanation of the Constitution is, it is an excellent starting point for reading about this era. Also see a yet older work, John Fiske, *The Critical Period of American History, 1783–1789* (1883).

More recent works revising these once influential books include Merrill Jensen, *The Articles of Confederation* (1940) and *The New Nation* (1950); Jackson T. Main, *The Antifederalists* (1961) and *Political Parties Before the Constitution* (1973); Frederick W. Marks, *Independence on Trial* (1973); Forrest McDonald, *We the People: Economic Origins of the Constitution* (1958); Andrew C. McLaughlin, *The Confederation and the Constitution* (1962); J. N. Rakove, *The Beginnings of National Politics* (1979); and Marion L. Starkey, *A Little Rebellion* (1955). For an overview, see Gordon S. Wood, *The Creation of the American Republic* (1969). The finest recent book on understanding the Constitution is Garry Wills, *Interpreting America: The Federalist* (1978).

Useful biographies of the men Jefferson called "demigods" include: Irving Brant, *James Madison the Nationalist* (1948); Jacob E. Cook, *Alexander Hamilton* (1982); J. T. Flexner, *George Washington and the New Nation* (1970); and John C. Miller, *Alexander Hamilton: Portrait in Paradox* (1959).

George Washington and the first "cabinet," a body for which the Constitution did not provide.

WE THE PEOPLE
PUTTING THE CONSTITUTION TO WORK
1789 - 1800

During the debate over the Constitution, one question never arose: Who would be the first president of the United States? The Revolution had produced many heros but, in the words of Henry Lee of Virginia, one man stood "first in war, first in peace, first in the hearts of his countrymen"—George Washington. True to script, the first electoral college voted unanimously to install Washington in what was, at the time, an office unique in the world. When he swore the presidential oath on April 30, 1789, the republic was launched.

THE FIRST PRESIDENCY

Washington possessed qualities that were indispensable to the launching of a government designed from scratch. He was committed to the republican ideal. Dignity and a sense of duty were the foundations of his personality. He was aware that he set a precedent each time he signed a bill into law or greeted a guest at dinner, and he confidently accepted the burden.

Setting Precedents

It is fortunate that Washington was a republican. Lionized as he was in 1789, he could likely have been crowned a king. Some members of the Order of Cincinnatus, an association of Revolutionary War officers, wanted to do just that. It was also suggested that the president be addressed as "Your Elective Majesty." But Washington rebuffed hints of crowns and sceptres and settled for "Mr. President" as quite adequate a title.

Not that Mr. President was self-effacing, nor least of all "one of the boys." Washington was fussy about the dignity of the office he held. He lived surrounded by servants in livery and powdered wigs. He drove about New York (the first national capital under the Constitution) in a splendid carriage drawn by matching cream-colored horses. He looked and acted like the prince of a smallish European state. When, at a reception, Hamilton bet Gouverneur Morris that he would not slap Washington on the back, and Morris did, the president stared him down with such icy disdain that Morris retreated stammering from the room. Morris never regained Washington's favor. He remembered his moment of informality as the costliest bet he had ever won.

In being as much monument as man, Washington won respect abroad. No European statesman feared the United States, but neither did any mistake George Washington for a head-scratching bumpkin who had had a bit of luck on a battlefield.

The Cabinet

Washington was as able a head of government as he was dignified a head of state. As a planter and general, of course, he was accustomed to wielding authority. Rather rarer a quality among leaders was his awareness of his own limitations and need of advice. Far from jealous of brighter people (as was, for instance, George III), Washington conscripted those he believed the country's best men to serve as his advisors. The chief of these, supervising operations of the five "executive departments" created by the Constitution, were five "secretaries" soon known collectively as the cabinet.

George Washington's inauguration at Federal Hall, New York City, April 30, 1789.

In creating the first cabinet, Washington balanced political tendencies and sectional sensitivities. From Virginia came Attorney General Edmund Randolph and Secretary of State Thomas Jefferson. By naming Randolph, an opponent of the Constitution until the last moment, Washington extended a hand of reconciliation to the anti-Federalists. Jefferson, by virtue of his agrarian book of 1785, *Notes on the State of Virginia*, was recognized as a spokesman for farmers who were suspicious of the non-democratic features of the new government.

To balance the Southerners, Washington named General Henry Knox of Massachusetts as Secretary of War. Knox was a wartime crony but, more important, as the chief military official under the Confederation, he represented continuity from old government to new. Postmaster-General Samuel Osgood of Massachusetts was a former anti-Federalist like Randolph.

The dynamic Alexander Hamilton of New York was Washington's Secretary of the Treasury. Partly because his conservative instincts were in tune with the president's, partly because the most urgent challenges facing the new government were financial, Hamilton's importance was second only to Washington's.

Hamilton's Goals and Policies

To pay the government's running expenses, Hamilton asked Congress to enact a 5 percent tariff on imports. The duty was low, not enough to impede sales of foreign goods in the United States, but its revenues were enough to pay the bills during normal times. A 5 percent tariff would not, however, provide enough money to cope with a crisis. In an emergency—war being the most obvious—the government would have to borrow. Therefore, Hamilton set out to establish a good "credit rating" for the nation.

This was no easy chore. The Confederation Congress had been grievously remiss in paying its debts. Some $12 million was owed to foreign banks and governments, $44 million to American citizens. The new government's borrowing power was crippled by the old government's neglect.

The First Debate

Hamilton proposed to wipe the slate clean by funding the entire Confederation era debt at face value. That is, by trading new government bonds for the old ones— "restructuring the debt," we might say—the Federalist government would immediately demonstrate its fiscal reliabilty. Few in Congress objected to repaying foreign creditors in full. The United States was a cash-poor country. Big future loans would have to be floated abroad. But Hamilton's insistence on paying American creditors in full led to a serious debate.

The issue, according to James Madison, was profiteering. Most of the domestic debt dated to the war years when thousands of Americans bought government bonds. As the years passed and the Confederation Congress failed to pay interest on these debts, let alone principal, many bondholders lost hope and sold their notes to speculators at big discounts. By 1789, most of this public paper was in the strongboxes of financial adventurers, not in the hands of the original buyers.

Nor had all of the adventurers been so very adventurous. As Madison told Congress in opposing the funding bill, some speculators, knowing in advance what Hamilton would propose, had scoured rural villages and towns buying up all the old government debts they could find, sometimes at a few cents on the dollar. In our parlance, they had traded on "insider information."

Should Congress reward such speculators? Madison said no. Instead, he proposed to pay the face value of the debt plus 4 percent annual interest to original lenders who still held the old bonds. Speculators who had bought public paper at bargain rates were to receive half the face value of their notes, with the remainder going to the original lenders.

Morally, Madison's argument held great appeal. He

ALMIGHTY DOLLAR

The word "dollar" is from the German *Taler*. The first silver coin by that name was the *Joachimstaler,* minted in what is now Czechoslovakia in the sixteenth century. The Dutch called similar coins *daler* and our spelling of the word comes from the Spanish, who then governed the Netherlands.

But why, in 1785, should the infant United States have adopted the Spanish dollar rather than the British pound sterling as its basic monetary unit? In part, the decision was just one of many knee-jerk anti-British actions during the 1780s. (The ever-patriotic Thomas Jefferson first suggested the dollar.) More to the point than hurt feelings, however, there were more Spanish dollars circulating in the infant United States than British pounds. Coin had flowed from the colonies to Britain, but Americans enjoyed a favorable balance of trade with Spain and the Spanish colonies; silver dollars flowed in and accumulated.

Nevertheless, Americans, like other peoples, accepted any gold or silver coin offered to them. As late as the California Gold Rush of 1849, many businesses in San Francisco quoted their prices in pounds, shillings, and pence.

proposed to reward those people who had stepped forward during the times that tried men's souls, not conniving speculators. But Hamilton replied that morality was beside the point. The issue was the new government's credit, stability, and prosperity: the future. By rewarding capitalists, the funding bill would encourage them to be lenders in days to come. The wealthy—the key to a government's stability in Hamilton's view— would be wedded to the success of the new government by the money that government owed them. Such an alliance was characteristic of all the great commercial nations of Europe.

Such practical arguments, not to mention the fact that several dozen congressmen stood to profit personally from the funding bill, carried the day. The old debt was funded.

Assumption

Hamilton next proposed that the federal government assume responsibility for debts contracted by the state governments. By paying back loans that some states had ignored for a decade, the federal government would further strengthen its good credit. Indeed, assumption would enhance the prestige of the federal government *vis à vis* that of the states, a project dear to the hearts of nationalists like Hamilton.

Again, James Madison led the opposition. He argued that some states, such as his own Virginia, had retired much of their debt. By way of contrast, most northern states, notably Massachusetts, were still deeply in debt. If the federal government now assumed the obligations of all the states, Virginians and others would, in effect, pay twice. They had retired their own states' debts by paying state taxes. Now, by paying federal taxes, they would pay part of the debt run up by Massachusetts, South Carolina, and other delinquent states. Was this fair? Enough congressmen thought not that the assumption bill was defeated in the House of Representatives by a vote of 31 to 29.

Hamilton was too determined for so close a vote to stand. Knowing that Virginians wanted the permanent national capital located in the South, he worked out a deal with Thomas Jefferson, Madison's political ally. If the assumption bill were allowed to squeak through on a second vote, Hamilton would deliver the votes of enough Northern congressmen to move the capital to the South. Thus was selected the site of Federal City, soon renamed Washington, D.C., in woodland on the banks of the Potomac River. Hamilton's Assumption Bill passed 34 to 28.

The Bank of the United States

The third pillar of Hamilton's fiscal program was the Bank of the United States, a central financial institution in which all government monies would be deposited. With such vast resources at its disposal, the B.U.S. would be invested with immense power over other banks and the nation's finances in general. The B.U.S. was not, however, a government agency. While the president would appoint five of the 25 directors who made bank policy, the remaining 20 were to be elected by shareholders—Hamilton's men of capital, once again.

This time, Hamilton had nothing to trade to Jefferson in return for his support, and the Secretary of State had had his fill of the marriage of government and capital. When the bank bill passed Congress, Jefferson urged President Washington to veto it. He argued that Congress had overstepped its constitutional powers. Nothing in the document gave the government the power to create such an institution.

Washington was impressed by Jefferson's reasoning. But Hamilton won the day by arguing that nothing in the Constitution specifically prohibited Congress from chartering a national bank. Therefore, such an action was justified under Article I, Section 8, which authorized Congress "to make all laws which shall be necessary and proper for carrying into execution," among other things, the regulation of commerce, which the B.U.S. would certainly do. Section 8 also empowered Congress to "provide for . . . the general welfare," which in the

> ## BUCKS AND QUARTERS
>
> The money slang word *buck* dates to the eighteenth century, when the hide of a deer, a buckskin, was commonly used as a medium of exchange. Its value was approximately that of a Spanish dollar.
>
> The American dollar eventually was divided into *quarters* of twenty-five cents each (quite an odd breakdown in a decimal system). Before coins valued at less than a dollar were common, it was customary to make change by sawing a Spanish dollar into eight wedge-shaped pieces. Two of them—two bits—equaled a quarter of a dollar. (In fact, the Spanish dollar was divided into eight *reales*.) This is the origin of the now-dying custom of calling a quarter "two bits" and half a dollar "four bits."

estimation of men like Hamilton and Washington, the Bank would also do.

In the Bank debate, Jefferson and Hamilton interpreted the Constitution in fundamentally different ways. Jefferson's "strict construction" of the document held that if the Constitution did not spell out a governmental power in black and white, that power did not exist. Hamilton's "broad construction" of the Constitution held that Article I, Section 8 permitted Congress to exercise any legislative powers that were not specifically prohibited elsewhere in the Constitution. By the close of Washington's presidency, these incompatible visions would contribute to the emergence of opposing political parties.

Hamilton Spurned

The B.U.S. was the last hurrah in Hamilton's campaign to shape the economy of the republic. He failed to build the fourth pillar of his temple when Congress rejected the "Report on Manufactures" he submitted in December 1791. In this report, Hamilton argued that Congress should promote industry to augment the nation's well-established agricultural and commercial base. His means of doing so was the time-honored device of the protective tariff. By slapping high duties on, for example, British cloth and shoes, Congress could price those imports out of the American market. This would encourage investors to build textile mills and shoe factories in the United States, creating jobs and new founts of wealth.

Farmers were inclined to oppose a protective tariff, particularly Southern planters with slaves to clothe and shod. Agriculturalists were consumers of manufactured goods and Hamilton's tariff meant higher prices. Farmers also feared that the European nations that suffered from high American tariffs on manufactured goods would retaliate by enacting high tariffs on American agricultural produce. Some overseas traders also opposed Hamilton's tariff. Many of them lived by carrying British cloth, shoes, and iron goods across the Atlantic. The temporary coalition was too much for even Hamilton's deft political touch. The tariff remained low, just enough to pay the government's expenses.

TROUBLES ABROAD

Washington was re-elected without opposition in 1792 and his second term, like the first, was on balance a success. He managed to carry out most of the policies about which he felt strongly and to establish sensible precedents for his successors to imitate. Most important, he presided over the establishment of a stable government for 4 million people and (on the map, at least) 900,000 square miles of territory.

The United States of America, so recently a gaggle of small ex-colonies, was a functioning republic when, in 1797, the 65-year-old Father of his Country returned to the plantation home where he had spent so little of his life.

Clouds on the Horizon

Washington's success was not unblemished. In his Farewell Message, published in September 1796, Washington warned the country about four ongoing problems he had been unable to resolve.

First, Washington urged—virtually begged—his countrymen not to form political parties. Washington regarded parties as selfish combinations of people who were willing to sacrifice the common good in order to benefit their own narrow interests.

Second, Washington admonished Americans to "discountenance irregular opposition" to the authority of their government. That is, they should voice their opposition to policies they disliked peacefully through legal channels, rather than resort to resistance and rebellion.

Third, he regretfully identified the beginnings of sectionalism in the United States. He feared that too many Americans pledged allegiance to North or South rather than to the republic as a whole. Division along sectional lines, fraught with the potential for civil war, must be nipped before it bloomed.

Finally, Washington warned against "the insidious wiles of foreign influence," the attempts by European diplomats to entangle the United States in their chronic, wasteful wars. Honor alliances already in effect, Washington said, but make no new permanent commitments to other countries.

RED HOT REVOLUTIONARY

Although he later regretted some of the excesses of his enthusiasm, Jefferson was an uncritical admirer of the French Revolution during its early years. Early in the Reign of Terror of 1793–94, when the French government executed thousands of French men and women, he wrote:

The liberty of the whole earth was depending on the issue, and was ever such a prize won with so little innocent blood? My own affections have been deeply wounded by some of the martyrs of this cause. But rather than it should have failed I would have seen half the earth desolated; were there but an Adam and Eve left in every country, it would be better than as it now is.

Revolution in France

There was nothing abstract about the turmoil in Europe during the 1790s. In 1789, France exploded in a revolution that, within a few years, pushed far beyond what the Americans had done. At first rebelling against the extravagance and excesses of the monarchy, the French revolutionaries soon set about redesigning their society from bottom to top.

Americans rejoiced almost unanimously at the events of 1789. Had not the Declaration of Independence spoken of the inalienable rights of all humanity? Now their ally in the struggle against Great Britain was joining them as a land where liberty flourished. It became fashionable for Americans to festoon their hats with a cockade of red, white, and blue—the badge of the French revolutionaries. When Lafayette sent Washington the key to the Bastille, the gloomy fortress where the French kings had imprisoned political dissidents, the president displayed it proudly to his guests. Nor were most Americans perturbed when the revolution turned against the institutions of monarchy and aristocracy. Had not the Americans themselves renounced kingship and forbidden citizens to accept titles of nobility?

Then, however, the French Revolution moved beyond liberty to the ideals of equality and fraternity. Conservatives like Washington and Hamilton could not be comfortable with talk of wiping out social distinctions. Even Thomas Jefferson, pro-French and given to exuberant boosting of tumult and uprisings, worried that the French were moving too far too fast.

Terror and Reason

Indeed, in January 1793, as Washington's first term of office was ending, King Louis XVI was beheaded. His queen, Marie Antoinette, followed him to the scaffold within the year. During the Reign of Terror that followed, French radicals known as Jacobins guillotined or drowned thousands of nobles and political rivals. The Terror shocked and sickened those who knew of it with all the impact of the shock of the Holocaust in the mid-twentieth century. Never had Europe seen anything like it.

Then, the virtual dictator of France for a year, Maximilien Robespierre, launched a campaign to wipe out religion. He converted Paris's cathedral of Notre Dame into a "Temple of Reason" where paunchy politicians and perfumed actresses performed rituals that struck many as ridiculous, others as blasphemous.

Few Americans thought fondly of the Catholic Church. However, Robespierre attacked all revealed religion and American preachers shuddered when they heard Americans admiring his campaign. William Cobbett, an Englishman living in the United States, observed with distaste that crowds of city people guillotined dummies of Louis XVI "twenty or thirty times every day during one whole winter and part of the summer." He also reported fist fights between gangs of pro-English "Anglomen" and pro-French "cutthroats."

Choosing Sides

Cobbett was observing a point of conflict that contributed to the birth of the political parties that Washington warned against. Americans who supported the French were inclined to favor an expanded democracy and the curtailment of social privilege at home. Working people in the cities, small and middling farmers, and many wealthy Southern planters who resented the favors that Hamilton's financial program lavished on merchants and capitalists turned increasingly to Thomas Jefferson as their spokesman and began to call themselves Jefferson Republicans. Jefferson, who left Washington's cabinet in 1793, gladly accepted the leadership of the coalescing movement.

Conservatives such as Washington, Hamilton, and Vice President John Adams, calling themselves Federalists, were neither enamored of democracy, which they equated with mob rule, nor hostile to social distinctions, which they regarded as buttresses of social stability. Until 1793, they were content to attack the principles of the French Revolution on a philosophical level. Then, Great Britain declared war on France. Under the terms of the alliance of 1778, it appeared that the United States was obligated to assist France in the fight.

The reasons for staying out of the Anglo-French war were more than philosophical. The Royal Navy was supreme on the Atlantic, and Washington rightly feared that full-scale war would prove too heavy a burden for the young government. Trusty Alexander Hamilton found the legal loophole that kept the United States out. He argued that the treaty of 1778 was invalid on two counts: it had been contracted with the French monarchy, which no longer existed, and it provided that the United States must help France only if Great Britain were the aggressor, which, with some justification, the British denied.

Washington announced that the United States would be neutral, "impartial toward the belligerent powers." This might have averted crisis had it not been for the arrival in Charleston in April 1793 of the French minister, Edmond Charles Genêt, or, as this rather preposterous character styled himself, Citizen Genêt.

Citizen Genêt

Genêt was young, bombastic, and as subtle as flags and fireworks. Soon after stepping ashore, he began to commission American shipmasters as privateers, armed raiders under contract to France to seize British ships. Within a short time, a dozen of these raiders brought 80 British merchant vessels into American ports. There Genêt presided over "trials" at which he awarded the prizes to the captors. Genêt also attended dozens of dinners held in his honor, at which he spoke as though he were the governor of a French colony.

By the time Genêt presented his credentials to the president, Washington was livid. Genêt's lack of diplomatic etiquette was bad enough to a man who would not be slapped on the back. Much worse, Genêt's privateers

---

CITIZEN GENÊT

The French revolutionaries hated the symbols of inequality as much as the reality of it. They tried to eliminate all titles, not only those of nobility (duke, countess, and marquis), but also *Monsieur* and *Madame*, forms of address that were then reserved for gentlemen and ladies. During the early stages of the French Revolution, it was declared that everyone was to be addressed as *Citoyen* and *Citoyenne*, or "Citizen" and "Citizeness." King Louis XVI was brought to trial as "Citizen Capet," and when Edmond Genêt arrived in the United States as minister, he called himself Citizen Genêt. His Jeffersonian friends briefly adopted the custom, referring to one another as "Citizen."

The Russian revolutionaries of 1917 did much the same thing when they abolished traditional Russian forms of address in favor of *Tovarich*, or "Comrade." In countries like the United States and Britain, the problem has been resolved by upgrading everyone to the level of "Mr." and "Mrs."—titles that previously were reserved to members of the gentry.

promised to drag the United States into a war with Britain that the president was determined to sit out. Washington received the Frenchman coldly and ordered him to subdue his politicking and to cease bringing British prizes into American ports.

Genêt bowed, retired, and continued to appear at dinners and demonstrations, adding jibes at the president to his speeches. When he directly defied Washington by recommissioning a captured British vessel, the *Little Sarah*, as a privateer, Washington ordered him to return to France.

This was bad news. Genêt was a member of a political faction that had been ousted back home and the Reign of Terror was in full swing. To return to France meant a rendezvous with Madame la Guillotine. Suddenly abject, Genêt asked Washington for asylum, and the president granted it. Most remarkably, he quieted down, married into the wealthy Clinton family of New York, and lived a long, contented life as a gentleman farmer in the Hudson River Valley.

A British Threat

Genêt's retirement did not end the threat of war with Britain. The British kept it boiling by insisting on their right to fight the war at sea under the Rule of 1756. This policy asserted that the ships of neutral countries could not trade in ports from which they had been excluded before the war began.

The targets of the proclamation were American merchants who were shipping grain, livestock, and other basic provisions to the French West Indies: Martinique, Guadeloupe, and Saint-Domingue (present-day Haiti). Before the war, the French had excluded Americans from this trade. Once at war with Britain, however, the French feared they could not supply their islands themselves. Therefore, they invited the Americans into the business.

It was a bonanza business. Merchants from New England, New York, and Pennsylvania reaped huge profits. The Anglo-French war had brought back the commercial prosperity of the colonial period that had proved so elusive during the 1780s. As so often before and since, wartime was a good time to be a neutral in the business of trade.

British merchants did not necessarily begrudge the Americans their short-term profits. However, they did worry that their country might well win the war in Europe only to discover that New England Yankees had taken over the trade of the West Indies. Thus the Rule of 1756. Thus the fact that during 1793 and 1794, British warships seized 600 American merchant vessels, about half of them in West Indian waters, a few within sight of American shores.

American shipowners were not delighted, but neither were they unduly disturbed. Overseas trade was a high-risk enterprise in the best of times. The wartime business with the West Indies was so lucrative that they were able to absorb the losses. Moreover, in New England, the upper classes were generally sympathetic to the British. Wealthy merchants were inclined to wink at British depredations in the interest of seeing the diabolical French atheists go down to defeat.

Impressment

The pro-French party, on the other hand, was not averse to picking a fight with Mother England. Jeffersonian propagandists—such as former seaman, erstwhile poet, and vituperative newspaper editor, Philip Freneau—railed against the British seizures of American ships as an affront to national honor. Seamen and their families had a more personal grievance, the Royal Navy's interpretation of the ancient practice of impressment.

Britain (and other seafaring nations) empowered the captains of warships to replace seamen who had died or deserted by means of an impromptu draft. If a ship were in port, its press gangs roamed the streets forcing likely young men into service. At sea, Men of War ordered merchant vessels to heave to—the proverbial shot across the bow—and press gangs boarded them. Impressment was highly unpopular. News of a press gang in an English town sent young men scurrying into cellars or fleeing to the countryside. Seamen on a signaled merchantman feigned crippled legs or idiocy. Few men with a choice between merchant service and the Royal Navy, with its brutal discipline, opted for king and country.

If British seamen hated impressment, Americans were infuriated when warships flying the Union Jack took crewmen from their own ships. Britain claimed the right to impress only British subjects from American ships, but there were plenty of these. Conditions and pay were superior in the American merchant marine. But the issue was further complicated by conflicting definitions of citizenship. Britain claimed that British birth made a person a lifelong British subject. The United States insisted that an immigrant became a naturalized American citizen after five years of residence in the United States. Many men were caught in the middle, exacerbating the sensitive issue of national independence.

Jay's Treaty: Peace at a Price

In April 1794, faced with a growing clamor for war, Washington sent the Chief Justice of the Supreme Court, John Jay, to England to appeal for peace. This alone was enough to raise the hackles of the anglophobic Jeffersonians, especially when the news trickled back

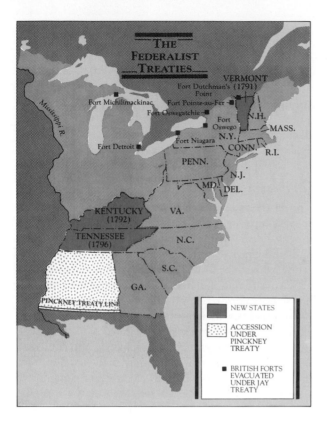

THE
FEDERALIST
TREATIES

VERMONT
Fort Dutchman's (1791)
Point
Fort Michilimackinac   Fort Pointe-au-Fer
Fort Oswegatchie   N.H.
Fort
Oswego   MASS.
N.Y.
Fort Niagara
CONN.
Fort Detroit   R.I.
PENN.
N.J.
MD.   DEL.
KENTUCKY
(1792)   VA.
TENNESSEE
(1796)   N.C.
S.C.
GA.
PINCKNEY TREATY LINE

Mississippi R.

NEW STATES

ACCESSION
UNDER
PINCKNEY
TREATY

BRITISH FORTS
EVACUATED
UNDER JAY
TREATY

that Jay was gaily hobnobbing in London society and had kissed the hand of the queen.

That fuss was nothing compared with the reception given the treaty that Jay brought home. The British made few concessions. They agreed to evacuate the western forts, which should have been transferred to the Americans in 1783. Britain also agreed to compensate American shipowners for vessels seized in the West Indies and to allow some trade with British possessions. In return, the Americans pledged not to discriminate against British shipping and to pay debts owed to British subjects from before the Revolution.

But nothing was said about impressment, the issue most charged with emotion. As for the British evacuation of the western forts, the fulfillment of a promise that had been made and broken a decade earlier hardly soothed the wounded pride of Republican patriots.

Party Conflict

Protest swept the country. When Washington submitted Jay's Treaty to the Senate for ratification, he was attacked personally for the first time, and not gently. Jay resigned from the Supreme Court and joked uneasily that he could travel the length of the country by the light of the effigies of him that were burned by furious Republicans. Crowds shouted: "Damn John Jay! Damn every one that won't put lights in his windows and sit up all night damning John Jay!"

It was, to say the least, an expression of party spirit, because Washington, Adams, Hamilton, and other Federalists did not damn John Jay. They believed that however imperfect his treaty, he had done the country a service by preserving the peace. They did not yet call themselves a party; with Washington in power, the Federalists dared not embrace open factionalism. But the lines between two political parties, already penciled in, were drawn a bit more clearly.

Pinckney's Treaty

A happier consequence of Jay's Treaty was an advantageous agreement with Spain. The Spanish too had been warring with revolutionary France. By the end of 1794, however, Spain wanted out of the conflict. France, then fighting practically the whole of Europe, was willing to come to terms. But the Spanish feared that the reconciled British and Americans might join together to invade their province of Louisiana. Not two years earlier, Citizen Genêt had proposed such an enterprise to pro-French Americans.

To placate the United States, Spanish ministers met with diplomat Thomas Pinckney and acquiesced in practically every demand that the Americans had made on them since 1783. In Pinckney's Treaty (officially the Treaty of San Lorenzo), Spain agreed to the American version of the boundary between the United States and Louisiana; to open the Mississippi River to American navigation (the Spanish owned the western bank); and to grant Americans the "right of deposit" in New Orleans. That is, Americans were empowered to store their exports (mostly foodstuffs and timber) in New Orleans, and to carry on commercial transactions in the city.

These concessions were of vital importance to the westerners, the more than 100,000 people who, by 1795, had settled in Kentucky (admitted to the Union in 1792) and Tennessee (admitted 1796), and the several thousand who lived in what is now Ohio.

WESTERN PROBLEMS

Life on the frontier contrasted sharply with the comfort and security of the thirteen coastal states. The killing labor involved in wrenching a farm out of dense forest combined with infectious disease and malnutrition to generate a death rate west of the Appalachians as high as it had been in seventeenth century Virginia and Maryland. Isolation from the eastern states meant that manufactured commodities were expensive when they were available at all. Atop these hardships was the determination of the Native Americans who lived between the Appalachians and the Mississippi to hold their ancestral lands.

Dark and Bloody Ground

Today, when we conjure up images of Indian wars, we are apt to think of the Great Plains in the later nineteenth century. Here were the dramatic battles of pulp novel and film, the Seventh Cavalry in dusty blue uniforms battling mounted warriors of Sioux and Comanche. In fact, the confrontations of the late eighteenth century between Americans and the tribes of the Ohio Valley—Miamis, Shawnees, Ottawas, Ojibwas (Chippewas), Sauks, and Foxes—were far fiercer and bloodier than any other Indian wars.

The tribes of the Eastern Woodlands were more numerous than the Plains Indians. By the 1790s, they were capable of fighting massive pitched battles in the dense forests of the region. George A. Custer's column at the endlessly celebrated battle of the Little Big Horn in 1876 numbered 265 men. In Ohio in 1794, General "Mad Anthony" Wayne led an army ten times that number. Because of the large numbers of casualties in Kentucky, Native Americans and white pioneers alike called the place "the dark and bloody ground."

President Washington was eager to clear the Ohio Valley of Native Americans. Not only was it a matter of national pride that the federal government actually govern all its territories, but many wealthy planters, of whom Washington was one, were deeply involved in land speculation in the Northwest Territory. They "owned" thousands of acres of virgin forest that they found difficult to sell to settlers as long as the Miamis and Shawnees maintained independence of action.

In 1790, Washington sent Josiah Harmer to find and defeat the Miamis and Shawnees under the war chieftain Little Turtle. Poorly supplied, wracked by dysentery and malaria, and handicapped by unfamiliarity with the country, Harmer's men were decimated near the site of present-day Fort Wayne, Indiana. The next year, a better-prepared expedition under Arthur St. Clair met the same fate, with 600 soldiers killed.

The Miamis and Shawnees, with their loose ties to the British in Canada, remained supreme in the Northwest Territory until August 1794, when General Wayne defeated them at the Battle of Fallen Timbers near Toledo. (The trees on the battlefield had been leveled by a tornado.) The victory would have won more praise for Washington among Westerners than it did if the president had not also dispatched an army against farmers in western Pennsylvania.

Of Pioneers and Whiskey

The men and women of the frontier were heavy drinkers, and their drink was whiskey. A jug sat on shop counters; every general store doubled as a saloon. People swigged whiskey like wine with their meals and like water with their work. Preachers refreshed themselves with it during sermons. The image of the hillbilly asleep next to his jug of moonshine was not invented by cartoonists. Future president William Henry Harrison said that he "saw more drunk men in forty-eight hours succeeding my arrival in Cincinnati than I had in my previous life."

Why whiskey? It was the beverage of the Celtic Fringe back in Britain, and the Scotch-Irish were the dominant ethnic group in the West of the 1790s. There were no breweries for beer, nor apple trees for cider in a newly won land. Then, there was disease. Settlers on the woodlands frontier suffered miserably from the alternating chills and fevers of malaria, which they called the "ague." The first medicine for which they reached was alcohol. The isolation of western life promoted heavy drinking. Travelers on the Ohio Valley frontier invariably recorded conversations with men, and especially women, who commented mournfully on the lack of company. Whiskey was a companion, not loquacious but undemanding.

It was also cheap. The corn or rye from which the creature was made was easy to grow, even in partly cleared forest. When a farm was a few years old, pioneers turned to wheat and rye, which also made a tolerable mash. Fuel for distillation was costless. Many family farmers kept a small still percolating day and night, turning out raw white whiskey. Commercial distillers established large operations on major waterways throughout the Ohio Valley.

Of Whiskey and Rebellion

Whiskey was also a cash crop. The Westerners could not ship their grain until the Mississippi River, into which the Ohio flows, was opened to American trade in 1795. The cost of transporting a low-value bulk commodity such as grain over the Appalachians was prohibitive. A pack horse could bear 200 pounds, about four bushels of grain; four bushels did not sell for enough to buy the horse's feed.

However, a horse could carry the equivalent of 24 bushels if it was converted into two eight-gallon kegs of liquor. A gallon of whiskey could be sold for 25 cents or more. Even then the profit was small. Hamilton's excise tax of 1791 (seven cents on the gallon!) wiped it out.

*Angry Westerners tar and feather an excise officer during
the Whiskey Rebellion of 1794.*

Just as Daniel Shays's men had done in Massachusetts in 1786, the Pennsylvania farmers roughed up tax collectors and rioted in river towns.

Washington and Hamilton, who had been alarmed by the Shaysite disorder, recognized a peerless opportunity to demonstrate the contrast between the weakness of the old Confederation and the authority of the new government. The president himself set out at the head of 15,000 troops to suppress the "rebellion." He left the expedition when the rebels scattered. But Hamilton, who had a yen for military glory, pushed on and arrested a few men who were tried, convicted of treason, and sentenced to death. Washington pardoned them, calling them mental defectives. Perhaps they were; perhaps it was just Washington's way of showing his contempt for the rebels.

In one sense, the suppression of the Whiskey Rebellion was a farce. An army as large as the one that had defeated the British—and far larger than that at Fallen Timbers—was organized to crush a rebellion that could

not be found. But the political significance of the episode was profound. The Federalist Hamilton was delighted to assert the national government's right to enforce order in one state with troops raised in other states.

FEDERALISTS VERSUS REPUBLICANS

By the summer of 1796, when Washington announced that he would retire and warned Americans against forming political parties, two parties existed in everything but name. On every controversy that arose during Washington's presidency, Americans not only disagreed, they also divided along much the same lines.

Party Lines

The Federalists supported Hamilton's financial policy; abominated the French Revolution as a source of atheism and social disorder; were open to friendship with England; accepted Jay's Treaty; and believed that the national government should act decisively and powerfully to maintain internal order, as Washington had done in western Pennsylvania.

Vice President John Adams and Alexander Hamilton were the chief spokesmen for the Federalist group, which also included John Jay, the wealthy Pinckneys of South Carolina, and—because no matter what he said about parties, he agreed with the policies of the Federalists—George Washington himself. Very wealthy people were inclined to be Federalists. In the North (especially New England), where money had been made in trade and speculation, the urban rich were almost unanimously Federalists.

The Jefferson Republicans generally opposed Hamilton's financial policy, particularly those provisions that enriched speculators. Farmers (and some great planters) believed that they paid the taxes that financed funding and assumption while benefiting little from those policies. Republicans were friendly to the ideals of the French Revolution, although not necessarily pleased by excesses such as the Reign of Terror. Republicans were generally antagonistic toward Great Britain, none more so than Jefferson. In a way, the Republicans wanted the Revolutionary War to go on forever. The Republicans despised Jay's Treaty. With an affection for democratic values that the Federalists spurned, the Republicans worried about an overly powerful national government quick to use soldiers against protesters such as the Whiskey Rebels.

Electioneering in 1796

Thomas Jefferson was the Republican candidate for president in 1796. Officially, Vice President John Adams of Massachusetts was the Federalists' man, and diplomat Thomas Pinckney of South Carolina was the Federalist vice-presidential candidate. However, Alexander Hamilton designed a scheme to manipulate the electoral college and put Pinckney in Adams's place. Whereas Pinckney was his loyal ally, Hamilton did not like Adams and knew he would have little influence with him. The result of Hamilton's scheme, however, was anticipated by no one.

In 1796, presidential electors did not vote separately for president and vice president. Each elector wrote two names on his ballot. The candidate with the largest number of votes was named president, the candidate with the second largest vote became vice president. Because nine states then empowered their legislatures to select members of the electoral college (popular elections were held in only six states), Hamilton was able to

John Adams, second U.S. president.

persuade some Federalist politicians in the South to cast one of their two votes for Pinckney, but the other—that should have gone to Adams—to some other person with no chance of winning. He hoped that enough Southern Republicans would vote for Pinckney to give him a larger total than Adams.

WASHINGTON THE VILLAIN

Although no one dared oppose him in the election of 1792, Washington was not universally worshiped. Indeed, the invective heaped on him by editor Benjamin Bache (who was Benjamin Franklin's nephew) exceeds anything to be found in newspapers today. In December 1796, Bache wrote, "If ever a nation was debauched by a man, the American nation has been debauched by Washington." When Washington turned over the presidency to John Adams in March 1797, Bache exulted, "If ever there were a period for rejoicing, it is this moment. Every heart, in unison with the freedom and happiness of the people, ought to beat high in exultation, that the name of Washington ceases from this day to give a currency to political iniquity and to legalize corruption." In another place, Bache warned, "The American people, Sir, will look to death the man who assumes the character of a usurper."

HOW THEY LIVED

LIFE ON THE LOG-CABIN FRONTIER

The end of hostilities after the Battle of Yorktown led to the rapid settlement of western Pennsylvania, a land of ridges, rolling hills, and mixed hardwood and conifer forests. The American victory meant that the Proclamation of 1763, which forbade white settlement west of the Appalachians, was null and void. More important, when the fort at Pittsburgh was transferred from the redcoats to the Continental soldiers in their blue and buff, the power of the Indians of the region, who were British allies, was sharply reduced.

Perhaps the social disruptions that accompany every war also played a part in populating western Pennsylvania. In raising its armies, the Revolution wrenched thousands of young men from their homes and accustomed ways of life at a critical time in their lives. As young adults, they faced decisions about the future. When the war was over, many veterans found it impossible to return home and take up life where they had left off. In the United States, such people could head west, to a frontier as unsettled as themselves. During the 1780s (and for half a century to come), the West was centered in what is, geographically, the Eastern Woodlands.

The author of an article about the Pennsylvania frontier that appeared in *The Columbian Magazine* for November 1786 did not mention the recently concluded war. But "the first settler in the woods," whom the author describes as a kind of social misfit, sounds very much like a Revolutionary War veteran: the pioneer was "generally a man who has outlived his credit of fortune in the cultivated parts of the State." Not a very good citizen, he was an anarchic, irreligious, and hard-drinking individual who "cannot bear to surrender up a single natural right for all the benefits of government."

The pioneer moved on when too many people began to crowd into his neck of the woods—when he could hear the barking of his nearest neighbor's dog or see the curl of smoke from his nearest neighbor's fire. He sold out to a settler who improved the primitive farm and who, in turn, made way for the solid citizen whose habits obviously relieved the author of the *Columbian* article. In the third wave came the "settler who is commonly a man of property and good character."

"The *third* and last species of settler" meant the end of the log-cabin frontier literally as well as figuratively, for the newcomer built a solid house and barn of quarry stone. At last there could be schools, churches, law and order—a civilized town. The writer for the *Columbian* left no doubt as to where his hopes for the country lay. Nevertheless, he granted the obvious: that neither the third nor the second phase of settlement was possible without the pioneers who had been willing to face the hardships of the log cabin in return for freedom and independence.

Pioneers opening up forest land tried to arrive at their destination in April when winter's snows had melted, but the overarching trees were not yet in full foliage. Their first task was to build a cabin and stable in order to be sheltered by the third week of May, when, in Pennsylvania, the year's crop of corn, beans, and squash had to be planted. The pioneers' fields were not pretty; they were not really fields. The pioneers adopted the Indian method of cultivation, killing the great oaks and maples by girdling their bark about two or three feet from the ground and planting wherever sun shone through the bare

---

The plan might have worked if Adams's supporters in New England had not caught wind of it. They retaliated by withholding votes from Pinckney. The result was that Adams won, but Pinckney did not finish second. Thomas Jefferson did. The president was the titular leader of one of the two political parties. The vice president was the actual leader of the other. Then, as now, the vice presidency was not a powerful office. But if the 61-year-old John Adams had died in office, his chief political rival, instead of a member of his own party, would have taken his place.

"His Rotundity"

In retrospect, it is possible to admire John Adams. He was a moderate at heart who acted according to stern and steadfast principles and, in the end, for the good of his country as he saw that good. He could be humorous.

When whisperers said that he had sent General Pinckney to London to procure four trollops for his and Adams's use, he responded, "I do declare upon my honor . . . , General Pinckney has cheated me out of my two." He was "always honest and often great," in Benjamin Franklin's words.

However, it is easier to admire Adams at a distance. He was also, as Franklin added, "sometimes mad." Impossibly vain and peevish, with a furious temper and a bottomless capacity for intolerance, Adams could be absurdly pompous. When wits sniggered at his short, dumpy physique ("His Rotundity," they whispered) and gossiped about his wife, Abigail (his only trusted advisor), Adams cut himself off, almost a hermit. He spent astonishingly little time in the national capital, Philadelphia, until the last year of his presidency. During his four years as president, he passed one day in four at the Adams's home in Quincy, Massachusetts. (By comparibranches. In the rich organic soil, created by the fallen leaves and toppled trees of centuries, even this primitive agriculture produced a crop of 40 to 50 bushels an acre, harvested in October.

Cattle and horses—generally bony, unhealthy-looking beasts—were allowed to roam, at most hobbled by the length of rope or leather thong that tied together two legs. There were few predators in the forests that would attack such large animals, and the frontier family with the most casual work habits had little time for tending livestock.

Most families also owned hogs. They too ran loose and were hunted rather than rounded up when pork was needed. Indeed, with the forests teeming with game, meat shortage was less of a problem than keeping the "domestic" and wild animals out of the corn fields.

Toward this end, the log-cabin pioneer built a rude zigzag fence. It was a marvelous adaptation to the conditions of the forest frontier—abundant wood and land, scarce labor. Logs could be split into rails using one tool, and the zigzag pattern required no post holes. The zigzag was not a very good fence. The rails were toppled by hungry hogs and easily leapt by deer. But it sufficed, and sufficient was the talisman of the family struggling against the wilderness.

The log cabin was another adaptation to forest conditions. Again, only one tool was required to build one. With their axes, the pioneers easily felled small trees, hewed (squared) them if they chose, and cut the notches that made it possible to build a cabin wall without upright timbers. In all but the rudest cabins—and many were but three-sided structures that faced an open fire—the only task requiring more than a single man's and woman's labor was raising the roof beam, itself a log. For this job, other frontier families were called on to help, and the event became a social occasion. Even the sniffy author of the *Columbian* article, who had little good to say about the pioneer, was moved to admire the cooperation involved in performing such tasks "without any other pay than the pleasures which usually attend a country frolic." The roofing itself consisted of split rails or a thatch of rye straw.

Not only did the log cabin go up quickly, but it was a strong house. Its walls were thick and almost invulnerable to arrowhead, musket ball, or fire. (To burn a log cabin, it was necessary to set fire to the roof.) Finally, if the logs were well chinked with moss and mud, they provided better insulation against cold than sawn clapboards did.

The sturdiness of the well-built log cabin was attested to by the fact that the people who came in the second wave of settlement purchased the pioneer log cabin, added on to it, laid floor boards, and shingled the roof. Otherwise they found the pioneer's dwelling quite serviceable. Even the third settler, the permanently fixed farmer, often found a use for the cabin as a hog shed or corn crib after building a stone house.

By the middle of the nineteenth century, the log cabin entered American folklore as a symbol of the opportunity the nation provided its citizens. A man who was born in a log cabin could hope to rise, as Abraham Lincoln had done and James A. Garfield would do, to the highest office in the land.

son, Washington was absent fewer than one day in eight.) Absence and Adams's inheritance of Washington's last cabinet, which was as bumbling a group as the first had been brilliant (and which reported every bit of business to Hamilton), made the president a man with only half a party behind him.

Another War Scare

Like Washington in his second term, Adams was preoccupied with the threat of war. This time, France was the potential enemy. Angered by Jay's Treaty, the French government ordered its navy and privateers to treat American ships as fair game. By the time Adams took the oath of office, 300 American vessels had been seized. Moreover, the French defined American sailors captured off British ships (many of whom had been pressed involuntarily into service) as pirates who could legally be hanged. In Paris, the French threatened to arrest the American minister, Charles Cotesworth Pinckney. In the United States, the French minister, Pierre Adet, railed publicly against Adams almost as intemperately as Genêt had assailed Washington.

Hamilton's supporters, the "High Federalists" who had reacted calmly to British seizures of American ships, demanded war with France. Determined to keep the peace, Adams dispatched to Paris two special ministers, John Marshall and Elbridge Gerry, to join Pinckney in asking for negotiations.

The XYZ Affair

The three diplomats were shunned. Weeks passed, and they could not get near the French foreign minister, Charles Maurice de Talleyrand. Finally, Talleyrand sent word through three henchmen, identified in code as X,

A Federalist political cartoon attacking France after the X, Y, Z Affair, 1798.

Y, and Z, that the foreign minister would be delighted to talk to the Americans if they agreed in advance to a loan of $12 million and a personal gift to Talleyrand of $250,000.

Bribes of this sort were routine in diplomacy; but the amount was excessive, and the tempers of the Americans were worn thin from waiting and humiliation. "Not a sixpence," Pinckney snapped, and the Americans walked out. Pinckney's reply was dressed up (and changed into American currency) back in the United States as "millions for defense but not one cent for tribute."

The High Federalists celebrated the news of Talleyrand's insult. Hamilton pressured Adams to mobilize an army of 10,000 men, and Washington agreed to become its titular commander on the condition that Hamilton

THE VICE PRESIDENCY

The vice president's only constitutional function is to preside over the Senate, and on the very rare occasions a vote is tied, to cast the deciding ballot. No ambitious politician has ever been happy in the post. John Adams called it "the most insignificant office that ever the invention of man contrived." When Theodore Roosevelt was nominated for the job in 1900, he feared that his political career had come to an end. John Nance Garner, vice president between 1933 and 1941, said the job wasn't "worth a pitcher of warm spit." Finley Peter Dunne, who wrote a popular newspaper column in Irish-American dialect around the turn of the twentieth century, summed it up: "Th' prisidincy is th' highest office in th' gift iv th' people. Th' vice-presidincy is th' next highest an' the lowest. It isn't a crime exactly. Ye can't be sint to jail f-r it, but it's a kind iv a disgrace."

PRIVATEERS

In order to expand their striking power beyond the number of warships in their navies, governments often commissioned "privateers." Captains of private vessels were given authority to wage war against the merchant ships of the enemy. Obviously, it was often not easy to distinguish between a legal privateer and a pirate, who preyed on any country's ships regardless of who was at war with whom. In fact, many privateers became pirates when the war was over, and governments frequently refused to accept their enemy's commissons as legal. Captured privateers often were hanged for piracy. It was a profitable, but dangerous, business.

be second in command. Not only did this mean Hamilton would jump rank over a number of Revolutionary War officers, it humiliated Adams and caused him to worry about a military coup.

Adams was more comfortable with the navy. He came from a shipbuilding state, and sea power posed no threat to domestic order. Moreover, while it was difficult to say where France and America might fight on land, an undeclared war already raged on the seas. Adams authorized the construction of 40 frigates and lesser warships, a huge increase over the three-vessel navy that he had inherited from Washington.

Repression of Dissent

Jefferson's Republicans remained generally pro-French. They trumpeted loudly and widely against all preparations for war. They were egged on by French diplomats and by a group of Irishmen who had fled to America after the failure of a rebellion against England. Both Adams's Federalists and Hamilton's High Federalists responded to this protest with a series of laws called the Alien and Sedition Acts of 1798.

One act extended the period of residence required for American citizenship from five to fourteen years. This was a tacit admission that most newcomers to the United States supported the Republicans. A second Alien Act allowed the president to deport any foreigner whom he deemed "dangerous to the peace and safety of the United States." A third gave the government authority to move expeditiously against enemy aliens at home. The Alien Acts were scheduled to expire shortly after Adams's term expired in 1801; they were unmistakably aimed at the Jeffersonian Republicans.

The Sedition Act

Although some foreigners fled the country for fear of arrest, the Alien Acts were not enforced. But the Sedition Act was. This law called for stiff fines and prison sentences for persons who published statements that held the United States government in "contempt or disrepute." Twenty-five cases were brought to trial, and ten people were convicted. Two Jefferson men in Newark, New Jersey, were imprisoned under the act when John Adams was saluted in the city by a volley of gunfire. One of them said, "There goes the president and they are shooting at his ass." The other responded, "I don't care if they fire through his ass." A court presided over by George Washington's nephew, Bushrod Washington, ruled that these were seditious words exciting resistance to lawful government.

Other prosecutions under the Sedition Act were not so comical. In an effort to crush the political opposition,

Federalists convicted four important Republican newspaper editors for the same crime. Thomas Jefferson, at his home, Monticello, received alarmed and angry letters from his supporters in every part of the country.

The Virginia and Kentucky Resolutions

Reading them, Jefferson and his chief advisor, James Madison, became convinced that the Alien and Sedition Acts were unconstitutional. The Federalist Congress, they believed, had not merely adopted obnoxious laws, it had overstepped the powers vested in it by the Constitution. In particular, Congress had violated the Bill of Rights. But who was to declare when Congress (and the president who signed an act) had acted unconstitutionally? The answer Jefferson and Madison gave was to haunt American history for half a century and contribute to the tragic Civil War of 1861 to 1865.

In the Virginia and Kentucky Resolutions, adopted in the legislatures of those states in 1798 and 1799, Madison and Jefferson wrote that the federal government was a voluntary compact of sovereign states. Congress, therefore, was the creation of the states. When Congress enacted a law that a state deemed to be unconstitutional, that state had the right to nullify the law within its boundaries. Acting on this principle, the Virginia and Kentucky legislatures declared that the Alien and Sedition Acts did not apply in those states.

In effect, the Virginia and Kentucky Resolutions marked a return to the supremacy of states which, under the Articles of Confederation, none had denied. In doing so, they challenged the supremacy of the federal government which, presumably, the Constitution had been written to establish. Nothing came of this challenge in 1799. No other state assembly adopted the Virginia and Kentucky Resolutions. The death of George Washington in December 1799 briefly calmed political tempers and, as the election of 1800 drew nearer, it became increasingly obvious that instead of helping the Federalists, the Alien and Sedition Acts were so unpopular that they improved the chances of a Republican victory.

The Very Peculiar Election of 1800

As it happened, Jefferson's victory over Adams in 1800 was nearly as tight as Adams's victory over Jefferson in 1796, and it was marked by an electoral college snafu with far more calamitous implications. Jefferson won 73 electoral votes to Adams's 65. The only significant change in the political alignment of the states from 1796 was the switch of New York from the Federalist to the Jefferson Republican column. This neat trick—with 19 electoral votes, New York was the third biggest prize in presidential elections—was the handiwork of a man who was Hamilton's rival for control of the state and his equal in political scheming.

Aaron Burr, only 44 years old, brilliant and imaginative, was the Republican vice-presidential candidate who swung New York into the Republican column. However, because none of the 73 Republican electors dropped Burr's name from his ballot so that Burr would finish in second place, the official count showed the New Yorker tied with Jefferson.

The Constitution provided (and still provides) that when no candidate wins a majority of votes in the electoral college, the House of Representatives, voting by states, not by individuals, chooses the president. In 1800, this gave the Federalists the balance of power. The votes of nine states were required for election; the Republicans, who dutifully voted for Jefferson, controlled only eight state delegations in the House.

A Vote for Stability

When the first ballot was taken, Jefferson received eight votes to Burr's six; two states were evenly divided. The Federalists voted mainly for Burr, some because they believed that Jefferson was a dangerous radical, others because they hoped to throw their Republican rivals into disarray. To his credit, Burr refused to urge on his supporters. At the same time, he did not instruct his few Republican supporters or Federalist friends to vote for Jefferson. He remained in seclusion.

After 35 deadlocked ballots, a Delaware Federalist, James A. Bayard, fearing that the crisis would destroy the national government his party had toiled to build,

announced that he would change his vote to Jefferson on the next ballot. In the end, he did not have to do so. Hamilton's agents had contacted Jefferson and extracted vague commitments that he would continue Federalist foreign policy and maintain the Hamiltonian financial apparatus. Just as important, Hamilton despised Burr. If Burr became president, Hamilton said, he would form an administration of "the rogues of all parties to overrule the good men." He conceded that Jefferson had at least a "pretension to character."

It was not much of a compliment, but it was enough. Hamilton pressured a few Federalist congressmen from key states to abstain. This enabled Jefferson to be elected on the thirty-sixth ballot on February 17, 1801.

Recognition of Political Parties

The original method of selecting the president was based on the premise that electors dedicated to the health of the republic would select "the best man" to be president, and the second best to be vice president. It worked only so long as George Washington was on the scene. The election of 1796 showed that party politicians were willing to manipulate the electoral process to serve factional ends. The election of 1800 demonstrated that parties were permanent fixtures of the American political process.

This meant that the original procedure of electing the president was no longer workable. Ratified in 1804, the Twelfth Amendment provided that, henceforth, electors would vote separately for president and vice president—the system that survives today.

For Further Reading

Although a generation old, still the best overview of the Federalist period is John C. Miller, *The Federalist Era* (1960). The person of George Washington loomed over the 1790s, so that biographies of him cited in previous chapters remain basic reading. In addition, see Marcus Cunliffe, *Man and Monument* (1958); J. T. Flexner, *George Washington: Anguish and Farewell* (1972); Forrest MacDonald, *The Presidency of George Washington* (1974); Edmund S. Morgan, *The Genius of George Washington* (1980); and Garry Wills, *Cincinattus: George Washington and the Enlightenment* (1984).

On the Adams presidency, particularly the election of 1796, see Stephen G. Kurtz, *The Presidency of John Adams* (1957); also Manning Dauer, *The Adams Federalists* (1953) and J. R. Howe, *The Changing Political Thought of*

John Adams (1966). Adams took his intelligent wife's views more seriously than most presidents have done; see Lynne Withey, *Dearest Friend: A Life of Abigail Adams* (1981).

The emergence of political parties in America is treated (with quite different interpretations) in William D. Chambers, *Political Parties in a New Nation* (1962); Joseph Charles, *The Origins of the American Party System* (1956); and Richard Hofstadter, *The Idea of a Party System* (1969). Providing special insights into the Jeffersonians are Daniel Boorstin, *The Lost World of Thomas Jefferson* (1948); Noble Cunningham, *The Jeffersonian Republicans* (1957); Merrill Peterson, *Thomas Jefferson and the New Nation* (1970). On Jefferson's great rival, see Jacob E. Cook, *Alexander Hamilton* (1982) and John

C. Miller, *Alexander Hamilton: Portrait in Paradox* (1959).

Standard sources for specific episodes of the 1790s include Harry Ammon, *The Genêt Mission* (1973); Leland D. Baldwin, *Whiskey Rebels: The Story of a Frontier Uprising* (1939); Gerald A. Combs, *The Jay Treaty* (1970); and Samuel F. Bemis, *Jay's Treaty* (1923) and *Pinckney's Treaty* (1926); Leonard W. Levy, *Legacy of Suppression: Freedom of Speech in Early America* (1960); James M. Smith, *Freedom's Fetters: The Alien and Sedition Laws and American Civil Liberties* (1956).

Thomas Jefferson's splendid home, Monticello, which he himself designed.

THE AGE OF THOMAS JEFFERSON

EXPANSION AT HOME, FRUSTRATION ABROAD
1800 - 1815

In April 1962, President John F. Kennedy played host to an assembly of Nobel Prize winners. He opened the proceedings by saying: "This is the most extraordinary collection of talent, of human knowledge, that has been gathered at the White House, with the possible exception of when Thomas Jefferson dined here alone."

It was more than a witty remark. Few people—far fewer political figures—have been so broadly learned and versatile in their skills as was Thomas Jefferson, the tall, slightly stooped man with graying red hair who took the presidential oath of office in March of 1801.

THE SAGE OF MONTICELLO

Jefferson was the author of the nation's birth certificate, the Declaration of Independence. He was governor of Virginia during the Revolution and minister to France under the Articles of Confederation. He was the first Secretary of State; and a shrewd political strategist who created the party that made him president in 1801.

Jack of All Trades

But Jefferson was more than a politician. He was a philosopher, happy when he could sit quietly in his study and think. He read and spoke several European languages and studied Indian tongues. His English was precise in its vocabulary and mellifluous in its rhythms. No other president wrote better than he did—and he wrote *more* than any other two presidents. The definitive edition of his works and letters fills 20 volumes and the project is complete only for the years of his pre-presidential career. No one who wrote to Jefferson received a form letter in reply. Many put a whim to paper and were favored with a disquisition.

Jefferson founded the University of Virginia, designing its curriculum and its buildings. He designed his own home, Monticello, and (anonymously) entered the competition among architects to design the president's mansion—the White House.

He dabbled in natural science. He invented the dumbwaiter, the swivel chair, and perhaps decimal coinage. He was a gourmet who may have introduced pasta to the United States. He spent up to $2,800 a year on wines for his table and up to $50 a day on groceries when a turkey could be bought for 75 cents. He employed a French chef, possibly the first American to do so. He once risked arrest to smuggle a desirable strain of rice out of Piedmont in Italy.

On the Other Hand

But Jefferson was no demigod, as he said the men who wrote the Constitution were. He knew profoundly that slavery was wrong, but continued to defend it, and to hold slaves. His detestation of Great Britain was pathological, a colossal blind spot. His vision of the future was shallow. He could be narrow-minded, peevish, and vindictive. He was no orator, partly out of shyness, partly because he was intensely self-conscious of a lisp.

Thomas Jefferson, a portrait by Rembrandt Peale (1805).

Nor was Jefferson universally admired. John Adams envied his popularity and rarely missed an opportunity to snipe at his reputation. Alexander Hamilton thought him soft-headed and frivolous. Other Federalists believed that he was an immoral "voluptuary" and a dangerous radical. During the presidential campaign of 1800, the *Connecticut Courant* warned that Mad Tom's election would mean "your dwellings in flames, hoary hairs bathed in blood, female chastity violated, children writhing on the pike and the halberd." Not yet exhausted, the editor continued, "murder, rape, adultery, and incest will be openly taught and practiced" in a Jeffersonian America. More phlegmatic anti-Jeffersonians contented themselves with the ribald tale (likely true) that one of Jefferson's slaves, Sally Hemmings, was his concubine.

JEFFERSON AS PRESIDENT

Jefferson was not oblivious to his critics and he knew he owed his election to some Federalists in the House of Representatives. In his eloquent inaugural address, he attempted to win over these moderate opponents by saying that "every difference of opinion is not a difference in principle. We have called by different names brethren of the same principle. We are all republicans, we are all federalists."

"NATURAL ARISTOCRACY"

Thomas Jefferson believed in the democratic principle that, on balance, the mass of people would choose to do the correct thing. He found arguments to the contrary unconvincing, because if "man can not be trusted with the government of himself, can he, then, be trusted with the government of others?" Federalists like John Adams disagreed. They believed that the people in a mass were a danger to the liberties of others and themselves. Government should be trusted to those with the leisure, education, and virtue to practice it intelligently. (Hamilton, of course, thought that the people were "a great beast.")

In the end, however, Jefferson and Adams were not so far apart. By "all men are created equal," Jefferson did not mean that all possessed equal talents. In a long correspondence with John Adams, when both were retired from politics, he agreed entirely with his old enemy that there was "a natural aristocracy among men. The grounds of this are virtue and talent"—inborn faculties.

Continuities

As president, Jefferson did quietly abandon some of his pre-presidential positions and adopt Federalist policies that, as leader of the opposition, he had condemned. Nothing more was heard from him or his Secretary of State, James Madison, about the doctrine of nullification they had formulated in the Kentucky and Virginia Resolutions.

Jefferson allowed parts of Hamilton's financial program to work for him. Although he had called the Bank of the United States unconstitutional, he did not try to hinder its operations. Jefferson claimed he had no choice. "This vice is entailed on us by the first error," he said, meaning that the government had a contract with the Bank until 1816. Still, he appointed no agrarian radical as Secretary of the Treasury, but the Swiss-born Albert Gallatin, who proved to be as responsible a money-manager as his Federalist predecessors.

Republican Simplicity

Jefferson brought a startlingly new style to the presidency. He sincerely disliked the pomp and ritual that Washington and Adams had fancied. Instead, he shook hands rather than bowing. He abolished the presidential levees (regularly scheduled, highly formal receptions) and, much to the annoyance of some officials and diplomats, he paid scant heed to the rules of protocol that assigned a rank of dignity, a chair at table, a precisely fixed position in a procession to every senator, representative, judge, cabinet member, and minister from abroad. Not even at state dinners were seats assigned; guests scrambled for places that they thought suited their dignity. Indeed, Jefferson preferred small parties at which he wore bedroom slippers and served the meal himself.

Jefferson's taste for "republican simplicity" was made easier by the move of the capital, the summer before his inauguration, from sophisticated Philadelphia to Federal City, Washington, D.C. It was no city at all in 1800, but a bizarre hodgepodge of half-completed public buildings, ramshackle boarding houses, stables, vast tracts of wooded wilderness, and precious few private homes.

Abigail Adams had done her laundry in the "ballroom" of the White House. Jefferson spent the night before he was inaugurated in a drafty rooming house, taking his breakfast with other boarders. For years, there would be no place in Washington for congressmen's families. Social life was masculine and on the raw side: smokey card games, heavy drinking, brawls, and even gunfights. Strangers got lost trying to find their way from the president's mansion to the Capitol, not in a warren of alleys but on muddy trails cut through forest and brush.

Making Changes

Jefferson's innovations were not exclusively stylistic. He pardoned the people who were still imprisoned under the Sedition Act (all of them his supporters, of course). He restored the five-year residency requirement for citizenship, and replaced Federalist office-holders with Republicans. He and Gallatin slashed government expenditures. The army's budget was halved from $4 million to $2 million annually; the navy's was devastated from $3.5 million to $1 million. Within a few years of such frugality, the national debt was reduced from $83 million to $57 million.

But such actions hardly constituted the "Revolution of 1800," as Jefferson called his election. Indeed, the most significant innovation in governance during Jefferson's presidency was effected by one of the president's bitterest enemies (although his distant cousin), the Federalist Chief Justice of the Supreme Court, John Marshall.

Marbury v. Madison

On the day before John Adams turned the White House over to Jefferson, Adams hurriedly appointed 42 Federalists to the bench. Federal judges served for life, so Adams was securing long-term employment for loyal supporters. In addition, he wanted to ensure that the judiciary, which was independent of both the presidency and Congress (also under Republican control in 1801) would remain a bastion of Federalist principles.

Adams was setting a precedent. The appointment of "midnight judges" would become standard operating procedure for outgoing presidents whose party had been defeated at the polls. Like incoming presidents who would follow him, Jefferson could only sit and steam to contemplate the salaries that had been lost to his own Republicans.

Except, that is, in the case of one William Marbury. Thanks to the inefficiency and oversight that would also become a feature of American government, the document that entitled Marbury to his job was not delivered before March 4, when Jefferson took the oath of office. On the face of it, Adams' dereliction was immaterial. According to the Judiciary Act of 1789, the Secretary of State—Under Jefferson this was James Madison—was obligated to deliver Marbury's commission. When Madison refused to do so, Marbury sued for a writ of *mandamus*, a court order that means "we compel" a government official to perform the duties of his office.

By 1803, the case was before the Supreme Court. As it would continue to be for more than 30 years, the Court was then dominated by Chief Justice John Marshall. The force of his personality was such, his willingness to do the lion's share of the Court's work was so eager, and his legal mind was so acute, that Marshall almost always had his way. In his ruling in the case of *Marbury v. Madison*, he scolded Madison for unseemly behavior. However, instead of mandating the Secretary to deliver Marbury's commission, Marshall ruled that a section of the law under which Marbury had sued was unconstitutional. Congress, Marshall said, had no constitutional right to give the federal courts certain powers that the Judiciary Act of 1789 accorded them.

The Doctrine of Judicial Review

Marbury v. Madison was a remarkable coup. By sacrificing the paycheck of one Federalist politico and canceling part of one Federalist law, Marshall asserted the Supreme Court's right to decide which acts of Congress were

Plan for the construction of Washington, D.C., 1792. The first president to live in the city was John Adams, who moved there from Philadelphia in 1800.

constitutional and which unconstitutional and therefore void. He decreed that the Supreme Court not only judged cases according to the law, the Court judged the validity of the law itself.

Nothing in the Constitution explicitly vested the Court with this substantial power. Jefferson and Madison had tried to claim it for the state legislatures in the Virginia and Kentucky Resolutions. But John Marshall effectively won it for the Supreme Court. Just to rub a little salt in Jeffersonian wounds, Marshall ruled at the same session that the Republicans' Circuit Court Act of 1802 could remain on the books because the Supreme Court (John Marshall) had decided it was constitutional.

Jefferson was helpless to fight the battle on high ground. Instead, he approved of a campaign of machination and low blows against the Federalist judiciary. First, the Republicans impeached and removed from office a Federalist judge in New Hampshire, John Pickering. That was easy; Pickering was given to drunken tirades in court, and was probably insane. Jefferson's men then inched closer to Marshall by impeaching Supreme Court Justice Samuel Chase. Chase was a poor jurist, grossly prejudiced in his rulings, overtly political, often asinine. But the Senate refused to find him guilty of the "high crimes and misdemeanors" that are the constitutional grounds for impeachment. Marshall's "Revolution of 1803," the principle of judicial review, was secured and remains the law of the land to this day. Like other presidents unhappy with the Supreme Court, Jefferson had no choice but to wait until seats fell vacant. Eventually, he was to name three members of the Court.

THE LOUISIANA PURCHASE

If Marshall added a twist to the Constitution, Jefferson gave it a mighty wrench in the most important action of his first term, the purchase of Louisiana from France. The Louisiana of 1803 was not merely the present-day state of that name. As a French colony—Spanish between 1763 and 1800—Louisiana covered some 828,000 square miles. The province included the better part of the thirteen states that, today, lie between the Mississippi River and the Rocky Mountains. Louisiana cost the United States $15 million, less than three cents an acre. Its purchase was the greatest real-estate bargain of all time.

Sugar and Foodstuffs

So grand a deal was imaginable only because the French emperor, Napoleon Bonaparte, first toyed with the idea of reasserting French power in North America and then abandoned the project. His scheme was inspired by the value, but also the weakness, of France's possessions in the West Indies: the islands of Martinique, Guadaloupe, and Saint-Domingue (present-day Haiti).

These colonies were producers of sugar and coffee, both lucrative commodities in the world market. They were grown on French-owned plantations by gangs of black slaves who were worked as hard and treated as badly as any in the world. The blacks grew little but sugar and coffee. Food production was neglected. So, grain and meat to feed the slave population had to be imported, much of it from the United States.

Napoleon's plan was to force Spain, a client state, to return Louisiana to France. There were only about 50,000 people of European descent in Louisiana but the endless lands bordering the Mississippi River were ripe for development. With Louisiana, Napoleon could feed the people of his sugar islands from within a new French–American empire. In 1801, secretly, Napoleon regained Louisiana.

A Vital Interest

Almost immediately, on Napoleon's orders, the Spanish governor in Louisiana revoked the right of deposit that had been guaranteed to U.S. citizens in Pinckney's Treaty—the right of Americans to store and trade their products in New Orleans. The American response, in many quarters, was near panic. The free navigation of the Mississippi River was absolutely vital to the 400,000 Americans who lived beyond the Appalachians in Ohio, Kentucky, and Tennessee. Each year they rafted 20,000 tons of produce down the Mississippi, the only way they could market it. To Westerners, in James Madison's words, the great waterway was "the Hudson, the Delaware, the Potomac, and all the navigable rivers of the Atlantic formed into one stream." As Jefferson put it, "There is on the globe one single spot, the possessor of which is our natural and habitual enemy. It is New Orleans," the city that controled the mouth of the Mississippi.

Congress voted funds to call up 80,000 state militiamen as a show of force. But it was an empty bluff. Any attack on New Orleans would require a naval blockade of the port as well as an overland assault, and Jefferson was in the process of eviscerating the American navy. The British, sworn enemies of Napoleon, would gladly help, but such an alliance was repugnant to the man who had written the Declaration of Independence.

An Offer Not to be Refused

Fortunately for Jefferson, there was an alternative to war. He instructed his minister in France, Robert R. Livingston, to offer Napoleon $2 million for a tract of land on the lower Mississippi where the Americans might build their own port. (Congress had voted him that sum.) In January 1803, impatient that no news had arrived from France, Jefferson sent James Monroe to Paris to offer as much as $10 million (a sum that had appeared in no congressional appropriation) for New Orleans and West Florida—the present-day Mississippi and Alabama Gulf coast.

When Monroe arrived, he was stunned to learn that, just a few days earlier, the French foreign minister, Charles Maurice de Talleyrand of the XYZ Affair, had offered all of Louisiana to Livingston for $15 million.

This remarkable turnabout had little to do with American wants and needs. Louisiana had, simply, been rendered worthless to Napoleon. Black rebels in Haiti, France's most valuable West Indian colony, had battered a crack French army commanded by General Charles Leclerc. Some 30,000 French troops were killed or incapacitated in battle and from tropical fever. "Damn sugar," Napoleon said on hearing of the debacle, "Damn coffee. Damn colonies! Damn niggers!" He told Talleyrand to sell Louisiana.

Constitutional Niceties

The transaction was quickly sealed despite the fact that it was utterly without constitutional sanction. The Founding Fathers had made no provision for purchasing territory nor, as was required by the terms of the sale, for immediately conferring U.S. citizenship on the people of Louisiana. But it was far too great an opportunity to be rejected.

Some Federalists called Jefferson a hypocrite for abandoning his strict constructionist theory of the Constitution. Jefferson—one hopes with some sheepishness—wrote that "what is practicable must often control what is pure theory." He instructed his supporters in Congress that "the less we say about constitutional difficulties respecting Louisiana the better." Even members of Jefferson's party far more zealous in their strict construc-

tionism, like John Randolph and John Taylor, kept their peace.

The Magnificent Journey

The acquisition of Louisiana aroused Jefferson's lifelong interest in natural science and in the still mysterious interior of the continent. Even before the Senate ratified the Louisiana Purchase, he persuaded Congress to appropriate $2,500 to finance an expedition across the continent for the purposes of looking for a feasible overland trade route (the "Northwest Passage" again), of gathering scientific data, and of holding "conferences with the natives on the subject of commercial intercourse."

Jefferson entrusted the mission to a Virginia neighbor, Meriwether Lewis, and William Clark, Lewis's friend and former commanding officer. He must have yearned to go himself for he attended to the most minute details of preparation, even listing in his own hand the provisions that the explorers should carry with them.

The actual trek exceeded anything ventured by conquistadores or voyageurs. Lewis, Clark, and a motley crew of 40 rowed, poled, and pulled their skiffs up the Missouri to the river's spectacular falls (present-day Great Falls, Montana). After portaging 16 miles, they enlisted the help of the Mandan, Shoshone, Nez Percé, and other tribes to find a tributary of the Columbia River. Following the great drainage, they reached the Pacific on November 15, 1805. There they spent four and a half months, during which time, as latter-day residents of Oregon and Washington will readily appreciate, it rained every day but twelve.

National Heroes

Lewis and Clark arrived back in St. Louis in September 1806. Not only was their trip a prodigious feat of exploration, but they collected a large body of information about the plant and animal life of the continent. Less welcome was the intelligence that there was no easy route to the Pacific.

THE NORTHWEST PASSAGE

The dream of finding a "Northwest Passage" to Asia never did die. When President Thomas Jefferson sent Meriwether Lewis and William Clark across North America in 1804, there was still a wan hope that a workable passage to the Pacific was possible. Throughout the nineteenth century, intrepid sailors attempted to trace an all-water route around the top of North America. Several expeditions spent years locked in polar ice. When, in 1958, the nuclear submarine *Nautilus* circled the continent by cruising under the ice of the North Pole, commentators implied that there was a Northwest Passage after all.

A BLACK EXPLORER

William Clark took one of his slaves on his famous trek. York was Clark's personal servant, and, in the informality the wilderness made necessary, he contributed to the expedition as an equal. Meriwether Lewis recorded that when many Indians first saw York, they believed he was a white man wearing paint. Only after trying to rub his color from him did they accept York's explanation of himself. Lewis noted that "instead of inspiring any prejudice, his color served to procure him additional advantages from the Indians."

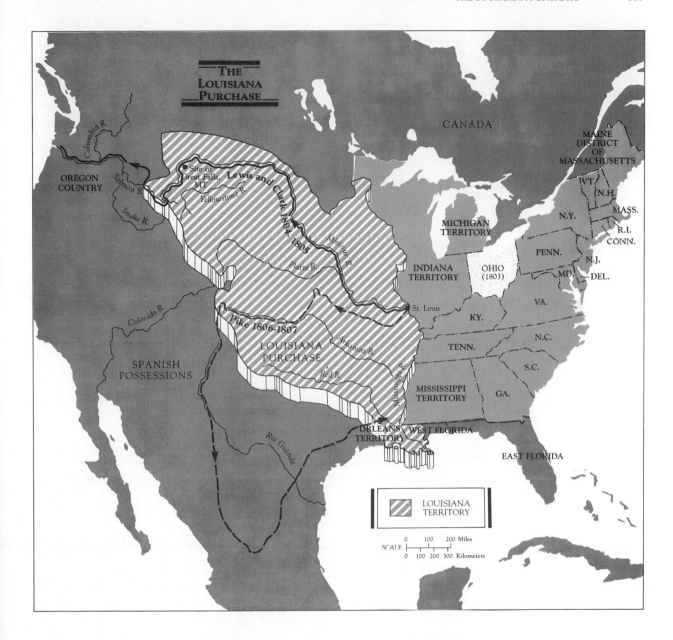

Lewis and Clark were among the last Americans to confront Indians untouched by Western civilization. Their experience is instructive. While there were a few uneasy moments with the Sioux, the explorers engaged in nothing resembling a battle with the dozens of tribes they met. (Incredibly, only one member of the party died.) Almost all the native peoples of the interior were curious, hospitable, and helpful. York, Clark's black slave (who was freed at the end of the expedition) was a source of endless fascination among the Native Americans by virtue of the color of his skin. The Shoshone, with whom the expedition could communicate through an Indian woman who served as interpreter and guide, Sacajawea, gave key advice toward finding the Pacific, which they themselves had never seen. The tribes of the

Northwest coast, of course, had long dealt with American and European seamen, whalers, and fur traders. One of their favorite expressions, Lewis and Clark discovered, was "son of a pitch."

Jefferson thought that the country traversed by Lewis and Clark would provide land for Americans for a thousand generations. His estimate was off by about 997, for the lands of the Louisiana Purchase and beyond were settled by 1890. But the West served Jefferson's Republican party very well. Ohio became the seventeenth state in 1803 and, voting Republican like Kentucky and Tennessee, contributed to Jefferson's easy reelection the next year. The Federalists carried only fourteen electoral votes, those of Connecticut and Delaware. Jefferson's shrewd politicking and Federalist blunders had made the

York, the sole black on the Lewis and Clark expedition, was a source of fascination to several Western Indian tribes.

party of Hamilton and Washington the provincials and Mad Tom's Republicans the national party.

The Further Adventures of Aaron Burr

Quirks of fate and the Louisiana Purchase also figured in the bizarre career of Aaron Burr. His fortunes had begun to tumble downhill immediately after his election as vice president in 1801 when Jefferson (somewhat unfairly) concluded that Burr had schemed to steal the presidency. Jefferson gave Burr no more to do than John Adams had given Jefferson and he denied the master-politician access to the federal patronage (appointive offices with which to reward political allies, government contracts to benefit supporters). Burr found—as his successors would—that the vice presidency provided him with no power and nothing to do.

Some evidence indicates that Burr plotted with a group of New England Federalists called the Essex Junto to detach New York and New England from the United States. If true, the plan depended on Burr's winning the election for governor of New York in 1804, when Jefferson dropped him from the national ticket. However, Burr was defeated, in large part because of Alexander Hamilton's sometimes vituperative opposition.

OHIO, THE FORTY-EIGHTH STATE

Government was so informal during the age of Jefferson that Congress admitted members from Ohio without officially admitting the state to the Union. The boundaries of what was thought to be the seventeenth state were approved and Ohio's congressmen took their seats on March 1, 1803. However, the vote to admit Ohio had not been taken. The oversight was rectified only 150 years later when Congress voted to admit the forty-eighth state on August 7, 1953.

Always rivals, Burr and Hamilton were now enemies and bitter in their published insults. When Burr remarked on an old sexual indiscretion in Hamilton's past, Hamilton responded with a nasty slur on Burr's integrity. Unable to up the verbal ante, Burr challenged Hamilton to a duel.

Hamilton disapproved of dueling. His son had recently been killed in one. But the feud was beyond shrugging off and, on July 11, 1804, the two men and their seconds rowed across the Hudson River to Weehawken, high on the New Jersey Palisades. They fired at one another from twenty paces. Hamilton's bullet went astray; some said he deliberately shot high. Burr's pierced Hamilton's abdomen, penetrated his liver, and lodged in his spine. He lived just 30 hours.

The first Secretary of the Treasury was never a beloved man, but his death shocked the nation. Burr was indicted for murder in both New York and New Jersey and had to flee to the South, while friends ironed out the legal difficulties. Still vice president, Burr returned to Washington, but his political career was finished. Not yet 50 years of age, energetic, and possessed of a keen imagination, he turned his gaze toward the West.

The Burr Conspiracy

There, Burr conferred amidst great secrecy with James Wilkinson, the territorial governor of Louisiana and a character so devious that, by comparison, Burr resembled George Washington. He met with other prominent Westerners, including Andrew Jackson of Tennessee, and even the head of the Ursuline Convent in New Orleans. Burr's oddest associate was one Harman Blennerhasset, an Irish refugee who lived opulently on an island in the Ohio River. Enamored of Burr's plans (whatever they were), Blennerhasset financed the construction of a flotilla of 13 flatboats, including a fabulously outfitted barge for Burr with glass windows, a fireplace, a promenade deck, and a "wine cellar." With 60 men, they meandered down the Ohio and the Mississippi.

Burr and Blennerhasset were accused variously of planning to invade Spanish Mexico or to spark a secession of the western states and territories from the United States. Or both, depending on what circumstances allowed and whose word is to be believed. Jefferson was prepared to believe the worst. When Wilkinson accused Burr of plotting treason, Jefferson had the New Yorker arrested and returned to Richmond, where he was tried before Chief Justice John Marshall.

Marshall was apt to snipe at anything dear to Jefferson's heart and he insisted on defining treason in the strictest of terms. However, there was no need for him to rig the trial. The prosecution's case was sloppy; few accusations were corroborated by second witnesses; the unsavory Wilkinson was a weak reed on which to support gossip, let alone a prosecution. Nothing of substance was proved against Burr and he was acquitted. The most significant event in the trial was Marshall's issue of a subpoena to Jefferson. The president refused to appear, citing the independence of the executive branch (which he had denigrated before his election).

Burr moved abroad for a few years before returning to New York. One more scandal was to pepper his remarkable career. During a messy divorce scandal, his second wife titillated New Yorkers by claiming to have been the only woman to have slept with both George Washington and Napoleon Bonaparte.

FOREIGN WOES

Like Washington and Adams, Jefferson found that settling foreign affairs was more troubling a challenge than setting domestic policy. Domestic policy, after all, was a matter of effecting an ideology. How foreign affairs turned out was at least half in the hands of foreigners.

In fact, Jefferson's ideology helped to set him up for even greater frustration abroad when he allowed the Adams navy to dwindle. He soon learned that a nation with vital interests in international trade had to be able to protect its international traders.

The Barbary Pirates

One trouble spot was the Mediterranean where the economy of the Barbary ("Berber") states of Morocco, Algiers, Tunis, and Tripoli was based in part on piracy and extorting a kind of "protection money" from seafaring nations. If a nation paid an annual tribute, the fearsome Barbary corsairs ignored their vessels. If it refused, that nation's sailing ships were fair game for attack, and the sailors aboard fair game for prison or slavery.

So effective were the Barbary pirates that even mighty Britain paid annual tribute to the various beys and pashas, judging it cheaper to buy safe passage for merchant ships in the Mediterranean than to make constant war. Before Jefferson became president, the United States paid too. Through the 1790s, the price of flying the American flag in Barbary waters cost about $2 million. In 1795, 119 American sailors were held in Algiers. It took a ransom of $800,000 to free them, and a 36-gun frigate to buy a three-month moratorium on other seizures.

The indignity of such commerce rankled on Jefferson, so when the pasha of Tripoli seized the crew of an American ship and demanded ransom, Jefferson ordered a punitive expedition to, in the words of the Marine Corps hymn, "the shores of Tripoli." Despite four years of in-

HOW THEY LIVED

GIVING BIRTH

A woman who married during the Federalist or Jeffersonian era could expect to be pregnant about seven times during her life—if she did not die as a young woman, in childbirth or otherwise. During the 1790s, there were almost 300 live births for every 1,000 women between the ages of 15 and 44—more than one woman in four delivered each year—as compared with 84 pregnancies for each 1,000 women in 1970. Pregnancy, childbirth, and the nursing of infants were a far more important part of a woman's existence in 1790 than they are in the late twentieth century. Indeed, giving birth to children was generally considered to be the chief reason for a woman's existence.

Almost every child was delivered at home. The few hospitals that existed were reserved for the seriously ill or injured, and childbirth was eminently normal. Most children were delivered by female midwives (the word means "*with* a woman") and in the company of the mother-to-be's own mother, sisters, neighbors, friends, and even older daughters. Historian Catherine M. Scholten has shown that childbirth was a communal event, the climactic shared experience of women. Except during the early stages of labor, when the husband might be called in to pray with or comfort his wife, men were usually excluded.

The midwife might have served an apprenticeship, or she might have slipped into the job as a consequence of accidentally getting "catched" in a number of childbirths and therefore developing a reputation as someone who knew what to do. In any event, while midwifery lacked the formal recognition in the United States that it had in England, it was very definitely a profession. The tombstone of one Boston woman says that she "by the Blessing of God has brought into this world above 3,000 Children."

In part, the presence of other women was a practical matter. Water had to be heated, and linens washed. In the event of a prolonged labor, food had to be prepared. Because in the eighteenth century few women gave birth lying on their backs in bed but, instead, squatting or standing, the mother depended on other women for physical support. Moreover, it was common practice for a recent mother to remain in bed for at least four weeks after childbirth. Her friends performed her household duties during this final phase of confinement.

But the attendants also served important cultural, social, and psychological purposes. By their presence and the exclusion of men, they emphasized the uniquely feminine character of the suffering involved in childbirth at a time when liquor was the only anesthetic available. The pains of bearing children were still generally thought of as God's punishment for the sin of Eve. By their presence—because they too had undergone childbirth or could expect to do so—the attendants were sharing in the travail.

Moreover, as Scholten discovered, they cheered the mother-to-be by distracting her with gossip, comparing her labor with more difficult labors they had witnessed (or suffered), and even making her laugh by telling bawdy jokes.

Already in the 1790s, however, the supervision of childbirth was being taken away from women by male physicians who had been trained in obstetrics. This trend began in England during the 1740s and 1750s, when Dr. William Smellie was appalled by the incompetence of many midwives. "We ought to be ashamed of ourselves," he told physicians, "for the little improvement we have made in so many centuries." Smellie invented the forceps used for assisting difficult births.

The development of obstetrics as a branch of medicine also reflected society's general drift away from literally interpreted religion. In 1804, Peter Miller, a student at the University of Pennsylvania, home of the country's best medical school, wrote that the dangers of pregnancy and the death of so many infants involved enough sorrow for women. It was absurd to cling to the belief that the moment of birth should also be a travail. Dr. William Dewees, a pioneer of medical obstetrics in the United States, asked, "Why should the female alone incur the penalty of God?"

In the cities and particularly among the upper and middle classes, male physicians supplanted female midwives in a surprisingly short period of time. In Boston and Philadelphia (and probably in other large cities) during the Federalist period, physicians were called into childbirth cases only when there were serious difficulties. By the 1820s, doctors virtually monopolized the delivery of children in urban areas.

The survival rate among both mothers and newborns improved with the triumph of medical obstetrics. (Although the significant advance took place only later in the nineteenth century, when the Hungarian Ignaz Semmelweiss and the English surgeon Joseph Lister discovered that "childbirth fever" [puerperal fever] was caused by the failure of most physicians even to wash their hands.) However, the triumph was not entirely progressive. The demands of a sexual modesty that was in fact prudery, which was strongest among the upper and middle classes, forced doctors to ask questions of "a delicate nature"—just about all questions about childbirth—through another woman. It was an unwieldy procedure at best, and in emergencies it was potentially dangerous.

In addition, the birth had to be carried out under covers, with the physician working entirely by touch. Indeed, even such an awkward process offended some people. In *Letters to Ladies, Detailing Important Information Concerning Themselves and Infants,* published in 1817, Dr. Thomas Ewell told of a husband who "very solemnly . . . declared to the doctor, he would demolish him if he touched or looked at his wife." Finally, as is common with scientific advances, there was a human cost. Transforming childbirth from a communal event into a private medical operation destroyed an important social relationship among women.

The bombardment of Tripoli, one of the repeated American attempts during 1801–1805 to subdue the Barbary States.

termittent naval bombardment and a daring amphibious attack led by Stephen Decatur, the issue could not be forced. In 1805, Jefferson gave up and paid Tripoli $60,000 in return for the release of captive Americans, a transaction that was not immortalized in song. Barbary Coast piracy and slave trading continued for another decade when Decatur returned to North Africa, Britain unleashed its fleet in the Mediterranean, and France began to establish imperial control over the region.

Europe at War

Far more serious a foreign threat than the Barbary states was the war between France and England that broke out shortly after the purchase of Louisiana. Jefferson was gladly neutral, of course, and, at first, American ship-

owners were delighted to reap profits by trading with both sides. Especially lucrative was the re-export business, West Indian products brought to the United States and then shipped to Europe under the neutral American flag. In two years, the re-export business quadrupled in value from $13 million to $60 million.

Then, in 1805, the Anglo-French war took a critical turn. At the Battle of Trafalgar, Lord Horatio Nelson destroyed the French fleet, thus establishing a British supremacy on the high seas that would last for a hundred years. Retaliating on land, Napoleon defeated the armies of Austria, Prussia, and Russia in rapid succession. France was supreme on the continent of Europe.

Caught in the Middle Again

The British and French then settled down into a kind of cold war, each aiming to cripple the economy of the other. The British issued the Orders in Council, forbidding neutrals to trade in Europe unless their ships first called at a British port to purchase a "license." New England merchants, who inclined to be pro-British, could have lived with the Orders. However, Napoleon retaliated with the Berlin and Milan decrees of 1806 and 1807, enacting what he called the Continental System: any neutral vessels that observed the Orders in Council would be seized by the French.

American merchants were caught in the middle. Within a year, the British seized 1,000 American ships

---

TRIBUTE TO THE PASHA

The annual payment to the pasha of Tripoli, which Jefferson attempted to cancel in 1801, consisted of $40,000 in gold and silver, $12,000 in Spanish money, and an odd assortment of diamond rings, watches, and fine cloth and brocade. The rulers of the Barbary States sincerely thought of these as gifts of friendship rather than as extortion. For example, in 1806 the bey of Tunis, who also received tribute, sent Jefferson a gift of four Arabian horses.

and the French about 500. Even then, the profits that poured in from voyages that were completed more than compensated for the losses. One Massachusetts senator calculated that if a shipowner sent three vessels out and two were seized—dead losses—the profits from the third left him a richer man than he had been. Statistics bear him out. In 1807, at the height of the commerce raiding, Massachusetts merchants earned $15 million in freight charges alone.

Impressment Again

The crisis was complicated by a renewal of the impressment problem of the 1790s. Chronically short of sailors, British naval captains once again began to board American merchantmen and draft crewmen whom, they insisted, were British subjects. There were plenty of such men on American vessels. Conditions under the American flag were much better than on British ships, the pay sometimes three times as much. As many as 10,000 seamen of British birth—about one-fourth of the total—may have been working for American ships masters in the early nineteenth century.

The trouble was, many of them had become American citizens, a transfer of allegiance British captains did not recognize. Yet other men impressed into the Royal Navy were American by birth. About 10,000 bona fide citizens of the United States (by American standards) were forced into the Royal Navy during the Napoleonic Wars. Some 4,000 were released as soon as they reached a British port but, at sea, arrogant or merely desperate naval officers were grabbing more.

The impressment crisis came to a head in June 1807, when, not far from the Virginia shore, H.M.S. *Leopard*, with 50 guns, ordered the lesser American frigate *Chesapeake* to stand by for boarding. The American captain refused the importunate command and the *Leopard* fired three broadsides, killing several sailors. A British press gang then boarded the *Chesapeake* and removed four men, including two American blacks who had once served in the Royal Navy.

The patriotic uproar was deafening. The *Chesapeake* was no merchantman taking a chance on a commercial expedition, but a naval vessel in American waters. Jefferson had to act. He chose what he called "peaceable coercion."

The Embargo

Under the Embargo Act of 1807, American ships in port were forbidden to leave. Foreign vessels were sent to sea in ballast (carrying boulders or other worthless bulk in their hulls). All imports and exports were prohibited. The Embargo was economic war, designed to force the British, who also benefited from American trade, to respect American claims.

For Jefferson, who had seen economic boycott bring Parliament around during his revolutionary youth, embargo was a logical course of action. In 1807, the British were at odds not with their own colonies but with a foreign enemy they feared was sworn to destroy their nation. Moreover, a broad spectrum of Americans suffered from the Embargo. Staple farmers lost their foreign markets, their livelihood. The ports of New England languished as fit ships rode at anchor, generating no profit and rotting in harbor. The Federalist party, badly maimed in the election of 1804, began to make a comeback behind a new, younger generation of leaders.

By the end of 1808, the Embargo had cost the American economy three times the price of a war. Jefferson had already decided to retire after two terms. Rather than leave his handpicked successor the burden of his error, he approved Congress's repeal of the Embargo.

Little Jeremy Applejohn

The president elected in 1808, James Madison, had been Jefferson's doggedly faithful disciple and aide for 15 years. A profound student of political philosophy, Madison believed in both Jefferson's exaltation of farmers as the country's most valuable citizens and the nationalism that had made him an active proponent of the Constitution.

He was not, however, particularly cut out to be a head of state. He commanded quiet mockery rather than public respect. Short and slight, he complained incessantly of aches, pains, and ailments. (His health was good enough: Madison lived on, sniffling, moaning, and groaning until he was 85.) His face was pinched, leading writer Washington Irving to quip that "Little Jeremy" looked like a "withered applejohn," that is, an apple that had been dried for two years. But Madison had his charms. Despite his unprepossessing appearance and lack of wealth, he had won the hand of a vivacious and fashionably buxom widow, Dolley Payne Todd, who added a sparkle to Washington society that had been lacking in the presidency of the widower Jefferson.

Non-Intercourse and Macon's Bill No. 2

Madison was particularly ill-suited to handle the international crisis that had confounded Jefferson. He was "too timid" in the words of his enemy, Fisher Ames, "wholly unfit for the Storms of War," according to his supporter, Henry Clay of Kentucky. Madison's first attempt to resolve the conflict over trade, the Non-Intercourse Act, opened trade with all nations except England and France. It provided that the United States would resume trading with whichever of the two belligerents agreed to respect the rights of American shipping. David Erskine, the pro-American British minister to Washington, negotiated a favorable treaty, and Madison renewed trade with Britain. Then, back in London, the British Foreign Office repudiated the agreement. Madison was humiliated.

In May 1810, the Republicans tried a new twist. Under Macon's Bill No. 2, they reopened commerce with both England and France, with the condition that as soon as either agreed to American terms, the United States would cut off trade with the other. In other words, the United States would take its licks at sea for the nonce, and then collaborate with the belligerent power that ceased administering them.

So bizarre a policy was asking for trouble from a trickster like Napoleon. With no intention of denying French captains the pleasure of taking American prizes, he revoked the Continental System, and Madison, as Macon's Bill No. 2 required, declared an end to trade with England.

Remarkably, Macon's Bill No. 2 actually worked. On June 16, 1812, feeling the loss of American business, the British canceled their Orders in Council. But it was too late. The British foreign minister, Robert Viscount Castlereagh, had given no advance hint of his intentions. On June 18, 1812, with the good news of diplomatic victory just catching the winds out of England, Madison bowed to pressure at home and asked the Congress for a declaration of war.

THE TWO TERM TRADITION

When George Washington rejected the certainty of reelection to the presidency for a third term, he made no point of principle about it. He was old and tired; he had served his country much of his adult life. In 1805, however, shortly after taking the oath of office a second time, Thomas Jefferson wrote of Washington's example: "I shall follow it, and a few more precedents will oppose the obstacle of habit to anyone after a while who shall endeavor to extend his term. Perhaps it may beget a disposition to establish it by an amendment to the Constitution."

For more than a century, the habit persisted despite several attempts to break it. Andrew Jackson retired after two terms in 1837. So did Ulysses S. Grant in 1877, although, four years later he changed his mind and tried, unsuccessfully, to run again. Theodore Roosevelt also retired after nearly eight years in office, rather frankly because he was somewhat intimidated by the precedent. He too tried later to win the White House back. Woodrow Wilson and Calvin Coolidge both observed the "habit" against their deep felt personal wishes. Only in 1940, with the world descending into the horrors of the Second World War, did Franklin D. Roosevelt seek and win a third term (and four years later a fourth).

It was this shattering of tradition, rather than the precedents of which Jefferson spoke, that resulted in the constitutional amendment Jefferson suggested. Franklin D. Roosevelt so dominated American politics for twelve years, usually overwhelming his opponents, that the longer-suffering Republican party proposed in 1947 the Twenty-Second Amendment to the Constitution, which forbids a president to serve more than two terms. Ironically, the first president to be affected by the restriction was Republican Dwight D. Eisenhower who was popular enough to win a third term in 1960 but could not run. Without him, the Republicans lost the White House for eight years during which liberal policies the party opposed were enacted.

THE WAR OF 1812

On the face of it, the War of 1812, like the attack on Tripoli, was fought to defend the rights of American shipping on the high seas. However, mercantile New England was largely hostile to the war and the Federalist party, representing the commercial capitalist class, was entirely so. The demands for war came from Jefferson Republicans representing agricultural regions, most of them a goodly distance from salt water.

The War Hawks

In New England and New York, antiwar Federalists, some of them sufficiently angry to threaten secession from the United States, won election to Congress in

Jefferson's successor James Madison and his vivacious wife, Dolley.

numbers unprecedented since 1800. The mercantile states of New England, New York, and New Jersey voted 34 to 14 against declaring war. Not a single Federalist congressman voted for the declaration.

The backing for "Mr. Madison's War," as New Englanders disdainfully called it, came entirely from the Jefferson-Republican party and largely from the South and the West. A noisy, belligerent claque of young congressmen known as "War Hawks" gave Madison the votes and encouragement he needed to get his declaration approved. Pennsylvania, the South, and the West voted 65 to 15 in favor of the declaration of war.

In part, the grievances of these agricultural regions were economic. In one way, farmers who lived by exporting their crops suffered more from British depredations at sea than merchants did. As a whole, the American merchant class never ceased to make money, even when the British were most active in seizing their ships. However, when a farmer's crop went unsold, it rotted—a total loss.

Perhaps more important, the War Hawks were generally young with the cocky belligerence of youth, and extremely nationalistic. Their outrage at "the injuries and indignities" heaped on their country by arrogant Britain was genuine and profound. Added to wounded pride, the western War Hawks resented Britain's contin-

ued aid to the Indians of the Northwest Territory, with whom their constituents were chronically in conflict. They wanted to break the back of Indian military power. The more exuberant of the War Hawks spoke of invading, conquering, and annexing Canada, the Indians' safe sanctuary.

On to Canada!

The War Hawks had reason to believe that Canada would be easy pickings. Many Americans had settled in Upper Canada, the rich lands north of Lake Ontario. Many Canadians openly voiced a preference for the American political system over their colonial status under Great Britain. Militarily, the situation looked to be bright. With the war against Napoleon in Europe nearing its climax, the British had left a mere 2,200 professional soldiers in North America. To defend Canada, they depended on a confederacy of Native American tribes led by a remarkable Shawnee chief, Tecumseh. But, late in 1811, before Mr. Madison's war was declared, Tecumseh's considerable force was shattered by William Henry Harrison, the territorial governor of Indiana.

"Panther Lying in Wait"

Tecumseh (Shawnee for "Panther Lying in Wait") had a reputation as a warrior dating back to the Indian vic-

Shawnee warrior Tecumseh.

tories over Josiah Harmer and Arthur St. Clair in the early 1790s. In 1798, he formed a warm friendship with an Ohio settler, James Galloway, lived with his family, and studied in Galloway's library of 300 books. In 1808, Tecumseh proposed to Galloway's daughter, Rebecca, and she agreed to marry him on the condition that Tecumseh abandon Indian ways and live like an American settler.

Tecumseh was not hostile to the civilization of the whites, far from it: not more than a handful of settlers in Indiana could have claimed an education better than his. But a revival of Indian culture was sweeping through the tribes of the Great Lakes basin when Rebecca Galloway set her terms. The movement, partly religious, partly political, was inspired by Tecumseh's brother, a one-eyed reformed drunkard, Tenskwatawa or "The Prophet." Tenskwatawa preached that Indians must reject white ways, particularly alcohol, and return to their ancestral traditions. Firearms and Christianity were the only elements of white culture that Tenskwatawa found appealing.

The Prophet also called for an end to wars between tribes. With the white population growing daily in Ohio and Indiana, it was time for all Indians together to draw a line in the sand and tell the invaders, "no further!" The Prophet urged his supporters to join him at Tippecanoe, a town built where a creek of that name flowed

into the Wabash River. It was there that Tecumseh rose to be the confederacy's military leader.

Governor Harrison respected Tecumseh but his fear of his leadership was greater. In November 1811, when Tecumseh was absent, he swooped down on Tippecanoe and destroyed it. In August 1812, when a three-pronged attack on Canada began, the Indians were reeling.

A Battle of Bunglers

For all their advantages, the American campaign was a fiasco on almost every front. One army was led by a general who was so fat that he could not sit on a horse and had to be hauled about in a cart. On the Niagara River, New York militia refused to advance and delayed their return home only long enough to watch a quarrel between two American commanders escalate into a duel (which the Canadians across the river also enjoyed). Surprised at American ineffectiveness, the Canadians counterattacked and captured Detroit, while their Indian allies destroyed the stockade at Chicago, then called Fort Dearborn.

The Northwest would have been laid wide open to further Canadian advance had it not been for the seamanship of Captain Oliver Hazard Perry. On September 10, 1813, although outgunned by the Canadian-British flotilla, he secured control of Lake Erie for the Americans. Receiving his famous message, "We have met the enemy and they are ours," William Henry Harrison then led 4,500 men toward York (Toronto), the capital of Upper Canada. The British defenders proved as inept as the Americans and, according to Tecumseh, cowards. He told the commanding British general, "We must compare our father's conduct to a fat dog that carries its tail upon its back, but when afrightened drops it between its legs and runs off." Harrison defeated the British-Indian force at the Battle of the Thames (where Tecumseh was killed), and burned the public buildings in the city.

In the meantime, the British invaded New York via the route John Burgoyne had followed during the War for Independence. They were stopped by Captain Thomas Macdonough, only 30 years of age, at the Battle of Lake Champlain. Ironically, while Americans won few victories on land, and those largely symbolic, American naval forces on both the lakes and the ocean won most of their encounters.

Nevertheless, the British revenged the burning of York when, in August 1814, they launched a daring amphibious raid on Washington, D.C. The troops burned the Capitol and the White House, and British officers claimed that they ate a dinner, still warm, that had been set for James and Dolley Madison. Indeed, the president narrowly escaped capture when, at a battle he

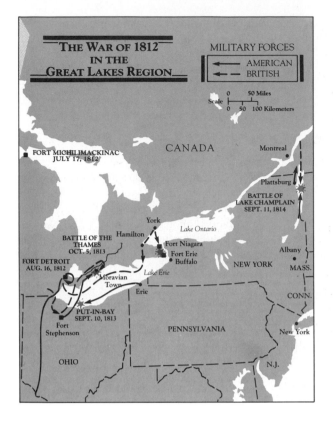

THE WAR OF 1812
IN THE
GREAT LAKES REGION

MILITARY FORCES
— AMERICAN
- - BRITISH

Scale 0   50 Miles
      0   50 100 Kilometers

CANADA

FORT MICHILIMACKINAC
JULY 17, 1812

Montreal

Plattsburg

BATTLE OF
LAKE CHAMPLAIN
SEPT. 11, 1814

York

Lake Ontario

Hamilton

BATTLE OF THE
THAMES
OCT. 5, 1813

Fort Niagara
Fort Erie
Buffalo

Albany

FORT DETROIT
AUG. 16, 1812

Moravian
Town

Lake Erie

NEW YORK

MASS.

Erie

CONN.

PUT-IN-BAY
SEPT. 10, 1813

Fort
Stephenson

PENNSYLVANIA

New York

N.J.

OHIO

drove out to view, the American army fled without fighting.

New Orleans

The British had not wanted the American war. But when Napoleon abdicated in the spring of 1814, freeing a large army for American service, they combined the beginning of peace talks at Ghent in Belgium with a plan to seize lower Louisiana from the United States. An army of about 8,000 excellent troops was dispatched under General Sir Edward Pakenham to attack New Orleans from the south. What augured to be a disaster for the Americans turned out to be a most amazing victory, the salvation of the War Hawks' battered morale, and the making of a most remarkable national hero, Andrew Jackson of Tennessee.

A self-taught lawyer, slave-owning planter, land-speculator, Indian-fighter, and duelist, Andrew Jackson assembled a force of 2,000 Kentucky and Tennessee volunteers, New Orleans businessmen, two battalions of free blacks, some Choctaw Indians, and artillerymen in the employ of the pirate-businessman Jean Lafitte. Jackson threw up earthworks five miles south of Louisiana's great port, the Mississippi River on his right, an impenetrable mangrove swamp on his left. In front of the gimcrack defenses was an open field.

Too confident, Pakenham sent his men through the morning fog on a frontal assault. Lafitte's cannoneers raked them with grapeshot and, when the redcoats were 200 yards from the earthworks, riflemen opened up with "a leaden torrent no man on earth could face." More than 2,000 redcoats fell dead. The army that had helped topple Napoleon broke and ran. Miraculously, only seven Americans were killed, four of them when they ran after the retreating British. (After the battle, Jackson hanged as many American soldiers for desertion as were killed during it.)

The Treaty of Ghent, which restored British-American relations to what they had been before the war, was actually signed before the Battle of New Orleans was fought. Nevertheless, the news of the astonishing victory had an electrifying effect. Such a glorious end to an ill-conceived and calamitous war seemed a reaffirmation of the nation's splendid destiny. When, within three years, Jackson crushed the powerful Creek tribe in the Southeast and Stephen Decatur returned to the Barbary Coast to sting the Algerians, Americans could feel that they had taken a prominent place in a world where armed might was one of the measures of greatness.

According to another of those measures, a nation's sway over vast territory, the United States was already capturing the attention of Europe. Unlike the nations of Europe, however, which expanded piecemeal at the expense of neighbors by annexing new provinces after victorious wars, the American people simply moved west into land they regarded as empty, theirs by the grace of God bestowed upon a people he had chosen for his own.

"THE STAR-SPANGLED BANNER"

It is to the War of 1812 that Americans owe their national anthem. On the night of September 13/14, 1814, a lawyer named Francis Scott Key was being detained on a British ship, which he had boarded in order to arrange for the release of a prisoner. While he was aboard, the British shelled Fort McHenry, the chief defense for the city of Baltimore. Fort McHenry resisted capture, and the sight of the American flag waving atop it on the morning of September 14 inspired Key's lyrics, which he wrote while being rowed back to shore.

Most singers have said that Key did the nation no favor by choosing as his music a popular English song, "To Anacreon in Heaven." Perhaps because it was a drinking song, sung and heard by people who did not care, "Anacreon" resisted (and still resists) attractive voicing.

Curiously, "The Star-Spangled Banner" has not been the national anthem for very long. Although unofficially sung since Key published it on September 20, 1814, the song was not officially adopted by Congress until 1931.

During the War of 1812, the British captured Washington, D.C.

For Further Reading

A classic that exemplifies the best of history-writing in the nineteenth century, as well as providing an excellent overview of the Jefferson-Madison years is Henry Adams, *History of the United States During the Administration of Thomas Jefferson and James Madison* (1889-91). For twentieth-century scholarship, see Marshall Smelser, *The Democratic Republic, 1801-1815* (1968). On Jefferson, see Daniel Boorstin, *The Lost World of Thomas Jefferson* (1948); Noble Cunningham, *The Jeffersonian Republicans* (1957); Dumas Malone, *Jefferson the President: First Term, 1801-1809 (1970)* and *Jefferson the President: Second Term, 1809-1813* (1974); and Merrill Peterson, *Thomas Jefferson and the New Nation* (1970). Controversial but a superb read is Fawn Brodie, *Thomas Jefferson: An Intimate Biography* (1974). Also see Richard E. Ellis, *The Jeffersonian Crisis: Courts and Politics in the Young Republic* (1971).

Alexander Deconde, *The Affairs of Louisiana* (1976) treats the great purchase in detail. The standard work on the Lewis and Clark expedition is David F. Hawke, *Those Tremendous Mountains* (1980) but students should also go to the horse's mouth, Bernard DeVoto, ed., *The Journals of Lewis and Clark* (1953). Jefferson's problems with John Marshall are treated in Richard Ellis, *The Jeffersonians and the Judiciary* (1971). For Marshall himself, see R. K. Faulkner, *The Jurisprudence of John Marshall* (1968) and Leonard Baker, *John Marshall: A Life in Law* (1974). For that other great nemesis of "Mad Tom," see Nathan Schachner, *Aaron Burr* (1984). On the milieu in which these characters moved, see James S. Young, *The Washington Community, 1801–1828* (1966.)

James Madison is the subject of a number of studies, including Irving Brant, *The Fourth President: A Life of James Madison* (1970) and Ralph Ketcham, *James Madison* (1971). On problems of "Jemmy Applejohn's" administration, see James M. Banner, *To the Hartford Convention* (1970); Linda K. Kerber, *Federalists in Dissent* (1970); Bradford Perkins, *Prologue to War: England and the United States, 1805–1812* (1961). Reginald Horsman remains our chief resource on the War of 1812 in his *Causes of the War of 1812* (1962) and *The War of 1812* (1969).

The DeWitt Clinton Railway, 1831.

BEYOND THE APPALACHIAN RIDGE

THE WEST IN THE EARLY NINETEENTH CENTURY

The Appalachian Mountains, a series of parallel ridges, rise in the southwestern corner of Maine and angle southwesterly into Georgia and Alabama. Known as the Catskills, the Poconos, the Alleghanys, the Blue Ridge, and the Smokeys at various points, they divide the springs and rains and snows that feed the creeks and rivers that flow into the Atlantic from those that feed the great Mississippi River system.

The Appalachians are not high as mountains go, but they were a formidable obstacle in the eighteenth century. Few natural passes traversed them, and most of those were but narrow gaps. In 1763, the British chose the Appalachian divide as a reasonable boundary between land which colonials might develop and land reserved for the Indian nations.

Independence erased the line of 1763 from the map, but not the wrinkle from the earth. In 1790, the first federal census takers counted only a few thousand intrepid pioneers living west of the mountains. The white population of the United States remained concentrated in the thirteen original states, looking to the Atlantic Ocean as their sole portal to the world outside.

THE FIRST AMERICAN WEST

The Battle of Fallen Timbers, Pinckney's Treaty, and Jefferson's obsession with the mouth of the Mississippi signaled a shift in orientation. By 1830, fully a quarter of the American population dwelled west of the Appalachians. Only a minority of these Westerners had been born in the Mississippi Valley, but the values of all had been shaped by the experience of cutting Eastern ties, packing up possessions, and striking off to where land was cheap and therefore, as Americans saw it, the future lay. Opportunity was synonymous with land in the mind of Americans and, thus, with "the West."

The West would continue to loom large over the American economy and society for the rest of the nineteenth century, and grip the American imagination until today. Indeed, in a sense, the American West became as much an idea as a physical place. In the United States, the word "frontier" took on a meaning scarcely to be heard in European usage. To Europeans, the frontier was a boundary between nations. To Americans, the word came to mean the less precise zone where white settlement and civilized institutions petered out, and wilderness and Indians still held sway. In Europe, frontiers moved in fits when victorious nations annexed the land of others. In North America, the frontier was in constant motion, ceaselessly shifting as restless men and women pushed into the setting sun.

Prodigious Growth

During the first decades of the nineteenth century, the American frontier moved bullishly beyond the Appalachian ridge. Between 1800 and 1820, the population of present-day Mississippi grew from 8,000 to 75,000. Alabama, with about 1,000 whites and blacks in 1800, was home to 128,000 in 1820, not counting large Indian nations.

The states north of the Ohio River were populated even more rapidly. In 1800, there were 45,000 white people in Ohio. Ten years later, the population was 230,000. By 1820, trans-Appalachian Ohio was the fifth largest state in the Union. By 1840, there were 1.5 million Ohioans. Only New York, Pennsylvania, and Virginia had larger populations. The state of Ohio was home to more people than Finland, Norway, or Denmark.

Between 1800 and 1840, the population of Indiana grew from almost nil to 686,000; Illinois, from a few hundred whites to 476,000. In 1800, American Michigan consisted of one wretched lakefront fort inherited from the French and British. In the 1830s, New Englanders flocked as thickly as passenger pigeons to Michigan's "oak openings," small fertile prairies amidst hardwood forests. By that time, the Mississippi River itself had ceased to lie beyond the frontier. Missouri, on the west bank, was a ten-year-old state, and home to an economy gearing up to support emigration farther west.

A People on the Move

The existence of land for the taking is not enough to explain this extraordinary, incessant movement of people. Russia was blessed with even more land than the United States, and a larger, far poorer population, but its "East"—Siberia—attracted few Russians. As a people, Americans seemed inherently restless, as agitated as the "painters" (panthers) that they chased deeper into the woods. To Europeans, and sometimes to themselves, Americans seemed incapable of putting down roots.

The young couple saying their marriage vows and promptly clambering aboard a wagon to head west was as familiar a scene in New England villages as stone fences meandering over cornfields. During the first decades of the century, Virginians headed across the mountains as rapidly as a high birth rate could replace them. In central and western Pennsylvania, site of a major wagon road west, the economy was closely tied to emigration. Inns and the stables of horse traders dotted the highway. A small Pennsylvania valley gave its name to the Conestoga wagon its people manufactured, a high-slung, heavy-wheeled vehicle designed for travel where there were no roads.

"In the United States," marveled Alexis de Tocqueville, the most singular of tourists, "a man builds a house in which to spend his old age, and he sells it before the roof is on." An Englishman looking over lands in the Ohio Valley reported that if he admired the improvements a recent settler had made on his property, the man was likely to propose selling everything on the spot so that he could begin again farther west. Americans joked that in the spring, the chickens crossed their legs so that they could be tied up for the next push west. Abraham

Life on the frontier was lonely, toilsome, and hard; but the opportunity represented by the West transfixed Americans.

Lincoln's father was a Virginian who moved to Kentucky, then Indiana, then Illinois.

Patterns of Settlement

A few of these pilgrims were simply antisocial. Others wanted as much company as they could persuade to follow them. Some meant to create the same way of life they knew back East, only better, with more land between their home and that of their neighbor.

MICHIGAN BOUND

As they sang of military victories and political candidates, Americans also sang of the experience of going west. There were dozens of songs about every destination that promised a better life. This one celebrated Michigan:

> *Come all ye Yankee farmers who wish to*
> *   change your lot,*
> *Who've spunk enough to travel beyond your*
> *   native spot,*
> *And leave behind the village where Pa*
> *   and Ma do stay,*
> *Come follow me and settle in Mich-i-gan-i-ay.*

Yet others were developers—a profession still with us and sometimes still honored—dreamers, schemers, and promoters of new Edens, Romes, Manchesters, New Yorks. Indeed, the men who, like Tom Lincoln, made a business of clearing a few acres and building a cabin to sell to a newcomer, were developers of a sort. Rather more important were those who bought large tracts of land, trumpeted its glories, and sold "subdivisions" at a profit.

Town boosters named streets before a tree had been felled in the intersections. Some of them were merchants or even manufacturers who planned to stay and prosper as the country grew. Others were professional boomers who made their bundle and moved on as rootless as hunters and trappers, never investing another thought in their creation and momentary domicile.

Squatters and Soldiers

The pioneer easiest to remember is the snaggletoothed frontiersman in a ragged buckskin shirt and coontail cap, wresting the forest from the Indians and fields from the forest, and grunting to his wan, washed-out wife in her filthy bonnet and calico smock, corncob pipe clenched in yellow teeth. An appalling sight, no doubt, many were; but James Madison was a bit unfair to lump such

Four engravings from O. Turner's History of the Holland Purchase *show how a New York farm was developed from wilderness over a forty-year period. The pattern held throughout the trans-Appalachian frontier as well.*

ABRAHAM LINCOLN AND JEFFERSON DAVIS

Both Abraham Lincoln and Jefferson Davis—opposing presidents during the Civil War—were born in log cabins on the Kentucky frontier. Lincoln's parents migrated there from Virginia in 1782, Davis's from Virginia in 1793. The two men were born within a year of each other—Davis in 1808, Lincoln in 1809.

In 1810, like many restless Kentuckians, the Davis family moved southwest to the rich cotton lands of Mississippi, where they became one of the richest slaveowning families in the state. Other Kentuckians went northwest, and Lincoln's father, a ne'er-do-well named Tom Lincoln, was among them. When Abraham was seven his family moved to Indiana and, when he was eleven, to Illinois. There, in Salem and Springfield, he became a successful attorney.

Perhaps because he realized that it was only a quirk of fate—the direction that their families had chosen when, with so many Americans, they "moved on"—that had made Davis the slaveowner and himself the antislavery politician, Lincoln refused to take a self-righteous attitude toward southern slaveowners. "They are just what we would be in their situation," he said.

people together as "evil-disposed persons." Mostly they were just dirt poor, and they tamed many an acre so that handsomer progeny could deny they ever existed.

The military was the cutting edge on some frontiers. Soldiers posted in the West to keep an eye on Indians had to be fed, clothed, and entertained. Shopkeepers, saloon keepers, and log-cabin prostitutes clustered around such lonely military installations. The security the fort provided encouraged trappers, hunters, and others who tramped the woods to congregate there in winter and during times of Indian trouble. Their needs stimulated the growth of a mercantile economy before there was much tillage in the neighborhood. Detroit and other towns gathered about old French and British outposts developed in such a way.

The Urban Frontier

In other parts of the West, cities actually came first. Only after a fairly advanced, if not necessarily refined, urban life had evolved did the hinterland fill in with farmers to provision the town. In such places, there never was a subsistence agriculture. The first farmers in such regions found a market ready-made and a broad range of suppliers and services welcoming them to town.

Places like Cincinnati, Louisville, Lexington, and Nashville were true, if small, cities before agriculture was well developed in the surrounding country. Occupying good locations at which river-farers could tie up their

keelboats and rafts, these cities served as jumping-off points for emigrants. When the cotton lands of the lower Mississippi Valley began to boom, sending out calls for provisions for their slaves, the citizens of such river ports responded with shipments of grain and livestock. Cincinnati, "the Queen City of the West," became famous for its slaughterhouses and packing plants when, not many miles away, the great hardwood forests blocked the sun from the earth and lonely men and women battled malnutrition and malaria.

In 1815, when there were no more than 15 steam engines in the whole of France, a nation of 20 million people, Kentucky boasted six steam mills that turned out cloth and even paper. Before the War of 1812, St. Louis had a steam mill that was six stories high. Like medieval burghers determined to outdo the cathedral of the next nearest city, Cincinnati built a mill that was nine stories high. Pittsburgh and Lexington, towns of 5,000 and 8,000 respectively, actually manufactured steam engines. Such places were no mere clearings in the wilderness where men bit off other men's ears to settle a disagreement.

Speculation as a Way of Life

Rapid development encouraged heated financial speculation. Many people went to Ohio or Michigan or Ala-

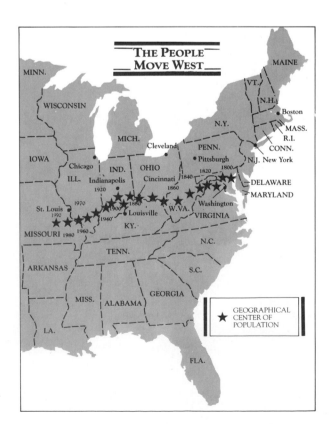

bama neither to farm, run a shop, salt and pack pork, nor invest in factories. They were speculators pure and simple, men with some money and plenty of plans to grow rich by the timeless, if risky, game of buying land cheap and selling it dear. Some were sharpers by anyone's definition, interested in nothing but lining their pockets. However, in a country where growth was the essence of life, almost everyone with a few dollars to spare, or able to borrow them, was attracted to the "inevitability" of rising values.

The speculative mentality made the price at which the government disposed of its land a matter of considerable political interest. (All western land, except for Indian claims and a few old French grants, was government land.) Under an ordinance of 1785, the federal government offered tracts of 640 acres at a minimum price of $1 an acre—cash.

Farmers protested that 640 acres were more than a family could work, and $640 far more than ordinary folk could raise. From the old Federalist point of view, the complaint was irrelevant. The land would be developed by the inevitable demand for it by a growing population. Administrative efficiency and the Federalist inclination to favor men of capital dictated that the government be a wholesaler, disposing of the land in large chunks and leaving the retailing of small farms to "the private sector."

Jeffersonian Land Policy

By way of contrast, the Jefferson Republicans believed in disposing of land in such a way as to favor the people who actually settled on it with plow and mule. The Jeffersonian idealization of the independent, small family farmer mandated a liberal land policy: "the price of land is the thermometer of liberty—men are freest where lands are cheapest." In 1804, a Jeffersonian Congress authorized the sale of tracts as small as 160 acres. The minimum price was $2 an acre but a buyer needed a down payment of only $80, and could pay the balance of $240 over four years.

The Land Act of 1804 made the government a retailer and a very obliging one. However, it neither shut out sharpers nor satisfied poor farmers. Introducing credit purchase actually benefitted speculators because, unlike conservative emigrants fearful of debt, speculators had no compunctions about borrowing heavily and making down payments on as much land as possible. The idea was to sell to latecomers before the second installment came due.

Feeding such speculation, irresponsible "wildcat banks" sprang up all over the West. On printing presses carted over the mountains, they churned out paper money with which speculators paid the government land

office and counted on a rise in values to make good their notes. For a while after the War of 1812, the wildcat banks did quite well. Land sales soared. In 1815, the government sold about 1 million acres; in 1819, more than 5 million.

Much of it went for higher than the minimum price because, before land was let go at $2 an acre, it was offered at auction. This practice also favored speculators. Settlers with small purses found themselves priced out of the market by those who did not care how much borrowed money they handed across the counter at the Land Office. Someone, surely, perhaps another sanguine speculator, would soon be willing to go a higher price. Some government lands in the cotton belt sold for more than $100 an acre—on paper.

Of Booms and Busts

The speculative boom in western lands depended, as do all speculations, on greed and the human species' marvellous capacity for self-delusion. Speculations are built on the principle of the "greater fool": one person pays an irrationally high price for a commodity—land or stocks or gold or, in seventeenth century Holland, tulip bulbs—on the assumption that there is a "greater fool" than he coming around the corner willing to pay even more. A great deal of money has been made in speculations. Mother Greed is a tireless bearer of fools.

A great deal of money has been lost in speculations as well. For, when the supply of potential buyers runs dry, and some speculators conclude that prices have peaked and can only decline, the result is often a crash. It takes but a few big plungers selling to "get out of the market" for prices to plummet. Because speculators deal in borrowed money, any significant drop in values causes a "panic" to sell so that, at least, some loans may be repaid. Indeed, if the lenders—the bankers—are the first to decide that values are going down, they can start the panic by calling in their loans, thus forcing speculators to sell at whatever prices they can get.

The Panic of 1819

This is what happened in 1819. The directors of the Bank of the United States, a generally conservative group of gentlemen, began to worry about the free-wheeling practices of the western banks and called in the money they owed to the B.U.S. Having lent out their resources to speculators, the wildcat banks called in those loans so as to avoid bankruptcy. When the speculators—no greater fools being on the horizon—were unable to sell land and pay their debts, the whole paper structure came tumbling down.

Speculators, as rich in acres as Charlemagne, could not meet their installment payments. The wildcat banks folded by dozens, leaving those thrifty souls who had deposited money in them broke. The B.U.S. lost money. Worthless bank notes went to the outhouse. The land reverted to government ownership.

In 1820, chastized by the panic, Congress abolished credit purchases and tried to dispose of the lands that had reverted to the government by reducing the minimum tract for sale to 80 acres, and the minimum price per acre to $1.25. With financial recovery, the speculators were back. In the meantime, Westerners on the bottom had devised various ways of dealing with them and other problems of living beyond the mountains.

PROBLEMS AND PROGRAMS

"Squatters" were emigrants to the West who began to develop farms on the public domain before they bought the land on which they stood. Such improved property was particularly attractive to speculators, since a cabin and a cleared field substantially increased the land's value. When the government surveyors and Land Office arrived, many squatters saw their claims "jumped," the home they had built on government land purchased at auction by a newly arrived slicker with a wad of borrowed bank notes in his purse.

In some areas, squatters combated these speculators by vigilante action. They banded together into "land clubs" and promised physical reprisals against anyone bidding on a member's land. Not infrequently, they made good on their threats and such ructions have made for many a thrilling book and film. But speculators could hire strongarms more than a match for farmers, and the law was, after all, on their side. In the end, squatters turned to the makers of law to fight their battles.

"Old Bullion" Benton

One spokesman for western settlers was Thomas Hart Benton, known as "Old Bullion" because he distrusted paper money issued by banks, preferring gold bullion. Born in North Carolina, Benton first entered politics in Tennessee but ran afoul of the state's premier citizen, Andrew Jackson (they fought a bloody tavern brawl in which Jackson was seriously wounded). Therefore, Benton opted for Missouri where he was among the earliest American settlers. Although well-read in the classics and supremely eloquent, Benton knew how to turn on the boisterous bluff that appealed to rough-hewn Westerners. "I never quarrel, sir," he told an opponent in a debate. "But sometimes I fight, sir; and when I fight, sir, a funeral follows, sir."

Elected senator in Missouri shortly after the Panic of 1819, Benton inveighed at every turn against bankers,

---

WESTERN RHETORIC

The following introduction was made to a small group of land speculators just before an auction for the sale of public lands:

My name, sir, is Simeon Cragin. I own fourteen claims, and if any man jump one of them, I will shoot him down at once, sir. I am a gentleman, sir, and a scholar. I was educated at Bangor, have been in the United States Army, and served my country faithfully. I am the discoverer of the Wopsey, can ride a grizzly bear, or whip any human that ever crossed the Mississippi, and if you dare to jump one of my claims, die you must.

---

paper money, and land speculators. He fought consistently throughout his long career for a land policy that would shut them out of the West.

Benton's pet project was preemption, or, as it was popularly called, "squatter's rights." Preemption provided that the man who actually settled on and improved land before the government officially offered it for sale would be permitted to purchase it at the minimum price. He would not be required to bid at an auction against speculators.

Another Benton program was graduation: land that remained unsold after auction would be offered at one-half the government minimum, and after a passage of time, at one-quarter. In a word, the price of the land was graduated downward in order to increase the number of people able to afford it. Eventually, Benton hoped, land that went unsold would be given away to people willing to settle it.

Benton's sentiments were soundly Jeffersonian. He favored those who tilled the soil, "the bone and sinew

---

THE LONG RIFLE

The gun that won the trans-Appalachian West was the Kentucky long rifle. It had a 44-inch barrel and enough maple stock to make it the height of an average man. It weighed only about eight pounds, however, and was a muzzle loader. To load it, the butt was placed on the ground, a light charge of coarse black powder (measured by dead reckoning) was poured down the muzzle into the breech, and a ball wrapped in greased linen or a leather patch was rammed home. (The patch was to seal the compression of the explosion and to ensure that the bullet "took" the rifling, the spiraling groves that gave it spin and therefore accuracy.) Even in the most practiced hands, the long rifle fired only about three times in four. Our phrase "flash in the pan" came from the all-too-common phenomenon of a charge that flashed without hurtling the ball on its way.

of the republic" in Jefferson's words, over financial interests associated with Alexander Hamilton and, in Benton's era, the Whig party.

Sectional Tensions

Opposition to liberal land policy was particularly strong east of the Appalachian ridge. The means by which public land was disposed of in Illinois or Missouri was of keen interest to people who lived on the oldest streets of Plymouth and the James neck of Virginia. To them, the western lands were a national resource—their wealth as well as that of westerners—a fount from which the government's expenses were to be paid. They feared that if the national domain was sold off as quickly and as cheaply as Benton and others wished, the old states would lose population and their property taxes would increase to make good the loss.

Northern factory owners feared that if emigrating to the West was too easy and cheap, their supply of laborers would shrink. The workers that remained, being in short supply, would demand higher wages.

Well-to-do Southern planters, increasingly dependent on slave labor, feared that disposing of western lands too cheaply would force the federal government to depend more heavily upon the tariff—import duties— to finance its operations. As consumers of the cheap British cloth, shoes, and other products that would be larded with new duties, they preferred to finance the government through land sales. Land policy, whether it was to be closely monitored or liberal, was an issue that, in the early nineteenth century, threatened to set section against section.

Handsome Henry Clay

The man who stepped forward with a plan to avert such a division was himself a Westerner, Henry Clay. Perhaps because he made his home in Kentucky, a state a generation older than Benton's Missouri, Henry Clay was concerned with wedding the West to the old states as well as with populating it. He wanted to see land gotten into the hands of actual settlers. But he also wanted to see it used to integrate the economies of North, South, and West. Clay was a nationalist, common enough a type in American history. He was a politician with a vision of the future beyond the next election day, a species now believed extinct.

Born in Virginia in 1777, Henry Clay trained as a lawyer and settled in Lexington at 21 years of age. He prospered as a planter, a land speculator, and especially as a politician. Elected to the House of Representatives in 1810, Clay won notoriety as one of the most bellicose of the War Hawks who helped push President Madison into war in 1812. When the fighting bogged down into

Henry Clay promoted continentalism by supporting federal financing of internal improvements.

stalemate, Madison named Clay to represent the War Hawk element at the peace talks in Ghent.

In Kentucky, in Europe, and in Washington, Clay had a taste for the good life. Keenly intelligent, famously handsome, graciously mannered, witty, ever-sociable, he charmed women and won the friendship and loyalty of men. He was equally at home sipping claret from crystal and sitting down to a game of faro that ended only when the whiskey was gone. Although he was a poor shot and killed no one, Clay fought several duels, almost a prerequisite of success in western politics at the time.

But Clay's prominence—he hovered near the center of power in the United States for four decades—owed only incidentally to his style. Like Benton, he worked to build up the West. Transcending Benton and other Westerners, Clay had a vision of a great and united nation that owed much to Alexander Hamilton but lacked Hamilton's indifference to the welfare of ordinary folk.

The Open Road

Clay's special cause as a young politician was federally financed internal improvements, particularly the building of better roads to tie the far-flung sections of the United States together. This was decidedly a Western

*Though plank roads provided a bumpy ride for travelers,
they were an improvement over muddy, rutted trails.*

cause. Although the roads and highways of the Eastern seaboard were wretched by the standards of western Europe, more than a century of population and development had resulted in a network of sorts. Beginning about 1790, the states and counties of the Northeast had graded and graveled old trails. The Old Post Road between Boston and New York allowed year-round long-distance travel on that important route, albeit an uncomfortable trip.

The Old Post Road was maintained by public monies. Other Eastern highways were privately constructed toll roads known as turnpikes because entrances were blocked with a pole resembling a pike that was "turned" to allow access when the toll was paid. One of the most successful, the Lancaster Pike, connected the rich farm town of Lancaster, Pennsylvania to Philadelphia, some 60 miles away.

By 1820, there were 4,000 miles of such toll roads in the United States. Some were surfaced with crushed rock, or macadam, a British import that was the ancestor of blacktop paving. A cheaper surfacing, more likely in the West, was made of planks laid parallel like railroad tracks, or even of logs laid crosswise. For the obvious reason, the latter were called corduroy roads. The ride they provided was bumpy and shattered many a hub and axle, but they kept a narrow, spoked wagon wheel out of the mud.

Federal Finance

Few entrepreneurs were willing to invest in even the cheapest road in the sparsely populated West. So-called roads there were usually nothing more than old Indian trails, sometimes widened to accommodate a wagon but, even then, often blocked by stumps. They guided the

way to neighbors, church, or river town well enough, but they could not accomodate commerce.

Nor could the young Western states afford to do much about the problem. They were caught in the vicious circle of needing good roads in order to attract population and move their products out, while lacking the population and, therefore, the tax base necessary to finance them.

The solution to Westerners such as Henry Clay was the federal government. As citizens of states that had been created by the Union, rather than states that were creators of it (to the end of his life, Thomas Jefferson referred to Virginia as "my country"), Westerners were more apt to look to Congress and president for aid than Easterners were. Moreover, the construction of a highway system in the vast West was a massive project. As men like Clay saw it, only the federal government could bear the expense.

Clay worked tirelessly on behalf of the first federal construction project in the West—the National Road that connected Cumberland, Maryland, on the Potomac River, with Wheeling on the Ohio River. It cost $13,000 per mile to build and was completed in 1818. Delighted by what this access to ocean-going commerce meant for Kentucky, Clay worked to have the National Road extended to Vandalia, Illinois. He was always ready to listen when fellow Westerners proposed new internal improvements.

Clay was uncommonly successful as a highway lobbyist, but he had formidable opponents. Many Southerners, nationally minded before the War of 1812, began to worry about the cost of internal improvements—and the taxation needed to pay for laying crushed stone, dredging rivers, and the like. Some Westerners, such as General Andrew Jackson, Clay's arch-rival for leadership of the section, feared that government finance of improvements was unconstitutional. Moreover, while Clay was blameless, many manipulators made fortunes on unnecessary or wasteful projects—there is something about a government appropriation—thus generating opposition to Clay's free-spending.

Until the 1820s, representatives of the New England states were also inclined to oppose spending federal money on internal improvements. Their own road system was adequate, so little federal money would be spent in their backyards. However, as the richest section of the country, the Northeast would pick up the biggest part of the bill in taxes. Moreover, until the Embargo and the War of 1812 disrupted the shipping business, New England's elite thought in terms of the Atlantic as the fount of their economic life. Factory owners feared that an improved West would attract their own people.

The American System

To counter such sectional thinking, Clay revived Alexander Hamilton's gospel of "continentalism." He urged Americans to seek their future, first of all, on the North American continent. He called his program the American System.

First, Clay argued that Northeastern industrialists had no reason to fear the consequences of internal improvements in the West. A populous West, connected to the Northeast by good roads, would provide a massive domestic market for the manufactured goods of New England and the Middle Atlantic states. He confronted the problem of taxes by compromising the Jeffersonian principle that western lands were to be disposed of as cheaply as possible. While not calling for extremely high prices—Clay supported graduation, for example—he proposed that revenues from land sales pay the greater part of the costs of internal improvements. He appealed to manufacturing interests by advocating a high tariff that would protect Northeastern factories from foreign competition.

To Westerners, largely farmers who might otherwise oppose a high tariff, Clay pointed out that a flourishing industry would lead to large urban populations of workers who would buy western food products. Higher prices for manufactured goods—the consequence of the high tariff—were a small price to pay for such a bonanza. To complete the circular flow of products among the regions, the South would supply the mills of New England with cotton.

The capstone of Clay's nationalistic program was the Second Bank of the United States. Chartered in 1816, its role in the American System was to regulate the money supply needed to fuel the integrated economy.

The weak link in Clay's program was the South, to which he did not offer very much. Southerners needed

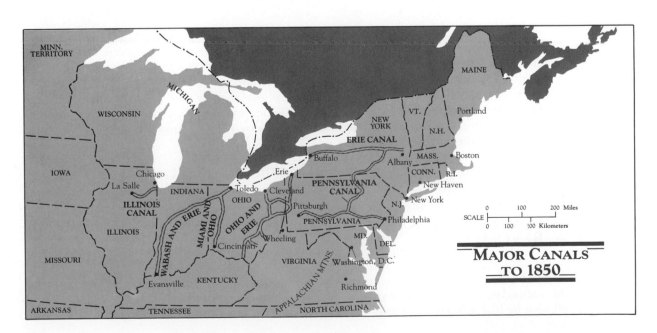

MAJOR CANALS TO 1850

WORKING AND PLAYING IN FRONTIER OHIO

When Europeans traveled through newly opened parts of the United States, like much of Ohio during the 1810s and 1820s, they were impressed by the feats of labor necessary to make a home in raw wilderness. They invariably complained about the food of the frontier—greasy fried pork and corn-meal mush or fire-roasted corn bread. And they were shocked by the heavy drinking in which everyone seemed to indulge.

But most of all they shuddered at the isolation of those who were building a life in a new country. The Europeans who wrote books about their American experiences were sophisticated and literate; they were accustomed to a full and stimulating social life. So they were disturbed by the loneliness endured by American westerners, particularly the women whose daily chores centered around solitary cabins in the woods.

Mrs. Frances Trollope, an English woman who wrote a celebrated book on *The Domestic Manners of the Americans,* blamed the emotional excesses of western revivalist religion on the absence of any form of recreation, of release from daily toil and tedium, even in the comparatively large river port of Cincinnati. "It is thus," she wrote, in the shrieking, howling, and rolling about the floor she witnessed at churches, "that the ladies of Cincinnati amuse themselves; to attend the theatre is forbidden; to play cards is unlawful; but they work hard in their families and must have some relaxation."

Just a few miles outside of Cincinnati, Mrs. Trollope met a hard-bitten frontier woman who showed off her farm and boasted that it produced almost everything the household needed. Economically, the family was self-sufficient but for tea, sugar, and whiskey. Socially, the situation was somewhat different. When Mrs. Trollope prepared to leave, her hostess sighed and said, "Tis strange for us to see company; I expect the sun may rise and set a hundred times before I shall see another *human* that does not belong to the family."

There is no distortion in this picture. Frontier life was extremely lonely for a great many pioneers. But not for all. During the 1820s, people in northern Ohio, an even newer region than the neighborhood of Cincinnati, managed to have a rich social life. William Cooper Howells, a printer who saw Ohio develop from wild forest into a populous industrial state, looked back on the parties of his youth with fond nostalgia. The point Howells made in his memoirs, *Recollections of Life in Ohio from 1813 to 1840,* was that Ohio pioneers combined amusement and diversion with work.

The raising of a family's log cabin or barn was done collectively by the people who lived within a radius of a few miles. The host had cut all the logs in advance and brought them to the site; sometimes, though, this job too was done by means of a community "log-roll." The men who best handled an ax took charge of notching the logs at each end and raising them into position by hand. With a team for each of the four walls, the job went quickly. When the walls rose too high to reach from the ground, the logs were lifted by means of young, forked trees to men straddling the tops of the walls. "The men under-

---

no help in finding profitable markets for their cotton, and needed to make no concessions to sell it. The mills of Manchester and Leeds and Bradford in England gobbled up all the fiber that Southern planters could grow. With the exception of a few special interest groups like Louisiana sugar planters, who wanted tariff protection against West Indian competitors, Southerners inclined to oppose Clay's program. To them, the American System meant bigger price tags on the manufactured goods that they, as agriculturists, had to buy.

THE TRANSPORTATION REVOLUTION

In the end, Clay had to be content with squeezing bits and pieces of his comprehensive program through Congress, not at all what he had in mind. Moreover, many of his victories were momentary; acts were repealed when his enemies, who were numerous, captured Congress and the White House. The American economy was to be integrated less by vision and legislation at the national level than by state action and by innovations in transportation that conquered seasons, leveled mountains, and diverted the course of rivers.

The Erie Canal

New York led the way in what was a revolution in transportation. In 1817, after years of prodding by De Witt Clinton—the mayor of New York City who had become state governor in 1816—the New York legislature voted funds to dig a canal from the Hudson River to Lake Erie, from Albany to Buffalo. With picks, shovels, mules, and wagons, gangs of rough, muscular laborers, many of them immigrants from Ireland, excavated a ditch 4 feet deep, 40 feet wide, and, when it was completed in 1825, 364 stood handling timber," Howells wrote, "and accidents seldom happened, unless the logs were icy or wet or the whisky had gone around too often." Howells himself, still quite a young man in Ohio's early years, took pride in taking on the job of "cornerman." While others built the walls, he "dressed up" the corners with an ax and guided the final logs into place. "It was a post of honor." The job was less laborious than that of raising the walls, but it took a head that "was steady when high up from the ground."

When a gathering of men for such a purpose took place there was commonly some sort of mutual job laid out for women, such as quilting, sewing, or spinning up a lot of thread for some poor neighbor. This would bring together a mixed party, and it was usually arranged that after supper there should be a dance or at least plays which would occupy a good part of the night and wind up with the young fellows seeing the girls home in the short hours or, if they went home early, sitting with them by the fire in that kind of interesting chat known as sparking.

In addition to log-rolling and barn- and cabin-raisings," "grubbing out underbrush" and the tedious task of processing flax (for linen and oil) were often done in conjunction with a community party. Other tasks—splitting logs into rails for fences, for example—were spiced up by holding a competition. Abraham Lincoln first ran for political office on his reputation as a virtuoso rail-splitter. But by far the most enjoyable kind of work party, remembered wistfully in practically every reminiscence of the frontier, was the husking bee. Not only was the job less laborious than the others and the occasion of a contest and a party, but husking bees took place in the autumn, when the harvest was done and the weather cool. It was the season when good food was most abundant and spirits were highest.

The ears of corn to be husked were divided into two piles. Two captains chose up sides, alternately selecting their teams from among the young men and boys and sometimes also from among the women and girls. Then

the two parties fell to husking, all standing with the heap in front of them, and throwing the husked corn to a clear space over the heap, and the husks (for animal fodder) behind them. From the time they begin till the corn was all husked at one end, there would be steady work, each man husking all the corn he could, never stopping except to take a pull at the stone jug of inspiration that passed occasionally along the line.

When one team had finished husking, they let out a great shout (which was the signal to lay a community dinner on the table), briefly exchanged taunts for the excuses of the losers, and then finished the husking along with them. Another "rule of the game" that increased interest was the provision that a boy who husked a red ear could claim a kiss from one of the girls at the party. But Howells concluded: "I never knew it necessary to produce a red ear to secure a kiss when there was a disposition to give or take one."

miles long. (The canal was later enlarged to 7 feet deep and 70 feet wide.)

The Erie Canal was expensive—$7 million, or almost $20,000 per mile. Skeptics waited for the state of New York to buckle under such a financial burden and declare bankruptcy. But when the ditch was finished, it opened up the Great Lakes basin to New York City's merchants and shippers by the cheapest means of transportation—water. Both city and state boomed. Linking the West with ocean-going commerce, New York quickly bypassed Philadelphia to become the country's biggest city.

Travel on the Erie Canal was slow. Mules on towpaths dragged the long, flat-bottomed canal boats at a lazy four miles an hour. But it transformed the laborious adventure of emigrating to the West into an excursion. For a cent a mile, a pilgrim could put himself into Buffalo and the Great Lakes basin: northern Ohio, Indiana, Illinois, and Michigan and Wisconsin. For five cents a mile, a man with a taste for comfort could travel the Erie Canal "first class." Far more important, it cost only $8 a ton to move factory goods west or western crops east. That was a 90 percent cut in the cost of overland transport!

The Canal Craze

Before the Erie Canal was dug, there were only about 100 miles of canal in the United States. (The longest one ran 28 miles.) Now, those who had laughed at "Clinton's Folly" went berserk in their rush to imitate it. Many were fools, laying out canals where mules feared to tread.

One of the most unlikely was the Mainline Canal in Pennsylvania. Smarting under the loss of business to New York City, Philadelphia merchants pressured the state legislature into pumping millions into this dubious venture. Actually, the Mainline Canal was shorter than the Erie but, while the New York route rose only 650 feet above sea level at its highest point, and required 84 locks to control its muddy water, the Mainline Canal

The Erie Canal made possible the cheap overland transportation of goods.

rose 2,200 feet and was regulated by 174 locks. At the Allegheny ridge, the highest in the Pennsylvania Appalachians, boats had to be hauled out of the canal and over the mountain on rails laid on a fantastic inclined plane. Miraculously, the Mainline Canal was completed, but it was a bust: too slow, too expensive, too many bottlenecks crowded with swearing boatmen in the mountains—where no boatman belonged.

All in all, some 4,000 miles of ditch were dug in imitation of the Erie Canal (and equally successful canal systems in western Europe). Another 7,000 miles were on the drawing boards when the bubble burst, as burst it did. While many of the canals were of inestimable use to locals, only a few made enough money to cover the money invested in them. So many states drained their treasuries to fund poorly advised projects that many politicians, including westerners, swore never again to finance internal improvements. As late as 1848, the constitution of the new state of Wisconsin forbade the expenditure of tax money on such ventures.

Railroads

The canal craze was also brought to an end by the appearance of a far better means of overland transportation—the railroad. As Pennsylvania's venture showed, canals were plausible only where the terrain was unhistrionic and the supply of water plentiful and constant. Even the most successful canals, like the Erie, were out of commission during the winter months when they froze. The railroad never provided transportation as cheaply as canal boats did. But railroads could run almost anywhere faster and, barring catastrophic blizzards, every day of the year.

The first railroads in the United States were constructed in 1827, just two years after the first railroad in the world proved workable in England. One line connected the granite quarries of Quincy, Massachusetts, with the Neponset River. The other carried coal from Carbondale, Pennsylvania, to the Lehigh River. Both were only a few miles long and served single-business enterprises, supplementing existing routes and means of transportation.

The potential of the railroad lay in using it, like the Erie Canal, as the "trunk" of a transportation system independent of traditional, "natural" routes. The first entrepreneurs in the United States to recognize this were Baltimoreans, merchants determined to put their city back in the competition with New York for the trade of the West. In 1828, work began on America's first trunk line, the Baltimore and Ohio.

Construction of the B&O was repeatedly stalled by financial difficulties, but the line was finally completed to Wheeling on the Ohio River in 1853. In the meantime, dozens of less ambitious railroads were constructed. By 1848, there were more than 6,000 miles of railroad track in the United States, while fewer than 3,000 miles of track existed in all the rest of the world.

Triumphs and Limitations

The railroad conquered time, and with time the isolation of the West. At the end of the War of 1812, it took more than seven weeks to ship a cargo from Cincinnati to

---

THE NEW YORK AND ERIE RAILROAD

In order to offset the economic advantages that the Erie Canal had brought to the northern counties of New York state, the southern counties proposed to build a railroad between the Hudson River and Lake Erie. Chartered on April 24, 1832, the New York and Erie Railroad (later the Erie Railroad) covered 446 miles between Piermont on the Hudson (26 miles from New York City) and Dunkirk (instead of Buffalo) on Lake Erie.

By 1851 trains carried President Millard Fillmore and his cabinet to Dunkirk on the then longest continuous railroad line in the world. Secretary of State Daniel Webster set out on the jaunt, it was reported, "on a flat car, at his own request, a big easy rocking-chair being provided for him to sit on. He chose this manner of riding so that he could get a better view and enjoy the fine country through which the railroad passed."

While the railroad could not provide as cheap transportation as did canal boats, it could go where canals could not. This early train is on one of the first lines to cross the Appalachian Mountains.

New York (by keelboat, wagon, and river boat). In 1852, when the two cities were connected by rail, it took six to eight days.

The cost of constructing a railroad was immense. In addition to securing right of way and hiring armies of laborers, a railroad company had to buy its own rolling stock. (A canal or turnpike company simply collected tolls from users with their own vehicles.) As a result, despite the total mileage of American railroads, few individual lines went very far. Indeed, competitive jealousies among the companies worked against true systems connecting distant points. Railway entrepreneurs built their lines in different gauges (the distance between the tracks), so that the cars of competing lines could not be used on them.

Most canals and railroads linked the West to the Northeast. However, the nation's great natural north-south artery, the Mississippi River, was not neglected during the revolution in transportation.

"Old Man River"

It could not have been otherwise. With its great tributaries, the Ohio and the Missouri, and dozens of smaller but navigable waterways, the Father of Waters tapped the central third of the continent. Westerners who lived on the Mississippi system could easily ship their corn or livestock to New Orleans on large log rafts that, broken up and sawed into lumber, were themselves a source of income.

The problem was in bringing goods back upstream. Sailing ships could not do the job. The Mississippi is a broad waterway but its current was mighty, and its channels narrow and shifting, the playthings of capricious sandbars. High riverbanks periodically stole the wind from sails. Large sailing vessels could not buck the current much beyond New Orleans; smaller boats carried too little to be worthwhile.

Some cargo was rowed upriver, some gotten north by poling small skiffs. Both were arduous tasks and extremely expensive. Half-savage keelboatsmen, such as the Ohio River's legendary Mike Fink, literally pulled their vessels upstream. The keelboater lashed a heavy line to a tree on the riverbank and, from the deck of the craft, heaved the ropes in, then repeating the process with another tree farther on.

It was no job for the languorous, nor was it an efficient way to move bulk. It took about six weeks for a huge raft to float pleasantly downstream from Pittsburgh, where the Ohio River begins, to New Orleans. It took four to five months to bring a much smaller tonnage back with even more raw-handed men drawing wages. It was more expensive to ship a cargo of English cloth or furniture from New Orleans to Illinois than to sail it from England to New Orleans.

Steamboat A-Coming

The marvel that resolved this dilemma was the flatbottomed steamboat, which was a long time coming. James Watt, the Scotsman who first harnessed the power of steam pressure for the purpose of pumping water out of mines, regarded ships as the second most important application of his discovery. In 1787, a Connecticut Yankee named John Fitch succeeded in making a practical steamboat. During the summer of the Constitutional Convention in Philadelphia, with several delegates witnessing the spectacle, he ran his 45-foot steamer down and up the Delaware River.

The "Lord High Admiral of the Delaware," as Fitch commissioned himself, built several larger steamers and briefly provided regular service between Philadelphia and Burlington, New Jersey. But he was a starcrossed man, obstreperous and obnoxious with his most generous backers. Nor was his humor improved by the indifference of Eastern capitalists who still thought in terms of the sea. They could not imagine how a vessel in which a good portion of the hold was committed to carrying fuel could compete with a sleek sailing ship drawing its energy from God's good sky.

In fact, the age of sail was far from over. For more than a century after the perfection of the steamship, clipper ships and great steel-hulled windjammers dominated

many world trade routes, particularly the long ones around Cape Horn. But steamboats conquered the rivers. Robert Fulton understood this. In 1807, his *Clermont* wheezed and chugged up the Hudson River from New York City to Albany at five miles per hour. The *Clermont* was three times as long as John Fitch's boat, but the dimension that thoughtful people noticed was that it drew only seven feet of water. The boat was able to clear obstacles that would have upended a sailing ship with less capacity.

Queens of the Mississippi

The steamboat paid its way on Eastern rivers like the Hudson. (Fulton's success helped to inspire the campaign to dig the Erie Canal.) But it was in the West that the great vessels found their natural home. In 1817, only ten years after the *Clermont*'s maiden voyage, there were 17 steamboats on the Mississippi. By 1830, there were 187 of them with new ones being constructed more quickly than old ones blew up.

Boiler explosions were no small problem. In order to minimize the weight of the boats, boilers were constructed more flimsily than experience and good sense prescribed. Nevertheless, Mississippi riverboat captains found it difficult to resist a race. As on the railroad, speed sold tickets and attracted shippers, so despite the opulence of some river boats, a trip on one was a bit of a gamble. At the peak of the steamboat age, 500 people died in accidents each year.

Designers competed just as frantically to adapt boats to the Western rivers. The greatest natural obstacles were the shifting sand bars of the Mississippi and Missouri, and "snags," fallen trees that were to the river what icebergs were to the North Atlantic, quiet predators capable of tearing a gaping hole in a wooden hull.

In 1841, the *Orphan Boy* was completed and eased on to the water. It could carry 40 tons of freight plus passengers. But even when fully loaded, it skimmed through water only two feet deep! The *Orphan Boy* was the ultimate, but a good many paddle-wheelers needed only three or four feet. Not only was this quality necessary to navigate the Father of Waters and the even trickier Missouri River, it enabled the boats to tie up at almost any bank in order to take on the cordwood they burned in prodigious quantities.

Symbols of a New Era

The locomotive and the steamboat knit the far-flung reaches of the United States together as neither Alexander Hamilton nor the young Henry Clay had imagined possible. In the words of a Cincinnati booster, they brought "to the remotest villages of our streams, and to the very doors of our cabins, a little Paris, a section of Broadway, or a slice of Philadelphia to ferment in the minds of our young people." The moving machines belching acrid smoke symbolized a sense of nationality as surely as the person of George Washington had symbolized the common cause of independence and constitutional union.

When the steamboat was still in its infancy, however, and the first railroad a decade in the future, Americans were already drawing together in their hearts, or so it seemed. In the wake of the War of 1812, a sense of American nationhood seized on the imaginations of the people of West, North, and even—ever so briefly—the South.

For Further Reading

On the early American West, see Ray A. Billington, *America's Frontier Heritage* (1967); R. S. Philbrick, *The Rise of the West, 1754–1830* (1965); Dale Van Every, *The Final Challenge: The American Frontier, 1804–1845* (1964); and Malcolm J. Rohrbough, *The Trans-Appalachian Frontier* (1978). Every inquiry into the American West should include the historian who founded Western history, Frederick Jackson Turner, *The Frontier in American History* (1920).

Important studies dealing with topics treated in this chapter include Richard D. Brown, *Modernization: The Transformation of American Life, 1600–1865* (1976); Elliott Brownlee, *Dynamics of Ascent: A History of the American Economy* (1979); Thomas C. Cochran, *Frontiers of Change: Early Industrialists in America* (1981); Eugene S. Ferguson, *The Americanness of American Tech-nology* (1975); F. W. Gates, *The Farmer's Age: American Agriculture, 1815–1860* (1960); Walter Havighurst, *Voices on the River: The Story of the Mississippi Waterways* (1964); L. C. Hunter, *Steamboats on the Western Rivers* (1949); Philip D. Jordan, *The National Road* (1948); Douglas C. North, *The Economic Growth of the United States, 1790–1860* (1951); R. M. Robbins, *Our Landed Heritage: The Public Domain* (1942); Ronald E. Shaw, *Erie Water West: A History of the Erie Canal, 1792–1854* (1966); George R. Taylor, *The Transportation Revolution, 1815–1860* (1951); Richard C. Wade, *The Urban Frontier* (1964); Sam B. Warner, Jr., *The Urban Wilderness* (1972).

Pertinent biographies are William Chambers, *Old Bullion Benton: Senator from the New West* (1970) and Glyndon D. Van Deusen, *The Life of Henry Clay* (1937).

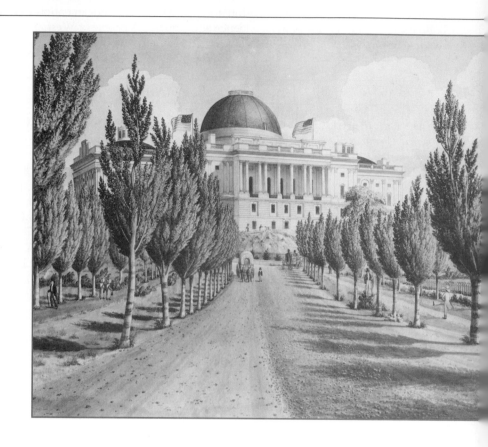

"View of the Capitol" in 1824, by Charles Burton.

A NATION AWAKENING

POLITICAL, DIPLOMATIC, AND ECONOMIC DEVELOPMENTS 1815 - 1824

Henry Clay's vision of an integrated national economy did not spring full-blown from his personal

ruminations. The idea of an American System was born in an era when a strong sense of nationalism

permeated American society and culture. The era had its beginnings in 1815 with Andrew Jackson's

victory at New Orleans and Stephen Decatur's punishment of the impudent Algerians. The news of

both events was celebrated with the discharging of muskets and pistols, flag-waving, shouting, singing,

and patriotic oratory.

THE ERA OF GOOD FEELINGS

For a decade after the divisive War of 1812, Americans in every section of the country embraced an image of themselves as a new chosen people—unique and blessed on the face of the earth, unsullied by the corruptions of Europe, nurtured by their closeness to nature, committed in the marrow of their bones to liberty, democracy, and progress. In 1821, in his inaugural address, President James Monroe was to declare that the United States would "soon attain the highest degree of perfection of which human institutions are capable."

It was during this period that the Fourth of July became a day of raucous popular celebration. Formerly reserved for religious services and decorous promenades in city squares, the Glorious Fourth burst into prominence as a day when everyone paid noisy homage to the nation with games, informal feasting, overdrinking, and boisterous gaiety.

Patriotic Culture

It was an era of patriotism in popular art. Woodcarvers and decorators trimmed canal boats, sailing ships, stagecoaches, and private homes with patriotic motifs: screaming eagles clutching braces of arrows; the idealized, vigilant female figure that represented liberty; and the flag, the only national ensign in the world that had growth and progress sewn into its design. Between 1816 and 1820, six new stars were added to Old Glory as six new states entered the Union.

The needlepoint samplers girls made to display their skills began to depict patriotic themes as often as religious themes: the Stars and Stripes, or the saying of some national hero like Decatur's "My Country right or wrong." Newspapers published exuberant verses that touted the national glories. Songwriters churned out lyrics that celebrated American grandeur.

Best Sellers

In 1817, William Wirt wrote a biography of Patrick Henry that implied that Virginians had led the movement for independence and had fought the war single handed. Offended patriots from other states looked for (and dependably found) patriotic demigods of their own.

Less controversial because of its singular subject was Mason Locke Weems's book, *The Life and Memorable Actions of George Washington*. Although originally published in 1800, Weems's unblushing study in hero worship peaked in popularity during the 1810s and 1820s, running through 59 editions. It was Weems who originated the story of the boy Washington chopping down the cherry tree and the tale of an older Washington throwing a silver dollar the width of the Rappahannock River. So noble was the Father of His Country that he could not fib; so far was he above other nations' leaders that even in physical strength he was a superman.

Another influential author of the time was Noah Webster, whose *American Spelling Book*, first published in 1783, sold more than 60 million copies. The "blue-backed speller" was the text from which most American schoolchildren learned that the "American tongue" was superior to Old World English because Webster had stripped it of "affectations." Many of the differences in spelling between American English and British English (lab*or* and col*or* as opposed to lab*our* and col*our*, theat*er* as opposed to theat*re*, *jail* for *gaol*) owe to Webster's linguistic chauvinism. His *American Dictionary of the English Language*, published in 1828, genuinely distinguished American English by including hundreds of words adopted from Indian tongues.

James Monroe

The gentleman who presided over this outpouring of national pride was, like three of the four men who preceded him in the presidency, a Virginian—James Monroe of Westmoreland County.

His is a blurred figure in the history books, a personality with few hard edges. His achievements can be listed. He studied law with Jefferson and was Jefferson's most trusted diplomat. He negotiated the Louisiana Purchase. Year after year, he served his patron and James Madison—as Secretary of State. It is difficult to find a public smear of his character. Jefferson wrote of him to Madison: "Turn his soul wrong side outwards, and there is not a speck on it."

It can be noted that people thought his wife one of the most beautiful women in the country. Portraits reveal that the fifth president was eccentric in his dress; he wore the old-fashioned, skin-tight knee breeches of the Revolutionary era, while his contemporaries pulled on utilitarian trousers.

But a two-dimensional figure in an oil painting is what James Monroe remains. Perhaps it is because he was so very successful as president, calmly meeting and promptly dispatching every problem that rose to face him. History, like the audience at a play, thrives on conflict and grows dull and torpid in times of stability. James Monroe had the political good luck, and the historical misfortune, of being president during an *entr'acte*, an interlude of calm between two times of crisis.

Political Stability

The Founding Fathers' hopes for a government without political parties briefly came to pass under Monroe. The

THE ERA OF GOOD FEELING 217

NATIONAL PROPRIETY

Noah Webster not only Americanized English, he was also very concerned that it be proper. He prepared an edition of the Bible in which he left out words "offensive to delicacy." Webster wrote:

Many words are offensive, especially for females, as to create a reluctance in young persons to attend Bible classes and schools, in which they are required to read passages which cannot be repeated without a blush; and containing words which on other occasions a child ought not to utter without rebuke.

Federalists, revived during the War of 1812, collapsed when the shooting was over. After Jackson's victory at New Orleans, their opposition to the war seemed more like disloyalty than good sense.

The number of congressmen styling themselves Federalists declined from 68 during the war to 42 in 1817 and 25 in 1821 (as compared with 158 Jeffersonian Republicans). By 1821, there were only 4 Federalists in a Senate of 48 members. Old John Adams, in retirement in Quincy, Massachusetts, took scant interest in the evaporation of the party that he had helped to found. His son, John Quincy Adams, joined the party of Thomas Jefferson and became Monroe's Secretary of State.

During the 1810s, Republican congressmen and senators met in caucus to choose their presidential candidate and therefore, in effect, the president. Monroe handily defeated Federalist Rufus King in 1816. King won the electoral votes of only Delaware, Connecticut, and Massachusetts. The next year, when Monroe visited Boston, where Jefferson had been loathed and Madison despised, he was received as a hero. A Boston newspaper

---

A YANKEE-DOODLE SONG

One of the most joyously patriotic songs to come out of the War of 1812 was "The *Constitution* and the *Guerrière*," about a two-ship battle that ended in an American victory:

It oft-times has been told
How the British seamen bold
Could flog the tars of France so neat
*   and handy, O!*
But they never found their match
Till the Yankees did them catch.
Oh the Yankee boys for fighting are
*   the dandy, O!*

---

congratulated him for inaugurating an "era of good feelings."

In 1820, Monroe was unopposed in the presidential election. (One member of the electoral college cast his vote for John Quincy Adams so that no president but Washington would have the distinction of being his country's unanimous choice, and to set up Quincy Adams as the party's nominee in 1824.) With only one political party, the United States had, in effect, no parties at all.

Smooth Sailing

There was another side to the consensus of the Era of Good Feelings, an indifference toward presidential politics. In 1816, William Crawford of Georgia could probably have won the Republican presidential nomination over Monroe, but Crawford did not think the prize worth a fight. His supporters simply did not attend the party caucus at which the candidate was to be named.

Nor was there much popular interest in general elections. In 1816, only 6 of 19 states chose presidential electors by statewide popular vote; in 1820, only 7 of 24 states did. In most of the others, the state legislatures made the choice, and they treated the task as though it were routine, confirming the governor's proclamation of a Thanksgiving holiday, or a pension for a retiring doorkeeper. In 1820, the returns from Richmond, Virginia, a city of 12,000 people, revealed that only 17 men had bothered to vote.

There is nothing intrinsically wrong in a subdued presidency and popular indifference to politics, particularly according to the tenets of the Jeffersonian faith, to which James Monroe subscribed. Jefferson had said that the government that governed least governed best. The absence of deeply divisive issues during Monroe's tenure in office reflected the relative prosperity of the times and the American people's concern with westward expansion and economic growth. Moreover, so what if Monroe was neither a mover nor a shaker? Movers and shakers often do a good deal of mischief; Monroe did none. He was a conscientious, competent, and hard-working executive. His administration was efficient and, without a popular clamor to distract them, he and his nationalistic Secretary of State, John Quincy Adams, had an unbroken string of diplomatic successes.

Making Up with the Mother Country

In the Rush-Bagot Agreement of 1817, the United States and Britain agreed to limit the number of armed vessels on the Great Lakes. It was the first major concession that the former mother country had made to the upstart Americans since the Revolution. More important, the partial disarmament set the pattern for future policies that established the world's longest unfortified international boundary.

In 1818, Britain and the United States established the southern boundary of British Canada at 49° north latitude, a line that now runs west from Lake Superior to Puget Sound. Although American claims in the Pacific Northwest were flimsy, and concrete American interests there next to nil, the British conceded Americans equal rights in what was called the Oregon country: present-day Oregon, Washington, the Idaho panhandle, and British Columbia.

Florida Is Secured

With Spain, Monroe-Adams diplomacy reaped even greater rewards. By 1819, the Spanish Empire was quaking. Rebellions had broken out in practically every province, and rebel armies won most of the battles against demoralized loyalist troops. The leaders of the independence movement—Simon Bolivar, José de San Martín, and Bernardo O'Higgins—paid flattering homage to the example set for them by the United States. Their praises of the United States as the beacon light guiding their own march to freedom provided more fodder for the Americans' bumptious national pride. The United States was the first nation to recognize the independence of the Latin American republics, beginning with Colombia and Mexico in 1822.

The disintegration of the Spanish Empire also gave Florida to the United States. The peninsula never had been a very valuable or secure part of the Spanish Empire. Thinly populated, Florida had been held by the British for 20 years after 1763. In 1818, in pursuit of Indian enemies, Andrew Jackson brazenly crossed the border, ignored Spanish authority, and (on foreign soil) executed two British subjects for treason to the United States!

When the Spanish minister in Washington protested Jackson's incursion, Secretary of State Adams responded by offering to buy Florida. For $5 million, Spain agreed. Adams had only to confirm Spain's version of the disputed boundary between American Louisiana and Spanish Texas (at the present eastern border of the state of Texas), which was no concession at all. The United States had never seriously contested the Mexican boundary. In the Adams-Oñis Treaty, the United States was guaranteed every acre to which the country had a reasonable claim.

The Monroe Doctrine

John Quincy Adams was also the author of the American statement of policy that has immortalized Monroe's name. In December 1823, the president wrote in a message to Congress (and to Europe) that the United States was no longer to be considered an appendage of the Old World. With an "essentially different" destiny, the United States pledged not to dabble or intervene in European affairs. In return, Europe was to consider the Western Hemisphere closed to further colonization. Monroe said that any such attempts would be defined in Washington as "an unfriendly disposition." In other words, he threatened war.

The proclamation of the Monroe Doctrine (a name given it only decades later) was prompted by two developments that disturbed the sensitive Quincy Adams. The first was expanded Russian exploration and fur trapping south of Alaska, which was Russian since 1741 by right of discovery. The Russians built an outpost, Fort Ross, provocatively close to Spanish San Francisco, and in February 1821, the Czar ordered foreign ships to keep at least a hundred miles clear of Russian America's shores. Far more important, Adams was troubled by rumblings in Austria and France. He feared those countries would send troops to the Western Hemisphere to help Spain regain control of its lost colonies.

Asserting American Identity

Neither threat amounted to anything. The Russians were interested in the plush pelts of the California sea otter, and by the 1820s, trappers had just about wiped out the animals in California's coves. In 1824, the Russians abandoned Fort Ross and withdrew to Alaska. The French and Austrians discovered that they faced far more compelling problems than rescuing Spain's colonies and lost pride. The plan for a trans-Atlantic invasion was stillborn.

Which was just as well: in 1823, the United States was probably not up to dispatching an effective army to Mexico, let alone to South America. If the Adams-Monroe closure of the New World to further colonization had any force, it was because the British, now utterly dominant on the Atlantic, wanted Latin America independent.

In fact, the British foreign minister, George Canning, had proposed that Great Britain and the United States jointly proclaim the Americas closed to further colonization. Previously restricted in the extent of their trade in the rich markets of the old Spanish Empire, the British

---

FORTUNE TELLING

In the early nineteenth century, some upper-class families amused themselves on a boy's fourth birthday by putting him in front of a pair of dice, a piece of fruit, a purse, and a silver knife. It was prophesied that if he picked up the knife, he would become a gentleman of leisure; the purse, a businessman; and the fruit, a farmer. If he picked up the dice, everyone had a good laugh.

This fabric, with its patriotic design, illustrates the patriotism of the early nineteenth century.

were the chief beneficiaries of Spanish American independence.

Adams decided to act alone in asserting the different destiny of the Western Hemisphere so that the United States would not look like "a cock-boat in the wake of the British man-of-war." To nationalistic American sensibilities, British friendship could be as threatening as British antagonism, and Adams planned to run for president in 1824.

Nationalism in the Courtroom

While Quincy Adams and Monroe proclaimed the national dignity of the American republic to the world, Chief Justice John Marshall buttressed the constitutional primacy of the national government at home in a series of decisions that are still basic to American law. Marshall never again invalidated a law of Congress as he had done in *Marbury v. Madison*. Instead, while cultivating a reputation for heroic physical laziness and squalid personal appearance, he dominated his fellow Supreme Court Justices until 1835. In chambers by day, at the boarding house where several justices lived together by evening, over lawbooks and tumblers brimming with whiskey, Marshall whittled away at the power of the states which, good Federalist to the end, he regarded as dangerous to the Union.

In *Fletcher v. Peck* (1810), the Marshall Court declared a state law unconstitutional, thus establishing the right of the Supreme Court to act in matters that concerned one state alone. The decision might be considered the judicial equivalent of Washington's suppression of the Whiskey Rebellion. In *Martin v. Hunter's Lessee* (1816), Marshall established the Court's authority to reverse the decision of a state court. In *McCulloch v. Maryland*

(1819), Marshall prevented the state of Maryland (and all states) from taxing the nationally chartered Bank of the United States. "The power to tax is the power to destroy," the Court declared. No state had the right to interfere with the national government's obligation to legislate on behalf of the common good, as the Constitution commissioned it to do.

In *McCulloch*, Marshall also propounded his views on the extent of governmental power. If the goal was legitimate and the law did not run counter to the Constitution, Congress and the president had the power to enact whatever legislation they chose to enact. It did not matter that the government in Washington was not specifically authorized by the Constitution to take a certain action (such as the establishment of a national bank). This was the issue that had caused the first split between Hamilton and Jefferson. Now with Hamilton and Hamilton's party both dead, John Marshall made "broad construction" of the Constitution the prevailing law of the land.

John Marshall served as Chief Justice during the administrations of six presidents, three of whom served two full terms while he lived. It would be difficult to argue that any of them contributed more to the shaping of American government than he. In 1833, the only Supreme Court Justice of the Marshall era whose legal mind rivaled his own, Joseph Story, published *Commentaries on the Constitution of the United States*. Essentially, it was a commentary on fundamental American law as John Marshall perceived it.

THE INDUSTRIAL REVOLUTION IN AMERICA

Alexander Hamilton would have honored John Marshall. Another of Hamilton's dreams for the United States—and Jefferson's worst nightmare—also headed for fulfillment during the second and third decades of the nineteenth century. To some extent in the West, but particularly in New England and the Middle Atlantic states, manufacturing came to rival agriculture in economic importance, and population began a significant shift from farms and villages to the towns and cities where factories were centered. In this process, the people of the Northeastern states were early participants in the Industrial Revolution.

What Industrialization Meant

Machine technology, the factory system of making goods, and the rapid growth of industrial cities were not revolutionary in the sense that people's lives were changed overnight. But the consequences of machines

Modern urban areas such as Brooklyn were more like villages in the early nineteenth century, as this painting illustrates.

that made goods quickly and cheaply changed the terms of human existence far more profoundly than did any battle, or the beheading of any king or queen.

For example, in the United States today, less than 8 percent of the population lives on farms. Save for a few eccentrics, no people produce more than a tiny fraction of the food they consume and the goods they use. They buy the commodities of life with money received for performing very specialized jobs. The typical farm family raises only one or two crops for market, and purchases the same mass-produced necessities and luxuries that city dwellers buy.

Before industrialization, in colonial and early national America, the situation was reversed. Roughly 90 percent of the population (the proportion was constantly declining) lived on farms or in farm villages, and personally produced a goodly proportion of the food they ate and the goods they used. For most people, very little was purchased: shoes; some clothing; tools such as axes and guns; pottery and tin- or pewterware; some services such as milling flour, shoeing horses, and so on. As for other necessities, ordinary people improvised them from materials on hand.

The pre-industrial farmer or shopkeeper had to be "handy." A man with a door to hang made the hinges himself; a woman who kept a tidy house made the broom with which she swept it. Heavy work, such as log-rolling and raising a roof beam on the frontier, husking corn, or

cutting ice from a pond, were done cooperatively by neighbors. In all but the half dozen largest cities, townspeople of some means kept gardens of an acre or so, often a dairy cow, commonly a brood sow. The Industrial Revolution changed that kind of unspecialized, largely self-sufficient life into the specialized, interdependent economy we know today.

It Started with Cloth

The first industrial machines were devised for the manufacture of textiles. This should not be surprising, because cloth is a universal necessity but making it by hand is both tedious and demanding, complicated and time-consuming.

In North America, as in much of the Western world, clothmaking was largely woman's work, and the process took up much of the spare time of that half of the population. On poor and even middling American farms, cloth was made at home from scratch. Natural fiber from animals (wool) or plants (cotton and flax for linen) had to be gathered, cleaned, carded (untangled, combed), spun into thread or yarn, dyed, and then woven or knitted by hand into a fabric that could warm a body, cover a bed, protect a wagonload, or propel a ship.

Because the process took so much time and required hard-learned skills at every turn, fabric was expensive. The poor dressed in hand-me-downs scarcely better than rags. People of modest means made do with one set of clothing for work, another for "Sunday-go-to-meeting."

Cottage Industry

Well-to-do people dressed rather more handsomely, of course, and they did not spin and weave. Cloth also had to be made in quantity for plantation slaves, soldiers, and sailors. Before industrialization, the needs of such groups were met by "cottage industry," or what was sometimes called "the putting-out system."

It worked in this way. Farm wives and daughters contracted with a cloth dealer, sometimes called a factor, to receive fiber from him and spin it into yarn or thread in their homes. Working in odd, snatched moments, they were paid not by the hour but by the piece. They were, in our terms, independent contractors. The women and children (and sometimes men) in another family might weave cloth under the same system, again in their spare time.

This system of production did not significantly disturb traditional social structure and values. Households involved in cottage industry were able to participate in the money economy to the extent of what their women earned. Socially, however, these women remained farmwives, daughters, and spinsters (unmarried women in a household). They were not "textile workers." Their values and the rhythm of their lives were essentially the same as those of their neighbors who did not spin or weave.

In the middle of the eighteenth century, this system began to change. English inventors devised water-powered machines that spun thread and wove cloth at many times the speed that hand spinners and weavers could do it, and, as a result, at a fraction of the cost. With a monopoly of this technology, Britain prospered, supplying the world with cheap fabric. Not only were most women from Canada to Calcutta delighted to be spared the tedium of spinning and weaving, but the machine-made cloth was cheap enough for almost all to buy, and it was generally of better quality than homemade cloth. England found a market for its cheap cloth everywhere in the world. Comparable machines were rapidly developed for other forms of manufacture.

The Importance of Power

The key to exploiting the new machines was power—a fast-moving river, or somewhat later, the steam engine. A water wheel or mighty, hissing piston could turn hundreds of machines much faster than any foot-driven spinning wheel. Power is where it is found or made, however. The process of making cloth had to be centralized, brought under one roof; the machines had to be run for as long as there was light by which to see. Industrialization created the factory and a new pace of labor governed by the clock, the tirelessness of the machines, the capitalist's need to use his investment to the utmost.

Industrialization also created a class of workers who

Slater Mill, established in Rhode Island in 1790, was the first successful cotton spinning factory in the United States.

did nothing but tend machines. No longer was thread spun by a farm wife in odd moments. The industrial textile worker spent six days a week, from dawn to dusk, at the factory. Because she worked virtually all the daylight hours, she had to live close to the factory. The mill-hand was a town dweller, no longer the farmer's daughter. A new social class emerged—the urban, industrial working class that Karl Marx would later name the proletariat.

Early Factories

The British protected their monopoly of industrial technology as a magician guards his bag of tricks. It was, of course, illegal to export machinery and the plans for them. Indeed, engineers and mechanics expert in building or repairing textile machines were forbidden to leave the country.

One such engineer was Samuel Slater, 23 years old in 1790, and quite clever enough to know that the knowledge that provided him comfort in England would make him rich abroad. Rather than risk being caught with plans for spinning machines, Slater committed to memory several long and intricate lists of specifications. He slipped away from his home and shipped off to America as a farm laborer. There he made contact with a Rhode Island merchant, Moses Brown, who had tried without success to build spinning machines. "Thee said thee could make the machinery," Brown wrote to him, "why not do it?"

Brown and a partner put up the money, and Slater contributed the expertise. In 1790, they opened a small water-powered spinning mill in Pawtucket, Rhode Island. The little factory housed only 72 spindles, a picayune operation compared with what was to come. Still, they were the equivalent of 72 spinning wheels in 72 cottages, and each of the Slater devices turned many times faster and spun much longer than any farm wife could manage.

The capital investment was substantial but operating expenses small. The whole mill could be run by one supervisor and nine children between the ages of seven and twelve. Their labor cost Slater and Brown 33 to 60 cents per worker per week. Within a few years, both men were rich. Slater lived to be one of New England's leading industrialists, owning mills in three states.

There were other such acts of technological piracy. In 1793, two brothers from Yorkshire, John and Arthur Schofield, came to Byfield, Massachusetts, and established the first American woolens mill. Francis Cabot Lowell smuggled plans for a power loom out of England. Throughout the nineteenth century, Englishmen would bring valuable technological advances in their sea trunks.

High Labor Costs

Once aroused, however, Americans proved more than able to advance the industrial revolution on their own. Alexander Hamilton had observed "a peculiar aptitude for mechanical improvements" in the American people. In the 1820s, a foreign observer marveled that: ". . . everything new is quickly introduced here. There is no clinging to old ways; the moment an American hears the word 'invention' he pricks up his ears."

One reason for the American infatuation with the machine was the labor shortage that had vexed employers since the earliest colonial days. Land was abundant and cheap in the United States. Opportunities for an independent life were so ample that skilled artisans demanded and generally won premium pay. In the early nineteenth century, an American carpenter made about three times as much in real income as his European counterpart. Even an unskilled worker in the United States could live considerably better than the day laborers of the Old World. What was sauce for the worker, however, was poison to the men who hired help. The machine, which did the job of many handworkers, was inevitably attractive to them.

Inventors Galore

Thus, Oliver Evans of Philadelphia earned a national reputation when he contrived a continuous-operation flour mill. One man was needed to dump grain into one end of an ingenious complex of machinery. Without further human attention, the grain was weighed, cleaned, ground, and packed in barrels. Only at this point was a second man required to pound a lid on the keg. Evans had saved millers half their payroll.

In 1800, Eli Whitney announced a system for casting small iron parts that promised to displace gunsmiths, one of the most skilled and best-paid of pre-industrial craftsmen. Muskets and sidearms were expensive because the lock (firing device) was made up of a dozen or more moving parts, several of which were tiny and quite delicate. Each was individually fashioned by hand so that no two guns were the same; every one was "custom made." Not only was crafting a firearm time consuming and expensive, but repairs required the attention of an artisan who was as skilled as the man who made the gun, for he had to fashion replacement parts from scratch.

Whitney's innovation was to make the molds for the parts of a gun so precise that one component cast in them was enough like every other that they could be used interchangeably. He appeared before a congressional committee with ten functional muskets constructed from interchangeable parts, took them apart, shuffled the components, and reassembled ten working muskets. His dramatic little show won him a government contract to make 10,000 more.

Many cultures produce inventors. The United States was one of the few to raise the inventor to the status of a hero. Even bastions of tradition embraced practical science. In 1814, Harvard College instituted a course called "Elements of Technology." In 1825, Rensselaer Polytechnic Institute, a college devoted entirely to the new learning, was founded at Troy, New York. Others followed in quick succession for Americans found nothing bizarre in teaching engineering side by side with Greek and Latin. Indeed, they were more likely to be suspicious of those who studied the classics.

A COUNTRY MADE FOR INDUSTRY

A cultural predilection to technology was only one of America's advantages in the industrial revolution. The United States was also blessed with the other prerequisites of an industrial society: resources necessary to feed the new machines; capital, surplus money to finance the building of factories; and labor, people to work them.

Resources

For a providentially minded people, it was as if the Creator had shaped the northern states with water-driven mills in mind. From New England to New Jersey, the country was traversed with fast-running streams that, dammed and channeled, provided power for factories. When steam power proved superior to water power, there were dense forests and rich deposits of coal to stoke the boilers. America's forests and strong agricultural base produced what raw materials the new industry required, from lumber to leather to hemp for rope. At the same time the textile industry was growing in New England, cotton cultivation expanded throughout the South to provide enough of the snowy fiber for both England and America.

Capital

Money available for investment in industry came from the merchants and shippers of the Northeast. Ironically, many of these capitalists were practically forced to convert their wealth from ships into mills by the restrictions on trade that they thought would be the ruin of them. In 1800, at the beginning of the Napoleonic Wars, there were only seven mills in New England, with a total of 290 spindles. After Jefferson's Embargo, Madison's Non-Intercourse Acts, and the War of 1812 had disrupted shipping for 15 years, there were 130,000 spindles in 213 factories in Massachusetts, Connecticut, and Rhode Island alone. Aware of a good thing once they saw it, industrialists continued to expand. By 1840, there were 2 million spindles in the United States.

Banking Creates Money

Banks, a new phenomenon in the early nineteenth century, made it easier to channel capital where it was needed. Not everyone was pleased at the multiplication of lending institutions from 30 in 1801 to 88 in 1811. A bank issued more money in paper certificates than it actually had on hand in gold and silver. In 1809, anticipating the obsession of Thomas Hart Benton, John Adams growled that "every dollar of a bank bill that is issued beyond the quantity of gold and silver in the vaults represents nothing and is therefore a cheat upon somebody."

However, so long as the people who built a mill, supplied it with fiber, and worked the machines accepted the paper dollars lent by a bank to the millowner, and so long as their grocers, landlords, and business associates accepted the paper money from them, it did not matter that the bank owned only $100,000 in gold and issued $1 million in paper. So long as the people who traded in the bills believed that they could present the paper to the bank and receive gold, capital was increased tenfold. So long as confidence and optimism were in rich supply, banks were a source of energy as powerful as the 32-foot falls of the Merrimack River.

Industry and Politics

With the increasing importance of industrial interests in the Northeast, the section's political interests shifted. Traditionally, New England shipowners had been suspicious of a high tariff on imported goods. If taxes on imports were high, fewer Americans bought them; thus, there was less business carrying manufactures across the

---

INGENUITY

The American fascination with gadgets and novel mechanical devices is almost as old as the republic. As foreign observers were to note, some wryly, some aghast, Americans seemed to leap into tinkering without planning. As one superb engineer liked to say, "Now, boys, we have got her done. Let's start her up and see why she doesn't work."

Between 1790 and 1800, Americans took out 306 patents. Between 1850 and 1860, the Patent Office cleared more than 28,000. Just a year earlier, in 1849, a young lawyer named Abraham Lincoln took out a patent for a device designed to float steamboats over shoals. He never learned if it worked because he did not start it up.

HOW THEY LIVED

LOW BRIDGE, EVERYBODY DOWN

Thomas Jefferson inscribed his opinions on so many subjects that he may be excused for a gaffe now and then, such as when he heard of New York's plan to connect the Hudson River to the Great Lakes by digging a great ditch. Jefferson wrote: "Talk of making a canal of three hundred and fifty miles through the wilderness—it is little short of madness."

The Erie Canal opened in November 1825, less than a year before Jefferson died. He had no opportunity to study the returns and recant his judgment: a fabulous excavation 4 feet deep and 40 feet wide, the breadth of a large state; a rise of 500 feet west of Troy scaled by means of 82 locks; natural waterways traversed by aqueducts, the most dramatic features of any canal; travel time from Albany to Buffalo cut from 20 days to 8, later to 6; the cost of moving a ton of freight that distance slashed from $100 to $10, later to $5; the stupendous $7 million cost of digging the ditch repaid with interest in just 12 years; Ohio and Indiana growing faster than older Kentucky and Tennessee; New York City eclipsing Philadelphia as the nation's largest metropolis.

Then again, Jefferson might not have revised his opinion of the adventure. He had written in *Notes on Virginia*, "let our workshops remain in Europe," that "mobs" of workers who do not till the soil "add just so much to the support of pure government, as sores do to the strength of the human body." The 3,000 Irishmen who were lured to New York to dig the ditch and who were joined by thousands of others to maintain and "navigate" the canal when it was done comprised one of the "great cities" that Jefferson also thought quite mad, albeit a city of a very strange shape.

They were a primitive lot, the "canal bhoys," fresh off the horrid, wretched little potato patches from which the English landlords allowed them to feed themselves. Only a sense of history rare among peasants, a rich oral tradition, and their deep Roman Catholic piety raised them above barbarism. The cash wages they were paid to shovel and heave the dirt of upstate New York threatened to return them to it.

Sordid brothels, gambling dens, and prototypes of the American saloon followed the work crews. The drunken, eye-gouging, ear-biting "ructions" were prodigious. As portions of the canal were opened and work camps became towns and cities built around locks, depots for horses and mules, and junctures of feeder canals, the atmosphere hardly changed: it just moved from tents to clapboard and brick buildings. Canal boats moved around the clock. The canal towns roared around the clock.

The fact that the boisterous, brawling boatmen worked an economic miracle did not often enter into the reflections of the proper New Englanders who traveled the canal. The authors of many accounts seem to have trembled for their personal safety each of the 325 miles they were aboard one of the "queer-looking Noah's Ark boats."

Ironically, they were not only quite secure, they were enjoying a trip that was palpably more bearable than any alternative, rather comfortable for some, and elegant for those who could pay the fare on a first-class boat.

The most expensive way to travel on the canal was on the packets. At least 80 feet long and 15 wide, they main-

---

ocean. Alexander Hamilton failed to get the tariff he wanted partly because New England merchants, strong Federalists on other issues, joined with farmers (who were consumers of manufactured goods and wanted the lowest prices possible) to defeat him.

As late as 1816, many New England congressmen voted against high tariffs. One of them was Daniel Webster, a 34-year-old representative from New Hampshire who numbered Portsmouth shipmasters among his legal clients. By 1823, when Webster returned to Congress, he had moved to Massachusetts and become counsel and confidant to several manufacturers. Now, he was a strong and eloquent supporter of a high tariff. If "infant industries" were to grow, they had to be protected from competition with the cheaper goods that the older and better developed British manufacturers could produce.

Labor

Industrialization eventually undercut and almost destroyed handicraft. Many people were needed to tend the machines in the new mills, and the United States lacked England's surplus of "sturdy beggars" roaming the countryside and overcrowding the cities. Only a few white Americans were desperately poor. Few who could freely choose among farming profitably, moving west, or working in small independent shops were attracted to low-paying, highly disciplined factory work.

The difficulty of recruiting labor from among traditional groups was reflected in the failure of the "Fall River system." In Fall River, Massachusetts, the mill-owners attempted to hire whole families to work in the mills. It was an honest mistake. The family was the unit of production on the traditional farm and in the artisan's shop. But the system did not work very well in the factories.

The Lowell Girls

Rather more successful, because it found a niche within the traditional social structure, was the system developed by Francis Cabot Lowell, who established several large tained a schedule, whereas other boats moved when they were loaded. The packets were towed around the clock by three trotting horses, which were consequently changed often. Because the passengers' quarters on a packet were quite comfortable, horses that were resting were not brought aboard, as was done on second- and third-class boats. The big companies that ran packets—the Pilot, Telegraph, Merchant's, Washington, Citizen's, and Commercial—maintained large stables at intervals of ten to twelve miles.

For five cents a mile, a first-class passenger moved at between four and six miles per hour. The packets overtook slower boats by means of a procedure that was routine but, nonetheless, the occasion of some altercations. The slower boat slackened its line and the line of the quicker, horses straining, was passed over it. Requiring even more dexterity was when the towpath changed sides: the horses cleared a bridge and galloped up and over it. The best of the canal men took pride in negotiating this maneuver without so much as a tug on boat or horse-collar.

On a packet, men and women could sit on stuffed sofas in the saloon, which ran the length of the boat. Meals were served in the saloon. Allowing for the era's comparative disinterest in gourmandaise, complaints about the cooking on the first-class boats was rare. At locks and stables, or when heavy traffic slowed the pace, passengers could walk the towpath ahead of the vessel.

At night, the saloon was efficiently divided into separate quarters for men and women. The sofas became beds. "Upper bunks" folded from the cabin walls. They were not roomy, scarcely more than five feet long with just enough "hip room" to roll over without unduly disturbing the passenger above.

If one was not apprehensive of the rough boatmen, nor interested in the often lovely scenery, the trip could be boring. Plenty of people played cards dawn to dusk, or idly bowed fiddles or played other instruments. As ever in America, there were preachers, clambering aboard when they were allowed, walking along the towpath shouting admonitions if they perceived a promising response among the travelers.

Second-class boats were usually smaller than a packet and carried their own horses and freight as well as passengers. They kept no schedule, but cast off when they were full.

The boat was towed into a lock (usually by a two-horse or mule team). The water was completely drained whence the boat sat on a scale. The toll was paid, and passengers in a hurry hoped that there would be no more interruptions "from Albany to Buffalo." Fare was one and a half cents a mile with food. In 1836, Jacob Schramm and a party of Germans made the trip on a second-class boat in seven days for only $8. They provided their own meals, easy enough to do with, by that year, towns lining the way.

Third-class boats, really freight scows willing to take an impecunious traveler aboard, cost even less, and delays could be interminable. Even then, the trip was safe and far easier than an overland trek. About the greatest danger on the Erie Canal was to fail to hear the boatman call, "Low bridge, everybody down," and to have one's head smartly rapped by a stone span while the boat traveled under it at four miles per hour.

mills at Waltham, Massachusetts in 1813, and a whole town that he named Lowell in 1826. Lowell dispatched recruiters to roam rural New England. They persuaded farmers to send their young daughters to work in the mills. For 70 hours a week at the machines, the girls and young women earned $3, paying half of that for room and board at company-supervised lodging houses.

The long workweek put off no one. It was normal enough a regimen for a farm family. The money was attractive, too. Farming the rocky New England soil never made anyone rich, and Yankee farmers burdened with large families inevitably liked the idea of subtracting one diner from the table, especially if that diner was a daughter who, by going to Waltham or Lowell for a few years, could save a dowry large enough to attract a suitable husband. The "Waltham system" was successful precisely because it drew on a body of people for whom there were few other opportunities.

The trick was to persuade strait-laced New Englanders to allow girls of 16 and 17 to leave home. Lowell worked it by providing a closely regulated life for his employees during off-hours as well as working hours. The Lowell girls lived in company-run dormitories, attended church services, and were kept busy (as if 70 hours at work were not enough!) with a variety of educational and cultural programs.

Most of the first American industrial workers were women—and children! In 1820, about half the factory hands in Massachusetts mills were under 16 years of age. A society of farmers, in which everyone down to six years of age had assigned chores, did not find this inhumane. And the pace of the early factory was slower than it would become. In some mills, girls were permitted to entertain (respectable) visitors while they watched their spindles. English visitors commented that American factories were idyllic compared with England's "dark, satanic mills."

In time, the American factory, too, would become a place of stultifying toil. But it is difficult to find many horrors in the first phase of American industrialization.

The Lowell Offering *(1845) was a literary magazine produced by women who worked in the Lowell, Massachusetts, mills.*

Artists depicted mills as objects of beauty and town pride. By way of contrast with what later builders would erect, those structures that have survived are regarded as architectural gems.

THE SOUTH AT THE CROSSROADS

While Westerners tamed land, and Northerners set about building a society dominated by mills and swelling cities, Southerners reaffirmed their agrarian heritage. There were those who would have had it otherwise. In 1816, when Daniel Webster was still speaking for the shipping interests of old New England, John C. Calhoun of South Carolina dreamed of cotton factories in his own state.

But Calhoun's attraction to industrialization, like his War Hawk supernationalism during the War of 1812, was already doomed. His future lay in defending Southern sectionalism, the plantation system, and the institution of slavery on which they rested. Ironically, this brilliant political theorist (and somewhat less able politician) was chained to such anachronistic institutions because of one of the most dramatic technological breakthroughs of the new era.

Slavery in Decline

When John C. Calhoun was born in 1782, black slavery appeared to be dying out. The Northern states took steps to abolish human bondage during the last years of the eighteenth century. Slavery was never vital to the Northern economy, so that Northerners could afford to practice the Revolution's principle of liberty.

Slavery was also declining in the South during the Revolutionary era. The world price of tobacco, one of the few crops for which slave labor was profitable, collapsed. On top of that, many of the old Chesapeake and Carolina tobacco fields were exhausted. Other slave-raised crops, such as South Carolina's rice and indigo, lost some luster when British subsidies were lost following independence (although South Carolinians remained the least apologetic defenders of slavery).

Southerners, as well as Northerners, were moved by the ideals of the Declaration of Independence. Thomas Jefferson, its author, agonized throughout his life over the injustice of human bondage. In their wills, Jefferson, George Washington, and many other planters freed at least some of their slaves. Few spoke of slavery as anything better than a tragic social burden, a necessary evil. Thomas Jefferson called the institution "a wolf held by the ears." "We can neither hold him nor safely let him go." As late as 1808, only a few Southerners objected when Congress (as the Constitution allowed) outlawed further importation of blacks from Africa. At the peace talks in Ghent in 1815, American and British commissioners discussed the possibility of cooperating in suppressing illegal traders. It is reasonable to wonder whether the tragic institution would have been peacefully abolished in the United States (as it was in the British Empire) had it not been for the "absurdly simple contrivance" invented by Eli Whitney.

The Cotton Gin

In 1793, seven years before his demonstration of interchangeable parts, Eli Whitney visited a plantation near Savannah, Georgia. There he saw his first cotton plant and learned from a friend that it flourished everywhere in the upland South. Cotton fiber was worth 30 to 40 cents a pound—a fabulous price for the by-product of a weed—but the upland cotton could not be exploited commercially because of the costs of separating the precious fiber from the plant's sticky green seeds. This job could be done only by hand, and the most nimble-fingered of people could process no more than a pound of fluff a day, hardly enough to justify hiring employees to do it, let alone setting an expensive slave to the job.

On the frost-free sea islands off the coast of South Carolina and Georgia, cotton had been cultivated profitably since 1786. But the variety planted there was "long-staple" cotton, with shiny, smooth, black seeds that could be popped out of the fiber by running the cotton bolls between two rollers. When this method was tried with the cotton of the uplands, however, its sticky green seeds were crushed, fouling the fiber with oil.

Whitney's device was so simple that a planter who had a decent collection of junk on the grounds could make a workable version. In fact, the ease of constructing the cotton "gin" (short for engine) denied Whitney the fortune he deserved for inventing it. His patents were simply ignored.

Essentially, Whitney dumped the bolls into a box at the bottom of which were slots too small for the seeds to pass through. A drum studded with wire hooks revolved so that the hooks caught the fibers and pulled them through the slots, leaving behind the seeds without crushing them. Another drum, revolving in the opposite direction, brushed the fiber from the wire hooks.

It was a magnificent device. A single slave cranking a small gin could clean ten pounds of cotton a day ($3 to $4 at 1790 prices). A somewhat larger machine tended by several people and turned by a horse on a windlass could clean 50 pounds a day ($15 to $20!). Once steam-powered gins were introduced, the capacity for producing cotton was limited not by the processing problem but by the number of acres that a planter could cultivate.

The Revival of Slavery

Technology had come to the South, but not industry. The effects of Eli Whitney's machine were the revival of the South's traditional one-crop economy, the domination of Southern society by large planters, and the reinvigoration of slavery. Like tobacco, cotton was well adapted to gang-cultivation. The crop required plenty of unskilled labor: plowing, planting, "chopping" (weeding, an endless process in the hot, wet, fertile South), ditch digging, picking, ginning, baling, and shipping.

Moreover, the fertile upland "black belt" that extends from South Carolina and Georgia through eastern Texas was natural cotton country. Seduced by the same charms of riches that turned Western farmers into speculators and doughty New England merchants into industrial capitalists, Southerners streamed into the "Old Southwest" (Alabama, Mississippi, and northern Louisiana) and eventually into Arkansas across the Mississippi River. In 1800, excluding Indians, there were about 1,000 people in what is now Alabama. In 1810, there were 9,000; in 1820, 128,000! The growth of Mississippi was less dramatic but not lethargic: 1800, 8,000; 1810, 31,000; 1820, 75,000.

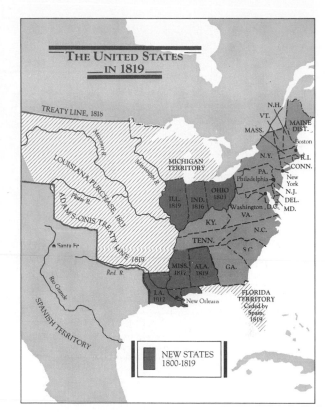

Nor was this an emigration of buckskin-clad frontiersmen with no more baggage than a long rifle and a frying pan. Wealthy planters from the old states made the trek, bringing both their bondsmen and women with them. In 1800, there were 4,000 blacks in Alabama and Mississippi. In 1810, there were 17,000, virtually all of whom were slaves; in 1820, there were 75,000. Almost half the population of Mississippi was black and in bondage.

The price of slaves soared, doubling between 1795 and 1804. Blacks who had been becoming financial burdens in Maryland and Virginia became valuable commodities in the new cotton South. The most humane masters found it difficult to resist the temptation of the high prices offered for their "prime field hands," males between 18 and 30 years of age. Slaveowners from as far north as New Jersey liquidated their human holdings to cotton planters.

The Missouri Crisis

There were still a few slaves in the North to be sold in 1819. Most states had adopted a gradualist approach to emancipation, by which no person born or brought into the state after a certain date could be enslaved. (There were a handful of aged slaves in New Jersey as late as the Civil War.)

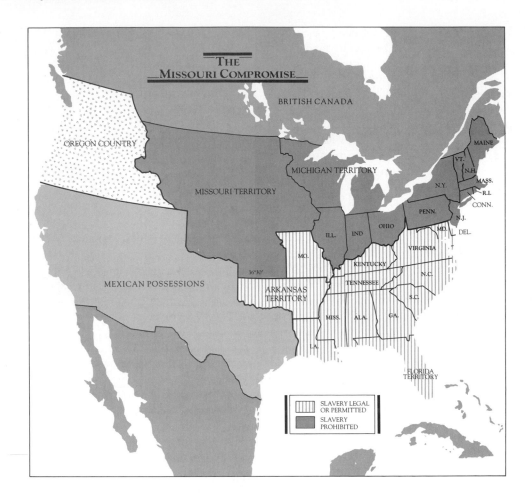

But there was also, by 1819, a clear-cut line between the "slave states" and the "free states." North of the Mason-Dixon line (the Maryland-Pennsylvania border) and the Ohio River, slavery was either forbidden or in the process of being abolished. South of it, the institution remained a vital part of society and economy. In 1819, quite in the middle of Monroe's "era of good feelings," the sectional character of the institution became, briefly, an explosive issue.

It was ignited by the application of Missouri Territory to be admitted to the Union as a state. Although west of the Mississippi River, all but a tiny fraction of Missouri lay north of the Ohio River, the traditional boundary between slave states and free states. Quite able to read a map and voicing moral objections to slavery, Congressman James Tallmadge of New York proposed that Missouri be admitted only after its state constitution was amended to forbid the further importation of slaves and to free all slaves within the state when they reached 25 years of age. In a word, Missouri would eliminate slavery gradually as the Northern states had done or were doing.

Some Northern representatives and senators leapt into the opening Tallmadge had cut. One described slavery as "a sin which sits heavily on the soul of every one of us." On hearing of such rhetoric, old Thomas Jefferson wrote from Monticello that he was startled as though he had heard "a firebell in the night." John Quincy Adams expressed concern. What worried both wise men was that once the morality of the discussants enters a debate, conflicts are not easily resolved by cutting a deal or trading quids for quos. Indeed, Southern congressmen, particularly representatives of cotton states like Mississippi and Alabama, replied to their Northern censors in fierce and furious language.

The Compromise

Ever unflappable, James Monroe was not unduly disturbed. A Virginian who was ambivalent (or perhaps equivocal) as to the future of slavery, he encouraged compromise in Congress. The deal was actually devised, however, by another Southerner who wanted no part of moral imprecations in discussions of slavery—Henry Clay.

Earning the nickname "The Great Compromiser" for his scheme, Clay proposed that Missouri be admitted to the Union as those who wrote its constitution wished, as a slave state. This soothed Southern tempers. In order to mollify Northerners for whom slavery was an important issue, Clay proposed that the southern boundary of Missouri, 36° 30′ north latitude, be extended through the remainder of American territory—to the scarcely known crest of the Rocky Mountains. North of that line, slavery was "forever prohibited." In territories south of 36° 30′, which meant only Arkansas Territory and recently acquired Florida, the citizens living there could decide whether the state would be slave or free.

Passions cooled; tempers eased. Congressmen who had glared at one another shook hands and turned to other business. But Jefferson's firebell continued, however muted, to echo in the distance and with a new timbre to its peal. Clay's compromise also involved an informal institutionalization of a "balance" between free states and slave states. There were 22 states in the Union in 1819, 11 free, 11 slave. When Missouri was admitted, Congress also agreed to detach the Maine District from Massachusetts and admit it as a free state.

For 30 years, Congress would admit states virtually in pairs, preserving the balance. But because the Missouri Compromise forbade slavery in the major part of the Louisiana Purchase, it was inevitable that, sooner or later, a territory would seek admission to the Union as a free state with no slave state to balance it.

Indeed, the population of the free North was increasing much more quickly than the population of the South. Until 1810, the two sections had grown at an uncannily similar rate. In 1820, however, despite the explosive growth of Mississippi and Alabama, there were nearly a million more people in the North than in the South, 5,219,000 to 4,419,000. As the disparity increased—and all signs said that it would—the "good feelings" that made James Monroe's presidency such a happy one were bound to be among the casualties.

For Further Reading

Comprehensive histories of this era include George Dangerfield, *The Era of Good Feelings* (1952) and the same author's more recent *The Awakening of American Nationalism, 1815–1828* (1965). Research discoveries subsequent to Dangerfield's work have been incorporated in John Mayfield, *The New Nation, 1800–1845* (1981). A superb social history in part covering these years is Daniel Boorstin, *The Americans: The National Experience* (1965). For economic development, see the approriate chapters of Douglas C. North, *The Economic Growth of the United States, 1790–1860* (1961) and Elliott Brownlee, *Dynamics of Ascent: A History of the American Economy* (1979).

The standard biography of the president of the Era of Good Feelings is William P. Cresson, *James Monroe* (1971), of his secretary of state, Samuel F. Bemis, *John Quincy Adams and the Foundation of American Foreign Policy* (1949). See also Henry F. May, *The Making of the Monroe Doctrine* (1975) and Dexter Perkins, *The Monroe Doctrine* (1927). On the major political issue of the Monroe presidency, see Glover Moore, *The Missouri Controversy* (1953) and Donald L. Robinson, *Slavery in the Structure of American Politics, 1765–1820* (1979).

Early American industrialization has been a subject of lively inquiry in recent decades. Students should see Thomas Cochran, *Frontiers of Change: Early Industrialism in America* (1981); Allan Dawley, *Class and Community in Lynn* (1976); Thomas Dublin, *Women at Work: The Transformation of Work and Community in Lowell, Massachusetts, 1826–1860* (1979); David J. Jeremy, *Transatlantic Industrial Revolution: The Diffusion of Textile Technologies Between Britain and America* (1981); Bruce Laurie, *The Working People of Philadelphia, 1800–1850* (1980); Leo Marx, *The Machine in the Garden: Technology and the Pastoral Ideal in America* (1964).

Andrew Jackson rose from humble roots, and his military feats made him a popular hero. A huge crowd turned out for his inauguration in 1829, as represented in Robert Cruikshank's lithograph, The President's Levee, or All Creation Going to the White House.

15

HERO OF THE PEOPLE

ANDREW JACKSON AND A NEW ERA
1824 - 1830

The single party system of the Monroe years had its virtues. At the top, at least, administration was efficient. In Congress, debate was candid and eloquent, and usually carried out on a higher plane than in eras when partisanship has reigned. At its best, party loyalty is less edifying than loyalty to home, country, or principle. At worst, it is a poison that rewards tawdry, sycophantic hacks who mouth "the party line."

The national leaders of the "era of good feelings" were not hacks. They appreciated the ideals that underlay the Founding Fathers' dislike of party and faction. But there were personally ambitious men among them, and a single party organization could not accommodate the hunger of all of them for advancement. There were simply not enough nominations to high office to go around.

So, in 1824, the Jefferson Republican party went bust. By 1828, politically active Americans had aligned themselves into two camps that, within a few more years, coalesced into full-blown parties. With an eye on the Federalist-Jeffersonian competition of the first American party system, some historians describe the reshuffling of the 1820s as the second party system.

THE SKEWED ELECTION OF 1824

D uring the quarter century the Jefferson Republicans dominated national politics, three traditions grew up around the presidency: King Caucus, the Virginia Dynasty, and an orderly succession to the White House by the Secretary of State, who had been appointed by his predecessor. In 1824, in part because the demands of each contradicted the other two, in part because so many politicians wanted to be president, two of these institutions were toppled and the third was discredited.

King and Dynasty

The first to be dethroned was "King Caucus." This was the name given (by those who did not much like it) to the method by which the Jeffersonians nominated their presidential and vice-presidential candidates between 1800 and 1824. In election years, Jefferson Republican members of Congress met in caucus (that is, as members of the party) and decided by vote whom they would support in the election. Until 1824, unsuccessful candidates accepted the decision of King Caucus; so did party members in the states.

In fact, fights within the caucus were without much spirit or lasting rancor. Monroe opposed Madison in 1808, lost, and three years later became his Secretary of State. William Crawford opposed Monroe in 1816, lost narrowly because of his own half-heartedness, and entered Monroe's cabinet. Partly by chance, but also because of the gentility with which caucus fights were fought, Madison and Monroe both stepped from the office of Secretary of State into the White House. An orderly means of succession seemed to be established with presidents, like Roman emperors, adopting their heirs.

In fact, people spoke of a "Virginia Dynasty" in the

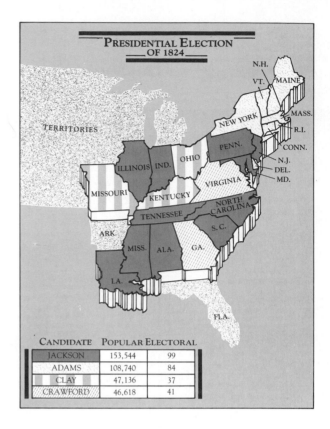

CANDIDATE	POPULAR	ELECTORAL
JACKSON	153,544	99
ADAMS	108,740	84
CLAY	47,136	37
CRAWFORD	46,618	41

presidency. All three of the Jefferson Republican presidents—Jefferson, Madison, and Monroe—were Virginians. Only one of the first five presidents, John Adams, was not from the Old Dominion. Until 1824, it was all quite tidy.

In that year, however, the Secretary of State was John Quincy Adams, so much a Massachusetts man that most Southern Jeffersonians regarded him as a Federalist in

CAUCUS

Caucus is an Americanism. In 1818, the witty editor of the *Edinburgh Review*, who did not like much about the United States, referred to it as "the cant word of the Americans," and British newspapers did not commonly use it—mis-use it, actually—until the end of the nineteenth century. However, it appears without self-consciousness in John Adams's diary as early as 1763, and others remembered its employment in New England in the early eighteenth century. Most plausibly, the word has an Algonkian origin. In his history of Virginia, Captain John Smith cites the word *ca-cawaas-saugh,* meaning "one who advises." Early in the eighteenth century, New Englanders frequently adopted such Indian words as names of men's clubs.

disguise. They were suspicious of Quincy Adams's strident nationalism and disliked his belief that the national government should exercise extensive powers in shaping both economy and society. Most Southern politicians hoped to make the Secretary of the Treasury, William Crawford, the party's presidential nominee.

Crawford was from Georgia but, having been born in Nelson County, Virginia, he was regarded as the Virginia Dynasty's legitimate heir. Indeed, quite at odds with Quincy Adams, Crawford was an orthodox Jeffersonian who feared a powerful central government and favored strict construction of the Constitution. President Monroe supported his candidacy and Crawford was annointed by King Caucus. However, only Crawford supporters attended the party caucus in 1824. Others repaired to their own states where state legislatures named three additional candidates.

Too Many Candidates Cloud the Stew

For a while, it appeared that New York Governor DeWitt Clinton, the builder of the Erie Canal, and South Carolina Senator John C. Calhoun would enter their names in the contest. Clinton dropped out when he attracted little support outside his state, and Calhoun settled for second-best, running as vice president with two other candidates.

One of them was John Quincy Adams. His supporters ignored King Caucus and rallied around the tradition that the Secretary of State should succeed to the presidency. They also liked Adams because of his assertive and successful foreign policy, his support of a high tariff to protect young industries, and his belief that the federal government should take an active role in promoting economic prosperity, including a federally financed program of internal improvements. Adams was nominated by the Massachusetts state legislature.

Henry Clay, nominated by the legislature of Kentucky, shared most of Adams's views. The two men differed in little but their aversion to one another's personal habits. When they had been negotiators together at Ghent, the high-living Clay mocked the hard-working Adams as dull and prudish. Adams, in turn, looked on Clay's drinking, gambling, and womanizing as dissolute and depraved. Now, in 1824, they divided the votes of those who favored their nationalistic economic program.

Unfortunately for Clay, he could not fully exploit his carefully cultivated image as a man of the growing progressive West. There was another Westerner in the contest, Andrew Jackson of Tennessee, who was a military hero to boot. So magical was his name as the conqueror of the British and half a dozen Indian tribes that it did not matter that Jackson's political principles were something of a mystery, perhaps even to "the Ginral" himself. Only on the question of currency and banking was Jackson known to have taken a strong stand. Although quite rich, Jackson detested banks and paper money. He had been ruined in a financial panic in the 1790s and, as Americans were soon to learn, Andrew Jackson did not forget a grudge.

In 1824, Jackson's supporters did not allow voters to forget New Orleans, nor the fact that Jackson was a man of action who crossed the Appalachians poor and by hook and crook and wiles and will—the American way—became a hero and the master of a grand plantation and a hundred slaves.

Indecisive Results

This appeal to sentiment and the support of Calhoun, who was also Jackson's vice-presidential candidate, was enough to win Jackson more popular and electoral votes than either Adams, Crawford, or Clay. He was also the only candidate to win at least one state in Northeast, South, and West. But Jackson's totals fell short of a majority in the electoral college. As after the election of 1800, the responsibility of naming the president fell to the members of the House of Representatives, voting by state.

Under the terms of the Twelfth Amendment to the Constitution (adopted in 1804), the House made its selection from among the top three finishers in the electoral college, which eliminated Clay. William Crawford also seemed to be out of the running as he had suffered a stroke that left him bedridden and unable to speak. Crawford's supporters insisted that he would recover, and, in time, he did. But they were unable to arouse any enthusiasm outside the Southern states that he had carried in the general election.

Jackson's followers were confident of victory. As they saw it, the House of Representatives was morally bound to ratify the election of the man preferred by more voters than any other. It was a good argument—the democratic argument—but it did not carry the day. Instead, because of the political beliefs and personal ambitions of the influential Henry Clay, and perhaps the impulsive decision of Stephen Van Rensselaer, an elderly congressman from New York, the second-place finisher in the election, John Quincy Adams, won the prize.

"Corrupt Bargain!"

Van Rensselaer, who cast the vote that threw the New York delegation and the election to John Quincy Adams, said that while he was praying for guidance, he glanced at the floor, saw a piece of paper on which was written "Adams," and took it as a sign from on high. Long before this providential moment, however, Clay had made his decision for Adams and, as Speaker of the House, he was in a position to reward congressmen who

This bandanna celebrates Andrew Jackson as the hero of New Orleans.

succumbed to his arguments. Clay favored Adams because, despite their personal distaste for one another, they agreed on most national questions. Jackson, on the other hand, was a sworn enemy of one of Clay's favorite projects, the Bank of the United States.

Moreover, Clay wanted to be president, and Jackson was surrounded by would-be successors: Calhoun of South Carolina (who easily won election as vice president); John Eaton of Tennessee; and Richard M. Johnson of Clay's own Kentucky. There was no room in the Jackson crowd for Henry Clay.

Adams, on the other hand, was a cranky, solitary man with few close friends. Nor, because he had spent much of his life abroad as a diplomat, was Adams surrounded by and tied to a circle of political associates. Clay could reasonably hope to be his successor.

Clay and Adams did not sit down across a table and hammer out a tit-for-tat understanding. Clay was a man for a deal in a smoke-filled room—how else win the title "Great Compromiser"?—but Adams was too stubborn, too well-schooled in propriety, too self-righteous even, to "talk turkey." His distaste for the manual labor of politics that left the hands dirty would, soon enough, shatter his career as a national politician. Nevertheless, when Clay threw his influence in the House of Representatives behind Adams, and Adams later appointed Clay Secretary of State, the losers of 1824 were sure that they had been cheated by two cynical schemers.

John Randolph of Roanoke, a Crawford supporter, drew on the novel *Tom Jones* to sneer at the union of

"the puritan and the blackleg," an insult that led Clay to challenge him to a duel. (No one was hit.) The Jacksonians settled for shouting "bargain" and "corruption." They vowed to obstruct the Adams presidency and plan their revenge.

A New Party

Between 1824 and 1828, Jackson's loose alliance of supporters coalesced into a new political party. It included Jackson's Western following and Southerners led by John C. Calhoun, a formidable base. To ensure a national majority, however, the Jacksonians had to break the grip of the Adams-Clay forces in the populous Northeast. Toward this end, Martin Van Buren, an ambitious New Yorker, called on Jackson at his Tennessee mansion, the Hermitage, and put his influence in his native state at the General's service.

The South, the West, and New York—this was the consortium that had allowed Jefferson and Aaron Burr to throw the first Adams out of office in 1800. Also like the Jefferson Republicans of 1800, the Jacksonians appealed to the ordinary fellow—the "Common Man"—and depicted their opponents as the party of privilege. This was mostly buncombe. The leaders of the Jackson party were of the same social class as the politicians surrounding Quincy Adams and Clay, and Andrew Jackson was no common man. But the Jacksonian appeal to democracy versus a conniving elite came naturally after the "corrupt bargain" controversy. "Let the people rule!" the Jacksonians cried even before Quincy Adams was inaugurated: Let them have the president that most of

John Quincy Adams was a well-qualified but unpopular president.

them chose in 1824. Seizing on the theme, the Jacksonians called themselves Democratic-Republicans, soon abbreviated to Democrats.

THE AGE OF THE COMMON MAN

Like his father, John Quincy Adams brought impressive credentials to the White House. On paper, no one—surely not the laconic General Jackson—was better qualified for the job. While Jackson could claim to have been slashed in the face by a British officer at the age of fourteen (for refusing to shine the soldier's shoes), John Quincy Adams at that age had been in high government service, as secretary to the American minister in Russia. He had been a diplomat in several European countries. He had also been senator from Massachusetts, and a Secretary of State whose successes still rank him among the most able ever to hold that post.

Another Unhappy Adams

Also like his father, Adams's qualifications ended with the long list of his accomplishments. Temperamentally, he was out of tune with his times, unable to provide what more and more Americans were coming to demand in a leader. In an age of magnetic political personalities—of Clay and Jackson and Calhoun—no one loved John Quincy Adams. Among a people beginning to prize equality above other political goals, and easy informality in society, Adams was standoffish, pompous, and sniffily self-conscious of his abilities, his learning, his ancestry, and his achievements, which he felt earned him the right to be president. He found it difficult to accept the point of view that high office should be awarded on any other basis than superior merit. He never doubted that he was the best that his generation had to offer.

INTERVIEWING THE PRESIDENT

John Quincy Adams may have been aloof, but he was certainly more accessible than are presidents of the twentieth century. It was his custom to rise early, walk alone from the White House to the Potomac River, shed his clothes, and take a swim quite naked. A woman journalist, who had attempted for weeks to get an interview with the president, hit on the idea of following him on one of those expeditions. While he was in the water, she sat on his clothes and refused to budge until Adams answered all of her questions! He did, while treading water, and in a better humor than that in which he held office hours while clad in frock coat and cravat.

Most damaging of all in an age when political horse-trading was frank, fast, and furious, John Quincy Adams tried to stand above partisan politics. He allowed open enemies to hold office under him. To have removed them and filled the posts with his supporters, he felt, would have been to stoop to the shabby politics of which—unjustly in his opinion—he had been accused in the "corrupt bargain" controversy.

Adams was also thin-skinned and short-tempered. He took criticism and sometimes mere suggestions as affronts to his office and his person. He cut himself off from possible allies who had honest, minor disagreements with him. By the end of his term, he had a smaller political base in Washington than had any previous president, including his unhappy father.

A Democratic Upheaval

If Adams's personality was quirky, his social assumptions did not differ appreciably from those of his five predecessors. The staunchest Jeffersonians, despite their democratic talk, had been self-conscious members of an elite of wealth, education, manners, and talent.

During the 1820s, however, it was outdated to think in terms of a "natural aristocracy" (or at least to speak of it in public). During the 1820s and 1830s, politics ceased to be largely the concern of the leisured, educated classes and came to preoccupy much of the white male population. The foremost foreign commentator on American attitudes, Alexis de Tocqueville, wrote that "almost the only pleasure which an American knows is to take part in government." A less sympathetic visitor to the United States, Mrs. Frances Trollope, was appalled that American men would rather talk politics than mend their fences and tend their crops.

In part, this great democratic upheaval was the fruit of half a century of democratic rhetoric. Natural aristocrats that the Jeffersonians may have been themselves, they had said that the people should rule, and the idea caught up with them. The democratic upheaval of the 1820s and 1830s was also the consequence of the extraordinary growth and energy of the young republic. An increasingly prosperous people needed to struggle less in order to survive and had more time to think about public affairs. With issues like the tariff, land policy, and internal improvements bearing heavily on individual fortunes, ordinary folk had good reason to do so.

Finally, the wave of democratic spirit that swept Andrew Jackson on its crest had some peculiarly Western sources. In attempting to attract population, the young Western states extended the right to vote to all free, adult white males and enacted other laws designed to appeal to people of modest station. Kentucky, for example, abolished imprisonment for debt in 1821; no longer could a man or woman be jailed for financial misfortune.

Democratization was an Eastern and urban movement, too. Fearful of losing population to the West, most Eastern states responded to liberal Western voting laws by adopting universal white manhood suffrage. In 1824, about half the states still insisted on some property qualifications in order to vote. By 1830, only North Carolina, Virginia, and Rhode Island retained such laws on their books, and Rhode Island's conservatism in the matter was deceptive. Still governed under the state's seventeenth-century colonial charter, which could not be easily amended, Rhode Island was rocked by a brief violent uprising in 1842, Dorr's Rebellion, which resulted in extending the vote to all adult white males.

In 1824, one state in four chose presidential electors in the state legislature. The others chose electors by popular vote in one form or another. By 1832, only planter-dominated South Carolina still clung to the less democratic method. Finally given the right to vote, people did. In 1824, the first presidential election in which there was widespread participation, about one-quarter of the country's adult white males cast ballots. In 1828, one-half of the eligible voters voted and, in 1840, more than three-quarters of the electorate participated in the national election.

The "Workies"

Some of these new voters built new parties around social issues. During the 1820s, a number of workingmen's parties sprang up in the Eastern cities. Called the "Workies" and supported largely by skilled artisans who had recently won the right to vote, these organizations pushed for a variety of reforms to protect mechanics, as skilled craftsmen were called: the abolition of imprisonment for debt, which hit the independent artisan hard; mechanics' lien laws, which gave wokers first claim on a bankrupt employer's assets; and free public education for all children. To the workingman of the Northeast, education was the equivalent of the Westerner's free land, the key to moving up in the world.

The workingmen's parties had their local victories, especially in New York. But they dwindled when visionaries, such as Scottish-born reformer Frances Wright, tried to convert them to demanding broader reforms. Wright, for example, fought for female equality and "free love," the freedom of all, unmarried and married, to enjoy sexual partners not their spouses.

Mainstream politicians of every persuasion had little interest in modifying the legal status of women, which meant challenging the supremacy of the male head of household. As for free love, mechanics were as likely as manufacturers to dally, but if anything, their publicly avowed sexual morals were more conservative than those of the elite. Artisans were conscious that their social status was superior to that of the urban underclass, which they associated with (among other things) promiscuity. Fanny Wright's titilating preachments had little appeal and contributed to the drift of workingmen's party voters to the Democrats.

The Anti-Masonic Party

Another expression of the democratic upheaval of the 1820s and 1830s was the Anti-Masonic party, which was founded in upstate New York when a bricklayer named William Morgan wrote an exposé of the Society of Freemasons. Morgan did not have so very much to say. Originally an association of free-thinkers who were skeptical of revealed religion (many of the Founding Fathers, including George Washington, had been members), the Freemasons had become a social club for generally well-to-do men.

Most of Morgan's revelations had to do with rituals, secret handshakes, and other hocus-pocus. For example, he quoted the order's initiation ceremony, in which a new member swore "to keep all Masonic secrets under the penalty of having his throat cut, his tongue torn out, and his body buried in the ocean." This is not the sort of thing that, as a rule, post-adolescents take seriously. However, some Masons took it very seriously, or so it seemed. Morgan disappeared, and, a short time later, a corpse that may have been mutilated according to regulations was fished out of the Niagara River.

The apparent murder inspired an extraordinary movement. According to politicians who pointed out that Morgan was a bricklayer and that most Masons were prosperous farmers, merchants, bankers, and the like, the order was a conspiracy aimed at keeping the common man down. Secrecy, they added, had no place in a free, open society. It was through the handshakes, code words, and other signs exposed by Morgan that Masons recognized one another, favored brother Masons in business to the disadvantage of others, and schemed to control the economy and the government.

The Anti-Masons benefited from the traditional views about the sanctity of the family that Fanny Wright flaunted. By maintaining that some secrets must be shared only with brother Masons, Anti-Masons said, the order was insinuating itself between husband and wife. If a husband were required to keep secrets from his own spouse, he was violating the marriage contract as surely as if he were a free lover.

The Anti-Masonic movement spread, especially in the Northeast. A brace of leaders who would later play an important part in national politics first came to the fore as Anti-Masons: Thaddeus Stevens, Thurlow

Weed, William H. Seward, and Millard Fillmore. In 1832, the party's candidate for president, William Wirt, won 33,000 votes and carried the state of Vermont. In the same year, the party elected 53 candidates to Congress.

Jackson was a Mason. Consequently, while quite democratic in some of their views, the Anti-Masons were hostile to his Democratic Party. Most of them remained in opposition to Jackson when their party's appeal faded, drifting into the anti-Jackson Whig party.

Nominating Conventions

The Anti-Masonic episode was brief, a conjunction of class resentment, political paranoia, and no small dollop of cynical opportunism. By no means did all the party's leaders believe that a conspiracy of handshaking Freemasons were on the verge of seizing control of the republic.

During its heyday, however, the Anti-Masonic party made a lasting contribution to American politics. In Baltimore in 1831, the Anti-Masons were the first to hold a national party convention. With the caucus system of making presidential nominations dead, and nomination by state legislatures not firmly established, the major parties imitated the Anti-Masonic example. The first Democratic convention met in 1832, nominating Andrew Jackson. The anti-Jackson Whigs followed suit a few years later.

The national convention was seen as a democratic reform, bringing party activists from throughout the country together in one place. Indeed, Martin Van Buren defended political parties as well as conventions as an alternative to the sectionalism that chronically threatened to split the Union in two or three. Conventions remained a vital part of the democratic process until the late twentieth century when instantaneous electronic media and the spread of the presidential primary system turned the quadrennial meetings into meaningless (and boring) television shows.

THE REVOLUTION OF 1828

Thomas Jefferson had called the election of 1800 the "Revolution of 1800." But in 1800, there had been not nearly so great a break with what had gone before as there was in Andrew Jackson's victory in the election of 1828. His election ended the era of sedate transfers of power from incumbent president to Secretary of State. Jackson was the first chief executive to come from a Western state. Indeed, he was the first president who was not from Virginia or Massachusetts. And the cam-

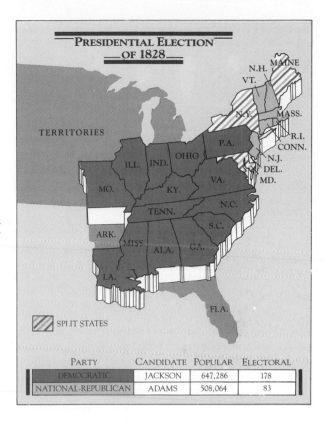

PARTY	CANDIDATE	POPULAR	ELECTORAL
DEMOCRATIC	JACKSON	647,286	178
NATIONAL-REPUBLICAN	ADAMS	508,064	83

paign that led to his election was noisier, harder fought, and "dirtier" than any the United States had experienced.

Slinging Mud

Personally, Jackson followed precedent by taking no part in the campaign of 1828. He sat in his Tennessee mansion while his supporters fired insulting salvos at President Adams. They depicted the incumbent as a usurper, an elitist, a man with effete European tastes who squandered money by filling the White House with elegant furniture and its cellar with European wines. The Democrats made a great fuss over Adams's purchase of a billiard table. Billiards, by virtue of the high cost of the table, was a game of aristocrats. (In fact, Adams paid for his toy out of his own pocket.)

Alarmed by the effectiveness of these tactics, the Adams men replied that Jackson was a savage and a murderer. Calling themselves National-Republicans, they reminded voters that Jackson had executed two British subjects in Spanish Florida in 1818 (conveniently forgetting that Adams had supported him after the fact). They printed broadsides that listed the men whom Jackson had killed in duels and the soldiers whom he had ordered shot during military campaigns.

But the assault that most stung Jackson was the claim that he and his beloved wife, Rachel, were adulterers.

The "Coffin Handbill," published by pro-Adams forces, presented Andrew Jackson's war deeds and duels as evidence of his barbarism.

The circumstances surrounding their marriage, some years earlier, were murky. At the least, Rachel Jackson's divorce was not final when the two wed, thus requiring them to go through a mortifying second ceremony, and they may have lived together before the first wedding. Laxity in observing marriage customs has never been rare in isolated places like the American frontier. But whatever Rachel Jackson's attitudes as a young woman, by 1828 she was a prim and proper old lady, and she was tortured by the ugly gossip. When she died shortly after the election, Jackson blamed Adams and his supporters for his deeply felt loss.

In the meantime, Jackson's party responded in kind, digging up an old tale that, as minister to Russia, Quincy Adams had procured the sexual favors of a young American girl for the dissolute czar. (Not likely.) Then there were whispers of bizarre perversions in the Adams White House. (Less likely yet; Quincy Adams was past 60 in 1828.) Mudslinging had come to American politics with a vengeance. Everything was fair game for discussion—except public issues.

DON'T VOTE FOR JACKSON

Among the campaign mud that found its way into print in 1821 was this aspersion on Andrew Jackson's lineage:

General Jackson's mother was a COMMON PROSTI-TUTE, brought to this country by the British soldiers! She afterwards married a Mulatto Man, with whom she had several children, one of which number GENERAL JACKSON IS ONE!

The Symbol of His Age

But it was not mud that won the election of 1828 for Jackson. The party organization, he, Vice President Calhoun, and Martin Van Buren put together turned that trick. Jackson swept to victory with 56 percent of a total vote that was more than three times as large as the vote in 1824, and a 178-83 victory in the electoral college. The upswing in popular participation carried over to Inauguration Day in 1829 when 10,000 people crowded the streets of Washington. They shocked genteel society with their drinking, coarse shouting, and boisterous invasion of the White House. Invited there by the new president, the mob muddied the carpets, broke crystal stemware, and stood on expensive upholstered sofas and chairs in order to catch a glimpse of their gaunt, white-haired hero.

The adoring mob was so unruly that Jackson's friends feared that he might be injured. They spirited him away through a window, and he spent his first night as president in a hotel. Back at the executive mansion, worried servants lured the mob outside to the broad lawn by setting up bowls of lemonade and whiskey punch and tables heaped with food.

The man whom these people worshiped was by no sensible definition a common man. Jackson's talents were exceptional, his will and integrity extraordinary. Nor was he the vicious desperado whom the Adams forces depicted. Jackson was a gracious, courtly gentleman whose public manners, as more than one person announced with an air of surprise, were the equal of royalty's.

It was also said of Jackson, however, that he was entirely comfortable sitting on a stump, chewing and spitting tobacco, and conversing with the most rugged, plain-spoken and poor men of the frontier. If he had become wealthy and ready to defend to the death every last cent and slave's straw hat that he owned, he never forgot his humble origins. Jackson was the first of the log-cabin presidents, the first to reap the rewards of his country's respect for self-made men.

Jackson thought well enough of himself, but he also believed that his success was due to the openness of American society. All people were not equally talented, in his view, but the good society provided everyone the opportunity to exploit his abilities and enjoy the fruits of his labor unimpeded by artificial social and economic obstacles. Government's task was to preserve this opportunity by striking down obstacles to it, such as laws that benefited some and, therefore, handicapped others.

Jackson's view of government was, therefore, essentially negative. He believed that government should, as much as possible, leave people, society, and the economy alone so that natural social and economic forces could operate freely. The common term for this point of view is *laissez-faire*, French for, "leave it alone."

Attitudes of a Hero; Attitudes of a People

Jackson's vision of equal opportunity extended only to white males, but in this too, as in his attitudes toward women, children, blacks, and Indians, he also represented the dominant opinion of his era.

Jackson believed that women lived in a different "sphere" from males. While menfolk struggled in an often brutal world, women guarded home and hearth. They were superior to men in religious and moral sensibility; indeed, it was because of these fine faculties that they had to be sheltered from a public life that was hardening at best, corrupting at worst. Jackson and most Americans, including women, agreed with the clergyman who preached the "Gospel of Pure Womanhood." Woman's "chastity is her tower of strength, her modesty and gentleness are her charm, and her ability to meet the high claims of her family and dependents the noblest power she can exhibit to the world."

The reward due women for accepting their divinely decreed private, submissive role in the world was the sacred right to be treated with deference. Jackson himself was famous for his chivalry. Rough as the old soldier's life had been, he was properly prudish in mixed company. Even in the absence of the ladies, he habitually referred to them as "the fair." Adding the word "sex" would have violated his sense of delicacy.

Toward children, visitors were amazed to discover, Jackson was indulgent. The man who had aroused armies to bloodlust and had slaughtered hundreds without wincing, and the president who periodically exploded in rages that left him (and everyone else) trembling, beamed quietly as young children virtually destroyed rooms in the White House before his very eyes. The British minister wrote that he could not hear the president's conversation because the two men were surrounded by caterwauling children. Jackson smiled absent-mindedly and nodded all the while. At table, the president fed children first, saying that they had the best appetites and the least patience.

Such indulgence was not universal in the United States. Many New Englanders tried to raise children by the old Puritan book. But Europeans commented in horror that American children generally, and especially in the West, had the manners of "wild Indians." Some also noticed that American children were more self-reliant than European children because of the freedom that was allowed them. It was this quality—"standing on your own two feet"—that Jackson and his countrymen valued in their progeny.

Democracy and Race

Toward Native Americans and blacks, Jackson also shared the prejudices of his age. Blacks were doomed to be subject to whites by Bible or Mother Nature or both. Blacks *were* slaves; American blacks were fortunate to have such enlightened masters. As a Southerner, Jackson did not trouble himself with the implications of the doctrine of equal rights. Having lived with both the Declaration of Independence and human bondage for 50 years, most Americans found them quite compatible.

As a Westerner, Jackson thought a great deal about Indians. He spent much of his life fighting them and taking their land. More than any single person, he was responsible for crushing the military power of the great Southeastern tribes—the Creeks, Choctaws, Cherokees, Chickasaws, and Seminoles.

Although he was ruthless in these wars, Jackson was not the simple "Indian-hater" his enemies sometimes

Andrew Jackson, a portrait by Thomas Sully.

HOW THEY LIVED

DUELING AND BRAWLING THE AMERICAN WAY

The duel—a prearranged fight with deadly weapons between gentlemen—originated in the medieval practice of the Wager of Battle. A form of ordeal, the Wager pitted a person accused of a crime against his accuser. If the accused won, he was declared innocent. Although condemned by religious leaders, the Wager of Battle survived in France until the 1500s. The duel rose in fashion to take its place.

A duel was not concerned with guilt or innocence of a crime; it had no standing in the law. The issue in dueling was a gentleman's honor. A man who thought himself or a woman under his protection insulted challenged the defamer to meet on the field of honor. It was not necessary to fight to the death, as it had been in the Wager. Merely following the intricate code of manners that governed dueling established one's honor. A majority of duels ended when blood was drawn or, if by pistols, when each party discharged his weapon in the general direction of the other. The point was good manners. Only gentlemen dueled. The vulgar multitude brawled.

Colonial Americans did not duel. Careful scholars have found records of only a dozen such fights between 1607 and 1776. Then, during the Revolutionary War, French officers such as Lafayette, Rochambeau, and de Grasse introduced the Code Duello to their American friends. A decade later, when French aristocrats fled the revolution in their country and settled in Louisiana, they made New Orleans the dueling capital of America. (On one Sunday in 1839, ten duels were fought in the Crescent City. A woman wrote that the young men of society kept score of their duels, as a young lady kept score of proposals of marriage.)

Dueling spread as rapidly as sudden wealth created self-made men (particularly southerners) who were in a hurry to prove their gentility. Librarian of Congress Daniel Boorstin has written that "of southern statesmen who rose to prominence after 1790, hardly one can be mentioned who was not involved in a duel."

It is only a slight exaggeration. Button Gwinnet, signer of the Declaration of Independence from Georgia, was killed in a duel in 1777. James Madison fought a duel in 1797. Maryland-born Commodore Stephen Decatur fought one duel in 1801 and was killed in another in 1820. William H. Crawford, Secretary of the Treasury under Monroe and presidential candidate in 1824, fought a duel. John Randolph of Roanoke fought two, the second in 1826 with Henry Clay of Kentucky, who also fought other men. Hero of the common man Senator Thomas Hart Benton of Missouri fought a number of duels and killed at least one of his opponents. Sam Houston of Texas fought a duel. A great many southerners who were prominent in the Confederacy were involved in duels; among them were William L. Yancey, Vice President Alexander H. Stephens, and General John C. Breckinridge. Confederate president Jefferson Davis was challenged to a duel by Judah P. Benjamin, who later became a fast friend and served in three cabinet positions. Romantic legend has it that duels were fought over ladies. In fact, as implied in this list, many were fought over politics.

The most famous American duelist was Andrew Jackson, seventh president of the United States, who did fight over insults to his wife. Some of his enemies said that Jackson was involved in a hundred duels. That is un-

---

portrayed. He found much to admire in Native Americans, their closeness to nature, and their courage in resisting their conquerors. There was an unmistakable tinge of tragic regret in his statement to Congress that the white and red races simply could not live side by side and, therefore, the Indians would simply die out. It was unfortunate; it was also the dictate of progress. Race, in Jackson's world, was a mighty force before which all beliefs bent.

Government by Party

Attitudes are not policies, but President Jackson lost no time in establishing the latter. As the first president to represent a political party frankly and without apologies, he made it clear that he would replace those federal officeholders who had opposed him with his own supporters. One of Jackson's men, William Marcy of New York, phrased the practice of rewarding party members as "to the victor belong the spoils."

There were about 20,000 federal jobs in 1829, and Jackson eventually dismissed about one-fifth of the people in them. Even considering the fact that some federal officeholders supported him, that was by no means a clean sweep. In fact, John Quincy Adams, who never dismissed anyone, privately admitted that many of the people Jackson fired were incompetent.

As for those who were able, when Jackson's critics claimed that the men who were best qualified by education and training should hold government jobs, Jackson answered with quite another theory. He said that each government job should be designed so that any reasonably intelligent, freeborn American citizen could perform it adequately. In another time, we would say he was defining bureaucracy.

The debate over the spoils system was noisy but brief.

likely. Even Old Hickory was not so tough or so lucky as to survive that many tests of honor and marksmanship.

However, the written terms of one of Jackson's duels have survived. In 1806, Jackson faced Charles Dickinson, a Nashville lawyer:

It is agreed that the distance shall be 24 feet, the parties to stand facing each other, with their pistols drawn perpendicularly. When they are ready the single word fire to be given at which they are to fire as soon as they please. Should either fire before the word is given, we [the seconds of both parties] pledge ourselves to shoot him down instantly. The person to give the word to be determined by lot, as also the choice of position.

Neither Dickinson nor Jackson fired before the word was given, but Dickinson fired first, gravely wounding but not felling Jackson. "Back to the mark, sir," Jackson said when Dickinson staggered in fear of what was to come. Then, according to Jackson's enemies, Jackson's pistol misfired, and in violation of the Code Duello, he pulled the hammer back and fired again. This breach of honor haunted Jackson for the rest of his life, for Dickinson died from the dubious shot.

Perhaps it was because of this slur on his character that when a man whom Jackson considered no gentleman challenged him some years later, Jackson refused to duel. But he offered to shoot it out in some "sequestered grove" as long as both parties understood that it was not an affair between social equals.

Actually, according to *The Code of Honor, or Rules . . . in Dueling*, written by a governor of South Carolina, a gentleman who had been insulted by a social inferior was to cane him, that is, to flog the impudent lout about the head and shoulders with a walking stick. But Jackson's action points up the fact that in the West, dueling merged undetectably into plain brawling. An Alabama law of 1837 that outlawed dueling also forbade the carrying of the decidedly ungentlemanly weapons "known as Bowie knives or Arkansas Tooth-picks." The people who carried bowie knives were not likely to have read the "Twenty-eight Commandments of the Duel."

Of course, dueling was by no means an exclusively southern and Western practice. Alexander Hamilton and Aaron Burr were not southerners. Benedict Arnold was from Connecticut; De Witt Clinton, from New York; and Nathaniel Greene, from Rhode Island—they all fought duels. Moreover, the practice was just as illegal in the South as it was in the North. Killing a person in a duel was murder, punishable by death. South Carolina imposed a fine of $2,000 and a year in prison for seconds as well as duelists. Officeholders in Alabama were required to take an oath that they never had dueled or acted as seconds.

But Daniel Boorstin is certainly correct to say that the prevalence of dueling in the South up to the Civil War reflected the propensity of upper-class southerners to regard the unwritten laws of honor, manliness, decency, and courage as more important than the laws of legislatures.

When the anti-Jackson forces eventually came to power in 1840, they carved up the spoils of office far more lustily than Jackson's men had done. For half a century, the ruling party's patronage of its members was an established part of American politics.

ISSUES OF JACKSON'S FIRST TERM

When he became president, Jackson did not have particularly strong opinions on the questions of the tariff and of internal improvements. In his first address to Congress, he called for a protective tariff, but he later drifted (again without passion) to the Southern position of a tariff for revenue only.

Internal Improvments

As a Westerner, Jackson understood the need for good roads and river channels free of snags and sandbars. As an advocate of laissez-faire and of strict construction of the Constitution, however, he worried that it was not constitutional for the federal government to finance them. In 1830, when he vetoed a bill to construct a road between Maysville and Lexington, Kentucky, he told Congress that if the Constitution was amended to authorize such projects, he would approve them.

In the Maysville Road veto, Jackson seems to have been as interested in taking a slap at Henry Clay as in protecting constitutional niceties. The projected road would have been completely within Clay's home state of Kentucky, adding immeasurably to Clay's popularity. Later, Jackson quietly approved other internal improvement bills when the expenditures promised to win votes for his own party.

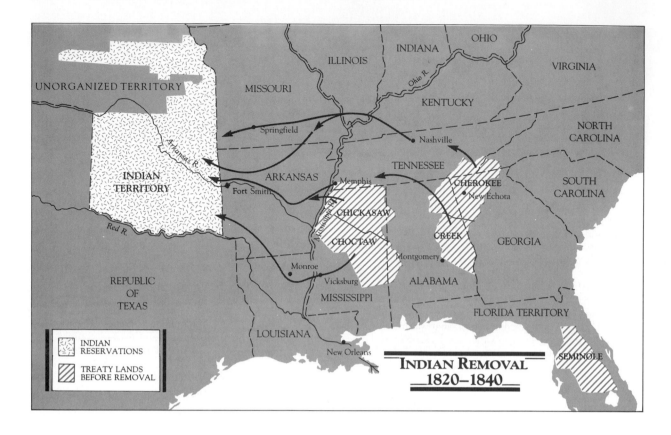

On the rising constitutional issue of the day, the division of power between the federal government and the states, Jackson was again inconsistent according to how his personal sensibilities and party interests were involved. When the issue was Georgia's attempt to ignore the federally guaranteed rights of Indians, Jackson allowed the state to have its way. But when South Carolina attempted to defy his power as president, he moved quickly and decisively to crush the challenge—coming close to dusting off his old uniform, polishing his sword, and personally leading an army south.

Indian Removal

The rapid settlement of the trans-Appalachian West brought large numbers of whites into lands formerly held exclusively by large Indian tribes. Congress and Presidents Monroe and Adams agreed that this situation was unworkable. To them, white ways and Indian ways were incompatible. To resolve the conflict, they advocated a policy of "Indian removal," the relocation of the tribes to an Indian Territory west of the Mississippi River that would be guaranteed to them "forever."

To implement removal meant scrapping old treaties that had made the same promise. Various agreements had given the Indians lands east of the Mississippi "as long as the water runs and the grass grows." Neverthe-

less, faced with a combination of inducements and threats, most of the trans-Appalachian tribes agreed to "removal" farther west. Others rebelled. The Sac and the Fox of Illinois and Wisconsin rose up under Chief Black Hawk, but were defeated. The Seminoles of Florida, their numbers augmented by runaway slaves, also fought back. They were never decisively defeated, but escaped into the swamplands, from where, between 1835 and 1842, they fought an effective holding action against the army.

The Cherokee Go to Court

Still other tribes, such as the Choctaws of the Old Southwest, were defrauded. Federal agents bribed renegade chiefs to sign removal treaties that were then enforced on the entire people. Another of the Civilized Tribes, the Cherokees, seemed to win their fight to remain in their ancestral homeland.

Like the Creeks, Choctaws, and Chickasaws, the Cherokees had adopted a good many white ways. They gave up their semi-nomadic hunting and gathering economy and farmed intensively, raising cash crops such as cotton as well as crops for use. They kept black slaves and lived in houses that combined traditional and white American building techniques. In 1821, the tribe adopted an 86-character alphabet that a half-Cherokee, half-white silversmith named Sequoyah had developed for their language. They printed newspapers and books and operated a school system, one of the best in the South. When they pleaded their interests, they emphasized values they held in common with the larger society: "In truth, our cause is your own. It is the cause of liberty and justice. It is based on your own principles, which we have learned from yourselves. . . . In your kindness, on your humanity, on your compassions, on your benevolence, we rest our hopes."

According to their treaty with the United States government, the Cherokees were entitled to remain where they were. The tribe was recognized as a semi-sovereign nation within the United States. Therefore, they refused every attempt of the federal government to force them out.

The state of Georgia was more determined. Unlike in Congress, where the Cherokees had friends, the government of Georgia was dominated by people who wanted the Cherokee lands and were willing to ignore federal treaties to get them. A Georgia court forced the issue by convicting a white missionary of a crime committed in Cherokee territory and, therefore, according to treaty, under tribal jurisdiction. The missionary and the Cherokee nation appealed the case of *Worcester v. Georgia* to the Supreme Court.

Chief Justice John Marshall had no more confidence

in the ability of whites and Native Americans to live side by side than did Andrew Jackson. He had waffled on an earlier dispute between the Cherokees and Georgia. But Marshall was a staunch defender of the sanctity of federal contract, which is precisely what the treaty with the Cherokees was. He ruled that the state of Georgia had no authority in Cherokee territory, threw out the conviction of Worcester, and made it clear that Georgia could not force the Cherokees to give up their land.

The Trail of Tears

That seemed to settle the matter, and the Cherokee nation celebrated. But Georgia gambled. The state had gone for Jackson in 1828, and the president was a lifelong Indian fighter. Georgia defied the Supreme Court, held on to its prisoner, engineered some fraudulent agreements with Cherokees who could be bought, and began the forcible removal of the tribe.

Georgia won its bet. "John Marshall has made his decision," Jackson was quoted as saying. "Let him enforce it." Thus began the Trail of Tears, the 1,200 mile trek of the Cherokees and some other Southeastern peoples to what is now Oklahoma. General John E. Wool, sent to supervise the forced march, commented distastefully of white Georgians who witnessed its start, like "vultures ready to pounce on their prey and strip them of everything they have."

Two thousand died in camps waiting for the migration to begin, another 2,000 on the trail. About 15,000 Cherokee made it to Oklahoma scarred and demoralized. It would take two or even three generations to recover, and the survivors remembered the betrayal of its own constitutional principles by the white nation that had robbed them of their homeland and whose ways they had embraced.

The Tariff of Abominations

If Georgia succeeded in defying the federal government, neighboring South Carolina did not. The issue that brought Jackson into conflict with the Palmetto State and his own vice president, John C. Calhoun, was the tariff.

In 1828, Congress passed an extremely high protective tariff, which no one completely liked, but which a majority accepted and John Quincy Adams signed. While most Southern planters hated this "Tariff of Abominations," South Carolina's cotton planters were enraged. They believed that their crop was paying the whole country's bills and underwriting industrial investment.

They had a point. Cotton accounted for fully half of the wealth that poured into the United States from abroad. Some of this income was indirectly diverted to

Sequoyah's invention of the Cherokee alphabet of 86 letters enabled thousands of Cherokees to read and write in their own language.

the North by the tariff that required everyone, including Southern cotton planters, to pay higher prices for manufactured goods. South Carolina's problem was constitutional. A congressional majority, with the concurrence of the president, had decided that the national wealth should be employed in part to promote industrial development. Those who wanted cheap prices and had no interest in an industrial future, like the South Carolinians, were in a minority. The Tariff of Abominations might not look fair under a southern sky; but it was eminently constitutional.

The Doctrine of Nullification

South Carolina's most eminent politician, Vice President John C. Calhoun, looked to the Constitution for a solution. In 1829, he secretly penned *The South Carolina Exposition and Protest*, an ingenious and mischievous interpretation of the document.

The *Exposition* took up where Jefferson's and Madison's Virginia and Kentucky Resolutions had left off. Calhoun stated that the Union had not been formed by the people of America (as John Marshall and other nationalists said), but by the people acting through the individual states of which they were citizens. This was not mere hair-splitting, for it meant that the states were sovereign, and not the federal government. That is, the states were the fundamental, indivisible units of government which had formed a compact, the Union, for the benefit of the states.

When, Calhoun continued, the Union enacted a law to which a sovereign state objected, as South Carolina objected to the Tariff of Abominations, that state had the right to nullify that law (prevent its enforcement) within its borders until such time as three-quarters of the other states overruled its decision. (Calhoun was here referring to the amendment process of the Constitution, which requires the ratification of three-fourths

of the states.) In such an event, Calhoun concluded, the nullifying state could choose between capitulation to the decision of the other states, or secession from the Union.

South Carolina Acts; The President Responds

Jefferson and Madison never had to act on their theory. When they wrote the Virginia and Kentucky Resolutions, they had had hopes of winning control of the federal government, which they did. Subsequently, they lost interest in their (now inconvenient) doctrine of state sovereignty.

Calhoun and his supporters had hoped that the Tariff of Abominations would be repealed after Jackson was elected president, thus leaving the *Exposition* in the abstract. However, in 1832, Congress adopted another high protective tariff, and Jackson signed it into law. South Carolinians blew up, and elected a convention that declared the Tariff of 1832 "null and void" within the borders of the sovereign state of South Carolina.

Jackson said that South Carolinians could write whatever they chose on paper, but if they refused to collect the tariff and send the proceeds to Washington, he personally would lead an army into the state. Congress responded to his request for authority to do so with the Force Bill. Crisis was averted, however, when no other state nullified the tariff, leaving South Carolina in isolation. Calhoun met quietly with Henry Clay to work out a compromise tariff just low enough that South Carolina could save face. In 1833, the state rescinded its nullification of the tariff. But South Carolina did not repudiate the principle of nullification.

Jackson let it ride. It was all on paper like Marshall's decision in the Cherokee case. He had had his way, and he had identified a new enemy—his own vice president.

For Further Reading

Unsurprisingly, Andrew Jackson and what he meant for America have fascinated historians, and they have differed radically in their findings. For an overview of the era, see Glyndon G. Van Deusen, *The Jacksonian Era, 1828–1848* (1959). Clashing interpretations may be found in Richard Hofstadter, *The American Political Tradition and the Men Who Made It* (1948); Marvin Meyers, *The Jacksonian Persuasion* (1957); Edward Pessen, *Jacksonian America* (1978); Robert Remini, *Andrew Jackson*

(1966); Arthur M. Schlesinger, Jr., *The Age of Jackson* (1945); and John W. Ward, *Andrew Jackson; Symbol for an Age* (1955).

Indeed, yet other explanations of the great upheaval of the 1820s can be found in books with a narrower focus, including: Lee Benson, *The Concept of Jacksonian Democracy* (1964); J. C. Curtis, *Andrew Jackson and the Search for Vindication* (1976); William W. Freehling, *Prelude to Civil War: The Nullification Controversy in*

South Carolina, 1816-1836 (1966); Walter E. Hugins, *Jacksonian Democracy and the Working Class* (1960); Richard P. McCormick, *The Second American Party System: Party Formation in the Jacksonian Era* (1966); Edward E. Pessen, *Most Uncommon Jacksonians: The Radical Leaders of the Early Labor Movement* (1967); Robert Remini, *The Election of Andrew Jackson* (1963); M. P. Rogin, *Fathers and Children: Andrew Jackson and the Destruction of American Indians* (1975).

On Indian removal, see John Ehle, *Trail of Tears* (1988); Michael Green, *The Politics of Indian Removal* (1982); Ronald Satz, *American Indian Policy in the Jacksonian Era* (1974).

Attempted assassination of Andrew Jackson by Richard
Lawrence in 1835. Lawrence fired two pistols at the
president, but both misfired.

IN THE SHADOW OF ANDREW JACKSON

PERSONALITIES AND POLITICS, 1830 - 1842

When Andrew Jackson became president in 1829, few who knew him expected that he would serve for more than one term—if he lived to finish that. To his supporters scattered around the country, Jackson might have been Old Hickory—a tough and timeless frontiersman who stood as straight as a long rifle. In person, he was a frail, 62-year-old wisp of a man who often looked to be a day away from death.

Over 6 feet tall, Jackson weighed only 145 pounds. No other president was so frequently ill as he.

Jackson suffered from lead poisoning (he carried two bullets in his body): headaches, diarrhea, kidney disease, and edema (a painful swelling of the legs). He was beleaguered by coughing fits. During his White House years, he suffered two serious hemorrhages of the lungs.

VAN BUREN VERSUS CALHOUN

Jackson's choice of a vice president, therefore, was a matter of some interest. In giving his approval to John C. Calhoun in 1828, Jackson was not simply pocketing South Carolina's electoral votes. He was naming his heir apparent as president and leader of the Democratic party.

John C. Calhoun

Like Jackson, Calhoun was of Scotch-Irish background, the descendant of those eighteenth-century emigrants described, in practically every account of them, as quick-tempered and pugnacious. Calhoun was indeed, again like Jackson, a man of passion and stubborn, steely will. Portrait painters captured a piercing, burning gaze just an eyelash short of open rage, never the slightest hint of

John C. Calhoun as an old man: dignified, cheerless, unyielding, without optimism.

a smile, never a posture that would indicate that Calhoun knew even odd moments of peace of mind. Photographers, coming along later in his life, confirmed their impression.

Already by 1828, in fact, Calhoun was the captive of an obsession. He feared that the social institutions that were the backbone of his beloved South Carolina and much of the South—black slavery and the plantation aristocracy that owed its eminence and privileges to owning slaves—were mortally threatened by the rapid growth of population in the North, the increasing power of industrial capitalists, and what those developments meant for the policies of the national government in the not too distant future.

In this fear, Calhoun made a sharp break with his own youth. The young Calhoun had been both a nationalist and an exponent of industrialization. In 1815, he wanted to "bind the nation together with a perfect system of roads and canals." In 1816, he introduced the bill that chartered the Second Bank of the United States, arguing the desirability of centralizing the nation's financial power. Young man Calhoun urged South Carolinians to build steam-powered cotton mills in the midst of their fields, monopolizing the profits in their coveted crop from seed to bolt of cloth.

But when the South did not industrialize and the North did, thence demanding high protective tariffs that raised the prices of the manufactured goods that Southern agriculturalists bought outside the section, Calhoun changed his tune. He became a defender of agrarian society, the plantation system, and when voices were raised about the morality of slavery, a vociferous exponent of that institution and enemy of its critics. He opposed protective tariffs and was critical of internal improvements because of the taxes they meant and even of the Bank of the United States he had helped to found.

Jackson found few faults in such sentiments, but the two men differed as to the relationship between the federal and state governments. The president believed the national government supreme. In *The South Carolina Exposition and Protest*, Calhoun proclaimed the state governments sovereign.

So fundamental a difference was quite enough to sour Jackson on his vice president. However, philosophical differences were exacerbated by a tempest on the Washington social scene which also served to create a rival to Calhoun as Jackson's heir.

Peggy O'Neill Eaton

The center of the storm was Peggy O'Neill, the fetching daughter of a Washington hotel keeper. Peggy was married to a sailor who, as seamen are inclined, was rarely at home. In her husband's absence, she found solace and several children in the arms of one of her father's boarders, Tennessee congressman John Eaton, whom Jackson made his Secretary of War.

The affair was well worth a whisper and a giggle, but not a good deal more. Such irregular conjunctions were by no means unheard-of in the capital. Washington was no longer the largely male city that it had been when Jefferson was president, but there was still a shortage of living quarters suitable to families that lived well at home. Many congressmen continued to leave their wives behind and board at hotels. Inevitably, some found lady friends and, as long as they exercised minimal discretion, little was made of it. Henry Clay was said to have been a roué. Richard M. Johnson, vice president between 1837 and 1841, lived openly with a black woman who was also his slave.

Still, Clay's affairs were quiet and Johnson left his mistress at home when he attended social functions. When Peggy O'Neill's husband died at sea and Eaton married her, he expected Washington society to receive her. Instead, there ensued a great hullabaloo. It was too much to expect women who had been faithful lifelong to the gospel of true womanhood to sip tea with a fallen sister. Peggy O'Neill Eaton was roundly and brusquely snubbed.

One of the leading snubbers was Floride Calhoun, the sternly moralistic wife of the vice president. The wives of the cabinet members followed her example, and it aggravated Jackson. When his own niece, who served as his official hostess, refused to receive Peggy Eaton, Jackson told her to move out of the White House. Still mourning the death of his wife, which he blamed on sexual scandalmongers, Jackson also happened to be charmed by the vivacious Peggy. He actually summoned a cabinet meeting to discuss the subject (as he hardly ever did on political and economic issues), and pronounced her "as chaste as a virgin." He told his advisers to command their wives to receive her socially.

This was too big an order, even for the General. If women were excluded from politics and the professions, the rules of morality and social life were flatly within their sphere. Peggy Eaton continued to find little conversation at social functions. Only Secretary of State Martin Van Buren, who as a widower had no wife to oblige, dared to be seen admiring her gowns and fetching her refreshments.

The Rise of the Sly Fox

Charm and chitchat came naturally to Van Buren. His worst enemies conceded his grace and wit. His portraits, quite unlike Calhoun's, show a Dutchman's twinkle in the eye and a good-natured, intelligent smile.

But Martin Van Buren was much more than a jolly Dutchman. He was a diabolically clever politician, almost always several moves ahead of his rivals, particu-

larly when they were impassioned true believers like Calhoun. Van Buren's wiles earned him the nickname "the Sly Fox of Kinderhook" (his hometown in New York).

He wrote no expositions, but he was the most successful—at least, the most "modern"—political organizer of his time. He owed his high position in Jackson's cabinet to delivering most of New York's electoral votes in 1828. He understood that a political party, whatever its ideals, had to be a vote-gathering machine, rewarding the activists who marshaled votes by appointing them to government positions. And he was very ambitious for himself. Van Buren's sensitivity to the feelings of Peggy Eaton may have been quite sincere, but his actions also served to win Jackson's favor. He also offered the impulsive president a way out of the Eaton mess when the affair threatened to paralyze the administration and destroy the Democratic party.

He, Van Buren said, would resign as Secretary of State, and Eaton would give up his post as Secretary of War. The other members of the cabinet, whose wives were causing the president so much anxiety, would have no choice but to follow their example. Jackson would be rid of the lot, but no particular wing of the Democratic party could claim to have been punished.

Jackson appreciated both the strategy and Van Buren's willingness to sacrifice his prestigious office in order to help him. He rewarded Van Buren by naming him minister to England, then, as now, the plum of the diplomatic service.

Calhoun Seals His Doom

The Sly Fox of Kinderhook was lucky, too. While he calculated each turning with an eye on a distant destination, Calhoun blundered and bumped into posts like a half-blind cart horse. For example, while the Eaton affair was still rankling Jackson, the president discovered in some old cabinet reports that, ten years earlier, Secretary of War Calhoun had favored punishing the General for his unauthorized invasion of Florida. Confronted with the evidence, Calhoun tried to lie his way out of his fix. The president cut him off by writing, "Understanding you now, no further communication with you on this subject is necessary."

Nor, it turned out, was there much further communication between Jackson and his vice president on any subject. In April 1830, Jackson and Calhoun attended a formal dinner during which more than twenty of Calhoun's cronies offered toasts in favor of states' rights and nullification. When it was the president's turn to lift a glass, he rose, stared at Calhoun, and toasted, "Our Union: It must be preserved." Calhoun got the last word of the evening. He replied, "The Union, next to our liberty, the most dear." But Jackson took satisfaction from the fact that, as he told the story, Calhoun was trembling as he spoke.

The old duelist delighted in such confrontations. Van Buren took pleasure in his enduring good luck for he was in England during the nastiest period of the fight between Jackson and Calhoun, when even the slyest of foxes might easily have slipped.

Then Calhoun blundered again, guaranteeing that Van Buren would succeed Jackson. Seeking personal revenge, Calhoun cast the deciding vote in the Senate's refusal to confirm Van Buren's diplomatic appointment. This brought the New Yorker back to the United States, but hardly in disgrace. Completely in Jackson's good graces by this time, Van Buren was named vice-presidential candidate in the election of 1832, an assignment he might not have received had Calhoun left him in London.

THE WAR WITH THE BANK

Unlike his campaigns in 1824 and 1828, Jackson's bid for re-election in 1832 was fought over a real issue—the future of the Second Bank of the United States. The Second B.U.S. had been chartered in 1816 for a term of 20 years. After a shaky start (the Panic of 1819), it fell under the authority of Nicholas Biddle, a courtly Philadelphian who administered its affairs cautiously, conservatively, profitably, and, so it seemed, to the benefit of the federal government and the national economy. The B.U.S. acted as the government's financial agent, providing vaults for its gold and silver, paying government bills out of its accounts, investing deposits, and selling bonds (borrowing money for the government when it was needed).

The Powers of the Bank

Every cent that the government collected in excise taxes, tariffs, and from land sales was deposited in the B.U.S., making it a large, fabulously rich, and powerful institution. Its 29 strategically located branches controlled about one-third of all bank deposits in the United States, and did some $70 million in transactions each year.

With such resources, the Bank held immense power over the nation's money supply and, therefore, the economy. In a foolish but revealing moment, Nicholas Biddle told congressmen that the B.U.S. was capable of destroying any other bank in the country.

What he meant was that at any moment the B.U.S. was likely to have in its possession more paper money issued by a state bank than that state bank had specie (gold and silver) in its vaults. If the B.U.S. were to

---

POP ART

In 1834, when the hero of the common man still sat in the White House, Nathaniel Currier of New York democratized American art. He began to sell cheap prints featuring natural wonders, marvels of technology such as locomotives, battles, portraits of prominent people, and scenes of everyday life, both sentimental and comical.

Currier and Ives (the partner arrived in 1852) sold their prints for as little as 25 cents for a small black and white print, up to $4 for a hand-colored picture measuring 28 by 40 inches. They were cheap enough to be afforded by the poor, just expensive enough to be acceptable as a wall-hanging in a self-conscious, middle-class household.

More than 7,000 Currier and Ives prints were produced by a process that can only be called "industrial." Some experts specialized in backgrounds, others in machinery, others in individual faces, yet others in crowd scenes. By the late nineteenth century, it was a rare American who could not have identified "Currier & Ives" to an enquirer.

---

present this paper for redemption in specie, the issuing bank would be bankrupt and the investment in it wiped out.

On a day he was more tactful, Biddle said that his bank exercised "a mild and gentle but efficient control" over the economy. That is, simply because the state banks were aware of the sword that the B.U.S. held over them, they maintained larger reserves of gold and silver than they might otherwise have done. Rather than ruining banks, the B.U.S. ensured that they operated more responsibly.

A Private Institution

Biddle was as proud of the public service he rendered as of the Bank's annual profits. Nevertheless, the fact remained that the Bank was powerful because it controlled the national money supply—a matter of profound public interest—but was itself a private institution. B.U.S. policies were made not by elected officials, nor by bureaucrats responsible to elected officials, but by a board of directors responsible to shareholders.

This was enough in itself to earn the animosity of a president who abhorred powerful special interests. Biddle therefore attempted to make a friend of the president by free-handed loans to several key Jackson supporters, and he designed a plan to retire the national debt—a goal dear to Jackson's heart—timing the final installments to coincide with the anniversary of the Battle of New Orleans. To no avail: Jackson shook his head and explained to Biddle that it was not a matter of disliking the B.U.S. more than he disliked other banks; Jackson did not trust any of them. "You are a den of vipers and thieves," he told bankers. "I intend to root you out, and by the eternal God, I will root you out." Biddle turned to Congress for friends.

The Enemies of the Bank

Biddle needed friends. The Bank had many enemies who, except for their opposition to it, had little else in common.

First there was the growing financial community of New York City—the bankers and brokers who would soon be known collectively as "Wall Street." Grown wealthy from the Erie Canal and from New York's role as the nation's leading port, they were keen to challenge the Philadelphia financier's control of the nation's money supply. Second, the freewheeling bankers of the West disliked Biddle's restraints. Caught up in the optimism of the growing region, these bankers wanted a free hand to take advantage of soaring land values. Oddly, the president, who hated all banks, had the support of a good many bankers in his hostility toward the B.U.S.

A third group that wanted to see the B.U.S. declawed was even more conservative in money matters than was Biddle. Hard-money men like Jackson were opposed to the very idea of an institution that issued paper money in quantities greater than it had gold and silver on hand. Eastern workingmen had good reason to support the hard-money position: they were often paid in bank notes that, when presented to shopkeepers, were worth less than their face value because of the shakiness of the banks that issued them.

B.U.S. notes were "as good as gold." Nevertheless, the working-class wing of the Democratic party, called "Locofocos" in New York, lumped Biddle along with the rest and inveighed against his monopolistic powers.

Clay Fires the First Shot

For all the hostility toward the B.U.S., Jackson did not pick the fight that escalated into what was called "the Bank War." Henry Clay fired the first shot when, in January 1832, he was nominated for the presidency by supporters calling themselves National-Republicans. Although the Bank's charter did not expire for four more years, Clay persuaded Biddle to apply for a new charter immediately. A majority of both houses of Congress would support the bid, putting Jackson, as Clay saw it, on the spot.

That is, if Jackson gritted his teeth and signed the Bank bill for fear of bucking a congressional majority, all would be well and good. The B.U.S. was one of the pillars of Clay's American System, as the first Bank of the United States had been a pillar of Hamilton's design. If Jackson vetoed the bill, Clay would have an issue on which to wage his presidential campaign. Clay believed that, because the Bank had proved its value to the national economy, he would defeat Jackson by promising to rescue it.

Clay was not the last presidential nominee to believe

A satirical "bank note" expressing the intense dislike of banks by "hard-money" Jacksonian Democrats.

that, presented with an issue, voters would decide on the basis of it rather than be dazzled by symbols. Jackson vetoed the Bank bill, Clay ran on the issue, and went down resoundingly to defeat. Jackson was still a hero, still the reed vibrating in harmony with the popular mood. He won 55 percent of the popular vote and 219 electoral votes to Clay's 49. (Anti-Masonic candidate William Wirt won 7 electoral votes, and South Carolina gave its 11 votes to John Floyd.)

Financial Chaos

In September 1833, six months after his second innauguration, Jackson took the offensive. He ceased to deposit government monies in the Bank, putting them instead into what were called his "pet banks," state-chartered institutions. The B.U.S., however, continued to pay the government's bills out of its account. Within three months, federal deposits in the B.U.S. sank from $10 million to $4 million. Biddle had no choice but to reduce the scope of the Bank's operations. He also chose, no doubt in part to sting Jackson, to call in debts owed the Bank by other financial institutions. The result was a wave of bank failures that wiped out the savings of thousands of people, just what Jackson had feared B.U.S. power might mean.

Under pressure from the business community, Biddle relented and reversed his policy, increasing the national supply of money by making loans to other banks. This action, alas, fed a new speculative boom. To Jackson's chagrin, many of the 89 pet banks to which he had entrusted federal deposits proved to be among the least responsible in using the money. They, too, fed the speculation.

In 1836, Henry Clay made his contribution to what would be the most serious American depression since the time of Jefferson's Embargo. He convinced Congress to pass a distribution bill under the terms of which $37 million was distributed to the states for expenditure on internal improvements. Presented with such a windfall, local politicians reacted as politicians sitting on a cash bonanza often do: they spent freely, crazily, backing the least worthy of projects and the sleaziest of promoters. Values in land, both in the undeveloped West and in Eastern cities, soared. Federal land sales rose to $25 million in 1836. Seeking to get a share of the freely circulating cash, new banks were chartered at a dizzying rate. There had been 330 state banks in 1830; there were almost 800 in 1837.

And there was no Bank of the United States to cool things down gradually, for its national charter had expired the previous year. Instead, action was left to Jackson, then in his last year of office, and he did the only thing within his power: he slammed a lid on the sale of federal land, the most volatile commodity in the boom. In July 1836, he issued the Specie Circular, which required that government lands be paid for in gold and silver coin; paper money was no longer acceptable.

Jackson's action stopped the runaway speculation, but with a heavy foot on the brake rather than the tug on the reins that the B.U.S. might have used. Western speculators who were unable to pay their debts to the government went bankrupt. Moreover, gold and silver were drained from the East, which contributed to a panic and depression there

The Giant of His Age

Jackson's financial policy was a disaster, based on ignorance and pig-headedness. It would have destroyed the career and reputation of a lesser man as, indeed, it did in the instance of Jackson's successor, Martin Van Buren. By the time the economy hit bottom, however, Jackson had retired to Tennessee. Seventy years old now, the man whom many thought would be lucky to live through one term, enjoying the "easy and dignified retirement" of a presidency that an old soldier deserved,

Andrew Jackson became a symbol of a democratic upheaval that changed the character of American politics.

had cut and chopped his way through eight pivotal years in the history of the nation.

Indeed, though aching and coughing, Jackson would live for nine more years, observing from his mansion home an era that unfolded in his shadow. He was never a wise man. His intelligence was limited; his education spotty; his prejudices often ugly. He was easily ruled by his passions and confused them with the interests of his country. His vision of America was pocked with more flaws than that of many of his contemporaries, including his enemies.

But for all this he was the symbol—the personification—of a democratic upheaval that changed the character of American politics. He presided over a time of ferment in nearly every facet of American life. He set new patterns of presidential behavior by aggressively taking the initiative in making policy. He called upon the presidential veto power more often than had all his six predecessors put together.

Jackson also impressed his personality on a political party and an era that would end only when the slavery issue tore the entire country apart. Even the party that his enemies formed during his second term was held together, to a large extent, by hostility toward him and his memory. And his political foes managed to succeed only when they imitated the methods of the Jacksonian Democrats.

THE SECOND AMERICAN PARTY SYSTEM

By 1834, Jackson's triumphs had forced a new realignment of American national politics. In the congressional elections that year, the old National-Republican followers of Quincy Adams and Clay joined with former Jackson supporters who objected to one or another of his policies—his promiscuous use of the veto, his highhanded treatment of the Indians, his war against the Bank—and called themselves the Whigs. Even South Carolinians, who agreed with Jackson on almost every point except his hostility toward nullification and John C. Calhoun, sometimes called themselves Whigs.

The word *Whig* was borrowed from English history and from the American Revolution. In Britain, the Whig party was traditionally the group inclined to reduce the power of the monarchy and to increase the sway of Parliament. During the early years of the American War for Independence, revolutionaries, emphasizing their opposition to the king, were as apt to call themselves Whigs as patriots. In Jacksonian America,

members of the new Whig party said that the monarch to be reined in was "King Andrew I."

To some degree, the Whigs were held together by a negative impulse, their common opposition to Jackson. They included supporters of the American System who believed that the federal government should take the initiative in shaping economic development. In Louisiana, however, sugar planters, who took little interest in other aspects of economic planning, supported the Whigs because they stood for a high tarriff on cheap foreign sugar.

In the North, the Whig party included high-tariff industrialists, of course, as well as most people of education, means, and pretension to social status. During the 1830s, Anti-Masons drifted into the party. Traditionalist New Englanders, suspicious of anything attractive to Southerners, like the Democratic party, inclined to Whiggery. So did those few blacks who were permitted to vote, and the upper and middle classes of city and town who found the vulgarity of lower-class Democrats and the spoils system offensive to their old Republican ideals.

Maryland Senator James Pearce summed up these Whig ideals when he said that Democratic party rule meant the rejection of "refining and uniting influences and of a highly educated and cultivated class" as well as the triumph "of the disorganizing over the conservative, of the leveling over the elevating, of selfishness over humanity, of partisanship over patriotism." In 1834, this patchwork alliance was enough to win 98 seats in the House of Representatives and almost half the Senate—twenty-five seats to the Democrats' 27.

The Godlike Daniel

Except for Henry Clay, the most prominent Whig was Daniel Webster of Massachusetts. At the peak of his powers, he was idolized as a demigod in New England. The adoration owed mostly to his personal presence and his peerless oratorical powers. He was indeed a specimen of a statesman. With a great face that glowered darkly when he spoke, his eyes burned like "anthracite furnaces." A look from him, it was said, was enough to win most debates. Webster was described as "a steam engine in trousers" and "a small cathedral in himself." An admirer said he was "a living lie because no man on earth could be so great as he looked."

In fact, Webster was not a fraction so great as he looked. Although an able administrator and an effective diplomat, Webster possessed a less than shining character. Of humble origin, he took too zestfully to the high life available to the eminent. He dressed grandly, adored good food, and savored the company of the wealthy. He was an alcoholic. He invested his money as foolishly as he spent it and was constantly in debt. This tied him yet more closely to the New England industrialists who regularly sent him money. During the Bank War, Webster indirectly threatened to end his services as legal counsel to the Bank unless Nicholas Biddle paid him off. (Biddle did.)

Webster came to expect money in the mail after every speech on behalf of the tariff or even the ideal of the Union. As a result, while he remained popular in New England, his not-so-secret vices and venality provided an easy target for the Democrats and made him an object of suspicion among fellow Whigs who took personal integrity as seriously as they took public virtue.

Union and Liberty

And yet, it was this flawed man who gave glorious voice to the ideal that was to sustain the indisputably great Abraham Lincoln during the first years of the Civil War. In 1830, when Calhoun and Jackson were toasting the relative values of union versus liberty, Webster rose in the Senate to tell the nation that "Liberty and Union, now and forever," were "one and inseparable."

He was replying to Robert Hayne of South Carolina, a fine orator who, when Calhoun was vice president, represented him on the floor. Hayne identified the doctrine of nullification with American liberty. Webster declared that, on the contrary, the Constitution was the wellspring of liberty in the United States, and the indissoluble union of the states was its greatest defense. "It is, Sir, the people's Constitution, the people's government, made for the people, made by the people, and answerable to the people." The Liberty and Union speech turned a political abstraction (the Union) into an object for which people would be willing to die. (It also provided three generations of schoolchildren with a memorization piece.)

1836: Whigs Versus a Democrat

Differences within the Whig party prevented its convention of 1836 from agreeing on a platform. The delegates could not even agree on a compromise candidate to oppose Martin Van Buren, the Democratic nominee. Consequently, Whig leaders decided on the curious tactic of trying to throw the election into the House of Representatives, as had happened in 1824.

That is, the Whigs named three candidates to run against Van Buren in those parts of the country where each was most popular. Webster ran in lower New England. Hugh Lawson White of Tennessee was the candidate in the South. In the Northwest and upper New England, the Whigs' man was William Henry Harrison, the hero of the Battle of Tippecanoe. Although the

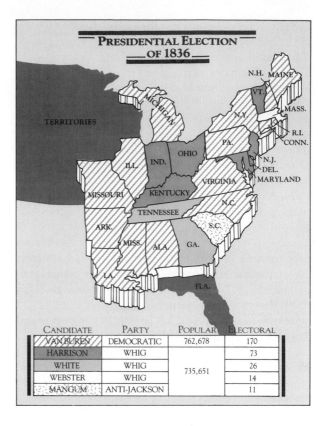

CANDIDATE	PARTY	POPULAR	ELECTORAL
VAN BUREN	DEMOCRATIC	762,678	170
HARRISON	WHIG		73
WHITE	WHIG	735,651	26
WEBSTER	WHIG		14
MANGUM	ANTI-JACKSON		11

battle was a quarter of a century in the past, the party hoped that the memory was still strong among a people ever hungry for new lands.

The strategy failed. While all three Whigs (and cantankerous South Carolina's candidate, Willie P. Mangum) won some electoral votes, Van Buren carried states in every section and a comfortable 170 to 124 majority in the electoral college. The Whigs held their own in Congress, still the minority but, with South Carolina unpredictable, in a good position for attack.

Depression

Election to the presidency was just about the last good thing that happened to Martin Van Buren. When his administration was just a few months old, the country reaped the whirlwind of runaway speculation and Jackson's Specie Circular. Drained of their gold and silver, several big New York banks announced in May 1837 that they would no longer redeem their notes in specie. Speculators and honest workingmen alike found themselves holding paper money that even the institutions that issued it would not accept as valid.

In 1838, the country sank into depression. In 1841 alone, 28,000 people declared bankruptcy. Factories

Martin Van Buren still looks the good-natured bon vivant in this daguerreotype of him as an elderly man.

closed because their products did not sell. Several citics were unsettled by riots of unemployed workers. Eight Western state governments defaulted on their debts.

Van Buren tried to meet the fiscal part of the crisis. A good Jacksonian, he attempted to "divorce" the government from the banks, which he blamed for the disaster. He established the subtreasury system, by which, in effect, the government would keep its funds in its own vaults. The Clay and Webster Whigs replied that what was needed was an infusion of money into the economy, not a withdrawal of it. But they could not carry the issue.

Van Buren also maintained the Jacksonian faith in laissez-faire by refusing to take any measures to alleviate popular suffering. The Founding Fathers, he said (in fact voicing Jackson's sentiments), had "wisely judged that the less government interfered with private pursuits the better for the general prosperity."

Whatever the virtues of Van Buren's position—whatever the convictions of most Americans on the question of government intervention in the economy—it is difficult for any administration to survive a depression. The president, who reaps the credit for blessings that are none of his doing, gets the blame when things go badly, how-

ever nebulous his responsibility for the misfortune. By early 1840, the Whigs were sure that hard times would give their candidate the White House.

"Tippecanoe and Tyler Too"

But who was to be the candidate? In that year of likely victory, Henry Clay believed that he deserved the nomination. For 25 years, he had offered a coherent national economic policy that, for the most part, had become Whig gospel. For half that time, he had led the fight against the Jacksonians. More than any other individual, he personified the Whig party.

But Clay's great career was also his weakness. In standing at the forefront for more than a quarter of a century, Clay inevitably had made mistakes and enemies. Victory-hungry young Whigs like Thurlow Weed of New York argued against nominating Clay. Better, Weed said, to choose a candidate who had no political record, but who, like Jackson in 1824 and 1828, could be painted up as a symbol. The first and foremost object of a political party, Weed and others said, was to win elections. Only then could it accomplish anything.

The ideal candidate, therefore, was William Henry Harrison, an old Western war-horse like Jackson, the victor of Tippecanoe, who had the added recommendation of descent from a distinguished Virginia family; his father had signed the Declaration of Independence. Harrison had run better than any other Whig in the peculiar election of 1836, and he was associated with no controversial political position whatsoever. Indeed, in 1836, his "handlers" forbade him to "say not one single word about his principles or his creed, let him say nothing, promise nothing. Let no [one] extract from him a single word about what he thinks. . . . Let use of pen and ink be wholly forbidden as if he were a mad poet in Bedlam."

Harrsion was nominated in 1840. To appeal to Southerners, John Tyler of Virginia was nominated vice president; "Tippecanoe and Tyler Too!"

A WHIG MARCHING SONG

Let Van from his coolers of silver drink wine,
*   And lounge on his cushioned settee;*
Our man on his buckeye bench can recline,
*   Content with hard cider is he.*
Then a shout from each freeman—a shout from each State,
*   To the plain, honest husbandman true,*
And this to be our motto—the motto of Fate—
*   "Hurrah for Old Tippecanoe!"*

HOW THEY LIVED

GOING TO COLLEGE

A university student today would have difficulty recognizing the colleges of the early nineteenth century. A student's life during the Jacksonian era more closely resembled college life in the Middle Ages than in the late twentieth century.

For example, all but a few colleges and universities were private institutions; as late as 1860, only 17 of the 246 colleges and universities in the United States were state institutions. Rather, most were maintained by one or another Protestant denomination in order to train ministers and to indoctrinate other young men in their principles, and they were funded by student tuition and by the subsidies that were granted by their affiliated churches. This was particularly true of the colleges that were founded during the Jacksonian era, many of which were inspired by the evangelical commitment to reform society.

Colleges were all-male institutions. Higher education was still regarded as the final polishing of a cultivated man, the foundation for public life and for the practice of the professions, particularly the ministry. Women, whose social role most people perceived as domestic and private, had no need for formal learning.

This attitude was beginning to change, however. In 1833, Ohio's Oberlin College, a hotbed of reformism, began to admit women students. A few colleges and universities followed suit, but the real expansion of educational opportunities for women came not with coeducation but with all-female institutions. The first of these were Georgia Female College in Macon (now Wesleyan College) and Mount Holyoke College in South Hadley, Massachusetts, founded by Mary Lyon in 1837.

College was not vocationally oriented, as it is today. That is, students were not taught the specific skills involved in the career they had selected. The young man who wanted to become an accountant, an engineer, an architect, or a businessman in the early nineteenth century apprenticed himself to someone skilled in those callings and learned "on the job." Women mastered skills thought proper to them at home. Although some universities had established medical and law schools, apprenticeship was also the most common means of preparing for those professions, too.

At college the curriculum remained much as it had been for centuries, a strictly prescribed course of study in the liberal arts and sciences (*liberal* in this case meaning "suitable to a free man"). Students learned the ancient languages (Latin, Greek, sometimes Hebrew), literature, natural science, mathematics, and political and moral philosophy—according to the beliefs of the church that supported the institution. Some colleges had added modern languages and history by the Jacksonian period, but there were no "electives"; every student took the same courses.

The colleges were small. Except for the very oldest, such as Harvard and Yale universities, and for some public institutions, such as Thomas Jefferson's University of Virginia, the typical student body numbered only a few dozen and the typical faculty perhaps three or four professors and an equal number of tutors. While faculty members and students came to know one another by sight and name, relations between them were not informal and chummy. On the contrary, professors erected a high wall of formality and ritual between themselves and those whom they taught, both out of the belief in the principle of hierarchy and out of the fear that too much friendliness would lead to a breakdown in discipline. Historian Joseph F. Kett has pointed out that stiff-necked behavior by instructors often owed to the fact that many of them were little older and sometimes even younger than most of

Marketing an Image

At first the Whigs planned to campaign simply by talking about Harrison's military record. Then, a Democratic newspaper editor made a slip that opened up a whole new world in American politics. Trying to argue that Harrison was incompetent, the journalist sneered that the old man would be happy with an annual pension of $2,000, a jug of hard cider, and a bench on which to sit and doze at the door of his log cabin.

Such snobbery toward simple tastes and the humble life were ill suited to a party that had come to power as the champion of the common man. The Whigs, who had suffered Democratic taunts that they were the elitists, charged into the breach. They hauled out miniature log cabins at city rallies and at country bonfires. They bought and tapped thousands of barrels of hard cider. They sang raucous songs like:

> Farewell, dear Van,
> You're not our man,
> To guide our ship,
> We'll try old Tip.

Stealing another leaf from the Jacksonian campaign book of 1828, the Whigs depicted Van Buren as an effeminate fop who sipped champagne, ate fancy French food, perfumed his whiskers, and flounced about in silks and satins.

It was all nonsense. Harrison lived in no log cabin but

their students. For example, Joseph Caldwell became *president* of the University of North Carolina when he was only 24 years old.

Student behavior was regulated by long lists of detailed rules. Students were expected to toe the line not only in class but also in their private lives. Attendance at religious services was mandatory at most private institutions. Strict curfews determined when students living in dormitories turned out their lamps. Even impoliteness might be punished by a fine or suspension. Students were expected to be deferential at all times.

This was the theory, at any rate. In practice, college students were at least as rambunctious as students of every era and more rebellious than any, save the generation of the 1960s. They defied their professors by day—the distinguished political philosopher Francis Lieber had to tackle students he wanted to discipline—and they taunted them by night. A favorite prank was stealing into the college chapel and ringing the college bell until dawn. They threw snowballs and rocks through the windows of their tutors' quarters. They led the president's horse to the roof of three- and four-story buildings. Students at Dickinson College in Pennsylvania sent a note to authorities at Staunton, Virginia, where the college president was visiting, informing them that an escaped lunatic headed their way would probably claim to be a college president and should be returned under guard.

Other student actions were rebellions and not just pranks. Professors were attacked by mobs angry at strict rules or poor food. Professors sometimes were stoned, horsewhipped, and fired on with shotguns. At the University of Virginia in 1840, Professor Nathaniel Davis was murdered. Writing to his own son at college in 1843, Princeton professor Samuel Miller warned against so much as sympathizing with potential rebels. Miller lived in fear of student uprisings, perhaps because one rebellion at Princeton was so serious that the faculty had to call in club-wielding townspeople to help put it down.

Why so much discontent? One reason is that the rules of college life had been written at a time when most college students were 14 to 18 years old, while, by the early nineteenth century, college students were often in their mid-twenties. Adults simply were not inclined to conform to behavior appropriate to adolescents, and in a society that took pride in individual freedom, they were quite capable of reacting violently to constraint.

Moreover, many college students lived not in dormitories but in their own lodgings in nearby towns. They fraternized largely with other students and developed a kind of defiant camaraderie directed against all outsiders. Enjoying broad freedoms in their off-campus lives, they were unlikely to conform to strict rules of behavior when they were at the college.

Finally, while the rules were strict, enforcement was often inconsistent. "There were too many colleges," writes Joseph F. Kett, "and they needed students more than students needed them." Faculty members who were nervous for their jobs would overlook minor offenses until they led to greater ones, at which point, suddenly, they drew the line. Inconsistency, as ever, led to contempt for would-be authority.

Colleges might expel or suspend the entire student body for "great rebellion." However, financial pressures apparently resulted in their readmission for the price of a written apology. Samuel Miller described student rebels as "unworthy, profligate, degraded, and miserable villains," but if they had the tuition, there was always a place for them somewhere.

in a large and comfortable mansion. He was no simple country bumpkin but rather the opposite, a pedant given to boring academic discourse on subjects of little interest to ordinary, hard-working people. Van Buren, while quite the dandy, was also an earthy man who held much more democratic ideas than did old Tip.

But nonsense worked (as it often has since). Although Van Buren won 47 percent of the popular vote, he was trounced in the electoral college by 60 to 234. Jacksonian chickens had come home to roost. Rarely again would a presidential election be contested without great fussing about irrelevancies and at least an attempt to avoid concrete issues. Moreover, with their successful appeal to the sentiments of the "common man," the Whigs of 1840 demonstrated that the democratic upheaval of the preceding two decades was complete. Never again would there be political profit in appealing to the superior qualifications of "the better sort" in the egalitarian United States. What may be most notable about the election campaign of 1840 is that a political candidate was marketed like a commodity—"packaged"—long before the techniques of modern advertising had been conceived in the world of commerce.

Fate's Cruel Joke

Wherever William Henry Harrison stood on specific issues, he was fully in accord with one fundamental Whig

This 1840 campaign banner shows William Henry Harrison walking from a humble log cabin to greet a wounded soldier. In fact, Harrison lived in a fine house but chose to present himself to voters as a simple man.

During the campaign of 1840, the Whigs' great paper ball covered with slogans was rolled throughout the Midwest and Northeast to shouts of "Keep the ball rolling!"

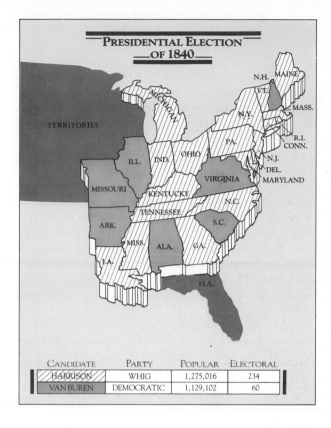

CANDIDATE	PARTY	POPULAR	ELECTORAL
HARRISON	WHIG	1,275,016	234
VAN BUREN	DEMOCRATIC	1,129,102	60

lecturing the country on republican virtue, he passed away.

John Tyler

At first, the Whigs did not miss a stride. Clay lectured "Tyler Too" that he should consider himself an acting president, presiding over the formalities of government while a committee of Whigs chaired by Clay made the real decisions. John Quincy Adams, now a Whig representative from Massachusetts, concurred. Tyler would have none of it. A nondescript man who had little imagination and a provincial view of national problems, Tyler insisted that the Constitution authorized him to exercise the same full presidential powers that he would have had if elected to the office.

Still, Tyler tried hard to get along with Clay. He went along with the abolition of the subtreasury system, and, although a low-tariff man, he agreed to an increase of rates in 1842 as long as the rise was tied to ending federal financing of internal improvements. Tyler also supported Clay's attempt to woo Western voters from the Democrats with his Preemption Act of 1841. This law provided that a family that had "squatted" on up to 160 acres of public land could purchase it at the minimum price of $1.25 per acre without having to bid against others.

A President Without a Party

But Tyler was not a real Whig. He had split with Jackson over King Andrew's arrogant use of presidential power. As a planter, his views on other issues were closer to those of John C. Calhoun (and Jackson!) than to those of the nationalistic Northern and Western Whigs. Most important, Tyler disliked the idea of a national bank and warned Clay not to try to force one on him.

Clay did try, and Tyler vetoed one bank bill after another. Furious, the majority Whigs expelled the president from the party, and Tyler's cabinet resigned (except Secretary of State Webster, who wanted to complete some touchy negotiations with Great Britain). Clay left the Senate in order to prepare for the presidential campaign of 1844.

After the blow-up, Tyler's cabinet was made up of nominal Southern Whigs much like Tyler himself. He hoped to piece together a new party of states' rights Whigs and Democrats for the contest of 1844. Toward this end, he named John C. Calhoun Secretary of State.

But party loyalty was too strong among both Whigs and Democrats for Tyler's scheme to work. In effect, he served as a president without a party. The major political consequence of his presidency was the beginning of the

principle—that Congress should make the laws and the president execute them. He was, apparently, quite willing to defer to the party professionals, particularly Clay, in framing policy. With large Whig majorities in both houses of Congress, the Great Compromiser had every reason to believe that, if not president in name, he would direct the nation's affairs. Old Tip dutifully named four of Clay's lieutenants to the cabinet and set before Congress a positive program that had Clay's name written all over it.

But Harrison refused to defer to Clay or to Daniel Webster when it came to oratory. Harrison politely turned down the inaugural address Webster wrote for him, having prepared his own. It was the longest, dullest inaugural address on record, a turgid treatise on Roman history and its relevance to the United States of America circa March 1841. Not even historians could have enjoyed it because it was delivered outdoors on a frigid, windy day. Harrison himself caught a bad cold.

For weeks he suffered, half the time in bed, half the time receiving Whig officeseekers as greedy as the Democrats of 1828. Then, he took permanently to bed with pneumonia. On April 4, 1841, exactly one month after deterioration of the Whig party in the South. States' righters like Tyler and Calhoun drifted back toward the Democratic party. In time, the great planters would not only return to the party of Jackson, but they would take it over.

British-American Friction

The major accomplishment of the Tyler administration was in the area of foreign affairs: solving a series of potentially dangerous disputes with Great Britain, and paving the way for the annexation of the Republic of Texas.

The first was a Whiggish goal that was engineered by Daniel Webster. One of the problems was a boundary dispute between Maine and New Brunswick. According to the Treaty of 1783, the line ran between the watersheds of the Atlantic and the St. Lawrence River. Both sides had agreed to the boundary as shown by a red line that Benjamin Franklin had drawn on a map.

The map disappeared, however, and in 1838, Canadian lumberjacks began cutting timber in the Aroostook Valley, which the United States claimed. A brief "war" between the Maine and New Brunswick militias ended with no deaths, and Van Buren managed to cool things down. But he could not resolve the boundary dispute.

The Canadian-American line immediately west of Lake Superior was also in question, and two other points of friction developed over American assistance to Canadian rebels and over the illegal slave trade in which some Americans were involved. The slavery issue waxed hotter late in 1841, when a group of blacks on the American brig *Creole* mutinied, killed the crew, and sailed to Nassau in the British Bahamas. The British hanged the leaders of the mutiny but freed the other slaves, enraging sensitive Southerners.

The Webster–Ashburton Treaty

Neither England nor the United States wanted war, but old rancor and the British determination to build a road through the disputed Aroostook country repeatedly stalled a settlement. Fortuitously, Webster found a kindred spirit in the high-living British negotiator, Lord Ashburton, and over brandy and port wine they worked out a compromise. Webster made a big concession to the British, too much as far as many New Englanders were concerned. But never above a little chicanery, Webster actually forged Franklin's map to show a "red line" that gave Maine less territory than he had negotiated, and he warned that the United States had better take what it could get. (The real map surfaced some years later, and showed that the United States was shorted.)

Ashburton was generous, too. He ceded a strip of territory in northern New York and Vermont to which the United States had no claim, and also about 6,500 square miles at the tip of Lake Superior. While wilderness at the time, the area around Lake Superior later became known as the Mesabi Range, one of the world's richest iron-ore deposits.

When the Senate ratified the Webster–Ashburton Treaty in 1842, every outstanding issue between the United States and Britain was settled, except the two nations' joint occupation of Oregon on the Pacific coast. Webster had good reason to be pleased with himself, and he joined his fellow Whigs in leaving John Tyler's cabinet.

For Further Reading

Once again, see Glyndon G. Van Deusen, *The Jacksonian Era, 1828–1848* (1959) for an overview and John W. Ward, *Andrew Jackson: Symbol for an Age* (1955) to appreciate the political values that informed the 1820s and 1830s. The appropriate chapters of Richard Hofstadter, *The American Political Tradition and the Men Who Made It* (1948) are, since the book was published forty years ago, stimulating. Richard P. McCormick, *The Second American Party System Formation in the Jacksonian Era* (1966) is essential.

Martin Van Buren, if almost forgotten in popular culture, is the subject of three excellent recent biographical studies: D. B. Cole, *Martin Van Buren and the American Political System* (1984); John Niven, *Martin Van Buren:* *The Romantic Age of American Politics* (1983); and M. L. Wilson, *The Presidency of Martin Van Buren* (1984). For his hapless nemesis, see Margaret Coit's now classic *John C. Calhoun: American Portrait* (1950) and the more critical Richard N. Current, *John C. Calhoun* (1966).

Dealing with the Bank War are Bray Hammond, *Bank and Politics in America from the Revolution to the Civil War* (1957); Robert Remini, *Andrew Jackson and the Bank War* (1967); and John McFaul, *The Politics of Jacksonian Finance* (1972). Sympathetic to Biddle's position is Thomas P. Govan, *Nicholas Biddle: Nationalist and Public Banker* (1959).

D. W. Howe, *The Political Culture of the American Whigs* (1979) is a fine survey of a subject long neglected except in biographies. Among the best biographies of the Whigs are Glyndon Van Deusen, *The Life of Henry Clay* (1937); Clement Eaton, *Henry Clay and the Art of American Politics* (1957); Richard N. Current, *Daniel Webster and the Rise of National Conservatism* (1955); Sydney Nathan, *Daniel Webster and Jacksonian Democ-* racy (1973); M. G. Baxter, *One and Inseparable: Daniel Webster and the Union* (1984). On the election of 1840 and its aftermath, see R. G. Gunderson, *The Log Cabin Campaign* (1957) and O. D. Lambert, *Presidential Politics in the United States, 1841–1844* (1936).

Sidney Smith, an English clergyman and wit generally known for his compassion, exquisitely lacerated American culture in 1820:

> In the four quarters of the globe, who reads an American book? or goes to an American play? or looks at an American picture or statue? What does the world yet owe to American physicians or surgeons? What new substances have their chemists discovered? or what old ones have they analyzed? What new constellations have been discovered by the telescopes of Americans?—what have they done in the mathematics?

Few of Smith's readers would have disagreed, including those Americans who imported the *Edinburgh Review*, the magazine he founded. "I must study politics and war," John Adams had told his wife, Abigail, in 1780, "that my sons may have liberty to study mathematics and philosophy. . . commerce and agriculture, in order to give their children a right to study painting, poetry, music, architecture, statuary, tapestry, and porcelain." In the 1820s, Americans were still studying those disciplines concerned with the accumulation of wealth.

Then, especially after Andrew Jackson became president, American political practices, and the everyday lives of Americans pricked the interest of literate Europeans and soon became something of a mania.

AS OTHERS SAW US

Before 1828, about 40 books written about the United States were published in Europe. After 1828, when the election of Andrew Jackson seemed to roll in an era dominated by the common man, the drollery of such a notion enchanted educated Europeans. Hundreds of books about Americans were published in little more than a decade. Most of them were in English but a considerable number were in French and German, and the odd title in Spanish, Italian, Polish, and the Scandinavian languages. To sate the appetite of European readers (and their own curiosity), successful authors such as Frederick Marryat and Charles Dickens crossed the Atlantic to describe the scenery, wonder over the curiosities, explain the political institutions, and scrutinize the manners, morals, quirks, and crotchets of the American people. The best of these books were *Democracy in America* by a French aristocrat, Alexis de Tocqueville, and *Domestic Manners of the Americans* by an English gentlewoman, Frances Trollope.

Alexis de Tocqueville

In his first volume, published in 1835, Tocqueville explained the workings of American political institutions, emphasizing their democratic character. In the second volume, published in 1840, he commented on the social attitudes and customs of Americans.

Tocqueville found much to admire in the United States, and in Americans. Because he was a traditionalist, he was surprised to discover how well democratic government worked, and he admitted it. He had no trouble liking Americans as individuals. However, because Tocqueville believed that spiritual values, tradition, a sense of security, and continuity in human relationships were essential to a healthy society, he was concerned that Americans seemed always to be on the move. Tocqueville was disturbed by an undiscriminating love of the new and contempt for the old, and most of all the relentless pursuit of money in Jacksonian America. In one of his most disturbing passages, Tocqueville wrote that American individualism not only makes "every man forget his ancestors, but it hides his descendants, and separates his contemporaries from him; it throws him back forever upon himself alone, and threatens in the end to confine him entirely within the solitude of his own heart."

Frances Trollope

The subject of Mrs. Trollope's book, published in 1832, was "domestic manners," everyday life. With an eye as keen as an eagle's and a wit as sharp as its talons, she swooped through American parlors, dining rooms, kitchens, drawing rooms, cabins, steamboats, theaters, churches, and houses of business—and liked very little of what she found. Like Tocqueville, Mrs. Trollope was disturbed by the materialism, individualism, and instability of American society. On the former, she cited an Englishman who had lived in the United States for a long time who told her "that in following, in meeting, or in overtaking, in the street, on the road, or in the field, at the theatre, the coffee house, or at home, he had

MISS MARTINEAU

While Americans execrated Mrs. Trollope, they rather liked the book written about them by another English visitor, Harriet Martineau. Miss Martineau was disturbed by many of the things that had bothered Mrs. Trollope. But it was obvious from her *Society in America* (1837) that she personally liked Americans and thoroughly enjoyed her lightning-fast trips throughout the United States. While traveling through the country, the rather deaf Miss Martineau thrust a huge ear-horn into the faces of everyone she met and shouted questions at them.

This domestic scene is typical of what Mrs. Trollope might have seen during her visit to America.

never overheard Americans conversing without the word DOLLAR being pronounced between them."

Mrs. Trollope had a terrible time in Jacksonian America. She observed, and was far from alone in her observations, that Americans rushed through hastily prepared meals. They jogged rather than walked down the street. (Frederick Marryat wrote that a New York businessman "always walks as if he had a good dinner before him and a bailiff after him.") Americans fidgeted when detained by some obligation lest they miss something in another part of town. When they did bring themselves to sit down, they whittled wood—so unable were they to be still.

"The Very Houses Move"

More than one foreign observer remembered as a symbol of their American experience the spectacle of a team of sweating horses pulling a house on rollers from one site to another. Nothing, it seemed, was rooted in the United States, neither the homes nor the mighty oak trees that Westerners mowed down like hay, nor customs nor social relationships nor religious beliefs that had served humanity well for centuries.

Such instability was not without its casualties, and dollar worship was not without its native as well as foreign critics. Many people failed through no fault of their own in the first frantic decades of the nineteenth century. The topsy-turvy, boom-and-bust financial cycle turned rich men into debtors and threw workers out of jobs that barely kept their families fed.

In the older agricultural regions of the Eastern states, people who had once been secure on little farms found that they were flirting with destitution as foodstuffs cheaper than those they produced were transported from Western farms by new canals and, later, by railroads. They felt manipulated by bankers and cheated by businessmen. Townspeople became disoriented as canals and railroads integrated them into an impersonal national economy and exposed them daily to a more diverse world

HOW THEY LIVED

THE REPUBLIC OF PORKDOM

Today, a good many Americans would regard a tender corn-fed filet mignon as the *ne plus ultra* of fine eating. The ground-beef hamburger comes as close to being a national dish as is possible in a pluralistic society. Beef is unquestionably America's favorite meat; Americans consume almost two pounds of it to every pound of pork, including bacon and ham, that they eat.

Americans of the early nineteenth century prized beef too, but, while they ate quite as much meat per capita as we do, beef was far less common on their tables than pork. Indeed, according to a writer in *Godey's Lady's Book*—the combination *Ladies Home Journal*, *Ms.*, and *Vogue* of the era—put it,

The United States of America might properly be called the great Hog-eating Confederacy, or the Republic of Porkdom. [In the] South and West . . . it is fat bacon and pork, fat bacon and pork only, and that continually morning, noon, and night, for all classes, sexes, ages, and conditions; and except the boiled bacon and collards at dinner, the meat is generally fried, and thus supersaturated with grease in the form of hog's lard.

Even slaves on well-managed plantations were provided with half a pound of salt pork a day.

Beef was less common, first of all, because it was relatively much more expensive than it is today. Cattle had to be transported on the hoof, which meant that cities could be supplied only from the near hinterland. Farmers on comparatively expensive real estate in the older states could generally do better cultivating their land than leaving it in pasture. Only with the development of the Great Plains after the Civil War, did the price of beef decline. Even then, in 1900 Americans ate as much pork as beef.

Unlike cattle, hogs flourished on wasteland, multiplying their weight 150 times in eight months on nuts and roots in the woods, fallen orchard fruit unfit for consumption, harvested gardens and grainfields, and offal—garbage. They required next to no attention. Indeed, the "bony, snake-headed, hairy wild beasts," the American "razorback," needed no protection. (A farmer's fields and the farmer himself needed protection from them!)

Hogs were ideally suited to a nation where land was abundant and labor was scarce, and they thrived. As early as 1705, Robert Beverley wrote in his *History of Virginia* that "hogs swarm like Vermine upon the Earth, and are often accounted such . . . When an Inventory of any considerable Man's Estate is taken, the Hogs are left out." In the southern states in 1850, there were two hogs for each human being.

Hogs had another recommendation over steers. They could be slaughtered where they were raised and cheaply preserved, butchered, and packed in salty brine in barrels to keep for a year or to be shipped to urban markets. Salt deposits were very important to early western pioneers because of the necessity of preserving pork. Cities on the Ohio and Mississippi rivers, such as Cincinnati and St. Louis, owed much of their growth to their role as meatpackers. Poor people owed their survival to salt pork. "I hold a family to be in a desperate way," a character in a James Fenimore Cooper novel put it, "when the mother can see the bottom of the pork barrel."

Scraping the bottom of the barrel is not the only catch phrase that survives in the language from the days of the Republic of Porkdom. We still use the term *pork barrel bill* to describe those congressional enactments, usually rushed through at the end of a session, that spend federal money in just about every district in which incumbents from the majority party are up for election—a highway improvement here, an agricultural station there, a defense installation somewhere else. The phrase conveys an image once familiar to every American—the none too pleasant appearance of chunks of pork bobbing about in a barrel of brine.

---

than that their parents had been confronted with in a lifetime: strangers passing through, some of them to pluck the locals as they went; immigrants from abroad coming to dig the ditches, gravel the roadbeds, and work in the new factories; promoters urging their children to strike for the West, where they would prosper.

Westerners, of course, were displaced by definition. They were freed from old restraints, moral as well as economic, but also deprived of the comforts of family connections, tightly knit insular communities, and institutions that were not as mobile as individuals. Small wonder, then, that in addition to being a time of extraordinary economic growth, the age of Jackson was an era when people groped for explanations of change and

attempted, in their spiritual lives, to come to terms with it.

RELIGION IN THE EARLY NINETEENTH CENTURY

During the last two decades of the eighteenth century, organized religion had declined both in the numbers of church members and in influence. The Anglican Church had suffered because it was so closely tied to England; there was not even an Anglican bishop in the colonies. The Congregationalists had supported the war for independence, but, in the 1790s, they had bitterly opposed Thomas Jefferson. When he triumphed in 1800 and blood did not run in the gutters of Hartford and Portsmouth—as many ministers had predicted—Congregationalism lost its hold on many New Englanders.

The educated middle and upper classes abandoned old-time Calvinism because its overriding doctrine of predestination no longer accorded with the abundant, benign world they saw around them. Oliver Wendell Holmes wrote a light-spirited poem about one-doctrine religion called "The Deacon's Masterpiece":

> Have you heard of the wonderful
>   one-hoss shay,
> That was built in such a logical way
> It ran a hundred years to a day?

And then suddenly collapsed.

In the same years that the Jacksonians came to power, Massachusetts and Connecticut, the last states to pay ministers out of tax monies, ceased to do so. It was a sharp break with the Puritan past.

The Second Great Awakening

If the old churches suffered, old-time religion did not disappear so much as it changed form, adapting to the democratic spirit of the new era. In the Second Great Awakening, as in the First of the mid-eighteenth century, eloquent preachers such as Charles Grandison Finney crisscrossed New England and New York with the message that human nature was tainted, just as the Puritans had preached. Unlike the Puritans, however, Finney and others said that not just a few "Elect" were saved through God's grace; everyone who repented and prayed for deliverance from their sinful natures would be blessed. Religion was voluntary. Salvation depended not on God's will, but on every individual's decision. "Don't wait," Finney said, "Do it!" Such an admonition could not have dropped from a Puritan's lips.

Revivalism

The "revival" of religion, which dated from the turn of the century, became a fixture of Jacksonian life. The well-turned revivalist sermon began with an emotional description of the capacity of human beings for evil, of which sensible people have never needed proof. The second part of the sermon detailed the gruesome sufferings of hell, for which all sinners were destined. Again, it was not a difficult message to put across to poor people who suffered hellishly enough in the physical world. Like good politicians, however, the revivalists concluded on a note of hope. Any person, in this "equal opportunity" religion, could be saved if he or she repented and declared faith in Jesus Christ.

While the revivalism of the Second Great Awakening spread to some extent through every state, and people of every social class were converted, revival fires burned hottest in rural New England and in New York—long-settled regions that seemed to be left behind by the nineteenth century—and on the frontier, where life was also hard and uncertain.

Tenting on the Old Camp Ground

Because few frontier settlements had buildings that were large enough to hold a crowd, the early Western revivalists held their meetings in openings in the forest, which sometimes were cleared especially for the purpose. Beginning at Cane Ridge and Gasper River, Kentucky at the turn of the century, people who lived isolated, lonely lives responded to calls to come—tenting by the thousands—more than 20,000 in one instance. Camp meetings attracted would-be converts (and plenty of scoffers) from as far away as 200 miles.

Such a concentration of humanity was itself exhilarating on the sparsely populated frontier. But there was something else. The atmosphere of the camp meeting was electrifying. As many as 40 preachers simultaneously harangued the crowd. Some spoke from well-constructed platforms; others, from atop stumps. The meeting went on day and night for a week or more. When the day's final pleas tailed off in the early morning hours, the moans of excited people could be heard from every direction as the thousands fell asleep in tents or under their wagons.

Conversions were passionate. People fell to their hands and knees, weeping uncontrollably. Others

---

UNITARIANS

Unitarianism originated in 1785 when a Boston church struck from its services all references to the Trinity because the notion seemed idolatrous as well as superstitious. The denomination spread rapidly throughout New England as the church of enlightened, generally well-to-do people. (A working-class equivalent of Unitarianism was Universalism.)

The Unitarian God was tailored to fit the worldly optimism of a comfortable people. He was not a distributor of justice and retribution but a kindly, well-wishing father. In the words of William Ellery Channing, the most famous early-nineteenth-century Unitarian preacher, God had "a father's concern for his creatures, a father's desire for their improvement, a father's equity in proportioning his commands to their powers, a father's joy in their progress, a father's readiness to receive the penitent, and a father's justice for the incorrigible." He was not the God of John Winthrop and Jonathan Edwards.

scampered around on all fours, barking like dogs. A common manifestation was the "jerks." Caught up in the mass hysteria, people lurched about, their limbs jerking quite beyond their control. Rumors spread that a man who cursed God had been seized by the jerks and broke his neck.

Small wonder that European tourists listed the camp meeting as one of the two peculiarly American sights that they "just must see." (The other was the slave auction.) Indeed, many Americans went just for the show and the chance to exploit the occasion with thieving, heckling preachers, heavy drinking, and sexual philandering.

Circuit Riders

The excesses of the camp meeting led inevitably to a reaction against them by sincere believers. Even the Methodists, who were among the earliest organizers of frontier revivals, drew back from what often seemed like carnivals. In place of the periodic camp meeting, they offered the circuit rider, a minister who was assigned to visit ten or twenty little Western settlements that were too poor to support a resident parson. Intensely devoted, poorly paid, and usually unmarried, the circuit riders rode through slashes in the woods in all weather. They preached, performed marriages and baptisms, took their rest and meals in the cabins of the faithful, and rode on. The most famous, Finis Ewing and Peter Cartwright, were rarely off their horses for more than three days at a time over more than three decades.

Other denominations imitated the Methodists because, when towns grew to more than a dozen or so cabins, individualistic Americans were rarely able to agree on one denomination to serve the whole community. A town of a thousand might support half a dozen churches: Methodist (or Free Methodist, for the denominations divided and multiplied freely); Baptist (or Primitive Baptist or Free Will Baptist); Presbyterian; Disciples of Christ; and so on.

Nor were all the denominations offshoots of the older churches. New religions sprouted and bloomed like sunflowers in Jacksonian America. Most of them withered and died with the first frost, but others have survived to this day. The two most durable homegrown American religions of the period originated in a part of rural New York State that was called "the burned-over district," because fiery revivals flared up there so often.

The Adventist Episode

Sometime before 1831, a Baptist named William Miller calculated that Christ's Second Coming to earth—the end of the world—would occur between March 21, 1843, and March 21, 1844. He began to preach his message throughout the Northeastern states and most listeners hooted him. But Miller convinced tens of thousands with the complex mathematical formula by which he had come to his unnerving conclusion.

Along with an energetic disciple, Joshua V. Himes of Boston, Miller published a newspaper and regularly preached two or even three long sermons a day. At the beginning of the fateful year, a magnificent comet appeared in the sky for a month, and converts flocked to join Miller's Adventists. (*Advent* means "coming" or "arrival.") Many sold their possessions and contributed the proceeds to the sect, which led critics to accuse Miller and Himes of conscious fraud.

On March 21, 1844, in order to be first to greet the Lord, several thousand people throughout New York and New England climbed hills in their "Ascension Robes" (sold by Himes). When Christ did not arrive, Miller discovered an error in his computations and set the date of the Second Coming at no later than October 22, 1844. Again some towns frothed with hysteria as the day approached, and an even greater disappointment descended upon them when Christ still did not appear. Miller himself was bewildered and broken-hearted. He returned to his home in upstate New York, where he died in 1849.

A disciple named Hiram Edson eventually reorganized some of the Millerites around the vaguer belief that Christ would return *soon*. Because Edson observed the Jewish sabbath, Saturday, rather than Sunday as a day of worship, this remnant of the Millerite excitement became known as Seventh-Day Adventists.

The Mormons

The Church of Jesus Christ of the Latter-Day Saints, or Mormons, another distinctively American religion, also originated in the burned-over district. The founder of the church was Joseph Smith, a boy from a farm family suffering from the decline of Eastern agricultural regions. Smith had a reputation for being a solitary daydreamer who preferred wandering the rolling hills of the region to the tedious chores of farm life. At the age of 17 he was "visited" by an angel. When he was 20, he told his family and some neighbors that an angel, Moroni, had shown him where some mysterious gold plates were buried. Somewhat later, Moroni provided Smith with spectacles called Urim and Thummim, which enabled him to read the strange inscriptions on the plates.

The story he translated was *The Book of Mormon*, a Bible of the New World that told of descendants of the Hebrews in America, the Nephites, and the history of their wars with the Lamanites, or Indians. Christ had founded Christianity among the Nephites, as he had done among the Jews in Palestine. Then in 384 A.D., the Lamanites wiped out the Nephites. However, their story survived in the book Smith published in 1830.

Tales similar to Smith's had long circulated in the folklore of the burned-over district. To many Americans, told from childhood that their country was a new Eden, there was nothing preposterous in the idea that Christ should have visited the New World as well as the traditional Holy Land. To those who were unsettled by the frenzied pace of the age of Jackson, it was not surprising that God should make his truth known in upstate New York in 1830. It was a time, as one of Smith's early converts, Orson Pratt, wrote, when "wickedness keeps pace with the hurried revolutions of the age." Poet John Greenleaf Whittier, who was not a Mormon, wrote of the Saints that "they speak a language of hope and promise to weak, heavy hearts, tossed and troubled, who have wandered from sect to sect, seeking in vain for the primal manifestation of divine power."

Persecution

Smith offered a way out of the era, but he was also his era's child. He extended the priesthood of his new religion to all white males, thus appealing to the Jacksonian yearning for equality, and he tapped the mystique of the West by taking his congregation first to Ohio, then to Missouri, and finally, in 1840, to Nauvoo, Illinois, where the Mormons prospered. By 1844, Nauvoo was the largest city in the state.

Their extraordinary prosperity as a group, and the Mormons' undisguised dislike of outsiders, whom they called Gentiles, begat envy and resentment, the same sort of dislike of secret, closed societies that had produced the Anti-Masonic movement. Nevertheless, because the Mormons of Nauvoo voted as a bloc, they were courted by both Whig and Democratic parties. Joseph Smith could undoubtedly have been elected to high office in Illinois by trading Mormon votes for a major party endorsement.

Instead, in 1844, he spurned both Whigs and Democrats and declared that he would be an independent candidate for the presidency. This news, added to fears of the well-armed Mormon militia of 2,000, the Nauvoo Legion, which Smith commanded, led to his arrest. On June 27, with the complicity of officials, he and his brother were murdered in the jail at Carthage, Illinois.

Safe in the Desert

Without their extraordinary leader, the Mormons might well have foundered, had not an even more remarkable (and politically shrewder) individual grappled his way to the top of the highly structured church hierarchy. Brigham Young, a Vermonter like Smith, also received revelations directly from God. The most important of these was the command that the Latter-Day Saints move beyond the boundaries of the sinful country that oppressed them.

Young organized the great westerly migration of the Mormons down to the last detail. Advance parties planted crops that would be ready for harvesting when the thousands arrived on the trail. For his Zion, Young chose the most isolated and inhospitable region known to explorers, the basin of the Great Salt Lake.

"This is the place," he said, looking down from the Wasatch Mountains, and there the Mormons laid out a tidy city with broad avenues and irrigation ditches that were fed with water from the surrounding peaks. The desert bloomed. Within a few years, more than 10,000 people lived in the Salt Lake basin.

In one respect, Young was frustrated. At the same time that the Mormons were constructing their Zion, American victory in a war with Mexico brought them back under the American flag. Young did not fight the troops who arrived to raise the flag, but he made it clear that real federal control of Utah, which the Mormons called Deseret, depended on cooperating with him. Prudently, the authorities gave in and named Young territorial governor.

Despite its large population, Utah was not admitted to the Union until 1896. The Mormons practiced polygamy, which fascinated Europeans like the adventurer, Sir Richard Burton, as camp meetings and slave auctions had done. Young himself had 27 wives and 56 children. Congress refused to grant statehood until Young's successor received a revelation that polygamy was to be abandoned.

UTOPIAN COMMUNITIES

Unlike members of traditional churches, Mormons lived in highly regulated communities in which individual rights and an individual's freedom to accumulate private riches were subordinated to the good of one another; indeed, the early Mormons practiced a form of communism. Such experiments held great appeal to people who were distressed by the poverty and moral misery that were, along with material progress, the fruits of a wide-open competitive economy. Some of the communities, like the Mormon Zion, had a religious foundation. Others were based on secular social theories.

Rappites and Shakers

The Rappites were an import, 600 German followers of George Rapp who came to the United States in 1803 and founded communities at Harmony, Pennsylvania;

Salt Lake City, the Jerusalem of the Mormons, as it appeared in the 1860s, only a few years after Brigham Young founded the settlement on barren desert land.

New Harmony, Indiana; and Economy, Pennsylvania. The members of the sect held property in common and practiced celibacy. Because, like the Millerites, the Rappites believed that Christ would return to earth at any time, they saw no need to perpetuate the human race.

The Rappites died out quickly because of their celibacy and because they discouraged non-Germans from joining their communities. A group with similar beliefs, the Shakers, had a longer history, since they courted converts and adopted children out of orphanages.

The Shakers were founded and brought to the United States in 1774 by an English woman, Mother Ann Lee, who had had a vision of Adam and Eve in intercourse. Deducing that sexual intercourse was the original sin of

the Bible, she forbade all such congress among her followers. Lee also taught that God had a female as well as a male nature—"Holy Mother Wisdom"—and insisted on the equality of the sexes. By 1810, there were 11 Shaker communities in the United States, mostly in the Northeast; by 1845, there were 18, with a combined population of 4,000.

The Shakers practiced celibacy. Men and women lived in different parts of their towns. Property was communal, and people who joined the Shakers turned over what they owned to the whole. However, there were no hints of fraud such as haunted Miller and Himes.

The Shakers were not persecuted and ridicule of them was rarely malicious. Celibacy was considered peculiar, but it did not offend conventional morality, as did "free love" and Mormon polygamy. Indeed, as a group that needed converts in order to survive, the Shakers were unfailingly polite, cooperative, and fair in their dealings with outsiders. They lived very simply, exciting no resentment of their prosperity. In fact, the Shaker communities were popular tourist attractions because of the fine workmanship and elegant simplicity of their crafts, which they sold in order to support themselves, as well as their neatness. "There is no dirt in heaven," Mother Lee had written, binding her followers to the most fastidious of housekeeping habits.

Setting an Example: The Utopians

The religious communities had two purposes in withdrawing from society: to live in what they believed was

---

WHOLE LOT OF SHAKIN' GOIN' ON

The true name of the Shakers was the United Society of Believers in Christ's Second Appearing. But outsiders began calling them "Shakers" because, among their other practices, they performed rhythmic dances (in groups, not men with women). They accepted this name despite its probably having been attached to them with derision. A century earlier, the Society of Friends had become known as Quakers in much the same way. Deriders had made fun of the admonition of the founder of the movement to "quake" on hearing the word of God.

Shakers gathered to perform the rhythmic dances that were part of their religion. People were tolerant of them perhaps because, unlike many other utopians of the early nineteenth century, the Shakers practiced celibacy.

the godly way in order to save their own souls, and to set an example that others might follow. Other utopians, although not necessarily irreligious, were primarily interested in the social aspect of their communities. They had theories about what was wrong with the larger society (which almost always included its material preoccupations and commitment to private property) and sought to show the world, by the contentment of their alternative way of life, how the whole society should be organized.

The most famous of these utopian communities was also one of the first to come to grief. New Harmony, Indiana, was purchased from the Rappites in 1825 by Robert Owen, a British industrialist who, in an age of "dark, satanic mills," had created a model of paternalism at his textile mill in New Lanark, Scotland. About a thousand people responded to Owen's call to build a community at New Harmony in which all property was to be held in common, and life was to consist not of drudgery for the enrichment of others but of joyous work for the good of all.

Unfortunately, the idealists at New Harmony were joined by many people who were interested only in the weekly philosophic discussions and, in the meantime, an easy life financed by Owen's fortune. Believing deeply in the goodness of human nature, Owen was incapable of throwing out freeloaders. In 1827, disillusioned and a good deal poorer, he returned to Scotland. Within a short time, denied income from the society they had rejected, New Harmony broke up, and the old Rappite

fields, orchards, and vineyards went to seed and weeds.

The Icarians, who followed the teachings of the Frenchman Etienne Cabet, also believed in the common ownership of property. In 1848, they established communities in Texas, and, in 1849, on the site of the abandoned Mormon settlement at Nauvoo, Illinois. One faction of the movement survived until 1895. Another Frenchman, Charles Fourier, founded a larger utopian movement that established more than 20 "phalanxes," or cooperative associations, throughout the North and Midwest. Most of them lasted only a few months; again, bickering and laziness undid the idealists.

Fruitlands

A similarly doomed colony was Fruitlands, the project of Bronson Alcott, a magnificent eccentric who is best remembered as the father of the author Louisa May Alcott. A lovable daydreamer, the friend of most of the important writers and thinkers of the period, Alcott was totally incapable of coping with the facts of workaday life. He inaugurated his communal lesson to the world by planting several fruit trees—about a foot or two from the front door of the community house, dropping the shovel when he was done, and returning to his meditations and endless colloquies with the extraordinary collection of crackpots and loons who gathered at Fruitlands.

One, whose name was Abram Wood, announced his defiance of corrupt worldly ways by deciding that his name was really Wood Abram. Another would not weed the garden because he insisted that weeds had as much right to grow as did vegetables. Samuel Larned lived for one year on nothing but crackers (so he said) and the next on apples. A woman who could no longer stand the vegetarian diet and ate a piece of meat at a neighboring farm was banished as if she were a murderess. Another Fruitlander said that the way to break loose from empty social conventions was to greet people, "Good morning, God damn you!" Everyone at Fruitlands agreed that cows were disgusting, but that central vision was not enough to sustain the vitality of the community.

Through it all, Mrs. Alcott kept things afloat by doing most of the work. It is not clear if this sturdy, stoical, and resourceful woman ever took seriously a word her husband said.

Oneida: A Success Story

Most of the American utopias were founded on the belief that private property was the source of injustice and human unhappiness. In this, they were rebelling against the most conspicuous phenomenon of the period—the helter-skelter competition for riches. In addition to private property, John Humphrey Noyes attacked the institution of marriage. Wedlock, he said, was itself a form of property: under American laws and customs, the husband effectively owned his wife, and, therefore, both were miserable.

Instead of preaching celibacy as an alternative, Noyes devised the concept of "complex marriage." In the community he founded at Oneida, New York, in 1847, every man was married to every woman. Couples who chose to have sexual relations for pleasure (the initiative was the lady's) could do so, but not for the purpose of procreation. Noyes was an early exponent of what came to be called eugenics, improving the quality of the human race (and therefore society) by allowing only those who were superior in health, constitution, and intellect to have children. (His method of birth control was male continence.)

Oneida's practice of "free love," like the Mormons' polygamy, enraged the community's neighbors, and Noyes had to flee to Canada to escape arrest. Oneida, however, enjoyed a long life. The community prospered from its manufacture of silverware, silks, and a superior trap for fur-bearing animals. Finally abandoning com-

Members of the Oneida community founded by John Humphrey Noyes believed that every man was married to every woman, a concept they called "complex marriage." They abandoned the concept in 1879.

plex marriage in 1879 and communal property in 1881, the surviving Oneidans reorganized as a corporation.

TRANSCENDENTALISM

Philosophically, Noyes is called a Perfectionist. He believed that Christ's redemption of humanity was complete. Individuals had it within themselves to be perfect—that is, without sin—and therefore above rules that had been written for the imperfect. People only had to face up to their own perfection, and it would be so. Those who did not, those who said no one could be perfect this side of heaven, were compromising with sin when no compromise was necessary.

Perfectionism was not so very far out of step with the popular spirit of the Jacksonian era. It was a time when, figuratively speaking, Americans believed that everything was within human competence. Noyes's error was to take the implications of his philosophy literally. When he put sinlessness into practice at Oneida by approving behavior that offended more conventional Americans, he suffered their censure.

Ralph Waldo Emerson, by way of contrast, became American's favorite philosopher by calling Perfectionism by another name—transcendentalism—and by avoiding its implications in the way he led his life.

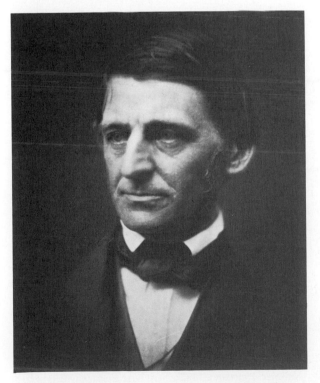

Ralph Waldo Emerson was America's popular philosopher.

The Sage of Concord

Emerson was the Unitarian pastor of the same church in Boston where Cotton Mather had preached gloom and doom a century earlier. Emerson's own view of human nature glowed with warmth and love, but, despite his comfortable congregation's approval, he found the pulpit constraining. In 1832, he announced that he could no longer accept the Unitarian practice of celebrating the Lord's Supper. He resigned and moved to Concord, Massachusetts, then well outside Boston.

"The profession is antiquated," Emerson said of preaching. But within a few years, he was preaching again, albeit from a lectern rather than a pulpit. He shook his head sagely that people should cling to superstition, yet his own message was a welter of notions far more mystical than the Christianity of Boston.

Emerson's philosophy of transcendentalism explicitly defied criticism that it was vague or contradictory. Based on feelings rather than reason, transcendentalism exalted a vague concept of nature over civilization, personal morality over laws, and the individual's capacity within himself to be happy, or sinless. When his ideas were criticized as fuzzy or contradictory, Emerson responded that the critic was not morally capable of understanding that "consistency is the hobgoblin of little minds" and that the truly enlightened human being could dispose "very easily of the most disagreeable facts."

The word *transcend* means "to go beyond, to rise above." As used by Emerson and his disciples, it meant to go above reason and beyond the material world. God was not a being, but a force. God was the "oversoul," which was within all men and women because it was in nature. "Standing on the bare ground," Emerson wrote, "my head bathed by the blithe air and uplifted into infinite space—all mean egotism vanishes. I become a transparent eyeball; I am nothing; I see all; the currents of the Universal being circulate through me."

The writer Herman Melville, a contemporary of Emerson, called this sort of thing "gibberish." But while Melville struggled to eke out a living with his writing, Emerson was lionized as the greatest mind of his time. While Melville scrutinized the problem of evil in the world, Emerson ignored it as among other disagreeable phenomena. His buoyant, bubbly optimism was brilliantly tailored to his era. Today he would host a television talk show on PBS or sing "soft rock" at the White House.

Other Transcendentalists

Emerson's close friend Henry David Thoreau was the introspective son of a Concord pencil manufacturer. Unlike the publically proper Emerson, Thoreau flaunted his eccentricity. In 1845, he constructed a small cabin in a wood Emerson owned near Walden pond, just outside Concord. There he wrote *A Week on the Concord and Merrimack Rivers* (published in 1849) and *Walden* (1854), an account of his reflections while sitting by the pond.

Although *Walden* is the masterpiece of transcendentalism, it is marred by the same half-baked dilettantism that robs Emerson's works of lasting value. Thoreau wrote as though he had seceded from civilization and struck off into the wilderness:

> I wanted to live deep and suck out all the marrow of life, to live so sturdily and Spartan, like as to put to rout all that was not life, to cut a broad swath and shave close, to drive life into a corner, and reduce it to its lowest terms.

But Walden was no Rocky Mountain fastness. It was a short walk to Concord, a walk that Thoreau took often when he felt like a decent meal or needed nails to patch up his cabin. Living deep and sucking the marrow out of life was rather like camping in the backyard. There was a sense of having things both ways—the mystical perception of being above the tawdry materialism of the United States, while enjoying its benefits—about much of what the transcendentalists did.

Bronson Alcott was a frequent visitor to the Emerson home. So were the Unitarian ministers William Ellery Channing and George Ripley. (In 1841, Ripley founded a transcendentalist utopia, Brook Farm, at West Roxbury, Massachusetts.) Other visitors included authors James Russell Lowell, Nathaniel Hawthorne, and Margaret Fuller, a prolific writer who was the first literary critic for the *New York Tribune*.

Dissenters

Hawthorne and Fuller were never fully sympathetic with the transcendentalist euphoria. Both were romantics, like Emerson and his circle. But when Hawthorne looked into the human heart, he found evil rather than the divinity perceived by Emerson's transparent eyeball; and Fuller was impatient with the transcendentalists's contentment to issue broad political pronouncements instead of cutting a broad swath and shaving close in real political action.

"The heart, the heart," Hawthorne wrote, "there was the little yet boundless sphere wherein existed the original wrong of which the crime and misery of the outward world were merely types." He made guilt, sin, and moral decay the themes of *Twice-Told Tales* (1837), the classic *The Scarlet Letter* (1850), and *The House of the Seven Gables* (1851). In *The Blithedale Romance* (1852), Hawthorne roundly satirized the transcendentalist utopian community at Brook Farm.

Just as he disagreed with the transcendentalists's belief in human perfectability, Hawthorne disagreed with their

Nathaniel Hawthorne, unlike most New England writers of his era, looked pessimistically on human nature.

Political activist Margaret Fuller published a scathing indictment of the arguments against female equality in 1845, three years before the emergence of an organized feminist movement in America.

politics. Whereas virtually all his New England literary friends were Whigs, Hawthorne was a Democrat. It may have been an affiliation of convenience. Except for Emerson, few Americans were able to live by writing. When Hawthorne's college crony Franklin Pierce, a Democrat, became president in 1853, he named Hawthorne American consul in England.

Margaret Fuller lived and died a romantic's life. She married an Italian aristocrat in 1847, participated in the rebellion of Giuseppe Garibaldi, and died in a shipwreck while returning to the United States. She was capable of the fullest-blown transcendental crowing: "I myself am more divine than any I see," she wrote to Emerson in 1838. But she was also a hard-headed thinker and a political activist, a radical where Hawthorne was a conservative. In 1845, fully three years before the emergence of feminism as a social and political movement, Fuller published *Woman in the Nineteenth Century*, a scathing rejoinder to the arguments against female equality.

Fuller died too soon to participate in the organized feminist movement or in the even greater reform movement of the nineteenth century, the fight against slavery. But she was, in her writings, a bridge between the reflective thought of her age and its busy devotion to practical social action.

For Further Reading

For background and context, see Perry Miller, *The Life of the Mind in America from the Revolution to the Civil War* (1966); I. H. Bartlett, *The American Mind in the Mid-Nineteenth Century* (1967); Russell B. Nye, *Society and Culture in America, 1830–1860* (1974); and Lewis Perry, *Intellectual Life in America* (1984). S. E. Ahlstrom, *A Religious History of the American People* (1972) and Martin E. Marty, *Righteous Empire: The Protestant Experience in America* (1970) and the same author's more recent *Pilgrims in Their Own Land: 500 Years of Religion in America* (1984) are also valuable.

An old but perennially delightful book with a somewhat jaundiced view of American enthusiasms, particularly revivalism, during this era is Gilbert Seldes, *The Stammering Century* (1928). Also on revivalism, see Bernard R. Weisberger, *They Gathered at the River* (1958) and C. A. Johnson, *The Frontier Camp Meeting* (1955). Other titles dealing with religious and utopian sects in the nineteenth century include: Leonard J. Arrington, *Great Basin Kingdom* (1958); A. E. Bestor, *Backwoods Utopias* (1950); Fawn M. Brodie, *No Man Knows My History: The Life of Joseph Smith* (1945); Martin Cardin, *Oneida* (1969); Whitney R. Cross, *The Burned-Over Dis-*

trict (1950); Henri Desroche, *The American Shakers: From Neo-Christianity to Neo-Socialism* (1971); Klaus J. Hansen, *Mormonism and the American Experience* (1981); and Robert O. Thomas, *The Man Who Would Be Perfect* (1977).

For leading cultural figures of the era, see Perry Miller, ed., *The Transcendentalists* (1950), a collection of their writings, Paul F. Boller, *American Transcendentalism, 1830–1860* (1974) and the following biographical studies: Gay Wilson Allen, *Waldo Emerson: A Biography* (1981); Paul Blanchard, *Margaret Fuller: From Transcendentalism to Revolution* (1978); David P. Edgel, *William Ellery Channing: An Intellectual Portrait* (1955); Walter Harding, *Thoreau: Man of Concord* (1960); John McAleer, *Ralph Waldo Emerson: Days of Encounter* (1984); and Joel Porte, *Representative Man: Ralph Waldo Emerson in His Time* (1979).

Alexis de Tocqueville, *Democracy in America*, particularly the second volume, is available in several editions, including abridgements, and is essential to every student of American history. See also Frances Trollope, *Domestic Manners of the Americans*.

An illustration from a membership certificate for the New York City Tract Society, a group organized to disseminate religious literature.

HEYDAY OF REFORM
FIGHTING EVIL, BATTLING SOCIAL PROBLEMS

The Mormons accepted authoritarian leaders and tried to flee the United States because, in part,

they were bewildered and demoralized by the rampant democracy and divisive individualism and

competitiveness of Jacksonian America. The utopians tried to secede from American society

because they found its materialism to be deadening and corrupt. In their bizarre way, the Mille-

rites on the hills, eyes cast yearningly toward the heavens, wanted out of society. Even the

transcendentalists, who kept one hand free to dip into the American cornucopia, strived to be spiritually apart from the material obsessions of the multitude.

For all its progress and achievement, Jacksonian America was a place of imperfection and social tension. For a person inclined to see the casualties, it was obvious that they were as numerous as the successes in the land of opportunity.

THE PRACTICAL REFORMERS

A small but conspicuous number of Americans, mostly Northerners, mostly from the same comparatively privileged social class that produced transcendentalism, were moved by evangelical religious fervor to believe that, as every soul could be saved, so could society be perfected. Rather than withdrawing from materialistic, competitive America, they labored within the belly of the beast to put at least some things right. Indeed, these reformers believed it was their moral duty as Christians to bear witness against evils, social as well as personal. They also believed it the moral obligation of the community—the United States—to remedy wrongs.

Many of the evangelical reformers were practical people, even "specialists." While far from immune to panaceas and quacks with cosmic visions, such practical reformers concentrated their energies on specific social evils.

Thomas Gallaudet and the Deaf

Such was Thomas Gallaudet, an Episcopal clergyman who was pained by the unique handicap of the deaf, and society's indifference toward people without hearing. Traditionally, Americans (and other Western peoples) regarded deafness, blindness, and other physical impairments as, variously, punishment for sin, trials designed by God for the purpose of sanctification, or simply, an unhappy circumstance visited on some by the roll of life's dice. Whichever the case, physical handicaps were personal misfortunes under which the sufferer was to bear up, cared for by family or community. The individual who strived to overcome a handicap was of interest and edifying, but the handicap itself was personal, not society's concern.

Gallaudet, a good evangelical, believed that the Christian was his brother's keeper, and the isolation of the deaf, particularly those who were deaf from birth, fascinated him. He was confounded when he attempted to communicate with the deaf and, in 1815, hearing of techniques of teaching lip-reading and sign language developed in England, he crossed the Atlantic to study

REFORMERS AND PERFECTIONISM

John Humphrey Noyes tried to make the connection between Perfectionism and the reform movements of the day explicit when he wrote: "As the doctrine of temperance is total abstinence from alcoholic drinks, and the doctrine of antislavery is immediate abolition of human bondage, so the doctine of perfectionism is the immediate and total cessation from sin." However, very few of the reformers supported him because they either failed to see the connection or feared what might happen to their movements if they associated their ideals with the unpopular apostle of "free love."

them. There, he was disgusted to learn that the methods were considered trade secrets, an article of commerce to be guarded as closely as a textile manufacturer guarded the plans for carding machines. To Gallaudet, the tools by which good might be done for others were not commodities to be bought and sold.

In France, fortunately, he found a teacher of the deaf whose views on helping the afflicted accorded with his own. The two men returned to the United States and, in 1817, founded the American Asylum, a free school for the deaf in Hartford, Connecticut. True to his ideals, Gallaudet taught his methods to every interested party and encouraged others to establish institutions like the American Asylum in other cities.

Samuel Gridley Howe and Laura Bridgman

Samuel Gridley Howe was a physician who, after fighting in the Greek war for independence from the Turks, returned to Boston with a comrade-in-arms who shared his interest in educating the blind. Howe organized the Perkins Institute for the Blind in Boston. Not only did he publicize his techniques, but, being a bit of a showman, Howe toured the country with a young girl named Laura Bridgman who was both deaf and blind. Howe had established communication with her, laying to rest the widespread assumption that even such seriously handicapped people were mentally deficient and forever helpless. Even overwhelming impediments to human fulfillment, Howe said, could be overcome if men and women were willing to make an effort to aid the afflicted.

Dorothea Dix

The plight of the mentally deficient and the insane aroused less sympathy than that of the physically handicapped. Traditionally, the retarded and harmless idiots had been cared for by their families and communities, allowed to wander, given petty chores of which they were capable, and otherwise ignored or mocked. Dangerous lunatics were locked up at home or by the legal authorities.

The line between violent insanity and criminality was blurred. Many a lunatic was hanged for his actions; others were recognized as having no moral responsibility but, nonetheless, confined in prisons or "hospitals," like London's famous Bedlam, where treatment consisted of little more than restraint. In Bedlam, and several American asylums (the word means "refuge"), it was not uncommon for guards to charge admission to visitors and goad the inmates into performing antics.

In 1841, Dorothea Lynde Dix, a teacher at a school for wealthy girls in Massachusetts, discovered that in the Cambridge House of Correction insane people were locked in an unheated room, even in the depths of the Massachusetts winter. Thirty-nine years of age, Dix had lived a genteel, quite sheltered life. She was pious and shy and often ill. But her traumatic discovery of the evils in the treatment of the insane galvanized her. She became one of the most effective reformers of the century.

Single-handedly at first, she investigated conditions at other Massachusetts institutions, including the state asylum at Worcester, and, in 1843, she drafted a memorial on the subject that was presented to the state legislature. The once quiet schoolteacher ringingly denounced the inhumanity of the state. Harmless, sweet-natured imbeciles were confined with dangerous maniacs in "cages, closets, cellars, stalls, pens!" They were fed slops and "chained, naked, beaten with rods, and lashed into obedience!"

Dix's ugly revelations did not square with New Englanders' proud image of themselves as the nation's most enlightened people. ("O New England," Noah Webster wrote, "how superior are thy inhabitants in morals, literature, civility, and industry!") Hearing Dix, the Massachusetts legislature immediately passed a bill to enlarge the state asylum and improve conditions elsewhere. Dix then set out to carry her message throughout the nation and the world. She persuaded Congress to establish St. Elizabeth's Hospital for the Insane and fifteen states to build humane asylums. She traveled to Europe, where she moved both Queen Victoria and the pope to improve treatment of the mentally deficient.

Crime and Punishment

Another institution that attracted the notice of practical reformers was the penitentiary. Large prisons for long-term convicts were themselves new to the United States. Until the end of the eighteenth century, lawbreakers were rarely given long prison terms. The most serious crimes were punished by hanging; there were as many as

Early treatment of the insane included locking them in cages or strapping them into tranquilizing chairs. Dorothea Dix denounced such inhumane treatment and prompted reform.

16 capital offenses in some states, rape and homosexuality as well as murder and treason. Other major felonies merited a public flogging or physical mutilation. In Massachusetts as late as 1805, counterfeiters, arsonists, wife beaters, and thieves were whipped or had their ears cropped or their cheeks branded with a hot iron. Petty offenses—drunk and disorderly, disturbing the peace—were punished with fines or the humiliation of a dunking, the stocks, or the pillory.

During the 1790s, influenced by the theories of the Italian criminologist Cesare Beccaria, most states reduced the number of capital offenses, abolished mutilation, restricted the use of whipping, and turned instead to prison sentences as a means of punishing crime. Unfortunately, legislatures were rarely as generous in appropriating funds for maintaining penal institutions as they were in changing the criminal code. Conditions of confinement were generally execrable. Connecticut, for example, used an abandoned mine shaft as its state penitentiary.

In hand-on-shoulder lockstep, prisoners march into the dining room at Sing Sing Prison in New York. Rigid discipline and strict rules were thought to be an important part of reforming criminals.

Prison Reform

Most people agreed that the purposes of prison were the punishment of the wrongdoer and the protection of society. As reformers pointed out, however, the security of society was not served if prison sentences transformed petty offenders into hardened criminals. In confining minor offenders with habitual criminals, the penitentiaries acted as schools of crime.

Such observations led to the idea of the prison as a correctional institution, a place for rehabilitation and education. A lively controversy developed between exponents of what was called the Pennsylvania System and those of the Auburn System, which was named after the town in which New York's state prison was located. Pennsylvania kept its convicts in solitary confinement; they rarely left their tiny, individual cells. The theory was that the inmates would meditate on their crimes and leave prison determined not to offend again.

The flaws of the system were twofold: maintaining individual cells was extremely expensive, and total isolation resulted in numerous cases of mental breakdown. In order to save money, Pennsylvania set its prisoners to working to pay their own bills. New York's Auburn Penitentiary addressed the problem of isolation by marching prisoners each day to large workrooms and a common dining hall. Conversation was forbidden, both to prevent education in crime and to keep order. Eventually, the Auburn System was adopted by other states, including Pennsylvania.

Another innovation of the period was the "house of refuge," in which juveniles were kept isolated from adult criminals. By 1830, New York City, Philadelphia, and Boston maintained such facilities. After 1830, the practice of public executions declined. Reformers rejected the ancient belief that the sight of a man dangling from a rope provided a grim lesson for onlookers when as many as 10,000 people eagerly flocked to witness an execution in New Jersey. It was obvious from the spectators' ribald behavior that they were there to enjoy a good show, not for the purposes of moral edification.

MORAL UPLIFT

Such undesirable behavior among the masses inspired a second kind of evangelical reform during the early 19th century. While reformers like Gallaudet, Howe, and Dix directed their energies toward alleviating the misfortunes and injustices suffered by a few, others addressed social problems that seemed rampant, afflicting the many and, therefore, corrupting the entire society.

Demon Rum

For example, Americans drank heavily and always had. In part, their bibulousness owed to the fact that grain was abundant and cheap in the United States. More was grown than was needed for consumption as food or could

ON THE WAGON

The phrase *on the wagon* means "no longer drinking alcoholic liquor." To publicize their cause, temperance groups hauled a water wagon through the streets of towns and cities and urged people to climb aboard. This vehicle—like a float in a parade—was so common that "going on the wagon" became a universally understood saying. Another catch phrase of the temperance movement has been lost: *cold-water man*, which meant "a person who did not drink."

By 1835, there were 5,000 temperance societies in the United States. This wall poster advertised a convention attended by several anti-alcohol organizations in New England.

find ready markets abroad. English ale and porter, along with apple cider and rum, were the everyday beverages of ordinary people in the East. In the West, the daily tonic was whiskey distilled from corn or rye. Wine and brandy—most of it imported—were fixtures of middle-class and upper-class life.

Few social occasions lacked alcohol. The hospitable family's first act upon receiving a guest was to uncork a bottle or to tap a barrel. Urban workingmen insisted that they needed liquor for strength, and employers of both craftsmen and unskilled laborers provided a ration, sometimes a substantial one, as part of the day's pay. Farmers were notorious for the "little brown jugs" that accompanied them in their fields.

By 1820, the annual consumption of spirits (not including beer, cider, and wine!) was more than seven and a half gallons for each American man, woman, and child. There were about 15,000 licensed distilleries in the country, and private stills were as common as chicken coops on backcountry farms.

Temperance

Drunkenness was universally regarded as sinful and socially disruptive. Cotton Mather had preached temperance for moral reasons in the early eighteenth century. During the 1780s, Dr. Benjamin Rush, a Philadelphia physician, described the physically destructive effects of excessive bibbing.

With the blossoming of the evangelical spirit during the 1830s, reformers assailing alcohol added two more arrows to their quiver. First, they published statistics showing that a substantial number of crimes were committed by people who were drunk. Second, they drew a connection between poverty and drinking. A few said that the miseries of poverty led to drunkenness. Most, steeped in moralism and the evangelical sense of individual responsibility, believed that drunkenness was the reason for poverty.

Once evangelicals took up the theme of temperance in drinking, the movement spread rapidly. By 1835,

there were 5,000 temperance societies in the United States with a membership of more than 1 million. In 1840, six reformed sots founded a national organization, the Washington Temperance Society. Two years later, a much more militant association, the Sons of Temperance, began to promote sobriety as a basic religious duty, virtually an eleventh commandment.

One of the Sons' most effective lecturers was John B. Gough, another former drunk. He rallied audiences with the lurid language of the fire-and-brimstone revivalist: "Crawl from the slimy ooze, ye drowned drunkards, and with suffocation's blue and livid lips speak out against the drink." Wherever Gough spoke, weeping men and women swore off the bottle.

Prohibition

Temperance reformers quarreled and split as promiscuously as did utopians and religious fundamentalists. One line of division ran between the advocates of temperance in the use of alcohol and the complete abstainers. The former argued traditionally that drunkenness was the evil, and not alcohol itself. They lodged no objection to the occasional sip of wine or restorative dram. The abstainers, observing that alcohol was addictive, concluded that it was inherently sinful. Temperance was not enough—it was necessary to swear off drink completely in order to live morally.

This split took on political significance when the teetotalers divided between moral suasionists, who regarded abstinence from drink as an individual decision, and legal suasionists, who considered the prohibition of the manufacture and sale of liquor as a means of reforming society.

In 1838, Massachusetts experimented with an act that was designed to cut down consumption among the poor. The Fifteen Gallon Law prohibited the sale of whiskey or rum in quantities smaller than fifteen gallons. However, the temper of the Age-of-Jackson man ran against any device that openly provided privileges to the rich, who could afford bulk purchases of spirits. The Fifteen Gallon Law was repealed within two years.

In 1845, New York adopted a more democratic law, which authorized local governments to forbid the sale of alcohol within their jurisdictions. Within a few years, five-sixths of the state was "dry." In 1846, the state of Maine, led by Neal Dow, a public-spirited Portland businessman, adopted the first statewide prohibition law. By 1860, thirteen states had followed suit. But the custom of drinking was too much a part of the culture to be abolished by well-meaning ordinances. Prohibition laws were flagrantly violated and, by 1868, they had been repealed in every state but Maine.

The temperance and prohibition movements were strongest in the Northeast; three-fourths of all temperance societies were located there. They were also, for the most part, native Protestant movements that were supported by evangelical reformers and largely directed toward native-born Protestant Americans. In the 1830s and 1840s, however, the crusade against alcohol took on a new dimension because of the huge influx of immigrants who had different customs, among which was (as far as reformers were concerned) an inordinate devotion to beer and whiskey.

The Stresses of Immigration

Only 8,400 Europeans came to the United States in 1820, hardly enough to excite notice. More than 23,000 arrived in 1830, however, and 84,000 in 1840, In the midcentury year, at least 370,000 people stepped from crowded immigrant ships onto wharves in the Eastern seaports while, in the distant West, the immigration from China first made its appearance.

Not only were they numerous, the immigrants of midcentury were, for the most part, people adhering to re-

---

THE PLEDGE

Although it did not ease the fears of Protestant nativists, there was a temperance movement among Irish Catholics in the United States. In 1840, an Irish priest, Theobald Mathew, toured the United States and administered "The Pledge" to more than half a million Irish Catholic immigrants and their children, swearing them into the Teetotal Abstinence Society.

---

ligious faiths scarcely known in the United States and, in many cases, they spoke languages other than English.

Thus, while 3,600 Irish came to the United States in 1820, most of them Protestant, 164,000 arrived in 1850, most of them Roman Catholic. Immigration authorities counted only 23 Scandinavian immigrants in 1820 and 1,600 in 1850, a number that would nearly triple within two years. In 1820, 968 Germans entered the United States; in 1850, 79,000 arrived.

Scandinavian and German immigrants inclined to cluster in large communities, retaining their languages and preserving Old-World customs. Among these was the convivial German beer garden, where entire families gathered to drink lager beer, first introduced to the United States in this era. To a teetotaler, the Irish were worse. Most of them spoke English, but they were notoriously given to gathering in city saloons and on construction sites to drink whiskey. And they were Roman Catholic, as were about half of the German immigrants. Between 1830 and 1860, when the general population slightly more than doubled, the Roman Catholic population of the United States increased tenfold—from 300,000 to more than 3 million.

The Whore of Babylon

The growth of Catholicism in the United States was difficult for many Protestants to accept. Since the days of the Puritans, they had been taught that the Church of Rome was the Bible's Whore of Babylon, not merely another Christian denomination but a fount of evil.

This prejudice took on new life in the second quarter of the nineteenth century because the pope of Rome, the spiritual leader of the world's Catholics, was also the political head of a reactionary and repressive state. In the Papal States of central Italy, dissidents were jailed and, it was believed, tortured. The political principles of Catholicism seemed to be the very antithesis of American traditions of democracy and liberty. Because of the intense devotion of most Irish immigrants to their faith and the authority of their priests, many Protestants feared that they were the shock troops of political reaction.

Moreover, the vast majority of the Irish immigrants were destitute. Landless in their native home, they had been forced to emigrate because of extreme deprivation and, in the 1840s, because of the failure of the island's potato crop. Once in the United States, they were willing to accept work at almost any rate of pay, prompting Protestant workingmen to regard them as a threat to the traditionally high standard of living that at least skilled mechanics enjoyed. When economic uneasiness combined with the evangelical crusade against the new immigrants' religious beliefs and their apparently heavy drinking, the result was a social and political movement.

Anti-Catholicism and the Know-Nothings

The famous painter and inventor of the telegraph, Samuel F. B. Morse, wanted to cut off the immigration of Catholics. Street wars between Protestant and Irish Catholic workingmen regularly erupted in Northeastern cities. In 1834, aroused by stories that Catholic priests kept nuns for sexual purposes, murdering the infants born of such unions, a mob burned an Ursuline convent in Charlestown, Massachusetts. In Philadelphia in 1844, 20 people were killed and over a hundred injured in anti-Catholic riots.

Anti-Catholicism took on a political form with the founding of the Order of the Star-Spangled Banner, a secret organization that was dedicated to shutting off further immigration. The order's members came to be known as "Know-Nothings" because, when asked by outsiders about the organization, they replied, "I know nothing."

After 1850, the Order came above ground as the American party. Capitalizing on the disintegration of the Whigs, the anti-Catholic, anti-immigrant movement swept to power in several states, including Massachusetts. At its peak, the American party elected 75 congressmen, and a former Whig president, Millard Fillmore of New York, ran as its presidential nominee in 1856. Anti-Catholicism was by no means considered an unacceptable bigotry.

Missionaries

Only a minority of Protestants believed in taking political action against Roman Catholics. The majority was indifferent to the faith of the newcomers, or stood by the guarantees of religious freedom in the First Amendment to the Constitution. Many of these people, however, approved of attempts by various missionary societies to convert Catholics and other peoples. As Timothy Dwight of Yale University explained in splendidly bib-

The sudden flood of immigrants into the United States created a period of social turmoil, as reflected in this lithograph of an 1844 anti-Irish riot in Philadelphia.

lical imagery, America's mission was to hasten the day "when the *Romish* Cathedral, the Mosque, and the Pagoda, shall *not have one stone left upon another which shall not be thrown down.*"

The American Tract Society (founded in 1814) and the American Bible Society (1816) distributed literature among the Catholic population. By 1836, the Tract Society estimated that it had sold or given away more then 3 million copies of publications that explained Protestant beliefs.

Another small group concentrated on converting the few Jews in the United States, but most of the missionaries' energies were directed overseas. Partly because the numerous denominational colleges of the United States turned out many more ministers than there were pulpits to fill, and partly because evangelicals felt responsible for the wrongs wreaked by Americans in other parts of the world, groups such as the American Board of Foreign Missions raised money to send zealous young men and women to preach the gospel far beyond the boundaries of the United States.

Blue Hawaii

American missionaries worked among the Native American tribes of the West and traveled to Africa, India, and China. No part of the world, however, exerted a greater attraction to Americans than the Sandwich Islands, or Hawaii.

In 1819, a young Hawaiian Christian told recent graduates of Andover Theological Seminary of the harm done to his homeland by sailors and whalers, Americans prominent among them. Discovered in 1778 by the great British explorer Captain James Cook, the islands' central Pacific location made them an ideal place for whalers from New Bedford and Nantucket to stop in order to refit their vessels, replenish their provisions, and recover from scurvy on island fruits. Not incidentally, the seafarers also introduced diseases unknown to Hawaiians that devastated the population. Between 1778 and 1804, the native population was halved, from about 300,000 to 150,000.

Because they also brought fascinating modern goods to a people who had lived simply from the sea, the visitors irrevocably corrupted Hawaiian culture. Back in New England, evangelicals who felt responsible for their own deaf, blind, and insane found it easy to consider the sins visited on the Hawaiians a burden upon themselves.

Blue-Nosed New Englanders

As early as 1820, young ministers and their wives, sisters, and mothers shipped out to Hawaii. They met with a mixed reception. While many Hawaiians converted to

Lucretia Coffin Mott played an important part in the feminist movement for a generation.

Christian denominations, and the missionaries had some success protecting the native people from the depredations of their less moral countrymen, they were greeted with some resistance when they forced proper Boston behavior on the natives. The most celebrated example of the missionaries' incapacity to distinguish theology from custom was their insistence that in the warm, humid climate of the Islands, Christian girls and women dress in full-length calico and flannel "Mother Hubbard" dresses.

Women were the backbone of missionary efforts in Hawaii and elsewhere. In a way, this curious phenomenon reflected the consequences of the westward movement back home. Because young men were freer than young women to break old ties and strike off on their own, New England was left with a surplus of women of marriageable age for whom there were no spouses. Evangelical reform, being within the realm of morality, was considered an acceptable outlet for the energies of such spinsters. Single women were prominent in every reform movement from temperance to abolitionism.

But there was more to the flowering of social activism among American women than demographics. In consecrating their lives to the deaf, the poor, the missions, and other good works, some otherwise privileged and comfortable middle-class women were able to protest, however obliquely, the private, domestic, and dependent status that American society assigned them. This discontent found an outlet in the emergence of feminism as a social movement.

THE WOMEN'S MOVEMENT

In the summer of 1848, a group of women called for a convention to be held at Seneca Falls, New York, to consider the "Declaration of Sentiments and Resolutions" they had drafted. The declaration was a deadly serious parody of the Declaration of Independence. "When in the course of human events," it began, "it becomes necessary for one portion of the family of man to assume among the people of the earth a position different from that which they have hitherto occupied, but one to which the laws of nature and nature's God entitle them, a decent respect to the opinions of mankind requires that they should declare the causes that impel them to such a course. . . ."

Feminism

The injustices suffered by women included the denial of the right to vote even when it was extended to "the most

THE FOUNDING MOTHERS

While individuals such as Fanny Wright and Margaret Fuller raised eloquent objections to the inequality of the sexes before 1848, that year marks the beginning of feminism as a social and political movement in the United States. Three of the four women who can be called the Founding Mothers of American feminism were present in the little town of Seneca Falls, New York, during the second week of July 1848 when the "Declaration of Sentiments and Resolutions," a biting parody of the Declaration of Independence, was presented to the country.

Lucretia Coffin Mott (1793–1880) and Elizabeth Cady Stanton (1815–1902) had been friends for a number of years by virtue of their participation in the cause of abolition. In 1840, they tried to register as delegates to an international antislavery convention in London (it was Stanton's wedding trip), but they were refused admission because they were women. The injustice and the absurdity of it—people committed to the equal rights of the races defending the inequality of the sexes—rankled on them. But not until eight years later did they conclude that the rights of women deserved the same kind of fight as did the rights of blacks. Mott and Stanton were principal authors of the declaration "that all men and women are created equal" and the demand for "immediate admission of all to the rights and privileges which belong to them as citizens of the United States."

Both remained active in the long and mostly frustrating battle for female equality until their deaths at ripe ages. They were good-humored people—Stanton, a portly mother of seven, could be downright garrulous—living disproof of the sour-faced fanatics that enemies of the women's movement liked to depict feminists as being. However, they were not afraid to defy the powerful social convention that women should take no part in public life. In 1861, Stanton addressed the New York State legislature; she called for a reform of divorce laws, which, like those in other states, discriminated against and even sealed the social exorcism of divorced women.

Amelia Jenks Bloomer (1818–94), by way of contrast, was a shy, retiring woman who was more comfortable alone with a pen than at the speaker's lectern. Ironically, her name was affixed to what was, at mid-century, considered the ultimate proof that the women's movement was ridiculous—the reform costume known as "bloomers."

Mrs. Bloomer attended the Seneca Falls convention but did not sign the declaration. Over the next several years, she drew closer to Stanton and increasingly devoted her temperance newspaper, *The Lily,* to questions of sexual inequality. In 1851, Bloomer began to advocate reform in women's dress. Female fashion at the time consisted of tightly laced corsets, layers of petticoats, and floor-length dresses that had to be held up in the dusty, muddy, or garbage-strewn streets. The corset was dangerous—literally maiming vital organs—and a kind of shackle. It was difficult to do much of anything in the constrictive garb but to wear it.

The bloomer costume dispensed with the corset in favor of a loose bodice, substituted ankle-length pantaloons for the petticoats, and cut the outer skirt to above the knee. It was, in fact, not new in 1851, when Elizabeth Smith Miller, not Amelia Bloomer, dared to wear it in public. Women at the utopian colony of New Harmony had worn something like the reform costume, as had otherwise quite conventional women at lake and seaside resorts. But Miller and Bloomer wanted to make it standard wear. Because Mrs. Bloomer was its best-known exponent in the pages of the widely circulated *Lily* (and because her name suggested the billowing pantaloons), bloomers they came to be called.

Mrs. Bloomer wore the reform costume for about ten years. However, Stanton and her principal associate after 1852, Susan B. Anthony, gave up on it after only one year. Like many reformers before and since, they discovered that when they tried to emphasize issues that lay close to the heart of women's inferior status, enemies and journalists were more interested in the highly eccentric dress they wore.

As the century progressed, the most important feminist issue became the vote, woman suffrage, and the name of Susan B. Anthony (1820–1906) became synonymous with it. Ironically, like her friend Mrs. Stanton, Anthony considered the woman's plight as much broader than mere disenfranchisement. But as the vote alone was regarded by otherwise conservative women as a "respectable" demand they would support, Anthony went along for the sake of unity.

An unmarried woman, Susan B. Anthony was able to devote all her time to the movement. The other Founding Mothers, burdened with the duties of marriage and motherhood, were unable to do so. For more than half a century—from 1852, when she was refused permission to speak at a temperance convention, until her death in 1906—she labored tirelessly for the cause that was still unfulfilled at the time of her death. Not until the Nineteenth Amendment to the Constitution was ratified in 1920 was the right of women to vote guaranteed.

All four of the Founding Mothers had connections with the Quakers, a sect that almost alone in the United States took the education of girls seriously. All but Bloomer had some formal schooling, which was very unusual in early-nineteenth-century America. Every one of them was also interested in other reform movements: temperance, peace, costume, abolitionism (and some trivial quackeries). And all believed in principle that the emancipation of women depended on more than gaining the right to vote.

Elizabeth Cady Stanton was one of the original participants in the 1848 Seneca Falls convention for women's rights.

exclusion of women from the professions and other gainful employment.

Only 68 women and 32 men signed the document, but the Seneca Falls Declaration got national attention—sympathetic in reform newspapers, scornful and mocking in more conventional publications. Among the organizers of the conference were Lucretia Coffin Mott and Elizabeth Cady Stanton, who continued to play an important part in the feminist movement for a generation. Among the spectators was Amelia Jenks Bloomer, a temperance reformer who was soon to become famous as the advocate of a new style of dress that bore her name. Bloomers gave a woman the freedom of trousers without exposing her legs, or the shape of them.

Stepping Aside

But the expectations of 1848—that equal rights for women was a demand whose time had come—were soon dashed to pieces. Americans, including most women, were not ready to think seriously about the civil equality of women. Even the vote, only one of the Seneca Falls demands, lay years in the future.

The community of evangelical reformers, while generally sympathetic to women's rights in theory, urged the feminists to set their problems aside until a reform that they considered far more important was carried out. This was the abolition of slavery, a cause that was entering its final phase when the first women's rights convention was called. Stanton and Mott, who had been abolitionists before they became feminists, tacitly agreed. They never silenced the call for women's rights, but they stepped to the side in the belief that when the slaves were freed, the women's cause would have its day. Indeed, the over-arching evil of slavery seemed, by 1850, to absorb the energies of every other reform movement.

ignorant and degraded men"; the forfeiture by a married woman of control over her own property; the nearly absolute control of the husband over a wife's behavior, which "made her, morally, an irresponsible being"—a state utterly reprehensible to an evangelical; and the

---

For Further Reading

Basic general studies of nineteenth-century reform include C. S. Griffin, *Thy Brother's Keepers: Moral Stewardship in the United States, 1800–1865* (1960) and *The Ferment of Reform* (1967); Arthur M. Schlesinger, *The American as Reformer* (1960); Alice F. Tyler, *Freedom's Ferment: Phases of American Social History to 1860* (1944); R. G. Walters, *American Reformers: 1815–1860* (1978).

On specific reforms, see Ray A. Billington, *The Protestant Crusade, 1800–1860* (1938); F. L. Byme, *Prophet of Prohibition: Neal Dow and His Crusade* (1961); M. E. Lender and J. K. Martin, *Drinking in America: A History*

(1982); H. E. Marshall, *Dorothea Dix: Forgotten Samaritan* (1937); Blake McKelvey, *American Prisons: A Study in American Social History Prior to 1915* (1936); W. G. Rorabaugh, *The Alcoholic Republic: An American Tradition* (1979); David J. Rothman, *The Discovery of the Asylum* (1970); I. R. Tyrrel, *Sobering Up: From Temperance to Prohibition* (1979); Carl Wittke, *The Irish in America* (1956).

For feminism: Lois Banner, *Elizabeth Cady Stanton* (1980); Carl M. Degler, *At Odds: Women and the Family in America from the Revolution to the Present* (1980); Eleanor Flexner, *Century of Struggle: The Women's Rights*

Movement in the United States (1975); Aileen S. Kraditor, *Up From the Pedestal: Selected Writings in the History of American Feminism* (1968); Gerda Lerner, *The Woman in American History* (1970); Alma Lutz, *Susan B. An-thony* (1979); William L. O'Neill, *Everyone Was Brave: The Rise and Fall of Feminism in America* (1970); Mary P. Ryan, *Womanhood in America* (1975).

This Currier and Ives depiction of a cotton plantation shows all the various activities of picking time but is highly idealized— designed to adorn the wall of a household in which slavery was regarded as a benevolent institution.

19

A DIFFERENT COUNTRY

THE EVOLUTION OF THE SOUTH

Doodling at his desk one day, Thomas Jefferson drew up a list of character traits in which, he suggested,

Northerners and Southerners differed. Northerners were cool and sober, he wrote; Southerners were

fiery and voluptuary. Northerners were hard-working, self-interested, and chicaning (devious); South-

erners were lazy, generous, and candid. Northerners were "jealous of their own liberties, and just to

those of others"; Southerners were "zealous for their own liberties, but trampling on those of others."

No doubt he had a point. Jefferson usually did. But to fix upon the differences between the people of the North and those of the South distorts the reality that they were much more alike than not. Southerners and Northerners shared a common linguistic, religious, cultural, and political heritage. By 1826, the year of Jefferson's death, they also shared 50 years of national history.

Politically, North and South had *tended* to line up on sectional lines during the early nineteenth century. The Jefferson Republicans and the Democrats counted on a core of Southern votes to build their majorities; the Federalists, National Republicans, and Whigs on primacy in the New England states. Nevertheless, Jefferson and Jackson won the presidency only because they attracted many Northern votes too. The Whigs competed with the Democrats as equals in the South until the 1850s. Zachary Taylor, one of only two Whigs elected president, was from Louisiana.

Despite the perturbation in South Carolina over the tariffs of 1828 and 1832, neither import duties, internal improvements, nor the question of a national bank seriously threatened the federal union.

SOUTHERN ANTISLAVERY

Until the 1830s, slavery was not a particularly divisive issue between the people of the two sections. The institution was indeed abolished or in the process of abolition in the North while it remained a building-block of society in the South. Still, New York did not finally abandon the institution until 1827, and there were a few slaves in New Jersey—all quite legal—as late as 1860. Except in a few states like Massachusetts and New Hampshire, where slavery was abolished at a blow in the Revolutionary Era, middle-aged Northerners could tell the young firsthand of the days when there were slaves among them. Few Northerners regretted doing away with the institution; equally few found the fact that Southerners preserved it to be intolerable.

Manumission and Race

Until the 1830s, in fact, the fate of slavery was still an open question in the South. Many of the most powerful Southerners, the very people who owed their wealth, leisure, and status to the forced labor of their human property, worried openly about the undesirable social, economic, and moral consequences of the institution. Thomas Jefferson agonized over slavery to the end of his life. "I tremble for my country when I reflect that God is just," he wrote of the South and its slaves. "The Almighty has no attribute which can take side with us in such a contest"—between enemies of slavery and de-

---

JEFFERSON'S CURIOUS BEQUEST

Like many planters, Thomas Jefferson freed some of his slaves in his will. Sally Hemmings, whom Jefferson's enemies had claimed, with some reason, to have been his mistress, was not among them. She was bequeathed to Jefferson's daughter, Patsy. Rather than giving the lie to the accusation that Jefferson used a slave sexually, the curious bequest may be circumstantial evidence that Sally Hemmings was indeed what the Federalists said she was. That is, the state of Virginia required manumitted slaves to leave the state. To have freed Sally Hemmings, who was then well along in years, would have forced her to leave her lifelong friends and her children.

---

fenders of the institution. Jefferson hoped that the passage of time would prepare slaves for total emancipation and lead masters to accept it.

In fact, it was not unheard of for wealthy planters of Jefferson's era to manumit—to free—their slaves in their wills. George Washington was honored for doing so. Less celebrated Southerners frequently rewarded individual slaves with freedom for extraordinary services. In 1833, Virginian John Randolph freed 400 blacks with a single stroke of his pen, the largest manumission in American history.

The possibility of total abolition arose periodically in the states of the upper South. But, in the end, every state below the Mason-Dixon line and the Ohio River opted to preserve it. The decisive factor was the racialism that was, simply, an assumption of the era. Most white Southerners (and white Northerners, for that matter) quite sincerely believed that blacks, as a people, were their innate inferiors in intelligence, initiative, even moral fiber.

Social and Economic Considerations

To whites of this frame of mind, it was one thing for Northerners to set blacks free. The black population was insignificant in most Northern states. In 1830, there were 125,000 blacks in the Northeast, amidst a total population of 5.54 million. There were but 42,000 blacks in the states of the Old Northwest, with 1.6 million people. So small a minority could be ignored, disdained, and pushed aside, as Northern blacks were. There was no concern that their exotic, and therefore undesirable, traits would overwhelm the culture. The black population was not "a social problem."

But blacks were the backbone of the agricultural workforce in the South, and a substantial part of the population, 2.16 million in 1830 as compared to 3.54 million whites. If such numbers, firmly under control as slaves,

A Perpetual Exercise of Boisterous Passions

More than a few Southern slave owners hated slavery because of what the institution did to them. George Mason of Virginia wrote in 1774:

Practised in the Arts of Despotism and Cruelty, we become callous to the Dictates of Humanity, & all the other finer feelings of the Soul. Taught to regard a part of our Species in the most abject and contemptible Degree below us, we lose that Idea of the Dignity of Man, which the hand of Nature had implanted in us. . . . Habituated from our Infancy to trample upon the Rights of human Nature, every generous, ever liberal Sentiment, if not extinguished, is enfeebled in our Mind. And in such an infernal School are to be educated our future Legislators and Rulers.

Writing a few years later, Thomas Jefferson echoed Mason's sentiments:

There must doubtless be an unhappy influence on the manners of our people produced by the existence of slavery among us. The whole commerce between master and slave is a perpetual exercise of the most boisterous passions, the most unremitting despotism on the one part, and degrading submissions on the other. Our children see this and learn to imitate it . . . . The parent storms, the child looks on, catches the lineaments of wrath, puts on the same airs in the circle of smaller slaves, gives loose to the worst of passions and thus nursed, educated, and daily exercised in tyranny, cannot but be stamped by it with odious peculiarities.

were suddenly or even gradually freed to compete with poor whites at the bottom of Southern society, Southerners who thought about the question usually concluded, the result would be profound cultural decay, social dislocation, even chaos.

Before about 1830, there was little that was malicious or apocalyptic in Southern statements of this sort. Indeed, there was a melancholy sense of fatefulness in the ruminations. In continuing to hold blacks as slaves, many planters of the late eighteenth and early nineteenth centuries sincerely believed that they were not so much preserving their own social standing as shouldering a tragic burden that had been strapped to their backs by history. They were protecting the blacks from the hostility of poor whites (of whom the elite's opinion was not exalted). They were preserving their society from anarchy.

The Colonization Movement

The American Colonization Society, founded in 1817, tried to provide such troubled Southerners with an alternative to slavery on the one hand, chaos on the other.

With the active support of such distinguished Southerners as Madison, Monroe, Marshall, and Clay, the Society proposed to raise money with which free blacks would be transported to West Africa. By ridding the South of free blacks, the advocates of colonization believed, they would avert racial conflict, encourage individual slave owners to free their human property, and inspire state legislatures to adopt laws abolishing the undesirable institution.

In 1821, the Society financed the emigration of a few former slaves to Sierra Leone, a colony established by the British as a refuge for blacks freed from bondage within the British Empire. The next year, the Society purchased a stretch of African coastline south of Sierra Leone and helped establish the black Republic of Liberia, with its capital at Monrovia (named for President Monroe). All told, about 11,000 American blacks settled in Liberia. They established a government patterned on the American model and, less happily, reduced the native people of the region to a kind of servitude with themselves on top.

But colonization quickly proved an unrealistic program. There were 1.5 million slaves in the United States in 1820, and 2.16 million in 1830, far more people than could be colonized on a small strip of African seacoast. Moreover, few free blacks were willing to go to Africa. Most were generations removed from their African roots—which were not in Liberia in any case—and felt no attraction to an unknown land. Virginia, Georgia, and Arkansas may not have been hospitable homes, but home they were. West Africa was not.

As for Southern whites, the longer the price of cotton boomed on the world market, the less was heard about the antislavery aspects of colonization. When the Mississippi Colonization Society was founded in 1829, its announced purpose was to rid the state of free blacks. Its officers disassociated themselves from the old goal of encouraging planters to free their slaves. Even in the upper South, where little cotton was grown, the profitability of selling surplus slaves "down the river" dulled the appeal of colonization. Except for one last debate, by 1830 the Southern antislavery movement was quite dead.

The Last Debate

In December 1831, Governor John Floyd of Virginia asked the legislature to consider a plan to phase out slavery over a period of years, and to compensate slave owners for their losses. In other words, for the good of the state, taxpayers would accommodate those who suffered for it. For three weeks in January 1832, the delegates discussed the proposal, for the most part moderately and intelligently.

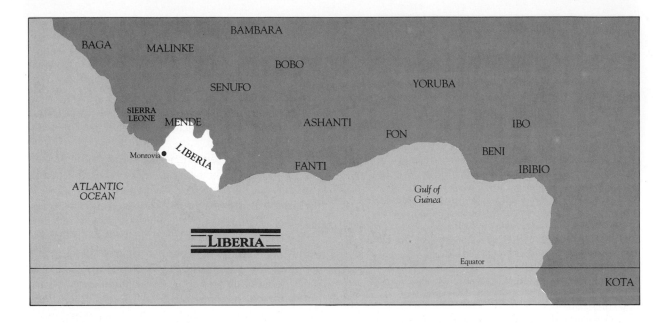

LIBERIA

Even the staunchest proslavery men were defensive. Typically, they introduced their speeches by regretting the fact that slaves had ever been introduced into Virginia, and by saying that the state would be a better place if it had been developed by free white labor. However, they concluded, the past was history; blacks constituted about half of Virginia's population; so large a population of free blacks was out of the question; and the colonization movement was obviously a failure. Thus, however unfortunate it was for the Old Dominion, Virginia must continue to be a slave state.

The assumption that a biracial society would not work carried the day—but just barely. At the end of January, the legislature rejected the Floyd plan by 73 to 58. A switch of only eight votes would have altered the course of American history, for the other states of the upper South—Delaware, Maryland, and Kentucky—could not have ignored abolition in Virginia. Had those states phased slavery out, slavery would not have split the Union across the middle, but would have been the peculiar institution of a few, generally lightly populated states in the Deep South. As it was, once the Virginia debate was over, no powerful party of Southern whites ever again considered the possibility of ridding themselves of the tragic institution.

THREATS TO THE SOUTHERN ORDER

Both Floyd's proposal and the Virginia legislature's rejection of it were profoundly influenced by two events that electrified the South in 1831: the appearance in the North of a new kind of antislavery agitator, and an uprising of slaves in Southampton County, Virginia, under the leadership of Nat Turner.

Early Abolitionists

While the mainstream debate over slavery revolved around its political justice, economic wisdom, and social consequences, there always had been a few voices raised about the morality of human bondage. Many eighteenth-century Quakers, such as John Woolman of New Jersey and Anthony Benezet of Philadelphia, had spoken publicly of the sinfulness of slavery. During the 1820s, Benjamin Lundy preserved this tradition, calling for gradual abolition and the colonization of blacks in Haiti, Canada, or Texas (then a part of Mexico). Educated blacks, notably the mathematician and astronomer Benjamin Banneker, published moral arguments against slavery and drew support from white religious groups and communities of free blacks in both North and South.

With few exceptions, these abolitionists treated the subject as one to be discussed calmly and moderately, in terms of one Christian concerned about the soul of another. Their fraternal attitude toward slave owners was typified by the Boston Unitarian William Ellery Channing, who told Southerners, "We consider slavery your calamity and not your curse." None of them used language as harsh as had Virginians Thomas Jefferson or John Randolph in discussing slavery.

David Walker and William Lloyd Garrison

In 1829, language and mood took on new forms. In that year, a free black dealer in cloth living in Boston, David

Although this photograph was taken after the Civil War, the scene would have been the same in 1830 or 1850.

The Philadelphia Anti-Slavery Society, 1851. Lucretia Coffin is seated second from the right.

NOTABLE PEOPLE

JOHN BROWN (1800–59)

Lieutenant Israel Green rushed through the shattered door with a swarm of marines. One of the hostages pointed to a bearded man, "This is Osawatomie." Green tried to run him through with his sword, but it bent double. The officer exploded in a rage beyond his control. He beat the old man with the pommel of his sword until he collapsed, and then Green continued to pound him.

It was October 18, 1859. "Osawatomie" was John Brown, an abolitionist who had led a 21-man "army" into Harper's Ferry, Virginia (now West Virginia). His goal had been to rally the slaves of the area and escape into the Appalachians. From the fastnesses of the mountains, Brown would wage guerilla war on slavery, which he called "the sum of villainies," and on slaveowners, whom he called "Satan's legions."

John Brown's raid was a farce. It would be written off as laughable had it not been for the bloodshed and the hatreds, fears, and foibles it revealed in the minds of Americans North and South.

It was finished 36 hours after it began. Brown squandered any chance for success when, instead of dashing into the mountains, he holed up in the federal arsenal at Harper's Ferry, waiting for a slave uprising in a region where there were few slaves and the whites were less than consecrated to the "peculiar institution." (One of the fatalities was Harper's Ferry's mayor, whose will freed his slaves; when the Civil War began, western Virginia refused to join the Confederacy because of a widespread dislike for wealthy slaveowners.)

Brown almost squandered his chance for immortality as a martyr to the antislavery cause when, with his holy war obviously doomed, he tried to barter the safety of his hostages for his own freedom, as if what he had done was a prank. But his raid had revealed the white South's frantic fear of slave rebellion. It also unveiled the fact that many abolitionists were willing to condone and abet a man who complained of "terrible gatherings" in his head. John Brown's fate was out of his hands; his name was saved for history. Within a few years, soldiers would march into battle singing,

John Brown's body Lies a-mouldering in the grave,
But his soul goes marching on.

John Brown was born in Connecticut, the son of a tanner, in 1800. His father imbued him with a passionate Calvinistic obsession with evil and the need not ony to resist sin, but to battle it. Two hundred years earlier, Brown would have been a doughty Massachusetts pioneer, a maker of towns against all the odds of wilderness. In the twentieth century he would have warred against whiskey or sexual immorality. In the mid-nineteenth century, like many Americans of evangelical bent, his ardor fastened on the national sin of slavery.

Brown failed at business—several businesses. It is not clear when he joined his sons in Kansas in 1855, if he was at all interested in having to go at a homestead on the plains. He may well have been attracted to Kansas only by the fact that there the debate over slavery had been transformed into violent confrontation. Proslavery "Jayhawkers" and "Border Ruffians" from western Missouri, seeing that they were simply out-voted, bullied and terrorized the growing antislavery majority. Much more omi-

---

Walker, published a pamphlet called *The Appeal*. After reviewing the traditional arguments about the immorality and injustice of slavery, Walker stated that unless whites abolished the institution, blacks had a moral duty to rise up in violent rebellion.

William Lloyd Garrison, a spare, intense young white man of 24 who was working for Benjamin Lundy in Baltimore, did not believe in violent rebellion. Among the many evangelical reform movements he supported was pacifism, opposition to all wars. And yet, when Garrison founded his antislavery newspaper in Boston in January 1831, *The Liberator*, his language was belligerent and incendiary, and aimed not only at the institution of slavery—the sin—but at the sinners, slave owners.

"I am aware," Garrison wrote in the first issue of his paper,

that many object to the severity of my language; but is there not cause for severity? I will be as harsh as truth, and as uncompromising as justice. On this subject I do not wish to think, or speak, or write, with moderation. No! no! Tell a man whose house is on fire to give a moderate alarm; tell him to moderately rescue his wife from the hands of the ravisher; tell the mother to gradually extricate her babe from the fire into which it has fallen;—but urge me not to use moderation in a cause like the present.

It was a declaration of war. To Garrison, the day of discourse and compromise was gone. Slavery was evil, pure and simple; slave owners and those who accommodated them—accepted them as individuals—were doers of evil. Garrison described the slave owner's life as "one of unbridled lust, of filthy amalgamation, of swaggering braggadocio, of haughty domination, of cowardly ruffianism, of boundless dissipation, of matchless insolence, of infinite self-conceit, of unequalled oppression, of more than savage cruelty."

This sort of thing does not usually go down well with the subjects of it. Indeed, Garrison was unpopular in the North. (He would have been wracked with doubt that the devil was in him had he been a hero of the masses.)

nous, and accounting for the fact that abolitionists who called themselves pacifists would support Brown, the administrations of Presidents Franklin Pierce and James Buchanan positively abetted winning Kansas for slavery by horsewhip and gun.

As early as 1851, Brown had said that if blacks had any sense of "manhood," they would kill anyone who tried to enforce the Fugitive Slave Act. By 1854, prominent abolitionists were no longer responding with frowns of disapproval. In August 1856, he reacted to a proslavery raid on Lawrence, Kansas, by riding to a cabin on Pottawatomie Creek and hacking to death five proslavery settlers (who had nothing to do with the Lawrence raid).

Brown was now a fugitive, wanted for murder. Incredibly, however, he toured New York and New England more or less openly. He addressed public meetings, was cordially received by prominent citizens, and given money by six well-to-do abolitionists. The fruit of the Kansas-Nebraska Act and the Dred Scott Decision was not to protect slavery, as too many southerners foolishly believed, but to turn otherwise conservative moralists into exponents of holy war and retribution against men guilty of nothing more than the fact that they approved of the institution of slavery.

Brown may have kept the specifics of his plans from the "Secret Six," but all knew that he intended violence. Among other things, he ordered a thousand pikes from a forge in Connecticut. When the raid at Harper's Ferry failed and Brown was arrested, tried, and sentenced to hang, all but one of the six went into hiding. They had savored Brown's tales when they were told in parlors but, like Brown in that faltering moment in the arsenal, they were not willing to face up to the consequences when revolutionary reveries are translated into action.

The one backer who stood his ground, Thomas W. Higginson, frankly stated that Brown's execution would do more good than if he were pardoned or even if his raid had succeeded. Higginson was correct and prophetic. In jail, Brown himself grasped the point and deported himself not as an avenging angel or field marshall of the holy war, but as a calmly dedicated Christian awaiting his destiny and salvation. His perception was brilliant—"I am worth inconceivably more to hang than for any other purpose"—his actions, really for the first time, were indisputably rational and selfless.

In the long run, John Brown's significance was indeed to make the war against slavery a mass movement—in the form of the blue-coated thousands of the Union Army. In the short run, his raid revealed just how unsure white southerners were of their "contented darkies". There had been no slave revolt in the South since Nat Turner's Rebellion a generation earlier. White southerners pointed to that fact in defense of their institution. But John Brown, for all his failures, laid bare the fact that they did not really believe their own boasts.

Southerners joined hands with Brown and Higginson in looking forward to Brown's execution. But they were acting out of fear and vengeance rather than on the basis of reasoned calculation. The same might be said of the secession movement that began almost exactly a year after the hanging in December 1859.

Even in Boston, a center of antislavery sentiment, Garrison was hooted and pelted with stones when he spoke in public. On one occasion, a mob threw a noose around his neck and dragged him through the streets. He was rescued only when the aggressiveness of a group of abolitionist women momentarily shocked the mob. (Garrison was also a supporter of women's rights.)

In the South, Garrison was regarded as a monster. Not because he was against slavery, at least not at first: antislavery Southerners loathed him as intensely as did proslavery Southerners. Garrison and other extremist abolitionists were hated because they were believed to be inciting bloody slave rebellion. In 1831, the fear of slave rebellion in the South was no abstract speculation.

Nat Turner

Nat Turner, a slave of Southampton County, Virginia, was a queer amalgam of mystic dreamer and hardheaded realist. Literate—unusual among slaves—he pored over the Bible, drawing his own interpretations of its meaning. The rebellion he led in August and September 1831 was triggered by a solar eclipse that he took as a sign from God.

And yet, Turner's revolt had a very practical goal—personal liberty—and Turner had a realistic conception of the odds that faced him. He planned with care, divulging his scheme to only a few trusted friends who swore with him to fight to the death. On the night of August 21, 1831, armed with little more than farm tools, the little group moved like lightning. They swept across Southampton County, killing 60 whites and recruiting more supporters from among the slaves.

The rising was over quickly, but before the rebels were rounded up after six weeks in hiding, there were 70 in the band. Forty, including Nat Turner, were hanged. Others, who were not directly responsible for spilling blood, were sold out of state. Undoubtedly, other blacks, including the innocent, were murdered by angry or frightened whites who did not bother to report the deaths.

WANTED: NAT TURNER

Five feet 6 or 8 inches high, weighs between 150 and 160 pounds, rather bright complexion, but not a mulatto. Broad shoulders, large flat nose, large eyes. Broad flat feet, rather knock-kneed, walks brisk and active. Hair on the top of the head very thin, no beard, except on the upper lip and at the top of the chin. A scar on one of his temples, also one at the back of his neck. A large knot on one of the bones of his right arm, near his wrist, produced [by] a blow.

The Fear of Rebellion

Turner's rebellion was not the first to throw a scare into white Southerners. In 1800, a black named Gabriel, sometimes called Gabriel Prosser, plotted an uprising in Richmond that may have passively involved as many as a thousand slaves. In 1822, a free black in Charleston, Denmark Vesey, had been accused of organizing a conspiracy to murder whites. Runaway slaves in Georgia joined with Seminole Indians to raid outlying plantations and free the slaves there. At one time or another, planters in every part of the South suspected slaves of plotting rebellion.

No doubt many of the suspected plots were figments of over-wrought imaginations; but there was nothing imaginary about Nat Turner, and a tremor of fear ran through the white South. In some parts of Louisiana, Mississippi, and South Carolina, blacks outnumbered whites by 20 to 1. Mary Boykin Chesnut, a South Carolinian of the planter class, was not observing a demographic curiosity when she described her family's plantation at Mulberry as "half a dozen whites and sixty or seventy Negroes, miles away from the rest of the world."

If many white Southerners shared such anxieties, their belief in black inferiority meant that few were willing to admit that blacks, left to their own devices, were capable of mounting a rebellion. To white Southerners, it was no coincidence that Turner's uprising followed the fiery first issue of *The Liberator* by only eight months. They took note of the fact that Turner knew how to read. They blamed white abolitionists like Garrison for the tragedy.

WHITE SOUTHERNERS CLOSE RANKS

Once Virginia made its landmark decision to remain a slave state, the South stood almost alone in the Western world. The Northern states had abolished the institution; the Spanish-speaking republics of the Americas had done so; Great Britain was in the process of emancipating the slaves in its colonies. In the entire Christian world, only the Spanish colonies of Cuba and Puerto Rico and the independent empire of Brazil still preserved the institution.

After 1832, Southerners faced up to the fact that American Negro slavery was a "peculiar institution," a way of life almost unique to them, and they moved on three fronts to protect it. First, they insulated the South from outside ideas that threatened slavery, and they suppressed dissent at home. Second, white Southerners ceased to apologize to themselves and others for slavery. Instead of calling it a historical tragedy or a necessary evil, they devised the argument that slavery was "a positive good" that benefited slave owner, slave, and society as a whole. Third, they reformed the state slave codes (the laws that governed the peculiar institution), both

The masthead of William Lloyd Garrison's antislavery newspaper.

Slaves beside their living quarters in South Carolina.

improving the material conditions under which slaves lived and instituting stricter controls over the black population.

Suppression of Dissent

Most Southern states passed laws that forbade the distribution of abolitionist literature within their borders. Officials screened the federal mails and seized copies of *The Liberator* and other antislavery newspapers and books. Georgia's legislature actually offered a reward of $5,000 to any person who would bring William Lloyd Garrison into the state to stand trial for inciting rebellion.

Even if the resolution was meant to be symbolic, a state legislature's willingness to sanction a felony illustrates the depth of bitterness in the South toward abolitionists. In border states like Kentucky, abolitionists such as John Gregg Fee and the politician Cassius Marcellus Clay (a relative of Henry) were generally unmolested, but they were the exception. The expression of antislavery opinions was no longer acceptable below the Mason-Dixon line.

Nor even in Washington: beginning in 1836, Southern congressmen annually nagged the House of Representatives to adopt a rule providing that every petition dealing with slavery that the House received be tabled, set aside with no discussion on the floor. Former president John Quincy Adams, now a member of Congress, argued that this "gag rule" violated the right to free speech. Quincy Adams was no abolitionist. He considered crusaders like Walker and Garrison to be dangerous and irresponsible fanatics. But he insisted on the constitutional right of abolitionists to be heard, and because

---

SOUTHERN ANXIETIES

Both antislavery and proslavery Southerners feared slave rebellion. The chief difference between them was in the tone in which they spoke of blacks.

Thomas Ritchie, an antislavery Virginian: "To attempt to excite discontent and revolt, or publish writings having this tendency, obstinately and perversely, among us, is outrageous—it ought not to be passed over with indifference. Our own safety—the good and happiness of our slaves, requires it."

Edward D. Holland, a proslavery South Carolinian: "Let it never be forgotten that our NEGROES are truly the *Jacobins* of the country; that they are the *anarchists* and the *domestic enemy*, the *common enemy of civilized society*, and the barbarians who would, IF THEY COULD, become the DESTROYERS of our race."

he criticized Southerners for quashing the right of petition, the lifelong nationalist came to be lumped with the abolitionists as an enemy.

A Positive Good

Shortly after Virginia's debate on the future of slavery, a professor of economics at the College of William and Mary, Thomas Roderick Dew, published a ringing defense of the slave system as a better way of organizing and controlling labor than the wage system of the North. By 1837, most Southern political leaders were parroting and embroidering on Dew's theories. In the Senate, John C. Calhoun declared that compared with other systems by which racial and class relationships were governed, "the relation now existing in the slave-holding states is, instead of an evil, a good—a positive good."

The proslavery argument included religious, historical, cultural, and social proofs of the justice and beneficence of the institution. The Bible, the positive-good propagandists argued, sanctioned slavery. Not only did the ancient Hebrews own slaves with God's blessing, but Christ had told a servant who wanted to follow him to return to his master and practice Christianity as a slave.

Dew and others pointed out that the great civilizations of antiquity, Greece and Rome, were slaveholding societies. Hardly barbaric in their eyes, slavery had served as the foundation of high culture since the beginning of recorded time. Slavery made possible the existence of a

---

CALHOUN'S CONSISTENCY

When abolitionists quoted the Declaration of Independence to proslavery Southerners—"all men are created equal"—the Southerners were generally forced to make convoluted interpretations of the phrase in order to excuse slavery. John C. Calhoun, at least, was consistent. "Taking the proposition literally," he said, "there is not a word of truth in it."

---

gracious and cultured upper class that, with its leisure, guarded the highest refinements of human achievement.

Southern planters took pride in the fact that, although elementary and secondary education in the South was inferior to that provided by the public-school systems of the North, more upper-class Southerners were college-educated than were members of the Northern elite. Even as late as 1860, there were more than 6,000 college students in Georgia, Alabama, and Mississippi and fewer than 4,000 in the New England states, which were, altogether, more populous.

As an aristocracy, Southerners said, the planters were closer to the tradition of the gentlemanly Founding Fathers than were the vulgar, money-grubbing capitalists of the North. Because gentlemen dominated politics in the South, the section was far better governed than was

These slaves were owned by Jefferson Davis.

RACISM IN SCRIPTURE

Defenders of slavery were hard pressed when abolitionists quoted the Bible on the equality of all men and women before God. A few went so far as to answer that blacks were a different species from whites, even though it was known that mating between species produces sterile offspring and the children of mixed parents in the South were both numerous and fertile.

Southerners were more comfortable when they went to the Bible. They quoted the story of Noah's son Ham, who had humiliated his father and was therefore cursed when Noah said, "a servant of servants shall he be unto his brethren." Blacks were human beings, proslavery Southerners agreed, but their race was "the mark of Ham." As Ham's descendants, they were doomed by God to be (borrowing from another source) "hewers of wood and drawers of water."

the North, where demagogues from the dregs of society could win election by playing on the whims of the mob, The planters liked to think of themselves as descended from the Cavaliers of seventeenth-century England. The South's favorite author was Sir Walter Scott, who spun tales of flowering knighthood and chivalry.

George Fitzhugh, Sociologist

But did all these "proofs" justify denying personal freedom to human beings? Yes, answered George Fitzhugh, a Virginia lawyer, in two influential books: *A Sociology for the South* (1854) and *Cannibals All!* (1857). He amassed statistics and other evidence with which he argued that the Southern slave lived a better life than did the Northern wageworker or the European peasant.

Like Dew and Calhoun, Fitzhugh argued that someone had to perform the drudgery in every society. In the South, menial work was done by slaves who were cared for from cradle to grave. Not only did the slave owner feed, clothe, and house his workers, but he also supported slave children, the injured and the disabled, and the elderly—all of whom were nonproductive. Fitzhugh delighted in pointing out that, by comparison, the Northern wageworker was paid only as long as there was work to be done and the worker was fit to do it. The wageworker who was injured was cut loose to fend for himself in an uncaring world: His children, the elderly, and the incompetent were no responsibility of capitalist employers.

Consequently, according to Fitzhugh, the North was plagued with social problems that were unknown in the South. The North teemed with obnoxious, nattering reformers; the lower classes were irreligious and, in their

misery, tumultuous. The free working class was tempted by socialism, communism, and other dangerous doctrines that threatened the social order. By comparison, Fitzhugh claimed, Southern slaves were contented, indeed happy. "A merrier being does not exist on the face of the globe," Fitzhugh wrote, "than the Negro slave of the United States."

Management

Fitzhugh equated happiness with the material conditions of slave life—housing, clothing, diet—and compared them favorably with the conditions under which the poorest wageworkers of the North lived. By the 1850s, when he wrote, most Southern state legislatures had defined minimum living standards as part of their slave codes, and magazines like the *Southern Agriculturalist* regularly featured exchanges among slave owners about how well they treated "their people."

The most commonly stated reason for keeping slaves adequately housed, clothed, and fed was practical: a healthy slave worked more efficiently and was less likely to rebel or run away. Also underlying the trend toward improvement in the conditions of slave life after the 1830s, was the South's determination to give the lie to the abolitionists' depiction of slavery as a life of unremitting horror. Planters who did provide decent accommodations for their slaves took pleasure in showing slave quarters to Northern or foreign visitors. They reassured themselves that they were just the beneficent patriarchs that the positive-good writers described. Less likely to be publicized were the measures of control that were devised in the wake of the Turner rebellion.

Control

By 1840, the states of the Deep South had adopted laws that made it extremely difficult for a slave owner to free his slaves. Virginia required recently freed blacks to leave the state. (The law was impossible to enforce effec-

SOUTHERN SUCCESS STORY

In 1841, John Hampden Randolph purchased a plantation in Iberville Parish (country), Louisiana. The price was astronomical, $30,000, but the down payment was only $863, the odd amount implying that Randolph was not rich in cash. He paid off the mortgage by planting cotton, but then switched to sugar. Before the outbreak of the Civil War, Randoph owned several thousand acres and 195 slaves. His sons were university educated, and he sent his daughters to a finishing school in Baltimore. In 1858, he built a 51-room mansion, Nottoway, which survives.

A slave displays scars from a brutal whipping. Such extreme cruelty was unusual, but many, perhaps most, slaves were whipped at one time or another.

job, the "paddyrollers" (patrollers) were brutal even with unoffending slaves. Blacks hated and feared them. Their mere presence and arrogance cast a cloud of repression over the plantation regions that few outsiders failed to notice.

Blacks who were not under the direct supervision of their masters or overseers were required by law to carry written passes that gave them permission to be abroad, even just a mile or two from their cabins. Free blacks—there were about 250,000 in the South by 1860, one to every 15 slaves—also had to protect carefully the legal evidence of their status. Kidnappings of free blacks, and sale of them as slaves elsewhere in the South, was not unknown.

The presence of free blacks presented a serious ideological problem for slave owners. One of the most effective means of controlling the slaves was to convince them that God and nature intended them to be slaves because of their race, and that they should be thankful to be under the care of their masters. But if slaves saw free blacks prospering, the argument flew to pieces. Slave owners also thought that free blacks were likely to stir up discontent among slaves, and they were probably right.

Religion could be an effective means of control, and careful masters paid close attention to the kind of preaching their property heard. Some owners took their slaves to their own churches where the minister was expected to deliver a sermon now and then based on biblical stories such as that of Hagar: "the angel of the Lord said unto her, return to Thy mistress, and submit thyself under her hands." Other masters permitted the blacks, who preferred an emotional Christianity enhanced with vestiges of West African culture, to have preachers of their own race. But these often eloquent men were instructed—specifically or indirectly—to steer clear of any topics that might cast doubt on the justice of slavery. Some toed the line. Others developed coded language and song by which they conveyed their protest. The idealized institution of John C. Calhoun and George Fitzhugh bore only an accidental relationship to slavery as it actually existed.

tively.) It was a crime in some Southern states to teach a slave to read.

County governments were required to fund and maintain slave patrols. These mounted posses of armed whites policed the roads and plantations, particularly at night. They had the legal right to break into slave cabins or demand at gunpoint that any black (or white) account for himself or herself. Usually rough, hard-bitten men who were so poor that they sorely needed the undesirable

For Further Reading

On the South and its distinctive characteristics, see Avery O. Craven, *The Growth of Southern Nationalism, 1848–1860* (1953); Clement Eaton, *The Growth of Southern Civilization* (1961) and *A History of the Old South* (1975); I. A. Newby, *The American South* (1979); and Charles S. Sydnor, *The Development of Southern Sectionalism, 1819–1848* (1948). Few historians today would subscribe to the conclusions in Wilbur Cash, *The Mind of the South* (1940), and yet it contains many perceptive insights. A contemporary "travel book" about the Old South well worth reading is Frederick Law Olmstead, *The Cotton Kingdom* (1861).

Of more specific concern but vital to understanding the subject are Dickson D. Bruce, *Violence and Culture in the Antebellum South* (1979); William J. Cooper, *The South and the Politics of Slavery, 1828–1856* (1978); Eugene Genovese, *The Political Economy of Slavery* (1962) and the same author's *The World the Slaveholders Made* (1969); Patrick Gerster and William Cords, eds., *Myth and Image in Southern History* (1974); Lewis C. Gray, *History of Agriculture in the Southern United States to 1860* (1933); James Oakes, *The Ruling Race: A History of American Slaveholders* (1982); Frank Owsley, *Plain Folk of the Old South* (1949); William R. Taylor, *Cavalier and Yankee: The Old South and American National Character* (1961); and Gavin Wright, *The Political Economy of the Cotton South* (1978).

"A Ride for Liberty—the Fugitive Slaves," painting by Eastman Johnson, ca. 1862.

THE PECULIAR INSTITUTION

SLAVERY AS IT WAS PERCEIVED AND AS IT WAS

In December 1865, the Thirteenth Amendment to the Constitution was ratified and became a part

of the basic law of the land. The Thirteenth is one of the shortest amendments, but in terms of what

it did, it was the most momentous. In providing that "neither slavery nor involuntary servitude . . .

shall exist within the United States," the Thirteenth wrote an end to the "Great Exception," a legal

and social institution that flew in the face of the ideals that Americans believed gave their nation special meaning to the world: the freedom of the individual, impartial justice, equality of opportunity, and government by the people—Slavery.

IMAGES OF SLAVERY

Since 1865, two images of slavery, one lush in romance, the other rife with horror, have competed for possession of the American memory. Both visions actually took shape before 1865, when slavery was still a living institution. The seeds of the former were planted by the positive-good theorists with the assistance of a Pennsylvania-born songwriter who spent only a few months of his life in the South. The latter was cultivated in abundant detail by Northern abolitionists who also, with a few exceptions, had little firsthand knowledge of the slave states.

Stephen Foster and the Sweet Magnolia

Stephen Foster was born in Pittsburgh in 1826. Musically inclined from youth, he was a pioneer of "pop music," one of the first Americans to support himself by composing songs that captured the fancy of a mass market. He wrote for traveling minstrel shows and sold sheet music, the songwriter's chief commodity before the invention of the player piano and the phonograph.

Foster's first successful song was "Oh! Susannah," a whimsical nonsense piece about the California gold rush of 1849 that is still popular in elementary school singalongs. Then, perhaps because the minstrel show was "set" in the South, with white (and sometimes black) performers rubbing burnt cork on their faces and joshing and singing in grotesquely exaggerated dialect, Foster turned to sentimental depictions of plantation life, often from the slave's perspective. In the world of "Old Folks at Home" and "Swanee River" (1851), "Massa's in de Cold, Cold Ground" (1852), "My Old Kentucky Home" (1853), and "Old Black Joe" (1860), slaves were uncom-

This idealized depiction of slaves by Eastman Johnson presented just the picture defenders of slavery wanted the world to see: simple, comfortable, contented slaves.

plicated, loving creatures who enjoyed a simple but secure and satisfying life attached to a kindly old "Massa" who beamed benignly on his loyal "darkies."

Dancing "darkies," grand houses, Spanish moss, the plunking of the banjo, the sweet scent of magnolia blossoms, and kindly white folks were the ingredients of Foster's South, and it is well to remember that he was immensely popular in the heyday of the abolitionist movement. Within a generation of the Thirteenth Amendment, this vision of antebellum Southern life was embraced by most white Americans, perhaps Northerners above all. In the industrial age of the late nineteenth century—dirty, urban, and paced by the relentless drive of the machine, it was consoling to dream nostalgically of a South that had never been. The tradition culminated in Margaret Mitchell's novel of 1936, *Gone with the Wind*, and Hollywood's classic film based on the book.

Theodore Dwight Weld and His Converts

Abolitionists depicted rather a different slavery. To these zealous black and white lecturers, journalists, and preachers who crisscrossed the Northern states, the slave's world was a hell of blacksnake whips, brutal slave catchers following packs of bloodhounds, children torn from their mothers' breasts to be sold down the river, squalor, disease, and near starvation under callous, arrogant masters, the sinister "slavocrats."

William Lloyd Garrison was far from alone in presenting this message to Northerners. Indeed, because of his rasping self-righteousness, he was probably less effective in the attack on slavery than people like Theodore Dwight Weld, a white evangelist, "as eloquent as an angel and powerful as thunder." Weld concentrated on converting prominent people to the antislavery cause. Two of his proselytes, Arthur and Lewis Tappan, were wealthy New York merchants who generously financed abolitionist institutions like Garrison's *Liberator*, Kenyon and Oberlin colleges in Ohio, and the American Anti-Slavery Society, founded in 1833.

Another Weld convert was James G. Birney, an Alabama planter who freed his slaves and ran as the presidential candidate of the antislavery Liberty party in 1840 and 1844. Weld married yet another abolitionist who had owned slaves, Angelina Grimké of a prominent South Carolina family.

Black Abolitionists

While the abolitionist movement steadily attracted white people, it was, unsurprisingly, most dependably supported by the free blacks of the North. Although generally poor, Northern blacks provided a disproportionate share of the money needed to publish antislavery

Sojourner Truth was a freed slave who devoted herself to abolition and women's rights movements.

newspapers and send antislavery lecturers. Several prominent abolitionist crusaders were black.

Sojourner Truth was the name taken by a physical giant of a woman born as the slave Isabella in New York in 1797. Freed under the state emancipation law of 1827, she worked as a domestic servant for several years and then burst on the abolitionist scene as one of the movement's most powerful orators. Sojourner Truth was illiterate to the end of her days—she died in 1893, at 96 years of age—but she transfixed audiences when she accompanied her speeches with songs she had written herself.

The most compelling of the black abolitionist orators was Frederick Douglass, who had been born a slave in Maryland in 1817. Escaping to Massachusetts, he educated himself and, in 1845, wrote his autobiography, which, until the publication of *Uncle Tom's Cabin* in 1851 and 1852, was the most widely read antislavery document. Unlike most white abolitionists, Douglass could speak firsthand of life in a slave society and his message was no less troubling. For a while, because his former master was pursuing him, Douglass lived in England, where he furthered his education.

Harriet Beecher Stowe

The decisive antislavery argument was that it reduced human beings to the status of livestock, mere property. However, rather than dwell on a point that seemed abstract to many people, black and white abolitionists alike focused on the physical deprivations and cruelties suffered by slaves. Some antislavery lecturers traveled with runaway slaves whose backs had been disfigured from brutal beatings.

The loudest single shot in the campaign was *Uncle Tom's Cabin, or Life Among the Lowly*, written by the daughter of a prominent family of Connecticut and New York, Harriet Beecher Stowe. Not only did her book sell an astonishing 300,000 copies within a year (the equivalent of 3 million copies today), but it was adapted into a play that was performed by dozens of professional and amateur troupes in small towns and cities alike. So influential was Mrs. Stowe's tale of Uncle Tom, a submissive and loyal old slave, that when Abraham Lincoln met her during the Civil War, he said, "So you are the little woman who wrote the book that made this great war."

First published as a serial in 1851 and 1852, the book version of Uncle Tom's Cabin *was widely read, selling 300,000 copies within a year.*

The underlying theme of *Uncle Tom's Cabin* is subtle: no matter how decent and well-intentioned the individual slave owner, he cannot help but do wrong by living with an inherently evil institution. In the story, Uncle Tom's original owner is the epitome of the paternalistic planter who genuinely loves his old slave—the Southern *beau ideal*. Nevertheless, when financial troubles make it necessary for him to raise money quickly, he is forced to sell his Tom. Heartbroken, the planter promises Tom that he will find him and buy him back as soon as he is able. Nevertheless, *he sells his beloved friend because he is able to do so!*

It was not, however, this insight into the peculiar institution that made *Uncle Tom's Cabin* so popular. Rather, the book's effectiveness owed to its graphic, lurid scenes of cruelty that Tom witnesses and suffers in the course of the story. Mrs. Stowe herself accepted this as the book's contribution. When Southerners angrily complained that she had distorted the realities of slavery, she responded in 1853 with *A Key to Uncle Tom's Cabin*, which set out the documentary basis of most of her accusations, much of it quotations from Southern newspapers.

Blacks never forgot this side of slavery, but with the ascendancy of the romantic version in the late nineteenth century, most white Americans did. Not until the civil-rights movement of the 1950s awakened the country to the tragic history of American blacks did the ugly face of the peculiar institution again impress itself on the popular consciousness.

WHAT SLAVERY WAS LIKE

Which image is correct? Both and neither. Although proslavery and antislavery partisans dealt with the peculiar institution as though it were monolithic, the same in Virginia and Texas, on cotton plantation and New Orleans riverfront, on vast plantation and frontier homestead, for field hand and big house butler, the reality of slavery was as diverse as the South itself.

The Structure of the Institution

The census of 1860, the last census that was taken while slavery was legal, revealed that nearly 4 million people lived in bondage. They were equally divided between males and females. All but a few lived in the 15 states south of the Mason-Dixon line and the Ohio River. West of the Mississippi River, Missouri, Arkansas, Louisiana, and Texas were slave states.

Only one white Southern family in four owned slaves. Even when those whose living depended directly on the

KING COTTON

Southern politicians repeatedly lectured Northerners that the South supported the national economy. That is, the money that cotton brought in from abroad provided most of the surplus capital that paid for the industrialization of the nation. This transaction was direct when protective tariffs on English-made goods forced Southerners to buy American-made goods.

The politicians were right. Cotton did industrialize the United States before the Civil War. However, Northern antislavery people had another way of considering this economic fact of life. Who, they asked, really produced the cotton? To a large extent, slaves did. And to that extent, the United States was industrialized by the forced labor of the blacks.

---

existence of the institution—overseers, slave traders, patrollers—are added in, it is clear that a minority of white Southerners had a direct material stake in slavery.

Those who were very rich and politically powerful because they owned slaves were particularly few. In 1860, only 2,200 great planters, less than 1 percent of the Southern population, owned 100 or more slaves. Only 254 persons owned 200 or more. Nathaniel Heyward of South Carolina was at the top of this pyramid; he owned 2,000 slaves on 17 plantations.

Actually more typical of the Southern slave owner was Jacob Eaton of neighboring North Carolina. On his 160-acre farm, he worked side by side with the slave family he owned. Eaton's yeoman class—small independent farmers who owned one to nine slaves—was the backbone of both the South and the slavery system. About 74 percent of Southern slave owners fell into this category. Another 16 percent of slave owners fell into the middle category of those who owned between 10 and 20 people. A mere 10 percent of slave owners owned more than 20 slaves.

If the big plantation was rare from a white perspective, life in the shadow of "the big house" was more common in the eyes of the blacks. By 1860, more than half the slaves lived on what we would think of as a "plantation" rather than a farm. Perhaps half a million belonged to members of the great planter class.

There were, oddly enough, a few black slave owners, even great planters. Andrew Durnford of New Orleans owned 77 slaves. When questioned about this, Durnford said frankly that his ownership of other blacks was self-interest. Owning slaves was the way to wealth in the South. Although he contributed to the American Colonization Society, Durnford freed only four slaves during his lifetime, another in his will.

First Light to Sundown

Few blacks enjoyed the comparative ease, comforts, and privileges of being domestic servants. Cooks, maids, butlers, valets, and footmen made life more pleasant for the great planters who could afford them, but they did not make money for Old Massa. The vast majority of slaves were field hands who raised a cash crop by means of heavy labor from first light to sundown the year round. For a slave owner to justify investing capital in a labor force rather than hiring free laborers and putting his capital elsewhere, it was necessary to keep the property hopping.

Cotton was by far the most important Southern product (the most important *American* product!). During the 1850s, an average annual crop of 4 million bales brought more than $190 million into the American economy from abroad. Cotton represented two-thirds of the nation's total exports and (in 1850) fully 1.8 million slaves out of 3.2 million worked it. Other cash crops that slaves raised were tobacco (350,000 slaves), sugar (150,000), rice (125,000), and hemp, from which rope, cloth, and paper were manufactured (60,000).

Southern farmers and planters strived to be self-sufficient. Therefore, slaves raised corn, vegetables, and hogs for food, and hay for fodder, as well as their cash crop. There was plenty of work to be done on farm or plantation the year round. The calendar of a cotton planta-

Most slaves were used as field hands and performed the heavy labor needed to raise such cash crops as cotton.

NOTABLE PEOPLE

MARY BOYKIN CHESNUT (1823–1886)

She was part of the elegant aristocracy at the pinnacle of southern society. Her father and her husband were United States senators. Her relatives owned dozens of large plantations and hundreds of slaves. She associated with only the rich and cultivated. She was waited on by slaves, and her days were filled with parties, dances, and receptions in big houses. Mary Boykin Chesnut was a southern belle and a grand lady who was expected to do little with her life but serve as her husband's hostess and as her elegant society's ornament. If she had not kept a diary during the Civil War years, we would know nothing but her name. Because she did keep one of the most revealing documents of the era, we know her as one of the South's most perceptive critics.

Mary Boykin was born on March 31, 1823. She attended Madame Talvande's School in Charleston, more a finishing school than an academy. Upper-class southern girls were expected to learn little but gracious manners. In 1840, seventeen years of age, she married James Chesnut, Jr., who was of the same social standing as herself. They honeymooned in Europe.

Mary Chesnut enjoyed the idle social whirl of the southern elite. Even when she was more than forty years old, her enthusiasm for gossip about belles and their beaus and hints of sexual scandal continued, and her reports of it have the ring of girlishness. She spent endless hours with other women simply sitting and talking. But Mary Chesnut did not quite fit in. She was an avid reader who devoured classical and contemporary authors alike. On more than one occasion, she breached the etiquette of her class by making it clear that she knew more about literature and even politics than did the gentlemen in her company.

Mary Chesnut never had children, an even more basic violation of the code of her class. Before she was married, a wealthy southern woman was expected to be beautiful and flirtatious but shy. After marriage, she was expected to be the mother of her husband's children, the means by which his line as an aristocrat was preserved. The failure of the Chesnuts to have children sorrowed Mary, but the distance it put between her and the ideal of southern womanhood probably contributed to her ability to dissect so shrewdly the society in which she moved.

Mary Chesnut hated slavery, but not for the same reasons that northern abolitionists did. In fact, she condemned them on the grounds that they did not know anything about the institution as it actually functioned, but spoke and wrote on the basis of abstract principles from ivory towers in New England. Like other white southerners, Mary did not believe that blacks were the equals of whites, but she felt that slavery corrupted the integrity and morals of her own people. She wrote of a relative who praised her slaves in extravagant terms when they were nearby. When the blacks left, the woman fearfully told friends that they were trying to poison her.

According to Mary Chesnut, a plantation was a house of concubines, with the men of the planter class abusing their authority over the young female slaves and making prostitutes of them. Mary's friends must have talked a great deal about this, for she wrote acerbically that women knew the identities of the fathers of every light-skinned black except those on their own plantations. The pain in her comments implies that she may have suffered from sexual humiliation.

After the war, the Chesnuts' wealth declined, but was not destroyed. Mary and James lived out their final years in comfortable obscurity in South Carolina. James died in 1885. Mary followed him the next year.

---

tion was packed with jobs major and odd except for a short period around Christmas, to which the slaves looked forward as "laying-by time."

Curiously, because slaves were expensive—up to $1,800 for a first-rate field hand, a healthy man in the prime of life—planters preferred to hire free black or Irish workers to perform unhealthy and dangerous tasks. Few would risk their costly human property on the jobs of draining swamps or working at the bottom of chutes down which 600-pound bales of cotton came hurtling at high speeds, sometimes flipping end over end.

The Rhythms of Labor

By the 1850s, a slave produced from $80 to $120 in value each year and consumed between $30 and $50 in food, clothing, and shelter. The margin of profit was not large enough to allow the small-scale slave owner to live without working in the fields along with his slaves.

Planters who owned up to about 20 slaves were less likely to perform menial tasks. But because slaves rarely worked any more than they were forced to (their share of the fruits of their labor was quite firmly fixed), the owner had to supervise them—constantly bribing, cajoling, threatening, or whipping them to move along. With more than 20 slaves, a planter could afford to hire a professional overseer or to put a straw boss or slave driver (himself a slave) in charge of supervision. On the very large plantations, masters had little direct contact with their field hands.

Slaves on larger plantations worked according to the task system or the gang system. Under the task system, a specific job was assigned each day. When it was done, the slave's time was his or her own. For some planters this was the most efficient form of organization because, when provided with an "incentive," however meager, the slaves worked harder. Others complained that the result of the task system was slipshod labor as their workers rushed through their tasks to get to their own chores or recreation. Under the gang system, slaves worked from sunrise to sundown in groups under a white overseer or black driver. It is impossible to know how frequently they felt the sting of the blacksnake. The lash was always in evidence, however, in black hand as well as white. Frederick Douglass wryly remarked that "everybody in the South wants the privilege of whipping someone else."

The Slave Trade

Slaves were defined in law as chattel property, personal movable possessions legally much the same as cattle, hogs, a cotton gin, a chair, or a share in a corporation. They could be bought, sold, bartered, willed, or given away as a present. In practice in the volatile cotton economy, the commerce in slaves was brisk and potentially quite profitable.

The slave trade was the ugliest face of slavery, as even strident defenders of the institution admitted. The general flow of the commerce was "down the river"—the Mississippi—from the older tobacco states to the cotton states of the Deep South. Professional slave traders bought blacks in Virginia and Maryland, and shipped them or marched them in coffles (groups chained together in a line) to New Orleans, where as many as 200 companies were in the business.

The slave auction was, in effect, an auction of human livestock. Foreigners, Northerners, and many Southerners were simultaneously disgusted and fascinated by them, much as American tourists in Mexico or Spain today react to bullfights. Prospective buyers crowded around the auction block, examining the teeth of the slaves in which they were interested, as they would examine those of horses; running them around to test their wind; wiping handkerchiefs over their bodies to determine if the auctioneer had dyed gray hairs black or rubbed oil into aged dry skin; and then raucously entering their bids.

Some abolitionists claimed that slaves were methodically bred like animals. Indeed, women were rewarded for bearing children, thus increasing their owners' wealth, and were described in auction advertisements as "good breeders." In Maryland, census takers discovered "plantations" on which the "work force" consisted of one adult male, half a dozen young women, and perhaps twice that many small children—not a group likely to get a lot done if agriculture was the idea. However, the gospel of the positive good required slave owners who

took it seriously to abhor such immorality, and slave breeding as a business was undoubtedly rare.

Masters aspiring to be patriarchs disapproved of everything about the slave trade, describing slave traders as base, crude, unworthy men. Nevertheless, as Harriet Beecher Stowe and others pointed out, without the slave trade there could be no slavery. If some humans were to be property, others had to have the right to buy and sell them. When there is trade, there must be brokers.

The Foreign Slave Trade

After 1808, it was a violation of federal law to import slaves. But when the price of slaves was high, some buccaneers were willing to try to bring in blacks from West Africa or Cuba.

It was a risky business. The Royal Navy patrolled African waters, and American naval vessels cruised the Atlantic and Gulf coasts. Nevertheless, an estimated 50,000 to 55,000 Africans and black Cubans were smuggled into the United States between 1808 and 1861. During the 1850s, several travelers in the South reported seeing a number of black men and women with filed teeth, tattoos, and ritual mutilations that were practiced only in Africa. On the eve of the Civil War, a slave vessel successfully made its way into Charleston harbor.

In the late 1850s, the price of slaves soared beyond the reach of all but the very wealthy. A group of Southern politicians met at Vicksburg, Mississippi, and formally demanded the reopening of the African slave trade. Such a law would never have passed Congress, but the Vicksburg Convention alarmed many Northerners and contributed to the hardening of sectional hostilities that contributed to the Civil War.

LIFE IN THE QUARTERS

The slave codes of the Southern states provided that slaves had no civil rights whatsoever. They could not own property under the law, therefore they could not legally buy and sell anything. They could not make contracts. They could not marry legally. They could not testify in court against any white person. They could not leave the plantation without their owner's written permission.

It was a crime for a slave to strike a white person under any circumstances, even self-defense. Slaves could not carry firearms. They could not congregate in more than small groups except at religious services under white supervision. They could not be abroad at night. In most Southern states, it was a crime for a white or another black to teach a slave to read.

The slaves' rights were those to life and, under most slave codes, a minimum standard of food, clothing, and shelter.

Humans Without Human Rights

The actual experience of slave life had little to do with the letter of the slave codes. For example, because it was not accounted murder when a master killed a slave during punishment, the legal right to life was almost unenforceable. Whipping was the most common means of corporal punishment, and 50 and more lashes—quite enough to kill a man—was not an uncommon sentence. In the end, the slaves' only real guarantee against death or brutal mistreatment at the hands of their masters was the gospel of patriarchy and their cash value.

There are few better guarantees than a man's self-esteem and his money, but neither was foolproof. Struggling slave owners had little time for noble theories. Slave owners and overseers did fly into uncontrolled rages and kill slaves. Because their property rights in their slaves inevitably took precedence over the slaves' few human rights, owners were rarely punished. After an incident of hideous torture in Virginia in 1858, with the slave victim dying after 24 hours of beating and burning, the law punished the sadistic master by imprisoning him. But he was not required to forfeit ownership of several other blacks.

A Diverse Institution

If the laws protecting slaves were not effective, it was also true that many slave owners were moved by personal decency and by their determination to live up to the

Slaves were kept in these cells in Alexandria, Virginia, until they were sold by the slave traders.

This photograph of a slave with instruments of punishment was widely distributed to raise money "for the benefit of colored people."

could not always be sure if the pork chop on the slave's table was the slave's own or stolen from him.

Some slaves were permitted to buy and sell outside the boundaries of the plantation and to keep the money. Along the Mississippi River, task system slaves working on their own time cut wood for the steamboats. Some sold chickens and eggs in nearby towns, and some slaves even kept shotguns for hunting. One remarkable character was Simon Gray, a skilled flatboatman who was paid $8 a month to haul lumber to New Orleans. Gray commanded crews of up to 20 men, including free whites, and kept detailed accounts for his owner. He eventually bought his own freedom.

A few masters permitted their slaves to save money in order to purchase their own, their spouse's, or their children's freedom. In at least one instance, a Kentucky judge actually enforced an agreement on a purchase price between a master and slave as a valid contract.

Another example of open violation of the slave code was on the model plantation of Joseph Davis, brother of Jefferson Davis, the future president of the Confederate States of America. Ignoring a Mississippi state law for-

ideal of the benevolent patriarch to care for their slaves far better than the law required, and sometimes in violation of the slave codes.

A family that owned only one or two slaves occasionally developed a relationship much like partnership with them. White owners and black slaves ate the same food, slept in the same cabin, and worked together intimately. On the whole, however, the slave on a large plantation was more likely to be better off, simply because of the poverty of the struggling small farmer.

After about 1840, large-scale slave owners generally provided simple but adequate rations. It was common to allow slaves to keep their own vegetable plots and even chickens; masters sometimes did not keep their own gardens and coops but bought vegetables and eggs from their slaves. Here and there was a master who allowed the blacks to raise hogs for their own use, but the master

WASHINGTON THE SLAVE OWNER

At the time of his death in 1799, George Washington owned 300 slaves at Mount Vernon and four additional plantations. The father-of-his-country's record as a patriarch was mixed. On the one hand, according to a visitor from Poland, the slaves' houses at Washington's River Farm were "more miserable than the most miserable cottages of our peasants." Washington himself expressed embarrassment over living conditions at River Farm.

On the other hand, Washington was deeply concerned to respect his slaves' family and marriage relationships. Children remained with their mothers until age 14. Slave husbands and wives were separated when one but not the other was needed elsewhere, and some of Washington's slaves were married to the slaves of other planters or to free blacks. However, Washington meticulously recorded who was tied to whom, and he refused to sell costly surplus slaves "because they could not be disposed of in families . . . and to disperse the families I have an aversion."

Moreover, Washington's plantations were within four miles and "nightwalking," conjugal visits, were a constant problem of which he complained but did little. In his will, Washington provided that his slaves be freed only after his wife's death because they had intermarried with Martha Washington's "Dower Negroes" and it "would excite the most painful sensations" if they were to be separated.

bidding the education of blacks, Joseph Davis maintained a school and teacher for the children of the quarters.

It is important to recall, however, that for every such master there was another who kept his slaves just sound enough to work and who agreed with the man who wrote without embarrassment to a magazine that "Africans are nothing but brutes, and they will love you better for whipping, whether they deserve it or not."

MODES OF PROTEST

Whether their master was kindly or cruel, their material circumstances adequate or execrable, the blacks hated their lot in life. While some, particularly domestic servants, were deeply and sincerely attached to their masters, and while slave rebellion was rare after Nat Turner, the blacks resisted slavery in other ways. When freedom became a realistic possibility during the Civil War, slaves deserted their homes by the thousands to flee to Union lines and, in the case of the young men, to enlist in the Union Army. As a South Carolina planter wrote candidly after the war, "I believed these people were content, happy, and attached to their masters." That, he concluded sadly, was a "delusion."

Malingering and Thieving

This honest man might have been spared his disappointment had he given deeper consideration to white people's stereotypes of the blacks under slavery. It was commonly held that blacks were inherently lazy and irresponsible and would not work except under close supervision. In fact, free blacks generally worked quite hard, and the same slaves whose laziness was a "constant aggravation" in the cotton fields, toiled in their own gardens from dawn to dusk on Sundays and often, by moonlight, during the week. In slavery, the only incentive to work hard for the master was negative—the threat of punishment—and that incentive was often not enough to cause men and women to ignore the blazing Southern sun. When the overseer or driver was over the hill, it was nap time.

Theft was so common on plantations that whites believed blacks to be congenital thieves. Again, the only incentive not to steal a chicken, a suckling pig, or a berry pie from the big-house kitchen was fear of punishment. If a slave was not caught, he had no reason to believe he had done wrong. One chicken thief who was caught in the act of eating his prize explained this point trenchantly to his master: if the chicken was master's property

and he was master's property, then master had not lost anything because the chicken was in his belly instead of scratching around the henyard. It is not known if this meditation saved the philosopher from a whipping.

Running Away

The most direct testimony of slave discontent was the prevalence of runaways. Only blacks who lived in the states that bordered the free states—Delaware, Maryland, Kentucky—had a reasonable chance of escaping to permanent freedom. A great many were successful "riding" the "Underground Railway," as rushing from hiding places in one abolitionist's home to another was called. Harriet Tubman, who escaped from her master in 1849, returned to the South 19 times to lead other blacks to freedom. (During the Civil War, Tubman was a Union spy behind Confederate lines.)

In calling for a stricter Fugitive Slave Act in 1850 (a law that gave the federal government the responsibility of returning slaves), Southerners estimated that as many as 100,000 blacks had escaped to the free states. Several times that number tried and failed.

Far more common was running away in the full knowledge that capture and punishment were inevitable. Nevertheless, the appeal of a few days or weeks of freedom, or the chance to visit a spouse or a friend on another plantation, was worth the risk to so many blacks that runaway slaves were a vexation in every part of the South.

Runaways in hiding relied on other blacks to conceal and feed them. The fact that they were hidden and fed at risk to their benefactors of corporal punishment reveals the existence of a sense of solidarity among the slaves that can never be fully understood by historians because the slaves kept no written records. But some indication of the quality of life in the slave quarters "from sundown to first light" can be conjectured from what is known of black religion and folklore.

Let My People Go

By the 1850s, most slaves had warmly embraced an emotional brand of Protestant Christianity that was basically Baptist or Methodist in temper. Religious services were replete with animated sermons by unlettered but charismatic preachers and exuberant rhythmic singing, the "Negro spirituals" loved by whites as well as by blacks.

In the sermons and spirituals, hymns that combined biblical themes with African musical forms, the slaves explicitly identified with the ancient Hebrews. While in bondage in Babylonia and Egypt, the Hebrews had been, in their simplicity and poverty, God's chosen people. In the afterlife, all human beings would be equal and happy.

This cry of protest was not lost on the whites. But as long as the slaves associated freedom with the next life, there was no reason to stifle the cry. What the black preachers told their congregations out of earshot of the master and mistress may well have been more worldly.

"Bred en Bawn in a Brier-Patch"

Another thinly masked form of protest was the folk tales for which black storytellers became famous, particularly the Br'er Rabbit stories that were collected after the Civil War as *Uncle Remus: His Songs and Sayings* by Georgia journalist Joel Chandler Harris. In these yarns, elements of which have been traced back to West African folklore, the rabbit, the weakest of animals and unable to defend himself by force, survives and flourishes through the use of trickery and complex deceits.

In the most famous of the Uncle Remus stories, "How Mr. Rabbit Was Too Sharp for Mr. Fox," Br'er Fox has the rabbit in his hands and is debating with himself whether to barbecue him, hang him, drown him, or skin him. Br'er Rabbit assures the fox that he will be happy with any of these fates as long as the fox does not fling him into a nearby brier-patch, which he fears more than anything. Of course, that is exactly what Br'er Fox does, whence Br'er Rabbit is home free. "Bred en bawn in a brier-patch, Br'er Fox," Br'er Rabbit shouts back tauntingly, "bred en bawn in a brier-patch." The slaves, unable to taunt their masters so bluntly, satisfied themselves with quiet trickery and coded tales about it.

It is worth noting that in the Uncle Remus stories, Br'er Rabbit now and then outsmarts himself and suffers for it. As in all social commentary of substance, the slaves were as sensitive to their own foibles as to those of their masters.

This slave family was fortunate in being able to pose five generations together. Historians disagree as to just how stable common family relationships were among nineteenth-century blacks.

UNCLE REMUS EXPLAINS

Many historians of slavery believe that because violent resistance by blacks was suicidal, many slaves (and post–Civil War Southern blacks) devised the technique of "playing Uncle Tom," that is, playing a docile role in front of whites in order to survive. Uncle Remus describes this behavior in "Why Br'er Possum Loves Peace." Mr. Dog attacks Br'er Coon and Br'er Possum. Br'er Coon fights back and drives Mr. Dog away, but at the price of taking some damage himself. In the meantime, Br'er Possum plays possum, plays dead.

Later, representing blacks who want to fight back, Br'er Coon berates Br'er Possum for cowardice. " 'I ain't runnin' wid cowards deze days,' sez Br'er Coon." Br'er Possum replies that just because he did not fight does not mean that he is a coward:

I want no mo' skeer'd dan you is right now . . . but I'm de most ticklish chap w'at you ever laid eyes on, en no sooner did Mr. Dog put his nose down yer 'mong my ribs dan I got ter laffin. . . . I don't mine fightin', Br'er Coon, no mo' dan you duz . . . but I declar' ter grashus ef I kin stan' ticklin.

Wit, not violence, was the way to deal with vicious whites. Note that it is Mr. Dog, not Br'er—Brother.

The Slave Community

Like Br'er Rabbit, slaves presented a different face to whites than among their own people. Often, individuals reinforced white beliefs in their inferiority by playing the lazy, dimwitted, comical "Sambo," quite devoted to "Ol' Marse" and patently incapable of taking care of themselves. Some observant whites noticed that Sambo was quick witted enough when surprised while talking to other slaves, or that he literally slaved in his own garden and only slept in the master's cotton fields.

For the most part, however, the vitality of black culture and the slave community remained concealed from whites. It can be read only in the folktales, sermons, and recollections of slavery gathered after emancipation. Perhaps the most striking demonstration of the resourcefulness of the blacks in sticking together for mutual support lies in the fact that family connections were powerful and productive. By 1865, when slavery was abolished, there were ten times as many slaves in the United States as had been imported from Africa and the West Indies. The American slave population was the only one in the Western Hemisphere to increase as a result of natural reproduction. Only after the blacks of South and Central America were freed did their numbers grow.

For Further Reading

Ulrich B. Phillips, *American Negro Slavery* (1919) and *Life and Labor in the Old South* (1929) presented sometimes romanticized, almost sympathetic portraits of slavery, and yet, despite the bias of the books, they contain much valuable information and are congenially written. Kenneth Stampp, *The Peculiar Institution* (1956) was an explicit response to Phillips and is equally valuable.

Since the 1960s, slavery has been exhaustively studied in virtually all its aspects. Just a few of hundreds of titles include Ira Berlin, *Slaves Without Masters* (1975); John Blassingame, *The Slave Community* (1972) and *Slave Testimony* (1977); Carl N. Degler, *Neither Black Nor White: Slavery and Race Relations in Brazil and the United States* (1971); Stanley Elkins, *Slavery* (1968); Robert Fogel and Stanley Engerman, *Time on the Cross* (1974), the findings of which are attacked in Herbert Gutman and Richard Sutch, *Slavery and the Numbers Game* (1975); and Paul A. David *et al.*, *Reckoning with Slavery* (1976).

See also George M. Frederickson, *The Black Image in the White Mind* (1971); Eugene Genovese, *The Political Economy of Slavery* (1962) and *Roll Jordan Roll* (1975); Herbert G. Gutman, *The Black Family in Slavery and Freedom, 1750–1925* (1976); Lawrence W. Levine, *Black Culture and Black Consciousness: Afro-American Folk Thought from Slavery to Freedom* (1977); Gilbert Osofsky, *Puttin' On Ol' Massa* (1969); Harold Rawick, *From Sundown to Sunup* (1967); and R. Starobin, *Industrial Slavery in the Old South* (1970).

Useful books pertaining to abolitionism include Ronald Abzug, *Passionate Liberator: Theodore Dwight Weld and the Dilemma of Reform* (1980); Anna Bontemps, *Free at Last: The Life of Frederick Douglass* (1971); M. L. Dillon, *The Abolitionists: The Growth of a Dissenting Minority* (1974); Louis Filler, *The Crusade Against Slavery* (1960); Aileen S. Kraditor, *Means and Ends in American Abolitionism: Garrison and His Critics on Strategy and Tactics, 1834–50* (1967); Gerda Lerner, *The Grimké Sisters from South Carolina: Rebels Against Slavery* (1967); Walter M. Merrill, *Against Wind and Tide: A Biography of William Lloyd Garrison* (1963); Benjamin Quarles, *Black Abolitionists* (1969); Gerald Sorin, *Abolitionism: A New Perspective* (1972); J. B. Stewart, *Holy Warriors: The Abolitionists and American Slavery* (1976); B. P. Thomas, *Theodore Dwight Weld: Crusader for Freedom* (1950); and

J. L. Thomas, *The Liberator: William Lloyd Garrison* (1963).

On the pro-slavery argument, see George M. Frederickson, *The Black Image in the White Mind* (1971); W. S. Jenkins, *Pro-Slavery Thought in the Old South* (1935); William Stanton, *The Leopard's Spots: Scientific Attitudes Toward Race in America, 1815-1859* (1960); and Harvey Wish, *George Fitzhugh: Propagandist of the Old South* (1943).

"Across the Continent" by Currier and Ives.

FROM SEA TO SHINING SEA

AMERICAN EXPANSION 1820 - 1848

With the acquisition of Louisiana in 1803, the boundaries of the United States appeared to be

complete for all time. Thomas Jefferson thought so. He believed that the land he purchased from

France would provide farms for sons and daughters of his beloved yeomanry for centuries. After Lewis

and Clark returned with the news that there was no easy route across the North American continent

to the Pacific, thus killing hopes of a direct trade with the Far East, there seemed little point in pushing

farther west.

The Atlantic Ocean and the Mississippi River were America's outlets to the rest of the world. The Rocky Mountains, imagined more than known, provided a pronounced natural boundary in the West. Indeed, rainfall was so sparse on the American slope of the Rockies that the treeless grasslands were thought of as a void fit for only the bison that wandered them and the mounted Indians who followed the great herds.

In the Southwest lay more desirable land just west of the state of Louisiana. Eastern Texas was fertile and well-watered. It was Mexican land but the founders of the Mexican Republic were hospitable toward the *norteamericanos*, whose war for independence and constitution had inspired many of them. During the 1820s, conflict between Mexico and the United States was unimaginable.

Things change. Within a few decades, the Mexican president Porfirio Diaz would lament of his country, "Poor Mexico, so far from God and so close to the United States."

MEXICO: SO CLOSE TO THE UNITED STATES

Even after Cortez and the conquistadors had looted the riches of the native Mexican cultures, the Viceroyalty of New Spain—Mexico—remained the jewel of the Spanish Empire. Spanish-born *gachupines* or *peninsolares* and Mexican-born white *criollos* monopolized the best lands and lived fat off the labor and skills of the Indians and mixed-blood *mestizos*. Mexico was home to the greatest of the indigenous New World civilizations, an amalgam of Spanish and Indian cultures. When the English settlers at Jamestown were starving, 300 poets competed for a prize in Mexico City. In 1609, Spanish adventurers established Santa Fe in the Sangre de Cristo Mountains of present-day New Mexico, in the heart of the North American continent. When Sydney Smith was mocking the absence of culture in the United States, an intellectual and literary life rivaling that of the lesser capitals of Europe flourished in Mexico City.

Mexico Expands North

Indeed, while Anglo-Americans were just beginning to penetrate the Appalachians, Spanish adventurers and friars were planting colonies deep in what is now the United States. The rivers of Texas, especially the Rio Grande, were dotted with *presidios* (military bases) and missions far more numerous than the old French trading posts along the Mississippi.

During the first years of American independence, a Franciscan priest, Junipero Serra, and his disciples established a string of missions in California, the farthest north at Sonoma above San Francisco. Local Indians were forced to live within the mission compound and to abandon traditional ways of life in favor of Spanish practices. Serra's missions also made it possible for a foot traveler along the Camino Real (or Royal Highway) to spend every night in a secure, hospitable mission compound. As in New Mexico, a gracious but simple way of life evolved among the small numbers of *californios* who lived in the northernmost Mexican province. Today, their culture has been swallowed up, their legacy surviving only in the Spanish-language place-names of California.

The Santa Fe Trade

In 1821, independent Mexico abandoned the Spanish restrictions on trade with the United States. William Becknell, an alert and enterprising businessman in Independence, Missouri, immediately set off in a wagon packed with American manufactures: cloth, shoes, tools, some luxury items. Feeling his way by compass, an eye for animal paths, and dead reckoning across what is now Kansas, he blazed an 800-mile trail to Santa Fe. The 7,000 inhabitants of the mountain community were so remote from the centers of Mexican population that they were starved both for imports and a market for their own produce. Becknell pocketed a fine profit selling the furs and gold that he brought back to Missouri.

Annually for 14 years, a convoy of wagons retraced Becknell's tracks. Only a few Missourians, such as the famous scout Kit Carson, actually settled in Santa Fe or nearby Taos, an Indian village, and those who did were happy to adapt to the gracious Spanish-Indian culture of the region. Nevertheless, the presence of even a few *sasones* (Saxons) in northernmost Mexico forged a link between an attractive country and the United States that was—no matter the flag that flew—stronger than the link between Santa Fe and Mexico City.

The Great American Desert

As for the American territory that the Santa Fe traders crossed, where the Stars and Stripes did fly, most Americans believed it was worthless. In what is now central Nebraska and Kansas, at about 100° west longitude, the land begins a gradual rise from an elevation of about 2,000 feet to, at the base of the Rockies, 6,000 to 7,000 feet. These high plains lie in the "rain-shadow" of the Rockies; before the westerly winds reach the plains, the moisture in them has been scooped out by the great mountains. Save for cottonwoods along the rivers, few trees grew on the great plains. The vastness of the landscape unnerved people who were accustomed to dense forests.

When Americans gazed over the windblown buffalo grass on the rolling plains, they thought not of farmland but of the ocean. The Santa Fe traders called their wagons prairie schooners. Less romantic military mapmakers labeled the country "the Great American Desert."

It was a mistake, of course, to believe that only land that grew trees naturally would support crops. However, it was true enough that the tough sod of the plains was more than a cast-iron or a fire-tempered wood plowshare could break and turn over. Many travelers observed that the grass that nourished 10 million bison would fatten cattle too. However, it was difficult to imagine how hypothetical steers might be transported to eastern markets. All agreed that the Indians of the plains, who were satisfied to trade with or charge "tolls" to the Santa Fe trekkers, were welcome to what they had.

The Texans

To the south, the Great Plains extended into Texas, then part of the Mexican state of Coahuila. There cattle could be grazed within easy driving distance of the Gulf of Mexico and shipped by water to New Orleans. As early as 1819, a Connecticut Yankee named Moses Austin was attracted by the possibilities of a grazing economy there, and he also noted the suitability of eastern Texas to cotton cultivation.

He died before he was able to implement his idea, but in 1821, his son Stephen Austin concluded his father's agreement with the Mexican government. Austin was licensed to settle 300 American families in Texas, each household to receive 177 acres of farmland and 13,000 acres of pastureland. In return, Austin promised that the settlers would abide by Mexican law, learn the Spanish language, and observe the Roman Catholic religion.

The earliest settlers may well have meant to keep their part of the bargain, but Texas was so far from the centers of Mexican power and culture, and the immigrants were so numerous (20,000 whites and 2,000 slaves by 1834), that Texas was inevitably American in culture and customs. Even so, because the province was prosperous and produced some tax revenues, there might have been no trouble. Then in 1831, Mexico abolished slavery, and in 1833, General Antonio Lopez de Santa Anna seized power. Slavery was as vital to the economy of Texas as it was in neighboring Louisiana, and Santa Anna proved to be less accommodating a Mexican president than his predecessors.

Santa Anna wanted to put an end to the squabbling that had plagued Mexican politics since independence and to promote a sense of Mexican nationality. He centralized the powers of government in the constitution he promulgated in 1835 and canceled foreign (that is, American) trading rights in Santa Fe. His reforms meant an end to the considerable autonomy the Texans had enjoyed and jeopardized their economic and cultural connections to the United States.

A small number of both anglo and hispanic Texans rebelled and seized the only military garrison in Texas, at San Antonio. At first, like the Americans of 1775, most of the rebels claimed that they were fighting only for the rights they had traditionally exercised as Mexican citizens. However, having far less in common with their mother country than the revolutionaries of 1775, some spoke of independence from the outset.

The Alamo and San Jacinto

Like King George III, Santa Anna had no intention of negotiating with his troublesome subjects. Rather, he welcomed the Texas uprising as an opportunity to rally the divided Mexican people around a national cause. In early 1836, he led an army of 6,000 to San Antonio, where he calculated that he could easily defeat the 200 Texans (and a few Americans) who were holed up in a former mission compound, the Alamo.

Among the defenders were men already famous in the United States. The garrison was commanded by William Travis, one of the most prominent Texans. Second in command was James Bowie, inventor of the double-edged long knife that many Westerners carried and that now bears his name. Best known was the Whig politician and humorist, David Crockett of Tennessee.

Santa Anna could have passed the Alamo by, leaving a small detachment to contain the garrison. The real threat lay farther east, where Sam Houston was frantically trying to raise an army among frontier farmers. Houston was having his troubles. Not every Texan supported him. By moving quickly, Santa Anna might easily have snuffed out the insurrection.

Instead, he sat in San Antonio for ten days, unable to comprehend why the defenders of the Alamo, whose cause was hopeless, would not surrender. When he realized that they were buying time for Sam Houston, he attacked at tremendous cost to his army and ordered all prisoners executed. Under an ancient but controversial rule of war, he had a right to do so: soldiers fighting a palpably hopeless cause lost their right to quarter. But

AMERICANS IN
THE MEXICAN
BORDERLANDS

MEXICAN FORCES
TEXAN FORCES
MEXICAN VICTORY
TEXAN VICTORY

standing on so antiquated a right, Santa Anna became the author of an atrocity. The executions (only a few women were spared) rallied virtually all Texans, including many of Mexican blood and culture, to the fight against the General-President.

On the banks of the Rio San Jacinto on April 21, Sam Houston routed the Mexican army and captured Santa Anna. In order to secure his release, Santa Anna agreed to the independence of Texas with a southern boundary at the Rio Grande rather than at the Rio Nueces, which had been the boundary of Mexican Texas. As soon as he was free, Santa Anna repudiated the agreement and

refused to recognize the Republic of Texas. But the demoralized Mexican army was in no condition to mount another campaign, and the Texans discreetly remained north of the Nueces.

The Lone Star Republic

In October 1836, Sam Houston was inaugurated president of a republic patterned on that of the United States. Texas legalized slavery and dispatched an envoy to Washington. Houston hoped that his old friend Andrew Jackson would favor annexation. Jackson liked the idea

This 1885 painting of the storming of the Alamo, done after a study of available sources, provides what is probably the most accurate view of the event.

of sewing the Lone Star of the Texas republic on the American flag. However, Congress was then embroiled in a nasty debate in which the question of slavery was being bandied about. Jackson did not want to complicate matters by proposing the admission of a new slave state. In order to spare his successor a problem, he delayed diplomatic recognition of the Republic of Texas until his last day in office.

Martin Van Buren opposed the annexation of Texas, and he was spared a debate on admission when the depression of the late 1830s distracted Americans from territorial questions. The Texans, disappointed and ever worried about Mexico, looked to Europe for an ally.

The British were happy to oblige. The British coveted Texas cotton and welcomed any opportunity to contain the growth of American power. Had it not been for the Texans' commitment to slavery, an institution which the British had recently abolished in the empire, there might have been more than a commercial connection between the old monarchy and the new republic.

THE OREGON COUNTRY

The American government was uneasy about British influence in Texas. Britons and Americans also stepped warily around one another on the western coast of North America in what was known as the Oregon country. This land of prosperous Indians, sheltered harbors, spruce and fir forests, and rich valley farmland was not considered the property of any single nation. This situation came about when the two empires with claims to it had withdrawn, one to the south and one to the north.

SANTA ANNA'S GIFT

Santa Anna's first presidency was ruined by Americans in Texas. However, he bore little animosity to the American people nor to the United States. He spent much of his exile between 1841 and 1844 in Staten Island, New York, where he passed on a then exotic habit to Americans. Santa Anna chewed chicle, sap from the sapodilla tree. When, in 1844, he hurried back to Mexico, he left a substantial supply in his home, which was found by one Thomas Adams who, a good American, marketed it as an alternative to chewing tobacco, a ubiquitous habit already thought filthy in polite society. Adams made a decent living from "chewing gum," but it made William Wrigley, Jr., rich when, in 1893, he hit on the idea of sweetening and flavoring the chicle, calling it "Juicy Fruit."

A Distant Land

Spain's claim to Oregon was never more than nominal. Spanish and Mexican influence ended at the mission town of Sonoma just north of San Francisco. So after 1819, when the boundary of Spanish America was set at 42° north latitude, the present southern line of the state of Oregon, the claim was itself overreaching.

The Russians had established a string of forts, timbering camps, and fur-trapping stations on the Pacific coast from present-day Alaska to Fort Ross, less than a hundred miles from San Francisco Bay. However, the czars had difficulty populating Siberia on the Russian mainland. Few Russians were interested in moving to permanent settlements even farther from Europe. Moreover, by the 1820s, the trappers had looted the coastal waters of the sea otters whose lush, warm furs had brought them there. Rather than get involved in a competition for territory that they could not defend, the Russians withdrew northward in 1825 and set the boundary of Russian America at 54° 40' north latitude, the present southern boundary of the state of Alaska.

Between 42° and 54° 40' lay the Oregon country into which Britons, Canadians, and Americans trickled. Because Oregon was far from their centers of power, the British and Americans agreed to what they called a "joint occupation," which was in truth very little occupation at all—more of an announcement that other nations were unwelcome.

The Mountain Men

The Americans, British, and Canadians in Oregon were few in number and not the sort to put down roots. Most were fur trappers scouring the chill creeks of the West in search of the pelt of the North American beaver. Furriers in New York, London, and Paris paid good prices for beaver; they sewed the pelts into plush coats for the wealthy, and chopped, steamed, and pressed the fur into felt, a versatile fabric with a worldwide market.

Even before William Becknell set out for Santa Fe, American and Canadian veterans of the War of 1812 were disappearing into the northern Rockies with large-bore rifles, iron traps, and a sense of relief at leaving civilization behind for eleven months a year. These "mountain men" never numbered more than a few hundred at any one time. They took Indian wives; they learned Indian lore calculated to foster survival in remote, rugged wilderness; and they sometimes lived with, sometimes battled against the tribes of the region. Other whites who dealt with the mountain men minded their manners, considering them to be savages themselves.

Jeremiah "Liver-Eatin'" Johnson waged a ten-year vendetta with the Crow tribe. He earned his colorful nickname when, to let the Crow know that it was he who killed one their warriors, he cut out and ate the livers of his victims. (Toward the end, Johnson later said, he just cut them out.) Jim Beckwourth, a mulatto born in Virginia, discovered the pass through the Sierra Nevada that rose to the lowest elevation. New York-born Jedediah Smith opened South Pass in Wyoming, the route that would be followed by most overland emigrants. Jim Bridger explored almost every nook of the Rockies. He was the first non-Indian to lay eyes on the Great Salt Lake.

Each year, in late summer or early fall, the trappers brought their furs to prearranged locations on the Platte, Sweetwater, or Big Horn rivers. For a few weeks, buyers from the British Hudson's Bay Company and John Jacob Astor's American firm, mountain men, and Indians of various tribes traded goods, drank whiskey, enjoyed a riotous orgy, now and then bit off the ear of an old pal who got out of line. Of more lasting significance was the knowledge of Western geography they imparted to the folks back home, particularly the fact that while it was a long hard trip, it was possible to cross overland to Oregon.

The Oregon Trail

Among the first to make the six-month journey for the purpose of settling in Oregon were missionaries. In 1834, the Methodists sent Jason Lee to preach the gospel to the Indians of Oregon. In 1835, four Flatheads visited the American Board of Foreign Missions and, so the board reported, persuaded them that Presbyterian was the gospel that they really wanted to hear. In 1836, Marcus and Narcissa Whitman carried it to them on foot. A few years later, the Catholic University at St. Louis sent Father Pierre-Jean de Smet to the Oregon country.

The trek usually began at Independence, Missouri. It was also there in 1843 that the first great wagon train was organized. A thousand Oregon-or-Busters outfitted and provisioned themselves, often packing oddly chosen mementos of home: cumbersome furniture and fragile china gewgaws. They swore to observe strict rules of behavior and cooperation for the duration of the crossing, and they hired mountain men as guides.

The Oregon Trail crossed Kansas to the Platte River and followed that broad, shallow course to Fort Laramie, the westernmost army outpost. The emigrants and their famous covered wagons then crossed the Continental Divide at South Pass and struggled through the Rockies to near the source of the Snake River, which flows into the great Columbia and the Pacific.

A wagon train made up to 20 miles a day (or as few as

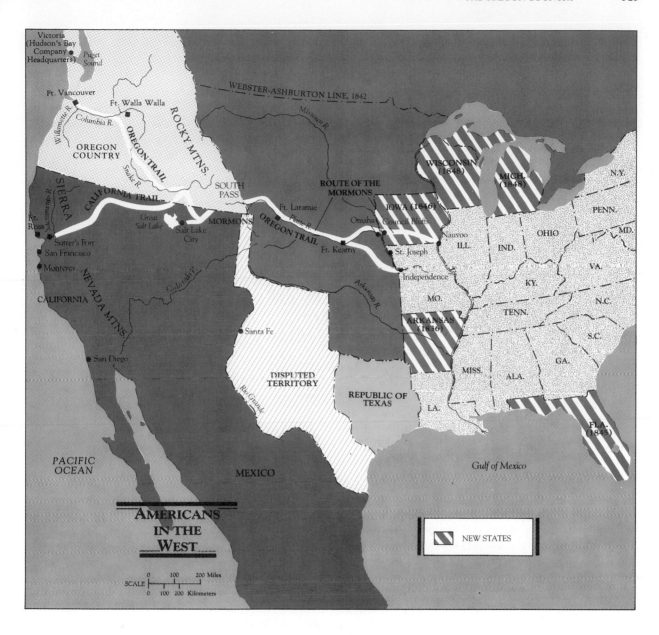

none at all), depending on the terrain and the weather. At night, exhausted by the tremendous labor of moving a hundred wagons and several hundred head of cattle, horses, and mules, the emigrants drew their prairie schooners into a hollow square or circle.

The Indians of the plains and mountains were not a serious threat to large, well-organized expeditions. While the Indians were hardly delighted to see large numbers of strangers crossing their ancestral lands (3,000 in 1845 alone), the whites were, at least, crossing

it and disappearing into the sunset. Although they warred constantly with one another, the tribes had few firearms and were, therefore, no match for the emigrants. The Oregon-bound travelers worried less about Indian attack than about theft. Indians made a game of stealing horses that strayed too far from the caravans. They also traded with the whites and picked up the discarded goods that littered the trail. Even before the stream of wagons wore deep ruts into the sod—which can still be seen today here and there—the Oregon Trail was marked like

A rare photograph of two wagon trains moving west. One, probably bound for Oregon, leaves the other, bound for California.

a highway with broken furniture, empty barrels, incapacitated wagons, the skeletons of worn-out cattle and horses, and simple grave markers that signaled the end of someone's dream. Death from accident or disease, particularly cholera, was common, but it was virtually impossible to lose the way.

Joint Occupation

By 1845, the American population of the Columbia and Willamette valleys had grown to 7,000 and the British-Canadian Hudson's Bay Company prudently moved its headquarters from the mouth of the Columbia to Vancouver Island. What is now the state of Washington served as a buffer zone between British and American population centers. Still, occasional clashes threatened the device of joint occupation that Daniel Webster and Lord Ashburton had worked out as recently as 1842.

The Americans wanted to end the joint occupation and annex Oregon to the United States. In July 1843, a group met at Champoeg and established a provisional territorial government under the American flag. A few

politicians back east supported them, as much to taunt the British as for any realistic hope of affecting policy. The idea of territorial expansion, previously something of a dirty concept because it involved seizing land that belonged to someone else, had taken on positive dignity. Expansion became a sacred duty for some Americans; they had come to believe that they had an obligation to increase the domain over which democracy and liberty held sway.

THE PUSH TO THE PACIFIC

This was the doctrine of Manifest Destiny. Dazzled by the nation's energy and progress, politicians and newspaper editors, mostly Democratic and largely Southern and Western, began to speak of the right, even the duty of Americans to take control of lands that were being wasted by "savage" aborigines and "backward" Mexicans or corrupted by the decadent British.

Legal claims, however universally recognized, were

less important to such people than the sacred mission of the United States to plant free, democratic institutions in Oregon and in thinly populated parts of Mexico. It remained for a New York journalist, John O'Sullivan, to coin a phrase. It was, he said, the "manifest destiny" of the United States—the nation's obvious fate—to expand from sea to sea. God and nature intended Americans to possess the North American continent.

The Texas Debate

In 1843, expansion became a matter of earnest debate. The Texans renewed their request for annexation, and won the support of a number of prominent Americans. Many Northern Democrats such as Lewis Cass of Michigan, James Buchanan of Pennsylvania, and Stephen Douglas of Illinois were enraptured by the idea of territorial expansion. They feared that until Texas was incorporated within the United States, it would be a standing temptation to the expansive British. Southern Democrats such as Calhoun and President John Tyler had an additional reason for favoring annexation. Slavery was legal in Texas; thus, if Texas were brought into the Union, the power of the proslavery bloc would increase.

For the same reason, many political and cultural leaders of New England strenuously opposed annexation. Northern Whigs and some Northern Democrats were determined that slavery should not expand beyond the states where it was already legal. Less hostile toward England than people of other sections, New Englanders did not object to the possibility of Great Britain's taking Texas. The British, at least, would abolish slavery there. Finally, the anti-Texas forces pointed out that admitting Texas would almost certainly lead to a war with Mexico in which the Mexicans, not the Americans, would be in the right.

Clay and Van Buren

Both of the likely presidential nominees of 1844 were unhappy to see Texas annexation shaping up as the principal issue of the campaign. Henry Clay knew that his Whig party, already strained by the slavery issues, could split in two over the issue. His likely opponent, Martin Van Buren, who commanded a safe majority of delegates to the Democratic nominating convention, had the same problem. The Democrats were torn between proslavery and antislavery factions. If the two old rogues took opposite stances on the question, the campaign would throw both parties into disarray. Therefore, they met quietly and agreed that both would oppose annexation, thus eliminating Texas as an issue.

"Dark Horse"

The first president to be described as a "dark horse," that is, a candidate whom no one much thought about before the campaign actually began, was James K. Polk. The phrase came from a novel published in England by Benjamin Disraeli, a future prime minister, in 1832: "A dark horse which never had been thought of, and which the careless St. James had never even observed in the list, rushed past the grandstand in sweeping triumph." Other "dark horses" elected president were James A. Garfield (1880) and Warren G. Harding (1920). Dark-horse candidates who lost the general election were William Jennings Bryan (1896) and Wendell Willkie (1940).

Their bargain presented the lame-duck President Tyler with an opportunity. He would be a third candidate and favor taking Texas. Tyler had no party organization behind him, so his announcement did not unduly disturb either Clay or Van Buren. Then occurred one of those unlikely events that change the course of history. Manifest Destiny Democrats revived a neglected party rule that a presidential nominee receive the support of two-thirds instead of a simple majority of the delegates to the convention. With his anti-Texas pledge, Van Buren was stymied.

After eight ballots ended in a deadlock, the convention turned to a "dark-horse candidate," that is, a candidate who was not considered a contender at the beginning of the race. He was James Knox Polk of Tennessee, a young protege of Jackson not yet 50 years old (he was called "Young Hickory"). Polk had been a Van Buren supporter who favored annexation, a perfect compromise candidate.

The Election of 1844

"Who is Polk?" the Whigs asked scornfully when they learned who was running against their hero, Clay. This snideness was unfair. Polk had been Tennessee's governor and served in the House of Representatives for 14 years, several as speaker. But his stature was midget indeed when his career and personality were set aside those of Henry Clay. Polk was a frail, small man with an air of melancholy about him. He was priggish; he disapproved of alcohol, dancing, and card playing.

At first, Henry Clay was overjoyed to be running against a political nobody. After three attempts, he would be president at last! The unpopular Tyler and the

HOW THEY LIVED

ZORRO AND THE CALIFORNIOS

Alta California—Upper California—was thinly populated when the United States seized it in the Mexican War, but it was far from an empty land. Indians were more numerous in California's mild climate than in any region of North America except the Eastern Woodlands a century and more earlier. And thousands of Mexicans had followed Spain's mission fathers north in the late eighteenth and early nineteenth centuries. Some of these *californios*, as they called themselves, clustered around small mercantile towns and *presidios* (military bases) such as San Diego, Los Angeles, Monterey, Yerba Buena (San Francisco), and Sonoma. Most, however, were ranchers living in isolation on vast government land grants. A few Americans, like John Bidwell and William Ide, as well as Europeans like the Dane, Peter Lassen, and the Swiss, John Augustus Sutter, had taken out grants.

They and the *californios* were rich in acres but they lived just a notch or two above subsistence. The only commodities California produced for the international market were hides and tallow, the fat of cattle and sheep cooked down for use in soap and candle manufacture. Neither brought in much money and few ships called at remote California ports. Even the richest *californios* lived in adobe homes, rarely more than one story high and rarely large. Furniture and most manufactures were made on the scene by Indian craftsmen. Diet was ample (plenty of beef!) and *californio* cuisine, while ingenious, was inelegant.

Nevertheless, the *californios* were proud of their independence and self-sufficiency and keenly conscious of their social status at the top of California's rather simple pyramid. Most of the grandees were of modest background but, just as the great planters of eighteenth-century Virginia took their values and mores from the English gentry, elite *californios* considered themselves *hidalgos*, Spanish noblemen, rightful rulers but also the benefactors of their lessers, both poor Mexicans and Indians. The top families intermarried, carefully planning the genealogies of their descendants.

Tight-knit as it was, the *californio* community was divided down the middle by the American invasion. Some, feeling little commitment to old Mexico, quickly made their peace with their gringo conquerors and salvaged at least some of their property and social position. Others resisted and won a few small battles before being overcome.

It was less the American victory, however, that inundated the *californios* (and non-Hispanic *hidalgos* like Sutter), than the great gold rushes of 1849 and 1850. The Spanish-speaking ranchers were left behind or literally overrun by the flood of gold-seekers. Among those who were ruined was Salomon María Simeón Pico, the son of a soldier who had been granted eleven Spanish leagues (48,829 acres, 19,756 hectares) between the Tuolumne and Stanislaus rivers, two of the richest gold-bearing streams. According to legend, Pico not only lost his herds and land, his wife was raped and beaten, dying soon thereafter.

It is not easy to separate legend from fact in Pico's subsequent career. It is clear that he became a masked highwayman on the old *camino real* between Santa María and Santa Barbara, and cut an ear off each of his mostly gringo victims to leave no doubt as to the identity of the perpetrator. (Pico strung his trophies and carried them on his saddle horn like a lariat.) It is less likely that he gave his cash earnings to impoverished *californio* families, but he was something of a popular hero among them even during his lifetime. Pico moved about California with impunity for eight years, aided no doubt by the fact that two brothers were mayors of San Luis Obispo and San Jose.

His most famous scrape with the law came in November 1851, when he shot the hat off the head of Los Angeles Judge Benjamin Hayes, who was presiding over the trial of three *californios* charged with murder. Although himself wounded, Pico escaped, helped by another *californio* who held off a pursuing sheriff with a sword. In 1857, Pico moved to Baja California. Three years later, he was arrested by Mexican authorities and summarily executed.

In the twentieth century, as "Zorro"—the Fox—a name Pico never used, the anti-American bandit became a popular culture hero in the United States. In 1919, writer Johnston McCulley collected the many Pico legends, deftly adapted them to appeal to an American readership, and published them as *The Curse of Capistrano*. Pico's fictional name was Don Diego Vega and he lived not in California's American era but earlier, when California was a Mexican province. His enemies were not gringos but corrupt Mexican authorities.

Unlike Pico the highwayman, Don Diego was a gracious *hidalgo* by day who donned a mask not for the purpose of robbery but to fight for justice and something much like what was called "the American Way." So admirable a gentleman could not be amputating ears and stringing them on rawhide, of course. Instead, McCulley's Zorro left his trademark by cutting a "Z" on his victims' cheeks.

Even that was too nasty for television. In the 1950s, when Zorro came into American livingrooms on the small screen, he contented himself to cut "Z" into the bark of trees, on the sides of buildings, or, bloodlessly on the clothing of his adversaries. Rather more remarkably, the television Zorro devoted a good deal of his time to protecting decent and well-meaning gringos from venal Mexicans.

FIVE STATES OF TEXAS?

Texas is not unique among the states because it was an independent republic before it became a state. Hawaii also claims that distinction. However, by the joint resolution of the American and Texan congresses that brought Texas into the Union, Texas reserved the right to divide into five states without further congressional approval. The advisability of splitting arose periodically in Texas politics because collectively, the states carved out of Texas would have ten United States senators rather than two.

obscure Polk would divide the pro-Texas vote; the anti-Texas vote, including the antislavery Democrats who would have voted for Van Buren, were his.

Then a piece of the sky fell. Tyler withdrew from the race, and every dispatch seemed to say that Manifest Destiny was carrying the day. Clay began to waffle on the expansion issue, and his equivocation alienated enough anti-Texas Whigs to cost him the election. In New York State, which Polk carried by a scant 5,000 votes (and with New York, the election), long-dependable Whig districts gave 16,000 votes to James G. Birney's abolitionist Liberty party.

Encouraged by the result of the election and egged on by Secretary of State Calhoun, Tyler moved on the Texas question. He could not muster the two-thirds vote in the Senate that a treaty required, but he had a simple majority of both houses of Congress behind him. Three days before Polk's inauguration, Congress approved a "joint resolution" annexing Texas. A few months later, the Texas Congress concurred, and Texas became the twenty-eighth state.

He Did What He Said He'd Do

The apparently mousy Polk proved to be a master politician, a shrewd diplomat, and, in terms of accomplishing what he set out to do, one of the most successful of presidents. When he took his oath of office, Polk announced he would serve just one term and during those four years he would secure Texas to the Union, acquire New Mexico and California from Mexico, and annex as much of the Oregon country as circumstances permitted.

Texas statehood was in the bag by Inauguration Day. The hard-working president immediately went to work on Oregon. Taking his cue from a chauvinistic slogan, "Fifty-four Forty or Fight!" (seizing all of Oregon for the United States up to the southern boundary of Russian

America at 54° 40′ north latitude) Polk alarmed the British by hinting of a war neither nation wanted. Having bluffed, Polk instructed his diplomats to inform the British that he would settle for an extension of the Webster-Ashburton line, at 49° north latitude, as the northern boundary of American Oregon. The Oregon country would be cut in half, with England retaining all of Vancouver Island.

In fact, the British got no more than they occupied and the Americans got no less than they could reasonably defend. Except for a minor adjustment of the line in the Strait of Juan de Fuca, worked out in 1872, the permanent northern boundary of the continental United States was final in 1846.

Polk was no less agreeable or candid about his designs on California and New Mexico. The United States had no legal claim in either province or the excuse that, as in Texas and Oregon, California and New Mexico were already peopled by Americans. Unassimilated gringos were few in New Mexico, and there were only about 700 Americans in California compared with 6,000 *californios*. In 1842, an American naval officer, Thomas ap Catesby Jones, somehow got it into his head that the United States was at war with Mexico, and he seized the provincial capital of California at Monterey. When he learned that he was mistaken, he had to run down the flag and sail off, rather the fool. But, embarrassed as Jones might have been, he was merely a few years ahead of his time. When Polk was unable to buy California and New Mexico for $30 million, he decided to take them by force.

An 1846 daguerrotype of United States General John Wool and his troops in Saltillo, Mexico.

General Zachary Taylor of Louisiana became an American war hero during battles against Mexico.

SHOWTIME

During the middle years of the nineteenth century, the traveling panorama was a cheap and popular diversion in urban and rural areas alike. On sheets of canvas sewn end to end, painters depicted historical events or natural wonders, along which paying customers walked, sometimes with printed explanations, sometimes listening to guides. Biblical scenes, Revolutionary War battles, portraits and deeds of notable Americans, and Indian massacres (and retribution) were particularly popular.

The largest was John Banvard's PANORAMA OF THE MISSISSIPPI, first unfurled in 1846. On canvas twelve feet high and three miles long (a mile and a half walk), Banvard showed 1,200 miles of Mississippi River from the Mouth of the Missouri to New Orleans. Panoramas gradually ceased to draw viewers in the late nineteenth century although Banvard's was updated by the insertion of Civil War battles and had a longer life than most.

War with Mexico

The luckless Santa Anna was back in power in Mexico City when Polk became president. This time, however, while he refused to discuss the sale of California and New Mexico, he moved cautiously, ordering Mexican troops in the north not to provoke the Americans. To no avail: Polk was determined to have war. He drew up an address asking Congress for a declaration on the basis of the Mexican government's debts with some American banks. In the meantime, he ordered General Zachary Taylor of Louisiana to take 1,500 men from the Nueces River in Texas to the Rio Grande. In April 1846, sixteen American soldiers were killed in a skirmish between Mexican and American patrols in the disputed region.

Feigning moral outrage, Polk rewrote his speech and declared that because of Mexican aggression, a state of war between the two nations already existed. Constitutionally, this was nonsense—Congress alone has the power to declare war. Americans had fought battles with the British and French at sea and sent punitive expeditions into the Barbary states and Florida, but the conflicts had not been called "wars." Even so, patriotic danders were up, and both houses of Congress approved Polk's action.

The Mexican army was actually larger than the American but the Mexican troops were ill-equipped, demoralized by incessant civil wars, and commanded by officers who owed their commissions to social status rather than merit. In less than two years, the Americans conquered much of the country.

In the summer of 1846, Stephen W. Kearny occupied Santa Fe without resistance. Then he marched his troops to California, where he found that the Americans and a few *californio* allies already had won a nearly bloodless revolution and had established the Bear Flag Republic. Kearny had only to raise the American flag and mop up a few scattered Mexican garrisons.

In September, Zachary Taylor took the offensive in northern Mexico, defeating Mexican armies at Matamoros and Nuevo León (also known as Monterrey). Although Old Rough and Ready, as his men called him, showed shrewd tactical judgment, the Nuevo León garrison escaped. Polk, who disliked Taylor, used this mistake as an excuse to divert some of Taylor's troops to a command under General Winfield Scott. Nevertheless, in February 1847, Taylor became a national hero when, with his shrunken army, he was attacked at Buena Vista by Santa Anna himself and won a total victory.

The next month, March 1847, General Winfield Scott landed at Vera Cruz and fought his way toward Mexico City along the ancient route of Hernando Cortez. He won a great victory at Cerro Gordo and an even bigger one at Chapultepec, where he captured 3,000 men and eight generals. On September 14, 1847, Scott donned one of the gaudy uniforms he loved (his men called him Old Fuss and Feathers) and occupied Mexico City, "the Halls of Montezuma."

NONVIOLENT CIVIL DISOBEDIENCE

Henry David Thoreau's preachment that a person was morally obligated to disobey an immoral law was given effective political form in the twentieth century by the leader of the Indian independence movement, Mohandas Gandhi, and by the leader of the American civil-rights movement, Martin Luther King, Jr. Both insisted on defying unjust laws. With those who said that their principle would lead to anarchy if everyone accepted it, Gandhi and King disagreed. Because they would not use violence and they would passively accept the punishment that the established government inflicted on them—in other words, go to jail—the majority of people would recognize the justice of their cause and change the law.

By the Treaty of Guadalupe Hidalgo, which was signed in February 1848, Mexico ceded to the United States the Rio Grande boundary, California, and the province of New Mexico, which included the Mormon Zion in Utah and the present-day states of Arizona and Nevada.

The United States paid Mexico $15 million and assumed responsibility for about $3 million that the Mexican government owed Americans.

Mexico was dismembered like a carcass of beef. One-third of its territory was taken largely because the United States was strong enough to do so. While the ineptitude of the Mexican military played a part in the national disaster, the partition of the country could not help but leave a bitterness in the historical memory of the Mexican people.

The Opposition

The Mexican War was generally popular in the United States. The army could accept only a fraction of the young men who volunteered to fight it. The fighting was easy; only 1,700 died in battle (although 11,000 soldiers succumbed to disease).

Nevertheless, the War had many vociferous critics. Many Whigs, including a young politician from Illinois named Abraham Lincoln, voted against the declaration. James Kent, a New York Whig, called the war "causeless and wicked and unjust" and said that "the acquisition of large Mexican territory would ruin us and our insti-

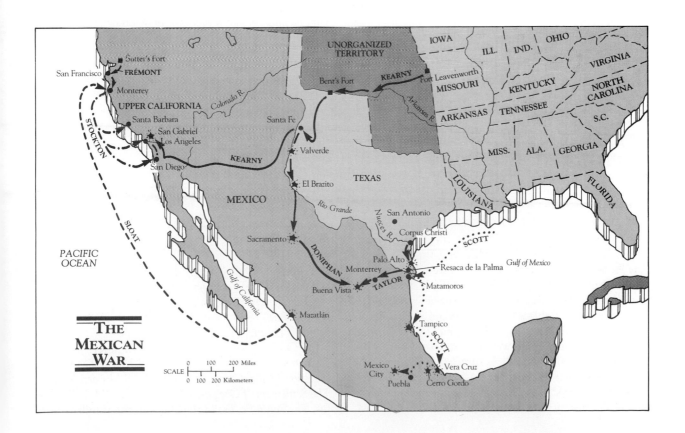

THE MEXICAN WAR

SCALE
0   100   200 Miles
0   100   200 Kilometers

tutions." In New England, a number of prominent politicians and clergymen condemned the war from platform and pulpit. Ralph Waldo Emerson and much of the Massachusetts intellectual establishment opposed it. Henry David Thoreau went to jail rather than pay a tax that he believed would help pay for adding new slave states to the Union. "Why are you in here, Henry?" asked Emerson, arriving to bail Thoreau out. "Why are you out there, Waldo?" Thoreau replied; he regarded it as a moral duty to obstruct the cynical war, even if just symbolically.

Not even the army was unanimously keen on the fight. Years later in his autobiography, then Captain Ulysses S. Grant remembered, "I was bitterly opposed to the measure, and to this day regard the war . . . as one of the most unjust ever waged by a stronger against a weaker nation. . . . Even if the annexation itself could be justified, the manner in which the . . . war was forced upon Mexico cannot."

In the House of Representatives, Whig congressman Thomas Corwin of Ohio said, "If I were a Mexican, I would tell you, 'Have you not room in your own country to bury your dead men? If you come into mine, we will greet you with bloody hands, and welcome you to hospitable graves.'" The vote in the Senate ratifying the Treaty of Guadalupe Hidalgo was only 38 to 14. Had four senators changed their votes, the treaty would not have been approved.

Expansion Run Amok

Cynical as the Mexican acquisition was, it was moderate compared with the suggestions of some American expansionists. Some Southerners wanted Polk to seize even more of Mexico, and he was leaning in that direction when the Treaty of Guadalupe Hidalgo arrived in Washington. When a rebellion broke out in the Yucatan Peninsula in 1848, Polk asked Congress to authorize the army, which was still in Mexico, to take over the tropical province. Curiously, some antislavery Northerners were sympathetic. Because slavery was illegal in Mexico and Mexicans were opposed to the institution, they believed, new American states carved from the country would come into the Union as free states.

The president also had designs on Cuba, where 350,000 slaves had long excited the imagination of proslavery Southerners. Polk wanted to present the Spanish government there with a choice between selling the rich sugar island or running the risk of a rebellion fomented by the United States, followed by military intervention.

This was the most bizarre suggestion concocted in the flush of victory, but not the most grandiose. J. D. B. De Bow, an influential Southern editor and publisher, wrote that it was the American destiny to absorb not only all of Mexico, but also the West Indies, Canada, and Hawaii. That was for appetizers. De Bow continued:

> The gates of the Chinese empire must be thrown down by the men from the Sacramento and the Oregon, and the haughty Japanese tramplers upon the cross be enlightened in the doctrines of republicanism and the ballot box. The eagle of the republic shall poise itself over the field of Waterloo, after tracing its flight among the gorges of the Himalaya or the Ural mountains, and a successor of Washington ascend the chair of universal empire.

No such golden age of empire followed the Mexican War. Indeed, the acquisition from Mexico, modest as it was by De Bow's standards, proved to be more than the old Union, just sixty years of age when the war ended, could digest.

For Further Reading

Ray A. Billington was the dean of Western history writers. See his *The Far Western Frontier, 1830–1860* (1956) and *Westward Expansion* (1974) for overviews. More "literary" and also reliable is Bernard DeVoto; see his *Across the Wide Missouri* (1947) and *The Year of Decision, 1846* (1943). Other important works on nineteenth-century expansion include Norman A. Graebner, *Empire on the Pacific: A Study in American Continental Expansion* (1955); Frederick Merk, *Manifest Destiny and Mission in American History: A Reinterpretation* (1963); D. M.

Pletcher, *The Diplomacy of Annexation: Texas, Oregon, and the Mexican War* (1973); John D. Unruh, *The Plains Across: The Overland Emigrants and the Trans-Mississippi West, 1840–1860* (1978); and Albert K. Weinberg, *Manifest Destiny* (1936).

On Oregon, see the contemporary Francis Parkman, *The Oregon Trail* (1849); Frederick Merk, *The Oregon Question* (1967); Malcom Clark, Jr., *The Eden-Seekers: The Settlement of Oregon, 1812–1862* (1981). L. R. Duffus, *The Santa Fe Trail* (1930) is still the standard work on that subject. On fur trappers and traders, see D. L. Morgan, *Jedediah Smith and the Opening of the West* (1953); P. C. Phillips, *The Fur Trade* (1961); and D. J. Wishart, *The Fur Trade of the American West, 1807–1840* (1979).

On Texas: E. C. Marker, *Mexico and Texas, 1821–1835* (1928); W. C. Binkley, *The Texas Revolution* (1952); Frederick Merk, *Slavery and the Annexation of Texas* (1972). The best biography of President Polk is Charles Seller, *James K. Polk: Continentalist* (1966).

This painting, entitled Bloody Kansas, *suggests the violence that erupted in Kansas after passage of the Kansas–Nebraska Act.*

APPLES OF DISCORD

THE POISON FRUITS OF VICTORY
1844 - 1854

American soldiers in Mexico suffered terribly from disease; a disproportionately large number of men in uniform died during the Mexican War. But the invasion force was small and the fighting was, in the end, rather short and easy. The army suffered no serious defeat and won several improbable victories. The news from every front—California, Santa Fe, beyond the Rio Grande, and from the "Halls of Montezuma" in the heart of Mexico—could not help but be thrilling back home. Americans lionized Generals Zachary Taylor and Winfield Scott, so much so that both would run for president.

Still, the nation's victory celebration was brief. The fruits of the conquest, vast new lands extending from the Rockies to the Pacific Ocean, proved to be apples of discord. They divided Americans on sectional lines even before the Treaty of Guadalupe Hidalgo officially transferred title to them to the United States. The increasingly volatile question of slavery was the cause of the trouble.

THE SECTIONAL SPLIT TAKES SHAPE

Slavery had been the subject of acrimonious debate before the Mexican War, of course. Since the 1830s, abolitionists had pretty constantly hurled anathemas from pulpit, platform, and press at Southerners, and slave owners had vilified abolitionists as incendiaries determined to inspire blacks to rebellion and massacre. The rhetoric on both sides was antagonistic, often ugly, and sometimes vicious.

Before the annexation of Texas and the Mexican War, however, the slavery debate lay at the periphery of national politics. Presidents and congressional leaders who recognized the issue as dangerous and divisive—a clear majority of the generation of Jackson, Benton, Clay, and Webster—found it advisable to avoid or hasten through political debates in which the peculiar institution raised its head.

Emancipation: A Dead Letter

The question of slavery came up all too often in Washington. Abolitionists and proslavery zealots in Congress could and did deliver impassioned sermons about good and evil, sinners and saints. Thomas Hart Benton became so disgusted by gratuitous injections of the slavery issue into discussions of apparently unrelated matters that he compared Congress's plight to the biblical visitation of plagues on Pharoah's Egypt:

You could not look on the table but there were frogs. You could not sit down at the banquet table but there were frogs, you could not go to the bridal couch and lift the sheets but there were frogs! We can see nothing, touch nothing, have no measures proposed, without having this pestilence thrust before us.

Benton and other practical politicians were disgusted because there were few points at which Congress had authority to touch the institution of slavery. The Constitution categorized slavery as a "domestic institution" of the states. This meant that short of a constitutional amendment abolishing slavery, the state governments alone possessed the power to decide whether or not their citizens would be permitted to own human property.

A constitutional amendment abolishing slavery was quite out of the question. Three-fourths of the states must agree to any change in the Constitution and, in the early nineteenth century, slave states were equal in number to free states. In fact, when war was declared on Mexico in May 1846, 15 of the 28 states were slave states. Strengthening and defending the peculiar institution at home as they were, Southern political leaders were not apt even to consider nationwide emancipation. It was this "sanction" of slavery that prompted William Lloyd Garrison to call the Constitution "a covenant with hell." But neither he nor other abolitionists could provide a workable way around the document. They were moral crusaders, not politicians.

Nibbling at the Edges

Antislavery politicians in Washington did try to attack slavery on the periphery. For example, the Constitution did give Congress the right "to exercise exclusive Legislation in all Cases whatsoever" concerning the District of Columbia. Consequently, abolitionist congressmen regularly called for abolition in Washington or, at least, banning the slave trade—the buying and selling of slaves in the capital.

Congress also had the right to legislate concerning slaves who ran away from their masters and crossed state lines. The Fugitive Slave Act of 1793, still on the books at midcentury, provided that such runaways be returned to their owners. (The law was frequently ignored or obstructed by antislavery Northerners, including officials.) Then, as a means of hobbling the institution, some antislavery Northern congressmen wanted to use the interstate commerce clause of the Constitution to prohibit the sale of slaves from any one state to another.

All of these issues aroused the passions of moderates who wanted to keep the slavery issue off center stage. To a large extent, they succeeded. The question that was to divide Americans down the middle, and engage moderates in political discussions of slavery, was the status of the peculiar institution in the territories.

The Wilmot Proviso

All agreed that Congress had authority to legislate in regard to slavery in the federal territories, American possessions that had not yet been accorded self-government as states. The Confederation Congress had done just that in the Northwest Ordinances of 1784 and 1787, forbidding slavery north of the Ohio River. The Constitutional Congress had decided the question of slavery in the Louisiana Purchase lands in the Missouri Compromise of 1820.

Indeed, the Missouri Compromise was the salvation of those politicians who wanted to keep the subject of slavery off the floor of Congress. It seemed to have settled the question for all time by permitting slavery in U.S. territories south of 36° 30′ north latitude, and prohibiting it to the north. Once Arkansas was admitted as a slave state in 1836, the only western land in which slavery was legal was eastern Oklahoma, then known as Indian Territory. In all other parts of the Louisiana Purchase, slavery was "forever prohibited" by a congressional act that had assumed an aura of permanence second only to the Constitution.

The annexation of Texas and the acquisition of new lands from Mexico upset the Missouri settlement. Many antislavery Northerners had opposed annexing Texas because it added a slave state in violation of the spirit of 1820. Proslavery Southerners supported the war with Mexico so exuberantly because they looked forward to annexing lands into which slavery could legally expand.

Determined to prevent this, Congressman David Wilmot of Pennsylvania attached a rider to several bills appropriating money to the army declaring that slavery would be forbidden in any lands taken from Mexico. This Wilmot Proviso passed the House of Representatives in both 1846 and 1847. Every Northern Whig and all but four Northern Democrats voted for it. Every Northern state legislature but New Jersey's endorsed it. A majority of Northerners stated quite clearly that they opposed the expansion of slavery anywhere. In the Senate, however, slave states held the edge in 1846 and 1847 and, with the help of a few Northern senators, the Wilmot Proviso was voted down.

John C. Calhoun led the argument against it. He said that the Constitution guaranteed to the citizens of all states who emigrated to the territories the same rights they enjoyed at home in the states. The citizens of some states had the legal right to own slaves. Therefore, Calhoun said, they had the right to take their slaves with them when they went West.

RIDERS

In the process of lawmaking, a *rider* is a clause, usually dealing with an unrelated matter, that is attached to a bill that is already under consideration in Congress or in a state assembly. The strategy of those who propose riders is to turn them into law despite considerable opposition. Opponents will so badly want the bill under consideration that they will pass it even with the objectionable rider. Thus Wilmot tried to attach his antislavery measure to an appropriations bill that was desperately needed. Only because the anti-Wilmot forces in the Senate were strong enough to vote it down did the Wilmot Proviso not cause a major crisis.

The Free Soil Party

When President Polk endorsed Calhoun's argument, a large number of Northern Democrats bolted and organized the Free Soil party. Some of them were abolitionists, but by no means all. As a party, the Free Soilers allowed that the people of the Southern states had every constitutional right to preserve slavery at home. In fact, most Free Soilers cared little about the plight of the blacks. There was a streak of racism in the rhetoric of many of them; a few wanted to ban free blacks, as well as slaves and slave owners, from the western territories.

The Free Soilers were heirs of the ideals of Thomas Jefferson. They believed that small family farmers were the backbone of the nation. The Mexican Acquisition, therefore, should be dedicated to the promotion and prosperity of such people, just as Jefferson had reserved the Northwest Territory for them in 1787. Slavery must be kept out of the West, for where there were slaves, there were slave owners; and slave owners, as the example of the Southern states amply demonstrated, used their economic edge over small farmers to stifle true democracy. "Free Soil! Free Speech! Free Men!," was their cry.

The Election of 1848

Polk did not run for reelection in 1848. A hard worker, he literally wore himself out expanding the nation and died less than four months after leaving Washington. In his place, the Democrats nominated one of his Northern supporters, the competent but gloriously dull Lewis Cass of Michigan, one of the few Northern congressmen to vote against the Wilmot Proviso.

The Whigs, having lost once again with their elder statesman Clay in 1844, returned to the winning formula of 1840—a popular general. They nominated the hero of the Battle of Buena Vista, Zachary Taylor of Louisiana. Because Taylor was a slave owner as well as a Southerner, Whig strategists hoped that he would carry Southern states that would otherwise be lost to the Democrats on the Wilmot issue.

Taylor was a most remarkable presidential candidate. "He really is a most simple-minded old man," said Whig educator, Horace Mann. "Few men have ever had more contempt for learning," wrote General Winfield Scott. "He doesn't know himself from a side of sole leather in the way of statesmanship," said Horace Greeley. A coarse, cranky, and blunt-spoken old geezer of 64 years, Taylor allowed that he had never bothered to cast a vote in his life. When the letter from the Whig party announcing his nomination arrived, he refused to pay the postage due on it. When the news of the honor finally broke through, he responded diffidently: "I will not say I will not serve if the good people were imprudent enough to elect me."

On their way West, immigrants break for lunch in a Kansas field.

The Free Soilers were able to put up a more distinguished and able candidate than either the Democrats or the Whigs, former president Martin Van Buren. Sixty-six years of age, he had come out against the expansion of slavery. (There was probably a whiff of the old Kinderhook opportunism in his stand; later, Van Buren had no difficulty supporting Democrats who favored expansion.)

Little Van did not have a chance, but his name on the ballot was decisive in his home state of New York. He won more votes there than Lewis Cass, throwing New York's 36 electoral votes to the Whig Taylor. Along with New York, as so many times earlier and later, went the election.

THE CALIFORNIA CRISIS

Moderates hoped that the Whig victory would cool the sectional passions aroused by the Wilmot Proviso and the rise of the Free Soilers. Although Taylor was himself a Southerner, and carried more than half the Southern states, he represented a party traditionally dedicated to compromise between North and South. He was, in fact, the victor in every New England state except New Hampshire.

But Old Rough and Ready was to know little harmony as president. Far from it: events in far-off California, unfolding even as he was nominated and elected, caused a crisis that almost split the North and South into warring parties in 1850.

Gold!

On the evening of January 24, 1848, a carpenter from New Jersey, James Marshall, took a walk along the American River where it tumbled through the foothills of California's Sierra Nevada. Marshall was an employee of Johann Augustus Sutter, a Swiss adventurer who had turned a vast Mexican land grant into a kind of feudal domain. Sutter's castle was an adobe fort near the Sacramento River, defended by cannons he had purchased from the Russians when they abandoned Fort Ross.

Marshall was building a sawmill for Sutter. He was inspecting the day's work on the mill race—the ditch that returned rushing water to the river after it turned the wheel that drove the saw—when he picked up a curious, heavy metallic stone. Returning to his crew, he said, "Boys, I think I have found a gold mine."

Indeed he had, and it meant the end of Sutter's mill. Sutter's workers dropped hewing timbers to shovel gravel from the bed of the American and other streams, separating the sand and silt from what proved to be plenty of gold dust and nuggets. For a moment, Marshall's discovery was the end of San Francisco. A foggy town of 500 souls, San Francisco was depopulated as its inhabitants, including most of the recently posted American military garrison, headed for the golden hills.

The next year—1849—80,000 people descended on California in the great "gold rush" that, as a mass emigration of zealous, single-minded souls, has been compared to the Crusades of the Middle Ages. By the end of the year, the population of California was about 100,000, more than that claimed by the states of Delaware and Florida. The Forty-Niners were producing $10 million annually in gold. Californians believed that their population and value to the nation merited immediate statehood. When Congress convened in December, they had already submitted a provisional state constitution that, among other things, prohibited slavery.

Trauma

The stunning rapidity of these events lay at the heart of the crisis that ensued. President Polk and proslavery Southerners had wanted Mexican lands, California most of all, to provide an outlet for the expansion of slavery. They had assumed, with good reason, that much of the Mexican Acquisition would be peopled slowly by emigrants from the adjacent southern states who, thanks to the defeat of the Wilmot Proviso, could take their slaves with them. In time, new slave states would emerge in Mexico's lost provinces.

But the Treaty of Guadalupe Hidalgo that gave California to the United States had not even been signed when James Marshall took his famous stroll. When the Forty-Niners demanded statehood, California had not yet been organized as a territory. Legally, it was still a conquered province, ostensibly under the control of the military. Proslavery Southerners saw their well-laid and

A would-be millionaire panning for gold in California.

HOW THEY LIVED

IN THE DIGGINGS

Very few of the forty-niners knew even the rudiments of how gold was mined. Only the Mexicans, who generally were called Sonorans in California after the Mexican state from which many came, and the Cornish from southwestern England had been miners before they came to the gold fields.

However, technological innocence was no great handicap in California in 1849 and the early 1850s because placer mining—recovering pure gold from the sands and gravels of creekbeds—required very little expertise. What placer mining called for was back-breaking toil, which the forty-niners were prepared to invest.

Placer mining is a mechanical process. In order to ascertain whether there was gold in a creek, a miner "panned" it. That is, he scooped up a pound or so of silt, sand, and pebbles in a sturdy, shallow pain; removed the stones by hand (making certain he did not discard any nuggets, chunks of gold); and then agitated the finer contents, constantly replenishing the water in the pan so that the lighter mud and sand washed over the sides while the heavier gold remained.

When miners (who usually worked in partnerships of two, three, or more) discovered enough "color" in a pan to warrant systematic mining of a placer, they staked a claim and built a "rocker" or a "long tom," two easily constructed devices that performed the washing process on a larger scale.

The rocker was a water-tight wooden box, three to five feet long and a foot or so across, that was built on a base like that of a rocking chair so that it could be tipped from side to side. On the bottom were a series of riffles made of wood or in the form of corrugated metal, and sometimes a sheet of fine wire mesh. These simulated the crevices in a creekbed, where the gold naturally collected. Into the rocker, by means of a sluice, ran a constant stream of water. While one "pard" shoveled gravel and sand into the box, another rocked it and agitated the contents with a spade or a pitchfork. As with panning, the lighter worthless mineral washed out (stones, again, were manually discarded), and the gold remained at the bottom to be retrieved at the end of the day, weighed, divided, and cached.

The long tom took more time to build but was easier to work and more productive. In effect, the water-bearing sluice was extended into a long, high-sided, water-tight box with a series of riffles built into the bottom. Using the long tom, all the partners could shovel gravel almost continuously. It was not necessary to agitate the contents. The long tom was also better adapted to "dry mining" than was the rocker. That is, in order to wash gold anywhere but in a creek, it was necessary to transport water to the site by means of a sluice.

The placer mines were known as the "poor man's diggings" because placer mining neither required much money nor gave the man with capital any advantage. The placer miner had to buy comparatively few tools and materials. At the same time, because just about everyone was dreaming of striking it rich, few were willing to work for wages, no matter how high they were set. The lucky discoverer of a valuable deposit had to take on partners. Gold mining became an industry with a conventional employer-employee relationship only when the placers were exhausted and attention shifted to the mountains from which the gold had been extracted through erosion. In order to win gold that was still locked in the earth, it became necessary to introduce hydraulic mining—literally washing a mountain down with high-pressure water cannon, thence retrieving the gold by washing—or quartz (hard-rock) mining—tunneling into the earth to dig out gold ore, gold compounded chemically with quartz or other worthless rock. Very little hard-rock gold was pure element. The ore had to be milled (crushed) and then smelted (melted to separate the gold from the other elements). Obviously, both hydraulic and hard-rock mining called for capital, and lots of it.

As long as the "poor man's diggings" held out, mining life was highly democratic and egalitarian. No one was allowed to stake a claim larger than he and his partners were able to mine within a season or two. Law and order in the mining camps was maintained by the informal common consent of the men who lived and worked in them. Except for small military units that were plagued with desertion, there was no formal legal authority in California until late 1850, and no estimable governmental presence over much of the gold fields for several years thereafter.

All the fruits of this democracy were not sweet. A man with the majority of a camp behind him could "get away with murder" or, at least, lesser crimes. The justice brought to others was frequently brutal. Miner democracy did not extend to other than native-born Americans and immigrants from Western Europe. Despite the fact that the forty-niners learned what they knew of mining from the Sonorans, they expelled them from all but the southern gold fields within a year. As Spanish-speaking people also, Chileans came up against prejudice.

Worst-treated of all were the Chinese. Because their culture was so alien and because they worked in large groups, thus spending less to live, the Chinese frightened the Californians; they feared that the "Celestials," as the Chinese were sometimes called, would drag down the standard of living for all. Very few Chinese managed to remain in mining and then only on deposits that had been abandoned by whites as too poor. For the most part they were forced to take less desirable jobs in towns and cities. There were a few blacks in the diggings. The photographs of black miners that survive show them in apparently equal partnership with whites.

well-executed plans to create a slave state on the Pacific pulverized like the rocks in California's streams.

Worst of all, if California were admitted to the Union, the South would lose its equality in the United States Senate. Southerners were already a minority in the House of Representatives, where seats are apportioned according to population. In 1849, there were about 9 million people in the South and 14 million in the North, and only three-fifths of the South's slaves were counted in apportioning House seats.

The Senate, therefore, where each state is represented by two members regardless of population, had assumed special significance to Southern sectionalists like Calhoun. In 1849, there were 15 slave states and 15 free states, a comforting equality. However, with no potential slave state on the horizon, and with two embryonic free states taking shape in Oregon and Minnesota Territories, California statehood looked like nothing less than a calamity.

A majority of Southern congressmen arrived in Washington in December 1849 declaring their opposition to California statehood. The North's toleration of abolitionists, they said, made it impossible for the South to trust the goodwill of any free state senators. Southerners needed numerical equality in the Senate in order to protect their interests.

Henry Clay's Last Stand

The Southern intransigents soon discovered that President Taylor was not on their side. The owner of more than 100 slaves did not mind saying that he would take up arms to protect his right to keep them. But Old Rough and Ready was a nationalist. For reasons of national pride, prosperity, and security, he insisted that California be admitted immediately. If it must be as a free state, so be it. He further angered Southern congressmen with his decision that a boundary dispute between Texas and what was slated to become New Mexico Territory be resolved in favor of New Mexico.

Tempers were boiling when Congress convened. The House of Representatives went through 63 ballots just to elect a Speaker, usually a formality. In the Senate the next month, Henry Clay, 72 years old now and beyond all hopes of becoming president, attempted to cap his career as the Great Compromiser by proposing a permanent solution to the slavery question.

Clay's Omnibus Bill was a compromise in the old tradition; it required both sides to make significant concessions in the interests of the common good, the Union. The bill provided that California be admitted as a free state and that the rest of the Mexican Acquisition be organized as territories with no reference to the status

---

IN THE WAY OF PROGRESS

Nowhere west of the Eastern Woodlands were Indians so numerous as in California. The mild climate and easily plucked wild foods supported dozens of mostly small tribes from the forests of the north to the deserts of the south. Most of the first Americans to come into contact with California Indians were contemptuous of them. Mountain man Jedediah Smith, who was familiar with most of the tribes of the West, said that "a great many of these Indians appear to be the lowest intermediate link between man and the Brute Creation. . . . They are either from indolence or from a deficiency of genius inferior to the Beaver." William Henry Dana, who reached California by sea, wrote that "the language of these people . . . is the most brutish and inhuman language. . . . It is a complete slabber."

Thus prejudiced, the Forty-Niners virtually enslaved California Indians to work in the mines. During 1848 and 1849, more Indians were digging gold in Sierra streams (for next to no reward, and no recognition) than were whites. During the 1850s and 1860s, when Indian labor was no longer so vital to the state's economy, a number of tribes were literally wiped out by armed action, disease, and dissipation.

---

of slavery there. This provision held out the possibility of future slave states in what is now Utah, Nevada, New Mexico, and Arizona.

The Texas land dispute was resolved in favor of the federal government (New Mexico Territory) but with face-saving concessions to Texas, including Congress's assumption of the large debt of the former Republic of Texas.

Clay ignored abolitionist demands that slavery be banned in the District of Columbia. The South had a strong constitutional point on that matter, and the mere suggestion of abolition angered those Southern moderates whom Clay was counting on to push through his Omnibus Bill. (Many of them brought slaves to Washington to serve as maids, cooks, and grooms.) However, he tried to mollify Northern sensibilities by proposing the abolition of the slave trade in the national capital. Slave auctions were ugly affairs, and it struck many moderate Southerners (like Clay) as a good idea not to hold them in the spotlight of the national capital.

To compensate slave owners for this symbolic rebuff, Clay included a new, stronger Fugitive Slave Act in his package. Until 1850, it was not overly difficult for antislavery officials in the North to protect runaway slaves within their jurisdiction. Clay's bill allowed special federal commissioners to circumvent local courts, arrest fugitive slaves in the North, and return them to their owners.

Failure

Not too many years earlier, the Omnibus Bill would have sailed through Congress amidst cheers, tossed hats, and invitations to share a bottle after adjournment. But Texas, the war, and California had changed the times and soured tempers. Extremists from both sections, and some congressmen who had been regarded as moderates, refused to accept the Omnibus Bill because it contained concessions they regarded as morally reprehensible.

Many Northerners, not just abolitionists, abhorred the new Fugitive Slave Act. By allowing federal officials to arrest people who had committed no crime under the laws of the states in which they resided, it made slavery quasi-legal everywhere. Southern extremists could not bring themselves to vote for the abolition of the slave trade in the District of Columbia. Texans and their allies opposed taking lands from that slave state and putting them into a territory into which the legality of slavery was not guaranteed. President Taylor's friends in Congress resented compensating Texas in any way.

The spirit of compromise was dead. New York's William H. Seward called the very idea of compromise "radically wrong and essentially vicious." Southern "fire-eaters," younger congressmen from slave states, pledged themselves to yield nothing. John C. Calhoun, once a master of cool reason and cold logic, was reduced to the sophistry of a cynical lawyer, defining the purposes he wanted to serve—the expansion of slavery and Southern political power—and devising convoluted theories and crazy schemes to justify them. For example, Calhoun proposed that there should be two presidents, one from the North and one from the South, each with the power of veto over congressional acts. The old man spent his last days, dying painfully of throat cancer, surrounded by a gaggle of romantic young disciples which, collectively, had half his brains.

Henry Clay, almost as decrepit, plugged away unsuccessfully among those who thought they were moderates. His cause was boosted when Daniel Webster delivered one of his greatest orations in support of the compromise. Concluding that "Liberty and Union" were "one and inseparable," Webster announced that in order to save the Union, he would vote even for the fugitive slave provisions of the Omnibus Bill. He was vilified for his speech in New England. Perhaps nothing better illustrates the growth of extremism in the North than the fact that prominent New Englanders who had winked at Webster's personal debauchery and panhandling of bankers and manufacturers for 30 years, denounced him

for taking the middle ground on a debate that was tearing the Union apart.

THE COMPROMISE OF 1850

Even if the Omnibus Bill had passed Congress, President Taylor would have vetoed it. He was too stubborn and willful to be a politician and his mind was set on two matters the Omnibus Bill defied. He insisted that California be admitted with no strings attached and that Texas must get nothing for giving up land to which the state had, in Taylor's view, no claim.

But, the bill never reached him. It failed and Henry Clay left Washington for Kentucky, old, weary, and at a loss. In the meantime, however, fate intervened to save his cause, and to bring to the fore a senator of unique resourcefulness who would be as important in the Senate of his era as Henry Clay had been in his own.

Death of a Soldier

First, fate swept truculent Zachary Taylor from the scene. On July 4, 1850, the president attended a patriotic ceremony on the Capitol Mall where, for several hours, he stood hatless in blazing sun listening to longwinded speeches. Returning to the White House, he wolfed down a large bowl of cucumbers and several quarts of iced milk.

A few hours later, the old man took to bed with severe stomach cramps, not surprising under the circumstances. Instead of leaving him alone, his doctors bled him and administered one powerful medicine after another—ipecac to make him vomit, quinine for his fever, calomel as a laxative, and opium for the pain they were causing him. Old Rough and Ready was murder on Mexicans and Texans, but he could not handle the pharmacopeia

---

NO NAME CITY

In the national capital in 1850, California meant sectional crisis. However, when the first California legislature met, the delegates were more interested in making their citizens feel more comfortable in the new state. The first law enacted by the legislature reduced the statute of limitations, so that Californians with perhaps murky pasts back East could not easily be extradited. The second enactment made it easier for an individual to change his name.

of the nineteenth century. On July 9, he died and was succeeded by Vice President Millard Fillmore.

Fillmore is remembered as our least memorable president, a joke repeated so often as to be worn bare. He had flirted with radical politics early in his career, and would do so again. But, by 1850, he was firmly within the moderate Whig camp of Clay and Webster. Although he did not declare publicly for compromise, it was generally believed he favored it.

The Little Giant

The senator who succeeded in putting together a compromise was Stephen A. Douglas of Illinois. Barely over five feet in height, Douglas was known as the "Little Giant" because of his success as a lawyer, his abilities as a speaker, and his role as tactical mastermind of the Illinois Democratic party. Only three years a Senator in 1850, Douglas nevertheless had the contacts and the guile to devise an ingenious strategy for shimming Clay's compromise into the lawbooks.

Instead of presenting the sharply divided House and Senate with a single Omnibus Bill, parts of which of-

fended nearly everyone, Douglas separated Clay's package into six component parts. These he maneuvered individually through Congress by patching together a different majority for each bill.

Thus, Douglas could count on Northern senators and representatives to support California statehood and the abolition of the slave trade in the District of Columbia. To these votes he managed to add those of just enough Southern moderates from the border states to slip the bills through. He could count on a solid Southern bloc for the Fugitive Slave Act and the Texas bill. To this group he added just enough Northern moderates to make a majority.

The "Compromise of 1850" was not really a compromise in the sense that both sides gave a little, took a little. A majority of both Northern and Southern congressmen refused to yield an inch. Only 4 of 60 senators voted for all of Douglas's bills, and only 11 for five of the six. (Even Douglas was absent from the vote on the Fugitive Slave Act.) Only 28 of 240 representatives voted for all of the bills.

Douglas's manipulations were brilliant; he had made extremely controversial bills into laws when a mere handful of his colleagues were committed to the spirit of compromise. His success also proved popular in the nation at large, where moderation appeared to be stronger than it was under the Capitol Dome. But Douglas did nothing to extinguish the fires of hostility that were smoldering in Congress.

Exit the Old Guard

In the Thirty-first Congress of 1849–1851, the nation's second generation of leaders, those who had governed the country since the passing of the Founding Fathers, rubbed elbows with the third generation, a new and very different breed. Andrew Jackson was already gone, dead at last in 1845. Henry Clay and Daniel Webster both passed on in 1852. Thomas Hart Benton survived until 1858, but only to discover that the new era had no place for him. Because he refused to defend slavery as a positive good and, like Webster, placed the Union above sectional prejudices, he lost his Senate seat in 1850, was defeated in a race for the House of Representatives from Missouri in 1856, and then lost when he ran for governor of the state.

John C. Calhoun would have won election after election had he lived to be a hundred. Alone of the giants of the Age of Jackson, he had made the transition—had led the transition!—from devotion to Union to extreme Southern sectionalism. But Calhoun did not survive to see the results of his unhappy career. On March 4, 1850, too ill to deliver his last speech to the Senate, an un-

Stephen A. Douglas, the Little Giant.

PUBLIC RELATIONS

Although few said so publicly, many Southern leaders privately admitted that they were glad to see the slave trade abolished in Washington, D.C. It was not a major market town, and everyone admitted that the auction block was slavery's ugliest face. With a large foreign population, which inclined to be antislavery, in the national capital at all times, the disappearance of the auction block in Washington could be considered a kind of public-relations measure, hiding an unpleasant reality from visitors.

The ending of the slave trade in Washington did not have that effect, however. There were slave auctions in both Arlington and Alexandria, Virginia, across the Potomac River, and diplomats and tourists found it quite easy to cross over to see them.

compromising attack on the North, he had to listen while it was read for him, his glazed eyes burning with defiance and hatred. Less than a month later, he was dead.

Enter a New Breed

Shortly before his death, Calhoun croaked to one of his disciples that it was up to the young to save "the South, the poor South." With each year of the 1850s, such "fire-eaters," so-called because of the heated invective with which they spoke of Northerners, displaced moderates in state legislatures, governorships, the House of Representatives, and the Senate.

The Whig party of the South, a refuge for moderates, dwindled. John Tyler had already led the states-rights Whigs back to the Democrats. After 1854, many of the compromise-minded followers of Henry Clay either left politics or embraced Southern extremism. Robert Toombs of Georgia, for example, supported the Compromise of 1850, but within a few years he was baiting Northerners in language as torrid as any Democrat's. A few old Southern Whigs were so respected as individuals that they continued to win elections under the label, or while voicing Whig principles as independents or nominal Democrats. Most of them were from the upper South, states where the fanatical proslavery spirit burned less brightly.

In the North, the abolitionists were proportionately less powerful than the fire-eaters in the South. Abolitionism remained unpopular with the majority of Northerners, in part because most Northern whites shared the racist beliefs of Southerners, in part because of the insufferable self-righteousness of some antislavery crusaders.

Nevertheless, there was a solid and militant antislavery delegation in Congress, including men whose abilities were rivaled only by their taste for antagonistic rhetoric. Among the ablest was William H. Seward of New York, a former Anti-Mason. Thaddeus Stevens of Pennsylvania was a staunch believer in racial equality whom Southerners hated above all other abolitionists, with the feeling mutual. Charles Sumner of Massachusetts was to succeed Daniel Webster as New England's most prominent Senator. Some of the antislavery congressmen, like Salmon B. Chase of Ohio, were Free Soilers. Most were Whigs who, after 1854, would join with the Free Soilers to form the Republican party.

Doughfaces

By no means were all Northern politicians hostile to slavery. A few Democrats spouted positive propaganda with the best of them. Others, most notably the dynamic Stephen Douglas, resembled the Northern Democrats of the Age of Jackson. They did not look on slavery as a healthy institution. They were apt to lament it as history's cruel trick on the United States, much as Thomas Jefferson had done. But their sensibilities were not outraged by its existence in the South and, for the sake of national unity and Democratic party victory at the polls, they were willing to tolerate the spread of the institution into the territories.

The Northern Democrats considered themselves to be the nation's moderates. Their political rivals were, after all, antislavery Whigs and Free Soilers, just as their allies, moderate Southern Democrats, had to cope with the intemperate fire-eaters. As the 1850s unfolded, however, the "moderate" Democrats steadily lost ground to politicians standing on the principles of the Free Soilers, and even to abolitionists.

Part of the difficulty was the mediocrity of presidential leadership during the 1850s. In the tense, troubled wake of the non-settlement of 1850, the country needed a Jackson or Clay, an Abraham Lincoln or a Franklin D. Roosevelt. It got a Franklin Pierce.

SLAVERY IN THE TERRITORIES

Franklin Pierce was handsome, amiable, an eloquent speechifier, and widely popular—until he served four unhappy, unsuccessful years in the White House. Indeed, Pierce thought that he was out of politics when the Democrats nominated him to run for president in 1852. The convention had deadlocked through 48 ballots and turned to him in desperation. He was one of the few Northerners who was acceptable to the Southern delegates.

Pierce won a narrow popular vote over Whig candidate Winfield Scott, but a near sweep in the electoral college. It was all a terrible mistake from first to last. As a fellow New Hampshireman commented, "Up here, where everybody knows Frank Pierce, he's a pretty considerable fellow. But come to spread him out over the whole country, I'm afraid he'll be dreadful thin in some places."

Then, Pierce's term began with a personal tragedy. Just before his inauguration, his son was killed in a railroad accident. Mrs. Pierce never recovered from her grief. Pained and preoccupied with his wife's distraction, Pierce leaned heavily for support on Southern friends, particularly his personal friend and Secretary of War, Jefferson Davis of Mississippi.

A Railroad to California

Davis was the brother of one of Mississippi's richest planters (and one of its most paternalistic slave owners). An able junior officer in the Mexican War, he had gone to the Senate and voted a Southern sectionalist line as senator. By Mississippi standards, however, Davis was a moderate. Although of a modest log-cabin background, he looked like an aristocrat, felt like one, and shunned shrill rhetoric. With presidential ambitions of his own, he hoped to make his mark as a national figure, the man who laid the groundwork for a transcontinental railroad that would tie California to the old states.

SLAVERY IN THE TERRITORIES

The Missouri Compromise provided that slavery was "forever forbidden" in the *territories* of the Louisiana Purchase lands north of 36° 30′, but did it also mean that states evolving out of those territories were also forbidden to legalize slavery? Probably not. Before he signed the Missouri Compromise, President Monroe consulted with his advisors and all of them, including John Quincy Adams, said that, no, once a territory had become a state, its domestic institutions were its own business. That was surely true. Had the people of the state of Maine chosen to legalize slavery as late as 1864, they were constitutionally free to do so. However, forbidding slavery in the territories meant that, in reality, states developing there would inevitably be free states. There would be no slave owners at the new state's constitutional convention and, as the examples of the Free Soil and Republican parties show, where there were no slave owners there was precious little interest in legalizing slavery.

The railroad would be a great national enterprise, and Davis wanted its eastern terminus in the South. The cities and states that handled the California trade would profit richly from it. From an engineer's point of view, the best route was southern, through Texas and crossing no mountain ranges of consequence until it reached the southern part of New Mexico Territory, just above the Gila River. There, in order to keep the line on the flat, it would be necessary to build in Mexican territory, which was unacceptable.

To remedy the problem, Davis and Pierce sent James Gadsden, a railroad agent, to Mexico City, where for $10 million, he purchased a 30,000-square-mile triangular tract of arid but level land. Davis, it appeared, had plucked a juicy plum for the South. None of the four other routes that had been suggested for the railroad was nearly so attractive. The most prominent of them, the so-called central route, originating in Iowa with connections to Chicago, climbed both the Rockies and the Sierra Nevada, the latter at 8,000 feet above sea level.

Moreover, once over the Iowa line, the central route entered the part of the Louisiana Purchase that had never been organized as a territory, but had been left for the proud Indians that roamed the Great Plains. Congress could not authorize a multimillion-dollar investment in country where there was no governmental authority. And Southern congressmen would not make things easier for Chicago and the central route by organizing territorial governments in areas where slavery was forbidden by the Missouri Compromise.

The Kansas-Nebraska Act

Unless, reasoned Stephen A. Douglas of Illinois, who wanted that railroad for Chicago, he could tempt Southern congressmen with a concession in the matter that had obsessed them for more than a decade, the expansion of slavery. In May 1854, Douglas introduced a bill to organize two new federal territories, Kansas and Nebraska. The bill explicitly repealed the section of the Missouri Compromise that prohibited slavery there. Instead, Douglas stated, the people of the Kansas and Nebraska Territories would decide for themselves whether they would allow or prohibit the institution. "Popular sovereignty," Douglas argued, was the democratic solution to the problem of slavery in the territories.

Southern congressmen jumped for the bait like trout after a cold winter. The Kansas-Nebraska Act opened to slavery land where it had been outlawed for 34 years—and apparently for all time. No one had any illusions about Nebraska. It bordered on the free state of Iowa and would inevitably be populated by antislavery Northerners. Kansas, however, abutted on Missouri, where slavery was not very important economically but where the institution was avidly defended.

Douglas's popularity soared in the South, a bonus, for he hoped to win the Democratic party's presidential nomination in 1856. As in 1850, he presented himself as a conciliator, the hero of both sections. To Southerners, he would be the man who opened Kansas to slavery. To Northerners, he would be the man who got the transcontinental railroad.

Thus did the Little Giant earn the title of "Doughface," a term used by antislavery Northerners to describe Northern Democrats who took one line at home, and another when addressing Southerners, reshaping their faces for the occasion as if they were made of dough. In fact, an ambitious Democrat had to be a Doughface in order to win his party's presidential nomination in the wake of the Mexican War. The Democratic party needed a Northern candidate to have a hope of winning. But because of the party's two-thirds rule, only a Northerner acceptable to the South, that is, friendly to Southern interests in the matter of slavery, could be nominated. Lewis Cass, the nominee in 1848, was a Doughface; so was Franklin Pierce and the Democratic nominee in 1856, James Buchanan.

The Republican Party

The Kansas-Nebraska Act killed the Whig party. When Southern Whigs voted for it along with the Southern Democrats, the Whigs of the North bade them farewell. Already, many Northern Whigs were abolitionists. Those who were not, like Abraham Lincoln of Illinois, regarded the Missouri Compromise as their party's greatest achievement. Willing to tolerate slavery in the South, unwilling to accept its expansion, the Northern Whigs joined with the Free Soilers to form the new Republican party.

So spontaneous was the explosion of anti-Kansas–Nebraska Act sentiment that the Republican party really had no single birthplace. The Republicans of Ripon, Wisconsin, later insisted that they were the first to use the name, but boosters in other towns had their claims. The fact is, the Republican party combusted spontaneously all over the North. Rather more striking, the Republican demand that the Kansas-Nebraska Act be repealed was so popular that the infant party actually captured the House of Representatives in the midterm election of 1854.

At first, the Republicans were a single-issue party of protest, not much different than the Free Soilers. But their leaders were experienced and cagey politicians who soon worked out a comprehensive program. The Republicans stole Douglas's thunder on the railroad question by insisting that the transcontinental be built on the

The first Republican Party presidential ticket, 1856: John C. Fremont and William L. Dayton appeal to the spirit of George Washington.

Central Route. They appealed to farmers who might be indifferent to the question of slavery in the territories by advocating a Homestead Act giving western lands to families that would actually settle and farm them.

From the Whig party, from which so many of them came, the Republicans brought the demand for a high protective tariff, thus winning some manufacturing interests to their side. Also appealing to industrial capitalists was the Republican demand for a liberal immigration policy, which would attract cheap European labor to the United States.

Also from the Whigs, Republicans inherited a disdainful vision of Democrats as vulgar, self-serving, and uneducated. Or, as poet Walt Whitman put it in a diatribe not to be topped, the Democrats he saw in Washington were

the meanest kind of bawling and blowing office-holders, office-seekers, pimps, malignants, conspirators, murderers, fancymen, custom-house clerks, contractors, kept-editors, spaniels well-train'd to carry and fetch, jobbers, infidels, disunionists, terrorists, mail-riflers, slave-catchers, pushers of slavery, creatures of the President, creatures of would-be Presidents, spies, bribers, compromisers, lobbyers, sponges, ruin'd sports, expell'd gamblers, policy-backers, monte-dealers, duellists, carriers of conceal'd weapons, deaf men, pimpled men, scarr'd inside with vile disease, gaudy outside with gold chains made from the people's money and harlot's money twisted together; crawling serpentine men, the lousy combinings and born freedom-sellers of the earth.

But the Republicans were not a national party, as the Whigs had been. They appealed only to Northerners. They did not even put up candidates for office in the slave states. Their hopes of national victory lay in a sweep of the free states, which would be quite enough to control the House and win the presidency. In that hope—government by a party frankly representing one section of the country—lay a threat to the unity of the country.

For Further Reading

The Civil War remains the central event of United States history; unsurprisingly, historians have studied the fighting and the sectional split leading up to the war more exhaustively than, perhaps, any other topic. The best single volume on the era is a recently published one: James McPherson, *Battle Cry of Freedom* (1988).

On the years charted by this chapter, see Avery O. Craven, *The Growth of Southern Nationalism, 1848–1860* (1953) and *The Coming of the Civil War* (1957); Alan Nevins, *Ordeal of the Union* (1947); David Potter, *The Impending Crisis, 1848–1861* (1976). Specifically concerned with the Free Soil movement are C. W. Morrison, *Democratic Politics and Sectionalism: The Wilmot Proviso Controversy* (1967); Eric Foner, *Free Soil, Free Labor, Free Men* (1970); F. J. Blue, *The Free Soilers: Third Party Politics* (1973); and John Mayfield, *Rehearsal for Republicanism: Free Soil and the Politics of Antislavery* (1980).

Joseph G. Rayback, *Free Soil: The Election of 1848* (1970) and K. J. Bauer, *Zachary Taylor: Soldier, Planter, Statesman of the Old Southwest* (1985) set the scene for the crisis of 1850. On the Gold Rush, see two old chestnuts: Rodman Paul, *California Gold: The Beginning of Mining in the Far West* (1947) and John W. Caughey, *Gold is the Cornerstone* (1949). The standard study of the Compromise of 1850 is Holman Hamilton, *Prologue to Conflict: The Crisis and Compromise of 1850* (1964).

Michael Holt, *The Political Crises of the 1850s* (1978) carries the story to the Kansas-Nebraska Act and beyond. See also James C. Malin, *The Nebraska Question: 1852–1854* (1953); David Potter, *The South and Sectional Conflict* (1968); and W. E. Gienapp, *The Origins of the Republican Party* (1986). On Douglas, see G. M. Capers, *Stephen Douglas: Defender of the Union* (1959). A sympathetic biography of Franklin Pierce is R. F. Nichols, *Young Hickory of the Granite Hills* (1931).

Fort Sumter the day after it was surrendered to the Confederate States of America.

THE COLLAPSE OF THE OLD UNION

THE ROAD TO SECESSION 1854 - 1861

The Kansas-Nebraska Act was an unmitigated tragedy. In sponsoring it, Stephen A. Douglas, the clever sectional compromiser of 1850, became the Pandora of disunion. Like the lady of the Greek myth, by making possible the expansion of slavery in the territories, Douglas opened a forbidden box filled with woes and troubles that took wing to plague the Union. Subsequent events, neatly traceable to the Kansas-Nebraska Act, led directly to the secession of most of the Southern states in 1861 and the terrible American Civil War.

In the ancient myth, Pandora was able to shut the lid of her box before hope escaped. The nation had its hopes after 1854 too, but one by one they were dashed by suspicion, hatred, and aggressive sectionalism.

BLEEDING KANSAS

K ansas Territory was the bone of contention that embittered North and South. Southerners who voted for the Kansas-Nebraska Act assumed that Kansas would enter the Union as a slave state, and before too long. The Republican party was sworn to repeal the Kansas-Nebraska Act and to restore the Missouri Compromise prohibition of slavery there, as soon as the Republicans gained a majority in Congress. In the meantime, New England abolitionists set out to win control of Kansas by working under the rules Douglas had written.

Northern Emigrants

Abolitionists such as Eli Thayer joined together to form the New England Emigrant Aid Company and other similar groups. They raised money to finance the emigration and settlement of antislavery Northerners willing to relocate in Kansas. Their success was extraordinary. Within two years after the Kansas-Nebraska Act,

Thayer's group alone sent 2,000 people to Kansas territory. Undoubtedly, their efforts and propaganda—for they praised the country as if they were selling farms there—encouraged many other Northerners to go on their own.

By way of contrast, comparatively few Southerners seemed interested in moving West. The fact was, no Southern region was so densely populated as New England. Western Missouri, which pro-slavery Southerners believed would populate the new territory, was itself an underpopulated frontier.

The pro-slavery forces were nearly as shocked by the size of the Northern emigration as they had been by California's application for statehood. The incipient slave state of Kansas might not be a slave state after all. To President Pierce and Jefferson Davis, so recently thinking of rails to the Pacific, Kansas became an obsession. Pierce, never happy in the Executive Mansion, was reduced to wretchedness. In the end, he was as glad as any other president before or since to get out of Washington. Once affable and charming, by 1861, he would be so twisted that when the Civil War did erupt, he publicly hoped for a Southern victory.

Border Ruffians

If few western Missourians moved across the line into Kansas, many of them, egged on from afar by Southern fire-eaters, were willing to take violent action against the Kansas "free-staters."

These "Border Ruffians," as they came to be called, were a poor and struggling people who, ironically, owned few slaves. But a generation of positive good propaganda and horror tales about slave insurrection had made them intensely racist and anti-Yankee. They understood that a free state of Kansas would be an attractive destination for runaway slaves and perhaps a place with a large free black population. Hundreds rode periodically across the territorial line to vote illegally in Kansas elections and to harass Northern settlers.

John Brown and Lawrence

Kansas was a lawless place. It is not possible to determine how many murders, beatings, and robberies were associated with the slavery controversy and how many reflected the disorder that was common to all American frontiers. Nevertheless, two incidents were clearly motivated by the slavery issue and might be said to have represented the first acts of violence in the Civil War.

On May 21, 1856, a gang of border ruffians rode into the antislavery town of Lawrence, Kansas, and set it afire. Only one person was killed, a Missourian who was crushed by a falling wall, but in other incidents, perhaps

---

BORDER RUFFIANS

The western counties of Missouri would have been breeding grounds for violence even if, after 1856, the slavery issue had not been injected to agitate the settlers there. Western Missouri was still raw frontier, an extremely poor farming and grazing country where reigned the lawless instability of America's move west. With the slavery issue added to this dangerous mix, the border counties produced a disproportionate number of dubious characters in the years immediately before, during, and after the Civil War. In addition to the sacking of Lawrence, Kansas, and John Brown's action on Pottawatomie Creek, western Missouri was prime recruiting ground for William C. Quantrill's notorious raiders, a Civil War unit given more to terroristic attacks on civilians than to fighting the Union Army. Quantrill's right-hand man, Bloody Bill Anderson, scalped the Northerners whom he killed. Future outlaws Jesse and Frank James and the Younger brothers came from this country, as did the "bandit queen," Myre Belle Shirley, or Belle Starr.

Fervent abolitionist John Brown directed the execution of five proslavery Kansans.

perpetrated by the same gang, several freestate settlers were murdered. Three days after the Lawrence Raid, in an act that he announced was retribution, a fanatical abolitionist named John Brown swooped down on a small settlement on the banks of Pottawatomie Creek and ordered five pro-slavery Kansans executed with a farmer's scythe.

Southern politicians, who had treated the pro-slavery violence in Kansas as something of a joke, screamed in humanitarian anguish. Northern abolitionists, who habitually condemned Southerners and, in particular, the border ruffians for their barbarity, were suddenly silent. A few actually praised John Brown as a Christian hero of the antislavery cause.

That a ritual murderer should be praised by people who were inclined to parade their moral rectitude indicates the degree to which the hatred between antislavery Northerners and pro-slavery Southerners had reached. Extremists on both sides no longer spoke and acted according to rational principles; they were in favor of any act done in the name of "the South, the poor South" or of the godly cause of antislavery.

Charles Sumner and Preston Brooks

Also in May 1856, Congress itself provided the stage for another bloody debacle. Senator Charles Sumner of Massachusetts, an abolitionist who found no contradiction between pacifism and vituperative oratory, delivered a speech on the floor of the Senate called "The Crime Against Kansas."

Sumner described persecution of free state settlers and blamed the violence on his Southern colleagues. All was pretty standard fare until Sumner added some gratuitous personal insults of an elderly senator from South Carolina, Andrew Butler. Butler suffered from a physical defect that caused him to drool when he spoke, and Sumner made some coarse allusions to his slobbering in connection with the barbarity of slave owners.

Two days later, Butler's nephew, a congressman named Preston Brooks, walked into the Senate, slinked to behind Sumner, who was seated at his desk writing, and proceeded to beat him senseless with a heavy cane. Brooks said that he was merely putting into practice the *Code Duello* of chivalry, which held that a gentleman avenged the personal insult of an equal by challenging him to a duel, but that one "caned" a social inferior.

In fact, Brooks's action made a mockery of chivalry. He had approached Sumner from behind. (Sumner, a big man, might well have floored Brooks had they met face to face.) Then, rather than merely humiliating Sumner with a few sharp raps, Brooks bludgeoned the senator to within an inch of death while Sumner, his legs tangled in his fallen desk, lay helpless to defend himself.

Instead of disowning Brooks as a bully and coward, Southerners feted him at banquets and made him gifts of dozens of gold-headed canes to replace the one that he had broken. The House voted against expelling him and, when Brooks resigned, his district resoundingly reelected him. At the same time, Northerners forgot that Sumner had stepped far beyond the bounds of common decency in his attack on Senator Butler, and made him a martyr. While Sumner recovered—it would be several years before he returned to the Senate—Massachusetts reelected him so that his empty desk would stand as a rebuke to the South.

A HARDENING OF LINES

In normal times, politicians who argue violently in Congress socialize quite cordially outside the Capitol. Even Andrew Jackson and Nicholas Biddle had been capable of civil words at parties and balls. By 1856, this ceased to be true. Both Northerners and Southerners carried firearms into the congressional chambers and ceased to speak with one another even on informal occasions.

Against this foreboding backdrop was held the presidential election of 1856.

The Election of 1856

Inevitably, the Democrats chose a Doughface, but he was not Stephen A. Douglas. The Little Giant, a hero in the South in 1854 when he opened the territories to slavery, lost his appeal after the events in Kansas. While making the great concession to Southerners, Douglas had, in classic Doughface fashion, told Northerners not to worry. The concession to slavery in the Kansas-Nebraska Act, he said, was purely symbolic, a gesture of goodwill to Southerners. In the end, Douglas said, Kansas would be a free state because of the superior population of the North and the unsuitability of Kansas to plantation agriculture. After the success of the New England Emigrant Aid Society in dispatching antislavery settlers to Kansas, his reasoning rang loudly and unpleasantly in Southern ears.

Instead, the Democrats nominated James Buchanan of Pennsylvania, a man of utterly pedestrian talent and, apparently, effete manner. (Andrew Jackson called him "Miss Nancy" behind his back.) Buchanan was profoundly lucky. He had been out of the country as minister to Great Britain between 1853 and 1856 and was, therefore, not closely associated with the Kansas controversy. However, he had won the favor of Southern extremists because he had been the party to a statement known as the "Ostend Manifesto," a call for the United States to purchase Cuba, which Southerners saw as a possible slave state, from Spain.

The Republicans chose John C. Frémont, famous as "the Pathfinder," the dashing leader of two exploration parties that had helped map the way to Oregon and California. Frémont was no giant of character or intellect. His greatest recommendation was his wife, Jessie Benton, the beautiful, willful, and intelligent daughter of Old Bullion. But in the mood of 1856, he was a logical choice for the Republicans: he was nationally known and admired, and he believed that the western lands should be reserved for family farmers.

Still, the Pathfinder suffered from two serious handicaps: he had abolitionist leanings, which scared off moderate Notherners, and he was a bastard at a time when illegitimacy still carried a stain of shame.

Despite these burdens and despite being unlisted on the ballot in every slave state, Frémont won a third of the popular vote. He might have defeated Buchanan had not former president Millard Fillmore been in the race on the Native American, or Know-Nothing, ticket. Anti-Catholicism was riding a wave as more and more Catholic Germans and Irish immigrated to the United

States. Fillmore actually outpolled Frémont in California and probably took enough votes from him in Pennsylvania and Illinois to throw those states and the election to Buchanan.

Dred Scott

Buchanan's presidency began with a bang. In his inaugural address he hinted that the issue of slavery in the territories would shortly be settled for all time. Two days later, on March 6, 1857, Americans learned what he meant when the Supreme Court handed down its decision in the case of *Dred Scott v. Sandford*.

Dred Scott was a slave in Missouri, the valet of an officer in the army. In 1834, he had accompanied his master to Illinois, where slavery was prohibited under the Northwest Ordinance of 1787, and, briefly, to a part of the Louisiana Purchase where slavery was then illegal under the Missouri Compromise. For four years, in other words, Scott had lived on free soil before returning to Missouri.

By 1846, he had become the property of an abolitionist who, rather than manumit Scott, saw an opportunity to strike a blow against the institution of slavery. With financial and legal help, Scott sued for his freedom on the grounds that part of his life he had been held as a slave in territory where Congress had prohibited slavery—a contradiction.

Dred Scott went to the Supreme Court to win freedom and lost.

Ironically, Missouri courts had released slaves with cases similar to Scott's, but that was before sectional animosity had cut so broadly through the political fabric of the nation. In the Missouri courts, Scott lost his case on the grounds that whatever his status may have been in Illinois in 1834, he became quite legally a slave again when he was returned to Missouri.

Chief Justice Taney: The Final Solution

Although every Supreme Court justice commented individually on Scott's appeal to them, Chief Justice Roger B. Taney, an old Jackson henchman from Maryland, spoke for the majority when he declared that as a black, Scott was not a citizen of the state of Missouri, which restricted citizenship to people of white race. Therefore, he could not sue in the state courts.

Instead of leaving the decision at that, which would have been unpopular in the North, but not sensational, Taney continued. He believed that he had discovered the constitutional solution to the question that was tearing the country apart. In fact, the doctrine Taney propounded was pure John C. Calhoun, the extreme Southern constitutional argument on the question of slavery in the territories.

Taney declared that the Missouri Compromise had been unconstitutional in prohibiting slavery in the territories because Congress was forbidden to discriminate there against the citizens of any of the states. State legislatures could outlaw slavery, to be sure. But territorial legislatures could not do so because they were the creatures of Congress, and therefore were subject to the Constitution's restraints on Congress.

The Republican Panic

Republicans, including moderates who had urged accommodating the South in some way, were enraged. They saw the history of the question of slavery in the territories as a step-by-step whittling away of the power of the people and the federal government to prevent the expansion of slavery.

That is, between 1820 and 1854, under the Missouri Compromise, slavery had been illegal in all territories north of 36° 30'. With the Kansas-Nebraska Act of 1854, slavery could be legalized in those territories if the settlers there chose to do so. With the Dred Scott decision of 1857, there was no way that a unanimity of settlers in a territory could prevent a slave owner from moving there with his human property. According to *Dred Scott v. Sandford*, popular sovereignty was as unconstitutional as the Missouri Compromise because a territorial legislature had no more authority than Congress did.

THE RACE ISSUE

Because few American whites believed in racial equality, it was to the interest of Northern Democrats to accuse the Republicans of advocating race mixture. "I am opposed to Negro equality," Stephen A. Douglas said in his debate with Abraham Lincoln in Chicago. "I am in favor of preserving, not only the purity of the blood, but the purity of the government from any mixture or amalgamation with inferior races."

The Democrats' line forced Republicans to reassure their constituents that opposition to slavery did not necessarily mean a belief in the equality of the races. Lincoln replied to Douglas: "I protest, now and forever, against that counterfeit logic which presumes that because I do not want a Negro woman for a slave, I do necessarily want her for a wife. . . . As God made us separate, we can leave one another alone, and do one another much good thereby."

Lincoln shrewdly took the debate back to the territorial question by saying, "Why, Judge, if we do not let them get together in the Territories, they won't mix there."

Republicans began to speak of a "slavocratic conspiracy," now involving the Supreme Court, which was determined to thwart the will of a majority of the American people. Their fury was fanned in October 1857 when pro-slavery settlers in Kansas, augmented by a good many Missouri residents, sent to Congress the "Lecompton Constitution," which called for admission of Kansas as a slave state. Then, although the Lecompton Constitution obviously did not represent the sentiments of a majority of Kansans, President Buchanan urged Congress to accept it.

Republicans were also enraged by the zest with which the federal government enforced the Fugitive Slave Act of 1850, seizing runaway slaves in free states and returning them to their masters in the South. In one case, a fugitive was pursued and caught at the cost of $40,000—an expensive bondservant indeed. In Milwaukee, an antislavery mob stormed a jail where a runaway slave had been taken and set him free.

Other abolitionists, particularly free blacks in the North, organized the "underground railroad," a constantly shifting network of households that began at the Ohio River and the Mason-Dixon line and sometimes in secret cellars, runaway slaves moved by night, led by professional "conductors" such as Harriet Tubman. Their destination was Canada—out of the country—the only place where they would be free of the slavocracy.

Harriet Tubman (left) stands with a group of slaves she helped escape to freedom.

Lincoln and Douglas: Two Northern Answers

Stephen A. Douglas did not take Taney's rebuke of popular sovereignty lying down. In a series of debates in Illinois in 1858, Douglas and a Springfield Republican who wanted his seat in the Senate, Abraham Lincoln, proposed two Northern solutions to the question of slavery in the territories.

"A house divided against itself cannot stand," Lincoln said in June 1858. "I believe that this government cannot endure half slave and half free." He meant that Southerners would not be satisfied with keeping slavery where it already existed. Since they had insisted in the Dred Scott decision and in the Fugitive Slave Act on imposing the institution on people who did not want it, the Southerners were forcing a showdown that, in the long run, would result in sectional conflict.

Douglas argued that popular sovereignty was still alive, kicking, and the best solution to the problem. When Lincoln reminded him that the Court had ruled it unconstitutional in the *Scott* decision, Douglas replied at Freeport, Illinois in August 1858 that a territorial legislature could keep slavery out by failing to enact a slave code. No slave owner would dare take his valuable human property to a country where there were no laws to protect his rights.

The Supreme Court might be able to overturn a territorial law, Douglas pointed out; but the Court could not force a territorial legislature to enact one it did not choose to enact. The Freeport Doctrine was diabolically ingenious, and Douglas won reelection to the Senate, very narrowly. But events proved that Lincoln was also correct about the intentions of the Southern extremists. When they were presented with the logic of the Freeport Doctrine, they went on the offensive again, demanding that Congress pass a national slave code that would protect slavery in all the territories.

John Brown: Another Solution Yet

John Brown had dropped out of sight after the murders on Pottawatomie Creek. But he was busy. Moving about New England behind a newly grown beard, he persuaded several well-to-do abolitionists who had abandoned pacifism that the time had come to strike violently at slavery. With their financial support, he organized a band of 22 insurrectionists, including some blacks and several of his own sons, at an isolated farm in Maryland. Just across the Potomac River, at the mouth of the Shenandoah, was Harpers Ferry, Virginia, site of one of the federal government's two major arsenals. Brown's plan was to seize the arsenal, capture guns and ammunition, and escape into the Appalachians, which rose steeply around the town.

From the mountains this guerrilla army would swoop down on plantations, free a few slaves at a time, and enlarge their corps. Soon, Brown predicted, black rebellions would erupt all over the South, resolving for all time the great moral and political problem of slavery.

Brown's critics later said that the scheme proved that the old man was out of his mind. He may well have been insane—he was certainly not the sort of fellow to invite to a favorite daughter's wedding—but there was nothing crazy about John Brown's military thinking. His plan prefigured in many ways the theory of guerrilla warfare that twentieth-century "national-liberation" movements put into practice with great success: operate from a remote and shifting base; avoid big battles in which conventional military forces have the overwhelming advantage; fight only small surprise actions when the odds favor the freewheeling guerrillas; win the friendship and support of the ordinary people, in Brown's case the slaves. The odds were never with him, but they were not prohibitive.

The Raid and the Reaction

Brown's most obvious mistake was to depart from his plan almost as soon as it was underway. On October 16, 1859, his little band hit and easily captured the arsenal. Then, however, he either lost his nerve or fooled himself into believing that the slaves nearby were on the verge of joining him. He holed up in the engine house of the arsenal, where he was promptly surrounded by United States marines under the command of Colonel Robert E. Lee. In two days Lee's professionals killed ten of Brown's followers and captured Brown. He was promptly tried for treason against the state of Virginia, found guilty, and hanged in December. Convicts did not sit endlessly on "death row" in 1859.

Most Northerners responded to the incident as Southerners did. They were shocked by the raid, and grimly applauded the speedy trial and execution of the old man. However, many prominent abolitionists were ominously silent, and a few openly praised Brown as a hero and a martyr. Ralph Waldo Emerson said that Brown's death made the gallows as holy as the Christian cross.

There was just enough of this kind of irresponsible palaver to arouse the Southern fire-eaters to a new pitch of hysteria. Brown's raid revived deep fears of slave rebellion, and here were Northerners praising a "lunatic" who had tried to start one. Southern editors and politicians wondered how they could continue to remain under the same government as people who encouraged their massacre.

It was true that the federal government had moved quickly and efficiently to crush Brown. Southerners had few complaints with Washington. But 1860 was an election year. What was to happen if the Republicans won the presidency, thus taking control of the federal police powers? Could the South still depend on protection against the John Browns, Nat Turners, Harriet Tubmans, and Ralph Waldo Emersons?

THE ELECTION OF 1860

The Southern extremists declared that if the Republicans won the election, the Southern states would secede from the Union; the Yankees should be aware of that possibility before they voted. Then, having threatened Northern voters, the same extremists not only failed to work against a Republican victory, but they guaranteed

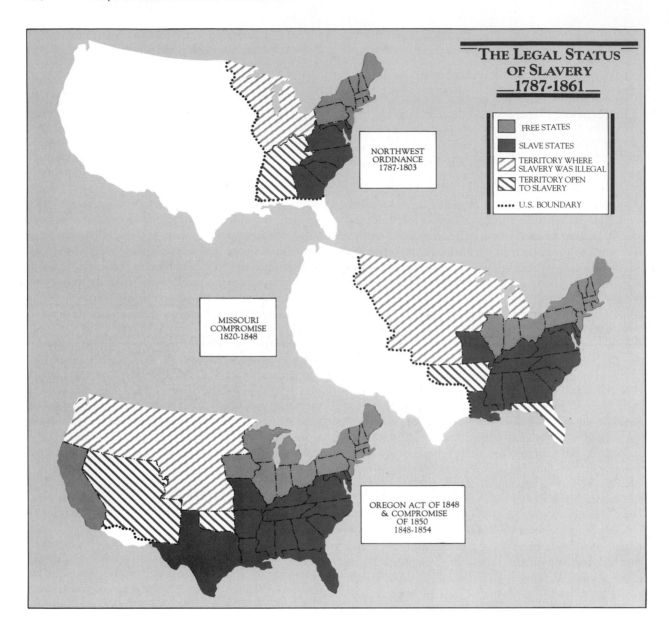

THE LEGAL STATUS
OF SLAVERY
1787-1861

FREE STATES
SLAVE STATES
TERRITORY WHERE
SLAVERY WAS ILLEGAL
TERRITORY OPEN
TO SLAVERY
······ U.S. BOUNDARY

NORTHWEST
ORDINANCE
1787-1803

MISSOURI
COMPROMISE
1820-1848

OREGON ACT OF 1848
& COMPROMISE
OF 1850
1848-1854

it. They split their own Democratic party along sectional lines.

The Democrats Split

The Democratic party was the last national institution in the United States. The Whigs were long gone, buried by the slavery issue. The large Protestant churches had broken into Northern and Southern branches—so had most fraternal lodges and commercial associations. The Republican party, of course, had an exclusively Northern membership. Only within the Democratic party did men from both sections still come together to try to settle their differences.

In April 1860, with the excitement of the Brown affair still hanging in the air, the Democratic convention met in Charleston. The majority of the delegates, including some Southern moderates, supported the nomination of

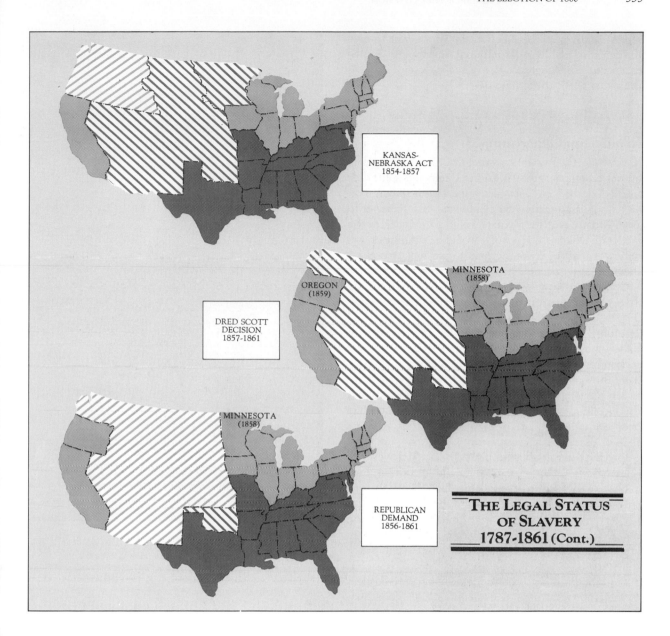

KANSAS-
NEBRASKA ACT
1854-1857

OREGON
(1859)

MINNESOTA
(1858)

DRED SCOTT
DECISION
1857-1861

MINNESOTA
(1858)

REPUBLICAN
DEMAND
1856-1861

THE LEGAL STATUS
OF SLAVERY
1787-1861 (Cont.)

Stephen A. Douglas. But the Southern extremists with-held their votes. The delegations of eight Southern states announced that they would support Douglas only if he repudiated the Freeport Doctrine and supported their demand for a federal slave code.

The Douglas forces pointed out that to do this would be to drive Northern Democrats into the Republican party. Unmoved by this reasoning, the eight hard-line delegations walked out of the convention. The forces recessed without nominating their leader, hoping to talk sense into the minority.

When the Democrats reassembled in Baltimore in June, the Southern extremists still refused to budge. Disgusted by what they considered political suicide, the regular Democrats nominated Douglas for president and chose a Southern moderate, Herschel V. Johnson of Georgia, as his running mate. The Southern Democrats then nominated John C. Breckinridge of Kentucky to represent them in the election. In an attempt to give the ticket a semblance of national support, the Southerners chose a Doughface from Oregon, Joseph Lane, as their vice-presidential candidate.

Republican Opportunity

Meanwhile, the Republicans met in Chicago. They were optimistic but cautious. With the Democrats split, they smelled victory. But they also knew that if they ran on too extreme an antislavery candidate—like Frémont in 1856—many Northern voters would scurry back to the moderate Douglas. Even worse would be winning on too radical a platform: Southerners would make good on their threat to secede.

Consequently, the Republican convention retreated from the rhetoric of previous years, and the delegates rejected party stalwarts such as William H. Seward and Salmon P. Chase. Both men were on the record with inflammatory anti-Southern statements. Seward had spoken of "a higher law than the Constitution" in condemning slavery and of an "irrepressible conflict" between North and South, precisely the sort of words that the Republicans of 1860 wished to avoid. Chase had been a militant abolitionist in Ohio politics for more than a decade.

Instead, the Republicans picked a comparatively obscure Midwesterner, Abraham Lincoln of Illinois. Lincoln was rock solid on the fundamental Republican principle: slavery must be banned from the territories. And his feelings about slavery were unequivocal. Lincoln called the institution "a monstrous injustice, . . . an unqualified evil to the negro, to the white man, and to the State."

But Lincoln was no abolitionist. He had steered clear of the Know-Nothings, thus maintaining a good relationship with German voters. And he was moderate, humane, ingratiating in his manner. In his famous debates with Douglas in 1858 and in a speech introducing himself to Eastern Republicans in New York City in February 1860, he struck a note of humility and caution. Not only was slavery protected by the Constitution in those states where it existed, he said, but Northerners ought to sympathize with slave owners rather than attack them. Lincoln himself had been born in Kentucky, a slave state. He knew that a quirk of fate would have made him a slave owner, so he found it easy to preach the golden rule. By choosing him, the Republicans believed that they were accommodating Southern sensibilities.

The Republicans adopted a comprehensive platform: a high protective tariff; a liberal immigration policy; the

A photograph of Abraham Lincoln, taken about the time he became the Republican candidate for president.

construction of a transcontinental railway; and a homestead act. In part, this platform was designed to win the votes of rather different economic groups: Eastern industrial capitalists and workers, and Midwestern farmers. In addition, by avoiding a single-issue campaign, the Republicans hoped to signal the South that they were not, as a party, antislavery fanatics. They also named a vice-presidential candidate who had been a Democrat as late as 1857, Hannibal Hamlin of Maine.

The Old Man's Party

A fourth party entered the race, drawing its strength from the states of the upper South: Maryland, Virginia, Kentucky, and Tennessee. Henry Clay's conciliatory brand of Whiggery—an inclination toward compromise

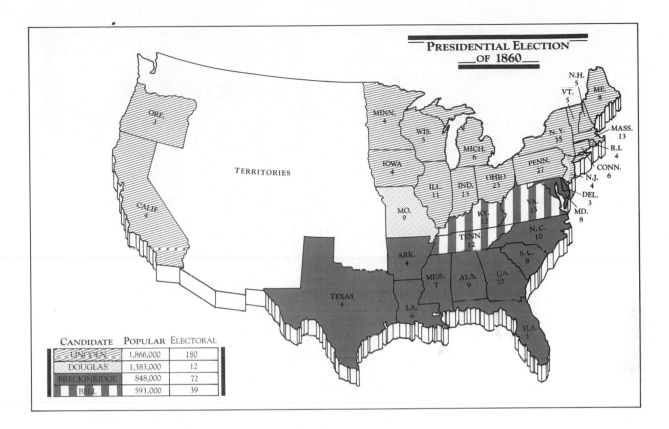

PRESIDENTIAL ELECTION OF 1860

Candidate	Popular	Electoral
LINCOLN	1,866,000	180
DOUGLAS	1,383,000	12
BRECKINRIDGE	848,000	72
BELL	593,000	39

and a deep attachment to the Union—survived in the border states. The platform of the Constitutional Union party consisted, in effect, of stalling: it was a mistake to force any kind of sectional confrontation while tempers were up; put off the difficult problem of slavery in the territories to a later, calmer day.

For president the Constitutional Unionists nominated John Bell of Tennessee, a protege of Clay, and for vice-president they chose the distinguished Whig orator Edward Everett of Massachusetts. But they found little support outside the border states. Republicans and both Northern and Southern Democrats sneered at them as "the old man's party."

Republican Victory

Abraham Lincoln won 40 percent of the popular vote, not much more than Frémont had drawn in 1856. But he carried every free state except New Jersey, which he split with Douglas, winning a clear majority in the electoral college. Breckinridge was the overwhelming choice of the South. He won a plurality in eleven of the fifteen slave states but a popular vote nationally of only 18 percent. Still, a majority of voters had preferred the candidates who appealed to sectional feelings and re-

jected the candidates who appealed to a spirit of nationalism, Douglas and Bell.

But not by much. Douglas won a mere twelve electoral votes (Missouri's nine and three from New Jersey), but he ran second to Lincoln in some Northern states and to Breckinridge in some states in the South. John Bell carried three of the border states and was strong almost everywhere. Even if the Douglas and the Bell votes had been combined, however, Lincoln would have won. Nevertheless, inasmuch as many Lincoln and some Breckinridge supporters were more interested in making a noise than fighting, it seems clear that most of the American people preferred some kind of settlement to the breakup of the Union.

South Carolina Leads the Way

If so, they did not get their wish. Having announced that Lincoln's election would lead to secession, the fire-eaters of South Carolina (where there was no popular vote for presidential electors) called a convention that, on December 20, 1860, unanimously declared that "the union now subsisting between South Carolina and the other States, under the name of the 'United States of America,' is hereby dissolved."

During January 1861, the six other states of the Deep South followed suit, declaring that a Republican administration threatened their "domestic institutions." Then came a glimmer of hope. The secession movement stalled when none of the other Southern states approved secession ordinances. At the same time they rejected secession, however, conventions in several border states declared their opposition to any attempt by the federal government to use force against the states that had seceded. By rebuffing the big talkers on both sides, the leaders of the border states hoped to force a compromise.

The outgoing president, James Buchanan, was not the man to engineer a compromise. No one had much respect for Old Buck, including his own advisers, mostly Southern, who now betrayed him. His Secretary of War, John Floyd of Virginia, transferred tons of war material to states that either had left the Union or were on the verge of leaving it. Floyd's act skirted close to treason.

Other Buchanan allies resigned their offices and left Washington, hardly pausing to remember the president who had worked on their behalf. The first bachelor ever to occupy the White House was quite alone, and he knew it. After a pathetic hand-wringing message sent to Congress in which he declared that while secession was illegal, he as president was powerless to do anything about it, Buchanan sat back to wait for the day he could go home to Pennsylvania.

An edition of the Charleston Mercury *announces the South's decision to secede from the Union.*

HOW THE UNION BROKE

As Buchanan slumped, Senator John J. Crittenden stood up. Like many Kentuckians, Crittenden had devoted his career to mediating between the North and the Deep South. Now he proposed, rather than divide the Union, divide the territories. Extend the Missouri Compromise line to the California border; guarantee slavery to the south of it, and forbid slavery to the north.

The Compromisers Fail

Because of the Dred Scott decision, Crittenden's plan could not be put into effect by congressional action; it was necessary to divide the territories by constitutional amendment. Crittenden hoped that the spectre of civil war, now chillingly real as military companies began to drill in cities and towns, would prompt both Northern and Southern states to act in haste.

With some encouragement they might have done so. There was a flurry of enthusiasm for Crittenden's compromise on both sides of the Mason-Dixon line. But before the Southern extremists were forced to take a stand, President-elect Lincoln quashed the plan. His reasons were political but nonetheless compelling. His Republican party was a diverse alliance of people who disagreed with one another on many issues. The one adhesive that bound them together was the principle that slavery must not expand into the territories. If Lincoln gave in on this point, he would take office with half of his own party sniping at him.

Lincoln also discouraged a second attempt at compromise, a peace conference that was held in Washington in February 1861. It was a distinguished assembly, chaired by former president John Tyler. Tyler had been a Southern extremist, and, a few months later, he would support the secession of Virginia. But he worked

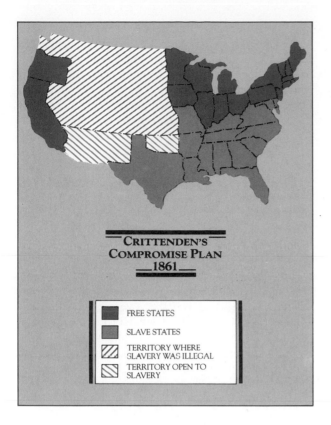

CRITTENDEN'S COMPROMISE PLAN 1861

■	FREE STATES
■	SLAVE STATES
▨	TERRITORY WHERE SLAVERY WAS ILLEGAL
▧	TERRITORY OPEN TO SLAVERY

already possess—and could be overturned by constitutional amendment at a later date. By February, in fact, the secessionists had lost interest in preserving the Union. They were caught up in the excitement of creating a new nation.

The Confederate States of America

According to secessionist theory, the seven states that left the Union were now independent republics. However, no Southern leader intended his state to go it alone. Although they were disappointed that eight of the fifteen slave states still refused to join them, they met in Montgomery, Alabama, shortly before Lincoln's inauguration and established their own "confederacy."

The government that the Southerners created differed little from the one that they had rejected. The Confederates declared that all United States laws were to remain in effect until amended or repealed, and they copied the Constitution of 1787 almost word for word. The few changes they made reflected the South's obsession with slavery and with Calhoun's political theories, and resulted in several curious contradictions. Thus, the Confederates defined the states as "sovereign and indepen-

hard for a settlement in February, proposing a series of constitutional amendments along the same lines as Crittenden's.

Once again, Lincoln drew the line on allowing slavery in the southern territories. Instead, he endorsed an amendment, passed by both houses of Congress, that would forever guarantee slavery in the states where it already existed. As he well knew, this was a purely symbolic gesture that granted nothing the South did not

LEE'S LOYALTY TO VIRGINIA

Robert E. Lee, perhaps the most respected active soldier in the army in 1861, was asked what he would do if there was a civil war. Would he support the North or the South? In effect, Lee replied neither; he would support his native state, Virginia:

"If Virginia stands by the old Union, so will I. But if she secedes (though I do not believe in secession as a constitutional right, nor that there is sufficient cause for revolution) then I will follow my native state with my sword and, if need be, with my life."

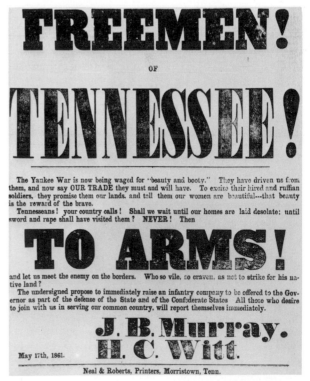

FREEMEN!
OF
TENNESSEE!

The Yankee War is now being waged for "beauty and booty." They have driven us from them, and now say OUR TRADE they must and will have. To excite their hired and ruffian soldiers, they promise them our lands, and tell them our women are beautiful—that beauty is the reward of the brave.

Tennesseans! your country calls! Shall we wait until our homes are laid desolate; until sword and rape shall have visited them? NEVER! Then

TO ARMS!

and let us meet the enemy on the borders. Who so vile, so craven, as not to strike for his native land?

The undersigned propose to immediately raise an infantry company to be offered to the Governor as part of the defense of the State and of the Confederate States. All those who desire to join with us in serving our common country, will report themselves immediately.

J. B. Murray.
H. C. Witt.

May 17th, 1861.

Neal & Roberts, Printers, Morristown, Tenn.

A Confederate recruitment poster defining the Civil War as a defense of home and hearth against foreign invaders.

dent" but called their new government "permanent." Even more oddly, the Confederates declared that individual states might not interfere with slavery, a restriction on states' rights that no prominent Republican had ever suggested.

The Confederates also modified the presidency. The chief executive was to be elected for a term of six years rather than four, but he was not permitted to run for a second term. While this seemed to weaken the office, the Confederates allowed the president to veto parts of congressional bills rather than, as in the Union, requiring the president to accept all or nothing.

Jeff Davis

As their first president, the Confederates selected Jefferson Davis. On the face of it, he was a good choice. His bearing was regal, he wore his dignity easily, and he was the model slave owner, the sort that Southerners liked to pretend was typical. Davis also seemed to be a wise choice because he was not closely associated with the secessionist movement. Indeed, Davis had asked his fellow Mississippians to delay secession until Lincoln had a chance to prove himself. When his state overruled

him, Davis delivered a moderate, eloquent, and affectionate farewell speech in the Senate. By choosing such a man, rather than a fire-eater, the Confederates demonstrated their willingness to work with Southerners who opposed secession, who were numerous. With Davis, the Confederacy could also appeal to the eight slave states that remained within the Union.

In other ways, the choice of Jefferson Davis was ill-advised. It was not so much the unattractive coldness of his personality. George Washington had been icier. Davis's weakness was that despite his bearing, he lacked self-confidence and was, consequently, easily irritated and inflexible. He proved incapable of cooperating with critics, even those who differed with him on only minor matters. He seemed to need yes-men in order to function, and, as a result, he denied his administration the services of some of the South's ablest statesmen.

Worse, Davis was a dabbler. Instead of delegating authority and presiding over the government, he repeatedly interfered in the pettiest details of administration— peering over his subordinates' shoulders, arousing personal resentments among even those who were devoted to him. He had been a good senator, he was not qualified to be the "Father of His Country."

Jefferson Davis, president of the Confederacy.

Abe Lincoln

By comparison, Abraham Lincoln knew the value of unity and competent assistants. Rather than shun his rivals within the Republican party, he named them to his cabinet. Seward became Secretary of State; Salmon P. Chase was Lincoln's Secretary of Treasury. After a brief misadventure with an incompetent Secretary of War, Simon Cameron, Lincoln appointed a Democrat, Edwin Stanton, to that post because his talents were obvious. Lincoln wanted able aides, not pals or toadies. Within their departments, Lincoln's cabinet officers were free to do anything that did not conflict with general policy. As a result, a cantankerous and headstrong group of men never seriously challenged his control of basic policy.

Lincoln differed from Davis in other ways. Far from regal, he was an awkward, plain, even ugly man. Tall and gangling, with oversize hands and feet, he impressed those who met him for the first time as a frontier oaf. His enemies called him "the baboon." Some of his supporters snickered at his clumsiness and were appalled by his fondness for dirty jokes.

But both friends and enemies soon discovered that the president was no yokel. Lincoln had honed a sharp native intelligence on a whetstone of lifelong study, and proved to be one of the three or four most eloquent chief

A crowd gathered in front of the unfinished Capitol Building to hear Abraham Lincoln's first inaugural address on March 4, 1861.

executives. And yet, behind his brilliance was a humility born of modest background that can be found in no other American president.

Long Odds

North and South were mismatched in more than their presidents. The population of the Union states was 22 million. The Confederacy's people numbered 9 million, of whom 3.5 million were slaves. In military terms, these figures meant that the North would have to enlist only 40% of its free males in military service between 1861 and 1865. The South, fielding a far smaller force, was to call on 90% of its eligible recruits.

Economically, the disparities between North and South were more exteme. There was literally an "industrial establishment" in the Union states for every industrial worker in the South. In value of industrial production, the Union edge was 10 to 1; in iron production, 15 to 1; in coal production 38 to 1; in textile production 14 to 1. There were more cotton spindles in the single city of Lowell, Massachusetts than in all the Confeder-

acy. The Union manufactured 32 firearms for every one the South turned out. Indeed, New England armories were to export firearms to Europe throughout the war.

And yet, the secessionists pushed on. As Alexander Stephens wrote of his native Georgia in December 1860, "The people run mad, they are wild with passion and frenzy, doing they know not what." By March 4, 1861, when Lincoln was sworn in before a glum Washington crowd, the Union was in tatters. In just two months, the Stars and Stripes had been hauled down from every flagstaff in the South except for one at Fort Pickens outside Pensacola, Florida, and another at Fort Sumter, a rocky island in the harbor of Charleston, South Carolina.

A War of Nerves

Neither of the forts threatened the security of the Confederacy. They were old installations that had been designed for defense and were manned by token garrisons. But symbols take on profound importance in uneasy times, and the Southern fire-eaters, itching for a fight, ranted about the insulting occupation of their country by a "foreign power."

Davis was willing to live with the Union forts for the time being. Unlike the hotheads, he understood that the Confederacy could not survive as long as only seven states adhered to it. His policy was to delay a confrontation with the North until he could make a foreign alliance or induce the eight slave states that remained in the Union to join the Confederacy. He feared that if he fired the first shot, the states of the upper South might support the Union.

The extremists disagreed. They believed that a battle, no matter who started it, would bring the other slave states to their side. Nevertheless, when the commander at Sumter announced that he would soon have to surrender the fort for lack of provisions, Davis had his way.

Within limits, Lincoln also favored delaying a confrontation. He believed that the longer the states of the upper South postponed a decision to secede, the less likely they were to go. Moreover, the leaders of Virginia, Kentucky, Tennessee, and Arkansas had formally warned him against using force against the Confederacy. If the Union fired the first shot, they would secede.

Finally, Lincoln did not have the people of the North solidly behind him. Northern Democrats would not support an act of aggression and Winfield Scott, Lincoln's chief military adviser, told him that the army was not up to a war of conquest. Some abolitionists who were also pacifists, such as Horace Greeley and William Lloyd Garrison, urged the president to "let the wayward sisters depart in peace."

NOTABLE PEOPLE

THE AGONY OF THE SOUTHERN WHIGS

Strictly speaking, there were no Southern Whigs in 1861 because there was no Whig party. It had ceased to exist after the passage of the Kansas-Nebraska Act when the Northern Whigs gave up in disgust on their proslavery fellows and joined with the Free-Soil Democrats to form the Republican party. The Southern Whigs, now only a minority party in a minority section, either joined the Democratic party or, if they had a strong enough electoral base to do so, continued in politics as independents.

But Democrat or independent in 1861, they were still Whigs at heart, disciples of Henry Clay with a strong sense of the glory of the united American nation and a tradition of distrust for Democrats. The secession crisis—the handiwork of Southern Democrats—and the Civil War that followed it were therefore an agony for them that no two faced in quite the same way.

Alexander Stephens (1812–83) fought secessionists in his home state of Georgia down to the hour that the state left the Union. Then, however, sadly loyal to his state, much like Robert E. Lee of Virginia, he pledged allegiance to the Confederacy, delivered a famous speech in which, rather un-Whiggishly, he said that slavery was the "cornerstone" of the Confederacy, and agreed to serve as vice president in what was viewed as a gesture of unity. Within a year, however, Stephens was at odds with Jefferson Davis. He began to spend less time in Richmond and more in Georgia, where he found himself, a former nationalist, in the unlikely position of fighting for states' rights against the former states-rights Democrat, Davis.

In February 1865, Stephens took on a job more congenial to a Whig. He led a Confederate delegation to Hampton Roads, Virginia, where he met with Lincoln and tried to arrange a compromise peace. The mission failed because Stephens had been instructed to insist on Confederate independence, and, with Union troops on the verge of striking a deathblow to Lee's Army of Northern Virginia, Lincoln refused even to discuss that possibility. Immediately after the war, Georgians elected Stephens to the Senate, but he was refused his seat by former Whig comrades who were now members of the Union's Republican party. Eight years later, now a Democrat like most Southern whites, he entered Congress, where he served for ten years without distinction.

Senator John J. Crittenden of Kentucky (1787–1863), a protégé and personal friend of Henry Clay, is a more appealing character than the unsteady Stephens. He believed in sectional compromise as intensely as did his teacher. The plan he devised early in 1861 appealed to a good many moderates who, like himself, did not think slavery an issue important enough to destroy the Union. Split the difference, Crittenden said; divide the territories between slave territories and free territories. But Lincoln could not agree; he had run on a platform that had promised no slavery in the territories, and the Crittenden Compromise provided for a similar division of all territories "hereafter acquired." To Lincoln, who had disapproved of the Mexican War, this seemed an open invitation to proslavery Southerners to provoke a war with Mexico or with Spain over Cuba in order to grab land suitable to the raising of those crops that were most profitably farmed by slaves.

Crittenden lived only to 1863, just long enough to suffer the personal tragedy of seeing one son fight for the Union and another for the Confederacy.

John Bell of Tennessee (1797–1869) was a slaveholder who agreed with the Republicans that slavery should *not* be allowed in the territories. Like Crittenden, he did not believe that the question was worth a war. Unlike Crittenden, he thought that the best way to avoid one was to follow the wishes of the majority and keep slavery restricted to the area where it was already established.

Curiously, Bell made few friends among the Republicans. The abolitionists among them saw Bell only as a slaveowner, and therefore an immoral man. But his position was by no means unattractive to Southerners, particularly those of the border states. Running for president in 1860 on the Constitutional Union ticket, Bell carried Virginia, Kentucky, and Tennessee and ran strong in Delaware, Maryland, Missouri, and elsewhere. More than a few Southerners were satisfied with the status quo or actually opposed slavery. Robert E. Lee was one who probably wished John Bell had won.

Robert Toombs (1810–85) was as erratic as Alexander Stephens. Capable of anti-Northern language as scorching as any Democrat's, he nevertheless opted for sectional compromise each time it was offered. Toombs supported the Compromise of 1850 and, in 1861, backed Crittenden's plan to head off secession. Unlike his fellow Georgian Alexander Stephens, however, Toombs actually helped to engineer Georgia's secession when the Republicans refused to meet the South halfway.

Named Confederate Secretary of State by Davis, Toombs quit after a few months in order to get into the fighting. He headed a brigade and fought bravely if without particular distinction. A wound at Antietam sent him home. When the war ended, he fled to England for fear of reprisals.

In 1867, Toombs returned to Georgia, where he refused to apply for a pardon, as many extreme secessionists had quickly done. Nevertheless, while taking this defiant stand, he stood up for compromise one more time in 1877 when the Republican party promised to withdraw all troops from the South if their dubiously elected presidential candidate, Rutherford B. Hayes, was permitted to take office without incident. The erratic course of Toombs's life may reflect nothing more than a mercurial personality; or it may illustrate the terrible strain placed on Southern Whigs who loved both the South and the United States.

Lincoln had no intention of doing that. He was determined to save the Union by peaceful means if possible, by force if necessary. He reasoned that if the Confederates fired the first shot, the border states might secede anyway, but at least the act of rebellion would unite Northerners behind him. If he delayed a confrontation indefinitely, he still might lose the border states and still have a divided, uncertain North.

This was the reasoning behind Lincoln's decision to resupply Fort Sumter. He announced that he would not use force against the state of South Carolina, and repeated his wish that the crisis be resolved peacefully; but he insisted on his presidential obligation to maintain the government's authority in Charleston harbor.

And so the war came. When the relief ship approached the sandbar that guarded Charleston harbor, the Confederacy attacked. On the morning of April 12, 1861, artillery under the command of General P. G. T. Beauregard opened up. The next day, Sumter surrendered. Davis was reluctant until the end. In a way, he lost control of South Carolina. His inability to control the Confederate states would haunt his administration for four years.

The Border States Take Sides

Oddly, the Battle of Fort Sumter served both Confederate and Union purposes. While Lincoln was able to call for 75,000 volunteers and to get them, his action pushed four more states into the Confederacy. Virginia, North Carolina, Tennessee, and Arkansas seceded from the Union, and in deference to Virginia's importance, the Confederate capital of the new nation was moved from Montgomery to Richmond.

Secessionist feeling was also strong in the slave states of Maryland, Kentucky, and Missouri. Lincoln was able to prevent them from seceding by a combination of shrewd political maneuvers and the tactful deployment of troops. Delaware, the fifteenth slave state, never seriously considered secession.

Then, in the contest for the border states, the North won a bonus. The mountainous western part of Virginia was peopled by farmers who owned few slaves and who traditionally resented the planter aristocracy that dominated Virginia politics and was now in favor of secession. The westerners had no interest in fighting and dying to protect the human property of the rich. In effect, the fifty western counties of Virginia seceded from the Old Dominion. By an irregular constitutional process, the Republicans provided the means for West Virginia to become a Union state in June 1863.

For the border states, the Civil War was literally a war between brothers. Henry Clay's and John Breckinridge's progeny fought on both sides. Several of President Lincoln's brothers-in-law fought for the South, and Jefferson Davis had cousins in the Union Army. The father-in-law of the great Confederate cavalryman, J. E. B. Stuart, served in the Union cavalry. At the battle of Port Royal (South Carolina), Union naval Captain Percival Drayton directed actions against Southern troops commanded by his brother, Thomas F. Drayton. The most poignant case was that of Senator Crittenden of Ken-

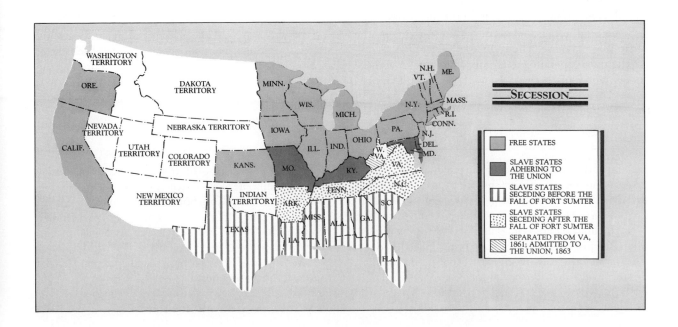

tucky, who had tried to head off war with a compromise. One of his sons became a general in the Union Army and another a general in the Confederate Army.

The Irony of Secession

However much the people of the border states disliked secession, they were not against slavery. In order to reassure them, Lincoln issued several pronouncements that the purpose of the war was to preserve the Union and not to abolish slavery. In emphasizing this war aim, he pointed up the irony of secession. While Southerners claimed that they had gone their own way in order to protect their peculiar institution, they actually had thrown away the legal and constitutional guarantees that they had had as U.S. citizens.

Under the Fugitive Slave Act, slaves who ran away to the Northern states were returned to their owners. In order to escape, slaves had to get to Canada, out of the country. With secession, "out of the country" was hundreds of miles closer—over the Tennessee–Kentucky or the Virginia–Maryland line. This fact was dramatized early in the war when several Union generals declared that slaves who had fled to Union lines were "contraband of war," subject to confiscation and therefore free. At first, Lincoln countermanded these orders so as not to antagonize the loyal border states, especially Kentucky. But it was obvious that the South had made it easier for slaves to get away than it had been before secession.

In leaving the Union as individual states, the Southerners had waived all legal rights to the territories, which were federal property. Their action was the most effective guarantee, short of a constitutional amendment, that slavery would be banned from the territories.

Some Southerners had no intention of giving up the territories, of course. The Indians of Oklahoma, for example, were generally pro-Confederate. But to win the Indian lands and, perhaps, New Mexico meant launch-

A recruiting poster calling for volunteers to fight for the Union.

ing the very war that Davis hoped to avoid. Secession was less a rational political act than it was the fruit of passion, suspicion, and sectional hatred blinding the Southern extremists to reality.

For Further Reading

Several of the books cited after the previous chapter also deal with events treated in Chapter 23, particularly Avery O. Craven, *The Growth of Southern Nationalism, 1848–1860* (1953) and *The Coming of the Civil War* (1957); James McPherson, *Battle Cry of Freedom* (1988); Alan Nevins, *Ordeal of the Union* (1947); David Potter, *The Impending Crisis, 1848–1861* (1976). Also see Eric Foner, *Politics and Ideology in the Age of the Civil War* (1980).

The events that promoted sectional bitterness in North and South during the 1850s are treated in Stanley W. Campbell, *The Slave-Catchers: Enforcement of the Fugitive Slave Law, 1840–1860* (1968); James C. Malin, *John Brown and the Legend of Fifty-Six* (1970); Don E. Fehrenbacher, *The Dred Scott Case: Its Significance in American Law and Politics* (1978); C. B. Swisher, *Roger B. Taney* (1935); R. W. Johansen, *The Lincoln-Douglas Debates* (1965); Stephen B. Oates, *To Purge This Land with Blood: A Biography of John Brown* (1970).

On the secession crisis, the standard works are Kenneth M. Stampp, *And the War Came: The North and the Secession Crisis, 1860–1861* (1950) and W. L. Barney, *The Road to Secession* (1972). See also Stephen A. Channing, *Crisis of Fear: Secession in South Carolina* (1970); R. A. Wooster, *The Secession Conventions of the South* (1962). Don Fehrenbacher, *Prelude to Greatness: Lincoln in the 1850s* (1962) is essential; Richard N. Current, *Lincoln and the First Shot* (1963) and *The Lincoln Nobody Knows* (1958) deal with the president's actions in 1861. For his predecessor, see P. S. Klein, *President James Buchanan* (1962), his Southern opposite number, Clement Eaton, *Jefferson Davis* (1977). See also Stephen B. Oates, *With Malice Toward None* (1979) and Benjamin P. Thomas, *Abraham Lincoln* (1952).

The aftermath of battle. Photograph by Timothy O'Sullivan, 1862.

TIDY PLANS, UGLY REALITIES

THE CIVIL WAR THROUGH 1862

The attack on Fort Sumter answered the first big question: there would be a shooting war. When

Lincoln called for 75,000 volunteers to preserve the Union, and Davis summoned the young men of

the South to defend the honor and independence of their homeland, both were flooded with enthu-

siastic recruits. By the summer of 1861, the Union had 186,000 soldiers in uniform and the Confed-

eracy, 112,000.

But what kind of war would it be? What would battle be like? Nowhere in the world had armies of such size clashed since the Napoleonic Wars in Europe half a century earlier. During the Mexican War, the United States had put no more than 10,000 men on a field. Now, just 15 years later, two American armies were faced with the challenge of feeding, clothing, sheltering, transporting, and controlling a mass of humanity 10 and 20 times that size.

The significance of numbers was not lost on the nations of Europe. High-ranking officers were dispatched to the United States to observe how the Americans managed their problem. The lessons they took back with them would inform military thinking in the Western world for 50 years.

THE ART AND SCIENCE OF WAR

The American Civil War took up where Napoleon and Wellington left off. American military men had been trained in a theory of battle formulated by a Swiss officer who had served in both the French and the Russian armies, Antoine Henri Jomini. A textbook based on Jomini's *Art of War* was the standard authority on tactics at West Point, where virtually all the major commanders of the Civil War had learned their craft.

Position, Maneuver, and Concentration

Jomini emphasized position and maneuver as the keys to winning battles or, better yet, in making battle unnecessary. The goal of the commanding general was to occupy high ground, and, when a battle threatened, ascertain the weakest point in the enemy's lines and concentrate power there. The commander who prepared more thoroughly, better exploited the terrain, and moved his troops more skillfully than his opponent would break through the opposing line and force the enemy from the field. The object then was to capture and occupy cities important in trade and government, forcing the enemy's capitulation. The idea was that, lacking what we would call a national "infrastructure," the enemy had nothing for which to fight. Napoleon defeated his enemies (excepting Russia) when he captured their major cities.

Jomini reduced all battle situations to twelve models. Therefore, commanders trained in his school, and with a brain in their heads, knew pretty much what their adversaries had in mind at all times. As long as both sides observed the "rules," there would be no long casualty lists. The general who was outfoxed knew that his duty was to disengage so that his men would be able to fight on another day under more favorable circumstances. Retreat was among the most vital of maneuvers

because it preserved an army as a functioning machine. Americans needed look no further than to George Washington's direction of their own Revolution to know that.

The Armies

The armies of the Civil War were divided into cavalry, artillery, and infantry with support units such as the Corps of Engineers (which constructed fortifications) and the Quartermaster Corps (entrusted with supply).

The cavalry's principal task was reconnaissance. Horse soldiers were the eyes of an army on whose information battle plans were based. Because cavalry units were mobile and fast, they could be used for raids, plunging deep into enemy territory, doing their damage, and high-tailing it out before being confronted by big guns and masses of infantry. In a pitched battle, cavalry was used to reinforce weak points in the lines and, if enemy troops were in retreat, to harass them. But cavalrymen were lightly armed by definition. For all the dash and flash, cavalry played a subsidiary role in pitched battle. Nevertheless, it was the glamorous service: The horses! The shades of the days of chivalry!

The artillery was slow to move and notoriously unglamorous. But, as Napoleon had shown, big guns were critical to both attack and defense. Before an attacking army moved, its artillery slugged away at enemy positions with exploding shells, "softening them up." In defense, the artillery greeted attackers with grapeshot (a charge of small iron balls) and canister (projectiles that exploded and filled the air with clouds of metal). Examinations of dead soldiers after Civil War battles revealed that an attacking army suffered far more from cannon than from small-arms fire.

As always before the nuclear age, the infantry was the

FED UP IN DIXIE

By no means did all white Southerners rally to the "Stars and Bars," as the Confederate flag was nicknamed. In the up-country South, the foothills on both sides of the Appalachian Ridge, few people owned slaves and many of them opposed secession as the darling of the great planters, whose political and economic domination they resented. Western Virginia and eastern Tennessee voted against secession and provided thousands of soldiers for the *Union* army. So did many counties in western North Carolina and northern Alabama. Once the war was underway, the Confederate government's practice of expropriating crops and livestock to feed its armies aggravated the situation. When food became expensive and scarce in cities like Richmond and even in the countryside, Southern women rioted in protest against the war.

backbone of the army. The cavalry might worry the enemy, and the artillery weaken him, but it was the foot soldiers who slugged it out face to face, took the most casualties, won and lost the battles. The commander of infantry was the commander of battle.

Battle

The basic infantry unit was the brigade of some 2,000 to 3,000 men. Under the command of a brigadier general, the soldiers formed double lines in defense or advanced over a front of about a thousand yards, again in two ranks. During the first campaigns of the Civil War, captains in the front lines tried to march the men in step, as had been the rule in the Napoleonic era. But with the greater firepower available by the 1860s, such formality was sensibly abandoned. It was enough that the men continued to run, trot, or simply walk into oncoming grapeshot, Minié balls (conical bullets), noise like a thunderstorm in hell, and a haze of black, sulfurous smoke. Junior officers led the charge so that the ranks of lieutenant and captain suffered high casualties. Other officers walked behind the lines in order to discourage stragglers. They were authorized to shoot men who panicked and broke ranks.

If the advancing army was not forced to turn back, the final phase of battle was hand-to-hand combat. The attackers clambered over the enemy's fortifications of earth and lumber. Attackers and defenders swung their muskets at one another like the baseball bats they played with in their spare time until the defenders broke and ran or the attackers were killed or captured. The men had bayonets, but during the Civil War, neither side succeeded in training soldiers to use them very well. The importance of mastering this difficult and deadly skill was one lesson that the European observers took home with them.

There was plenty of shooting but not a great deal of aiming. Except for special units of sharpshooters, foot soldiers were not marksmen. There was little sense in taking on the big and expensive job of training large numbers of men in the skill of hitting small targets at great distances. With a few important exceptions (Shiloh, Antietam, Gettysburg), Civil War battles were not fought in open country. The men confronted one another in dense woods on terrain broken by hills, stone fences, and ditches. They often could not see one another until they were almost close enough to touch.

Even in open country, hundreds of cannon and tens of thousands of muskets filled the air with a dense, acrid smog that, on a windless day, shrouded the battlefield. (Smokeless powder was still in the future.) If a soldier could shoot well, there was little he could aim at in order to prove it.

Billy Yank and Johnny Reb

As in all wars, the men who fought were quite young, most between the ages of 17 and 25, with drummer boys of but 12. They came from every state and social class, although when both sides adopted draft laws (the Confederacy in April 1862, the Union in March 1863), the burden fell more heavily on poorer farmers and working-class people.

The Union battery at Fredericksburg and photographer Timothy O'Sullivan were under fire by Confederate artillery when this photograph was taken.

This was because the draft laws included significant exemptions favoring the well-to-do. The Confederate law exempted men who owned 20 or more slaves. It was sorely resented by Johnny Reb, the common soldier, who rarely owned even one slave. Both the Confederate and Union draft laws allowed a man who was called to service to pay for a substitute at a price that was beyond the means of the ordinary fellow. In the North, a draftee could hire another to take his place or simply pay the government $300 for an exemption. In July 1863, working-class resentment of the law led to a week-long riot in New York City. Mobs of workingmen, especially Irishmen, sacked draft offices, attacked rich men, and harassed and lynched blacks, whom they considered the cause of the war and a threat to their jobs. Some 60,000 people were involved. At least 400 were killed, and some $5 million in property destroyed.

In the South, resistance to the draft was less dramatic. Nevertheless, thousands of draft dodgers headed west or into the Appalachians and the Ozarks, where some organized outlaw gangs, raided farms, and occasionally skirmished with Confederate troops. Most Southern opposition to the war centered in the poorer mountain counties.

Both Union and Confederate armies were plagued by a high desertion rate, about 10 percent through most of the war. Some individuals specialized in desertion, the bounty jumpers. Because some states and cities paid cash bonuses, or bounties, to men who signed up, a few men made a lucrative, if risky business of enlisting, skipping out at first opportunity, and looking for another unit offering bounties. In March 1865, Union military police arrested one John O'Connor. He confessed to enlisting, collecting a bounty, and deserting 32 times.

Shirking was not typical of either army. Over the course of the war, 1.5 million young men served in the Union Army, and more than 1 million, from a much smaller population, with the Confederate. Whatever their resentments, ordinary people thought they had something at stake in the conflict. Despite their exemption, Southern slave owners served in proportion to their numbers.

Army Life

The war they knew was not much like the war presented to the folks back home. In artists' paintings and drawings in newspapers, masses of men in blue and gray moved in order across open fields amidst waving flags and cloudlike puffs of white smoke. In reality, battle was a tiny part of military experience. Mostly, the war involved waiting, digging trenches, building breastworks, marching, carting supplies hither and yon, and being carted from one place to another in crowded trains.

The war meant poor food and shelter. In the South, supply was rarely efficient. Even when the Confederacy had enough uniforms, shoes, and food—which was not always—there were problems in getting them and the soldiers together. In the North, the inevitable profiteers sold the government tainted beef and shoddy blankets that fell apart in the rain. On both sides, physicians were unprepared to cope with so many patients; dysentery, typhoid, influenza, and other epidemic illnesses killed more soldiers than did enemy guns.

THE SOBERING CAMPAIGN OF 1861

Army life also involved drilling day in and day out. But those who rallied to the colors in the spring of 1861 thought of the war as an adventure, a vacation from the plow and hog trough that would be over all too soon for their taste. They trimmed themselves in gaudy uniforms. Some, influenced by pictures of Turkish soldiers in the recently concluded Crimean War, called themselves "Zouaves" and donned the Turkish fez and baggy pantaloons. Other units adopted names that would have been more appropriate to a boys' club. One Confederate regiment was called "The Lincoln Killers."

On to Richmond

Abraham Lincoln shared the illusion that the war would be short and painless. He waved off Winfield Scott's professional warning that it would take three years and 300,000 men to crush the rebellion. Lincoln asked the first volunteers, mostly members of state militias, to enlist for only 90 days. That would be enough. Southerners too spoke of "our battle summer." The soldiers and civilians on the two sides disagreed only as to who would be celebrating when the leaves fell in the autumn of 1861.

These pleasant illusions were blown away on a fine July day about twenty miles outside Washington. Believing that his volunteers could take Richmond before their short enlistments expired, Lincoln sent General Irvin McDowell marching directly toward the Confed-

"Brother against brother" was not just a romantic contrivance. The phenomenon was by no means uncommon. At the Union assault on Hilton Head, Naval Commander Percival Drayton commanded the U.S.S. Pocahantas, one of the vessels attacking Confederate troops under Brigadier General Thomas F. Drayton, his brother. Both were South Carolinians.

erate capital with 30,000 troops. Laughing and joking as they went, sometimes shooting at targets, the boys from Ohio and Massachusetts were accompanied by a parade of carriages filled with congressmen, socialites, newspaper reporters, and curiosity seekers. The crowd carried picnic lunches and bickered as to where in Richmond they would enjoy a late supper.

They were met by a Confederate force of about 22,000 under the command of General Beauregard up from Fort Sumter. The rebels had hastily dug in on high ground behind a creek called Bull Run, near a railroad crossing named Manassas Junction. McDowell attacked immediately, guessing the Confederate left flank to be the weakest point in the line. He was right about that. Although his troops were shocked by the ferocity of the musket fire that greeted them, they almost cracked the Southern line.

Had it cracked, the war would likely have been over, at least in the upper South. To the rear of Beauregard's line, the road to Richmond lay open. At the critical moment, however, 9,000 Virginians commanded by Joseph E. Johnston arrived on the field after a frantic train

ride from the Shenandoah Valley. A brigade under the command of Thomas J. Jackson, a 37-year-old mathematics instructor at Virginia Military Academy, shored up the sagging Confederate left. The Union soldiers fell back and then broke in hysteria, fleeing for Washington along with the panicked spectators.

Celebrations and Recriminations

The South had a victory and a hero. At the peak of the battle for the left flank, a South Carolinian rallied his men by shouting, "There stands Jackson like a stone wall." The name stuck, for it seemed appropriate to more than Thomas J. Jackson's performance on the battlefield. He was introspective and humorless, somewhat a figure of ridicule to his students before the war, a stern Scotch-Irish Presbyterian who lacked the human touch and was never loved by his troops, as some generals have been.

But his men stood in awe of him because Jackson came to life when the bullets whistled. He never yielded a line to the enemy, and he was a genius at maneuvering troops. For two years, Jackson would do what the South

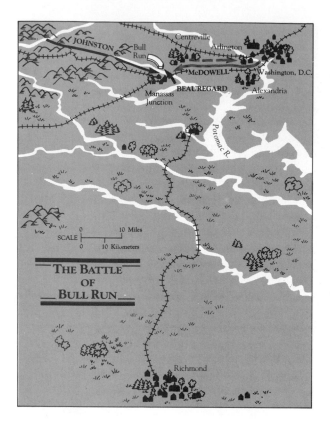

THE BATTLE
OF
BULL RUN

could show them off once or twice before the Union capitulated. And then they bickered. At a round of gala parties in Richmond, old personal jealousies erupted as blustering colonels and generals blamed one another for blunders real and imaginary.

In the North, however, the defeat at Manassas taught a sorely needed lesson. The spectacle of McDowell's troops throwing down their guns and trotting wild-eyed into Washington, where they lay down to sleep in doorways and on the sidewalks, alarmed Lincoln and brought him around to Winfield Scott's way of thinking. The war would be no summer's pastime but a long, hard fight. Lincoln asked Congress for 300,000 troops under three-year enlistments.

He also relieved Irvin McDowell from command of what was now called the Army of the Potomac, replacing him with George B. McClellan. The former president of the Illinois Central Railroad (for which Lincoln had been a lawyer), McClellan had a reputation as an organizer and administrator. In November 1861, Winfield Scott retired, and McClellan also took charge of the Union armies that were being drilled throughout the Midwest.

Northern Strategy

Though Scott was gone, a three-part strategy that he had outlined to Lincoln before the fighting began was

needed done, insert his men in critical positions and stand like a stone wall against Union assaults.

By way of contrast, General Beauregard's reputation suffered at Bull Run because he failed to follow up his victory by marching on Washington. Within a few months, he was replaced as Confederate commander in Virginia by Joseph E. Johnston, who had brought the troops and Stonewall Jackson from the Shenandoah Valley.

Elegant in goatee and personally as brave as a lieutenant, Johnston was a superior soldier. But neither Beauregard nor anyone else was to blame for the South's failure to capture Washington. As Johnston himself put it, "The Confederate Army was more disorganized by victory than that of the United States by defeat"; and a disorganized army is no army at all. All the better generals at Bull Run and deskmen like Robert E. Lee, who was President Davis's military adviser, emphasized the need for regrouping and hard training.

The Summer Lull

President Davis agreed, and he cautioned Richmond society that there was more fighting to come. But few seemed to listen. The common soldiers were cocky and overconfident as a result of their victory and minor casualties. Southern politicians spoke as though the war were over. Volunteer officers nagged their tailors to finish sewing gold braid on dress uniforms, so that they

Dour, distant, cold—Thomas "Stonewall" Jackson nevertheless won Robert E. Lee's ear, admiration, and respect.

This hastily scrawled sketch seems to be the most appropriate depiction of the panicked Union retreat from the first Battle of Bull Run.

now adopted. First, it was necessary to defend Washington with the Army of the Potomac and to maintain constant pressure on Richmond in the hope of capturing the city. This was important because Richmond was less than 100 miles from Washington, the seat of the Confederate government, and a railroad hub and a major industrial center, home of the Tredregar Iron Works which was to sustain Virginia's fighting machine during the war.

Second, because Lincoln and his advisers believed that the Ohio-Mississippi waterway was vital to the economic life of the Midwestern states, Union armies would strike down the great valley. Their object was to gain complete control of the Mississippi as soon as possible in order to permit Western farmers to resume the export of foodstuffs, by which they lived, and to split the Confederacy in two. Then the trans-Mississippi front (Arkansas, Louisiana, and Texas) could be neglected while the Union concentrated its force in the East.

Third, the Union would use its overwhelming naval superiority to blockade the South, strangling its export economy. If the Confederates were unable to sell cotton abroad, they could not buy the manufactures, particularly the munitions, that were essential in a lengthy war. Scott called this strategy the "Anaconda Plan" after the South American snake that slowly crushes its prey. The powerful Union would asphyxiate its foe.

On the face of it, an effective blockade was out of the question. The Confederate Atlantic and Gulf coastline was a labyrinth of inlets, sheltered channels, coves, bays, bayous, salt marshes, and lonely broad beaches. It was quite impossible to prevent every vessel from reaching shore or from making a break for the high seas. Never-

theless, an effective commerce could not be rowed through the surf or unloaded in swamps, and the commanders of the Union Navy felt confident that with time their ships could bottle up the Confederate ports.

Dixie's Challenge

Southern strategy had a simpler design but a flimsier foundation. In order to attain its basic goal—independence—the Confederacy needed only to turn back Union advances until the British or French, who showed some friendship to the Southern cause, came to the rescue, or until the people of the North grew weary of fighting and forced Lincoln to negotiate. In the broadest sense, the story of the Civil War tells how these hopes were dashed and how, although long frustrated and delayed, the Union strategy succeeded.

The Confederacy's hope of foreign intervention died first. In the case of France, it was doomed from the beginning by the personality of the French emperor, Napoleon III. On one day a scheming power politician who recognized that an independent Confederacy might be molded into a valuable French protectorate, Napoleon III was, on the next, a flighty romantic.

At first, while leading the Southerners on, he delayed when the more prudent British hesitated. (Napoleon did not want to move alone.) Then, when he was approached by a group of Mexican aristocrats who, in order to defeat a peasant revolution, offered to make an emperor of his nephew, Maximilian of Austria, Napoleon III saw a grander opportunity in America's tragedy. While the United States at peace would not have tolerated European interference in Mexico—it was not so

INDIANS IN GRAY AND BLUE

While blacks were a mainstay of the Union army, most Native Americans sat out the war, no doubt somewhat heartened that, for once, the whites were fighting among themselves. Some tribes formed units, however, particularly those from Indian Territory, where slavery was legal. About 5,500 Native Americans fought on the Confederate side, about 4,000 for the North. An Iroquois officer served on General Grant's staff.

long since expansionists had spoken of annexing the whole country themselves—the United States tearing itself apart was helpless to take action. Anyway, what self-respecting emperor wanted a dependency of quarrelsome, headstrong cotton planters when he could tread in the footsteps of Cortez? Not Napoleon III. By the end of 1862, he scarcely noticed the Southern diplomats who continued to court him.

The pro-Confederate sentiments of the British government were more solidly founded. The South was the principal source of cotton for the British textile industry and British industrialists generally supported Henry Lord Palmerston's Liberal government. Moreover, many English aristocrats looked upon the Southern planters as rough-cut kinsmen, flattering in their imitation of the British upper classes. Finally, a great many British politicians relished the opportunity to shatter the growing power of the American upstart.

However, whereas Napoleon III was impulsive, the British leaders were cautious. They would not throw in with the Confederacy until the rebels demonstrated that they had a real chance of winning. A combination of Southern blunders in export policy, bad luck, Union diplomatic skill, and a key Union victory at the Confederacy's brightest hour dashed the Confederate dream (and the British inclination) of redrawing the map of North America.

King Cotton Dethroned

The first Confederate blunder was Jefferson Davis's decision to blackmail England into supporting the Southern cause. He prevailed on cotton shippers to keep the crop of 1860 at home, storing it on wharves and in warehouses. The idea was to put the pinch on British mill owners so that they would set up a cry for war.

"Cotton diplomacy" did not work. English mill owners had anticipated war and shortages, stockpiling huge reserves of fiber. By the time these supplies ran out in 1862, cotton growers in Egypt and the Middle East were filling much of the gap created by the American war. To make matters worse, Union troops captured enough Southern cotton by 1862 to keep the mills of New England humming and even to sell some to Great Britain.

The Diplomatic War

In November 1861, a zealous Union naval officer almost scuttled the northern effort to keep England neutral. The captain of the *U.S.S. San Jacinto* boarded a British steamer, the *Trent*, and seized two Confederate diplomats who were aboard, James M. Mason and John Slidell. Northern public opinion was delighted. It was refreshing to hear for a change of an American warship bullying a British vessel. But Lincoln took a dimmer view of the incident. The British minister came close to threatening war. To the president, Mason and Slidell were two hot potatoes, and he took advantage of the first lull in the public celebrations to hasten them aboard a British warship. "One war at a time," he remarked to his cabinet.

No harm was done. In France, Slidell was frustrated by Napoleon III's Mexican ambitions and, in England, Mason proved no match for the Union minister, Charles Francis Adams, in the delicate game of diplomacy. Mason did manage to see two commerce-raiders, the *Florida* and the *Alabama*, constructed for the Confederacy and put to sea. But Adams cajoled and threatened the British government into preventing a sister ship and several Confederate rams from leaving port. He moved with great skill and energy through the salons of London, and kept Great Britain out of the war until the North turned the tide of war in its direction.

1862 AND STALEMATE

As Confederate hopes of bringing England in dimmed, the South increasingly looked to sympathizers in the North, defeatists, and antiwar activists to aid their cause. Some Northerners frankly favored the South, particularly people in the Union slave states and in the lower counties of Ohio, Indiana, and Illinois, a region with a strong Southern heritage. However, these "Copperheads," as Northerners who sympathized with the South were called (after the poisonous snake that strikes without warning), were never able to mount a decisive threat to the Union war effort. They were a minority, and Lincoln played free with their civil liberties in order to silence them.

Lincoln and the Copperheads

One of the president's most controversial moves against the opponents of the war was his suspension of the ancient legal right of *habeas corpus*, a protection against arbitrary arrest that is basic to both English and American law. At one time or another, 13,000 people were jailed, almost always briefly, because of alleged antiwar activity. Lincoln also used his control of the post office to harass and even suppress anti-administration newspapers.

The noisiest Copperhead was Clement L. Vallandigham, a popular Democratic congressman from Ohio. His attacks on the war effort were so unsettling that, after General Ambrose Burnside jailed him, Lincoln feared he would be treated as a martyr. The president solved the problem by handing Vallandigham over to the Confederates as though he were their agent. Identifying Vallandigham with treason was unfair but shrewd; in 1863, he was forced to run for governor of Ohio from exile in Canada. At home, or even in prison, he might have won. But he was defeated, and when he returned to the United States the next year, he was harmless enough that Lincoln was able to ignore him.

More worrisome than pro-Confederate Northerners was defeatism, the belief that the war was not worth the expense in blood and money. Each time Union armies lost a battle, more and more Northerners wondered if it would not be wiser to let the Southern states go. Or, they asked, was it really impossible to negotiate? Was Lincoln's Republican administration, rather than the Southern states, the obstacle to a negotiated peace?

It was impossible for Lincoln to secure reunion on any other basis than military victory. Even at the bitter end of the war, when the Confederacy was not only defeated but devastated, Jefferson Davis insisted on Southern independence as a condition of peace. As long as the South was winning the battles, any kind of negotiation was out of the question.

And the South did win most of the battles in 1861 and 1862. The show belonged to Stonewall Jackson and General Robert E. Lee, who was to succeed Joseph E. Johnston as commander of the Army of Northern Virginia when, at the Battle of the Seven Pines on May 31, 1862, Johnston was seriously wounded. Time after time, Lee and Jackson halted or drubbed the Army of the Potomac. Nevertheless, even in his most triumphant hour in the summer of 1862, Lee revealed that his military genius was limited by his supreme virtue, his self-conscious image of himself as a Virginia gentleman, the scion of a distinguished old family.

Lee's cause was not so much the Confederacy as the dignity of "Old Virginny." He had opposed secession; he did not like slavery, the obsession of the Southern hotheads; and he did not much like the hotheads, regarding them as rather vulgar parvenus. Consequently, Lee never fully appreciated the fact that while he was defending the Old Dominion with such mastery, the Southern cause was being slowly throttled at sea, in the dozens of coastal enclaves Union troops occupied, and in the Mississippi Valley.

The Campaign in the West

"We must have Kentucky," Lincoln told his cabinet. Without Kentucky—the southern bank of the Ohio River, he feared, the war would be lost. Even before the army recovered from the defeat at Manassas, Lincoln approved moving a large force into the state under the command of Generals Henry Halleck and Ulysses S. Grant. In early 1862, Grant thrust into Tennessee, quickly capturing two important forts, Henry and Donelson. These guarded the mouths of the Tennessee and Cumberland rivers, two waterways of far greater strategic value than muddy Bull Run. Moving on, however, General Grant fought the battle that taught both sides that they were not playing chess.

Moving up (south on) the Tennessee River unopposed, Grant intended to attack Corinth, in the northern-most part of Mississippi. He knew that Confederate General Albert Sidney Johnston planned to defend the town, but had no idea that Johnston was also prepared to attack. On April 6, 1862, while camped at Shiloh, Tennessee, Grant's armies were caught in their bedrolls by 40,000 rebels. Many were killed before they awoke. The others held on, but just barely. Only when, that night, Union reinforcements arrived under General Don Carlos Buell, did the Confederates withdraw.

A. S. Johnston, regarded by many military historians as one of the Confederacy's best field commanders, was killed at Shiloh. Other Confederate losses numbered

THE WAR IN THE WEST 1862

HOW THEY LIVED

FACING BATTLE

The Civil War battle experience was much the same whether the soldiers wore Union blue or Confederate gray—except that the troops of the North were almost always better supplied with shelter, clothing, shoes, medicines, food, and arms and ammunition. It is difficult to say how much this meant to the final outcome of the war. Cold, wet, tired, and ill soldiers are surely less effective than well-equipped ones, and Confederate troops without shoes—not an uncommon sight—were usually, but not always, exempt from charging enemy lines, a further depletion of the outnumbered southern force. Nevertheless, Johnny Reb, the Confederate foot soldier, won the respect of both his officers and his enemies as a formidable fighting man. As early as the second Battle of Bull Run in 1862, the commander of a unit called Toombs's Georgians told of leading so many barefoot men against the Yankees that they "left bloody footprints among the thorns and briars." Nevertheless, they followed him. Johnny Reb and his Union counterpart, Billy Yank, knew when they were going to fight. In only a few large-scale battles was an army caught by surprise. Jomini's "rules" were well-known by the generals on both sides, and preparations for massive attack were so extensive that getting caught napping, as Grant's men were at Shiloh, was rarely repeated. In fact, the men who would be *defending* a position were generally prepared for battle with extra rations and ammunition earlier than the attackers, who knew when they would be moving.

Two or three days' supply of food was distributed before a battle. A historian of the common soldier, Bell I. Wiley, suggests that in the Confederate ranks

this judicious measure generally fell short of its object because of Johnny Reb's own characteristics: he was always hungry, he

had a definite prejudice against baggage, and he was the soul of improvidence. Sometimes, the whole of the extra rations would be consumed as soon as it was cooked, and rarely did any part of it last for the full period intended.

This carelessness could have serious consequences because fighting was heavy toil; tales of units that were incapacitated by hunger at the end of a day's battle were common. Wiley points out that after Bull Run in the East and Shiloh in the West, however, few soldiers took other than close care of their canteens. Waiting, marching, and running in the heat, cold, and rain, and the grime and dust of battle made everyone intolerably thirsty.

As short a time as possible before the ensuing battle, each infantryman was given 40 to 60 rounds of ammunition to stash in the cartridge box he wore on a strap slung over a shoulder. (Soldiers rarely carred more than a few rounds of ammunition at other times because the powder got damp without meticulous care.) The Springfield repeating rifles took a round that looked like any modern cartridge. The muzzle-loading musket—which was used by all the Confederates and most of the Yankees—took a round that consisted of a ball and a charge of powder wrapped together in a piece of paper that was twisted closed at the powder end. To load the musket, a soldier bit off the twist so that the powder was exposed, pushed the cartridge into the muzzle of his gun, inserted the paper he held in his teeth to keep the ball from rolling out, and rammed a rod (fixed to his gun) into the barrel to the breech. Each time he fired, he had to fall to one knee in order to reload. That moment, and when men were retreating, were considered far more dangerous than when troops were advancing.

On the eve or morning of a battle, the commanding

11,000 of 40,000 troops engaged. The Union lost 13,000 of 60,000 men. Bodies were stacked like cordwood while massive graves were dug. Acres of ground were reddened with blood, and the stench of death sickened the survivors at their grisly job of cleaning up. Compared with the minor casualties at Bull Run—compared with the losses in most battles in any war—Shiloh was a horror.

Grant was temporarily discredited, accused of having been drunk on the morning of the attack. Soldiers of the two armies ceased to fraternize between battles, as they had done in the woods of Tennessee, where Confederate and Union guards had conversed in the night, traded tobacco for coffee, and, on at least one occasion, played a Sunday baseball game. Bull Run showed that there would be a long war; Shiloh showed that it would be bloody. Not even the victory of naval officer David G. Farragut a short time after Shiloh, which put the Union in control of New Orleans, could cure the sense of melancholy that followed the great battle.

The War at Sea

Confederate seamen on the commerce-raiders *Florida*, *Alabama*, *Shenandoah*, and about 15 other Confederate commerce-raiders got to see the world. These fast, heavily armed ships roamed both oceans to search out, destroy, or capture some 300 Northern merchantmen. They seized and sold $15 million in ships and cargo, and sunk 120,000 tons of Union shipping. Operating entirely on its own, one commerce-raider was still attacking Union ships three months after the war was over.

Life was less exhilarating for the Union sailors assigned to blockade the Confederate coast. Most of their wartime days were long and boring, spent slowly patrolling the waters outside Southern ports.

When the war began, the United States Navy was no formidable force. It was possessed of some 90 ships, of which about 50 were fit for service. Half of those were on duty in distant waters. However, not nearly so many naval officers deserted to the Confederacy as army offigeneral addressed his troops either personally or in written orations read by line officers. George McClellan was noted among Union commanders for his stirring orations in the tradition of Napoleon and Wellington. Confederate General Albert Sidney Johnston also took the high road in his speech before Shiloh:

The eyes and the hope of eight millions of people rest upon you. You are expected to show yourselves worthy of your race and lineage; worthy of the women of the South, whose noble devotion in this war has never been exceeded in any time. With such incentives to brave deeds and with the trust that God is with us, your general will lead you confidently to the combat, assured of success.

Because the Confederate cause was defense of a homeland, it could easily be put in such noble terms. The Union Army, however, had something of a morale problem during the early stages of the war because "the Union" was so abstract and Billy Yank was, after all, invading someone else's land.

After the Emancipation Proclamation, the morale of the Union soldiers improved, while that of the Confederates declined. Now, Billy Yank was fighting "to make men free"—a line from the favorite Union song—while some southern commanders were reduced to appealing to base instincts. For example, General T. C. Hindman exhorted in December 1862:

Remember that the enemy you engage has no feeling of mercy. His ranks are made up of Pin Indians, Free Negroes, Southern Tories, Kansas Jayhawkers, and hired Dutch cutthroats. These bloody ruffians have invaded your country, stolen and destroyed your property, murdered your neighbors, outraged your women, driven your children from their homes, and defiled the graves of your kindred.

Bell I. Wiley points out that toward the end of the war, Confederate soldiers fought most grimly and intensely when they were up against a black detachment on the Union line.

Grimness was lacking before the earliest battles. The men were high spirited on both sides. As the war ground on, the experienced soldiers tended to grow quiet and reflective before the fighting started. Some read their Bibles. Others—but not many, it seems—took a few quick pulls of whiskey. Friends made and remade promises to look for one another when the battle was over, to help those too seriously wounded to move, and to gather personal belongings to return to a friend's family if he was killed. During the final, brutal battles before Richmond, soldiers wrote their names and addresses on pieces of paper that they pinned to their clothing on the assumption that there would be no friends alive to care for their bodies. The waiting was usually over about dawn. The command to charge was given. And with a shout, the repeated "hoorays" of the Union troops, and the eerie "rebel yell" of the Confederates, the simultaneous excitement and dread of battle began.

cers did, and those Southern captains who resigned first returned their ships to Union ports. With expert command, and the overall leadership of Secretary of State Gideon Welles, the navy quickly set about strangling the Southern economy by capturing ports and preventing Southern "blockade runners" from getting into harbors in Confederate hands.

About 300 blockade runners—fast, sleek steamships with a low silhouette—made about 1,300 attempts to deliver rifles, lead, saltpeter (for making gunpowder), food, clothing, medicine, and luxury goods to Southern ports between 1861 and 1865. The Union Navy captured 136 of them (turning many into blockaders) and destroyed another 85.

The Monitor and the Merrimack

The Confederates seriously threatened to destroy the blockade only once, in March 1862. Out to the mouth of the Chesapeake steamed an old warship, the *Merrimack*, in brand new clothes. She had been covered over with iron plates forming the shape of a tent. The *Merrimack* was a ram, outfitted on its prow with an iron blade like a plowshare that could slice through a wooden hull. Cannonballs bounced off the sloping armor as though they were made of rubber. Within a few hours of her debut, the *Merrimack* sank several Union warships.

Left unopposed for a few weeks, this single ship might have broken the blockade of the Chesapeake. But the *Merrimack* did not have even a few days. The Union had an experimental vessel of its own, the even odder-looking *Monitor*. It too was ironclad, but resembled a cake tin on a platter skimming the waves. For five hours on March 9, 1862, the two ships had at one another, then disengaged.

Technically, the battle was a draw, but strategically an important Union victory. The *Merrimack* had to retreat for repairs, and, in May, the Confederates destroyed the vessel so that it would not be captured by the Union navy. Indeed, the Confederates destroyed most of the 52 ironclads they built or began construction on to keep them out of Union hands. The *Monitor*, however, proved to be just a prototype for many others like it.

McClellan and the "Slows"

In creating the Army of the Potomac, George McClellan made an invaluable contribution to the Union cause. Not only were his men better trained than most Southern troops, but they usually were better armed. While the Confederates had to import or capture most of their guns, McClellan and his successors had a limitless supply of munitions and constantly improved firearms. The Springfield repeating rifle, introduced toward the end of the war, allowed Union soldiers to fire six times a minute instead of once or twice.

The trouble with McClellan was that he would not exploit his tremendous edge. He was a man of contradictions. On the one hand, he loved to pose, strut, and issue bombastic proclamations to his men in the style of Napoleon and Wellington. On the other, when it came time to fight, he froze as though he were one of their statues. His problem was not entirely a matter of personality. McClellan was a Democrat. He did not want to crush the South. He believed that merely by creating an awesome military force, the Union could persuade the Confederates to give in without a bloody battle.

Moreover, McClellan was sincerely devoted to his soldiers. He could not bring himself to fight a battle in which the dead bodies would pile up as they had at Shiloh. Finally, he was a traditionalist. If there had to be a battle, he wanted overwhelming superiority. He could never get enough men to suit his conservative nature. To Lincoln, who did not like McClellan (the feeling was mutual), it was a simpler matter. Lincoln said that McClellan was ill; he had a bad case of "the slows."

The Peninsula Campaign

When McClellan finally did move in April 1862, he did not drive directly on Richmond. Instead, he moved by sea to historic Yorktown on the peninsula between the York and James rivers. Within a month, he had 110,000 troops poised to take Richmond from the south, bypassing the city's fortifications.

It could have worked—*should have worked*, Lincoln believed. The Confederate Army of Northern Virginia was outnumbered and caught by surprise. On the last day of May, Joseph Johnston was seriously wounded and Robert E. Lee hastily took charge. Instead of pouncing, however, McClellan sat and fiddled. He overestimated the size of the Confederate force that faced him and demanded reinforcements from Lincoln. But Lee seemed to be threatening Washington and Lincoln refused.

Lee had set one of the traps that fooled the Northerners time and again. He had sent Stonewall Jackson on a diversionary mission, feigning an assault on Washington that Jackson did not have the strength to bring off. But the ruse was successful, and Jackson then sped east to reinforce the Confederate armies that were defending Richmond. By the time McClellan gave in to the president's impatient demand for action, Johnston, Lee, and Jackson had 85,000 men to hold him.

Seven days of nearly constant battle followed between June 26 and July 2, 1862. Again overly cautious and outsmarted on the field, McClellan was fought to a standstill. Even then, he held a favorable position. His supply lines were intact; Confederate morale was badly shaken by the 25 percent casualties the South had suffered; and Richmond was only a few miles away, nearly within range of bombardment. A massive Union push in the summer of 1862 might have carried the day and ended the war.

But it was Lincoln's turn to make a mistake. He called off the Peninsula Campaign, ordering the troops back to Washington by ship, and replacing McClellan with General John Pope, who was to take the old Manassas route to Richmond.

Pope had won several victories in the West and was a favorite with the abolitionists in Congress because of his opposition to slavery. But he was an unimaginative general who was no match for the wily Lee and Jackson. At the end of August, Lee met him on the same ground as

Junior staff officers relax during the Peninsula Campaign. The young man reclining in the right foreground is Captain George Armstrong Custer, soon to be the war's youngest general. A decade later he rode to immortality at the Battle of Little Bighorn.

the first Battle of Manassas and beat him back much more easily than the Confederates had defeated Mc-Dowell.

Antietam

Lincoln had no choice but to recall McClellan to command, and the eastern theater bogged down into a stalemate that began to worry Jefferson Davis as much as it worried Lincoln. Davis's critics were not satisfied with Lee's brilliant defenses and wanted the war carried into the North. Indeed, with the chances of British intervention rapidly fading, a major victory on Union soil seemed to be the only way that Britain might be brought into the war.

Unfortunately, while Lee worked defensive miracles with inferior numbers, his army of 40,000 was not up to an advance when the enemy was 70,000 strong. Moreover, he suffered a fatal stroke of bad luck when his battle plans, wrapped around a pack of cigars, fell into McClellan's hands. The Union commander caught Lee be-

fore he was prepared to fight, at Sharpsburg, Maryland, near Antietam Creek.

The fighting was as vicious as at Shiloh. Lee lost a quarter of his army, and he was in no position to retreat safely back across the Potomac into Virginia. Stoically, he waited for the counterattack that could destroy his army. To Lee's surprise, McClellan did not move. He was down with "the slows" again. On the second night after the battle, hardly believing his luck, Lee slipped back to the safety of Virginia.

Emancipation: A Political Masterstroke

During the first year of the war, Lincoln continued to insist that his aim was not the destruction of slavery but the preservation of the Union. Not only did he constantly reassure political leaders from the loyal slave states, he twice countermanded orders of generals in the field that slaves within their Departments—in the Confederacy itself—were freed as acts of war. Nevertheless, Congress chipped away at the peculiar institution by

Following the Battle of Antietam, Lincoln posed at Major General John McClelland's headquarters. At left is Allan Pinkerton, Lincoln's bodyguard and later founder of the famous Pinkerton Detective Agency.

the Emancipation Proclamation was a master-stroke. It reassured loyal slave owners by allowing them to keep their slaves. It also served as an inducement to Confederate slave owners to make peace before January in order to save their property.

At the same time, the Emancipation Proclamation permitted Northern commanders to make use of blacks who, once Union armies were nearby, fled to freedom by the thousands. Many young black men wanted to join the army, but, so long as they were legally slaves, they could not be enlisted. Thanks to the Emancipation Proclamation, fully 150,000 blacks served in Union blue. One Billy Yank in eight was black, a fact that was revealed in few pictorial representations of the troops.

Black units were often assigned the dirtiest and most dangerous duty, for example, mining tunnels under Confederate fortifications. They were paid only half a white soldier's wages, about $7 a month. And yet, because they were fighting for freedom rather than for an abstraction such as the Union, black soldiers were said to bicker and gripe far less than whites did.

Fighting to Make Men Free

The Emancipation Proclamation also served Lincoln as a trial balloon. Without committing himself either way, he was able to test Northern opinion on the subject of freeing the slaves. When Union soldiers adopted Julia

declaring that those slaves employed in producing arms in the South and the slaves of people who had committed treason were free.

Antislavery feeling was on the upswing. In August 1862, when abolitionist newspaper editor Horace Greeley publicly demanded that Lincoln move against the hated institution, the president replied, "If I could save the Union without freeing any slave, I would do it; and if I could save it by freeing all the slaves, I would do it; and if I could do it by freeing some and leaving others alone, I would also do it."

In fact, Lincoln had already decided to free some slaves. In the summer of 1862, he read to his cabinet a proclamation that, as of a date yet to be decided, all slaves held in territory that was still under the control of rebel forces were henceforth free. Secretary of State William Seward persuaded Lincoln to keep the Emancipation Proclamation in his pocket until the North could win a major victory. Otherwise, Seward argued, Lincoln's proclamation might look like an act of desperation. The major victory was Antietam. On September 22, 1862, five days after the battle, Lincoln issued his Proclamation, to go into effect January 1, 1863.

Abolitionists roundly criticized Lincoln for a blow against slavery that did not free a single slave. (It freed no slave in lands where Lincoln had authority.) In fact,

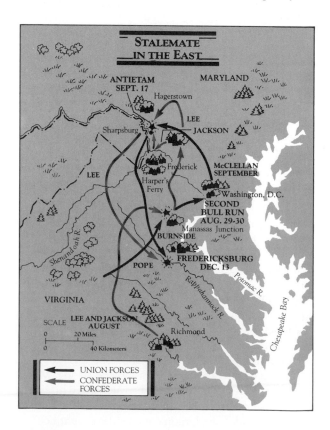

Ward Howe's abolitionist "Battle Hymn of the Republic" as their anthem—"let us fight to make men free"—Lincoln learned that by striking at slavery, he had improved Northern morale.

He also had ensured British neutrality. Dismayed by the Confederate defeat at Antietam, the pro-Confederate British government was almost completely silenced by the popularity of the Emancipation Proclamation among ordinary people. Long hostile to the institution of slavery, British public opinion slowly but irreversibly drifted to the side of the Union. Even textile workers, whose livelihood suffered because of the cotton shortage, issued statements supporting the new Union cause.

Finally, Lincoln mollified his critics within the Republican party. Called the Radicals because they wanted an all-out conquest of the South and a radical remaking of its social institutions, this group controlled the Joint Committee on the Conduct of the War, which frequently criticized Lincoln's policies. The Radical leaders, Thaddeus Stevens in the House of Representatives and Charles Sumner in the Senate, were not satisfied with the Emancipation Proclamation. They wanted a constitutional amendment that would abolish slavery in the Union as well as in the Confederacy. But Lincoln's action subdued them, particularly with a congressional election coming up. Lincoln also played for Radical support by once again dismissing the Democrat McClellan,

and appointing another antislavery general, Ambrose E. Burnside, as commander of Union forces in the East.

Stalemate

Burnside did not want the job. Quite an able corps commander, as McDowell and Pope were, he knew that he was not up to the complexities and responsibilities of directing an entire army. But, he was too good a soldier to turn Lincoln down and, on December 13, led a tragic attack against an impregnable Southern position on high ground near Fredericksburg, Virginia. Watching the slaughter of 1,300 Union soldiers (plus 9,600 wounded), General Lee remarked to an aide that "it is well that war is so terrible or we would grow too fond of it." Burnside retreated, in tears and broken. And the Union and Confederate armies settled down to winter quarters on either side of the Rappahannock River.

The war also bogged down in the West in 1862. After Shiloh, a Confederate force under General Braxton Bragg moved across eastern Tennessee into Kentucky in an attempt to capture the state. At Perryville on October 8, he fought to a draw against General Don Carlos Buell, decided his supply lines were overextended, and moved back into Tennessee. On the last day of 1862, Bragg fought another standoff with the Union Army at Murfreesboro. Both sides went into winter quarters—neither beaten, neither within sight of victory.

For Further Reading

On the Civil War, see James McPherson, *Ordeal by Fire: The Civil War and Reconstruction* (1982) and *Battle Cry of Freedom* (1988). Larger, longer works are Bruce Catton, *Centennial History of the Civil War*, 3 vols. (1961–1965); Shelby Foote, *The Civil War: A Narrative*, 3 vols. (1958–1974); and Alan Nevins, *The War for the Union*, 4 vols. (1959–1971). Also see Catton's *Mr. Lincoln's Army* (1951) and *Glory Road* (1952).

More specialized works on the military history of the war include, R. Beringer, *Why the South Lost the Civil War* (1986); on black soldiers, Dudley T. Comish, *The Sable Arm* (1966); Robert Durden, *The Gray and the Black* (1972); Herman Hattaway and Archer Jones, *How the North Won* (1983); Frank VanDiver, *Their Tattered Flags* (1965); Bell I. Wiley, *The Life of Johnny Reb* (1943) and *The Life of Billy Yank* (1952).

On politics in the war era, see Eric Foner, *Politics and*

Ideology in the Age of the Civil War (1980); Frank L. Klement, *The Copperheads in the Middle West* (1960); Emory Thomas, *The Confederate Nation* (1979); Frank Van Diver, *Jefferson Davis and the Confederate State* (1964).

Valuable biographical studies include T. L. Connelly, *The Marble Man* (1977) on Lee; Clement Eaton, *Jefferson Davis* (1977); Douglas S. Freeman, *Lee: A Biography* (1934–35); W. W. Hassley, *General George McClellan* (1957); William S. McFeeley, *Grant: A Biography* (1981); Stephen B. Oates, *With Malice Toward None* (1979); Benjamin P. Thomas, *Abraham Lincoln* (1952); Frank Van Diver, *Mighty Stonewall* (1957).

Two reference works are essential: M. M. Boatner, *The Civil War Dictionary* (1959) and E. B. Long, *The Civil War Day by Day* (1971), a comprehensive chronicle of events.

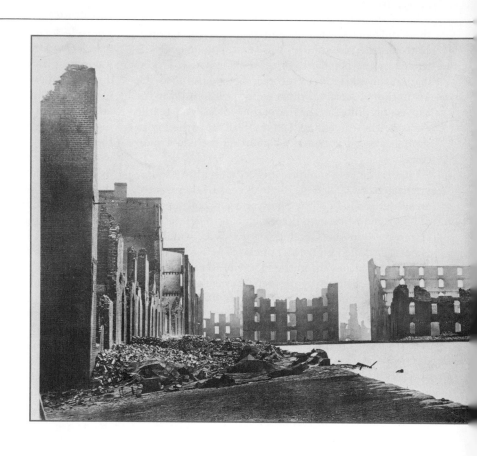

Pounded by Union artillery and burned by retreating Confederates, much of Richmond was a ruin in 1865.

DRIVING OLD DIXIE DOWN

GENERAL GRANT'S WAR OF ATTRITION 1863 - 1865

The war's second anniversary passed without observance. By the spring of 1863, the Confederacy was suffering severe shortages of men and goods, and a crazy rate of inflation wherever a money economy had not been abandoned for barter. In the Union, frustration smothered every encouraging word. Lincoln had men, money, and a strategy, but he could not find a general to do the job. In the East, the Confederates had defeated or stymied four commanders.

In the West, the situation was little more encouraging. Not even Kentucky was quite secure; there would be Confederate cavalry raids the breadth of the state throughout the war. Southern Louisiana and western Tennessee were occupied but elsewhere the smaller Confederate armies had, like Lee's in Virginia, fought the Union to a standstill.

THE CAMPAIGNS OF 1863

The third campaign of the war—1863—began with more bad news for the Union. However, by the end of the year, the tide unmistakeably turned against the South. A second attempt by Lee to invade the North ended in a Confederate disaster worse than Antietam. In the West, Union armies broke the stalemate and cut the Confederacy in two; and Lincoln finally found a general who knew how to win a war.

Hooker and Chancellorsville

After Ambrose Burnside's debacle at Fredericksburg, one of his most outspoken critics was General Joseph Hooker, called "Fighting Joe" because of his aggressiveness in the Peninsula Campaign. Hooker was a talented officer. He improved the medical, quartermaster, and commissary arms of his commands, emphasized intelligence, and was undeniably brave. He was to distinguish himself at Lookout Mountain before Chattanooga during the waning days of the war.

But Hooker was also an indiscreet blowhard, not a type the military treasures. He had left the military in 1853 when his public criticisms of fellow officers angered Winfield Scott. After Fredericksburg, he assailed Lincoln for weakness, saying that what the country needed for the duration of the war was a dictator. In one of the most unusual commissions ever given a military officer,

HOOKERS

The term "hooker" to refer to prostitutes entered general (if not polite) American usage during the Civil War. Many have thought that the new word owed to General "Fighting Joe" Hooker, who was not sufficiently spirited, some critics thought, in keeping whores away from the Army of the Potomac. However, "hooker" in its colloquial sense was included in the second edition of a *Dictionary of Americanisms* edited by John R. Bartlett, which was published in 1859. Apparently, the term originated in North Carolina and refers to the obvious, the practice of aggressive prostitutes in hooking their arms around those of potential clients on the streets.

"DIXIE" AND "THE BATTLE HYMN"

The unofficial anthems of the Confederate and Union soldiers, "Dixie" and "The Battle Hymn of the Republic," were each stolen from the other side. "Dixie" had been written for a minstrel show by Dan Emmett, the Ohio-born son of an abolitionist. The music to "The Battle Hymn of the Republic" (and its predecessor, "John Brown's Body") was an anonymous Southern gospel song, which first had been heard in Charleston, South Carolina, during the 1850s.

Lincoln told Hooker that only victorious generals could set up dictatorships. If Hooker could win the victory that the North needed, Lincoln would run the risk that Hooker was Napoleon Bonaparte.

Hooker proved to be no more capable in charge of a whole army than Burnside was. After several months' preparation, in early May he crossed the Rappahannock River with more than twice as many soldiers as Lee's 60,000. Lee took his opponent's measure and calculated he could take a chance. He divided his army, left his fortifications, and hit Hooker from two directions near the town of Chancellorsville. The Army of the Potomac suffered 11,000 casualties. Hooker was humiliated and his defeat seemed to confirm that Richmond, the goal of the Army of the Potomac, could not be taken.

However, the Battle of Chancellorsville exposed yet another mortal weakness in the South's fighting ability. In winning, Lee's losses were even larger than Hooker's. Whereas the North had a large population base from which to replace fallen men, the Confederacy did not. Moreover, Lee's losses at Chancellorsville included his "right arm," Stonewall Jackson. Returning from a reconnaissance mission, Jackson was accidentally shot and killed by his own troops. Lee said he could never replace Jackson and, whether or not he was correct, he never placed the same degree of confidence in any other general. Never again would the Army of Northern Virginia be so daring and so successful as it had been in 1862.

Fortress Vicksburg

In the West, the Union had not succeeded in accomplishing its major goal—control of the Mississippi. By holding fast to a 150-mile stretch of the river between Vicksburg, Mississippi, and Port Hudson, Louisiana, the rebels were able to shuttle goods and men from one end of the lower South to the other. Much worse, Midwestern farmers were unable to use the great river that was traditionally their avenue to market.

The key to the impasse was Vicksburg. "We may take all the northern ports of the Confederacy," Lincoln said, "and they can still defy us from Vicksburg. It means hog and hominy without limit, fresh troops from all the states of the far South, and a cotton country where they can raise the staple without interference."

The city sat on high cliffs at a bend in the river. A Confederate force commanded by a renegade Pennsylvania Quaker, John C. Pemberton, manned heavy artillery on the top of the bluffs. Vessels passing below the batteries ran the risk of destruction. Infantry could not approach the city from the north and east, for Vicksburg was protected by rugged woodland laced by creeks and bayous—a tangle of earth, brush, and water. Pemberton's defenders flourished there like Br'er Rabbit. Union attackers found it difficult to move. Vicksburg was as near and as far from the Union's western armies as Richmond was from the Army of the Potomac.

U.S. Grant

Then, within a few short weeks, an unlikely candidate for the laurels of heroism broke the western stalemate wide open. He was General Ulysses S. Grant, whose life had been a study in mediocrity. A West Point graduate, Grant had been cited for bravery as a young officer in the Mexican War but was then shunted off to duty at a lonely desert fort and to a cold, wet, and even lonelier outpost on the northern California coast. Grant took to the whiskey bottle and, after a dressing down by his superior, he resigned from the army. In business back in Illinois, he scraped by, dodging bankruptcy. When the Civil War began, he was a clerk in a relative's store.

The Civil War was a godsend for men like Grant. Critically short of officers, the army paid little attention to the past records of professionally trained soldiers who were willing to volunteer. Grant was given the command that won the first notable Union victory of the war, the capture of Forts Henry and Donelson in Tennessee. Then, however, came Shiloh and renewed suspicion of Grant's reliability. Lincoln was on the verge of giving up on him when the general hatched his plan to take Vicksburg.

Everyone who met Grant commented on his unimpressive presence. He was a short, dumpy man with a carelessly trimmed beard. Although he was far from being a daily drunkard, neither had he sworn off the bottle, and it showed. His uniform was perpetually rumpled, and usually stained. From a distance, he could be mistaken for an aging corporal who was about to be demoted. Even up close he seemed listless and stupid to many. But he was neither. If he did not look the part, Grant was capable of boldness equal to that of Stonewall Jackson, and he had Lee's easy confidence with large commands. His written reports were models of clarity and directness.

The Siege

At Vicksburg, Grant scored a feat of old-fashioned military derring-do and then sat down to an exercise in total war, not maneuvering with an army but assaulting the society and economy that supported the enemy troops. First, he transferred his army to the western bank of the Mississippi, marched them swiftly to a few miles below Vicksburg, and then recrossed the river, ferried by Navy gunboats that had raced by night under the Confederate guns.

Having flanked the rough country where Pemberton was so comfortable, Grant abandoned his lines of supply, a risky maneuver but one that confused the rebels. He charged to the east and forced a small Confederate force under Joseph E. Johnston to withdraw from the area. Grant feigned a full assault on Jackson, the capital of Mississippi, and then, before the Confederates had quite grasped his intentions, he reversed direction, turning back toward Vicksburg. The befuddled Pemberton was trounced in a series of brief battles. In a little more than two weeks, Grant won half a dozen confrontations and captured 8,000 Southern troops.

On May 19, with Pemberton still reeling from the turnaround and penned up in Vicksburg, Grant sat his

Ulysses S. Grant's unimpressive past made him an unlikely war hero.

men down to besiege the city. Nothing was settled yet. But Union forces had broken through where they had been stalled, and the Confederate government had cause for alarm.

The Gettysburg Campaign

Back in Richmond, some of Lee's advisers urged him to send part of the Army of Northern Virginia west to attack Grant from the rear, thus relieving Vicksburg. Lee decided instead to invade Pennsylvania. If he threatened Washington, he calculated, Lincoln would be forced to call Grant's troops to the East. In the meantime, there was a good chance that by moving quickly, Lee could catch the Army of the Potomac off guard and give it a drubbing.

It was a bold gamble. If Lee had succeeded, his reputation as a strategist would be as great as his reputation as a battlefield tactician. But he failed, ironically because in the midst of the most famous battle of the war, Lee made the most serious tactical mistake of his career.

At first, Lee had everything his way. He surprised the Union Army, and Lincoln, having lost faith in Hooker, changed commanders yet again. With Lee's troops somewhere on Northern soil—exactly where, no one knew— the president appointed a colorless but methodical general, George Gordon Meade, to find them and fight. Almost by accident, forward units of Meade's and Lee's armies bumped into each other on July 1, 1863, in the little town of Gettysburg, Pennsylvania. The Union soldiers were looking for Lee. The Confederate soldiers were looking for shoes.

Both armies descended on rolling farmland south of Gettysburg. Curiously, the Confederates occupied the battlefield from the north, the Yankees from the south.

Both established strong positions on parallel ridges about half a mile apart, the rebels on Seminary Ridge, the Union troops on Cemetery Ridge. Deciding to move before his enemy's entrenchments were complete, Lee attacked with his left flank and almost won the battle on the first day. His men pushed Meade's line back until it was curled into the shape of a fish hook. But the line held.

On July 2, Lee attacked at the other end of the Union line, at the "eye" of the fishhook. Once again, the rebels came within a few yards and a few hundred men of breaking through. But when the sun set on the second day, Union troops still held a steep bulbous knoll called Little Round Top. It was a valuable position. The troops that occupied Little Round Top could enfilade the open fields that separated the two armies; that is, they could shoot into an advancing army from the side, thus increasing the odds of finding a target.

That night, Lee's imagination failed him. Although badly outnumbered now, he decided on a mass frontal attack against the Union center. One of his generals, James Longstreet, argued long and loudly against a move that violated Jomini's cautions and was chillingly reminiscent of Burnside's charge into a powerful position at Fredericksburg. Longstreet pointed out that after two days the Union troops would be well entrenched on Cemetery Ridge. Better that the Confederates sit tight and force Meade, who was on his own ground, to attack

Confederate General Robert E. Lee.

CHANCELLORSVILLE AND GETTYSBURG

them. The advantage always rested with the defensive position.

Pickett's Charge

Stonewall Jackson might have persuaded Lee to defend or, alternatively, to try to turn the Union's right flank again. James Longstreet could not. But he was dead right. Just a few miles away, General Meade was betting on an assault to his center and he was ready for it. He concentrated his strength there, and, on the afternoon of July 3, he had the satisfaction of seeing his decision pay off. Between one and two o'clock, howling the eerie "rebel yell," 15,000 men in gray uniforms began to trot across the no man's land. This was Pickett's Charge, somewhat of a misnomer because the angry Longstreet was actually in command of it. The attack was a nightmare. The men were slaughtered first by artillery and then by Minié balls. The worst of the fire came from Little Round Top, which had been reinforced during the night.

About a hundred Virginians actually reached the Union lines. There was a split second of glory, but it lasted no longer. The attackers were immediately surrounded by a thousand Union soldiers and killed or captured.

Pickett's Charge lasted less than an hour. When the Confederate survivors dragged themselves back to Seminary Ridge, 10,000 men were dead, wounded, or missing. Five of twenty regimental commanders involved in the massive assault were wounded. The other fifteen were dead. So were two Confederate brigadier generals.

On July 4, a somber Robert E. Lee, with 28,000 fewer troops than he had brought into Pennsylvania, waited for the Union counterattack. It never came. Meade had learned the bloody lesson of Pickett's Charge. He would not expose his men to the horrors of crossing an open field into the mouths of cannon. By nightfall, a drizzle had become a downpour, making the Potomac impassable and setting up Lee's army for plucking. Defeated and huddled together, the Confederates were in a worse position than they were after Antietam. But the rain also discouraged Meade from launching an attack. When Lincoln got the news he fumed: "We had them within our grasp. We had only to stretch forth our hands and they were ours. And nothing I could say or do could make the Army move."

LOADED GUNS

Some 24,000 of 37,000 muskets and rifles that were collected from the battlefield at Gettysburg were still loaded, never fired that day. About 6,000 had between three and ten charges in them. The soldiers were so excited that they continued to reload without discharging their weapons.

High Tide

For all Lincoln's disappointments, Gettysburg was an important victory. It ravaged Southern morale: intelligent Confederates understood that their armies would never again be capable of an offensive campaign. Lincoln was still without the decisive, relentless general that would take advantage of the Union's numerical superiority. But that too was to change. Not long after the news of Gettysburg arrived in Washington, a spate of telegrams from the West informed the president that the long siege of Vicksburg had also ended on July 4, 1863.

Literally starving, after having stripped the streets of pets and the cellars of rats, the people of the city had surrendered to Ulysses S. Grant. Five days later, Port Hudson, Louisiana, the last Confederate outpost on the Mississippi, gave up without a battle. Union General Nathaniel Banks took 30,000 prisoners there. Within a week, the Confederacy lost several times more men than the rebels had put into the field at the first Battle of Bull Run.

The Tennessee Campaign

Worse followed bad. In September, a previously cautious Union general, William S. Rosecrans, boldly attacked the one remaining Confederate Army in the West. Rosecrans pushed Braxton Bragg out of Tennessee and into northern Georgia. Union troops then occupied Chattanooga, an important railroad center on the Tennessee River.

Like Grant at Shiloh, however, Rosecrans was surprised by a counterattack. On September 19, reinforced by grim Confederate veterans of Gettysburg, Bragg hit him at Chickamauga Creek. It was one of the few battles of the war in which the Confederates had the larger army, 70,000 to Rosecrans's 56,000. And numbers told. The rebels smashed through the Union right, scattering the defenders and making Chickamauga one of the bloodiest battles of the war. It would have been a total rout but for the stand on the Union left led by a Virginian who had remained loyal to the Union, George H. Thomas, the "Rock of Chickamauga." Thanks to Thomas's stand, the Union troops were able to retire in good order to the fortifications of Chattanooga.

Wisely, Bragg decided to besiege the city rather than attack it. But unlike Grant at Vicksburg, Bragg had other enemies than the army trapped inside the town. Grant himself marched his men to Chattanooga and brought 23,000 troops from the East by rail. Late in November, he drove Bragg's Confederates from their strongholds on Missionary Ridge and Lookout Mountain and back into Georgia.

The long campaign for Tennessee was over. It had taken two years longer than Lincoln had expected but at last the Confederacy was severed in two, and the stage was set for the final Union offensive. After Vicksburg and Chattanooga, there was no doubt about who was the man to lead it. Early in 1864, Lincoln promoted U. S. Grant to the rank of lieutenant general and gave him command of all Union forces.

TOTAL WAR

Grant had proved that he was a daring tactician of the old school. At Vicksburg, with dash and flash, he had outsmarted and outmaneuvered the enemy. Then he demonstrated his understanding that the nature of war had changed. He informed Lincoln that his object was not the capture of Confederate flags, commanders, cities, and territory, but the total destruction of the enemy's ability to fight.

The Union's superiority in numbers was overwhelming, and Grant intended to put his edge to work. He would force the Confederates to fight constant bloody battles on all fronts, trading casualties that the North could afford and the South could not. At the same time, he would destroy the Confederacy's capacity to feed, shoe, and arm its soldiers. He would complete on land what the naval blockade had begun—he would strangle the Southern economy.

Grant called off the gentleman's war. His kind of fighting was not chivalrous. It involved making war not only on soldiers but on a society. It was left to Grant's best general, the blunt-spoken William Tecumseh Sherman, to give it a name. "War is hell," Sherman said. He was a no-nonsense man, even unpleasant in his refusal to dress up dirty work with fuss, feathers, and pretty words.

Sherman's self-designed assignment was to move from his base in Chattanooga toward Atlanta, laying waste the rich agricultural production of the black belt. Grant, with General Meade as his field commander, would personally direct the onslaught against Richmond.

Grant Before Richmond

The war of attrition—the war of grinding down the Confederacy—began in May 1864. With 100,000 men,

---

UNSUNG CONFEDERATE HERO

Joseph Reid Anderson is only occasionally mentioned in the histories of the Civil War, but he was second only to Robert E. Lee in allowing the Confederacy to fight as long as it did. Anderson was the owner and manager of the Tredregar Iron Works of Richmond, Virginia, and he kept the huge factory running until April 1865, when the Confederacy itself fell.

A Union wagon train crosses a temporary bridge on the Rapidan River on its way to the Wilderness Campaign.

Grant marched into the Wilderness, wooded country near Fredericksburg where Burnside had been defeated. There Grant discovered that Lee was several cuts above any commander he had yet faced. Although outnumbered, Lee outmaneuvered Grant and actually attacked. While Grant's men suffered almost twice as many casualties as the Southerners, replacements rushed to the Union front. On the Southern side, Lee just counted his dead and sent his wounded men home.

Now it was Lee's turn to discover that he too was up against a new kind of rival. Instead of withdrawing to Washington where his men could lick their wounds and regroup, as all other Union commanders had done, Grant shifted his men to the south and attacked again, at Spotsylvania Court House. For five days, spearheaded in places by black troops, the Army of the Potomac assaulted the Southern trenches. Grant lost 12,000 men, again almost twice Lee's casualties. Northern congress-

men and editors howled. The man was a butcher! But Grant was unmoved. He sent a curt message to Washington: "I intend to fight it out on this line if it takes all summer."

It took even longer. Time after time, Lee rallied his shrinking army and somehow managed to scratch together enough munitions and provisions to keep his men in the field. Time after time, he threw Grant back. At Cold Harbor, south of Spotsylvania, the two fought another gory battle. Before they charged, Union troops wrote their names on scraps of paper and pinned the tags to their uniforms. They expected to die.

Petersburg and the Shenandoah

But still Grant came on, always swinging to the south. On June 18, he attempted to capture Petersburg, a rail center that was the key to Richmond's survival. He might have succeeded immediately but for the failure of General Benjamin Butler, a political general in charge of 30,000 reinforcements, to join him in time. This time, Grant was as shaken by his casualties as his critics were. Some 55,000 had been lost in the campaign, more men than Lee had under arms at the end of the year. One unit from Maine attacked with 850 soldiers and returned to the lines with 218. Grant finally paused and sat down to besiege Petersburg. It would last ten months, through the harshest winter of the war.

In the meantime, in July, Lee tried a trick that had

LINCOLN ON GRANT

General Grant was on the receiving end of torrid criticism throughout his command, but Lincoln always defended him. When the president was told that Grant was a drinker, he replied, "Give me the brand, and I'll send a barrel to my other generals."

A war hero second only to Grant in the eyes of Northerners, a savage sadist to Southerners, William Tecumseh Sherman is probably best described as having had fewer illusions about the nature of war than any other Civil War general.

Although born in Ohio, Sherman spent much of his life in the South, first as a junior officer at remote Texas forts (which he loathed) and then between 1859 and 1861 as head of a military academy in New Orleans (which he liked very much). Sherman was comfortable with Southerners and the Southern way of life, and he shared the views of white Southerners (and most white Northerners) toward blacks. Shortly before the war began, he told a group of New Orleanians that "Negroes in the great numbers that exist here must of necessity be slaves."

But Sherman was also a keen nationalist. When he went to New Orleans in 1859, he told his patrons that if Louisiana seceded, he would fight against them.

Beginning as a colonel under Grant, he advanced in rank and command each time Grant did. He was a gruff soldier, as was Grant, and almost as indifferent to the condition of his uniform.

Sherman took over as commander in the West when Grant went east to press the fight against Lee. He led his troops from Chattanooga to Atlanta, the last important Southern railroad center that was still functioning normally. After winning several hard-fought battles, he finally broke out of Tennessee, which half a dozen Union commanders had been unable to do.

However, occupation of Atlanta put Sherman in a dangerous position. The single-track railroad to Chattanooga on which his sixty-two thousand men depended for their supplies was vulnerable to Confederate raids, as General John B. Hood, in command of the Southern army, promptly demonstrated. Sherman's options were two: retreat to Chattanooga, leaving the southeastern quarter of the Confederacy free from war; or, in violation of standard military procedure, cut loose of supply lines and march three hundred miles through hostile country to the sea, where the Union navy could provision his army.

With Grant's approval (telegraphed to him), Sherman decided to march.

Giving up communications as well as supplies, his men would move in four columns on parallel routes, make ten miles a day, and live off what the land, sometimes called the "breadbasket of the Confederacy," had to offer. What they did not eat, Sherman ordered, they should destroy.

They did. By the time they entered the port city of Savannah, which was defended by only boys and old men, Sherman's trooops had cut a swath of destruction forty to sixty miles wide. In a letter to his father,

You can form no idea of the amount of property destroyed by us on this raid. All the roads in the state are torn up and the whole tract of country over which we passed is little better than a wilderness. I can't for the life of me think of what the people that are left there are to live on. We have all their Cattle, Horses, Mules, Sheep, Hogs, Sweet Potatoes and Molasses and nearly everything else. We burnt all the Cotton we met which was millions of pounds. . . . A tornado 60 miles in width from Chattanooga to this place 290 miles could not have done half the damage we did.

Saylor said that his detachment never lost pace because

worked before. He sent General Jubal Early on a cavalry raid toward Washington designed to force Grant into weakening his besieging army. Early was remarkably successful. His men actually rode to within sight of the Capitol dome and some tough-talking politicians began to stutter. But Early's raid was the Confederacy's last hurrah. Grant did not panic, and, this time, neither did Lincoln. The men stayed at Petersburg and raised Lee's bet. Grant sent a Union cavalry commander, Philip Sheridan, to intercept Early, preventing him from rejoining Lee.

Sheridan chased Early into the Shenandoah Valley, the fertile country to the west of Richmond that had served as a Confederate sanctuary and as Richmond's breadbasket for three years. Sheridan defeated Early three times. More important, he laid waste to the valley that had fed the Army of Northern Virginia for three years, burning houses, barns, and crops, and slaughtering what livestock his men did not eat. He reported that when he was done, a crow flying over the Shenandoah Valley would have to carry its own provisions.

Sherman in Georgia

General Sherman was even more thorough in scouring Georgia. He moved into the state at the same time that Grant entered the Wilderness. At first he met brilliant harassing action by Joseph E. Johnston. Then an impatient Jefferson Davis, unaware that Johnston's army was not up to a major battle, replaced him with the courageous but foolish John B. Hood, whom Sherman defeated. On September 2, 1864, Union troops occupied Atlanta. The loss of this major rail center was a devastating blow to Confederate commerce and morale.

Sherman's position was delicate. His supply lines ran to Chattanooga, more than one hundred miles away over an easily raided single-track railroad. A bold move by the Confederates would have isolated him in the middle they were constantly replacing their tired mules with fresh ones, killing those they no longer needed to deny their use to the Georgians. The same went for cattle. Sherman's army left Atlanta with five thousand head and entered Savannah with ten thousand. They killed so many along the way that the stench of death hung over north Georgia.

They created "Sherman sentinels," charred chimneys that stood where once a house had been, and tied "Sherman bow ties," iron rails torn up from the Atlanta–Savannah railroad that were heated and then twisted around telegraph poles and trees. They looted large plantations so thoroughly that the occupants had little choice but to leave or starve. One household, consisting of two white women and their slaves, rose early in the morning to eat what they could scrape up before the Yankees came, which they did every day for two weeks. On another plantation, the soldiers discovered that the owner, who had fled, had hidden his valuables in a cabbage patch and had replanted the garden. They admired his cleverness, but took or destroyed everything.

Sherman had three reasons for his scorched-earth policy. First, he had to feed his men, who were completely separated from other Union forces. Second, he did not want to fight the pursuing Confederate Army until he had reestablished supply lines, so he had to destroy *their* sources of supply. Finally, and most important, Sherman wanted to punish the South and Southerners for causing what he regarded as an unnecessary as well as a costly war. "We are not only fighting hostile armies, but a hostile people," Sherman had said. "We must make old and young, rich and poor, feel the hand of war."

Southerners believed that he went too far, inflicting suffering on defenseless women and children. "I almost felt as if I should like to hang a Yankee myself," wrote Georgian Eliza Frances Andrews in her diary when she saw the "burnt country" around Milledgeville, then the state capital.

In fact, Sherman had ordered his men not to enter private homes; they were to burn only public buildings and railroad properties and bridges. And he made it clear that he would enforce the military penalty for rape and murder, which was death.

Sherman was no sadist, motivated by pleasure in causing suffering. He approached the job of the March to the Sea with a sense of grim necessity. Once in Savannah, with no sound military reason for burning the town or mistreating the people, he administered a liberal truce. When General Johnston surrendered to him in April, Sherman allowed him terms far more generous than Grant had allowed Lee.

By then, of course, the war was over. While it was still on, however, Sherman insisted on facing up to the fact that it was a dirty business and there was no way it could be made mannerly and clean. "Its glory is all moonshine," Sherman said in 1879. "It is only those who have neither fired a shot, nor heard the shrieks and groans of the wounded who cry aloud for blood, more vengeance, more desolation. War is hell." Sherman's real crime was that he refused to encourage the illusion that war could possibly be anything else.

of hostile territory where—with Grant committed to Petersburg—he could not be relieved. Once again, the new Union leadership turned difficulty into triumph. Sherman ordered the people of Atlanta to evacuate the city, and he put it to the torch. He then set out to the southeast, moving quickly in order to avoid a set battle that he could not afford to fight. His men were instructed to destroy everything of use to the Confederacy in a swath 60 miles wide. They not only tore up the railroad between Atlanta and Savannah, but they burned the ties and twisted the iron rails around telegraph poles. "Sherman bow ties," they called them.

Sherman's purpose was twofold. First, he wanted to make it difficult for the Southern army (under Johnston's command once again) to feed itself. Second, he wanted to punish the people of Georgia. Those who had caused and supported the war would suffer for it. This was total war carried into the realm of social responsibility.

Sherman reached Savannah on December 10 and cap-

tured it two weeks later. Resupplied from the sea, Sherman then turned north to join Grant. He would continue to scorch the southern earth and join Grant at Petersburg for the final battle of the war.

The Sudden End

That final battle was never fought. In February 1865, Jefferson Davis tried to make peace by sending the Confederate vice president, Alexander H. Stephens, and two other men to meet with Lincoln and Secretary of State Seward on a ship off Hampton Roads, Virginia. The South was reeling, but, preposterously, Davis insisted on Confederate independence as a condition of peace. The conference broke up.

Late in March, Lee tried to draw Grant into a battle in open country. By this time, he had 54,000 men to Grant's 115,000, and he was easily pushed back. On April 2, knowing that his 37-mile-long lines were too

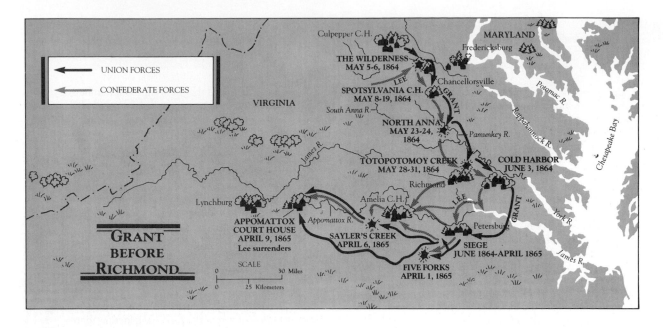

much for his numbers to man, Lee abandoned Petersburg (and therefore Richmond) and made a dash west. He hoped to turn south, resupply in untouched North Carolina, and link up with Johnston for a last stand.

With help from Sheridan, Grant cut him off. Desertions had reduced Lee's proud army to 30,000 men, and some of them were shoeless. On April 7, Grant called for a surrender, and, two days later, he met Lee at Appomattox Court House in Virginia. The terms were simple and generous. The Confederates surrendered all equipment and arms except for the officers' revolvers and swords. Grant permitted both officers and enlisted men to keep their horses for plowing. After taking an oath of loyalty to the Union, the Southern troops could go home.

Jefferson Davis, who seemed to have lost his sense of reality, ordered Johnston to fight on. The veteran soldier, who had not fared well by Davis's whims, knew better than to obey. On April 18, he surrendered to Sherman at Durham, North Carolina. The ragged remnants of two other Confederate armies gave up over the next several weeks.

THE BATTLE OF THE CRATER

Early in the siege of Petersburg, one of the war's most bizarre battles occurred. Miners from Pennsylvania dug a tunnel under a salient in the Confederate lines and planted four tons of gunpowder beneath a critical point in the fortifications. The plan was to detonate the charge and send a massive assault force led by a crack unit of black troops.

At almost the last moment, the selected shock troops were replaced by a less experienced white unit. Some said the reason for the change was the staff's apprehension that the Union command would be accused of treating black troops as cannon fodder. (The charge had been levied before.) Others said that the change was to deny blacks the opportunity of leading an attack that could end the war immediately, as indeed a breakthrough at "the crater" might very well have done.

In any case, victory was not the issue of the battle. Instead of leading the charge around the massive 170-foot-long, 60-foot-wide, 30-foot-deep crater, the first wave incredibly massed into it and others followed. They were easy targets for the Confederate counterattack that restored the defenders' lines at a cost of 4,000 Union losses.

THE AMERICAN TRAGEDY

The United States has never fought a more destructive war. More than one-third of the men who served in the two armies died, were wounded, permanently maimed, or captured by the enemy. Some 620,000 were killed (360,000 Union, 260,000 Confederate) as compared with 680,000 in *all* other American wars. At Antietam (the bloodiest single day), there were 25,000 casualties, four times the American losses on D-Day during World War II; the 6,500 killed at Antietam were double those killed in the War of 1812 or the Mexican War.

Put another way, the 620,000 dead were from a nation with, in 1860, a population of about 30 million. Considering that half the population was female and 7 or 8 million males were either too old or too young for military service, more than one out of every twenty-five men who were "eligible" to die in the war did lose their lives.

This ruined stretch of railway near Atlanta was destroyed by Sherman's troops on their way to Savannah. In other places they made bonfires of the ties and melted the rails over them.

Union troops at Appomattox Court House shortly after Lee's surrender to Grant, April, 1865.

In some Southern states, more than one-quarter of all the men of military age lay in cemeteries.

Assassination

There was one more casualty to be counted just a few days after the fall of Richmond. On April 14, Good Friday, President Lincoln, his wife, and a few friends attended a play at Ford's Theater in Washington. Shortly after ten o'clock, Lincoln was shot point blank in the head by a zealous pro-Confederate, John Wilkes Booth. Lincoln died early the next morning.

Booth was one of those unbalanced characters who pop up periodically to remind us of the role of the irrational in history. An actor who had delusions of grandeur, Booth had organized a cabal including at least one mental defective to avenge the Confederacy by wiping out the leading officials of the Union government. Only he succeeded in his mission, although one of his co-conspirators seriously wounded Secretary of State Seward with a knife.

As he escaped, Booth shouted, "Sic semper tyrannis!" which means "thus always to tyrants" and was the motto of the state of Virginia. Booth fled into Virginia; on April 26, he was cornered and killed at Bowling Green. In July, four others were hanged for Lincoln's murder, including a woman, Mary Surratt, in whose boarding-house the plot was hatched. But vengeance did not bring the president back, and his loss proved to be inestimable, perhaps more for the South than for the North.

Father Abraham

To this day, Lincoln remains a central figure of American history. More books have been written about him than about any other American. He was the epitome of the American Dream. He rose from modest frontier origins to become the leader of the nation in its greatest crisis.

Lincoln was not overwhelmingly popular as a president. The Radicals of his own party assailed him because of his reluctance to make war on slavery. Northern Democrats vilified him because the war dragged on and the casualties mounted to no avail. People of all points of view mocked his ungainly appearance and bemoaned his lack of dignity. As late as September 1864, with the casualties before Petersburg at horrible levels, Lincoln thought it likely he would lose his bid for reelection to the Democratic party candidate, General George McClellan.

Lincoln weathered McClellan's threat thanks in part to political machinations; he made Nevada a state, although it consisted of little more than half a dozen mining camps of uncertain future. By pushing through admission, he gained three electoral votes for his party. He also directed his generals to put Republican troops on furlough on election day so that they could vote for him, while he kept units that were favorable to McClellan on isolated duty. Lincoln also appealed to prowar Democrats by dropping the name "Republican" and calling himself the Union party candidate. For vice president he chose a Democrat from Tennessee, Andrew Johnson.

But Lincoln did not win the election of 1864 on the basis of political ploys. He won because he had quietly gained the respect of the majority of the people of the North by the example of his dogged will, personal humility, and eloquent humanitarianism. In a speech dedicating a national cemetery at Gettysburg in November 1863, he stated American ideals more beautifully (and succinctly) than anyone had done since Jefferson's preamble to the Declaration of Independence. His second inaugural address, delivered in Washington a month before Lee's surrender, was simultaneously a literary masterpiece, a signal to Southerners that they could lay down their arms without fear of retribution, and a plea to Northerners for a compassionate settlement of the

A poster advertising a reward for the capture of Lincoln's assassin, John Wilkes Booth, and his accomplices.

The Lincoln conspirators on the gallows about to be executed.

national trauma. "With malice toward none," he concluded, "with charity for all; with firmness in the right, as God gives us to see the right, let us strive on to finish the work we are in."

CONSEQUENCES OF THE CIVIL WAR

The military triumph of the Union guaranteed several fundamental changes in the nature of the American republic. Once and for all, the constitutional unity of the states was defined beyond argument. The states rights theories of John C. Calhoun, so compelling in the abstract, were buried without honor at Appomattox. The United States was not a federation of independent and sovereign states. It was a nation, one and indivisible.

Politicians have described themselves as states' righters since the Civil War. To some extent, the line between state and national jurisdiction remains unsettled to this day. But never again after 1865 would anyone suggest that a state could leave the Union if its people disapproved of some national policy.

A New Political Majority
The political dominance of the South was destroyed by the Civil War. Since the founding of the republic, Southerners had played a role in the government of the country out of all proportion to their numbers. Eight of the fifteen presidents who preceded Lincoln came from slave states. Southern slave owners had been president two years out of three. At least two of the seven Northerners who had held the office—Pierce and Buchanan—were pro-South in their policies. After Lincoln and Andrew Johnson, no resident of a former Confederate state would occupy the White House until Lyndon B. Johnson in 1963, and he was more Westerner than Southerner. Only in 1976, with the election of Jimmy Carter of Georgia, was a self-acknowledged Southerner accepted by the American people as their leader.

Twenty of thirty-five pre-war Supreme Court Justices had been Southerners. There was always a Southern majority on the Supreme Court.

Until the Civil War, two-thirds of the Speakers of the House had been Southerners. Since the time of Andrew Jackson, Southerners had dominated Congress through a combination of political skill, agrarian alliance with Western farmers, and threat of secession. In making good on its threat to secede, the Southern bloc destroyed this alliance. The Democratic party remained a major force in New York and the agricultural states of the North. But the Republicans held the edge above the Mason-Dixon line, and never again would a coalition of farmers dominate the government in Washington.

In its place, Northeastern industrial and financial interests came to the fore. Businessmen had been late in joining the antislavery coalition. To bankers, great merchants, and factory owners, the Republican party was of interest more because of its economic policies than because of its hostility to slavery. With the war concluded, however, these forces held a strong position and could exploit the sentimental attachment of many voters to the "Grand Old Party."

New Economic Policies
During the war, the Republican Congress passed a number of bills that would have been defeated had Southerners been in their seats and voting. In July 1862, about

---

UNION AND NATION

Before 1861, "United States" as gramatically a plural; since 1865, it has been a singular. That is, before the Civil War, one said, "The United States *are* . . ." Since, we have said, "The United States *is* . . ."

Lincoln quietly charted the transformation in his speeches. In his First Inaugural Address (March 1861), he used the word "Union" 20 times, "nation" not once. In his First Messager to Congress (July 1861), he said "Union" 49 times and "nation" thrice. In the Gettysburg Address, Lincoln never said "Union" but referred to "nation" five times.

the time of Antietam, both houses approved the Pacific Railways Act. As modified later in the war, this act gave 6,400 square miles of the public domain to two private companies, the Union Pacific and the Central Pacific railroads. These corporations were authorized to sell the land and use the proceeds to construct a transcontinental railway, the ultimate internal improvement. In 1864, while Grant slogged it out with Lee before Richmond, Congress gave the Northern Pacific Railroad an even more generous subsidy. These acts revolutionized the traditional relationship between private enterprise and the federal government.

The tariff was another issue on which Southern agricultural interests had repeatedly frustrated the manufacturers of the Northeast. Since 1832, with few exceptions, the Democratic party had driven the taxes on imported goods ever downward. The last tariff before the war, passed in 1857 with the support of Southern congressmen, had set rates lower than they had been since the War of 1812.

In March 1861, even before secession was complete, the Republican Congress rushed through the Morrill Tariff, which pushed up the taxes. In 1862 and 1864, rates went even higher. By 1867, the average tax on imported goods stood at 47 percent, about the same as it had been under the act of 1828 that the Southerners had called the Tariff of Abominations and that Calhoun had called fit grounds for secession.

The South had long frustrated the desire of Northern financial interests for a centralized banking system. Hostility to a national bank was one of the foundation stones of the old Democratic party. During the war, with no Southern congressmen in Washington and with the necessity of financing the Union Army looming over Congress, New York's bankers finally got their way.

Financing the War

The Union financed the war in three ways: by heavy taxation, by printing paper money, and by borrowing,

that is, selling bonds abroad and to private investors within the United States. The principal taxes were the tariff, an excise tax on luxury goods, and an income tax. By the end of the war, the income tax provided about 20 percent of the government's revenue.

The government authorized the printing of $450 million in paper money. These bills were not redeemable in gold. Popularly known as "greenbacks" because they were printed on one side in a special green ink, they had value only because the federal government declared they must be accepted in the payment of debts. When the fighting went badly for the North, they were traded at a discount. By 1865, a greenback with a face value of $1 was worth only 67 cents in gold.

This inflation was miniscule compared with that in the Confederacy, where government printing presses ran amok. In June 1861, there were $1.1 million in Confederate notes in circulation in the South; by January 1864, the total was $826.8 million. A citizen of Richmond had to pay $25 for a pound of butter and $50 for a breakfast. By 1865, prices were even higher, and some Southern merchants would accept only gold or Union currency, including greenbacks!

The banking interests of the North were uncomfortable with the greenbacks. However, they profited from the government's large-scale borrowing. By the end of the war, the federal government owed its own citizens and some foreigners almost $3 billion, about $75 for every person in the country. Much of this debt was held by the banks. Moreover, big financial houses like Jay Cooke's in Philadelphia reaped huge profits in commissions for their part in selling the bonds.

Free Land

Another momentous innovation of the Civil War years was the Homestead Act. Before the war, Southern fear of encouraging the formation of more free states in the territories had effectively paralyzed any attempt to liberalize the means by which the federal government disposed of its western lands. In May 1862, the system was overhauled. The Homestead Act provided that every head of family who was a citizen or who intended to become a citizen could receive 160 acres of public domain. There was a small filing fee, and homesteaders were required to live for five years on the land that the government gave them. Or, after six months on the land, they could buy it outright for $1.25 per acre.

A few months after approving the Homestead Act, Congress passed the Morrill Act. This law granted each loyal state 30,000 acres for each member whom that state sent to Congress. The states were to use the money that they made from the sale of these lands to found agricultural and mechanical colleges. In subsequent years, the founding of 69 land-grant colleges greatly ex-

---

DON'T SWAP HORSES

Until the end of the nineteenth century, candidates for the presidency did not actively campaign. They did, however, urge on their supporters. In the wartime election of 1864, Lincoln himself provided his party's slogan by telling a leading supporter the story of the Dutch farmer who said he never swapped horses in the middle of a stream. Indeed, Americans never have changed presidents voluntarily during a war. Even during the unpopular war in Vietnam, it took the retirement of Lyndon B. Johnson in 1968 to put Republican Richard M. Nixon in the White House. With the war still on in 1972, Nixon won reelection by a landslide.

panded educational opportunities, particularly in the West.

Again, it was a free-spending policy which parsimonious Southern politicians would never have accepted, and the revolutionary infusion of government wealth into the economy spawned an age of unduplicated expansion—and corruption.

Free People

No consequence of the Civil War was so basic as the final and irrevocable abolition of slavery in the United States. In a sense, the peculiar institution was doomed when the first shell exploded over Fort Sumter. Slavery was not only an immoral institution, but by the middle of the nineteenth century, it was hopelessly archaic. It is the ultimate irony of wars that are fought to preserve outdated institutions that war itself is one of the most powerful of revolutionary forces. Precariously balanced institutions such as slavery rarely survive the disruptions of armed conflict. Once hundreds of thousands of blacks had left their masters to flee to Union lines, once virtually all the slaves had learned of the war, it was ridiculous to imagine returning to the old ways. Even if the South had eked out a negotiated peace, even if the North had not elected to make emancipation one of its war aims, slavery would have been dead within a decade.

And yet, many Southerners refused to recognize this reality until the end. Several times the Confederate Congress turned down suggestions, including one from General Lee, that slaves be granted their freedom if they enlisted in the Confederate Army. Only during the last two months of the conflict did any blacks don Confederate uniforms, and those few never saw action.

Blacks in Uniform

On the other side of the lines, 186,000 blacks, the majority of them runaway slaves, served in 16 regiments of the Union Army (and 30,000 in the Navy). They fought in 449 engagements, including 39 major battles. Sixteen black soldiers and four black sailors won the Congressional Medal of Honor.

Blacks were less interested in preserving the Union than in freeing slaves. This was one reason why some of their white commanders, such as Thomas Wentworth Higginson, preferred black troops to white.

Their superiority lies simply in the fact that they know the country, which White troops do not; and, moreover, that they have peculiarities of temperament, position, and motive, which belong to them alone. Instead of leaving their homes and families to fight, they are fighting for their homes and families; and they show the resolution and sagacity which a personal purpose gives. It would have been madness to attempt with the bravest White troops what I have successfully accomplished with Black ones.

The bravery of black Americans won the admiration of a great many Northerners. President Lincoln, for example, confessed that he was surprised that blacks made such excellent soldiers, and he seems to have been revising the racist views that he formerly shared with most white Americans.

For a time, at least, so did many Union soldiers. Fighting to free human beings, a positive goal, was better for morale than fighting to prevent secession, a negative aim at best. By 1864, as they marched into battle, Union regiments sang "John Brown's Body," an abolitionist hymn, and Julia Ward Howe's more poetic "Battle Hymn of the Republic":

> As He died to make men holy,
> Let us die to make men free.

Because the Emancipation Proclamation did not free all slaves, in February 1865 Radical Republicans in Congress proposed, with Lincoln's support, the Thirteenth Amendment to the Constitution. It provided that "neither slavery nor involuntary servitude, except as a punishment for crime . . . shall exist within the United States." Most of the Northern states ratified it within a few months. Once the peculiar institution was destroyed in the United States, only in Brazil, some Moslem countries, and a few remote parts of sub-Saharan Africa was the holding of human beings in bondage still condoned.

For Further Reading

The works listed at the conclusion of Chapter 24 are relevant to this chapter as well. See also E. D. Fite, *Social and Industrial Conditions in the North During the Civil War* (1976); J. F. C. Fuller, *Grant and Lee* (1957); Paul D. Gates, *Agriculture and the Civil War* (1965); Leon F. Liwack, *Been in the Storm So Long* (1979); Robert P. Sharkey, *Money, Class, and Party* (1959); Hans A. Trefousse, *The Radical Republicans* (1969); Bell Wiley, *Southern Negroes, 1861–1865* (1938) and *The Plain People of the Confederacy* (1943).

Freedmen pose for a photographer in Richmond, Virginia, 1865.

BRINGING THE SOUTH BACK IN

THE RECONSTRUCTION OF THE UNION

When the guns fell silent in 1865, the people of the South looked about them to see a society, an

economy, and a land in tatters. Some Southern cities, such as Vicksburg, Atlanta, Columbia, and

Richmond, were flattened, eerie wastelands of charred timber, rubble, and freestanding chimneys.

Few of the South's railroads could be operated for more than a few miles. Bridges were gone. River-

borne commerce, the lifeblood of the states beyond the Appalachians, had dwindled to a trickle. Old commercial ties with Europe and the North had been snapped clean. All the South's banks were ruined.

Even the cultivation of the soil had been disrupted. The small farms of the men who had served in the ranks lay fallow by the thousands, many of them never to be reclaimed by their former owners. Great planters who had abandoned their fields to advancing Union armies discovered that weeds and scrub pine were more destructive conquerors. The former slaves who had toiled on the land were often gone, looking elsewhere for a place to start new lives as free men and women. Between 1860 and 1870, the number of horses, milch cows, and hogs in the South declined by about a third. The value of farms declined by almost half.

THE RECONSTRUCTION DEBATE

In view of the widespread desolation, the word *reconstruction* would seem to be an appropriate description of the twelve-year period following the Civil War. But the word does not refer to the literal rebuilding of the South, the laying of bricks, the spanning of streams, the reclaiming of the land.

Reconstruction refers to the political process by which the eleven rebel states were restored to a normal constitutional relationship with the twenty-five loyal states and their national government. It was the Union, that great abstraction over which so many had died, that was reconstructed.

Lincoln's Plan to Reconstruct the Union

Blood was shed during Reconstruction too, but little glory was won. Few political reputations—Northern or Southern, white or black, Republican or Democratic—emerged from the era without a stain. More than one historian has suggested that Abraham Lincoln comes down to us a heroic and sainted figure only because he did not survive the war.

Indeed, the Reconstruction policy Lincoln proposed as early as 1863 was soundly repudiated by members of his own party. Lincoln anticipated the problems he did not live to face. He described as "a pernicious abstraction" the constitutional issue with which both sides in the bitter Reconstruction debate masked their true motives and goals.

By the end of 1863, Union armies controlled large parts of the Confederacy, and ultimate victory was reasonable to assume. To provide for a rapid reconciliation of the sections, Lincoln declared on December 8, 1863, that as soon as 10 percent of the voters in any Confederate state took an oath of allegiance to the Union, the

POCKET VETO

Section 7 of Article I of the Constitution provides that if a president vetoes an act of Congress, he shall return the act to Congress within ten days "with his Objections." If he fails to do so, the act becomes law without his signature.

However, if Congress enacts a bill and then adjourns before ten days have passed, as was the case with the Wade-Davis bill, the president can veto it without explanation simply by failing to sign it, figuratively leaving it in his coat pocket. Thus, the pocket veto.

people of that state could organize a government and elect representatives to Congress. Moving quickly, Tennessee, Arkansas, and Louisiana complied.

Congress Checks the President

However, Congress refused to recognize the new governments, leaving the three states under the command of the military. Motives for checking Lincoln's plan varied as marvelously as the cut of the chin whiskers that politicians were sporting, but two were repeatedly voiced. First, almost all Republican congressmen were alarmed by the broad expansion of presidential powers during the war. No president since Andrew Jackson (still a villain to those Republicans who had been Whigs) had assumed as much authority as Lincoln had—at the expense of Congress. Few congressmen wished to see this trend continue during peacetime, as Lincoln's plan for Reconstruction proposed.

Second, Radical Republicans, abolitionists who had been at odds with Lincoln over his reluctance to move against slavery, objected that Lincoln's plan made no allowances whatsoever for the status of the freedmen, as the former slaves were called. They took the lead in framing the Wade-Davis bill of July 1864, which provided that only after 50 percent of the white male citizens of a state swore an oath of loyalty to the Union could the Reconstruction process begin. Then, the Wade-Davis bill insisted, Congress and not the president would decide when the process was complete.

Lincoln responded with a pocket veto and, over the following months—the last of his life—hinted that he was ready for compromise. He said he would be glad to accept any former rebel states which opted to reenter the Union under the congressional plan and he let it be known he had no objection to giving the right to vote to blacks who were "very intelligent and those who have fought gallantly in our ranks." He urged the military governor of Louisiana to extend the suffrage to some blacks and was quoted as saying that "the restoration of the Rebel States to the Union must rest upon the principle of civil and political equality of both races."

Prisoners from the Front, *by Winslow Homer (1866). As this painting depicts, soldiers were allowed to return home—to a shattered society and ruined economy.*

Stubborn Andy Johnson

Like Lincoln, Andrew Johnson of Tennessee grew up in stultifying frontier poverty. Unlike Lincoln, who taught himself to read as a boy and was ambitious from the start, Johnson was illiterate as an adult. He was working as a tailor when he swallowed his pride and asked a school-teacher in Greenville, Tennessee, to teach him to read and write. She did, later married him, and encouraged Johnson to pursue a political career. Andrew Johnson had more political experience than Lincoln or, for that matter, most U. S. presidents. Johnson held elective office on every level, from town councilman to congressman to senator and, during the war, governor.

Experience, alas, is not the same thing as aptitude. Whereas Lincoln was an instinctive politician attuned to the realities of what he could and could not accomplish, Johnson was unsubtle, insensitive, willful, and stubborn. His reputation was not helped by the fact that he was ill when sworn in as vice president, bolted several glasses of brandy for strength, and took the oath of office drunk and thick-tongued.

Nevertheless, Johnson had the goodwill of the Radicals because he had several times called for the harsh punishment of high-ranking Confederates. (He wanted to hang Jefferson Davis.) But he quickly lost Radical support when, like Lincoln, he insisted that he, the president, possessed the authority to decide when rebel states were reconstructed. Thus ensured the debate over what Lincoln had called "a pernicious abstraction."

Johnson: They Are Already States

Johnson based his case for presidential supervision of Reconstruction on the assumption that the Southern states had never left the Union because it was constitutionally impossible to do so: the Union was one and inviolable; it could not be dissolved. Johnson and the entire Republican party and most Northern Democrats had held to that principle in 1861. Johnson stuck by it in 1865.

There had indeed been a war and an entity known as the Confederate States of America. But individuals had fought the one and created the other; states had not. Punish the rebels, Johnson said—he approved several confiscations of rebel-owned lands—but not Virginia, Alabama, and the rest. They were still states in the United States of America. Seating their duly elected representatives in the Congress was a purely administrative matter. The president, the nation's chief administrator, would decide how and when to do it.

Obstinate, often vulgar, Andrew Johnson was a self-taught student of the Constitution. Rigorous adherence to it, as he read it, and a reflexive distaste for the idea of black citizenship doomed his early friendly relationship with the Radical Republicans.

Logic Versus Horse Sense

There was nothing wrong with Johnson's logic; he was an excellent constitutionalist. The president's problem was his inability (or stubborn refusal) to see beyond constitutional tidiness to the world of human feelings, flesh, and blood—especially blood.

The fact was, virtually every senator and representative from the rebel states—Johnson was an exception—had left their seats in the winter and spring of 1861, and Congress and the president had functioned as the Union through four years of war. More than 600,000 people

OLD THAD STEVENS

Few Radical Republicans were as sincerely committed to racial equality as Thaddeus Stevens of Pennsylvania. In his will he insisted on being buried in a black cemetery because blacks were banned from the one where he normally would have been interred.

Nevertheless, even Stevens came to terms with the racism of those northern whites who refused the vote to the blacks in their own states. In order to win their support for black suffrage in the South, Stevens argued that the situation was different in the South because blacks made up the majority of loyal Union men there. "I am for negro suffrage in every rebel state," he said. "If it be just, it should not be denied; if it be necessary, it should be adopted; if it be a punishment to traitors, they deserve it."

had been killed and most Northerners blamed these deaths on arrogant, antagonistic, rich Southern slave owners who, when Johnson announced that he would adopt Lincoln's plan of Reconstruction (with some minor changes), began to assume the leadership in their states that they had always held.

Nor did Johnson's reputation as a man who wanted rebels punished seem to hold up. By the end of 1865 he pardoned 13,000 Confederate leaders, thus making them eligible to hold public office. In elections held in the fall under Johnson's plan, Southern voters sent many of these rebels to Congress, including four Confederate generals, six members of Jefferson Davis's cabinet, and as senator from Georgia, former Confederate Vice President Alexander H. Stephens.

The Radicals: They Have Forfeited Their Rights

To Johnson's argument, Charles Sumner, the Radical Republican Senator from Massachusetts, replied that the former Confederate states had committed "state suicide" when they seceded. They were not states. Therefore, it was within the power of Congress to admit them. Thaddeus Stevens of Pennsylvania, leader of the Radicals in the House of Representatives, came to the same conclusion by arguing that the Southern states were "conquered provinces." Therefore, they had the same status as the federal territories of the West.

These theories suited the mood of most Northerners very well, but they were constitutionally indefensible. An obscure Republican, Samuel Shellabarger of Ohio, came up with a formula that both appealed to angry, war-weary Northerners and made constitutional sense: the rebel states had forfeited their rights as states. Congress's Joint Committee on Reconstruction found that "the States lately in rebellion were, at the close of the war, disorganized communities, without civil government, and without constitutions or other forms, by virtue of which political relations could legally exist between them and the federal government." Such a state of affairs meant that only Congress could decide when the eleven former Confederate states might once again function as members of the Union.

The Radicals

Congress refused to seat the senators and representatives who were sent to Washington under the Johnson plan. The leaders of the resistance were Radical Republicans, former abolitionists for the most part who, whatever constitutional arguments they put forward, were determined to crush the Southern planter class they had hated for so long and, with varying degrees of idealism, wanted to help the black freedmen who had, for so long, been victimized and exploited by the slave owners.

Some Radicals like Stevens and Sumner and Benjamin "Bluff Ben" Wade of Ohio believed in racial equality. George W. Julian of Indiana proposed to confiscate the land of the planters and divide it, in forty-acre farms, among the blacks; with economic independence they could guarantee their civil freedom and political rights. Other Radicals wanted to grant the freedmen citizenship, including the vote, for frankly political purposes. Black voters would provide the backbone for a Republican party in the South, which did not exist before the war.

The Radicals were a minority within the Republican party. However, they were able to win the cooperation of party moderates because of Johnson's repeated blunders and a series of events in the conquered South that persuaded a majority of Northern voters that Lincolnian generosity would mean squandering the Union's military victory and making a mockery of the cause for which so many soldiers had died.

Freedmen pose with their reading books in front of their log schoolhouse.

THE CRITICAL YEAR

The reaction of most blacks to the news of their freedom was to test it by leaving the plantations and farms on which they had lived as slaves.

Many flocked to cities that they associated with blacks who had been free before the war. Others, after a period of wandering, gathered in ramshackle camps in the countryside, eagerly discussing the rumor that each household would soon be alloted "forty acres and a mule." Without a means of making a living in a stricken land, these congregations of people were potentially, and in some cases were in fact, dens of hunger, disease, crime, and disorder.

The Freedmen's Bureau

In order to prevent chaos in conquered territory, Congress had created the Bureau of Refugees, Freedmen, and Abandoned Lands, popularly known as the Freedmen's Bureau. Administered by the army under the command of General O. O. Howard, the Bureau provided relief for the freedmen (and some whites) in the form of food, clothing, and shelter; attempted to find jobs for them; set up hospitals and schools run by idealistic black and white women from the Northern states, sometimes at the risk of their lives; and otherwise tried to ease the transition from slavery to freedom. When the Freedmen's Bureau bill was first enacted, Congress had assumed that properly established state governments would be able to assume responsibility for these services within a year after the end of the hostilities. The Bureau was scheduled to expire in March 1866.

In February 1866, however, the process of Reconstruction was at a standstill. Congress had refused to recognize Johnson's state governments but had not created any to its own liking. The former Confederacy was, in effect, still under military occupation. So, Congress passed a bill extending the life of the Bureau.

Johnson vetoed the bill and, a month later, he vetoed another congressional act that granted citizenship to the freedmen. Once again, his constitutional reasoning was sound. The Constitution gave the states the power to rule on the terms of citizenship within their borders, and Johnson continued to insist that the state governments he had set up were legitimate.

He might have won his argument. Many Americans took their constitutional fine points seriously and Radical demands for black civil equality ran against the grain of white racism. However, the actions of the Johnson government toward blacks, and the apparent refusal of many Southern whites to acknowledge their defeat in the war, nullified every point Johnson scored.

The Black Codes

Because blacks as slaves had been the backbone of the Southern labor force, the Southern legislatures naturally expected the blacks to continue to bring in the crops after the war. The freedmen wanted the work. Far from providing farms for them, however, the Johnsonian state governments did not even establish a system of employment that treated the blacks as free men and women. On the contrary, the black codes defined a form of second-class citizenship that looked to blacks and many whites like a step or two back into slavery.

In some states, blacks were permitted to work only as domestic servants or in agriculture, just what they had done as slaves. Other states made it illegal for blacks to live in towns and cities. In no state were blacks allowed to vote or to bear arms. In fact, few of the civil liberties listed in the Bill of Rights were accorded them.

Mississippi required freedmen to sign twelve-month labor contracts before January 10 of each year. Those who failed to do so could be arrested, and their labor sold to the highest bidder in a manner that (to say the least) was strongly reminiscent of the detested slave auction. Dependent children could be forced to work. Blacks who reneged on their contracts were not to be paid for the work that they already had performed.

The extremism of the black codes alienated many Northerners who would gladly have accepted a less restrictive form of second-class citizenship for the freedmen. (Only a few Northern states allowed black people full civil equality.) Northerners were also disturbed when whites in Memphis, New Orleans, and smaller Southern towns rioted, killing and injuring blacks, while the Johnson state governments sat passively by.

The Fourteenth Amendment

Perceiving the shift in mood, in June 1866, Radical and Moderate Republicans drew up a constitutional amendment on which to base congressional Reconstruction policy. The long and complex (and later controversial) Fourteenth Amendment banned from holding high federal or state office all high-ranking Confederates unless they were pardoned by Congress. This struck directly at many of the leaders of the Johnson governments in the South.

The amendment also guaranteed that all "citizens of the United States and of the State wherein they reside," —in other words, blacks—were to receive fully equal treatment under the laws of the states.

If ratified, the Fourteenth Amendment would preclude Southern states from passing any more laws like the black codes. However, it also promised to cancel Northern state laws that forbade blacks to vote, and in that aspect of the amendment Johnson saw an opportunity. Calculating that many Northerners, particularly in the Midwest, would rather have Confederates in the government than grant full civil equality to blacks, Johnson decided to campaign against the Radicals on the amendment issue in the 1866 congressional election.

DISCOURAGING REBELLION

Among other provisions of the Fourteenth Amendment, the former Confederate states were forbidden to repay "any debt or obligation incurred in aid of insurrection or rebellion against the United States." By stinging foreign and domestic individuals and banks that had lent money to the rebel states, the amendment was putting future supporters of rebellion on notice of the consequences of their actions.

The Radical Triumph

The first step was the formal organization of a political party. Therefore Johnson, along with conservative Republican allies such as Secretary of State Seward and a few senators, and some Democrats called a convention of the National Union party in Philadelphia. The message of the convention was sectional reconciliation; to symbolize it, the meeting was opened by a procession of northern and southern Johnson supporters in which couples made up of one Southerner and one Northerner marched arm in arm down the center aisle of the hall.

Unhappily for Johnson, the first couple on the floor was South Carolina governor James L. Orr, a huge, fleshy mountain of a man, and Massachusetts governor John A. Andrew, a little fellow with a way of looking intimidated. When Orr seemed to drag the mousy Andrew down the length of the hall, Radical politicians and cartoonists had a field day. Johnson's National Union movement, they said, was dominated by rebels and preached in the North by cowardly stooges.

In the fall, Johnson sealed his doom. He toured the Midwest seeking support—he called it his "swing around the circle"—and from the start discredited himself. Johnson had learned his oratorical skills in the rough-and-tumble, stump-speaking tradition of eastern Tennessee. There, voters liked a red-hot debate between politicians who scorched each other and the hecklers that challenged them.

Midwesterners also liked that kind of ruckus, but not, it turned out, from their president. When Radical hecklers taunted Johnson and he responded gibe for gibe, Radicals shook their heads sadly that a man of so little dignity should be sitting in the seat of Washington and Lincoln. Drunk again, they supposed.

The result was a landslide. Most of Johnson's candidates were defeated. The Republican party, now led by the Radicals, controlled more than two-thirds of the seats in both houses of Congress, enough to override every veto that Johnson dared to make.

RECONSTRUCTION REALITIES AND MYTHS

The Republicans' Reconstruction program was adopted in a series of laws that were passed by the Fortieth Congress in 1867. These dissolved the Southern state governments that had been organized under Johnson and partitioned the Confederacy into five military provinces, each commanded by a major general. The army would maintain order while voters were registered—blacks and those whites who were not specifically disenfranchised under the terms of the Fourteenth Amendment. The constitutional conventions that these voters elected

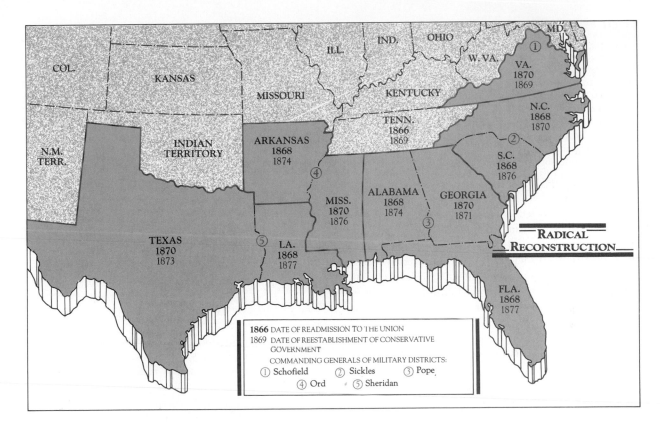

were required to abolish slavery, give the vote to adult black males, and ratify the Thirteenth and Fourteenth Amendments. After examination of their work by Congress, the reconstructed states would be admitted to the Union, and their senators and representatives could take their seats in the Capitol. The Radicals assumed that at least some of these congressmen would be Republicans.

The Readmission of the Southern States

Tennessee complied immediately with these terms and was never really affected by the Radical experiment in remaking the South. Ironically, it was Andrew Johnson, as military governor during the war, who had laid the basis for a stable government in the "Volunteer State."

In 1868, largely as a result of the black vote, six more states were readmitted. Alabama, Arkansas, Florida, Louisiana, North Carolina, and South Carolina sent Republican delegations, including some blacks, to Washington. In the remaining four states—Georgia, Mississippi, Texas, and Virginia—because some whites obstructed every attempt to set up a government in which blacks would participate, the military continued to govern until 1870.

In the meantime, with Congress more firmly under Radical control, Thaddeus Stevens, Charles Sumner, and other Radicals attempted to establish the supremacy of the legislative over the judicial and executive branches of the government. With the Supreme Court

they were immediately successful. By threatening to reduce the size of the Court or even to try to abolish it, the Radicals intimidated the justices. Chief Justice Salmon P. Chase decided to ride out the difficult era by ignoring all cases that dealt with Reconstruction issues—just what the Radicals wanted.

As for the presidency, Congress took partial control of the army away from Johnson and struck at his right to choose his own cabinet. The Tenure of Office Act forbade the president to remove any appointed official who had been confirmed by the Senate without first getting the Senate's approval of the dismissal.

The Impeachment of Andrew Johnson

Although Johnson had attempted to delay and obstruct congressional Reconstruction by urging Southern whites not to cooperate, the strict constitutionalist in him had come to terms with the Radicals's control of the government. He had executed the duties assigned him under the Reconstruction acts. However, he decided to defy the Tenure of Office Act for the same constitutional reasons. To allow Congress to decide if and when a president could fire a member of his own cabinet was a clear infringement of the independence of the executive branch of the government. In February 1868, Johnson dismissed the single Radical in his cabinet, Secretary of War Edwin Stanton.

Strictly speaking, the Tenure of Office Act did not

WAS JOHNSON IMPEACHED?

Andrew Johnson *was* impeached, the only American president to be so. *Impeachment* is not removal from office but the bringing of charges, the equivalent of indictment in a criminal trial. The official who is found guilty of the articles of impeachment is convicted and removed from office (and may be sent to prison or otherwise penalized if convicted in a subsequent criminal trial). Johnson was *not* convicted of the charges brought against him.

apply to Stanton's dismissal because he had been appointed by Lincoln, not by Johnson. Nevertheless, as the Constitution provided, the House of Representatives drew up articles of impeachment, passed them, and appointed a committee to serve as Johnson's prosecutors. The Senate acted as the jury in the trial, and the Chief Justice presided.

A President on Trial

All but two of the eleven articles of impeachment dealt with the Tenure of Office Act. As expected, Johnson's defenders in the Senate argued that it did not apply to the Stanton case, and, in any event, its constitutionality was highly dubious. The other two articles condemned Johnson for disrespect of Congress. These charges were undeniably true; Johnson had spared few bitter words in describing the Radicals who seemed to dominate both houses. But the president's defenders argued that sharp and vulgar language did not approach being the "high crimes and misdemeanors" that the Constitution stipulates as the reason for impeachment.

Removal of an impeached federal official requires a two-thirds majority of the Senate. In 1868, that meant 36 senators had to vote for conviction, no more than 18 for acquittal. The actual vote in Johnson's case was 35 to 19. He remained in office by a single vote.

A ticket of admission to the Senate gallery to witness the impeachment of Andrew Johnson.

Actually, it was not so close. About six Moderate Republican senators had agreed privately that if they were needed to acquit, they would vote for acquittal. They wanted to avoid going on record as favoring the president. Johnson had little support in the North, and they were practical politicians. However, they did not believe that the president should be removed from office simply because he was at odds with Congress. Moreover, if Johnson were removed from office, his successor would have been Ben Wade of Ohio, a Radical of such dubious deportment—he was a notorious foulmouth—that by comparison Johnson was a statesman. Finally, 1868 was an election year. Andy Johnson's days were numbered. The immensely popular Ulysses S. Grant would be the Republican nominee. Victory in November was a sure thing.

The Fifteenth Amendment

Grant easily defeated New York governor Horatio Seymour in the electoral college by a vote of 214 to 80. However, the popular vote was much closer, a hair's breadth in some states. Nationwide, Grant won by 300,000 votes, and, some rudimentary arithmetic showed, he got 500,000 black votes in the Southern states. Grant lost New York, the largest state, by a very thin margin. Had blacks been able to vote in New York (they were not), Grant would have carried the state easily. In Indiana, Grant won by a razor-thin margin. Had blacks been able to vote in that Northern state (they were not), it would not have been close.

In other words, the future of the Republican party seemed to depend on the black man's right to vote in the Northern as well as the Southern states. Consequently, the Moderates in Congress supported Radicals in drafting a third "Civil War Amendment." The Fifteenth forbade states to deny the vote to any person on the basis of "race, color, or previous condition of servitude." Because Republican governments favorable to blacks still controlled most of the Southern states, the amendment was easily ratified. The Radical Reconstruction program was complete.

Legends

By the end of the nineteenth century and increasingly after 1900, a legend of Reconstruction took form in American popular consciousness. Most white people came to believe that Reconstruction was a time of degradation and humiliation for white Southerners. Soldiers bullied them, and they languished under the political domination of ignorant former slaves who were incapable of good citizenship, carpetbaggers (Northerners who went South in order to exploit the tragedy of defeat), and scalawags (white Southerners of low caste who cooperated with blacks and Yankees). A verse in the anti-radical New York *World* read:

This photograph of Ulysses S. Grant is a print from a restored glass plate negative.

I am a carpet-bagger—
   I've a brother scalawag—
Come South to boast and swagger
   With an empty carpet bag
To rob the whites of greenbacks
   And with the blacks go bunk
And change my empty satchel
   For a full sole-leather trunk.

For the "Black Reconstruction" governments, the legend continued, were hopelessly corrupt as well as unjust. The blacks, carpetbaggers, and scalawags looted the treasuries and demeaned the honor of the Southern states. Only by heroic efforts did decent white people, through the Democratic party, redeem the Southern states once they had retaken control of them. Some versions of the legend glamorized the role of secret terrorist organizations, such as the Ku Klux Klan, in redeeming the South.

The Kernel of Truth

As in most legends, there was a kernel of truth in this vision of Reconstruction. The Radical governments did spend freely. There was plenty of corruption in Southern government; for example, the Republican governor of Louisiana, Henry C. Warmoth, banked $100,000 during a year when his salary was $8,000. In 1869, the state of

Florida spent as much on its printing bill as had been spent on every function of state government in 1860.

Sometimes the theft was open and ludicrous. Former slaves in control of South Carolina's lower house voted a payment of $1,000 to one of their number who had lost that amount in a bet on a horse race. Self-serving carpetbaggers were numerous, as were vindictive scalawags and incompetent black officials.

The Legend in Perspective

Large governmental expenditures were unavoidable in the postwar South, however. Southern society was being built from scratch—an expensive proposition. It was the lot of the Radical state governments to provide social services—for whites as well as blacks—that had simply been ignored in the Southern states before the Civil War. Statewide public school systems were not founded in the South until Reconstruction. Programs for the relief of the destitute and the handicapped were likewise nearly unknown before Republicans came to power.

Corrupt politicians are inevitable in times of massive government spending, no matter who is in charge; shady deals were not unique to Southern Republican governments during the 1860s and 1870s. The most flagrant theft from public treasuries during the period was the work of Democrats in New York, strong supporters of white Southerners who wanted to reduce the blacks to peonage. In fact, the champion Southern thieves of the era were not Radicals but antiblack white Democrats.

WHAT IF JOHNSON HAD BEEN CONVICTED?

What would it have meant for the structure of American government if Andrew Johnson had been removed from office for, in effect, disagreeing with Congress? It might have been a major step toward the parliamentary form of government that is practiced in most representative democracies. Whereas in the United States the executive branch of government is separate from the legislative branch, in parliamentary systems like that of Canada and Great Britain, the prime minister, the head of government, must be a member of Parliament and have the support of a majority of the members of Parliament. If the prime minister loses that support, he or she loses the office and Parliament elects a new prime minister or is dissolved, and new elections held. The American presidency would still have been constitutionally independent had Johnson been removed, but the precedent probably would have emboldened later Congresses to remove presidents of whose policies they disapproved. As it was, Johnson's acquittal and, in 1974, Richard Nixon's resignation before he was impeached, have helped to preserve the independence of the executive branch.

NOTABLE PEOPLE

BLACKS IN CONGRESS

Better a white crook than a black crook; better a white grafter than a black of stature and probity. Such was the view of the "Redeemers," white Democrats who wrested control of Southern state governments from the Republican party during Reconstruction. They depicted black officials as incompetent, corrupt, and uninterested in the welfare of the South as a whole. With most Southern whites contemptuous of the recently freed slaves, it was an effective appeal. Other issues paled into near invisibility in what seemed the blinding urgency in asserting "white supremacy."

At low levels, many black officeholders were incompetent and self-serving. A few high in state administrations were venal grafters. That their Redeemer challengers were rarely better and often worse did not, however, lend a reflective bent to Southern voting behavior. Rather, race was all.

While none of the blacks who sat in Congress in the wake of the Civil War may be said to have been statesmen of the first order, as a group they were as able and worthy a lot as the era's other "ethnic delegations" in the Capitol, any random selection of farmer-congressmen or businessmen-congressmen, any Northern or Western state delegation of either party, any random selection of 22 Redeemers.

Between 1869 and 1901, 20 blacks served in the House, two in the Senate. South Carolina, where blacks outnumbered whites, sent eight; North Carolina four; Alabama three; and Virginia, Georgia, Florida, Louisiana, and Mississippi one each. Both black senators, Hiram K. Revels and Blanche K. Bruce, represented Mississippi, where potential black voters also outnumbered whites.

Thirteen of the 22 had been slaves before the Civil War, the others were lifelong free blacks. Their educational attainment compared well with that of Congress as a whole. Ten of the black congressmen had gone to college, five had graduated. Six were lawyers (rather less

than among all congressmen—nothing for which to apologize); three were preachers; four farmers. Most of the others were skilled artisans, by no means "the dregs of society" as the Redeemers ritually portrayed them.

Hiram Revels was a Methodist pastor. He was born in North Carolina in 1822 but, as a free black, prudently removed to Indiana and Ohio where, during the Civil War, he organized a black regiment. The end of the war found him in Natchez where a cultivated and conservative demeanor (and a willingness to defer to white Republicans) made him an attractive candidate for the Senate.

Blanche K. Bruce was born a slave in 1841, but he was well educated: his owner leased him to a printer. In 1861, he escaped from his apparently lackadaisical master and, in the wake of the Union troops, moved to Mississippi. His record in the Senate was conservative and quiet.

The most durable of the black congressmen was J. H. Rainey of South Carolina. He sat in Congress between 1869 and 1879, winning his last election in the year of the Hayes-Tilden debacle. In most of his district, blacks outnumbered whites by 6 to 1 and 8 to 1. He was retired in the election of 1878 only as a consequence of widespread economic reprisals against black voters and some little violence.

Rainey's parents had bought their freedom long before the Civil War but, in 1862, he was drafted to work on the fortifications in Charleston harbor, a condition that was tantamount to enslavement. However, Rainey escaped to the West Indies and worked his way to the North, returning to his home state early during Reconstruction.

Rainey was indeed vindictive toward the white South, exploiting racial hostilities as nastily as any Redeemer on the other side. Most of the black congressmen were, unsurprisingly, preoccupied with civil rights issues. No doubt, had South Carolina's blacks retained the fran-

---

After a Republican administration in Mississippi ran a clean, nearly corruption-free regime, the first post-Reconstruction treasurer of the state absconded with $415,000. This paled compared to the swag E. A. Burke, the first post-Reconstruction treasurer of Louisiana, who took $1,777,000 with him to Honduras in 1890.

As for the carpetbaggers, many of them brought much-needed capital to the South. They were hot to make money, to be sure, but in the process of developing the South, not as mere exploiters. Many of the scalawags were by no means unlettered "poor white trash," as the legend had it, but Southern Whigs who had disapproved of secession and who, after the war, drifted naturally, if briefly, into the Republican party that their Northern fellow Whigs had joined.

Blacks in Government

The blacks who rose to high office in the Reconstruction governments were rarely ignorant former field hands, but well-educated, refined, even rather conservative men. Moreover, whatever the malfeasances of Reconstruction, blacks could not be blamed; they never controlled the government of any Southern state. For a short time, they were the majority in the legislatures of South Carolina (where blacks were the majority of the population) and precisely one-half of the legislature of Louisiana. Only two blacks served as United States senators, Blanche K. Bruce and Hiram Revels, both cultivated men from Mississippi. No black ever served as a governor, although Lieutenant Governor P. B. S. Pinchback of Louisiana briefly acted in that capacity when the chise, Rainey would have exploited racial hostility as destructively as his opponents.

However, Rainey was by no means oblivious to other questions. By the end of the 1870's, he used his modest seniority to work for Southern economic interests that transcended the color line. He defended the rights of Chinese in California on conservative "pro-business" Republican, as well as racial, grounds and attempted to improve relations with the black republic of Haiti.

George H. White was the last black to sit in Congress from a Southern state before the passage of the Civil Rights Act of 1965. Born a slave in 1852, he attended Howard University in Washington (then a black institution) and practiced law in North Carolina.

In 1896, he won election to the House of Representatives by adding a number of white Populist votes to a black Republican bloc. At the time, some Southern Populists, like Thomas Watson of Georgia, preached interracial political cooperation in an attempt to build a solid agrarian front to the "Bourbons" into which the Redeemers had been transformed. Unlike the Northern Populists, who fastened on the Republican party as their chief enemy, Southern Populists sometimes saw allies in black Republican voters. Their issues were agrarian: almost all Southern blacks tilled the soil.

This put black politicians like White in an impossible situation. Preferment in the national Republican party required him to adhere to a line that, under President William McKinley, also elected in 1896, became conservative and imperialistic. White spoke out on behalf of a high tariff—albeit on the grounds that it favored the working man: "the ox that pulls the plow ought to have a chance to eat the fodder"—and favored the Spanish-American War.

Inevitably, his positions alienated those whites who had helped elect him. Moreover, Southern Populism was undergoing a momentous transformation during the late 1890s. Shrewd Democratic party politicians like Benjamin "Pitchfork Ben" Tillman combined a populistic appeal to poor whites with an incendiary hatred of blacks.

Racial hatred was the staple of demagogues like Tillman (and, soon enough, Tom Watson in Georgia). However, they also hammered on the fact that Southern blacks voted overwhelmingly Republican and that meant a "plutocratic" federal government.

Conservatives like White were easy targets and, in 1898, the North Carolina Populists switched sides, supporting the Democratic candidate and almost ousting White after only one term.

He knew his political future was doomed and compensated for "an organization man's" first term by speaking out loudly during his second about what was happening in the South (while most white Republicans merely shrugged). Only after 1898 did he fasten almost exclusively on civil rights issues, describing himself as "the representative on this floor of 9,000,000 of the population of these United States."

By 1900, black voters in White's district had been reduced to a fragment. He did not even bother to stand for reelection and sure humiliation. Instead, in his farewell speech in 1901, he delivered his finest oration, an eloquent speech that served as the coda to Reconstruction's failure to integrate blacks into the American polity:

> *These parting words are in behalf of an outraged, heartbroken, bruised and bleeding, but God-fearing people, faithful, industrial, loyal people, rising people, full of potential force. The only apology that I have to make for the earnestness with which I have spoken is that I am pleading for the life, the liberty, the future happiness, and manhood suffrage for one-eighth of the entire population of the United States.*

white governor was out of the state. Whatever Reconstruction was, its color was not black.

Redemption

The crime of Reconstruction in the eyes of most Southern whites was that it allowed blacks the opportunity to participate in government. The experiment failed because black voters were denied an economic foundation on which to build their civil equality, and because Northerners soon lost interest in the ideals of the Civil War.

Because they had no land, the blacks of the South were dependent on landowners for their sustenance. When Southern landowners concluded that it was in their interest to eliminate the blacks from political life, they could do so by threatening with unemployment.

Unprotected former slaves could not command the respect of poorer whites, who provided most of the members of terrorist organizations like the Ku Klux Klan, which was founded in 1866 by former slave trader and Confederate general Nathan Bedford Forrest. These nightriders—identities concealed under hoods—frightened, beat, and even murdered blacks who insisted on voting. Congress outlawed and, within a few years, effectively suppressed the Klan and similar organizations like the Knights of the White Camellia, but in the meantime, many blacks had been terrorized into staying home on election day.

Congress was unable to counter the conviction of

Hiram Revels (left) and Blanche K. Bruce (right), both of Mississippi, were elected to the United States Congress during Reconstruction.

increasing numbers of white Southerners that only through "white supremacy," the slogan of the Southern Democratic parties, could the South be redeemed. In most Southern states, where whites were the majority, an overwhelming white vote on this issue alone was enough to install legislators and governors who promptly found effective ways to disenfranchise the blacks.

In the North and West, each year that passed saw the deterioration of interest in the rights of Southern blacks. At no time had more than a minority of Northern whites truly believed blacks to be their equals. As an era of unprecedented economic expansion unfolded in the wake of the Civil War, and unprecedented scandals rocked the administration of Ulysses S. Grant, to whom the protection of black civil rights was entrusted, support for Reconstruction dwindled. Albion W. Tourgee, a white Northerner who fought for black civil equality in North Carolina, wrote that trying to enforce the Fourteenth and Fifteenth Amendments without federal support was "a fool's errand."

THE GRANT ADMINISTRATION

Ulysses S. Grant was the youngest man to be president up to his time, only 46 years old when he took the oath of office in 1869. In some ways, his appearance remained as unimpressive as when reporters caught him whittling

sticks on the battlefield. Stoop-shouldered and taciturn, Grant has a peculiar frightened look in his eye in most of the photographs of him, as though he knew that he had risen above his capabilities.

In fact, Grant hated the duties and power of the presidency. It was the perquisites of living in the White House that he fancied. He took with relish to eating caviar and tournedos béarnaise and sipping the best French wines and cognac. The earthy general whose uniform had looked like that of a slovenly sergeant developed a fondness for expensive, finely tailored clothing.

Indeed, the elegant broadcloth on his back was the emblem of Grant's failure as president. Money and fame had come too suddenly to a man who had spent his life struggling to survive. Both he and his wife were overwhelmed by the adulation heaped on him. When towns and counties took his name, and when cities made gifts of valuable property and even cash—$100,000 from New York alone—Grant accepted them with a few mumbled words of thanks. He never fully understood that political giftgivers were actually paying in advance for future favors. Or, if he did understand, he saw nothing wrong in returning kindness with the resources at his disposal. Among the lesser of his errors, he gave federal jobs to any of his and his wife's relatives who asked and, a seedy lot, they were not bashful. Worse, Grant remained as loyal to them as he had been loyal to junior officers in the army. In the military, backing up subordinates when they slip up is a virtue, essential to morale. Grant never quite learned that in politics backing up subordinates who steal is less than admirable.

Black Friday

Grant's friends, old and new, wasted no time in stealing. Unlucky in business himself, the president luxuriated in the flattery lavished on him by wealthy men. In 1869, two unscrupulous speculators, Jay Gould and Jim Fisk, made it a point to be seen in public with the president, schemed secretly with Grant's brother-in-law, Abel R. Corbin, and hatched a plot to corner the nation's gold supply.

That is, having won Corbin's assurance that he would keep Grant from selling government gold, Gould and Fisk bought up as much gold and gold futures (commitments to buy gold at a future date at a low price) as they could. Their apparent control of the gold market caused the price of the precious metal to soar. In September 1869, gold was bringing $162 an ounce. Gould's and Fisk's plan was to dump their holdings and score a killing.

Finally grasping that he was an accomplice, on Friday, September 24, Grant dumped $4 million in government gold on the market and the price collapsed. Gould and Fisk suffered very little. Jim Fisk simply refused to honor his commitments to buy at the higher-than-market price and hired thugs to threaten those who insisted he do so. (High finance could be highly rough-and-tumble during the Grant years.) But businessmen who needed gold to pay debts and wages were ruined by the hundreds, and thousands of workingmen lost their jobs. The luster of a great general's reputation was tarnished before he had been president for a year.

Other Scandals

During the construction of the Union Pacific Railway in the years following the Civil War, the directors of the U.P. set up a dummy corporation called the Crédit Mobilier. This company charged the U. P. some $5 million for work that actually cost about $3 million. The difference went into the pockets of Union Pacific executives. Because the U.P. was heavily subsidized by the federal government, and therefore under close scrutiny, key members of Congress were cut in on the deal. Among the beneficiaries was Schuyler Colfax, Grant's vice president. Speaker of the House James A. Garfield also accepted a stipend.

Three of Grant's appointees to the cabinet were involved in corruption. Carriers under contract to the Post Office Department paid kickbacks in return for exorbitant payments for their services. The Secretary of War, William W. Belknap, took bribes from companies that operated trading posts in Indian reservations under his authority. He and his subordinates shut their eyes while

Grant's presidential campaign ribbon commemorated his march into Richmond, Virginia, during the Civil War.

the companies defrauded the tribes of goods that they were due under the terms of federal treaties. Grant insisted that Belknap leave his post, but since Belknap was Grant's old crony, the president refused to punish him on behalf of cheated Indians.

Nor did Grant punish his Secretary of the Treasury, Benjamin Bristow, or his personal secretary, Orville E. Babcock, when he learned that they had sold excise stamps to whiskey distillers in St. Louis. Whenever the president came close to losing his patience (which was considerable), Roscoe Conkling or another stalwart reminded him of the importance of party loyalty. Better a few scoundrels escape than party morale be damaged and the Democrats take over.

The Liberal Republicans

Although the full odor of the Grant scandals was loosed only later, enough scent hung in the air in 1872 that a number of prominent Republicans broke openly with the president. Charles Sumner of Massachusetts, a senator since 1851 and chairman of the Senate Foreign Relations Committee, split with the president over Grant's determination to annex the island nation of Santo Domingo to the United States. Without Sumner's opposition to imperialism and a land-grab by cynical Republican profiteers, Grant would surely have succeeded.

Carl Schurz of Missouri and E. L. Godkin, the British-born editor of *The Nation* magazine, were appalled by the steamy atmosphere of corruption in Washington and the treatment of public office as a way of making a living rather than as performing a public service. Schurz and Godkin (but not Sumner) had also given up on Reconstruction (which, whatever his personal sentiments, Grant enforced). Although not necessarily convinced that blacks were inferior to whites, they had concluded that ensuring civil rights for blacks was not worth the instability of government in the South, nor the continued presence of troops in the Southern states. Better to allow the white Redeemers to return to power.

The Election of 1872

This was also the position of the man whom the Liberal Republicans named to run for president in 1872, the editor of the *New York Tribune*, Horace Greeley. It was a terrible choice, for Greeley was a lifelong eccentric. Throughout his 61 years, Greeley had clambered aboard almost every reform and far-out bandwagon that had rattled down the road, from abolitionism and women's rights at one end of the spectrum to vegetarianism, spiritualism (communicating with the dead), and phrenology (reading a person's character in the bumps on his or her head) at the other.

Even in his appearance, Greeley invited ridicule. He looked like a crackpot with his round, pink face exaggerated by close-set, beady eyes and a wispy fringe of white chin whiskers. He wore an ankle-length overcoat on the hottest days, and be carried a brightly colored umbrella on the driest. Sharp-eyed Republican cartoonists like Thomas Nast had an easy time making fun of Greeley.

To make matters worse, Greeley needed the support of the Democrats to make a race of it against Grant. He condemned blacks as "simple, credulous, ignorant" patsies of greedy carpet-baggers and scalawags and called for Republicans to "clasp hands across the bloody chasm" with Southern Democrats. This was asking too much of Republican party regulars. Voters who disapproved of Grant disapproved much more of Southern Democrats.

Moreover, throughout his editorial career, Greeley had printed just about every printable vilification of the Democrats—particularly Southerners—that the English language offered. The Democrats did give him their nomination. But Southern whites found it difficult to support such a leader. A large black vote for Grant in seven Southern states helped give the president a 286 to 66 victory in the electoral college.

THE TWILIGHT OF RECONSTRUCTION

The Liberals returned to the Republican party. For all their contempt for the unhappy Grant, upon whom the scandals piled during his second term, the Liberals found their flirtation with the Democrats humiliating. Among them, only Charles Sumner remained true to the cause of the Southern blacks. His Civil Rights Act of 1875 (passed a year after his death) guaranteed equal accommodations for blacks in public facilities such as hotels and theaters and forbade the exclusion of blacks from juries. Congress quietly dropped another provision forbidding segregated schools.

The Act of 1875 was the last significant federal attempt to enforce equal rights for the races for 80 years. Not only had Northerners lost interest in Civil War idealism, Southern white Democrats had redeemed most of the former Confederacy. By the end of 1875, only three states remained Republican: South Carolina, Florida, and Louisiana.

The Disputed Election

The Democratic presidential candidate in 1876, New York governor Samuel J. Tilden, called for the removal of troops from these three states, which would bring the white supremacy Democrats to power. The Republican candidate, Governor Rutherford B. Hayes of Ohio, ran on a platform that guaranteed black rights in the South, but Hayes was known to be skeptical of black capabilities and a personal friend of a number of white Southern politicians.

When the votes were counted, Hayes's opinions seemed to be beside the point. Tilden won a close popular vote, and he appeared to sweep the electoral college by a vote of 204 to 165. However, Tilden's margin of victory included the electoral votes of South Carolina, Florida, and Louisiana, where Republicans still controlled the state governments. After receiving telegrams from party leaders in New York, officials there declared that in reality Hayes had carried their states. According to these returns, Hayes had eked out a 185 to 184 electoral vote victory.

It was not that easy. When official returns reached Washington, there were two sets from each of the three disputed states—one set for Tilden, and one for Hayes. Because the Constitution did not provide for such an occurrence, a special commission was established to decide which set of returns was valid. Five members of each house of Congress and five members of the Supreme Court sat on this panel. Seven of them were Republicans, seven were Democrats, and one, David Davis of Illinois, a Supreme Court justice and once Abraham Lincoln's law partner, was known as an independent. Because no one was interested in determining the case on its merits, each commissioner fully intending to vote for his party's candidate, the burden of naming the next president of the United States fell on Davis's shoulders.

He did not like it. No matter how honestly he came to his decision, half the voters in the country would call for his scalp because he had voted down their candidate. Davis prevailed on friends in Illinois to get him off the hook by naming him to a Senate seat then vacant. He resigned from the Court and, therefore, the special commission. His replacement was a Republican, and the stage was set for the Republicans to "steal" the election.

The Compromise of 1877

The commission voted on strict party lines, eight to seven, to accept the Hayes returns from Louisiana, Florida, and South Carolina—thus giving Rutherford B. Hayes the presidency by a single electoral vote. Had that been all there was to it, there might have been further trouble. At a series of meetings, however, a group of prominent Northern and Southern politicians and businessmen came to an informal agreement that was satisfactory to the political leaders of both sections.

The "Compromise of 1877" involved several commitments, not all of them honored, for Northern investment in the South. Also not honored was a vague agreement on the part of some conservative Southerners to build a "lily-white" Republican party in the South based on economic and social views that they shared with Northern conservatives.

As to the disputed election, Hayes would be permitted to move into the White House without resistance by either Northern or Southern Democrats. In return, he would withdraw the last troops from South Carolina, Florida, and Louisiana, thus allowing the Democratic party in these states to oust the Republicans and destroy the political power of the blacks.

Despite the proclamations before Inauguration Day that Democrats would fight if Tilden were not elected, there was no trouble. This was not because the men who hammered out the Compromise of 1877 were so very powerful. It merely reflected the growing disinterest of Americans in the issues of the Civil War and Reconstruction and their increasing preoccupation with the fabulous economic growth of the country. The Southern blacks, of course, were the casualties of this watershed year, but since the price they paid was suppression, few whites heard their complaints and fewer were interested.

For Further Reading

James McPherson, *Ordeal by Fire: The Civil War and Reconstruction* (1982) is the best recent account of Reconstruction. See William A. Dunning, *Reconstruction: Political and Economic* (1907) for the old harshly critical view of the era's policies that dominated American historical thinking for half a century, and for a rejoinder, W. E. B. DuBois, *Black Reconstruction* (1935). John Hope Franklin, *Reconstruction After the Civil War* (1961) provides a briefer objective account, as does Herman Belz, *Reconstructing the Union* (1969). A splendid account of the reaction of blacks to freedom is Leon F. Liwack, *Been in the Storm So Long* (1979).

Valuable studies of special topics include Richard N. Current, *Three Carpetbag Governors* (1967); Stanley Kutler, *Judicial Power and Reconstruction Politics* (1968); Eric McKitrick, *Andrew Johnson and Reconstruction* (1960); Robert C. Morris, *Reading, 'Riting, and Reconstruction: The Education of Freedmen in the South, 1861–1870* (1981); Willie Lee Rose, *Rehearsal for Reconstruction* (1964); Hans A. Trefousse, *The Radical Republicans* (1969); A. W. Trelease, *KKK: The Ku Klux Klan Conspiracy and Southern Reconstruction* (1971); and C. Vann Woodward, *Reunion and Reaction: The Compromise of 1877 and the End of Reconstruction* (1951).

This political cartoon of the 1880s shows Uncle Sam weighing the Democratic and Republican parties represented as roosters. Because they balanced, a few votes could, and did, win an election for either party.

PARTIES, PATRONAGE, AND PORK

POLITICS AS SPORT AND BUSINESS

The presidents of the late nineteenth century are not an exciting lot. Their portraits arranged side

by side on a wall—Grant, Hayes, Garfield, Arthur, Cleveland, Harrison, Cleveland again—they

resemble a line of mourners at a Midwestern funeral. They were protective of their dignity, to be sure,

and grandly bewhiskered. They were competent to perform executive duties (except, possibly, Grant),

devoted family men, sober-sided and drab (except Chester A. Arthur), and uninspiring across the

board.

This lack of presidential charisma is one reason why twentieth-century Americans find the presidents of the late nineteenth century so unappealing. In our age of sparkling electronic media and short attention spans, it is the personable performer who has the edge in winning elections. Moreover, twentieth-century Americans have gotten used to vigorous chief executives, men who seized the initiative in domestic and foreign matters alike. By way of contrast, between 1868 and the end of the century, presidents believed Congress should take the lead. The president was to execute laws, steer the government, and, when necessary, apply a constitutional brake.

Finally, there is no doubt that what was most vital in late nineteenth-century America lay not in politics but in the fabulous growth of American industry, the creation of big business, and the development of the great "Wild West" so central to American popular culture. The historian might easily be tempted to rush through the whole subject of politics with a few words—except for two striking facts.

First, politics was itself a business in the late nineteenth century, from the White House down to city hall. Politics reflected the nation's preoccupation with getting ahead, with developing and organizing for material gain. Second, Americans of that era loved their political game. In no other period of American history did a higher percentage of eligible voters actually exercise the franchise. Despite the fact that their isolation made it difficult for many rural voters to get to the polls in wintry Novembers, and the fact that many blacks' constitutional right to vote was nullified in practice by fear of economic or violent reprisals, fully 80 percent of those who were eligible to vote in the 1870s, 1880s, and 1890s did vote. In our own time, by comparison, about half the eligible voters turn out at a typical election.

HOW THE SYSTEM WORKED

Presidential elections brought out the most voters of all. In part this was because, nationally, the two major parties were so evenly matched. A man (and in a few states after 1890, a woman) found plenty of evidence that a single vote really could make a difference. Between 1872, when Grant won reelection by a smashing 750,000 votes, and 1896, when William McKinley ushered in a new political era of Republican dominance with an 850,000 vote plurality, presidential elections were close. Two (1880 and 1884) were decided by fewer than 40,000 votes in a total of 9 to 10 million. In 1876 and 1888, the winning candidates had fewer supporters than the losers: the winners collected their prize in the electoral college.

In 1892, the victorious Democrat, Grover Cleveland, scored a respectable popular majority. Even then his share of the vote cast was well under half of the total, 46.1 percent. In fact, the only presidential candidate of either party between 1872 and 1896 to win an absolute majority of the popular vote was Samuel J. Tilden, the fellow who lost the "Stolen Election" of 1876.

Solid South and Republican Respectability

The parties were not so well balanced by region nor among distinct social groups. With the exception of Connecticut, which was evenly divided, New England voted heavily Republican. In the section where Federalism, Whiggery, and abolitionism had been strongest, an enduring distaste for the party of Jackson and the old slave owners prevented Democrats from winning more than occasional elections.

The upper and middle classes of the Northeast and Midwest were generally Republican. They thought of the G.O.P., or the "Grand Old Party," as a bastion of morality and respectability, another legacy of the Whigs to the Republican party. Ironically, most big cities in the North, which were run by cynical, if not corrupt political machines, also voted Republican. (The most important exception was Democratic New York.) Finally, those blacks who retained the right to vote were staunch Republicans. Although they got scant attention from the G.O.P. after 1877, blacks still thought of it as the party of Lincoln and emancipation.

The Democrats built their national vote upon the foundation of the "Solid South." Except for blacks and those Appalachian whites who had opposed secession, Southern whites were doggedly loyal Democrats. Not a single former slave state, Union or Confederate, including West Virginia, voted Republican in a presidential election during the late nineteenth century. The Democrats also invariably won New York City by appealing to immigrants, and they commanded the major part of the immigrant and white ethnic vote elsewhere. Many Midwestern farmers voted Democratic. In a year of difficulties on the farm, the Democratic party could and did win their states. Farther west, in new states to be admitted during the period, Democrats were often in the majority.

YELLOW DOG DEMOCRATS

In eastern Texas and other parts of the South, white voters took pride in the name, "Yellow Dog Democrats." They meant that they were so loyal to their party that if the Republican candidate for office was Jesus Christ, and the Democratic candidate an old yellow dog, they would vote for the yellow dog.

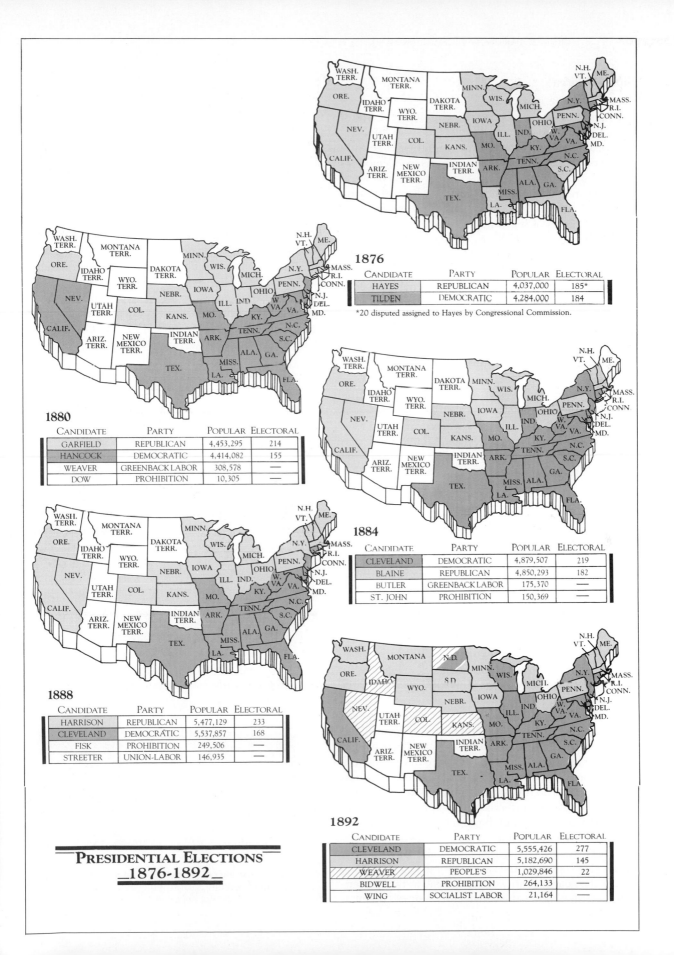

1876

CANDIDATE	PARTY	POPULAR	ELECTORAL
HAYES	REPUBLICAN	4,037,000	185*
TILDEN	DEMOCRATIC	4,284,000	184

*20 disputed assigned to Hayes by Congressional Commission.

1880

CANDIDATE	PARTY	POPULAR	ELECTORAL
GARFIELD	REPUBLICAN	4,453,295	214
HANCOCK	DEMOCRATIC	4,414,082	155
WEAVER	GREENBACK LABOR	308,578	—
DOW	PROHIBITION	10,305	—

1884

CANDIDATE	PARTY	POPULAR	ELECTORAL
CLEVELAND	DEMOCRATIC	4,879,507	219
BLAINE	REPUBLICAN	4,850,293	182
BUTLER	GREENBACK LABOR	175,370	—
ST. JOHN	PROHIBITION	150,369	—

1888

CANDIDATE	PARTY	POPULAR	ELECTORAL
HARRISON	REPUBLICAN	5,477,129	233
CLEVELAND	DEMOCRATIC	5,537,857	168
FISK	PROHIBITION	249,506	—
STREETER	UNION-LABOR	146,935	—

1892

CANDIDATE	PARTY	POPULAR	ELECTORAL
CLEVELAND	DEMOCRATIC	5,555,426	277
HARRISON	REPUBLICAN	5,182,690	145
WEAVER	PEOPLE'S	1,029,846	22
BIDWELL	PROHIBITION	264,133	—
WING	SOCIALIST LABOR	21,164	—

PRESIDENTIAL ELECTIONS
1876-1892

Swing States

Because of these steady voting patterns, the outcome of national elections turned on the vote in a handful of "swing" states, particularly Illinois, Indiana, Ohio, and New York. In each of these states, with their large blocs of electoral votes, hard-core Republicans and Democrats were about equal in number. Political decisions were, therefore, in the hands of independents who might swing either way depending on local issues, party organization, the personalities of the candidates, or a passing whim. Several presidential elections during the period were decided in New York State, where the result depended on how big a majority the New York City Democrats could turn in to counterbalance the Republican edge upstate.

Party leaders believed that the personal popularity of a candidate in the swing states could make the difference. Consequently, a disproportionate number of late nineteenth-century presidential and vice-presidential nominees came from Indiana, Ohio, and New York.

In the elections held between 1876 and 1892, the major parties filled twenty presidential and vice-presidential slots. Eighteen of the twenty (or 90 percent) were filled by men from the four key states. Eight were from New York, and five more from Indiana. Neither party was particularly interested in finding "the best man" for the job. They wanted to win an election. To do so they had to carry the swing states.

Bosses at Conventions

National conventions, which met every four years, played a much more important role in party politics than they do today. The difference was communications. Today, political leaders from every part of the country can discuss affairs with any other by picking up the phone or by hopping on a plane. In the late nineteenth century, congressmen saw one another in Washington on a regular basis. However, governors and state and city political bosses, who were often the real powers in party politics, did not.

Consequently, when they did gather at their quadrennial meetings, they wheeled and dealed, bargained and traded, made and broke political careers. There was no army of pushy television reporters around to shove a microphone in the midst of every group of politicians which gathered on the floor of the barn-like convention halls. Newspaper reporters could be kept away by strong-arm bodyguards, often ex-boxers, when the discussion promised to be interesting.

Today, the primary system almost inevitably assures that a party's presidential candidate will be known long before the delegates answer the roll call at the conventions. At the end of the nineteenth century, nomina-

tions were more likely to be decided at the convention, perhaps on the floor, or just as likely by bosses in hotel corridors and suites over oysters, beefsteak, and freeflowing whiskey. Ordinary delegates, whose livelihood depended on party bosses, did as they were told. They went to conventions for the festivities.

In the Democratic party, the most important bosses were the head of New York's Tammany Hall, who reliably delivered that city's vote, and the Bourbon leaders of the Solid South. (They were named for their extreme conservatism, like that of the Bourbon kings of France—not after Kentucky's famous corn liquor.) In the Republican party, men like Boss Matthew Quay of Pennsylvania and Boss Thomas C. Platt of New York traded the support of their delegations for the promise of a prestigious cabinet post or a healthy share of the lucrative government offices and contracts that a victorious party had at its disposal.

The Patronage

The spoils system had come a long way since the days of Andrew Jackson and William Marcy, for the United States had become quite a big country. There was a lot of patronage—government jobs for the party faithful—to go around: 50,000 jobs in Grant's time, 250,000 by the end of the century. Some government jobs involved real work. There was a postmaster in every town and hundreds of postal employees in the cities. Indian agents administered the government's treaty obligations to the tribes. In some federal bureaucracies like the Customs Service, there was enough paperwork to bury thousands

Presidential politics in the nursery: This soap doll was one of dozens of novelties peddled during the election campaign of 1896.

One-Party Politics

When Judge M. B. Gerry sentenced Alfred E. Packer to death for murdering and eating five companions during a blizzard in Colorado in 1873, he stated as a reason for his decision: "There were seven Democrats in Hinsdale County, but you, you voracious, man-eating son-of-a-bitch, you ate five of them."

of clerks wearing green visors and plastic cuffs to protect their white shirts from smudges of ink and graphite.

Who got these jobs? To a large extent, they were filled by supporters of the party in power. Political activists who worked to get the vote out were rewarded with government employment. In return, in election years their party assessed them a modest percentage of their income to finance the campaign. The result was politics for its own sake. The party scratched the jobholder's back; the jobholder reciprocated.

The higher ranking the party official, the more rewarding the job. The post of Collector of Customs in large ports was particularly lucrative. In addition to a handsome salary, Collectors were paid a share of all import duties on goods reclaimed from smugglers who had been caught at their work. This curious incentive system made for a remarkably uncorrupt Customs Service. There was more to be made in catching violators than in taking bribes from them.

This toy scale weighed the comparative merits of Democrat Grover Cleveland and Republican Benjamin Harrison.

Thus, Collector of the Port of New York Chester A. Arthur earned an average $40,000 a year between 1871 and 1874, and in one big case he shared a bounty of $135,000 with two other officials. He was the best paid government official in the country, earning more than even the president. And he was assessed a handsome sum for the privilege by the Republican party. On a rather more modest level, a handful of Southern blacks benefited from the patronage when the Republican party was in power. Some federal appointments in the South went to black people.

Pork

Other party supporters were rewarded with contracts for government work in "pork-barrel" bills. At the end of each congressional session, congressional coalitions pieced together bills to finance government construction projects in each member's district—a new post office here, a government pier there, the dredging of a river channel somewhere else. The idea was not so much to get needed work done, but to reward businessmen who supported the proper party with a share of what was, during the 1880s, an annual surplus of $100 million in the Treasury.

Thus, the River and Harbor Bill of August 1886 provided for an expenditure of $15 million to begin over 100 new projects, although 58 government projects that had been started two years earlier remained unfinished.

Of course, there was not a job or contract for every voter. In order to turn out the vast numbers they did, the parties exploited the emotional "politics of memory," the very rational politics of pensions, and ballyhoo that would have horrified Washington, Adams, Jefferson, and even William Henry Harrison.

The Politics of Memory

If most Republicans forgot the blacks, they remembered the Civil War. G. O. P. orators specialized in "waving the bloody shirt," reminding Northern voters that Democrats had caused the Civil War. Lucius Fairchild, a Wisconsin politician who had lost an arm in battle, literally flailed the air with his empty sleeve during campaign speeches. Even more flamboyant was Indiana politician Oliver P. Morton. "The Democratic party," Morton crowed, "may be described as a common sewer and loathesome receptacle, into which is emptied every element of treason North and South, every element of inhumanity and barbarism which has dishonored the age."

The Civil War loomed over the period. Between 1868 and 1901, every president but the Democrat Grover Cleveland had been an officer in the Union Army. When Cleveland, believing that sectional bitterness was fading, issued an order to return captured Confederate battle flags to their states for display at museums and war monuments, an angry protest in the North forced him to back down and contributed to his failure to win reelection the next year.

The man who defeated Cleveland in 1888, Benjamin Harrison, was still waving the bloody shirt after 20 years and not apologizing for it. "I would a thousand times rather march under the bloody shirt, stained with the lifeblood of a Union soldier," Harrison told voters, "than march under the black flag of treason or the white flag of cowardly compromise." Dwelling on a divided past could not possibly be constructive, but it won elections, even for the Democrats in the South. They waved the Confederate Stars and Bars, reminding voters of the nobility of the lost cause and of the white supremacy that the Democratic Redeemers had salvaged from that cause and from the "Black Republicans."

Vote Yourself a Pension

In their pension policy, the Republicans converted the bloody shirt into dollars and cents. Soon after the war ended, Congress had voted to fund pensions to Union veterans who were disabled from wartime wounds and diseases. The law was strictly worded, perhaps unfairly so, as many claimed. Many genuinely handicapped veterans did not qualify under its terms. Instead of modifying the law, however, Northern congressmen took to introducing special pension bills that provided monthly stipends for specifically named constituents who had persuaded them that their case was just.

By the 1880s, the procedure for awarding special pensions had become grossly abused. Congressmen took little interest in the truthfulness of the petitioner or the worthiness of his grievance. (One applicant for a pension had not served in the army because, he said, he had fallen off a horse on the way to enlist.) They simply introduced every constituent request as a bill. When

almost all Republicans and many Northern Democrats had a few special pension bills in the hopper, the bills were rushed through collectively by voice vote. Instead of declining as old veterans died, the cost of the pension program actually climbed. In 1866, 127,000 Union veterans received pensions valued at $15.5 million. By 1885, the cost had risen to $56 million; by 1888 to $80 million. Pensions made up one of the largest line items in the federal budget, and a veterans' lobby, the Grand Army of the Republic (G.A.R.), came to serve effectively as a Republican political-action committee in return for them.

The G.A.R.

In 1888, Congress passed a new general pension bill that granted an income to every veteran who had served at least 90 days in the wartime army and was disabled for any reason whatsoever. An old soldier who fell off a stepladder in 1888 was eligible under its terms.

President Cleveland vetoed the law in the name of fairness and economy. The Republicans then ran against Cleveland in that year with the slogan "Vote Yourself a Pension." Cleveland's opponent, Benjamin Harrison told voters, "When you lifted your hands and swore to protect and defend the Constitution and the flag, you didn't even know what your pay was to be. . . . My countrymen, it is no time now to use an apothecary's scale to weigh the rewards of the men who saved the country."

Harrison won the election. The next year, he signed an even more generous Dependent Pensions Act and appointed the head of the G.A.R., James "Corporal" Tanner, to distribute the loot. "God help the surplus," Tanner said, referring to the money in the Treasury. He meant it. By the end of Harrison's term, Tanner had increased the annual expenditure on pensions to $165 million, with a million pensioners on the rolls. Local wits took wry notice of young women who married doddering old Billy Yanks who had a gleam in their eyes and a check in the mail. Widows of Civil War veterans were

In 1902, forty years after Antietam and Shiloh, members of the Grand Army of the Republic were still a staple of Memorial Day parades. They were almost always Republican voters.

entitled to eight dollars a month plus two dollars per child.

Northern Democrats posed as the party of principle in the controversies over the bloody shirt and pensions. In the South, however, Democrats played the Civil War game in reverse. State governments provided benefits for Confederate veterans.

PRESIDENTS AND PERSONALITIES

As a legacy of the Grant scandals, a presidential candidate's reputation for honesty was a popular campaign cry. In 1876, the Republicans turned to Rutherford B. Hayes, and the Democrats to Samuel J. Tilden—in part because, as governors of Ohio and New York respectively, they had never stolen a cent. When Hayes's supporters stole the election of 1876, the Democrats delighted in calling him "His Fraudulency" or "Rutherfraud" B. Hayes.

Hayes, Integrity, and Oblivion

In truth, Hayes was amiable and obliging within the law, but studiously honest. A Civil War hero who was twice seriously wounded, he was the first president who trav-

eled for pleasure rather than on military or diplomatic missions. Perhaps most interesting about Hayes, who was president during a severe depression and widespread violence between workers and employers, he had serious reservations about the desirability of the capitalist system. (His wife had very serious reservations about alcoholic beverages. She would not serve them at the White House, earning the by-no-means affectionate nickname, "Lemonade Lucy.")

As president, Hayes pleased few people besides Lucy. Old Radical Republicans were ired by his abandonment of Southern blacks (to which he was bound by the Compromise of 1877). Neither of the Republican party's two major factions, the "Stalwarts" (Grant supporters) or the "Half-Breeds" (critics of Grant), believed that Hayes allotted them as much patronage than they deserved. There never was a question of renominating him; even Hayes yearned to hit the tourist road. Long before his term ended, two prominent Republicans announced their intention of succeeding him. One was James G. Blaine of Maine, leader of the Half-Breeds. The other was Ulysses S. Grant, out of office four years, just back from his own world tour, and nearly bankrupt. He needed the salary, and he resented the fact that in becoming president earlier he had been obligated to give up his lifetime pay as a general. And the leader of the Stalwarts, an old Radical who despised Blaine, Roscoe Conkling of New York, persuaded Grant that it was his duty to run.

THE SURPLUS

Many late nineteenth-century congressmen voted for dubious veterans' pensions and pork barrel bills because spending won votes. However, there was also a profoundly good economic reason to get rid of the government's money during the 1880s. Bizarre as it seems to us today, with the federal government drowning in debt, in the 1880s the United States Treasury collected about $100 million more in taxes each year than it spent. Each dollar that came to rest in the Treasury was a dollar less in circulation, feeding the economy. Allowing the surplus to grow meant risking a depression.

Reducing revenue was out of the question. More than half the government's collections came from the tariff, which was backed by powerful interests. So, the government spent on pensions, often dubious internal improvements, and during the 1890s, on the construction of a large modern navy.

Even then, it took a major depression and war to wipe out the surplus. In 1899, after the war with Spain, the government had a deficit of $90 million. There have been years since when more money flowed into the Treasury than out, but there has never again been cause to worry about a surplus.

ORDINARY PEOPLE

Presidents were not so remote and sheltered from the people in the late nineteenth century, as Garfield's assassination shows. When he was shot, the president of the United States was waiting for a train on a public platform.

An incident that involved Rutherford B. Hayes after he left the White House illustrates the point more amusingly. While attending a GAR encampment, Hayes was stopped by a policeman, who brusquely pulled him back to a pathway, and gave him a finger-shaking lesson because he was walking on the grass. Likewise, President Grant, who never lost his love for fast horses, was written a ticket by a Washington officer for speeding.

Garfield: A Dark Horse

Neither Blaine nor Grant was able to win a majority of the delegates to the Republican convention. They were frustrated by the ambitions of several "favorite son" candidates, men who came to Chicago backed only by their own states. The hope of the "favorite son" is that there will be a deadlock between the front runners, which would force the tired delegates to turn to them as compromise candidates.

Finally, after 34 ballots, the Blaine men recognized that the cause of their hero was lost. Instead of turning to one of the favorite sons whom they held responsible for their disappointment, they switched their votes to a man whose name was not even in nomination, James A. Garfield of Ohio. On the thirty-sixth ballot, he became the Republican candidate.

Garfield was a Half-Breed, a Blaine supporter, but he played on Roscoe Conkling's bottomless vanity by traveling to New York to seek the boss's blessing and to promise him a share of the patronage. Garfield went to the polls with a united party behind him.

The Democrats, having failed to win with an anti-war Democrat in 1868 (Seymour), a Republican maverick in 1872 (Greeley), and a reformer in 1876 (Tilden), tried their luck with their own Civil War general, Winfield Scott Hancock. An attractive if uninspiring man, he made the election extremely close. Garfield drew only 10,000 more votes than Hancock, just 48.3 percent of the total.

Another President Is Murdered

Garfield was a much more intelligent and substantial man than his opportunistic career would indicate. Whether or not he would have blossomed as president cannot be known, for he spent his four short months as an active chief executive sorting out the claims of Republican party workers to government jobs. At one point he exclaimed in disgust to Blaine, his Secretary of State who wanted very badly to be president, that he could not understand why anyone pursued the post, considering all its trivial, tawdry concerns.

Garfield tried to placate both wings of the party. But when he handed the choicest plum of all, the post of Collector of Customs of the port of New York, to a Blaine man, Roscoe Conkling openly broke with the president. He and his protege in the state Republican machine, Thomas Platt, resigned their seats in the Senate. Their intention was to remind Garfield of their power in the New York Republican party by having the state legislature reelect them.

By the summer of 1881, it appeared that Conkling and Platt had lost their battle. The Garfield—Blaine Half-Breeds had succeeded in blocking their reelection. But the issue was finally resolved by two gunshots in a Washington train station. On July 2, 1881, Charles Guiteau, a ne'er-do-well preacher and bill collector who had worked for the Stalwarts but had not been rewarded with a government job, walked up to Garfield as he was about to depart on a holiday and shot him twice in the small of the back. After living in excruciating pain for eleven weeks, the second president to be murdered died on September 19.

"I am a Stalwart! Arthur is president!" Guiteau shouted when he fired the fatal shots. He meant that the new president was none other than Conkling's longtime ally, Vice President Chester A. Arthur. The deranged

SPIKED ORANGES

Lucy Hayes allowed no alcoholic beverages in the White House—or so she thought. According to Washington newspapermen, a bibulous lot, they bribed White House servants to serve them punch and oranges spiked with rum—or so they thought. After he left the presidency, Hayes insisted that the joke was on the drinkers. He said that he and his wife knew of the journalists' plan and had their servants spike the drinks and fruit with a nonalcoholic beverage that tasted like rum.

TURKEY

Roscoe Conkling was a physical-culture enthusiast. He exercised daily and was extremely proud of his exceptional physique. This provided his enemy, James G. Blaine, with an easy target when he described Conkling's "haughty disdain, his grandiloquent swell, his majestic, over-powering turkey-gobbler strut."

CONKLING THE IDEALIST

Although he is chiefly remembered for his cynical attitude toward the patronage and party loyalty, Roscoe Conkling remained truer to the Radical Republican ideals of his young manhood than did most members of his party. Until his death in 1888—he froze to death in a blizzard—Conkling's extremely successful law firm was instructed to take cases from blacks at nominal or no cost.

Guiteau expected Arthur to free him from prison and reward him for his patriotic act.

Once in office, however, Chet Arthur, recently the "prince of spoilsmen," proved to be an able and uncorrupt president who signed the first law to limit a party's use of government jobs for political purposes.

Civil-Service Reform

The Pendleton Act of 1883 established the Civil Service Commission, a three-man bureau that was empowered to draw up and administer examinations that applicants for some low-level government jobs were required to pass before they were hired. Once in these civil-service jobs, employees could not be fired simply because the political party to which they belonged lost the presidency.

At first, only 10 percent of 131,000 government workers were protected by civil service. But the Pendleton Act also empowered the president to add job classifications to the civil-service list at his discretion.

Ironically, because the presidency changed party hands every four years between 1880 and 1896, each incumbent's desire to protect his own appointees in their jobs—a violation of the spirit of civil-service reform—led by the end of the century to a fairly comprehensive civil-service system.

After Democrat Grover Cleveland was elected in November 1884, but before he took office in March 1885, outgoing President Chester Arthur protected a number of Republican government employees by adding their jobs to the civil-service list. Cleveland did the same thing for Democratic government workers in 1888, Benjamin Harrison for Republicans in 1892, and Cleveland again for Democrats in 1896. By 1900, 40 percent of the federal government's 256,000 employees held civil-service positions. About 30 percent of government clerks were women, an unlikely proportion at a time when jobs were given out in order to win votes.

Another provision of the Pendleton Act was the abolition of the assessment system. That is, the parties were forbidden to insist that those of their members who held government positions "donate" a percentage of their salaries for political campaign chests each election year. Until the presidency of Benjamin Harrison (1889–93), the professional politicians were at a loss as to how to replace these revenues. Harrison's Postmaster General, John Wanamaker, came up with the solution. He levied "contributions" on big businessmen who had an interest, direct or ideological, in Republican victory at the polls. This method, with the Democrats finding their share of big business support, and later drawing from the treasuries of labor unions, remained the chief means of financing national political campaigns until the 1970s.

Honest Chet Arthur

Chester A. Arthur may have been president illegally. Enemies said he was not born in Fairfield, Vermont, as he claimed, but in a cabin a few miles north—in Canada (a president must be American born). However that may have been, the urbane and elegant Arthur, resplendent in his furs and colorful waistcoats compared to the gray dour look of the Republicans around him, did a good job in the White House.

Arthur wanted a second term. He tried to mend fences with the Stalwarts by twice offering Roscoe Conkling (a superb lawyer) a seat on the Supreme Court. He tried to woo the Half-Breeds by deferring to Secretary of State James G. Blaine's judgment in foreign affairs. Blaine would have none of it and resigned from the cabinet. With Conkling's political career in eclipse, Blaine easily won the Republican nomination for the presidency, again at Chicago, in the summer of 1884.

1884: Blaine versus Cleveland

Blaine expected to win the election as well. As usual, New York State seemed to be the key to victory, and Blaine believed that he would run more strongly there than most Republicans. Some old Liberal Republicans, now known as Mugwumps (an Algonkian word for "big chief," a reference to their self-righteous pomposity), had deserted the party, announcing that the Democratic candidate, Grover Cleveland, was the more honest man.

Blaine expected to make up this defection and more by winning the Irish vote, which usually did not go Republican. He was popular in the Irish-American community because, in an era when Republican leaders frequently disdained the Catholic Church, Blaine had Catholic relatives. Moreover, for reasons of his own, Blaine liked to "twist the lion's tail," taunt the British, the ancestral enemy in many unsmiling Irish eyes. Finally, news broke that seemed a bonus: it was revealed that while he was a lawyer in Buffalo, Grover Cleveland had fathered an illegitimate child. The stringent sexual

NOTABLE PEOPLE

JAMES ABRAM GARFIELD (1831–1881)

Perhaps if he had lived longer, he would be better understood. As it is, James A. Garfield of Cuyahoga County, Ohio, is one of the most puzzling (and disappointing) personalities of the late nineteenth century. A man of exceptional intelligence and talent, he has gone down in history as just another lackluster politician in an age that was crowded with them. Perhaps it would have been different if he had made a mark as president. But he was fatally shot just four months after his inauguration in March 1881, the fourth president to die in office, and the second to be assassinated. And yet, even before his dark-horse nomination and election in 1880, Garfield had failed to distinguish himself from his run-of-the-mill colleagues. Perhaps, understanding the character of politics in his era, Garfield consciously strived to be a mediocrity.

James Abram Garfield was born in a log cabin, the last of the frontier presidents. Poverty stricken then, the family was devastated when Garfield's father died and young James had to shoulder the responsibility of supporting his mother. He worked on a canal boat, developing the powerful physique that, after he was shot in 1881, enabled him to survive for two months while infection festered painfully in his body.

Like Lincoln, Garfield educated himself, not merely to read and write but well enough to gain admission to Williams College. There he distinguished himself, mastering the demanding classical curriculum that was still the rule in colleges. Although he entertained friends by simultaneously writing in Latin with his right hand and Greek with his left, Garfield's erudition was not limited to tricks. His diaries reveal a man who was familiar with history (although not with literature, save the Bible) and who understood, as did very few of his politician contemporaries, the forces of industrialization and urbanization that were changing America.

After serving as an officer in the Civil War, brevetted as a general, Garfield entered Congress as a Radical Republican. He was a leader, becoming Speaker of the House, but also a straight party man who risked nothing with imaginative speeches and viewpoints, of which he seemed to have been capable. Indeed, while the details are vague, it appears that he accepted some money from the Crédit Mobilier company during Johnson's presidency.

In 1880, Garfield was elected to the Senate from Ohio and attended the Republican national convention as floor manager for presidential hopeful John Sherman. When the convention deadlocked and turned quickly to Garfield as its nominee, he remained silent. Sherman was convinced that he had been betrayed. In fact, Garfield allowed his opportunities to develop without either encouraging them or choking them off—again, standard operating procedure for a politician of the Gilded Age.

He was nominated and elected, but served only four months in good health. Ironically, this exceptional individual who forced himself to be a political hack was struck down at fifty years of age because of one of the most sordid aspects of that era's politics that Garfield tolerated—the patronage.

On July 2, 1881, the president was waiting for a train when Charles Guiteau, an insane man to whom Garfield had refused to give a government position, pumped two bullets into the small of his back. Had the wounds been inflicted in the late twentieth century, Garfield would have been up and around in a few days, the slugs would have been located by x-ray and easily removed, and the danger of infection eliminated with antibiotics. No vital organs were damaged; no bones were broken. But because one bullet was lodged against Garfield's spine, the doctors were afraid to operate. Instead, they treated the president by probing with metal rods and by "irrigating," flooding the worst wound with water. It did more harm than good. After living in excruciating pain for eleven weeks, Garfield died on September 19.

Garfield's single contribution to American political development occurred two years after his death, when Congress enacted the Pendleton Act, which instituted the civil service in the United States. Garfield was a martyr to the principle that lower-level government employees remain in their jobs no matter which party is in power. But would he have signed the bill had he been alive and well in the presidency at that time? As with almost everything about the man, it is impossible to say. On the one hand, he had lived happily with the spoils system during the two decades he had sat in Congress. On the other hand, when he was at the top, the tyranny of the patronage disgusted him. Referring to the fact that most of his time as president was spent dividing up the spoils among his supporters, Garfield exclaimed, "My God! What is there in this place that a man should ever want to get into it!"

code of the period seemed to dictate that such a libertine should not be president.

Cleveland nimbly neutralized the morality issue by publicly admitting the folly of his youth and explaining that he had tried to make amends by financially supporting the child. Indeed, the Democrats turned the scandal to their advantage when they argued that if Cleveland had been indiscreet in private life, he had an exemplary record in public office, whereas Blaine, who was admirable as a husband and family man, had engaged in several dubious stock deals as a congressman from Maine. Put Cleveland into public office where he shined, they said, and return Blaine to the private life that he richly adorned.

Grover Cleveland was the only Democratic president of the late nineteenth century, elected in 1884 and 1892. He was defeated in 1888.

age was done. The Irish voters trundled back into the Democratic column and blizzards upstate snowed many Republican voters in. New York State and the presidency went to Grover Cleveland.

In 1888, four years later, Cleveland was undone in his bid for reelection by a similarly trivial incident. A Republican newspaperman, pretending to be an Englishman who was a naturalized American citizen, wrote to the British ambassador in Washington asking which of the two candidates, Cleveland or Benjamin Harrison of Indiana, would be the better president from the British point of view. Foolishly, the ambassador replied that Cleveland seemed to be better disposed toward British interests. The Republican press immediately labeled Cleveland the British candidate. Thousands of Irish Democrats in New York, who were reflexively hostile to anything or anyone the British favored, voted Republican and helped give that swing state to Harrison.

This sort of folderol, and the color and excitement of political rallies, seemed to make the difference in an era when the two parties were so evenly balanced. Unlike late twentieth-century Americans, who are flooded with entertainment from a dozen media and to whom elections are just one show among many, late nineteenth-century Americans enjoyed politics as a major diversion. They flocked to rallies in numbers almost unknown today in order to hear brass bands, swig lemonade or beer, and listen to speeches that were more show than statement of principle.

ISSUES

How Little Things Decide Great Elections

Just a few days before the election, disaster struck the Blaine campaign. The confident candidate made the mistake of dining lavishly with a group of millionaires in Delmonico's, the most regal restaurant in New York City. It was not a good idea when he wanted the votes of poor men. Before another group, he ignored the statement of a Presbyterian minister, Samuel Burchard, who denounced the Democrats as the party of "rum, romanism, and rebellion," that is, of the saloon, the Roman Catholic Church, and Southern secession.

This was pretty ordinary stuff in Republican oratory of the period, but Blaine was not fighting the campaign with an ordinary strategy. He was wooing Irish-American votes, and the Irish were sensitive about their Catholic religion. When Democratic newspapers plastered the insult "romanism" across their front pages, Blaine rushed to express his sincere distaste for this kind of bigotry and to explain that had he heard Burchard's words, he would have called him on them. But the dam-

Principles and issues did play a part in late nineteenth-century politics. Within the Republican party, a shrinking minority of leaders tried to revive the party's commitment to protecting the welfare of southern blacks until as late as 1890. When President Grant tried to seize Santo Domingo in 1870, he was frustrated by the resistance of senators from his own party who were impelled by old anti-expansionist prejudices.

However, both episodes illustrate the fact that differences of principle and opinion were more likely to lie within the parties rather than to distinguish one from the other. The political party's business was to win power. Having cooperated in that effort, politicians lined up on issues with only casual or self-serving nods toward the organization to which they belonged.

Even the question of the tariff, the nearest thing to an issue that distinguished Republicans from Democrats, found members of both parties on each side. The level at which import duties were set could inspire orators to sweating, thumping, prancing paroxysms of holy passion. But their position on the issue, low tariff or high protective tariff, depended on the place their constituents occupied in the economy, not on the party to which they belonged, an abstract principle, or even social class.

The Tariff

With the exception of the growers of a few crops that needed protection from foreign producers—like Louisiana's sugar cane planters—farmers inclined to favor a low tariff. Corn, wheat, cotton, and livestock were so cheaply produced in the United States that American farmers were able to undersell local growers of the same crops in large parts of Europe and Asia—if other countries did not levy taxes on American crops in response to high American duties on the goods that those countries shipped to the United States. Moreover, low duties on imported manufactured goods meant lower prices on the commodities that consumers of manufactured goods, such as farmers, had to buy.

The interest of agriculturalists in keeping import duties down meant that the Democratic party, with its powerful Southern agrarian contingent, was generally the low-tariff party. However, Republican congressmen representing rural areas also voted for lower rates.

While industrialists, who wanted to protect their factories from foreign competition, were generally Republican and set the high-tariff tone of that party, equally rich and powerful railroad owners and bankers often supported lower duties. Some remained contentedly within the Republican party in the company of other wealthy capitalists; others—the grand financier August Belmont, for example—were Democrats. As far as bankers like Belmont were concerned, the more goods being shunted about the country the better, no matter whether they were foreign or domestic in origin. Railroaders had an added incentive to support a low tariff. They were huge consumers of steel for rails, which was one of the commodities that received the most protection.

In the late nineteenth century, high-tariff interests had their way. After bobbing up and down from a low of 40 percent (by no means a "low" tariff) to a high of 47 percent, rates were increased to 50 percent in the McKinley Tariff of 1890. That is, on the average, an imported item was slapped with a tax that was equivalent to half of its value.

When a depression followed quickly on the act, Grover Cleveland and the Democrats campaigned against the McKinley rates and won the election of 1892. But the tariff that Congress prepared, the Wilson-Gorman bill, lowered duties to a level of 39.1 percent of the value of imports. This rate was good enough for Cleveland's supporters in commerce and finance, but too high for the farmers who had voted for him. The president's

rather wishy-washy way out of his quandary encapsulates the fact that tough issues were intra-party problems, not questions that divided the two parties. Cleveland did not sign the Wilson-Gorman bill; he did not veto it; he let it become law by ignoring it. When a party was divided on an issue, the president had to play to both sides.

Money

The issue that would, in the 1890s, shatter the political equilibrium of the 1870s and 1880s was money. The question was: what should be the basis of the circulating currency in America's rapidly expanding economy? Should it be gold and paper money redeemable in that metal from the bank that issued the note? Or should the supply of money be monitored and regulated by the government in such a way as to adjust to changing economic needs?

The controversy had its roots in the Civil War. In 1862, in order to help finance the war effort, the Union government authorized the printing of about $450 million in paper money that was not redeemable in gold. The greenbacks, so called because they were printed in green ink instead of gold on the obverse, were accepted at face value by the federal government. That is, their value in payment of taxes or other obligations was established in the law.

As long as the war went badly and the government's word was of dubious value, individuals involved in private transactions insisted on discounting the greenbacks, redeeming them in gold at something less than face value. Even after the war was won, bankers remained suspicious of any paper money that was not redeemable in gold. Successive secretaries of the Treasury, who shared the conservative views of the bankers, were determined to retire the greenbacks. When the notes flowed into the Treasury in payment of taxes, they were destroyed and were not replaced by new bills.

The result was deflation: a decline in the amount of money in circulation and, therefore, an increase in the value of gold and of paper money that was redeemable in gold. Prices dipped; so did wages. It took less to buy a sack of flour or a side of bacon than it had when the greenbacks had flowed in profusion. That meant that the farmer who grew the wheat and slopped the hogs received less for his efforts.

Farmers, who were usually in debt, were hit hardest by deflation. They had borrowed heavily to increase their acreage and to purchase machinery when the greenbacks had been abundant and prices therefore high. After the Treasury began to retire the greenbacks, the farmers found themselves obligated to repay these loans in money that was more valuable and more difficult to get.

For example, a $1,000 mortgage taken out on a farm during the 1860s represented 1,200 bushels of grain. By the 1880s, when a farmer might still be paying off his debt, $1,000 represented 2,300 bushels.

The Greenback Labor Party

Protesting the retirement of the greenbacks as a policy that enriched banker-creditors at the expense of producer-debtors, farmers formed the Greenback Labor party in 1876. In an effort to convince industrial wage-workers that their interests also lay in an abundant money supply, the party chose as its presidential candidate Peter Cooper, New York philanthropist and an exemplary, popular employer

Cooper made a poor showing, but in the congressional race of 1878 the Greenbackers elected a dozen congressmen, and some Republicans and Democrats rushed to back their inflationary policy. However, President Hayes's monetary policy was as conservative as Grant's had been, and in 1879, retirement of the greenbacks proceeded apace. In 1880, the Greenback Labor ticket, led by a Civil War general from Iowa, James B. Weaver, won 309,000 votes, denying Garfield a popular majority but, once again, failing to affect policy.

In 1884, Benjamin J. Butler led the Greenbackers one more time, but received only one-third of the votes that Weaver had won in 1880. The demand to inflate the currency was not dead. Indeed, within a decade the structure of American politics was turned upside down and inside out because of it. But the greenbacks were gone. Just as, after all the fuss and fury had died down, industrialists had their way on the tariff, banking interests got the money policy they wanted. When political parties are not built around principles and issues, the best organized interest groups within the parties usually prevail.

POLITICS IN THE CITY

By 1896, silver had replaced the greenbacks as the talisman of those Americans who wanted to inflate the nation's money supply. Both the Republican and Democratic parties were shaken by a fierce debate in which gold and silver became sacred symbols. The political atmosphere was religious, evangelical, even fanatical. "Gold bugs" and " free silverites" both believed they were engaged in a holy war against the other in which there could be no compromise, no quarter. The political equilibrium of the 1870s and 1880s was shattered, not

---

CITIZENSHIP

The New York machine naturalized newly arrived immigrants almost as soon as they stepped off the boat. The record day was October 14, 1868, when a Tweed judge swore in 2,109 new citizens, three a minute. One James Goff attested to the "good moral character" of 669 applicants. Two days layer, Goff was arrested for having stolen a gold watch and two diamond rings.

---

to mention the minor role issues had played in distinguishing the parties.

The Democratic party convention of 1896 was the most tumultuous since the party of Jefferson and Jackson destroyed itself at Charleston in 1860. Richard Croker, the leader of New York City's Democrats, was bewildered by the fury in which the members of his party were running about, arguing, shaking their fists. He listened to an agitated gold versus silver debate and impatiently shook his head. He could not understand what the fuss was about. As far as he was concerned, gold and silver were both money, and he was all for both kinds.

The Political Machine

Urban politics in the late nineteenth century resembled national politics in some ways. Issues were of secondary importance. What counted first was winning elections. The big city political party existed, like a business, for the benefit of those who "owned" it. The technique of

---

VOTE EARLY, VOTE OFTEN

Because voter-registration methods were quite lax in the nineteenth century, it was not difficult to march a group of men from one precinct house to the next, voting them in each one. When Tim Sullivan was a low-level worker in the New York machine, he used this system with his "repeaters"—unemployed men who voted "early and often" for the price of a day's wages or a day's drinking money:

When you've voted 'em with their whiskers on, you take 'em to a barber shop and scrape off the chin fringe. Then you vote 'em again with the side lilacs and a mustache. Then to a barber again, off comes the sides and you vote 'em the third time with the mustache. If that ain't enough and the box can stand a few more ballots, clean off the mustache and vote 'em plain face.

The emphasis was on the products and the processes for making them. The center of the fair was not the hallowed Declaration, but Machinery Hall, a structure that covered twenty acres and housed the latest inventions and technological improvements: from typewriters and the telephone through new kinds of looms and lathes and a dizzying variety of agricultural machines.

Towering above all the pulleys and belts, five times the height of a man, and weighing 8,500 tons, was the largest steam engine ever built, the giant Corliss. Hissing, rumbling, chugging, and gleaming in enamel, nickel plate, brass, and copper, the monster powered every other machine in the building. It was literally the heart of the exposition. It was to the giant Corliss that President Ulysses S. Grant came to open the fair. When he threw the switch that set Machinery Hall in motion, he wordlessly proclaimed that Americans were not just free and independent, but they were hitching their future to machines that made and moved things quickly, cheaply, and in astonishing quantities—industry!

A LAND MADE FOR INDUSTRY

Between 1865 and 1900, the population of the United States more than doubled from fewer than 36 million to 76 million people. The wealth of the American people grew even more rapidly than their numbers. At the end of the Civil War, the annual production of goods was valued at $2 billion. It increased more than six times in thirty-five years, to $13 billion in 1900.

Even in 1860, the United States had been the fourth largest industrial nation in the world with more than 100,000 factories capitalized at $1 billion. But before the Civil War there was no doubt that the United States was first and foremost a farmer's country. More than seven people in ten lived on farms or in small towns serving farmers. In 1860, scarcely more than a million people worked in industrial jobs. Because many of them were women and children who did not vote, factory workers were an inconsequential force in politics.

By 1876, change was everywhere. Railroads were so central to the national economy that a strike by railway workers the next year shook the country to its foundations. By 1900, $10 billion was invested in American factories, and five million people worked in industrial jobs. During the first years of the 1890s, the industrial production of the United States surpassed that of Great Britain to make the United States the world's premier industrial nation. Industrial workers, although still politically weak, were becoming a social force with which to reckon.

An Embarrassment of Riches

Viewed from the late twentieth century, this success story seems to have been as predestined as John Winthrop's reception in heaven. All the ingredients of industrial transformation were heaped upon the United States in an abundance that no other country has enjoyed.

In contrast to the plight of undeveloped countries today, Americans were rich in capital and able to welcome money from abroad without losing control of their own destinies. Once the Union victory in the Civil War assured foreign investors that American government was stable and friendly to commercial and industrial interests, the pounds, guilders, and francs poured in. By 1900, over $3.4 billion in foreign wealth fueled the American economy. Thanks to investors from abroad, Americans had to divert only 11 to 14 percent of their national income into industrial growth. This compares agreeably with 20 percent in Great Britain half a century earlier and in the Soviet Union some decades later. Because the cost of industrial development was so "cheap" in the United States, the experience of industrialization was far less painful in the New World than in the Old. Americans sacrificed less on behalf of the future than other industrial peoples have had to do.

The United States was also blessed in both the size and character of its labor force. The fecund and adaptable farm population provided a pool of literate and mechanically inclined people to fill the skilled jobs the new industry created. Unlike peasants of Asia and Europe who were attached to an ancestral plot of ground and often suspicious of unfamiliar ways, American farmers had always been quick to move on at opportunity's call. In the late nineteenth century, not only did the opportunity of the new industry beckon seductively, the labor-saving farm machinery that factories sent back to the farm made it possible for farm families actually to increase production of crops while their sons and daughters packed themselves off to the city.

During these same years, Europe's population underwent a spurt of growth with which the European economy could not keep pace. Cheap American food products undersold crops grown at home, helping to displace European peasants. They emigrated to the United States by the hundreds of thousands each year, filling low-paying, unskilled jobs. At every level in the process of industrialization, the United States was provided a plenitude of clever hands and strong backs.

A Land of Plenty

No country has been so blessed with such varied and abundant natural resources as has the United States: lush agricultural land producing cheap food; seemingly inexhaustible forests supplying lumber; rich deposits of gold, silver, semi-precious metals, and dross such as phosphates and gravel. Most important of all in the industrial age were huge stores of coal, iron, and petroleum.

The gray-green mountains of Pennsylvania, West Virginia, and Kentucky seemed to be made of coal, the indispensable fuel of the age of steam. In the Marquette range of Michigan was a mountain of iron ore 150 feet high. The Mesabi range of Minnesota, just west of the birdlike beak of Lake Superior, was opened in the 1890s to yield iron ore purer and in greater quantity than any other iron mining region in the world.

The United States had a huge, ready-made market for mass-produced goods in its constantly growing population. And with the growth of industry (and the political influence of the industrial capitalist class), government in the United States proved quick to respond to the needs of manufacturers.

"Yankee Ingenuity"

So were inventors. "As the Greek sculpted, as the Venetian painted," wrote an English visitor to the Centennial Exposition, "the American mechanizes." Actually, the new invention that turned the most heads at the great fair, the telephone, was the brainchild of a Scot who came to the United States via Canada, Alexander Graham Bell. Millions of people picked up the odd looking devices he had set up and, alternately amused and amazed, chatted with companions elsewhere in the room. Young men at the fair dropped a hint of what was to come by "ringing up" young ladies standing across from them, casually striking up conversations that, lacking proper introductions, would have been unacceptable face to face.

It was probably true that only in the United States could Bell have parlayed his idea into the gigantic enterprise it became, the American Telephone and Telegraph Company. As a writer in the *Saturday Evening Post* at the end of the century put it:

The United States is the only country in the world in which inventors form a distinct profession. . . . With us, inventors have grown into a large class. Laboratories . . . have sprung up almost everywhere, and today there is no great manufacturing concern that has not in its employ one or more men of whom nothing is expected except the bringing out of improvements in machinery and methods.

The Telephone

Bell was a teacher of the deaf who, while perfecting a mechanical hearing aid, realized that if he linked two of the devices by wire, he could transmit voice over distance. Unable to interest the communications giant Western Union in his telephone, he set up a pilot company in New York and the telephone seized the American imagination. Rutherford B. Hayes put a telephone in the White House in 1878. By 1880, only four years after they first heard of the thing, 50,000 Americans were paying monthly fees to hear it jangle on their walls. By 1890, there were 800,000 phones in the United

Young women quickly monopolized the profession of telephone operator when Bell's companies found "boys" to be imprudent and impolite.

States; by 1900, 1.5 million people in the tiniest hamlets knew all about "exchanges," "party lines," and bored, nasal-voiced "operators."

Many systems were useful only locally. But as early as 1892, eastern and midwestern cities were connected by a long-distance network, and rambunctious little western desert communities noted in their directories that "you can now talk to San Francisco with ease from our downtown office." Instantaneous communication was an invaluable aid to business and, important to some entrepreneurs, it left no written records of dubious transactions such as letters and telegrams did.

The Wizard of Menlo Park

Even more celebrated than Bell was Thomas Alva Edison. Written off by his boyhood teachers as a dunce, Edison was, in fact, befuddled throughout life by people who pursued knowledge for its own sake. He was the ultimate, practical American tinkerer who looked for a need—and an opportunity to make money from it—and went to work. Despite an obnoxious personality, Edison became a folk hero because he approached invention in a no-nonsense all-American way. He said that genius was 1 percent inspiration and 99 percent perspiration. He took pride in his work, not his thoughts. With a large corps of assistants sweating away in his research and development laboratory in Menlo Park, New Jersey, he took out more than a thousand patents between 1876 and 1900.

Most of these patents were for improvements in existing processes. (He perfected a transmitter for Bell.) However, a few of Edison's inventions were seedbeds for wholly new industries: the storage battery, the motion-picture projector, and the phonograph. The most important of his inventions was the incandescent light bulb, a means of converting electricity into stable, controllable light.

Electric Light

Edison solved the theoretical principle of the electric bulb—the 1 percent inspiration—almost immediately. Within a vacuum in a translucent glass ball an electrically charged filament or thread should burn (that is, glow) indefinitely. The perspiration part was discovering the fiber that would do the job. In 1879, after testing 6,000 materials, Edison came up with one that burned for 40 hours, enough to make it practical. Before he patented the incandescent light bulb early the next year, Edison improved the filament enough to make it work for 170 hours.

The financier, J. P. Morgan, who loathed the telephone—he glowered and shouted at it whenever he used it—was fascinated by Edison's invention. His house and

CLOUDED CRYSTAL BA[LL]

The fabulous success of Americans in explo[ring] nology can obscure the fact that technologi[cal] often faced massive resistance in selling the[ir] tions, and often themselves failed to unders[tand the] tential of what they had done.

This has been vividly true in the commu[nications] field. Thus, in 1845, the Postmaster Genera[l passed up an] opportunity to purchase the patent for the t[elegraph for] $100,000 because "under any rate of postag[e that could] be adopted, its revenues could [not] be mad[e to equal the] expenditures." Within a generation, a priva[te] company, Western Union, was one of the m[ost profita]ble giants of American business. In 1876, W[estern] Union's president, William Orton, turned d[own an op]portunity to buy Alexander Graham Bell's [patent,] saying "What use could this company make [of an elec]trical toy?"

In 1907, a businessman told radio pione[er Lee de] Forest that "all the radio . . . apparatus that [the country] will ever need" could be put in a single roo[m. In 1985] there were 500 million radio receivers in th[e United] States. If they were spread out evenly throu[ghout the] country, no person, even in the wilderness [of Alaska,] would be more than 233 feet from the chat[ter of a disc] jockey.

In 1926, De Forest himself said of televi[sion that] while it was theoretically and technically v[iable,] "commercially and financially I consider it [an impossi]bility, a development of which we need wa[ste little time] dreaming." As for the phonograph, its inve[ntor, Thomas] Edison said it was "not of any commercial [value." To]day—every day in the United States—Am[ericans buy] 50,000 TV sets (and throw out 20,000 old [ones). The] record industry manufactures 574,000 reco[rds] daily, 342,000 "singles," and imports anoth[er . . .] disks.

bank in New York were among the first [il]luminated structures in the United Stat[es. He re]alized that many people disliked gas, the p[rincipal source] of nighttime light. Although clean enou[gh (unlike ker]osene), gas could be dangerous. Hundre[ds of deaths were] caused when, in a moment of ignoranc[e, carelessness,] or drunkenness, people blew out the fl[ame instead of] turning off the gas. Hotel managers nerv[ously papered] the walls of rooms with reminders that [one did not "blow out"] gas.

The incandescent bulb succeeded as [had] the telephone. From a modest start in Ne[w York City] with about 80 customers, Edison's inve[ntion caught on so] quickly that by 1900, more than 3,000 t[owns and cities] were electrically illuminated. Within a few more years, gaslight virtually disappeared, and the kerosene lantern survived only on farms and in the poorer sections of the cities.

gold, silver, semi-precious metals, and dross such as phosphates and gravel. Most important of all in the industrial age were huge stores of coal, iron, and petroleum.

The gray-green mountains of Pennsylvania, West Virginia, and Kentucky seemed to be made of coal, the indispensable fuel of the age of steam. In the Marquette range of Michigan was a mountain of iron ore 150 feet high. The Mesabi range of Minnesota, just west of the birdlike beak of Lake Superior, was opened in the 1890s to yield iron ore purer and in greater quantity than any other iron mining region in the world.

The United States had a huge, ready-made market for mass-produced goods in its constantly growing population. And with the growth of industry (and the political influence of the industrial capitalist class), government in the United States proved quick to respond to the needs of manufacturers.

"Yankee Ingenuity"

So were inventors. "As the Greek sculpted, as the Venetian painted," wrote an English visitor to the Centennial Exposition, "the American mechanizes." Actually, the new invention that turned the most heads at the great fair, the telephone, was the brainchild of a Scot who came to the United States via Canada, Alexander Graham Bell. Millions of people picked up the odd looking devices he had set up and, alternately amused and amazed, chatted with companions elsewhere in the room. Young men at the fair dropped a hint of what was to come by "ringing up" young ladies standing across from them, casually striking up conversations that, lacking proper introductions, would have been unacceptable face to face.

It was probably true that only in the United States could Bell have parlayed his idea into the gigantic enterprise it became, the American Telephone and Telegraph Company. As a writer in the *Saturday Evening Post* at the end of the century put it:

The United States is the only country in the world in which inventors form a distinct profession. . . . With us, inventors have grown into a large class. Laboratories . . . have sprung up almost everywhere, and today there is no great manufacturing concern that has not in its employ one or more men of whom nothing is expected except the bringing out of improvements in machinery and methods.

The Telephone

Bell was a teacher of the deaf who, while perfecting a mechanical hearing aid, realized that if he linked two of the devices by wire, he could transmit voice over distance. Unable to interest the communications giant Western Union in his telephone, he set up a pilot company in New York and the telephone seized the American imagination. Rutherford B. Hayes put a telephone in the White House in 1878. By 1880, only four years after they first heard of the thing, 50,000 Americans were paying monthly fees to hear it jangle on their walls. By 1890, there were 800,000 phones in the United

Young women quickly monopolized the profession of telephone operator when Bell's companies found "boys" to be imprudent and impolite.

States; by 1900, 1.5 million people in the tiniest hamlets knew all about "exchanges," "party lines," and bored, nasal-voiced "operators."

Many systems were useful only locally. But as early as 1892, eastern and midwestern cities were connected by a long-distance network, and rambunctious little western desert communities noted in their directories that "you can now talk to San Francisco with ease from our downtown office." Instantaneous communication was an invaluable aid to business and, important to some entrepreneurs, it left no written records of dubious transactions such as letters and telegrams did.

The Wizard of Menlo Park

Even more celebrated than Bell was Thomas Alva Edison. Written off by his boyhood teachers as a dunce, Edison was, in fact, befuddled throughout life by people who pursued knowledge for its own sake. He was the ultimate, practical American tinkerer who looked for a need—and an opportunity to make money from it—and went to work. Despite an obnoxious personality, Edison became a folk hero because he approached invention in a no-nonsense all-American way. He said that genius was 1 percent inspiration and 99 percent perspiration. He took pride in his work, not his thoughts. With a large corps of assistants sweating away in his research and development laboratory in Menlo Park, New Jersey, he took out more than a thousand patents between 1876 and 1900.

Most of these patents were for improvements in existing processes. (He perfected a transmitter for Bell.) However, a few of Edison's inventions were seedbeds for wholly new industries: the storage battery, the motion-picture projector, and the phonograph. The most important of his inventions was the incandescent light bulb, a means of converting electricity into stable, controllable light.

Electric Light

Edison solved the theoretical principle of the electric bulb—the 1 percent inspiration—almost immediately. Within a vacuum in a translucent glass ball an electrically charged filament or thread should burn (that is, glow) indefinitely. The perspiration part was discovering the fiber that would do the job. In 1879, after testing 6,000 materials, Edison came up with one that burned for 40 hours, enough to make it practical. Before he patented the incandescent light bulb early the next year, Edison improved the filament enough to make it work for 170 hours.

The financier, J. P. Morgan, who loathed the telephone—he glowered and shouted at it whenever he used it—was fascinated by Edison's invention. His house and

---

CLOUDED CRYSTAL BALLS

The fabulous success of Americans in exploiting technology can obscure the fact that technological pioneers often faced massive resistance in selling their inventions, and often themselves failed to understand the potential of what they had done.

This has been vividly true in the communications field. Thus, in 1845, the Postmaster General rejected an opportunity to purchase the patent for the telegraph for $100,000 because "under any rate of postage that could be adopted, its revenues could [not] be made equal to its expenditures." Within a generation, a private telegraph company, Western Union, was one of the most profitable giants of American business. In 1876, Western Union's president, William Orton, turned down an opportunity to buy Alexander Graham Bell's telephone, saying "What use could this company make of an electrical toy?"

In 1907, a businessman told radio pioneer, Lee De Forest that "all the radio . . . apparatus that the country will ever need" could be put in a single room. In 1985 there were 500 million radio receivers in the United States. If they were spread out evenly throughout the country, no person, even in the wilderness of Alaska, would be more than 233 feet from the chatter of a disc jockey.

In 1926, De Forest himself said of television that while it was theoretically and technically workable, "commercially and financially I consider it an impossibility, a development of which we need waste little time dreaming." As for the phonograph, its inventor Thomas Edison said it was "not of any commercial value." Today—every day in the United States—Americans buy 50,000 TV sets (and throw out 20,000 old ones). The record industry manufactures 574,000 record albums daily, 342,000 "singles," and imports another 66,000 disks.

---

bank in New York were among the first electrically illuminated structures in the United States. Morgan realized that many people disliked gas, the principal source of nighttime light. Although clean enough (unlike kerosene), gas could be dangerous. Hundreds of fires were caused when, in a moment of ignorance, forgetfulness, or drunkenness, people blew out the flame instead of turning off the gas. Hotel managers nervously plastered the walls of rooms with reminders that the lights were gas.

The incandescent bulb succeeded as dramatically as the telephone. From a modest start in New York in 1882 with about 80 customers, Edison's invention spread so quickly that by 1900, more than 3,000 towns and cities were electrically illuminated. Within a few more years, gaslight virtually disappeared, and the kerosene lantern survived only on farms and in the poorer sections of the cities.

Young Thomas Edison, already America's most honored inventor.

utilizing massive natural sources of power at isolated places such as Niagara Falls.

Like Bell's telephone, Tesla's alternating current confronted the single significant impediment Americans faced in their drive toward massive industrial development. The very vastness of the country, while a treasure trove of resources, was also an obstacle to development. The United States spanned a continent that was dissected by rivers, mountains, and deserts into regions as large as the other industrial nations of the time. If geography had the last word, the United States would have remained a patchwork of distinct manufacturing regions in which small factories produced goods largely for the people of the vicinity alone. Indeed, this is a fair description of manufacturing in the United States through the period of the Civil War.

THE RAILROAD REVOLUTION

The steam railroad conquered America's awesome geography. The steam-powered locomotive, belching acrid smoke, its whistle piercing the air of city and wilderness, tied the country together on its "two streaks of rust and a right of way." Railroads made it possible for Pittsburgh steel makers to bring together the coal of Scranton and the iron of Michigan as if both minerals were found just across the county line. Thanks to the railroad, the great flour mills of Minneapolis could scoop up the cheap spring wheat of the distant Northwest, grind it into flour, and put their trademarked sacks into every cupboard in the country.

Because so many Western railroads found their way into Chicago, the Windy City quickly eclipsed river-based Cincinnati as "hog butcher to the world" and the nation's dresser of beef. Live-stock fattened on range-land a thousand miles away rolled bawling into Chicago in rickety railroad cars and then rolled out—packed in cans, barrels, and refrigerator cars—to the East Coast and from there around the world.

No single electric company dominated the industry in the way that American Telephone and Telegraph controlled Bell's patents. Nevertheless, like the railroads, the great regional companies were loosely associated by interlocking directorates and the influence of the investment banks. Edison, a worse businessman than scholar, saw most of his profit go to backers like Morgan. He ended his working life as an employee of mammoth General Electric, the corporate issue of his inventive genius.

The Problem of Bigness

George Westinghouse became a millionaire from his invention of the air brake for railroad trains. By equipping every car in a train with brakes, operated from a central point by pneumatic pressure, Westinghouse solved the problem of stopping long strings of railroad cars. Not only did his air brake save thousands of lives, but it led to bigger profits for railroads by making longer trains possible.

Once established, Westinghouse turned his attention to the development of alternating current electricity, which Edison had stubbornly resisted. Edison's direct current served very well over small areas, but it could not be transmitted over long distances. When Nikola Tesla, an immigrant from Croatia in the Austro-Hugarian empire, perfected a means to transmit alternating current, Westinghouse leapt ahead of Edison by fully

Inefficiency and Chaos

By 1865, the United States was already the world's premier railway country with about 35,000 miles of track. With a few exceptions, however, individual lines were short, serving only the hinterlands of the cities in which they terminated. In the former Confederacy, there were 400 railroad companies with an average track length of only 40 miles each. It was possible to ship a cargo between St. Louis and Atlanta by any of 20 routes. Competing for the business in cutthroat rate wars, not a single Southern line was financially secure.

NARROW GAUGE

The short, narrow-gauge feeder lines that snaked into canyons and around mountains to bring out ore or logs were not so colossal as the great trunk lines, but the engineering required to build them was often more demanding. For example, the California Western that brought redwood logs down to the port of Fort Bragg, California, was only 40 miles long but never ran in a straightaway for as much as a mile, crossed 115 bridges, and went through one tunnel 1,122 feet long.

Few lines actually linked up with one another. Goods to be shipped over long distances, and therefore on several lines, had to be unloaded (hand labor added to costs), carted across terminal towns by horse and wagon (another bottleneck), and reloaded onto another train. No two of the six railroads that ran into Richmond shared a depot. Before the Civil War, Chicago and New York were linked by rail on the map, but a cargo going the entire distance had to be unloaded and reloaded six times.

Early railroaders actually encouraged inefficiency in order to discourage takeovers by companies interested in consolidation. They deliberately built in odd gauges (the distance between rails) so that only their own locomotives and rolling stock could run on their tracks. As narrow as two feet apart in mountainous areas, the distance between rails ran to five feet in the South. Until 1880, the important Erie Railroad clung to a monstrous six-foot gauge. The Illinois Central, the nation's third largest railroad, employed two different gauges.

Lack of coordination among railroads presented shippers and passengers with another headache. Each railway company scheduled its trains according to the official time in its headquarters city. But local time varied even in cities just a few miles apart. When it was noon in Washington, D.C., it was 12:24 P.M. in Baltimore, 70 miles away (and 11:43 in Savannah, Georgia). The Baltimorean in Washington who tried to catch a 12:00 train home might discover that his watch was quite right for Baltimore, but that he was nearly half an hour too late to make the trip that day. In the train station in Buffalo, which served the New York Central and the Michigan Southern, three clocks were necessary: one for each railroad, and one for local time, which was different yet. In the Pittsburgh station there were six clocks. Traveling from Maine to California on the railroad, one passed through 20 "time zones." In fact, there were 80 such "zones" in the United States.

The Consolidators

Charles F. Dowd introduced the idea of four official time zones in 1870; his plan was enacted into law at the behest of the railroads in 1883. Long before that, men like J. Edgar Thomson of the Pennsylvania Railroad and Cornelius Vanderbilt of the New York Central labored outside the law, and often in conflict with it, to bring order out of the chaos of independently owned "short lines."

They secretly purchased stock in small railroad companies until they had control of them, then drove other competitors out of business by means of ruthless rate wars. They built the "Pennsy" and the New York Central ever westward from New York to Chicago and, thus, connections with lines that ran to the Pacific. All along

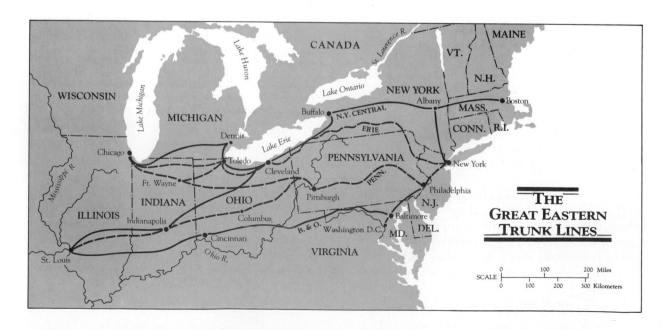

THE GREAT EASTERN TRUNK LINES

their "main lines," feeders tapped the surrounding country.

Thomson was all business, a no-nonsense efficiency expert with little celebrity outside railroad and government circles. Vanderbilt, who began his working life as a ferryman in New York City's crowded harbor, was colorful and often in the news. Ferrying was a rough business, no place for a milquetoast, and as a young man, the Commodore, as Vanderbilt styled himself (dressing in a mock naval uniform), fired more than one cannon at a competitor's harbor barge.

Vanderbilt gave up brawling as his shipping empire and responsibilities grew, but he was as tough and unscrupulous behind a broad oak desk as he had been at the tiller of a ferry. Once, when a reporter suggested that he had broken the law in a conflict with a rival, Vanderbilt snapped back gruffly, "What do I care about the law. Hain't I got the power?"

He had, and he used it masterfully to crush competition. By the time of the Civil War, Vanderbilt had a near-monopoly of New York harbor commerce. He even controlled the business that hauled New York City's monumental daily production of horse manure to farms in Staten Island. Vanderbilt's waterborne transportation empire led him naturally into moving the commerce of America's greatest city overland, too.

The Commodore was never quite respectable. His rough-and-tumble origins resonated in his speech. He was a friend of Victoria Woodhull and Tennessee Claflin, two eccentric sisters who preached free love. The mention of his name caused ladies and gentlemen of genteel New York society to shudder—for a while. Because he said out loud what other businessmen did quietly—that ethics and social responsibility did not always make good business—he was an easy target for moralists. Vanderbilt could not have cared less. Like many of the great capitalists of the era, he regarded his fortune—$100 million when he died—as adequate justification for what he did.

Pirates of the Rails

Compared to another breed of early railroader, men like Thomson and Vanderbilt can be justified very easily. In addition to making millions for themselves, they built transportation systems of inestimable social value. The Pennsy was famous for safe roadbeds in an age of frequent, horrendous railroad accidents. The New York Central pioneered the use of steel rails and was equipped with the life-saving Westinghouse air brake while other lines halted (or failed to halt) their trains mechanically. The Commodore's son and heir, William Vanderbilt was best known for saying "The public be damned!" but he also played a major part in standardizing the American gauge at the present 4 feet, 8 1/2 inches.

In contrast, some early railroaders simply took, making their fortunes by destroying what others had built. The most famous of these pirates were a trio that owned the Erie Railroad and actually succeeded in bilking Cornelius Vanderbilt. The senior member of the "Erie Gang" was Daniel Drew, a pious Methodist who knew much of the Bible by heart, but put a very liberal interpretation on the verse in Exodus that said, "Thou shalt not steal."

James Fisk, only 33 years old in 1867, was another sort altogether. No Bible for "Jubilee Jim"; he was a stout, jolly extrovert who fancied garish clothing, tossed silver dollars at street urchins, and caroused openly in New York's gaslit restaurants and cabarets with showgirls from the vaudeville stage who, at the time, were considered little better than prostitutes. (One of them, Josie Mansfield, was his undoing; in 1872, Fisk was murdered by another one of her suitors.)

A third, Jay Gould, was a man of the shadows. While Drew went to church and Fisk slapped on cologne, Gould slipped home to his respectable Victorian family. Furtive in appearance as in fact, tight-fisted, and close-mouthed, Gould was probably the brains of the Erie Ring. Certainly he lasted the longest, becoming almost respectable and marrying a daughter to a European nobleman. But when it came to making money, Gould was at one with his partners in the Erie Gang: the consequences of their piracy for others, let alone society, were quite beside the point.

The Erie War

In control of the Erie Railroad, the three men knew that Vanderbilt wanted their property and was secretly making large purchases of Erie stock. In order to separate him from as much of his fortune as possible, they watered Erie's stock; that is, they marketed shares in the dilapidated railroad far in excess of the Erie's real assets, from $24 million to $78 million in a few years when virtually nothing was done to improve the line. As Vanderbilt bought, they pocketed the money that should have gone into expanding the Erie's earning power.

WATERING STOCK

Daniel Drew was notorious for watering the stock in companies he owned. A popular story about him had it that he had started young. As a young drover, Drew would bring his cattle to the New York market, where he would pen them up with salt and no water. The next morning, before he sold them, he would drive them into a creek, where the groaning beasts bloated themselves. At market, they were fat, sleek, and largely phony.

The Commodore came to his senses and went to the judges, whom he regularly bribed, to indict the trio. Forewarned, Drew, Fisk, and Gould escaped to New Jersey, where they owned the judges. (It was said in the streets that they rowed across the Hudson River in a boat filled with bank notes.) A settlement was pieced together. In the meantime, the Erie amassed the worst accident record among world railroads and the company was devastated as a business. The Erie did not pay a dividend to its stockholders until the 1940s. For 70 years, what profits there were went to make up for the thievery of three men over six years.

THE TRANSCONTINENTAL LINES

In the Northeast and South, the creation of railroad systems was partly a matter of consolidating short lines that already existed. This movement peaked during the 1880s, when the names of 540 independent railway companies disappeared from the business registers. In the West, railroad lines were extensive, integrated transportation systems from the start. Beyond the Mississippi, creating railroad systems was a matter of construction from scratch.

Public Finance

The great transcontinental railroads were built and owned by private companies but (with one exception: James J. Hill's Great Northern) financed by the public. The sparsity of population between the Mississippi Valley and the western states of California and Oregon (and Washington after 1889) made it impossible to attract private investors. Railroad building was expensive. To lay a mile of track required bedding more than 3,000 ties in gravel and attaching 400 rails to them by driving 12,000 spikes. Having built that mile in Utah or Nevada at considerable expense, a railroader had nothing to look forward to but hundreds more miles of arid desert and uninhabited mountains.

With no customers along the way, there would be no profits and, without profits, no investors. The federal government had political and military interests in binding California and Oregon to the rest of the Union, and, in its land, the public domain, the government had the means with which to subsidize railroad construction.

The Pacific Railway Act of 1862 granted to two companies, the Union Pacific and the Central Pacific, a right-of-way of 200 feet wide between Omaha, Nebraska, and Sacramento, California. For each mile of track that the companies built, they were to receive, on either side of the tracks, ten alternate sections (square

miles) of the public domain. The result was a belt of land 40 miles wide, laid out like a checkerboard on which the U.P. and C.P. owned half the squares. (The rest was reserved for disposition under the Homestead Act or by direct government sale.)

The railroads sold their land, thus raising money for construction and creating customers. Or, just as important, they could use the vast real estate as collateral to borrow cash from banks. In addition, depending on the terrain, the government lent the two companies between $16,000 and $48,000 per mile of track at bargain interest rates.

The Romance of the Rails

As in the consolidation of eastern trunk lines, the business operations of the transcontinentals was sometimes a wee bit shady—as in the case of the Crédit Mobilier. However, the actual construction of the line was a heroic and glorious feat. The Union Pacific, employing thousands of Civil War veterans and newly immigrated Irish pick-and-shovel men, the "Paddies," laid over a thousand miles of track. The workers lived in shifting cities of tents and freight cars built like dormitories. They toiled by day, and bickered and brawled with gamblers, saloon keepers, and whores by night. Until the company realized that it was more efficient to hire professional gunmen as guards, the workers kept firearms with their tools in order to fight off those Indians who may have sensed that the iron horse meant the end of their way of life.

The builders of the Central Pacific had no trouble with Indians, but a great deal with terrain. Just outside Sacramento rose the majestic Sierra Nevada. There were passes in the mountains through which the line could snake, but they were narrow and steep. Under the direction of a resourceful engineer, Theodore D. Judah, 10,000 Chinese chipped ledges into the slopes, built roadbeds of rubble in deep canyons, and bolted together trestles of timbers two feet square. They were paid $26 to $36 a month and, as they had worked in the gold mines, operated in crews of twelve to twenty, each group having its own cook.

The snows of the Sierra proved to be a difficult problem, not only for the builders but for the eventual operation of the line. To solve it, the workers constructed snowsheds miles long. In effect, the transcontinental railroad crossed part of the Sierra Nevada indoors. Once on the Nevada plateau, the experienced C.P. crews built at a rate of a mile a day for an entire year.

The U.P. and C.P. joined at Promontory Point, Utah, on May 10, 1869. The final days were hectic. Because the total mileage that each company constructed deter-

Ten thousand immigrant Chinese laborers built the Central Pacific Railway across the West. Here workers complete the Secrettown Trestle in the Sierra Nevada.

mined the extent of its land grants, the two companies raced around the clock. The record was set by the crews of the Central Pacific. They built 10.6 miles of more-or-less functional railroad in one day (just about the same length of track the company laid down during the whole of 1864). That involved bedding 31,000 ties, and connecting 4,037 iron rails to them with 120,000 spikes!

Railroad Mania

Seeing that the owners of the U.P. and C.P. had become instant millionaires, other ambitious men descended on Washington in search of subsidies. In the euphoria of the times, Congress in 1864 was doubly generous to the Northern Pacific, which planned to build from Lake Superior to Puget Sound. In the territories, the N.P. received 40 alternate sections of land for every mile of railway built! The Atchison, Topeka, and Santa Fe ran

from Kansas to Los Angeles. The Texas Pacific and Southern Pacific linked New Orleans and San Francisco at El Paso, Texas (Jefferson Davis's route in the days before the Kansas-Nebraska Act). In 1884, the Canadians (who were even more generous with government land) completed the first of their two transcontinental lines, the Canadian Pacific. Never before had there been such an expenditure of effort and wealth to accomplish the same purpose in so short a time.

The costs were considerable. The federal government gave the land-grant railroads a total of 131 million acres. To this, the state governments added 45 million acres. Totaled up, an area larger than France and Belgium was given to a handful of capitalists. In addition, towns along the proposed routes enticed the builders to choose them as sites for depots by offering town lots, cash bounties, and exemption from taxes.

These gifts were not always offered with a glad hand.

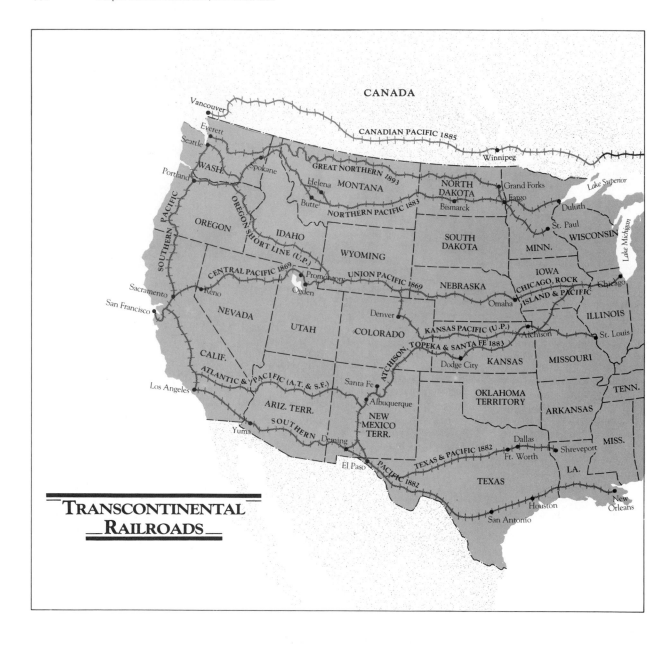

TRANSCONTINENTAL
RAILROADS

The town fathers knew that if a railroad bypassed a town, the town might die, taking their fortunes and status with it. Aware of this, railroaders did not hesitate to set communities against one another like roosters in a cock fight. The Atchison, Topeka, and Santa Fe, popularly known as "the Santa Fe," did not originally enter the city of that name. Nearby Albuquerque offered the better deal and got the major depot.

The Panic of 1873

Western railroaders made money by building railroads with public and borrowed money, not by actually operating them. As a result, they built too much railroad too soon. When the time came to pay the high operating costs and to pay off loans out of fees paid by shippers and passengers, many of the new companies found that there were just not enough customers to go around. In 1872, only one railroad in three made a profit.

On September 18, 1873, a Friday, the chickens came home to roost. Jay Cooke and Company, a bank that had loaned heavily to western railroads, including the richly endowed Northern Pacific, announced that the firm was bankrupt. Jay Cooke and Company was not an ordinary bank. It was the most prestigious house of finance in the United States, the government's chief agent during the Civil War. Its failure caused a panic: speculators rushed to sell their stocks and the market

LAND FOR SALE

In order to promote land that it owned in Nebraska, the Burlington and Missouri River Railroad offered a number of come-ons. A would-be purchaser had to pay his own fare to go out to look at the land, but the railroad would refund his fare if he bought. Once a landowner, he would receive a free railroad pass, as well as "long credit, low interest, and a twenty percent rebate for improvements." Prices were not extravagant. The Union Pacific disposed of pretty good Nebraska land at $3 to $5 an acre.

their gates, workers lost their jobs, the shops they frequented went broke.

THE ORGANIZERS

In a free, unregulated economy, the cycle of boom and bust was inevitable and, since the age of Jackson, Americans as a people had been committed to the ideal of a free and unregulated economy. They believed that their country's peculiar virtue lay in the fact that competition

crashed. By the end of 1873, 5,000 businesses had declared bankruptcy and a half million workers were jobless. The depression of the 1870s was the worst in American history up to that time.

It would not be the last. A by-product of fabulous economic growth was a wildly erratic "business cycle." For a time the industrial capitalist economy boomed, luring investment and speculation, encouraging expansion and production. Sooner or later, the capacity of railroads to carry freight and factories to produce goods outpaced the capacity of the market to absorb their services and products. When that happened, banks closed, investments and savings were wiped out, factories locked

BUILDING THE RAILROADS

Track-laying is a science. A light car, drawn by a single horse, gallops up to the front with its load of rails. Two men seize the end of a rail and start forward, the rest of the gang taking hold by twos. They come forward at a run. At a word of command the rail is dropped in its place, less than thirty seconds to a rail for each gang, and so four rails go down to the minute. Close behind come the gangers, spikers, and a lovely time they make of it.

William Bell

LAND GRANTS TO RAILROADS

ONE-HALF OF ALL LAND IN AN 80-MILE-WIDE AREA WAS GRANTED TO **NORTHERN PACIFIC**

NOTABLE PEOPLE

THE FIELD BROTHERS

The economic explosion of the late nineteenth century created opportunities from the bottom to the top of American society. Immigrants who had flirted with starvation in the old country found subsistence and comfort. Ordinary Americans moved up into the middle class as skilled workers, managers, and small businessmen. Scions of the old elite, of comfortably fixed, educated, and genteel families who would have been content to have been local eminences in the early nineteenth century found that, in the new America, they had a vast, national arena in which to make their marks.

The Field family of Connecticut is a case in point. Of *Mayflower* vintage, the Fields had produced generation upon generation of farmers, Congregationalist ministers, merchants, and local political leaders. The family was ancient and respectable, but quite unknown beyond its township. Opportunity for the Reverend David Field, born in 1781, meant a midlife exchange of a pulpit in tiny Haddam, Connecticut, for one in Stockbridge, Massachusetts, a scarcely larger town. Four of his six sons, by way of contrast, became national figures in the law, business, technology, and popular culture.

The eldest of them, David Dudley Field (1805–94), was America's foremost legal reformer. As a lawyer in New York, he observed that the century-old tangle of ordinances that had worked well enough in a small commercial city were inadequate in a burgeoning metropolis and commercial empire. He labored, much of the time drawing on his own resources, to sift, reform, and codify city and state law. Late in his life, he turned to international law, particularly rules governing the conduct of nations during wartime.

New York State adopted David Dudley Field's codification of criminal law in 1881, but not the reforms of the civil code which he proposed. By the 1880s, his influence had been somewhat tarnished by his political and business associations. Field had defended "Boss" William Marcy Tweed, the head of the corrupt political machine that governed New York City during the 1860s, as well as the notorious robber barons Jim Fisk and Jay Gould. However, many of his proposals were incorporated into the English Judicature Acts of 1873–75, which later spread to British colonies throughout the world.

David Dudley Field had the curious experience of arguing cases before the Supreme Court when his younger brother was an associate justice. Stephen Johnson Field (1816–99), also an attorney, was a Forty-Niner, rushing off to California in search of gold or, perhaps, litigants. He settled in the boomtown of Marysville, was elected

mayor and, in 1857, was named Justice of the California Supreme Court in 1857. Stephen Field was a Democrat but also a staunch supporter of the Civil War. In 1863, Abraham Lincoln named him to the U. S. Supreme Court.

On the high court, he proved to be conservative in cases involving business, but also a defender of civil liberties. Indeed, his insistence on defending the rights of Chinese immigrants in California may have cost him further advancement in public life. He was several times considered as a favorite-son candidate for the presidency, but was denied the prize because he had offended white workingmen with his "pro-Chinese" judicial decisions.

Cyrus Field (1819–92) was a technological visionary of extraordinary persistence. A successful paper manufacturer before he was 30, in 1854 he turned to promoting the idea of a cable between Europe and North America over which telegraphic messages could be sent. Such a device would obviously be of inestimable value to business, but the difficulties of laying such a cable seemed overwhelming. Indeed, Field's first attempt at laying a cable between Ireland and Newfoundland in 1857 broke and a second, in 1858, lasted just three weeks.

In 1865, Cyrus Field tried again, this time using the largest ship in the world, the British-built *Great Eastern*. Almost 700 feet long and 120 feet across, the "great iron ship" was an engineering marvel that was never used properly. Able to power itself by sail, paddle wheel, or screw, it could carry 4,000 passengers and 2,000 crew. Instead of exploiting its size in long voyages, such as between Britain and Australia, the *Great Eastern's* owners put it on the Atlantic run, where it did not compete well with smaller ships. Repeatedly, its owners went bankrupt.

Cyrus Field saw the *Great Eastern* as a massive cable factory with enough power to run all the mills of Manchester. He outfitted the ship to reel out the continuous, fragile wire that would tie together Old World and New. In 1865, he lost a cable once again but, on July 27, 1866, the connection was made. Despite his achievement, Cyrus Field did not die wealthy. A bit too trusting of his business associates, including Jay Gould, he saw his fortune evaporate by the time of his death.

The youngest Field brother, Henry Martyn Field (1822–1907), was a Presbyterian minister who wrote adulatory biographies of David Dudley and Cyrus (but not, oddly, Stephen). However, he too made his mark as a communicator. During the 1890s, with the American middle class large, energetic, and curious, he wrote bestselling travel books for vicarious sojourners.

A construction crew in the Montana Territory in 1887 is shown laying track for the Manitoba Railway, which ran between Seattle, Washington, and St. Paul, Minnesota.

STEEL AT ONE CENT A POUND

Just as John D. Rockefeller liked to point out that kerosene was cheaper after Standard Oil came to monopolize the refining industry, Andrew Carnegie had a neat justification of his organization of the steel industry:

> *Two pounds of ironstone mined upon Lake Superior and transported nine hundred miles to Pittsburgh; one pound and one half of coal, mined and manufactured into coke, and transported to Pittsburgh; a small amount of manganese ore mined in Virginia and brought to Pittsburgh—and these four pounds of materials manufactured into one pound of steel, for which the customer pays one cent.*

Produced in quantity, steel could be used in buildings, bridges, and, of particular interest in the late nineteenth century, superior rails for trains. Until the mid-nineteenth century, however, the costs involved in producing this "super-iron" were so great that steel was used mostly in small, expensive items: knives and other blades, precision instruments, bearings for machinery, and the like.

By the time of the Civil War, working independently

Andrew Carnegie, steel manufacturer and master of vertical integration.

was open to anyone having the will and wherewithal to have a go at it.

Once a businessman reached the top of the economic pyramid, however, he was apt to become disenchanted with the competitive ideal. To the entrepreneur who was no longer scrambling but in charge of a commercial or industrial empire valued at millions of dollars and employing thousands of people, free-wheeling competitors threatened stability and order, like so many yapping dogs at his heels.

In the late-nineteenth century, Andrew Carnegie in steel, John D. Rockefeller in oil, and other canny businessmen devoted their careers to minimizing the threat of competition. Carnegie organized his company so efficiently that he could determine the price structure of the entire steel industry without regard to what other steel makers did. Rockefeller destroyed his competitors by fair means and foul, and simply gobbled them up.

Steel: The Bones of the Economy

Steel is the element iron after carbon and other "impurities" have been burned out at high temperatures. Engineers were well aware of its potential in construction. Steel is much stronger than iron per unit of weight.

of each other, two ironmakers, Henry Bessemer of England and William Kelly of Pennsylvania and Kentucky, developed a method by which steel could be made in quantity at a reasonable price. No one grasped the significance of their discovery more quickly than Andrew Carnegie, an immigrant from Scotland who, beginning as a telegrapher, became a high-ranking executive of the Pennsylvania Railroad. Already a rich man by the end of the Civil War as a result of speculations in oil and the manufacture of iron bridges (his company built the first span across the Mississippi), he decided to sell everything and concentrate on steel, "putting all his eggs in one basket, and then watching that basket." In 1873, he began construction of a huge Bessemer plant in Braddock, Pennsylvania, outside Pittsburgh.

A Head for Business

Carnegie knew apples as well as eggs—how to polish them. He named his factory after J. Edgar Thomson, the president of the Pennsy, which would be a major customer of Carnegie Steel. But Carnegie also knew to locate the great works outside of Pittsburgh, which was served by the Pennsylvania Railroad alone. In Braddock, Carnegie could play several railroads against one another, winning the most favorable shipping rates. Nor was it luck that Carnegie built his mill during the depression of 1873. For the next 25 years, he took advantage of hard times, when the price of everything was down, to expand his factories, scrap old methods, and introduce new technology.

Carnegie also prided himself on spotting talent, putting it to work for him, and rewarding it. Charles Schwab, later the president of United States Steel and the founder of Bethlehem Steel, was an engineer's helper at Carnegie Steel whom Carnegie promoted and made a partner.

"Vertical Integration"

Carnegie's major contribution to business organization was his exploitation of the principle of "vertical integration." That is, in order to get a leg up on his competitors, he expanded his operation from a base of steel manufacture to include ownership of the raw materials from which steel was made and the means of assembling those raw materials at the factory. For example, Bessemer furnaces were fueled by coke, which is to coal what charcoal is to wood—a hotter-burning distillation of the mineral. Rather than buy coke from independent operators, Carnegie absorbed the 5,000 acres of coalfields and 1,000 coke ovens owned by Henry Clay Frick, who became a junior partner in Carnegie Steel. Carnegie and Frick then added iron mines to their holdings.

While never completely independent of trunk-line railroads, Carnegie controlled as much of his own shipping as he could. He owned barges that carried iron ore from Michigan and the Mesabi to his own port facilities in Erie, Pennsylvania. He owned a shortline railroad that brought the ore from Erie to Homestead. By eliminating from his final product price the profits of independent suppliers, distributors, and carriers, Carnegie was able to undersell competing companies that were not vertically integrated and, therefore, had to include the profits of independent suppliers in their final product price.

Vertical integration served Andrew Carnegie very well. His personal income rose to $40 million a year in 1900. He lived much of the time in a castle in Scotland not far from where his father had worked as a weaver. His company steadily assumed a more dominant role in the steel business. In 1870 there were 167 iron and steel firms around Pittsburgh. By the end of the century there were 47.

In 1901, 66 years old and bored with business, Carnegie threatened to combine most of these into a behemoth that would threaten companies organized by the banker J. P. Morgan with an all-out price war. Morgan was persuaded to buy Carnegie out for $500 million, the largest personal commercial transaction ever made. Morgan then created the first billion dollar corporation, United States Steel. It consisted of 213 steel mills, 41 iron mines, 112 ore barges, 57,000 acres of coalfields, and 1,000 miles of railroad.

The Corporation

Carnegie was progressive in many ways, always open to the new. But he organized his company as a partnership, disdaining the business structure that was the chief means of consolidation in the late nineteenth century, the corporation. Corporate structure—selling small "shares" in a company on the open market—was advantageous to both investors and business organizers. Widely dispersed ownership meant widely dispersed risk. The investor who owned some shares in a number of companies did not lose everything if one of those companies failed. American law also provided investors with the privilege of "limited liability." That is, the corporation's legal liability was limited to the assets of the corporation, and did not extend to the assets of shareholders. (If an individually owned business or partnership went bust, creditors could seize the other assets of the owners, including home and personal property.)

These inducements made it possible for entrepreneurs to raise the huge amounts of capital needed to finance expensive industrial enterprises. However, by reserving controlling interest to themselves, they did not have to share decision making with small investors. Abuses were common enough. Pirates like the Erie Ring could drain

A ladle used in a nineteenth-century steel mill dwarfs the men standing nearby.

a corporation of its assets, enrich themselves personally through their control of corporate policy, allow the company to go under, and walk away with their ill-gotten personal fortunes.

New Uses for Equal Rights

The Fourteenth Amendment to the Constitution, designed to secure equality under the law to all citizens, proved to be more valuable to corporations than to the black former slaves for which it was written. After dodging the question for several years, the Supreme Court ruled in *Santa Clara County v. the Southern Pacific Railroad* (1886) that a corporation was a "person" under the meaning of the Fourteenth Amendment. The states were forbidden to pass laws that applied specifically to corporations and not to flesh-and-blood persons because such laws denied corporate persons civil equality.

However, while corporations enjoyed the civil rights of citizens who walked and talked, it was difficult to exact the same responsibilities of it. Men and women could be sent to jail for violating the law. Corporations could not.

John D. Rockefeller

While thousands of businessmen organized corporations, they all fade from sight in the shadow of the solemn, muscular, well-dressed, and deeply religious person of John Davison Rockefeller. Beginning his career as an accountant, Rockefeller avoided service in the Civil War by hiring a substitute. He made a small fortune selling provisions to the Union Army, but a small fortune was only an appetizer. Rockefeller had a voracious appetite for riches. Outside of home and Sunday school,

which he taught, he talked of little but business. After swinging a lucrative deal as a young man, he danced a two-step jig and exclaimed "Bound to be rich! I'm bound to be rich!"

Rockefeller disapproved of smoking and drinking, in part because of his Baptist faith, but in part because cigars and whiskey cost money that could be invested to make more money. He carefully recorded how he spent every dime; he spent few frivolously. He would remove his stovepipe hat and bend down to pick up a penny. John D. Rockefeller would have succeeded no matter what his business. The one he chose proved to be as basic to modern society as steel.

Black Gold

Crude oil has been seeping to the surface of the earth since before there were human beings to step into it and growl. It is mentioned in a Mesopotamian cuneiform tablet. Europeans used it as a lubricant. The Seneca Indians of western Pennsylvania ate it as a laxative. That classical American huckster, the snake-oil salesman, bottled the stuff, flavoring "Seneca Oil" with sugar and spices and tossing in a healthy shot of alcohol, thence claiming it cured everything from "female weakness" to rainy days. The farmers who lived around Titusville in

John D. Rockefeller, builder of Standard Oil, philanthropist.

INC. AND LTD.

In the United States, a limited liability corporation is distinguished by the word "Corporation" in its name or the abbreviation "Inc.," meaning "incorporated." In Great Britain, the comparable designation is "Ltd.," meaning "limited."

western Pennsylvania were more likely to hate the gunk. It fouled the soil, polluted streams, and, if it caught fire, it filled the air with billows of noxious smoke.

In 1855, an organic chemist, Benjamin Silliman, discovered that one of the components into which crude oil could be broken down was kerosene, a liquid that could be safely burned to heat a house or cookstove, or illuminate the night. It was a timely discovery. In the 1850s, overharvesting had desolated the world's population of whales. Whale oil, used to illuminate middle and upper-class homes—the poor used candles or went to bed—had soared in price. Kerosene was cheap; even the poor could afford it. In 1859, seeing the opportunity, a former army officer named Edwin Drake went to Titusville, Pennsylvania and devised a drill and pump system by which crude oil could be extracted in commercial quantities.

The Pennsylvania oil rush that followed was as wild as the gold rush of 1849. Drilling for oil, like panning for gold, required only modest capital, so thousands of men dreaming of instant riches descended on the "oil fields" of western Pennsylvania. John D. Rockefeller, living in nearby Cleveland, Ohio, came and looked. But he did not like what he saw, neither the social disorder and moral laxity, nor the fact that the independent drillers, competing fiercely to stay afloat, repeatedly declared price wars on one another, slashing the price at which they sold their black gold to refiners. A few drillers got rich; many more went broke. It was not Rockfeller's kind of business.

"Horizontal Integration"

Oil refining was a fragmented business too; there were 250 companies engaged in it as late as 1870. However, operating a refinery called for rather more capital than sinking a drill-bit into the ground and saying a prayer. Rockefeller recognized that, unlike drilling, which would always attract "wildcatters" who might get lucky, hit a gusher, and become a major competitor overnight, the refining end of the business was manageable. It was a kind of "narrows" on the river of oil that flowed from well to consumers. Like the robber barons of medieval Europe who built castles at narrow places on the Rhine and Danube, thence deciding which boat might pass and

which might not, the company that controled the narrows of oil business—refining—would be able to determine production and prices. It did not matter how many wild-eyed visionaries roamed the countryside with a drilling rig. If there was one refiner, they would sell their crude at the price the refiner was willing to pay.

Controlling an entire industry by controling a key phase of its process is known as horizontal integration. Instead of setting the standards for an industry by integrating a portion of the business from top to bottom, from source of raw materials to market (as Carnegie did in steel), horizontal integration meant establishing an effective monopoly across the industry.

This is what Rockefeller and his associates—his brother William, Samuel Andrews, and Maurice Clark—accomplished. In 1870, their Standard Oil Company of Ohio refined 3 or 4 percent of the nation's oil. Within twenty years, Standard Oil controlled 90 percent of American refining capacity. They worked this magic by persuading strong and cooperative competitors to throw in with them, and by driving weak and uncooperative refiners out of the business.

Rebates

Rockefeller ground some refineries down by attacking them in cutthroat rate wars. With generally superior facilities, Standard Oil was able to take losses over the short term that less efficient competitors could not bear. On one occasion, Rockefeller bought up every barrel stave and hoop in the oil region. Competitors could not ship their products for lack of containers. On another, a private army of 250 Standard Oil men forcefully prevented a refining company from building a pipeline to New York City.

Much more effective was the "draw-back" or "rebate." Because Standard Oil could promise railroads a fixed, large amount of oil to carry east each day, Rockefeller demanded of them and got a refund of part of their published rate list—under the table. With smaller competitors paying the published rates, Rockefeller had a huge advantage when it was time to sell. For a short period, Rockefeller got a rebate from the Erie Railroad for each carload of kerosene his competitors shipped! This was his price to the Erie for continuing to use the line himself. The rebate was particularly effective in fighting the refiners of Pittsburgh, who were served by only one railroad which, therefore, did not have to bargain.

The Standard Oil Trust

In order to win these wars, Rockefeller had to occupy a commanding position in the refining industry. At the beginning of the consolidation, however, he and his associates lacked the vast capital resources that would have been necessary to buy out other large producers. The solution, designed by Rockefeller's lawyers, Samuel C. T. Dodd and John Newlon Camden, was to adapt the ancient legal device of the trust to the running of a business.

Traditionally, the trust was the means by which the property of a minor or an incompetent was managed on his or her behalf. That property was put into the care of a trustee whose obligation was to see to it that the property was well-administered. Rockefeller, Andrews, and Clark, and Henry Flagler explained to their major competitors that if they surrendered control of their refineries to the Standard Oil Trust, for which they would receive trust certificates, they would be spared the duties of management and the risks of competition while, because the trustees would coordinate the use of the combined facilities, their income would soar. The wiser refiners saw the point and agreed (and became very wealthy).

Rockefeller, once in control of a near monopoly, was able to mop up those refiners who held out and to calculate precisely how much oil the market could absorb, how much, therefore, to produce, and at what price to sell.

The goal of the trust was not to drive prices up to extortionate levels. Rockefeller enjoyed telling hostile interrogators that with each step toward monopoly, Standard had reduced the retail price of a gallon of kerosene. The goal of the trust, he said, was economic order, not rapacious profiteering.

Rockefeller had no apologies for what he did. He remained a scathing critic of the gospel of competition to the end of his days. However, the fact that a handful of men could dictate the doings of an entire, vital industry—Standard Oil was run by only nine trustees—aroused a storm of fear and resentment in the land.

For Further Reading

For overviews of American economic development, see the following books: Elliott Brownlee, *Dynamics of Ascent: A History of the American Economy* (1974); Thomas C. Cochran and William Miller, *The Age of Enterprise* (1942); Vincent P. DeSantis, *The Shaping of Modern America, 1877–1916* (1973); John A. Garraty, *The New Commonwealth, 1877–1890* (1968); Samuel P. Hays, *The Response to Industrialism, 1885–1914* (1957); Robert Higgs, *The Transformation of the American Economy* (1971); Matthew Josephson, *The Robber Barons* (1934); Glenn Porter, *The Rise of Big Business, 1860–1910* (1973); Robert H. Wiebe, *The Search for Order* (1967).

Valuable special studies include Roger Burlingame, *Engines and Democracy: Inventions and Society in Mature America* (1940); A. F. Chandler, *The Visible Hand: The Managerial Revolution in American Business* (1977); Thomas C. Cochran, *Railroad Leaders, 1845–1890* (1953); Robert W. Fogel, *Railroads and American Eco-*

nomic Growth (1964); Edward C. Kirkland, *Dream and Thought in the Business Community, 1860–1900* (1956) and *Men, Cities, and Transportation* (1948); Gabriel Kolko, *Railroads and Regulation* (1965); James McCague, *Moguls and Iron Men* (1964); Elting E. Morison, *From Know-How to Nowhere: The Development of American Technology* (1974); Walter T. K. Nugent, *Money and American Society, 1865–1880* (1968); George R. Taylor and R. D. Neu, *The American Railroad Network, 1861–1900* (1956).

One of the finest recent biographies is Robert V. Bruce, *Alexander Graham Bell and the Conquest of Solitude* (1973). For other personages mentioned in this chapter see Matthew Josephson, *Edison* (1959); Harold C. Livesay, *Andrew Carnegie and the Rise of Big Business* (1975); Allan Nevins, *A Study in Power: John D. Rockefeller* (1953); and J. F. Wall, *Andrew Carnegie* (1971).

Wealthy New Yorkers celebrate their prosperity with crowns of laurel at an elegant dinner.

LIVING WITH LEVIATHAN

REACTIONS TO BIG BUSINESS AND GREAT WEALTH

In *Democracy in America*, written more than twenty years before the Civil War, Alexis de Tocqueville

admired the broad distribution of wealth in the United States. Except for slaves, few Americans

seemed to be so poor that they could not hope to improve their lot. At the same time, few were so

rich that they had coalesced into an aristocracy, a distinct social class permanently ensconced above

the mass of the population.

Today, it is clear that Jacksonian America did not apportion its wealth so equitably as Tocqueville believed. Nevertheless, the gap between dirt poor and filthy rich was not nearly so yawning as it was to become. By the late nineteenth century, industrialization and the growth of big business created a class of multimillionaires whose fortunes were so great that it was absurd to imagine them slipping into the anonymous masses. Cornelius Vanderbilt amassed $100 million in his lifetime. His son, William, doubled that to $200 million in a few years. By 1900, Andrew Carnegie was able to pocket $480 million in a single transaction. John D. Rockefeller gave away such a sum within a few years. He could afford it. In 1892, his wealth totaled $815,647,796.89.

To many observers, the industrial and financial aristocracy's control of technology, transportation, industry, and money seemed to mock the American dream of equality of opportunity. How could an ordinary fellow succeed against such entrenched power and privilege? Social critics railed at the new elite. Substantial social movements protested the new inequities. But, in the end, Americans came to terms with a society that was both richer and poorer than the one which Alexis de Tocqueville had measured.

REGULATING THE RAILROADS AND TRUSTS

Railroads attracted a few critics as soon as they made their appearance in the United States. Poets and philosophers looked on "the machine in the garden" as a defilement of nature. Here and there, city dwellers banded together to fight plans to run tracks down the streets on which they lived and shopped, literally endangering lives.

But such nay-sayers were few. Most Americans welcomed the iron horse at first, especially those people who lived in isolated rural areas. To them, the railroad offered the possibility of shipping their produce to market, thereby earning money with which to escape a life of mere subsistence.

A Short Honeymoon

Even in the countryside, however, the honeymoon between railroad and farmer was brief. As an officer of the Illinois Central put it, "the people are in favor of building a new road and do what they can to promote it. After it is once built and fixed, then the policy of the people is usually in opposition." Ordinary people were infuriated that pirates like Drew, Fisk, and Gould made money only to the extent that they abused the railroad as a means of transportation. Western townsfolk discovered that the railway barons' arrogance did not end with their

demands for free sites for depots. Along the transcontinental lines, virtually every important piece of business had to be "cleared" with the local railway manager. Farmers learned that the railroads were less their servants, carting their produce to market, than the masters of their fate.

California's "Big Four"—Collis P. Huntington, Leland Stanford, Mark Hopkins, and Charles Crocker—it was said, "owned" the state, thanks to their control of the Southern Pacific Railroad, which absorbed the Central Pacific. In addition to its stranglehold on transportation, the S.P. was, next to the federal government, California's biggest landowner. Indeed, instead of disposing of its land grant cheaply, as the transcontinental lines did, the S.P. held tight to its holdings in California's fertile central valley, driving the price of an acre up ten times or more than the $3 to $5 charged elsewhere in the West.

By the end of the century, the S.P. actually used its tremendous leverage to drive small farmers and ranchers out of business. The line's political officer, William F. Herrin, was widely considered to be the boss of the state legislature, monitoring every law that was passed in the interests of the S.P. Novelist Frank Norris summed up the Southern Pacific for many Californians in the title of his novel, *The Octopus* (1901), its tentacles reaching into every corner of the Golden State.

The Farmer's Grievances

The farmers of the Mississippi Valley also discovered that the railroad did not necessarily usher in a golden age. A big problem, as they saw it, was monopoly. In most areas, one line handled all the traffic. Consequently, the rates at which farmers shipped their wheat, corn, or livestock to markets in the East were at the mercy of the shippers. Too often for goodwill to prevail, farmers saw their margin of profit consumed by transportation costs.

Most infuriating was the railroads' control of storage facilities, the grain elevators that stood close to the depot in every railway town. The farmer had to pay the company storage fees until the railroad sent a train to haul away his grain. Obviously, it was often to the railroad's interests to delay scheduling shipment as long as possible. The company alone determined how long a farmer had to store his produce and, therefore, how large his fee was. In just a few months, a railroad could gobble up a year's income.

Attempts to Regulate

In the early 1870s, an organization of farmers, the Patrons of Husbandry (or Grangers, as members were called) won control of the state legislature of Illinois

Gift for the Grangers, *a lithograph made in 1873*
celebrates the Patrons of Husbandry, a farmers'
organization.

and considerable influence in adjoining states. Allied with small-business men, who also felt squeezed by railroads, they passed a series of "Granger laws" that set maximum rates that railroad companies could charge both for hauling and storing. Several other state governments followed Illinois's lead.

The railroad barons launched a legal counterattack, hiring high-powered corporation lawyers like Richard B. Olney and Roscoe Conkling to challenge state regulatory legislation before the Supreme Court. At first, the Grangers prevailed. In the case of *Munn v. Illinois* (1877), a Supreme Court dominated by old-fashioned Lincoln Republicans declared that when a private company's business affected the public interest, the public had the right to regulate that business for the common good.

Nine years later, the times and the personnel of the Supreme Court had changed. In 1886, justices on cordial terms with the new order wrote several pro-railroad doctrines into the law of the land. The most important was handed down in the Wabash case of 1886 (*Wabash, St. Louis, and Pacific Railway Co. v. Illinois*). In this decision, the Court reinterpreted the interstate-commerce clause of the Constitution in such a way as to protect large railroad companies. That is, the Constitution provides

that only Congress can regulate commerce between and among states. In the Wabash case, the Court ruled that because the Wabash Railroad ran through several states, the Illinois legislature could not regulate freight rates even between two points within Illinois. The Wabash decision left state governments with authority over only short, generally insignificant local lines that could not have been exploitative even if their owners had been obsessed with being so.

The Interstate Commerce Commission

The Wabash decision was not popular. Rural politicians and urban reformers condemned the Court as the tool of the railway barons. If only Congress could bridle the iron horse, they shouted from Grange halls and from the stages of city auditoriums, let Congress do so. In 1887, Congress did, enacting the Interstate Commerce Act.

On the face of it, the law brought the national railroads to heel. It required railroads to publish their rates. Special under-the-table rebates were forbidden. Railroads were forbidden to charge less for long hauls along routes where there was competition than for short hauls in areas where a company had a monopoly. The Interstate Commerce Act also outlawed the pooling of business by railroads, a practice by which, many shippers believed, they were controlled and fleeced. To enforce the act and to regulate rates, Congress created a permanent independent federal commission, the Interstate Commerce Commission.

The Interstate Commerce Act calmed anti-railroad protest, but it did not have much effect on railroad policy. The I.C.C., simply, did not have the power it needed to carry out its mission. If the Commissioners wished to compel a railroad to comply with their regulations, they had to take the company to the same courts that had, all along, favored the railroads over the state legislatures. Commissioner Charles A. Prouty commented, "If the I.C.C. was worth buying, the railroads would try to buy it. The only reason they have not is that the body is valueless in its ability to correct railroad abuses."

In fact, the railroads did not have to buy the I.C.C. because it was given to them. The Harrison, Cleveland, and McKinley administrations—1889 to 1901—were all sympathetic to big business and packed the Commission with railroaders and lawyers friendly to the industry.

The Money Power

By the early 1890s, the trunk lines of the country had come under the control of five great alliances of railroad men and bankers. By 1900, these had effectively fallen under the sway of two mighty New York investment banks, J. P. Morgan and Company and Kuhn, Loeb and

Company, the latter in league with Union Pacific president, Edward H. Harriman.

This development was due to the fact that, when the government ceased to subsidize construction, the railroads had to look to other sources for the huge amounts of capital needed to lay second tracks, modernize equipment, and buy up competitors. Because the railroad system had been over-built in the first place, profits rarely provided the kind of money such expensive endeavors required. Shortages of capital grew even more serious a problem during the recurrent business recessions of the period. Income sank during such downturns, but fixed costs (such as maintenance) remained the same.

The traditional means of raising capital—offering shares of stock to the public—was simply not up to these needs, particularly during recessions. Into the gap stepped the investment banks. These institutions served both as sales agents, finding moneyed buyers for railway stock at a commission, and as buyers themselves. In return for these services, bankers such as John Pierpont Morgan insisted on a say in the formation of railroad policy, placing a representative of the bank on the client's board of directors.

Because every large railroad needed financial help at one time or another—every transcontinental but the Great Northern went under during the depression of 1893 to 1897—Morgan's and Kuhn Loeb's men soon sat on every major corporate board, creating an interlocking directorate. Like all bankers, their goal was a steady, dependable flow of profit, and their means to that end was to eliminate wasteful competition. They called a halt to the periodic rate wars among the New York Central, Pennsylvania, and Baltimore and Ohio railroads in the Eastern states. In 1903, J. P. Morgan tried to merge the Northern Pacific and the Great Northern, two systems with parallel lines between the Great Lakes and the Pacific Northwest. Competing for traffic, he believed, hurt them both.

Banker control had its benefits. No longer did unscrupulous pirates like the Erie Gang ruin great transportation systems for the sake of short-term killings. The integration of the nation's railways also resulted in a gradual but significant lowering of fares and freight rates. Between 1866 and 1897, the cost of shipping a hundred pounds of grain from Chicago to New York dropped from 65 cents to 20 cents, and the rate for shipping beef from 90 cents per hundredweight to 40 cents. J. P. Morgan's self-justification was identical to that of John D. Rock-

J. P. Morgan, the titan of American finance for a generation.

"The Scourge of the West": the railroad as arrogant exploiter backed up by the power of government.

efeller: competition was wasteful and destructive; consolidation better served the nation as a whole, as well as the cream of its capitalists.

J. P. Morgan

But the control of so important a part of the economy by a few men with offices on Wall Street called into question some very basic American ideals. Where was individual freedom and opportunity, many people asked, when a sinister "money power" headed by the imperious Morgan could decide on a whim the fate of millions of farmers and working people?

A resplendent and cultivated man who owned yachts that were larger than the ships in most countries' navies, and collections of rare books and art that were superior to those in most countries' national museums, Morgan never attempted to disguise his power or his contempt for ordinary mortals. In return he was feared, held in awe, and hated.

Morgan shook off all such criticism. In the end, he was vulnerable only to ridicule. An affliction of the skin had given him a large, bulbous nose that swelled and glowed like a circus clown's when he was angry. Making fun of it, however, was the only foolproof way to make

it light up, and Morgan rarely rubbed elbows with the kind of people who would notice his single human weakness.

An Age of Trusts

In addition to railroaders, Morgan found plenty of company among the industrialists whose trusts and other devices for doing business he organized for fees of a million dollars and more. The trust was most useful in industries in which, like oil, there was a single critical stage of manufacture that involved relatively few companies. Some of John D. Rockefeller's most successful imitators were in sugar refining (the sugar trust controlled about 95 percent of the nation's facilities) and whiskey distilling. In 1890, James Buchanan Duke of Durham, North Carolina, founded the American Tobacco Company, a trust which coordinated the activities of practically every cigarette manufacturer in the United States. In effect, he dictated the terms by which tens of thousands of tobacco growers did business.

By 1890, many Americans had become convinced that when a few men could control a whole industry, the principle of economic opportunity and the foundations of American democracy were in jeopardy.

The Sherman Antitrust Act

Responding to public pressure in that year, Congress passed the Sherman Antitrust Act, which declared that "every contract, combination, in the form of trust or otherwise, or conspiracy, in restraint of trade or commerce among the several states, or with foreign nations, is hereby declared to be illegal." The Sherman Act authorized the Attorney General to move against such combinations and force them to dissolve, thus reestablishing the independence of the companies that had formed them.

The Sherman Act was no more successful in halting the consolidation movement than the Interstate Commerce Act was in controlling the power of the railroads. Critics said that the Sherman Act was a sham from the beginning, designed to quiet unease but not to hurt big business. In fact, the weakness of the law lay in the inability of congressmen to comprehend this new economic phenomenon. Real monopoly was so unfamiliar to the lawmakers that they were unable to draft a law that was worded well enough to be effective. The language of the Sherman Act was so ambivalent that a shrewd lawyer—and the trusts had the best—could usually find a loophole.

Moreover, while congressmen could take fright at a popular uproar, the courts were immune to it. The Wabash case was only one of a series of decisions by the Supreme Court that ensured the survival of the biggest of businesses. In the first major case tried under the Sherman Act, *U.S. v. E. C. Knight Company* in 1895, the Court found that a nearly complete monopoly of sugar refining in the United States did not violate the law because manufacture, which the sugar trust monopolized, was not a part of trade or commerce, even though its sugar was sold in every state.

Nor was the executive branch keen to attack big business. President Grover Cleveland's Attorney General, Richard B. Olney, was a former corporate lawyer. Under Benjamin Harrison and William McKinley, the other presidents of the 1890s, the Justice Department was similarly pro-business. During the first ten years of the Sherman Act, only eighteen cases were instituted and four of these were aimed at labor unions, also "conspiracies in restraint of trade."

Consequently, rather than heralding doomsday for the trusts, the years between 1890 and 1901 were a golden age. The number of state-chartered trusts actually grew from 251 to 290. More telling, the amount of money invested in trusts rose from $192 million to $326 million. By the end of the century, there was no doubt that the demands of modern manufacturing meant that massive organizations were here to stay. But whether they would continue to be the private possessions of a few Bells, Morgans, Carnegies, and Rockefellers was still open to debate.

RADICAL CRITICS

The Interstate Commerce and Sherman Antitrust laws were enacted by mainstream politicians who believed that the individual pursuit of wealth was a virtue—men who wished only to restore the opportunity to succeed and the possibility of competing that the big business combinations had apparently destroyed. Outside the mainstream, radical critics of the new industrial capitalism raised their voices and wielded their pens in opposition to the new order itself. At least briefly, some of them won large followings.

Henry George and the Single Tax

A lively writing style and a knack for simplifying difficult economic ideas made journalist Henry George and his single tax the center of a short-lived but momentous social movement. In *Progress and Poverty*, published in 1879, George observed what was obvious, but also bewildering to many people. Instead of freedom from onerous labor, as the machine once seemed to promise, the machine had put millions to work under killing conditions for long hours. Instead of making life easier and fuller for all, the mass production of goods had enriched the few in the "House of Have," and impoverished the millions in the "House of Want."

George blamed neither industrialization nor capitalism as such for the misery he saw around him. Like most Americans, he believed that the competition for comfort and security was a wellspring of the nation's energy. The trouble began only when those who were successful in the race grew so wealthy that they ceased to be entrepreneurs who built, and became parasites who lived off the "rents" their property generated.

George called income derived from mere ownership of property "unearned increment," because it required no work, effort, or ingenuity of its possessors. Property grew more valuable and its owners richer only because other people needed access to it in order to survive. Such value was spurious, George said, and government had every right to levy a 100 percent tax on it. Because the revenues from this tax would be quite enough to pay all the expenses of government, all other taxes could be abolished. "The single tax" became the rallying cry of George's movement. It would destroy the idle and parasitic rich as a social class. The entrepreneurship and competition that made the country great would flourish without the handicaps of taxation.

THE LAST DANCE OF THE IDLE RICH: THE BRADLEY MARTIN BALL OF 1897

In the winter of 1896/97, Americans were wrestling with a depression greater than the depression of the 1870s, bad times that would be exceeded only during the Great Depression of the 1930s. Businesses had failed by the thousands. Several million people were out of work. People had been evicted from farms and homes by the hundreds of thousands. The treasuries of charitable organizations were strained to the breaking point; some had given up in despair and closed their doors. Jobless people had marched on Washington; others had rioted; yet others plodded on day by day—gathering coal along railroad tracks, or picking through the garbage pails behind expensive restaurants. In November 1896, a presidential candidate who was called the Great Commoner, William Jennings Bryan, was defeated by William McKinley, who, fairly or not, was widely described as a tool of the moneyed interests. It was an unhappy time, with class sensibilities keen, resentments explosive.

Sometime during that winter, at breakfast in his Fifth Avenue mansion, Bradley Martin, one of high society's grandest adornments, had an idea. "I think it would be a good thing if we got up something," he told his wife and brother, Frederick. "There seems to be a great deal of depression in trade; suppose we send out invitations to a concert."

Mrs. Martin complained that a concert would benefit only foreigners. Most professional musicians in the country at that time were German and Italian, and she wanted to do something for Americans. "I've got a far better idea," she said. "Let us give a costume ball at so short notice that our guests won't have time to get their dresses from Paris. That will give an impetus to trade that nothing else will."

The conversation was recorded by Frederick Townshend Martin with no intention of making his brother and sister-in-law look either vicious or ridiculous. In fact, he justified their economic theories, explaining that "many New York shops sold out brocades and silks which had been lying in their stockrooms for years."

The ball was held on February 10, 1897, in the ballroom of the Waldorf-Astoria Hotel, which had been decorated to resemble the palace of the French kings at Versailles. To the Martins' set, it was a glorious success. According to experts, there was never such a display of jewels in New York. Financier August Belmont came in gold-inlaid armor that cost him $10,000. The costumes of others were inferior only by comparison. One woman said that in order to help the particularly hard-pressed Indians, she had had native Americans make her Pocohontas costume. Bradley Martin himself made a curious selection.

As the host at Versailles, he had first claim to be Louis XIV, the Sun King, who had built the great palace and was universally conceded to be the most glorious of the French monarchs. But Bradley chose to be his great-grandson, Louis XV. He would not have wanted to be Louis XVI, who had been beheaded because of his and his predecessors' extravagance in a country where the poor suffered wretched misery.

"Everyone said it was the most brilliant of the kind ever seen in America."

Not quite everyone. Even before the first waltz, Martin and his "idle rich" friends were being villified from pulpit, editorial desk, and political platform for their callous decadence in a difficult time. Much more significant, the ball was criticized by more than one business leader. If idle heirs such as the vapid Martin did not know that such affairs caused resentment, class hatred, and (in more than one instance in the past) social revolution, sensible businessmen did. Two years after the ball, in his book *The Theory of the Leisure Class*, sociologist Thorstein Veblen would give a name to Bradley Martin's life style, "conspicuous consumption." However, already by that time, America's wealthy were learning to enjoy their riches quietly. Indeed, looking back after several decades, two distinguished historians, Charles and Mary Beard, called the Bradley Martin ball of 1897 the "climax of lavish expenditure" in the United States. "This grand ball of the plutocrats astounded the country, then in the grip of a prolonged business depression with its attendant unemployment, misery, and starvation."

It was not only the fear of social upheaval that wrote an end to conspicuous consumption on a grand scale. To a large extent, high-society affairs like the ball were the doings of women, the wives and daughters of rich businessmen. After the turn of the century, many of them rebelled against their enforced idleness and frivolity and began to take an interest, even a leading role, in social and political causes: votes for women, of course, but also Prohibition, suppression of the white-slave racket (prostitution), amelioration of lower-class suffering, and other social programs of the Progressive era.

Not Mrs. Bradley Martin and her husband, of course. Unreconstructable denizens of the ballroom, they carried on as before. But not in New York. The ball was so unpopular there that city hall slapped a large tax increase on the Martin mansion on Fifth Avenue. In a huff, the Martins moved to London. Brother Frederick Townshend Martin wrote of this relocation with an air of despondency; the United States had lost two valuable citizens.

George's gospel was popular enough that in 1886 he narrowly missed election as mayor of New York, a city where real-estate values and "unearned increment" from land were higher than anywhere in the world.

Edward Bellamy Looks Backward

Another book which became the Bible of a protest movement was Edward Bellamy's novel of 1888, *Looking Backward, 2000–1887*. Within two years of its publication, the book sold 200,000 copies (the equivalent of more than a million in 1990) and led to the founding of about 150 "Nationalist clubs," made up of people who shared Bellamy's vision of the future.

The story that moved them was simple and soon to be rather conventional in its gimmick. A proper young Bostonian of the 1880s succumbs to a mysterious sleep and awakes in the United States of the twenty-first century. There he discovers that technology has produced not a world of sharp class divisions and widespread misery (as in 1887), but a utopia that provides abundance for all. Like George, Bellamy was not opposed to industrial development in itself.

Capitalism no longer exists in the world of *Looking Backward*. Through a peaceful democratic revolution—won at the polls—the American people have abolished competitive greed and idle unproductive living because they were at odds with American ideals. Instead of private ownership of land and industry, the state owns the means of production and administers them for the good of all. Everyone contributes to the common wealth. Everyone lives decently, and none miserably or wastefully, on its fruits.

Bellamy's vision was socialistic. However, because he rooted it in American values rather than in the internationalism of the Marxists, he called it "Nationalism." The patriotic facet of his message made his gospel palatable to middle-class Americans who, while troubled by the growth of fantastic fortunes and of wretched poverty, found foreign ideologies and talk of class warfare obnoxious and frightening.

Socialists and Anarchists

Nevertheless, Marxist ideology, including the doctrine of class conflict, found adherents in the United States. Some old-stock Americans were converted to Marxian socialism. For the most part, however, Marxism found its adherents among immigrants and the children of immigrants. Briefly after 1872, the General Council of the First International, the official administration of world socialism, made its headquarters in New York, where Marx sent it to prevent the followers of his anarchist rival, Mikhail Bakunin, from winning control of it.

The Marxists taught that the capitalist system of wage slavery—workers laboring for wages in the employ of a capitalist class that owned the means of production, the factories and machines—would fall under its own weight to socialism and then communism, under which, respectively, the state and the workers themselves would own the factories and machines, administering them for the good of all.

Some Marxist socialists held that in democratic countries like the United States, this social revolution would be voted in peacefully. Social Democratic movements flourished in a number of cities, most notably in Milwaukee, where an Austrian immigrant, Victor L. Berger, built a party that, after 1900, would govern the city for several decades.

Other Marxian socialists held that the overthrow of capitalism would inevitably be violent. The most extreme of these revolutionaries were the anarchists, some of whom held that individuals could hasten the great day through "the propaganda of the deed," acts of terrorism against the ruling class. Anarchists figured prominently in an incident in Chicago in 1886 in which, ironically, they were not responsible for the bloodshed that occurred.

Haymarket

In May 1886, workers at the McCormick International Harvester Company, the world's largest manufacturer of farm machinery, were on strike. The Chicago police were blatantly on the side of the employers, and over several days they killed four workers. On May 4, a group of anarchists, mostly German but including a Confederate Army veteran of some social standing, Albert Parsons, held a rally in support of the strikers at Haymarket Square, just south of the city center.

The oratory was red-hot; but the speakers broke no laws, and the crowd was orderly. Indeed, the rally was about to break up under the threat of a downpour when a platoon of police entered the square and demanded that the assembly disperse. At that instant, someone threw a bomb into their midst, killing seven policemen and wounding 67. The police fired a volley, and four workers fell dead.

News of the incident fed an antianarchist hysteria in Chicago. Authorities rounded up several dozen individuals who were known to have attended anarchist meetings, and authorities brought eight to trial for the murder of the officers. Among them was Parsons and a prominent German agitator, August Spies.

The trial was a farce. No one on the prosecution team knew or even claimed to know who had thrown the bomb. (His or her identity is still unknown.) Nor did the prosecution present evidence to tie any of the eight to the bombing. One, a deranged young German named Louis Lingg, was a bomb maker, although even he had a plausible alibi. Several of the defendants had not been at the rally. Parsons had been ill in bed that evening and, indeed, had been ill since before the rally was called.

All these facts proved to be irrelevant. Chicago was determined to have scapegoats, and, although the charge was murder, the Haymarket anarchists were tried for their ideas and associations. Four were hanged. Lingg committed suicide in his cell; and the remaining three were sentenced to long prison terms.

The Social Gospel

Taking a more moralistic approach to the tensions of the late nineteenth century were a number of influential Protestant clergymen. Troubled by the callousness of big business, preachers of the "Social Gospel" emphasized the Christian's social obligations, his duty to be his brother's keeper.

Walter Rauschenbusch began his ministerial career on the frontiers of Hell's Kitchen, one of New York City's worst slums. "One could hear human virtue cracking and crushing all around," he wrote. To Rauschenbusch, poverty was the cause of crime and sin, and mass poverty was the result of allowing great capitalists a free hand in enriching themselves. Later, as a professor at Rochester Theological Seminary, Rauschenbusch

A New York tenement photographed by Jacob Riis.

taught the obligation of the churches to work for both the relief of the poor and a more equitable distribution of wealth.

Washington Gladden, a Congregationalist, called unrestricted competition "antisocial and anti-Christian." He did not propose the abolition of capitalism, but he did call for regulation of its grossest immoralities. Late in life, Gladden described John D. Rockefeller's fortune as "tainted money" and urged his church not to accept contributions from the millionaire.

The Social Gospel appealed to many middle-class people, often modestly well-to-do themselves, who did not suffer directly from the power of the very wealthy but who were offended by the extravagance and idleness of their lives. William Dean Howells, the editor of the *Atlantic Monthly*, wrote a novel about a successful manufacturer of paint (*The Rise of Silas Lapham*, 1885) who finds the idleness of wealth discomfiting. He "rises," finds purpose and happiness again, only when he loses his fortune and is forced to return to productive work. Howells even convinced an old friend from Ohio, former president Rutherford B. Hayes, to go on record late in his life as an advocate of the peaceful abolition of capitalism.

DEFENDERS OF THE FAITH

Such a barrage of criticism did not, of course, go unanswered. At the same time that great wealth was taking its knocks, it was reaping the praise of defenders. In part, like the critics, they drew on traditional American values to justify the new social system. In part, also like the critics, the defenders created new philosophies, original with the era of industrial capitalism.

Social Darwinism

Thoughtful and reflective people who were at peace with their era found a justification for great wealth and even dubious business ethics in a series of books, essays, and lectures by the British philosopher Herbert Spencer. Because Spencer seemed to apply Charles Darwin's celebrated theory of biological evolution to human society, his theory is known as "Social Darwinism."

According to Spencer, as in the world of animals and plants, where species compete for life and those best adapted survive, the "fittest" people rise to the top in the social competition for riches. Eventually, in the dog-eat-dog world, they alone survive. "If they are sufficiently complete to live," Spencer wrote, "they do live, and it is well that they should live. If they are not sufficiently complete to live, they die and it is best they should die."

The intellectual tough-mindedness of Social Darwinism made Spencer immensely popular among American businessmen who were proud of their practicality. The Englishman was never so celebrated in his own country as he was in the United States. Although a vain man, Spencer was positively embarrassed by the adulation heaped on him at banquets sponsored by American academics and rich businessmen. Social Darwinism accounted for brutal business practices and underhand methods, justifying them as the natural "law of the jungle."

The language of Social Darwinism crept into the vocabulary of both businessmen and politicians who represented business interests. John D. Rockefeller, Jr., told a Sunday school class that "the growth of a large business is merely the survival of the fittest. The American Beauty Rose can be produced in the splendor and fragrance which bring cheer to its beholder only by sacrificing the early buds which grow up around it. This is not an evil tendency in business. It is merely the working out of a law of nature and a law of God."

But few American millionaires were true Social Darwinists. The very ruthlessness of the theory made it unpalatable to rich families who, in their personal lives, were committed to traditional religious values. Moreover, businessmen are rarely intellectuals, and Spencer's philosophy and writing style were as thick and murky as Rockefeller crude oil. Understanding him demanded careful study, such as businessmen rarely had the time to do. As a result, his explanation of the new society was more influential among scholars.

William Graham Sumner

The most important of these was a Yale professor, William Graham Sumner. He was uncompromising in his opposition to aiding the poor, putting government restrictions on business practices, and interfering in any way whatsoever with the law of the jungle. "The men who are competent to organize great enterprises and to handle great amounts of capital," he wrote, "must be found by natural selection, not political election."

Sumner's rigorous consistency also led him to oppose government on behalf of capital. He opposed protective tariffs. To subsidize American manufacturers by taxing imports was just as unnatural to him as was regulating the growth of trusts. If American manufacturers were not fit to compete with European manufacturers in a free market, Sumner said, they were not fit to survive. Likewise, Sumner opposed government intervention in strikes on behalf of employers. He believed that the strike was a natural test of the fitness of the employers' and the workers' causes. The outcome of a strike determined which side was "right."

To businessmen who used government trade policy and courts to their own purposes, Sumner's impartial applications of "natural law" were going too far. They had no objection to the right kind of government action.

After the turn of the century, the principles of Social Darwinism were turned on their head by the sociologist Lester Frank Ward of Brown University. Whereas Sumner argued that nature in society must be allowed to operate without restraint, Ward suggested that human society had evolved to a point where natural evolution could be guided by government policy. Just as farmers improved fruit trees and ranchers improved livestock through selective breeding, government could improve society by intervening in the naturally slow evolutionary process. Ward's "Reform Darwinism" influenced two generations of twentieth-century liberals.

The Success Gospel

The Gospel of Success had far more influence among nineteenth-century capitalists than Social Darwinism did. The United States had been built on the desire to prosper, Success Gospellers said. Therefore, if competition for riches was a virtue, what was wrong with winning? Far from a reason for anxiety or evidence of social immorality, the fabulous fortunes of America's wealthy families were an index of their virtue. The Rockefellers, Carnegies, and Morgans deserved their money.

Success manuals, books purporting to show how anyone could become a millionaire, were read as avidly as the works of George and Bellamy, and by far more people. All much the same, the manuals drew on the widespread assumptions that hard work, honesty, frugality, loyalty to employers and partners, and other "bourgeois virtues" drawn from Benjamin Franklin inevitably led to success. Having succeeded, America's millionaires deserved not resentment but admiration and imitation.

Shrugging off his enemies, John D. Rockefeller said flatly, "God gave me my money." A Baptist minister from Philadelphia, Russell B. Conwell, made a fortune delivering a lecture with a similar theme. In "Acres of Diamonds," which the eloquent preacher delivered to paying audiences more than 6,000 times, Conwell said that great wealth was a great blessing. Not only could every American be rich, but every American should be rich. If a person failed, the fault lay within, not with society. "There is not a poor person in the United States," Conwell said, "who was not made poor by his own shortcomings." The opportunities, the "acres of diamonds," were everywhere, waiting to be collected.

Conversely, those who already were rich were by definition virtuous. "Ninety-eight out of one hundred of the rich men of America are honest. That is why they are rich."

Horatio Alger and "Ragged Dick"

Through the 130 boys' novels written by a minister who lost his pulpit in clouded circumstances, Horatio Alger, the Success Gospel was conveyed to the younger generation. Alger's books sold 20 million copies between 1867 and his death in 1899, and 100 million by 1920.

He enjoyed this success despite the fact that he was no writer. His prose was wooden, his characters were snipped from cardboard, and his plots were variations on two or three simple themes. All assume as a given that one of the paramount goals of life is to get money. All teach that wealth is within the grasp of everyone because almost all Alger's heros are lads grappling with destitution. They are also honest, hard-working, loyal to their employers, and clean-living. "Ragged Dick," Alger's first hero and the prototype for "Tattered Tom," "Lucky Luke Larkin," and dozens of others, is insufferably courteous and always goes to church.

Curiously, Ragged Dick et al. do not get rich slowly through hard work. At the beginning of the final chapter, the hero is often as badly off as on page one. Then, however, he is presented with what amounts to a visitation of grace, a divine gift that rewards his virtues. The child of a rich industrialist falls off the Staten Island Ferry; or a rich girl stumbles into the path of a runaway brewery wagon drawn by panicked horses; or she slips into the Niagara River just above the falls. Because the Alger hero acts quickly, rescuing her, the heroic lad is rewarded with a job, marriage to the daughter, and eventually, the fortune of his grateful father-in-law. While appealing to the adolescent boy's yen for adventure, the novels also touched the American evangelical belief in divine grace. Thus, just as He did with Rockefeller, God gave Ragged Dick his money as reward for his virtues.

Philanthropy

The flaw in the Success Gospel as a justification of great fortunes was the obvious fact that many rich men got their money by practicing the opposite of the touted virtues—dishonesty, betrayal of partners and employers, reckless speculation—and they grew richer while living a life of sumptuous, decadent ease. The ethics of John D. Rockefeller's business practices were not nearly so bad as his many enemies said, but there was no question that he cut corners. Similar suspicions surrounded practically every rich family in the country.

Perhaps in part to compensate for the negative marks on their reputations, many wealthy businessmen turned to philanthropy as a kind of retroactive justification of their fortunes. Horatio Alger supported institutions that housed homeless boys in New York City. Russell B. Conwell founded Temple University, where poor young men could study very cheaply and improve themselves. Le-

Booker T. Washington (center) won the support of many wealthy benefactors with his "Atlantic Compromise." To his left is steel magnate Andrew Carnegie at the dedication of Tuskegee Institute.

land Stanford built a wholly new "Harvard of the West" in California. Rockefeller and other industrial millionaires gave huge sums to their churches, to art galleries and museums, and to universities. In retirement, Rockefeller took particular interest in helping black Americans break out of the prison that racial discrimination had built around them.

Andrew Carnegie devised a coherent theory that justified fabulous fortunes on the basis of stewardship. In a celebrated essay entitled "Wealth," he argued that the unrestricted pursuit of riches made American society vital and strong, but it also made the man who succeeded a steward, or trustee. He had an obligation to distribute his money where it would provide opportunities for poor people to join the competition of the next generation. Indeed, Carnegie said that the rich man who died rich, died a failure.

Carnegie retired from business in 1901 and devoted the rest of his life to granting money to libraries, schools, and useful social institutions. He was so rich, however, that despite extraordinary generosity, he died a multimillionaire.

PRIVATE CARS

Partial to yachts, J. P. Morgan never owned a private railroad car, which was one of the status symbols of the late nineteenth century. In George Gould's, guests for dinner were expected to dress formally; Gould's liveried waiters served the food on solid gold plates. The Vanderbilt family's car, called the "Vanderbilt," could not accommodate all the guests whom they wished to entertain, so they had a new one built and called it "Duchess" after Consuelo. At Palm Beach, a favorite pleasuring ground of the rich, twenty to thirty private cars were sometimes parked in a special section of the train yard. When Morgan wished to go to a place he could not reach by water, he had to rent an opulent private car. On one occasion, he rented a whole train of private cars to transport east coast Episcopalian bishops to a conference in San Francisco.

HOW THE VERY RICH LIVED

Probably nothing reconciled ordinary Americans to the existence of multimillionaires more than the sheer fascination of the multitudes with the splendor in which the very rich lived. As Thorstein Veblen, an eccentric sociologist, observed in several books written at the end of the century, the very wealthy literally lived to spend money for the sake of proving that they had money. Veblen called this showy extravagance "conspicuous

There could only be one reason for dining on horseback: The diners could afford to do it. This was at Sherry's Ballroom in New York in 1903.

consumption," and the propensity to throw it away "conspicuous waste."

Conspicuous Consumption

Having much more money than they could possibly put to good use, the very rich competed in spending it by hosting lavish parties for one another, by building extravagant palaces, by purchasing huge yachts that were good for little but show, by adorning themselves with costly clothing and jewelry, and by buying European titles for their daughters.

Some high-society parties lasting but a few hours cost more than $100,000. At one, hosted by the self-proclaimed prince of spenders, Harry Lehr, 100 dogs dined on "fricassee of bones" and gulped down shredded dog biscuit prepared by a French chef. The guests at one New York banquet ate their meal while mounted on horses (trays balanced on the animals' withers). The horses munched oats out of sterling-silver feedbags, possibly making more noise than their riders. At a costume affair, guests let it be known that they had spent more than $10,000 each on their fancy dress.

It was the golden age of yachting. Cornelius Vanderbilt's *North Star* was 250 feet long. Albert C. Burrage's *Aztec* carried 270 tons of coal; it could steam 5,500 miles without calling at a port for fuel. As on land, J. P. Morgan was champion at sea. He owned three successively larger, faster, and more opulent yachts called *Corsair*. Morgan had a sense of humor; a corsair is a pirate's vessel.

Nowhere was consumption more conspicuous and lavish than at upper-class resorts such as Newport, Rhode Island. A summer "cottage" of 30 rooms, used for only three months a year, cost $1 million. Coal baron E. J. Berwind spent $1.5 million to build "The Elms." William K. Vanderbilt outdid everyone with "Marble House." That cottage cost $2 million; the furniture inside, $9 million.

Those places were for vacations. At home in the cities, the millionaires created neighborhoods of mansions such as New York's Fifth Avenue, a thoroughfare given over to grand houses for twenty blocks; Chicago's Gold Coast, which loomed over the city's lakeshore; and San Francisco's Nob Hill, from which palaces looked down on the city like bastions of medieval barons.

A Lord in the Family

A fad of the very rich that aggravated many Americans was the rush during the 1880s and 1890s to marry daughters to European nobles. Nothing more clearly dramatized the aristocratic pretensions of the new elite. Wealthy families took pride in the price that they paid to have an earl or a duke as a son-in-law. It was a two-way bargain. An American daughter got a title to wear to Newport; an impoverished European aristocrat got

The lavish interior of "The Breakers," built by Cornelius Vanderbilt as his summer house, in Newport, Rhode Island.

money with which to maintain himself in fine wines, horses, and hounds.

Thus, heiress Alice Thaw was embarrassed on her honeymoon as countess of Yarmouth when creditors seized her husband's luggage. She had to wire her father for money to get it out of hock. Helena Zimmerman, the daughter of a coal and iron millionaire from Cincinnati, married the duke of Manchester. For twenty years, their bills were paid by the father of the duchess out of the labor of workers living on subsistence wages.

The most famous American aristocrats were the heiresses of two of the original robber barons, Jay Gould and Cornelius Vanderbilt. Anna Gould became the Countess Boni de Castellane. Before she divorced him in order to marry his cousin, the higher-ranking Prince de Sagan, the count extracted more than $5 million from Jay Gould's purse. Consuelo Vanderbilt was married against

her wishes into the proudest family in England. Both when Consuelo married the duke of Marlborough and when she divorced him, the payoff ran to several million. The duke may have been the only individual ever to get the better of the Vanderbilt family.

Women as Decor

The role of young heiresses in the game of conspicuous waste helps illustrate the curious role of the women of the new social class. They were more idle than their menfolk. A role in business or public life was denied them and they had none of the homemaking duties of middle-class women to occupy their time.

What, then, to do? In effect, the women of the wealthiest classes became their families' chief conspicuous consumers. The rich woman's role was to reflect her husband's accomplishment in amassing wealth; she was a glittering display piece for costly clothing and jewelry. Mrs. George Gould, daughter-in-law of the crusty Jay, went through life known for little but the fact that she owned a pearl necklace that was worth $500,000. No one ever mentioned Mrs. Gould in any other context. Her life revolved around the moments when she entered ballrooms, all eyes on her pearls.

Women's fashions were designed to emphasize their wearers' idleness. Indeed, fashion, by its very nature, is conspicuously wasteful. In keeping up with changes, the whole point of fashion, the wealthy woman demonstrated that it made no dent in her husband's fortune if

Mrs. George Gould's identification with her half-million dollar pearl necklace was so total that she was never photographed without it.

tieth century, was a completely useless headgear. It offered neither protection nor warmth. But it did prevent a man from so much as bending down to dust his patent-leather shoes. "White collar," displaying clean linen at wrist and neck, made it clear that the wearer did no work that would soil his clothing.

Unlikely Neighbors

For the most part, ordinary Americans knew of the shenanigans of the very rich only through hearsay and the popular press. Farmers and factory workers did not vacation at Newport or attend costume balls and ducal weddings at Blenheim palace. The nature of urban life in the late nineteenth century was such, however, that the idle rich could not conceal their extravagance from the middle and lower classes.

The rich employed legions of servants to maintain their mansions. The grandeur and waste of upper-class life was well-known to these poorly paid people. (Two million women worked in domestic service at the end of the century.) More important, because it was impossible to commute long distances in the congested cities, whether for business or social life, the wealthy lived not in isolated suburbs but close to the centers of New York, Boston, Philadelphia, Chicago, and other great cities.

The tradesmen who made daily deliveries of groceries, meat, vegetables and fruit, ice, coal (for heating), and other necessities, not to mention repairmen and those who delivered durable goods, were intimately familiar with the kind of wealth that their customers enjoyed. Marginal workers who were employed by the service and the light manufacturing industries of the center city walked daily past palaces and saw the rich come and go in lacquered carriages tended by flunkies in livery.

she annually discarded last year's expensive clothing to make room in her closet for the latest from Paris.

Fashion reflects social status in other ways. When wealthy women laced themselves up in crippling steel and bone corsets, which made it difficult for them to move, let alone perform any physical work, they were making it clear that they did not have to do such work and were purely decorative. They had servants to care for every detail of their lives.

Men's clothing reflected social status, too. The tall silk hat, the badge of the capitalist well into the twen-

Popular Culture

In newspapers aimed at a mass readership, in popular songs, and in the melodramas favored by working people, the idleness and extravagance of the "filthy rich" were favorite themes. The wealthy were depicted with a mixture of envy and resentment. New York's Tin Pan Alley, the center of the sheet-music industry, preached a combination of pity for the "bird in a gilded cage," the wealthy woman, and the traditional moral that because

---

LELAND STANFORD

When he was president of the Southern Pacific Railroad, Leland Stanford ordered that all employees of the company stand at attention in a line along the track when his private trains passed through. All Southern Pacific locomotives traveling in the other direction were to blow their whistles in salute.

YOU CAN TAKE IT WITH YOU

At the Vanderbilt family tomb on Staten Island, watchmen punched a time clock every hour on the hour around the clock. William Vanderbilt, son of the Commodore, had a deathly fear of graverobbers.

poor people worked, they were more virtuous. There were plenty of evil capitalists, greedy landlords, and exploitative employers in the Horatio Alger books.

In the popular melodramas of the day, simple plays with no subtlety of character and a completely predictable plot, right-living poor people were pitted against an unscrupulous rich villain. "You are only a shopgirl," said the high-society lady in a typical play. "An honest shopgirl," replied the heroine in stilted language, "as far above a fashionable idler as heaven is above earth!" (The poor but virtuous shopgirl was often rewarded in the final act by marriage to a rich young man; she consequently took up the life of idleness that she had condemned through two and a half acts.)

Juicy Scandals

Ordinary people studiously followed the scandals that periodically rocked high society. In 1872, "Jubilee Jim" Fisk was shot to death by a rival for the affections of his showgirl mistress, Josie Mansfield. Newspaper readers could find a moral in the fact that Fisk's great wealth and power could not save him from a violent death at the age of 38. Nevertheless, a good part of the story's appeal were the details of Fisk's sumptuous personal life, on which the newspapers lovingly dwelled.

Even more sensational was the 1906 murder of architect Stanford White by millionaire Harry Thaw. During his trial, Thaw accused White of having seduced his beautiful fiancée, Evelyn Nesbit. Her testimony concerning the famous White's peculiarities behind closed doors simultaneously titillated the public and served as a moral justification for the murder. (Thaw went free.) Such scandals were the stock in trade of nationally circulated periodicals, such as the *Police Gazette* and *Frank Leslie's Illustrated Newspaper*, that appealed to the work-

Readers of sensationalist newspapers were awed by the beauty of Evelyn Nesbit and titillated by the sex scandal in which she was involved.

ing classes. By the end of the century, many large daily papers also took to bumping conventional news to the back pages when an upper-class scandal came up in the courts.

For Further Reading

Most of the works cited at the conclusion of Chapter 28 are relevant here, particularly Vincent P. DeSantis, *The Shaping of Modern America, 1877–1916* (1973); John A. Garraty, *The New Commonwealth, 1877–1890* (1968); Samuel P. Hays, *The Response to Industrialism, 1885–1914* (1957); Glenn Porter, *The Rise of Big Business, 1860–1910* (1973); and Robert A. Wiebe, *The Search for Order* (1967). Also see Sigmund Diamond, *The Reputation of American Businessmen* (1959) and L. Galambos, *The Public Image of Big Business in America* (1975).

Justifications and defenses of the new order are studied in John G. Cawelti, *Apostles of the Self-Made Man in America* (1966); Sidney Fine, *Laissez-Faire and the Welfare State: A Study of Conflict in American Thought, 1865–1901* (1956); Richard Hofstadter, *Social Darwinism in American Thought* (1944); Edward C. Kirkland, *Dream and Thought in the Business Community* (1956); and Irwin Wyllie, *The Self-Made Man in America* (1954).

Criticisms of the new commonwealth are the focus in C. A. Barker, *Henry George* (1955); Gabriel Kolko, *Railroads and Regulation* (1965); Samuel T. McSeveney, *The Politics of Depression: Political Behavior in the Northeast, 1893–1896* (1972); Andrew Sinclair, *Corsair: The Life of J. Pierpont Morgan* (1981); John L. Thomas, *Alternative America: Henry George, Edward Bellamy, Henry Demarest Lloyd* (1983); and Thorstein Veblen, *The Theory of the Leisure Class* (1899).

Entrance to a West Virginia coal mine.

FACTORIES AND IMMIGRANT SHIPS

THE PEOPLE WHO BUILT MODERN AMERICA

Leland Stanford and James J. Hill thought of themselves as the men who had built the railroads. So

did most Americans. John D. Rockefeller took pride in the Standard Oil Company as his personal

creation, and, whether they liked the results or not, Americans agreed with him. Newspapers and

magazines referred to Andrew Carnegie as the nation's greatest steelmaker. In the popular mind, vast

industries were associated with powerful individuals, just as battles were identified with generals:

Sherman had marched across Georgia; Grant had taken Richmond; Vanderbilt ran the New York

Central. J. P. Morgan even spoke of his hobby, yachting, in personal terms. "You can do business with anyone," he huffed, "but you can only sail a boat with a gentleman."

In reality, Morgan and his friends merely decided when and where the boat was to go. It took 85 grimy stokers and hard-handed sailors to get Morgan's *Corsair* out of New York harbor and safely into Newport or Venice. In the same way, Stanford, Hill, Rockefeller, and other great businessmen directed the creation of industrial America, but the edifice was built by anonymous millions of men and women who wielded the shovels and needles and tended the machines that whirred and whined in numberless factories and mills.

A NEW WAY OF LIFE

A merica's working people could not be kept below decks like the crew of the *Corsair*. While the population of the United States grew rapidly in the late nineteenth century, more than doubling between 1860 and 1900, the size of the working class quadrupled. In 1860, 1.5 million Americans made their living in workshops and mills, and another 700,000 in mining and construction. By 1900, 6 million people worked in manufacturing and 2.3 million in mining and construction, increases of four times and 3.3 times, respectively. Wageworkers, once a decided minority, now constituted a distinct and significant social class.

Bigger Factories, Better Technology

The size of the work place also grew, a fact of profound importance for the quality of workers' lives. In 1870, the average workshop in the United States employed eight people and was owned by an individual or by partners who lived nearby and who personally supervised the business, often working at the bench with their employees. Generous or peevish as they might be, such bosses were personally involved in the lives of their workers. They heard of childbirths, the death of a parent, the luck of a brother, and they discussed matters such as wages, hours, and shop conditions face to face with the people who were affected by them. Even Pittsburgh's iron and steel mills, the largest factories in the country in 1870, employed on average just 90 workers.

By 1900, the average industrial worker labored in a shop with 25 employees. Plants employing a thousand were common. The average payroll of a Pittsburgh steel plant was now 1,600, and a few companies listed 10,000 people on the payroll. Carnegie Steel employed 23,000.

Girls work at a thread-winding machine at the Loudon Hosiery Mill in London, Tennessee, in 1910.

The men who directed the affairs of such concerns rarely stepped on the floor of a shop. They were interested in wages, hours, and conditions only insofar as they were entries in the ledgers that lined the walls of their offices.

The increased application of steam power and improved machinery affected workers in other ways. The highly skilled craftsman, trained for years in the use of hand tools, ceased to be the backbone of the manufacturing process. Not many crafts actually disappeared (as they would in the twentieth century), and some, like the machinist's trade, increased in importance. But in most areas, steam-powered machines took over from artisans, performing their jobs more quickly and often better.

JOHN HENRY

Ironically, considering that few blacks held industrial jobs in the nineteenth century, a black man became the symbol of the decline of the skilled worker in the face of the new machines. "The Ballad of John Henry," written about 1872 and immediately popular among working people, told the story of a black miner's contest with the newly introduced steam drill. There are several versions. Most of them end in tragedy for the human being. John Henry might defeat the steam drill in a contest to sink steel in rock, but he dies from the pace, "with his hammer in his hand."

Many machines were tended by unskilled or semi-skilled men, women, and children who merely guided the device at its task. Unlike craftsmen, these workers were interchangeable, easily replaced because their jobs required little training. Consequently, they could be poorly paid, and they commanded scant respect from employers, small-business men, professionals, politicians, and skilled workers. "If I wanted boiler iron," said one industrialist, "I would go out on the market and buy it where I could get it cheapest; and if I wanted to employ men I would do the same."

Wages

In dollars, the wages of many workers declined during the final decades of the nineteenth century. However, real wages, or purchasing power, generally rose as the cost of food, clothing, and housing dropped more radically than did hourly pay. Taken as a whole, the industrial working class enjoyed almost 50 percent more purchasing power in 1900 than in 1860.

This statistic can be misleading. The skilled "aristocracy of labor"—such workers as locomotive engineers, machinists, master carpenters, printers, and other highly trained craftsmen—improved their earnings much more than did the unskilled workers at the bottom of the pile. The average annual wage for all manufacturing workers in 1900 was $8.37 a week. Unskilled workers were paid about ten cents an hour on the average, about $5.50 a week. A girl of twelve or thirteen, tending a loom in a textile factory, might take home as little as $2 a week after various fines (for being late to work, for example) were deducted from her pay. As late as 1904, sociologist Robert Hunter estimated that one American in eight lived in poverty.

Hours

Hours on the job varied. Most government employees had enjoyed an eight-hour day since 1868. Skilled workers, especially in the building trades (bricklayers, carpenters, plumbers), generally worked ten. Elsewhere, factory workers were counted lucky if they worked twelve-hour days. During the summer months, many mills ran sunup to sundown, as long as sixteen hours—with only one shift.

The average work-week was 66 hours long in 1860, and 55 hours in 1910. People were on the job five and a half or six days a week; half-day Saturday was considered a holiday. In industries that had to run around the clock, such as steel (the furnaces could not be shut down), the workforce was divided into two shifts on seven-day schedules. Each shift worked for twelve hours. At the end of a two-week period, the day workers switched shifts with the night workers. This meant a "holiday" of 24

hours once a month. The price of the holiday was working for 24 hours two weeks later while the other shift enjoyed its vacation.

True holidays were few: Memorial Day, Fourth of July, Christmas, a few more. However, because of the erratic swings in the business cycle, factory workers had plenty of unwanted time off. Some industries were highly seasonal. Coal miners, for example, could expect to be without wages for weeks or even months during the summer, when homes were not heated. In times of depression, unemployment soared. During the depressions of the 1870s and 1890s, about 12 percent of the working population was jobless for extended periods.

Conditions

While some employers attended to safety conditions, a safe work place was far from the rule in the nineteenth century. Between 1870 and 1910, there were 10,000 major boiler explosions in American factories, or just under one per workday. Between 1880 and 1900, 35,000 American workers were killed on the job, almost five per day. Railroads had a particularly horrid record. Every year, one railroad worker in 26 was injured seriously, and one in 400 was killed. Textile workers without some fingers and ex-textile workers without hands were fixtures in every mill town. In lumber mill towns, the old-timer with all his digits was a wonder of the world.

In many cases, injured workers and the survivors of those who were killed on the job received no compensation. In others, employer compensation amounted to little more than burial expenses. In the coal fields, the mine owners thought themselves generous if they al-

A newsboy peddles papers in St. Louis, Missouri.

lowed a dead miner's son, who was younger than the regulation age, to take a job in the mines in order to support his mother.

Employer liability law was stacked against workers. Most courts insisted that employers were not liable for an employee's worker injury unless the plaintiff bore no responsibility whatsoever for the accident in question. Short of the collapse of a factory roof, a complete lack of employee culpability was difficult to prove, particularly by a worker who could not afford a skilled lawyer. Courts ruled that if an employee was hurt because his machine was dangerous and he knew it, the employer was not liable. It did no good to plead that the injured worker would have been fired had he refused to tend the device. Under the law, the choice to stay on the job, and therefore part of the responsibility for his injury, was his.

Occupational diseases—the coal miner's "black lung," the cotton-mill worker's "white lung," and the hard-rock miner's silicosis—were not recognized as the employer's responsibility. Poisoning resulting from work with chemicals was rarely identified as job-related.

WHO WERE THE WORKERS?

Skilled workers inclined to be males of old-stock British or Irish origin. Unskilled jobs were generally filled by children, women, and recent immigrants. In some industrial towns, one-half to three-quarters of the workforce was foreign-born.

Child Labor

In 1900, the socialist writer John Spargo estimated that 1.8 million children under 16 years of age were employed full time. They did all but the heaviest kind of work. Girls as young as twelve tended dangerous looms and spinning machines in textile mills. "Bobbin boys" of ten hauled heavy wooden boxes filled with spindles from spinning rooms to weaving rooms and back again. Children swept filings in machine shops. Boys of eight worked the "breakers" at coal mines, hand picking slate from anthracite in filthy, frigid wooden sheds.

In city tenement "sweat shops," whole families and their boarders sewed clothing or rolled cigars by hand, and children worked as soon as they were able to master the simplest tasks. In cities, children practically monopolized messenger-service work, light delivery, and some kinds of huckstering.

In part, child labor was the fruit of greed. On the grounds that children had no nonworking dependents to support, employers paid them less than they paid adults. But the phenomenon also provides an example of "cultural lag." Children had always worked and it took time for society to face up to the reality that factory labor was essentially different from chores on a family farm or in a small workshop. Where relations in the small shop were personal, the sharply limited capacity of children, particularly fatigue when set to tedious, repetitive tasks, was easy to recognize and take into account. Placed in a niche in a massive factory, the child laborer became nothing but a number on an accountant's sheet.

Women Workers

Cultural lag also played a part in the large numbers of women in industry. The first industrial workers had been female, partly because women had long been the mainstay of cloth making in Western culture, partly because the founders of the first American textile mills—like the Lowells—had not been able to imagine factory work as a suitable lifetime career for the head of a family. In devising the "Lowell system," the well-meaning pioneers of the factory system had believed that they had reconciled industrialization with the old way of life.

The increasing demands of growing industry, and the heavy nature of much factory work, soon resulted in an industrial work force that was predominantly male. Nevertheless, the difficulty of supporting a family on one person's income forced working-class women to continue to labor for wages even after they married. In 1900, almost 20 percent of the total work force was female. About half the workers in textiles were women, and the percentage in the needle trades and other home manufactures was much higher.

With few exceptions, women were paid less than men for performing similar tasks for the same number of hours, sometimes half as much. Abysmally low pay was particularly characteristic of the largest female occupation. In 1900, 2 million women were employed for subsistence wages or less in domestic service: cooking, cleaning, and tending the vanities and children of the well-to-do.

No Blacks Need Apply

While a few blacks found factory jobs in the most menial positions—as sweepers, for example—industrial jobs went mostly to whites. Blacks remained concentrated in agriculture and in low-paying service occupations: domestic servants, waiters, porters, and the like. In 1900, more than 80 percent of the black population lived in the South, most of them on the land.

The industrial color line was most clearly drawn in the South. When the cotton textile industry moved south at the end of the century, the millowners drew on

A small girl working alongside her mother and scarcely older sister in a Louisiana oyster cannery.

the poor white population for its work force. Implicitly, and sometimes explicitly, employees were informed that if they proved troublesome (that is, if they complained about wages, hours, and conditions), the companies could always tap the huge, poor black population. Their own racial prejudices served to keep Southern white workers the poorest industrial work force in the country. Rather than risk the loss of poorly paid jobs to blacks, they accepted low wages and a low standard of living.

ORGANIZE!

However poorly industrial work paid, it was preferable to other alternatives open to people at the bottom of society. The majority of workers, most of the time, tacitly accepted unattractive wages, hours, and conditions of labor. They expressed their discontent (or desperation) as toilers have done since they constructed the ziggurats. Absenteeism was high in factories, particularly on "Blue Monday" after beery Sunday. And in good times, when getting another menial job was not difficult, workers unable to take holidays sufficient to health and sanity simply quit on a minute's notice.

Sabotage was a word yet to be invented, but the practice was well-understood. When the pace of work reached the dropping point, or a foreman stepped beyond the bounds of tolerable behavior, it was easy enough to jam or damage a machine so that it appeared to be an accident—and take a break while it was being fixed. An angry worker who had made up his mind to quit might decide literally to "throw a monkey wrench into the works" or to slash the leather belts that turned the looms, drills, stampers, lathes—that ran the entire factory.

A Heritage of Violence

When workers were powerless to remedy their conditions "through channels," violence was common. During the nationwide railroad strike of 1877, a spontaneous outbreak that had its roots in a serious depression, workers did not merely walk off the job, but they stormed in mobs into railroad yards and set trains and buildings on fire. In a few places, they fought pitched gun battles with company guards and, toward the end of the unsuccessful strike, with troops who had been called out to put them down.

At Andrew Carnegie's Homestead Works in 1892, a strike led by the Amalgamated Association of Iron and

DIVIDE AND CONQUER

A Western lumber magnate explained that in order to have a tractable work force, an employer should hire from several ethnic groups: "Don't get too great a percentage of any one nationality. For your own good and theirs mix them up and obliterate clannishness and selfish social prejudices."

Steel Workers actually besieged the giant factory and forced the withdrawal of a barge bringing 300 armed guards into the town. Less colossal conflicts characterized labor disputes in many industries. They were nowhere more bloody and bitter than in the coal mines of Pennsylvania and in the hard-rock gold and silver mines of the mountainous West.

The Molly Maguires

During the early 1870s, many Irish coal miners in northeastern Pennsylvania gave up on the possibility of improving the conditions of their unhealthful and dangerous work through peaceful means. Within the semisecret atmosphere of a fraternal lodge, the Ancient Order of Hibernians, they formed a secret society called the Molly Maguires. The Mollys then launched an effective campaign of terrorism against the mine owners and particularly the supervisors. They systematically destroyed mine property and murdered loyal company men rather than merely beating them up. (In which case, the victims could have identified their attackers.)

Because of the ethnic dimension of the conflict—almost all the miners were Irish; almost all the bosses were American or Cornish—the Molly Maguires were able to maintain an effective secrecy. Their enemies did not know who they were, how numerous they were, or how much support they had in the community. To this day, historians must conjecture a good deal when discussing the Mollys.

In any case, the mine owners had the last word. They brought in an Irish-American undercover detective,

WOMEN IN THE WORK FORCE

There was at least one woman in each occupation listed by the Census Bureau in 1890. More than 225,000 were running farms, and 1,143 listed their occupation as clergyman. Women outnumbered men as teachers and as waiters (the latter by five to one). There were 28 female lumberjacks. In all the United States, however, out of 12,856 wheelwrights (makers and repairers of wagon wheels) there was only one woman.

James McParland, an employee of the Pinkerton Agency, which specialized in breaking up unions. McParland infiltrated the Mollys and gathered evidence that led to the hanging of nineteen men and the end of terrorist action in the mines.

The Union Makes Us Strong

At best, violence is a risky mode of protest and resistance. In a stable and free society, organizing for strength seemed more appropriate and likelier to yield results. "One out of many," "in numbers there is strength," the sacredness accorded to the federal union in the Civil War—all such American mottos and ideals fed the imaginations of working people who were determined to improve their lot.

The first American union dated from before 1800, an association of shoemakers in Philadelphia, the Knights of St. Crispin. Workingmen's associations had been the backbone of the Jacksonian political movement in the Eastern states. By the early 1870s, skilled workers such as machinists, iron molders, carpenters, locomotive engineers, and firemen had formed thousands of local trade groups that totaled about 300,000 members.

For the most part, these scattered organizations had little to do with one another. Developing at a time when industry was decentralized, the unions inevitably lagged behind the employers in recognizing the need for national organization. By the end of the Civil War, however, the outlines of the new industrial order had been sketched in. In 1866, William Sylvis, a visionary iron puddler (a man who made castings from molds), founded the National Labor Union and devoted the last three years of his life to its cause, traveling by foot around the Northeastern states and rallying workers of every occupation in churches, in fraternal lodges, or under the stars.

Sylvis believed that the workers' future depended on political action. He formed alliances with a number of reform groups, including the women's suffrage movement and farmers' organizations that were lobbying for a cheap currency. The National Labor party put up candidates in the presidential election of 1872 but with so poor a showing that the party and the N.L.U. folded. From a membership of 400,000 in 1872, the N.L.U. disappeared within two years.

The Knights of Labor

A different kind of national labor organization already had emerged to take the place of the National Labor Union. Organized in 1869 by a group of tailors led by Uriah P. Stephens, the Noble and Holy Order of the Knights of Labor spread its message secretly. Stephens was aware that many bosses simply fired the union men

Women delegates to a Knights of Labor convention held in 1886.

in their employ. When the Knights announced meetings in newspaper advertisements, therefore, they did not reveal their meeting place or even their name, but identified the group as "******".

The Knights of Labor also differed from the N.L.U. in their disinterest in political action as an organization. Members were urged to vote, but Stephens believed that the interests of working people would ultimately be served by solidarity in the work place, not at the ballot box.

Some Knights spoke as if they believed in class conflict, irreconcilable differences between producers and parasites—workers and farmers on the one hand, capitalists on the other. But their concept of class lines was far less precise than that of the Marxists; they barred from membership only saloonkeepers, lawyers, and gamblers, hardly professions that included all the bosses of industrial America. In fact, Stephens himself disliked the idea of class conflict and looked forward to a day when all men and women of good will would abolish the wage system and establish a cooperative commonwealth.

Women were welcome in the Knights. So were blacks and unskilled workers, who usually were overlooked as union material in the nineteenth century. However, the Knights failed to appeal to one group that was essential to the success of any labor organization. Roman Catholics, particularly Irish-Americans, were the single largest ethnic group in the working class.

As the name of his organization implies, Stephens surrounded the Knights of Labor with the mystery, symbolism, ritual, secret handshakes, and other rigamarole that was common to American fraternal organizations. A lifelong Freemason, Stephens based the Knights' ritual

on that of his own lodge. The trouble was that, traditionally, the Masons were hostile to Catholicism, and the pope forbade members of the Church to join secret societies of any sort. The Catholic suspicion of the Knights was a serious drawback. Without Catholic support, no labor organization could prosper.

Terence Powderly

In 1879, Stephens was succeeded as Grand Master Workman by Terence V. Powderly, a misleadingly mild-looking man with a handlebar moustache. Himself a Roman Catholic, Powderly brought the Knights into the open and toned down the Masonic flavor of their rituals. He then persuaded an influential Catholic bishop, James Gibbons, to prevail on the pope to remove his prohibition of Catholic membership in the union.

The Knights grew at a dazzling rate under Powderly. With 110,000 members in 1885, the organization claimed 700,000 the next year. Ironically, for Powderly disliked strikes, the major impetus of this growth was a remarkable strike victory by the Knights against Jay Gould's Missouri Pacific Railroad. Gould had vowed to destroy the union. "I can hire half the working class to kill the other half," he growled. But when he tried to cut wages, the Knights closed down his line and forced him to meet with their leaders and agree to their terms.

The easy victory and the explosive growth of the union proved to be more curse than blessing. Powderly and the union's general assembly were unable to control the new members. Instead of working together according to a national policy, which was the rationale of a national labor organization, local leaders, who were often new to the concept of unionism, were encouraged by the victory in the Missouri Pacific strike to go it alone in a dozen unrelated directions. Powderly fumed and sputtered and refused to back the rash of strikes in 1885 and 1886. But he could not stop them.

Jay Gould got his revenge, completely crushing a strike against the Texas Pacific Railroad, another of his

---

THE YELLOW-DOG CONTRACT

Yellow-dog contracts, which were forced on employees by some companies, were meant to intimidate as much as anything else. The penalty for violating such a contract was dismissal, which employers did often enough without such documents. Employees had to agree that "in consideration of my present employment I hereby promise and agree that I will forthwith abandon any and all membership, connection, or affiliation with any organization or society, whether secret or open, which in any way attempts to regulate the conditions of my services or the payment therefor."

many properties. Then, in 1886, the Haymarket tragedy was unfairly but effectively imputed to the Knights. Membership plummeted. Workers wanted union; not many wanted chaos.

Samuel Gompers and the A.F.L.

In the same year as Haymarket, a national labor organization dedicated to union and stability for *some* workers was put together by a few dozen existing associations of skilled workers. The American Federation of Labor's guiding spirit was a cigar maker, born in London of Dutch-Jewish parents, an emigrant to the United States as a boy.

Samuel Gompers astonished his fellow workers (and their employers) with his intelligence, learning, toughness in bargaining, and eloquence on the soapbox. He was a homely, even ugly man, squat and thick of body with a broad, coarse-featured face. But this uncomely character had very definite ideas about how labor organizations could not only survive in the United States, but become one of the interlocking forces that governed the country.

Practicality

First of all, Gompers believed that only skilled craftsmen could effectively force employers to negotiate with them. When bricklayers refused to work, and all the bricklayers in a locality stuck together, the employer who wanted bricks laid had no choice but to talk. When the unskilled hod carriers (workers who carried the bricks to the bricklayers) went out, however, employers had no difficulty in finding other men with strong backs and empty stomachs to take their place. Therefore, Gompers concluded, the A.F.L. would admit only skilled workers.

Second, the goal of the A.F.L. unions was "bread and butter," higher wages, shorter hours, better working conditions. Gompers had no patience with utopian dreamers, particularly socialists. What counted was the here and now, not "pie in the sky." Unions with utopian programs not only distracted workers from the concrete issues that counted, but were easy targets for suppression by the bosses who were able (as in the Haymarket incident) to convince Americans that labor organizations threatened the very foundations of their society.

Third, while Gompers believed that the strike, as peaceful coercion, was the union's best weapon, he made it clear that A.F.L. unions would cooperate with employers who recognized and bargained with them. Make unions partners in industry, he told employers, meaning A.F.L. unions that supported the capitalist system, and radical anticapitalist organizations would wither and die.

The Friends of Friends

Gompers, who lived until 1924, served as president of the A.F.L. every year but one (when A.F.L. socialists defeated him). He did not see his hopes come to fruition, but he made a start. With his carrot-and-stick approach to dealing with employers—striking against those who refused to deal with the A.F.L., cooperating with those who accepted unions—he saw the A.F.L. grow from 150,000 members in 1888 to more than 1 million shortly after the turn of the century.

Most employers continued to hate him and the A.F.L. as dearly as they hated socialists and revolutionary labor unions. "Can't I do what I want with my own?" Cornelius Vanderbilt had asked years before about his company's policies. The majority of American industrialists continued to believe that the wages they paid and the hours their employees worked were no one's business but their own. Their argument was that the worker who did not like his pay had the right to quit. In 1893, such hardnosed antilabor employers formed the National Association of Manufacturers to destroy unionism wherever it appeared. The N.A.M. remained the most important antiunion organization into the twentieth century.

In 1900, a more enlightened group of manufacturers led by Frank Easley and Marcus A. Hanna, a former Rockefeller associate, came to the conclusion that labor unions were a permanent part of the American industrial scene. The choice was not between unions and no unions. The choice was (as Gompers had preached for more than a decade) between conservative, procapitalist unions that were willing to cooperate with employers and desperate, revolutionary unions that were determined to destroy capitalism.

Easley and his associates chose Gompers's A.F.L. and joined with him in 1900 to form the National Civic Federation, which was to work for industrial peace through employer—union cooperation.

Conservative Unionism

By the turn of the century, Gompers' anti-radicalism and opposition to organizing the unskilled, once practical policies, hardened into ideology and prejudice. On more than one occasion, Gompers actually used A.F.L. unions to destroy promising unions formed by unskilled workers.

The A.F.L.'s opposition to unrestricted immigration began as a hard-headed, bread-and-butter policy—to keep wages up—and took on a racialist aspect. Gompers, though himself a Jewish immigrant, denounced Jews from Eastern Europe as being incapable of becoming good American citizens. His opinions of the Japanese and Chinese on the West Coast were rabid.

The A.F.L. unions generally opposed the organization of women (20 percent of the work force) and blacks, who were not numerically important outside of agriculture but were potentially of supreme interest to any working-class movement because they could be used as strikebreakers. The result was that while the lot of the skilled workers steadily improved in the late nineteenth and early twentieth centuries, only 3 percent of "gainfully employed" Americans were members of labor organizations. A union movement, the A.F.L. was; a working-class organization, it was not.

HOLD FAST!

Some immigrants may have believed that the streets of the United States were paved with gold, but there is no sign of that fantasy in an immigrants' manual of 1891 that advised:

Hold fast, this is most necessary in America. Forget your past, your customs, and your ideals. Select a goal and pursue it with all your might. No matter what happens to you, hold on. You will experience a bad time, but sooner or later you will achieve your goal.

THE NATION OF IMMIGRANTS

"So at last I was going to America! Really, really going at last!" These words were written by Mary Antin, recalling her feelings as a girl in a *shtetl*, a Jewish village in the Russian Empire, when her family decided that their future lay in the United States. "The boundaries burst!" she went on. "The arch of heaven soared! A million suns shone out for every star. The winds rushed in from outer space, roaring in my ear, 'America! America!'"

No one ever caught the thrill of moving to the New World with such exuberance. It may have been Mary Antin's genius with her adopted language. Americans thought so: they bought 85,000 copies of *The Promised Land* when it was published in 1912. Or her joy may have been because, as Jews, her mother and father had come to the United States not merely to improve their standard of living, but to survive.

In 1881, a czar who had relaxed anti-Jewish laws in Russia was assassinated. His dim-witted son, Alexander III, persecuted the Jews and tacitly encouraged Christian peasants to rampage through the *shtetls* on bloody *pogroms* (from the Russian word meaning "riot" or "devastation"). Frustrated by the poverty and desperation of their own lives in that oppressive and poor country, they beat and killed Jews with no fear of the law. As they had before and would again, the Jews moved on. Between about 1881 and 1914, fully one-third of the Jewish population of Russia left the country, most of them bound for the United States. It was one of the greatest relocations of a people in such a short period in the history of the world.

The Flood

And the Jews were not the largest ethnic group to come to the United States during the late nineteenth and early twentieth centuries. Between 1890 and 1914 (when the outbreak of the First World War temporarily choked off immigration), some 3.6 million Italians cleared the Immigration Service. And there were others: Irish, Scots, Welsh, English, Scandinavians, Germans—the so-called "Old Immigration" that continued in large numbers through the late nineteenth century—and Poles, Lithuanians, Ukrainians, Russians, Serbians, Croatians, Slovenes, Armenians, Greeks, and, from Asia, Chinese and Japanese.

Immigration was part and parcel of the American historical experience (and is so again). The word itself, meaning movement *to* a place, was coined by an American, as more appropriate to Americans than emigration, movement *from* a place. Not even the Indians, the "native Americans," had originated in the Western Hemisphere. Throughout most of the colonial period, immigrants were as important to American growth as the natural increase of population. The Revolution and the uncertain period that followed slowed down the flow of newcomers, but not even the dangers of sea travel during the War of 1812 could quite close it down. After 1815, Europeans came over in numbers that increased almost annually. Only during serious depressions, when jobs were scarce, and during the Civil War, when a young man might be drafted before he shook down his sea legs, did the influx slow down.

From 10,000 in 1825, immigration topped 100,000 in 1845. Except for the first two years of the Civil War, the annual total never dipped below that figure. In 1854, a record 428,000 foreigners stepped ashore. In 1880, 457,000 immigrants made landfalls in Boston, New York, Philadelphia, Baltimore, New Orleans, and dozens of smaller ports. Only a crippling depression during the 1890s pushed the annual total below 300,000. After the turn of the century, during each of six years, more than 1 million people arrived to make homes in the United States. Always an abundant stream, sometimes swollen, immigration had become a flood.

A sign in four languages helps immigrants at Ellis Island.

Old Immigrants, New Immigrants

But there was more to the immigration after 1880 than a mere increase in numbers. Before 1880, a large majority of immigrants listed the British Isles, the Netherlands, Germany, or Scandinavia as their place of birth. While these northern and western Europeans continued to arrive in large numbers after 1880, an annually larger proportion of newcomers after that year originated in southern Italy; the Ottoman (Turkish) Empire; Greece; and the Slavic, Hungarian, and Rumanian parts of the Austro-Hungarian Empire. And from Russia, which then included much of Poland, came both Christian and Jewish Russians, Poles, Lithuanians, Latvians, Estonians, and Finns.

Before 1880, only about 200,000 people of southern and eastern European origin lived in the United States. Between 1880 and 1910, about 8.4 million arrived. In 1896, this New Immigration exceeded the Old for the first time. By 1907, New Immigrants were almost the whole of the influx. Of 1,285,349 legal immigrants who were registered that year, just about 1 million began their long, difficult journey in Southern and Eastern Europe.

Birth Pains of a World Economy

Although only parts of Europe, North America, and Japan may be described as having been "industrialized" in the nineteenth century, the effects of this economic revolution were felt everywhere save the most remote jungles and mountain valleys. A decline in infant mor-

tality and an increase in life expectancy, side effects of the new technology, resulted in a giant leap in population in agricultural lands as well as in the industrial countries.

World production of foodstuffs soared too, but unequally. The biggest gains were made where agriculture was itself becoming mechanized, as in the United States. In those parts of the world where peasants remained the agricultural work force, food production did not keep up with population growth. Thus, the grain from the broad American prairies and increasingly from Canada undersold grain raised on small plots by peasants in countries such as Italy and Poland, the granary of Eastern Europe. Even in Italy and Poland, American and Canadian grain was cheaper than the home-grown product.

The bottom fell out of the standard of living in the industrial world's hinterlands. During the latter decades of the nineteenth century, southern Italian farm workers made between $40 and $60 a year, Polish farm workers about the same. The cash income of peasants in southern China was too small to be worth calculating. When large landowners in Europe attempted to consolidate and modernize their holdings, the result was to push people off the land even more efficiently than declining incomes had.

The Jews of Russia felt the effects of the worldwide Industrial Revolution in their own way. Generally forbidden by Russian law to own land, most of them were old-fashioned artisans who handcrafted clothing, shoes, household goods. Others were peddlers, some fixed in one place, others wanderers. Both craftsmen and peddlers found that their way of life was undercut by modernization. The shoes made by a Warsaw cobbler could not compete with cheap, machine-made shoes from England. The peddler who wandered around Russian Poland trying to sell handmade clothing learned the same lesson.

Fleeing Militarism

Finally, people on the bottom in Germany, in the Austro-Hungarian, Russian, and Ottoman empires, and in some smaller nations were cursed by the drive to build up modern military forces. In the period before the First World War, conscription into the army could mean a life sentence. Terms of service were ten to twelve years in Austria-Hungary. With a little bad luck, they could be 25 years—a lifetime—in Russia. Even when the term was just a few years, army life was brutalizing. For generations, peasants and immigrants to the United States related chilling tales of self-mutilation by young men who were trying to escape the press gangs; they chopped off their toes or fingers, or blinded an eye. Clearly, it was better to go to the United States.

EUROPEAN IMMIGRATION

"OLD IMMIGRATION" AREAS—DOMINATED IMMIGRATION BEFORE ABOUT 1880

"NEW IMMIGRATION" AREAS—DOMINATED IMMIGRATION AFTER ABOUT 1880

Promoting Immigration

Many American industrialists encouraged immigration Until the Foran Act of 1885 made it illegal to do so, some companies paid immigrants' fares if they signed contracts agreeing to work for their patrons when they arrived in the United States. James J. Hill plastered every sizable town in Sweden and Norway with posters that described the richness of the soil along his Great Northern Railroad. (South Dakota was nicknamed the "Sunshine State" in a promotional campaign; some advertisements had palm trees swaying in the balmy Dakotan breezes.) The American Woolens Company circulated handbills in southern Italy that showed an immigrant worker with a sleek, perfumed handlebar moustache carrying a heavy sack of money from a mill to a *banco* across the street. In the West, railroaders and other employers handsomely paid Cantonese labor recruiters to import gangs of Chinese coolies to do heavy construction work at minuscule wages.

Employers liked immigrant labor because it was invariably cheaper than American labor, because immigrants would take menial, dirty jobs that Americans shunned, and because the newcomers were almost always more docile than old-stock Americans. So far from familiar surroundings and customs, they hesitated to complain. Since many intended to work in America only temporarily, a few months or a few years, and then return to their homelands, they were likely to accept very low wages, live on next to nothing, and take no interest in joining a union or going on strike.

From the national perspective, immigrant labor was pure asset. On the average, more than 60 percent of the arrivals on late nineteenth-century immigrant ships were able-bodied males; the percentage was higher among Italians and Greeks. The "old country" had borne the expense of supporting them during their unproductive childhood years and was still, often enough, supporting their women and children. In the United States, immigrants were producers pure and simple. It was a very profitable arrangement.

ETHNIC AMERICA

In addition to the general push and pull that affected all immigrants to some degree, each ethnic group had its unique experience that strongly influenced both the decision to make a home in a new land and the reception that greeted it.

HOW THEY LIVED

THE IMMIGRATION EXPERIENCE

The immigrant's trek began with a walk. Most of the people who came to the United States after 1880 were peasants, from rural villages that were far from a seaport or a railroad line. So they walked, a circumstance that put a stricter limit on the amount of baggage they could carry to America than did the rules of the steamship companies. Some might fill a handcart and sell it in a buyer's market when they reached their port of embarkation. More commonly, they carried a cheap suitcase or a bundle filled with their few possessions: clothing; a down-filled pillow or comforter; perhaps a favored cooking pot; a treasured keepsake; sometimes a vial of the soil of the native land that they would never see again.

In Italy, they usually walked all the way to the seacoast, to Genoa in the north or to Naples in the south. In Greece, which is made up of peninsulas and islands, there would usually be a ferry ride to Piraeus, the port of Athens. From deep within Russia, Lithuania, Poland, and Germany, there would be a train ride—more likely in boxcars than in passenger wagons. Even the Russians and Poles headed for a German port, Bremen or Hamburg, because while the czarist government provided both Christian peasants and Jews with excellent reasons to leave, the absence of a first-class commercial port in Russia prevented exploitation of the emigrant trade at home. Indeed, despite the threat of persecution, Russian and Polish Jews often had to enter Germany illegally, paying people who lived on the frontier to smuggle them across and secure a semblance of legal passports and exit visas.

Tickets, at least, were cheap. By the 1890s, heated competition among steamship companies in both northern and southern Europe pushed the price of transatlantic passage in steerage (the lowest class) below $20 and sometimes as low as $10. There were humiliating but important ceremonies on departure day: a rude bath and fumigation for lice on the docks, and a more than casual examination by company doctors for contagious diseases (especially tuberculosis), insanity, feeble-mindedness, and trachoma (an inflammation of the eye that leads to blindness and was common in Italy and Greece at the time). On the other side of the Atlantic, United States immigration authorities would refuse entry to anyone who suffered from these diseases, and the company that had brought them over was required to take them back. With paying passengers waiting in New York for passage home—there was a reverse migration too—captains were careful to make sure that they would not lose money on the return voyage. Moreover, while the horrors of shipboard epidemic were considerably reduced from what they had been in the age of sail, highly contagious diseases were not to be taken lightly.

The immigrants were crowded together. Immigrant ships held as many as a thousand people in steerage. There were no cabins, only large compartments formed by bulkheads in the hull. The only privacy was the minimum that could be created by hanging blankets around the few square feet of deck to which a family could enforce its claim. Bickering was constant, and fistfights were common. Except when the weather was bad, almost everyone preferred sitting on the open deck to huddling in the hold.

Most captains prohibited cooking of any kind, except perhaps the brewing of tea on the open deck. Meals were included in the price of passage and were taken in shifts; the last breakfast ran into the first dinner, and so on. Despite the efforts of the German and Italian governments to regulate the quality of food and cookery, the ship at sea was pretty much on its own, and emigrants were unlikely to complain about the quality of service once they arrived in America. Food was cheap, and the cause of constant complaint. Even when meals were good and prepared in sanitary galleys, the ship's cook could not please every passenger; the immigrants tended to be conservative in their culinary tastes, and devoted to a regional or village

The Smooth Road of the British

The people of England, Scotland, Wales, and the Protestant north of Ireland continued to be among the major immigrant groups of the nineteenth century. Between the Civil War and the turn of the century, 1.9 million Britons came to the United States. They were almost immediately at home among a people who derived primarily from their stock: in appearance, they were indistinguishable from the vast majority of white Americans; they practiced the religious faiths that were most common in the United States; and they were familiar with the basic culture, folkways, and most importantly, the language.

To be sure, they spoke with identifiable accents that distinguished them from native-born Americans. But those accents are so rarely mentioned in the historical sources that it seems clear that the foreign birth of English, Scottish, and Welsh immigrants separated them in no meaningful way from the mainstream of American society. Andrew Carnegie, Alexander Graham Bell, James J. Hill, and several of John D. Rockefeller's associates were British, but their places of birth were of no consequence to their careers or historical images.

Among the most significant as a group in the building of the American economy were the Cornish "Cousin Jacks." Miners in their homeland in England's south-cuisine. Immigrant manuals recommended the smuggling on board of a sausage or two, or some fruit and vegetables, in order to escape from the poor fare.

Between meals the travelers chatted, sewed, played games, sang, danced, studied English in small groups, read and reread manuals and letters from friends and relatives who were already in the United States, exchanged information and misinformation about their new home, and worried that they might have made a mistake. Days could be interminable, but the voyage was not a long one by steamship. Depending on the port of embarkation and the size of the ship, it took from eight days to two weeks to arrive in New York harbor.

Indeed, an immigrant steamer that arrived at the same time as many others might lie at anchor in lower New York harbor for almost as long as it had taken to cross the Atlantic. In 1892, the United States Immigration Service opened a facility designed specifically for the "processing" of newcomers on Ellis Island, a landfill site in New York harbor that had served as an arsenal. Laid out so that a stream of immigrants would flow in controlled lines through corridors and examination rooms to be inspected by physicians, nurses, and officials, Ellis Island, its architects boasted, could handle 8,000 people a day. Fifteen thousand immigrants passed through on some days, and thousands more had to wait before they could be checked.

Processing at Ellis Island was an experience that few immigrants ever forgot. Crowds milled and shoved for position before they entered the maze of pipe railings that took them from station to station. Instructions boomed over loudspeakers in half a dozen languages; children wailed; and anxious parents called for their lost children. The first person to examine the immigrants was a doctor who was expected to make an instant diagnosis of afflictions for which the newcomers might be denied entry. If he saw a facial rash, he marked a large *F* on the immigrant's clothing with a piece of soft white chalk. People

so marked were cut out of the herd and examined more closely. *H* meant suspected heart disease; *L* meant limp and examination for rickets (children were made to do a little dance); and a circle around a cross meant feeble-mindedness and thus immediate return to the ship. Thousands of families were faced with the awful decision, which had to be made within moments, whether to return to Europe with a relative who had been forbidden entry or to push on.

Those who pushed on were quickly examined for trachoma and other eye diseases and brusquely interviewed by an immigration officer. Everyone was prepared for the trick question: "Do you have a job waiting for you?" Immigrant manuals cautioned readers in capital letters *NOT* to reply in the affirmative. The Foran Contract Labor Law of 1885 forbade the making of pre-arrival agreements to work. Previously—and surreptitiously after 1885—labor jobbers had impressed immigrants into jobs under virtually slavelike conditions, or, at least, many immigrants believed that they had no choice but to work for what the Italians called the *padrone*, or "master."

About 80 percent of those who had entered the building were given landing cards that enabled them to board ferries to the Battery, the southern tip of Manhattan Island. The United States government was through with them, and the horde of agents who made their living by offering "services" now took charge. Again in a babel of languages, previously arrived countrymen shouted that they could offer jobs, provide train tickets, change currency, recommend an excellent boarding house. Some, but not many, were honest. Every large ethnic group in the United States eventually founded aid societies to provide newcomers such services and to protect them from being swindled within hours of their arrival in the land of opportunity.

---

west, the Cornish brought skills that were indispensable to the development of American mining (coal, iron, lead, and precious metals). The English, Scots, and Welsh eased into positions at every level in every occupation and industry.

The Catholic Irish

The story is a little different for the people of southern Ireland, then officially a part of Great Britain but far from British in sentiment. Almost all of the 3.4 million Irish who came to the United States between 1845 and 1900 spoke English, and they too were familiar with the

rudiments of Anglo-American culture. However, they differed from the British in two important ways.

First, they were members of the Roman Catholic Church, which many nineteenth-century American Protestants feared and hated out of historical memory. Indeed, in 1887 anti-Catholic prejudice was revived with the formation of the American Protective Association, which was especially strong in the Midwest. Members of the A.P.A. took an oath to "strike the shackles and chains of blind obedience" to the Roman Catholic Church from the minds of communicants, but their chief activity seemed to be discrimination against ordinary Catholics.

GOING HOME

The immigrant ships were not empty when they steamed eastward across the Atlantic. Plenty of immigrants returned to Europe disillusioned or in quite a good mood because they had intended to go home once they had made money in the land of opportunity. It is estimated that 370,697 British nationals, including Irish people, returned during the 1880s. Between 1875 and 1910, 18 percent of Swedish immigrants went home. In the depression year of 1875, about half the German immigrants to the United States turned around. Many Italian emigrants were virtual commuters known as "birds of passage." They shipped to the United States (or South America), worked for six months or so, living frugally and saving, and then returned to *bell'Italia* where they lived on their earnings until they were broke and it was time to commute once again. After the turn of the century, about one Italian returned to Italy for every three that arrived in America. The Greeks were thought to be the most likely to return. Between 1908 and 1931, about 40 percent of Greek immigrants made the trip back home.

Second, the Irish arrived not only much poorer than other Britons, but practically starved. Their land had been exploited by England for centuries. Brutalized by poverty, the Irish were considered by their English lords to be semibarbaric, stupid, and addicted to drunken riot as their recreation. Many Americans, especially the "WASPs" who dominated American society, culture, and economy, adopted the common English prejudice. Although Irish behavior was little different from the behavior of any people ground down by poverty, many of the idealistic Republicans who had fought against similar stereotypes when they had been applied to blacks were the most extreme Irish-baiters. Employers hung the sign "NINA" (No Irish Need Apply) on their gates and in their shop windows.

And yet, Irish-Americans took with zest to their adopted home. Numerous enough that they could insulate their personal lives from anti-Catholic prejudice, the Irish parlayed their cohesiveness and natural bent for oratory into a formidable political force. By the time of the Civil War, the Democratic party organizations in heavily Irish cities such as Boston and New York were catering to the interests of the Irish community and reaping rewards in an almost unanimous Irish vote. By the 1880s, Irish immigrants and Irish-Americans dominated urban politics in much of the East and Midwest, and in San Francisco. Ironically, it was their considerable power on the West Coast that led to the first legislation to restrict immigration—of the Chinese.

Guests of the Golden Mountain

In 1849, seamen brought the news to the Chinese port of Canton that a *gum shan*, a mountain of gold, had been discovered in California. In a country plagued by overpopulation, flood, famine, epidemic disease, and civil warfare, the people of the southern Chinese province of Kwang-tung listened avidly to the usual distortions of life across the ocean. "Americans are a very rich people," one promoter explained. "They want the Chinaman to come and will make him welcome . . . . It will not be strange company."

By 1852, 20,000 Chinese had arrived in California. The richest mines had long since been discovered and skimmed. For the frugal Chinese, accustomed to a destitution unknown in America, this was of no moment. Accustomed to working communally in groups of twelve

Chinese immigrant posed with his possessions to prove to relatives back home that he had been successful in America.

SUI GENERIS

The population of Ireland in 1840 was estimated to have been 8 million. In 1980, the population of the country was a bit less than 4 million. Surely the Emerald Isle is the only part of the world with fewer people today than 140 years ago, let alone less than half the number. Leaving is, perhaps, the central fact of Irish culture.

to twenty, and paid just $26–$36 a month—too little for a white Forty-Niner, they made a living taking over diggings that Caucasians had abandoned. Other Chinese found employment in menial jobs that whites disdained: cook, laundryman, farm worker, domestic servant. By 1860, there were 35,000 Chinese immigrants in California. Most of them were young men who hoped to return home after they had made their fortune. There were only 1,800 Chinese women in the state, a good many of them prostitutes. In San Francisco, Sacramento, Marysville, and most mining camps of any size, lively Chinatowns flourished.

Race and a radically different culture kept the Chinese separate. "When I got to San Francisco," wrote Lee Chew, later a wealthy businessman, "I was half-starved because I was afraid to eat the provisions of the barbarians. But a few days living in the Chinese Quarter and I was happy again."

Leaders of the *Gum Shan Hok*—the Guests of the Golden Mountain—also encouraged the immigrants to stick to themselves. "We are accustomed to an orderly society," explained a leader of the San Francisco Chinatown, "but it seems as if the Americans are not bound by rules of conduct. It is best, if possible, to avoid any contact with them."

After the construction of the transcontinental railroad began in 1864, Chinese immigration stepped up. Previously about 3,000 to 6,000 a year had come to

IRISH-AMERICAN PATRIOTISM

In 1835, John England, the Roman Catholic bishop of Charleston, provided an explanation of why the Irish took so adeptly to politics: "The Irish are largely amalgamated with the Americans, their dispositions, their politics, their notions of government; their language and their appearance become American very quickly, and they praise and prefer America to their oppressors at home."

California; after 1868, the annual number jumped to 12,000 and 20,000, peaking at 23,000 in 1872.

Keeping John Chinaman Out

As long as there was plenty of work, hostility to the Chinese was restrained. But in 1873, the West lapsed into a depression along with the rest of the country. In 1877, when the Chinese represented 17 percent of California's population, a San Francisco teamster named Denis Kearney began to speak to white workingmen at open-air rallies in empty sandlots. He blamed the joblessness not on impersonal economic forces, but on the willingness of the Chinese to work for less than an American's living wage. Kearney led several rampages through Chinatown, but, much more important, the anti-Chinese movement inspired politicians to choke off the Asian immigration. In 1882, Congress enacted the Exclusion Act, which forbade the Chinese to come. A few hundred continued to enter legally every year (mostly women to become wives of *Gum Shan Hok* already here), and illegal immigration via Canada helped somewhat to augment the Chinese-American population.

To some extent, Filipinos and Japanese replaced the Chinese in the Asian immigration. Filipinos had free access to the United States after their country was made an American colony in 1898. Japanese began to trickle in, usually via Hawaii, where they were an important factor in the agricultural labor force. Caucasians resented them as much as they had disliked the Chinese, but because Japan had a strong government that was sensitive to racial slights, the U.S. Congress did not adopt a Japanese exclusion law until 1924, when most other immigrant groups were also shut out.

The Germans and the Political Motive

In general, the large German immigration to the United States owed to the same worldwide economic forces that displaced other peasant peoples. After 1848, however, there was also a strong political dimension to the German removal. The failure of a series of liberal revolutions in several German states—revolutions aimed at establishing a democratic system and individual rights much like those that existed in the United States—forced the exile of many leading German liberals. The most famous German exile in the United States was Carl Schurz, who became a senator from Missouri and a member of Rutherford B. Hayes's cabinet.

Many of the 4.4 million Germans who came to the United States between 1850 and 1900, an average of about 100,000 a year, were also influenced by fears that life would be intolerable under the new reactionary governments in their homeland.

Because many of them had been landowners in Europe, albeit not rich ones, German immigrants generally had enough money when they reached the United States to move westward and take up free or cheap land. Wisconsin became heavily German in the last half of the nineteenth century. By 1900, more Milwaukeeans spoke German, at least as their first language, than English. There were other heavily German areas in Missouri and Texas.

Adapting to America

Like the Germans, Scandinavians inclined to become farmers in the United States. Norwegians predominated in whole counties in Wisconsin and Minnesota. Swedes were numerous in other parts of Minnesota and in the Pacific Northwest. Finns, who speak an entirely different language from the Swedes but are historically tied to them in many respects, were important in yet other regions, particularly in logging country and in the iron mines of the Mesabi Range.

Ethnic groups that predominated over large areas found adaptation to the New World comparatively easy since they could approximate familiar Old World ways of life. They founded schools taught in their native languages, newspapers and other periodicals, European-style fraternal organizations (the Germans' athletically oriented *Turnverein*, or the Norwegians' musical Grieg Societies, named after their national composer), and so on. They continued to eat familiar food and raise their children by traditional rules. They were numerous enough to deal with "Americans" from a position of strength.

The problems that such immigrants faced were common to all settlers of a new land. Olë Rolvaag, a gloomy Norwegian-American writer, focused on the loneliness of life on the northern prairies, an experience that was shared by all pioneers there regardless of ethnic background: He did not write about cultural alienation. Indeed, he wrote in Norwegian and, like Isaac Bashevis Singer in the late twentieth century, became known as an American novelist only in translation.

Sephardic and German Jews

Other immigrant groups had a comparatively easy time adapting because they were few and cosmopolitan. The best example is the Sephardic Jews (Jews descended from and still somewhat influenced by the customs of Spanish and Portuguese forebears). Small in numbers, generally well-educated and well-fixed, they eased into middle- and upper-class society even before the Civil War, particularly in Rhode Island and New York, and in cities like Charleston and New Orleans. Considering the fewness of their numbers, they contributed a remarkable number of prominent citizens. Jefferson Davis's strongest supporter in the Confederacy was Judah P. Benjamin, a Sephardic Jew who served in three cabinet posts. Supreme Court Justice Benjamin Cardozo had a Sephardic background. So did the twentieth-century financier and presidential adviser, Bernard Baruch of South Carolina.

By 1880, there was also a small German Jewish community in the United States, perhaps 150,000 people. The majority were small-scale tradesmen or businessmen—rare was the Southern town without its Jewish-owned drygoods store. Some German Jews, such as Levi Strauss, pioneered in the founding of the ready-made clothing industry; others carved out places for themselves in finance, usually independent of the long-established American banking community, which was WASP-dominated and generally closed to outsiders (August Belmont was the most successful). The Guggenheim syndicate was one of the nation's leading owners of metal mines by the turn of the century.

The German Jews clung to their religious heritage, but otherwise quickly adopted American mores and customs. Indeed, led by Rabbi Isaac Mayer Wise of Cincinnati, German Jews in the United States preferred Reform religious observance, which is highly secular and closely equivalent to liberal Protestantism, to the Orthodox, fundamentalist Judaism of the Jews of the New Immigration.

The Trauma of the New Immigration

Adapting to their new homes was not so easy for most of the New Immigrants who arrived after 1880. Very few of the newcomers from southern and Eastern Europe had much money when they arrived. Most were illiterate, and their Old World experience in peasant village and *shtetl* did not prepare them for life in the world's greatest industrial nation during its era of most rapid development.

However serious the immigrants' reasons for leaving ancestral homes, the homes were still ancestral, the rhythms of life familiar, the customs second nature. Wherever their origins, the New Immigrants had been accustomed to a rural and traditional way of life that was the very antithesis of life in the United States, whether on a commercial farm or in the crowded streets of the big city.

Not only was the circle of friends and acquaintances small in the Old World, but the number of people with whom the peasant or Jewish shopkeeper dealt in the course of life was limited to a comparative few who, in any case, spoke a familiar language and thought according to similar (or, at least, well-understood) values.

In the United States, however, all but a very few landsmen or *compagni* were alien, and everyone spoke incomprehensible languages. The immigrants, at home for better or for worse in Europe or Asia, were foreigners, a minority in the United States.

Strangest of all for people who came from traditional, pre-industrial cultures where life was regulated and slowed by the seasons, the weather, the use of hand tools, American life was regulated and rushed by the tyrannical clock and powered by the relentless churning of the dynamo. In the industrial society of the late nineteenth century, Americans were even more self-driven than they had been when Alexis de Tocqueville's head had been set spinning by the American pace. This was particularly true in the big cities where a majority of the New Immigrants settled and which, in the minds of other Americans, were intimately associated with the newcomers.

For Further Reading

The general histories listed in the bibliographies of Chapters 27–29 are all pertinent to this chapter as well. Specifically dealing with immigrants are: Rowland T. Berthoff, *British Immigrants in Industrial America* (1953); Leonard Dinnerstein and David Reimers, *Ethnic Americans: A History of Immigration and Assimilation* (1975); Nathan Glazer and Daniel P. Moynihan, *Beyond the Melting Pot* (1970); Oscar Handlin, *The Uprooted* (1951); Marcus L. Hansen, *The Immigrant in American History* (1940); John Higham, *Send These to Me: Jews and Other Immigrants in Urban America* (1975); Maldwyn A. Jones, *American Immigration* (1960); Dale Steiner, *Of Thee We Sing* (1986); and Philip A. M. Taylor, *The Distant Magnet* (1970).

Books with a focus on working people include David Brody, *Workers in Industrial America* (1979); Robert V. Bruce, *1877: Year of Violence* (1959); Melvyn Dubofsky, *Industrialism and the American Worker, 1865–1920* (1975); Foster R. Dulles and Melvyn Dubofsky, *Labor in America* (1984); Herbert G. Gutman, *Work, Culture, and Society in Industrializing America* (1976); Harold C. Livesay, *Samuel Gompers and the Origins of the American Federation of Labor* (1978); David Montgomery, *Workers' Control in America: Studies in the History of Work, Technology, and Labor Struggle* (1979); Daniel Nelson, *Managers and Workers: Origins of the New Factory System in the United States, 1880–1920* (1975); Henry Pelling, *American Labor* (1960); Daniel T. Rogers, *The Work Ethic in Industrial America, 1850–1920* (1974); and Philip Taft, *The A.F. of L. in the Time of Gompers* (1929).

"Street Arabs"—homeless, abandoned boys in New York Ci

BRIGHT LIGHTS AND SQUALID SLUMS

THE GROWTH OF BIG CITIES

Once in the United States, immigrants discovered that their most ordinary practices—even the way

they looked—struck Americans of older stock as exotic. Even those "WASPs" who had grown

accustomed to the restrained Roman Catholic worship of the Irish and the Germans found themselves

troubled by the mystical Catholicism of the Poles and the public ceremonies of the Italians. Indeed,

Irish bishops joined Methodists in worrying about the "paganism" implied in the magnificently

bedecked statues of the Madonna and the gory, surrealistic depictions of the crucified Christ that peasants from Sicily and the Campania carried through the streets of San Francisco, Chicago, New Orleans, and New York, accompanied by the unlikely music of brass bands.

The Orthodox services of the Greeks, Russians, Ukrainians, Serbians, and other Balkan peoples seemed to feature even more ornate vestments and mystifying rituals than the Catholic Mass. The Jews and the Chinese, of course, were not even Christian and therefore all the more out of line with American traditions.

The newcomers looked different from Americans. The Greeks, Armenians, Assyrians, Lebanese, and Italians were generally swarthy in complexion, a formidable handicap in a nation that was drawing a sharp color line. Polish women often arrived clad in colorful babushkas, aprons, and billowing ground-length skirts of the Eastern European peasant. The impoverished Jews dressed drably enough for late-nineteenth-century American taste, but the men, if religious, wore full beards and never removed their hats. Their Saturday sabbath attracted attention principally because the Jews turned Sunday into a combination holiday and major market day, which offended the sabbatarian sensibilities of some Protestants.

Americans who visited immigrant neighborhoods were unsettled because the smells in the air were alien. Clinging to their traditional diets, which were often based on pungent seasonings and the use of much more onion and garlic than old-stock Americans deemed humane, the immigrants seemed determined to resist American ways all the while they lived in the country.

CITIES AS ALIEN ENCLAVES

In his novel of 1890, *A Hazard of New Fortunes*, William Dean Howells sent Basil March, a genteel and educated middle-class American, on a ride on an elevated train in New York City. March "found the variety of people in the car as unfailingly entertaining as ever" but he felt like a foreigner in his own country. Even the Irish, who ran the city, were outnumbered by "the people of Germanic, Slavonic, of Pelagic [Mediterranean], of Mongolian stock. . . . The small eyes, the high cheeks, the broad noses, the puff lips, the bare, cue-filleted skulls, of Russians, Poles, Czechs, Chinese, the furtive glitter of Italians, the blond dullness of Germans; the cold quiet of Scandinavians—fire under ice—were aspects that he identified, and that gave him abundant suggestion for the . . . reveries in which he dealt with the future economy of our heterogeneous commonwealth."

A Patchwork Quilt

The cities, particularly in the Northeast and Midwest, where 80 percent of the New Immigrants settled, seemed to be salients established and secured by invading armies. By 1890, one-third of the population of Boston and Chicago had been born abroad, as were one-quarter of Philadelphia's people. When their children, who seemed to old-stock Americans as obdurately foreign as their parents, were added to this total, the anxiety of "American" residents and visitors to the cities is easy to understand.

In fact, the immigrants threatened no one. Members of each ethnic group clustered together into "ghettos" that were exclusively their own. A map of New York, wrote journalist and photographer Jacob Riis, himself a Danish immigrant, "colored to designate nationalities, would show more stripes than the skin of a zebra and more colors than the rainbow." Jane Addams sketched a similar patchwork in the poor part of Chicago, where she established one of the first American settlement houses, agencies to help the immigrants, Hull House. The same was true of most large eastern and midwestern cities and of many smaller industrial towns. In Lawrence, Massachusetts, a woolens manufacturing town, more than twenty languages and probably twice that many distinctive dialects were spoken.

There were ghettos within ghettos. In New York City's Greenwich Village, an Italian community, people from the region of Calabria effectively controlled housing on some streets, immigrants from Sicily on others. On such regional blocks, Italians from a specific village would sometimes be the sole occupants of an "Agrigento tenement," and so on. Grocery stores and restaurants advertised themselves not as Italian but as purveyors of Campanian or Apulian food. Priests frequently ministered to the same people whom they had known back in Italy; lawyers often represented the same clients.

The same held true for Jewish neighborhoods, where Galician Jews (Galicia was a Polish province of Austria–Hungary) looked with suspicion on Jews from Russian-speaking areas. Romanian Jews fastidiously set up their own communities, and the better established and assimilated German Jews wondered what the world was coming to. Christian Germans divided on Lutheran and Catholic lines; Serbians and Croatians as to whether they wrote their common language in the Latin or the Cyrillic alphabet.

The Impulse to Assimilate

The desire to assimilate, to become "American," varied in intensity from group to group, and among individuals within a group. Some immigrants found solace in the familiar language, familiar customs, familiar foods, and

Chinese immigrants being examined for glaucoma (grounds for deportation) at Angel's Island, San Francisco.

fellowship of "Little Italy," "Jewville," and "Polack Town," and clung tenaciously to the neighborhood. The ethnic ghetto was a buffer against the prejudice of old-stock Americans and the hostility of other ethnic groups with whom its inhabitants competed for the lowest-level jobs. Even an educated immigrant from the Austro-Hungarian Empire found himself disoriented in his attempts to "shift" from old to new ways of thinking and reacting.

I never knew if my reactions would be in line with the new code of conduct and had to think and reflect. Whenever I decided on the spur of the moment I found myself out of sympathy with my environment. I did not feel as they felt and therefore I felt wrongly according to their standards. To act instinctively in an American fashion and manner was impossible, and I appeared slow and clumsy. The proverbial slowness of foreigners is largely due to this cause.

Others seized avidly on what they took to be "American" ways with an extraordinary enthusiasm. This was perhaps best illustrated in the large Jewish community of New York's Lower East Side, which in its earliest years was sharply divided between those who clung to the medieval ways of the Russian and Polish *shtetls* and the big-city-wise and sophisticated younger immigrants and

children of immigrants who often scorned their elders' "greenhorn" ways

Avenues of Advancement

Hard work at menial jobs was the economic lot of most immigrants. The urban political machine, which had room at or near the top for anyone who could deliver votes, provided an avenue of advancement for a few who recognized the opportunities it provided for the "boss" of the ethnic ghetto. Others joined the American quest for material success by pursuing careers in areas that were not quite respectable, and, therefore, less attractive to members of established social groups—show business, professional sports, and organized crime, that is, illegal business. The roster of surnames of leading entertainers, boxers, baseball players, and gangsters over a period of decades reads almost like the strata of a canyon that geologists read, each layer dominated by members of a new, aspiring ethnic group.

Immigrant Aid Institutions

The ethnic groups themselves established institutions to assist their countrymen in adjusting to the new life.

Some encouraged assimilation, some clannishness. Sephardic and German Jewish families who were comfortably established in the United States founded the Hebrew Immigrant Aid Society to minister to the needs of the penniless Eastern European Jews who flocked into the cities. The Young Men's and Young Women's Hebrew Associations, dating back to 1854, expanded several times over during the last decade of the century.

Among the Catholic population, which grew from 6 million in 1880 to 10 million in 1900 (making Roman Catholicism the country's largest single denomination), traditionally charitable religious orders such as the Franciscans and the Sisters of Mercy established hospitals and houses of refuge in the slums. The St. Vincent de Paul Society functioned much like the Salvation Army, providing food, clothing, and shelter for the utterly desperate, but without the military trappings.

Curiously, a sort of ethnic prejudice helped to hamstring the older Jewish and older Catholic communities in responding to the needs of the New Immigrants. Sephardic and German Jews worried that the numbers, poverty, and provincialism of the Eastern European newcomers would arouse an anti-Semitic spirit among Christians that would be turned on them, too. The American Catholic Church was dominated by Irish-Americans who were little more cordial toward Italians, Poles, and other new Catholic nationalities than were old-stock Protestants. Only after an encyclical of 1891, *Rerum Novarum*, in which the pope proclaimed a Catholic Social Gospel, did the Church hierarchy take much interest in the material well-being of its communicants.

Then the Church was torn between serving as an agency of assimilation and maintaining its high standing among Catholic immigrants—who often clung to their religion with more piety than they had in Europe—by encouraging a "fortress mentality" toward the dominant Protestant culture. Indeed, the Church approved of parishes organized along ethnic rather than geographical lines. In places like Detroit and New Orleans, there might be an Italian, a Polish, a Lithuanian, and a geographical parish church—that is, an Irish–German one—within a few blocks of one another.

Settlement Houses

Old-stock Americans created the settlement house, an idea patterned after Toynbee Hall located in a notorious London slum, to assist immigrants in coming to terms with their new country.

During the 1880s, a number of middle-class Americans who were imbued with the New England conscience that dictated concern for others traveled to England to learn how Toynbee worked. They found that the house provided food and drink to the disinherited, as traditional charities had, but also child care for working mothers, recreational facilities, and courses of study in everything from household arts to the English language and social skills needed to function in the larger society. The young men and women who worked at Toynbee Hall also told the Americans that they had been morally elevated by their sacrifices and exposure to a misery that they had not known in their own lives.

The first American settlement house was the Neighborhood Guild, set up in New York City in 1886. More

Hester Street in New York City was home to a large community of Jewish immigrants in the early 1890s.

famous, however, because of the powerful personalities of their founders, were Jane Addams's Hull House in Chicago (1889), Robert A. Woods's South End House in Boston (1892), and Lillian Wald's Henry Street Settlement in New York (1893). From comfortable middle-class backgrounds, well-educated, and finely mannered, Addams, Woods, and Wald were exemplars of the American middle class who were determined to fight the materialism of their own people, the misery suffered by poor city dwellers, and to keep traditional American values alive by educating immigrants in them. What they did not always understand was that in the great metropolises that took shape in the late nineteenth century, a new American culture and code of values was emerging.

OF THE GROWTH OF GREAT CITIES

Americans had an ingrained prejudice against cities that dated back to Thomas Jefferson, but they were also, by the end of the nineteenth century, one of the world's most urban peoples. The proportion of city dwellers in the total population, the number of cities, and the size of cities all increased at a faster rate in the United States than in any other country in the world.

In 1790, when the first national census was taken, only 3.4 percent of Americans lived in towns of 8,000 people or more. By 1860, the eve of the Civil War, 16 percent of the population was urban, and by 1900, 33 percent was.

The increase in the number of cities is rather more striking. In 1790, only six American cities boasted populations of 8,000 or more. The largest of them, Philadelphia, was home to 42,000 people. In 1860, 141 municipalities had at least 8,000 people within their limits; by 1890, 448 did, and by 1910, 778! Fully twenty-six cities were larger than 100,000 in 1900, and six of them topped 500,000. Philadelphia counted 1.3 million people at the turn of the century and, at that, had slipped to third place behind New York and Chicago.

From Country to City

Although the influx of immigrants was largely responsible for the tremendous growth of cities at the end of the century, Americans migrated from country to city too. Dismayed by the isolation of farm life, ground down by the heavy tedious labor, and often as not reaping few rewards for their toil, they heard of well-paying jobs for literate, mechanically inclined people. Or they visited cities and were dazzled by the bright lights, the abundance of company, the stimulation of a world in constant

motion, and the stories of the fortunes that might be made in business.

Parents, rural ministers, and editors of farm magazines begged, threatened, and cajoled in an effort to keep the children of the soil at home, but their efforts met with limited success. While the total number of farm families grew during the late-nineteenth century, the proportion of farmers in the total population declined, and in some regions, with a nearby city beckoning, even the numbers dropped. During the 1880s, more than half the rural townships of Iowa and Illinois declined in population, while Chicago underwent its miraculous growth. In New England, while the overall population of the region increased by 20 percent, three rural townships in five lost people to the dozens of bustling mill towns that lined the fast-moving rivers and to the metropolises of Boston and New York.

For the most part, the American migration from farm to city was a white migration. Only 12 percent of the 5 million blacks in the United States in 1890 lived in cities. Nevertheless, about 500,000 blacks moved from the rural South to the urban North during the final decade of the century, foreshadowing one of the most significant population movements of the twentieth century.

The Walking City

While rapid growth was the rule in cities large and small, the most dramatic phenomenon of American urbanization in the late nineteenth century was the emergence of the gigantic metropolises, the six cities of more than 500,000 people that dominated the regions in which they sat like imperial capitals. Philadelphia doubled in size between 1860 and 1900, when William Penn's "green countrie towne" claimed 1.3 million people. New York, with 33,000 people in 1790, and over 1 million in 1860, quadrupled its numbers until, by 1900, 4.8 million lived within its five "boroughs." New York was the second largest city in the world, smaller only than London.

Chicago's crazy rate of growth as the hub of the nation's railroad system amazed Americans and foreigners alike. With only a few more than 100,000 people in 1860, Chicago increased its size twenty times in a generation, numbering 2.2 million inhabitants in 1900.

Before the 1870s, cities so vast were unimaginable. When the mass of a city's population moved around by foot, city growth was limited in area to a radius of a mile or two, as far as a person could walk from home to workplace or a housekeeper could walk to market in an hour or so. To be sure, the well-to-do owned horses and carriages in the walking city and could, therefore, live a greater distance from their places of business and entertainment. But not too far. A horse moves only margin-

HOW THEY LIVED

BIG CITY SWEATSHOPS

In the early nineteenth century, four Americans in five wore clothing that had been made to order. The wealthy took their wants to the little shops in every town and city where fine garments were expertly made by hand from fabric to finished product. With great skill, tailors and seamstresses worked not from patterns, as someone interested in sewing would do today, but from fashion plates, carefully drawn pictures in magazines of people dressed in the latest styles. By the early nineteenth century, Paris was already considered the authority in such matters.

The middle classes, which began to pay more attention to "fashion" in the nineteenth century, depended on their womenfolk for their garb. That is why needlecraft learned at a mother's knee was such an important part of a young girl's education; clothing her family would be one of her most important duties as a wife and mother.

As for the poor, they made do with castoffs either scavenged or purchased from merchants who specialized in buying and reconditioning used clothing. The fact that most garments were made to fit an individual did not mean that any particular item had been made to fit the person who, at a given time, was wearing it.

Only sailors, slaves, and—after 1849—miners in the West were likely to wear clothing such as virtually everyone does today, ready-made in quantity to standard sizes and sold "off the rack." Sailors were not generally in a port long enough to be fitted and a garment sewn. (The first ready-made clothing stores were called "sailors' shops.") The slaves had no choice in the matter of what they put on their backs, and their owners, wanting to provide them some protection from the elements at a minimum cost, became an attractive market for enterprising tailors who abandoned the custom trade and took to producing rough, cheap garments in quantity. Miners, like sailors, were in a hurry, and they lived in an almost entirely masculine society. Their demand for sturdy, ready-made clothing provided the impetus for the founding in 1850 of the Levi Strauss Company of San Francisco, today perhaps the best-known manufacturer of ready-made clothing in the world.

By 1900, things had changed. Nine Americans in ten were wearing ready-made togs. A "Clothing Revolution," as historian Daniel Boorstin has called it, had taken place as a consequence of technology with, curiously, a boost from the American Civil War.

The technology was supplied by inventions such as the sewing machine, patented by Elias Howe in 1846, and powered scissors that could cut through eighteen pieces of fabric at once, thus making the parts for eighteen garments of exactly the same size. The standard sizes were provided by the United States government when the Civil War made it necessary to buy uniforms for hundreds of thousands of men. The army's Quartermaster Corps measured hundreds of recruits and arrived at sets of proportions that provided a fit for almost all. It was a simple step to do the same for women's sizes after the war ended, and ready-made clothing shops began to displace tailors and seamstresses. The department store, which appeared at the end of the century, was built around its selection of every kind of clothing. The great mail-order houses such as Montgomery Ward and Sears Roebuck were able, with everyone knowing his or her size, to sell garments by mail.

How were the new ready-made clothes manufactured? Not, ironically, in factories. There was little outsize machinery involved in the making of garments (sewing machines were treadle or electrically powered) and a great deal of handwork (finishing buttonholes, installing linings). Thus it was possible to farm out the work to people in their homes, just as, before the invention of cloth-making machinery, spinning and weaving had been farmed out.

Whereas the old putting-out system usually had in-

---

ally faster than a pedestrian and rather more slowly when the streets are choked with people wending to and fro. Indeed, the most common layout of a mill town was a factory or two at the geographical center of the city and residential areas surrounding it in concentric circles; or, more likely, because mills were generally located near rivers, in semicircles fronting the water. The workers clustered close by. With a twelve-hour day to work, there was little time for commuting. The small businessmen who owned the shops lived behind them. The millowners, their top supervisors, and professionals lived on the outskirts. They were not strangers to the crowding, noise, dirt, and turmoil of the walking city, but when the opportunity to flee presented itself, they were quick to seize it.

Farthest out of all, beyond the built-up neighborhoods, paved streets, and sewers, were ramshackle shantytowns inhabited by people with only a marginal role to play in the city's life. Unlike today, when the homeless crowd into the core cities, in the nineteenth century, the limitations inherent in foot and horse travel left the outskirts, a form of banishment, to them.

Getting Around

One of the earliest means by which wealthy and middle-class people could put some distance between their residences and center city was the horsecar line. With charters from city hall, entrepreneurs strung light rails down major thoroughfares and ran horse-drawn streetcars volved the wives and daughters of farmers, leaving people on the land, the new putting-out system engaged people who lived in city slums and who depended exclusively on needlework for their livelihood.

The system was called "sweating," and the places in which the garmentmakers worked were called "sweatshops" because of the peculiarly exploitative character of the system. A manufacturer of clothing kept a small headquarters; at the most, the material was cut to pattern in his "factory." Then, the pieces of a garment were handed out on a weekly or daily basis to people, usually Jewish or Italian immigrants, who took them home to their tenement apartments. There the whole family—perhaps some boarders, perhaps even some neighbors—sat down during all the daylight hours to make up the garments. Sometimes a household saw a coat (usually called a cloak in the nineteenth century) or a gown through from components to completion. Other households specialized in different phases of the process, such as roughing the garment in, or finishing work. Some sweatshops made buttonholes, others sewed pockets, and so on.

The key to the system was that everyone involved was paid by the piece—so much per jacket, so much per lining. A complex hierarchy of subcontracting developed in which it was to the interest of all to pay those below them in the chain as little for their work as possible. That is, a man who provided finished cloaks to the manufacturer received a fixed rate for each garment that he delivered. In order to make a profit, he had to pay less than that rate to those households that had done the work. If the head of a household sweatshop had boarders or neighbors sewing, he had to pay them even less. Everybody was "sweating" their income out of somebody else.

Moreover, just as in factories, employers were inclined to cut the piece rate as a worker's productivity increased or when someone else told the manufacturer whom he supplied (who sweated him) that others were willing to work for less. In order to compete, he sweated the people under him.

In turn, everyone in the chain had to take less for their work. The operator of a Chicago sweatshop explained the results to a Congressional committee in 1893:

Q. *In what condition do you get the garments?*
A. *They come here already cut and I make them up.*
Q. *What is the average wage of the men per week?*
A. *About $15 a week.*
Q. *How much do the women get?*
A. *About $6. They get paid for extra hours. . . .*
Q. *Are wages higher or lower than they were two years ago?*
A. *Lower. There are so many who want to work.*
Q. *How much do you get for making this garment?*
A. *Eighty cents.*
Q. *How much did you get for making it two years ago?*
A. *About $1.25.*
Q. *Is the help paid less now?*
A. *Yes, sir.*

A cloakmaker, Abraham Bisno, told the same panel that he had earned about $20 a week in 1885 for completing fewer garments than he had sewn in 1890, when he had made $13 to $14 a week. In 1893, he was being paid $11 a week for even greater productivity.

As the rate per piece fell, sweatshop workers increased their hours in the unhealthful, poorly ventilated tenements. Only when urban states such as New York and Illinois passed laws that forbade such work in residences was there any improvement in conditions. But, often as not, the driving exploitation of the sweat system was merely transferred to an unhealthful, poorly ventilated factory that was little different from a tenement flat.

---

with seats open to the public. Cheap as the fares were, usually five cents, they were still too expensive for most working people, who continued to walk to work. However, skilled artisans, white-collar workers, and small-business men took advantage of the quick, cheap transportation to move away from their places of business: north on the island of Manhattan in New York, west across the Schuylkill River in Philadelphia, north and west in Chicago, and west out of Boston.

Making possible even more distant residential neighborhoods was the steam-powered elevated train, or El, which ran at high speeds above the crowded streets on ponderous and ugly steel scaffolding. In 1870, New York completed the first El on Ninth Avenue, and the range of the trains, soon up to the northern tip of Manhattan,

encouraged the middle classes to move even farther away from Wall Street and the once leafy, now crowded Bowery. In making the suburbs more accessible, the Els also served to begin the process of pushing the residents of the shantytowns into inner-city housing abandoned by the middle classes.

Electric Trolleys

The utility of elevated trains was limited by the high cost of constructing them. Only the richest, largest (and most corrupt) cities were able and willing to shoulder the expense. Moreover, no sooner did the Els stimulate residential construction along their routes, where they ran at ground level, than the noisy, dirty, and dangerous

Grid-lock in the horsedrawn age. Because a horse could panic or collapse, traffic jams in the late nineteenth century were often worse than they are today.

locomotives roused the ire of the very people who rode on them to work and recreation.

Consequently, it was the electric trolley car, pioneered by inventor-businessman Frank J. Sprague, that decisively turned the walking city into a memory and ensured the sprawl of the great metropolises. Economical, fast but easy to stop, clean, quiet, even melodious in their rattling and ringing of bells, the trolleys were the key to the growth of big cities and assets to smaller ones. Richmond was the first to build a system in 1887. By 1895, fully 850 lines crisscrossed American cities on 10,000 miles of track. They were as important to the urbanization of the United States as the railroads were to the settlement of the West.

Building Up

By enabling the construction of residential neighborhoods miles from city business districts, the trolleys made it possible for many more people to congregate in city centers for work, business, and entertainment. This caused real-estate values to soar to absurd heights.

The practical solution was obvious enough: multiply the square footage of midtown properties by building multi-storied structures such as steam- or electric-powered elevators theoretically made possible. Even with the elevators at hand, however, there was still a catch in vertical construction. In order to support the weight of tall buildings built of stone or brick, the weight-bearing walls had to be so thick on the lower floors, virtually solid like the pyramids of Egypt, as to defeat the whole purpose of building up.

Once again, technology provided the solution in the form of extremely strong I-shaped steel girders. With these at their disposal, architects were able to abandon the very concept of weight-bearing walls and design skeletons of steel on which, in effect, they hung decorative siding of cast iron or of stone. The potential height of steel buildings seemed almost limitless. They could rise so high as to scrape the sky. Indeed, once the method was perfected, corporations competed to erect the tallest tower, as medieval cities had competed to build the tallest cathedral spire.

In time, New York was to become the most dramatic

of the skyscraper cities; but Chicago architects pioneered in the design of "tall office buildings," as Louis H. Sullivan, the most thoughtful of architects, rather prosaically described his graceful structures. In an article in *Lippincott's Magazine* in 1896, Sullivan explained how through the use of "proud and soaring" vertical sweeps, "a unit without a single dissenting line," the artistic form of the skyscraper reflected the essence of its construction. In the twentieth century, Sullivan's even more imaginative protégé, Frank Lloyd Wright, was to apply the principle of "form following function" to a wide variety of structures.

Building Over

Another technological innovation that contributed to the expansion of cities was the suspension bridge, which erased wide rivers as barriers to urban growth. Its pioneer was a German immigrant, John A. Roebling, who came to the United States in 1831 as a canal engineer and set up the first American factory for twisting steel wire into cable. Roebling's associates scoffed at his contention that if a bridge were hung from strong cables instead of built up on massive pillars that had to stand in the water,

much broader rivers could be spanned. Obsessed with the concept of a suspension bridge, Roebling devoted his life to perfecting a design. Before the Civil War, he had several to his credit, including an international bridge over the Niagara River near the Falls.

Roebling planned his masterpiece for the East River, which separated downtown New York, a city bursting at the seams, from the roomy seaport of Brooklyn on Long Island. While working on the site in 1869, he was injured, contracted a tetanus infection, and died. Without delay, his equally devoted son, Washington A. Roebling, carried on the work. He too suffered serious injuries; he was crippled from the "bends," later associated with deep-sea divers, as a result of working too long below water level on the foundations of the towers. Nevertheless, from a chair in a room overlooking the great span, now called the Brooklyn Bridge, he saw it completed in 1883. It was admired for its beauty as well as its engineering.

In providing easy access to Manhattan—33 million people crossed it each year—the bridge ignited a residential real-estate boom in Brooklyn; within a few years, Brooklyn was the fourth largest city in the United States. But the bridge also spelled the end of Brooklyn as an

A network of trolley car lines served San Francisco's transportation needs. Note "cow catchers" designed to save humans as well as errant animals from slipping beneath the wheels.

The Flatiron Building, an early skyscraper, photographed around 1905. Today it is dwarfed by its neighbors. .

independent city. Increasingly a satellite of Manhattan, Brooklyn was legally incorporated into the city of New York in 1898.

The Great Symbol

The Brooklyn Bridge was dedicated with a mammoth celebration. President Chester A. Arthur proclaimed it "a monument to democracy." Sides of beef were roasted in the streets, oceans of beer and whiskey disappeared, brass bands competed in raising a din, races were run, prizes were awarded, dances were danced, and noses were punched. A fireworks display of unprecedented magnificence topped off the festivities, illuminating the fantastic silhouette from both sides of the East River. The Brooklyn Bridge was a celebration of the city.

It was also an indictment of the city. On the morning of the gala, one dissenting newspaper editor groused that the Brooklyn Bridge had "begun in fraud" and "continued in corruption." It was no secret to anyone that much of the $15 million that the project had cost had gone not into concrete, steel, and Roebling cable but into the pockets of crooked politicians.

The glories of the bridge were also marred by its cost in human lives. At least 20 workers were killed building it, and others just vanished, probably falling unnoticed. Many more were maimed. Then, just a few days after the dedication, a woman stumbled while descending the stairs that led from the causeway to the ground, and someone shouted, "The bridge is sinking!" In the stampede that followed, 12 people were trampled to death.

THE EVILS OF CITY LIFE

City people died at a rate not known in North America since the seventeenth century. At a time when the national death rate was 20 per 1,000 (20 people in each 1,000 died annually), the death rate in New York City was 25 per 1,000. In the slums, it was 38, and for children under five years of age, 136 per 1,000. The figures were only slightly lower in the other big cities, and in parts of Chicago they were higher. In one Chicago slum as late as 1900, the infant mortality rate was 200; one child in 5 died within a year of birth. By way of comparison, the infant mortality rate in the United States today is less than 20 per 1,000, and the total death rate is less than nine.

Too Many People, Too Little Room

City people died primarily because of impossibly crowded living conditions, another consequence of high real-estate values. In Philadelphia and Baltimore, the poor crowded into two- and three-story brick "row houses" that ran for 200 yards before a cross street broke the block. In Boston and Chicago, typical housing for the New Immigrants was in old wooden structures that had been comfortable homes for one family; in the late nineteenth century, they were crowded by several families, plus boarders. In New York, the narrow confines of Manhattan Island made the crowding even worse. Former single-family residences were carved into tenements that housed a hundred or more people.

In 1866, the New York Board of Health found 400,000 people living in overcrowded tenements with no windows, and 20,000 living in cellars below the water table. At high tide, their "homes" filled with water. The board closed the cellars and ordered 46,000 windows cut in airless rooms; but in 1900, people whose memories dated back to 1866 said that conditions were even worse than ever.

Jacob Riis, a newspaper reporter who exposed urban living conditions in a book of 1890, *How the Other Half Lives*, estimated that 330,000 people lived in a square mile of slum—986.4 people an acre. New York was more than twice as crowded as the London that had turned Charles Dickens's stomach, and parts of it were more populous than Bombay, the American's image of a living hell. On one tenement block in the Jewish section of the Lower East Side, just a little larger than an acre, 2,800 people lived. In one apartment of two tiny rooms there, Riis found a married couple, their twelve children, and six adult boarders.

When architect James E. Ware designed a new kind of building to house New York's poor, he worsened the situation. His "dumbbell" tenement, named for its shape, ostensibly provided 24 to 32 apartments, all with ventilation, on a standard New York building lot of 25 by 100 feet. However, when two dumbbells were constructed side by side, the windows of two-thirds of the living units opened on an air shaft, sometimes only two feet wide, that was soon filled with garbage, creating a threat to health worse than airlessness. Nevertheless, the dumbbells met city building standards, and by 1894, there were 39,000 of them in New York, housing about half the population of Manhattan.

Health

Such crowding led to epidemic outbreaks of serious diseases like smallpox, cholera, measles, typhus, scarlet fever, and diphtheria. Quarantining of patients, the indispensable first step in dealing with highly contagious diseases in the nineteenth century, was out of the question in slums: where were the unafflicted people to go? Even less dangerous illnesses like chicken pox, mumps, whooping cough, croup, and the various influenzas were killers in the crowded cities. Common colds were feared as the first step to pneumonia.

In his famous book, Jacob Riis took readers on a tour of a tenement: "Be a little careful, please! The hall is dark and you might stumble. You can feel your way, if you cannot see it. Close? Yes! What would you have? All the fresh air that enters these stairs comes from the hall-door that is forever slamming." He paused at the entrance to a windowless apartment. "Listen! That short, hacking cough, that tiny, helpless wail. . . . The child is dying of measles. With half a chance it might have lived; but it had none. That dark bedroom killed it."

Sanitation

The crowding itself was the chief cause of poor sanitation. Whereas free-roaming scavengers—chickens, hogs, dogs, and wild birds—handily cleaned up the garbage in small towns, and backyard latrines were adequate in disposing of human wastes, neither worked when more than a hundred people lived in a building and shared a single privy. City governments provided for waste collection, but even when honestly administered (which was the exception), sanitation departments simply could not keep up.

Horses compounded the problem. They deposited tons of manure on city streets daily, and special squads could not begin to keep pace. Moreover, on extremely hot and cold days, old and poorly kept horses keeled over by the hundreds; sometimes in New York the daily total topped 1,000. Although by law the owner of the dead beast was required to dispose of the carcass, this often meant dumping it into the river. More often, because the task was so formidable, owners of faltering nags cut their horses out of harness and disappeared. In summer, the corpses bloated and began to putrefy within hours.

In the poorest tenements, piped water was available only in shared sinks in the hallways, which were typically filthy. Safe water had been so heavily dosed with chemicals that it was barely palatable. The well-to-do bought bottled "spring water" that had been trucked into the cities. Other people depended on wells in the streets that were inevitably fouled by runoff.

Tenement apartments did not have bathrooms. Children washed by romping in the water of open fire hydrants or by taking a swim in polluted waterways. If you did not come home tinged gray or brown, one survivor of New York's Lower East Side remembered, you had not washed. When a bath was necessary, adults went to public bathhouses where there was hot, clean water at a reasonable price. Many of these establishments were quite respectable; others became known as dens of immorality.

Vice and Crime

As they always are, slums were breeding grounds of vice and crime. With 14,000 homeless people in New York in 1890, many of them children—"street arabs"—and work difficult to get and uncertain at the best of times, many found the temptations of sneak thievery, pocket

HORSE AND BUGGY DAYS

A horse dead was a sanitation problem in big cities, but so was a horse alive. Each horse produced as much as 25 pounds of manure each day. In New York City in 1900 there were about 150,000 horses. The potential litter problem, therefore, weighed about 1,800 tons. Most manure merely dried and crumbled where it dropped, blowing or washing away in time. Some was scooped up by the city or private entrepreneurs and sold to farmers on the outskirts of the city as fertilizer.

Dead horses left to rot in the streets compounded New York's growing sanitation problems at the turn of the century.

picking, purse snatching, and, for the bolder, violent robbery too much to resist. As early as the 1850s, police in New York were vying with (or taking bribes from) strong-arm gangs that were named after the neighborhoods where they held sway: the Five Points Gang, Mulberry Bend, Hell's Kitchen, Poverty Gap, the Whyo Gang.

They occasionally struck outside their areas, robbing warehouses and the like, and preying on the middle- or upper-class fops who took to slumming in these neighborhoods. But, like today, the gangs' typical victims were slum dwellers struggling to survive and escape the slum: the workingman who paused for a beer before he took his pay envelope home, the small-business men who were forced to make regular payments or risk physical violence. Whereas the homicide rate declined in German and British cities as they grew larger, it tripled in American cities during the 1880s. Although the prison population rose by 50 percent, the streets in some sections grew more dangerous.

By the end of the century, the more sophisticated gangs moved into vice, running illegal gambling operations, opium dens, and brothels. Prostitution flourished at every level of society, and there was a plentiful supply of impoverished girls and young women who had no other way to survive. The lucky ones set themselves up as mistresses or in fancy houses that catered to the wealthy. More common was the wretched slattern who plied her trade in the slums under the "protection" of a gang.

An Urban Culture

And yet, for all the horror stories, which no one savored more than the people who lived in the cities, for all the lurid accounts of urban life in books, newspapers, magazines, sermons, lectures, plays, and scandalized reports by people who visited New York, Chicago, Kansas City, or other "dens of pestilence," a vital, exciting, and excited urban culture developed in American cities. City people compared rural "yokels" and "hayseeds" unfavorably to themselves. Once established, city people were unlikely to move to the country or even to be attracted by jobs beyond the municipal limits.

The cities continued to grow at an extraordinary rate, both from immigration and the influx from the towns and countryside. Indeed, had it not been for the existence of a more traditional American frontier larger than any that had gone before, it is likely that the rural population would have declined in the late nineteenth century, as it was to do in the twentieth century.

For Further Reading

Again, see the overviews listed after several of the chapters immediately preceding this one: Vincent P. De-Santis, *The Shaping of Modern America, 1877–1916* (1973); John A. Garraty, *The New Commonwealth, 1877–1890* (1968); Samuel P. Hays, *The Response to Industrialism, 1885–1914* (1957). Even allowing that urbanists have been among the most productive of historians in recent decades, A. M. Schlesinger, *The Rise of the City, 1878–1898* (1933) is still an essential source.

To augment and correct Schlesinger in particulars, see Robert H. Bremner, *From the Depths: The Discovery of Poverty in America* (1956); Howard Chudakov, *The Evolution of American Urban Society* (1975); John Higham, *Send These to Me: Jews and Other Immigrants in Urban America* (1975); Blake McKelvey, *The Urbanization of America, 1860–1915* (1962); Zane Miller and Patricia Melvin, *The Urbanization of Modern America* (1987); Thomas L. Philpott, *The Slum and the Ghetto* (1978); Barbara Rosenkrantz, *Public Health and the State* (1972); Stephan Thernstrom, *The Other Bostonians: Poverty and Progress in the American Metropolis* (1973); Sam B. Warner, *Streetcar Suburbs: The Process of Growth in Boston, 1870–1900* (1971) and *The Urban Wilderness: A History of the American City* (1972); and Morton White, *The Intellectual Versus the City* (1962).

Books focusing on immigrants but with a special concern for urban life include Nathan Glazer and Daniel P. Moynihan, *Beyond the Melting Pot* (1970); Oscar Handlin, *The Uprooted* (1951); Leonard Dinnerstein and David Reimers, *Ethnic Americans: A History of Immigration and Assimilation* (1975); John B. Duff, *The Irish in the United States* (1971); Irving Howe, *World of Our Fathers* (1976); Alan Kraut, *The Huddled Masses: The Immigrant in American Culture, 1880–1921* (1982); Humbert Nelli, *The Italians of Chicago* (1970); Moses Rischin, *The Promised City: New York's Jews* (1962); Thomas Sowell, *Ethnic America: A History* (1981); Virginia Yans-McLaughlin, *Family and Community: Italian Immigrants in Buffalo* (1977).

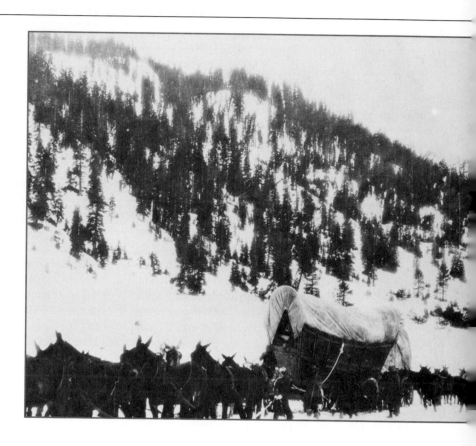

Mule-drawn supply wagons hauling provisions to a mountain mining camp.

THE LAST FRONTIER

WINNING THE REST OF THE WEST

1865 - 1900

In long-settled parts of the world, the frontier is the place where the territory of one sovereign state

comes to an end, and the territory of another state begins. In Europe, the crest of the Pyrenees marks

the frontiers of Spain and France, the Rhine River the frontiers of France and Germany. In grainy

films of the 1930s, European frontiers were places of locomotives hissing on sidings, grim customs

agents interrogating travelers, zebra-striped barricades lowered across tracks and roadway.

European frontiers have moved about frequently enough as a consequence of dynastic marriages and wars. But redrawing a frontier in Europe has long meant detaching from one country lands that were already populated and attaching them to another sovereignty.

In the United States, the word *frontier* came to mean something entirely different. To Americans, the frontier was the vaguely demarcated zone where lands they had settled ended and undeveloped country began. Because the course of American expansion began on the eastern rim of the continent, the frontier usually took the form of a line that ran from north to south, and that was more or less constantly moving westward. On and beyond that line was not a sovereign state to Americans, but wilderness country to be tamed and made their own.

The presence of numerous Indians beyond the frontier, living on ancestral lands, might have complicated Americans' assessment of "the West." But, in the long run, the Western Indians were to be swept aside as the tribes of the East had been.

THE LAST FRONTIER

The Census Bureau's definition of "settled land" was not very rigorous. While Americans of the late-twentieth century would consider a square mile on which only two, three, or four people lived to be something on the order of howling wilderness, the Census Bureau defined a square mile as "settled" if but 2.5 persons lived there. Even at that, at the time of the Civil War, the part of the United States that was beyond the frontier comprised roughly half the nation. With the exception of California, Oregon, and Washington Territory on the West Coast, where 440,000 people lived; the Great Salt Lake basin, where the Mormon Zion had grown to be home to a population of 40,000; and New Mexico, which was the seat of a gracious culture and home to 94,000 mostly Spanish-speaking citizens, the American frontier ran north to south about 150 to 200 miles west of the Mississippi River. Settlers had barely spilled over the far boundaries of Minnesota, Iowa, Missouri, and Arkansas. Half of the state of Texas was beyond the frontier at the end of the Civil War.

An Uninviting Land

Rather more striking in view of what was to happen in the late nineteenth century, most Americans believed that this West would never be settled. Americans thought agriculturally; pioneering meant bringing land under tillage, and, except for isolated pockets of fertile, well-watered soil, none of the three geographical regions of the West was suitable to agriculture. And those isolated pockets of good land were too far from the markets and the sources of manufactured goods that any settlers would need in order to prosper.

In the middle of the "last West" lay the majestic Rocky Mountains, which range from Alaska to New Mexico. The snowy peaks of the Rockies were familiar to Easterners from landscape paintings by artists who had accompanied the transcontinental wagon trains or military expeditions, or, having learned of the natural glories of the American landscape, had traveled west on their own, easel and canvases packed in their lumbering wagons. The very grandeur of the Rockies, however, told Americans that the mountains could not support a population living as people did in the older regions.

West of the Rockies and east of California's Sierra Nevada lay the high desert and the Great Basin—the mountainous and arid home of birds, snakes, lizards, rodents, comical armadillos, cactus, creosote bush, sagebrush, and tumbleweed. The soil was rocky, thin, and often alkaline. This region is called a basin or sink because its rivers lose heart in their search for an outlet and pool up in the desert, disappearing into the earth and evaporating in the sun. The Mormons had worked miracles in one of those sinks, the Great Salt Lake basin. But no part of the West seemed less inviting to Americans than this genuine desert.

East of the Rockies stretched the Great Plains, also a land of little rain and no trees. A short grass carpeted the country, and rivers like the Missouri and the Platte meandered through it, making the Great Plains less forbidding than the Great Basin. Nevertheless, there was simply not enough rainfall on the plains to support staple agriculture as Americans knew it.

The Native Peoples of the West

Some people did live in this last great region, of course. In addition to the Mormons and the *nuevos mexicanos*, hundreds of thousands of Indians continued to cling proudly to traditional, sometimes ancient ways of life. Even the parts of the Great Basin most forbidding to whites supported the Ute, Paiute, and Shoshone who coped with the torrid summers by dividing into small foraging bands and seeking higher elevations.

Farther south, in the seemingly more hostile environment of present-day Arizona and New Mexico, the Pima, Zuñi, and Hopi had been farming the desert intensively for centuries before the explorations of Francisco de Coronado. Their pueblos (a Spanish term, of course), were communal houses or groups of apartments, sometimes perched high on sheer cliffs, where a delicately integrated culture evolved. The Navajo, more numerous than the other peoples in the desert south of the Grand

Native Americans commemorate a buffalo kill by donning ceremonial dress.

Canyon (and comparative newcomers there) lived in family groups spread out over the country. The Navajo were skilled weavers of cotton when the introduction of Spanish sheep provided them with the opportunity to raise their craft into a durable art. Both the Navajo and the Pueblo Indians feared the warlike raiders of the Apache tribes, who dwelled farther south but ranged widely in search of booty.

In what was then called Indian Territory, present-day Oklahoma, the "civilized tribes," which had been forced out of Georgia and Alabama during the Age of Jackson, had rebuilt their amalgam of native and European cultures: an intensive cash-crop agriculture, a town life, a written language, a school system, and newspapers. Indian Territory came to loom large in the American imagination after the Civil War because, beyond the pale of state and effective federal law, it was an attractive sanctuary for some of the most famous outlaws and "badmen" of the era.

But the Indians who most intrigued Easterners were, curiously, those who were most determined to resist the whites and their ways, the tribes of the Great Plains. Thanks to the writings of intrepid travelers such as historian Francis Parkman and painters Alfred J. Miller, Karl Bodmer, and George Catlin, the Comanche, Cheyenne, and Arapaho peoples of the central and southern plains, and the Mandan, Crow, Sioux, Nez Percé, and Blackfoot peoples of the northern half of the grasslands were a source of awe and admiration to Easterners and of apprehension to those whites who came into their country to compete with them.

Plains Culture

Everything in the lives of the Plains Indians—economy, social structure, religion, diet, dress—revolved around two animals: the native bison and the horse, which was introduced to the Plains out of Mexico. The bison not only provided food, but its hides were made into clothing, footwear, blankets, portable shelters (the conical tepees), bowstrings, and canvases on which artists recorded heroic legends, tribal histories, and genealogies. The bison's manure made a tolerable fuel for cooking and warmth in a treeless land where winters were harsh.

Fortunately, the shaggy beasts were abundant beyond numbering. During the early 1860s, near the end of the bison's reign, Colonel Charles Goodnight wrote of a herd:

The noise resembled low rumbling thunder, and the earth trembled under their pounding hooves. [We] moved up on a light eminence, and as far as the eye could reach, North, South and West, a distance of not less than 10 miles in either direction, the whole country was covered with what appeared to be a monstrous moving brown blanket, the length and breadth of which could not be determined. The number of animals it contained was beyond the human mind to estimate.

The Plains Indians were nomadic. Except for the Mandan, they grew no crops but trailed after the herds of bison on their horses, to southern grazing grounds in the winter, and back north to fresh grass in the summer. It was not an ancient way of life, like that of the Southwestern pueblos. Runaway horses from Mexican herds had been domesticated only about 150 years before the Plains Indians were confronted by white Americans. Nevertheless, in that short time the Indians had developed their stirrupless, saddleless, and bitless mode of riding, which was quite independent of Mexican example and awe inspiring to American observers. "Almost as awkward as a monkey on the ground," wrote painter George Catlin in 1834, "the moment he lays his hand upon a horse, his face even becomes handsome, and he gracefully flies away like a different being."

The wandering ways of the Plains tribes brought them into frequent contact with one another and with Indians who had developed different cultures. While they traded and could communicate with remarkable subtlety through a common sign language, the tribes were just as likely to fight one another. Since the Indians had no concept of private ownership of land, their wars were not aimed at territorial conquest, but at capturing horses, tools, and sometimes women, and at demonstrating courage, the highest quality about which a Great Plains male could boast. The English word *brave*, given to Plains warriors as a noun, was not chosen on a whim.

With only about 225,000 native Americans roaming the Great Plains in 1860, war was not massive, but it was chronic. A permanent peace was as foreign to the Indians' view of the world as the notion that an individual could claim sole ownership of eighty acres of grassland.

By the 1860s, every Plains tribe knew about the "palefaces" or "white-eyes." They did not like the Pony Express riders or wagon trains that traversed their homeland, and they occasionally skirmished with the white wayfarers. But the galloping express riders and emigrants did move on. Indeed, the wagon trains were welcome to the extent that they traded, abandoned, or neglected to secure horses, textiles, iron tools, and rifles, all of which improved the Indians' standard of living.

THE PONY EXPRESS

The Pony Express looms large in the folklore of the American West. It would be strange if it were otherwise, the memory of lone riders trotting and even galloping across half a continent carrying a few pounds of government dispatches and very expensive private letters from "back East" to California. But it was, in fact, a short-lived enterprise, set in motion in April 1860 and shut down just eighteen months later.

The "technology" of the Pony Express was primitive. Indeed, its string of some 190 relay or "stock" stations between St. Joe, Missouri and California represented no essential improvement on the means by which the emperors of ancient Persia communicated with their far-flung lands. Some eighty young men, based at "home stations" seventy-five to one-hundred miles apart, raced against a demanding schedule with bags of dispatches and letters. Each ten or fifteen miles of their way, they changed their frothing ponies for fresh mounts at a relay station. All in all, the Pony Express kept some 500 horses in sound condition at all times.

Primitive as it was, however, the Pony Express cut twelve full days off the time it had taken for Washington to communicate with Sacramento, and vice versa (via steamship and the Isthmus of Panama).

The Pony Express was never intended as more than a stopgap until the telegraph and railroad more substantially bound East to West. However, it might have had a longer life had not the Civil War intervened in the spring of 1861. The trouble with the Pony Express was its fragility. Expecting the mail to get through when the elements were the only obstacles was doughty enough. In wartime, it was simply foolish.

The Destruction of the Bison

This state of *détente* between Indians and Americans began to change when Congress authorized the construction of the Pacific railroad. The crews that laid the tracks of the Union Pacific and Kansas Pacific across the plains were not interested in staying. But unlike the California and Oregon emigrants, their presence led directly to the destruction of the bison.

The killing of the bison began harmlessly enough. In order to feed the work crews cheaply, the Union Pacific Railroad hired hunters like William F. "Buffalo Bill" Cody to kill the beasts. The workers could hardly consume enough of the lean, beeflike meat to affect the size of the herds, which numbered perhaps fifteen million bison in 1860. However, when a few of the hides were shipped back east and caused a sensation as fashionable "buffalo robes," wholesale slaughter began.

A team of marksmen, reloaders, and skinners could down and strip a thousand bison in a day. Buffalo Bill alone shot 4,280 in seventeen months. Living in huge herds, the animals were not startled by loud noises and stood grazing, pathetically easy targets, as long as they did not scent or see human beings. With dozens of such teams at work, the bison population declined at a startling rate.

The railroad companies encouraged the slaughter because, merely by crossing over the flimsy iron tracks, a herd of bison could obliterate the line. To apply the finishing touches, wealthy Eastern and European sportsmen chartered special trains and, sometimes without

An advertisement for buffalo robes, which were fashionable in the 1870s.

stepping to the ground, they shot trophies for their mansions and clubs. By the end of the century, when preservationists stepped in to save the species, only about 600 American buffalo remained alive. It was the most rapid extirpation of a species in history, but no more rapid than the extinction of the culture of the people whose fate was tied to the bison.

JUST CAUSE

It would be a simpleton's mistake to think that all soldiers thought of the Indians as little more than vermin to be run to ground. Captain Frederick Benteen, who was at the Little Bighorn but not with Custer's doomed party, wrote of the effectiveness of the Sioux attack: "We were at their hearths and homes, their medicine was working well, and they were fighting for all the good God gives anyone to fight for."

The Cavalry

The United States cavalry accompanied the railroad's construction crews, ostensibly to enforce the Indians' treaty rights as well as to protect the workmen. Some of these troops were captured Confederate soldiers who elected to take an oath of loyalty and serve in the West as preferable to languishing in prisoner camps. After the war, they were joined by Northern whites and former slaves who had enlisted and found army life preferable to hard-scrabble farming back home.

Some soldiers and officers learned to respect the tribes and tried to deal fairly with them. General George Crook, who is remembered as the most able of the army's Indian fighters, preferred being known for his just dealings with the natives. Other officers shared the opinion of General Philip H. Sheridan, who was reputed to have told a Comanche chief at Fort Cobb in 1869, "The only good Indian is a dead Indian."

Overall, of course, the sympathies of the army were with the railroaders, miners, cattlemen, and eventually farmers who intruded on Indian lands. Whites believed in an elaboration of Manifest Destiny, that because the Indians, like the Mexicans, used the land so inefficiently, their claim to it was not equal to their own. From 1862, when the final era of Indian wars began with a Sioux uprising in Minnesota, until 1890, when the power of the last untamed tribe was shattered at Wounded Knee, South Dakota, the United States cavalry finished what the buffalo hunters had begun, the destruction of a way of life.

The Last Indian Wars

Like war between the tribes, war between Plains Indians and whites was largely a war of small skirmishes with few pitched battles. Between 1869 and 1876, for example, the peak years of the fighting, the army recorded 200 distinct "incidents," a number that did not include many unopposed Indian raids and confrontations between civilians and the tribes. But the total casualties on the army's side (and possibly the Indians's) was less than in any of several Indian–white battles in the 1790s.

The army preferred to fight decisive battles. But the Indians generally clung to traditional hit-and-run attacks that exploited their mobility and allowed them to escape fights in which, with their inferior arms and numbers, they were at a disadvantage. The result was frequent frustration among the soldiers and a cruelty toward the enemy such as had not been seen in the Civil War. In 1871, Commissioner of Indian Affairs Francis Walker explained that "when dealing with savage men, as with savage beasts, no question of national honor can arise. Whether to fight, to run away, or to employ a ruse, is solely a question of expediency."

By 1876, the army's victory seemed complete. Little by little, the soldiers in their ever-dusty blue had hemmed in the wandering tribes and whittled away at their ability to subsist. The typical state of a surrendering tribe was near-starvation, with a goodly proportion of the young men dead. But Indian resistance was not quite at an end.

Custer's Last Stand

In June of the centennial year, an audacious Civil War hero and colonel of the Seventh Cavalry, George Armstrong Custer, led 265 men into a battle with the Sioux on Montana's Little Bighorn River. In a rare total victory for the Indians, everyone in Custer's party was killed. Although a completely unexpected defeat, "Custer's Last Stand" thrilled Americans. Denied in life the advancement that he believed his record and talents had merited, "Yellow Hair," as the Sioux called him, became a romantic hero in death. A brewery commissioned an imaginative painting of the Battle of the Little Bighorn by Cassilly Adams and within a few years distributed 150,000 reproductions of it.

Senior officers who had disapproved of the flamboyant and impetuous Custer, and thought him to blame for the disaster, kept their mouths shut. Only in the next century would the episode be fully appreciated from the Indians' point of view, as a final great military victory brilliantly engineered by Sioux war chiefs. At the time, however, the tribes' joy was short-lived. Most of the victors were under control within the year.

Good Intentions, Tragic Results

In 1881, a Colorado writer, Helen Hunt Jackson, published A Century of Dishonor, one of the decade's bestsellers. In meticulous detail and with little distortion of fact, she detailed the cynicism with which the United States government had dealt with the Indians since independence. The list of Indian treaties was the list of broken treaties. Time and again, according to Jackson, "Christian" whites had cheated "savage" Indians of their land, had herded them onto reservations on lands judged to be the least useful, and then had chipped away at those.

By 1876, the government had ceased to make treaties

A drawing of the battle of Little Bighorn by Red Horse, 1881.

MOVING AMIDST THE HOSTILES

A cavalry detachment in the West, unlike its movie versions, was accompanied by huge wagon trains of equipment, often 150 vehicles. In addition to a rider, each horse carried 80 to 90 pounds of equipment. With such a load, a horse needed to be rested frequently. This was accomplished without arresting progress by dividing the soldiers on the march into two troops. One troop walked until it was half a mile ahead of the plodding wagon train. Then, the soldiers dismounted to rest and graze their horses until the wagons were half a mile ahead. As they caught up, the other troop moved on ahead and repeated the maneuver. In this way, there was always a troop, in two columns, on either side of the precious supplies to warn off raiders.

with the Indians. Those Indians who did not resist American control were defined as wards of the federal government; they were not citizens but were under Washington's protection and enjoyed a few special privileges. After the publication of *A Century of Dishonor*, many Easterners demanded that the government use this wardship in a just manner.

In 1887, Congress approved the Dawes Severalty Act. Intentions were the best. Assuming that the traditional Indian life was no longer feasible, the supporters of the Dawes Act argued that the Indian peoples must be Americanized; that is, they must become self-sustaining citizens through adoption of the ways of the larger society. Under the Dawes Act, the tribes were dissolved and the treaty lands were distributed, homestead-style, 160 acres to each head of the family (itself not a plausible concept to most tribes), and an additional 80 acres to each adult member of the household. Lands left over were sold to whites. In order to avoid further despoliation, remaining Indian land could not be sold or otherwise disposed of for 25 years.

The supporters of the Dawes Act overlooked a number of vital facts. First, few of the western Indians were farmers; traditionally they had been hunters, gatherers, and traders. Second, the reservation lands were rarely suited to agriculture; they had been allotted to the Indians precisely because they were unattractive to white farmers. Third, tracts of a few hundred acres in the arid West were rarely enough to support efficient white farmers, let alone novices at tillage. Finally, no western tribe thought in terms of private ownership of land as vested in a nuclear family. The tribe, which the Dawes Act aimed to relegate to the dustheap, was the basic social unit to the native Americans. The defeated Indians were de-

moralized by the forced disintegration of their culture and individuals too often were debauched by idleness and alcohol. When it was again permitted by law, they would be stripped of much of their land, too.

Wounded Knee

Among these desperate people appeared a religious teacher in the tradition of Tecumseh's brother, The Prophet. Jack Wilson, or Wovoka, a Paiute who had lived with a white Christian family and had been fascinated by the doctrine of redemption, wandered the West preaching a religion that appealed to thousands of Indians. His message was that by performing a ritual dance, the Indians, who were God's chosen people, could prevail on the Great Spirit to make the white man disappear. This "Ghost Dance" would bring back to life the buffalo herds and the many Indians who had been killed in the wars. The old way of life, which in the 1880s most adult Indians vividly remembered, would be restored.

This sort of belief, simultaneously edifying and pathetic, is common among peoples who have seen their world turned upside down. In parts of the Southwest that were untouched by Wovoka's religion, defeated Indians turned to peyote, a natural hallucinogenic drug, as a way to escape a bewildering, intolerable reality.

To understand the appeal of the Ghost Dance religion, it is necessary to recall just how rapidly the culture of the Plains Indians was destroyed. The Dakota Sioux, for example, did not go to war with the whites until the end of the 1860s. Within another decade, the survivors had been herded on the Pine Ridge Reservation in South Dakota. There, on Wounded Knee Creek, when the Dakotas took avidly to the Ghost Dance religion, and the soldiers guarding them heard that there were guns in the camp, a war of nerves set in. In December 1890, some shots from within the encampment led to a mas-

A CENTURY OF DISHONOR

"It makes little difference . . . where one opens the record of the history of the Indians; every page and every year has its dark stain. The story of one tribe is the story of all, varied only by differences of time and place; but neither time nor place makes any difference in the main facts. Colorado is as greedy and unjust in 1880 as was Georgia in 1830, and Ohio in 1795; and the United States Government breaks promises now as deftly as then, and with added ingenuity from long practice."

Helen Hunt Jackson,
A Century of Dishonor (1881)

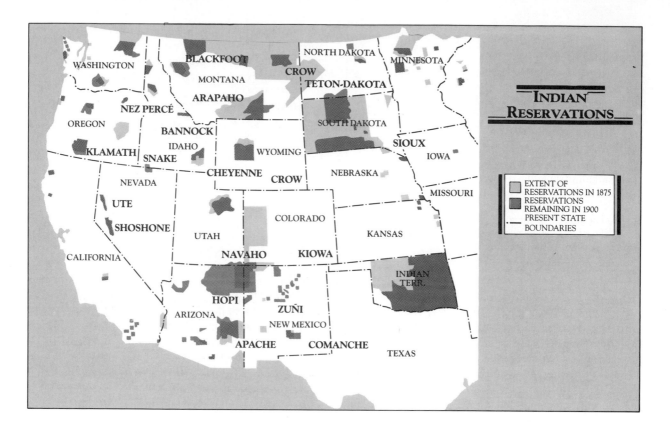

INDIAN
RESERVATIONS

EXTENT OF
RESERVATIONS IN 1875
RESERVATIONS
REMAINING IN 1900
PRESENT STATE
BOUNDARIES

sacre of the surrounded Indians. About 200 people, half of them women and children, were killed.

THE CATTLE KINGDOM

As the Indians lost the West, Americans won it. Indeed, the final decades of the nineteenth century stand as the greatest era of economic expansion in American history.

In 1870, American forests yielded about 12.8 billion board feet of lumber. By 1900, this output had almost tripled to about 36 billion. Although this increase reflects in part the development of forest industries in the Southern states, the region of greatest expansion was a new one, the Pacific Northwest.

In 1870, Americans were raising 23.8 million cattle. In 1900, 67.7 million head of the stupid, bawling creatures were fattening on grasslands, mostly in the West, and in Western feedlots.

Annual gold production continued only slightly below the fabulous levels of the gold-rush era, until the

end of the century, it was nearly double the totals of 1850. Annual silver production, only 2.4 million troy ounces in 1870, stood at 57.7 million in 1900.

The First Buckaroos

Acre for acre, cattlemen won more of the West than any other group of pioneers. They were motivated to bring the vastness of the Great Plains into the American economy by the appetite of the burgeoning cities for cheap meat, and they were encouraged in their venture by the disinterest in the rolling arid grasslands of anyone save the Indians. Their story thrills Americans (and other peoples) to this day partly because it was romanticized, partly because the cattle kingdom was established so quickly and just as quickly destroyed.

The cowboy first rode into American legend just before the Civil War. In the late 1850s, enterprising Texans began to round up herds of the half-wild longhorns that ranged freely between the Nueces River and the Rio Grande. They drove them north over a trail that had been blazed by Shawnee Indians to Sedalia, Missouri, a railroad town with connections to Chicago. Although the bosses were English-speaking, many of the actual workers were Mexican. They called themselves *vaqueros*.

Vaquero, "cowboy," entered the English language as buckaroo. Indeed, while Anglo-Americans soon comprised the majority of this mobile work force, and former black slaves were a substantial minority of it, much of what became part of American folklore and parlance about the buckaroos was of Mexican derivation. The cowboy's colorful costume was an adaptation of functional Mexican work dress. The bandana was a washcloth that, when tied over the cowboy's mouth, served as a dust screen, no small matter when a thousand cattle were kicking up alkali grit. The broad-brimmed hat was not selected for its picturesque qualities but because it was a sun and rain shield. Manufactured from first-quality beaver felt, the sombrero also served as a drinking pot and washbasin.

The pointed, high-heeled boots, awkward and even painful when walking, were designed for riding in the stirrups, where a *vaquero* spent his workday. The "western" saddle was of Spanish design, quite unlike the English tack that Americans in the East used. Chaps, leather leg coverings, got their name from chaparral, the ubiquitous woody brush against which they were designed to protect the cowboy.

Meat for Millions

The Civil War and Missouri laws against importing Texas cattle (because of hoof-and-mouth disease) stifled the cattle driving business before it was fairly begun. However, in 1866, when the transcontinental railroad reached Abilene, Kansas, a wheeler–dealer from Illinois, Joseph G. McCoy, saw the possibilities of underselling steers raised back East with Texas longhorns. McCoy built a series of holding pens on the outskirts of the tiny Kansas town, arranged to ship cattle he did not then have with the Kansas Pacific Railroad, and dispatched agents to southern Texas to induce Texans to round up and drive cattle north to Abilene on a trading route called the Chisholm Trail.

In 1867, McCoy shipped 35,000 "tall, bony, coarseheaded, flat-sided, thin-flanked" cattle to Chicago. In 1868, 75,000 of the beasts, next to worthless in Texas, passed through Abilene with Chicago packers crying for more. In 1871, 600,000 "critters" left the pens of several

The Sioux camp near Pine Ridge, South Dakota, in 1891.

HOW THEY LIVED

PUNCHING COWS

It took three or four months to drive a herd of cattle from the vicinity of San Antonio, Texas, to a railhead town in Kansas and to be asked to join a trail crew was a coveted honor among the young men of the country. The wages were low, only $1 a day plus board and as good a bed as the sod of the Great Plains provided. But because a lot of money and many lives rested on every member of a crew, only those who had impressed a trail boss with their skills and reliability were invited to go.

A trail crew consisted of the trail boss, usually the owner of the cattle; his *segundo*, or assistant; a cook; a wrangler, who was in charge of the *remuda*, or herd of horses that accompanied the expedition; and a hand for each 250 to 300 cattle. Most herds were made up of between 2,500 and 3,000 cattle, so 10 to 12 cowpunchers, or buckaroos, was typical. (The "cows" were really steers, males that had been castrated at their first roundup; the "punchers" got their name because one of their jobs was to punch the cows into corrals and loading chutes—using poles.)

A herd moved about ten to fifteen miles a day, the animals grazing as they got the chance. The usual procedure for getting a herd along was for two men to ride "lead" or "point," one on either side of the milling steers; two to ride "swing" and "flank," in pairs at regular intervals alongside the herd; and two or three to ride "drag," behind the herd to hurry up stragglers.

Each position had its peculiarities and was assigned in rotation or with an eye to a particular cowpuncher's abilities or his personal standing at the moment in the trail boss's graces. Riding point was the most dangerous in the event of a stampede, but it was also the most prestigious and most pleasant in terms of dust and odor (unless there was a powerful tailwind). Conversely, riding drag was the safest but also the least desirable job, not only because of the quality of the air that 3,000 animals left behind, but also because there was not a moment in which some independent-minded "dogies" were not determined to set off on their own.

The day's drive started at first light and ended as late toward dusk as the trail boss could find satisfactory grass and water, but the cowboy's work was not done. After a big dinner at the chuck wagon, the hands had to "ride night." In two-hour shifts, pairs of riders circled the herd in opposite directions, looking out for predators and soothing the nervous steers. Some folklorists (and some old cowpunchers) say that the western singing and guitar-playing tradition developed as a means of keeping a herd calm; music soothed the generally docile if not the savage beast. Indeed, night riding was as dangerous as it was detested for its theft of sleep. Almost all stampedes started at night, tripped by a bolt of lightning, a steer dodging a coyote, or, to human reckoning, no reason whatsoever. Except for river crossings—there were four major and numerous minor watercourses between Texas and Kansas—the stampede was the most frequent cause of death written on the wooden markers that dotted the Shawnee, Chisholm, and Goodnight-Loving trails. (Indians were not a serious threat to the cow puncher's life, although they stole his cattle when they could.)

There would be no strumming guitar in the pouring rain that came often enough. Then the night riders donned their yellow oilskin slickers that covered their whole saddle, and gently cursed, or slept. It was said that a cowpuncher who had a good night horse could sleep in the saddle, since his mount even knew to wake him at the end of the two-hour shift.

Cowboys on the long drive might bring along a horse or two of their own, but the boss supplied the tough, wiry work ponies. They were geldings, about seven to ten for each hand. (Stallions fought, and mares were considered too temperamental for the job.) Each had a unique identity and job. There were morning horses and afternoon horses. The night horse had singular qualities already noted. The cowboy used the strong rope horse to help pull a stray out of a bog or for some other problem involving a lasso. A highly specialized but important horse was the water horse, a good swimmer on which a cowboy could count to get him across as much as a mile of strong current with steers rolling their wild, pink-rimmed eyes and thrashing about on every side. The most talented mount was the cutting horse, which knew exactly how a steer would act without the rider's instructions. The best were as agile as sheepdogs.

The cowboy's attachment to his horse, the butt of many Hollywood jokes, was nevertheless genuine. The cowpuncher was a horseman; he shunned work that had to be done on foot. Everyone had stories of crews that quit rather than slop hogs or milk dairy cows.

If passionate in general, however, the cowboy's attachment to horses in the particular was fickle. He did not own the mounts on which he worked, and at the end of the trail they were sold off along with the cattle. Only a few hands returned home to Texas overland. After they had spent most of their money on liquor, women, and cards, cowboys climbed aboard an eastbound train, rode it to the Mississippi River, and struck south by riverboat.

The "long drive," from grazing land to railhead town, often covered several hundred miles or more.

Kansas railroad towns to end up on American dinner tables.

The profits were immense. A steer that cost about $5 to raise on public lands could be driven to Kansas at the cost of one cent a mile ($5 to $8) and sold for $25 or, occasionally, as much as $50. Investors from as far as England went west to establish ranches that were as comfortable as big-city gentlemen's clubs. The typical cattleman at the famous Cheyenne Club never touched a gun and he sat on a horse only for the photographer. Instead, he sank into plush easy chairs, ignited a Havana cigar, and discussed account books, very often in an English accent, with his fellow businessmen.

The railhead continued to push westward, and with it went the destination of the cowboys, who were soon arriving from the North as well as the South. The migration of the railhead was alright with most of the citizens of towns like Abilene. They concluded after a few seasons that the money to be made as a cattle trading center was not worth the damage done to their own ranches and farms by hundreds of thousands of cattle. The wild atmosphere given their towns by the rambunctious cowboys, many of them bent on a blowout after months on the trail, was even less conducive to respectable civic life. As a cow town grew, its "better element" demanded churches and schools in place of saloons, casinos, and whorehouses. The stage was set for the "taming" of a town, which is the theme of so many popular legends.

Never, though, did the cowboys lack for someplace to take their herds. There were always newer, smaller towns to the west to welcome them. In Kansas alone, Ellsworth, Newton, Wichita, Dodge City, and Hays had their "wide-open" period.

Disaster

The cattle kingdom lasted only a generation, ending suddenly as a result of two natural disasters.

The profits to be made in cattle were so great that exploiters ignored the fact that grassland has its limits as the support of huge herds. Vast as the plains were, they were overstocked by the mid-1880s. Unlike the bison, which had migrated vast distances each season, allowing the Plains to rest, the cattle stayed put. Clear-running springs were trampled into unpotable mud

The cowboy's "long drive" ended in a railhead town surrounded by stockyards.

holes. Weeds never before noticed replaced the grasses that had invited overgrazing. (The worthless, if romanticized, tumbleweed was an immigrant from Russia.) Hills and buttes were scarred by cattle trails. Some species of migratory birds that once passed through twice a year simply disappeared; the beefsteaks on hoof had beaten them to their food.

Then, on January 1, 1886, a great blizzard buried the eastern and southern plains. Within three days, three feet of snow drifting into 20- and 30-foot banks suffocated the range. Between 50 and 85 percent of the livestock froze to death or died of hunger. About 300 cowboys could not reach shelter and died; the casualties among the Indians never were counted. When spring arrived, half the American plains reeked of death.

The summer of 1886 brought ruin to many cattlemen who had survived the snows. Grasses that had weathered summer droughts for millennia were unable to do so in their overgrazed condition; they withered and died, starving cattle already weakened by winter. Then, the next winter, the states that had escaped the worst of the

blizzard of 1886 got sixteen inches of snow in sixteen hours and weeks more of intermittent snowfall.

The End of a Brief Era

The cattle industry recovered, but only when more prudent and methodical businessmen took over the holdings of the speculators of the glory days. Cattle barons like Richard King of southern Texas foreswore risking all on the open range. Through clever manipulation of land laws, King built a ranch that was as large as the state of Rhode Island. If not quite so grand in their success, others imitated King's example in Texas, Wyoming, Montana, and eastern Colorado.

Even more important in ending the days of the long drive and the cowboy as a romantic knight-errant was the expansion of the railroad network. When new east-west lines snaked into Texas and the states on the Canadian border, and the Union Pacific and Kansas Pacific sent feeder lines north and south into cow country, the cowboy became a ranch hand, a not-so-freewheeling employee of large commercial operations.

The Cowboy's Life

Even in the days of the long drive, the world of the cowboy bore scant resemblance to the legends that came to permeate American popular culture. Despite the white complexion of the cowboys in popular literature and in Western films of the twentieth century, a large proportion of cowboys were Mexican or black. In some cases, these workers and the whites acted and mixed as equals. Just as often, however, they split along racial lines when they reached the end of the trail, frequenting segregated restaurants, barber shops, hotels, saloons, and brothels.

Black, white, or Hispanic, they were indeed little more than boys. Photographs that the buckaroos had taken in cow towns like Abilene and Dodge City (as well as arrest records, mostly for drunk and disorderly conduct), show a group of very young men, few apparently much older than 25. The life was too arduous for anyone but youths—days in the saddle, nights sleeping on bare ground in all weather. Moreover, the cowboy who married could not afford to be absent from his own ranch or farm for as long as the cattle drives required.

The real buckaroos were not constantly engaged in shooting scrapes such as made novels and movies so exciting. Their skills lay in horsemanship and with a rope, not with the Colt revolver that they carried to signal co-workers far away. Indeed, toting guns was forbidden in railhead towns. With a drunken binge on every cowboy's itinerary, the sheriff or marshal in charge of keeping the peace did not tolerate shooting irons on every hip. Those who did not leave their revolvers in camp outside town checked them at the police station.

THE WILD WEST IN AMERICAN CULTURE

The legend of the cowboy as a romantic, dashing, and quick-drawing knight of the wide-open spaces was not a creation of a later era. On the contrary, all the familiar themes of the Wild West were well-formed when the cold, hard reality was still alive on the plains. Rather more oddly, the myths of the Wild West were embraced

William F. Cody (tall man with hat in back row) poses with Plains Indians chiefs at Pine Ridge, South Dakota, just weeks after the Wounded Knee massacre.

not only by Easterners in their idle reveries, but by the cowboys themselves.

Play-Acting

The most important creator of the legendary Wild West was a none too savory character named E. Z. C. Judson. A former Know-Nothing who was dishonorably discharged from the Union Army, Judson took the pen name Ned Buntline, and between 1865 and 1886, churned out more than 400 romantic, blood, guts, and chivalric novels about Western heroes. Some of his characters he invented; others were highly fictionalized real people. Called pulps after the cheap paper on which they were printed or dime novels after their price, the books by Judson and his many competitors were devoured chiefly, but not exclusively, by boys.

Buntline's mythical world appealed even to those who should have known better. During the 1880s, while living as a rancher in North Dakota, future president Theodore Roosevelt helped capture two young cowboys who had robbed a grocery store. In their saddlebags, Roosevelt found several Ned Buntline novels that no doubt featured outlaws who were unjustly accused.

The tiny town of Palisade, Nevada, on the Central Pacific railroad line, won the reputation in Eastern newspapers as a den of cutthroats because brawls and gunfights broke out so regularly when passengers left the train for refreshment. In fact, the fights were staged by locals in part to twit Eastern fantasies, in part because they were just plain bored.

American Heroes

In the pulps and later in films, Americans discovered that the bank and train robbers Jesse and Frank James, and several cohorts from the Clanton family, were really modern-day Robin Hoods who gave the money they took to the poor. When Jesse was murdered, his mother made a tourist attraction of his grave, charging admission and explaining that her son had been a Christian with an inclination to read the Bible in his spare time.

Belle Starr, the moniker of one Myra Belle Shirley, was immortalized as "the bandit queen," as pure in heart as Jesse James was socially conscious. Billy the Kid (William Bonney), a Brooklyn-born homicidal maniac, was romanticized as a tragic hero who had been forced into a life of crime by a callous society. James Butler "Wild Bill" Hickok, a gambler and clothes-horse who killed perhaps six people before he was shot down in Deadwood Gulch, South Dakota, in 1876, was credited with dozens of killings, all in the cause of making the West safe for women, children, and psalm books. Calamity Jane (Martha Cannary), later said to have been Wild Bill's para-

Sitting Bull, a woman, and three of his children pose with two white visitors to the Standing Rock reservation in 1882.

mour, wrote her own romantic autobiography in order to support a drinking problem.

Calamity Jane and other "living legends" of the West personally contributed to the mythmaking by appearing in Wild West shows that traveled to cities in the East and in Europe, where they dramatized great gun battles. The most famous of these shows was the creation of "Buffalo Bill" Cody who easily made the transition from hunter to impresario. Among his featured performers was Sitting Bull, the Hunkpapa Sioux chief who had overseen the defeat of George Custer. Reality and myth were cruelly confused in Sitting Bull's life. After a successful career in show business, he returned to the Rosebud Reservation where, during the Ghost Dance excitement, he was accidentally killed by two Indian policemen who were arresting him on suspicion of fomenting rebellion.

Some creators of the legendary West were conscientious realists; Frederic Remington, whose paintings and bronze statues of cowboys and Indians are studiously representative, is a fine example. Others, while romantics, were talented artists; Owen Wister, an aristocratic Easterner, created the finest prototype of the Western knight without armor in *The Virginian*, published in 1902. If the cowboy gave you his word, Wister wrote, "he kept it; Wall Street would have found him behind the times. Nor did he talk lewdly to women; Newport would have thought him old-fashioned."

THE MINING FRONTIER

The folklore of the precious-metal mining frontier is second only to the legend of the cowboy in the American imagination. Deadwood Gulch, for example, where Wild Bill Hickok was gunned down and Calamity Jane spent much of her life, was no cow town but a gold mining center.

Gold and Silver Rushes

After the richest of the California gold fields played out, prospectors in search of "glory holes" fanned out over the mountains and deserts of the West. For more than a generation, they discovered new deposits almost an-

nually and very rich ones every few years. In 1859, there were two great strikes. A find in the Pike's Peak area of Colorado led to a rush that was reminiscent of that of 1849. At about the same time, gold miners in northern Nevada discovered that a "blue mud" that had been fouling their operations was one of the richest silver ores ever discovered. This was the beginning of Virginia City and the Comstock Lode. Before the Comstock pinched out in the twentieth century, it yielded more than $400 million in silver and gold.

In 1862, Tombstone, Arizona, was founded on the site of a gold mine; in 1864, Helena, Montana, rose atop another. In 1876, rich placer deposits were discovered in the Black Hills of South Dakota (then forbidden to whites by Indian treaty). The next year, silver was found at Leadville, Colorado, almost two miles above sea level in the Rockies.

During the 1880s, the Coeur d'Alene in the Idaho panhandle drew thousands of miners, as did the copper deposits across the mountains in Butte. In 1891, the Cripple Creek district in Colorado began to outproduce every other mining town. In 1898, miners rushed north to Canada's Klondike, Alaska's Yukon, and then to Nome, where the gold was on the beach. As late as 1901,

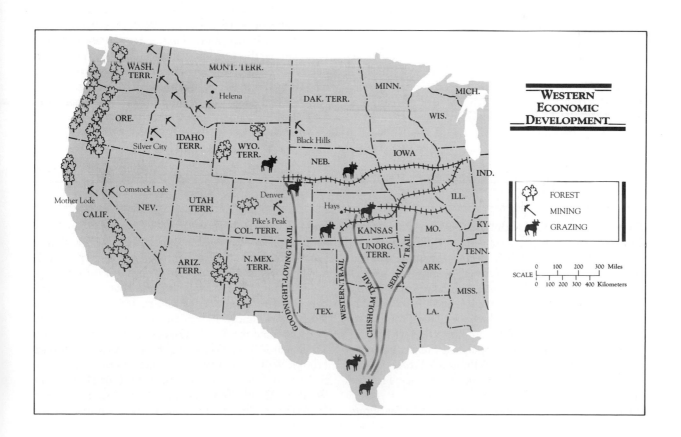

there was an old-fashioned rush when the classic grizzled old prospector in a slouch hat, Jim Butler, drove his pick into a desolate mountain in southern Nevada and found it "practically made of silver." From the town of Tonopah, founded on its site, prospectors discovered rich deposits in Goldfield, a few miles away.

Mining Camps and Cities

Readers of the dime novels of the time and film viewers since have avidly savored the vision of boisterous, wide-open mining towns, complete with saloons rocking with the music of tinny pianos and the shouts of bearded men. The live-for-today miner, the gambler, the prostitute with a heart of gold are permanent inhabitants of American folklore. Nor is the picture altogether imaginary. The speculative mining economy fostered a risk-all attitude toward life and work.

However, efficient exploitation of underground (hard rock) mining required a great deal of capital and technical expertise, both to finance the operation and to build the railroads that hauled ore out. Consequently, the mining camps that were home to from 5,000 to even 10,000 people within a short time of their founding were also cities with a variety of services and a social structure more like that of older industrial towns than the towns of the cattleman's frontier.

In 1877, only six years after it was founded on a vein of gold, Leadville, Colorado boasted several miles of paved streets, gas lighting, a modern water system, thirteen schools, five churches, and three hospitals. It was hardly the tiny, false-front set that is used to represent mining towns in Hollywood films.

"Camps" such as Virginia City in Nevada, Deadwood Gulch in South Dakota, and Tombstone in Arizona are best remembered as places where legendary characters like Wild Bill Hickok and Wyatt Earp discharged their revolvers; but they were also the sites of huge stamping mills (to crush the ores) that towered over the landscape, and of busy exchanges where mining stocks were traded by agents of San Francisco, New York, and London bankers.

In Goldfield, the last of the wide-open mining towns, one of the most important men in the camp was the urbane Wall Street financier Bernard Baruch (who may have been outdressed by some of the locals). The Anaconda Copper Company of Butte, Montana, was one of the nation's ranking corporate giants. The Guggenheim mining syndicate was supreme in the Colorado gold fields. Rockefeller's Standard Oil was a major owner of mines in Coeur d'Alene. If it was wild, the mining West was no mere colorful diversion for readers of dime novels, but an integral part of the national economy. In fact, the gold and silver that the hard-rock miners tore from the earth stood at the very center of a question that divided Americans more seriously than any other after the end of Reconstruction—what was to serve as the nation's money.

The miners and mine owners alone could not make an issue of the precious metals from which coins were minted, goods bought and sold, and debts incurred and paid off—or not paid off. There were too few of them. However, as the century wound to a close, the money question became of great interest to a group of people who formed a major part of the American population, and who had once been its most important segment, the farmers of the land.

For Further Reading

Three good books deal with "the West" in general from rather different perspectives: Ray A. Billington, *Westward Expansion: A History of the American Frontier* (1967); Thomas D. Clark, *Frontier America: The Story of the Westward Movement* (1969); and Frederick Merk, *History of the Westward Movement* (1978). Also valuable is Robert A. Wiebe, *The Search for Order* (1968). An essential book is that by the "founding father" of frontier history, Frederick Jackson Turner, *The Frontier in American History* (1920). Also see Billington's *Frederick Jackson Turner* (1973) and *America's Frontier Heritage* (1967).

Useful special studies include Allan C. Bogue, *From Prairie to Corn Belt* (1963); E. Dick, *The Sod-House Frontier* (1937); Dee Brown, *Bury My Heart at Wounded Knee* (1970); E. E. Dale, *The Range Cattle Industry* (1930); David Day, *Cowboy Culture: A Saga of Five Centuries* (1981); Robert R. Dystra, *The Cattle Towns* (1968); Gilbert C. Fite, *The Farmer's Frontier, 1865–1900* (1966); Joe B. Frantz and J. E. Choate, *The American Cowboy: The Myth and the Reality* (1955); William S. Greever, *The Bonanza West: The Story of the Western Mining Rushes* (1963); William T. Hagan, *American Indians* (1961); E. S. Osgood, *The Day of the Cattleman* (1929); Rodman W. Paul, *Mining Frontiers of the Far West, 1848–1880* (1963); J. M. Shagg, *The Cattle Trading Industry* (1973);

Fred A. Shannon, *The Farmer's Last Frontier* (1967); Duane A. Smith, *Rocky Mountain Mining Camps* (1967); Henry Nash Smith, *Virgin Land: The American West as Symbol and Myth* (1950); J. R. Swanson, *The Indian Tribes of North America* (1953); Robert M. Utley, *Last Days of the Sioux Nation* (1963); Wilcomb E. Washburn, *The Indian in America* (1975); Thomas H. Watkins, *Gold and Silver in the West* (1960); and Walter P. Webb, *The Great Plains* (1931).

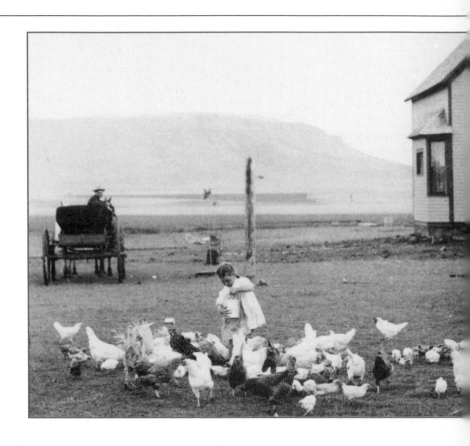

*The grandeur and isolation of a plains farm are captured in t[...]
traveling photographer's masterpiece.*

STRESSFUL TIMES DOWN HOME

THE CRISIS OF AMERICAN AGRICULTURE 1865 - 1896

Ever since the world's first farmer poked a hole in the ground and inserted a seed, tillers of the soil

have understood that they were engaged in a game of chance with nature. Farming was a gamble,

betting a year's living on such uncertainties as the day of winter's final frost and summer's yield of

sunshine and rain. Farmers were at the mercy of capricious insects and birds. Illness at harvest time

could mean twelve months of deprivation.

But farmers have also known that their work was the bedrock on which civilization was based. It was they who produced the first necessity of life after air and water. The farmer was the man, in the words of a song of the 1890s, "who feeds them all."

American farmers were, perhaps, particularly conscious of their role in society. They believed they were the nation's most valuable citizens, the "bone and sinew" of the republic. So they had been told by Thomas Jefferson and succeeding generations of politicians fishing for their votes.

In the final decades of the nineteenth century, the staple farmers of the West and South discovered that the grand old truisms were not necessarily so. In the new America of gigantic railroads, multimillion dollar corporations, mighty investment banks, and a marketplace that extended to the obscurest corners of the earth, the powers of nature could seem to be secondary, almost innocuous by comparison with diabolical economic forces—and the power of people whom farmers came to think of as parasites, sucking them dry. In the 1890s, welling anger and resentment down on the farm culminated in a radical political movement that shook the confidence of the conservative men who had governed the United States since the end of the Civil War.

THE BEST OF TIMES, THE WORST OF TIMES

Farmers rarely led the way on the last frontier; miners, cattlemen, and soldiers clearing the land of Indian claims were the usual pioneers. Subsistence agriculture attracted no one. Commercial agriculture was feasible in the late-nineteenth-century West only after the railroad arrived to connect field and barnyard to hungry Eastern and foreign cities. Once the railroad made its appearance, however, settlers with plow and little more fairly inundated the last frontier.

Success Story

Never in the history of the world have people put new land to the plow as quickly as Americans (and immigrants) did in the final three decades of the nineteenth century. As of 1870, when the railway building boom was at full tilt, Americans had brought a total of 408 million acres of land under cultivation, an average of 1.6 million acres of new farmland a year. Between 1870 and 1900, a single generation of farmers put 431 million acres of virgin soil to the plow, more than between 1607 and 1870, and an average of 14.4 million acres each year.

Crop production increased just as sharply. By 1900, American farmers were producing up to 150 percent more of the staple grains—corn and wheat—than they had in 1870. Hogs, a by-product of corn, numbered 25 million in 1870 and 63 million in 1900.

The ravenous appetites of American and foreign city dwellers encouraged this amazing growth. The expansion of the railroads made it possible for crops raised by a Great Plains farmer to feed the inhabitants of Chicago and New York, London and Warsaw. Even at that, however, the pioneer farmers of the West had to overcome formidable difficulties to accomplish what they did.

Cool, Clear Water

American farmers and immigrants from northern Europe were accustomed to summer rains nourishing their crops. From the Atlantic Seaboard to as far west as Missouri and eastern Kansas, 32 to 48 inches of rain fell each year, more in the deep South. West of about Wichita, Kansas, however, annual precipitation declined to 16–32 inches a year, with much of it during the winter. Yet farther west in the "rain-shadow" of the Rocky Mountains, at about the eastern boundary of Colorado, rainfall dropped to 16 inches or less per year. This was the "Great American Desert" which an early explorer had called "almost totally unfit for cultivation." The central valley of California was just as arid with no rain during the summer months worth counting on.

The Californians solved their problem with large-scale irrigation. They formed cooperative "ditch companies" that tapped the water of the San Joaquin, Sacramento, and numerous other rivers that rose in the Sierra Nevada, channeling it to their crops. Irrigation brought them into conflict with hydraulic miners who, in washing down whole mountainsides to win their grains of gold, clogged the rivers and irrigation ditches with mud. The more numerous farmers won the contest in California's courts, shutting down the hydraulic operations.

To some extent, "dry farming" on the Great Plains was based on a delusion. The summers of the 1870s and early 1880s, when cultivators arrived in the region, were abnormally rainy. This convinced the settlers and some experts, such as Charles Dana Wilber, that "rain follows the plow." When they broke the primeval sod, farmers believed, they permanently altered the climate by liberating moisture from the earth that would return indefinitely in the form of heavier rains.

There was nothing to this theory, as the devastating drought of 1887 was to show, but Great Plains farmers did make the most of what moisture they had by plowing more deeply than Eastern farmers did. The thick layer of dust that settled in the foot-deep furrows acted as a mulch, conserving moisture.

Large California-style ditch companies were out of the

question on most of the Great Plains. By mid-summer the level of the largest rivers dropped too low to be tapped, and smaller streams disappeared. Some farmers individually irrigated their fields from wells on which they mounted pre-fabricated windmills. However, the cost of the windmills and of drilling a well, between $1 and $2 a foot, was too much for most settlers to risk when they had no idea whether they would hit water at 25 or 200 feet.

A Treeless Land

Save for groves of cottonwood along the muddy rivers, there were no trees on the Great Plains and, therefore, no lumber with which to build. Importing wood for a respectable frame house had to be delayed until after a family had harvested a few crops and squirreled some money away. In the meantime, pioneers lived in sod houses, which were constructed of blocks cut from the tangled plains sod. Sod houses were rather snug in the winter, but they dripped mud in the spring thaw and became hellholes of choking dust during the long arid summers. Many Western farmers died in them after many years, still just dreaming of clapboards and windows.

Building fences was more urgent. Crops needed to be protected from open-range cattle, and the settler's own livestock kept under control. But cheap as fence lumber

> ### MAKING A SOD HOUSE
>
> To make a sod house, pioneers mowed about an acre of grassland, preferably when it was slightly moist, and hitched mules or oxen to a "grasshopper plow" that turned up the sod in strips about a foot wide and 4 to 5 inches thick. These were chopped into blocks with a spade and, grass side down, the "Nebraska marble" was laid like bricks. The walls of a sod house had to be two to three feet thick in order to support the roof, which was made of wooden rafters with a layer of sod grass-side up on top. Door and window frames were made from old packing crates.
>
> A sod house was fireproof, quite snug in winter and cool in summer, but it dropped dirt and dust constantly and, in heavy rains, it might be necessary to cook, eat, and sleep with an umbrella overhead.

was, the cost of ringing a 160-acre farm with wooden posts and rails was beyond the means of nearly all. The solution to their problem came in 1872 when Joseph Glidden of Illinois perfected a machine that mass-produced cheap barbed wire. With the flimsiest of scavenged fenceposts, a Great Plains farmer could erect a steel "hedge" so efficient that a starving cow would lie down and die rather than push through it to grass. In

A couple stand with their prized possessions in front of their sod house in Custer County, Nebraska, about 1886.

Mechanization on the farm: Horse-drawn reapers like this did the work of many men.

1875, Glidden sold 600,000 pounds of barbed wire at $20 per hundred pounds. By 1880, he had cut this price in half and sold 80.5 million pounds of the stuff. By the end of the century, barbed wire could be bought at just $1.80 a hundredweight.

Barbed wire's effectiveness was the cause of numerous clashes between settlers who used it (sometimes called "nesters"), and open-range cattlemen accustomed to running their animals freely on the plains. When fences prevented their cattle from reaching streams and water holes, one cattleman retaliated by damming up streams above nester land, cutting fence wire into useless shreds, and, in Johnson County, Wyoming, hiring gunfighters to terrorize them.

Machines in the Land

Barbed wire was but one of hundreds of technology's contributions to the fabulous expansion of agriculture. A chilled steel plow invented by Oliver Evans in 1877 sliced through sod and heavy soils. Disc harrows cultivated wide swaths with each pass, allowing "dry farmers" to tend more acres than they needed to back East. Manufacturers like John Deere and International Harvester developed machines that planted seeds, shucked corn, threshed wheat, bound shocks, and shredded fodder for livestock. The value of farm machinery in use in the United States increased from $271 million in 1870 to $750 million in 1900.

Machinery made the American farmer of the late nineteenth century the most productive in the world and, potentially, able to cultivate six times as much land as his father had farmed back East before the Civil War. That is, plowing and seeding wheat by hand, harvesting

it with a sickle, and threshing with a flail, a pre-war farmer had to spend between 50 and 60 hours to harvest about 20 bushels of wheat per acre. With a gang plow and a horse-drawn seeder, harrow, reaper, and thresher—all of which were in widespread use by 1890— a farmer produced a much larger crop after only eight to ten hours of work per acre.

Hard Times

On the other hand, machinery cost money that most farmers simply did not have. Already short-term debtors, borrowing each year for seed and provisions during the growing season, the typical farmer of the late nineteenth century was also a long-term debtor, owing money for his machines even if he got his land for free.

What was worse, beginning about 1872, the western growers of wheat, corn, and livestock watched their incomes sag and, by the 1890s, utterly collapse. A crop that in 1872 brought a farmer $1,000 in real income (actual purchasing power) was worth only $500 in 1896. A man who was 48 years old in 1896, still an active working farmer, had to turn out twice as many hogs or double the bushels of corn or wheat as he had produced as a young man of 24, just to enjoy the same standard of living that he had known in 1872. It was not comforting to know that a quarter century of backbreaking toil had yielded nothing but the prospect of more struggle. By the 1890s, the price of corn was so low (eight cents a bushel) that some farmers had to forgo buying coal and to burn their grain for winter warmth.

Those that were unable to pay their debts went under. Between 1889 and 1893, some 11,000 Kansas farm families lost their homes when they failed to make their mortgage payments. In several western counties of Kansas and Nebraska during the same period, nine out of every ten farmsteads changed hands. The number of farm tenant families—those that did not own the land they worked—doubled from 1 to 2 million between 1880 and 1900, most of the increase coming after 1890. For every three landowning farm families in the North and West, there was one tenant family. For them, farming was no longer the basis of independence and hope for the future, but grinding toil for the sake of putting a meal on the table and keeping the banker from the door.

The South: Tenants and Sharecroppers

Tenancy was far more common in the South, particularly in the cotton belt. Below the Ohio River, there were as many tenant farmers as there were families working land they owned. Among blacks, tenants and sharecroppers outnumbered landowners by almost five to one.

The South's tenancy problem had different origins, dating to Reconstruction. Having freed blacks from bondage, the then dominant Republicans failed to provide the freedmen the means to survive on their own. After some consideration, the Republicans rejected proposals to confiscate the large plantations and divide them into forty-acre farms for the blacks who had worked them as slaves. With a few exceptions, land was left in the hands of those who owned it before the war.

But how were the crops to be got in? The former slaves refused to work in gangs for wages. It was too reminiscent of the patterns of life under slavery. Even if they had been willing, the landowning planters had no money with which to pay wages. They were themselves impoverished; the blacks had been their capital.

The solution to the problem was a system of cultivation that, on the face of it, seemed fair to both landowner and worker, sharing the crop. Plantation owners partitioned their land into family farm-size plots on which a cabin, usually quite rude, was constructed. In return for the use of the house and the land, sharetenants, who provided their own daily bread, mule, plow, and seed, turned over to the landlord one-quarter to one-third of each year's crop. Sharecroppers were tenants who were too poor to supply mule, plow, and seed. The landlord provided everything in return for one-half of the crop.

As a means of production, the system worked. Southern cotton production reached its 1860 level in 1870 and exceeded the pre-war record (1859) a few years later. As in the West, however, greater production was accompanied by a drastic decline in wholesale prices. The price

A sharecropper's cabin in North Carolina, 1919.

BLACK SODBUSTERS

With the collapse of Reconstruction, Benjamin "Pap" Singleton, a black carpenter from Nashville, concluded that blacks could make decent lives for themselves only by doing what so many whites were doing—moving West. He came to be known as the "Moses of the Colored Exodus" by traveling throughout the South urging blacks to migrate to Kansas and found black colonies. His message touched a chord in some communities. By the end of 1878, more than 7,000 "Exodusters" took out homesteads in Kansas. In 1879, another 20,000 arrived, founding communities such as Nicodemus, which still preserves its black pioneer heritage.

At first glad for the immigrants, Kansas soon launched a campaign of discouragement to counter Singleton's work. While propagandists publicized the usual rosy lies among potential white immigrants, they told southern blacks about the hardships and risks of farming on the Great Plains (all true enough), for fear that the state would become a black refuge.

of a pound of cotton fell to six cents by the 1890s, and briefly in 1893 to a nickel, $30 for a bale it took six strong men to lift.

Debt Bondage

One result of declining prices was a physically and morally debilitating poverty. Pellagra, a fatal niacin-deficiency disease unknown even in slavery times, became a problem of epidemic proportions in the South. Another consequence was a form of debt bondage that, wrote Charles Oken in 1894, "crushed out all independence and reduced its victims to a coarse species of servile labor."

The victims were white as well as black, for many farmers with modest holdings lost them to creditors, usually merchants. The ledgers of one Southern merchant, T. G. Patrick, show that during one season he provided about $900 worth of seed, food, tools, and other necessities to a farm owner named S. R. Simonton. When the price of cotton dropped well below Simonton's expectations that fall, he was able to repay only $300, leaving Patrick with a lien against his property of $600. Simonton cut his costs drastically the following year to just $400, but the accumulated debt of $1000 was too much for Patrick to carry. He took Simonton's land and Simonton became his tenant.

Once a tenant or sharecropper, the Southern farmer's debts bound him to the land as if he were a medieval serf. Tenants and sharecroppers also bought their necessities on credit from a general merchandiser, often their landlord, putting up as collateral their share of the crop. If the income from their share did not cover the year's debt, the merchandiser put a lien on the next year's harvest, quite effectively binding the cropper to work for him indefinitely. There was no quitting and moving out. To try to flee such a debt was a criminal offense punishable by imprisonment.

There was, of course, an element of security in debt bondage; the cropper who owed money to his landlord was not likely to be evicted. But there had been such an element of security in slavery too.

Hayseeds

Southern black farmers needed no tutoring to know that their race excluded them from full participation in the mainstream of American politics and social life. The color line was drawn ever more clearly in the South as the nineteenth century waned. White farmers of the South and West experienced a more subtle deterioration in their political power and status. Not only did the proportion of agriculturalists in the population decline annually, but the legislators whom farmers sent to Washington and the state capitals seemed all too often to forget their grimy constituents once they made the acquaintance of back-slapping lobbyists for railroads, industry, and banks.

A newly confident urban culture depicted the man of the soil in popular fiction, songs, and melodramas as a thick-skulled yokel, a ridiculous figure in a tattered straw hat with a hayseed clenched between his teeth, who allows traveling salesmen to sleep with his daughter. Rather more serious chroniclers of rural life such as Hamlin Garland sympathized with farmers but wanted no part of their lives. In his popular book of 1891, *Main-Travelled Roads*, Garland depicted rural life as dreary and stultifying.

Tens of thousands of farmers' sons and daughters fol-

THE FARMER FEEDS THEM ALL

When the Lawyer hangs around and the Butcher cuts a
  pound,
Oh the farmer is the man who feeds them all.
And the preacher and the cook go a-strolling by the brook
And the farmer is the man who feeds them all.

Oh the farmer is the man, the farmer is the man,
Lives on credit 'till the fall.
Then they take him by the hand and they lead him from the
  land
And the middle man's the one that gets them all.
                                        Song of the 1890s

lowed Garland in his flight to the city. In part, they despaired of ever making a living on the land. In part, they were lured by the social and cultural attractions of the city. "Who wants to smell new-mown hay," playwright Clyde Fitch wrote in 1909, "if he can breathe gasoline on Fifth Avenue instead?" With each son and daughter who opted for urban fumes, farmers who clung to the Jeffersonian image of themselves became further dejected, agitated, and demoralized.

PROTEST AND ORGANIZATION

To ward against jokes and jeers, farmers could repair to the good old gospel of agrarianism, the confidence that they were peculiarly valuable to society. They could and did disdain the cities as sinks of iniquity and sin. In speech and sermon, and in the pages of magazines catering to country people, politicians, preachers, and journalists repeated the old shibboleths. In sturdy pillars of American popular culture, like the McGuffey's Readers in which urban and rural schoolchildren alike learned their ABCs, and values on the side, the ennoblement of farm life was alive and well.

Rural Renaissance

And yet, American farm life was undeniably isolated, arduous, and often dreary, the winds on the Great Plains dispatching men and women to the state asylum in numbers high enough to worry the doughtiest Jeffersonian. Aside from church—which was not for everyone—and moments snatched on shopping trips to town, there was little to relieve the tedium and monotony, especially for farm women, whose lives were far more isolated than those of their menfolk.

In the 1870s, farmers and their wives joined the Patrons of Husbandry, the Grange, which sponsored dances, fairs, even lecturers who spoke on everything from the date of creation to the habits of the people of Borneo. In the 1880s, new organizations—the Agricultural Wheel, the Texas State Alliance, The Southern Alliance, the Colored Farmers' National Alliance—mushroomed all over the countryside to take over many of the same functions.

Their value was inestimable, particularly for women. A leader of the Southern Alliance, the largest of the regional organizations, declared that it "redeemed woman from her enslaved condition, and placed her in her proper sphere." Indeed, women were to play an active role in the agrarian movement at every level.

Originally, both the Grange and the Alliances were avowedly non-political. Inevitably in the hard times, however, farmers getting together asked themselves what—or who—was to blame for their woes? The Grangers attacked the railroads for exploiting them, and successfully regulated their rates by electing sympathetic politicians to state legislatures. Then they saw their work wiped out by the Wabash decision of 1886. The Alliances and Wheels taught that the truculent individualism of the farmer in a highly organized society contributed to their distress and encouraged members to form cooperatives and other economic combinations.

The Co-op Movement

In consumer cooperatives, farmers banded together to purchase essential machinery in lots and therefore more cheaply. Money pools, associations much like contemporary credit unions, sprouted all over the Midwest. Through these associations, which were capitalized by members and operated on a nonprofit basis, farmers hoped to eliminate their dependence on banks. While many survived to serve the credit needs of their members for generations, money pools suffered from the opposition of bankers and the inexperience of their own amateur administrators. Farmers too often put friends rather than professionals in charge of the money pools, and the rate of mismanagement and embezzlement was sadly high.

Producer cooperatives were designed to counter the power of the railroads over farmers' lives after the Supreme Court's decision in the Wabash case of 1886 struck down the Granger laws regulating charges for storing grain. Corn-belt farmers pooled funds and built their own grain elevators in the expectation they could keep their crop off the market until they liked the selling price. By the mid-1890s, there were more than 1,600 producers' co-ops among dairy farmers alone.

But co-ops could not remedy the problem that was at the root of agricultural distress: American staple farmers were too many and too good for their own good. Too much land had been opened to settlement by too many railroads too quickly. Improvements in farm machinery and new methods resulted in far more grain, livestock, and fiber than the market could absorb.

Sinister Forces

Some agrarian leaders recognized overproduction as a problem. Canadian-born "Sockless Jerry" Simpson of Kansas called on the federal government to carve out new markets for American farm goods abroad. Mary Elizabeth Lease of Kansas, one of the nation's first women lawyers and an orator of fiery intensity, told farmers to "raise less corn and more hell." But that was a slogan, not a program. To the individual farmer, the only solution to declining prices was not to plant less corn but more, thus worsening the situation.

Moreover, few farmers believed that overproduction was the sole or even the chief cause of agrarian distress. Mother Lease herself pointed out that the streets of American cities teemed with hungry, ill-clad people while foodstuffs rotted in Kansas and cotton went unsold in Alabama. She and other agrarian leaders—Simpson, Ignatius Donnelley of Minnesota, William Peffer of Kansas, Thomas Watson of Georgia—said that sinister, parasitical forces were at work like thieves in the night to enrich themselves at the expense of men and women who produced wealth. Their villains included the great railroaders, politicians and judges pliantly in their employ, and most of all the "money power," a conspiracy of bankers and lawyers who manipulated the nation's currency.

THE MONEY QUESTION

Money is a medium of exchange, a token that the people of a society agree represents value. It makes the exchange of goods and services more workable than simple barter: so much grain in return for so many pairs of shoes or so many hours of labor. Obviously, money is essential to all but the most primitive economies.

The value of money can change. At the time of the first European settlements in North America, the tribes of the Eastern Woodlands used wampum, or strings of beads made of shell, to represent value when they exchanged corn, hides, and other goods. Strings of wampum were difficult to make and, therefore, scarce. However, when Europeans introduced glass beads in great quantity into this economy at little cost to themselves, buying valuable pelts for a pittance, but refusing to accept the beads in return when the Indians tried to purchase iron tools, weapons, and other European products, wampum was soon worthless to everyone.

Gold and Silver

Rather than wampum, the economically sophisticated nations of the world used precious metals—gold and silver—as their medium of exchange. They were rare, durable, and limited in supply. There was little danger that the world would suddenly be flooded with either, as the Eastern Indians were flooded with beads.

Thus, the value they represented was stable and dependable. The farmer who received gold for his crop knew that the suppliers of the goods his family needed would accept the gold at the value he put on it. It did not even matter which country's emblem was stamped on a coin. The weight of the gold in it determined its

worth. In the United States, the Treasury minted coins of large denomination in gold: $5 coins, $10 coins (called "eagles"), and $20 coins ("double eagles").

Coins of smaller denomination (dimes, quarters, dollars) were minted in silver, which was more common than gold and therefore less valuable, but also limited in quantity. In 1837, Congress determined that the value of silver as money would be pegged to that of gold at a ratio of 16:1. That is, an ounce of gold was legally worth 16 ounces of silver, it being estimated that there was in the world just about sixteen times as much silver as gold. Put another way, for every 16 ounces of silver a miner presented to the mint for sale, he would receive one ounce of gold.

Large commercial transactions were carried out in paper money issued by banks pledged to redeem it in silver or gold. The value of this paper depended, of course, upon people's confidence in the ability of the bank in question to hand precious metal over the counter when presented with its own notes.

The Greenbacks

During the Civil War, finding itself with too little gold and silver to support the army, the Lincoln administration issued a new kind of paper money, some $433 million in bills called "greenbacks" because they were printed on the obverse (like our own money) in green ink. The greenbacks were not redeemable in gold or silver. Their value depended entirely upon the government's agreement to accept them in payment of most obligations, such as taxes.

Government acceptance of the greenbacks gave them value as a medium of exchange. However, no one considered them "as good as gold" (or silver) and their value fluctuated, sometimes wildly, depending on the success or failure of the Union army or a twist in federal financial policy. At the end of the Civil War, it took $157 in greenbacks to buy $100 in coin.

Inflation or Deflation

Discounted as they were, the abundant greenbacks nevertheless circulated; the Union did, after all, survive and continue to accept them. Indeed, the greenbacks won many friends because, by increasing the amount of money in circulation, they inflated wages and prices, including prices at which farmers sold their crops. The Civil War was a prosperous time down on the farm. Looking back on it in bleaker days, many farmers associated the good times with the greenbacks. They argued that the federal government should continue to use them to regulate the amount of money in circulation in order to accommodate the needs of a dynamic people. The

NOTABLE PEOPLE

THE NEW SOUTH: THE PROPHET AND THE BUILDER

In speech after speech throughout the South, he told the story of a funeral that he had attended in rural Georgia. "They buried him in a New York coat and a Boston pair of shoes, and a pair of breeches from Chicago and a shirt from Cincinnati." The coffin, continued Henry W. Grady (1851–89), the wisecracking editor of the Atlanta *Constitution,* was made from northern lumber and hammered together with northern-forged nails. "The South didn't furnish a thing on earth for that funeral but the corpse and the hole in the ground."

Grady's point, to which he devoted most of his short life, was that the South must abandon its traditional reliance on agriculture and promote industrialization. The North's industry explained why the Confederacy had been defeated and why, in the wake of the war, the South suffered in company with the agricultural Plains. Only by accepting the realities of the modern world would the South prosper and escape its status as a backwater.

Although Grady lived to see few of his ideas come to fruition, during the very period that southern agrarians like Thomas E. Watson were vilifying urban, industrial America, Southerners scored the kind of successes that Grady had called for. Beginning with a federal grant of almost 6 million acres of forest land in 1877, southern syndicates laid the basis of a thriving lumber and turpentine industry in the vast pine woods of the section. Birmingham became the "Pittsburgh of the South," the center of a booming steel industry, following the discovery of coal and iron in northern Alabama in the early 1870s. By 1890, Birmingham was making more pig iron than was Pittsburgh. ("Pigs" are iron ingots, intermediate products ready for further processing.)

The southern oil industry was largely a twentieth-century development; the great Texas gusher, Spindletop, came through in 1901. Likewise the southern textile industry. Most of the New England textile mills migrated to the South after 1900, although, even before Grady died in 1889, the trend of "bringing the factory to the fields" was to some degree under way.

The Southerner who was most successful in bringing the factory to the fields was not a maker of cloth but a maker of cigarettes and bad habits. James Buchanan "Buck" Duke (1856–1925) started out as a tobacco grower, a good southern agrarian on the face of it. In 1881, he was shown a new machine that rolled cigarettes by the hundreds per minute, and his head began to spin in contemplation of its possibilities. All cigarettes were then rolled by hand, mostly by the smoker. Like a chess player, Duke had to see several moves ahead. To make money from manufacturing cigarettes, it was neces-

sary not only to mass-produce them cheaply, but also to change Americans' tobacco habits.

In the late nineteenth century, "decent" women did not smoke (at least in public), upper- and middle-class men smoked cigars or pipes, and workingmen and the lower classes in the South were inclined to chew tobacco. Cigarettes were around. The soldiers in the Civil War had taken to them because they could carry papers and a pouch of tobacco but not cigars. After the war, however, the white cylinders were considered to be effete, a boy's smoke behind the barn. Duke would have to change that image, and he did.

Buying the patent to the cigarette-rolling machine, he encouraged adolescents to cultivate the habit by selling a pack of twenty for only a nickel and by including inside each pack a "trading card" that featured pictures and brief biographies of military heroes and popular athletes, mostly boxers and baseball players. No one better understood the wisdom in putting together a long-term market than "Buck" Duke. All the while he created his consumers, he improved machinery and bought out competitors. By 1889, his company accounted for half the cigarettes sold in the United States, and Duke had only begun.

In 1890, he set up a trust along the lines laid out by John D. Rockefeller. Through it he gained control of his major competitors, R. J. Reynolds and P. J. Lorillard, and built an almost perfect monopoly. Indeed, through loose arrangements with British cigarette manufacturers, Duke had a major say in the tobacco-processing industry on two continents. Only federal antitrust action in 1911 forced him to disband his gigantic corporation. By that year, he controlled 150 factories, and, even at that, his reputation as the South's greatest home-grown business mogul was being challenged by the directors of the recently founded Coca-Cola Company of Atlanta.

Like the Yankee moguls whose methods he adopted, "Buck" Duke was a generous philanthropist. His most enduring monument is Duke University, which had been a small, local college before it received an endowment from Duke and changed its name; it is now an architecturally magnificent Gothic-style campus in Duke's hometown of Durham, North Carolina. Until the militant antismoking campaigns of the 1970s, Duke was one of the few universities in the United States where students and faculty could light up the "coffin nails" that had built the institution wherever and whenever they chose. That practice has been abandoned, but his statue, which stands in front of the university's cathedral-size chapel, portrays James Buchanan Duke gently tapping the ash from his cigar.

supply of gold and silver did not expand rapidly enough to keep up with the explosive economy of the United States.

Bankers and big businessmen thought otherwise. They dealt in large sums of money and feared having the value of their vast properties—and the money others owed to them—reduced in value by politicians seeking favor with voters. These monetary conservatives insisted that money had absolute, natural value, determined by the amount of gold in existence and, until the 1870s, by the amount of silver.

With their close ties to the executive branch of the government in the wake of the Civil War, the conservatives generally had their way. By February 1868, $45 million in greenbacks had been retired from circulation, simply burned when paid to the government in taxes. Money grew scarcer and therefore more valuable: deflated. Wages and prices, including the prices at which farmers sold their crops, declined.

The protest was so widespread that, in October 1868, Congress ordered the Treasury Department to stop retiring the greenbacks. But the inflationist victory was short-lived. In 1875, ascendant conservatives ordered that for every $100 issued by banks (money theoretically backed by gold), $80 in greenbacks be retired. In 1879, Secretary of the Treasury John Sherman ordered that all payments to the government be made in specie, or coin, effectively destroying the greenbacks. Between 1865 and 1878, the amount of all kinds of money in circulation in the United States shrunk from $1.08 billion to $773 million. Whereas in 1865 there had been $31.18 in circulation for every American, in 1878 there was $16.25.

The Greenback Party

In an attempt to stem this deflation, many farmers, working people, and some small business men joined together to form the Greenback Labor Party, which was dedicated to the single issue of inflating the currency. Like most third parties in American history, the Greenbackers attracted few voters. In 1880, Civil War General James B. Weaver of Iowa won 308,578 votes. In 1884, Greenback candidate Benjamin F. Butler won just 175,370 votes, not many more than the Prohibitionist party candidate received. By 1884, people who wanted the currency inflated had turned to another form of money for their salvation—silver coin.

Silver to the Fore

Between 1837 and 1873, the price of silver was legally pegged to the price of gold at a ratio of 16:1. During the 1860s, however, American mines produced proportionately less silver than gold. Therefore, mine owners pre-

A cartoonist uses the image of the bicycle, still a "newfangled contraption," to argue against attempting to value silver coin on a par with gold money.

ferred to sell not to the United States Mint, which paid the official price, but to private or foreign buyers, who were willing to pay more, an ounce of gold for just fourteen ounces of silver or less.

In 1873, confronted with the fact that little silver was being presented to the Mint, Congress enacted the Demonetization Act, ceasing the purchase of silver. The silver dollar was dropped from the list of coins the government minted. Silver became an ordinary commodity like wheat, hogs, lumber, or petticoats, its value (in gold) set by the laws of supply and demand. President Grant signed the bill without ado.

Already as the ink was drying, however, the relative supply of silver and gold was changing again. New silver strikes and new methods of mining it were resulting in a vast increase in production of the white metal. In 1861, only $2 million worth of silver had been mined in the United States compared to $43 million worth of gold. In 1873, the value of silver and gold mined was about equal, $36 million each. During the rest of the 1870s, silver production increased so rapidly that its price on the private market, the only market now open to miners, collapsed.

Politician friends of mining interests like the excitable Democrat Richard "Silver Dick" Bland of Missouri and Senator Henry W. Teller of Colorado began to denounce the Demonetization Act as "The Crime of '73." They accused the government of conspiring with bankers to punish silver miners for their very success. There was no "Crime of '73"; no one could have anticipated the explosive growth of silver production when the Demonetization Act was passed but the most sanguine Western prospector.

Nevertheless, when silver production did rise, monetary conservatives were undoubtedly relieved that the government was no longer buying and minting it, thus inflating the currency and reducing the value of their property. The "Gold Bugs," as Bland and Teller called them, began to look upon abundant silver as a threat to the value of their money as serious as the greenbacks.

By themselves, mine owners and miners would have been powerless to force the government to resume the purchase and minting of silver. Even after the admission of mineral-rich Colorado in 1876, mining interests were significant in only a handful of states. However, inflationist congressmen from agricultural states—mostly Southern and Western Democrats, but also including Republicans—seized on silver coinage as a way to get more money in circulation. In the depression year of 1878, they forced the conservatives to agree to a compromise. The Bland-Allison Bill of that year required the Secretary of the Treasury to purchase between $2 million and $4 million of silver each month for minting into money. The silver dollar was back.

The Sherman Silver Purchase Act

The silver dollar was back, but the principle of bi-metalism (both gold and silver as money, the value of one pegged to the other) was not. In both the Republican and Democratic administrations of the 1880s, the Treasury was safely in the hands of conservatives dedicated to gold as the sole standard of value. The government almost invariably bought the minimum $2 million in silver required by law. In effect, the silver dollars that were minted were tokens akin to paper money, themselves backed by gold.

Meanwhile, the national production of silver continued to grow and the market price of the metal plummeted. By 1890, it took nearly 20 ounces of silver to buy an ounce of gold. In the minds of inflationists and silver producers, the old lost ratio of 16:1 took on a mythic, sacred significance.

In 1889 and 1890, the balance of power tipped to the side of the inflationists. Two states in which silver was an important commodity (Montana and Idaho) and four in which inflationist farmers were a majority (the two

Dakotas, Washington, and Wyoming) entered the Union, bringing 12 new silver senators to Washington.

The result was the Sherman Silver Purchase Act of 1890. Like the Bland-Allison Act, it was a compromise. The Sherman law required the Secretary of the Treasury to purchase 4.5 million ounces of silver each month, in effect the entire monthly production of the nation's silver mines at that time. However, the government bought silver at the market price, which continued to decline, from a ratio of 20:1 in 1890 to 26.5:1 in 1893. Consequently, the Sherman Act failed to relieve discontent in the mining regions and led to violent strikes as mine owners attempted to cut costs by forcing down wages.

Farmers, who favored silver coinage as a means of inflating the currency and raising prices, were also disappointed. Although he signed the Sherman Act, President Benjamin Harrison was a gold standard man. He treated silver coins as if they were tokens—paper money—instructing the Secretary of the Treasury to pay all the government's bills in gold. To distressed farmers already inclined to look for sinister forces at work in the night, the presidency itself seemed in the employ of the money power.

THE POPULISTS

By 1890, the Alliance movement was at flood tide. The Southern Alliance had 1.5 million members, the Colored Farmers Alliance a million, other groups combined about the same. Feeling their strength, the leaders of the various regional organizations gathered in Ocala, Florida in December to draw up a list of grievances and consider the possibility of organizing a third party.

Hesitation

By December 1890, Kansas farmers had already organized a statewide People's Party, calling themselves Populists after the Latin word for people, *populus*, and winning control of the state legislature. At Ocala, however, old Republican and Democratic loyalties were too strong, and racial anxieties too gnawing for the delegates to take the same leap.

Southern white farmers hesitated because they had made inroads in the Democratic party and feared that if they split the white vote in the South by forming a new party, blacks would regain the political equality they had held through the Republican party during Reconstruction. Indeed, the leaders of the Colored Farmers Alliance were reluctant to give up their allegiance to the Repub-

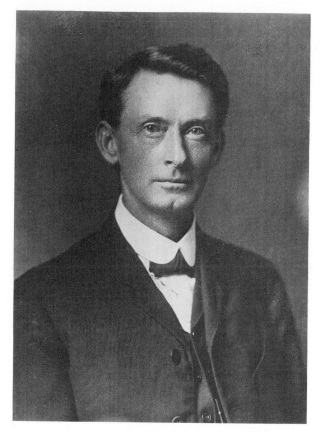

Thomas E. Watson, a Populist from Georgia, advocated the principle that social class was more important than race. He had a knack for inflammatory journalism and oratory.

lican party, which had, however uncertainly, defended civil rights for blacks.

But events were already underway to undermine old loyalties. In July 1890, the same month the Silver Purchase Act was passed, the Republican majority in the United States Senate failed to enact the Force Bill, a law designed to protect the right of Southern blacks to vote. In effect, the Republicans abandoned Southern blacks to their own fate. Some black Southerners called for a new party. Some Southern whites like Tom Watson of Georgia, a diminutive lawyer who had been cheated out of elective office by the Democratic machine, called for an alliance between black and white farmers. In a magazine article published in 1892, he told white and black farmers:

You are kept apart that you may be separately fleeced of your earnings. You are made to hate each other because upon that hatred is rested the keystone of the arch of financial despotism which enslaves you both. You are deceived and blinded that you may not see how this race antagonism perpetuates a monetary system which beggars both.

The Omaha Convention

In February 1892, delegates from the various Alliances and Wheels, and more than a few self-appointed spokesmen for the farmers and silver miners, met in Omaha, Nebraska to form a new party. They gladly adopted the name "Populist" from the Kansas party that had already sent several congressmen and Senator William Peffer to Washington.

To symbolize the fact that farmers of North and South had bridged the sectional chasm that had made them enemies, the Populists nominated former Union General and Greenbacker James B. Weaver for president, and former Confederate General James G. Field for vice-president. No one expected them to win, and they did not. Grover Cleveland, the Democratic candidate, won a comfortable victory in the electoral college despite carrying only 46 percent of the popular vote. And Weaver did well enough, winning more than a million votes and carrying Kansas. At Omaha, the Populists were planning for November 1896, not 1892, when they expected to restore democracy and justice to a corrupted country.

Indeed, what most struck observers about the Omaha convention was the evangelical fervor with which the Populists addressed public questions, as if they were embarked not on a political campaign, but on a crusade against satanic evil itself. "We meet on the verge of a nation brought to the verge of moral, political, and material ruin," Ignatius Donnelley of Minnesota wrote in the preamble to the party platform, "Corruption dominates the ballot box, the legislatures, the Congress, and touches even the ermine of the bench." William Peffer, looking like a biblical prophet with his waist-length beard, railed like one about the iniquities of the land. "Conspiracy" was a word on everyone's lips, the conspiracy of the great railroads to defraud the shipper, the conspiracy of politicians to destroy democracy, the conspiracy of the money power, even the conspiracy of Jews.

"The people are at bay," Mother Lease said, "let the bloodhounds of money beware." When the platform was finally approved, according to one not too sympathetic reporter, "cheers and yells . . . rose like a tornado . . . and raged without cessation for thirty-four minutes, during which time women shrieked and wept, men embraced and kissed their neighbors, locked arms, marched back and forth, and leaped upon tables and chairs in the ecstasy of their delirium."

A Far Reaching Program

The atmosphere was, no doubt, disarming. And yet, the platform the Populists wrote was far from lunatic. On the contrary, it was a comprehensive program for reform

The hatred of farmers for bankers sometimes took the form of anti-Semitism, hatred of Jewish bankers. One book that blamed Jews particularly for the ruination of the American farmer was Ignatius P. Donnelly's novel *Caesar's Column*. One character's explanation of why Jewish bankers were exploiting farmers is curious: past anti-Semitism with a Darwinian twist:

Christianity fell upon the Jews, originally a race of agriculturists and shepherds, and forced them, for many centuries, through the most terrible ordeal of persecution the history of mankind bears record of. Only the strong of body, the cunning of brain, the long-headed, the persistent, the men with capacity to live where the dog would starve, survived the awful trial. Like breeds like; and now the Christian world is paying, in tears and blood, for the sufferings inflicted by their bigoted and ignorant ancestors upon a noble race. When the time came for liberty and fair play the Jew was master in the contest with the Gentile. . . . They were as merciless to the Christians as the Christians had been to them.

that, if enacted, would have transformed American development, and not necessarily for the worse.

Indeed, the Populists' political reforms were in large part, although not by them, to become the law of the land. They called for the election of United States Senators by popular vote, rather than by state legislatures, a reform instituted in the Seventeenth Amendment to the Constitution in 1913. They demanded the universal use of the Australian, or secret ballot, to prevent landlords and employers from intimidating their tenants and workers into voting as the bosses chose. By the early twentieth century, public ballots had been abolished everywhere but in New England town meetings.

The Populists introduced the concepts of the initiative, recall, and referendum to American government. The initiative allows voters, through petition, to put measures on the ballot independent of action by legislatures and thus, in theory, free of manipulation by professional lobbyists and their accomplices. The recall allows voters, also through petition, to force a public official to stand for election before his or her term is up. The Populists hoped that the recall would discourage politicians from backing down on campaign pledges. The referendum allows voters to vote directly on laws rather than indirectly through their representatives; it is the means by which initiative measures and recall petitions are decided. All three are accepted procedure in many states today.

The most controversial Populist demand was for the abolition of national banks and for government ownership of railroads and the telegraph. Enemies pointed to this plank as evidence that the Populists were Socialists.

They were not; virtually all of them were landowners or tenants who aspired above all to own land. However, they believed that "natural monopolies"—huge enterprises that could be run efficiently only under a single management—should not be in private hands. To the Populist mind, decisions that affected the interests of all should be made democratically, not by combinations of private parties interested only in their own enrichment.

The Populists also called for a postal savings system, so that ordinary people might avoid depositing their money in privately owned banks, and for a graduated income tax. In 1892, the federal income tax was 2 percent for all; the Populists wanted the wealthy to pay a higher percentage of their income than the modest farmer or wageworker paid.

Finally—as only one plank of many—the Populists addressed the silver question. They called for an increase in the money in circulation of $50 per capita. This inflation was to be accomplished through the free and unlimited coinage of silver, its value pegged to that of gold. In the summer of 1892, this was perhaps the mildest of the Populist demands. It represented only an adjustment of the Sherman Act then in effect. In just over a year, however, "Free Silver" was to become the Populists' obsession, nearly destroying their ardor for the rest of the Omaha platform.

The Panic of 1893

In February 1893, ten days before Grover Cleveland took the oath of office, the Reading Railroad, a major Eastern trunk line, announced it was bankrupt. For two months the stock market was jittery, and then it collapsed. Hundreds of banks and thousands of businesses joined the Reading in receivership. By November, the country was sunk in a depression greater than that of the 1870s.

Needing money or fearing for the safety of their government bonds, both American and British financiers rushed to redeem them. Cleveland, who was more firmly committed to the gold standard than Harrison, was true to his word. He instructed the Secretary of the Treasury

In the Wilson-Gorman Tariff of 1894, provision was made for an income tax of 2 percent on all incomes of $4,000 or more, a pretty modest tax by today's standards. It was widely condemned by men of means, and in the case of *Pollock* v. *Farmers' Loan and Trust Co.* (1895), the Supreme Court ruled that because the tax was a direct tax that did not fall on all equally, it was unconstitutional. Only after the Sixteenth Amendment was adopted in 1913 was it constitutional to tax the wealthy at a higher rate than the poor.

Coxey and his secretary leading his army to Washington, D.C.

to redeem all demands in gold alone. By fall, the government's gold reserve—the actual metal in its vaults—sunk to below $100 million, the level regarded by conservatives as the absolute minimum for maintaining the government's credit.

A Most Unpopular Man

Cleveland blamed the crisis, and the panic that led up to it, on the Sherman Act. "To put beyond all doubt or mistake" the commitment of the United States to the gold standard, the president called for its repeal and a frightened Congress obliged him. That lost him the support of Democrats from the mining states. Then the news leaked that, at the height of the crisis, Cleveland

had called on J.P. Morgan for help in increasing the government's gold reserve. Throughout the South and Midwest, more Democrats denounced him.

In 1894, Cleveland's Attorney General, a former railroad attorney, Richard B. Olney, helped to crush a strike of workers against the Pullman Company, a manufacturer of railroad cars, and of railway workers who sympathized with them. Their leader, a charismatic former brakeman, Eugene V. Debs, was jailed, and working people all over the country turned against Cleveland. The president blundered even in his treatment of Jacob Coxey, an Ohio businessman who led a march of unemployed men to Washington to ask for relief. Coxey was arrested for walking on the grass.

Few presidents have been so unpopular as was Grover

Cleveland in his second term. And with each blow to his prestige, the Populists celebrated. In their eyes, Cleveland's Democrats and the Republicans were indistinguishable. Both parties were the puppets of the money power. The people did indeed seem to be at bay. The Populists expected to come to power in 1896. The word "revolution" was being voiced in many gatherings of "the bone and sinew of the republic."

For Further Reading

For background and context, see Vincent P. DeSantis, *The Shaping of Modern America, 1877–1916* (1973) and Robert H. Wiebe, *The Search for Order, 1880–1920* (1967). The genuinely classic studies of the subject, with contrasting visions, are Gilbert C. Fite, *The Farmer's Frontier, 1865–1900* (1966) and Fred A. Shannon, *The Farmers' Last Frontier. Agriculture 1860–1897* (1945). Also see Allan C. Bogue, *From Prairie to Corn Belt* (1963); E. Dick, *The Sod-House Frontier* (1937); and Walter P. Webb, *The Great Plains* (1931).

On farmers' movements, see Solon J. Buck, *The Granger Movement* (1913); R. F. Durden, *The Climax of Populism* (1965); Lawrence Goodwyn, *Democratic Promise: The Populist Movement in America* (1976); John D. Hicks, *The Populist Revolt* (1931); the appropriate chapters of Richard Hofstadter, *Age of Reform* (1955); J. Morgan Kousser, *The Shaping of Southern Politics: Suffrage Restriction and the Establishment of the One-Party South, 1880–* 1910 (1974); Walter T. K. Nugent, *Money and American Society, 1865–1880* (1968) and *The Tolerant Populists: Kansas Populism and Nativism* (1963); Norman Pollock, *The Populist Response to Industrial America* (1966); Theodore Saloutos, *Farmer Movements in the South, 1865–1933* (1960); Irwin Unger, *The Greenback Era: A Social and Political History of American Finance, 1865–1879* (1964); Allen Weinstein, *Prelude to Populism: Origins of the Silver Issue, 1867–1878* (1970); and C. Vann Woodward, *The Strange Career of Jim Crow* (1974).

P. E. Coletta, *William Jennings Bryan: Political Evangelist, 1860–1908* (1964) and Louis W. Koenig, *Bryan: A Political Biography of William Jennings Bryan* (1971) present somewhat different views of the man who came to personify agrarian aspirations. The model biography of the leading Southern Populist is C. Vann Woodward, *Tom Watson: Agrarian Rebel* (1938).

The Rough Riders, soon to win fame in the writings of Colonel Theodore Roosevelt, on a training exercise.

THE DAYS OF McKINLEY

THE UNITED STATES BECOMES A WORLD POWER 1896 - 1903

Only a few presidential elections have been so anxious and tense as the election of 1896. Even as the year began, politicians were calling the contest more important than any since 1860, when the Union itself hung in the balance. This time, the fissure in America was social rather than sectional, class arrayed against class. The terrible depression, the "revolt of the hayseeds," the violent strikes, the mass demonstrations, and the passions the silver issue had engendered lent a sense of foreboding to every political discussion.

WATERSHED

The election of 1896 was a watershed. When it was over, the political era that had begun with the end of Reconstruction would be dead, and a new one underway. No one knew what the new era would be like when the campaign began. That depended upon which party and which candidate won the electoral college in November. Thus the anxiety.

Mark Hanna and Bill McKinley

Meeting in St. Louis in June, the Republican convention was placid on the surface. Most Republican agrarians had long since bade farewell to the Grand Old Party and signed on with the Populists. A small free silver contingent from the mining states, led by Senator Teller of Colorado, caused a minor ruckus trying to win concessions for their cause. But the convention was dominated by "Gold Bugs." When they rebuked Teller, he and his followers walked out. The convention was left to people of like mind and, with little folderol, they chose as their presidential candidate a man who was a model of conservatism, prudence, respectability, and sobriety, William McKinley of Ohio. Or, rather, as the Populists and Democrats were soon to claim, they sat back and allowed a beefy Cleveland industrialist, Marcus Alonzo Hanna, to choose their candidate for them.

Bald, scowling Mark Hanna was nearly 60 in 1896. He had made a fortune in coal and iron, was close to the Rockefellers, and was well-known in industrial circles as a feisty spokesman for moderation and flexibility in dealing with conservative labor unions. Hanna railed against exploitative capitalists as scorchingly as he condemned labor radicals.

Only in the 1890s, after the descent of the depression, did Hanna take an interest in national politics. He had ambitions of his own, but also the realism to know that he could not jump from the corporate board room to the Executive Mansion. Instead, he devoted his energies to promoting the candidacy of his fellow Ohioan, former representative and governor William McKinley of Canton.

McKinley, the Republican party's chief expert on the tariff, was himself ambitious. Theodore Roosevelt later said that McKinley looked into every introduction and conversation for the advantage it might mean to him. And yet, without Hanna clearing the way and pushing him on, it is unlikely that McKinley would have won the Republican nomination in 1896. The issue that was tearing the country apart—gold standard versus free silver—simply did not interest him very much.

Moreover, while his dignity commanded respect,

McKinley lacked the presence and personality that made people stand up and applaud. William Allen White said that "he was destined for a statue in the park and he was practicing the pose for it." McKinley was easy to overlook and underestimate. Mark Hanna was the wheeler-dealer who marched into an office, cigar blazing, and planted a hefty haunch on the desk of the person he wanted to see. Many Republicans and Democrats alike assumed that McKinley was his puppet.

The Frightening Boy Bryan

The partnership of energy and solemnity proved indispensable to the Republicans in 1896 because the Democratic party candidate, nominated at a frenzied convention in July, was a tornado of energy. William Jennings Bryan, scarcely beyond the 35 years of age the Constitution requires a president to be, was a two-term congressman from Nebraska, a newspaperman, and regionally famous as a platform orator. His one and only subject for four years had been the free coinage of silver, and Bryan had polished a single speech, the "Cross of Gold," to a mathematical precision in phrasing, timing, and theatrical gesture. Deeply religious himself, Bryan enlisted God in the cause of silver coinage. He identified the gold standard with the crucifiers of Christ, silver with democracy and Christianity.

If the intensity with which he spoke was set aside, Bryan was a rather conservative man. He did not approve of much of what the Populists held dear except for free silver. But his language and apparently irresponsible youth were enough to frighten Republicans. They called him "Boy Bryan" and "the boy orator of the Platte," scornfully but also with trepidation. The Democrats, committed to the cause of silver when the Chicago convention was planned, gladly scheduled him and his Cross of Gold to close out the debate on the currency question.

Later, it would be said that when Bryan spoke he transformed himself from an obscure delegate into a presidential candidate by acclamation. In fact, he and his supporters had paved the way for his nomination almost as carefully as Mark Hanna had worked for McKinley. And yet, Bryan's speech and the Democratic party's ringing endorsement of free silver were so electrifying that the Western farmers began to celebrate a November victory in July. For, late in the month, the Populists nominated Bryan too.

The Populists Join the Democrats

Meeting in St. Louis, the Populists were presented with a difficult decision. If they maintained their party's independence by nominating a candidate of their own, they would split the free silver vote and put Bill Mc-

William Jennings Bryan carries a cross of gold in this cartoon by Grant Hamilton, who viewed Bryan as a despoiler of the Bible.

Kinley in the White House. If they nominated Bryan—and just about everyone but Mark Hanna agreed on this in July—they would easily elect a man whose evangelical style suited them and whose position on free silver was perfect.

However, Bryan was pointedly clear in his opposition to the comprehensive Populist program for reform. For the sake of a free silver president, the Populists would, by nominating Bryan, throw away their grand plans for America and, fused to the older, larger Democratic party, their very identity.

Urban Populists like Henry Demarest Lloyd urged the party to think in long-range terms. He told the Populists to maintain their independence and the integrity of their program, accept defeat in 1896, and work toward 1900. Some Southern Populists like Tom Watson of Georgia had another reason for opposing fusion. In the South, the conservative enemy was not Republican but Democratic. To fuse with the Democrats in the South meant suicide, and breaking the connections that Watson had been trying to forge between white and black farmers. Southern blacks would not vote for the Democratic party, the party of white supremacy.

But Midwestern Populists like Jerry Simpson wanted fusion. "I care not for party names," he said, "it is substance we are after, and we have it in William J. Bryan." The Populists from the mining states agreed; free silver had always been the heart of their rebellion. The party nominated Bryan and, to seal the partnership, nomi-

nated Tom Watson for vice president, asking the Democrats to accept him as their candidate too. Bryan ignored them. He accepted Populist support but made no concessions to them, not even the symbolic one of taking a Populist for vice president.

Waves Against a Rock

Rallying voters was Bryan's forte. Handsome, tireless, and completely at home among ordinary, hard-working farm people—whether exhorting them or gobbling up potato salad and chowchow after a speech—Bryan revolutionized presidential campaigning in the United States.

Before 1896, with a few halting exceptions, presidential nominees had been quiet, as though it were an insult to the dignity of the office to woo votes like a candidate for town councilman in an Appalachian hollow. Not Bryan. His speaking tour took him more than 13,000 miles by train. He delivered 600 speeches in 29 states in only 14 weeks, more than six speeches a day. The roaring enthusiasm of the crowds that greeted him, at least in the West and South, confirmed him in his zeal and threw bankers and industrialists into a panic.

Panic was what Mark Hanna wanted to see. He pressured wealthy Republicans (and more than a few conservative Democrats) into making large contributions to McKinley's campaign. By the time of the election, Hanna had spent more on posters, buttons, rallies, picnics, advertisements, and a corps of speakers who dogged Bryan's steps than had been spent by both parties in every election since the Civil War. (The Republicans printed five pamphlets for every American voter.)

THE CROSS OF GOLD

The following lines are the first and last from William Jennings Bryan's electrifying speech at the 1896 Democratic convention:

I would be presumptuous, indeed, to present myself against the distinguished gentlemen to whom you have listened if this were a mere measuring of abilities; but this is not a contest between persons. The humblest citizen in all the land, when clad in the armor of a righteous cause, is stronger than all the hosts of error. I come to speak to you in defense of a cause as holy as the cause of liberty—the cause of humanity. . . .

If they dare to come out in the open field and defend the gold standard as a good thing, we will fight them to the uttermost. Having behind us the producing masses of this nation and the world, supported by the commercial interests, the laboring interests, and the toilers everywhere, we will answer their demand for a gold standard by saying to them: you shall not press down upon the brow of labor this crown of thorns, you shall not crucify mankind upon a cross of gold.

Hanna was so successful a fund-raiser that, before election day, he began to return surplus contributions.

Knowing that the phlegmatic McKinley could not rival Bryan on the stump, Hanna kept his candidate at his modest home in Canton, Ohio, instructing Republican speakers to compare McKinley's self-respect with Bryan's huckstering. In fact, McKinley's campaign was as frantic as Bryan's and nearly as tiring. Delegations of party faithful came in a steady stream to Canton, where they marched through the town behind a brass band and gathered on McKinley's front lawn. McKinley delivered a short speech from the porch, answered a few prearranged questions, and invited "all his friends" to join him for lemonade or beer, depending on the delegation's attitude toward alcohol (which had been discreetly ascertained by party workers when the visitors arrived at the railroad depot). About 750,000 friends visited McKinley's home that summer and fall, trampling his lawn "as if a herd of buffalo had passed through."

Momentous Results

Bryan won more votes, 6.5 million, than any candidate in any previous election. But McKinley won 7 million and, in the electoral college, gathered 271 votes to Bryan's 176. It was the first time in a quarter of the century that any presidential candidate had won an absolute majority. What happened? As late as September, professional politicians believed that Bryan was well ahead.

Candidate William McKinley between speeches on his front porch in Canton, Ohio.

First, although Bryan's supporters were noisy, his appeal was fatally limited to Democrats from the Solid South, hard-pressed staple farmers of the West, and to a few numerically insignificant groups like Western metal miners. McKinley swept the Northeast, including the swing states, and also the largely agricultural states of North Dakota, Minnesota, Wisconsin, Iowa, Michigan, and Illinois. Many farmers whose conditions were not desperate accepted the Republican contention that Boy Bryan was a dangerous radical. That has never been a desirable label in American politics.

Nor did Bryan win much support among factory workers and city people generally. He hardly tried. Imbued with rural prejudices against big cities and the "foreigners" who lived there, he made only one speaking tour in vital New York State and was quoted as having called New York City "the enemy's country," as though it were inhabited solely by bankers and grain speculators. Fourteen of the fifteen biggest cities were controlled by Republican machines and they delivered the vote to William McKinley.

Some industrialists tried to intimidate their employees into voting for the Republican candidate. The Baldwin Piano Works posted notices on the eve of election day to the effect that if Bryan won, the plant would close for good the day following. But Bryan's weakness in the industrial districts was not due to such tactics. His single-issue free silver campaign offered little to factory workers. They found more convincing the Republican claim that a high-tariff policy protected their jobs.

Finally, Mark Hanna shrewdly judged the instincts of a newly important element in American politics, the growing middle class of small-business men, professional people, salaried town dwellers, and highly skilled, well-paid working men. Preoccupied with their respectability and considering themselves to be the new bone and sinew of the American republic, they were frightened by Bryan and the ragged, restive farmers whom he represented. These people committed themselves to the Republican party as "the party of decency." For 40 years after 1896, they made the Republican party the majority party.

The End of Populism

As Watson and Lloyd had feared, fusion with the Democrats meant extinction for the Populists. Having sacrificed their comprehensive reform program for the chance of winning free silver with Bryan, they had nothing left when the votes were counted against him. In the South, Populists who had worked to build a party based on interracial cooperation turned against the blacks (most of whom voted Republican in 1896) to become prominent exponents of white supremacy. In the West, the party withered away, in part because of the electoral

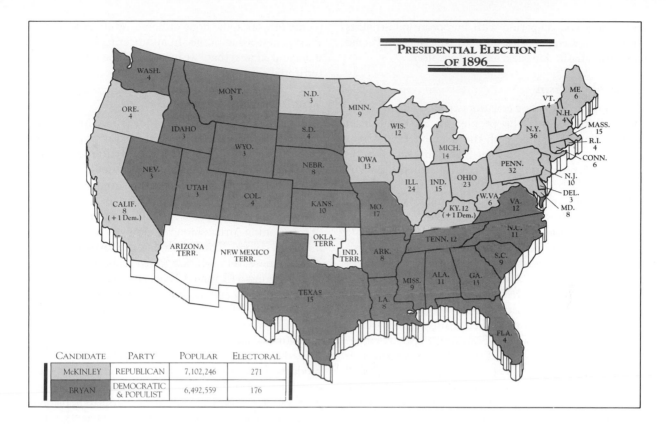

PRESIDENTIAL ELECTION OF 1896

CANDIDATE	PARTY	POPULAR	ELECTORAL
McKINLEY	REPUBLICAN	7,102,246	271
BRYAN	DEMOCRATIC & POPULIST	6,492,559	176

rebuke, and in part because, slowly under McKinley, the wholesale prices of farm products began to rise.

The agricultural depression lifted for a number of reasons. Newly discovered gold deposits in Canada and Alaska inflated the currency somewhat and helped raise prices. Several poor growing seasons in Europe created an increased demand for American farm products. Finally, farmers, like most of the American people, were distracted in 1898 by the McKinley administration's decision to win the United States a place among the empires of the world. Tom Watson was to say, "The blare of the bugle drowned the voice of the reformer."

AMERICAN IMPERIALISM

McKinley hoped to have a quiet presidency. He would have liked to have watched over the economic retrenchment of the nation after the years of depression and agitation. His confidence in the vitality and resilience of American business convinced him that prosperity was just around the corner. All he had to do was wait patiently.

McKinley got his prosperity. Even before he was inaugurated in March 1897, the economic indicators began to show improvement. Peace and quiet were more elusive. Little as the role suited him, McKinley led the American people into a series of overseas adventures that transformed a nation that had been born in an anticolonial revolution into an empire with colonies in both hemispheres.

The Myth of Isolationism

Not that the United States had been isolated from world affairs before McKinley became president. Far from it. The American government maintained busy diplomatic missions in all important capitals, had fought a war with Mexico in the interests of expansion, and several times came close to war in defense of American prestige. In 1889, only a typhoon that sunk German and American warships near Samoa prevented a full-scale naval encounter with a major European power.

Trade made the United States an active participant in world affairs. American ships and sailors were a common sight in the world's most exotic ports. As early as 1844, the United States had signed a trade treaty with the Chinese Empire, as far off and foreign a place as Americans could imagine. In 1854, a naval squadron under Commodore Matthew Perry had anchored off Yokohama, Japan, and had threatened to bombard the city unless the Japanese agreed to abandon their country's genuine isolationism and begin to purchase American goods.

By 1870, American exports totaled $320 million, mostly agricultural produce bound for Europe. By 1890, $857 million in goods was sold abroad, with American manufacturers competing with European industrialists in peddling steel, textiles, and other products in Pacific countries, Latin America, and Europe itself.

Anticolonialism

If Americans were not isolationists, neither were they imperialists. Neither the people nor most statesmen wanted anything to do with the scramble for colonies that engrossed Europe and newly powerful Japan in the late nineteenth century. To Americans, there was a difference between taking the West from a handful of Mexicans and Indians, and establishing suzerainty over distant and densely settled lands with long cultural traditions. Repeatedly, attempts to annex Cuba and the Dominican Republic were squelched in Congress. With the exceptions of Alaska and the tiny Pacific island of Midway, both acquired in 1867 and neither with much population, the United States possessed no territory that was not contiguous to the states.

Two deep convictions worked against the occasional proposals that the United States take such colonies. First, the country had been founded in a war against an empire. Could the heirs of the first great anticolonial rebellion take over the lands of other peoples? Second, the vastness of the American continent provided a more than adequate outlet for American energies. There was

A pro-expansion cartoon shows a sword-bearing Uncle Sam rolling up his sleeves for a fight.

plenty of work to be done at home. William McKinley shared these assumptions. In all sincerity, he said in his inaugural address that "we must avoid the temptation of territorial expansion."

The Nature of Imperialism

But times were changing. By 1897, the United States was the single most important industrial power in the world. Consciousness of this greatness stirred many people to believe that the United States should assume its rightful place among the great nations, and in the 1890s, the great nations were imperialist nations.

The European powers were well along in the process of partitioning Africa among themselves. Indochina was a French colony. The Dutch flag flew over Indonesia. The Japanese were securing Korea and the Chinese island of Formosa (Taiwan). Russia had designs on northern China. Germany and Italy, latecomers to the scramble, looked in Africa and Asia for areas to annex. India, the finest prize of all, was British.

The initial impulse toward empire was economic. Colonies were a source of raw materials and a market for the products of the mother country. Colonialism also generated an emotional justification of its own. Colonies were a source of pride. British imperialists took pleasure in seeing "all that red on the map." (Mapmakers usually colored British possessions in red.) The Germans seized parts of Africa that had little economic value, such as the Namib desert, just for the sake of having colonies.

In England and later in the United States, this bumptious chauvinism was known as "jingoism," from a British song of 1877, "We do not want to fight, But by jingo, if we do . . ." To the jingoes, being strong enough to overcome less advanced peoples was reason enough to do so. Finally, imperialism fed on itself like a sport. Nations seized colonies simply to prevent competitors from doing so.

Some young American politicians such as Henry Cabot Lodge of Massachusetts and Theodore Roosevelt of New York itched to join the scramble. They worried publicly that, in their wealth and prosperity, Americans were becoming soft and flabby. The country needed war now and then in order to toughen up. Roosevelt, a body-building enthusiast, often drew analogies between individuals and nations, between boxing matches and battles.

Anglo-Saxons

Lodge, Roosevelt, and other expansionists were influenced by a theory of race that had evolved in part out of Social Darwinism. Whereas Herbert Spencer had applied his doctrine of "survival of the fittest" to relationships within a society, disciples such as Harvard historian John Fiske and Congregationalist minister Josiah Strong applied it to relationships among different races and cultures. In separate publications of 1885, Fiske and Strong wrote that the Anglo-Saxons (British and Americans) were obviously more fit to govern than were other peoples. According to Strong's *Our Country*, the Anglo-Saxons were "divinely commissioned" to spread their superior political institutions throughout the world. It was not a betrayal of American ideals to take over other lands. There was a racial and religious duty to do so.

Strong believed that inferior races eventually would die out. An influential political scientist at Columbia University, John W. Burgess, stated flatly in 1890 that the right of self-determination did not apply to dark-skinned peoples. He wrote that "there is no human right to the status of barbarism."

Alfred Thayer Mahan

Also in 1890, the expansionists found a highly calculating spokesman in naval captain Alfred Thayer Mahan. In a bestseller in both Europe and America, *The Influence of Sea Power Upon History*, Mahan argued that the great nations were always sea-faring nations possessing powerful navies. He chided Americans for having allowed their own fleet to fall into decay. (In 1891, jingoes who wanted war with Chile had to quiet down when they were informed the Chilean navy might humiliate the American fleet.) Mahan urged a massive program of ship construction, and Congress responded with large appropriations.

A modern steam-powered navy needed coaling stations at scattered points throughout the world. That in itself required taking colonies, even if they were only dots on the globe like Midway, or building bases in ostensibly independent countries like Hawaii, where in 1887, the United States cleared a harbor at the mouth of the Pearl River on the island of Oahu.

Fears for an America Without a Frontier

Another theory of history that fired up the expansionist movement was based on the announcement of the Director of the Census in 1890 that the frontier no longer existed. In 1889, Congress opened western Oklahoma to white settlement; the last large territory that had been reserved for the sole use of Indians was occupied by whites literally overnight.

At the 1893 meeting of the American Historical Association, a young historian named Frederick Jackson Turner propounded a theory that the frontier had been the key to the vitality of American democracy, social stability, and prosperity. Turner was interested in the past, but the implication of his theory for the future was unmistakable. With the frontier gone, was the United States doomed to stagnation and social upheaval? To some who found Turner convincing, the only solution was to establish new frontiers abroad. Throughout the 1890s, American financiers pumped millions of dollars into China and Latin America because they felt that investment opportunities within the United States were shrinking.

By 1898, America's attitude toward the world was delicately balanced. Pulling in one direction was the tradition of anticolonialism. Tugging the other way were jingoism, Anglo-Saxonism, and apprehensions for the future. All it took to decide the direction of the leap was a sudden shove. That was provided by a Cuban war for independence that began in 1895.

THE SPANISH AMERICAN WAR

On a map, Cuba looks like an appendage of Florida, a geographical curiosity that had long attracted the notice of some Americans. Cuba was also a historical curiosity because, along with Puerto Rico, it alone in the Western Hemisphere had remained under Spanish control after the Latin American wars of independence. Rebellion was chronic in Cuba, but weak as Spain was, the old monarchy was able to hold fast to its last American jewel.

The uprising of 1895 was more serious. Smuggling in arms and munitions provided by Cuban exiles in the United States, the rebels won the support of a large number of ordinary Cubans, perhaps the majority. Until the 1890s, the island had been rather prosperous, exporting sugar to the United States, but the Wilson-Gorman Tariff of 1894 practically shut out Cuba's sole export and caused an economic crisis.

It was a classic guerrilla war. The Spanish army and navy controlled the cities of Havana and Santiago and most large towns. By day, Spanish soldiers moved with little trouble amongst a seemingly peaceful peasantry. By night, however, docile field workers turned into fierce rebels and sorely punished the Spanish troops. As in most guerrilla wars, fighting was bitter and cruel. Both sides were guilty of atrocities.

Americans were generally sympathetic to the Cubans. Their interest in the conflict was excited into near hysteria when two competing newspaper chains decided that the rebellion could be used as ammunition in their circulation war.

The Yellow Press

William Randolph Hearst's New York *Journal* and Joseph Pulitzer's New York *World* were known as the "yellow press" because they relied on gimmicks to appeal to readers. The nickname came from one of those gimmicks: "The Yellow Kid," the first comic strip to appear in a newspaper. The Hearst and Pulitzer chains could squeeze the most lurid details out of celebrated murder and sex cases, and they pioneered the "invented" news story. In 1889, Pulitzer's *World* sent Elizabeth S.

HOW THEY LIVED

REMEMBERING THE *MAINE:* SOLDIERS IN THE SPANISH-AMERICAN WAR

Secretary of State John Hay called it "a splendid little war." Undersecretary of the Navy Theodore Roosevelt resigned his post in order to fight in it. William Allen White remembered the glad excitement with which the declaration of war had been received in the Midwest: "Everywhere over this good, fair land, flags were flying, . . . crowds gathered to hurrah for the soldiers and to throw hats into the air." The celebrants' favorite cry was, "Remember the *Maine;* to hell with Spain." Americans regarded the occasion as an opportunity to prove the arrival of the United States as a world power and, at home, as a chance to seal the reunion of North and South by having northern and southern boys join together to fight Spain. While McKinley would not allow political rival William Jennings Bryan to go abroad and make a military reputation, he was delighted to appoint old Confederate officers like Fitzhugh Lee and General Joseph Wheeler to active command.

But, as historian Frank Freidel points out, for the soldiers in the ranks "it was as grim, dirty, and bloody as any war in history." He adds: "Only the incredible ineptitude of the Spaniards and the phenomenal luck of the Americans" kept the Spanish-American War small and short—splendid.

While the navy proved ready to fight on an instant's notice, the army was not ready for anything. In 1898, the army was only 28,000 strong, and those troops were scattered the length and breadth of the country. Congress had authorized increasing this force to 65,700 in wartime, but despite a rush of enlistments, the army never grew this large. The young men who rallied to arms in every state preferred to join the state militias or new units of volunteers, in which enlistments were for two years unless discharged earlier (as almost all would be).

In 1898, the militias numbered 140,000 men, but regular army officers justly suspected their training and equipment and generally preferred volunteer units in the regular army. Indeed, training was generally inadequate across the board because of the rush to get into action, and supplies were worse. Companies mustering, mostly in the southern states, were issued heavy woolen winter uniforms and Civil War-vintage Springfield rifles. Much meat that was provided the recruits was tainted, and sanitary conditions in the crowded camps were such that filth-related diseases such as typhoid and dysentery ravaged them. When the dead were counted at the end of 1898, 379 men were listed as killed in combat, while 5,083 men were listed as dead of disease.

There was no difficulty in getting volunteers. While 274,000 eventually served in the army, probably an equal number were turned down. Among these rejects were Frank James, brother of the late train robber Jesse James, and William F. "Buffalo Bill" Cody, who annoyed the War Department by writing a magazine article entitled "How I Could Drive the Spaniards Out of Cuba with Thirty Thousand Indian Braves." Martha A. Chute of Colorado was discouraged in her offer to raise a troop of women, as was William Randolph Hearst in his suggestion to recruit a regiment of professional boxers and baseball players. "Think of a regiment composed of magnificent men of this ilk," the editor of the *New York Journal* wrote. "They would overawe any Spanish regiment by

"Nellie" Bly around the world in an attempt to break the record of the fictional hero of Jules Verne's novel, *Around the World in Eighty Days.* (She did it, completing the trip in 72 days, 6 hours, and 11 minutes.)

It was easy to move from this kind of promotionalism to puffing up Spanish atrocities. The yellow press dubbed the Spanish military commander in Cuba, Valeriano Weyler, "The Butcher" for his repressive policies, which included the establishment of concentration camps. Warring against a whole population, Weyler tried to stifle the uprising by herding whole villages into camps; everyone who was found outside the camps could be defined as enemies to be shot on sight. This strategy was inevitably brutal, and Cubans died in the camps by the thousands from malnutrition, disease, and abuse.

Real atrocities were not enough for Hearst and Pulitzer. They transformed innocuous incidents into horror stories and invented others. When Hearst artist Frederic Remington wired from Havana that everything was peaceful and he wanted to come home, Hearst ordered him to stay: "You furnish the pictures. I'll furnish the war." One sensational drawing showed Spanish officials leering at a naked woman accused of espionage. In fact, the woman had been searched quite properly in private by female officers.

McKinley's Dark Hour

McKinley tried to calm tempers. The business community had substantial investments in Cuba, about $50 million in railroads, mines, and sugar-cane plantations, and they feared the revolutionaries more than the Spanish. McKinley and his advisers wanted Spain to abandon its harsh policies and placate both Cubans and bellicose Americans by liberalizing government on the island.

The Spanish responded to his pressure. In 1898, a new government in Madrid withdrew Weyler and proposed autonomy for Cuba within the Spanish Empire. McKinley's administration was satisfied. But the war came anyway, largely because of two unforeseeable events.

On February 9, Hearst's New York *Journal* published a letter that had been written by the Spanish ambassador in Washington, Enrique Dupuy de Lome. In it, Dupuy their mere appearance." Nevertheless, the "Rough Riders," a motley collection of cowboys, athletes, and gentlemen like Colonel Theodore Roosevelt, was mustered. But because of shipping problems, the Riders had to leave their horses in Florida when they sailed for Cuba and fight on foot.

In fact, there were few battlegrounds in Cuba or in the Philippines that were suited to cavalry attack. Both are tropical countries, and most of the fighting was done in summer and much of it in jungle. The army tried to prepare for jungle warfare by authorizing the recruitment of up to 10,000 "immunes," young men who were thought to be immune to tropical diseases. However, medicine's comparative ignorance of the nature of tropical diseases combined with racism to make the immune regiments no more serviceable than any others. Whereas the original idea had been to fill these units with men who had grown up in marshy areas of the Deep South, within months recruiters were turning away white Louisianians from the bayous and accepting blacks from the upcountry South and even urban New Jersey. They were believed to possess a genetic immunity to malaria, yellow fever, and other afflictions of the tropics.

Blacks played a large part in both the Cuban and the Philippine campaigns. When the war broke out, there were four black regiments in the regular army: two infantry and two cavalry, the Ninth and the Tenth Horse Regiments. All four saw action. In fact, while Theodore Roosevelt was describing the capture of San Juan Hill as an accomplishment of the Rough Riders, other witnesses believed that the Rough Riders would have been devastated had it not been for the Tenth Negro Cavalry, which was immediately to their left during the charge. While the Rough Riders made a lot of noise, the Tenth simply did their job. In the words of the restrained report of their commander, later to be General of the Armies, John J. "Black Jack" Pershing: "The 10th Cavalry charged up the hill, scarcely firing a shot, and being nearest the Rough Riders, opened a disastrous enfilading fire upon the Spanish right, thus relieving the Rough Riders from the volleys that were being poured into them from that part of the Spanish line."

About 10,000 blacks served in the war, 4,000 of them in the "immunes." A study done of white regiments indicates that the Spanish-American War was generally a poor man's fight and, rather more surprising, a city man's fight.

From largely rural Indiana, for example, of those volunteers who listed their occupation, only 296 were farmers. There were 322 common laborers, 413 skilled laborers, and 118 white-collar workers (clerks). Only 47 in the regiment were professional men, and 25 were merchants. A survey of a Confederate volunteer unit reveals similar figures. Several historians state that the army was far less representative of the occupations of the general population than were the armies of the two world wars.

In age, it was typical, however. The average age of the soldiers was 24. Their average height was 5 feet 8 inches, and their average weight was 149 pounds, both less than the averages today.

de Lome told a friend that McKinley was "weak, a bidder for the admiration of the crowd." It was by no means an absurd assessment of the president, but it was insulting. McKinley himself was riled, and war fever flared higher.

Six days later, on February 15, 1898, the battleship *U.S.S. Maine* exploded in Havana harbor with a loss of 260 sailors. To this day, the cause of the disaster is unknown. The explosion may have been caused by a coal fire that spread to the magazine. A bomb may have been planted by Cuban rebels in an attempt to provoke the United States into declaring war on their behalf. Or it may have been the work of Spanish diehards who opposed their country's new liberal policy in Cuba. So charged was the atmosphere that some people suggested that William Randolph Hearst had planted the bomb for the sake of a headline!

In any case, with the yellow press raging, many Americans accepted the least credible explanation: the Spanish government, which was trying to avoid war at all costs, had destroyed the *Maine*.

McKinley vacillated for a month and a half. He flooded Spain with demands for a change of policy. As late as March 26, Mark Hanna urged him to keep the peace, and on April 9 the Spanish government gave in to every demand McKinley had made on them. In the meantime, however, fearing that to continue resisting the war fever would cost the Republicans control of Congress in the fall elections, McKinley caved in. On April 11, practically ignoring the Spanish capitulation, the president asked Congress for a declaration of war and got it.

The "Splendid Little War"

Declaring war was one thing. Fighting the Spanish was quite another. The regular army numbered only 28,000 men, most of whom were in the West keeping an eye on Indians. The army was not up to launching an invasion even just a hundred miles from Florida.

The spanking new navy was ready, however, but it struck first not in Cuba but halfway around the world in Spain's last Pacific colony, the Philippines. On May 1,

Joseph Pulitzer's World *speculated on the cause of the* Maine *disaster in the same edition in which the explosion was reported.*

acting on the instructions of Assistant Secretary of the Navy Theodore Roosevelt (the Secretary of the Navy was ill), Commodore George Dewey steamed a flotilla into Manila Bay and, in just three hours, destroyed seven Spanish ships without losing a single sailor.

But Dewey had no soldiers with which to launch an attack on land. For more than three months, he and his men sat outside Manila harbor, baking in their steel ships, while Filipino rebels struggled with the Spanish garrison. In August, newly arrived troops finally took the capital. Although they did not know it, a peace treaty had been signed the previous day.

For, by that time, American troops had also conquered Cuba and Puerto Rico. Secretary of State John Hay called their campaign a "splendid little war" because so few Americans died in battle. In order to celebrate so gaily, however, it was necessary to overlook the more than 5,000 soldiers who died from typhoid and tropical diseases.

Although the Spanish army in Cuba outnumbered the Americans until the last, both commanders and men were paralyzed by defeatism. They might have been overcome more easily than they were but for the ineptitude of the American commanders, General Nelson A. Miles and General William R. Shafter, who was so fat that he had to be helped into the saddle of an extremely large horse when it was time to move.

Despite shortages of food, clothing, transport vehicles, medical supplies, ammunition, and horses, an army of 17,000 was landed in Cuba in June and defeated the Spanish outside Santiago at the battles of El Caney and San Juan Hill. (With 200,000 soldiers in Cuba, the Spanish had stationed only 19,000 in Santiago.)

The victory allowed Americans to forget the poor management of the war and gave them a popular hero. Theodore Roosevelt had resigned from the Navy Department to accept a colonelcy in a volunteer cavalry unit called the "Rough Riders." It was a highly unmilitary group, made up of cowboys from Roosevelt's North Dakota ranch, show business fops, upper-class polo players and other athletes, and even some ex-convicts. The Rough Riders had to fight on foot because the army had been unable to get their horses out of Tampa, Florida, but they fought bravely in the hottest action on San Juan Hill.

EMPIRE CONFIRMED

In August, the Spanish gave up. American troops occupied not only Manila in the Philippines and much of

DEWEY'S BLUNDER

Commodore George Dewey became a national hero by virtue of his victory at Manila Bay during the Spanish-American War. A group of conservative Democrats hoped to nominate him for the presidency in 1900 in order to head off William Jennings Bryan, who was still regarded as something of a radical. At first Dewey refused because he did not believe that he was qualified for the office. He later changed his mind, explaining that "since studying the subject, I am convinced that the office of the president is not such a very difficult one to fill." As a result of his candor, Dewey lost the support of virtually everyone, and Bryan was nominated once again.

Cuba, but also the island of Puerto Rico, which had been seized without resistance. But what should be done with these prizes? Suddenly, the imperialism controversy was no longer an academic debate. It involved three far-flung island countries that were inhabited by millions of people who spoke Spanish or Malayan languages, who clung to traditions very different from those of Americans, and who did not want to become colonial subjects of the United States.

To the dismay of the imperialists, the independence of Cuba had been guaranteed before the war had begun. In order to get money from Congress to fight Spain, the administration had accepted a rider drafted by Senator Teller of Colorado. The Teller Amendment forbade the United States to take over the sugar island. Therefore, the great debate over imperialism centered on Puerto Rico and the Philippine Islands.

The Debate

The anti-imperialists were a disparate group, and their arguments were sometimes contradictory. In Congress, they included idealistic old Radical Republicans like George Frisbie Hoar of Massachusetts, former Liberal Republicans like Carl Schurz, and much of the old Mugwump wing of the party. Some Republican regulars also opposed taking colonies; among them was Thomas B. Reed of Maine, the no-nonsense, dictatorial Speaker of the House who otherwise despised reformers. Finally, a substantial part of the Democratic party, led by William Jennings Bryan, opposed annexation of any former Spanish lands. Henry Teller himself became a Democrat in 1900 because of his opposition to imperialism.

The anti-imperialists reminded Americans of their anticolonial heritage. "We insist," declared the American Anti-Imperialist League in October 1899, "that the subjugation of any people is 'criminal aggression' and open disloyalty to the distinctive principles of our government. We hold, with Abraham Lincoln, that no man is good enough to govern another man without that man's consent."

Some of the anti-imperialists appealed to racist feelings. With many people ill at ease because of the nation's large black population, was it wise to bring millions more nonwhite people under the flag? When Congress finally decided to take the Philippines and pay Spain $20 million in compensation, House Speaker Reed resigned in disgust, grumbling about "ten million Malays at two dollars a head."

But racist feelings worked mostly in favor of the imperialist group. Shrewd propagandists like Roosevelt, who was now governor of New York; Henry Cabot Lodge; and the eloquent Albert J. Beveridge, senator from Indiana, preached that the white race had a duty

Theodore Roosevelt and his "Rough Riders" cavalry unit.

and a right to govern "inferior" peoples. "God has not been preparing the English-speaking and Teutonic peoples for a thousand years for nothing but vain and idle self-contemplation and self-admiration," Beveridge told the Senate. "No! He has made us the master organizers of the world to establish system where chaos reigns."

Well-grounded fears that if the United States abandoned the Philippines, Japan or Germany would seize them motivated other politicians to support annexation. Such anxiety was especially significant in deciding McKinley's mind on the question. But most of all, the American people were in an emotional, expansive mood. Coming at the end of the troubled, depressed, and divided 1890s, annexation of colonies seemed a way to unite the country.

Hawaii

McKinley found it easier to come out for annexation of the Philippines and Puerto Rico because the United States already had taken its first real overseas colony. In

July 1898, shortly after the Spanish-American War began, Congress had annexed the seven main islands and 1,400 minor ones that made up the mid-Pacific republic of Hawaii. Shortly thereafter, Guam, Wake, and Baker islands were added as coaling stations for the navy.

The annexation of Hawaii was long in the making. Some of the descendants of American missionary families in the islands had grown rich by exporting sugar to the United States, and they had won the confidence and support of the Hawaiian king, Kalakaua. Until 1890, they were content with their independent island paradise.

Then, the McKinley Tariff of 1890 introduced a two-cent-per-pound bounty on American-grown sugar. This encouraged enough mainland farmers to produce cane or sugar beets that Hawaiian imports declined sharply. Unable to affect American tariff policy from outside, the Hawaiian oligarchy concluded that it must join the islands to the United States and benefit from the subsidy.

The plan was squelched before it got started. In 1891,

Kalakaua died and was succeeded by his sister, Liliuoka-lani, who was determined to maintain the independence of the islands. She announced that the theme of her reign would be "Hawaii for the Hawaiians" and intro-duced a series of reforms aimed at undercutting *haole* or white control of the economy and legislature.

Alarmed, the oligarchy acted quickly with help from the American ambassador in Honolulu. He declared that American lives and property were in danger and landed marines from the *U.S.S. Boston* who quickly took control. Back home, imperialists in the Senate intro-duced a treaty of annexation, but before they could push it through, Grover Cleveland was sworn in as president (March 4, 1893), and he withdrew the proposal.

Cleveland was not obdurately opposed to annexa-tion. But he wanted to know how the Hawaiian people felt, and he sent an investigator, James H. Blount, to the islands. Blount reported that very few ethnic Hawaiians wanted to be part of the United States; they wanted independence and the restoration of Queen Liliuoka-lani. Cleveland ordered the marines to return to their ships and to the naval base at Pearl Harbor.

The Hawaiian whites had gone too far to chance re-storing Queen Liliuokalani. They maintained control and declared Hawaii a republic. As long as Cleveland sat in the White House, they bided their time and quietly cultivated Republican senators. In the excitement of the Spanish War, Hawaii was annexed by means of a joint resolution of the American Congress and Hawaiian leg-islature, the same device under which Texas had joined the Union.

Many Hawaiians continued to resent the takeover. Liliuokalani spent much time in the United States trying to win financial concessions for herself and the islands' natives. But as the white population grew and the islands attracted Japanese and Chinese immigrants, the native Hawaiians declined into a weak minority. Like Native Americans, they became foreigners in their own home-land. The islands' famous anthem, *Aloha Oe*, which was written by Liliuokalani, translates as "Farewell to Thee."

The Philippine Insurrection

Securing the Philippines was not so easy. If the war with Spain had been something like splendid, the war that

Sanford B. Dole, a businessman and the first governor of the territory of Hawaii, seated next to Queen Liliuokalani, the last monarch of Hawaii.

followed was a great deal like ugly. Like the Cubans, the Philippine people were experienced in guerrilla warfare. Led by Emilio Aguinaldo, a well-educated patriot who was as comfortable in the jungle as he was in the library, the rebels withdrew from the American-occupied cities to the jungle and fought only when the odds favored them.

In response, the American army of occupation was expanded to 65,000 men by early 1900, but even then the troops could make little progress outside the cities. The American commanders were unable to draw the *insurrectos* into a conventional battle in which superior fire power told the tale.

The fighting took a vicious turn. The Filipinos frequently decapitated captives. The Americans, frustrated by their failures, tropical heat, insects, and diseases, retaliated by slaughtering whole villages that were thought to be supporting the rebels. The army never did defeat the Filipinos. The rebellion ended only when, in March 1901, General Arthur MacArthur succeeded in capturing Aguinaldo. Weary of the bloodshed, Aguinaldo took an oath of allegiance to the United States and ordered his followers to do the same. (He lived quietly and long enough to see Philippine independence established in 1946.) More than 5,000 Americans died in the cause of suppressing a popular revolution, a queer twist in a conflict that had begun, three years before, in support of a popular revolution.

The China Market

The Philippines provided a superb base for Americans engaged in the China trade and investors interested in developing the large but weak and impoverished "Middle Kingdom." On the face of it, China too was ripe for imperialist plucking. The emperor had little power outside Beijing; powerful regional warlords battled one another in the provinces; and most of the imperialistic nations of Europe, plus Japan, had carved out "spheres of influence" in China where their own troops maintained order and their own laws governed their resident citizens' behavior.

However, the most powerful of the powers in China, Great Britain, opposed the partition of China. Longer an imperial power and therefore more conscious than Japan, Russia, Germany, and Italy of the headaches and expense that attended imperial glory, the British believed that with their efficient industrial complex they could dominate the market of an independent China.

American businessmen disagreed with the British assessment of how economic competition in China would turn out, believing that they would win the lion's share of the prodigious purchases 160 million Chinese were capable of making. However, this projection put them in complete agreement with the British policy of preventing the other imperialist nations from turning their spheres of influence into full-fledged colonies and shutting the door on free competition.

The Open Door Policy

Just as John Quincy Adams had beaten the British to promulgating the Monroe Doctrine, McKinley's Secretary of State, John Hay, rushed ahead of Great Britain to circulate a series of memoranda called the "Open Door notes." These declarations pledged the imperial powers to respect the territorial integrity of China and to grant equal trading rights in their spheres of influence to all other countries.

Anticolonialist as it was, the Open Door policy by no means established the self-determination of the Chinese people, nor ended military intervention by outsiders. In 1900, when antiforeign rebels known as Boxers (the Chinese name of their religious movement was "Righteous Harmonious Fist") besieged 900 foreigners in the British legation in Beijing, American troops joined the soldiers of six other nations in defeating them. The victory encouraged beliefs in white superiority (despite the Japanese contribution) and convinced other nations that cooperation in maintaining the Open Door was the best policy in China.

Chinese Boxers captured by soldiers of the U.S. Cavalry in Tianjin, China.

McKinley Reelected, McKinley Murdered

In 1900, the Democrats again nominated William Jennings Bryan to run against McKinley. Bryan tried to make imperialism the issue but the campaign fizzled. Americans were either happy with their overseas possessions or simply indifferent to the question of imperialism. McKinley sidestepped the issue and pointed to the nation's new prosperity; the Republican slogan was "Four More Years of the Full Dinner Pail." Prosperity carried the day. Several states that had voted for Bryan in 1896 went Republican in 1900, including Bryan's home state of Nebraska.

A new vice president stood at McKinley's side on Inauguration Day. Theodore Roosevelt had moved quickly from his exploits in Cuba to the governorship of New York. There, however, he alienated the Republican boss of the state, Thomas C. Platt, by refusing to take orders and even attacking some corrupt members of Platt's machine. When McKinley's vice president, the obscure Garrett Hobart of New Jersey, died in 1899, Platt saw a chance to get rid of the troublesome Rough Rider. He would banish him to the political burial ground of the vice-presidency.

Mark Hanna, who was accustomed to consider all contingencies, had his reservations. What would happen to the country, Hanna asked McKinley, if something happened to him, and the manic Roosevelt became president? The president was almost 60 at a time when that was a ripe old age.

Something did happen to McKinley. On September 6, 1901, the president paid a ceremonial visit to the Pan-American Exposition in Buffalo. Greeting a long line of guests, he found himself faced by a man who extended a bandaged hand. The gauze concealed a pistol of large bore and Leon Czolgosz, an anarchist who "didn't believe one man should have so much service and another man should have none," shot the president several times in the chest and abdomen. Eight days later, McKinley died. "Now look," Hanna shook his head at the funeral, "that damned cowboy is president."

A Flexible Imperialist

Unlike the "accidental presidents" who preceded him, "Teddy" Roosevelt was to leave an indelible mark on the office. The young New Yorker (42 years old when he took office) knew only one way to do anything: rush into the lead and stay there. Nowhere was his assertive personality more pronounced than in his foreign policy, a peacetime extension of the zest that had taken him bellowing up San Juan Hill.

Roosevelt's actions varied according to the part of the world with which he was dealing. With the European nations he insisted that the United States be accepted as an equal, active imperial power. Although friendship between Great Britain and the United States had been long in the making, Roosevelt sped it along by responding cordially to every British request for cooperation. Toward Latin America, Roosevelt was often arrogant. He told both Latin Americans and Europeans that the whole Western Hemisphere was an American sphere of influence. Toward Asia, Roosevelt continued to practice the "Open Door."

During Roosevelt's presidency, American capital poured into China. International consortia developed mines, built railways, and set up other profitable enterprises. In 1905, the president applied his policy of equilibrium in China by working through diplomatic channels to end a war between Russia and Japan. Much to the surprise of most Europeans, Japan handily defeated Russia and threatened to seize complete control of Manchuria and other parts of northern China. Through a mixture of threats and cajolery, Roosevelt got both sides to meet at Portsmouth, New Hampshire, to work out a treaty that maintained a balance of power in the area and guaranteed Chinese independence.

High-Handedness in Latin America

In Latin America, Roosevelt was not so compromising. He made it clear to the European nations that the United States held a preeminent position in the Western Hemisphere. In 1904, when disputes between Venezuela and the Dominican Republic on the one hand, and European commercial powers on the other threatened to result in European invasions, Roosevelt proclaimed what came to be called the Roosevelt Corollary to the Monroe Doctrine. In order to protect the independence of American states, the United States would, if necessary, exercise an "international police power" in the Western Hemisphere. In other words, while European nations still had to keep out of the Americas, the United States would intervene south of the border if circumstances called for such action.

Roosevelt wasted no time putting his corollary to work. United States Marines landed in the Dominican Republic and took over the collection of customs, seeing to it that European creditors were paid off. From 1904 until the 1930s, the United States intervened in a number of Latin American countries: Cuba, Nicaragua, the Dominican Republic, and Haiti. These actions may have pleased European investors, but they created a reservoir of ill-will among Latin Americans who felt bullied by the great Anglo colossus of the north. No action offended Latin Americans more than Roosevelt's high-handed seizure of the Panama Canal Zone, which the president considered his greatest achievement.

In 1911, when the construction of the canal was nearly complete, Roosevelt reflected (quite accurately) that only his decisiveness had moved the project along. "If I had followed traditional, conservative methods," he said, "the debates on it would have been going on yet.

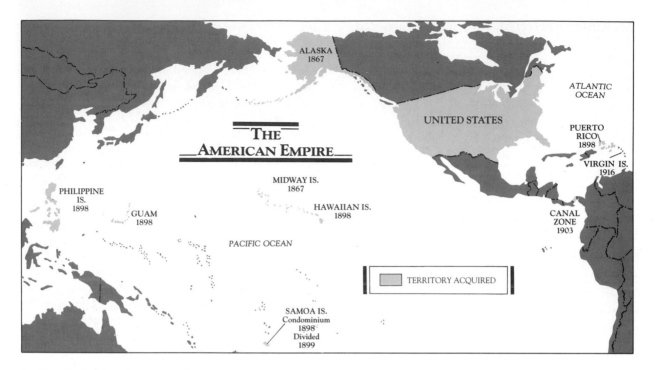

But I took the Canal Zone and let Congress debate; and while the debate goes on the Canal does also."

A Path Between the Seas

Naval officers had long recognized the value of a quick route between the Atlantic and the Pacific. During the Spanish-American War, the battleship *Oregon*, stationed in San Francisco, took 67 days to steam the 12,000 miles to Cuba via Cape Horn. Had there been an isthmian canal, the voyage would have been but 4,000 miles.

A French company had started to dig a canal across Panama, then part of Colombia, in the 1880s. But the project was abandoned because of financial and engineering difficulties and the ravages of malaria and yellow fever among the builders. Three out of five Frenchmen and women in Panama died; the mortality was undoubtedly higher among the laborers, mostly blacks from Jamaica. The horrors of the French experience convinced most American experts that the "path between the seas" should be dug not in Panama, but in Nicaragua, which was more healthful and provided the lowest crossing of the American landmass between the Arctic and Tierra del Fuego.

It was a Nicaraguan canal that Secretary of State Hay had in mind when he negotiated a treaty with Britain, promising the United States full control of the project. Congress also favored the Nicaragua route. Then, however, two of the most effective lobbyists of all time, an agent of the French company that held rights to the Panama route, Philippe Bunau-Varilla, and an American wheeler-dealer, William Nelson Cromwell, went to

work in Washington's restaurants, the cloakrooms of Congress, and in the White House itself.

Their goal was win approval of the Panama route, then sell the assets of the French company in Panama, including an American-built railroad, to the United States. There was no good reason why their proposal should have been accepted. Even if the United States opted for the Panama route, the French company's rights on the isthmus were due to expire and most of its equipment was useless. Nevertheless, Bunau-Varilla and Cromwell somehow won over President Roosevelt and key members of Congress.

Roosevelt Takes Panama

Then the project stalled in Bogota. The Colombian government turned down the American offer to pay Colombia $10 million (the Colombians wanted $25 million) and an annual rental fee of $250,000. Rather than take a step backward, Roosevelt conspired with Bunau-Varilla to start a revolution in Panama. On November 2, 1903, the president moved several warships to the vicinity, and the next day, the province erupted in riots and declared its independence. On November 6, the United States recognized the new republic of Panama. On November 18, the first foreign minister of Panama, none other than the Frenchman Bunau-Varilla, signed a treaty with the United States that granted perpetual use of a ten-mile-wide "canal zone" across the isthmus on the terms that Colombia had refused.

None of Roosevelt's successors in the presidency were quite so arrogant in dealing with Latin America. For example, Roosevelt's hand-picked successor, William

OLD BOYS

Most of Theodore Roosevelt's advisors were drawn from his own social class. They were gentlemen of old, genteel families who assumed without much reflection that they were the people intended to govern the United States. They wore their duties lightly. Cabinet meetings could seem like a clubroom full of joshing old boys.

When T. R. asked Attorney-General Philander C. Knox to prepare a legal justification of his actions in the detachment of the Isthmus of Panama from Colombia, Knox replied, "Oh Mr. President, do not let so great an achievement suffer from any taint of legality." After a long, blustering explanation of his actions to the cabinet, T. R. asked, "Well, have I defended myself?" Secretary of War, later of State, Elihu Root replied, "You certainly have, Mr. President. You have shown that you were accused of seduction and you have conclusively proved that you were guilty of rape."

Theodore Roosevelt took immense personal satisfaction in securing American rights to dig the Panama Canal and in 1906 traveled to Panama to inspect the construction project.

Howard Taft, tried to replace "gunboat diplomacy" with "dollar diplomacy," the attempt to influence Latin America (and China) through investment rather than armed force. In 1921, over the protests of Roosevelt's old ally Henry Cabot Lodge, the United States attempted to make amends to Colombia for Roosevelt's high-handed actions by paying the $25 million that the Colombians originally had demanded for the right to dig the Panama Canal.

But such gestures could not change America's "big brother" behavior or the simmering resentment of many people in Latin America. The plunge into imperialism established intervention as an essential part of American diplomacy. Every president from Theodore Roosevelt to Herbert Hoover (1929–1933) used troops to enforce their wishes in Latin America. Lyndon B. Johnson, Ronald Reagan, and George Bush revived the policy.

For Further Reading

The essential background of the political upheaval at the end of the nineteenth century can be found in Vincent P. DeSantis, *The Shaping of Modern America, 1877–1916* (1973); H. Wayne Morgan, *From Hayes to McKinley: National Party Politics, 1877–1896* (1971); and Robert H. Wiebe, *The Search for Order, 1880–1920* (1967).

Valuable special studies include Howard K. Beale, *Theodore Roosevelt and the Rise of America to World Power* (1956); Robert L. Beisner, *From the Old Diplomacy to the New, 1865–1900* (1975); C. S. Campbell, *The Transformation of American Foreign Relations, 1865–1900* (1976); Robert F. Durden, *The Climax of Populism: The Election of 1896* (1965); Frank Freidel, *The Splendid Little War* (1958); Lloyd Gardner, Walter Le Feber, and Thomas McCormick, *The Creation of the American Empire* (1973); Ray Ginger, *Altgeld's America: The Lincoln Ideal and Changing Realities* (1958); Paul F. Glad, *The Trumpet Soundeth* (1960) and *McKinley, Bryan, and the People* (1964); G. Grunder and W. E. Livezey, *The Phil-*

ippines and the United States (1951); S. L. Jones, *The Presidential Election of 1896* (1964); Walter R. Le Feber, *The New Empire: An Interpretation of American Expansion, 1860–1898* (1963); Ernest R. May, *Imperial Democracy: The Emergence of America as a Great Power* (1961); David McCullough, *The Path Between the Seas* (1977); Dwight C. Miner, *Fight for the Panama Canal* (1966); Thomas J. Osborne, *American Opposition to Hawaiian Annexation, 1893–1898* (1981); J. W. Pratt, *Expansionists of 1898: The Acquisition of Hawaii and the Spanish Islands* (1936) and *America's Colonial Experiment* (1950); William A. Russ, Jr., *The Hawaiian Republic, 1894–98* (1961); and William A. Williams, *The Tragedy of American Diplomacy* (1959).

See the biographies of Bryan by P. E. Coletta and Louis W. Koenig listed at the conclusion of Chapter 33; Margaret Leech, *In the Days of McKinley* (1959); H. Wayne Morgan, *William McKinley and His America* (1963); and Edmund Morris, *The Rise of Theodore Roosevelt* (1979).

Adventurous cyclists on Minerva Terrace, Yellowstone National Park.

GAY NINETIES AND GOOD OLD DAYS

AMERICAN SOCIETY IN TRANSITION, 1890 - 1917

As 1899 drew to a close, editors and writers of letters to editors bickered about the significance of the New Year's Day that was approaching. One faction declared that New Year's Day 1900 would mark the beginning of a new century. Another rushed to point out that the first century A.D. had not ended with the last day of A.D. 99, but with the last day of A.D. 100. Therefore, the twentieth century would begin at the stroke of midnight on January 1, 1901, a year in the future.

They were quite right, of course. The year 1900 was the last year of the nineteenth century, not the first year of the twentieth. Nevertheless, the titillation of writing so portentously sounding a date as 1900 on their next letter to the editor meant more to people than did the dictates of arithmetic. Many Americans rang out the old century on December 31, 1899, and rang in the new in the wee hours of January 1, 1900. The newspapers say that the celebrations were particularly festive that night.

MIDDLE AMERICA

Many political historians have celebrated 1900 as the dividing line between an age of conservative hegemony and an age of reform, the Progressive Era. In many ways, however, 1900 seems less a watershed year than the midpoint of a quarter-century when the American middle class that we know came into its own, brimming with confidence and plans.

Dark Corners

To a black, to an Indian of the Plains or a Mexican of the Southwest, to a white workingman in a marginal job, or to many of the nearly 12 million immigrants who

A white mob preparing to lynch a black man in Paris, Texas, in 1893.

came to the United States between 1890 and 1910, the decades that spanned the year 1900 were not rosy. During most of the 1890s, the United States languished in hard times. It was the decade of Wounded Knee, bloody labor battles, an era when the lynching of blacks in the South reached epidemic proportions. In 1899, a mob in Palmetto, Georgia, could announce in advance that a man would be burned alive so that thousands could flock aboard special excursion trains to witness the spectacle.

Life expectancy at birth for native-born white Americans was about 45 years, lower for blacks and immigrants, much lower for Indians. Infant mortality in New York City was worse than it had ever been. Nationwide, people were six times more likely to die of influenza than they are today, sixty times more likely to die of syphilis, and more than eighty times more likely to die of tuberculosis. Diseases that are not major problems in the late twentieth century—typhoid, scarlet fever, strep throat, diphtheria, whooping cough, measles—were common killers in the 1890s and 1900s.

And yet, when people who lived through the years around the turn of the century remembered them, they were apt to call the final decade of the nineteenth century the "Gay Nineties," to recall a decade of nickelodeon music and Coney Island, of a night of vaudeville and a week at the seaside, of beer gardens and ice cream parlors, of the bicycle craze and winsome Gibson Girls.

The first years of the twentieth century have lived on in popular consciousness as the original "good old days." The era before World War I is the slice of time to which popular novelists and film makers repair when they want to portray an America that is recognizable but unmistakably better. Life was less complex in this engaging vision. The summer sun was cozier, the hot dogs tastier, the baseball more exciting, the cars more adventurous, the boys more gallant, the girls prettier, the melodies more lilting.

A Golden Age

The turn of the century has cast such an alluring glow over time because middle-class values and aspirations have dominated American culture in the twentieth century, and in the 1890s and early 1900s the modern middle class came into its own. The troubles of poor farmers, factory workers, blacks, Indians, Mexicans, and recent immigrants were real and often tragic. But such people were not at the center of things, writing definitions, as was that class of people who, while not rich, did not have to struggle in order to survive. The middle class reached unprecedented numbers at the turn of the century, numerous enough to create and sustain a distinctive lifestyle and to support a bustling consumer economy and technology devoted to physical comfort, conveni-

Children romping in the surf at Coney Island, 1889.

ence, individual self-improvement, and the enjoyment of leisure time.

Increasingly well-educated, the new middle class quietly shelved the zealous, religious piety of their parents and grandparents. They embraced instead the proper pleasures of their rich nation. The people of the "good old days" were by no means oblivious to social evils. Far from it; they were also the citizens of the "Progressive Era," a time of rampant reform. But progressivism was itself the manifestation of a confident people. War and revolution were not yet constant companions of daily life.

Teddy

The buoyant temper of the period was personified in the man who, in September 1901, succeeded William McKinley as president. Theodore Roosevelt was climbing a mountain in the Adirondacks when he received the news of McKinley's death. He rushed to Buffalo, took the oath of office, and confided to a friend, "It is a dreadful thing to come into the presidency in this way.

But it would be a far worse thing to be morbid about it." Roosevelt intended to enjoy the presidency, as his fellow Americans intended to make the most of life. And no other chief executive before or since has had such a "bully" time living at 1600 Pennsylvania Avenue.

Both critics and friends of the president poked fun at his personal motto: "Walk softly and carry a big stick." They said that they observed Roosevelt wildly waving clubs around often enough, but rarely knew him to walk softly. Quite the contrary. Everything that Roosevelt did was accompanied by fanfare. He seemed to swagger and strut about like an exuberant adolescent, hogging center stage and good naturedly drowning out anyone who dared to compete for the spotlight. He insisted on being, as one of his children put it, the bride at every wedding and the corpse at every funeral. "The universe seemed to be spinning round," wrote Rudyard Kipling, "and Theodore was the spinner."

Roosevelt shattered the image of solemn dignity that had been nurtured by every president since Rutherford B. Hayes. He stormed about the country far more than had any predecessor, delivering dramatic speeches, mix-

HOT DOG

The hot dog is second only to the hamburger as a symbol of *cuisine américaine*, but its origins are hotly disputed. Not the origins of the mild sausage itself: it was being made commercially in Frankfurt, Germany, and Vienna, Austria, in the early nineteenth century. (Thus the alternative names, frankfurter and wiener—Vienna in German is *Wien*.) The disputed point is: who first put one of the things in a soft roll and provided the classic condiments of yellow mustard, chopped onion, and sweet pickle relish?

Some partisans claim that the deed was first done at the amusement park at Coney Island; hot dogs were once called "coney islands," too. Others credit Anton Feuchtwanger, who sold the sausages so quickly at the St. Louis World's Fair in 1904 that he had to add the roll so that his customers did not burn their hands. Yet others say the roll was first added at a New York Giants baseball game in April 1900 where they were first called "dachsund sausages." A popular cartoonist of the time who liked his baseball, Tad Dorgan, provided the more durable name "hot dog."

ing gleefully with crowds of all descriptions, camping out, climbing mountains, and clambering astride horses and atop farm and industrial machines. When a motion-picture photographer asked him to move for the ingenious new camera, Roosevelt picked up an ax and furiously chopped down a tree.

The Strenuous Life

Of an old family of Dutch origin, Roosevelt had been sickly as a youth. He was hopelessly nearsighted and suffered from asthma. As an adolescent, however, he took up body-building and revealed his tremendous inner energy. He fought on the Harvard boxing team and rode with cowboys in North Dakota. As Police Commissioner of New York City, he accompanied patrolmen on night beats as dangerous as any in the world. When the war with Spain broke out, he left his office job and joined the army. In dozens of articles and books, he wrote of the glories of "the strenuous life."

Roosevelt liked to show off his large, affectionate, and handsome family with himself at stage center, a stern but generous patriarch. He sported a paunch (fashionable at the turn of the century), a close-snipped moustache, and thick pince-nez that dropped from his nose when he was excited, which was often. His teeth were odd, all seemingly incisors of the same size and about twice as many as there should be. He displayed them often in a broad grin that he shed only when he took off after enemies whom middle-class Americans also found it easy to dislike: Wall Street bankers, Socialists, impudent Latin Americans.

William McKinley had concealed his fondness for cigars so as not to be a bad example to young men. Roosevelt had no compunctions about puffing away in public. What was the harm in a minor vice that brought a man pleasure? More than any other individual, Roosevelt taught Americans to believe that their president should be a good fellow and part showman.

The Symbol of His Age

Roosevelt had many critics. But most Americans, especially those of the vibrant new middle class, found him a grand fellow indeed. They called him "Teddy" and named the lovable animal doll they bought for their children, the teddy bear, after him. He was the first president to be routinely identified by his initials, T.R. Even Elihu Root, a stodgy Eastern aristocrat who served as both Secretary of War and Secretary of State, waxed playful when he congratulated the president on his forty-sixth birthday in 1904. "You have made a very good start in life," Root said, "and your friends have great hopes for you when you grow up." The British ambassador quipped, "You must remember that the president is about six years old."

Kansas journalist William Allen White, the archetype of the middle-class townsman, wrote that "Roosevelt bit

Horseback riding was one of Theodore Roosevelt's many athletic pursuits.

me and I went mad." White remained a lifelong devotee of "the Colonel," as did Finley Peter Dunne, the urbane Chicagoan who captured the salty, cynical humor of the big-city Irish in his fictional commentator on current events, Mr. Dooley. Radical dissenters hated Roosevelt (who hated them back with interest). But they were at a loss as to how to counter his vast popularity. Labor leaders and Socialists stuck to the issues when they disagreed with him. There was no advantage in attacking Teddy Roosevelt personally.

Although Roosevelt was a staunch believer in Anglo-Saxon superiority, he won the affection of blacks when he ignored the squeals of Southern segregationists and invited Booker T. Washington to call on him in the White House. Woman suffragists, gearing up for the last phase of their long battle for the vote, petitioned rather than attacked him. Elizabeth Cady Stanton addressed him from her deathbed in 1901 as "already celebrated for so many deeds and honorable utterances."

Much mischief was done during Theodore Roosevelt's nearly eight years in office. He committed the United States to a role as international policeman that damaged the nation's reputation in many small countries. He was inclined to define those who disagreed with him in moral terms, a recurring and unfortunate characteristic of American politics since his time.

But the happy symbiosis between the boyish president and the majority of the American people may be the most important historical fact of the years spanning the turn of the century. Like the man who was their president between 1901 and 1909, the worldly middle class of the Gay Nineties was confident, optimistic, and glad to be alive.

An Educated People

The foundation of middle-class vigor was wealth. American society as a whole had grown so rich that despite the disproportionate fortunes of the great multimillionaires, millions of people in the middle could afford to indulge interests and pleasures that had been the exclusive property of tiny elites in earlier epochs and other countries. Among these was education beyond "the three r's—'readin', 'ritin', and 'rithmetic.' " During the final third of the nineteenth century, and especially after 1890, the American educational system expanded and changed to accommodate the numbers and aspirations of the new class.

There were no more than about 300 secondary schools in the United States in 1860 (a country of 31.4 million people), and only about 100 of them were free. While girls were admitted to most public elementary schools, very few attended beyond the first few grades.

Colleges and universities—about 560 in 1870—ca-

tered to an even more select social set. They offered the traditional course in the liberal arts (Latin, philosophy, mathematics, and history) that was designed to polish young gentlemen rather than to train people for a career. The handful of "female seminaries" and colleges that admitted women before the Civil War also taught the ancient curriculum mixed with a strong dose of evangelical religion.

After about 1880, educational facilities rapidly multiplied and changed character. By 1900, there were 6,000 free public secondary schools in the United States, and by 1915, there were 12,000, educating 1.3 million pupils. Educational expenditures per pupil increased from about $9 a year in 1870 to $48 in 1920. Secondary schools no longer specialized in preparing a select few for university, but offered a wide range of courses leading to jobs in industry and business, from engineering and accounting to agriculture and typing.

A New Kind of University

The Morrill Land Grant Act of 1862 and the philanthropy of millionaires combined with the middle class's hunger for learning to expand the opportunities for higher education. The Morrill Act provided federal land to the states for the purpose of serving the educational needs of "the industrial classes," particularly in "such branches of learning as are related to agriculture and mechanic arts." Thus it not only fostered the founding of technical schools in which middle-class youth might learn a profession, but put liberal-arts training within the reach of those who sought it. Many of the great state universities of the West owe their origins to the Morrill Act.

Gilded Age millionaires competed for esteem as patrons of learning by constructing buildings and by endowing scholarships and professorial chairs at older institutions. Some even founded completely new universities. The story was told that railroad king Leland Stanford and his wife traveled to Harvard with the notion of erecting a building in memory of their son, who had died. As President Charles W. Eliot was explaining how much it had cost to construct several of Harvard's splendid buildings, Mrs. Stanford suddenly realized that they could afford to build their own university! And they did; Stanford University in Palo Alto, California, was founded in 1885.

Cornell (1865), Drew (1866), Johns Hopkins (1876), Vanderbilt (1872), and Carnegie Institute of Technology (1905) were universities that bear the names of the moguls who financed them. In Philadelphia, Success Gospel preacher Russell B. Conwell established Temple University in 1884 explicitly to educate poor boys ambitious to rise in social station. John D. Rockefeller pumped millions of dollars into the University of Chicago (1890), making it one of America's most distinguished centers of learning within a decade. George Eastman, who made a fortune from Kodak cameras, gave to the University of Rochester.

The Midwestern and Western state universities, beginning with Iowa in 1858, generally admitted women to at least some programs. In the East, however, separate women's colleges were founded, again with the support of wealthy benefactors. Georgia Female College (Wesleyan) and Mount Holyoke dated from before the Civil War. In the later decades of the century they were joined by Vassar (1861), Wellesley (1870), Smith (1871), Radcliffe (1879), Bryn Mawr (1880), and Barnard (1889). Vassar's educational standards rivaled those of the best men's colleges, but it was necessary to maintain a kind of "head start" program in order to remedy deficiencies in the secondary education provided even well-to-do girls.

Studying for Careers

The transformation of higher education was not simply a matter of more colleges, universities, and students. While some institutions, such as Yale, clung to the traditional liberal arts curriculum, the majority of schools adopted the "elective system" that was pioneered by the College of William and Mary, Washington College in Virginia, and the University of Michigan, and most effectively promoted by President Eliot of Harvard. Beginning in 1869, Eliot abandoned the rule that every student follow precisely the same sequence of courses. Instead, he allowed individuals to choose their field of study. "Majors" included traditional subjects but also new disciplines in the social sciences, engineering, and business administration. The new emphasis on university education as preparation for a career reflected the aspirations of middle-class students who had not yet arrived financially and socially.

From Germany, educators borrowed the concept of the professional postgraduate school. Before the 1870s, young people who wished to learn a profession attached themselves to an established practitioner. A would-be lawyer agreed with an established attorney to do routine work in his office, sweeping floors and helping with deeds and wills, in return for the right to "read law" in the office and to observe and question his teacher. After a few years, the apprentice hung out his own shingle. Many physicians were trained the same way. Civil and mechanical engineers learned their professions "on the job" in factories. All too often, teachers received no training and were miserably paid, about $200 a year in rural states.

Women, Minorities, and the New Education

Exceptional women who were dauntless enough to shake off the ridicule of their male classmates could be found in small numbers at every level of the new system. By the mid-1880s, the word *co-educational* and its breezy abbreviation, "coed," had become part of the American language. The first female physician in the United States, Elizabeth Blackwell, was accredited only in 1849. In 1868, she established a medical school for women in New York City. By that date, the Woman's Medical College of Pennsylvania already was recognized, however grudgingly, as offering one of the nation's most effective programs of medical education.

Female lawyers were unusual at a time when women were not considered equal to men before the law. In 1873, the Supreme Court approved the refusal of the University of Illinois to admit women by declaring that "the paramount mission and destiny of women are to fulfill the noble and benign offices of wife and mother." By the end of the century, dozens of women practiced law, among them the Populist wife and "Mother" Mary Lease. Antoinette Blackwell, sister-in-law of Elizabeth, paved the way for the ordination of women ministers, and by the turn of the century, the more liberal Protestant denominations, such as the Unitarians and Congregationalists, had ordained some women.

Also in small numbers, well-to-do Jews and Catholics began to take advantage of the new educational opportunities. The Sephardic and German Jews were a secular people who preferred to send their sons to established institutions rather than found their own. The Catholic Church, on the other hand, the largest religious denomination in the United States but mainly a church of the lower classes, preferred to found its own colleges. Church policy was to prepare the sons and daughters of the Catholic middle class for active careers in business and the professions while simultaneously shoring up their loyalty to their faith by means of rigorous schooling in Church doctrine, history, and observance.

The most famous Catholic colleges dated from before the Civil War: Notre Dame and Villanova were founded in 1842; Holy Cross (1843) and Boston College (1863) were explicitly created as foils to aristocratic Harvard. Thomas Jefferson's and John Quincy Adams's dream of a national university was fulfilled by the Roman Catholic Church with the founding in 1889 of the Catholic University of America in Washington, D.C. It is difficult to imagine either the Virginian or the New Englander quite happy about the sponsor.

On a much smaller scale, educational opportunities for blacks also expanded. The traditional universities in New England and many of the sectarian colleges of the Ohio Valley continued to admit a small number of very

NELLIE BLY

The 1890s were a watershed decade in the public status of women in the United States. Led by the methodical Carrie Chapman Catt, the American Woman Suffrage Association began to win the vote for women where the movement of Elizabeth Cady Stanton and Susan B. Anthony had met only frustration. Social workers like Jane Addams and Lillian Wald proved too assertive and effective to be written off as eccentric spinsters. In the popular press, Charles Dana Gibson celebrated "the Gibson girl," an assertive, independent young lady who bore little resemblance to the frail violet who had been the ideal of the Gospel of True Womanhood.

At the very beginning of the decade, Elizabeth Cochran, the orphan daughter of a Pennsylvania miller, came to personify the "new woman" while remaining rather distant from the organized woman's movement. Cochran's aloofness toward the feminists may have owed to a childhood of struggle. (Feminists were overwhelmingly middle-class.) Born in 1864, she was forced by her father's death to go to work. Almost entirely self-educated, Cochran was to parlay her talents and a knack for self-promotion into international celebrity and, via an odd route, riches.

In 1885, while working at a menial job to support her mother, Cochran wrote a letter to a Pittsburgh newspaper editor who had helplessly bemoaned the fact that women who did not marry seemed useless to society. Eloquently and forcefully, Cochran called for opening employment opportunities for girls (who were "just as smart" as boys and "a great deal quicker to learn"). In that way, the single woman could prove herself, be independent, and cease to concern gentlemen like the editor of the *Pittsburgh Dispatch*.

The editor (who became a lifelong friend) was sufficiently impressed that he hired Cochran as a reporter. Using the pen name Nellie Bly (from a Stephen Foster song), she wrote a series of exposés of working and living conditions in the city ten years before the age of the muckraker is said to have begun. Nellie Bly also pioneered the technique of the undercover reporter, actually taking jobs in factories and writing her articles in the first person.

When pressure was brought on the *Dispatch* to relegate Nellie to the society pages, where women "belonged," she moved to New York and pushed her way into a job with Joseph Pulitzer's booming *World*. She was an immediate sensation when she managed to have herself committed to a municipal asylum for insane women. She lived as an inmate for ten days, and penned another blistering first-person exposé.

Nellie was sincerely interested in social reform but far from oblivious to her own interests. Her most famous project for Pulitzer was a masterpiece of self-promotion and one of journalism's first manufactured stories. As a girl, Nellie had read Jules Verne's novel *Around the World in Eighty Days*, in which a British dandy and his valet girdled the globe with unbelievable speed. A number of adventurers had tried to beat the fictional record and failed. Nellie locked herself up with train and steamship time-tables and told the *World* that she could make the trip in 75 days. The editors were interested but said that if they financed such a project, a man would have to carry the banner. A woman on such a journey would "need a protector" anyway, her editor said. "Even if it were possible for you to travel alone, you would have to carry so much baggage that it would detain you in making rapid changes." Nellie replied, "Very well. Start the man and I'll start the same day for some other newspaper and beat him."

Nellie Bly left Jersey City under the *World's* auspices on November 14, 1889 and, after a trip that sometimes seemed leisurely as she waited for steamships to depart, returned to her point of departure via a special transcontinental train on January 25, 1890. Her trip took 72 days.

Suffragists courted Nellie Bly for their cause, but she was uninterested. As early as 1885, when she brought herself to the attention of the *Pittsburgh Dispatch* with her plea on behalf of employment opportunities for women, she expressed oblique disdain for organized feminism. Fighting for jobs for women, she wrote, "would be a good field for believers in women's rights. Let them forego their lecturing and writing and go to work; more work and less talk." After her famous journey, Nellie declined to join the Women's Suffrage Party. "If I became a suffragette," she wrote, "I would play into the hands of my critics. They may not like me, but they respect me. Joining your group would identify me as a partisan. I can help your movement more by putting into practice what you've been preaching."

Again Nellie expressed her disdain for "mere talk." She also disliked what she regarded as the feminists' lack of feminity, remembering late in life that "they looked to be neither men nor women, so queer and nondescript was their attire." She told Susan B. Anthony that "if women wanted to succeed, they had to go out as women. They had to make themselves as pretty and attractive as possible." On rather a different level, Nellie Bly was arguing for what Carrie Chapman Catt was effecting of the American Woman Suffrage Association, espousing expanded rights for women because they were different from men, rather than because they were the same.

The fact was, Nellie Bly was a loner, marching to her own drummer. Shortly after her return from her world trip, she quit journalism to marry a well-to-do manufacturer, 72 years of age to her 31. When he died in 1904, she ran his factory, designed a steel barrel, provided social and medical services and recreational facilities for her employees, and paid women the same wages received by men, a practice then almost unheard of. Unfortunately, her Iron Clad Manufacturing Company went bankrupt because of theft by an employee with whom Nellie was having an affair. She was absolved of complicity in the corruption but was soon broke herself, writing in 1919 that "I have exactly $3.65 and a trunk full of Paris evening dresses." William Randolph Hearst gave her a job writing a column for the New York *Journal* but she never regained her celebrity. She died in 1922.

Tuskegee students in a history class.

well-qualified blacks. W. E. B. Du Bois, a founder of the National Association for the Advancement of Colored People, earned a Ph.D. at Harvard. Hamilton S. Smith earned a law degree from Boston University in 1879 (the first African American to do so), and when he could not make a living as an attorney, attended the Howard University School of Dentistry.

Howard was a private university educating the small but dynamic black middle class. In the North as well as the South, philanthropists and state governments founded institutions for blacks only. Beginning with Lincoln University in Pennsylvania (founded as the Ashmun Institute in 1854), idealistic benefactors supported schools such as Howard in Washington (1867) and Fisk in Nashville (1866). After Booker T. Washington's Atlanta Compromise speech of 1895 and the Supreme Court's decision in *Plessy v. Ferguson* (1896) gave the go-ahead to segregation at all levels of education, Southern state governments founded "agricultural and mechanical" schools patterned after Alabama's Tuskegee Institute (1881), at which blacks could train for manual occupations.

The accomplishments of these institutions should not be underestimated. Few scientific researchers of the time were more productive than Tuskegee Institute's great botanist, George Washington Carver. Nevertheless, the educational level of blacks lagged so far behind that of whites that in 1910, when only 7.7 percent of the American population was illiterate, one-third of blacks above the age of ten could neither read nor write.

A LIVELY CULTURE

Americans continued to buy the books of European authors and the works of the older generation of American poets—Emerson, Longfellow, Whitman, Whittier. Emily Dickinson of Amherst, Massachusetts, a recluse who was virtually unknown until after her death in 1886, was immediately recognized as one of the country's finest writers. But it was first of all an age when novelists flourished, some growing quite rich from the demand for their books.

Twain and James

Samuel Langhorne Clemens, or Mark Twain, was quintessentially and comprehensively American. A Mis-

*W.E.B. Du Bois, a founder of the National Association
for the Advancement of Colored People.*

The Arena, the *Atlantic* published a mix of poetry, stories, and elegant essays that sometimes dealt with contemporary issues but usually at a fastidious distance.

Howells was a realist. He had no patience with the high-flown, preposterous motives and beliefs that sentimental writers imputed to their characters. In *The Rise of Silas Lapham* (1885), a novel about a successful industrialist, when one sister loses a suitor to another, she does not react selflessly, nor does the sister who gets her man think seriously of sacrificing herself. Nevertheless, neither Howells nor the *Atlantic* would have considered dealing graphically with sexual matters or the degradation that poverty and squalor created. Because the proper upper and middle classes themselves considered such discussions unacceptable, the writings of realists like Howells are sometimes lumped with romanticism and sentimentalism as part of "the genteel tradition."

Naturalistic writers defied the taboos, some of them with considerable success. In *Maggie: A Girl of the Streets* (1893), Stephen Crane depicted the poor not as noble and selfless but as miserable and helpless. In *The Red Badge of Courage* (1895), the Civil War is described as something other than glory, bugles, bravery, and flying colors (if anything, a more daring venture than a book about a prostitute). In *McTeague* (1899) and *The Octopus* (1901), Frank Norris dealt with people driven almost mechanically by animal motives.

The most popular of the naturalists was Jack London. His *Call of the Wild* (1903) is comparable to Huckleberry Finn in that it is simultaneously a grand take of adventure (about a dog) and, at a deeper level, a profound commentary on the human condition. Theodore Dreiser broke with a moralistic literary convention (that nevertheless survived) by allowing characters like *Sister Carrie* (1900) to enjoy rich lives despite sinful pasts. Dreiser's success was doubly remarkable because, from a Midwestern German household, his treatment of the English language was adversarial at best, and often downright cruel.

A Hunger for Words

The genteel tradition was also challenged by a new type of magazine that made its appearance in the 1880s and 1890s. Catering to the new, hungry, but not so ethereally intellectual middle classes, these periodicals illustrate the interaction of industrial technology, the larger reading public, and the emergence of modern advertising that was first exploited in 1883 by Cyrus H. K. Curtis and his *Ladies' Home Journal*.

Improved methods of manufacturing paper, printing, and photoengraving, as well as cheap mailing privileges established by Congress in 1879, inspired Curtis to found a magazine for women who were hungry for a world

sourian, he deserted a Confederate militia to go west to Nevada, and eventually settled in Hartford, Connecticut, when he became able to choose his style of life. Brilliantly capturing both the hardships and ribald humor of frontier life in *Roughing It* (1872), he earned an international reputation with *The Adventures of Tom Sawyer* (1876) and *The Adventures of Huckleberry Finn* (1885). Readers sometimes missed the profound and subtle social criticism in Twain's work (as an old man, he grew increasingly melancholy and cynical), but they read him with pleasure for his wit and mastery of the American language.

Twain's favorite settings and themes were robustly Western. The other great novelist of the period, Henry James, settled in England because he found American culture stultifying, and he set most of his novels in the Old World and peopled them with cultivated, cosmopolitan characters. But like Twain, his goal was to define America. In *The American* (1877), *The Europeans* (1878), and *Daisy Miller* (1879), James dealt with the relationship of open, albeit less cultivated, American characters with a jaded and decadent European culture.

Realism and Naturalism

An able novelist in his own right, William Dean Howells presided over the American literary establishment as editor of the *Atlantic Monthly*. Like *Harper's*, *Forum*, and

Samuel L. Clemens, known to his wide readership as Mark Twain.

beyond the kitchen and parlor but who found few opportunities in business and the professions. The *Ladies' Home Journal* sold for only ten cents (compared with the thirty-five-cent *Atlantic* and *Harper's*) and emphasized women's interests. It was not a feminist publication. On the contrary, editor Edward Bok preached a conservatism that reassured homemakers that their conventional prejudices were proper and right and middle-class people generally that they were a "steadying influence" between "unrest among the lower classes and rottenness among the upper classes."

Somewhat more daring were the new general-interest magazines of the 1890s, such as *McClure's*, *Munsey's*, and *Cosmopolitan*. They too cost a dime, thus putting them within reach of a large readership. (The *Saturday Evening Post*, which Cyrus Curtis bought in 1897, sold for only a nickel.) Without stooping to sensationalism, they presented readers with a livelier writing style than the established journals and a lavish use of photographs and illustrations.

McClure's and *Munsey's* pioneered the then curious economics of selling their publications for less than it cost to print and mail them. They made their profit from building up big subscription lists and selling advertising to manufacturers of consumer goods wanting to reach

people who had extra money to spend. The subscription list of *McClure's* increased from 8,000 in 1893 to 250,000 in 1895 (with $60,000 in advertising per issue), and that of *Munsey's* grew from 40,000 to 500,000 during the same two years. By 1900, the combined circulation of the four largest magazines totaled 2.5 million per month, more than all American magazines combined only twenty years earlier.

Libraries and Lyceums

The cultural hunger of the middle class was also expressed in the construction of free public libraries. Again, men suddenly grown rich gave millions to build them. Enoch Pratt donated $1 million to Baltimore for its library. Wealthy lawyer and presidential candidate Samuel J. Tilden gave New York City $2 million, and William Newberry founded one of the nation's greatest collections of books and valuable manuscripts in Chicago with a munificent bequest of $4 million. Beginning in 1881, the self-taught Andrew Carnegie made libraries his principal philanthropy. Before his death in 1919, Carnegie helped found 2,800 free public libraries.

The old lyceum idea of sending lecturers on tour to speak to people who lived far from big cities was revived

Two musical classics, one now international, were written in 1893. *Happy Birthday to You* began as *Good Morning to You* and was written by Patty Smith Hill, a pioneer of the kindergarten movement who taught at the Teacher's College of Columbia University. Irving Berlin tried to steal it from Hill in 1921, but she sued and won.

The lyrics of *America the Beautiful* were put to the music of a hymn by Katherine Lee Bates, a professor of English at Wellesley College. Congress annually receives petitions demanding that the song, which celebrates American beauty and natural grandeur, replace the militaristic (and unsingable) *Star-Spangled Banner* as the national anthem.

AMERICANS AT PLAY

Promoters founded more than 200 Chautauqua-type resorts, some in the mountains, some at the seaside. Enough people could afford to take a holiday from work that a flourishing tourist economy based on leisure time soon grew up.

Nevertheless, old assumptions died hard. Resort promoters found it advisable to provide at least the appearance of "usefulness" for the vacations they offered. If the middle class trekked to Lake Chautauqua or Lake George in New York and to Long Beach or Atlantic City in New Jersey primarily for rest and relaxation, they could tell others and convince themselves of the cultural and educational aspects of their holiday. They were not just wasting time.

Taking the Cure

A similar conjunction of relaxation and constructive use of time underlay the resorts that were devoted to good health. Owners of mineral springs claimed miraculous powers for their waters. Baths in naturally heated mineral waters or in hot mud were prescribed as nostrums for dozens of afflictions. "Hydropathy," a nineteenth-century medical fad, taught that virtually constant bathing and drinking water improved health. For decades, the wealthy had made prosperous summer resorts of places like Saratoga Springs in New York and White Sulphur Springs in Virginia where "taking the cure" could be done in pleasant surroundings among congenial people. Now thousands of middle-class people followed them, again rationalizing their desire for relaxation by extolling the health benefits of their holiday.

Leisure and the Working Class

Working people could not afford to take off a week for the mountains or seaside. However, leisure came to play a part in their lives, too. Great urban greens, beginning with New York's magnificent Central Park, provided free relief on weekends for the teeming masses of the city's slums. Working people in large cities were also able to enjoy themselves at the commercial "amusement parks" that sprang up as a means by which trolley car companies could exploit their investments to the fullest.

Traction companies made a profit only from those parts of their lines that traversed the crowded parts of the cities and then only on workdays. However, the expense of center-city real estate required them to build their sprawling car barns (storage and repair facilities) outside the city. If they were not required by law to run trolleys on Saturday and Sunday, they still wanted to make constant use of their expensive equipment.

---

in 1868 by James Redpath. Offering large fees, Redpath persuaded the most distinguished statesmen, ministers, and professors of the day to deliver highly moral and usually informative addresses in auditoriums and specially erected tents in hundreds of small cities and towns.

Chautauqua

The lyceum movement was a throwback to the antebellum period, when only the very wealthy traveled away from home and the middle class still held fast to the Calvinist beliefs that toil was the human fate and idleness (such as casual travel) was a sin. The lyceum scheduled programs in the evening, when the day's toil was done.

The phenomenon that was born in 1874 at Lake Chautauqua in New York's Allegheny Mountains was more characteristic of the new age. The "Chautauquas" originally were eight-week summer training programs for Sunday-school teachers. During the 1890s, however, cheap excursion fares on the trains made it feasible for people who might have little interest in active church work to make the trip for the sake of the cool mountain air and relaxation. To accommodate them, the Chautauqua organizers broadened their program to include lecturers on secular subjects.

By the turn of the century, a middle-class family spending a few weeks at Lake Chautauqua could expect to hear lectures by individuals as prominent as William Jennings Bryan and to watch "magic-lantern" (slide) shows about the Holy Land, Persia, or China presented by professional world travelers. Distinguished professors, including plenty of quacks, expounded on their theories about human character, happy marriage, or childrearing. German oom-pah bands, Hawaiian dancers, trained dogs, Italian acrobats, and Indian fire-eaters provided lighter entertainment.

Competing amusement parks line the street at Coney Island.

In order to encourage people to ride the trolleys be-yond the city centers, the traction companies encour-aged the construction of amusement parks "at the end of the line" or, in many cases, built "playlands" them-selves. Perhaps the most famous was New York's Coney Island, located on the ocean in Brooklyn. The fare from downtown New York was five cents, with children riding free. Once there, for a dollar or two, a large family could ride the mechanical amusements, such as George C. Tilyou's Bounding Billows, Barrel of Love, and Human Roulette Wheel. They could imitate Buffalo Bill at shooting galleries, visit side-shows and exotic "Somali Villages," or simply loll on the beach with a picnic lunch or "a weird-looking sausage muffled up in two halves of a roll."

These homely pleasures were as exciting to working people as was a trip to Saratoga to the new middle class. Most important, Coney Island, Philadelphia's Willow Grove, Boston's Paragon Park, and Chicago's Chelten-ham Beach represented an organized industry—the manufacturing, packaging, and merchandising of leisure time.

Working-class leisure was more frankly devoted to simple "fun" than were the middle-class Chautauquas. Nevertheless, insistence that even a day at Coney Island was educational and healthful demonstrated the perva-siveness of traditional ideals. Sordid sideshows were touted with moralistic spiels. Knocking over weighted bottles for a prize of a Kewpie doll was defined as honing a valuable skill. Even suggestive dancing by "hoochie-koochie girls" such as Fatima, the sensation of the Chi-cago World's Fair of 1893 who toured the country for a decade, was described as glimpses into the culture of the Turkish Empire. A writer in prim *Harper's Weekly* ap-proved of the "trolley parks" because they were "great breathing-places for millions of people in the city who get little fresh air at home." In a nation not quite free of its Calvinistic past, every hour had to have a purpose.

The First Fitness Craze

Good health was also the rationale for a series of sporting manias that swept over the United States at the turn of the century. To some extent, the concern for bodily health was a contribution of German immigrants, whose *Turnvereine*, clubs devoted to calisthenics, were old-

THE FIRST COCAINE CRAZE

The Western world learned of the invigorating effects of chewing the coca leaf when the Spanish conquered the Inca empire in the sixteenth century. Over the next three centuries, the odd European (and American) experimented with the drug; but only after 1860, when the plant was crystallized into "cocaine," a hundred times more powerful than the leaves, did its use spread throughout society. Parke-Davis, a drug manufacturer, called it "the most important therapeutic discovery of the age, the benefit of which to humanity will be incalculable." The American Hay Fever Association praised it to the skies. Nor were the drug's social "benefits" neglected. In 1878, a magazine touted it as "the cure for young people afflicted with timidity in society." Cocaine was added to patent medicines and soft drinks.

By the end of the century, however, the addictive qualities of cocaine were well-documented. Reformers crusaded against it, and use by the middle class sharply declined. Cocaine came to be associated with blacks, as a 1903 release by the American Pharmacological Association indicates: "The state of Indiana reports that a good many of its Negroes and a few white women are addicted to cocaine." In 1914, the police chief of Atlanta blamed 70 percent of the city's crime on cocaine. What had been almost "high-fashion" became the vice of a despised underclass in a generation.

country carry-overs like democratic socialism and beer gardens. However, it was obvious as early as the mid-nineteenth century that the urban population walked less and got less exercise generally than had its farmer forebears. In the first issue of the *Atlantic Monthly* in 1858, Thomas Wentworth Higginson asked, "Who in this community really takes exercise? Even the mechanic confines himself to one set of muscles; the blacksmith acquires strength in his right arm, and the dancing teacher in his left leg. But the professional or businessman, what muscles has he at all?" Only a society with plenty of spare time could take Higginson's question to heart.

Croquet, archery, and tennis, all imported from England, enjoyed a vogue in the 1870s. Roller skating was even more popular. Great rinks like San Francisco's Olympian Club, with 5,000 pairs of skates to rent and a 69,000-square-foot floor, charged inexpensive fees that were within reach of all but the poorest people. But no sporting fad was as widespread as bicycling.

Bicycles

Briefly during the 1860s, French "dandy horses" were seen on American city streets. These crude wooden vehicles were powered by pushing along the ground. About 1876, the "bone crusher," with its six-foot-high front wheel, made its appearance; by 1881, when the League of American Wheelmen was founded, more than 20,000 intrepid young Americans were devoting their idle hours to pedaling furiously about parks and city streets.

While some praised bicycling as a "health-giving outdoor exercise," moralists condemned the sport for promoting casual relations between young people of the opposite sex. While young men and ladies might leave home for a Sunday ride in proper groups of their own sex, they found it easy to strike up acquaintanceships in parks far from the eyes of parents and chaperone aunts. More than one worried preacher thought that the bicycle was a first step toward moral chaos.

Indeed, it was on the pneumatic tires of the bicycle that many emancipated young women of the 1890s escaped into a refreshing new freedom. The "safety bicycle," which had much the same design as bicycles today, took the risk of broken bones out of the sport. On Sundays, the streets were full of them, and a goodly number carried young women in candy-striped blouses with billowing sleeves, sporty broad-brimmed hats, and full free-flowing skirts.

The Gibson Girl

The "new look" woman of the 1890s took the name of the "Gibson Girl" after the popular magazine illustrator, Charles Dana Gibson, who "invented" her. Gibson's vision of ideal American womanhood charmed the nation from Newport high society to working-class suburbs. The Gibson Girl was by no means a feminist. She took little interest in women's suffrage or other political issues. Essentially, she remained an object of adoration—fine-featured, trim, coy, flirtatious, even seductive.

The Gibson Girl was novel. She was no shrinking violet. She did not faint after the exertion of climbing a staircase. She played croquet, golf, and tennis. She rode a bicycle without chaperones. She was quite able to take care of herself; one of Gibson's favorite themes was the helplessness of young men in the hands of his self-assured young ladies.

Theodore Roosevelt's daughter, Alice, who became a national sweetheart when the popular waltz "Alice Blue

WOMEN IN GOVERNMENT

Just as the black cowboy virtually had been forgotten, few historians have noted that women played an important part in government long before they could vote. At the turn of the century, nearly one government worker in three was female. The federal bureaucracy was very much a woman's world.

The typewriter created secretarial jobs for women in large business offices where formerly all employees were male.

Gown" was named for her, might have been sculpted by Gibson, and middle-class women adopted her style. Photographs of mill girls leaving textile factories in Massachusetts and of stenographers in offices in New York reveal an air of Gibson Girl self-assurance. The new independence of women was also indicated by the fact that they were marrying later. In 1890, the average age for a woman on her wedding day was 22, two or three years older than it had been in 1860.

Technology and the Lives of Women

Technology played a part in creating the new, active, and independent woman. The telephone, for example, permitted a familiarity with men that was forbidden to "young ladies of breeding" face to face.

Also much noted by people of the time was the fact that Bell's American Telephone and Telegraph Company turned to young ladies to handle the job of connecting callers to each other. The company fired the young men whom it originally had hired because their conversation on the wires was flippant and occasionally obscene; also anticipating the future, they took advantage of anonymity to shock or insult proper middle-class subscribers.

Unlike factory work, which was menial and dirty, a job as an operator was socially acceptable for middle-class girls. In addition to finding an escape from the plush prison of the parlor, thousands of women earned an income independent of their parents and husbands. Alexander Graham Bell, unknown to both parties, was a partner with American feminists in their movement to emancipate women.

The Changing Office

Another invention that created jobs for women, and therefore a sense of independence, was the typewriter. Because handwriting was often illegible, and potentially costly in business, dozens of inventors had taken a stab at creating a "writing machine." But the first practical typewriter was perfected only in 1867 by Christopher Latham Sholes, and first marketed in 1874 by the Remington Arms Company, a firearms manufacturer in search of a product with which to diversify its interests.

Before the use of the machine became standard in business, almost all secretaries were men. They not only wrote letters for their employers, but they ran various errands and sometimes represented the boss. The typewriter made it possible for businessmen to split the secretarial profession into assistant and typist. Men continued to perform the more responsible and better-paid job, rising to a status that would be described as "junior executive" today. The mechanical task of transcribing letters and business records into type went to women.

Like the job of telephone operator, that of typist did not require higher education. Nor was it heavy labor, an important consideration in an age that defined respectable young ladies as "delicate." And the job did not usually involve much responsibility, which nineteenth-century men were disinclined to allot to women. By 1890, 15 percent of clerical workers were female; by 1900 almost 25 percent were.

SPORTS

The turn of the century was also a golden age of organized sport. Although football (with somewhat different rules from today) was a game played almost exclusively by university students, people of all social classes avidly followed the fortunes of the nearest "Ivy League" team. Basketball, which was invented in Springfield, Massachusetts in 1891 by Dr. James Naismith, a physical education instructor who was looking for a sport that his students could play during the rigorous New England winter, was still in its infancy. The spectator sports that obsessed Americans were baseball and boxing. Both had evolved from traditional folk recreations, but by the end of the nineteenth century, both were organized as money-making enterprises.

The National Pastime

Baseball developed out of two ancient children's games, rounders and town ball, which had been brought to the United States by English immigrants. According to Albert G. Spalding, a professional pitcher for clubs in Boston and Chicago, systematic rules for the sport were first drafted by Abner Doubleday of Cooperstown, New York, in 1839. The story was poppycock. There is no evidence Doubleday invested a minute in thinking about the game. Spalding devised the tale to promote the sporting goods manufacturing company that made him a millionaire. In reality, baseball "just growed"; there was little agreement on a number of important rules until after the Civil War.

While many towns organized teams to play neighbors on special occasions, the professional sport emerged from upper-class baseball "clubs" such as the New York Knickerbockers. Soon concerned more with defeating rivals than with enjoying an afternoon of exercise, the clubs began to hire (at first secretly and despite noisy protest) long-hitting and fast-pitching working-class boys to wear their colors. In 1869, the first openly professional team, the Cincinnati Red Stockings, went on tour and defeated all comers.

When people proved willing by the thousands to pay admission fees to see the difficult game played well, businessmen in large Eastern and Midwestern cities organized cooperative associations. The National League was founded in 1876; the American League, "the junior cir-

The first World Series in 1903 was played between Boston and Pittsburgh.

cuit," dates from 1901. The first World Series between the champions of both leagues was played in 1903.

Teams were focal points of civic pride. Important games often received more attention in the newspapers than did foreign wars. After Brooklyn became a borough of New York City in 1898, its baseball team, the Trolley Dodgers, became the former city's sole symbol of an independent identity, its antidote to the Brooklyn Bridge.

Boxing and Society

Fights between two strong men may be humanity's oldest spectator sport. In 1867, because boxing was becoming a "manly art" practiced by the upper class, an English sportsman, the Marquis of Queensberry, devised a code of rules that was quickly adopted throughout Europe and the United States. The Queensberry rules hardly made for a gentle sport. One read that "all attempts to inflict injury by gouging or tearing the flesh with the fingers or nails and biting shall be deemed foul."

As with baseball, the opportunities to make money from paid admissions encouraged promoters to search out popular heroes. The first to win a national reputation was a burly Irish Bostonian named John L. Sullivan, who started out by traveling the country and offering $50 (and later $1,000) to anyone who could last four rounds with him. Between 1882 and 1892, "the Boston Strong Boy" bloodied one challenger after another, personally collecting as much as $20,000 a fight and making much more for the entrepreneurs who organized his bouts.

The crowds that watched great championship bouts and most baseball games included comparatively few working people. However, they followed their heroes in the new sports pages of the newspapers, which, as with baseball, devoted column after column to important fights. Because Sullivan and his successor as heavyweight champion, Gentleman Jim Corbett, were Irish, they became objects of ethnic pride. So entangled in the culture did the sport become that when a black boxer rose to the top, he caused an anxiety that reached into the halls of Congress.

Jack Johnson

Blacks played baseball with whites during the earliest professional years. The catcher on a team that toured

CONSUMER GOODS

By 1909, thirteen of the largest industrial firms in the United States were involved in the production of consumer goods, including tobacco, whiskey, meat, petroleum products, and tires for automobiles.

the world in the 1880s was black. However, the same wave of racism that initiated the Jim Crow Laws in the 1890s led to the segregation of the sport. A first baseman from Iowa, Adrian "Cap" Anson, led the fight to keep black players out of the two major leagues.

Black boxers did fight whites and, in 1908, one of them, Jack Johnson won the heavyweight crown and proceeded to batter every challenger who stepped forth. Such a feat by a black man rankled many white Americans. Johnson aggravated the hatred for him by gleefully insulting every "great white hope" who challenged him. A tragically indiscreet man, he flaunted his white mistresses at a time when the color line was being drawn across practically every American institution.

Southern states, which had been the most hospitable to professional prize fights, forbade Johnson to fight within their borders. Politicians raved at every Johnson victory and gaudy public appearance. Congress actually passed a law that prohibited the interstate shipment of a film of Johnson's victory over former champion Jim Jeffries in Reno in 1910. Finally, in 1912, racism defeated him not in the ring but through an indictment under the Mann Act, which forbade "transporting women" across state lines "for immoral purposes." (Johnson had taken his common-law wife to another state.)

Johnson fled to Europe, but was homesick and agreed to fight the white boxer Jess Willard in Havana in 1915. He lost, and it was widely believed that he threw the match as part of a deal with the Justice Department by which he could reenter the United States without fear of arrest. A famous photograph of the knockout shows Johnson on his back, apparently relaxed and unhurt, and shielding his eyes from the Caribbean sun. Jack may have had his last jibe at good-old-days America, but the days were good enough for the white middle class that few people noticed.

For Further Reading

Overviews of the era are Vincent P. DeSantis, *The Shaping of Modern America, 1877–1916* (1973); Ray Ginger, *The Age of Excess* (1965); William L. O'Neill, *The Progressive Years: America Comes of Age* (1975); and Robert H. Wiebe, *The Search for Order, 1880–1920* (1967). On

general social and cultural history, students should look at Frederick Lewis Allen, *The Big Change* (1952); Van Wyck Brooks, *The Confident Years, 1885–1915* (1952); and the classic Mark Sullivan, *Our Times* (1926–1935). Studies of special topics include G. W. Chessman,

Governor Theodore Roosevelt (1965); Carl M. Degler, At Odds: Women in the Family in America from the Revolution to the Present (1980); Ann Douglas, The Feminization of American Culture (1977); Foster R. Dulles, America Learns to Play (1940); Ray Ginger, Altgeld's America: The Lincoln Ideal and Changing Realities (1958); Otis L. Graham, Jr., The Great Campaigns: Reform and War in America, 1900–1928 (1971); Jack D. Kirby, Darkness at the Dawning: Race and Reform in the Progressive South (1972); J. R. Krout, Annals of American Sport (1924); Margaret Leech, In the Days of McKinley (1959); Henry F. May, The End of American Innocence (1959); H. Wayne Morgan, William McKinley and His America (1963); George E. Mowry, The Era of Theodore Roosevelt (1958); Steven A. Reiss, Touching Base: Professional Baseball and American Culture in the Progressive Era (1980).

Three fine books about "Teddy" are John M. Blum, The Republican Roosevelt (1954); W. H. Harbaugh, Power and Responsibility: The Life and Times of Theodore Roosevelt (1961); and, best of all, Henry F. Pringle, Theodore Roosevelt (1931).

Members of the Women's Trade Union League demonstrating in New York.

A GENERATION OF REFORM

THE EMERGENCE OF THE PROGRESSIVES AFTER 1900

In 1787, when his contemporaries were writing the Constitution—in part out of fear of social turmoil—Thomas Jefferson was in France. The Bastille had not yet been attacked, Paris was peaceful, but Jefferson had the fire of revolution in his blood. During this period, he wrote several letters in which he said that periodic revolution was essential to the health of a free society. "A little rebellion, now and then, is a good thing," he wrote to James Madison, "as necessary in the political world as storms in the physical." To another friend a few months later he added, "The tree of liberty must be refreshed from time to time with the blood of patriots and tyrants."

Does political progress depend on periodic violent uprisings? The history of the United States seems to say not. During a 200-year epoch that has been marked by just such instability and tumult in the world, only once has the United States been shaken by a revolution, the secession of the Southern states in 1861; and it was neither progressive nor successful.

A mechanism for peaceable change was, of course, written into the Constitution in the form of the amendment process. But much more important, periodically in American history—in predictable cycles, some historians think—people whose means and privileges put them far above the masses have themselves risen up, quite without violence, to rid themselves of political and social abuses, pruning the deadwood and disease from Jefferson's tree of liberty. Such a welling of the reform spirit was the "Progressive Era" spanning, roughly, the first two decades of the twentieth century.

THE PROGRESSIVES

The far-reaching reforms the people called progressives demanded and, for the most part, put into effect after 1900, were not original with the new century. The movement inherited ideas from the Mugwumps, the Social Gospel, the half-century-old women's movement, urban social workers, Populism, even the sundry varieties of socialism that bloomed for a season in the late nineteenth century.

What was new about the progressives was the fact that where their predecessors appealed to relatively small social groups and antagonized (or simply did not interest) the majority, the progressives rallied much of a generation to most of their causes.

Middle America

Their chief appeal, however, and the source of almost all progressive leaders, was the new middle class of small-business men and professionals: lawyers, physicians, ministers, teachers, journalists, social workers, and the wives and daughters of the middle classes whose first reform was personal, to break free of nursery, parlor, and chapel. Few progressive leaders came from the industrial and financial elite. Few rose from the masses of laboring people and poor farmers. The progressive movement was middle class in its heart and head.

The progressives were acutely aware that they were "in between." Eternally knocking about in the back of

The Progressives came from the new middle class, such as the Drummond family posing on the back porch of their New York home.

the progressive mind was the assumption that what was best about America was its middle class—people not so rich as to endanger the republic, not so poor as to have no stake in it. Indeed, many progressives felt that the middle class was threatened by plutocrats from above, and from below by the potentially dangerous mob.

Thus, virtually all progressives were committed to curtailing the power of the great corporations and banks or, at least, to control the manner in which that power was used. Most progressives intended for the Rockefellers and the Morgans to behave in ways that were compatible with the good of society, as the progressives defined it.

While the progressives were concerned with the material and moral welfare of those below them on the social ladder, they also feared the masses. In the cities, progressive reformers often voiced concern that the slums were tinderboxes of anger, ready to explode in destructive anarchy. In the Midwest and West, most progressive leaders had been staunch anti-Populists because they saw the farmers' rebellion as an upheaval of the impoverished, uneducated, and unwashed. William Allen White, a leading progressive journalist, first made his name as the author of a scathing anti-Populist manifesto called "What's the Matter with Kansas?" Years later, a little sheepishly, White explained that he had written the piece not because an idea had occurred to him in his study, but because he had been jostled on a street corner in Emporia, Kansas, by "lazy, greasy fizzles" whose vulgarity had offended him, and whose inclination to push and shove frightened him.

Many progressives saw clearly the relationship between the power of great wealth and dangerous restiveness among the exploited poor. Early in the century, Woodrow Wilson of New Jersey put the thought in a curious way when he blamed the automobile, then a plaything of the rich, for the spread of socialism. Driving their cars around recklessly, frightening horses, killing chickens, and scattering ordinary folks, Wilson wrote, the rich were bringing their arrogance to every country road in the nation.

Righteous Optimists

Louis D. Brandeis, a Louisville lawyer who helped design the Democratic party's reform program, was Jewish. Alfred E. Smith and Robert F. Wagner, progressive politicians in New York State, were Irish and German,

respectively, and Roman Catholic in religion. W. E. B. Du Bois, who helped to found the National Association for the Advancement of Colored People, was black. But they were exceptions. Most progressive leaders were "WASPs" from "old stock," people whose American roots ran through several generations.

Most were urban in background, brought up in cities or towns. Even those progressive politicians who represented rural states, such as Robert M. La Follette of Wisconsin and George Norris of Nebraska, had grown up in small towns. As boys, they had rubbed elbows with farmers, but they had not walked behind plows or milled about anxiously next to their wagons as agents weighed, graded, and put a price on the year's crop. Like William Allen White, La Follette had been an anti-Populist during the 1890s.

Progressive political leaders were inclined to be moralistic to the point of self-righteousness, ever searching for the absolute right and absolute wrong in every political disagreement. California's Hiram Johnson irked even his most devoted supporters by his clenched-teeth sanctimony. Robert M. La Follette did not know what a sense of humor was. To "Fighting Bob," life was one long crusade for what was right. Theodore Roosevelt described the beginning of an election campaign in biblical terms: "We stand at Armageddon and do battle for the Lord." Woodrow Wilson, stern of visage in wing collar and pince-nez, eventually destroyed himself because he would not compromise with his critics in order to save the most important cause of his life.

And yet, while their noses were ever to the wind for hint of foul odors, the progressives believed that progress was indeed possible because human nature was intrinsically good. "Our shamelessness is superficial," wrote Lincoln Steffens, "beneath it lies a pride which, being real, may save us yet." They were optimists.

A Coat of Many Colors

Almost all progressives believed that a powerful government, active in taking the initiative and holding it, was the key to improving America. In this statism they were rather unlike earlier reformers who were as apt to consider government a part of the problem. Jane Addams, whose main work concerned helping the urban poor, said that private institutions like her Hull House were "today inadequate to deal with the vast numbers of the city's disinherited."

As for the corporations that threatened American ideas, the progressives believed that a powerful state was the only agency that could bring them to heel. The goals were still Jeffersonian, Herbert Croly wrote in *The Promise of American Life*, published in 1909, the welfare of the many determined by the will of the many. But, to

REFORM

What is reform? One dictionary defines it as "to change into a new and improved condition; removal of faults or abuses so as to restore to a former good state, or bring from bad to good." In the context of American history, *reform* has also come to mean peaceful, usually gradual change, as opposed to violent and sudden change, which Americans define as *revolution*.

Croly, the old Jeffersonian principle of "the less government the better" had been rendered obsolete by the magnitude of social problems and the vast power of the plutocrats. Croly would have "Jeffersonian ends" served by "Hamiltonian means," the power of the state.

Beyond a commitment to active government, progressivism was variety, a frame of mind rather than a single coherent movement. There were Democratic progressives and Republican progressives. In 1912, breakaway Republicans formed the Progressive party. Some progressives considered some socialists to be kin.

On specific issues, progressives differed among themselves as radically as they differed from the "Old Guard" against whom they battled. For example, while many progressives believed that labor unions had the right to exist and fight for the betterment of their members, others opposed unions for the same reason that they disliked powerful corporations: organized special-interest groups were at odds with the American ideal of serving the good of the whole. On one occasion, a few leaders of the National American Woman Suffrage Association said that women should work as strikebreakers if by so doing they could win jobs currently held by men.

Some progressives were ultranationalists. Others clung to a humanism that embraced all people of all countries. Some progressives were expansionists. Senator Albert J. Beveridge of Indiana saw no conflict in calling for broadening democracy at home while urging the United States to rule colonies abroad without regard to the will of their inhabitants. Others were anti-imperialists, even isolationists who looked on Europe as a fount of corruption.

Progressives disagreed on the subject of laws regulating child labor. By 1907, about two-thirds of the states, governed or influenced by progressives, forbade the employment of children under fourteen years of age. However, when progressives in Congress passed a federal child-labor law in 1916, the progressive President Woodrow Wilson expressed grave doubts before signing it. Wilson worried that to forbid children to work infringed on their rights as citizens. This was essentially the same reasoning that was offered by the conservative

Supreme Court in *Hammer v. Dagenhart* (1918), which struck down the law.

Race

Many, perhaps most, progressives could not imagine blacks as citizens participating fully and actively in American society. Some were frank racists, especially the Southern progressives: Governor James K. Vardaman of Mississippi, Governor Jeff Davis of Arkansas, Senator Benjamin "Pitchfork Ben" Tillman of South Carolina. As president of Princeton University, Woodrow Wilson helped to segregate the town of Princeton on racial lines, including even sidewalk water fountains. As president of the United States, he approved the introduction of "Jim Crow" practices in the federal government. Other progressives tolerated racial discrimination out of habit or because they feared the consequences of equality when 45 percent of all black Americans were illiterate.

Other progressives regarded racial prejudice and discrimination as among the worst evils afflicting America. Journalist Ray Stannard Baker wrote a scathing and moving exposé of racial segregation in a series of articles entitled "Following the Color Line." In 1910, white progressives, including Jane Addams, joined with the black Niagara Movement to form the National Association for the Advancement of Colored People. Except for his color, W. E. B. Du Bois, the guiding spirit of the Niagara Movement, was the progressive *par excellence*: genteel, middle class, university educated, and devoted to the idea that an elite should govern. Du Bois believed that a "talented tenth" of the black population would lead the race to civil equality in the United States.

Forebears

So diverse a movement had a mixed ancestry. From the Populists' Omaha Platform, the progressives took a good deal. As William Allen White remarked, the progressives "caught the Populists in swimming and stole all of their clothing except the frayed underdrawers of free

FILTHY LUCRE

Progressives were morally appalled by money grubbing. When he was president, Theodore Roosevelt expressed this sentiment when he tried to have "In God We Trust" deleted from American coins. "It seems to me," he wrote, "eminently unwise to cheapen such a motto by use on coins, just as it would be to cheapen it by use on postage stamps and advertisements." A few coins were struck without "In God We Trust," but Congress, failing to appreciate T.R.'s point, restored it.

silver." They called for the direct election of senators and a graduated income tax that would hit the wealthy harder than the poor and middle classes (both enacted by constitutional amendment in 1913). Progressives also favored the initiative, referendum, and recall. Some, but by no means all, progressives wanted to nationalize the railways and banks. Many more believed that local public utilities such as water, gas, and electric companies, being natural monopolies, should be government-owned.

The progressives also harkened back to the "good government" idealism of the Liberal Republicans and Mugwumps. Indeed, in the progressives' intense moralism, their compulsion to stamp out personal sin as well as social and political evils, they sometimes sounded like the evangelical preachers of the early nineteenth century.

In exalting expertise and efficiency, and in their belief that a new social order must be devised to replace the social chaos of the late nineteenth century, the progressives owed a debt to people whom they considered their enemies. Marcus A. Hanna, described as a conservative when he died in 1904, had spent half his life preaching the collaboration of capital and organized labor as an alternative to class conflict.

Frederick W. Taylor, the inventor of "scientific management," was rarely described as a progressive and personally took little interest in politics. Nevertheless, in his conviction that the engineer's approach to solving problems could be fruitfully applied to human behavior, he was a forebear of the progressive movement. The progressives believed that society could be engineered as readily as Taylor engineered machine tools and the way a man wielded a shovel.

PROGRESSIVISM DOWN HOME

Progressivism originated in the cities. In the last years of the nineteenth century, capitalizing on widespread disgust with the corruption that had become endemic to municipal government, a number of reform mayors swept into office and won national notoriety. They were not, as had been their predecessors in the 1870s and 1880s, easily ousted after a year or two.

Good Government

One of the first of the city reformers was Hazen S. Pingree, a shoe manufacturer who was elected mayor of Detroit in 1890. Pingree spent seven years battling the corrupt alliance between the owners of the city's public utilities and Detroit city councilmen. In nearby Toledo,

Ohio, another businessman, Samuel M. Jones, ran for mayor as a reformer in 1897. Professional politicians mocked him as an addleheaded eccentric because he plastered the walls of his factory with the golden rule and other homilies. But Jones also treated his employees fairly, including sharing profits with them. As "Golden Rule" Jones, he took control of Toledo and proved to be a no-nonsense administrator. Within two years, he rid Toledo's city hall of graft.

Another progressive mayor from Ohio was Cleveland's Thomas L. Johnson. A former single-taxer, Johnson was elected in 1901. Not only did he clean up a dirty government, but he actively supported woman suffrage, reformed the juvenile courts, took over public utilities from avaricious owners, and put democracy to work by presiding over open "town meetings" at which citizens could make known their grievances and suggestions.

Lincoln Steffens, a staff writer for *McClure's*, called Cleveland "the best-governed city in the United States." Steffens was the expert; in 1903, he authored a sensational series of articles for *McClure's* called "The Shame of the Cities." Researching his subject carefully in the country's major cities, he named grafters, exposed corrupt connections between elected officials and dishonest businessmen, and demonstrated how ordinary people suffered from corrupt government in the quality of their daily lives.

Steffens's exposés hastened the movement for city reform. Joseph W. Folk of St. Louis, whose tips put Steffens on the story, was able to indict more than thirty politicians and prominent Missouri businessmen for bribery and perjury as a result of the outcry that greeted "The Shame of the Cities." Hundreds of reform mayors elected after 1904 owed their success to the solemn, bearded journalist.

The Muckrakers

No single force was more important in spreading the gospel of progressivism than the mass-circulation magazines. Already well-established by the turn of the century thanks to their cheap price and lively style, journals such as *McClure's*, the *Arena*, *Collier's*, *Cosmopolitan*, and *Everybody's* became even more successful when their editors discovered the popular appetite for the journalism of exposure.

The discovery was almost accidental. Samuel S. McClure himself had no particular interest in reform. Selling magazines and advertising in them was his business, hobby, and obsession. When he hired Ida M. Tarbell and Lincoln Steffens at generous salaries, he did so because they wrote well, not because they were reformers. Indeed, Tarbell began the "History of the Standard Oil Company," exposing John D. Rockefeller's dubious business practices because of a personal grudge: Rockefeller had ruined her father. Steffens was looking for a story, any story, when he stumbled upon the shame of the cities.

But when Tarbell's and Steffens's sensational exposés caused circulation to soar, McClure and other editors were hooked. The mass-circulation magazines soon brimmed with sensational revelations about corruption in government, chicanery in business, social evils like child labor and prostitution, and other subjects that lent themselves to indignant, excited treatment. In addition to his series on racial segregation, Ray Stannard Baker dissected the operations of the great railroads. John Spargo, an English-born socialist, discussed child labor in "The Bitter Cry of the Children." David Graham Phillips, who later succeeded as a novelist dealing with social themes, revealed that the United States Senate, elected by state legislatures, had become a kind of "millionaires' club."

Theodore Roosevelt called the new journalists "muckrakers" after an unattractive character in John Bunyan's religious classic of 1678, *Pilgrim's Progress*. The writers were so busy raking through the muck of American society, he said, that they failed to look up and see its glories in the stars and the crown that could be their own.

He had a point, especially when after a few years the quality of the journalism of exposure deteriorated into sloppy research and wild, ill-founded accusations made for the sake of attracting attention. During the first decade of the century, no fewer than 2,000 articles and books of exposure were published. Inevitably, the conscientious muckrakers ran out of solid material, and muckraking as a profession attracted incompetent hacks and sensation-mongers.

But the dirt could be real enough, and the early reform journalists were as determined to stick to the facts as to arouse their readers' indignation. Their work served to

---

NOTHING BUT THE FACTS, MA'AM

The Muckrakers were keenly aware that part of the revolution they worked in American journalism was to sensationalize it. Lincoln Steffens chafed under the regime in which "reporters were to report the news as it happened, like machines, without prejudice, color, and without style; all alike." Ray Stannard Baker wrote impatiently that "facts, facts piled up to the point of dry certitude, was what the American people really wanted." Both were to remain true to high standards of journalistic integrity, but that was not true of many muckrakers.

---

transmit the reform impulse from one end of the country to the other. The ten leading muckraking journals had a combined circulation of three million. Because the magazines were also read in public libraries and barbershops, and just passed around, the readership was many times larger.

In the Jungle with Upton Sinclair

Upton Sinclair was probably the most influential muckraker of all. An obscure young socialist, in 1906 he wrote a serialized novel, *The Jungle*, about how ethnic prejudice and economic exploitation in Chicago turned a Lithuanian immigrant into a revolutionary determined to smash the capitalist system. The message did not particularly appeal to the editors of the mass-circulation magazines, and Sinclair turned to a Socialist party weekly newspaper, the *Appeal to Reason*, to run it. (Even the *Appeal* had a big readership; one issue sold over one million copies.) In its pages, *The Jungle* was a mighty success. As a book, it sold 100,000 copies, even reaching the desk of President Theodore Roosevelt.

Sinclair's book may have converted a few of its readers to socialism (although its literary quality decayed rapidly in the final chapters when the protagonist takes up the red flag.) However, the passages that made it a bestseller were those that luridly described the conditions under which meat was processed in Chicago slaughterhouses. *The Jungle* publicized well-documented tales of rats ground up into sausage, workers with tuberculosis coughing on the meat they packed, and filth at every point along the disassembly line.

"I aimed at the nation's heart," Sinclair later lamented, "and hit it in the stomach." He meant that within months of the publication of *The Jungle*, a federal meat-inspection bill that had been languishing in Congress was rushed through under public pressure and promptly signed by President Roosevelt. It and a second Pure Food and Drug Act, which forbade food processors to use dangerous adulterants (the pet project of a chemist in the Agriculture Department, Dr. Harvey W. Wiley), expanded government power in a way that had been inconceivable a few years earlier.

Efficiency and Democracy

In 1908, Staunton, Virginia introduced a favorite progressive municipal reform, the city-manager system of government. The office of mayor was abolished. Instead, voters elected a city council, which then hired a nonpolitical, professionally trained administrator to serve as city manager. Proponents of the city manager system reasoned that democracy was protected by the people's control of the council; but because the daily operations of the city were supervised by an executive who was free of political influence, they would be carried out without regard to special interests. By 1915, over 400 mostly medium-size cities had followed Staunton's example.

The "Oregon system" was the brainchild of one of the first progressives to make an impact at the state level. William S. U'ren, a former Populist and single-taxer, believed that the remedy for corruption in government was simple: more democracy. The trouble lay in the ability of efficient, well-organized, and wealthy special interests to thwart the good intentions of the people. Time after time, U'ren pointed out, elected officials handily forgot their campaign promises and worked closely with the corporations to pass bad laws or defeat good ones.

In 1902, U'ren persuaded the Oregon legislature to adopt the initiative, recall, and referendum. The Oregon system also included the first primary law. It took the power to nominate candidates for public office away from the bosses and gave it to the voters. Finally, U'ren led the national movement to choose United States senators by popular vote rather than in the state legislatures.

U'ren lived to the ripe old age of 90, long enough to see twenty states adopt the initiative and thirty, the referendum. A number of progressive states also instituted primaries of one kind or another, but until the 1970s, the primary was a less popular idea. In the South, the "white primary," by which Democratic party candidates were chosen, was used in the interests of racism: since most whites were Democrats, the primary was the contest that counted; and because the primary was an election within a private organization, blacks could be legally excluded from it.

"Fighting Bob"

The career of Wisconsin's "Fighting Bob" La Follette is a history of progressivism in microcosm. Born in 1855, he studied law and served three terms as a Republican in Congress before 1890. He showed few signs of the crusader's itch until a prominent Republican offered him a bribe to fix the verdict in a trial. La Follette flew into a rage at the shameless audacity of the suggestion, and he never quite calmed down for the rest of his life.

In 1900, he ran for governor in defiance of the Republican organization, attacking the railroad and lumber interests that dominated the state. He promised to devote the resources of the government to the service of the people, and his timing was perfect. A state that recently had rebuffed the Populists was ready for reform, and La Follette was elected. As governor, he pushed through a comprehensive system of regulatory laws that required every business that touched the public interest to conform to clear-cut rules and submit to close inspection of its operations.

The "Wisconsin Idea"

La Follette went beyond the negative, or regulatory, powers of government to create agencies that provided positive services for the people. La Follette's "Wisconsin idea" held that in the complex modern world, people and government needed experts to work on their behalf. A railroad baron could not be kept on a leash unless the government had the support of knowledgeable specialists who were as canny as the railroad men. Insurance premiums could not be held at reasonable levels unless the state was able to determine what profit was just and what was rapacious. The government could not intervene to determine what was fair in a labor dispute unless it had the help of the labor experts and economists.

La Follette formed a close and mutually beneficial relationship with the University of Wisconsin. His organization generously supported the institution, making it one of the nation's great universities at a time when most state-supported schools were little more than poorly funded agricultural colleges. In return, distinguished professors like Richard Ely, Selig Perlman, and John Rogers Commons put their expertise at La Follette's disposal. The law school helped build up the first legislative reference library in the United States so that assemblymen would no longer have to rely on lobbyists to draft their laws.

The university's School of Agriculture not only taught future farmers, but carried out research programs that addressed problems faced daily in Wisconsin's fields and barns. La Follette even made use of the football team. When enemies hinted there would be trouble if he spoke at a political rally, he showed up in the company of Wisconsin's burly linemen, who folded their arms and surrounded the platform. There was no trouble.

Perhaps La Follette's most original contribution to progressivism was his application of machine methods to the cause of reform. He was idealistic. But he was not naive. In order to ensure that his reforms would not be reversed, he built an organization that was more finely integrated than Boss Tweed's. Party workers in every precinct got out the vote, and if they did not violate La Follette's exacting demands for honesty in public office, they were rewarded with government patronage.

In 1906, La Follette took his crusade to Washington as a United States senator. He held that office until his death in 1925 and made several unsuccessful tries at winning the presidency. In Wisconsin and elsewhere he was loved as few politicians have been. He was "Fighting Bob," incorruptible and unyielding in what he regarded as right. La Follette's thick, neatly cropped head of brown hair combed straight back, which turned snow white with years, waved wildly during his passionate speeches. He looked like an Old Testament prophet, and, in a way, La Follette devoted his life to saving the soul of American society, as Jeremiah had done for Israel.

Progressives in Other States

In New York State, Charles Evans Hughes came to prominence as a result of his investigation into public utilities and insurance companies. Tall, erect, dignified, with a smartly trimmed beard such as was going out of fashion at the turn of the century, he lacked the charisma of La Follette and other progressives. If they were humorless in their intensity, Hughes was "a cold-blooded creature" (in the words of the hot-blooded Theodore Roosevelt). But he was unshakably honest as governor of New York between 1906 and 1910.

William E. Borah was not elected as a senator from Idaho in 1906 as a progressive. On the contrary, his career in politics had been characterized by a close and compliant relationship with the mining and ranching interests that ran the state. Once in the Senate, however, Borah usually voted with the growing progressive bloc. This record and his isolationism—like many Westerners, Borah believed that the United States would be corrupted by close association with foreign powers—guaranteed his reelection until he died in office in 1940.

Progressivism in California

Hiram Johnson of California came to progressivism by much the same path as had La Follette. A prim, tight-lipped trial lawyer from Sacramento, Johnson won fame by taking over the prosecution of the corrupt political machine of Boss Abe Ruef in San Francisco.

At first it appeared to be an ordinary graft case. Ruef and his allies, Mayor Eugene E. Schmitz and a majority of the Board of Aldermen won office by appealing to ethnic voters. They collected payoffs from brothels, gambling dens, and thieves in return for running a wide-open city. In the wake of the great San Francisco earthquake and fire of 1906, Ruef set up a system by which those who wished to profit from the rebuilding had to clear their plans with him. Scarcely a street could be paved or a cable-car line laid out until money changed hands. On one occasion, Ruef pocketed $250,000, of which he kept one-quarter, gave one-quarter to Schmitz, and distributed the remainder among the aldermen whose votes were needed to authorize public works. Like other city bosses, Ruef bought and sold judges in lawsuits.

But Johnson discovered that Ruef not only was associated with vice and petty graft, but was intimately allied with the most powerful corporation in the state, the Southern Pacific Railroad. The distinguished and ostensibly upright directors of the Southern Pacific, men whom Johnson had admired, were tangled in a web that stretched to include profiting from the misfortune of the wretched syphilitic whores on the city's notorious Barbary Coast.

The never equanimous Johnson was transformed into "a volcano in perpetual eruption, belching fire and smoke." In 1910, he won the governorship on the slogan, "Kick the Southern Pacific out of politics." Never again would he assume that great wealth and a varnish of propriety indicated a decent man. Indeed, his sense of personal rectitude was so great that it cost him a chance to be president. In 1920, Republican party bosses such as Johnson loathed asked him to run as vice president in order to balance the conservative presidential nominee, Warren G. Harding. Johnson turned them down in a huff. As a result, when Harding died in office in 1923, he was succeeded by the conservative Calvin Coolidge instead of the volcano from California.

ON THE FRINGE

Most progressives advocated municipal ownership of public utilities, but they were staunchly anti-socialist. Indeed, progressive politicians like La Follette and Johnson warned that the reforms they proposed were necessary to preserve the institution of private property from a rising Red tide in American politics.

This message had a special urgency in the early years of the twentieth century because the Socialist party of America, founded in 1900, came close to establishing itself as a major force in American politics. Pieced together by local Socialist organizations and frustrated former Populists, the Socialist party nominated labor leader Eugene V. Debs for president in 1900, and he won 94,768 votes. In 1904, running again, Debs threw a scare into progressives and conservatives alike by polling 402,460.

ATTEMPTED MURDER?

In late May 1908, Robert La Follette led a filibuster against a financial bill of which he disapproved. He spoke for nearly seventeen hours before giving up. Through much of this time, La Follette sipped a tonic of milk and raw eggs prepared in the Senate dining room. After he had been taken violently ill on the floor, it was discovered that there was enough ptomaine in the mixture to kill a man. Because no one else suffered from eating in the Senate dining room that day, many assumed that La Follette's enemies had tried to kill him.

Debs and Berger

In many ways, Debs resembled a progressive politician. He was a fiery, flamboyant orator, a master of the theatrical and gymnastic style of public speaking that not only was necessary in an age when sound amplification was primitive, but was favored by Americans in their preachers and politicians. He was more a moralist than either an intellectual or politician. He freely admitted that he had little patience with the endless ideological hairsplitting of which other Socialists were quite fond. And Debs' followers worshiped him as progressives worshiped La Follette, Borah, and Roosevelt.

The adulation and loyalty accorded him made him a presidential candidate five times between 1900 and 1920. In 1912, he won almost one million votes, 6 percent of the total.

But Debs differed from the progressives in other ways. He did not seek to smooth over the conflict between classes, but to exhort the working class to take charge. If he was not an ideologue, he nevertheless agreed with the Marxists that the class that produced wealth should decide how that wealth was to be distributed.

Full of hope in 1908, the Socialist party chartered its own train, "the Red Special," to carry Eugene V. Debs on his presidential campaign.

Victor Berger of Milwaukee more clearly linked socialism and progressivism. An Austrian immigrant, middle-class in background, Berger forged an alliance among Milwaukee's large German-speaking population, the labor movement, and the city's reform-minded middle class. His Social Democratic party (a part of Debs' Socialist party) soft-pedaled revolutionary rhetoric and promised Milwaukee honest government and efficient city-owned public utilities. Once, while he and Debs were being interviewed by a journalist, Debs said that capitalists would not be compensated when their factories were taken from them; their "property" had been stolen from working people, and theft would not be rewarded. Berger countered that, no, capitalists would be compensated for their losses. Property might well be theft, but Berger would not frighten his middle-class supporters with loose talk about confiscation.

In 1910, Berger was elected to the House of Representatives, and Socialist candidates for mayor and city council were swept into power in Milwaukee. To radical members of the party, Berger's "sewer socialism," a reference to his emphasis on city ownership of utilities, was nothing more than progressivism. Berger thought otherwise. He insisted that by demonstrating to the American people the Socialists' ability to govern a large city, the Socialist party would win their attention to the revolutionary part of its program.

Labor's Quest for Respectability

Berger also hoped to advance the fortunes of socialism by capturing the American Federation of Labor. Socialists were a large minority in the union movement and a majority among members who were not Roman Catholic. At the A.F.L.'s annual conventions, the Socialists challenged the conservative leadership of Samuel Gompers and several times came close to ousting him from the presidency.

In the end they failed. Presenting a moderate face to the American people was also central to Gompers' strategy for establishing the legitimacy of the labor movement, and his version of moderation included support of progressive capitalism. His glad willingness to cooperate with employers won him many friends among progressives (and some conservatives such as Mark Hanna). In 1905, President Theodore Roosevelt intervened in a coal miners' strike. During the William Howard Taft administration (1909–13), progressives established a Commission on Industrial Violence with a membership that was skewed in a pro-union direction. Progressive Democratic President Woodrow Wilson named Samuel Gompers to several prestigious government posts and appointed a former leader of the A.F.L.'s United Mine Workers, William B. Wilson, to be Secretary of Labor.

Victor L. Berger (1860–1929)

Victor L. Berger was born into a middle-class family in Nieder-Rehbach in the Austro-Hungarian Empire and educated at the universities of Vienna and Budapest. In 1878, he emigrated to the United States, settling briefly in Bridgeport, Connecticut. In 1881, he moved to Milwaukee, which had a large German-speaking population. A schoolteacher, Berger took an active role in the rich ethnic life of the German community, especially in the city's Old World oriented social democratic organizations. By the early 1890s, he was the most prominent Socialist in Milwaukee, and in 1897, he became editor of the *Wisconsin Vorwarts,* the movement's newspaper.

The German bloc was the core of the Milwaukee party, but Berger concluded that in order to succeed, the Socialists had to leave European preoccupations behind and attract old-stock Americans to the movement. In 1895, he converted Eugene V. Debs, the popular and quintessentially American labor leader, to socialism. In 1897, along with Debs and several other regional Socialist leaders, Berger founded the Social Democratic party of America, a broadly based alliance of Marxist, Populist, utopian, and Christian socialist groups. In 1901, Berger helped engineer the alliance with Morris Hillquit of New York that resulted in the formation of the Socialist party of America. In the same year, he also became editor of the *Social Democratic Herald,* the new English-language organ of his Milwaukee party that signaled his concerted campaign to win non-German support in his city.

Berger deeply admired liberal American political institutions, and he was convinced that socialism could triumph in the United States only when Socialists abandoned the notion of violent revolution and won majority support. In Milwaukee, he devised a strategy that became the model for the municipal socialist movement of the early twentieth century. The Milwaukee Social Democratic party deemphasized its ultimate revolutionary goal so as not to frighten off middle-class reformers. In an age of gross municipal corruption, the Berger Socialists offered scrupulously honest and efficient government. They attracted non-Socialist members of the union movement by pledging prolabor legislation and support during strikes. The Socialists even won the support of many businessmen by promising stable labor relations. In one election campaign, Berger boasted that there would be fewer strikes when the Socialists came to power. Finally, by municipalizing public utilities (with generous compensation), Berger sought to demonstrate the workability of socialism as well as his party's competence to govern.

Following this formula, the Milwaukee party grew steadily through the first decade of the century. In 1910, it won a sweeping victory, sending Berger to Congress and electing the mayor and the majority of the city council. Other local parties, molded on Berger's design, won comparable victories in other cities—Butte, Schenectady, Berkeley—thus increasing Berger's prestige in Socialist party councils.

As a member of the party's National Executive Committee, however, Berger was not so flexible as he was in city politics. From the time the party was founded, he fought a running battle with the "revolutionist" left-wing Socialists on the issues of revolutionary militance and the party's relationship with the labor movement. The leftists scorned Berger's immediate program as "sewer socialism," and called for an unequivocally socialist plan. They argued that working for piecemeal reforms strengthened capitalism rather than hastening the day when the Socialists would take control, and they denounced Berger as nothing but a progressive. Berger, never slow to retaliate to criticism, said that the revolutionists' irresponsible

---

The union movement grew in the favorable climate of the Progressive era, but by no means sensationally. Membership in the A.F.L. rose from about 500,000 in 1900 to 1.5 million in 1910, with some 500,000 workers holding cards in independent organizations. This was a pittance among a nonagricultural labor force of almost 20 million.

The "Wobblies"

The most important unions outside the A.F.L. were the cautious and conservative Railway Brotherhoods (of Locomotive Engineers, Firemen, Brakemen, etc.) and the radical Industrial Workers of the World, or, as members were called, "the Wobblies." Founded in 1905 by Socialists and other radicals who were disgusted by Gompers' conservatism and his reluctance to organize un-

skilled workers, the I.W.W. also found friends among progressives, but more often sent chills racing down their spines.

Progressives supported West Coast and wheatbelt Wobblies when, between 1909 and 1913, the hobo members of the union waged a series of "free speech fights" to protect their right to recruit members by speaking from street corner soapboxes. Progressive sensitivity to traditions of personal liberty and common decency was agitated when policemen assigned to destroy the union arrested Wobblies for reading publicly from the Declaration of Independence and the Constitution. In 1912, progressive organizations, particularly women's clubs, helped the I.W.W. win its greatest strike victory among immigrant textile mill workers in Lawrence, Massachusetts. They publicized the horrendous living conditions in Lawrence, lobbied congressmen, and took rhetoric and policies held the party back.

Much more serious was the split between the two groups on the union question. The left wingers considered the A.F.L. irretrievably committed to preserving capitalism and urged the party to support a truly socialist union that would organize the unskilled majority of the work force and work toward the overthrow of the system. After 1905, they advocated an informal alliance between the Socialist party and the Industrial Workers of the World, a revolutionary industrial union that, after 1909, fought and won several well-publicized strikes.

Berger opposed the I.W.W. from the beginning because he feared that it would damage the A.F.L., which, however antisocialist, was a genuine working-class organization. After 1909, he argued that the I.W.W. endorsement of revolution and sabotage alienated the very middle-class reformist elements to whom his faction was appealing with increasing success. In 1913, Berger took the lead in engineering a divorce of the two movements by successfully removing William D. "Big Bill" Haywood from the National Executive Committee. Haywood was the chief spokesman for an alliance between party and union, and Berger forced him out on the grounds that Haywood advocated violent sabotage.

In the wake of Haywood's recall, party membership declined, and in the autumn of 1913, most of the Socialist party's electoral gains of the previous years were lost. In 1916, Berger's long-standing wish to replace Eugene V. Debs with a moderate Socialist as presidential candidate was realized with the nomination of Allen Benson. But despite an increased electorate, Benson won less than two-thirds of Debs's 1912 total.

The next year, the United States entered the world war, and the party revived in Milwaukee and nationally. The only national political body to stand unequivocally against the war, the Socialist party attracted many non-Socialist antiwar voters and thus increased its strength throughout the country. In 1918, Berger won back the congressional seat that he had lost in 1912.

By this time, however, the federal government had moved against the party for its opposition to the war. The *Milwaukee Ledger* (a Socialist daily that had been founded by Berger in 1911) lost its cheap mailing privileges, and several editions were confiscated by the Post Office. Berger was convicted of having violated the Espionage Act of 1917, a law that declared practically all antiwar agitation to be illegal. By a vote of 309 to 1, Congress refused to seat him on this basis, and after Berger won a special election to fill the seat in 1919, again turned him down.

In 1921, the Supreme Court overturned Berger's conviction. In 1923, he finally took his place in Congress and served until 1928, when he was ousted in the Republican landslide of that year. With the 1920s, however, the Socialist party was in disarray. The success of the Bolsheviks in Russia had led to the growth of a largely foreign-born Communist faction in the Socialist party, which, after Berger and Morris Hillquit expelled them in 1919, formed two Communist parties. By 1923, both Communist parties and the now almost completely reformist Socialist party were tiny sects with a combined membership that was smaller than the socialists alone had claimed before 1919.

Anti-Communist himself by this time, Berger drifted slowly but steadily away from socialism. In 1928, he supported Alfred E. Smith for president solely because the Democratic nominee was opposed to Prohibition. On July 16, 1929, Berger was struck by a streetcar in Milwaukee, and he died of his injuries three weeks later.

the children of strikers into their homes, a masterful public-relations ploy.

The capacity of middle-class progressives to back the Wobblies could not, however, go much beyond well-wishing. The Wobblies called loudly and gaily for revolution, precisely what progressives were determined to avoid. Although the I.W.W. officially renounced violence, including violent sabotage, individual members spoke of driving spikes into logs bound for sawmills and throwing hammers into the works of harvesters, threshers, and balers. And, although the first blow was more often thrown by employers than workers, fistfights, riots, and even murder characterized enough Wobbly strikes to besmirch the union's reputation.

Nor were middle-class progressives alone in considering the I.W.W. beyond the pale. No one used fiercer language in denouncing the organization than Samuel Gompers. In 1913, Victor Berger and a prominent New York Socialist, Morris Hillquit, led a movement within the Socialist party that successfully expelled the leader of the I.W.W., William D. "Big Bill" Haywood, from the party's National Executive Committee.

Feminism and Progressivism

Another "-ism" with an ambivalent relationship to the progressive movement was feminism. In 1900, the struggle on behalf of equal rights for women was more than fifty years old. Despite the tireless work of leaders like Elizabeth Cady Stanton and Susan B. Anthony, the victories had been few. In their twilight years at the beginning of the Progressive Era, Stanton and Anthony could look back on liberalized divorce laws, women voters in six Western states, a movement unified for the

Strikers—both men and children workers—march in Lawrence, Massachusetts, 1912.

moment in the National American Woman Suffrage Association, and the initiation of a new generation of leaders including Carrie Chapman Catt and Anna Howard Shaw, a British-born physician.

But the coveted prize, a constitutional amendment that would guarantee women the right to vote, seemed as remote as it had at Seneca Falls in 1848. Most articulate Americans, women as well as men, continued to believe that women's delicacy and fine moral sense made it best that they remain in a separate sphere from men. If women participated in public life, they would be sul-

lied as men had been and lose their vital moral influence in the home.

In fact, when Anthony died in 1906, success was fewer than fifteen years away. The democratic inclinations of the progressives made it increasingly difficult for them to deny the franchise to half the American people. Even progressive leaders who had little personal enthusiasm for the idea of female voters publicly supported the cause.

Changing Strategies

Much more important in accounting for the victory of the suffrage movement was a fundamental shift in its appeal. Under the leadership of Carrie Chapman Catt, the National American Woman Suffrage Association came to terms with progressive prejudices and quietly shelved the comprehensive critique of women's status in American society that the early feminists had developed, including doubts about the institution of marriage. The suffragists also downplayed the traditional argument that women should have the right to vote because they were equal to men in every way.

A few "social feminists" clung to the old principles. Charlotte Perkins Gilman, an independently minded New Englander, argued in *Women and Economics* (1898)

WOBBLIES

Members of the I.W.W. were called Wobblies by both friends and enemies. There are several explanations of the origin of their name; according to one, they were so strike prone that they were "wobbly" workers. The story the I.W.W. favored told of a Chinese restaurant operator in the Pacific Northwest who would give credit only to Wobblies because they could be depended on. When someone asked for a meal on credit, the restaurant owner, unable to pronounce the name of the letter *W*, asked "I-Wobbly-Wobbly?"

that marriage was itself the cause of women's inequality. Alice Paul, a Quaker like many feminists before her, insisted that the suffrage alone was not enough to solve "the woman question."

But most of the middle-class suffragists argued that women should have the right to vote precisely because they were more moral than men. Their votes would purge society of its evils. Not only did the suffragists ingeniously turn the most compelling anti-suffrage argument in their favor, but they told progressives that in allowing women to vote they would be gaining huge numbers of allies. In fact, women were in the forefront of two of the era's most important moral crusades, the struggle against prostitution and the prohibition movement.

White Slavery

To earlier generations, prostitution had been an inevitable evil that could be controlled or ignored by decent people, but not abolished. Most states, counties, and cities had laws against solicitation on the grounds that streetwalking "hookers" were a public nuisance. Somewhat fewer governments declared the quiet sale of sex to be a crime. Even where prostitution was nominally illegal, it was common to tolerate "houses of ill repute" that were discreetly operated (and usually made contributions to worthy causes such as the welfare of the police).

Communities in which men vastly outnumbered women cow towns, mining camps, seaports, migrant farm-worker and logging centers—typically tolerated red-light districts in a corner of town. A stock figure of small-town folklore was the woman on the wrong side of the tracks who sold favors to those sly or bold enough to knock on her door.

In the large cities, prostitution ran the gamut from lushly furnished and expensive brothels for high-society

Under Carrie Chapman Catt, women suffragists emphasized their respectability.

VOTES FOR WOMEN? T.R. SAYS: IT DOES NOT MATTER

"Personally, I believe in woman's suffrage, but I am not an enthusiastic advocate of it, because I do not regard it as a very important matter. I am unable to see that there has been any special improvement in the position of women in those states in the West that have adopted woman's suffrage, as compared to those states adjoining them that have not adopted it. I do not think that giving the women suffrage will produce any marked improvement in the condition of women. I do not believe that it will produce any of the evils feared, and I am very certain that when women as a whole take any special interest in the matter they will have suffrage if they desire it."

swells, such as Sally Stanford's in San Francisco, to "the cribs," tiny cubicles rented by whores who catered to working men. With their pay so low, thousands of New York working women moonlighted as prostitutes at least part of the time. Novelists Stephen Crane (*Maggie: A Girl of the Streets*, 1892) and Upton Sinclair (*The Jungle*) both dealt with the theme of tacitly forced prostitution.

The world's oldest profession had affronted proper people long before the Progressive era. In most places, the middle class was content to declare the trade illegal and then tolerate it out of their sight. Some cities restricted prostitution to neighborhoods far from middle-class residential areas, such as New Orleans's Storyville, San Francisco's Barbary Coast, and Chicago's South of the Loop.

The progressives, spearheaded by women's organizations, determined to wipe out the institution. During the first decade of the twentieth century, most states and innumerable communities passed strict laws against all prostitution and enforced them rigorously. In 1917, prodded by the United States Navy which had a training camp near New Orleans, even storied Storyville, the birthplace of jazz, was officially closed. By 1920, all but a few states had anti-prostitution laws on the books.

The Limits of Progressive Moralism

Action on the federal level was more complicated. Prostitution was clearly a matter for the police powers of the states and localities. However, progressives were so convinced that government held the key to social reform and must act at every level that, in 1910, they joined with some conservatives to put the interstate commerce clause of the Constitution to work in the cause. Senator James R. Mann of Illinois sponsored a bill that struck against the probably exaggerated practice of procurers luring poor girls from one part of the country to become

prostitutes elsewhere. The Mann Act forbade transporting women across state lines "for immoral purposes." It was this law under which the boxer Jack Johnson was prosecuted.

Of course, neither local, state, nor federal law abolished prostitution. The campaign may be the best example of the progressives' excessive faith in the powers of the government. Brothels continued to operate, albeit less openly and probably with more police graft than before. Streetwalkers, previously the most despised and degraded of whores, became the norm because they were less easily arrested. Wealthy men continued to maintain paid mistresses and created the "call girl," a prostitute who stayed at home until "called" by a hotel employee or pimp who worked the streets and hotel lobbies.

Prohibitionism

The nineteenth-century impulse to combat the evils of drink never quite died. Temperance advocates and out-

A prostitute poses for the camera. Ending prostitution became a goal of the Progressives and members of the women's movement in the early 1900s.

right prohibitionists had battled back and forth with the distillers of liquor and with ordinary people who simply enjoyed a cup of good cheer. By 1900, however, anti-alcohol crusaders were emphasizing social arguments over their moral distaste for drunkenness and, in so doing, won widespread progressive support.

The prohibitionists pointed out that the city saloon was often the local headquarters of the corrupt political machines. Close the saloons, the reasoning went, and the bosses would be crippled. Moreover, generally overlooking the fact that poverty caused a widespread drinking problem among the working classes, the prohibitionists argued that the misery of the working classes was the result of husbands and fathers spending their wages on demon rum and John Barleycorn. Because the public bar was then an all-male institution, the temperance movement formed a close alliance with feminists.

Carry Nation of Kansas was one woman who suffered her whole life with a drunken husband and poverty. Beginning in 1900, she launched a campaign of direct action, leading hatchet-wielding women into saloons where, before the bewildered eyes of saloonkeeper and customers, they methodically chopped the place to pieces.

Frances Willard, head of the Woman's Christian Temperance Union, opposed such tactics. She and her followers also entered saloons, but instead of breaking them up, they attempted to shame drinkers by kneeling to pray quietly in their midst. In addition, the W.C.T.U. turned to politics, supporting woman suffrage for its own sake as well as for the purpose of winning the final victory over liquor.

Increasing numbers of progressives adopted the reform. Only in the big cities, mostly in the eastern states, did socially minded politicians like Alfred E. Smith and Robert Wagner of New York actively fight the prohibitionists. The large Roman Catholic and Jewish populations of the cities had no religious tradition against alcohol; on the contrary they used wine as a part of religious observance. Elsewhere, libertarian progressives argued that the government had no right to interfere with the individual decision of whether or not to drink.

Nevertheless, the possibilities of moral improvement, of striking a blow against poverty, and of joining battle against the political manipulations of the big distillers and brewers converted many progressives to prohibition, and in the waning days of the movement (though they were not thought to be waning at the time), they had their way.

For Further Reading

Once again, see Vincent P. DeSantis, *The Shaping of Modern America, 1877–1916* (1973) and Robert H. Wiebe, *The Search for Order, 1880–1920* (1967) for context. William L. O'Neill, *The Progressive Years: America Comes of Age* (1975) is perhaps the most readable survey of the era written in recent years. However, the following general interpretations are also quite valuable: Arthur Ekirch, *Progressivism in Practice* (1974); Lewis L. Gould, *Reform and Regulation: American Politics, 1900–1916* (1978); Otis L. Graham, Jr., *The Great Campaigns: Reform and War in America, 1900–1928* (1971); the appropriate chapters of Richard Hofstadter, *The Age of Reform* (1955); Gabriel Kolko, *The Triumph of Conservatism* (1963); Christopher Lasch, *The New Radicalism in America* (1965); and George E. Mowry, *The Era of Theodore Roosevelt* (1958).

More narrowly focused books about progressives with excellent insights are John D. Buenker, *Urban Liberalism and Progressive Reform* (1973); D. M. Chalmers, *The Social and Political Ideas of the Muckrakers* (1964); Carl M. Degler, *At Odds: Women in the Family in America from the Revolution to the Present* (1980); Louis Filler, *Crusaders for American Liberalism* (1939); Samuel T. Hays, *Conservation and the Gospel of Efficiency: The Progressive Con-*servation Movement, *1890–1920* (1959); David M. Kennedy, *Birth Control in America: The Career of Margaret Sanger* (1970); Jack D. Kirby, *Darkness at the Dawning: Race and Reform in the Progressive South* (1972); Roy Lubove, *The Progressives and the Slums* (1962); George E. Mowry, *The California Progressives* (1951); William L. O'Neill, *Everyone Was Brave: The Rise and Fall of Feminism* (1969); J. T. Patterson, *America's Struggle Against Poverty* (1981); Jean Quandt, *From the Small Town to the Great Community: The Social Thought of Progressive Intellectuals* (1970); James H. Timberlake, *Prohibition and the Progressive Movement, 1900–1920* (1963); James Weinstein, *The Corporate Ideal in the Liberal State, 1900–1918* (1968); and Robert H. Wiebe, *Businessmen and Reform* (1962).

Important biographical studies include John M. Blum, *The Republican Roosevelt* (1954); David McCullough, *Mornings on Horseback* (1981); W. H. Harbaugh, *Power and Responsibility: The Life and Times of Theodore Roosevelt* (1961); R. S. Maxwell, *La Follette and the Rise of Progressivism in Wisconsin* (1956); Henry F. Pringle, *Theodore Roosevelt* (1931); David P. Thelen, *Robert M. LaFollette and the Insurgent Movement* (1976).

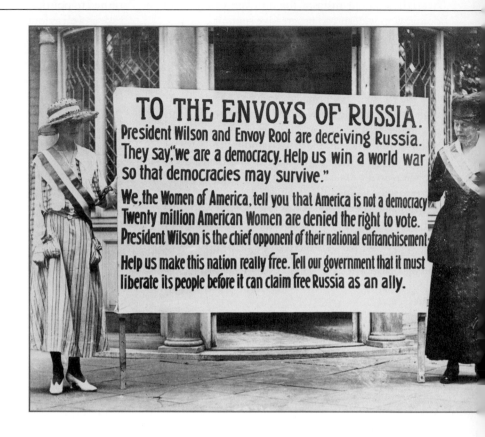

Feminists deliver a message to diplomats from the short-lived liberal democratic government of Russia, 1917.

VICTORS AT ARMAGEDDON

THE PROGRESSIVES IN POWER
1901 - 1916

By 1904, the progressive movement commanded the allegiance of a large bloc of senators and congressmen from both major parties, and the president himself, Theodore Roosevelt. The irony that he, the scion of an old and privileged family, should be the titular leader of a popular protest movement was not lost on T.R. In a letter to the decidedly nonprogressive Senator Chauncey Depew of New York, who was also chairman of the board of directors of the New York Central Railroad, Roosevelt wrote in mock weariness: "How I wish I wasn't a reformer, Oh Senator! But I suppose I must live up to my part, like the Negro minstrel who blackened himself all over!"

Was T.R. also mocking the progressives, and his own sincerity? Perhaps in part. But then, it was not so bizarre that T.R. was willing to use his powers as president to chastize and discipline those powerful industrial capitalists whom he considered to be "malefactors of great wealth." His family's fortune and status were pre-industrial; he was a member of an old American elite that had been slighted and shunted aside by the *nouveax riches* of the late nineteenth century. Moreover, despite the sigh of resignation to duty in the letter to Depew, Roosevelt loved to be in the thick of things. During his nearly eight years in the White House, reform was where the action was.

T.R. TAKES OVER

At first, Roosevelt moved cautiously. He was well aware of the fact that the bosses of the Republican party distrusted him as a "damned cowboy." Mark Hanna openly discussed his interest in the 1904 Republican presidential nomination with party leaders like Tom Platt of New York and Matthew Quay of Pennsylvania. And the Republican machine was beholden to the likes of them who had created it, and not to the young and accidental president.

But no one was to contest T.R.'s claim on party leadership in 1904. Mark Hanna died suddenly in February that year, Matt Quay a short time later. Even had they lived and been hale and hearty, they would have had to step aside for the damned cowboy. In a little more than two years, Roosevelt had left them in the dust, building up an immense personal following and quietly replacing members of the Old Guard in government positions with his own men. Ever graceful in his maneuvers, he eased the McKinley-Hanna men who were mediocrities out of his cabinet, and he won the loyalty of those he kept by giving them an authority and autonomy that they had not enjoyed under McKinley.

Among the McKinley appointees whom he kept in office were Secretary of State John Hay; Secretary of War Elihu Root (who succeeded Hay in the State Department in 1905); Attorney General Philander C. Knox; Secretary of the Interior E. A. Hitchcock; and Secretary of Agriculture James Wilson. All were competent.

Busting Taboos and Trusts

Roosevelt had no fear of ability in his subordinates. He was happy and able to delegate responsibility because

Theodore Roosevelt aggressively enforced antitrust laws. In this cartoon he is depicted as a powerful lion tamer whipping the trusts into shape.

there was no doubt in his or in the public's mind as to who was in charge. Thus, in April 1902, he directed Attorney General Knox, a former corporation lawyer, to have a go at the most powerful corporate organizers in the United States. His target, the Northern Securities Company, had been designed by J. P. Morgan and railroaders Edward H. Harriman and James J. Hill to end struggles for control of the railroads in the northern quarter of the country. Funded by the nation's two richest banks, Northern Securities was a holding company that was patterned after Morgan's United States Steel Corporation.

Morgan was shocked by Roosevelt's prosecution. Under McKinley, the Sherman Antitrust Act had languished, almost unused. In a pained and revealing moment, the great financier wrote to Roosevelt, "If we have done anything wrong, send your man to my man and we can fix it up." The message was not apt to appeal to the president, who read it as an invitation to sit in Morgan's waiting room.

Roosevelt blithely ignored the invitation and Knox

pushed on in the courts. In 1904, they won; the Supreme Court ordered the Northern Securities Company to dissolve, and progressives cheered. When Roosevelt instituted additional antitrust suits, forty in all, of which he won twenty-five, progressives nicknamed him the "trust-buster."

It was an overstatement. Roosevelt did not believe that bigness in business was itself an evil, and he continued to socialize on good terms with the millionaires with whom Knox was contending in the courts. Indeed, in 1907 he allowed Morgan's United States Steel Company to gobble up a major regional competitor, Tennessee Coal and Iron without public statement.

The trust-buster's criteria for determining what made one business combination "good" and another "bad" were vague. In a way, his antitrust suits were drama and symbol. Roosevelt wanted to show big business and the American people that he and the United States government were in charge. In the Tennessee Coal and Iron case, J.P. Morgan had to send his man, hat in hand, to see T.R.'s man, and not vice versa.

The Workingman's Friend

Quite as startling as trust-busting was Roosevelt's personal intervention in the autumn of 1902 in a strike by 140,000 anthracite miners. The men's demands were moderate. They wanted a 20 percent increase in pay, an eight-hour day, and their employers to recognize and negotiate with their union, the United Mine Workers. The mine owners refused to yield on a single point. Theirs was a competitive, unstable business; with so many companies engaged in mining coal, the price of the commodity fluctuated radically and unpredictably. Employers traditionally avoided long-term commitments to anyone—buyers, shippers, or employees.

Most of the coal operators were entrepreneurs of the old hard-nosed school, easy for muckraking reporters to caricature, which they did. Their property was their property and that was that; they would brook no interference in their use of it, least of all by grimy employees. George F. Baer, the ringleader of the operators and more pious than prudent, stirred up a furious public reaction when he told a journalist that he would never deal with

Striking miners, members of the United Mine Workers, parade in their Sunday best during the 1902 coal strike.

the U.M.W. because God had entrusted him with his company's mines.

By way of contrast, union leader John Mitchell was depicted in the progressive press as a moderate, modest, and likable man. T.R., keenly sensitive to public opinion, knew where the applause was to be had. Moreover, Mitchell was a conservative union leader, constantly engaged in a battle with socialists in the U.M.W. Roosevelt was inclined to help him win his factional battle by giving him a boost in his fight with the operators. In October, the president let it be known that if the strike dragged on through the winter with no settlement, he might use federal troops to dispossess the owners and open the mines. Knowing the Rough Rider was capable of so drastic and dangerous an act, the ubiquitous Morgan stepped in and pressured the mine owners to go to Washington to work out a settlement.

The result was a compromise that rather favored the owners. The miners got a 10 percent raise and a nine-hour day; the operators were not required to recognize the U.M.W. as the agent of the workers. (Baer and the others refused even to meet face to face with Mitchell.) Nonetheless, the miners were elated. So were people who counted on coal to ward off winter's cold. But the big winner, as in most of his chosen battles, was Theodore Roosevelt. He had reversed the tradition of using federal troops to help employers break strikes and had forced powerful industrialists to bow to his will on behalf of a "square deal" for workingmen.

Teddy's Great Victory

By 1904, T.R. was basking in the sun of a nation's adulation. He was unanimously nominated and presented with a large campaign chest. The Democrats, hoping to capitalize on the grumbling of some conservatives over the president's actions and remarks about arrogant businessmen, did a complete about face from the party's agrarianism of 1896 and 1900. They nominated a Wall Street lawyer and judge with impeccable social credentials but also a record of sympathy for labor, Alton B. Parker, to oppose him. The urbane but colorless Parker was the antithesis of Boy Bryan and, Democratic bosses hoped, a foil to the histrionic Roosevelt.

Parker was hopelessly stodgy, but even the second most colorful politician in the country would have looked like a cardboard cutout next to T.R. Not even Parker's friends on Wall Street voted for him. If they disliked T.R.'s antitrust adventures, they recognized that Roosevelt hewed to conservative lines in advocating an anti-inflationary money policy and a high tariff, which were of far greater importance to business interests than courtroom spats. J. P. Morgan, recently stung in the Northern Securities case, donated $150,000 to Roosevelt's campaign.

The president won a lopsided 57.4 percent of the vote, more than any candidate since popular totals had been recorded. His 336–140 electoral sweep was the largest since Grant's in 1872, and he did it without the help of the Southern states. Building on the coalition of money and respectability that had been put together by McKinley and Hanna in 1896, T.R. enlarged the Republican majority by appealing to progressives.

THE PRESIDENT AS REFORMER

The only sour note for the Republicans in a giddy election week was the remarkable showing of the Socialist party candidate, Eugene V. Debs. His 400,000 votes amounted to only 3 percent of the total, but represented an astonishing fourfold increase over his vote in 1900. Roosevelt did not like it either. Increasingly after 1904, he seized every opportunity—and created more than a few—to denounce anticapitalist radicals.

Perhaps his most gratuitous attack followed the arrest and illegal extradition late in 1905 of Charles Moyer and Big Bill Haywood, the leaders of the militant Western Federation of Miners. Charged with murder in Idaho, the two radicals were, in effect, kidnapped by authorities in Denver, Colorado. Roosevelt shrugged off the irregularity of the arrest because the two were "undesirable citizens." Moyer and Haywood's lawyer, Clarence Darrow, justifiably complained that with the president of the United States making such statements, a fair trial was not likely. (Nevertheless, both men were acquitted.)

At the same time he assailed the Socialists, Roosevelt set out to co-opt them by unleashing a whirlwind of reform. He was determined to eliminate the abuses that gave the Socialists their easiest targets.

The Railroads Derailed

As they had been for thirty years, the railroads remained a focus of popular resentment. The freewheeling arrogance of many directors and the vital role of transportation in the national economy preoccupied progressives at every level of government. Prodded by regional leaders, most notably Senator Robert La Follette, Roosevelt plunged into a long, bitter struggle with the railroad companies. In 1906, he won passage of the Hepburn Act. This law authorized the Interstate Commerce Commission to set maximum rates that railroads might charge their customers and forbade them to pay rebates to big shippers. This prohibition had been enacted before but had not been effectively enforced; the Hepburn Act gave the I.C.C. some teeth. More than any of T.R.'s previous actions, it blasted the railroaders' traditional immunity from government interference.

Also in 1906, Congress passed an act that held railroads liable to employees who suffered injuries on the job. By European standards, it was a mild compensation law, but in the United States, it marked a sharp break with precedent, which held employees responsible for most of their injuries.

Purer Food

Affecting more people, and thereby making for better headlines, was the Pure Food and Drug Act and the Meat Inspection Act, both signed in 1906, that eliminated adulteration of foods (by large processors), enforced stringent sanitary standards on them, and put the lid on the patent-medicine business, which marketed dangerous and addictive drugs as "feel-good" nostrums.

By requiring food processors to label their products with all ingredients used in making them, and providing hefty penalties for violators, the Pure Food and Drug Act eliminated sometimes toxic and often worthless preservatives and fillers from canned, bottled, and sacked foodstuffs. The Meat Inspection Act provided for federal inspection of meat-packing plants to eliminate the abuses that Upton Sinclair had detailed so gruesomely in *The Jungle*.

Big meat packers like Armour, Swift, Wilson, and Cudahy grumbled about the federal inspectors, notebooks in hand, puttering about their abattoirs. But, in time, they learned that meat inspection worked in their favor and to the detriment of smaller regional slaughterhouses. That is, with their greater resources, the big meat packers were able , however grudgingly, to comply with the federal standards. By way of contrast, smaller companies, able to stay in business only by slashing costs at every turn, found the expense of sanitation in an inherently gory business to be beyond their means.

The big packers actually made advertising hay of the inspection stamps on their products: the government approved of them! Small companies closed their doors or restricted their sales to the states in which they were located. (Like all national reforms, federal meat inspection applied only to firms involved in interstate commerce.) Some progressives were not pleased to be helping big business against small, but T.R. was not one of them. It was not bigness itself to which he objected, but irresponsibility in business.

War on Drugs

Proportionately, there were probably more drug addicts in the United States at the turn of the century than in the 1980s. Some were hooked on opium or morphine and had minimal difficulty meeting their needs at unregulated pharmacies. Others were addicted to any of the various patent medicines advertising themselves as cure-alls. Even Lydia Pinkham's Vegetable Compound, decorously packaged and aimed in fine print at ladies suffering from "female complaints" was a rather strong alcoholic elixir laced liberally with opiates.

The Pure Food and Drug Act, which restricted the use of addictive drugs and required labeling of ingredients, undercut the patent medicine business. Soft drink companies were also affected, for some, including the gigantic Coca-Cola Company of Atlanta, had used a by-product of cocaine processing in their beverages to give it a "kick." Coca-Cola actually introduced caffeine as a stimulant as early as 1902 but, with the passage of federal drug legislation in 1906, was able—like the big meat packers—to advertise its "purity."

Resources in Jeopardy

Theodore Roosevelt and his progressive allies were not always far-seeing. Many of their enactments were the fruit of passionate impulse or playing to their constituents. In their campaign to conserve natural resources, however, they looked to the distant future and created monuments for which they are quite rightfully honored.

As a lifelong outdoorsman, T.R. loved camping, riding, hiking, climbing, and hunting. As a historian, he was more sensitive than most of his contemporaries to the role of the wilderness in forging the American character. He actively sought and gained the friendship of John Muir, the adopted Californian and Alaskan who had founded the Sierra Club in 1892. Muir's interest in nature was aesthetic, cultural, and spiritual. He wanted to protect from development such magnificent areas of untouched wilderness as Yosemite Valley, which he had helped to establish as a National Park in 1890. Roosevelt shared these sentiments.

The motives of progressive conservationists such as T.R.'s tennis partner and America's first trained forester,

---

AMERICAN ESSENCE

Coca-Cola, which William Allen White called "the sublimated essence of all that American stands for," had its beginning as a kind of health food. An Atlanta druggist concocted it in 1886 as an alternative to alcohol. Within a year, a pious Methodist named Asa G. Candler purchased all rights to "Coke" for $2,300 and sold it as a "brain tonic," promoting its kick. Indeed, until 1902, Coke was made with coca leaves and may have been addictive; Southerners called it "dope." Candler's advertising was certainly addictive. By 1908, the Coca-Cola Company had plastered 2.5 million square feet of billboard and walls with posters. By 1911, more than a million dollars a year was spent on promoting the elixir.

Gifford Pinchot of Pennsylvania, were somewhat different. While by no means oblivious to the cultural and aesthetic values of wilderness, Pinchot's major concern was protecting forests and other natural resources from rapacious exploiters interested only in short-term profits. He wanted to ensure that future generations of Americans would have their share of timber and other nonrenewable natural resources such as minerals, coal, and oil to draw on, as well as grasslands, and water for drinking and generating power.

Roosevelt had good reason to worry about the nation's natural resources. Lumbermen in the Great Lakes states had already mowed down once endless forests, moved on, and left the land behind them to useless scrub and shoddy. Western ranchers put too many cattle on delicate grasslands, turning them into deserts. Coal and phosphate mining companies and drillers for oil thought in terms of open account books and not of the fact that, in a century, the United States could run out of these vital resources. Virtually no one in extractive industries worried that they were destroying watersheds vital to urban water supplies, polluting rivers, and sending good soil into the sea.

Americans had always been reckless with the land, none more so than the pioneers of legend. But there was a big difference between what a few frontiersmen could do to it with axes and horse-drawn plows and the potential for destruction of irresponsible million-dollar corporations.

Conservation

The National Forest Reserve, today's National Forest System, dates from 1891, when Congress empowered the president to withhold forests in the public domain from private use. Over the first ten years of the law, Presidents Harrison, Cleveland, and McKinley had declared 46 million acres of virgin woodland off limits to loggers without government permission.

Enforcement had been desultory until, prodded by Pinchot, Roosevelt began to prosecute "timber pirates," who raided public lands and cattlemen who abused government-owned grasslands. Within a few years, Roosevelt added 125 million acres to the national forests, as well as reserving 68 million acres of coal deposits, almost 5 million acres of phosphate beds (vital to production of munitions), a number of oil fields, and 2,565 sites suitable for the construction of dams for irrigation and generation of electrical power.

Progressives cheered. Some of the "multiple uses" to which the national forests were dedicated—recreation, preservation—won the plaudits of groups like the Sierra Club. Others—flood control, irrigation, development of hydroelectric power—pleased social planners. The prin-

Theodore Roosevelt and Sierra Club founder John Muir in Yosemite National Park.

ciple of "sustained yield," managing forests to ensure an adequate supply of lumber into the indefinite future, appealed to the big lumber companies with their huge capital investments, and encouraged them to employ foresters on their own lands.

In the West, however, an angry opposition developed. Cattlemen, clear-cut loggers, and private power companies banded together in an anti-conservation movement that succeeded, in 1907, in attaching a rider to an agricultural appropriations bill that passed Congress. It forbade the president to create any additional national forests in six Western states. Roosevelt had no choice but to sign the bill; the Department of Agriculture could not have functioned otherwise. But he had one last go at what he called the "predatory interests." Before he wrote his name on the bill, he reserved 17 million acres of forest land in the interdicted states.

Concern for the Farm

Theodore Roosevelt's conservation campaign remains one of the single most important contributions of his presidency. Nevertheless, his policies could hurt ordinary people as well as special interests. For example, he and Pinchot helped Los Angeles, the burgeoning metropolis of southern California, to grab the entire Owens River, 300 miles to the north, for its water supply. The president regarded the mammoth construction project, now known as the Los Angeles Aqueduct, as a showpiece of resource development and public control of electrical power. In the process, however, he helped to destroy the fertile Owens Valley. Then a land of prosperous, self-reliant small farmers, it would become by 1930 an arid region of sagebrush, dust storms, and tarantulas.

Had Roosevelt lived to see its results, he might well have regretted his action. He was a devotee of the family farm as one of the essential American institutions. He established the Country Life Commission, which lamented the steady disappearance of this way of life and submitted to Congress a number of recommendations designed to help family farmers. Conservative congressmen who had soured on their progressive president refused even to publish the report.

The Reformer Retires

In two major speeches in 1908, Roosevelt called for a comprehensive, even radical, program that included federal investigation of major labor disputes and close regulation of both the stock market and businesses that were involved in interstate commerce. But Congress sidestepped virtually all of his proposals because the damned cowboy had become a "lame duck." It was a presidential election year and, four years earlier, celebrating his great victory in 1904, T.R. had impulsively declared that "a wise custom which limits the President to two terms regards the substance and not the form, and under no circumstances will I be a candidate for or accept another nomination." Having served three and a half years of McKinley's term, Roosevelt had defined himself as a two-term president.

In 1908, he almost certainly regretted his vow. Except, perhaps, for Calvin Coolidge and Ronald Reagan, Theodore Roosevelt relished his job, and flourished in it, as no other president has. Unlike Coolidge and Reagan, who treated the presidency as a personal honor, he was a worker and a marvelous success. He was not yet 50 years old in 1908 and as popular as ever with the voters. He would undoubtedly have won reelection had he been willing to forget his pledge not to run.

But he kept his word and settled for hand-picking his successor, which no president had been able to do since Andrew Jackson in 1836. That William Howard Taft, then Secretary of War, was not the man whom either conservative or progressive Republicans would have chosen indicates just how high Roosevelt was riding.

A CONSERVATIVE PRESIDENT IN A PROGRESSIVE ERA

Taft never would have been nominated without Roosevelt's blessing. He would not have dreamed of running for president. Regularly in his correspondence he dashed

William Howard Taft on a Republican campaign banner of 1908.

off the exclamation "I hate politics!" and he meant it. He was a lifelong functionary, not a politician. His only elective post prior to 1908 was as a judge in Ohio. Taft remembered that job as the most congenial he had ever held, for his temperament was judicial. Slow to think, sober, cautious, reflective, dignified, Taft worked well in a study, but he was no showman.

Amidst a people who savored Roosevelt's gymnastic style, Taft's very body militated against him. He weighed over 300 pounds, and was truly at ease only when he settled into a swivel chair behind a desk or sank into an overstuffed couch with other easygoing men. His single form of exercise, golf, did not help his image; batting a little white ball around an oversize lawn was considered a sissy's game in the early twentieth century.

Taft was no reactionary. He had loyally supported Roosevelt's reforms, and T.R. calculated that he, more than anyone else, would carry out the Square Deal. So did other progressives. They supported him, as did the conservative wing of the Republican party. Anyone was preferable to the man whom they had begun to refer to privately as "the mad messiah."

The Election of 1908

The election was an anticlimax. The Democrats returned to William Jennings Bryan as their candidate, but the thrill was gone. The Boy Orator of the Platte, no longer young, was shopworn beyond his years. He had grown jowls and a paunch as penance for his lifelong vulnerability to the deadly sin of gluttony, and he was rapidly losing his hair.

Moreover, his loyal supporters, the staple farmers of the Midwest, were no longer struggling to survive. They were beginning to dress like the townsmen they had jostled in 1896 and to build substantial homes. Even the issue of 1900, imperialism, was dead. Taft, who had served as American governor of the Philippines, could claim credit for having transformed the anti-American Filipinos, whom he called his "little brown brothers," into a placid and apparently content colonial population. Puerto Rico was quieter. Hawaiians did the hula for increasing numbers of American tourists. Central America simmered but the specter of American power kept the lid on. Thousands of men were digging their way across Panama under American direction, thrilling the nation.

The upshot was that a lethargic Bryan won a smaller percentage of the popular vote than in either of his previous tries. The Socialist party was also disappointed in the results. Bubbling with optimism at the start of the campaign, they chartered a private train, the "Red Special," on which candidate Debs crisscrossed the country. The crowds were big and enthusiastic. But Debs's vote was only 16,000 higher than in 1904 and represented a smaller percentage of the total. It appeared that Roosevelt's tactic of undercutting the socialist threat with a comprehensive reform program had worked.

Taft Blunders

Taft lacked both the political skills and the zeal to keep the campaign going. For example, even though he initiated 90 antitrust suits during his four years as president, twice as many as Roosevelt had launched in seven and a half years, no one complimented him as a trustbuster. Taft had managed to alienate the progressives immediately after taking office when he stumbled over an obstacle that T.R. had danced around quite nimbly, the tariff.

In 1909, duties on foreign goods were high, set at an average 46.5 percent of the value of imports by the Dingley Tariff of 1897. Republican conservatives insisted that this rate was necessary in order to protect the jobs of American factory workers and to encourage industrial investment by capitalists. Some Midwestern progressives disagreed. They believed that American industry was strong enough to stand up to European manufacturers in a fair competition. To maintain the Dingley rates was to subsidize excessive corporate profits by allowing manufacturers to set their prices inordinately high. Farmers were twice stung because the European nations, except Great Britain, retaliated against the Dingley Tariff by levying high duties on American agricultural products. Ominously, in the election of 1908, several Western states that had supported Roosevelt returned to the Democratic column.

T.R. had let Republican conservatives have their way on the tariff, placating (or distracting) progressives by pounding the tub on other reforms. By 1909, evasion was no longer possible, and Taft called Congress into special session for the purpose of tariff revision. The House of Representatives drafted a reasonable reduction of rates in the Payne bill. In the Senate, however, Nelson Aldrich of Rhode Island, a trusty ally of industrial capitalists, engineered 800 amendments to what became the Payne-Aldrich Act. On most important commodities, the final rate was higher than under the Dingley Tariff.

Taft was in a bind. Politically, he was committed to lower rates. Personally, however, he was more comfortable with the aristocratic Aldrich and the five corporation lawyers in his cabinet than with low-tariff men in the Senate, who were Democrats or excitable Republican progressives like La Follette and Jonathan Dolliver of Iowa. After equivocating, Taft worked out what he thought was a compromise in the Roosevelt tradition. The conservatives got their high tariff but agreed to a 2 percent corporate income tax and a constitutional amendment that legalized a personal income tax. (It was ratified in 1913 as the Sixteenth Amendment.) Instead of emphasizing the progressive aspects of this arrangement, as T.R. surely would have done, Taft described the Payne-Aldrich Act as "the best tariff that the Republican party ever passed."

The Insurgents

This angered the Midwestern Republican progressives, especially after Taft came out in favor of a trade treaty with Canada that threatened to dump Canadian crops on the American market. But they broke with the new president only when he sided with the reactionary Speaker of the House of Representatives, Joseph G. Cannon of Illinois, against them.

"Uncle Joe" Cannon offended the progressive Republicans on several counts. He was so hidebound a conservative as to be a stereotype. As Speaker of the House and chairman of the House Rules Committee, he put progressives on unimportant committees and loaded the meaningful ones with Old Guard friends. Finally, while the progressives inclined to be highly moralistic, even priggish in manner, Uncle Joe was a crusty tobacco chewer, a hard drinker who was not infrequently drunk, and a champion foulmouth.

The proper Taft also found Cannon's company unpleasant. However, the president believed in party loyalty, and when a number of Midwestern Republican progressives, calling themselves Insurgents, voted with Democrats to strip Cannon of his near-dictatorial power, Taft joined with the Speaker to deny the Insurgents access to party money and patronage in the midterm election of 1910. The result was a Democratic victory and Cannon was out of the speakership, never to return.

Pinchot Forces a Break

It is impossible to say how Theodore Roosevelt would have handled the quarrel between Cannon and the Insurgents. But he assuredly would not have done what Taft did in a dispute between Secretary of the Interior Richard A. Ballinger and Chief Forester Gifford Pinchot.

When Ballinger released to private developers a number of hydroelectric sites that Pinchot had persuaded Roosevelt to reserve, Pinchot protested to Taft and won the president's grudging support. However, when Pinchot leaked his evidence against Ballinger to *Collier's* magazine, which was still in the muckraking business, Taft fired him. This may have been exactly what Pinchot wanted. He acted as if he were prepared, almost immediately booking passage to Italy, where his friend and patron, former president Roosevelt, was vacationing. Pinchot brought with him an indictment of Big Bill Taft as a traitor to the cause of reform.

Enter Stage Left the Conquering Hero

Roosevelt was having a bully time on his extended world tour. He had left the country shortly after Taft's inauguration to give his successor an opportunity to function outside his predecessor's aura. First Roosevelt traveled to East Africa, where he shot a bloody swath through the still abundant big game of Kenya and Tanganyika (Tanzania). He bagged over 3,000 animals, a good many of which he had stuffed for the trophy room of his home at Oyster Bay, Long Island.

Then he went to Europe to bask in an adulation that was scarcely less fierce than he enjoyed at home. He hobnobbed with aristocrats and politicians, who thought of him as the ultimate American, much as Benjamin Franklin had been considered in eighteenth-century France. Roosevelt topped off his year-long junket by representing the United States at the funeral of King Edward VII, shining in the greatest collection of royalty ever assembled.

And yet, something was missing. Roosevelt longed for the hurly-burly of politics, and he was all too willing to believe Pinchot's accusations. When he returned to the United States in June 1910, he exchanged only the curtest greetings with the president. He spoke widely on behalf of Republican congressional candidates, at first playing down the split between regulars (conservatives) and Insurgents (progressives). Then, at Osawatomie, Kansas, in September 1910, Roosevelt proclaimed what he labeled the "New Nationalism," a comprehensive program for further reform. To Republican conservatives, it was frighteningly radical.

Among other proposals, Roosevelt called for woman suffrage, a federal minimum wage for women workers, abolition of child labor, strict limitations on the power of courts to issue injunctions in labor disputes, and a national social-insurance scheme that resembled present-day Social Security. He struck directly at Taft's policies by demanding a commission that would set tariff rates "scientifically" rather than according to political pressures. He supported the progressive initiative, recall, and referendum, including a new twist, a referendum on judicial decisions. This was enough in itself to aggravate the legalistic Taft, but in demanding a national presidential-primary law under which the people, and not professional politicians, would make party nominations, Roosevelt also hinted that he was interested in running for the presidency again.

Challenging Taft

Taft was not the only politician who worried about Roosevelt's presidential plans. Robert La Follette had been preparing to seek the Republican presidential nomination in 1912, and believed he had a chance to defeat Taft, that is, if Roosevelt did not also run. Little as he liked doing it, he sent mutual friends to ask Roosevelt his intentions, implying that he would drop out if T.R. was running. Roosevelt responded that he was not interested in the White House. In January 1911, La Follette organized the Progressive Republican League to promote his candidacy.

Most progressive Republicans supported La Follette, including Roosevelt backers who not so secretly hoped that their real hero would change his mind. In fact, Roosevelt was itching to run. When, in March 1912, La Follette collapsed from exhaustion during a speech, Roosevelt announced with unseemly haste, "My hat is in the ring."

La Follette was not seriously ill, and he never forgave T.R. for having, as he believed, used him as a stalking-horse. But "Fighting Bob" was no match for the old master when it came to stirring up party activists, and his campaign fell apart. Roosevelt swept most of the thirteen state primary elections, winning 278 conven-

NOTABLE PEOPLE

THE FATHER OF THE AMUSEMENT PARK: GEORGE C. TILYOU, 1862–1914

George C. Tilyou was born to Irish-American parents in 1862. When he was three years old, his father leased a lot on the beach in the then independent community of Coney Island for $35 a year. It was a brilliantly timed act. The end of the Civil War was the signal for the runaway growth of resorts in the United States, and Coney Island was strategically located, far from the congestion of New York City but close enough to be convenient for a stay of a few days. The wealthy came first, sometimes by yacht, but also middle-class people to whom Newport, Rhode Island, and Palm Beach, Florida, were just names. Tilyou's hotel, the Surf House, catered to the middling sort. In fact, because Tilyou, Sr., was active in Democratic party politics, at any time his hostelry was likely to be filled with ward heelers and other political bosses from Manhattan and Brooklyn.

So George Cornelius Tilyou grew up, as they said at Coney, with sand in his shoes. Like two generations of Coney natives, he found it difficult to leave the place, and when he did, as on a wedding trip to the Columbian Exposition in Chicago in 1893, it was to pick up ideas for how to develop the Beach as a resort.

It developed as a resort for the middle and working classes, soon abandoned by the yachting and horsey sets, and Tilyou recognized the opportunities in providing mass, cheap entertainment. He was one of the first and by far the most successful operators of amusement parks, as shrewd a psychologist as Phineas T. Barnum and, when he died, a rich man.

Tilyou's first venture into the vacation business came in 1876 when the Centennial Exposition in Philadelphia attracted people from all over the nation to the east coast.

Calculating that they had money to throw away, the 14-year-old Tilyou filled old medicine bottles with sea water and cigar boxes with Coney beach sand which he sold for 25 cents each. He made enough from dubious but classic resort "gifts" with which to dabble in beachfront real estate. The township did not sell land on the beach but, instead, leased it to people who were part of the political machine, who then sublet choice business locations to others, sometimes at extraordinary profits. Because of his contacts, Tilyou was able to open a theater that featured some of the leading vaudeville acts of the era.

Then he made what appeared to be a fatal mistake. He broke with the political boss of Coney, John Y. McKane, who protected brothels and illegal gambling dens and organized a party devoted to the policy that Coney's future rested on becoming a wholesome family resort. Tilyou denounced McKane for his grafting and when the boss weathered the attack, Tilyou found himself shut out of the profitabe leasing deals.

In 1893, however, McKane was jailed for stuffing ballot boxes and Tilyou was back in business. In that same year he discovered the Ferris wheel at the Chicago World's Fair and the young impresario's career took off.

The Ferris wheel was the hit of the fair. It was 250 feet in diameter, almost as high when it was mounted as a football field is long. Suspended on the gigantic circle were 36 "cars," like railroad carriages, each of which held 60 people. The most nominal admission fee promised tremendous profits.

Although he was on his honeymoon, Tilyou was obsessed with the fantastic toy and only briefly disconcerted when he learned that its inventor had already sold it. He

---

tion delegates to Taft's 48 and La Follette's 36. If La Follette was beaten, however, the suddenly aroused Taft was not, and he had a powerful weapon in his arsenal.

Taft controlled the party organization. As president, he appointed people to thousands of government jobs, wedding their careers to his own success. In the Republican party, this power of the patronage was particularly important in the Southern states, where the party consisted of little more than professional officeholders, including some blacks, who made their living as postmasters, customs collectors, agricultural agents, and the like. While the Republicans won few congressional seats and fewer electoral votes in the South, a substantial bloc of delegates to Republican conventions spoke with a Dixie drawl. They were in Taft's pocket and, along with Northern and Western party regulars they vastly out-numbered the delegates Roosevelt had won in the primaries.

Consequently, when the convention voted on whether Taft or Roosevelt would be awarded 254 dis-

puted seats, Taft delegates won 235 of them. Roosevelt's supporters shouted "Fraud!" and walked out. They formed the Progressive party, or, as it was nicknamed for the battle with the Republican elephant and the Democratic donkey, the Bull Moose party. (In a backhanded reference to La Follette's allegedly poor health and Taft's obesity, Roosevelt had said that he was "as strong as a bull moose.")

DEMOCRATIC PARTY PROGRESSIVISM

In one piece, the Republican party was unambivalently the nation's majority party, as four successive presidential elections had demonstrated. Split in two, however, the G.O.P. was vulnerable and the Democrats smelled victory. When the convention assembled in Baltimore, contracted with Ferris to build another for Coney. It was only half the size of the original, 125 feet in diameter with 12 cars holding 36 people each but the sign Tilyou erected back home in Coney Island was: "ON THIS SITE WILL BE ERECTED THE WORLD'S LARGEST FERRIS WHEEL!" Tilyou was making money before it was built. He sold concessions around it to various vendors, including one to a purveyor of a frankfurter sausage on a white milk roll, the first hot dog. Then Tilyou built a number of other "amusements," at first simple gravity devices such as giant sliding boards and seesaws but soon enough the electrically powered forerunners of devices still active on boardwalks and at fairs today. From another Coney entrepreneur, Paul Boyton, Tilyou copied the idea of fencing in a large "amusement park" and charging a single admission fee. Coney's clientele did not have the means for extravagant spending; better to commit them to a whole day at Steeplechase Park where they would have to buy their food and other extras rather than having them wander over to Steeplechase's competitors, Luna Park and Dreamland.

Steeplechase Park opened in 1897. Its centerpiece was a gravity driven "horse race" ride imported from England. People mounted wooden horses—a beau and his belle could ride on the same one—which rolled on tracks over a series of "hills" and entered the central pavillion at the Park where, upon exiting, the customers were mildly abused by a clown and costumed dwarf. The biggest hit of the Steeplechase was the jet of compressed air which shot out of the floor, blowing young ladies' skirts into the air amidst great shrieking and guffawing.

Innocent sexual horseplay was the idea in many of the mechanical amusements Tilyou constructed. Airjets were everywhere. Other amusements were designed to throw young ladies in such a position that their ankles were exposed or they landed in the laps of their escorts or, perhaps, someone whom they were interested in meeting. In an age when polite society was warily trying to come to terms with sex, dwelling on it through romantic euphemisms in popular songs, Tilyou's formula worked. For a time after the turn of the century, Steeplechase Park lost ground to newer amusement parks, Luna Park (featuring "a trip to the moon") and Dreamland, where holidaymakers could stroll through the streets of an Egyptian city, a Somali village, among Philippine headhunters, or see the eruption of Mount Pelee, the Johnstown flood, the Galveston tidal wave, or other natural disasters.

But it was Tilyou who really had the sand in his shoes. When Steeplechase Park burned to the ground in 1907—every wooden Coney Island attraction burned at one time or another—he simply hung up a sign:

I have troubles today that I didn't have yesterday.
I had troubles yesterday that I have not today.
On this site will be erected shortly a better, bigger, greater Steeplechase Park.

Admission to the Burning Ruins—10 cents.

Tilyou also built Steeplechase Pier in Atlantic City, a New Jersey oceanfront town that competed with Coney. He died in 1914, only 52 years of age. Coney's Steeplechase Park closed in 1967.

---

there was an abundance of would-be nominees ready to leap into the breach. As at the Republican convention, but for a rather different reason, the key to winning the party's presidential nomination lay in the Southern state delegations.

Because the South was "solid" in delivering electoral votes to the Democratic column, it held a virtual veto power over the nomination. The old two-thirds rule, so important in shaping Democratic party policy before the Civil War, had been reinstituted after it. In order to be nominated, a Democrat needed the votes of two-thirds of the delegates, and no one could approach that total if the Southern delegates opposed him as a group. A candidate with the Southern delegates solidly behind him had a handsome head-start on the nomination.

Democratic Hopefuls

In 1912, none of the leading candidates was offensive to the South, and each had Southern supporters; thus the usual Southern bloc was split. William Jennings Bryan was still popular with Southerners, and he was interested. As a three-time loser, however, he was not a very attractive candidate. Bryan's only hope was a deadlocked convention when he might be selected as a compromise candidate.

Oscar Underwood of Alabama was another minor hopeful; he commanded the support of the Southern "Bourbon" conservatives, but for that reason he was unacceptable to Southern progressives, who might more accurately be described as Populists who had learned to preach racism along with attacks on big business. Some progressives supported Judson Harmon of Ohio. Others backed Champ Clark, the "Old Hound Dawg" of Missouri, which was as much a Southern as a Western state. In fact, Clark went into the convention confident of winning. The man who left it a winner, however, was New Jersey governor Woodrow Wilson, who was nominated on the forty-sixth ballot.

A Moral, Unbending Man

Wilson was a Southerner himself; he had been born in Virginia and had practiced law in Georgia as a young man. He had abandoned the law, however, earned a Ph.D. degree, and ended up as a professor of political science at Princeton University. In 1902, he had been named president of Princeton, the first non-minister to hold that post at the still strongly Presbyterian school.

And yet, Wilson had more than a little of the Presbyterian clergyman in him. His father and both grandfathers had been parsons. So was his wife's father. He had been raised to observe an unbending Calvinist morality, and his sensitivity to the struggle between good and evil in the world was reflected in an ascetic, lean figure and a sharply chiseled, thin-lipped face. With his family and a few intimate friends, Wilson was fun-loving and playful, a fan of baseball and the cinema, liable to erupt in horseplay with his daughters, who adored him. Publicly, he was formal, sometimes even icy. A less talented man with such a personality would never have risen half so high as Wilson did.

In fact, his meteoric rise in politics was almost accidental. In 1910, he was merely an honored educator, the president of an Ivy League university. He had transformed the college from an intellectually lazy finishing school where rich young men made social contacts into an institution that commanded intellectual respect. But Wilson's stubbornness caught up with him in a rather trivial matter. He tried to close down Princeton's "eating clubs," exclusive student associations much like fraternities, and clashed with trustees and alumni dedicated to their preservation.

When he was offered the Democratic nomination for governor of New Jersey, he quit academic life. To everyone's surprise except, perhaps, Wilson's, he won the governorship in the traditionally Republican state, and the upset made him a national figure overnight. He was less social reformer than an honest-government progressive and set about cleaning up the state bureaucracy and the Democratic party. Like Teddy Roosevelt in New York a decade before, Wilson was soon at odds with the bosses of his own party in New Jersey. They were delighted when he decided to seek the presidency. Ironically, in terms of what was to follow, he offered himself to the party as a middle-of-the-road alternative to William Jennings Bryan and Champ Clark, a conservative.

The Campaign of 1912

In fact, Wilson's "New Freedom," as he called his program, was a decidedly less ambitious blueprint for reform than was Roosevelt's "New Nationalism." Wilson emphasized states' rights to the extent that he opposed the Progressive party's comprehensive social program as

WILSONIAN HORSEPLAY

Stern and forbidding in public, Woodrow Wilson's private personality was rather the opposite. On the morning after his wedding to his second wife in 1915, he was seen in a White House corridor doing a dance and singing, "Oh, you beautiful doll." His daughters by his first wife, Margaret, Jessie, and Eleanor, certainly showed no signs of moralistic browbeating. One of their amusements in the White House was to join tourists who were being shown around by guides and make loud remarks about the homeliness and vulgarity of the president's daughters.

strongly as Taft did. He considered Roosevelt's proposals to augur a dangerous expansion of government powers.

The two men differed even more sharply on the question of the trusts. Whereas T.R. had concluded that consolidation, even monopoly, was inevitable in a modern industrial society, and that the federal government should supervise and even direct the operations of the big corporations in the public interest, Wilson condemned this vision as "a partnership between the government and the trusts." Wilson believed that competition in business was still possible in modern America. In his view, the government's task was to play watchdog over business, ensuring and restoring free competition by breaking up the trusts. In 1912, he opposed the huge, permanent government apparatus that Roosevelt endorsed.

With the Republican organization in tatters and Taft practically dropping out of the race, it would have been difficult for Wilson to have lost the election. Nevertheless, he campaigned tirelessly and skillfully. Articulate,

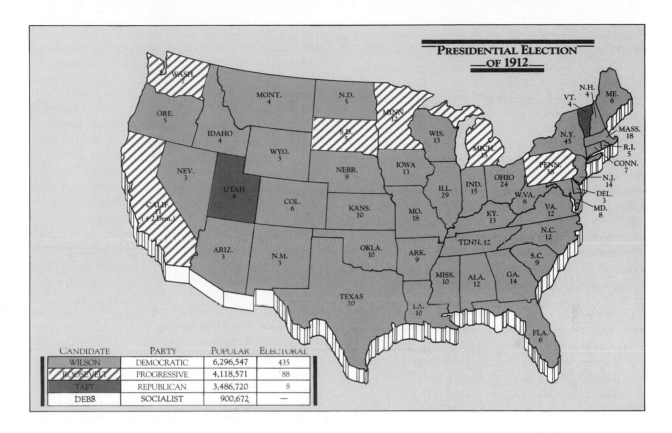

PRESIDENTIAL ELECTION —OF 1912—

CANDIDATE	PARTY	POPULAR	ELECTORAL
WILSON	DEMOCRATIC	6,296,547	435
ROOSEVELT	PROGRESSIVE	4,118,571	88
TAFT	REPUBLICAN	3,486,720	8
DEBS	SOCIALIST	900,672	—

as a college professor is supposed to be, Wilson was also exciting—as few college professors are. Lifelong dreams of winning public office flowered in eloquent speeches that left no doubt that the Presbyterian schoolmaster was a leader.

Wilson won only 41.9 percent of the popular vote but won by a landslide in the electoral college, 435 votes to Roosevelt's 88 and Taft's 8. Eugene V. Debs, making his fourth race as the Socialist party nominee, won 900,000 votes, 6 percent of the total. The big jump after four years of a conservative president seemed to indicate that it was necessary to reform in order to stifle the socialist challenge. Taft, the only conservative candidate, won but 23.2 percent of the total vote.

Tariffs and Taxes

T.R. had usually gotten his way by outflanking Congress, interpreting the president's constitutional powers in the broadest possible terms. Taft had deferred to congressional leaders, virtually collapsing before the most persuasive of them. Wilson's style was to act as a prime minister. He was not a member of Congress, as the British prime minister is a member of the House of Commons, but he could and did address Congress personally as though he were. He was the first president to appear

personally before Congress with his program since John Adams. Adams's successor, Thomas Jefferson, had suffered from a stammer and had set the precedent of communicating with Congress only through written messages.

Wilson's brief address was aimed less at persuading congressmen than at inspiring their constituents to put pressure on them, and it worked. A number of Democratic senators who had been dragging their feet on tariff revision fell into line. The Underwood-Simmons Tariff reduced the Payne-Aldrich rates by 15 percent and put on the free list several commodities that were controlled by trusts—iron, steel, woolens, and farm machinery—thus lowering prices on them.

The lower tariff reduced revenue for the government. To make up the losses, Wilson sponsored both a corporate and a personal income tax. It was not high by late-twentieth-century standards. People who earned less than $4,000 a year paid no tax. On annual incomes between $4,000 and $20,000, a tidy sum in 1913, the rate was only 1 percent. People in the highest bracket, $500,000 and up, paid only 7 percent, a fraction of the low brackets today. Nevertheless, by forcing the rich to pay proportionately more toward supporting the government, the tax provisions of the tariff law represented a triumph of progressive principles.

Wilson's Cabinet

Wilson designed his cabinet in order to unite the Democratic party behind him. The president never had "shined to" William Jennings Bryan, but he named him Secretary of State because Bryan had helped to nominate him and still owned the affection of many Western Democrats.

Most other appointments rewarded key components of the party, especially the South and, through Secretary of Labor William B. Wilson, the labor movement, whose support the president wanted and needed. The most valuable member of the cabinet was William G. McAdoo. As Secretary of the Treasury, he provided the president with shrewd advice on banking policy. When McAdoo married Wilson's daughter, he became a kind of heir apparent.

Three confidants did not sit in the cabinet. Joseph Tumulty, a canny Irish politician, served as Wilson's private secretary and reminded the president of the sometimes sordid realities involved in keeping together a political machine. Colonel Edward M. House, a Texas businessman, was a shadowy but not sinister figure. Self-effacing and utterly devoted to the president, House neither desired nor accepted any official position. In-

stead, he traveled discreetly throughout the United States and abroad, informally conveying the president's views and wants to businessmen and heads of state.

Louis D. Brandeis, a corporation lawyer who became an antitrust progressive, provided Wilson with both economic principles and a social conscience. The father of the New Freedom, Brandeis turned Wilson away from the limitations of the program after 1914 and toward a broader progressivism. In 1916, Wilson rewarded him by naming him to the Supreme Court, on which Brandeis served as one of the most influential liberal justices of the twentieth century. He was the first justice to consider sociological information along with legal precedent in adjudging the constitutionality of laws.

The New Freedom in Action

Two laws that reflected Brandeis's influence were the Federal Reserve Act of 1913 and the Clayton Antitrust Act of 1914. The first was designed both to bring order to the national banking system and to hobble the vast power of Wall Street. The law established twelve regional Federal Reserve Banks, which dealt not directly with people but with other banks. The Federal Reserve System was owned by private bankers who were required to deposit 6 percent of their capital in it. However, the president appointed the majority of the directors, who sat in Washington, theoretically putting the government in control of the money supply.

The greatest power of the Federal Reserve System was (and is) its control of the discount rate, the level of interest at which money is lent to other banks for lending to private investors and buyers. By lowering the discount rate, the Federal Reserve can stimulate investment and economic expansion in slow times. By raising the rate, the Federal Reserve can cool down an overactive economy that threatened to blow up in inflation, financial panic, and depression.

The Federal Reserve Act did bring some order to the national banking system. But it did not, as many progressives hoped, tame the great bankers. Indeed, because representatives of the private banks sat on the Federal Reserve Board, the long-term effects of the law were to provide Wall Street with an even more efficient, albeit more accountable, control of national finance.

In 1914, Wilson pushed his antitrust policy through Congress. The Clayton Antitrust Act stipulated that corporations would be fined for unfair practices that threatened competition, forbade interlocking directorates (the same men sitting on the boards of "competing" companies and thereby coordinating policies), and declared that officers of corporations would be held personally responsible for offenses committed by their companies. Another bill that was passed at the same time

A confident Woodrow Wilson at the peak of his powers.

created the Federal Trade Commission to supervise the activities of the trusts. This agency looked more like T.R.'s New Nationalism than the New Freedom Wilson had plumped for in 1912.

Wilson Changes Direction

After the congressional elections of 1914, Wilson shifted far more sharply toward the reforms that Teddy Roosevelt had promoted. Although the Democrats retained control of both houses, many progressives returned to their Republican voting habits in 1914 and cut the Democratic margin in the House. It was obvious to both the president and Democratic congressmen that if they were to survive the election of 1916 against a reunified Republican party, they would have to woo these progressive voters.

Consequently, Wilson agreed to support social legislation that he had opposed as late as 1914. He did not like laws that favored any special interest, farmers any more than bankers, but in order to shore up support in the West, he agreed to the Federal Farm Loan Act of 1916, which provided low-cost credit to farmers. Early in his administration, Wilson had opposed a child-labor law on constitutional grounds. In 1916, he supported the Keating-Owen Act, which severely restricted the employment of children in most jobs.

The Adamson Act required the interstate railroads to put their workers on an eight-hour day without a reduction in pay. Wilson even moderated his anti-black sentiments, although Washington definitely took on the character of a segregated Southern city during his tenure. Despite a lifelong opposition to woman suffrage, the president began to encourage states to enfranchise

FORM 1040

The income tax, somewhat as it is known today, was first collected in March 1914. The original tax was designed to have well-to-do Americans pay the bulk of the federal government's bills. At a time when the average worker made $800 a year, no person earning less than $3,000 (about $35,000 in today's values) paid the tax. The rate was just 1 percent after deductions, with a surtax of 6 percent on incomes over $500,000 (about $6 million today). In part because the income tax was progressive, hitting the well-to-do harder than the tariff and excise tax did, it was quite popular at first.

During World War I, however, the need for funds lowered the minimum taxable income to $1,000. What had been a tax on the upper classes became a tax on almost all who worked. In 1990, after the tax reforms of the Reagan administration, lower- and middle-income families pay disproportionately more of the government's expenses than they did before the income tax was adopted.

women and to hint that he supported a constitutional amendment that would guarantee the right nationwide.

By the summer of 1916, Wilson could say with considerable justice that he had pushed progressive reform farther than had any of his predecessors. He enacted or supported much of Theodore Roosevelt's program of 1912, as well as his own. By 1916, however, Americans' votes reflected more than their views on domestic issues. They were troubled about their nation's place in a suddenly complicated world. Simultaneous with the enactment of Wilson's New Freedom and more than a little of T.R.'s New Nationalism, Europe had tumbled into the bloodiest war in history.

For Further Reading

Overviews of the era are Vincent P. DeSantis, *The Shaping of Modern America 1877–1916* (1973); Arthur S. Link, *Woodrow Wilson and the Progressive Era* (1954); George E. Mowry, *The Era of Theodore Roosevelt* (1958); William L. O'Neill, *The Progressive Years: America Comes of Age* (1975); Robert H. Wiebe, *The Search for Order, 1880–1920* (1967).

Indeed, virtually all the books cited at the conclusion of Chapter 36 are relevant to this chapter as well. In addition, see D. F. Anderson, *William Howard Taft: A Conservative's Conception of the Presidency* (1973); John

Morton Blum, *Woodrow Wilson and the Politics of Morality* (1956); P. E. Coletta, *The Presidency of William Howard Taft* (1973); John A. Garraty, *Woodrow Wilson* (1956); Lewis L. Gould, *Reform and Regulation: American Politics, 1900–1916* (1978); Otis L. Graham, Jr., *The Great Campaigns: Reform and War in America, 1900–1928* (1971); Samuel T. Hays, *Conservation and the Gospel of Efficiency: The Progressive Conservation Movement, 1890–1920* (1959); and the multi-volume Arthur S. Link, *Woodrow Wilson* (1947–65).

The chaos behind the trenches: the Meuse-Argonne campaign.

AMERICA DISCOVERS EUROPE

WORLD WAR I
1914 - 1918

A few days before his inauguration in 1913, Woodrow Wilson was reminded of some difficulties in

American relations with Mexico. He thought about the problem for a moment and set it aside,

remarking, "It would be the irony of fate if my administration had to deal chiefly with foreign affairs."

Wilson did not fear such a challenge. His self-confidence was as sturdy as Theodore Roosevelt's.

But his academic and political careers had been devoted to domestic concerns. He had paid scant

attention to the thorny snarls in which relations among nations could be tangled, and he had never been particularly interested in them. When the Wilson of 1913 considered the rest of the world, it was on the basis of assumptions and sentiments rather than in terms of a coherent, deliberate policy.

WILSON, THE WORLD, AND MEXICO

Like most Americans, the president was proud that his nation's population and industrial power ranked it with a mere handful of nations as a great world power. Also like other Americans, he believed that the United States was unique among great and lesser powers alike. Protected from Europe by a broad ocean, the United States required no huge armies to defend its security but, instead, expended its resources in constructive ways. Founded on the basis of an idea rather than on inheritance of a common culture and territory, the American nation should act toward other countries in accordance with principles rather than out of narrow self-interest.

Moral Diplomacy

As a man with a moralistic view of the world, Wilson had roundly criticized Teddy Roosevelt's gunboat diplomacy. To bully small nations was to betray the principle of self-determination on which the United States had been founded. He pointedly announced that his administration would deal with the weak and turbulent Latin American countries "upon terms of equality and honor." As a progressive who was suspicious of Wall Street, Wilson also disapproved of Taft's dollar diplomacy. Shortly after he took office, Wilson canceled federal support of an investment scheme in China because he smelled an implied obligation on the part of the government to intervene in the event that the investors' profits were threatened. If Wall Street financiers wanted to risk money in China, *they* would have to risk it, not expect Uncle Sam to underwrite their scheme.

Wilson was influenced by the Christian pacifism toward which Secretary of State William Jennings Bryan also leaned. Bryan believed that war was justified only in self-defense. If nations would act cautiously and discuss their problems, they would not have to spill blood. With Wilson's approval, Bryan negotiated "cooling off" treaties with 30 nations. The signatories pledged that in the event of a dispute, they would wait and talk for one year—they would "cool off"—before declaring war. Bryan believed that during this year, virtually every dispute between nations could be resolved without the use of force.

The Missionary Position

High ideals, but once Wilson was in the cockpit, he found that applying them consistently was more difficult than flying the recently invented airplane. In part, this was because of the untidy and unruly characteristics of reality. In part, it was because Wilson was also impelled by assumptions that conflicted with the moral principles by which he had been raised and the progressive principles he had learned.

Wilson had no doubts about the superiority of the white race. Though by no means a lynch-mongering redneck, Wilson had the racial attitudes of a Southern gentleman, patronizing and indulgent but also firm in asserting his social "place." Atop his Southern heritage, the academy in which Wilson had spent his adult life was permeated with theories and pseudo-sciences assuming the white man's superiority. As president, Wilson found it difficult to act as an equal in dealing with non-

From the Los Angeles *Daily Times*

STILL SHAKING HIS FINGER

A cartoonist chided Wilson for being too lenient in dealing with Pancho Villa, June 1916.

white nations such as Japan and the racially mixed Latin Americans.

His commitment to diplomacy by good example was complicated by a missionary's impulse to dictate proper behavior. When weaker nations did not freely emulate American ways of doing things, Wilson could wax arrogant, patronizing, and demanding. If other peoples did not realize what was good for them, Wilson would teach them.

So he raised no objections to a California state law that insulted race-sensitive Japan by restricting the right of Japanese immigrants to own land. In 1915, he ordered marines into black Haiti when chaotic conditions there threatened American investments. The next year, he landed troops in the Dominican Republic under similar circumstances. These actions angered Latin Americans, but they were minor irritants compared with Wilson's ill-advised and fruitless interference in Mexican affairs.

¡Viva Madero!

In 1911, the Mexican dictator for 35 years, Porfirio Diaz, was overthrown following a revolution supported by practically every Mexican region and social group except the elite that Diaz had favored. Foreign investors, who had reaped rich rewards by cooperating with the dicta-

tor, waited and fretted, none more so than the British and the Americans. The leader of the revolution spoke of returning control of Mexican wealth to Mexicans, and Americans alone owned $2 billion in property in Mexico, most of the country's railroads, 60 percent of the oil wells, and more mines than Mexicans controlled. About 50,000 American citizens lived in Mexico.

Francisco Madero was the reflective idealist who headed the revolution. He and Wilson would have disagreed, but they might also have gotten along. Madero was cultivated, educated, and moderate, not given to acting rashly. Moreover, he shared Wilson's liberal political philosophy and admired American institutions.

They never had a chance to communicate. Quietly encouraged by American diplomats during the Taft administration, a group of Diaz's generals led by Victoriano Huerta staged a coup. Apparently making some of their plans in the American embassy, the rebels struck shortly before Wilson was inaugurated, murdered Madero, and seized control of the federal government.

¡Viva Carranza!

The murder offended Wilson. He said that he would not deal with "a government of butchers," and he pressured England to withdraw its hasty recognition of the Huerta

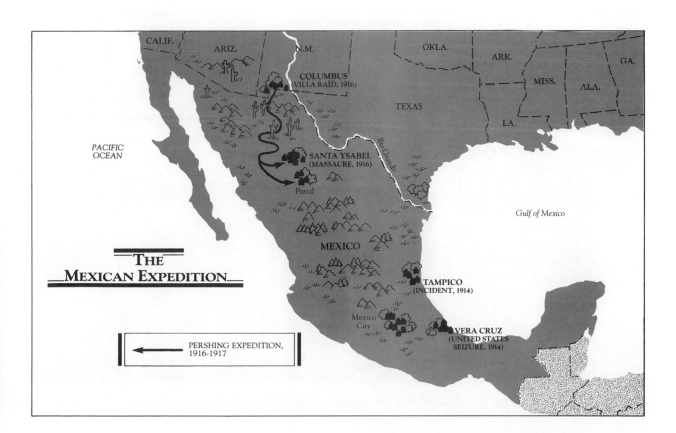

THE MEXICAN EXPEDITION

PERSHING EXPEDITION, 1916–1917

government. When peasant rebellions broke out in scattered parts of Mexico and a Constitutionalist army took shape behind a somber, long-bearded aristocrat, Venustiano Carranza, Wilson openly approved.

In April 1914, the United States intervened directly in the civil war. Seven American sailors on shore leave in Tampico were arrested by one of Huerta's colonels. They were freed almost immediately, but Huerta refused the demand of Admiral Henry T. Mayo for a twenty-one gun salute as an apology appropriate to the incident. Claiming that American honor had been insulted (and seeking to head off a German ship that was bringing arms to Huerta), Wilson ordered troops into the important port of Vera Cruz.

To Wilson's surprise, ordinary Mexicans joined the fight against the Americans, and street fighting in Vera Cruz claimed more than 400 lives. Wilson failed to understand that while Huerta was unpopular, the memory of the Mexican War was fresh in the Mexican memory. Rebel groups generally resented *gringo* interference as much as Huerta did. Even Carranza, in control of the north of Mexico, condemned the American landing.

Somewhat alarmed by his fix, Wilson agreed to an offer by Argentina, Brazil, and Chile to mediate the crisis.

¡Viva Villa!

Before anything could be settled, Carranza ousted Huerta. However, he then quarreled with one of his own generals, a bizarre, charismatic character who had been born Doroteo Arango, but was universally known as Pancho Villa. Alternately jovial and peevish, part-time bandit and part-time social revolutionary, Villa was romanticized by the young American journalist John Reed as "The Robin Hood of Mexico." Villa cleverly played for American approval and, for a time, Wilson was convinced that Villa represented democracy in Mexico.

But Wilson wanted stability most of all. When Carranza took Mexico City in October 1915, Wilson recognized his de facto control of the government. This stung Villa, prompting him to show his seamier side. Calculating that American intervention would destabilize Mexico and create an opportunity for him to seize power, Villa stopped a train carrying American engi-

Bandit and revolutionary Pancho Villa (center) with the leader of agrarian revolt in Mexico, Emiliano Zapata (right).

neers invited by Carranza to reopen mines, and shot all but one. Early in 1916, he sent a raid across the border into the dusty little desert town of Columbus, New Mexico, where his brigands killed 17 people.

Instead of allowing Carranza to root out and punish Villa, as was proper with neighboring nations that were sovereign equals, Wilson ordered General John J. Pershing and 6,000 troops, including the black Tenth Cavalry, to pursue and capture the bandit guerrilla. They were humiliated. In the arid mountainous state of Chihuahua that was his home, Villa easily eluded the American expedition, leading the soldiers on 300 miles of a zigzag route during which time they never gained sight of Villa's main force. Pershing's men did, however, exchange shots several times with Carranza's troops. In one clash, 40 died. While accomplishing nothing, Wilson had succeeded in alienating every political faction in Mexico.

In January 1917, he finally gave up and ordered "Black Jack" Pershing to return home. Only because Americans were faced by a more formidable enemy, the German Kaiser, were they able to make light of their humiliation at the hands of a man whom they considered an illiterate bandito.

THE GREAT WAR

By the beginning of 1917, Europe had been at war for two and a half years. In June 1914, an ethnic Serbian, Gavrilo Princip, had assassinated Archduke Franz Ferdinand of the Austro-Hungarian Empire, which included among its provinces two with a large Serbian population—Bosnia and Herzogovina. At first it appeared that the incident would pass. Sensational assassinations were regular news in turn-of-the-century Europe.

But Austro-Hungarian sensitivity to the decline of its once majestic empire, obligations among the great powers of Europe written into secret treaties, the weakness of the Russian Czar and the irresponsibility of the German Kaiser, and the reckless arms race in which the European nations had been engaged for a generation, plunged the Continent into war.

Tangled Alliances

Serbia, a Slavic nation, was an ally of Russia, which backed the little country in defying Austria. Austria-Hungary looked to powerful Germany for encouragement, and got it. France, sworn to revenge a defeat at the hands of the Germans in 1870, became involved because of French fears of German industrial might, which had led to secret agreements promising mutual support to Russia. England, traditionally aloof from European wrangles, had been frightened by Germany's construction of a worldwide navy (larger than America's and second only to Britain's), and had informal understandings with both France and Russia.

Many of the smaller nations of Europe were associated with either the Central Powers (Germany, Austria-Hungary, Italy, Bulgaria, Turkey) or the Allied Powers (England, France, Russia, eventually Italy, which, over time, switched sides). By August 1914, most of Europe was at war. Eventually, 33 nations would be involved.

Americans React

The American people reacted to the conflagration with a mixture of disbelief and disgust. For a generation, European rulers had filled the air with the sounds of saber rattling. Americans were used to that; their own Teddy Roosevelt was a master of bluff and bluster. But T.R., it seemed, had understood the difference between a military strut and a catastrophe. Until 1914, so had the Europeans. Even Kaiser Wilhelm II of Germany, an absurd and broadly ridiculed figure with his extravagant military uniforms, golden spiked helmet, comic-opera waxed moustache, and penchant for bombast, had acted prudently in the crunch. Like most Europeans, Americans concluded that the constant talk about war without going to war would continue indefinitely. They did not really believe that powerful, civilized countries would turn their terrifying technology for killing on one another.

Once European nations had done just that, Americans consoled themselves that their nation, at least, remained above such savagery. Politicians, preachers, and editors quoted and praised the wisdom of George Washington's and Thomas Jefferson's warnings against "entangling alliances." They blamed Europe's tragedy on Old-World corruptions, its kings and princes, religious intolerance, clash of cultures, nationalistic hysteria, and insane stockpiling of armaments that were superfluous if they were not used, suicidal if they were.

Never did American political and social institutions look so grandly superior. Never had Americans been more grateful to have turned their backs on Europe's ways. As reports of hideous carnage on the battlefield began to hum over the Atlantic Cable, Americans shuddered and counted their blessings. No prominent person raised an objection when President Wilson proclaimed absolute American neutrality. However, when the president also called on Americans to be "neutral in fact as well as in name, . . . impartial in thought as well as in action," he was, as he was wont to do, demanding too much of human nature.

Sympathy for the Allies

A large proportion of Americans looked to England as their ancestral as well as cultural motherland, and they were naturally sympathetic to Britain's cause. Wilson himself was an unblushing Anglophile. Before becoming president, he had vacationed regularly in Great Britain. He had written a book in which he broadly admired the British parliamentary form of government, and in his first year in office, he had resolved the last minor points of difference between England and the United States: a border dispute in British Columbia, a quarrel between Canadian and American fishermen off Newfoundland, and British objections to discriminatory tolls on the Panama Canal.

Hardly noted at first, but ominous in the long run, American and British capital were closely allied. British investments in the United States were vast, and when the cost of purchasing everything from wheat to munitions required that these holdings be liquidated, Americans bought them at bargain rates. Banks like the House of Morgan lent money to the English, at first with Wilson's disapproval, and acted as agents for Allied bond sales. By 1917, Great Britain owed American lenders $2.3 billion. It was a strong tie, when compared to the meager $27 million that the Germans managed to bor-row in the United States. Wall Street had good reason to favor a British victory or, at least, to pale at the thought of a British defeat.

Some Americans were sympathetic to France. The land of Lafayette was America's "oldest friend," the indispensable ally of the Revolution. Americans never had formally gone to war with the French. And France was, except for the United States, the only republic among the world's great powers, constitutionally pledged to civil equality and representative institutions.

WHAT'S IN A NAME?

The British called it the European War, and Americans were inclined to use that term until the United States intervened in April 1917. Then, a few idealistic but awkward tags were tried: War for the Freedom of Europe, War for the Overthrow of Militarism, War for Civilization, and—best known—Woodrow Wilson's War to Make the World Safe for Democracy. Only after 1918 did the Great War and the World War become standard—until 1939 when the outbreak of another great worldwide war made it World War I.

Multi-Culturalism

But Americans were by no means unanimously favorable to the Allies. One American in three was either foreign-born or a first-generation citizen, many of them with strong Old-World sentiments that made them pro-German or unfriendly toward the Allied Powers. Millions of Americans traced their roots to Germany or Austria-Hungary. While they had come to the United States for its economic opportunities, many of them gladly retained sentimental attachments to the old culture. Few German-, Austrian-, or Hungarian-Americans seriously believed or suggested that their adopted country take the side of the fatherland. But they did hope for American neutrality, and in heavily German areas like Wisconsin and other parts of the Midwest, they said so loudly. The National German League quickly grew to claim 3 million members and actively worked against intervention.

German-Americans joined with Irish-Americans in the German-Irish Legislative Committee for the Furtherance of United States Neutrality and the American Federation of Labor's National Peace Council. Many of the nation's 4.5 million people of Irish descent hated England. When the British crushed an Irish rebellion in 1916 (which was backed by Germany), a few prominent Irish-Americans declared for the German cause.

Similarly, many Russian and Polish Jews, who had suffered brutal persecution under the czars, supported Germany. They thought of Germany and Austria as countries where Jews enjoyed civil equality. Socialists, an important minority within both the Jewish and German-American communities, hated Russia above all other countries because of the cruelty of the czar's secret police.

With so diverse a population and such a tangle of conflicting loyalties, Wilson's policy of neutrality not only was idealistic, but was the only practical alternative, especially for a Democratic party politician who depended on ethnic voters. And it might have worked if Europe's "Great War" (as the First World War was called until the Second broke out) had been fought for clearly stated and limited goals, and had been concluded with an early victory by one side or the other.

The Deadly Stalemate

A quick victory was what the German General Staff had in mind. Germany's "Schlieffen Plan," which was framed in 1905, was to knock the modern French army out of the war by flanking it to the north. This meant invading France through neutral Belgium. Once in control of France's Channel coast, German troops would be able to keep the British army from landing in Europe and sweep down on Paris, just as the Germans had done in 1870.

In the meantime, von Schlieffen had said, weakened German forces on the Eastern Front would take a drubbing from the Russians. However, once France was defeated and Britain neutralized, troops from the Western Front could be sped to meet the Russians on railroads designed for just that purpose.

The Schlieffen Plan failed because, instead of providing a broad avenue into France, the Belgians resisted heroically. Capturing the single fortress city of Liège took the Germans twelve days, longer than they expected to be in Belgium. Frustrated, the invaders treated the Belgians with a chilling ferocity, earning a reputation as "the savage Hun," which profoundly influenced public opinion in the United States and elsewhere.

During the delay, the Russians advanced deeply into German territory, and the German General Staff lost its nerve. At a critical moment, the high command weakened the army on the Western Front in order to stop the Russians in the East. They did so, winning a tremendous victory at the Battle of Tannenberg. But the war bogged down into stalemate. Enemy armies dug entrenchments and earthworks and faced one another—along 475 miles in the west—across a "no man's land" of moonscape craters, spools of barbed wire, and the smell of death. For three years men on both sides would hurl themselves "over the top" and die by the tens of thousands for the sake of advancing the trenches a few miles.

The Technology of Killing

A revolution in military technology, and the failure of many generals to comprehend it, made the war unspeakably bloody. Although the airplane, first flown at Kitty Hawk, North Carolina, in December 1903, captured the imagination of romantics, it was of little importance in battle. (Ordinary soldiers considered pilots playboys; in fact, the life expectancy of British pilots at the front was two weeks.) Nor was poisonous mustard gas, used by both sides, a decisive weapon. Its results were devastating, but a slight shift in the wind blew the toxic fumes back on the army that had loosed it.

The machine gun, on the other hand, made the old-fashioned mass infantry charge, such as had dominated battle during the American Civil War, an exercise in suicide. When one army charged out of its trenches, enemy machine guns filled the air with a hurricane of lead that mowed down soldiers by the thousands. On the first day of the Battle of the Somme in July 1916, 60,000 young Britons were slaughtered or wounded, the majority of them within half an hour. By the time the Somme campaign sputtered to a meaningless end, Brit-

NOTABLE PEOPLE

WILLIAM D. HAYWOOD (1869–1927)

Big Bill Haywood was famous during the years before the Great War. As the head of the IWW, the Industrial Workers of the World, he came close to wielding real power as a leader of the unskilled industrial and agricultural working people so vital in the economy. But the war was to destroy Haywood's career and shatter his vision of what America should mean. Within a few years after the guns were stilled, he was a lonely exile who would never come home.

William D. Haywood was born in Salt Lake City in 1869. He became a miner in northern Nevada while still a teenager. Several times he turned to other work—cowboying, prospecting for a mine of his own, homesteading on the site of an abandoned army post. Haywood was a quintessential westerner, looking for the chance to improve himself, an implicit believer in the American gospel of opportunity that said the West was the place a man could best do such a thing.

Bad luck and the attractive wages gold and silver miners took home brought Haywood back to the mines of Silver City, Idaho. There he found his opportunity to rise within the Western Federation of Miners, the militant labor union of the miners, mill, and smelter workers of the region. His forceful personality and aptitude for running an organization brought him to the attention of the WFM's leadership in Denver. At the turn of the century, Haywood moved to the metropolis as the WFM's Secretary-Treasurer.

In Silver City, Haywood had supervised an orderly union local, negotiating wages and conditions across a table from the owners of the mines. Elsewhere in the West, union miners fought violent strikes with their employers, which were increasingly large corporations with headquarters in San Francisco, New York, and London.

The miners resented absentee control of the gold and silver they believed they had found and which they won from the earth. They worked daily with explosives and were apt, when pushed, to fight back with dynamite and guns. The bosses, when they sensed a chance to break the miners' unions and gain uncontested control of labor in the mining camps, were equally quick to use violence in the form of hired thugs and pliant local and state authorities. Bill Haywood found himself one of the leaders of an organization engaged in what was unmistakeably class warfare. He did not disdain the role. During the 1890s, he had concluded that some form of socialism, common rather than private ownership of the means of production, was the only way to achieve social justice in the United States.

The mine owners and their allies in government considered Haywood one of an "Inner Circle" of sinister conspirators whom they held responsible for the disorder. If he could be removed from the scene, they believed they could gain the upper hand in labor relations. In 1906, when a ne'er-do-well known as Harry Orchard confessed that he had murdered a former governor of Idaho on the orders of the "Inner Circle," Haywood was brought to trial in Boise.

The prosecution's case relied heavily on the testimony of the unsavory Orchard. Haywood's lawyer, Clarence Darrow, seized on this and defended him by prosecuting Orchard's character. Haywood was acquitted.

His career in the WFM was at an end. Other leaders of the union believed Haywood's tough talk was responsible for the trial (and may have believed him guilty of the crime). It mattered little to Haywood. The publicity had made him an eminent man. Intellectuals, particularly in New York's Greenwich Village, lionized him as a primal

---

ish losses totaled 400,000; French, 200,000; and German, 500,000.

The British developed the tank in the hopes of neutralizing German machine guns. The heavily-armored vehicles could drive directly into gun emplacements. But World War I tanks were slow, scarcely faster than foot soldiers. Attached to infantry units, tanks provided a minimum of protection to the hapless foot soldiers.

Incompetence at the top of every army contributed substantially to the bloodshed. Petty personal and national jealousies among generals of the Allies, especially between the English and the French, resulted in decisions that had little to do with the welfare of the common soldier or even the winning of the war.

The War at Sea

Americans were sickened by the news from Europe, but it was the war at sea that directly touched American interests. As in the past, naval war was economic war; it was aimed at destroying the enemy's commerce and, therefore, its ability to carry on the fight. Naval superiority allowed Great Britain to strike first, proclaiming a blockade of Germany.

According to the laws of war at sea, all enemy merchant ships were fair game for seizing or sinking, although it was required that crews and passengers be rescued. The ships of neutral nations, however, retained the right to trade with any nation as long as they were not carrying contraband (defined before the war as war materiel).

The laws of blockade, which had caused friction between the British and the Americans in the past, were more complicated, and in 1914 Great Britain introduced several new wrinkles. The British "blockaded" Germany by mining some parts of the North Sea. Ships, including those of neutrals, would risk being destroyed merely by exemplar of the working masses. He lectured widely, building his image with a simple, eloquent platform manner. He was elected to the Socialist party's National Executive Committee and twice represented the party at international conferences. He became an organizer for the IWW, the revolutionary union of unskilled workers he had helped found in 1905. He was in the headlines during strikes the IWW led in Lawrence, Massachusetts, in 1912 and Paterson, New Jersey in 1913.

In 1914, Haywood became Secretary-Treasurer of the IWW, in effect its leader. He introduced a degree of order to an organization that had been almost guerrilla-like in its operations. He regularized dues collections, set up an efficient national office in Chicago, and perfected a system for enrolling the dispersed casual workers who brought in the nation's grain harvest, previously a virtually unorganizable workforce.

Haywood's IWW opposed American entrance into World War I. Haywood was, however, very cautious in the issue. He believed that the workers' business lay "at the point of production," in the factory, field, forest, and mine, not in fighting causes that, however noble, were beyond their power to effect. He attempted to soft-pedal the IWW's antiwar line. He dropped bitterly sardonic antiwar lyrics from the IWW's songbook and said that it was a matter of personal choice whether or not members registered for the draft.

To no avail. In the fall of 1917, federal authorities launched nationwide raids of IWW headquarters. Either because they believed that the IWW was really treasonous, because they feared what the union's strength in the critical areas of agriculture, lumber, and copper could mean to the war effort, or simply because they saw a chance to use wartime hysteria as an opportunity to crush the anticapitalist IWW and Big Bill Haywood, the federal prosecutors did just that.

Long trials for sedition drained the IWW's resources and distracted its leaders from the business of running a union. Vigilante action against the IWW in the field reduced its membership. For all his cynical comments about the capitalist enemy, Haywood was shocked that he and more than a hundred other IWW leaders were found guilty of charges that bordered on the absurd.

By 1921 he was stunned by the shattering of the IWW. Like many American socialists, Haywood found consolation only in the success of the Bolsheviks in far-off Russia. Instead of reporting to prison, he slipped aboard a ship and sailed for the Soviet Union.

For a few years, while the Russian Communists deluded themselves that international revolution was just around the corner, Haywood acted like a leader of that campaign, appearing at ceremonies in Moscow. When the capitalist order proved far from dead in Europe and America, and the Soviet leaders engrossed themselves in domestic affairs, Haywood was first put in charge of a factory (he was apparently a failure at the job) and then pensioned off in a small apartment in the Russian capital.

He was delighted to receive American visitors but was miserable as an exile. There was no alternative. To return to the United States meant prison. In 1927, he suffered a stroke and died.

---

attempting to trade with Germany. The Royal Navy stopped many American ships on the high seas and took them to British ports for search. Britain also redefined contraband to mean almost all trade goods, including some foodstuffs. When neutral Holland, Denmark, and Sweden began to import goods for secret resale to Germany (pastoral Denmark, which never before purchased American lard, imported 11,000 tons of it in the first months of the war), the British slapped strict regulations on trade with those countries.

American objections were mild. The German market had not been important to American shippers, and wartime sales to England and France rose so dramatically that exporters needed no extra business. Trade with the Allies climbed from $825 million in 1914 to $3.2 billion in 1916, a fourfold increase in two years.

At first the Germans were indifferent to the British blockade. Their plan had been to win a quick victory on land, which rendered economic warfare moot. When the war stalemated, however, the German General Staff recognized the necessity of throttling England's import economy. The tool Germany developed for doing this was another creation of the new military technology, the *Unterseeboot* (undersea boat, or U-boat)—the submarine.

Submarine Warfare

Ironically, the modern submarine was the invention of two Americans, John Holland and Simon Lake. When the navy rejected their device as frivolous, however, they took their plans to Europe. The Germans recognized the submarine's potential and launched a construction program. By February 1915, Germany had a large enough flotilla of the vessels, each armed with nineteen torpedoes, to declare the waters surrounding the British Isles to be a "war zone." All enemy merchant ships within those waters were liable to be sunk, and the safety of neutral ships could not be absolutely guaranteed. Within days, several British vessels went to the bottom, and President Wilson warned the Kaiser of Germany's "strict accountability" for American lives and property lost to U-boats.

Because submarines were so fragile, the kind of warfare in which they engaged was particularly inhumane. On the surface, the submarine was helpless; a six-inch gun mounted inconspicuously on the bow of a freighter was enough to blow a U-boat to bits. Because submarines could dive only slowly, British merchant vessels were instructed to ram them.

Therefore, German submarines had to strike without warning, giving crew and passengers no opportunity to escape. And since submarines were tiny, their crews were cramped. There was no room to take aboard those who abandoned ship. Survivors of torpedoed boats were on their own in the midst of the ocean.

Many Americans grumbled that if the British block-ade was illegal, the German submarine campaign was immoral. The British were thieves, but the Germans were murderers, drowning seamen by the score. And more than seamen. The issue came to a head on May 7, 1915, when the English luxury liner *Lusitania* was torpedoed off the coast of Ireland, and 1,198 people of the 1,959 aboard were killed, including 139 Americans. What kind of war was this, many Americans asked, that killed innocent travelers? The New York *Times* described the Germans as "savages drenched with blood."

Wilson Wins a Victory

The Germans replied that they had warned Americans against traveling on the *Lusitania* through advertisements in major New York and Washington newspapers. They pointed out that the *Lusitania* had not been merely a passenger ship. It had been carrying 4,200 cases of small arms purchased in the United States and some high explosives. So many people were lost because the *Lusi-*

The front page of the New York Times *on May 8, 1915, announcing the sinking of the* Lusitania, *an English luxury liner.*

tania had gone down in only eighteen minutes, blown wide open not by the torpedo but by a secondary explosion. The British had been using innocent passengers as hostages for the safe conduct of war materiel.

Wilson was well aware of this and did not hold the British blameless in the tragedy. Nevertheless, Germany's military right to use the new weapon was less important to him than the principle of freedom of the seas for those not at war. He sent a series of strongly worded notes to Germany. The second was so antagonistic that the pacifistic Bryan feared it meant war. He resigned rather than sign it, and Wilson replaced him in the State Department with Robert Lansing, an international lawyer.

The Germans ceased attacking passenger vessels, and the uproar faded. Then, however, early in 1916, the Allies announced that they were arming all merchant ships, and Germany responded that the U-boats would sink all enemy vessels without warning. On March 24, 1916, a sitting duck, a French channel steamer on a scheduled run between Dieppe and Folkestone, the *Sussex*, went down with an American among the casualties. Wilson threatened to break diplomatic relations with Germany, the last step before a declaration of war, if "unrestricted submarine warfare" were continued.

The German General Staff did not want the United States to enter the war. Plans for a major offensive on all fronts were afoot, and the German navy did not have enough U-boats to launch a full-scale attack on British shipping. In the Sussex Pledge of May 4, 1916, the German foreign office promised to observe the rules of visit and search before attacking enemy ships. That effectively meant abandoning the use of the submarine, but it kept the United States out of the war.

AMERICA GOES TO WAR

Wilson had won a spectacular diplomatic victory at the beginning of his campaign for reelection. He was enthusiastically renominated at the Democratic convention, and his campaign was given a theme that did not entirely please him. The keynote speaker designed his speech around the slogan "He Kept Us Out of War."

He Kept Us Out of War—While Preparing for It

Wilson did not like the slogan because, as he confided to an aide, "I can't keep the country out of war. Any little German lieutenant can put us into war at any time by some calculated outrage." He meant that a submarine commander, acting on his own, could bark out the order that would torpedo the Sussex Pledge. Like many na-

Little as Wilson liked it, Americans who opposed involvement in World War I strongly supported him in the election campaign of 1916.

tional leaders before and since, Wilson had trapped himself in a position where control over a momentous decision was out of his hands. He, at least, had the wisdom to know it.

Wilson began to prepare for the possibility of war as early as November 1915, when he asked Congress to beef up the army to 400,000 men and fund a huge expansion of the navy. He was pushed into this "preparedness" campaign by his political enemy Theodore Roosevelt, who jabbed and poked at the fact that American forces totaled fewer than 100,000; that the Quartermaster Corps (entrusted with supply) had only recently begun using trucks; that at one point in 1915 the American artillery had only enough ammunition for two days' fighting with cannon that were a generation obsolete.

Wilson also had to contend with an anti-preparedness Congress led by Representative Claude Kitchin of North Carolina. With widespread backing among the Western and Southern progressives, on whom Wilson generally depended for support, the anti-preparedness forces pointed out that it had been "preparedness" that had led to Europe going to war in the first place. If the United States had the means to fight, they argued, it was all the more likely that the United States would fight. Wilson had to settle for a compromise, less of a military build-up than the Roosevelt forces wanted, more than Kitchin and his supporters liked.

The Election of 1916

While Wilson wrestled with the preparedness issue, the Republicans patched up their split of 1912. Progressives who were able to stomach T.R.'s aggressiveness wanted to maintain the Bull Moose party's independence. They met and nominated the Colonel to run. But Roosevelt wanted to win; he wanted the Republican nomination too. When he could not get it, he recommended his friend, Henry Cabot Lodge, who was warlike enough, but no progressive. So easily, in the heat of war, he had lost sight of the ideal of 1912. When the Republicans actually nominated Supreme Court Justice Charles Evans Hughes, progressive in the past but a moderate on the war issue, T.R. lost heart and dropped out of the race. William Allen White wrote that the Progressives were all dressed up with nowhere to go.

Hughes's integrity was unimpeachable. In dignity and presidential bearing, he was more than a match for Wilson. His distinguished gray beard was a reminder of the simpler days before the Great War. He spoke in high-sounding phrases. But Hughes was also a dull fellow on the speaker's platform, and he lacked Wilson's moral toughness. Nor did his views on the war issue differ much from the president's; he too wanted to avoid war, but knew the United States could be forced into it. Nevertheless, thanks to Theodore Roosevelt, who stormed about the country sounding like the German Kaiser, the Republican choice came to be known as the war candidate.

This undeserved reputation cost Hughes just enough votes to give the election to Wilson. It was very close. Hughes carried every Northeastern state but New Hampshire and every Midwestern state but Ohio. He went to bed on election night believing that he was president. Then one antiwar Western state after another turned in majorities for Wilson. When Wilson carried California by a paper-thin margin, he was elected, 277 electoral votes to 254. The election was on Tuesday.

Not until Friday did the American people know for certain who would lead them for the next four years.

Trying and Failing to Keep the Peace

Elated by the surprise but still nervous about the "little German lieutenant" who could plunge the United States into war, Wilson set out to mediate between the Allies and Central Powers. He had concluded that only by ending the war in Europe could he be sure of keeping the United States out of it. During the winter of 1916–1917, he believed that he was making progress, at least with the Germans. For a time, the British seemed to be the major obstacle to peace.

On January 22, 1917, Wilson outlined his peace plan to Congress. Only a "peace without victory," a "peace among equals" with neither winners nor losers, could solve the problem. The progressive idealist did not call for a mere cessation of hostilities. He proposed to pledge the warring powers to uphold the principles of national self-determination and absolute freedom of the seas, and to establish some kind of international mechanism for resolving future disputes.

But it was all an illusion. He and the American people were in for a rude awakening. The proposal was not even half-digested when, a week later, the German ambassador informed Wilson that on February 1, German submarines would begin sinking neutral as well as enemy ships in the war zone around Great Britain. With a fleet of 100 submarines, the German military planners be-

A banner headline on the New York American *reported the beginning of war between the United States and Germany, April 6, 1917.*

lieved that they could knock Great Britain out of the war within six months. They knew that breaking the Sussex Pledge meant almost certain American intervention. But because the United States was far from ready to intervene massively, the German leaders calculated that the war would be over before more than a token American force could be landed in Europe.

Wilson was crestfallen, then irate. He broke off diplomatic relations with Germany, as he had threatened to do, and asked Congress for authority to arm American merchant ships. When former progressive allies such as La Follette and Borah filibustered to prevent this, he denounced them as "a little group of willful men, representing no opinion but their own."

For the first time, the president was the leader of the war party. Nevertheless, Wilson did not abandon all hope of staying out until German submarines sent three American freighters to the bottom. On the evening of April 2, mourning that "it is a fearful thing to lead this great peaceful people into war," a solemn Wilson asked Congress for a formal declaration.

For four days a bitter debate shook the Capitol. Six senators and about fifty representatives fought to the end, blaming Wilson for having failed to be truly neutral and claiming that the United States was going to spill its young men's blood in order to bail out Wall Street's loans to England and to enrich the munitions manufacturers, the "merchants of death." In one of the most moving speeches, freshman Senator George Norris of Nebraska said, "We are going into war upon the command of gold. . . . We are about to put the dollar sign on the American flag."

Why America Went to War

In later years, some historians would say that Norris had been right. With varying emphases, they agreed that special interests had methodically maneuvered the United States into a war that did not concern the country. To the extent that Wall Street favored a British victory for the sake of its own profits and that the "merchants of death" fed off the blood of soldiers, they were correct.

But to say that certain interest groups wanted to go to war is not to say that they had their way with Wilson and Congress. Woodrow Wilson was as unlikely to take his cues from Wall Street and the Dupont munitions works as he was to seek advice on church polity from Theodore Roosevelt. To Wilson, the freedom of the seas was sacred, a right on which Americans had insisted since the 1790s. Moreover, the president shared in the profound shift in public sentiment from 1914 and even 1915, when virtually no American dreamed of declaring war, to the spring of 1917, when the majority favored

entering the conflict. The reasons for his about-face lie in the growing belief that Germany represented a force for evil in the world and the skillful propaganda of the British and pro-British Americans in encouraging this perception.

The Hun and His Kultur

The depiction of Germans as barbaric "Huns" practicing a diabolical *Kultur* (merely German for "culture," but having a sinister ring to it in American ears) had its origins in the German violation of Belgian neutrality. Figuratively at first, the British and French called the invasion "the rape of Belgium" and soon discovered the propaganda value of the word. In fact, the German occupation of the little country, while harsh, was generally no more brutal than the wartime controls the British slapped on the ever-rebellious Irish. But wall posters representing the broken body of a young girl being dragged away by a bloated, beast-like German soldier in

The art of the poster—expressing a thought instantly and forcefully—reached its apogee during World War I.

a spiked helmet elicited all the horrible implications that rape connotes.

German insistences that their troops observed all due proprieties toward civilians were undermined in October 1915, when the German army executed Edith Cavell, the British head of the Berkendael Medical Institute in Brussels. Although Cavell was guilty of acts that were considered espionage under international law (she helped a number of British prisoners escape), the execution of a woman for charitable deeds was profoundly stupid in an age when women were only rarely executed for murder.

The submarine war further angered Americans. Not everyone agreed with Wilson that the rights of neutrals could be absolute in a modern war. But repeated incidents of unarmed merchant seamen and innocent passengers drowning in the dark, cold waters of the North Atlantic touched a delicate nerve. Artists brilliantly aroused basic human fear in posters that showed seamen fighting vainly to swim while their ship sank in the moonlit background.

German saboteurs were probably not so active in the United States as British and pro-British propagandists claimed. Nevertheless, several German diplomats were caught red-handed in 1915 when a bumbling agent left incriminating papers on a train, and in 1916, the huge Black Tom munitions stores in New Jersey was completely destroyed in a suspicious "accident."

But the real blockbuster was a mere piece of paper. On February 25, 1917, while Wilson was searching for a last chance to avoid war, the British communicated to him a message that the German foreign minister, Arthur Zimmermann, had sent to the Mexican government. In the event that the United States declared war on Germany, Zimmermann proposed that Germany would finance a Mexican attack on the United States. Assuming Germany won, Mexico would be rewarded after the war with the return of some of the territory that it had given up in the Mexican War 70 years earlier, specifically the "lost provinces" of New Mexico and Arizona.

It was a foolish proposal. Mexico was still wracked by civil turmoil and was in no condition to make war on Guatemala, let alone the United States. Regardless, with the American people already angered, the Zimmermann Telegram persuaded many that the unprincipled Hun must be stopped.

The American Contribution

The Germans provoked the American intervention on a gamble. German leaders bet that their all-out U-boat attack would starve England into surrender before the Americans could contribute to the war effort. For three frightening months, it appeared as though they had guessed right. In February and March 1917, German submarines sank 570,000 tons of shipping bound to and

Warships defend a liner from submarine attack.

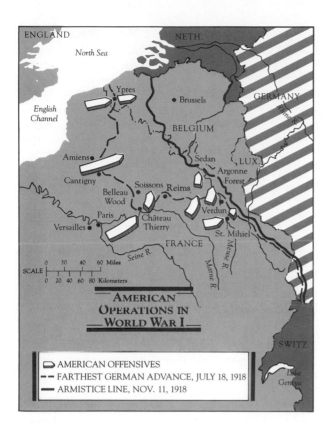

AMERICAN
OPERATIONS IN
WORLD WAR I

AMERICAN OFFENSIVES
FARTHEST GERMAN ADVANCE, JULY 18, 1918
ARMISTICE LINE, NOV. 11, 1918

moth *Vaterland*, renamed the *Leviathan*) and by launching a massive shipbuilding program, the Americans were soon producing two ships for every one that the Germans sank.

The Fighting Over There

Soldiers went too. General John Pershing arrived in Paris in July 1917 with the first units of the American Expeditionary Force, the First Infantry Division. This was primarily a symbolic gesture. Because Pershing refused to send poorly trained men to the front, the Germans were proved right in gambling that American reinforcements could not in themselves turn the tide. The first Americans to see action, near Verdun in October, were used only to beef up decimated French, British, and Canadian units.

The autumn of 1917 went poorly for the Allies. The Germans and Austrians defeated the Italians in the south and, in November, knocked Russia out of the war. A liberal democratic government that had deposed the czar in March 1917 proved unable to keep a mutinous Russian army supplied, and a group of revolutionary Communists, the Bolsheviks, led by Vladmir Ilyich Lenin, seized power on the basis of promises of "Peace and Bread." The Treaty of Brest-Litovsk, which the Germans forced on the Russians, was vindictive and

from England. In April, the total ran to almost 900,000 tons. A quarter of the British merchant fleet lay at the bottom of the sea. (All told, 203 U-Boats sank 5,408 ships during the war, some 11 millions tons.) At one point in April 1917, the British had enough food on hand to feed the island nation for only three weeks.

But the worst passed and the Germans lost their wager. At the insistence of American Admiral William S. Sims, merchantmen ceased to travel alone. Guarded by naval vessels, particularly the small, fast, and heavily armed destroyers (the nemesis of the U-boats), merchant ships crossed the Atlantic in huge convoys. Over the objections of the Royal Navy (but with the support of Prime Minister David Lloyd George), Sims succeeded in building his "bridge of ships."

As early as May 1917, U-boat kills dropped drastically, far below what the German navy claimed it could do. By July, the American navy took over most defense operations in the Western Hemisphere and sent 34 destroyers to Queenstown, Ireland (present-day Cobh) to assist the British. So successful was the well-guarded convoy system that only 200 out of 2 million American soldiers sent to France in 1917 and 1918 were drowned on the way. In the meantime, by commandeering more than a hundred German ships that were in American ports at the time war was declared (including the behe-

American soldiers move supplies during the Argonne offensive, the last large battle involving Americans before World War I came to an end.

WORLD WAR I CASUALTIES

	Total mobilized forces	Killed or died	Wounded	Prisoners & missing	Total casualties
United States	4,791,000	117,000	204,000	5,000	326,000
Russia	12,000,000	1,700,000	4,950,000	2,500,000	9,150,000
France	8,410,000	1,358,000	4,266,000	537,000	6,161,000
British Commonwealth	8,904,000	908,000	2,090,000	192,000	3,190,000
Italy	5,615,000	650,000	947,000	600,000	2,197,000
Germany	11,000,000	1,774,000	4,216,000	1,153,000	7,143,000
Austria-Hungary	7,800,000	1,200,000	3,620,000	2,220,000	7,020,000
TOTAL	58,520,000	7,707,000	20,293,000	7,187,000	35,187,000

harsh. News of it convinced many Americans that they had done well in going to war to stop the Hun's hunger for world conquest. By closing down the Eastern Front, however, the Germans were able to throw a bigger army into France.

In the spring of 1918, Germany launched a do-or-die offensive. The Allies fell back to the Marne River, close enough to Paris that the shelling could be heard on the Champs Elysées. But by this time there were 250,000 fresh American troops in France, including about 27,000 at Chateau-Thierry, near the hottest of the fighting. By June, when the Germans attempted one last drive, about 85,000 Americans helped hurl them back at Belleau Wood.

By late summer, 1918, the Americans in France represented the margin of victory over the Germans. In September, the Americans took over the attack on a bulge in the German lines called the St. Mihiel Salient, and succeeded in clearing it out. The final great American battle was along a 24-mile line in the Argonne Forest, a naturally rugged country just short of the border between France and Germany that had been transformed into a ghostly wasteland by four years of digging and shelling. It was in that position that over 1 million "doughboys" were sitting when, on November 11, 1918, the Germans surrendered.

Armistice

In the trenches and back home, Americans celebrated deliriously. Millions of people gathered in city centers throughout the country, dancing and whooping. They believed that the Yanks had won the war. After all, the Germans had stalemated the French and British until the boys had gone "over there," in the words of a popular song of the time. Then, just a year after the Americans had begun to fight, it was over.

The American intervention was invaluable to the Allied victory, but the unmitigated joy in the United States was possible only because the American sacrifice was a comparatively minor one. Over 100,000 Americans were dead, more than half of them from disease (particularly the influenza that swept the world in 1918) rather than from bullets. By comparison, 1.4 million French and almost 1 million British soldiers died. Three-quarters of all the Frenchmen who served in the armed forces were casualties. Both France and Britain were badly maimed. Germany and Russia were defeated. If it was not quite true that the United States had "won the war," it was certainly true that the United States was the only nation whose people could feel like victors.

For Further Reading

Several books cited above remain basic, particularly Vincent P. DeSantis, *The Shaping of Modern America, 1877–1916* (1973); Arthur S. Link, *Woodrow Wilson and the Progressive Era* (1954); George E. Mowry, *The Era of Theodore Roosevelt* (1958); William L. O'Neill, *The Progressive Years: America Comes of Age* (1975); and Robert H. Wiebe, *The Search for Order, 1880–1920* (1967).

Somewhat more narrowly focused or dealing with this era in part are E. H. Buehrig, *Woodrow Wilson and the Balance of Power* (1955); Foster R. Dulles, *America's Rise to World Power, 1898–1954* (1955); Lewis L. Gould, *Reform and Regulation: American Politics, 1900–1916* (1978); Otis L. Graham, Jr., *The Great Campaigns: Reform and War in America, 1900–1928* (1971); P. Edward Haley, *Revolution and Intervention: The Diplomacy of Taft and Wilson with Mexico, 1910–1917* (1970); George F.

Kennan, *American Diplomacy, 1900–1950* (1951); David Kennedy, *Over Here: The First World War and American Society* (1980); N. G. Levin, Jr., *Woodrow Wilson and World Politics: America's Response to War and Revolution* (1968); A. S. Link, *Wilson the Diplomatist* (1957) and *Woodrow Wilson: War, Revolution, and Peace* (1979).

Also see Ernest R. May, *The World War and American Isolation, 1914–1917* (1959); Walter Millis, *The Road to War* (1935); R. E. Quirk, *An Affair of Honor: Woodrow Wilson and the Occupation of Vera Cruz* (1962); Lawrence

Stallings, *The Doughboys* (1963); Charles C. Tansill, *America Goes to War* (1938); Russell Weigley, *The American Way of War: History of United States Military Policy and Strategy* (1973); and William A. Williams, *The Tragedy of American Diplomacy* (1959).

For military history, an excellent source is Russell Weigley, *The American Way of War: History of United States Military Policy and Strategy* (1973). See also A. E. Barbeau and F. Henri, *The Unknown Soldiers* (1974); and Lawrence Stallings, *The Doughboys* (1963).

*Film star Douglas Fairbanks drumming up sales of war bonds
on Wall Street.*

OVER HERE

THE FIRST WORLD WAR AT HOME

1917 - 1920

Woodrow Wilson called the Great War "a war to make the world safe for democracy." He sent the

doughboys to Europe, and threw the industrial might of the United States behind the Allies on the

understanding that there would be no victors in the traditional sense of the word, but instead a new

world order dedicated to settling disputes between nations justly and peacefully. He also called World

War I "a war to end wars."

And yet, while sincerely impelled by these high ideals, Wilson was also apprehensive. In April

1917, when his crusade had just begun, Wilson told a newspaper reporter, "Once lead this people into war, and they'll forget there ever was such a thing as tolerance. To fight you must be ruthless and brutal, and the spirit of ruthless brutality will enter into the very fiber of our national life." It was to be one of the tragic ironies of Wilson's life that he initiated some of the policies that made his prophecy come true.

THE PROGRESSIVE WAR

The First World War was simultaneously the apogee of progressivism, when reformers had a free hand in turning their ideals into policy, and the undoing of the progressive movement. For two years, progressive moralists and social planners of the New Nationalist stripe had their way in Washington. Within two years of the conclusion of the war, there was no progressive movement, only a few isolated voices crying in the wilderness of congressional minority, and getting no reply but echoes from the past.

The Movement Splits

The conflict in Europe split the progressives. A few of them itched to fight. The most famous was Theodore Roosevelt, a shrill, almost pathetic, figure in his waning years. When the United States finally intervened, T.R. asked for a command in Europe. Prudently, for this was no splendid little war, Wilson ignored him. In so doing, he permanently embittered many of Roosevelt's devotees.

Other Republican progressives, mostly Westerners such as La Follette, Norris, Borah, and Hiram Johnson, held out to the bitter end for American neutrality. After the declaration of war, they toned down their rhetoric in the interests of national unity. (And in order to save their careers: some newspaper cartoonists depicted them accepting medals from the German Kaiser.) But they never changed their opinion that going to war was a tragic blunder that had been foisted on the country by munitions makers and bankers. They prolonged the debate on the Conscription Act of 1917 for six weeks, finally forcing Congress to exempt men under 21 from the draft. Any warmth they might have felt for Wilson before April 1917 quickly dissipated thereafter.

Not so with most progressives. In Congress and out, the majority of them wholeheartedly supported the war. Like Wilson, they came to believe that imperial Germany represented a deadly threat to free institutions all over the world. Moreover, in the task of mobilizing resources in order to fight the Hun, and in the wave of patriotic commitment that swept the country, the pro-

gressives saw a golden opportunity to put their ideas for economic and social reform to work.

They were right on one count. It was impossible to wage modern total war and cling to the vision of a free, unregulated economy. Armies that numbered millions of men could not be supplied with food, clothing, shelter, medicine, and arms by companies that were free to do as their owners chose. France and England had clamped tight controls on their factories and farms. American progressives believed that the United States would have to do the same.

They were not disappointed. Suggestions for regulation of business that had been rejected in peacetime as too radical proved, in the emergency of wartime, to be less than was necessary. The federal government virtually took over the direction of the economy.

The Planned Economy

Some 5,000 government agencies were set up during the 20 months that the United States was at war, a statistical average of more than eight new agencies a day! Some were useless, wasteful bureaucracies that were established without careful thought and served little purpose save to provide desks, chairs, paper clips, and salaries for the functionaries who ran them. A few were failures. The Aircraft Production Board was commissioned to construct 22,000 airplanes in a year. That figure was unrealistic. But the 1,200 craft and 5,400 replacement motors that the board actually delivered to France were far fewer than a hustler with a hefty bank loan might have supplied.

Other agencies were quite successful. The Shipping Board, actually founded in 1916 before the declaration of war, produced vessels twice as fast as the Germans could sink them. Privately run shipbuilding companies, loaded with deadwood in management, would not have been up to that herculean task.

The United States Railway Administration, headed by Wilson's son-in-law and Secretary of the Treasury, William G. McAdoo, was created early in 1918 when the owners of the nation's railroads proved incapable of moving the volume of freight the war created. The government paid the stockholders a rent equal to their earnings in the prosperous pre-war years and simply took over. McAdoo untangled a colossal snafu in management within a few weeks, and reorganized the railroads into an efficient system such as the nation had never known. About 150,000 freight cars short of what was needed to do the job in 1917, American railroads enjoyed a surplus of 300,000 by the end of the war.

The various war production boards were coordinated by a superagency, the War Industries Board, which was headed by a young Wall Street millionaire, Bernard Baruch. His presence at the top of the planning pyramid indicated that the progressives had not won their campaign for a directed economy without paying a price. American industry and agriculture were regulated, indeed regimented, as never before. But democratically elected officials and public-spirited experts with no stake in the profits were not in the driver's seat. Businessmen were.

Herbert Hoover: The Administrator as War Hero

The task given to Food Administrator Herbert C. Hoover was even more difficult than McAdoo's, and his achievement was daily in the public eye. Hoover's job was to organize food production, distribution, and consumption so that America's farms could feed the United States, supply the huge Allied armies, and help maintain many European civilians.

Only 43 years old when he took the job, Hoover already was known as a "boy wonder." An orphan when still a boy in Iowa, Hoover moved to California and worked his way through Stanford University. A mining engineer, he decided to work abroad on new strikes rather than for established mining companies at home. He had his adventures; he and his wife were besieged in China during the Boxer Rebellion. Mostly, however, Hoover plugged away, made shrewd investments, was soon quite rich, and quite bored with the idea of making more money. Hoover's ambitions lay in public service. Like Andrew Carnegie, he believed that able, wealthy men had special responsibilities to society. Unlike Carnegie, who gave money away, Hoover meant to devote his talents for administration and organization to public service.

He got his chance when he happened to be in London at the outbreak of the Great War. He was asked to take over the problem of getting food to devastated Belgium and jumped at the challenge. He liquidated his business, quickly mastered the complex and ticklish task of feeding people in a war zone, and undoubtedly saved tens of thousands, if not hundreds of thousands, of lives.

Hoover did it without charm or personal flash. He was an intense, outwardly humorless person—all business. His method was to apply engineering principles to the solution of human problems. Progressives admired just such expertise, and the cool, methodical Hoover was a refreshing contrast to other humanitarians who moved about in a cloud of pious self-congratulation. It is an insight into the spirit of the times that he became a war hero comparable to "Black Jack" Pershing and America's dashing ace pilot, Eddie Rickenbacker.

Hooverizing America

Food was not rationed in the United States as it was in Europe. Hoover preferred voluntary action to coercion. He sponsored publicity campaigns that urged American families to observe Wheatless Mondays, Meatless Tuesdays, Porkless Thursdays, and so on. The program worked because compliance was easy, yet psychologically gratifying. Making do without a vital commodity one day a week was no real sacrifice, but doing so made civilians feel as though they were part of the fighting machine. And when a Meatless Tuesday was observed by millions, the savings were enormous.

Hoover also encouraged city dwellers to plant "Victory gardens" in their tiny yards. Every tomato that was raised at home freed commercially produced food for the front. His agency promoted classes in economizing in the kitchen and distributed cookbooks on how to prepare leftovers. The impact was so great that, half-seriously, Americans began to use the word *hooverize* to mean "economize." Chicago proudly reported that the housewives in that city had hooverized the monthly production of garbage down by a third.

Hoover increased farm production through a combi-

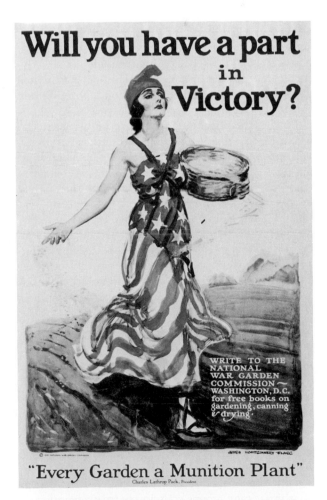

"Every Garden a Munition Plant"

A National War Gardens Commission poster encouraged citizens to plant home vegetable gardens, thus freeing commercial producers to concentrate on providing goods for the war effort.

nation of patriotic boosting and cash incentives. He helped increase wheat acreage from 45 million in 1917 to 75 million in 1919. American exports of foodstuffs to the Allies tripled over already high pre-war levels. Hoover was called "the Miracle Man," and another young Washington administrator, Undersecretary of the Navy Franklin D. Roosevelt, wanted the Democratic party to nominate him for president in 1920.

Managing People

People were mobilized too: workers and ordinary citizens as well as soldiers. In May 1917, Congress passed the Selective Service Act, the first draft law since the Civil War. Registration was compulsory for all men between the ages of 21 and 45. (In 1918, the minimum age was lowered to 18.) From the 10 million who registered within a month of passage (24 million by the end of the war), local draft boards selected able-bodied recruits according to quotas assigned them. Some occupational groups were deferred, but no one was allowed to buy his way out, as had been done during the Civil War. Indeed, authority to make final selections was given to local draft boards in order to silence critics who said that conscription had no place in a democracy. The draft contributed about 3 million young men in addition to the 2 million who volunteered.

About 21,000 draftees claimed to be conscientious objectors on religious grounds, although, in the end, only 4,000 insisted on being assigned to noncombatant duty, as medics or in the Quartermaster Corps. Approximately 500 men refused to cooperate with the military in any way, some for political rather than religious reasons. Under the terms of the Selective Service Act, they were imprisoned and, generally, treated poorly. Camp Leonard Wood in Missouri had an especially bad reputation. In Washington State, a man who claimed that Jesus had forbidden him to take up arms was sentenced to death. He was not executed, but the last conscientious objector was not freed from prison until 1933, long after most Americans had come to agree with him that the war had been a mistake.

SOCIAL CHANGES

War is a revolutionary or, at least, an agitator. The changes impressed on American society from the top in the interests of victory inevitably affected social relationships. Some groups consciously took advantage of the government's wants, needs, and preoccupations to achieve old goals. Others were merely caught up by the different rhythms of a society at war.

Labor Takes Its Seat

In order to keep the factories humming, Wilson made concessions to the labor movement that would have been unthinkable a few years earlier. He appointed Samuel Gompers, the patriotic president of the American Federation of Labor, to sit on Baruch's War Industries Board. In return for this recognition, Gompers pledged the A.F.L. unions to a no-strike policy for the duration of the conflict.

Because wages rose during the war, there were comparatively few work stoppages. Business boomed, and employers dizzy with bonanza profits did not care to jeopardize them by resisting moderate demands by their employees. Most important, the National War Labor Board, on which five A.F.L. nominees sat, mediated industrial disputes before they disrupted production and, in many cases, found in favor of the workers.

The quiet incorporation of organized labor into the decision-making process made the A.F.L. "respectable," as it never had been before. From 2.7 million members in 1914, the union movement (including independent unions) grew to 4.2 million in 1919.

Black Americans in Wartime

Like Gompers, leaders of black organizations hoped that by proving their patriotism in time of crisis, blacks would win an improved status. About 400,000 young black men enlisted or responded to the draft; proportionately, more blacks than whites donned khaki.

It was difficult to ignore the contradiction between Wilson's ringing declaration that the purpose of the war was to defend democracy and liberty and the second-class citizenship suffered by black people. W. E. B. Du Bois, the leader of the N.A.A.C.P., pointedly reminded the president of the dichotomy, and Wilson did go so far as to issue a strong condemnation of lynching. Nevertheless, mere war could not destroy deeply rooted racist sentiments. Black soldiers were assigned to segregated units and usually put to menial tasks such as digging trenches and loading trucks behind the lines. Only a few black units saw combat, although one regiment that did was awarded the Croix de Guerre for gallantry in battle by the French government.

Military segregation had its advantages for some blacks. To command black units, the army trained and commissioned more than 1,200 black officers. This was particularly gratifying to Du Bois, who staked his hopes for the future on the creation of a black elite.

Race Riot at Home

More important in the long run than service in the army was the massive movement of blacks from the rural and strictly segregated South to the industrial centers of the North. Before 1914, only about 10,000 blacks a year

Members of the 369th Infantry, a black regiment, returned to the United States in 1919 wearing medals given to them by the French government commending them for gallantry in battle.

drifted from the South to cities like New York, Philadelphia, Detroit, and Chicago. After 1914, when the risks of ocean travel choked off immigration from abroad while factories filling war orders needed workers, 100,000 blacks made the trek each year. It was not so great a leap in miles as the European immigration, but it was just as wrenching socially. From a Mississippi delta cabin to a Detroit factory and slum was a big change in way of life.

Those who served in the army, and most of those who moved north, were young people. They were less inclined to accept the daily humiliations that accompanied being black in white America. This was particularly true of the men in uniform, who believed that their service entitled them to respect.

The result was that 1917 was a year of racial conflict, with a frightening race riot in industrial East St. Louis,

Illinois. In Houston, white civilians fought a pitched battle with black soldiers, and twelve people were killed. Although both sides shared the blame for the riot, thirteen black soldiers were hanged and fourteen were imprisoned for life. Du Bois and the N.A.A.C.P. were only partly correct in their analysis of how the war would affect African Americans. Society made economic concessions to blacks in the interests of winning the war, but it did not grant civil equality.

It's a Woman's War

The women's suffrage movement, on the contrary, skillfully parlayed wartime idealism and fears into final victory for the long-fought cause. Imitating British and French examples, the armed forces inducted female volunteers, mostly as nurses and clerical workers. More important was the same labor shortage that created op-

A woman welder was unthinkable before the war created a labor shortage.

portunities in industry for blacks. Working-class women began doing factory work and other jobs that had been closed to them. Women operated trolley cars, drove delivery trucks, cleaned streets, directed traffic, and filled jobs in every industry from aircraft construction to zinc galvanization.

Middle-class women took the lead in organizing support groups. They rolled bandages, held patriotic rallies, and filled the holds of ships with knitted sweaters and socks and home-baked cookies for the boys in France. With women's contributions to waging the war so obvious, it was increasingly difficult for patriotic politicians to oppose suffrage with the argument that women belonged in the nursery minding infants.

Voting at Last

By 1917, the feminist movement was split once again into radical and conservative wings. Curiously, while the "radicals" and "conservatives" often had harsh words for one another, their different approaches both contributed to the victory of the suffrage movement. Thus, when the aggressive Women's Party led by Alice Paul demonstrated noisily in Washington, burning a copy of Wilson's idealistic Fourteen Points and chaining themselves to the fence in front of the White House, many politicians went scurrying for reassurance to the more

polite National American Woman Suffrage Association.

Led by Carrie Chapman Catt, the association shrewdly obliged them. Not only did most American women oppose such irresponsible behavior, Catt argued, but social stability and conservative government could be ensured only by granting women the vote. Their numbers would counterbalance the increasing influence of radicals and foreigners at the polls, not to mention the blacks who were demanding their rights.

The suffrage movement was too long in the field and too large to be denied. Even Wilson, who instinctively disliked the idea of women voting, announced his support. On June 4, 1919, a few months after the Armistice, Congress sent the Nineteenth Amendment to the states. On August 18, 1920, ratification by Tennessee put it into the Constitution. "The right of citizens . . . to vote," it read, "shall not be denied or abridged by the United States or by any State on account of sex." Carrie Chapman Catt had no doubt about what had put it over. It was the war, the former pacifist said, that liberated American women.

The Moral War

Another long progressive campaign already had been brought to a victorious end. Like the suffragists, the prohibitionists appeared to be stalled permanently on the eve of the war. In 1914, only one-quarter of the states had prohibition laws on the books, and many of those were casually enforced. With American intervention in the war, however, the anti-drinking forces added a new and decisive argument to their armory: the distilling of liquor consumed vast quantities of grain that were needed as food. Shortly after the declaration of war, Congress passed the Lever Act, a section of which forbade the sale of grain to distilleries.

Because many breweries were run by German-Americans, with their teutonic names emblazoned proudly on bottle and barrel, they were doubly handicapped in fighting the prohibitionists. Although Americans had developed a taste for cold lager beer, the beverage was still associated with Germans. Moralism, hooverizing, and the popular insistence on 100 percent Americanism all combined to bring about, in December 1917, the passage of the Eighteenth Amendment, which prohibited "the manufacture, sale, or transportation of intoxicating liquors" in the United States. It was ratified in 1919 and put into effect by the Volstead Act.

War usually leads to relaxation of sexual morality, as vast numbers of young men are removed from the social restraints of family and custom. The First World War proved to be no exception. However, well-meaning moralists in Wilson's administration hoped to take advantage of the mobilization of millions in order to instill

In 1920, for the first time, women in every state were eligible to vote.

high moral standards in the young men under their control. Josephus Daniels, the deeply religious Secretary of the Navy, thought of his ships as "floating universities" of moral reform. He gave orders to clear out the red-light districts that were a fixture in every naval port, and the army did the same in cities near its bases.

Prostitution was not eliminated by these orders any more than whiskey and beer drinking were abolished by the Eighteenth Amendment. But the short-term victories encouraged reformers in their belief that, among the horrors, the First World War was a blessing to social reform.

CONFORMITY AND REPRESSION

It was not a blessing on civil liberties. As Wilson had predicted, white-hot patriotism scorched the traditions of free political expression and tolerance of disparate ways of life. Of course, the principles of free speech and religious expression had been violated before the First World War. But never had violation of the Bill of Rights been so widespread as during the war, and never had the federal government so stridently supported, even initiated, repression.

The Campaign Against the Socialists

The Socialist party of America was the only important national political institution to oppose American intervention. In April 1917, just as war was being declared in Washington, the party met in emergency convention in St. Louis and proclaimed "unalterable opposition" to a conflict that killed working people and paid dividends to capitalists. Rather than hurting the party at the polls, this stance earned the party an increase in votes as many non-Socialists cast ballots for Socialists as the only way short of soap-boxing, a dangerous idea, to express their dissent.

Government moved quickly to head off the possibility of an antiwar bandwagon. The state legislature of New York expelled seven Socialist assemblymen simply because they objected to the war. Not until after the war did courts overrule the unconstitutional action. Victor Berger was elected to Congress from Milwaukee, but denied his seat by the House. When he then defeated the candidate supported by both the Democratic and Republican parties in the special election to fill the vacancy, Congress again refused to seat him. Berger's seat remained empty until 1923 when he was allowed to fill it. In the meantime, the Milwaukee Socialists' *Social Democratic Herald* and many other Socialist papers were denied cheap mailing privileges by Postmaster General

Albert S. Burleson. Most of them never recovered from the blow.

The most celebrated attack on the Socialists was the indictment and trial of the party's longtime leader Eugene V. Debs for a speech opposing conscription. In sending Debs to prison, the Wilson administration was taking a chance. The four-time presidential candidate was loved and respected by many non-Socialists. At his trial in September 1918, Debs's eloquence lived up to its reputation. "While there is a lower class I am in it; while there is a criminal element I am of it; while there is a soul in prison, I am not free," he told the jury. But in prosecuting and jailing him and other prominent Socialists such as Kate Richards O'Hare, the government also made it clear that dissent on the war issue would not be tolerated.

The Destruction of the I. W. W.

The suppression of the I.W.W. was more violent. There was an irony in this because, while the radical union officially opposed the war, Secretary-Treasurer "Big Bill" Haywood tried to play down the issue. For the first time since its founding in 1905, the I.W.W. was enrolling members by the thousands every month. Haywood hoped to ride out the patriotic hysteria of wartime and emerge from the war with a powerful economic organization.

But the government did not decide to move against the I.W.W. because of its paper position on the war. Unlike the Socialists, who numbered many articulate and politically active middle-class people among their supporters, the I.W.W. worked among the lowest ranks of the working class, people with little influence on public opinion. By 1917, however, most of these "Wobblies" were concentrated in three sectors of the economy that were vital to the war effort: among the migrant harvest workers who brought in the nation's wheat; among loggers in the Pacific Northwest; and among copper miners in Western towns like Globe and Bisbee in Arizona and Butte in Montana. And these "Wobblies" refused to abide by the no-strike pledge that Samuel Gompers had made on behalf of the American Federation of Labor.

The I.W.W. was crushed by a combination of vigilante terrorism and government action. In July 1917, a thousand "deputies" wearing white armbands in order to identify one another rounded up 1,200 strikers in Bisbee, loaded them on a specially chartered train, and dumped them in the Hermanas desert of New Mexico, where they were without food for 36 hours. The next month, I.W.W. organizer Frank Little was lynched in Butte, possibly by police officers in disguise. In neither case was any attempt made to bring the vigilantes to justice. President Wilson pointedly ignored Haywood's protest of the Bisbee deportation and his demand for action in the case of Little's murder.

In the grain belt, sheriffs and farmers had a free hand in dealing with suspected Wobblies. In the Sitka spruce forests of Washington and Oregon (Sitka spruce was the principal wood used in aircraft construction), the army organized the Loyal Legion of Loggers and Lumbermen to counter the popularity of the I.W.W. There, at least, conditions were improved as the union was repressed, but attacks on the I.W.W. were consistently vicious. Local police and federal agents winked at and even participated in everyday violations of civil rights and violence against Wobblies and their sympathizers.

Civil Liberties Suspended

The fatal blow fell in the autumn of 1917, when the Justice Department raided I.W.W. headquarters in several cities, rounded up the union's leaders, and indicted about 200 under the Espionage Act of 1917. Along with the Sedition Act of 1918, the Espionage Act outlawed not only overt treasonable acts, but made it a crime to "utter, print, write, or publish any disloyal, profane, scurrilous, or abusive language" about the government, the flag, or the uniform of a soldier or sailor. A casual snide remark was enough to warrant bringing charges, and a few cases were based on little more than that.

In *Schenck v. the United States* (1919), the Supreme Court unanimously upheld this broad, vague law. Oliver Wendell Holmes, Jr., the most liberal minded and humane Justice on the Court, wrote the opinion which established the principle that when "a clear and present danger" existed, such as the war, Congress had the power to pass laws that would not be acceptable in normal times.

Even at that, the government did not prove that the I.W.W. was guilty of sedition. In effect, the individuals who were sentenced to up to twenty years in prison were punished because of their membership in an unpopular organization. Many liberals who had no taste for I.W.W. doctrine but who were shocked at the government's cynical policy of repression fought the cases. In 1920, led by Roger Baldwin, they organized the American Civil Liberties Union to guard against a repetition of a shameful chapter in American judicial history.

Manipulating Public Opinion

The attack on the Socialists and the Wobblies was only one fulfillment of Wilson's prediction that a spirit of ruthless brutality would enter the fiber of American life. Americans in general were stirred to believe that they were engaged in a holy crusade, "a war to end war" against a diabolical foe. Violent acts against German-Americans and the very idea of German culture were commonplace.

Some of the innumerable incidents of intolerance that marred the wartime years were spontaneous; for example, a Midwestern mob dragged a German-American

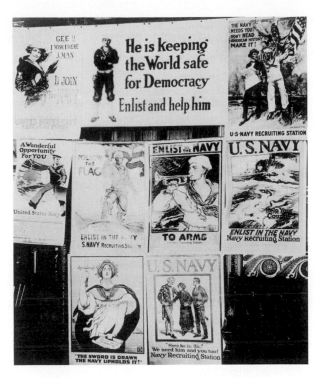

Poster art reached its apogee during World War I in the hands of government propagandists.

shopkeeper from his home, threw him to his knees, forced him to kiss the American flag, and made him spend his life savings on war bonds. But the fire of intolerance that burned from coast to coast was also instigated and abetted by the national government.

The agency that was entrusted with mobilizing public opinion was the Committee on Public Information. Ironically, it was headed by George Creel, a progressive newspaperman who had devoted his career to fighting the very sort of intolerance and social injustice he now found himself encouraging. Creel faced a twofold task. First, to avoid demoralization, the C.P.I. censored the news from Europe. The C.P.I. dispatches emphasized victories and suppressed or played down stories of setbacks and the misery of life in the trenches between battles. With most editors and publishers solidly behind the war, Creel had little difficulty in convincing them to censor their own correspondents.

Crushing Kultur

Second, and far more ominously, the C.P.I. took up the task of molding public opinion so that slight deviations from full support of the war were branded as disloyal. Obviously, all German-Americans could not be imprisoned. (Only 6,300 were actually interned compared with 45,000 of Great Britain's much smaller German community.) However, the C.P.I. could and did launch a massive propaganda campaign that depicted German *Kultur* as intrinsically vile.

The C.P.I. issued 60 million pamphlets, sent pre-written editorials to pliant (or merely lazy) newspaper editors, and subsidized the design and printing of posters conveying the impression that a sinister and ubiquitous network of German spies was operating in the United States. With money to be made in exploiting the theme, the infant film industry centered in Hollywood, California rushed to oblige. A typical title of 1917 was *The Barbarous Hun*. (Another film company was prosecuted in 1917 for releasing a film about the American Revolution that depicted British troops in an unfavorable light.)

At movie theaters before shows and during intermissions, a corps of 75,000 "Four-Minute Men," volunteers, delivered patriotic speeches of that length, 7.5 million such messages in all. Film stars such as Douglas Fairbanks, Charlie Chaplin, and Mary Pickford ("America's Sweetheart") appeared at Liberty Bond rallies and spoke anti-German lines written by the C.P.I.

Liberty Hounds and Boy Spies

The anti-German hysteria could take laughable form. Restaurants revised their menus so that sauerkraut became "liberty cabbage," hamburgers became "Salisbury steaks" (after a British lord), and frankfurters and wiener sausages, named after German and Austrian cities, became widely known as "hot dogs."

The real dog, the dachshund, had to be transformed into a "liberty hound." Towns with names of German origin chose more patriotic designations. German measles, then a common childhood disease, became "patriotic measles." Hundreds of schools and some colleges dropped the German language from their course offerings. Dozens of symphony orchestras refused to play the works of German composers, leaving noticeable holes in the repertoire. Prominent German-Americans who wished to save their careers found it advisable to imitate the opera singer Ernestine Schumann-Heinck. She was a fixture at patriotic rallies, her ample figure draped with a large American flag and her magnificent voice singing "The Star-Spangled Banner" and "America the Beautiful."

But the firing of Germans from their jobs, discriminating against German farmers, burning of German books, and beating and occasional lynching of German-Americans were not so humorous. Nor was the treatment of conscientious objectors by organizations of self-appointed guardians of the national interest with names like "Sedition Slammers," "Terrible Threateners," and even "Boy Spies of America." The members of such organizations stopped young men on the streets and demanded to see their draft cards. The largest of these groups, which were responsible for hundreds of

---

HOW THEY LIVED

"THEY DROPPED LIKE FLIES": THE GREAT FLU EPIDEMIC OF 1918

About 10 million people died as a result of battle during the four years of the First World War. Small wonder that the event staggered the confidence and morale of the European nations.

But the war was a modest killer compared with the "Spanish flu." During only *four months* late in 1918 and early in 1919, a worldwide flu epidemic, or pandemic, killed 21 million people. The American army in Europe lost 49,000 men in battle and 64,000 to disease, the majority of them to the flu. At home, fully 548,452 American civilians died, 10 times as many as soldiers felled in battle.

In the United States, the yet unnamed disease first appeared in March 1918, at Fort Riley, Kansas. After a dust storm, 107 soldiers checked into the infirmary complaining of headaches, fever and chills, difficulty in breathing, and miscellaneous aches and pains. Most curious to them, the illness had befallen them in an instant; one moment they were feeling fit, the next they could barely stand. Within a week, Fort Riley had 522 cases, and in a little more than a month, when the affliction abruptly disappeared, 8,000 cases. Almost 50 of the sick men died, not too disturbing a rate in an age when any number of contagious diseases forgotten today were considered deadly. Some doctors noted that these flu victims were in the prime of life and, presumably after basic training, in excellent condition. Moreover, most of them were strapping farm boys, who usually shook off such ailments as though they were colds.

It was wartime, however, and the soldiers from Fort Riley were shipped to Europe in May. The flu made a brief appearance in the cities of the eastern seaboard, but did not rival any of a number of epidemics, including a serious one in the United States in 1889 and 1890.

In Europe, the disease was far more deadly. In neutral Switzerland alone, 58,000 died of it in July. The deaths in the trenches on both sides of the line were enough, according to the German general Erich von Ludendorff, to curtail a major campaign. By June, the flu was sweeping Africa and India, where the mortality was "without parallel in the history of disease." That could be attributed to the wretched poverty of the subcontinent. But what of Western Samoa, where 7,500 of the island's 38,000 people died?

The total figures had not been calculated when the flu began a second and even more destructive tour of the world. The war had created ideal conditions for such a pandemic. People moved about in unprecedented numbers; 200,000 to 300,000 crossed the Atlantic to Europe each month, and many were carrying the unidentifiable germ. Moreover, war crowded people together so that conditions were also perfect for the successful mutation of viruses. With so many handy hosts to support propagation, the emergence of new strains was all the more likely.

That is apparently what happened in August, in western Africa, France, or Spain, which got the blame. A much deadlier variation of the original swept over the world, and this time the effects in the United States were cataclysmic.

In Boston, where it struck first, doubtless carried in by returning soldiers, 202 people died on October 1. New York City reported 3,100 cases in one day; 300 victims died. Later in the month, 851 New Yorkers died in one day, far and away the record. Philadelphia, which was particularly hard hit, lost 289 people on October 6; within one week, 5,270 were reported dead. The death rate for the month was 700 times its usual rate. Similar figures came in from every large city in the country. Just as worrisome, the disease found its way to the most obscure corners of the country. A winter logging camp in Michigan, cut off from the rest of humanity, was afflicted. Oregon officials reported finding sheep-herders dead by their flocks.

Most public officials responded about as well as could be expected during a catastrophe that no one understood. Congress, many of its members laid low, appropriated money to hire physicians and nurses and set up clinics. Many cities closed theaters, bars, schools, and churches,

---

illegal acts, was the American Protective League. At one time it numbered 250,000 members, many of whom probably had signed up simply to avoid having their loyalty questioned.

WILSON AND THE LEAGUE OF NATIONS

Why did Woodrow Wilson, a Jeffersonian liberal before the war, tolerate and even encourage such government-abetted behavior? The answer lies in the fact that the president's dream of building a new and just world order became an obsession with him. Like no president before him (but like several since), he lost interest in domestic affairs except insofar as they affected his all-consuming foreign policy concerns. The one-time enemy of big government presided over its extraordinary expansion. Repression of dissenters, even unjust and illegal repression, appeared to hasten the defeat of the Kaiser, so Wilson abandoned values that had guided his life.

The President's Obsession

In January 1918, Wilson presented to Congress his blueprint for the postwar world. It consisted of "Fourteen Points," which, Wilson insisted, were to be incorporated into the treaty that would eventually be made. Mostly, and prohibited public gatherings such as parades and sporting events. Others, notably Kansas City, where the political boss frankly said that the economy was more important, carried on as usual. Mystifying moralists, Kansas City was no harder hit than were cities that took extreme precautions. (Nationwide and worldwide, about one-fifth of the population caught the Spanish flu, and the death rate was 3 percent.)

Several city governments required the wearing of gauze masks and punished violators with fines of up to $100. Many photographs that were taken during the autumn of 1918 have a surreal quality because of the masks. San Franciscans, their epidemic at a peak on Armistice Day, November 11, celebrated wearing gauze. Some wretched poet wrote the lines:

> Obey the laws
> And wear the gauze
> Protect your jaws
> From septic paws

Philadelphia gathered its dead in carts, as had been done during the bubonic plague epidemics of the Middle Ages. The city's A. F. Brill Company, a maker of trolley cars, turned over its woodshop to coffinmakers. The city of Buffalo set up its own coffin factory. Authorities in Washington, D.C., seized a trainload of coffins headed for Pittsburgh.

Then, once again, the disease disappeared. There was a less lethal wave (perhaps another mutation) in the spring of 1919, with President Wilson one of the victims; and a leading historian of the phenomenon, Alfred W. Crosby, suggests that another minor epidemic in 1920 may have been a fourth wave. But the worst was over by about the time that the First World War ended, leaving physicians to reflect on the character of the disease and to wonder what they could do if it recurred.

There were some things to reflect on. The first has already been noted: the Spanish flu struck very suddenly,

offering individuals no way to fight it except to lie down and wait.

Second, the disease went fairly easy on those people who are usually most vulnerable to respiratory diseases, the elderly; and it was hardest on those who usually shake off such afflictions, young people. In the United States, the death rate for white males between the ages of 25 and 34 was, during the 1910s, about 80 per 100,000. During the flu epidemic it was 2,000 per 100,000. In a San Francisco maternity ward in October, 19 out of 42 women died. In Washington, a college student telephoned a clinic to report that two of her three roommates were dead in bed and the third was seriously ill. The report of the police officer who was sent to investigate was "Four girls dead in apartment." Old people died of the flu, of course, but the death rate among the elderly did not rise a point during the epidemic!

Third, people who had grown up in tough, poor, big city neighborhoods were less likely to get the disease and, if they got it, less likely to die of it than were people who had grown up in healthier environments.

These facts eventually led scientists to conclude that the Spanish flu was a mutation of a common virus that caused a flu that was nothing more than an inconvenience. It was postulated, although never proved, that the deadly germ was the issue of an unholy liaison between a virus that affected humans and another that affected hogs. Spanish flu became "swine flu."

Thus, poor city people, who were more likely to suffer a plethora of minor diseases, had developed an immunity to the virus that farm people had not. Because old people were spared in 1918 and 1919, it has been said that the Spanish or swine flu was related to the less fatal virus that had caused the epidemic of 1889 to 1890. Having been affected by it, the elderly were relatively immune to its descendant.

Wilson's points dealt with specific European territorial problems to be resolved, but several general principles were woven through the plan.

First, Germany must be treated fairly and generously in order to avoid the festering resentments that could lead to another war. Wilson was well aware that, for more than forty years before the war, French politicians had called for revenge for Germany's defeat of France in 1870. In practical terms, Wilson meant that Germany must not lose territory occupied by German-speaking people and must not be saddled with huge reparations payments—"fines" as punishment for the war—such as British and French leaders were at that very time telling their people would be paid.

Second, the boundaries of all European countries must

conform to nationality as defined by language. Like many others, Wilson believed that the aspirations of people to govern themselves had been a major cause of the war. No such concessions were to be made to the nonwhite peoples in Europe's colonies, however, although Wilson called for Germany's colonies to be disposed of on some basis other than as spoils of war divided among the victors.

Third, Wilson demanded "absolute freedom upon the seas, . . . alike in peace and in war." This was a reference to the German submarine campaign that Wilson blamed for American intervention, but it also hearkened to Britain's historical inclination to use British primacy on the waves to interfere with neutral shipping.

Fourth, Wilson demanded disarmament. It was obvious to all parties that the arms race of the two decades preceding the war had not been a deterrent but a major cause of the tragedy.

Finally and most important toward avoiding another Great War, Wilson called for the establishment of "a general assembly of nations," a kind of congress of countries, to replace the alliances and secret treaties that, he believed, had contributed to the tragedy of 1914. More than any other aspect of his program, the dream of a League of Nations came to obsess the president.

Wilson Fools Himself

As ultimate victory was ensured by an Allied breakthrough during the summer of 1918, Wilson turned virtually all his energies to planning for the peace conference to be held in Paris. He announced that he would personally head the American delegation, the first president to take so active a part in diplomatic negotiations.

The enormity of World War I justified such an innovation, but Wilson somewhat mistook his enthusiasm for remaking the world as reflecting the mood of the American people. In the congressional elections of 1918, held just a week before the armistice, the voters returned Republican majorities of 240 to 190 to the House of Representatives and of 49 to 47 to the Senate. The new Congress not only was Republican, but had a decidedly unidealistic tinge. Old bosses and professional politicians who had struggled against the reformers for a decade were coming back to Washington.

They were not all hidebound reactionaries, nor Wilson-haters, by any means. They were the kind of men who were willing to make deals. But Wilson did not try to cultivate their good will by including a prominent Republican among the delegates with whom he sailed to Europe on December 4. Nor did he recognize that, in choosing so many Republican regulars, the American people were reflecting a weariness with the idealism and rigorously active government of the Wilson administration.

Wilson also misinterpreted his reception in England, France, and Italy. Everywhere he went he was greeted with roaring cheers and blizzards of flowers thrown by adoring crowds. With a new democratic government in Germany surrendering on the basis of the Fourteen Points, Wilson believed that the people of Europe had risen to greatness, expressing their support for a peace without victors and a postwar world organized on principles of justice.

The Peace Conference

He could not have been more mistaken. The cheering crowds were welcoming not a visionary leader, but a conqueror, the man who, Europeans believed, had tilted the stalemated war in their favor, enabling their countries to win it. Their leaders, the men with whom Wilson

sat down in Paris, understood this. They had a much more realistic view than the American president of what the four years of terribly destructive war had meant to Europe. The peoples of the Allied nations wanted to avenge the bitterness of their sacrifices by tasting the sweet fruits of victory. For four years, the other three members of the "Big Four" had promised them those fruits. Now, in 1919, they paid lip service to Wilson's ideals, but once behind the closed doors of the conference room, they put their national interests first.

Indeed, Georges Clemenceau, the prime minister of France, commented wryly, "God gave us the Ten Commandments and we broke them. Wilson gives us the Fourteen Points. We shall see." Clemenceau was a cagey, tough, and bitter infighter whom a lifetime in politics, mostly in opposition, had turned into a cynic. He was determined to hang the blame for the war on Germany and to ensure that France would never again be attacked. Clemenceau wanted to strip Germany of valuable territory and saddle the German people with huge reparations payments that, on top of their massive war debt, would hobble Germany for a generation.

David Lloyd George of Great Britain was personally more cordial to Wilson. But he was a habitual backroom manipulator given to inconstancy and outright deceit; and he too had political demands to meet. His country had suffered dreadfully from the bloodletting and wanted reparations. Moreover, the Royal Navy had no intention of giving up its dominance on the high seas.

Vittorio Orlando of Italy was only casually interested in the larger questions. He went to Versailles to make sure that Italy was rewarded with Austrian territory, including several regions of the Alps that were home to 200,000 German-speaking people, and the port of Fiume on the Adriatic, a city that was largely Croatian in population. His goals directly contradicted Wilson's Point Nine. The Japanese delegate, Count Nobuaki Makino, not a member of the Big Four, was determined to retain the German colonies in the Pacific that Japan had seized. So much for Point Five.

Bit by bit the Allies drew new lines on Wilson's blueprint. When the president revealed how all-important the League was to him by insisting that its Covenant (constitution) be acted on early in the proceedings, they calculated that he would give in on other questions in order to save it. He did. The terms of the Treaty of Versailles, which Wilson brought home in July 1919, bore only a passing resemblance to the Fourteen Points he took to Europe eight months earlier.

Article 10

Europe's rejection of Wilson's call for national self-determination in Europe and just treatment of Germany did not much concern the senators who had the consti-

None of his three fellow heads of government at the Versailles Conference shared Wilson's ideals or hopes for the future.

tutional responsibility to approve or reject the treaty. On the contrary, only 12 of the 49 Republican senators, mostly the Western progressives who had opposed going to war in 1917, announced themselves to be "irreconcilable" in their opposition to the pact. Still fuming because the United States went to war in the first place, they meant to isolate the United States from corrupt Europe once again.

In March 1919, before Wilson returned from Versailles, the other 37 Republican senators signed a round robin declaring themselves to be "reservationists" on the issue. That is, while they considered the Treaty of Versailles as it stood to be unacceptable, they let the president know that they would vote to ratify if Wilson made some changes in it or accepted their reservations. What worried them most was Article 10 of the League Covenant, which pledged all member states to "preserve against external aggression the territorial integrity and . . . political independence of all members." Article 10 seemed to commit the United States to go to war if any other member of the League were attacked.

Wilson replied that Article 10 was merely a moral obligation on the part of members, and, long after his day, he would be proved correct; throughout its history, the League was unable to enforce its decisions. Nevertheless, having said that the article had little concrete meaning, Wilson refused to make a single concession to the worried senators. In his stubbornness, he created an opportunity for the chairman of the Senate Foreign Relations Committee, an old friend of Theodore Roosevelt who despised everything about the president, to destroy his dream.

The Fight for the League

Henry Cabot Lodge was a dapper, ill-tempered senator from Massachusetts who was not very popular with his colleagues. As stubborn and demanding as Wilson, he lacked a shred of Wilson's greatness. Lodge, however, proved in the battle over the League to be a much shrewder politician than the president. Perceiving that Wilson was growing less flexible, Lodge became open and cooperative with senators who disliked the League less avidly than he did. Understanding that the longer the debate dragged on, the less the American people would be interested in the League, Lodge played for time and welcomed every one of Wilson's refusals to compromise. He read the entire 264 pages of the treaty into the record of his committee's hearings, even though it already had been published and placed on every senator's desk.

Lodge guessed right, and Wilson, less reasonable with every day that passed, guessed wrong. Whereas the majority of Americans doubtlessly favored the League in the first months of 1919, their interest waned slowly but perceptibly as the months passed.

The climax came in September. With the treaty about to come before the Senate, Wilson undertook an exhausting 8,000-mile speaking tour. He believed that by

PRESTIGE

John Maynard Keynes, a member of the British delegation at the Versailles Peace Conference, wrote that Woodrow Wilson enjoyed a prestige and a moral influence throughout the world unequaled in history. His bold and measured words carried to the peoples of Europe above and beyond the voices of their own politicians. The enemy peoples trusted him to carry out the compact he had made with them; and the Allied peoples acknowledged him not as a victor only but almost as a prophet.

rallying the people behind him, he could pressure the reservationist senators to vote for the treaty. By September 25, when he moved into Colorado, the crowds seemed to be with him. At Pueblo, however, his speech was slurred, and he openly wept. Wilson either suffered a mild stroke at that time or was on the verge of a nervous breakdown. His physician hastily canceled the remainder of the tour and rushed him back to Washington. A few days later, he crumpled to the floor of his bedroom, felled by a cerebral thrombosis, a blood clot in the brain.

The Invisible President

No one really knows just how seriously Wilson was disabled over the next several months. His protective and strong-willed wife isolated him for six weeks from almost everyone but his physicians. She screened every document brought to him and returned them with shaky signatures at the bottom. When suspicious advisers insisted on seeing him, they discovered that his left side was paralyzed and his speech was halting. However, he appeared to be in complete control of his wits. To a group of senators who told him, "We've all been praying for you," he replied, "Which way, Senator?"

Wilson did not meet officially with his cabinet for six months, and photographs of that occasion show a haggard old man with an anxiety in his eyes that cannot be found in any earlier picture. The clarity of his thinking undoubtedly was affected. But since Wilson in the best

ROUND ROBIN

A round robin is a petition or statement that is signed by several people with no one of them identified as the leader or instigator. All sign around the text of the document in order to disguise the order of signing. The intent of the round robin is precisely the opposite of that of John Hancock in signing his name so prominently to the Declaration of Independence.

of health had refused to consider compromising with Lodge, the president's removal from the scene probably had little effect on the final outcome of the battle.

That outcome was defeat. In November, on Wilson's instructions, the Democratic senators voted with the irreconcilables to kill the treaty with the Lodge reservations by a vote of 55 to 39. When the treaty was introduced without the reservations, the reservationists and the irreconcilables defeated it against the Democrats. In March, over Wilson's protest, 21 Democrats worked out a compromise with the reservationist Republicans and again voted on the treaty. The 23 Democrats who went along with Wilson's insistence that he get the original treaty or no treaty at all made the difference. They and the irreconcilables defeated it.

The Election of 1920

Wilson believed that he could win the Treaty of Versailles and the League of Nations in the presidential election of 1920. Incredibly, given his shattered health and the tradition against a third term, he wanted to be the Democratic party's nominee. That was too much for even the most faithful Democrats to swallow. They chose Governor James M. Cox of Ohio, a lackluster party regular who looked like a traveling salesman. For vice-president the Democrats nominated a staunch but slight young Wilsonian with a magical name, the Undersecretary of the Navy, Franklin D. Roosevelt. The Democrats were pessimistic. But perhaps the Roosevelt name on the Democratic ticket would win enough progressive votes to put the party across.

The Republicans expected to win. The congressional elections of 1918 had seemed to show that despite six years of Democratic government, the Republicans remained the majority party. As is common when parties are optimistic, there was a fight for the nomination between General Leonard Wood, an old comrade of Theodore Roosevelt, and Illinois governor Frank O. Lowden, who had a reputation as an innovative scientific farmer. Both arrived in Chicago with large blocs of votes, but neither had a majority.

Early in the proceedings, a group of reporters cornered a political wheeler-dealer from Ohio named Harry M. Daugherty and asked him who he thought would be nominated. Daugherty replied genially: "Well boys, I'll tell you what I think. The convention will be deadlocked. After the other candidates have failed, we'll get together in some hotel room, oh, about 2:11 in the morning, and some 15 men, bleary-eyed with lack of sleep, will sit down around a big table and when that time comes Senator Harding will be selected."

Senator Harding was Warren G. Harding. A Daugherty crony, Harding was a handsome, likable man who was considered one of the least competent figures in Congress. Perhaps because of that, he was acceptable to almost everyone. Because Harding had been a "mild reservationist" on the treaty issue, as usual taking an innocuous stand, Henry Cabot Lodge (in whose "smoke-filled room" at the Blackstone Hotel the nomination took place) undoubtedly believed that he could control him.

The Great Bloviator

During the campaign, Harding waffled on the treaty, sometimes appearing to favor it with reservations and at other times hinting that he would let the issue quietly die. If there was a theme to his campaign, it was the need for the country to cool off after almost two decades of experimental reform and white-hot wartime crusading. This circumstance allowed Harding to implement his technique of "bloviation." Bloviating, as Harding was happy to define it, was "the art of speaking for as long as the occasion warrants, and saying nothing." In Boston, in September, Harding said that "America's need is not heroism but healing, not nostrums but normalcy, not agitation but adjustment, not surgery but serenity, not the dramatic but the dispassionate, not experiment but equipoise, not submergence in internationality but sustainment in triumphant nationality."

The acerbic journalist H. L. Mencken said that Harding's speech reminded him of "stale bean soup, of college yells, of dogs barking idiotically through endless nights." But he added that "it is so bad that a sort of grandeur creeps through it." A Democratic politician remarked that the normalcy speech "left the impression of an army of pompous phrases moving over the landscape in search of an idea."

But Harding did have an idea. The great bloviater had sensed that no specific issue, including the League of Nations, was as important to the American people in 1920 as "a return to normalcy," and he was right. He won 61 percent of the vote, more than any candidate who preceded him in the White House since popular votes were recorded, and a landslide record that held up until 1964.

Wilson lived on quietly in Washington until 1924, a semi-invalid specter out of the past, frustrated and bitter. Unlike the pedestrian Harding, he was a giant who loomed over an age. His intelligence, dignity, steadfastness, and sense of rectitude overshadowed even Theodore Roosevelt, something T.R. himself must have sensed in his final, pathetic years. Wilson's end was therefore more tragic than that of any other president, including those who were assassinated. For Wilson, like the tragic heroes of great drama, was murdered by his own virtues.

For Further Reading

The regnant study of the American homefront during World War I is David Kennedy, *Over Here: The First World War and American Society* (1980). See also Ellis W. Hawley, *The Great War and the Search for a Modern Order: A History of the American People and their Institutions, 1914–1920* (1979); the early chapters of William E. Leuchtenburg, *The Perils of Prosperity, 1914–1932* (1958); Arthur S. Link, *Woodrow Wilson: War, Revolution, and Peace* (1979); Preston Slosson, *The Great Crusade and After* (1930); Daniel M. Smith, *The Great Departure: The United States in World War I, 1914–1920* (1965); and the later chapters of Robert H. Wiebe, *The Search for Order, 1880–1920* (1967).

Worthwhile diplomatic studies include Thomas A. Bailey, *Woodrow Wilson and the Lost Peace* (1944) and *Woodrow Wilson and the Great Betrayal* (1945); John M. Blum, *Woodrow Wilson and the Politics of Morality* (1956);

John A. Garraty, *Henry Cabot Lodge* (1953); N. G. Levin, Jr., *Woodrow Wilson and World Politics: America's Response to War and Revolution* (1968); the classic Harold Nicholson, *Peacemaking: 1919* (1939); and Ralph Stone, *The Irreconcilables: The Fight Against the League of Nations* (1970).

On economic mobilization, see Robert Cuff, *The War-Industries Board: Business-Government Relations During World War I* (1973). On social aspects of the wartime experience, see Maurine W. Greenwald, *Women, War, and Work: The Impact of World War I on Women Workers in the United States* (1980); Frederick C. Luebke, *Bonds of Loyalty: German-Americans and World War I* (1974); Frederick L. Paxson, *American Democracy and the World War* (1948); William Preston, Jr., *Aliens and Dissenters: Federal Suppression of Radicals, 1903–1933* (1953).

A few speakeasies were as grand as any pre-Prohibition night c

THE TROUBLED DAYS OF WARREN G. HARDING

TRANSITION YEARS

1919 - 1923

The 1920s have come down to us with a ready-made personality, a nickname that purports to capture the flavor of the decade. In the popular imagination, in novels and films and in television shows, the 1920s are the "Roaring Twenties." The picture is familiar: exhausted by the prolonged fervor of the Progressive Era, unsettled and then disillusioned by a righteous war that failed to save humanity from itself, the American people set out to have a little fun, and ended up by having a lot.

Images of the Roaring Twenties readily flood the mind: speakeasies, college boys and flapper girls defying traditional morality during breaks between dancing to the exciting new jazz music played by black musicians; bootleggers and gangsters, somehow menacing and engaging at the same time. The 1920s were the golden age of sport: Babe Ruth's Yankees and John McGraw's Giants were the superteams of baseball; Harold "Red" Grange was the saint of the religion of football; Jack Dempsey and Gene Tunney were prize fighters as mythic as Odysseus and Hercules. Robert T. "Bobby" Jones of Georgia made golf a popular sport for both participants and spectators, and William "Big Bill" Tilden did the same for tennis.

Radio made its debut: the first commercial broadcast told of Warren G. Harding's landslide victory in the presidential election of 1920. The movies were a fixture of everyday life in the cities and towns—and in their golden age, what with Charlie Chaplin, Rudolph Valentino, and Clara Bow, the "It" girl. The automobile, the modern world's amulet of personal freedom, was everywhere, from the homely, accessible Model T Ford to the Stutz Bearcat, Dusenberg, and Cord, still among the most glorious creations of the auto maker's craft.

The list can go on, but at any length it will be a distortion. Only a small proportion of the American population—the wealthy and the comfortably fixed middle classes who lived in cities and towns—enjoyed even a semblance of the legend's roaring good times. And the gravy years were not ten, but five or six in number, beginning only after Calvin Coolidge became president in 1923. In the meantime, there were the troubled days of Warren G. Harding.

THE WORST PRESIDENT

During the four years that preceded the reign of "Silent Cal" Coolidge, from 1919 to 1923, American life was beset more by contradictions, uncertainties, and fears than by diverting good times. In fact, during the two years immediately before and the two immediately after the inauguration of President Harding in March 1921, American society was on edge, and so was the man whom many historians consider to have been the worst president.

Gamaliel

A newspaperman, Warren Gamaliel Harding worked his way up in politics on the basis of a friendly smile, a firm handshake, the reliable support of the Republican party line in his newspaper, the Marion Star, and the happy discovery by Ohio's political bosses to whom, whenever they asked a favor, Warren G. Harding said yes.

He loved the Senate, where voters sent him in 1914. The job suited his temperament. Being a senator called for making the occasional speech—Harding was good at that—but as only one senator among 96, he was not expected to take the lead in anything. The Senate was a club in which members watched out for one another. No one objected that Harding helped old cronies find government jobs that they were unfit to perform, and the affable Ohioan had plenty of time to enjoy the all-night poker and bourbon parties with his pals that were his second most favorite recreation.

Because newspaper reporters were rather more restrained in dealing with the private lives of public officials than they are today, Harding got only slightly more censorious treatment in the press. He was widely thought to be among the least effective of Senators, but his adulterous relationships with several mistresses, while no secret, were never publicized. Only after his death did one of Harding's ladies, Nan Britton, go to the newspapers with the story that Harding had fathered her illegitimate daughter.

A DECENT MAN

It is easy to look back and feel sympathy for this weak man because Harding himself had no illusions about his intelligence or his moral capacity for leadership. He freely and openly admitted that he could not hope to be "the best president," and said he would try to be "the best-liked."

Such a man did not belong in public life, but Harding was personally kind and decent. After the sour experience with the brilliant but imperious Wilson, the American people did not regard an ordinary mind and a self-effacing personality as handicaps.

Harding displayed his humanity when, at Christmas 1921, he pardoned Eugene V. Debs and other Socialists who had opposed the war. (Vindictive toward the end, Wilson had refused to do so.) Harding personally put pressure on the directors of the United States Steel Corporation to reduce the work-day in their mills to eight hours, not because he challenged their asserted "right" to do with their property as they chose, but because he was appalled at the idea of a twelve-hour day for a factory worker.

Perhaps most striking was Harding's reaction when political enemies whispered that he was part black. In an era when most white people thought in at least mildly racist terms, that kind of talk could ruin a career. Other

PRESIDENTS AND BASEBALL

In 1910, William Howard Taft instituted the custom that the president throw out the first ball of the baseball season in Washington, D.C. Perhaps the most avid presidential baseball fan was his successor, Woodrow Wilson, who drove often to Griffith Stadium where he watched the Washington Senators play from his limousine in foul territory beyond the right-field flagpole. (A spare player stood nearby to shield Wilson from errant foul balls.)

Warren G. Harding, Herbert Hoover, Franklin D. Roosevelt, and Harry S Truman were also fans, and Jimmy Carter was a pretty good softball player. Ronald Reagan had been a baseball announcer as a young man, and had portrayed the great pitcher, Grover Cleveland Alexander, in a film of 1952. As president, however, he rarely remained at a game longer than ceremony required. In April 1989, by way of contrast, newly elected George Bush took Egyptian President Hosni Mubarak to a game and both stayed to the end.

politicians would have responded with a lawsuit or an indignant racist diatribe that outdid their accusers for spleen. But Harding merely shrugged, an extraordinary response in that era. How did he know whether or not one of his forebears "had jumped the fence."

Smart Geeks

Harding made several excellent appointments to his cabinet, or had them pushed on him by political expedience. As Secretary of Commerce, he picked Herbert Hoover, whom Franklin D. Roosevelt had wanted to run against Harding in the election of 1920. In fact, Hoover was a Republican by inheritance, temperament, and philosophy and, while he must have been slightly appalled by Harding, he accepted. Harding was ill at ease with the prissy, all-business Hoover, but knew that he needed the advice of men like him. He called Hoover (not to his face) "the smartest geek I know."

As he had done during the First World War, Hoover worked quietly. He mollified conservative Republicans by encouraging the formation of private trade associations in industry and agriculture rather than, in the manner of the progressives, putting the government in the driver's seat. Hoover's hope was that these organizations would eliminate waste, develop uniform standards of production, and end "destructive competition."

As Secretary of State, Harding named Charles Evans Hughes, a gesture to the progressive wing of the Republican party, with which Hughes had been associated. A man of moderate temperament, an able if unimaginative Supreme Court Justice between 1910 and 1916, Hughes

had waffled on the issue of the League of Nations, just as Harding had done.

By 1921, that issue was dead but, because the Senate had not ratified the Treaty of Versailles, the United States was still officially at war with Germany. Hughes ironed out that diplomatic technicality by prevailing on Congress to pass a simple resolution that the war was over and by extending recognition to the new German republic.

The Treaty of Washington

Hughes then presented his alternative to the League of Nations as a means of keeping the peace. He called the world's nine most important naval powers to an international conference in Washington to discuss naval disarmament. The delegates, who expected the usual round of receptions and meaningless platitudes that most such conferences entailed, followed by backroom horsetrading, were shocked when Hughes opened the conference by proposing a detailed plan for disarmament. All the naval powers were to scrap many of their capital ships (battleships and battle cruisers) and cancel plans for future naval construction.

Most diplomats agreed that the arms race had been instrumental in bringing on the First World War. Therefore, the delegates in Washington had little choice but to listen, particularly when Hughes reminded them that by limiting the size of their navies, their governments could save millions of dollars: the construction of even a single capital ship was a major line item in a national budget.

In the Treaty of Washington of 1921, the five major naval powers agreed to limit their fleets according to a ratio that reflected their interests and defensive needs. For each five tons that Great Britain and the United States floated in capital ships, Japan would have three, and France and Italy somewhat smaller fleets.

Each nation gave up ships, but each benefited too. Great Britain maintained naval equality with the United States, a primacy that American plans for ship construction would have destroyed. (The United States scrapped 30 battleships and cruisers that were under construction or on the drawing boards.) The American government slashed its expenditures, a high Republican party priority. Japan, which needed only a one-ocean navy whereas Britain and the United States had worldwide interests, got parity (or even superiority) in the Pacific. Italy and France, still reeling from the war, were spared the strain of an arms race, but retained naval strength in the Mediterranean.

The Harding Scandals

Unfortunately, the work of Hoover and Hughes just about sums up the accomplishments of the Harding administration. The president's other appointees were either servants of narrow special interests or outright crooks. Secretary of the Treasury Andrew Mellon pursued tax policies that extravagantly favored the rich and helped bring on the disastrous depression that would end the Roaring Twenties. More dismaying in the short run were those old cronies whom Harding favored with government jobs. No sooner were they settled in their Washington offices than they set about filling their pockets and ruining their generous friend.

Attorney General Harry Daugherty winked at violations of the law by political allies. Probably with Daugherty's connivance, Jesse L. Smith, a close friend of the president, sold favorable decisions and public offices for cold cash. Charles R. Forbes, the head of the Veterans Administration, pocketed money intended for hospital construction. Secretary of the Interior Albert B. Fall leased the navy's petroleum reserves at Teapot Dome, Wyoming, and Elk Hills, California, to two freewheeling oilmen, Harry Sinclair and Edward L. Doheny. In return, Fall accepted "loans" of about $300,000 from the two.

Fall also tarred Harding with his corruption because, some time earlier, he had persuaded the president to transfer the oil reserves from the navy's authority to that of the Interior Department.

By the summer of 1923, Harding realized that his administration was shot through with corruption. When he set out on a vacation trip to Alaska, he knew that it was only a matter of time before the scandals hit the newspapers and destroyed his name. His health was already suffering; the famous handsome face is haggard and gray in the last photographs.

Nevertheless, weak and obliging to the end, Harding allowed his friend Forbes to flee abroad, and he took no action against the others. Jesse Smith killed himself. Mercifully, perhaps, Harding died too, before he got back to Washington. Only later did Americans learn of the secrets that plagued him, from the corruption in his administration to the irregularities in his personal life. So tangled were the affairs of the Harding administration that scandalmongers suggested that Harding's wife had poisoned him, and they were widely believed. Actually, the president suffered a massive heart attack.

Who Says a Watched Pot Never Boils?

Democrats hoped—vainly, it turned out—that the Teapot Dome scandal would inundate the Republican administration.

SOCIAL TENSIONS: LABOR, RADICALS, IMMIGRANTS

If Harding's poignant tale is symbolic of his time, the social tensions that strained and snapped while he was in the White House ran far deeper than the personality of an unhappy man from Marion, Ohio. Had Harding been a pillar of moral strength and probity, the years he presided over would have been much as troubled as they were. Indeed, the tensions of the early 1920s began two years before Harding was inaugurated. As far as most Americans were concerned, the social conflicts that first broke into the open then were quite closely related: labor, political radicalism, and the presence of so many immigrants in an idyllic America that had never really existed.

1919: A Year of Strikes

During the First World War, the conservative trade unions of the American Federation of Labor seemed to become part of the federal power structure. In return for recognition of their respectability, most unions agreed not to strike for the duration of hostilities. Unfortunately, while wages rose slowly during 1917 and 1918, the prices of consumer goods, including necessities, increased quickly and then soared during a runaway postwar inflation. The end of the war also led to the cancellation of government contracts; tens of thousands doing war-related work lost their jobs, and the inevitable

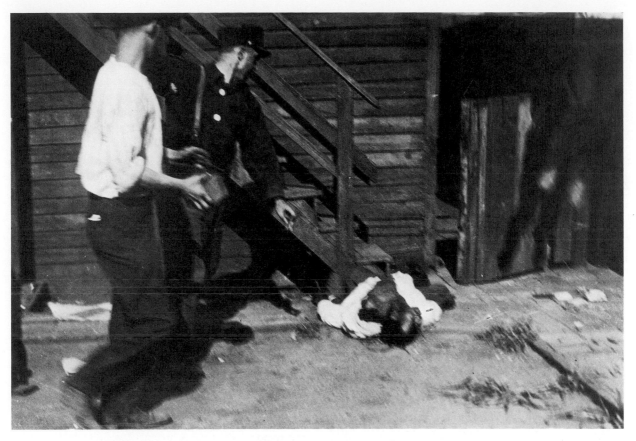

A black man lies wounded at the bottom of a staircase, the victim of the Chicago race riot of 1919.

occurred. 3,600 strikes during 1919 involving 4 million workers.

Striker grievances were generally valid, but, to the surprise of many workers, few Americans outside the labor movement were sympathetic. When employers described the strikes of 1919 as the handiwork of revolutionaries, aimed at destroying middle-class decency, much of America agreed. In Seattle, a dispute that began on the docks of the busy Pacific port turned into a general strike involving almost all the city's 60,000 workers. Most of them were interested in nothing more than better pay. However, the concept of the general strike was associated in the popular mind with class war and revolution. Mayor Ole Hanson was able to depict the dispute as an uprising that had been inspired by danger-ous foreign "Bolsheviks" like those who had taken over Russia during the war. With the help of marines, he crushed the strike.

Steelworkers Walk Out

The magnates of the steel industry employed similar methods to fight a walkout in September by 350,000

workers, largely in the Great Lakes region. The men had good reason to strike. Many of them worked a twelve-hour day and a seven-day week. It was not unusual for individuals to put in thirty-six hours at a stretch. That is, if a man's relief failed to show up, he was told to stay on the job or lose it. When the extra shift ended, his own began again.

For this kind of life, steelworkers took home subsis-tence wages. For some Slavic immigrants in the industry, that home was not even a bed to themselves. They contracted with a landlord to rent half a bed. After their wearying shift and a quick, cheap meal, they rolled under blankets still warm and damp from the body of a fellow worker who had just trudged off to the mill.

These wretched conditions were well-known. And yet, the heads of the industry, Elbert Gary of United States Steel and Charles Schwab of Bethlehem Steel, easily persuaded the public that the strike was the work of revolutionary agitators like William Z. Foster. Because Foster had a radical past (and future as the leader of the American Communist party) and because many steel-workers had ethnic roots in Eastern Europe, the nursery of Bolshevism, the strikers were almost universally condemned. The strike ended in failure although, under pressure from the president, working conditions were somewhat improved.

The Boston Police Strike

The Boston police strike of 1919 frightened Americans more than any other. While the shutdown of even a basic industry like steel did not immediately affect daily life, the absence of police officers from the streets caused a jump in crime as professional hoodlums and desperately poor people took advantage of the situation.

Boston's policemen, mostly Irish-Americans, were underpaid. They earned pre-war wages, not enough to support their families decently in a city where many prices had tripled. Nevertheless, they too commanded little public support. When Massachusetts governor Calvin Coolidge ordered the National Guard into Boston to break the strike, the public applauded. When Samuel Gompers asked Coolidge to restore the beaten workers to their jobs, the governor replied "there is no right to strike against the public safety by anybody, anywhere, anytime," and he became a national hero. His hard-line policy won him the Republican vice-presidential nomination in 1920 when the California progressive, Hiram Johnson, refused to balance the ticket by running with the conservative Harding.

Some of the strikes of 1919 ended in victory. Most failed, and the debacle ushered in a decade of decline for the labor movement. The membership of unions stood at over 5 million in 1919, but at only 3.6 million in 1929, despite the expansion of the nonagricultural working class during the same years.

Red Scare

Public reaction to the strikes of 1919 revealed widespread hostility toward recent immigrants and second-generation Americans. This xenophobia took more virulent form in the Red scare of 1919. Even before the Armistice was signed, a new stereotype had replaced the "bloodthirsty Hun" as the villain whom Americans had most reason to fear: the seedy, bearded, and wild-eyed Bolshevik. American newspapers exaggerated the many real atrocities that took place during the civil war that followed the Russian Revolution and invented tales of mass executions, torture, children turned against their parents, and women proclaimed the common property of all men. Already in an uneasy mood, Americans were prepared to believe the worst about a part of the world from which so many immigrants recently had come.

Many Americans believed that foreign-born Communists were a threat to the United States. In March 1919, the Soviets organized the Third International, or "Comintern," an organization explicitly dedicated to fomenting revolution around the world. So it seemed to be no accident when, in April, the Post Office discovered 38 bombs in the mail addressed to prominent capitalists and government officials. In June, several bombs reached their targets. One bomber who was identified—he blew himself up—was a foreigner, an Italian. And in Chicago in September 1919, two American Communist parties were founded with the press emphasizing the immigrant element in the membership. Many Americans concluded that the Red threat was closely related to the large number of immigrants and their children within the United States.

In reality, a small minority of ethnic Americans were radicals, and many of the prominent Socialists and Communists boasted impeccable WASP origins. Max Eastman, the editor of the radical wartime magazine *The Masses*, was of old New England stock. John Reed, whose *Ten Days That Shook the World* remained for many years the classic English-language account of the Russian Revolution, was a Harvard boy from Portland, Oregon. Debs and William Z. Foster had no ethnic ties to Southern or Eastern Europe. William D. Haywood observed that he could trace his ancestry "to the Puritan bigots." Moreover, neither they nor the foreign-born radicals posed a real threat to established institutions. Within a few years, the combined membership of the two Communist parties and the Socialist party numbered only in the thousands.

The Palmer Raids

But popular dread of Communists was real enough, and the temptation to exploit it for political gain was overwhelming. Wilson's attorney general, A. Mitchell Palmer, tried to ride the Red scare into a presidential nomination by ordering a series of well-publicized raids on Communist headquarters.

Although an investigation found that only 39 of those he had arrested could be deported under the law, Palmer nonetheless put 249 people on a steamship dubbed "the Soviet Ark" and sent them to Russia via Finland. On New Year's Day 1920, Palmer's agents again swooped down on hundreds of locations, arresting 6,000 people. Some of them, such as a Western Union delivery boy, merely had the bad luck to be in the wrong place at the wrong time. Others were arrested while merely peering into the windows of Communist storefront offices. Nevertheless, all were imprisoned for at least a short time.

Palmer's popularity fizzled in the spring of 1920. He predicted that there would be mass demonstrations on May Day, the international socialist and communist holiday, and nothing happened. By midsummer, the great scare was over, but anti-foreign feeling continued to affect both government policy and popular attitudes throughout the 1920s.

Sacco and Vanzetti

The two most celebrated victims of the wedding of anti-radicalism to xenophobia were Nicola Sacco and Bartolomeo Vanzetti. In 1920, the two Italian immigrants were arrested for an armed robbery in South Braintree, Massachusetts, in which a guard and a paymaster were killed. They were found guilty of murder and sentenced to die in the electric chair.

Before they could be executed, the American Civil Liberties Union, Italian-American groups, and labor organizations publicized the fact that the hard evidence against Sacco and Vanzetti was scanty and, at least in part, invented by the prosecution. The presiding judge, Webster Thayer, had been openly prejudiced against the defendants because they were anarchists and Italians; Thayer was overheard speaking of them as "damned dagos."

At the same time, Sacco and Vanzetti won admiration by acting with dignity during their trial, steadfastly maintaining their innocence but refusing to compromise their political beliefs. "I am suffering," Vanzetti said in court, "because I am a radical and indeed I am a radical; I have suffered because I was an Italian, and indeed I am an Italian . . . but I am so convinced to be right that if you could execute me two times, and if I could be reborn two other times, I would live again to do what I have done already."

Despite a movement to save them that reached international proportions, Sacco and Vanzetti were finally executed in 1927. Although recent research has indicated that at least Sacco was almost certainly guilty of the Braintree murder, that question lost its relevance to both sides during the 1920s.

The Passing of the Great Race

In 1883, the American poet Emma Lazarus had written, "Send these, the homeless, tempest-tost to me, I lift my lamp beside the golden door." As if they had heard her, European immigrants continued to pour into the United States at high levels until 1915, when all-out naval war made the Atlantic too dangerous for large numbers of people to cross. In 1918, immigration into the United States declined to 110,000.

Even before the war, many Americans of WASP and "Old Immigrant" stock had become nervous about the large numbers of Eastern and Southern Europeans among them—or rather, about the immigrants who clustered in ethnic ghettos in the larger cities. Unlike earlier arrivals, including the once-despised Irish, the "New Immigrants" seemed determined not to become Americans.

Around the turn of the century, this essentially cultural and social anxiety took on racist overtones as re-

spected anthropologists began to describe significant genetic distinctions among the European peoples. The most important of these writers was William Z. Ripley, whose *Races of Europe* was published in 1899. Ripley divided Caucasians into the Teutonic, Alpine, and Mediterranean races. While all three had their redeeming traits (the Mediterranean Italians, for example, were credited with a finely developed artistic sense), there was no question that Teutons—Britons, Germans, Northern Europeans generally—were the ones who were committed to liberty and to the American way of life. Slavic peoples got very bad reviews.

In 1916, a lawyer and natural scientist of some repute, Madison Grant, took up where Ripley left off. In *The Passing of the Great Race*, Grant maintained that, through intermarriage with old stock Americans, the New Immigrants were literally destroying, through dilution, the nation's prized genetic heritage. The book was immensely successful, running through several editions. (During the war, Grant demoted the Germans out of the Great Race.) After the war, when immigration soared again—to 805,000 in 1921—the time for action seemed to have come.

Immigration Restriction

There was a precedent for restricting immigration on the basis of race. In 1882, Congress had excluded the Chinese from the United States. In that same year, Congress determined that criminals, idiots, lunatics, and those likely to become a public charge (people with

---

ANTI-SEMITISM

The hatred of Jews that was to acquire nightmarish proportions in Germany had its counterpart in the United States, albeit never so vicious or significant as it was under Adolf Hitler. For a time during the 1920s, automobile millionaire Henry Ford sponsored a newspaper, the *Dearborn Independent,* that insisted, as Hitler did, that Jews in general were party to an "international conspiracy" to destroy Western Christian civilization. The most astonishing aspect of this kind of anti-Semitism was that it posited an alliance between wealthy, conservative Jewish bankers like the Rothschild family of Europe and their worst enemies, Socialists and Communists who were Jews.

These allegations never were taken very seriously in the United States. However, anti-Semitism was acceptable and even respectable when it took the form of keeping Jews out of some businesses (banking, ironically) and social clubs. Moreover, a number of universities applied Jewish "quotas" when they admitted students. Jews were admitted, but only up to a certain percentage of each class.

glaucoma, tuberculosis, and venereal disease were the chief targets) could no longer enter the country. By 1900, pressure groups such as the Immigration Restriction League began to call for an immigration law that would discriminate against other genetic inferiors— Southern and Eastern Europeans, in brief, the New Immigrants.

Four times between 1897 and 1917, Congress tried to discriminate against the New Immigrants by enacting bills requiring all newcomers to pass a literacy test. Few peasants from Southern and Eastern Europe could read and write. Four times, however, three times by Woodrow Wilson alone, the bills were vetoed. The importance of ethnic voters to the Democratic party, and the demand of a still expanding industry for cheap labor, stymied the restrictionists.

Then the election of 1920 brought the Republicans to power. In 1921, Congress enacted and President Harding signed a law limiting annual immigration to 350,000 people. Each European nation was entitled to send 3 percent of the number of its nationals who had been residents of the United States in the base year of 1910. In 1924, an amendment reduced the number of immigrants from outside the Americas to 150,000, the quota to 2 percent, and changed the base year to 1890. Because most Southern and Eastern Europeans had begun to emigrate to the United States only after 1890, the quotas of such poor countries as Poland, Czechoslovakia, Hungary, Romania, Yugoslavia, Bulgaria, Greece, and Italy were very low. For example, the annual quota for Italy was a minuscule 6,000, and was inevitably filled within the first few months of each year.

By way of contrast, the quotas for the comparatively prosperous countries of Northern and Western Europe, the nations of the Old Immigration, were generous and rarely filled. The annual quota for Great Britain under the 1921 law was 65,000, one-fifth of the total. During the 1930s, an average of only 2,500 Britons emigrated to the United States each year.

SOCIAL TENSIONS: RACE, MORAL CODES, RELIGION

The 1920s were also a time of anxiety and tension in relations between the two major American races, between people who held fast to traditional moral codes and those who rejected them, and (closely allied to the moral issue) between rural people and urban people.

Black Scare

Having supported the war effort with extraordinary enthusiasm, African Americans looked forward to a greater measure of equality after the Armistice. The 200,000 young black men who had served in the army in Europe had been exposed to a white society in which their color was not a major handicap. Although they had been segregated within the armed forces, they had found that the French people looked on them as Yanks of a different color, nothing more or less, and had been grateful for their help against Germany. At home, blacks who moved to northern cities experienced a less repressive life than they had known in the rural South and felt freer to express themselves.

But white America had not changed its mind about race. In 1919, of the 78 blacks who were lynched, 10 were veterans; several were hanged while dressed in their uniforms. Race riots broke out in 25 cities with a death toll of more than a hundred. The worst of the year was in Chicago, where a petty argument on a Lake Michigan beach in July mushroomed into vicious racial war. White and black gangs with guns roamed the streets shooting at anyone of the wrong color whom they stumbled across. In all, 38 people were killed and more than 500 were injured.

Black Nationalism

In this charged and disillusioning atmosphere emerged a remarkable character. Born in the British colony of Jamaica, Marcus Garvey came to the United States in 1916. He concluded that whites would never accept blacks as equals, and, filled with a glowing pride in his own race, he rejected integration. Garvey's alternative to the violent racial conflicts of the postwar years was the joining together of blacks throughout the world to organize a powerful black nation in Africa.

Garvey's Universal Negro Improvement Association (U.N.I.A.) was based on pride in race, the strong organizing point of all racial-separatist movements. "When Europe was inhabited by a race of cannibals, a race of savages, naked men, heathens, and pagans," Garvey told cheering throngs in New York's Harlem, turning white stereotypes of blacks upside down, "Africa was peopled by a race of cultured black men who were masters in art, science, and literature."

He made little headway in the South, but in the North, urban blacks who already were uprooted found his call for a return to Africa appealing, at least in the abstract. Estimates of U.N.I.A. membership as high as 4 million were probably exaggerated, but many more African Americans than that listened to Garvey's message with open minds and enjoyed the pageantry of nationhood with which he surrounded himself.

Garvey bedecked himself in ornate, regal uniforms and commissioned paramilitary orders with exotic names such as "The Dukes of the Niger" and the "Black Eagle

Wearing ornate uniforms and commissioning paramilitary orders, Marcus Garvey led a large black nationalist movement that was born in response to the violent racial conflict that scarred America in 1919.

Flying Corps." Even veterans in the fight for racial equality were influenced by Garvey's magic. W. E. B. Du Bois wrote, "The spell of Africa is upon me. The ancient witchery of her medicine is burning in my drowsy, dreamy blood."

The popularity of black nationalism unnerved whites who were accustomed to a passive black population. When Garvey ran afoul of the law with one of the dozens of his business enterprises, the authorities moved against him with an enthusiasm that bore little relation to the seriousness of his offense. Whether because of mismanagement or fraud, Garvey's Black Star Line, a steamship company, had sold worthless stock through the mails at $5 a share. Some 35,000 blacks lost $750,000, a comparatively minor take during the 1920s. Nevertheless, the government pressed its case for five years, draining the resources of the U.N.I.A.

The Ku Klux Klan

Marcus Garvey's ritual, costume, and ceremony were reflected in a white racist organization of the same era,

the Ku Klux Klan. The twentieth-century K.K.K. was founded in 1915 by William Simmons, a Methodist minister. After viewing *The Birth of a Nation*, a film that glorified the anti-black movement of the post–Civil War period, Simmons began organizing, first in the South but, by 1919, in the North and West as well.

Under Hiram Wesley Evans, the K.K.K. gave local units and officials exotic names such as Klavern, Kleagle, Grand Dragon, and Exalted Cyclops. Evans was a shrewder businessman than Garvey. The Klan's central office retained a monopoly of "official" bedsheet uniforms that all members were required to buy. The Klan provided a cash incentive for local organizers by giving them a percentage of all money that they collected, a kind of franchised bigotry. By the mid-1920s, membership may have risen as high as 4.5 million.

In the South, the K.K.K. was primarily an anti-black organization. Elsewhere, K.K.K. leaders exploited whatever hatreds, fears, and resentments were most likely to keep the bedsheet orders rolling in. In the Northeast, where Catholics and Jews were numerous, Klan leaders inveighed against them. Immigrants generally were a handy target. In the Owens Valley of California, a region of small farmers whose water was drained southward to feed the growth of Los Angeles, the big city was the enemy. In the Midwest, some Klaverns concentrated their attacks on saloonkeepers who ignored Prohibition and "lovers' lanes" where teenagers flaunted traditional morality on weekend nights.

Setting aside the hocus-pocus and the mercenary motives of the central office, the Klan represented the belief of generally poor, Protestant, and small-town people that the America they knew was under attack by immigrants, cities, and modern immorality. Nevertheless, the Klan prospered in cities too. The twentieth-century metropolis was an unsettling phenomenon, but it continued to attract people of every kind.

Klan power peaked in 1924. In that year, the organization boasted numerous state legislators, congressmen, senators, and even governors in Oregon, Ohio, Tennessee, and Texas. In Indiana, state Klan leader David Stephenson was a virtual dictator. At the Democratic national convention of 1924, the Klan was strong enough to prevent the party from adopting a plank that was critical of its bigotry.

The K.K.K. declined as rapidly as the U.N.I.A. In 1925, Grand Dragon Stephenson was found guilty of second-degree murder in the death of a young woman whom he had kidnapped and taken to Chicago. In an attempt to win a light sentence, he turned over evidence showing that virtually the whole administration of the K.K.K. was involved in thievery and that Indiana Klan politicians were thoroughly corrupt. By 1930, the K.K.K. had dwindled to 10,000 members.

HOW THEY LIVED

HOW THEY PLAYED THE GAME

Originally, baseball was a gentleman's game, played by wealthy amateurs for the pleasure of competition. By the turn of the twentieth century, this had changed. Baseball became a business, potentially very lucrative. The players were paid for their skills by teams organized into two major leagues, the National and the American. The profits to the owners, who called themselves "sportsmen" and their properties "clubs," lay in paid admissions to games. Because the better the team, the more people willing to pay to attend, it stood to reason that clubowners would seek to build winning teams. However, it did not always work that way. While the players indeed competed with one another to win games, the sportsmen did not compete with one another to win the best players.

In order to avoid bidding wars among themselves for the services of star pitchers, hitters, and fielders, the club-owners devised the "reserve clause," an agreement that every player was required to sign. The reserve clause was based on the dubious assumption that a baseball player was a professional like a physician or lawyer and not a lowly employee. Unlike a machinist or miner who, of course, as industrial employers never tired of saying, were free at all times to quit their job and find another, the professional baseball player was not free to do so. In signing the reserve clause, he agreed that he could not leave to play with another team without the owner's consent. His services were reserved unless the clubowner "sold" or "traded" him to another owner with whom the player then had no choice but to come to terms—if he wanted to stay in baseball.

As in other businesses, practices varied from team to team, but perhaps the most frankly businesslike of the owners was Cornelius "Connie Mack" McGillicuddy, who also managed his Philadelphia Athletics of the American League. The dominant team in baseball in the years before the First World War, the A's won six league pennants and three world series. Mack twice built up powerhouse teams in that era and then broke them up, selling his star players off for a cash profit. And again by the end of the 1920s he created a team that was better than the New York Yankees of the era. Once again Mack cashed in, selling off his players.

There was no reconciling the concept of sportsmanship or a sense of civic responsibility with Mack's policies, and yet, simply because he continued to manage the A's into his 90s, he was touted as one of the grand old men of the "game."

Charles A. Comiskey, owner of the Chicago White Sox, was another kind of businessman. Until the First World War he was content with mediocre players to whom he paid the lowest salaries in either major league. Then, during the war, while attendance in all cities declined, the White Sox jelled behind such stars as hard-hitting outfielder Joseph "Shoeless Joe" Jackson and third baseman George "Buck" Weaver. After finishing high in the standings in 1917 and 1918, the White Sox won the American League pennant in 1919 and were regarded by most sports journalists as unbeatable in the World Series, particularly because the National League champion was an old team but an upstart champion, the Cincinnati Red Stockings.

There was trouble in the White Sox team, however. While their sterling play had caused attendance and profits to soar, Comiskey had actually taken the lead in calling for a league-wide paycut. At a time when wages in almost every job were rising, the two leading White Sox pitchers, who won 50 games between them, were paid a combined salary of only $8,600. Adding insult to exploitation, Comiskey allowed his champion players consider-

Wets and Drys

To some extent, the Klan was a manifestation of hostility between cities and country and small towns. This social conflict was also evident in the split that developed after the Eighteenth Amendment went into effect in 1920. Violation of the Prohibition law was widespread. While some bootleggers smuggled liquor into the country from Mexico, the West Indies, and Canada, individual liquor distillers in isolated corners of rural America continued to practice their ancient crafts, distilling "white lightning" and "moonshine" and battling government agents with guns as well as stealth.

Nevertheless, there was a clear geographical and social dimension to the political battle between "drys," people who supported Prohibition, and "wets," those who opposed it. The drys were strongest in the South and in rural areas generally, where the population was largely composed of old-stock Americans who clung to fundamentalist Protestant religions. The wets drew their support from the big cities, where Roman Catholics and Jews, who generally had little understanding of or sympathy for prohibition, were numerous. (Roman Catholics and Jews use wine in basic religious practices, e.g., the Eucharist and the Shabbat dinner.)

Wet mayors and city councils often refused to help federal officials enforce Prohibition. Democratic Mayor James J. Walker of New York openly frequented fashionable speakeasies (illegal saloons). Republican "Big Bill" Thompson of Chicago ran for office on a "wide-open-town" platform and won. As a result, smuggling, illegal distilleries and breweries, and theft of industrial ably lower expenses when they were on the road than any other team in either league.

The White Sox lost the World Series to the Red Stockings 5 games to 3. (Only in 1922 was the Series reduced to 7 games.) An investigation during the winter and spring revealed that it was no mere upset. Eight White Sox players, including stars Weaver and Jackson, had conspired with gamblers to throw the match and make a killing on longshot bets.

It was rumored that Comiskey had been aware of the fix all along but was willing to sacrifice the Series for the chance to intimidate future players. Indeed, although the eight accused "Black Sox" were acquitted in criminal court for lack of hard evidence, they were banned from playing professional ball for life by a newly installed Commissioner with broad powers to regulate the business, Judge Kenesaw Mountain Landis. Like the head of a government commission, Landis showed no reluctance to discipline owners whose actions threatened the good of the whole, but he backed the owners in disputes with players.

Not every club ownership was so cash-oriented as Mack or so exploitative as Comiskey. Indeed, during the same years that Landis was brushing up baseball's reputation for honesty at the top, an ugly, pot-bellied, spindly legged, and atrociously vulgar orphan from Baltimore was revolutionizing the game and winning huge salaries from ungrudging employers, the New York Yankees.

George Herman "Babe" Ruth started in baseball as a pitcher—quite a good one—for the Boston Red Sox. In 1919, the year of the Black Sox Scandal, while playing the outfield on days he did not pitch, Ruth hit 29 home runs, double that of any previous player. In fact, the major leagues did not even keep official home run statistics until 1921; baseball B. R.—before Ruth—was a game of tactics played by lithe, swift men who eked out runs one at a time with scratch hits off over-powering pitchers, and gritty base running. Tyrus J. "Ty" Cobb of the Detroit Tigers, a genuinely mean-spirited man whose specialty was sliding into second with file-sharpened cleats slicing the air, was the most respected player of the 1910s.

Now, with a single swing, the "Sultan of Swat" could put up to four runs on the scoreboard and the fans loved it. Purchased from the Red Sox by the Yankees for $100,000—itself an unprecedented windfall under the reserve clause—Ruth hit 59 home runs in 1921, the record until his own 60 in 1927. Rather than haggle with their godsend, the Yankee ownership paid him annually higher salaries. By the end of the decade, when his pay was higher than that of the president of the U.S., Ruth shrugged nonchalantly, "I had a better year than he did."

Not only did he make the Yankees the best team in baseball, Babe Ruth made them the richest. In 1923, New York opened the largest baseball stadium of the era, Yankee Stadium, which was properly nicknamed, "the house that Ruth built." Other owners and Commissioner Landis took notice too. If home runs sold tickets, they would have more home runs. The baseball itself was redesigned into a livelier "rabbit ball" and the slugger became the mythic figure in the game. Hack Wilson of the Chicago Cubs hit 56 home runs in 1930, setting the National League's record, and Jimmy Foxx of the Philadelphia Athletics was eclipsing Ruth himself by 1932 when he hit 58 (and was promptly sold by Connie Mack). The New York Yankees remained the team that most totally staked its fortunes on men who swung the heavy bat and the "club" that was the most liberal with a paycheck. It would not have much mattered to Connie Mack and Charles Comiskey, perhaps, but the Yankees were also, of course, the most successful team in the history of both the sport and the business.

and medicinal alcohol were commonplace and provided the basis for an extremely lucrative, if illegal, business. In Chicago by 1927, the Alphonse "Al" Capone bootleg ring grossed $60 million by supplying liquor and beer to the Windy City's speakeasies. (Capone also made $25 million that year from gambling and $10 million from prostitution.)

Gangsters as Symbols

As far as Al Capone was concerned, he was a businessman. He supplied 10,000 drinking houses and employed 700 people. He and other gangsters needed the administrative acumen of a corporate executive to run their affairs and the same kind of political influence that conventional businessmen courted. "What's Al Capone done?" he told a reporter. "He's supplied a legitimate demand . . . . Some call it racketeering. I call it a business. They say I violate the prohibition law. Who doesn't?"

With incredible profits at stake, rival gangs engaged in open, bloody warfare for control of the trade. More than 400 "gangland slayings" made the name of Chicago synonymous with mob violence, although other cities had only slightly better records.

Very few innocent bystanders were killed in these affrays. As conscious of public relations as other businessmen of the era, Capone and his ilk tried to keep their violence on a professional level. But Americans were appalled by the carnage, and they did not overlook the fact that most prominent gangsters were "foreigners." Capone and his predecessors in Chicago, Johnny Torrio and Big Jim Colosimo, were Italians. Dion

Ku Klux Klan members march in Washington, D.C., in August 1925, without the masks that concealed their identities.

O'Bannion (Capone's rival), "Bugsy" Moran, and Owney Madden were Irish. Arthur "Dutch Schultz" Flegensheimer of New York was of German background. "Polack Joe" Saltis came from Chicago's Polish West Side. Maxie Hoff of Philadelphia, Solly Weissman of Kansas City, and "Little Hymie" Weiss of Chicago were Jews.

BOTTOMS UP

One argument wets marshalled against Prohibition was that forbidding drinking resulted in an actual *increase* in drinking. The statistics, while fragmentary, do not bear their assertion out. Between 1906 and 1910, per capita alcohol consumption in the United States was 2.6 gallons per year. In 1934, the first year after the Prohibition Amendment was repealed, consumption stood at 1.2 gallons. Not until 1971, a generation after Prohibition, did per capita consumption of alcohol reach pre–World War I levels.

The death rate from chronic alcoholism peaked in the United States in 1907 at 7.3 per 100,000. By 1932, the last full year of Prohibition, the rate had declined to 2.5 per 100,000.

"Illegal business" attracted members of groups on the bottom of the social ladder because success in it required no social status or family connections, no education, and, to get started, little money. With less to lose than the respectable established people who patronized the speakeasies, ethnics had fewer compunctions about the high risks involved. But the majority of Americans were not inclined to take a sociological view of the matter. To them, organized crime was violent, and "foreigners" were the source of it.

Hollywood as Symbol

Show business was also a low-status enterprise that presented few competitive advantages to wealthy and established groups. The film industry, which was booming by 1919, had been largely dominated from the beginning by Jewish studio bosses such as Samuel Goldwyn and Louis B. Mayer. Consequently, when protest against nudity and loose moral standards in Hollywood films boiled over, it too took on an ethnic flavor. Preachers who demanded that controls be slapped on filmmakers were not above attributing immorality on the screen to

Renowned Federal agents, Izzy Einstein and Moe Smith (flanking an illegal still) became national celebrities by using comical tactics to trap bootleggers.

"non-Christian" influences aimed at subverting Protestant America.

By 1922, Hollywood's nabobs feared that city and state governments were on the verge of banning the showing of their films. They headed off the movement to do so by joining together to censor themselves. Sensitive to the ethnic angle in the anti-Hollywood campaign, they hired a man who was the epitome of the small-town Midwestern Protestant to be chief censor and film-industry spokesman. Will H. Hays of Indiana, Postmaster General under Harding, supervised the drafting of a code that forbade movies that allowed adultery to go unpunished or that depicted divorced people in a sympathetic light. The Hays Code went so far as to prohibit showing

Hooray for Hollywood

The first filmmakers set up shop wherever they happened to be. By the 1920s, however, the movie industry had become concentrated in Hollywood, one of the myriad communities that grew together to form greater Los Angeles. The official explanation of the choice of location was the weather; southern California is one of the sunniest parts of the nation, and early filmmakers depended on natural light. But there was another reason for choosing Hollywood. Like the organizers of many infant industries, filmmakers took considerable liberties with business law, particularly copyright and contract law. Everyone, it seemed, was engaged in a dozen lawsuits at all times. Hollywood was only a hundred miles from the Mexican border. If a case seemed to be getting serious, the filmmakers could make a quick dash out to Tijuana.

a married couple in bed together or, indeed, a double bed in the background of bedroom scenes. In the movies, couples slept in twin beds, and so powerful was the medium that separate beds became fashionable in three-dimensional society too.

The Evolution Controversy

The clash between traditional values and the worldly outlook of the twentieth century was clearest cut in the controversy that surrounded the theory of the evolution of species as propounded half a century earlier by the English biologist Charles Darwin. Although many scientists insisted that there was no contradiction between the biblical account of the creation of the world (if interpreted as literary) and Darwin's contention that species emerged and changed character over the eons, fundamentalist Protestants who insisted on the literal truth of every word of the Bible disagreed. Feeling threatened by fast-changing times and urged on by such influential leaders as William Jennings Bryan, the fundamentalists tried to prohibit the teaching of evolution in the public schools; in Tennessee, they succeeded in passing a law to that effect.

In the little Appalachian town of Dayton in the spring of 1925, a group of friends who had been arguing about evolution decided to test the new law in the courts. One of their number, a high school biology teacher named John Scopes, would deliberately break it. In front of adult witnesses, Scopes would explain Darwin's theory, submit to arrest, and stand trial. The motives of the men were mixed. The earnest young Scopes hoped that the law would be struck from the books. Some of his friends wanted to see it confirmed. Yet others, Dayton businessmen, could not have cared either way. They looked on a celebrated trial as a way to put their town on the map and to make money when curiosity-seekers, sensation-mongers, cause-pleaders, and reporters—the more the merrier—flocked to Dayton in search of lodgings, meals, and other services.

The "Monkey Trial"

Dayton's boosters succeeded beyond their dreams. The "Monkey Trial," so called because evolution was popularly interpreted as meaning that human beings were "descended" from apes, attracted broadcasters and reporters by the hundreds; among them was the nation's leading iconoclast, Henry L. Mencken, who came to poke fun at the "rubes" of the Bible belt.

Number-one rube in Mencken's book was William Jennings Bryan, quite aged now—he died shortly after the trial ended—who agreed to go to Dayton to advise the prosecution. Bryan wanted to fight the case on the strictly legal principle that, in a democracy, the people

Clarence Darrow for the defense and William Jennings Bryan for the prosecution at the Scopes "Monkey Trial," which addressed the question of evolution and its instruction in classrooms.

of a community had the right to dictate what might and what might not be taught in tax-supported schools. His advice was ignored. Their heads spinning from the hullabaloo and carnival atmosphere of the town, even the prosecuting attorneys wanted to debate religion versus science.

The defense, which had been put together and funded by the American Civil Liberties Union, also intended to fight the case on the basis of two significant principles. Led by the distinguished lawyer and libertarian Arthur Garfield Hays, the attorneys planned to argue that the biblical account of creation was a religious doctrine and therefore could not take precedence over science (evolution) because of the constitutional separation of church and state. The defense also insisted that freedom of intellectual inquiry, including a teacher's right to speak his or her mind in the classroom, was essential to the health of a democracy.

Hays was assisted by the era's leading criminal lawyer, Clarence Darrow, who loved publicity and the drama of courtroom confrontation more than legal niceties. Darrow regarded the trial as an opportunity to discredit fundamentalists by making their leader, Bryan, look like a superstitious old fool. Against his better judgment, Bryan allowed Darrow to put him on the stand as an expert witness on the Bible. Under the trees—the judge feared that the tiny courthouse would collapse under the crowd—Darrow and Bryan talked religion and science. Was the world created in six days of twenty-four hours each? Was Jonah literally swallowed by a whale?

Supporters of Darrow rested content that Bryan himself turned out looking like a monkey, but they lost the case. Scopes was found guilty and given a nominal penalty. It was a small consolation to the anti-evolutionists, who were crestfallen when Bryan admitted that some parts of the Bible may have been meant figuratively. In fact, the only winners in the Monkey Trial were Dayton's businessmen, who raked in outside dollars for almost a month, and the masters of ballyhoo. This was appropriate in itself, for by 1925, the second full year of Calvin Coolidge's "New Era," raking in money and ballyhoo were what America seemed to be all about.

For Further Reading

It is not the definitive history of the 1920s, but still the most enjoyable to read: Frederick Lewis Allen, *Only Yesterday* (1931). Also eminently readable and less subjective are William E. Leuchtenburg, *The Perils of Prosperity, 1914–1932* (1958); Robert K. Murray, *The Harding Era* (1967); and George Soule, *Prosperity Decade: From War to Depression, 1917–1929* (1947).

On the crisis of labor in 1919 and after, see Irving Bernstein, *The Lean Years* (1960); David Brody, *Labor in Crisis: The Steel Strike of 1919* (1965); Robert L. Friedheim, *The Seattle General Strike* (1965); and Francis Russell, *A City in Terror: 1919, the Boston Police Strike* (1975). On the xenophobia that was closely related to fears of a social uprising, see John Higham, *Strangers in the Land* (1955); Robert K. Murray, *Red Scare* (1955); and William Preston, Jr., *Aliens and Dissenters: Federal Suppression of Radicals, 1903–1933* (1963).

The history of African Americans during the 1920s has been the subject of several excellent books in recent decades. See Nathan J. Huggins, *Harlem Renaissance* (1972); Gilbert Osofsky, *Harlem: The Making of a Ghetto, 1890–1930* (1966); William Tuttle, Jr., *Race Riot: Chicago and the Red Summer of 1919* (1970); and Theodore G. Vincent, *Black Power and the Garvey Movement* (1971).

The response of white America to rapidly changing times is the subject of D. M. Chalmers, *Hooded Americanism* (1965); N. H. Clark, *Deliver Us From Evil* (1976); Ray Ginger, *Six Days or Forever* (1958); Kenneth T. Jackson, *The Ku Klux Klan in the Cities, 1915–1930* (1967); Don S. Kirschner, *City and Country: Rural Responses to Urbanization in the 1920s* (1970); Lawrence Levine, *Defender of the Faith; William Jennings Bryan, The Last Decade* (1965); and George M. Marsden, *Fundamentalism and American Culture* (1980).

Other social and cultural themes are treated in Loren Baritz, *The Culture of the Twenties* (1969); Isabel Leighton, *The Aspirin Age* (1949); Larry May, *Screening Out the Past* (1980); Humbert S. Nelli, *The Business of Crime* (1976); John Roe, *The Road and the Car in American Life* (1971); Andrew Sinclair, *Prohibition: The Era of Excess* (1962); and Robert Sklar, *Movie-Made America* (1975).

On the politics of the Harding era, see Wesley Bagby, *The Road to Normalcy* (1962); Stanley Cohen, *A. Mitchell Palmer: Politician* (1963); Robert K. Murray, *The Politics of Normalcy* (1973); Burt Noggle, *Teapot Dome: Oil and Politics in the 1920s* (1962); J. W. Prothro, *Dollar Decade: Business Ideas in the 1920s* (1954); Francis Russell, *The Shadow of Blooming Grove: Warren G. Harding in His Times* (1968); and Andrew Sinclair, *The Available Man* (1965).

In cities, the first traffic jam was not long in following the first automobile.

CALVIN COOLIDGE AND THE NEW ERA

WHEN THE BUSINESS OF AMERICA WAS BUSINESS
1923 - 1929

Vice President Calvin Coolidge was visiting his father in tiny Plymouth Notch, Vermont, when he

got the news of Harding's death. Instead of rushing to Washington to be sworn in by the Chief Justice

of the Supreme Court, Coolidge walked downstairs to the darkened farmhouse parlor, where his

father, a justice of the peace, administered the presidential oath by the light of a kerosene lamp. To

the very pinnacle of his political career, Coolidge was the epitome of unpretentious simplicity and

rectitude—or, some have suggested, of sloth and showmanship.

THE COOLIDGE YEARS

Coolidge was not a bit like his predecessor. Far from strapping and handsome, he was thin with a pinched face that, even when he smiled, seemed to say that he wished he were somewhere else. Alice Roosevelt Longworth, the acidulous daughter of Theodore Roosevelt, said that Coolidge looked as though he had been weaned on a pickle.

Whereas Harding's private life was suspect, even tawdry, Coolidge was a man of impeccably proper, even dreary personal habits. His idea of a good time was a good nap. As president, he spent 12–14 hours out of 24 in bed except on slow days, when he was able to sneak in a few extra winks. When in 1933 writer Dorothy Parker heard that Coolidge had died, she asked, "How could they tell?"

A Quiet Clever Man

Coolidge would have appreciated that. He may have been known as "Silent Cal," hesitant to say much of anything, but when he spoke he was witty. In an attempt to break the ice at a banquet, a woman seated next to Coolidge told the president of a friend who had bet her that untalkative Cal would not say three words all evening. "You lose," Coolidge replied, and returned to his appetizer, resuming the bland, inscrutable gaze that was his trademark. "I found out early in life," this fabulously successful politician once noted, "that you don't have to explain something you haven't said."

And he was clever. At a meeting of American heads of state in the West Indies, Coolidge was sitting in a semi-circle with his colleagues when a waiter began to walk down the line serving drinks. It was the Prohibition Era; if Coolidge took a drink while out of the country, it would make juicy front-page news, and American reporters and photographers (who were undoubtedly enjoying their West Indian daquiris) waited on tenterhooks for the waiter to reach Coolidge with his tray. If, on the other hand, Coolidge doughtily turned the waiter away, it would be a mild but stereotypically American insult to his hosts. Coolidge fooled everyone. The instant before the waiter tried to serve him, he bent down to tie his shoe, and remained hunched over until the waiter moved on.

Coolidge took a curious pleasure in posing for photographers in costumes that were ludicrous on him: wearing a ten-gallon hat or a Sioux Indian war bonnet; strapping himself into skis on the White House lawn; dressing as a hard-working farmer at the haying in patent leather shoes with a Pierce Arrow in the background. Perhaps the photos were Coolidge's quiet way of saying

An old hand at grabbing publicity, Calvin Coolidge posed in an Indian headdress for photographers.

that he was at one with the American people of the 1920s in enjoying novelties and pranks. On being asked about the costuming, he said that he calculated that "the American public wants a solemn ass as President and I think I'll go along with them."

He was assuredly at one with the majority of the American people in abdicating political and cultural leadership to the business community. Coolidge worshiped financial success and believed without reservation that millionaires knew what was best for the country. "The man who builds a factory builds a temple," he said. On another occasion, he put his faith with sublime simplicity: "The business of America is business."

Keeping Cool With Coolidge

And so, while Coolidge quickly rid the cabinet of the racketeers and hacks whom he had inherited from Harding, he retained Harding's appointees from the business world, most notably Herbert Hoover (with whom he was as uncomfortable as Harding was) and Secretary of the Treasury Andrew Mellon. He then sat back to preside over the most business-minded administration to his time. In return, business praised his administration higher than they built skyscrapers in New York and Chicago. The Republicans crowed about "Coolidge prosperity," the recovery from the erratic postwar economy that began in 1923, and, thanks to the president's unblemished record for honesty, the G.O.P. never suffered a voter backlash as a result of the Harding scandals.

On the contrary, the biggest of the scandals, Teapot Dome, hurt progressive Democrats, for the Wilsonian, William G. McAdoo, a leading contender for the Democratic nomination in 1924, had been an attorney for the oilman Edward L. Doheny. Although McAdoo knew no more of the crooked transaction than did Coolidge, people associated him more closely with the thieves than they did the Republicans. When Montana Senators Thomas J. Walsh and Burton Wheeler, who led the investigation into the oil leases, attacked the Republicans, they were squelched by the slogan "Keep Cool With Coolidge." The president's supporters chastised them for ranting and raving about past crimes that Coolidge had remedied in his quiet way. By the summer of the election year of 1924, it was clear that Coolidge had the confidence of the country.

The Election of 1924

Then the Democrats obliged by tearing themselves apart. The convention, held in New York, pitted the Empire State's favorite son, Alfred E. Smith, against William G. McAdoo, whose support came mostly from the South and the West. Smith was a Roman Catholic and had the backing of white ethnic voters in the Northeast and urban Midwest as a symbol of their arrival in American politics. McAdoo, although no bigot himself, drew support from Southerners and Westerners who regarded Catholicism with at best distaste, and from virulently anti-Catholic Ku Kluxers. So bitter was the split and vicious the whisper campaign that neither candidate would yield for more than a hundred ballots, long after it was obvious neither could win the nomination.

Finally, the weary delegates settled on a compromise candidate, Wall Street lawyer John W. Davis. He was not absent from his lucrative practice for long. Davis won a mere 29 percent of the vote to Coolidge's 54 percent. Aged Robert La Follette, trying to revive the Progressive party in 1924, captured 17 percent of the popular vote and carried his native Wisconsin.

For four more years, Calvin Coolidge napped through good times. It was eight months after he left office, in October 1929, that what businessmen called the "New Era" came crashing to an end. Ironically, in view of the impending Great Depression, Coolidge retired from office with great reluctance. It was whispered that when the Republican convention of 1928 took his coy statement, "I do not choose to run for president in 1928," as a refusal to run, and nominated Herbert Hoover to succeed him, Coolidge threw himself on his familiar bed and wept.

Mellon's Tax Policies

The keystone of New Era government was the tax policy sponsored by the Secretary of the Treasury, Andrew Mellon of Pittsburgh. Mellon looked less like the political cartoonist's stereotype of a big-business man—a bloated, fleshy moneybags—than like a sporting duke, but a moneybags he was. Trim, with chiseled aristocratic features, and dressed in deftly tailored suits and tiny pointed shoes that shone like newly minted coins, Mellon was one of the three or four richest men in the world, a banker with close ties to the steel industry.

Believing that economic prosperity depended on the extent to which capitalists reinvested their profits in economic growth, Mellon favored the rich by slashing taxes that fell most heavily on them. He reduced the personal income tax for people who made more than $60,000 a year, and by 1929, the Treasury was actually shoveling taxes back to large corporations. United States Steel received a nice refund of $15 million. Other big corporations were comparably blessed.

To compensate for the loss in government revenues, Mellon cut government expenditures. The costs of government that he conceded were indispensable were to be paid for in two ways. First, Mellon raised the tariff on imported products, a double benefit for industrial capitalists. In the Fordney-McCumber Tariff of 1922, import duties reached levels that had been unheard of for a generation.

Second, Mellon sponsored modest increases in regressive taxes, that is, taxes that fell disproportionately on the middle and lower class. The costs of some kinds of postal services increased. The excise tax was raised and a new federal tax was imposed on automobiles. Both were paid by consumers. To those who complained that these measures penalized the middle classes and to some extent the poor, Mellon replied that the burden on each individual was small, and that his overall scheme helped ordinary people as well as the rich.

Mellon contended that when businessmen reinvested their government-sponsored windfalls, they created jobs and, therefore, the means of a better standard of living for all. The share of the middle and lower classes in Coolidge prosperity would "trickle down" to them. Moreover, the inducement to get rich, encouraged by government policy, would reinvigorate the spirit of enterprise among all Americans.

For six years, from late 1923 to late 1929, it appeared as though Mellon was dead right. His friends toasted him as "the greatest Secretary of the Treasury since Alexander Hamilton." Just how much damage his policies did to the national economy would not be known until after the collapse of the New Era in 1929. As early as 1924, however, the policy of subordinating federal policy to the short-term interests of big business and banking was helping to make a shambles of the international economy.

The Legacy of the Treaty of Versailles

The fundamental weakness of the international economy during the 1920s was owed to the fabulous costs of World War I. The war had pushed every participant nation except the United States to the brink of bankruptcy (and Russia over the cliff). Germany, for example, spent more during four years of war than during the previous four decades of the nation's existence. Britain and France were also deeply in debt—$10 billion to the United States alone—and France bore the additional burden of having been the battlefield. Both countries demanded that Germany pay them $13 billion in reparations. In addition to fixing guilt for causing the war on the Germans, the money was earmarked for repaying the debts owed to Americans.

The result was a flow of international payments from Germany to Britain and France (and other smaller countries), and from there to the United States. The trouble was that too much wealth was drained from Germany for the economy of that important industrial nation to remain healthy. The gold went abroad. At home, paper German marks inflated crazily; in time it took bundles, even wheelbarrows full of paper money to buy food. By November 1923, one American dollar bought 4.2 billion marks. Economists warned that to continue to bleed Germany was to promote political extremism (including Adolf Hitler's Nazi party) and to threaten the economies of all the European nations.

Some British and French statesmen acknowledged the point but insisted that as long as they were obligated to make huge debt payments to the United States, they had no choice but to insist on German payments to them. The burden of finding a remedy was on Americans.

A Foreign Policy for Bankers

There were several ways out of the morass. First, the United States, the world's wealthiest nation, could invigorate European industry by importing more European products. The Fordney-McCumber Tariff, a vital part of Mellon's fiscal policy, shut the door on that idea. Alternatively, the United States could forgive Britain and France all or most of their debts, in return for which they would cancel reparations payments from Germany. The international economy would, so to speak, have a fresh start.

Unfortunately, an administration that was closely allied with banking interests would not do that. "They hired the money, didn't they?" Coolidge said of the French and British war debts, as though he were talking about a grocer having trouble paying for his automobile.

Indeed, American bankers were profiting doubly from the European financial mess by loaning money to the Germans to, in part, subsidize their reparations payments. Interest, and a little bit of principal, was coming in from everywhere.

And that fact, bank profits, was good enough for the Republican administrations of the 1920s. In the Dawes Plan of 1924 (named for Budget Director Charles G. Dawes) and the Young Plan of 1929 (named for Owen D. Young), the United States agreed to a rescheduling of reparations payments, but not to a reduction of the total burden.

The circular flow of payments continued. American bankers loaned money to Germany; Germany paid about $2.5 billion in reparations to Britain and France between 1923 and 1929; Britain and France paid $2.6 billion to American creditors. The European economy was steadily, if slowly, sapped, and the American economy was indirectly damaged: capital that was supposed to be reinvested at home to "trickle down" was devoted to a nonproductive balancing of international books that did nothing for American workers.

Isolationism?

After the Treaty of Washington, the Harding and Coolidge administrations resisted meaningful cooperation with other nations. There was no question of joining the League of Nations as more and more Americans became convinced that it had been a mistake to intervene in the war that produced it. America's international efforts on behalf of maintaining the peace were restricted to proclamations of goodwill much like William Jennings Bryan's "cooling off" treaties. In 1928, Secretary of State Frank B. Kellogg joined with French Foreign Minister Aristide Briand to write a treaty that "outlawed" war as an instrument of national policy. Eventually, 62 nations signed the Kellogg-Briand Pact, a clear indication that, as a broad and pious statement of unenforceable sentiment, the pact was meaningless.

Because the United States refused to cooperate internationally in any meaningful way, the foreign policy of the 1920s is usually described as "isolationist." This is, however, something of a misnomer. Towards Latin America, the Harding and Coolidge administrations were active and aggressive on behalf of the interests of American investors there.

American investments in Latin America climbed from about $800 million in 1914 to $5.4 billion in 1929. The United States replaced Great Britain as the chief economic power in Latin America, particularly in the nations of the Caribbean.

The poorer Latin American nations sorely needed capital, and to that extent every dollar invested there was potentially a boon—if the population of the host countries as a whole benefited from it. Unfortunately, American businessmen had little interest in how the Latin American countries were governed until their profits were threatened by political instability. They ignored the depredations of predatory native elites until they were in trouble.

When dictators in the "banana republics" were unable to contain popular resentments, American investors turned to Washington for protection of their profits. By 1924, American officials directly or indirectly administered the finances of ten Latin American nations. For at least part of the decade, the marines occupied Nicaragua, Honduras, Cuba, Haiti, and the Dominican Republic. The business of the entire Western Hemisphere was the business of Coolidge's America too.

PROSPERITY AND BUSINESS CULTURE

In the late twentieth century, it is easy to see the damage wreaked by the Coolidge administration. But the voters of the 1920s supported Silent Cal and his policies with unmistakeable enthusiasm. The Republican party held comfortable majorities in every Congress between 1920 and 1930. Only in the South and some thinly populated Western states, and in a few big cities, could the Democrats count on winning elections.

The Anticlimactic Election of 1928

In 1928, the 54 percent of the vote that Coolidge had won in 1924 rose to 58 percent. The victorious Republican candidate was Herbert Hoover, who was, in his energy and rather opaque written celebrations of business, even better an exemplar of the New Era than Silent Cal.

Hoover's opponent, Alfred E. Smith of New York, had spent four years mending fences with Southern and Western Protestants who had supported McAdoo in 1924. Smith was unable to win over the bigots, however. For the first time since Reconstruction, a number of prominent Southerners, including Methodist bishop James Cannon, urged voters to support the Republican party. Their reason was partly Smith's Roman Catholic religion. But they also drummed on Smith's opposition to Prohibition. Like many urban politicos, Smith not only urged repeal, he openly flaunted the law. Herbert Hoover probably disapproved of Prohibition personally, but in 1928 he called it "a great social and economic experiment, noble in motive and far-reaching in purpose." He was the "dry" candidate, Smith the "wet."

Smith also invited hostility from Southern, Western, and rural voters with his rasping, nasal New York accent. Heard over the radio—or "raddio" as Smith called it—his voice conjured up all the unsavory images associated with New York City for half a century.

Still, had he been a Kansas Presbyterian who never drank even patent medicines, Smith would have lost in 1928. Business and the Republican party reigned supreme because of the general prosperity of the New Era and because a great many Americans were sincerely convinced that businessmen were the new messiahs Woodrow Wilson had tried so hard to be.

The Shape of Prosperity

Industrial and agricultural productivity soared during the 1920s, even though there was not much increase in the size of the industrial work force, and the number of agricultural workers actually declined. Wages did not keep up with the contribution that the more efficient workers were making to the economy, however. While dividends on stock rose 65 percent between 1920 and 1929, wages increased only 24 percent.

Nevertheless, the increase in wages was quite enough to satisfy the working people who enjoyed them, particularly because consumer goods were relatively cheap and business promoted an alluring new way for a family to live beyond their means—consumer credit.

Buy Now, Pay Later

Before the 1920s, borrowing was something one did in order to build a business, get crops in the ground, or to save or improve an enterprise. In theory, borrowed money was invested in productivity, thus providing the means to retire the debt. Or, people borrowed in order to build or buy a home, in which case their debt was secured by real property. During the 1920s, for the first time, large numbers of Americans began to borrow simply in order to live more pleasurably. They went into debt not to produce but to consume and enjoy.

The chief agency of consumer borrowing during the 1920s was the installment plan. A refrigerator that sold for $87.50 could be ensconced in a corner of the kitchen for a down payment of merely $5 and monthly payments of $10. Even a comparatively low-cost item like a vacuum cleaner ($28.95) could be had for $2 down and "E-Z payments" of $4 a month. During the New Era, 60 percent of all automobiles were bought on time; 70 percent of furniture; 80 percent of refrigerators, radios, and vacuum cleaners; and 90 percent of pianos, sewing machines, and washing machines. With 13.8 million people owning radios by 1930 (up from virtually none in 1920), the Americans who basked in the glow of Coolidge prosperity were also up to their necks in hock.

Moralists pointed out that borrowing in order to consume marked a sharp break with American ideals of frugality—the axioms of Benjamin Franklin—but others spoke louder and in more seductive tones. They were the advertisers, members of a new profession dedicated to creating wants in people's minds—the advertising men called them needs—which people had never particularly noticed before.

Buy, Buy, Buy

The earliest advertisements, dating to antiquity, were announcements. In the eighteenth and nineteenth century, a merchant placed a tiny notice in a newspaper describing goods, perhaps unusual ones, available for purchase, or special "sale" prices on common products.

During the 1870s, Robert Bonner, the editor of a literary magazine, the New York *Ledger*, learned by accident the curious effectiveness of repeating a message over and over. He intended to place a conventional one-line ad in a newspaper—"Read Mrs. Southworth's New Story in the *Ledger*"—and the compositor misread his specification of "one line" as "one page." The line ran over and over, down every column. To Bonner's surprise,

THE TIN LIZZIE

Although Americans did not invent the automobile, they democratized it by putting cars within the reach of almost everyone. But striving for simplicity (shunning all "extras," including a choice of color), by adapting the assembly line to the manufacture of cars, and by refusing to change his design, Henry Ford managed to whittle the price of a brand-new Model T to $260 in 1925. That is more than $2,000 in today's dollars, but still considerably less than the cheapest new car on the market. By 1927, Ford had sold 15 million tin lizzies, as Model T Fords were affectionately known, more than all other auto makers combined.

LET'S HAVE A LOOK UNDER THE HOOD

Americans and Britons speak a different language when they talk about their cars. What Americans call the hood, the British call the bonnet. Some other differences:

American English	British English
clunker or junker	banger
gas	petrol
generator	dynamo
headlight	headlamp
muffler	silencer
station wagon	estate wagon
trunk	boot
windshield	windscreen

The different vocabularies provide a little case study in how languages develop. The automobile roared into history long after the United States and Great Britain had gone their separate political and cultural ways, but before instantaneous electronic communication allowed words coined on one side of the Atlantic to become immediately familiar on the other.

Because the early automobile was largely a French development, many American automotive terms were taken from the French language: *automobile* itself, *cabriolet* (later shortened to *cab*), *chassis*, *chauffeur*, *coupe*, *garage*, *limousine*, and *sedan*.

the blunder did not bankrupt him; his magazine sold out in one afternoon.

The lesson was unmistakeable. During the 1890s, C. W. Post, without a cent to his name, borrowed enough money to plaster an entire city with the name of his new breakfast cereal, Post Toasties, and was a millionaire within a month. Bombarded by the name in newspapers, on billboards, painted on the sides of buildings, slipped under doors on leaflets, people bought. By the 1920s, advertisers had moved on to making the extravagant claims of the snake oil salesman, telling outright lies, and bringing sexual titillation into the game: suggestive young ladies in advertisements for such products as soda pop and tickets on railroads.

Advertising became a profession and the pros styled themselves as practical psychologists. They sold goods by exploiting anxieties and, in the words of Thorstein Veblen, "administering shock effects" and "trading on the range of human infirmities which blossom in devout observances, and bear fruit in the psychopathic wards." In the age of Coolidge, the makers of Listerine Antiseptic, a mouthwash, invented a disease, "halitosis," of which the symptoms included nothing more than a curter greeting than usual from a friend: "Even your best friend won't tell you." Listerine made millions. Fleisch-

Advertisements were positively artistic by the 1920s.

mann's yeast, losing its market as people began buying instead of baking their bread, advertised their product as excellent for curing constipation and adolescent pimples. The success of anxiety advertising resulted in the creation of underarm deodorants, a nicety without which humanity had functioned for millennia.

Chain Stores

With manufacturers of "small-ticket" items like toothpaste and mouthwash spending millions to create a demand for their products, it became advantageous to retail advertised goods on a nationwide basis too. Individual "Mom and Pop" grocery stores and locally owned and managed haberdasheries and sundries shops sold comparatively few cans of Chef Boy-Ar-Dee Spaghetti, Arrow shirts, and tubes of Ipana each month. Therefore, they paid the regional wholesaler a premium price. A centrally managed chain or franchise company, on the contrary, could buy the same goods for hundreds of stores at once, secure a better wholesale price, and keep shipping charges down through "vertical integration." The result was they sharply undersold "Mom and Pop," and their retail chains spread rapidly throughout the country.

By 1928, 860 grocery chains competed for the dollars of a population that was eating better. Among the biggest success stories between 1920 and 1929 were the first supermarkets: Piggly-Wiggly (from 515 to 2,500 stores),

Safeway (from 766 to 2,660 stores), and A & P (Atlantic and Pacific Tea Company, from 4,621 to 15,418 stores). Chains also came to dominate the sundries trade (F.W. Woolworth and J.C. Penney), auto parts (Western Auto), and, of course, the retailing of gasoline.

Image Advertising

"Image" advertising—associating a product with certain values or an attractive sort of person—characterized the selling of automobiles at a time when dozens of manufacturers competed for a share of the market. Pierce Arrows and Lincolns implied, none too subtly, that possession of one of these automobiles indicated a person of high social standing. Stutz Bearcat was the car of the sport and the swell. Dodge affected a stodgy and stolid comfortable "old shoe" family image. Henry Ford insisted that his car be presented as common and democratic.

By the end of the decade, there were 27 million cars registered by state departments of motor vehicles. Indeed, everything related to automobiles, from publicly financed highway construction to those new features of the American landscape, service stations and the roadside motor hotel or "motel," flourished during the New Era.

The Limits of Prosperity

A few economists joined the moralistic critics of runaway consumption, pointing out that the time would come when everyone who could afford a car, a washing machine, and other consumer durables would have them. They would no longer be buying, and the consumer industries would be in trouble.

Another major weakness of the Coolidge economy was that significant numbers of Americans did not share in the good times and were, therefore, shut out completely from the buying spree. The 700,000 to 800,000 coal miners and 400,000 textile workers and their dependents suffered depressed conditions and wages throughout the decade; they were not buying many cars and radios. Staple farmers were once again struggling to stave off bankruptcy. Even those who did well often lived in places where there was no electricity; they were buying no appliances that needed to be plugged in.

The Southern states generally lagged far behind the rest of the country in income and standard of living. Blacks, Native Americans, Hispanics, and other minority groups tasted Coolidge prosperity only in odd bites.

Business Culture

But economically deprived groups are rarely politically articulate when the mainstream society is at ease in its world, and in the 1920s, mainstream America was quite at ease. Business leaders hastened to take the credit for good times, and they got it.

In 1925, Sears, Roebuck opened its first retail store while continuing its catalogue sales.

On a local level, businessmen's clubs such as the Rotary, Kiwanis, Lions, and Junior Chambers of Commerce seized community leadership and preached boosterism: "If you can't boost, don't knock." Successful manufacturers like Henry Ford were looked to for wisdom on every imaginable question. Any man who made $25,000 a day, as Ford did during most of the 1920s, must be an oracle on whatever subject he chose to speak about. Even that man once the most hated in America, John D. Rockefeller, now in his eighties and retired to Florida, became a figure of respect and affection, thanks to Rockefeller philanthropy, Coolidge prosperity, and the skillful image building of the Rockefeller family's public relations expert, Ivy Lee.

The career of an advertising man, Bruce Barton, showed just how thoroughly the business culture dominated the way Americans thought. In 1925, Barton published a book called *The Man Nobody Knows*. It depicted Jesus as a businessman, a hale fellow well-met, a sport, an entrepreneur, and an advertising genius whose religion was like a successful company. Instead of finding Barton's vision blasphemous or laughable, Americans bought *The Man Nobody Knows* by the hundreds of thousands. It was a best seller for two years!

John Jacob Raskob of General Motors promoted the worship of business in popular magazines such as *The Saturday Evening Post*. Because the value of many kinds of property was rising throughout the 1920s under the stewardship of business, Raskob said that it was a simple matter for workingmen to save a little money and invest it, thus becoming capitalists themselves. To an astonishing degree, middle-class Americans who had a small nest egg in the bank believed him. They plunged their savings into one get-rich-quick scheme after another, feeding but at the same time dooming the speculative economy.

GET RICH QUICK

The most colorful get-rich-quick craze of the decade centered on Florida, previously a backward and isolated agricultural state. Improved train connections with Eastern and Midwestern population centers, retirement to Florida by such celebrities as Rockefeller and William Jennings Bryan, and the lively nationwide ballyhoo of ingenious promoters such as Wilson Mizner put people on notice of the Sunshine State's possibilities as a vacation and retirement paradise.

The Florida Land Boom

The development of places like Orlando, Fort Lauderdale, and Miami Beach would take time, of course, no one denied that. The way to make money from their growth, therefore, was to buy orange groves and sandy wasteland at bargain prices and hold the land for resale to the actual builders of vacation hotels and retirement homes. The number of people rich enough to make such a long-term committment, however, was small. In 1925, though, Florida's boosters attracted more modestly-fixed people to send their money south by promoting a get-rich-quick speculative fever that fed on itself.

As had happened repeatedly in the American West, the price of Florida land rose not because development was underway and residents were pouring in by the hundreds of thousands, but because speculator bought from speculator, each planning to sell to another as quickly as possible at an even higher price. Some lots in Miami Beach on which no one dreamed of building changed hands dozens of times within a few months, the price climbing with every sale. At the height of the craze, one issue of a Miami newspaper ran more than 500 pages of advertisements of land for sale. There were over 2,000 real-estate offices in the little city.

Since the price of every acre in Florida seemed to be skyrocketing, many Northerners were willing to buy sight unseen, and frauds were inevitable. More than a few snowbound dreamers in Chicago and Minneapolis purchased tracts of alligator-infested swampland from fast-talking salesmen who assured them that they were purchasing a site that Piggly-Wiggly or Woolworth's would find highly desirable. Others bought "beachfront lots" that were closer to the ocean than they counted on—underneath six feet of salt water at high tide. But

the major fuel of the mania was not fraud. It was a foolishness born of a culture that exalted business and money-making above all else.

As with all speculative crazes, the day inevitably arrived when there were no more buyers, no one willing to bet on higher prices in the future. After a few months of making mortgage payments on land that was not moving, would-be land barons decided, as herd-like as they had bought, to get out of Florida real estate with their winnings, to break even, or just to cut their losses. The market was flooded with offerings at ever lower prices. The speculators who were caught holding overpriced property saw paper fortunes evaporate; the banks that had loaned them money to speculate failed; people who had trusted those banks to invest their savings sensibly lost their accounts.

The Florida crash was triggered by a hurricane that hit Miami and showed, as Frederick Lewis Allen put it, what a soothing tropical wind could do to a vacation paradise when it got a running start from the West Indies. The price of land plunged within weeks to dollars per acre. Citrus farmers who had cursed themselves a thousand times for having sold their groves so cheaply at the beginning of the boom discovered that, thanks to a chain of defaults, they were back in possession of their orchards only a little worse for the wear of speculators tromping over it imagining hotels and happy beach loungers. Wilson Mizner, one of the architects of the boom and a big loser in the bust, was good humored about the debacle. "Always be pleasant to the people you meet on the way up," he said, "because they are always the very same people you meet on the way down." He went to Hollywood.

Buying on Margin

Middle-class America was almost as nonchalant as Mizner. Even before Florida busted, they began to fuel an-

NOTABLE PEOPLE

THE LONE EAGLE: CHARLES A. LINDBERGH (1902–1974)

Raymond Orteig was a wealthy French restauranteur living in New York whose two enthusiasms were Franco-American friendship and aviation. He believed that airplanes had a much brighter future than, in 1926, seemed likely. During the 1920s, the fragile but ever improved crafts served as toys for rich hobbyists, as showpieces at state and county fairs where nomadic "barnstormers" did aerial tricks such as walking on the wing of a plane in flight, and, here and there in the United States, as vehicles to deliver "air mail," which the Post Office regarded as an experiment.

Even the prospects of military aviation were dim. Despite the publicity that had been given aerial dog-fights during the First World War, planes had been more show than substance, playing no significant role in any action. In 1921 and 1923, General William Mitchell of the Air Service, a branch of the army, had proved in a series of tests that bombs dropped from planes could sink a capital ship (a captured German vessel); but in order to prove his point, Mitchell had disobeyed orders and won the enmity of his superiors. He was court-martialed, and his vision momentarily discredited.

But Orteig believed in the commercial potential, if not in the military uses, of airplanes. Partly to demonstrate the feasibility of long-distance trips, the only kind of transportation in which flying made sense, and partly because he enjoyed ballyhoo as well as most people in the 1920s, Orteig offered a $25,000 prize to the first plane to cross the Atlantic nonstop between France and the United States.

By the spring of 1927, a number of pilots, including First World War flying ace René Fonck, and polar explorer Admiral Richard A. Byrd, using huge biplanes powered by three motors, had tried and failed. Both survived their accidents, but in other attempts, including an east–west flight by two Frenchmen who almost made it to North America, six were dead and two were seriously injured.

In the meantime, in San Diego, California, another challenger for the prize had been making news. Charles A. "Slim" Lindbergh, Jr., a shy 25-year-old mail pilot from the Midwest, had a different approach to the problem. He had persuaded a group of St. Louis businessmen to finance the construction of a plane that would be capable of flying the Atlantic, and he had found a company, Ryan aircraft of San Diego, to build it. Instead of pinning his hopes on a massive machine powered by three large (and heavy) engines and flown by a crew (more weight), Lindbergh believed that the way to get to France was with a plane of the utmost simplicity, a machine designed to carry little more than gasoline and a single pilot.

Far from being the rickety wing and a prayer, as the press described the *Spirit of St. Louis*, it was the creation of careful calculation and engineering expertise that had no commercial value, but was designed down to the last rivet to do one thing: get off the ground with a maximum load of fuel. In effect, the *Spirit* was a flying gas tank. The press would dub the young pilot "Lucky Lindbergh" when he succeeded in his mission, but most of the luck involved in the venture was in the ease with which he persuaded his backers of his idea and found a builder who shared his confidence. Indeed, in getting the *Spirit* from San Diego to the airfield on Long Island from which he would depart, Lindbergh broke two aviation records: he made the longest nonstop solo flight to date (San Diego–St. Louis) and the fastest transcontinental crossing. It was no reckless experiment.

But that was how the press of the 1920s played it. Lindbergh was mobbed wherever he went in New York, and was depicted as the simple, plucky, American frontiers-

---

other speculative mania, driving up the prices of shares on the New York Stock Exchange.

Speculation in stocks had long been a game for a few very rich people. However, the prosperity of the 1920s created savings accounts for middle-class Americans, even after consumption. In order to tap their capital, stockbrokers offered the possibility of purchasing stock on an installment plan in which, so it seemed, there were no installments to pay.

That is, investors with just a few hundred or thousands of dollars to risk in the market could buy stocks "on margin." They bought shares of RCA-Victor, the New York Central, or Illinois Gadget by paying out as little as 10 percent of the quoted price of those companies' shares. In this way, they were able to hold title to ten times as many shares as they could afford to buy cash. A bank or broker loaned the speculator the balance of the stocks' actual price with the stocks themselves serving as collateral. This—the money the speculator owed—was "the margin." When the shares were sold, presumably at a big profit—the loan was paid off and the shrewd speculators pocketed the difference, also ten times what they would have made if they had bought with cash. At least that was how the 1.5 million Americans "playing the market" in 1926 understood margin to work.

The Bull Market

Beginning in 1927, that was how it did work for hundreds of thousands of people. Prices of shares began to soar as more and more people rushed to buy. During the summer of 1929, values went crazy. American Telephone and Telegraph climbed from $209 a share to $303; General Motors went from $268 to $391, hitting $452 on September 3. Some obscure issues enjoyed even more dizzying rises. And with each tale of a fortune made man sort of hero. He was not allowed to examine his plane without the presence of thousands of well-wishers, sensation-seekers, and even hysterics who wanted to touch him as though he were a saint. Historians have compared the fuss made over him with the adoration that Americans of the 1920s lavished on movie stars and boxing champions; but it seems more accurate to describe the preflight hoopla in terms of Daniel Boorstin's definition of a celebrity: a person who is well known for being well known.

On May 16, 1927, conditions for a takeoff were less than ideal. The airstrip was muddy from rains, which meant additional drag on the plane, and by the time that Lindbergh was ready to go, he was taking off with a tailwind, not recommended procedure even when the craft is not loaded to the utmost of its theoretical limitations. (At the last minute, Lindbergh called for an additional 50 gallons of gasoline in the tanks.)

But Richard A. Byrd's plane was sitting at the same field, mechanically ready to go but stalled by legal complications; and another challenger was almost ready. Impatient, emotionally geared for the moment, perhaps influenced by the press notices of his singularity, Lindbergh packed five sandwiches into the tiny cockpit and took off. Once he was airborne, the riskiest part of the venture was behind him. Unless he fell asleep. That, and occasional threats of ice on the wings, which would add weight to the plane, were the worries he later recalled as most serious. At ten o'clock at night, two days after his departure, he landed amidst a screaming mob of 100,000 people at Le Bourget Field, Paris.

Americans were popular in Europe during the 1920s, and Lindbergh was exalted as the greatest of them. Back home it was the same thing: ticker-tape parades, thousands of invitations merely to appear in towns and cities.

For a while, the soft-spoken hero luxuriated in the fame and money that came to him. In 1929, he married Anne Morrow, the daughter of the American ambassador to Mexico (Lindbergh was himself the son of a congressman), and as a team they continued to tour on behalf of the government and commercial aviation. The couple's infant son was kidnapped from their New Jersey home and, despite the payment of ransom, murdered. Police (and the Lindberghs) believed that the frenzied publicity surrounding the event contributed to the death of the child by frightening the abductor. After the trial, conviction, and execution of a carpenter, Bruno Hauptmann, which were criticized because of the relentless press coverage, the Lindberghs moved to Europe, where, they believed, they could escape the spotlight.

There, Lindbergh was impressed by the new German air force built up by Adolf Hitler and Hermann Goering, and he accepted a medal from the German dictator. After 1939, when he returned to the United States to lecture on behalf of the isolationist America First Committee, Lindbergh was criticized as being pro-Nazi. He was not, but he was an Anglophobe, and he believed that Germany would win the war that broke out in September 1939. Therefore, he opposed those who wanted to go to war before England fell.

Like most of the America Firsters, Lindbergh ceased his opposition to the war once the United States had entered it. He worked as a technical expert to aircraft companies, and, although over 40, he flew several missions in the Pacific theater. In the end, Lindbergh's accomplishment of 1927 overshadowed his politics of 1939 to 1941, and he was commissioned a general in the air force.

overnight, related breathlessly or with smug self-congratulation at country club, lodge hall, community dance, or, indeed, on the porch of the church on Sunday, more people were hooked, encouraged to carry their savings to stockbrokers, whose offices were as easy to find as auto parts stores.

Historically and ideally, the value of a share in a corporation represented the earning capacity of the company. The money that a corporation realized by selling shares was to be expended, theoretically, to improve the company's plant, equipment, marketing capacity, and in other productive ways. Thus, when the price of stock in General Motors or Radio Corporation of America rose during the late 1920s, it represented to some extent the extraordinary expansion of the automobile and radio industries.

During the speculative Coolidge Bull Market, however, the prices of shares also reflected nothing more

than the willingness of people to pay those prices because, as in Florida, they expected someone else to buy from them at yet greater prices. It was immaterial to such speculators that the companies in which they had put their money did not pay dividends or even use their capital to improve productive capacity. The rising prices of stocks fed on themselves. It became more profitable for companies to put their capital into speculation— making loans to margin buyers, for example—than into production. The face value of shares in the Coolidge Bull Market bore little relationship to the health of the American economy.

Politicians, either unable to understand what was happening or afraid to appear pessimistic in a time of buoyant optimism, reassured their constituents that there was nothing wrong. When a few concerned economists warned that the bull market was a bubble that had to burst, with calamitous consequences, others scolded

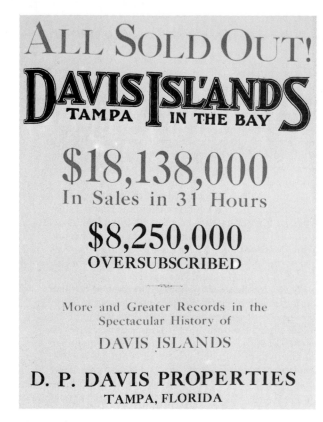

An advertisement typical of those prompting a Florida land boom among real-estate speculators in the 1920s.

them. President Coolidge told people that he thought stock prices were cheap, in effect encouraging others to rush to the broker.

The Inevitable

Joseph P. Kennedy, a Boston millionaire (and father of President John F. Kennedy), said in later years that he had sold off his stocks during the summer of 1929 after the man who shined his shoes had mentioned that he was playing the market. Kennedy reasoned that if such a poorly paid person was buying stock, there was no one left out there to bid prices higher. The inevitable crash was coming soon.

Kennedy was right. On September 3, 1929, the average price of shares on the New York Stock Exchange peaked and then dipped sharply. For a month, prices spurted up and down. Then on "Black Thursday," October 24, a record 13 million shares changed hands, and values collapsed. General Electric fell 47½ points on that one day; other major issues dropped almost as much.

On Tuesday, October 29, the wreckage was worse. In a panic now, speculators dumped 16 million shares on the market. Clerical workers on Wall Street had to work through the night just to sort out the avalanche of paperwork. When the dust settled early the next morning,

more than $30 billion in paper value had been wiped out.

It was phony value, representing little more than the irrational belief that prices could rise indefinitely. Nevertheless, the eradication of so many dollars profoundly shattered the confidence of businessmen and belief in the business culture of the 1920s. The Great Crash eventually contributed to the hardship of millions of people who could not have distinguished a share in Seaboard Air Lines from the label on a bottle of cognac.

Crash and Depression

The Great Crash of 1929 did not cause the Great Depression of the 1930s. That was the result of fundamental weaknesses in the economy that had little to do with the mania for speculation. But the crash helped to trigger the decline in the American economy that was well under way by New Year's Day 1930.

Middle-class families who had played the market lost their savings. Banks that had recklessly loaned money to speculators went broke. When they closed their doors, they wiped out the savings accounts of frugal people who looked on a bank as a vault to protect their money from robbers.

Corporations whose cash assets were decimated shut down operations or curtailed production, thus throwing people out of work or cutting their wages. Those who had taken mortgages during the heady high interest days of 1928 and 1929 were unable to meet payments and lost their homes; farmers lost the means by which they

---

JESUS AS ADVERTISING MAN

He would be a national advertiser today, I am sure, as he was the greatest advertiser of his own day. Take any one of the parables, no matter which—you will find that it exemplifies all the principles on which advertising textbooks are written.

1. First of all they are marvellously condensed, as all good advertising must be. Jesus hated prosy dullness.

2. His language was marvellously simple—a second great essential. All the greatest things in human life are one-syllable things—love, joy, hope, child, wife, trust, faith, God.

3. Sincerity glistened like sunshine through every sentence he uttered. The advertisements which persuade people to act are written by men who have an abiding respect for the intelligence of their readers, and a deep sincerity regarding the merits of the goods they have to sell.

4. Finally he knew the necessity for repetition and practiced it. No important truth can be impressed upon the minds of any large number of people by being said only once.

Bruce Barton, *The Man Nobody Knows* (1925)

Variety, *the show business newspaper, announced the stock market crash in theatrical parlance.*

made a living. This contributed to additional bank failures.

Virtually everyone had to cut consumption, thus reducing the sales of manufacturers and farmers and stimulating another turn in the downward spiral: curtailed production meant layoff; increased unemployment meant another reduction in consumption by those newly thrown out of work. And so it went, from buy, buy, buy to down, down, down.

For Further Reading

See these several general histories of the 1920s: Frederick Lewis Allen, *Only Yesterday* (1931); Loren Baritz, *The Culture of the Twenties* (1969); Paul A. Carter, *The Twenties in America* (1968); Ellis W. Hawley, *The Great War and the Search for a Modern Order: A History of the American People and Their Institutions, 1917–1933* (1979); William E. Leuchtenburg, *The Perils of Prosperity, 1914–1932* (1958); George Soule, *Prosperity Decade: From War to Depression, 1917–1929* (1947).

Focusing on politics are David Bumer, *The Politics of Provincialism: The Democratic Party in Transition* (1968); Otis L. Graham, Jr., *The Great Campaigns: War and Reform in America, 1900–1928* (1971); Oscar Handlin, *Al Smith and His America* (1958); John D. Hicks, *Republican Ascendancy, 1921–1933* (1960); Donald Lisio, *The President and Protest* (1974); E. A. Moore, *A Catholic Runs for President* (1956); Theodore D. Saloutos and John D. Hicks, *Twentieth Century Populism: Agricultural Discontent in the Middle West, 1900–1939* (1951); D. R. McCoy, *Calvin Coolidge: The Quiet President* (1967); Arthur M. Schlesinger, Jr., *The Crisis of the Old Order* (1957); William Allen White, *A Puritan in Babylon* (1938); Joan Hoff Wilson, *Herbert Hoover: Forgotten Progressive* (1975).

On economic and financial questions, see Irving Bernstein, *The Lean Years* (1960); C. P. Kinderberger, *The World in Depression* (1973); J. W. Prothro, *Dollar Decade: Business Ideas in the 1920s* (1954); and the incomparable John K. Galbraith, *The Great Crash* (1955).

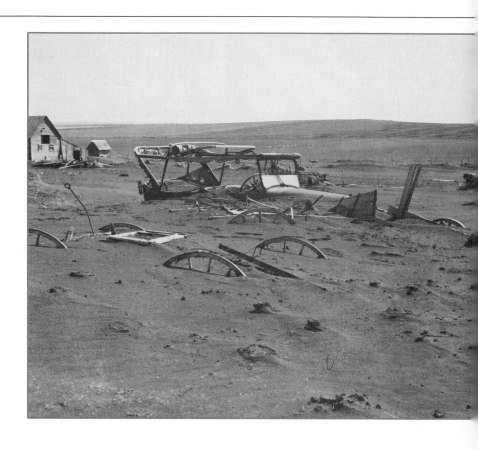

The aftermath of a series of dust storms, South Dakota, 1936.

NATIONAL TRAUMA
THE GREAT DEPRESSION
1930 - 1933

The stock market crash of late 1929 was a headlines story day after day. The depression that began

in 1930 made its impact less dramatically at first, but by the end of the year it engulfed the nation.

Bad economic times did not entirely dissipate until 1940, after the economy had been jolted into full

activity by the outbreak of war in Europe.

The Great Depression was not only the most serious economic crisis in American history, it was a

more jarring psychological and moral experience for the American people than any other event in their past except the Civil War. The Great Depression was a national trauma that left lifelong scars. Americans who had lived through the First World War and the Roaring Twenties found their recollections of those periods vague and inconsequential after 1930. People who came of age during the 1930s would remember the deprivation, anxieties, and struggles of the decade more vividly than they would remember the Second World War, the return of prosperity, and the beginning of the nuclear age in the 1940s. So large did the memory of hard times loom in their minds that they passed on to their children, who were born in the 1930s and early 1940s and never really experienced the depression, a sense that it was an important event in their own lives. Not until the later 1960s did a generation come of age for which the Great Depression was irrelevant "ancient history." Not until 1980, half a century after the depression began, did voters in a national election decisively repudiate the political "liberals" whom the Great Depression brought to the fore.

THE FACE OF CATASTROPHE

Not every memory of the 1930s was a bad one. On the contrary, many people were proud that when times had been worst, they nevertheless had survived and, what is more, had carried on vital cultural, social, and personal lives. Negative or positive, however, the depression generation was the last American generation to date whose character and values were forged in an era of economic decline, denial, and insecurity.

The Depression in Numbers

During the first year after the crash of the stock market, 4 million workers lost their jobs. By 1931, 100,000 people were being fired each week. By 1932, 25 percent of the work force was unemployed, 13 million people with about 30 million dependents. Black workers, "the last hired and the first fired," suffered a higher unemploy-

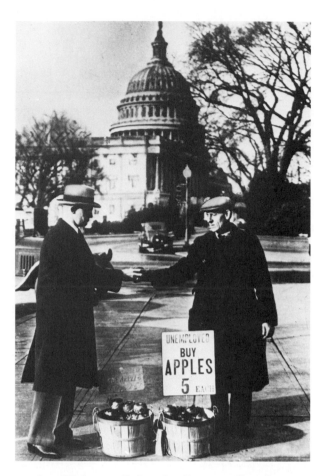

On a Washington, D.C., sidewalk, a man sells apples to support himself while unemployed.

ment rate than whites, 35 percent. In Chicago, 40 percent of those people who wanted work could not find it. In Toledo, 80 percent were unemployed. In some coal-mining towns like Donora, Pennsylvania, virtually no one had a job.

Employees who held on to their jobs took cuts in pay. Between 1929 and 1933, the average weekly earnings of manufacturing workers fell from $25 to less than $17. The income of farmers plummeted, and that was from a low base. By the winter of 1933, some corn growers were burning their crop for heat—shades of the 1890s—because they could not sell it at a profit. Growers of wheat estimated that it took five bushels to earn the price of a cheap pair of shoes. The wholesale price of cotton dropped to five cents a pound, laughably low if the consequences were not so tragic.

Banks failed at a rate of 200 a month during 1932, wiping out $3.2 billion in savings accounts. When New York's Bank of the United States went under in Decem-

---

A CHICKEN IN EVERY POT

The Republican party slogan in the election campaign of 1928 had been "A Chicken in Every Pot and Two Cars in Every Garage." In 1932, the advertising man who had coined it was out of work and reduced to begging in order to support his family.

ber 1930, 400,000 people lost their deposits. Much of the money was in small accounts that had been squirreled away by working people as a hedge against economic misfortune. When, understandably frightened, they withdrew their emergency funds, the downward spiral continued.

Hundreds of thousands of people lost their homes between 1929 and 1933 because they could not meet mortgage payments. One farm family in four had been pushed off the land by 1933, mainly in the cotton, grain, and pork belts of the South and Midwest. With their customers unable to buy, more than 100,000 small businesses went bankrupt, 32,000 in 1932 alone (88 per day). Doctors, lawyers, and other professionals reported huge drops in income. Some schools closed for lack of money; in others, teachers took sharp cuts or worked without pay as the only means of keeping them open. Some teachers in Chicago were not compensated for ten years. Others never were.

What Depression Looked Like

Even people who did not personally suffer were reminded of the depression at every turn. More than 5,000 people lined up outside a New York employment agency each week to apply for 500 menial jobs. They were hard to miss. When the city government of Birmingham,

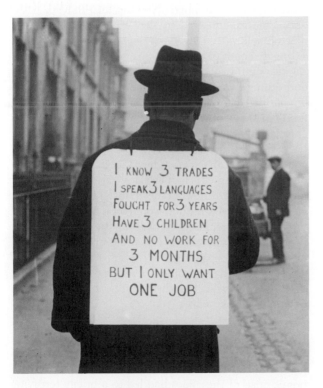

Unemployed working man, 1930.

Alabama, called for about 800 workers to put in an eleven-hour day for $2, 12,000 applicants showed up. In 1931, a Soviet agency, Amtorg, announced openings for 6,000 skilled technicians who were willing to move to Russia; 100,000 Americans said they would go. Once-prosperous workers and small-business men sold apples or set up shoeshine stands on street corners, claiming that they preferred any kind of work to accepting charity.

Charitable organizations were not up to the flood of impoverished people. Philadelphia's social workers managed to reach only one-fifth of the city's unemployed in order to provide $4.23 to a family for a week, not enough to buy food, let alone pay for clothing, rent, and fuel. Soup kitchens set up by both religious and secular groups offered little more than a crust of bread and a bowl of thin stew, but for three years, they were regularly mobbed by people who waited in lines that strung out for blocks. A journalist described the crowd at the Municipal Lodging House in New York City in 1930: "There is a line of men, three or sometimes four abreast, a block long, and wedged tightly together—so tightly that no passer-by can break through. For this compactness there is a reason: those at the head of the grey-black human snake will eat tonight; those farther back probably won't."

On the outskirts of most large cities (and right in the middle of New York's Central Park), homeless men and women built shantytowns out of scavenged lumber, scraps of sheet metal, flimsy packing crates, and cardboard boxes. The number of people who simply wandered the land brought the face of catastrophe to rural America. Because it was impossible to stay the flood, railroads gave up trying to keep people off the freight trains. Detectives for the Missouri Pacific railroad counted 14,000 people hopping the railroad's freights in 1928; in 1931, 186,000 rode the same rails. Rough estimates indicate that 1.5 million people were moving about in search of casual work, and others were simply moving about; railroad officials noted ever-increasing numbers of children in the trek.

This revelation, plus increased desertion of their families by unemployed men, a rise in the divorce rate, and a decline in the birth rate—from more than 3 million births in 1921 to 2.4 million in 1932—convinced some moralists and sociologists that the depression was destroying the American family. Others responded that hardship was causing families to pull together.

This was true of the tragic odyssey of the "Okies" and "Arkies." In the mid-1930s, the hardships of depression were compounded by a natural disaster in large parts of Oklahoma, Texas, Kansas, and Arkansas: dust storms literally stripped the topsoil from the land and blacked out the sun. In several counties of eastern Oklahoma, 90 percent of the population went on the dole. Some

NO ONE HAS STARVED

At the worst of times early in the Great Depression, it was common to say that "no one has starved." But some came close, as these two excerpts from the *New York Times* indicate:

MIDDLETOWN, N.Y., December 24, 1931.—Attracted by smoke from the chimney of a supposedly abandoned summer cottage near Anwana Lake in Sullivan County, Constable Simon Glaser found a young couple starving. Three days without food, the wife, who is 23 years old, was hardly able to walk.

DANBURY, Connecticut, September 6, 1932.—Found starving under a rude canvas shelter in a patch of woods on Flatboard Ridge, where they had lived for five days on wild berries and apples, a woman and her 16-year-old daughter were fed and clothed today by the police and placed in the city almshouse.

areas lost half their population as people fled across the desert to California, typically in decrepit Model T Fords piled with ragged possessions. Novelist John Steinbeck captured their desperation, and their plucky inner resourcefulness in *The Grapes of Wrath*, a popular novel published in 1939.

THE FAILURE OF THE OLD ORDER

Will Rogers, himself an "Okie" and the nation's most popular humorist, quipped that the United States would be the first country to go to the poorhouse in an automobile. He was trying to restore a sense of proportion to the way people thought about the Great Depression. No one was starving, President Hoover added in one of his many ham-handed attempts to ease tension.

In the broadest sense, both men were right. There was no plague or famine. Indeed, to many people the troubling paradox of America's greatest depression was that deprivation was widespread in a country that was blessed with plenty. American factories remained as capable as ever of producing goods, but they stood silent or working at a fraction of capacity because no one could afford to buy their wares. Farms were pouring forth food in cornucopian abundance, but hungry people could not afford to consume it. One of the most striking images of the early 1930s transformed a mild, white-haired California physician into an angry crusader. Early one Saturday morning, Dr. Francis E. Townsend looked out his window to see old women picking through the garbage pails of a store that was heaped high with foodstuffs.

The Tragedy of Herbert Hoover

Business and the Republican party had reaped credit for the soothing breezes of prosperity. Now they took the blame for the whirlwind of depression, and the recriminations were aimed particularly at the titular head of the party, Herbert Clark Hoover. The shantytowns where homeless thousands dwelled were called Hoovervilles; newspapers used as blankets by men who were forced to sleep on park benches were Hoover blankets; a pocket turned inside out was a Hoover flag; a boxcar on the railroad was a Hoover Pullman.

Still remembered as a great humanitarian when he entered the White House in 1929, Hoover was the callous torturer of the people a year later. Celebrated for his energy and efficiency as Secretary of Commerce, Hoover as president was perceived to be incompetent, paralyzed by the economic crisis. When Hoover made one of his rare public appearances, a motorcade through the hard-hit industrial city of Detroit, sidewalk crowds greeted him with dead silence and sullen stares. The president could not even take a brief vacation without arousing scorn. "Look here, Mr. Hoover, see what you've done," an Appalachian song had it. "You went a-fishing, let the country go to ruin."

In truth, Hoover's self-confidence decayed rapidly during his four years in the presidency. If never a warm man, Hoover had always exuded confidence, beaming smugly for photographers. Now he sat subdued, withdrawn, and embittered in the White House. Sitting down to talk with him, an adviser remembered, was like sitting in a bath of ink.

Critics unjustly characterized Hoover as uncaring, a do-nothing president, a stooge for the Mellons and other big businessmen. The president was moved by the suffering in the country. He gave much of his income to charity and urged others to do the same. Far from paralyzed, he worked as hard at his job as Woodrow Wilson and James K. Polk. Nor was he a Coolidge, letting business do as it pleased; Hoover led government to greater intervention in the economy than had any preceding president except Wilson. It would soon be forgotten, but the man who replaced Hoover in the White House, Franklin D. Roosevelt, several times criticized Hoover for improperly expanding the powers of government. It would be forgotten because Roosevelt would recognize, as Hoover never did, that the Republican administration had not done enough.

Hoover's Program: Not Enough

Something had to be done. A good many Americans personally recollected that the somewhat less severe economic crisis of the 1890s had led to a briefly terrifying social unrest among dispossessed farmers. Now, in the

Suffering from unemployment and poverty, these men constructed homes from scrap lumber at West Houston and Mercer Streets in New York. They were photographed by Bernice Abbott on October 25, 1935.

1930s, urban industrial workers—and the middle class—were suffering as they had not suffered in the depression of the 1890s.

The progressives (of whom Hoover had been considered one) had established the precedent that government was responsible for guiding the economy. Only in flush times like the Coolidge era could an administration abdicate its obligations and remain popular. Indeed, Hoover promptly broke with the immediate past by cutting Mellon's regressive consumer taxes in order to encourage purchasing and, therefore, production.

Hoover also broke with the Coolidge–Mellon policies of withdrawing the government from active intervention in the economy. He spent $500 million a year on public works, government programs to build or improve government properties. These projects created some jobs that would otherwise not have existed. The most famous

of them was the great Boulder Dam, now called Hoover Dam, on the Colorado River southeast of Las Vegas, Nevada. The great wall of concrete was the single most massive example of government economic planning and construction to its time and provided work and relief for thousands. But, of course, the Boulder Dam project did nothing in the short run for those who were not involved in building it. (In the long term, ironically the most conspicuous consequence of this water conservation and power-generation project was to transform Las Vegas into a pleasure dome of casinos.)

In the Reconstruction Finance Corporation (R.F.C.), established by Congress in 1932, Hoover created an agency to help banks, railroads, and other key economic institutions stay in business. The R.F.C. lent money to companies that were basically sound but were hamstrung by the shortage of operating capital.

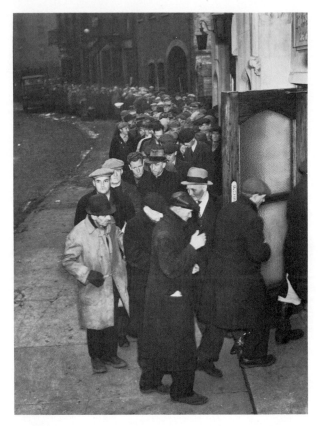

*A line of hungry men stretches into the darkness outside a
soup kitchen in New York City.*

The trouble was that cutting consumer taxes did nothing for those who were unemployed and therefore paying few taxes. Those who still had jobs inclined not to spend what little windfalls came their way but to squirrel them away against the day when they might be out of work. Moreover, there was a glut in the urban middle class of the "big ticket" consumer durables like appliances and automobiles, the sale of which might have put people to work.

The R.F.C. was a positively unpopular program. People in trouble saw it not as a recovery policy but as relief for big business while individuals were told to shift for themselves. The R.F.C. alone looked very much like an extension of Andrew Mellon's "trickle-down" economics; except in the arid early years of the Great Depression, little seemed to trickle down.

The Blindness of the Rugged Individual

More was needed—massive relief to get the poor, who were growing in numbers, over the worst of the crisis. This Hoover would not authorize. A self-made man himself, he had forgotten the role of talent, temperament, and good luck in getting ahead, attributing "success" to more values alone. He believed that "rugged individuals"—he used the phrase—who looked to no one but themselves, were the secret of American cultural vitality. For the federal government to encourage that trait of the national character was one thing; for the government to sponsor huge handouts was quite another. Federal relief measures were not, in Hoover's opinion, the first step in defeating the depression, but were the first step in emasculating the American spirit. There was a difference between helping Belgians devastated by war and helping Americans deprived by economic dislocations.

Hoover also clung to certain assumptions that prevented him from realizing just how much federal guidance was needed. Failing to recognize that state boundaries had no economic significance, he wanted the states to take the lead in fighting the depression. Viewing government as much like a business, he was particularly inflexible when it came to the ideal of a balanced budget and the government's power to manipulate the value of the currency.

Government, Hoover insisted, must spend no more money than it collected; the books must balance. As for money questions, Hoover knew that during every depression since the Civil War, only Greenbackers, Populists, and others regarded as radicals had proposed increasing the supply of money (deliberately inflating prices) in order to stimulate the economy. Each time they had been defeated, and each time the country had emerged from hard times more prosperous than before. Hoover was positive that this cycle would be repeated if the old faith were kept: if the budget were balanced and the dollar remained rooted in gold.

The Depression Goes International

For a few months, in 1931, Hoover's prediction that "prosperity was just around the corner" seemed to be coming true. Most economic indicators made modest gains. Then the entire industrialized world followed the United States into the economic pit. In May, a major European bank, the Kreditanstalt of Vienna, went bankrupt, badly shaking other European banks that had supported it, and toppling many. In September, Great Britain abandoned the gold standard. That is, the Bank of England ceased to redeem its paper money in gold bullion or coin. Worried that all paper money would lose its value, international investors withdrew $1.5 billion in gold from American banks, further weakening the financial structure and launching a new wave of local failures.

But the worst consequence of the European collapse was what it did to Hoover's state of mind. It persuaded him that America's depression was not the fault of domestic problems that he might help remedy, but of foreigners over whom he had no power. The most cosmopolitan president since John Quincy Adams had sunk to the ignorant provincial's easy inclination to blame others—foreigners. The result was that by 1932 his administration was paralyzed. The country was drifting as Hoover tacitly admitted that he was helpless and could only wait. Conditions worsened by the month.

AMERICANS REACT TO THE CRISIS

If Hoover's failure represented the inability of the New Era Republicans to cope with the depression, radicals were unable to offer a plausible alternative. Critics of capitalism believed that the crisis represented the death throes of the system and that they would soon be in power. To an extent, they, like Hoover, waited for inevitable forces beyond their control to summon them to the helm.

The Not-So-Red Decade

After polling only 267,000 votes in prosperous 1928, Socialist party presidential candidate Norman Thomas won 882,000 in 1932. Communist candidate William Z. Foster doubled his vote in those four years, from 49,000 to 103,000. But the combined anticapitalist vote of less than a million was minuscule compared with the 23 million cast for the Democrats in that year and even the 16 million won by the discredited Hoover. Thomas's total in 1932 was less than the Socialists had won twenty years before, when the electorate was much smaller and the economy was in much better health.

Later in the 1930s, American Communists made some gains among intellectuals and in the leadership of the labor movement. Distinguished writers such as Mary McCarthy, Edmund Wilson, and Granville Hicks joined the Communist party. Even F. Scott Fitzgerald, the chronicler of "flaming youth" during the 1920s, flirted with Marxist ideas that he did not really understand. Theodore Dreiser, the dean of American novelists, wanted to join the Communist party but was told by party leaders that he could do more good for the cause outside the organization than in. Perhaps they thought that if he wrote calls for revolution in his tortured version of the English language that it would all sound quite dull.

The Communist love of conspiracy and manipulation drove intellectuals out of the party as quickly as they joined. It also prevented the Communists from establishing a base in the labor movement despite making contributions to its growth that, in retrospect, can be seen to have been invaluable. Wyndham Mortimer of the United Automobile Workers, labor journalist Len De Caux, lawyer Lee Pressman, and many other Communists and "fellow travelers" (sympathizers who were not members of the party) devoted their lives to building up the union movement. However, most Communist organizers either denied or thickly camouflaged their affiliation with the party and their anticapitalist ideology. The result was that few rank-and-file union members were exposed to, let alone converted to, Communist ideas. When anti-Communist labor leaders took the offensive against the Reds in the 1940s, they found it easy to oust party members from the unions.

A Curious Response

Americans simply did not interpret the Great Depression as evidence that capitalism had failed. During prosperous times, Americans had believed that individual success was primarily due to individual initiative, and not to general social conditions. So their initial response to the depression was to blame themselves for the hardships that beset them. Sociologists and journalists reported on homeless hitchhikers who apologized for their shabby clothing. A walk through any big-city park revealed unsuccessful job seekers slumped on benches, heads in hands, elbows on knees, collars drawn up, wondering where they, not the system, had failed.

The Gillette Company, a manufacturer of razor blades, exploited the feeling of personal failure by running an advertisement that showed a husband reporting shamefully to his wife that he still had not found a job. The message was that employers had turned him down not because there were no jobs available but because he cut a poor appearance with his badly shaved whiskers. A maker of underwear put the responsibility for the unemployment of a bedridden man squarely on his own shoulders. He was out of work not because 13 million others were, but because he wore an inferior brand of undershirt and so caught a cold that he well deserved.

Long after the depression ended, it was the proud boast of many families that however bad things had gotten, they never had gone "on the county," never had taken handouts from public-welfare agencies. The unmistakable message was that coping with hard times was a personal responsibility. The implication for radicals who sought to direct anger and frustration against the system was not encouraging.

HOW THEY LIVED

WEEKNIGHTS AT EIGHT

Although commercial radio broadcasting began in 1920 and the first radio network, the National Broadcasting Company, was founded in 1926, it was during the Great Depression of the 1930s that the new medium of communication and entertainment found a place in the lives of almost all Americans. Radio receivers were ensconced in about 12 million American households in 1930. By 1940, they were in 28 million. Fully 86 percent of the American people had easy daily access to radio sets. They were designed not to look like electronic equipment but as a prized piece of furniture, the twentieth-century equivalent of the wardrobe. Some were sleekly modern "art deco," others gothic with the pointed, vertical arches of a medieval cathedral.

Hard times themselves were a big reason for the dramatic expansion of radio. During the 1920s, the average price of a receiver was $75, far out of reach of most families. During the 1930s, a serviceable set could be bought for $10 or $20, an amount that, with sacrifices, all but the utterly destitute could scrape up.

The New Deal also played a part in the radio boom. While most cities and towns were electrified before 1933, very little of the countryside was. Private power companies were not interested in the small return to be had from stringing wire into the hinterlands. By putting the advantages of electrification for country people above profits, Roosevelt's Rural Electrification Administration brought isolated farm families into the mainstream of society. With more than 57 million people defined as living in "rural territory" in 1940, the significance of radio to American culture may be said to have owed largely to New Deal reforms. Indeed, country people depended more on the crackling broadcasts of news, music, and dramatic programs for brightening their lives than did city dwellers.

Manufacturers that produced consumer goods rushed to advertise on the three networks: the Columbia Broadcasting System; the Mutual; and the National Broadcasting Company with its two chains, the red and the blue networks. (When antitrust proceedings forced NBC to dispose of one of its networks, the American Broadcasting Company was born.) In 1935, the first year for which there are reliable statistics, networks and local stations raked in $113 million from advertisers with operating expenses at an estimated $80 million. In 1940, expenses were up to $114 million, but advertising revenues had almost doubled to $216 million.

The manufacturers of Pepsodent toothpaste got the best bargain of all. In 1928, they contracted with two white minstrel-show performers who had a program in black dialect on Chicago station WGN. "Sam 'n' Henry" agreed to pick two new names and do their show nationally on the NBC network. The new show was called "Amos 'n' Andy," and from the start it won a popularity that, comparatively speaking, has probably never been duplicated in the history of the entertainment industry.

Basically, "Amos 'n' Andy" was a blackface minstrel show set in Harlem instead of on a southern plantation.

One of the two performers, Freeman Gosden of Richmond, said that he based the character of Amos Jones on a black boyhood friend. Amos was the honest, hardworking proprietor and sole driver of the Fresh Air Taxi Company—his cab had no windshield. Neither during the program's 32 years on radio nor after it had moved to television was Gosden's character offensive. However, Amos came to play a comparatively small part in the series as the program evolved. The chief protagonist was George (Kingfish) Stevens, a fast-talking con man who usually bungled his stings and ended up outsmarting himself. During the 1950s, black groups began to protest that the Kingfish, who was rather stupid underneath his pretensions and self-estimation, was an insulting stereotype.

The character of the Kingfish's usual mark, Andrew "Andy" H. Brown, also caused trouble. Andy was infinitely gullible, a character whom even the Kingfish easily swindled. He depended for survival on the con man's own ineptitude or on Amos's intervention.

Everyone in America, it sometimes seemed, listened to the program, which ran on weeknights at eight o'clock. Particularly interesting plots were discussed each day. Few needed to be told what Amos, Andy, and the Kingfish were like, or even the minor characters (also played by Gosden and his partner, Charles Correll): Lightnin', who swept up the hall of the Mystic Knights of the Sea; the shyster lawyer Algonquin J. Calhoun; Ruby Jones; and Sapphire Stevens, who made life as miserable for George as he made it for Andy.

In November 1960, "Amos 'n' Andy" went from radio to television in a weekly half-hour format featuring black actors who mimicked the voices that had been created by Gosden and Correll. Already, however, the program was an anachronism. The civil-rights movement was in full swing by 1960, pushing toward victory in the long campaign to establish full equality for blacks. The National Association for the Advancement of Colored People denounced "Amos 'n' Andy" as "a gross libel on the Negro."

The show's sponsors believed that blacks enjoyed the program as much as whites (which appears to have been so until the 1960s), and Gosden insisted that "both Charlie and I have deep respect for black men"; he felt that the show "helped characterize Negroes as interesting and dignified human beings." Today, it is easy to see the point. Even the most ridiculous characters on "Amos 'n' Andy" were stock comic figures in traditional comedy, and there was nothing derogatory in the depiction of Amos and Ruby Jones. Nevertheless, the NAACP had a point too. The social effects of ridiculing members of an oppressed group are mischievous at best. It is easy to shrug off riducule when it does not relate to reality or ignore stereotypes when the stereotyped group is well established. But in the fight in which blacks were engaged in the early 1960s, such ridicule and stereotypes stood in the way of justice. After 100 episodes, "Amos 'n' Andy" went off the air.

The Bonus Marchers' encampment on Anacostia Flats was destroyed by troops led by Douglas MacArthur and sent by a frustrated President Hoover.

Episodes of Violence

There was violence. Hungry, angry people rioted in St. Paul and other cities, storming food markets and clearing the shelves. Wisconsin dairy farmers stopped milk trucks and dumped the milk into ditches, partly in rage at the low prices paid by processors, partly to dramatize their need for help. In Iowa, the National Farmers' Holiday Association told hog raisers to withhold their products from the market—to take a holiday—and attracted attention by blockading highways. Eat your own products, Holiday Association leader Milo Reno told the Iowans, and let the money men eat their gold.

But these incidents were isolated and exceptional. For the most part, Americans coped with the depression peacefully and without a thought for revolution. In fact, the most violent episode of the early depression was launched not by stricken people but by the authorities. This was the demonstration and destruction of the

"Bonus Expeditionary Force" in Washington during the summer of 1932.

The Bonus Boys were 20,000 veterans of the First World War and their wives who massed in Washington to demand that Congress immediately, as a relief measure, vote them a bonus for their wartime service that had been scheduled for their old age. When Congress adjourned in July 1932 without having done so, all but about 2,000 of the demonstrators left the capital. Those who remained set up a Hooverville on Anacostia Flats on the outskirts of the city, policed themselves, cooperated with authorities, and were generally peaceful.

Hoover, thoroughly frustrated by the stubborness of the depression and his own abysmal unpopularity, persuaded himself that the Bonus Boys were led by Communist agitators. (Actually, the most influential organization among the Bonus Boys was the right-wing and militantly anti-communist American Legion.) The president sent General Douglas MacArthur to disperse them. MacArthur, a talented military man often blinded and made ludicrous by a sense of personal vanity, called on armored vehicles and tear gas to make short work of the protesters. However, when an infant died from asphyxiation and Americans mulled over the spectacle of young soldiers attacking old soldiers on presidential orders, Hoover's reputation sank even lower.

Midwestern Robin Hoods

Americans displayed their disenchantment with traditional sources of leadership in other, less direct ways. Businessmen, who had been almost universally lionized just a few years before, became objects of ridicule in films, on radio programs, and in the columns and comic strips of daily newspapers.

Perhaps the most curious example of cynicism toward traditional values was the admiration lavished on a new kind of criminal, the midwestern bank robber who exploited automobiles and the wide-open highways of the Midwest to flee the scene of his dirty work. A sensationalist press transformed John Dillinger, "Pretty Boy" Floyd, "Machine Gun" Kelly, Bonnie Parker and Clyde Barrow, and "Ma" Barker and her family-centered gang into Robin Hoods.

Unlike the businessmen-gangsters of Prohibition, the depression bank robbers were small-time, guerrilla operators who botched as many holdups as they pulled off. They were also reckless with their guns, killing bank guards and even innocent bystanders in their attempt to create an atmosphere of terror to cover their escape. But because they robbed the banks whose irresponsibility had ruined many poor people and because they came from poor rural (and WASP) backgrounds themselves, the outlaws aroused a kind of admiration among Midwesterners down on their luck.

Some of the gangsters themselves cultivated the image of Robin Hood. John Dillinger (who killed ten men) made it a point to be personally generous. "Pretty Boy" Floyd, who operated chiefly in Oklahoma, never had trouble finding people who would hide him from the authorities. Bonnie Parker actually sent doggerel epics celebrating the exploits of "Bonnie and Clyde" to newspapers, which gladly published them.

The Movies: The Depression-Proof Business

The film industry exploited this envy of a few who "beat the system" by making movies that slyly glamorized lawbreakers. Still fearful of censorship, the studios always wrote a moral end to their gangster films: the wrongdoer paid for his crimes in a hail of bullets or seated in the electric chair. But the message was clear: criminals played by George Raft, Edward G. Robinson, and James

In Dinner at Eight, *glamorous Jean Harlow made moviegoers forget the depression—at least for a few hours.*

Cagney were pushed into their careers by poverty and often had redeeming qualities.

The film industry did not suffer during the depression. Movies flourished during the worst years, occupying the central position in American entertainment that they would hold until the perfection of television. Admission prices were cheap. Each week, 85 million people paid an average of 25 cents (10 cents for children) to see Marie Dressler, Janet Gaynor, Shirley Temple, Mickey Rooney, Jean Harlow, and Clark Gable in a dizzying array of adventures and fantasies.

The favorite themes were escapist. During the mid-1930s, Shirley Temple, an angelic if chillingly saccharine little blonde girl who sang and danced, led the list of moneymakers. Her annual salary was $300,000, and her films made $5 million a year for Fox Pictures. Royalties from Shirley Temple dolls and other paraphernalia made her a millionaire. Director Cecil B. DeMille specialized in costume epics, expecially those that transported viewers into Biblical times.

Choreographer Busby Berkeley made millions for Warner Brothers by staging dance tableaux featuring dozens of beautiful starlets (transformed by mirrors and trick photography into hundreds). People bought tickets to Berkeley films to escape the gray rigors of depression life. For the same reason, they supported the production of hundreds of low-budget Westerns each year. The cowboy was still a figure of individual freedom in a world in which public events and private lives had become all too complexly interrelated.

By way of contrast, some directors specialized in didactic films on social themes that were often hard-hitting. Frank Capra's métier was films that lovingly celebrated old American values and threats to them. Typically, they pitted decent ordinary men and women against indolent, parasitical, and usually crooked businessmen and politicians.

Music, Music, Music

At first almost destroyed by the depression, the popular music business rebounded quickly to rank a close second behind the movies as the ordinary American's entertainment. Sales of records, about $50 million a year during the 1920s, collapsed in 1932 to $2.5 million. The chief casualties were the "hillbilly" and traditional black "blues" singers whose audiences were among the hardest hit social groups in the country. Companies like Columbia, Decca, and RCA discontinued their "race record" lines and only a few black and Appalachian artists, like Bessie Smith and the Carter Family, continued to make money.

The 78-rpm record, which cost only 35 cents, and the jukebox, that provided a play for a nickel, slowly revived the business. By 1939, there were 225,000 jukeboxes in the United States scratching up 13 million records a year. Sales of records increased from 10 million in 1933 to 33 million in 1938 (and then soared, with the return of prosperity, to 127 million in 1941).

The chief beneficiaries were the "big bands," which played "swing," an intricately harmonized orchestral jazz music intended for dancing. For 50 cents (and even less), a young "jitterbugger" could dance for three or four hours to the music of Benny Goodman, Harry James, or dozens of other groups. It was not an every-evening diversion. The 50 cents needed for admission was precious enough that the big bands had to rush from city to city and to towns too, on a series of one-night stands. Even the most popular orchestras might find themselves appearing in 30 different ballrooms in as many nights.

Nevertheless, they were lionized when they came to town. In the Palladium Ballroom in Hollywood, California, Harry James once drew 8,000 dancers in a single night, 35,000 in a week. At other capitals of swing music, like the Glen Island Casino in New Rochelle, New York, big bands earned extra revenue by playing for a radio audience. Because a good radio could be ensconced in the parlor for $10 or $20, and operated for the cost of

SAFE SEX DEPRESSION STYLE

Radio flourished during the Great Depression, playing a major role in the lives of children as well as adults. Many stations dedicated late afternoons and early evenings to juvenile programs featuring young heroes like Little Orphan Annie and Jack Armstrong, the All-American Boy, aviators and space explorers, and cowboys like the Lone Ranger and Tom Mix (who was a real person).

Most combined strident morality and patriotism with cliff-hanging adventure and encouraged habitual listening and consumption of the sponsor's product by offering premiums (secret decoder rings) and by forming "clubs." Tom Mix's club was called the Straight Shooters and required members to swear a pledge:

I promise to shoot straight with my parents by obeying my father and mother.

I promise to shoot straight with my friends by telling the truth always, by being fair and square at work and at play.

I promise to shoot straight with myself by striving always to be my best, by keeping my mind alert and my body strong and healthy.

I promise to shoot straight with Tom Mix by regularly eating good old Hot Ralston, the official Straight Shooter cereal, because I know Hot Ralston is just the kind of cereal that will help build a stronger America.

electricity, it was far and away most depression-era Americans' favorite form of entertainment.

THE ELECTION OF 1932

The nostalgic glow that could come to surround listening to a favorite radio program, or going to a ballroom or a movie palace decorated like a Turkish harem, meant that many people would think back about the Great Depression as quite a good time. In the summer of 1932, however, when the economy hit bottom, few people took the situation with a light heart. The country's mood during the presidential election campaign of that year was somber and anxious.

A Roosevelt for the Democrats

A Democratic victory was a foregone conclusion, and the Republicans resignedly renominated Herbert Hoover to bear the brunt of the reaction against the New Era. Democratic hopefuls, by way of contrast, fought a hair-pulling fight win a ticket to the White House. The chief candidates at the Chicago convention were John

Nance Garner of Texas, who had inherited the McAdoo Democrats from the South and West; Al Smith, the party's standard-bearer in 1928 who believed he deserved a second chance; and Governor Franklin D. Roosevelt of New York, once Smith's protégé but now a national figure in his own right.

When the beginnings of a convention deadlock brought back memories of 1924 and a bitterly divided party, a large number of Garner supporters switched to Roosevelt and gave him the nomination. With a nose for the dramatic, Roosevelt broke with tradition, according to which a nominee waited at his home to be informed of the convention's decision. He flew to Chicago (conveying a sense of urgency) and told the cheering Democrats that he meant to provide a "New Deal" for the American people. In so saying, Roosevelt simultaneously slapped at Republican policies during the 1920s (the New Era) and reminded people of both major parties that he was a distant cousin of the energetic president of the Square Deal, Theodore Roosevelt.

The Campaign

Hoover's campaign was dispirited. He was in the impossible position of having to defend policies that had failed. Roosevelt, on the contrary, like any candidate who expects to win, avoided taking controversial stands. Any strong position on any specific question could only cost him votes. At times, indeed, Roosevelt seemed to be calling for the same conservative approach to the economic crisis that Hoover already had tested; he warned against an unbalanced budget and reassured voters that he was no radical.

The most obvious difference between the president and his challenger was Hoover's gloomy personality and Roosevelt's buoyant charm. Roosevelt smiled constantly. He impressed everyone who saw him as he whisked around the country as a man who knew how to take charge, liked to take charge, and was perfectly confident in his ability to lead the country out of its crisis. The theme song of Roosevelt's campaign, which was blared by brass bands or played over loudspeakers at every whistle stop and rally, was the cheery "Happy Days Are Here Again."

Only after his lopsided victory—472 electoral votes to Hoover's 59—did it become clear that Roosevelt had spelled out no program for recovery. Because Inauguration Day came a full four months after the election, there was one more long winter of depression under Herbert Hoover. The repudiated president, now practically a recluse in the White House, recognized that a void existed and attempted to persuade Roosevelt to endorse the actions he had taken.

Roosevelt nimbly avoided making any commitments either in favor of or opposed to Hoover's policies. He took a quiet working vacation. He issued no statements of substance, but he was not idle. During the interregnum, Roosevelt met for long hours with experts on agriculture, industry, finance, and relief. Organized by Raymond Moley, a professor at Columbia University, this "brains trust," as reporters called it, marked a rather significant shift in the personnel of people who ran Washington. During the 1920s, the capital had been a businessman's town. Now they were turning over their apartments and selling their homes to academic intellectuals, men (and a few women) from universities who hungered to have a go at making policy.

For Further Reading

Arthur M. Schlesinger, Jr., *The Crisis of the Old Order* (1957) and *The Coming of the New Deal* (1959) provide a superb overview of the critical years of the early 1930s. See also Irving Bernstein, *The Lean Years* (1960); C. Bird, *The Invisible Scar* (1965); Albert Romesco, *The Poverty of Abundance: Hoover, the Nation, and the Great Depression* (1965) and Jordan A. Schwarz, *The Interregnum of Despair: Hoover, Congress, and the Depression* (1970); and Studs Terkel, *Hard Times* (1970). For background, refer once again to Ellis W. Hawley, *The Great War and the Search for a Modern Order: A History of the American People and Their Institutions, 1917–1933* (1979); John D. Hicks, *Republican Ascendancy, 1921–1933* (1960); and William E. Leuchtenburg, *The Perils of Prosperity, 1914–1932* (1958). Frederick Lewis Allen's sequel to *Only Yesterday, Since Yesterday* (1940) provides the same highly individual insights as his better-known book.

Valuable more broadly or more narrowly focused books include Roger Daniels, *The Bonus March* (1971); John K. Galbraith, *The Great Crash* (1955); John A. Garraty, *Unemployment in History: Economic Thought and Public Policy* (1979); Susan Estabrook Kennedy, *The Banking Crisis of 1933* (1973); C. P. Kinderberger, *The World in Depression* (1973); Donald Lisio, *The President and Protest* (1974); Van L. Perkins, *Crisis in Agriculture* (1969); Theodore Saloutos and John D. Hicks, *Twentieth Century Populism: Agricultural Discontent in the Mid-*

dle West, 1900–1939 (1951); Robert Sklar, *Movie-Made America* (1975); Peter Temin, *Did Monetary Forces Cause the Great Depression?* (1976); Raymond Walters, *Negroes and the Great Depression* (1970).

Franklin D. Roosevelt has been the subject of numerous biographies both political and personal. Among the most rewarding are James MacGregor Burns, *Roosevelt: The Lion and the Fox* (1956); Frank Freidel, *Franklin D. Roosevelt* (1952–73); Joseph P. Lash, *Eleanor and Franklin* (1971). Also see H. G. Warren, *Herbert Hoover and the Great Depression* (1956).

President Roosevelt visits a CCC camp in the Shenandoah National Park, 1933.

REARRANGING AMERICA

FRANKLIN D. ROOSEVELT AND THE NEW DEAL 1933 - 1938

A few days before his inauguration in 1933, Franklin D. Roosevelt visited Miami. From the crowd that surged around him, a jobless worker named Joe Zangara, later found to be unbalanced, stepped up and emptied a revolver at the gay party. Anton Cermak, the mayor of Chicago, who was with Roosevelt, died from his wounds. The president-elect escaped without a scratch.

The American people learned from the episode that they had chosen a leader who was cool in a crisis: Roosevelt barely flinched during the chaos of the shooting. But what else did they know about him? Not a great deal on March 4, 1933, and that little was not altogether reassuring.

THE PLEASANT MAN WHO CHANGED AMERICA

Henry Cabot Lodge had called him "a well-meaning, nice young fellow, but light"; Edith Galt Wilson—"more charming than able." In 1932, Walter Lippmann, a political columnist of liberal leanings, called Roosevelt "a pleasant man who, without any important qualifications, would very much like to be president." Many others wondered if a person who had enjoyed so pampered and sheltered a life was capable of appreciating the difficulties and suffering that had befallen millions of Americans.

Silver Spoon

The new president had been born into an old, rich, privileged, and rather idle New York family. Boyhood vacations were spent in Europe and at elegant yachting resorts in Maine and Nova Scotia. He attended the most exclusive private schools and was sheltered to the point of suffocation by an adoring mother. When Roosevelt matriculated at Harvard, Mother Sara Roosevelt packed up, followed him, and rented a house near the university so that she could keep an eye on her boy. F.D.R.'s wife, Eleanor Roosevelt, was from the same tiny and exclusive social set. Indeed, she was the president's distant cousin.

Franklin Roosevelt's cheery grin and ever-present cigarette holder became his trademarks.

Even the charm with which Roosevelt ran his campaign—the jaunty air, the toothy smile a bit too quick to take shape, an effortless knack of putting people at their ease with cheery small talk—was very much a quality of the socialite who, in the 1930s, was a popular satirical target of filmmakers. Roosevelt was the real life incarnation of a genial but fluffy character Cary Grant was to play in half a dozen movies: "Tennis, anyone?"

And yet, from the moment F.D.R. delivered his ringing inaugural address—"the only thing we have to fear is fear itself!"—the clouds over Washington parting on cue to let the March sun through, it was obvious that he was a natural leader. From the first day, Roosevelt dominated center stage as cousin Theodore had done 30 years earlier, and without the tiresome bluster and bullying. Where Teddy had been liked, F.D.R. was loved. Poor sharecroppers and blacks living in big city slums tacked his photograph on the walls of their homes next to prints of Christ in Gethsemane, and named their children for him.

Conversely, he was hated, as T.R. never was. It was said that some of the nation's wealthiest people despised him so much that they could not bear to pronounce his name. Much to the amused satisfaction of Roosevelt's supporters, they referred to him through clenched teeth as "that man in the White House," and as a "traitor to his class."

Long before F.D.R. died in office in 1945, after winning reelection four times, he was ranked by historians as among the greatest of the chief executives along with Washington, Lincoln, and Wilson (his one-time political idol). No succeeding generation of judges has demoted him.

Roosevelt's Contribution

Roosevelt's unbounded self-confidence was a major contribution to the battle against the depression. His optimism was infectious. The change of mood he brought to Washington and the country was astonishing, and shortly after assuming office he exploited his charisma by launching a series of "Fireside Chats" on the ubiquitous radio. In an informal living-room manner, he explained to the American people what he was trying to accomplish and what he expected of them. Millions listened avidly and trustfully.

AMERICAN ARISTOCRAT

Franklin D. Roosevelt was descended from or related by marriage to eleven presidents of the United States who had preceded him. Curiously, only one of them, Martin Van Buren, had been a Democrat.

F.D.R. THE PRAGMATIST

In a conversation with Secretary of Commerce Daniel Roper, Roosevelt made clear his practical policy-making: "Let's concentrate upon one thing. Save the people and the nation and if we have to change our minds twice a day to accomplish that end, we should do it."

But Roosevelt was much more than a charmer. He was not afraid to make decisions or to accept responsibility. He acted. One day after he was sworn in, he called Congress into special session for the purpose of enacting crisis legislation, and he declared a "bank holiday." Calling on emergency presidential powers that are rarely used, he ordered all banks to close their doors temporarily in order to forestall additional failures. Although the immediate effect of the bank holiday was to tie up people's savings, the drama and decisiveness of his action won wide approval.

In 1933, Justice Oliver Wendell Holmes, Jr. said that the president had "a second-class intellect." He was right; Roosevelt was by no means brilliant. He never fully understood the complex economic and social processes with which his administration had to grapple, and did not think it was necessary that he should. If an indifferent student, he had the professors at his command. He sought the advice of experts, his "brains trust" and was open to suggestions from all quarters. But because he never doubted his responsibilities as the nation's elected "chief," he maintained complete authority over his stable of headstrong intellectuals, many of them prima donnas. He stroked their vanities when it suited his purposes, played one brains truster against another, and retained the personal loyalty of some of those whose advice he rejected. Faces changed in the White House anterooms. Friends became critics. But Roosevelt never lacked talented advisers.

In the end, Roosevelt's greatest strength was his flexibility. "The country needs bold, persistent experimentation," he said. "It is common sense to take a method and try it. If it fails, admit it frankly and try another." Roosevelt's pragmatic approach to problems not only suited the American temperament, but contrasted boldly with Hoover's insistence on making policies conform to a badly rotted ideology.

A Real First Lady

Not the least of F.D.R.'s assets was his remarkable wife, Eleanor. Only much later, in the age of anything-goes journalism, did Americans learn that their marriage had been shattered by an affair between Franklin and Eleanor's one-time personal secretary, Lucy Mercer. Eleanor offered a divorce; Franklin begged off; Eleanor said that Lucy had to go, and she did.

Although she grew up privileged and sheltered, Eleanor Roosevelt developed a genuine compassion for the disadvantaged.

Not only would a divorce have killed Roosevelt's political career far short of the presidency, it would have denied him the services of his one aide who may be called indispensable. During the New Deal years, the homely, shrill-voiced Eleanor was thought of by friend and foe alike as the alter ego of the president. She was his legs and eyes, for F.D.R. was a cripple, paralyzed from the waist down by polio in 1921 and unable to walk more than a few steps in heavy, painful steel leg braces, while Eleanor Roosevelt was a locomotive. With little taste for serving tea and honoring Boy Scouts, she raced about the country, picking through squalid tenements, wading in mud in Appalachian hollows, and descending into murky coal mines to see how the other half made do. Whereas F.D.R. was cool, detached, and calculating, Eleanor was compassionate, deeply moved by the misery and injustices suffered by the "forgotten" people on the bottom of society.

She interceded with her husband to appoint women to high government positions. She supported organized labor when F.D.R. tried to straddle a difficult question. She made the grievances of African-Americans a particular interest. Much of the affection that rebounded to F.D.R.'s benefit in the form of votes was earned by "that woman in the White House."

THE HUNDRED DAYS

Never before or since has the United States experienced such an avalanche of laws as Congress passed and the president signed during the spring of 1933. By nature a cautious and deliberate body, Congress was jolted by the crisis and by Roosevelt's forceful demands to enact most of his proposals without serious debate, a few without even reading the bills through. During what came to be known as the Hundred Days, Franklin D. Roosevelt and his brains trusters were virtually unopposed. Conservative congressmen simply shut up, cowed by their own failure and the decisiveness of the New Dealers.

Saving Banks and Farms

The most pressing problems were the imminent collapse of the nation's financial system, the massive foreclosures on farm and home mortgages that were throwing people out on the streets and roads, and the distress of the millions of unemployed.

The Emergency Banking Act eliminated weak banks merely by identifying them. Well-managed banks in danger of folding were saved when the Federal Reserve System was empowered to issue loans to them. Just as important, when the government permitted banks to reopen, people concluded that they were safe. They ceased to withdraw their deposits and returned funds that they had already taken home and out of circulation. Roosevelt also halted the drain on the nation's gold reserve by forbidding its export and, in April, by taking the nation off the gold standard. No longer could paper money be redeemed in gold coin that was hoarded. Instead, the value of money was based on the government's word, and the price of gold was frozen by law at $35 an ounce. ("Well, that's the end of Western civilization," a Wall Street financier was quoted as saying.)

NEW HOUSEHOLD ECONOMY FOR MILLIONAIRES

Eleanor Roosevelt is generally attributed with being her husband's eyes and ears among ordinary people. However, when she was complimented by the *New York Times* during World War II for insisting that the ten servants in her household economize for the sake of the war effort, it was F.D.R. who indicated that he was the one who realized that his and Eleanor's privileged past had little to do with the lives of most Americans. In a note to her, he teased: "All I can say is that your latest newspaper campaign is a corker and I am proud to be the husband of the Originator, Discoverer and Inventor of the New Household Economy for Millionaires! Please have a photo taken showing the family, the ten cooperating servants, the scraps saved from the table.... I will have it published in the Sunday *Times*."

The New Deal attempted to halt the dispossession of farmers through the establishment of the Farm Credit Administration. This agency refinanced mortgages for farmers who had missed payments. Another agency, the Home Owners' Loan Corporation, provided money for town and city dwellers who were in danger of losing their homes.

Helping the Helpless

Nothing better illustrated the contrast between Hoover's hidebound inaction and Roosevelt's flexibility than the establishment of the Federal Emergency Relief Administration. Whereas Hoover had resisted federal relief measures on ideological grounds, the F.E.R.A. quickly distributed $500 million to states so that they could save or revive their exhausted programs for relieving the desperate plight of the poor. The agency was headed by Harry Hopkins, an Iowa boy become New York sidewalk social worker with a cigarette dangling from his lip and a fedora pushed back on his head.

Actually, Hopkins disliked the idea of handouts. He believed that people who were able to work should be required to do so in return for help. It did not matter to him that the jobs they did were not particularly useful. His point was that government-paid jobs should not only get money into the hands of those who needed it, but give relief workers a sense of personal worth.

Nevertheless, Hopkins recognized that the crisis of 1933 was so severe that money had to be gotten out into the country quick. Setting aside his insistence on work-for-pay in administering F.E.R.A., he won F.D.R.'s confidence with his able and energetic direction of the program. There was waste and bureaucratic boondoggling, but F.E.R.A. worked, creating hope where there had been ennui and despair.

Alphabet Soup: C.C.C., C.W.A., W.P.A.

New bureaucracies, with and without boondoggling, were the order of the day in 1933. With an initial appropriation of $500 million, the Civilian Conservation Corps (C.C.C.) employed 250,000 young men between the ages of 18 and 25 and about 50,000 First World War veterans. Organized into crews, they reforested land that had been raped by cut-and-run lumbermen and undertook other conservation projects in national parks and forests.

Ultimately, 500,000 people worked for the C.C.C., and it became one of the New Dealers' favorite programs. The C.C.C. not only relieved distress (employees were obligated to send part of their paychecks to their families), but accomplished many needed conservation measures, and got city boys into the fresh air of the woods and mountains, a moral tonic in which Americans placed great faith (and still do).

Critics of the C.C.C. fastened on the quasi-military

*In an effort to stave off panicky customers, President Roosevelt ordered banks to close their doors
for emergency "holidays."*

discipline with which the army ran the program, but the idea of relief through jobs rather than through charity remained a mainstay of the New Deal. The Civil Works Administration (C.W.A.), which Harry Hopkins headed after November 1933, put 4 million unemployed people to work within a few months. They built roads, constructed public buildings—post offices, city halls, recreational facilities—and taught in bankrupt school systems.

When the C.W.A. spent more than $1 billion in five months, F.D.R. shuddered and called a halt to the program. But private investors would not or could not take up the slack, and unemployment threatened to soar once again. In May 1935, the president turned back to Hopkins and Congress to establish the Works Progress Administration (W.P.A.).

The W.P.A. broadened the C.W.A. approach. In ad-

dition to basic construction, the agency hired artists to paint murals in public buildings, and writers to prepare state guidebooks that remain models of their kind. In the South, the W.P.A. sent out workers to collect reminiscences of old people who remembered having been slaves. The W.P.A. even organized actors into troupes that brought theater to people who never had seen a play. By 1943, when the agency was liquidated, it had spent more than $11 billion and had employed 8.5 million people. The National Youth Administration, part of the W.P.A., provided jobs for 2 million high school and college students.

Repeal

Roosevelt's support of the Twenty-first Amendment, the repeal of Prohibition, might be listed as one of the New

THE REGULATED SOCIETY

Regulatory agencies are established by Congress and given authority to act as watchdogs over specific aspects of American life. For example, the Interstate Commerce Commission (I.C.C.) regulates the movement of goods and people across state lines, assigning rights over certain routes to trucking companies, setting rates, settling disputes, and so on. The Federal Communications Commission (F.C.C.) keeps an eye on the practices of radio and television broadcasters. Today, 55 major regulatory commissions in the United States government turn out 77,000 pages of decisions and rules each year.

Deal's relief measures. On March 13, 1933, F.D.R. called for the legalization of weak beer, and when the amendment was ratified in December, most states quickly legalized more potent waters.

Certainly many people looked on the possibility of buying a legal drink as relief. An Appalachian song prais-

ing Roosevelt pointed to repeal of Prohibition as his most important act: "Since Roosevelt's been elected Moonshine liquor's been corrected. We've got legal wine, whiskey, beer, and gin."

The N.R.A.

The New Deal's relief programs were a great success. Although direct benefits reached only a fraction of the people who were hurt by the depression, they were the worst off who were helped, and the government's willingness to act in the crisis encouraged millions of other people. Nevertheless, relief was just a stopgap. F.D.R. and the New Dealers were also concerned with the problem of actual economic recovery, and in this area their accomplishments were less effective.

The National Industrial Recovery Act, which created the National Recovery Administration (N.R.A.), was a bold and controversial attempt to bring order and prosperity to the shattered economy. The N.R.A. was headed by General Hugh Johnson, something of a blowhard but also a peerless, inexhaustible organizer and cheerleader,

Eight thousand children form an eagle at a National Recovery Administration rally in San Francisco.

and a zealous believer in economic planning. Johnson supervised the drafting of codes for each basic industry and, before long, some less than basic industries too.

The codes set minimum standards of quality for products and services, fair prices for which they were to be sold, and the wages, hours, and conditions under which employees in various industries would work. Section 7(a) of the National Industrial Recovery Act was path-breaking in the area of labor relations; it required companies which signed the codes to bargain collectively with their workers through labor unions that had the backing of a majority of the company's employees.

The N.R.A. was designed to eliminate waste, inefficiency, and destructive competition—the goal of industrial consolidators since Vanderbilt and Rockefeller. In making the federal government the referee among companies and between employers and employees, the N.R.A. was the legatee of Theodore Roosevelt's New Nationalism of 1912 (Johnson was an old Bull Mooser), the mobilization of the economy during the First World War, and even Herbert Hoover's trade associations. The difference was that the N.R.A. codes were compulsory. A business was bound to its industry's code not by the moral suasion that Hoover had preferred, but by the force of law. Noncompliance led to prosecution by the government.

Blue Eagle Mania

Critics of the N.R.A., including some within the New Deal administration, likened it to the Fascist system that had been set up in Italy in 1922 by Benito Mussolini, and to the Nazi economy that was being instituted in Germany at the same time under Adolf Hitler. This was unfair. Mussolini and Hitler suppressed free labor unions; the N.R.A. promised them a part in making industrial policy.

More to the point was the criticism that the Blue Eagle functionaries went ridiculously far. Johnson was indeed code-crazy, wanting to regiment the most peripheral and even trivial businesses. There was a code for the burlesque "industry" that specified how many strippers were to undress per performance, what vestments they were to discard, and the quality of tassels and G-strings in N.R.A. houses. Had prostitution been legal in the United States, Johnson might have risen to even more ludicrous heights.

Such extremes were possible in part because of the enthusiasm with which Americans initially took to the N.R.A. Rooted on by the bombastic Johnson, 200,000 people marched in an N.R.A. parade in New York, carrying banners emblazoned with the N.R.A. motto, "We Do Our Part." The symbol of the N.R.A., a stylized blue eagle clutching industrial machinery and thunderbolts, was painted on factory walls, pasted on shop windows, and adopted as a motif by university marching bands.

For a brief time, Hugh Johnson seemed as popular as Roosevelt himself. He was certainly more conspicuous. Johnson stormed noisily about the country, publicly castigating as "chiselers" those businessmen who did not fall into line. He apparently inherited his bullying personality from his mother, who at an N.R.A. rally in Tulsa said that "people had better obey the N.R.A. because my son will enforce it like lightning, and you can never tell when lightning will strike."

THE NEW DEAL THREATENED; THE NEW DEAL SUSTAINED

The New Deal suffered its first setback not in Congress but at the Supreme Court. It was a conservative body in 1933, with six Harding, Coolidge, and Hoover appointees and one dating back to the presidency of William Howard Taft. Out of synchronization with the revolution in government, the "nine old men," as F.D.R. was to denounce them, declared two major pieces of New Deal legislation unconstitutional, and threatened others.

Death of the Blue Eagle

The N.R.A. met its death because of a suit brought by a small poultry company specializing in slaughtering chickens for use in the kosher kitchens of religious Jews. The Schechter brothers, owners of the company, found the sanitary standards required by the N.R.A. code for their industry incompatible with the ritual requirements of kosher slaughter. They claimed that N.R.A. regulations represented unjustifiable federal interference in intrastate commerce. (Their business was carried out almost entirely within New York State.) In 1935, the Supreme Court ruled unanimously that the Schechter Brothers were right, declaring that the National Industrial Recovery Act was unconstitutional.

The fuss was minimal. Both Roosevelt's and the people's enthusiasm for the N.R.A. had waned since 1933. Many codes were indeed so picayune as to seem impediments to economic recovery. Moreover, Congress moved promptly to salvage the one provision of the N.R.A. codes that had widespread support—Section 7(a). In the Wagner Labor Relations Act or National Labor Relations Act of 1935, the New Dealers reinstated the requirement that employers recognize and negotiate with labor unions that claimed the support of a majority of a company's employees.

In fact, the Wagner Act went further than Section 7(a) by setting up the National Labor Relations Board to investigate unfair labor practices and to issue "cease and desist" orders to employers found responsible for them. Most important, the law guaranteed the right of

The Union Cigar Company was by no means an industrial giant, but the collapse of its stock in the Great Crash of 1929 nevertheless made history. When the price of Union shares plummeted from $113.50 to $4 in one day's trading, the president of the company jumped to his death from a hotel room that he had rented for that purpose. The incident helped fuel a legend that rich men shouting "Ruined!" were hurling themselves wholesale from high buildings during late 1929 and early 1930. Cartoonists in newspapers and magazines had a field day with the theme. But it was only wishful thinking. When a historian researched the matter, he discovered that the suicide rate was higher in the months just preceding the crash than it was thereafter.

While many, perhaps most, middle-class investors and speculators were "ruined" in the collapse, the very rich suffered little more than a loss in paper wealth (relative richness) and not poverty. Still, the moneyed classes, which had been so at home during the age of Coolidge, very confident of their right and duty to govern the country, were stunned and even paralyzed by their failure. "I'm afraid," said Charles Schwab, chairman of the United States Steel Corporation, "that every man is afraid." Franklin D. Roosevelt, celestially noncommittal during his campaign for the presidency, may have had as much support from the nation's financial elite as did Hoover. Certainly the attitude of Wall Street and corporate boardroom alike was to give him a chance.

It did not last. By 1936, Roosevelt was being called "a traitor to his class" in society circles. Some of the jokes told about him and his wife, Eleanor, were vicious and ugly. Others were simply lame, as was this attack on Roosevelt's programs for putting people to work as welfare in disguise:

Q. Why is a WPA worker like King Solomon?
A. Because he takes his pick and goes to bed.

By 1937, when most people were wrestling with the recession of that year, the very wealthy were living comfortably again. Stock prices were up—although far below 1929 levels—and a new kind of social whirl made its appearance. Unlike the society of Mrs. Astor, J. P. Morgan, and Bradley Martin, with its regal ballrooms, private railroad cars, club parlors, and yachts, the café society of the late 1930s centered in Prohibition era speakeasies that had come above ground with repeal as restaurants and as clubs in which to sit and to dance all night, to see and to be seen. In New York City, the undisputed capital of café society, the chief seats were El Morocco, the Stork Club, and the "21" Club, which reveled in its cryptic speakeasy designation.

The young always had played an important part in the social whirl. Marrying daughters to European noblemen had been a way to display wealth during the late nineteenth century; youth had set the pace of fashion during the 1920s. In café society, however, the "rich, young, and beautiful" became the center of the piece.

What was more remarkable about café society was the interest that ordinary Americans took in its doings. Whom Alfred Gwynne Vanderbilt was dating was breath-

unions to represent those workers who voted for those unions in N.L.R.B.-supervised elections.

Farm Policy

A similar salvage operation preserved parts of the Agricultural Adjustment Act that the Supreme Court negated in 1936. Also enacted during the Hundred Days, the Agricultural Adjustment Act established yet another agency, the Agricultural Adjustment Administration (A.A.A.), which was to enforce the principle of "parity," for which farmers' organizations had fought throughout the 1920s.

"Parity" meant increasing farm income from the depths it plumbed in 1933 to the ratio that it had borne to the prices of non-farm products during the prosperous years of 1909 to 1914, a kind of golden age of agriculture as farmers looked back on it. The A.A.A. accomplished this by restricting farm production. Growers of wheat, corn, cotton, tobacco, rice, and hogs were paid subsidies to keep some of their land out of production. The costs of this expensive program ($100 million was paid to cotton farmers alone in one year) was borne by a tax on processors—millers, refiners, butchers, packagers—which was then passed on to consumers in higher food, clothing, and tobacco prices.

Because the crops of 1933 were already in the ground when the A.A.A. was established in May, it was necessary to destroy some of them. "Kill every third pig and plow every third row under," Secretary of Agriculture Henry A. Wallace said. The results were mixed. Many people were repelled by the slaughter of 6 million small pigs and 220,000 pregnant sows. Others not so sensitive wondered why food was being destroyed when millions were hungry. (In fact, 100 million pounds of the prematurely-harvested pork was diverted to relief agencies and inedible waste was used as fertilizer.) Nevertheless, the A.A.A. worked; the income of hog farmers began to rise immediately.

Fully a quarter of the 1933 cotton crop was plowed under, the fields left fallow. Unfortunately, because cotton farmers tended those fields still under cultivation more intensely, production actually rose in 1933. Within two years, however, cotton (and wheat and corn) prices rose by over 50 percent.

lessly reported in syndicated "society columns" by hangers-on such as Walter Winchell and "Cholly Knickerbocker." It was a news item if the heiress of an industrial fortune dropped in at El Morocco several times a week in order to dance the rhumba with her "agile husband." Naughtier gossip made reference to blond hubbies dancing the rhumba with willowy debutantes.

Debutantes (or debs), young women who were "coming out" into society, when in fact they had been lounging around night clubs since they were fifteen or sixteen, were the queens of café society. The leading deb of 1937 was Gloria "Mimi" Baker, whose mother replied to someone who called her a decadent aristocrat: "Why Mimi is the most democratic person, bar none, I've ever known." Indeed, café society was "democratic" in ways that earlier high societies had not been. Because status depended on beauty, on what passed for wit and talent, and on simply being well known and rich, the café set admitted movie stars, athletes, and even impoverished but slickly mannered nobles from Europe. They, in turn, were delighted to rub shoulders and dance the rhumba with the very rich.

Indeed, international "playboys" jumped at the opportunity to do more than be photographed at night clubs and race tracks they could not afford, and therein lay the great morality play of the 1930s and, possibly, part of the explanation for the fascination of many Americans with the doings of café society. Like people who attend high-speed automobile races, they were interested in the collisions as much as in the running.

Barbara Hutton, who had to stick to spartan diets in order to keep her weight down, was sole heiress to $45 million made in the five-and-tens of F. W. Woolworth. In 1933, she married Alexis Mdivani, who claimed to be a dispossessed Russian prince. Almost immediately after the marriage, the debonair Mdivani began to make her miserable, railing particularly at her weight problem. Drawing on the $1 million that Barbara's father had given him as a wedding present, the prince spent much of his time in the company of other women. In 1935, Barbara won Mdivani's consent for a divorce by giving him $2 million.

Almost immediately, she married a Danish count, Kurt von Haugwitz-Reventlow. Hutton showered him with gifts, including a $4.5 million mansion in London, but divorced him in 1937. The same photographers who snapped pictures of laughing, dancing debutantes at the Stork Club rushed about to get shots of tearful Barbara Hutton, the "poor little rich girl."

Some of the people who pored over them were sympathetic. "She's made mistakes," wrote columnist Adela Rogers St. Johns, "been a silly, wild, foolish girl, given in to temptations—but she's still our own . . . an American girl fighting alone across the sea." Others took pleasure in her repeated comeuppances. "Why do they hate me?" Barbara asked. "There are other girls as rich, richer, almost as rich."

A less desirable side effect of A.A.A. restrictions on production was the throwing of people off the land. Landowners dispossessed tenant farmers in order to get the subsidies that fallow land would earn. Between 1932 and 1935, 3 million American farmers lost their livelihood. Most of them were very poor black and white tenants who already were struggling to survive.

Anxious Days

Despite its negative effects, the New Dealers were devoted to the principles of the A.A.A. Its rejection by the Supreme Court was a far more serious blow than the loss of the Blue Eagle. Again, they salvaged what they could. In the Soil Conservation and Domestic Allotment Act, parity and the limitation of production were saved under the guise of conserving soil.

Much more worrisome was the fear that, piece by piece, the conservative Supreme Court would dismantle the entire New Deal. Roosevelt's supporters were particularly worried about the Rural Electrification Act and the law that had set up the Tennessee Valley Authority (T.V.A.).

The Rural Electrification Administration (R.E.A.) brought electricity to isolated farm regions that had been of no interest to private utility companies. It was vulnerable to Court action because it put the government into the business of distributing power, indirectly competing with private enterprise. The T.V.A. was farther reaching yet. It was a massive government construction, flood control, and electrification project that shaped an entire region, a model of government economic and social planning.

T.V.A.

The T.V.A. was the brainchild and lifelong darling of Senator George Norris, a Republican progressive who advocated economic planning and regional development engineered by the government. Although he was from Nebraska, Norris had fastened on the valley of the Tennessee River, in the southern Appalachians, as the place to put his ideas to work.

Almost every year, the wild Tennessee River flooded its banks and brought additional hardship to southern Appalachia, one of the nation's poorest areas. Norris's

A dam constructed by the Tennessee Valley Authority.

idea was to use the stricken region as a laboratory. The government would construct a system of dams both to control the raging floods and to generate electricity. In homes, the cheap power would bring the people of Appalachia into the twentieth century. The government-generated electricity would also make possible the construction of factories, especially for the manufacture of fertilizers, which would invigorate the economy of a chronically depressed region.

Norris also pointed out that by generating electricity itself, the government would be able to determine the fairness of the prices of power demanded by other companies elsewhere in the country. Until the 1930s, the actual cost of generating electrical power was something of a mystery outside of the business.

During the 1920s, Henry Ford had tried to buy key sites on the Tennessee River from the government, notably Muscle Shoals, a tumultuous rapids, in order to build a privately-owned power plant. Norris had fought Ford off in Congress, arguing that the Tennessee Valley provided an ideal laboratory for the testing of theories of regional planning. Fortunately for Norris, scandalous government giveaways of valuable property to profiteers like Ford, notably the oil reserves at Teapot Dome, were still alive in the public memory. However, while he had been able to keep Muscle Shoals and other sites in federal hands, Norris was unable to push through his plan

for government development of the Tennessee Valley until the election of F.D.R.

Creeping Socialism

Fiscal conservatives attacked the New Deal because of its astronomical costs. Herbert Hoover spoke of the decimal point in the government's debts "wandering around among the regimented ciphers trying to find some of the old places it used to know."

Predictably, the T.V.A. and R.E.A. were attacked as socialistic. Big business, which had approved F.D.R.'s banking reforms and, for a time, the N.R.A., launched a political offensive against programs that put the government into the production and distribution of electrical power. As early as 1934, having recovered from the demoralization of 1929, some bankers and big business men founded the American Liberty League, which accused Roosevelt of trying to destroy free enterprise and set up a dictatorship.

Most Liberty Leaguers were Coolidge-Mellon Republicans, but they were joined by some prominent Democrats, including the party's presidential nominees of 1924 and 1928, John W. Davis and Alfred E. Smith. Davis was a corporation lawyer and found his role familiar. Smith turned against Roosevelt in part because of his peeve over losing his chance to be president to a man whose rise in politics he had helped advance. Abandoning the sidewalks of New York for seats on a number of corporate boards, the once progressive Smith took increasingly reactionary positions on public questions.

Combatting such critics was like swatting mosquitoes for the able Roosevelt. A majority of Americans remained distrustful of big-business men, even still bitter towards them. F.D.R. labeled the Liberty Leaguers "economic royalists" and they never did have a large following.

The Supreme Court was another matter, a major threat to the New Deal. Making one of his rare political miscalculations, Roosevelt proposed a scheme to save his reforms by packing the Court with additional justices who would endorse it.

Reaction in both Congress and the nation at large was hostile. The New Deal was popular but Roosevelt's court-packing scheme did indeed look like tampering with the Constitution. Roosevelt quietly retreated and the crisis passed when the Court, perhaps alarmed, approved several key New Deal enactments. Then Father Time lent a hand; beginning in 1937, a series of retirements and deaths allowed Roosevelt to appoint a New Deal majority to the bench without tampering with the traditional size of the Court. When F.D.R. died in 1945, eight of the nine justices were his appointees.

THE SPELLBINDERS

F.D.R. made his court-packing proposal in 1937, at the beginning of his second term. For a while, however, it appeared that he might not win reelection. The threat came not from the American Liberty League or even the Republican party, but from three popular demagogues whom Roosevelt and his chief political strategist, Postmaster General James A. Farley, genuinely feared.

Father Coughlin

With the coming of depression, Charles E. Coughlin, a Canadian-born Roman Catholic priest, had transformed a religious radio program into a platform for his political beliefs. At first, Coughlin enlisted his mellow, baritone voice and Irish genius with the spoken word in support of Roosevelt. He was not a man to mince. "The New Deal is Christ's Deal," he said in 1933.

A year later, however, Coughlin became convinced that the key to solving the depression was a complete overhaul of the national monetary system, including the abolition of the Federal Reserve System. Despite Roosevelt's reputation among the "economic royalists" as a radical, the president had no patience for such extreme proposals. But because Coughlin had a huge and devoted following—perhaps 10 million listeners to some programs—his scathing attacks were a source of worry to F.D.R., Farley, and other tacticians.

Dr. Townsend

Dr. Francis E. Townsend, a California physician, rather a different sort than the high-voltage Coughlin, was at least equally a threat to Roosevelt's majority. Himself 66 years old in 1933, Townsend was appalled by the plight of the nation's aged citizens. He proposed that the federal government pay a monthly pension of $200 to all people over 60 years of age, with two conditions attached.

First, federal pensioners would be forbidden to work. Second, they would spend every cent of their pension within the month. His "Townsend Plan" not only would provide security for the nation's elderly, the kindly doctor told audiences all over the country, but would reinvigorate the economy by creating jobs for young men and women.

By 1936, 7,000 Townsend Clubs claimed a membership of 1.5 million. When Roosevelt rejected the plan as unworkable, Townsend went into the opposition and laid tentative plans to join his movement with those of Father Coughlin and of Roosevelt's most serious political rival, Senator Huey P. Long of Louisiana.

The Kingfish

Huey Long remains one of the most fascinating figures of the depression decade. After a stint as a traveling salesman, during which he learned he had a magical gift of gab, he became a lawyer. He never forgot the poor farmers among whom he had lived and worked. He built a successful political career as a colorful and often profane orator who baited the railroad and oil industry elite that ran the state. Unlike most Southern demagogues, however, Long did not resort to race-baiting to win votes. He accepted segregation, but he also won the support of many of those Louisiana blacks, mostly in New Orleans, who had held on to their right to vote, by providing services for them too.

A WELL-FUNDED CAMPAIGN

In 1934, radical novelist Upton Sinclair won the Democratic party's nomination for governor of California by proposing a comprehensive social welfare program known as EPIC, "End Poverty in California." President Roosevelt was less than delighted by the emergence of another spellbinder within his own party, and pretty much sat out the campaign. The Republican party spent $4 million in the successful effort to defeat Sinclair. By way of contrast, in 1932, the Republicans had spent only $3 million nationally in the campaign to reelect President Hoover.

AS MAINE GOES

In the nineteenth century, the people of Maine elected their governor in September, almost two months before the national presidential election. The saying "As Maine goes, so goes the nation" reflected the significance that was attributed to the results there. In the 28 presidential elections in which Maine voters participated, the state's record in picking the winner was 22 to 6, good but not foolproof, as Herbert Hoover learned in 1932: he won Maine, but few other states.

In 1936, Maine again looked to vote Republican. Democratic party campaign manager James Farley quipped. "As Maine goes, so goes Vermont." He was right on the button. F.D.R. won every state that year except Maine and Vermont!

As governor of Louisiana between 1928 and 1932, Long built roads and hospitals, and provided free textbooks and lunches for schoolchildren—social benefits that were almost unknown in the South and were far from universal in the North and West. Long was an ambitious and egotistic showman. He called himself "the Kingfish" after a clownish (and devious) character on the popular radio program "Amos 'n' Andy." He was the Kingfish, and all the other politicians were little fishes. He made Louisiana State University the best public university in the South and led cheers when L.S.U. played its great rival, the University of Alabama. Once, when a circus announced that it would open in Baton Rouge on the date of an important L.S.U. game, Long killed the competition by closing down the show on the grounds that lion tamers were cruel to animals.

The New Deal Supreme

People loved Huey Long, not only in Louisiana, which he continued to run even after entering the Senate in 1933, but all over the South and Midwest. He based his national ambitions on a plan called "Share the Wealth," which called for a heavy tax on the well-to-do and no personal incomes of more than $1 million a year. To people struggling for the necessities, it was an appealing program.

Because Long was the virtual dictator of the Pelican State ("I'm the Constitution around here," he said with a puckish smile), Roosevelt considered him a threat to democracy as well as to his own reelection in 1936. In the end, however, the president overcame him and Townsend and Coughlin by a combination of cooptation and good luck.

Roosevelt undercut Coughlin's financial program through his own moderate monetary reforms. To steal Townsend's thunder, he supported the Social Security Act of 1935. Its pensions were tiny compared with the $200 a month for which Townsend called. Nevertheless, it was a revolutionary law; for the first time, the United States government assumed responsibility for the welfare of people who were disabled or too old to work. Also in 1935, Roosevelt supported a revision of the income tax law that did not abolish huge incomes, as Long demanded, but taxed people in the upper brackets much more heavily than those in the lower.

In every case, the New Deal reforms were half a loaf. In no case was the program of the critics adopted. But so great was Roosevelt's personal popularity that his would-be rivals lost support and, eventually, lost heart. Townsend's clubs declined slowly, as did Coughlin's radio audience. In the end, the "radio priest" discredited himself by turning to a Nazi-like anti-Semitism and praising Adolf Hitler. Long was removed from the scene by fate; in 1935, he was assassinated by a young man whose family Long had injured in his power grab.

Thus, in the election of 1936, Roosevelt had to face only the affable and moderate Republican governor of Kansas, Alfred M. Landon. Offering no real alternative to the New Deal, Landon was swamped, winning majorities only in Maine and Vermont.

Louisiana politician Huey Long demonstrates his flair for theatrical oratory.

THE LEGACY OF THE NEW DEAL

Even before the election of 1936, Roosevelt had shifted the direction of his reforms. At first, he had viewed the New Deal as very much a new deal for everyone. With some reason, he believed he had saved the capitalist system from the kind of political extremism that the depression was nurturing elsewhere in the world. He felt betrayed when big business, instead of recognizing and rewarding his moderation, vilified him.

In 1935, threatened by the spellbinders and encouraged by his wife, with her ties to disadvantaged groups, F.D.R. became, in varying degrees, the president of the people on the bottom of society. Their response in the election of 1936 only heartened him to push on. It was in this break with "the classes" and partisanship on behalf of "the masses" that the legacy of the New Deal lies. Such phenomena have occurred without revolution only rarely in history.

African Americans Become Democrats

Roosevelt emphasized the economic problems of disadvantaged groups almost to the exclusion of other problems. On the question of civil rights for blacks, for example, F.D.R. was nearly silent. The Democratic party depended heavily on its Southern bloc for support, and Southern politicians were committed to white supremacy and Jim Crow segregation. As a concession to them, Roosevelt refused even to support a federal anti-lynching bill, and he tolerated the racial segregation of work gangs on government-supported building projects such as the T.V.A.

Under constant pressure from the N.A.A.C.P. (National Association for the Advancement of Colored People), from Eleanor Roosevelt, and from such individual African-American leaders as Mary McLeod Bethune, the New Dealers made sure that blacks shared in relief programs. Black Americans moved into more than a third of new housing units constructed by the federal government. As a result, the 1930s saw a revolution in black voting patterns. In 1932, about 75 percent of African American voters were Republicans; they still thought of the G.O.P. as the party of Lincoln and emancipation. For example, the only black congressman in 1932 was Oscar De Priest of Chicago, a member of the G.O.P.

By 1936, more than 75 percent of registered black voters were voting Democratic—even De Priest was defeated by a black New Dealer—and the trend continued for 30 years. The Democratic party might not have been the friend of the blacks, but it was the friend of the poor, and most blacks were just that.

Mary McLeod Bethune used her personal friendship with Eleanor Roosevelt to win concessions for blacks in New Deal policies.

The Growth of the Unions

Roosevelt also won the organized-labor movement to the Democratic party. Left to his own prejudices, he would have remained neutral in disputes between unions and employers. However, when militant unionists such as John L. Lewis of the coal miners (a lifelong Republican) and Sidney Hillman and David Dubinsky of the large needle-trades unions made it clear that they would throw their influence behind the president only in return for administration support, Roosevelt gave in. Lewis raised a donation of $1 million to the president's campaign for reelection in 1936. In return, Roosevelt had to be photographed accepting the check, smiling with approval on the burly, bushybrowed Lewis.

"The President wants you to join the union," the Committee on Industrial Organization told workers in basic industries after F.D.R. signed the Wagner Act. At first a faction within the American Federation of Labor, the Committee left the A.F.L. in 1937 to form an entirely new association of unions, the Congress of Industrial Organizations (C.I.O.). Massive, colorful campaigns won recruits in unprecedented numbers.

The Steel Workers' Organizing Committee, parent organization of the United Steel Workers, was founded in 1936. By May 1937, it had 325,000 members. The United States Steel Corporation, the nerve center of antiunionism in the industry, recognized the union as a bargaining agent without a strike.

The United Automobile Workers enlisted 370,000 members in a little more than a year. The story was similar among workers in other basic industries: rubber, glass, lumber, aluminum, electrical products, coal mining, the needle trades, even textiles. "The Union" came to have a mystical significance in the lives of many workers. Workers fought for the right to wear union buttons on the job. The union card became a certificate of honor. Old hymns were reworked to promote the cause. Professional singers like Woody Guthrie, Pete Seeger, and Burl Ives lent their talents to organizing campaigns.

Employer Violence

The sit-down strike was one of the most dramatic manifestations of worker militance. Beginning with automobile workers in the Fisher Body Plant of Flint, Michigan, in early 1937, workers shut down factories not by picketing outside the gates, but by occupying the premises and refusing to leave.

Not every employer responded as sensibly as United States Steel. Tom Girdler of Republic Steel called the C.I.O. "irresponsible, racketeering, violent, communistic" and threatened to fight the union with armed force. In this heated atmosphere occurred the "Memorial Day Massacre" of 1937, so called because Chicago police attacked a crowd of union members, killing ten and seriously injuring about a hundred.

Although he eventually came to terms with the United Automobile Workers, Henry Ford at first responded to the new unionism as did Girdler. He employed an army of toughs from the underworld and fortified his factories with tear gas, machine guns, and grenades. At the "Battle of the Overpass" in Detroit, Ford "goons" (as antiunion strong-arm forces were called) beat organizer Walter Reuther and other U.A.W. officials until they were insensible. Violence was so common in the coal fields of Harlan County, Kentucky, that the area became known in the press as "Bloody Harlan."

But such incidents, well-documented in photographs and newsreel films, redounded to the benefit of the union movement, and by the end of the depression decade, organized labor was a major force in American life. In 1932, there were 3.2 million union members. In 1940, there were 9 million, and by 1944, more than 13 million.

The Bottom Line

The greatest positive accomplishment of the New Deal was to ease the economic hardships suffered by millions

Police attack a crowd of union members during the "Memorial Day Massacre" in Chicago, 1937.

of Americans and, in so doing, to preserve their confidence in American institutions. In its relief measures, particularly those agencies that put jobless people to work, Roosevelt's administration was a resounding success.

As a formula for economic recovery, however, the New Deal failed. When unemployment dropped to 7.5 million early in 1937 and other economic indicators brightened, Roosevelt began to dismantle many expensive government programs. The result was renewed collapse, a depression within a depression. The recession of 1937 was not as serious as that of 1930 to 1933, but it provided painful evidence that for all their flexibility and willingness to experiment and spend, the New Dealers had not unlocked the secrets of maintaining prosperity during peacetime. Only when preparations for another world war led to massive purchases of American goods from abroad (and to rearmament at home) did the Great Depression end. By 1939, the economy was clearly on the upswing. By 1940, with Europe already at war, the Great Depression was history.

Through such programs as support for agricultural prices, rural electrification, Social Security, insurance of bank deposits, protection of labor unions, and strict controls over the economy, the federal government came to play a part in people's daily lives such as had been inconceivable before 1933. In the T.V.A., the government became an actual producer of electrical power and commodities such as fertilizers. It was not "socialism," as conservative critics of the New Deal cried, but in an American context it was something of a revolution.

Perhaps the most dubious side effect of the new system was the extraordinary growth in the size of government. Extensive government programs required huge bureaucracies to carry them out. The number of federal employees rose from 600,000 in 1930 to a million in 1940, a total that would rise more radically during the Second World War. To the extent that bureaucracies are concerned above all with their own survival and expansion, leading to the squandering of tax moneys and to aggravations in dealing with government, the New Deal contributed to American life, with its many blessings, a phenomenon that has, at one time or another, vexed every citizen to near distraction.

A Political Revolution

Between 1896 and 1933, the Republican party had been the nation's majority party. The only Democratic president during that era, Woodrow Wilson, won election only when the Republicans split and the Great War in Europe unsettled American politics at the bottom. During the 36 years before Roosevelt's election, the Democrats controlled the House of Representatives only ten years, and the Senate only six.

The Great Depression and the New Deal changed everything. F.D.R. and Jim Farley forged a new majority of the solidly Democratic South, Northern and Western liberals, blue-collar workers (particularly urban white ethnics), and African Americans, with substantial support among Western farmers and ranchers. The New Deal alliance was not without problems. Beginning in 1937, old-fashioned small-government Southern Democrats who disapproved of even the New Deal's minimal gestures toward blacks and the prominence in Washington of "Yankee" liberals, sometimes voted with Republicans against New Deal measures.

Roosevelt's charm and his refusal to push civil rights for blacks, plus grass-roots support for the New Deal among Southern whites, prevented the crack from widening into a real split during his presidency. The Democratic majority forged during the 1930s lasted for half a century. During the fifty years between 1930 and 1980, Republicans occupied the White House for sixteen years, but those presidents (Eisenhower, Nixon, and Ford) were moderates who had made their peace with New Deal institutions.

In Congress, the Democratic majority was even more striking. During the same fifty years between 1930 and 1980, Republicans held majorities in the Senate for only six years and in the House of Representatives for only four. The Republican party simultaneously controlled presidency, Senate, and House for a mere two years (1953 to 1955).

For Further Reading

First of all, see the biographical studies and general works listed at the conclusion of Chapter 42. Other basic studies of the New Deal are Paul Conkin, *The New Deal* (1975); William E. Leuchtenburg, *Franklin D. Roosevelt and the New Deal, 1932–1940* (1963); Arthur M. Schlesinger, Jr., *The Coming of the New Deal* (1959) and *The Politics of Upheaval* (1960). Frederick Lewis Allen, *Since Yesterday* (1940) is an enjoyable popular history.

On the several immediate crises faced by F.D.R. and the New Dealers, see Susan Estabrook Kennedy, *The Banking Crisis of 1933* (1973); C. P. Kinderberger, *The World in Depression* (1973); Roy Lubove, *The Struggle for Social Security, 1900–1935* (1968); Thomas K. McCraw, *T.V.A. and the Power Fight, 1933–1939* (1971); Michael Parrish, *Security Regulation and the New Deal* (1970); E. E. Robinson, *The Roosevelt Leadership* (1955); Elliott Rosen, *Hoover, Roosevelt, and the Brains Trust* (1977); Theodore D. Saloutos and John D. Hicks, *Twentieth Century Populism: Agricultural Discontent in the Middle West, 1900–1939* (1951); and Studs Terkel, *Hard Times* (1970).

On Roosevelt's critics: Allan Brinkley, *Voices of Protest: Huey Long, Father Coughlin, and the Great Depression* (1982); Abraham Holtzman, *The Townsend Movement* (1963); Irving Howe and Lewis Coser, *The American Communist Party* (1957); D. R. McCoy, *Angry Voices: Left of Center Politics in the New Deal Era* (1958); David A. Shannon, *The American Socialist Party* (1955); C. J. Tull, *Father Coughlin and the New Deal* (1965); and T. Harry Williams, *Huey Long* (1969).

On the labor movement, see Irving Bernstein, *Turbulent Years: A History of the American Worker, 1933–1941* (1970); and Sidney Fine, *Sit-Down: The General Motors Strike of 1936–1937* (1969). Other insightful monographs include Frank Freidel, *F.D.R. and the South* (1965); Paul A. Kurzman, *Harry Hopkins and the New Deal* (1974); Richard D. McKinzie, *The New Deal for Artists* (1973); Richard Polenberg, *Reorganizing Roosevelt's Government: The Controversy over Executive Reorganization, 1936–1939* (1966); Harvard Sitkoff, *A New Deal for Blacks* (1978); and George Tindall, *The Emergence of the New South, 1914–1945* (1967).

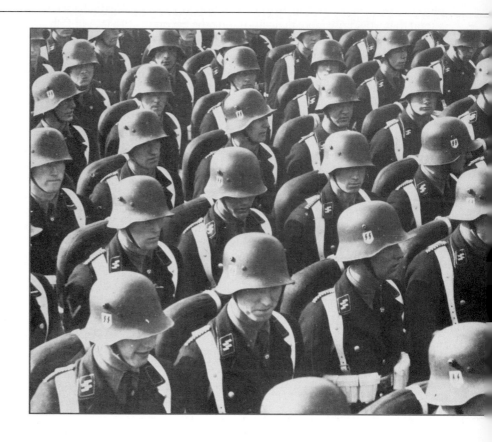

The SS, Hitler's elite paramilitary force.

HEADED FOR WAR AGAIN

FOREIGN RELATIONS
1933 - 1942

In 1933, the year Franklin D. Roosevelt became president, Germany also got a new leader. Adolf

Hitler, the head of the extreme right-wing National Socialist, or "Nazi" party, was named Chancellor

of the Weimar Republic's parliamentary government by the elderly President, war hero Paul von

Hindenburg. The two paid little attention to each other during their first years in office. F.D.R. had

his hands full fighting the Great Depression. Hitler was also preoccupied with the home front, working

from the first day he took office to destroy the Weimar constitution and seize absolute power.

696 Chapter 44: HEADED FOR WAR AGAIN

The character and values of the two men could hardly have differed more. The patrician Roosevelt was a liberal, dedicated to democratic principles. The middle-class, rather vulgar Hitler despised democracy and was contemptuous of individual freedoms. Nevertheless, comparisons were inevitable. Pundits noted that both men were virtuosos in using the radio and other modern forms of communication as a means to persuade. Roosevelt was at his best as a soothing voice in his Fireside Chats, quietly reassuring Americans that through reform they could preserve what was of value in their way of life. Hitler was at his best through loudspeakers, exhorting frustrated Germans to a hatred of the Weimar Republic, the foreigners who had humiliated Germany in the Versailles Treaty, and people whom he defined as enemies within: Socialists, Communists, and Jews.

Roosevelt and Hitler would eventually confront each other and clash, but only after Americans had experimented with a foreign policy designed to avoid entanglement in another foreign war.

NEW DEAL FOREIGN POLICY

When he first took office, Roosevelt seemed to be as casual as Woodrow Wilson about foreign policy. Like Wilson, he passed over professional diplomats in naming his Secretary of State. Roosevelt made a political appointment, the courtly senator from Tennessee Cordell Hull, whose elegant bearing belied his log-cabin origins.

Hull and Roosevelt were generally content to follow the guidelines that had been charted by Hoover and his Secretary of State, Henry L. Stimson. Where they departed from blueprint, their purpose was to reinforce the New Deal program for economic recovery at home.

The Good Neighbor

Roosevelt and Hull even embraced Hoover's phrase "good neighbor" to describe the role that they meant the United States to play in Central and South America. Following through on Hoover's announced intentions when he left office, Roosevelt withdrew U. S. Marines from Nicaragua, the Dominican Republic, and Haiti, where they had been keeping order. Like Hoover, he refused to intervene in Cuba despite the chronic civil conflicts that plagued the island republic and America's legal entitlement, under the Platt Amendment, to send in troops in times of trouble.

In 1934, when peace returned to Cuba under a pro-American president who later became dictator, Cordell Hull formally renounced the Platt Amendment. No

---

TWO DIFFERENT WORLDS

In December 1940, Adolf Hitler told Germans that there could be no reconciliation between Germany, on the one hand, and Great Britain *and the United States*, on the other. They were "different worlds."

The next month, President Roosevelt accepted Hitler's dichotomy and said that his world was devoted to the Four Freedoms, "freedom of speech and expression, freedom of worship, freedom from want, freedom from fear."

---

longer would the "Colossus of the North" be a bully, using its overwhelming power to force its way in the Caribbean. As a result of the about-face, no United States president was ever so well liked in Central and South America as was Roosevelt. Even when, in 1938, Mexico seized the properties of American oil companies and offered little compensation to the former owners, Roosevelt kept cool and took a conciliatory stand. A few years later, he worked out a friendly settlement.

By then, the Good Neighbor Policy was reaping concrete benefits for the United States. The Second World War had begun, but despite German efforts to win a foothold in the Western Hemisphere, most Latin American nations backed the United States, and the few neutrals that cozied up to Hitler were very cautious. Had a South American country permitted Nazi Germany to establish bases on its soil, it would have seriously inhibited the American contribution to the war in Europe and Asia.

The Stimson Doctrine

Toward Asia, New Deal diplomacy also moved along paths that had been staked out during the Hoover administration. The problem in the East, as policy-makers saw it, was to maintain Chinese independence and American trading rights in China—the Open Door Policy—in the face of an ambitious and expansion-minded Japan. The trouble was that China's government, headed by Generalissimo Chiang Kai-shek, was disorganized, inefficient, and increasingly corrupt.

Late in 1931, taking advantage of the chaos, Japanese military officers detached the province of Manchuria from China and set up a puppet state that they called Manchukuo. Hoover considered but rejected Stimson's proposal that the United States retaliate against Japan by imposing severe economic sanctions, denying Japan the American products that were vital to its industry and navy, particularly oil. Instead, Hoover announced that the United States would not recognize the legality of any territorial changes resulting from the use of force.

A young Chinese survivor of the Japanese air attack on Shanghai, 1937.

Curiously, this policy became known as the Stimson Doctrine.

The Stimson Doctrine was little more than a rap on the knuckles, rather more like one of those inexpensive and painless statements of moralistic disapproval that come from critics of foreign policy, rather than from those responsible for making it. Japanese militarists, driven by a compelling sense of national destiny, shrugged it off. In 1932, they launched an attack on Shanghai and casually tyrannized the population. In 1937, the Japanese bombed the city, one of the first massive bombings of a civilian population.

Nevertheless, Roosevelt went no further than Hoover had in 1932. He (and the League of Nations) responded to Japanese aggression with words alone. With economic problems so serious at home, no Western country would risk war with Japan for the sake of a China so dubiously governed and divided.

Recognition of the Soviet Union

Where Roosevelt and Hull parted ways with Hoover and Stimson, the cause was that all-pervasive reality, the depression at home. For example, in May 1933, Roosevelt scuttled an international conference that was meeting in London for the purpose of stabilizing world currencies. Delegates of 64 nations had gathered with Hoover's approval and, so they assumed, with Roosevelt's as well. Before discussions actually began, however, Roosevelt announced that he would not agree to any decisions that ran contrary to his domestic recovery program, specifically his decision to take the United States off the gold standard. The conference collapsed.

In November 1933, Roosevelt formally recognized the Soviet government, which four presidents had refused to do. In part this was a realistic decision that was long overdue. For good or ill, the party dictatorship headed by Joseph Stalin was firmly in control of the Soviet Union and its traditional territories. But Roosevelt was also swayed by the argument that the Soviet Union would provide a large and profitable market for ailing American manufacturers. This proved to be an illusion. Soviet Russia was too poor to buy much of anything from anyone. Nevertheless, it was the hope of stimulating economic recovery at home that made possible the end of a pointless sixteen-year policy of nonrecognition.

New Directions, Old Strictures

Increased trade was also the motive behind Secretary of State Cordell Hull's strategy of reducing tariff barriers through reciprocity. With a Southern Democrat's distaste for high tariffs, Hull negotiated reciprocal trade agreements with 29 countries. The high Republican rates of the 1920s were slashed by as much as half in return for other nations' agreements to lower their barriers against American exports.

Roosevelt probably would have liked his administration to take a more active part in the affairs of nations than the United States did. He admired his cousin Theodore Roosevelt's forcefulness, and he was an old Wilsonian, as was Hull. He had enthusiastically supported the League of Nations when it was first proposed and, while recovering from his polio attack during the early 1920s, had studied and written about foreign policy.

But F.D.R. was first and foremost a politician who thought about voters at every turn. He knew that it was political suicide for an elected official to wander too far from popular prejudices in any matter, and according to an authoritative public-opinion poll of 1935, 95 percent of all Americans were isolationists. They believed that the United States had no vital interests to protect in either Europe or Asia and wanted their government to act accordingly.

Suspicion of Europe was reinforced by the theory that the economic collapse of the Old World was responsible for the American depression. This feeling intensified between 1934 and 1936, when Senator Gerald Nye of North Dakota began a series of investigations into the political machinations of the munitions industry. Nye insisted that the United States had been maneuvered into the First World War by "merchants of death" such as the giant Du Pont Corporation and other companies, which had been only too willing to see young men slaughtered for the sake of bigger sales. This belief was popularized in a bestselling book of 1935, *The Road to War* by Walter Millis, and many academic historians took a similarly jaundiced view of the reasons why, in 1917, Americans had gone "over there."

Neutrality Policy

In a series of Neutrality Acts passed between 1935 and 1937, Congress said "never again" with an exclamation point. Taken together, the three laws warned American citizens against traveling on ships flying the flags of nations at war (no *Lusitanias* this time) and required belligerent nations to pay cash for all American goods they purchased and to carry them in their own ships. There would be no United States flagships sunk even by accident, and no American property lost because of a war among Europeans. Finally, belligerent nations were forbidden to buy arms in the United States and to borrow money from American banks. This law was designed to prevent the emergence of an active lobby of munitions makers and bankers with a vested interest in the victory of one side in any conflict.

Critics of the Neutrality Acts argued that they worked to the disadvantage of countries that were the innocent victims of aggression. Such nations would be unprepared for war, whereas aggressor nations would equip themselves in advance. This was certainly the message of Fascist Italy's invasion of Ethiopia in 1935 and of Japan's huge purchases of American scrap iron. But until 1938, Americans were interested only in avoiding a repetition of the events that had taken them into war in 1917. The majority wanted no part of trying to influence international behavior if it meant American involvement.

THE WORLD GOES TO WAR

Each year brought new evidence that the world was drifting into another bloodbath. In 1934, the Nazi government of Adolf Hitler began rearming Germany. In 1935, Hitler introduced universal military training and Italy invaded Ethiopia, one of but two independent nations in Africa. In 1936, Francisco Franco, a reactionary Spanish general, started a rebellion against the unstable democratic government of Spain and received massive support from both Italy and Germany, including combat troops who treated the Spanish Civil War as a rehearsal for a bigger show.

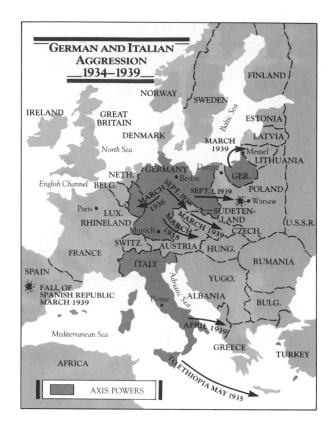

In July 1937, Japan sent land forces into China and quickly took the northern capital, then called Peiping, and most of the coastal provinces. In March 1938, Hitler forced the political union of Austria to Germany in the *Anschluss* (union), increasing the resources of what Hitler called the Third Reich, or empire. In September, claiming that he wanted only to unite all Germans under one flag, Hitler demanded that Czechoslovakia surrender the Sudetenland to him.

The Sudetenland was largely populated by German-speaking people. But it was also the mountainous natural defense line for Czechoslovakia, the only democratic state in central Europe. Nevertheless, in the hope that they could win peace by appeasing Hitler, England and France agreed to the takeover; Hitler mocked their misplaced goodwill within months. In March 1939, he seized the rest of Czechoslovakia, where the people were Slavic in language and culture and were generally fearful of or hostile to Germans.

The Aggressor Nations

In some respects, the three aggressor nations of the 1930s were very different. Japan was primarily motivated to expand into China for economic reasons. A modern industrial nation, Japan was poor in basic natural resources like coal and iron. China was rich in these raw materials, and Japanese leaders hoped to displace the

Hitler and Francisco Franco, 1940.

United States and Great Britain as the dominant imperial power on the Asian mainland.

Until the summer of 1941, Japanese policy-makers were split between fanatical militarists who believed they must have war with the United States (and looked forward to it) and moderates who believed they could best serve their country's purposes by coming to an understanding with the United States. American trade was important to Japan; indeed, the Asian nation was the third largest customer of the United States, importing vast quantities of American cotton, copper, scrap iron, and oil.

Italy under the Fascists seemed chronically locked into poverty. Dictator Benito Mussolini, a strutting buffoon in his public posing but ruthless in his use of power, made do with the appearance of wealth and might. Ethiopia was an easy touch, a destitute and backward country that had to send men with antiquated muskets and even spears to combat Mussolini's tanks. Only so weak a country could have fallen to Italy's poorly trained and equipped army. Mussolini's tanks were designed more for parades rather than for war. Some were made of sheet metal that could be dented with a swift kick. By itself, Mussolini's Italy represented no real threat to world peace, and Americans either applauded what

progress the Italian economy made under Fascist rule or laughed at newsreel films of Mussolini's slapstick antics.

Beyond his Charlie Chaplin moustache, there was nothing comical about the Nazi dictator of Germany. Adolf Hitler's strutting was all too serious because his theater was a potentially rich and powerful nation. Moreover, Hitler was far more cunning and deliberate than Mussolini. He knew what he wanted and had said as much in an autobiography entitled *Mein Kampf*, or *My Struggle*—German domination of the continent of Europe. While his strategy was not without flaws, Hitler seemed brilliantly to grasp just how much he could get away with in dealing with the other European powers and the United States. Or, as some have suggested, he was very lucky.

Perverted Nationalism

In other ways, the three aggressor nations were much alike. Japanese militarists, Italian Fascists, and German Nazis were all stridently antidemocratic. They sneered at the ideals of popular rule and individual liberties, regarding them as the sources of the world's economic and social problems. In the place of traditional principles of democratic humanism, they exalted the totalitarian

Mussolini on his favorite perch, in the Piazza Venezia, Rome.

state as mystically personified in a single person: Hiro-hito, the divine emperor of Japan; Mussolini, the Italian *Duce*; and Hitler, the German *Führer*.

The aggressor nations were militaristic. They wor-shiped armed force as the best means of serving their national purposes. If militarism could be less than omi-nous when practiced by a poor country like Italy, it was frightening when combined with fanatical Japanese na-tionalism or Nazi racism. The Japanese considered East Asia to be their garden, off limits to Westerners who had dominated the Eastern Hemisphere for a century. Japa-nese soldiers were sworn to solemn oaths to die serving emperor and homeland.

Nazi racism was criminal from its inception. Calling on ancient Germanic mythology and nineteenth-cen-tury pseudoscience, as well as populist anti-Semitism, it taught that "non-Aryans" were subhuman degenerates who had no claims on the master race save to serve it. After imprisoning, exiling, or silencing the German Communists, Socialists, and Democrats, Nazi paramili-tary organizations routinely brutalized German Jews. Hitler's government stripped Jews of civil rights and eventually, during the war, murdered those who re-mained in extermination camps along with millions of Jews from conquered lands, gypsies, congenitally hand-icapped people, political dissidents, homosexuals, and those bold or foolish enough to resist the Nazis.

And the War Came

Hitler had repeatedly pushed the Western democracies and gotten his way. In September 1939, when he in-vaded Poland, ostensibly to secure a German-speaking part of the country, Britain and France drew the line, declaring war. However, neither nation had prepared adequately to help Poland, and Hitler had neutralized the Soviet Union by signing a "nonaggression" pact with Communist dictator Joseph Stalin. Stalin knew that Russia was on Hitler's list but he distrusted England and France. He believed he was buying time to prepare, when he signed the treaty.

And territory for a buffer: while Hitler's legions in-vaded Poland from the west, Russian soldiers streamed into eastern Poland, and the tiny Baltic Sea states of Latvia, Lithuania, and Estonia.

An uneasy quiet fell on Europe during the winter of 1939–1940. Journalists spoke of a "phony war" in which neither side attacked the other with force. In fact, the French and British were committed to defensive war,

Japanese soldiers believed that Emperor Hirohito was divine and swore to fight to the death serving him.

remembering the terrible loss of life in World War I when the men went over the top. They huddled behind the Maginot Line, a system of fortifications to which the French had dedicated vast resources throughout the 1930s.

The Germans had other plans. Appreciating better than the British and French what the motor vehicle meant to armed conflict, they were preparing for *Blitzkrieg* (lightning war): massive land, sea, and air attacks with which, in the spring, the crack German armed forces overran Denmark, Norway, Luxembourg, Belgium, and the Netherlands. In June 1940, France collapsed, and the British managed to evacuate their troops and some French units from the little port of Dunkirk only by mobilizing virtually every ship and boat that was capable of crossing the English Channel. The motley fleet returned nearly 340,000 men to England to await a German invasion. They were demoralized, but they were not in German prison camps.

The Invasion of Russia

"We shall fight on the beaches, we shall fight on the landing grounds, we shall fight in the fields and in the streets, we shall fight in the hills; we shall never surrender," said the new British prime minister, Winston Churchill, and his eloquence inspired Americans as well as Britons. But few were truly confident that the British alone could withstand a German onslaught.

Instead of invading Great Britain with land forces, Hitler ordered relentless aerial bombardment of the country while Germany expanded its power to the south. Mussolini's Italy had joined the war against France (forming with Germany the Rome-Berlin Axis) and faced British and Anzac (Australian and New Zealand Army Corps) troops in Libya in North Africa. Then in June 1941, the Führer made what is widely regarded as his greatest strategic blunder: he invaded the Soviet Union.

Stalin, who would later depict himself as the savior of Russia, was oddly unprepared for the onslaught. Soviet forces disintegrated before the German *Wehrmacht* until the fall when, miraculously, the Red Army held. The fighting was barbaric on both sides. Hitler lost 750,000 men in the first year in Russia, more than in the entire war to that point.

Nevertheless, the *Wehrmacht* nearly surrounded Leningrad in the north and threatened Moscow. The next year, 1942, the Germans advanced farther, with Stalingrad in the south the chief objective. There the campaign was halted.

THE UNITED STATES AND THE WAR IN EUROPE

The fall of France, the heroic resistance of Britain, and to a lesser extent the invasion of Russia changed American attitudes toward neutrality. With the exception of neutral Sweden, Switzerland, and Eire, Britain and France were the last democracies in Europe. France was "America's oldest friend," and Britain, if the nation's oldest enemy, was nevertheless the cultural motherland with whom its daughter had largely reconciled.

Moreover, ugly pro-Axis and racist rhetoric in the United States by small but noisy Nazi organizations such as William Dudley Pelley's Silver Shirts and Fritz Kuhn's German-American Bund, as well as German machinations in Latin America, persuaded Americans that Hitler had no intention of stopping in Europe. During the "phony war" in March 1940, only 43 percent of Americans thought that a German victory in Europe would threaten them in any way. By July, almost 80 percent thought so. They viewed Hitler as a madman who wanted to conquer the world.

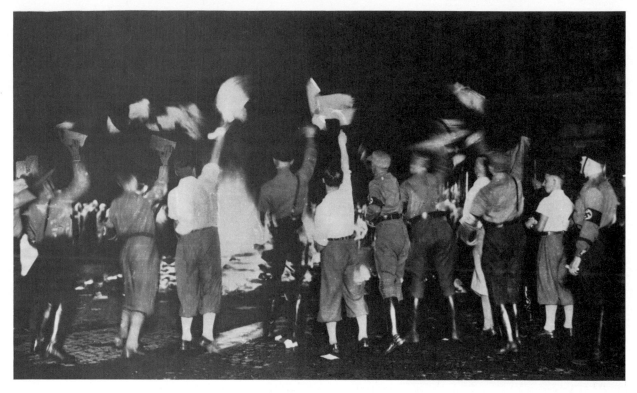

*Nazi repression included destroying ideas as well as people. Here, students burn "subversive"
books in front of the Berlin Opera House, May 1933.*

Roosevelt Leads the Way

Franklin D. Roosevelt played no small part in shaping this change of opinion. As early as 1938, when few Americans could conceive of getting involved in a foreign war, and the French and British governments were appeasing Hitler in the belief that he wanted peace, Roosevelt concluded that only a show of force—or the use of it—would stop the Führer. In this opinion he was one with Winston Churchill, then a bellicose gadfly in Parliament, later the wartime prime minister and F.D.R.'s close personal friend.

But whereas Churchill was in opposition and could snipe at Britain's policy of appeasement, waiting for events to rally public opinion behind him, Roosevelt was president. He could not afford to get too far ahead of the country, least of all in calling for preparation for war. His technique was to float trial balloons by delivering militant anti-Nazi speeches. If the reaction was hostile, he backed down; if friendly, he moved ahead.

In 1939, at F.D.R.'s behest, Congress amended neutrality policy so that war materials could be sold on a cash-and-carry basis. (That is, American ships were still banned from the trade.) In 1940, with a large majority of Americans worried about how a Nazi victory would affect them, he announced that he was trading 50 old destroyers the British needed to counter German submarines for eight naval bases in Bermuda, Newfoundland, and British colonies in the Caribbean. Roosevelt described the deal as a defensive measure and not involvement in the war, which, strictly speaking, was so. Preparedness was also the justification for the Burke-Wadsworth Act of September 1940, which instituted the first peacetime draft law in American history (the term of service was one year) and appropriated $37 billion to build up the navy and army air corps.

It was comparatively easy to win support for these measures. Nevertheless, when Roosevelt decided to break with tradition in 1940 and run for a third term as president, he felt it necessary to assure the American people that "your boys are not going to be sent into any foreign wars."

The Third Term

Despite the shift in public opinion in favor of fighting Hitler, Roosevelt feared that an antiwar Republican candidate might eke out a victory against another less eminent Democrat. (The alternatives to F.D.R. were uninspiring: the tobacco-spitting vice-president, John Nance Garner; Jim Farley, a political manager without a vision in his history; Joseph P. Kennedy, a businessman playboy who thought prejudices were principles.) Indeed, he remembered very well that Woodrow Wilson had won reelection in 1916 only by claiming the antiwar position for himself.

Therefore, Roosevelt blithely ignored the two-term tradition, and the Democrats were delighted with his decision. However, the war versus peace debate never materialized. The Republicans chose a man who did not disagree with Roosevelt on any essentials. Indeed, utilities magnate Wendell Willkie had been a Democrat most of his life. An attractive and personable Indianan who had relocated to Wall Street, Willkie made it clear that he differed only in degree from the popular incumbent.

Thus, Willkie criticized the undeniable waste of many New Deal programs without calling for their abolition. He assailed the vast presidential powers that Roosevelt had assumed as bordering on dictatorship, but he did not propose to dismantle the huge executive apparatus that the New Deal had created. Willkie claimed that he was the better bet to keep the United States out of war, but he did not oppose either arming for defense or aiding Great Britain. In short, he offered Americans the kind of choice that was better resolved by sticking to the leader who was already tested.

Still, Willkie ran a strong race. He captured Maine, Vermont, and eight Midwestern states and more popular votes than any losing candidate to that time, 45 percent of the total. But Roosevelt's popularity was too great to overcome. The president ran an incumbent's campaign. He did his job while the exuberant challenger barnstormed the country. His landmark third-term reelection, which broke the tradition established by Washington and Jefferson and challenged by only Grant and Theodore Roosevelt, was an anticlimax, and it did not interrupt the nation's drift toward war.

Undeclared War on Germany

A few weeks after the election, Roosevelt responded to Winston Churchill's plea for additional aid by sending the lend-lease bill to Congress. As enacted, Lend-Lease provided that the United States would serve as the "arsenal of democracy," turning out arms of all sorts to be "loaned" to Britain. Eventually, with lend-lease extended to the Soviet Union, such aid totaled $54 billion.

Because no amount of aid in materiel could help the British defend their shipping against "wolf packs" of German submarines, Roosevelt proclaimed a neutral zone that extended from North American waters to Ice-

LEND-LEASE

Britain could not afford to pay for the destroyers that Winston Churchill requested at the end of 1940. Britain had spent $4.5 billion in the United States for arms, and in December 1940 had only $2 billion in reserve. Roosevelt explained the "loan" of the ships to Britain with the follow parable:

Suppose my neighbor's house catches fire, and I have a length of garden hose. If he can take my garden hose and connect it up with his hydrant, I may help him to put out the fire.

Now what do I do? I don't say to him before that operation, "Neighbor, my garden hose cost me $15; you have to pay me $15 for it." What is the transaction that goes on? I don't want $15—I want my garden hose back after the fire is over.

land. He sent troops to Greenland, a possession of conquered Denmark, and ordered American destroyers to patrol the sea lanes, warning British ships of enemies beneath the waves. This permitted the British to concentrate their navy in the waters around their home islands.

The United States was at war in everything but name. Indeed, in August 1941, Roosevelt met with Churchill on two ships, the British *Prince of Wales* and the American *Augusta*, a cruiser, off the coast of Newfoundland. There they adopted what amounted to mutual war aims patterned after Wilson's Fourteen Points.

The Atlantic Charter called for self-determination of nations after the war; free trade and freedom of the seas; the disarmament of aggressor nations; and some new means of collective world security, a provision that would evolve into the United Nations.

It was only a matter of time before guns were fired. After a few ambivalent incidents involving German submarines and American destroyers, the *U.S.S. Reuben James* was sunk in October 1941 with a loss of 100 sailors. Prowar sentiment flamed higher.

A Nasty Debate

Roosevelt still did not ask Congress for a formal declaration of war. He hoped that Britain and the Soviet Union could defeat Germany without the expenditure of American lives, a commodity with which every wartime American president since Lincoln had been cautious. More important, Roosevelt did not want to go to war without a unified nation behind him. By the autumn of 1941, he had his majority. Most Americans had concluded, without enthusiasm but with resolve, that Hitler must be stopped at any cost. Even the Communist party,

HOW THEY LIVED

RATIONING AND SCRAP DRIVES

German submarines set a pair of four-man saboteur teams ashore in Florida and on Long Island. (They were immediately captured.) Japanese subs ran a few torpedoes up on California beaches, and several paper bombs, explosives held aloft and pushed by winds, detonated over Texas. Otherwise, the continental United States was physically untouched by the war that devastated most of Europe, half of China, and the cities of Japan. Considering the colossal scale of the American material contribution to the war, it is a remarkable testament to the nation's wealth that people on the home front experienced the war only in the form of shortages in consumer commodities and then not to a degree that could be called sacrifice.

Because the Japanese quickly gained control of 97 percent of the world's rubber-tree plantations in Malaya, automobile tires were the first consumer goods to be taken off the market. Washington froze the sale of new tires and forbade recapping early in 1942; the armed forces badly needed tires, and the national stockpile of rubber was only 660,000 tons, or just about what civilians consumed in a year. Huge quantities were collected in a scrap drive. One Seattle shoemaker contributed 6 tons of worn rubber heels that he had saved, and a Los Angeles tire dealer provided 5,000 tons of trade-ins. People cleared closets of old overshoes, and the Secretary of the Interior took to picking up rubber doormats in federal office buildings. Unfortunately, reclaimed rubber was not suitable to tire manufacture, and doormats were usually made of previously reclaimed rubber, so they were not particularly suitable for new doormats.

It was fear of a rubber rather than a gasoline shortage that accounted for the first controls on driving, although, on the east coast, which was dependent on tanker imports, gasoline was also short by the summer of 1942. The president proclaimed a nationwide speed limit of 35 miles per hour, and pleasure driving was banned. (Zealous officials of the Office of Price Administration jotted down license numbers at picnics, race tracks, concert halls, and athletic events.) In addition, the total miles a car could be driven was limited by the category of sticker issued to each owner. Ordinary motorists received "A" cards, entitling them to four gallons of gasoline a week, later three, and for a short time only two. A "B" card added a few gallons; these were issued to workers in defense plants for whom driving to work was necessary. Physicians and others whose driving was essential got "C" cards, a few more gallons. Truckers ("T") got unlimited gas, as did some others, including political bigwigs who got "X" cards (a source of resentment). Counterfeiting and selling of gas cards (usually "C" category) was common, as was theft from government warehouses. The OPA discovered that 20 million gallons' worth of cards were stolen in Washington alone.

Surplus gasoline could not be collected, but just about every other commodity that was vital to the war effort could be and was. Community organizations like the Boy Scouts sponsored scrap drives through 1942 and 1943, collecting iron, steel, brass, bronze, tin, nylon stockings (for powder bags), bacon grease (for munitions manufacture), and waste paper. Many of these campaigns were more trouble than they were worth, but not those that collected iron, steel, tin, and paper. Scrap iron and steel made a significant contribution to the national output, and about half of the tin and paper products came not from mines and forests but from neighborhood drives. So assiduous were the Boy Scouts in their scrap-paper drive of 1942 that in June the government had to call a halt to

which had opposed American intervention until Hitler invaded the Soviet Union, was now in the prowar camp, and much of the Eastern big-business establishment had concluded that Hitler represented a threat to American commercial primacy in the world.

There was, however, an opposition. Roosevelt did not worry about the antiwar agitation of extremist Hitler supporters such as Father Coughlin and members of the Bund and Silver Shirts. But he was concerned about the old-fashioned isolationists who formed the well-financed and active America First Committee. Former president Herbert Hoover, ex-New Dealer Hugh Johnson, and progressive intellectuals such as Charles A. Beard despised Hitlerism. Whatever hostility toward Great Britain they harbored was aimed at British imperialism; they feared that the United States would go to war to protect the British Empire, an unworthy goal in their eyes. Their priority in supporting the America First Committee was to avoid making the mistake of 1917 as they saw it—pulling British chestnuts out of the fire.

The America First Committee's case was weakened because most of its members agreed that the United States should arm for defense. Roosevelt and the rival Committee to Defend America by Aiding the Allies described every contribution to the British cause in just such terms, and this justification confounded the isolationists. Nevertheless, Roosevelt hesitated. He confided to Winston Churchill that he would not ask for war until some dramatic incident—in other words, a direct attack on the United States—rallied the America Firsters to his cause.

As it turned out, the bitter debate over intervention missed the point. Both sides in the argument trained their eyes on Europe and the Atlantic as the crisis area.

it; the nation's paper mills simply could not keep up with the supply of "raw materials."

The tin shortage was responsible for the rationing of canned goods. In order to buy a can of corn or sardines, as well as coffee, butter, cheese, meat, and many other food items, a consumer had to hand the grocer ration stamps as well as money. These stamps were issued regularly in books and served as a second, parallel currency. In order to buy a pound of hamburger, a shopper needed stamps worth 7 "points" as well as the purchase price. A pound of butter cost 16 points; a pound of cheese, 8 points; and so on. The tiny stamps—which were color-coded red (meat, butter), blue (processed food), green, and brown— were a tremendous bother. More than 3.5 billion of them changed hands every month. In order to restock shelves, a grocer had to turn in the stamps to a wholesaler, who, in turn, had to deposit them with a bank in order to make additional purchases.

Everyone had a complaint of one sort or another, although, except for butter, the allotments were not stringent. For example, the weekly sugar ration was 8 ounces a person, about as much as a dentist would wish on a patient in the best of times. In 1943, the standard of living was 16 percent higher than it had been in 1939, and by 1945, despite rationing, Americans were eating more food and spending more money on it than ever before. Among the major foods, only butter consumption dropped appreciably, from seventeen to eleven pounds per capita per year, and some home economists believed that because of butter rationing, a larger proportion of the population was eating it.

In fact, the OPA noticed a curious fact about consumer habits in the cases of coffee and cigarettes. Coffee was rationed because of the shortage of ships available to carry it from South America. When rationing began in November 1942 (one pound a person per five weeks), people began to hoard it. At restaurants, some diners would trade their dessert for an extra cup. When rationing of coffee was dropped in July 1943, sales of coffee dropped! Then, in the autumn of 1943, when a coffee stamp was inadvertently included in ration books, Americans anticipated that coffee would be rationed again and stripped the market shelves bare. When the OPA announced that there would be no coffee ration, sales dropped again.

Cigarettes were rationed because 30 percent of the industry's production was reserved for the armed forces, which comprised only 10 percent of the population. The government was, in effect, subsidizing the smoking habit among the men and women in the service. At home, the operation of the principle that scarcity equals status may also have caused an increase in the incidence of the bad habit.

A much more salutary consequence of wartime shortages was the popularity of gardening. There was no shortage of fresh vegetables, and they were never rationed. But because canned vegetables were and because truck and train space was invaluable, the government encouraged the planting of Victory gardens. Some 20.5 million individuals and families planted them, and by 1945, consumers were raising between 30 and 40 percent of all the vegetables grown in the United States. Nutritionists recognized that this was paying dividends in the national diet, but when the war was over, Americans quickly shed their good taste. By 1950, they had returned to canned vegetables and to the frozen products of Clarence Birdseye.

The dramatic incident was to occur in the Pacific, where Japan moved into the former French colonies of Indochina and continued its war against the indecisive government of Chiang Kai-shek. War in Asia was an old story. It seemed reasonable to conclude that it would go on indefinitely without a decisive turn in either direction. Roosevelt took a tougher line toward Japan after the occupation of Indochina, and negotiations with Tokyo continued into the summer and autumn of 1941.

AMERICA GOES TO WAR

All the while the Japanese "peace party," headed by Prince Fumimaro Konoye, continued to negotiate during the summer of 1941, the prowar faction of the imperial government, headed by General Hideki Tojo, increased its influence. When he was named premier in October 1941, Tojo gave the negotiators until early November to come up with a formula for peace that the United States would accept. But the minimum Japanese demand that Japan be recognized as the dominant economic power in China could not be reconciled with the Open Door Policy, to which the United States was deeply committed.

Pearl Harbor

Curiously, the Japanese and American governments concluded on the same day that they were unlikely to resolve their differences peacefully. Talks continued, but Secretary of State Hull told the War Department that it

Destruction of the American fleet at Pearl Harbor, December 7, 1941.

should take over responsibility for Japanese-American relations, and military commanders in the Pacific were warned that hostilities could begin at any minute. In fact, the Japanese had initiated preparations for attack that could not easily be reversed.

On December 7, 1941, it was launched. Admiral Iso-roku Yamamoto, a tragic figure who admired the United States and feared the result of a war he did not want, engineered a tactically brilliant aerial attack on Pearl Harbor, the huge American naval base on Oahu in the Hawaiian Islands. His planes sank or badly damaged 8 battleships, 7 other vessels, and 188 airplanes, and killed or wounded 3,435 servicemen. Yamamoto did not fully join in the celebrations that swept over his fleet and the people of Japan. The three American aircraft carriers that he believed would be at Pearl Harbor were at sea when the assault force arrived and thus escaped unscathed.

Yamamoto understood that air power was the key to war in the broad Pacific, and fretted about his bad luck. As a one-time resident of the United States, he also appreciated better than did the Tojo group how great American industrial might was compared with Japan's.

"I fear we have only awakened a sleeping giant," he told his officers, "and his reaction will be terrible."

The Reaction

The wounded giant awakened with a start. Pearl Harbor was attacked on Sunday. The next day, Roosevelt went before Congress and described December 7, 1941, as "a day that will live in infamy." He got his unanimous vote, or very nearly so. In both houses of Congress, only Representative Jeannette Rankin of Montana, a pacifist who had voted against entry into the First World War, refused to endorse the declaration of war.

In every city in the nation during the next several weeks, the army's and navy's enlistment offices were jammed with stunned and angry young men. Pearl Harbor was so traumatic an event in the lives of Americans that practically every individual remembered exactly what he or she had been doing when news of the attack was announced.

Quietly at the time, more publicly later, Roosevelt's critics accused him and other top officials of having plotted to keep Pearl Harbor and nearby Hickham Field,

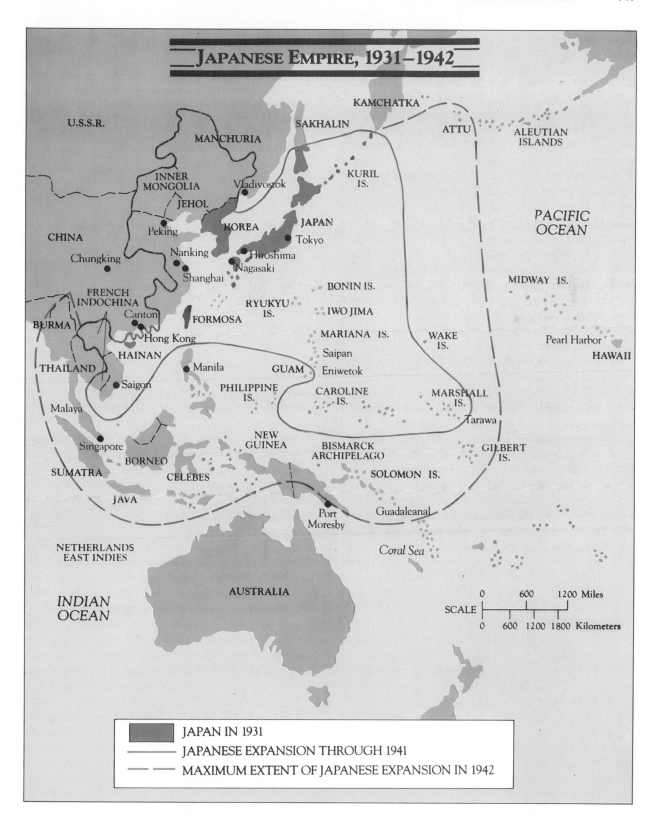

JAPANESE EMPIRE, 1931–1942

U.S.S.R.

MANCHURIA

KAMCHATKA

SAKHALIN

ATTU

ALEUTIAN
ISLANDS

INNER
MONGOLIA

Vladivostok

KOREA

KURIL
IS.

JEHOL

CHINA

Peking

Nanking

JAPAN

Tokyo

Chungking

Hiroshima

Shanghai

Nagasaki

PACIFIC
OCEAN

FRENCH
INDOCHINA

Canton

FORMOSA

RYUKYU
IS.

BONIN IS.

IWO JIMA

MIDWAY IS.

BURMA

Hong Kong

HAINAN

MARIANA IS.

Saipan

WAKE
IS.

Pearl Harbor

THAILAND

Saigon

Manila

GUAM

Eniwetok

HAWAII

Malaya

PHILIPPINE
IS.

CAROLINE
IS.

MARSHALL
IS.

Singapore

Tarawa

SUMATRA

BORNEO

NEW
GUINEA

BISMARCK
ARCHIPELAGO

GILBERT
IS.

CELEBES

SOLOMON IS.

JAVA

Port
Moresby

Guadalcanal

NETHERLANDS
EAST INDIES

Coral Sea

INDIAN
OCEAN

AUSTRALIA

SCALE

0   600   1200 Miles

0   600   1200   1800 Kilometers

JAPAN IN 1931

JAPANESE EXPANSION THROUGH 1941

MAXIMUM EXTENT OF JAPANESE EXPANSION IN 1942

an air base, completely unprepared for the attack. It was said that Washington knew the assault was coming but withheld vital intelligence from Hawaii, sacrificing thousands of American lives for the political purpose of getting the United States into the war.

In truth, the lack of preparation at Pearl Harbor was stupid and shameful. As early as 1924, air-power advocate Billy Mitchell had said that Pearl Harbor was vulnerable to air attack. In 1932, Admiral Harry Yarnell had snuck two aircraft carriers and four cruisers to within bombing range of Oahu before he was detected. Had his force been hostile, an attack comparable to that of December 7, 1941, would have ensued. In early December 1941, numerous indications that something was brewing either were ignored or reached the appropriate commanders after unjustifiable delays. At Hickham Field, fighter planes were drawn up wing tip to wing tip so that they could be protected against sabotage on the ground. This made destruction from the air all the simpler, and, even after the attack began, it was difficult to get the fighters into the air.

But to say that there was a deliberate conspiracy among the highest ranking officials in the United States government was absurd, an example of the paranoia that periodically taints American politics. The blunders of the military in Hawaii were just another example of the chronic incompetence inherent in all large organizations, and the key to the stunning Japanese victory was the brilliant planning behind it.

Nevertheless, there is no doubt that Roosevelt was relieved to get officially into the conflict with a united people behind him. He was totally convinced by December 1941 that the survival of democracy, freedom, and American influence in the world depended on the total defeat of the aggressor nations, which only American might could ensure.

Getting the Job Done

Of all the nations that went to war, only Japan, whose participation in the First World War had been nominal, celebrated at the start of it. In Europe and the United States, there was very little of the exuberance with which people had greeted the first days of the fighting in World War I. Among Americans, the attitude was that there was a job to be done.

The popular songs of the period were concerned with getting home again. There was a melancholy tenor to "I'll Be Seeing You" and "I'll Never Smile Again." The lyrics told of the sadness of separation, however necessary it might be. Few people were attracted by the foot-stomping patriotism of George M. Cohan's "Over There," the American anthem during the First World War.

OLD PERSONAL FRIENDS

Kichisaburo Nomura, the Japanese ambassador to the United States during 1941, had known President Roosevelt personally for 25 years. Nomura had been naval attaché at the Japanese embassy during the First World War, when Roosevelt had been Undersecretary of the Navy.

Once in the service, soldiers and sailors referred to the conflict as "W-W-2," a sardonically mechanical (or perhaps bureaucratic) description of a war that was reminiscent of the name of a New Deal public works project. Indeed, because the country had been through it before, and because the New Deal reforms had introduced the idea of government-supervised order to the national economy, mobilization of resources and people was far more orderly and effective than it had been 25 years earlier.

Organizing for Victory

The mobilization of fighting capacity began before Pearl Harbor. By December 1941, more than 1.5 million men were in uniform. By the end of the war, the total number of soldiers, sailors, and airmen, and women in auxiliary corps in every service climbed to 15 million.

The draft accounted for the majority of these "GI's," a name that referred to the "government issue" designation of uniforms and other equipage. Boards made up of local civic leaders worked efficiently and with comparatively few irregularities to fill the armed forces. The "Friends and Neighbors" who informed young men of their fate with the salutation "Greetings" exempted only the physically disabled and those with work skills designated as essential to the war effort, including farmers and agricultural workers. As time passed, another sad category of those exempted was adopted: "sole surviving sons," men of draft age all of whose brothers had been killed in action. In the windows of homes which lost a soldier, small red, white, and blue banners, with stars enumerating the loss, were sometimes hung. The lady of the house was called a "Gold Star Mother."

Money was mobilized too. When the war began, the government was spending $2 billion a month on the military. During the first half of 1942, the expenditure rose to $15 billion a month. By the time Japan surrendered in August 1945, the costs of the war totaled more than $300 billion. In less than four years, the American government spent more money than it had spent during the previous 150 years of national existence. The national debt, already considered high in 1941 at $48 billion, doubled and redoubled to $247 billion in 1945.

Instead of building automobiles, this Chrysler assembly line turned out tanks for the war effort.

A few businessmen continued to oppose government policy, particularly the wartime labor laws. One of the most graceless was Sewell L. Avery, head of the huge retail chain store Montgomery Ward. Roosevelt's policies had saved his company from bankruptcy, and during the war, full employment in the work force resulted in bonanza profits for retailers like him. But Avery had to be carried bodily to jail for refusing to obey a law that guaranteed his employees the right to join a union.

He was not typical. Most big-business men, including former opponents of the administration, accepted unionization and rushed to Washington to assist the government. They were responding in part to the need for national unity. Corporation executives also recognized that wartime expenditures meant prosperity. General Motors, for example, received 8 percent of all federal expenditures between 1941 and 1945, $1 of every $12.50 that the government spent.

Few criticisms came from the General Motors boardroom. Indeed, General Motors president William S.

Knudsen was one of the most prominent "dollar-a-year men," business executives who worked for Roosevelt in effect without pay. He headed the War Resources Board (W.R.B.), which had been established in August 1939 to plan for the conversion of factories for military production in the event of war. There was a bit of cynical palaver about the patriotic sacrifice dollar-a-year men were making but the country did need their organizational skills.

New Alphabet Agencies

After the congressional elections of 1942, which brought many conservative Republicans to Washington, Roosevelt announced that "Dr. New Deal" had been dismissed from the country's case and "Dr. Win-the-War" had been engaged. He explained that since there was now full employment, social programs were no longer necessary.

However, the New Dealers' practice of establishing

Henry J. Kaiser mass produced cheap Liberty ships that permitted the United States to fight a two-theater war.

government agencies to oversee public affairs was vastly expanded. In addition to Knudsen's W.R.B., the Supplies Priorities and Allocation Board (S.P.A.B.), under Donald M. Nelson of Sears Roebuck and Company, was commissioned to ensure that raw materials, particularly the scarce and critical ones, were diverted to military industries. The Office of Price Administration (O.P.A.) had the task of controlling consumer prices so that the combination of high wages and scarce goods did not lead to runaway inflation.

After Pearl Harbor, a National War Labor Board (N.W.L.B.) was set up to mediate industrial disputes. Its principal purposes were to guarantee that production was not interrupted and that wage increases were kept within government-set limits. This offended many of Roosevelt's former supporters in the labor movement, none of them more important than John L. Lewis of the United Mine Workers, who returned to the Republican party. But the N.W.L.B. also worked to ensure that employees were not gouged by avaricious employers. The board was reasonably successful. There were strikes, including a serious one led by Lewis in 1943. But labor relations were generally good, and union membership continued to rise.

The Office of War Mobilization (O.W.M.) was the most important of the new alphabet agencies. Theoretically, it oversaw all aspects of the mobilized economy, as Bernard Baruch had done during the First World War. It was considered to be sufficiently important that James F. Byrnes of South Carolina resigned from the Supreme Court to head it as a kind of "assistant president." Many believed that Byrnes's contribution to the war effort earned him the right to a presidential nomination.

Success

In essentials, Dr. Win-the-War's treatment was an overwhelming success. The size of the federal government swelled at a dizzying rate, from 1.1 million civilian employees in 1940 to 3.3 million in 1945. (State governments grew at almost the same rate.) Inevitably there was waste (agencies doing the same thing), inefficiency (agencies fighting at cross-purposes with one another), and corruption (many unessential jobs). But with national unity and military victory constantly touted as essential, the few critics of wartime problems, such as Senator Robert A. Taft of Ohio, sounded petty and were unable to carry the day. Taft was a carper. The most effective check on waste, inefficiency, and corruption, the Senate War Investigating Committee, was headed by a Democratic New Dealer, Senator Harry S Truman of Missouri.

The lessons learned during the First World War and the administrative skills of dollar-a-year businessmen and bureaucrats trained in the New Deal worked wonders on production. New factories and those formerly given to the manufacture of America's automobiles canceled civilian production and churned out trucks, tanks, the versatile jeeps, and amphibious vehicles in incredible numbers. In 1944 alone, 96,000 airplanes (260 per day) rolled out of American factories. Industrialist Henry J. Kaiser perfected an assembly line for producing simple but serviceable freighters, the so-called liberty ships. By 1943, his mammoth yards were christening a new one every day. Altogether, American shipbuilders sent 10 million tons of shipping down the ways between 1941 and 1945.

Such statistics would have been regarded as pipe dreams before the war. But they were duplicated in every basic industry, including steel, rubber, glass, aluminum, and electronics.

The Workers

Unemployment vanished as a social problem. Instead, factories running at capacity had difficulty finding people to fill jobs. There was a significant shift of population to the West Coast as the demands of the Pacific war led to the concentration of defense industries in such ports as Seattle, Oakland, San Diego, and Long Beach.

LIBERTY SHIPS

Mass production means making something no better than it has to be in order to function. The idea is to turn the product out in vast numbers, quickly and cheaply. Mass production is, obviously, the basis of the high standard of living enjoyed by the masses of people in the United States and other advanced nations. However, one of the most amazing applications of the principle was not in the manufacture of consumer goods, but of the "liberty ship," a freighter built to carry the goods of war.

Liberty ships were "no frills" boxcars of the seas, 441 feet long, 57 feet across the beam, with a rudimentary engine. Some 800 of them were lost during the war, most to enemy action, but more than a few as the victims of storms. Because they were welded rather than riveted together, liberty ships were not the sturdiest of vessels.

But welding was what made it possible for American shipyards employing men and women who had never before built ships to float a liberty ship in as few as 40 days after the keel was laid. Some 2,700 were built between 1941 and 1944. Toward the end of the war, several rolled down the ways each day. Liberty ships were so cheap that if one completed a single voyage (carrying freight enough to fill 300 railroad cars), it paid for itself. Their design was such a masterpiece of simplicity that, with just a few old salts aboard, inexperienced crews of 45 (plus 35 navy gunners) could sail them.

Among the new Californians (the population of the Golden State rose from 6.9 million in 1940 to 10.5 million in 1950) were hundreds of thousands of blacks. Finding well-paid factory jobs that previously had been closed to them, blacks also won a sense of security, which had been unknown to earlier generations, because of the generally antiracist policies of the young C.I.O. unions and F.D.R.'s executive order in 1941 that war contractors observe fair practices in employing blacks.

Economic equality for African Americans remained a long way in the future. Everywhere they went, Blacks found resentments and discrimination, and serious race riots in 1943. Nevertheless, prodded by Eleanor Roosevelt and pressured by influential black leaders such as A. Philip Randolph of the Brotherhood of Sleeping Car Porters, F.D.R. issued an executive order forbidding racial discrimination in companies that benefited from government contracts.

Women, including many of middle age who never had worked for wages, entered the work force in large numbers. The symbol of the woman performing "unwomanly" work was "Rosie the Riveter," assembling airplanes and tanks with heavy riveting guns. Indeed, women did perform just about every kind of job in the industrial economy. Rosie dressed in slacks, tied up her hair in a bandanna, and left her children with her mother. But off the job, she remained reassuringly feminine by the standards of the time.

Curiously, these genuinely independent women did not turn to traditional feminism. Comparatively little was heard of demands for equality during the war. On the contrary, woman after woman told newspaper reporters that she looked forward to the end of the war, when she could quit her job to return home as wife and mother within the traditional family system. There were exceptions, of course. Many women enjoyed the economic and social freedom. For the most part, however, the female wartime workers were an ideal wartime work force: intelligent, educated, energetic, impelled by patriotism, and generally uninterested in competing with the soldiers who eventually would come back and take their jobs.

Prosperity at a Price

Labor shortages inevitably produced a demand for higher wages. The unions grew stronger; membership rose from 10.5 million to 14.7 million. With a few exceptions, however, strikes were short and did not disrupt production. The N.W.L.B. mediated disputes, generally keeping raises within the limit of 15 percent over prewar levels that the government had set as an acceptable standard. This made the task of the O.P.A. all the easier.

The success of the O.P.A. was remarkable. Coveted consumer goods—coffee, butter, sugar, some canned foods, meat, shoes, liquor, silk, rayon, and nylon—were scarce because of rationing, but high wages gave workers the money to spend on what there was. (Real wages rose 50 percent during the war.) There was a black market, or illegal sale of rationed goods, but it never got out of control, and prices rose only moderately between 1942 and 1945. Instead of consuming wholesale, Americans pumped their wages into savings accounts, including $15 billion in loans to the government in the form of war bonds. It became a point of patriotic pride with some women to paint the seam of a nylon stocking on the calf of a naked leg (although a pair of real stockings remained a treasure).

There was an element of good-humored innocence in the way Americans fought the Second World War. If they did not believe that a world free of problems would follow victory, which few doubted lay ahead, Americans were confident that they and their allies were in the right. By the time the fighting was over, 290,000 Americans were dead. But shocking as that figure is at first glance, and bloody as some individual battles were, American suffering was insignificant compared with that of other nations. Indeed, keeping the casualty list short was one of Roosevelt's priorities throughout the conflict, and he succeeded. If Winston Churchill was right in describing the year 1940, when the British stood alone against Nazism, as "their finest hour," the Second World War was an hour of confidence and pride for Americans too, particularly in view of the difficult depression era that had preceded the war and the age of anxiety that was to follow.

For Further Reading

General studies of foreign policy during the 1930s are numerous. The following are among the most useful: Selig Adler, *Uncertain Giant: American Foreign Policy Between the Wars* (1966); Charles A. Beard, *American Foreign Policy in the Making, 1932–1940* (1946); Paul Conkin, *The New Deal* (1975); Robert Dallek, *Franklin D. Roosevelt and American Foreign Policy, 1932–1945* (1979); R. H. Ferrell, *American Diplomacy in the Great Depression: Hoover-Stimson Foreign Policy, 1929–1933* (1957); William E. Leuchtenburg, *Franklin D. Roosevelt and the New Deal, 1932–1940* (1963); and John E. Wiltz, *From Isolationism to War, 1931–1941* (1968). A book that has profoundly influenced the writing of diplomatic history in the United States in our time is William A. Williams, *The Tragedy of American Diplomacy* (1962).

More intensively focused are W. S. Cole, *America First: The Battle Against Intervention* (1953); Robert A. Divine, *The Illusion of Neutrality* (1962); Lloyd C. Gardner, *Economic Aspects of New Deal Diplomacy* (1964); Walter Johnson, *The Battle Against Isolationism* (1944); Manfred Jonas, *Isolationism in America, 1935–1941* (1966); Warren F. Kimball, *The Most Unsordid Act: Lend-Lease, 1939–1941* (1969); Basil Rauch, *Roosevelt: From Munich to Pearl Harbor* (1950); E. E. Robinson, *The Roosevelt Leadership* (1955); and Bryce Wood, *The Making of the Good Neighbor Policy* (1961).

Unsurprisingly, American-Japanese relations in the years leading up to Pearl Harbor have been extensively studied and yet remain a highly controversial subject. Just a few of the many books on the subject are Robert J. Burtow, *Tojo and the Coming of War* (1961); Herbert Feis, *The Road to Pearl Harbor* (1950); Akira Iriye, *After Imperialism: The Search for a New Order in the Far East, 1921–1933* (1965); Gordon W. Prange, *At Dawn We*

Slept: The Untold Story of Pearl Harbor (1981); and Robert Wohlsetter, *Pearl Harbor: Warning and Decision* (1962).

Biographical studies of key players in making foreign policy in this era are James MacGregor Burns, *Roosevelt: The Soldier of Freedom* (1970); Wayne S. Cole, *Gerald P.* *Nye and American Foreign Relations* (1962); Richard N. Current, *Secretary Stimson: A Study in Statecraft* (1954); Elting E. Morison, *Turmoil and Tradition: A Study of the Life and Times of Henry L. Stimson* (1960); and J. W. Pratt, *Cordell Hull* (1964).

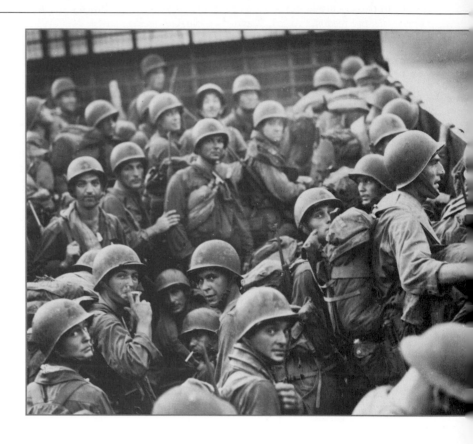

American troops approaching a Pacific beachhead during the Second World War.

AMERICA'S GREAT WAR

The United States at the Pinnacle of Power 1942 - 1945

Nazi Germany was defeated by British pluck, Russian blood, and American industrial might. By holding out alone against Hitler in 1940 and 1941, Britain prevented him from establishing an impregnable Nazi "Fortress Europe" in the West. The British saved the foothold that made an invasion of continental Europe possible. In sustaining appalling casualties—26 million people dead—the Soviet Union slowly sapped the might of the German *Wehrmacht*. The contribution of the United States was to keep both Britain and Russia afloat with Lend-Lease and, beginning in 1942, to turn the tide with the full force of the world's most powerful economy. The Pacific war against Imperial Japan—a huge effort in itself—was almost entirely an American show.

American strategists designed most of the formula that won World War II. American military administrators oversaw the huge and intricate apparatus of two military operations of unprecedented scale. Without the full participation of the United States, Germany and Japan might have been fought to a standstill. But they could not have been defeated. World War II was America's "Great War," the victory perhaps the chief contribution of the United States to Western civilization.

STOPPING JAPAN

As in World War I, the United States itself was not a battlefield in World War II, but Americans knew that they were in a fight between December 1941 and August 1945. Adults of the era were to remember—were to mark passages in their lives—by the dramatic events of the conflict: the day Pearl Harbor was attacked, D-Day when the invasion of Nazi-dominated Europe began, the day Franklin D. Roosevelt died, V-E Day and V-J Day, when Germany and Japan finally surrendered. The memories ended up sweet, to sustain the faith of a generation that their lives had meaning; but the memories began with defeat.

Humiliation and Anger

The first months after Pearl Harbor brought nothing but bad news to the United States. Immediately after Admiral Yamamoto paralyzed the American Pacific Fleet, the Japanese army advanced easily into Malaya, Hong Kong, the Philippines, Java, and Guam. Within a few weeks, the dramatic Japanese battle flag, rays emanating from the rising sun, snapped in the breezes of British Singapore and Burma, and the Dutch East Indies, present-day Indonesia.

There was heroism in the disaster. On the principal island of the Philippines, Luzon, 20,000 crusty GI's under General Douglas MacArthur and a larger force of Filipinos fought valiantly on the Bataan Peninsula and the rocky island of Corregidor in Manila Bay. At first the men, most of them professional soldiers, thought they would be relieved or evacuated. Slowly the sickening truth sank in: they were quite alone, isolated by an ocean from a helpless navy, the doomed "battling bastards of Bataan." Nevertheless, they grimly accepted the thankless, hopeless task of delaying the Japanese.

General MacArthur did not stay. Once President Roosevelt realized that the Philippines must fall, he ordered the nation's best-known general to flee to Australia. F.D.R. must have been tempted to let MacArthur fall into Japanese hands. He disliked and distrusted the general; as early as 1934 the president named MacArthur as one of the two most dangerous men in the United States, a threat to constitutional government. Indeed, outside a coterie of doggedly devoted aides, MacArthur riled much of the American military establishment. He was an egomaniac and a posturer, carefully cultivating an image complete with props—sunglasses, corncob pipe—a cooler "American" version of Benito Mussolini. "I studied dramatics under MacArthur," General Dwight D. Eisenhower wryly remarked.

Nevertheless, MacArthur was one of the army's senior professionals and F.D.R. believed him essential to winning the war against Japan. His connection with the Philippines was lifelong, intimate, and genuinely affectionate; his father had been military governor of the colony. When MacArthur fled the islands, he promoted his mystique and inspired the Philippine resistance, which proved to be heroic, with a radio message that concluded, "I shall return."

On May 6, the last ragged defenders of Corregidor surrendered. Humiliation in the worst military defeat in the nation's history gave way to furious anger when reports trickled into the United States of Japanese cruelty toward the prisoners on the infamous Bataan Death March. Of 10,000 men forced to walk to a prison camp in the interior, 1,000 died on the way. (Another 5,000 of the captives died in the camps before the war was over.)

Japanese Strategy

While the siege of Corregidor dragged on, the Japanese piled up victories elsewhere in South Asia and Oceania. Under the command of Admiral Yamamoto, Japanese strategy was to establish a defense perimeter of fortified islands distant enough from Japan that the Americans, upon recuperating from Pearl Harbor, could not bomb Japan's home islands or force a battle in which the Japanese could be decisively defeated. Then, Japanese policy-makers believed, they could negotiate a peace that left Japan in control of the resources of China and South Asia.

By early May 1942, the first phase of the plan—establishment of a distant perimeter—seemed near completion. Japanese soldiers occupied the Solomon Islands and most of New Guinea. At Port Moresby, however, Australian and American forces halted the advance, preventing for the time being any serious assault on Australia. Yamamoto then moved his fleet, as yet unscarred, to the Coral Sea off Australia's northeastern coast. His object was to cut supply lines between Hawaii

American soldiers surrender to the Japanese on the Philippine island of Corregidor in one of the bitterest military defeats in U.S. history.

and Australia, thus choking off the resistance in New Guinea.

The Coral Sea and Midway

On May 6 and 7, 1942, the Japanese and American fleets fought a stand-off battle. The battle of the Coral Sea was a unique naval encounter in that the ships of the opposing forces never steamed within sight of one another. Carrier-based aircraft did the fighting, against one another and against enemy vessels. The Japanese lost fewer ships and planes than the Americans, but the battle was no Japanese victory. Yamamoto felt obliged to abandon his plan to cut the southern shipping lanes between Hawaii and Australia. Instead, he looked to the central Pacific where Japanese supply lines were more secure. His object in the Central Pacific was the American naval and air base on the two tiny islands of Midway, about a thousand miles northwest of Hawaii. A base on Midway would secure half the ocean for Japan.

But there, between June 3 and June 6, 1942, the Japanese suffered a critical defeat. The American fleet under Admirals Raymond A. Spruance and Frank J. Fletcher lost the carrier *Yorktown* to Japanese dive bombers and torpedos. However, American planes destroyed four Japanese carriers.

It was far more than a one-for-four trade. Unlike the United States, Japan lacked the wealth and industrial capacity to replace so fabulously expensive a vessel as an aircraft carrier. Japan's offensive capacity was smashed just seven months after Pearl Harbor. Moreover, by holding Midway, the Americans controled the Central Pacific. Much earlier than he had planned, and closer to Japan than he had hoped, Yamamoto had to shift to defending what the Japanese had won.

The great commander did not live to see the disastrous end of the war that he had, in effect, predicted. By 1943, the Americans had cracked the Japanese navy's communications code and learned that Yamamoto would be flying over Bougainville in the Solomon Islands. They shot down his plane, and Yamamoto was killed. Japan never produced another naval commander of his sagacity nor, during the war, another statesman of his moderation and good sense.

Anti-Japanese Hysteria

Not even the megalomaniacs among Japan's military rulers seriously entertained the possibility of invading the United States. Nevertheless, the stunning Japanese victories of early 1942 and the success of a few submarines in torpedoing ships off the beaches of Oregon and

California caused ripples of invasion hysteria to wash over the Hawaiian Islands and the Pacific states. Newspaper magnate William Randolph Hearst, who had baited the Japanese with racial insults for 50 years, deluded himself into believing that his person was a prime Japanese target. He hurriedly moved out of San Simeon, his fantastic castle on an isolated stretch of the central California coast, for safer haunts inland. Humbler but equally nervous citizens organized patrols to keep an eye on the surf from the Canadian border to San Diego. For a few days, much of Los Angeles was on edge.

In many California, Oregon, and Washington communities, anger over Pearl Harbor coalesced with long-standing racial resentments of Japanese-Americans to result in spontaneous outbreaks of violence. Gangs of teenage toughs (and grown men) beat up Japanese and other Asians. People of Chinese and Korean descent took to wearing buttons identifying their origins in order to avoid problems.

West Coast politicians called for the internment of Japanese-born non-citizens (known as *Issei*) and even their native-born children, the *Nisei*. At first, officials of the Justice Department resisted them. Various investigations before the war had revealed that only a few Japanese-Americans, most of whom were known to the Federal Bureau of Investigation, were disloyal and might represent a threat of sabotage. Even the Japanese consul in Los Angeles had advised Tokyo that no help would be forthcoming from the Japanese-American community.

But when the Attorney-General, soon to be governor of California, Earl Warren, and the commanding general at San Francisco's Presidio joined the anti-Japanese clamor, Roosevelt gave in. Executive Order 9066 defined coastal areas as forbidden to "Japanese" residence, including American citizens. About 9,000 Nisei tried to leave the zone but many were thwarted by prejudice, turned back at the Nevada line or prevented from buying gasoline. In the first months of 1942, the federal government forcibly removed 110,000 Japanese-Americans from their homes, interning them in camps in seven states, from inland California to Arkansas.

Many liberals and more than a few government officials were appalled by the idea of American concentration camps. Because the criteria for relocation were ancestry and race, the federal government seemed clearly to be in violation of the Fourteenth Amendment to the Constitution. But feelings were too high for constitutional niceties. "If the Japs are released," Earl Warren said in June 1943 when there was talk of closing the camps, "no one will be able to tell a saboteur from any other Jap." In the case of *Korematsu v. the United States* in 1944, a Supreme Court dominated by New Deal liberals voted 6 to 3 to uphold an action that cost 110,000 people their freedom for several years and about $350 million in property.

A Better Record

In Hawaii, ironically, where about one-third of the population was of Japanese ancestry, the Nisei were treated brusquely but not grossly abused. A few thousand known sympathizers with Japan were arrested, but, as a vital part of the islands' work force, Hawaiian-Japanese had to cope with only informal prejudice and the inconvenience of martial law. After repeated requests for a chance to prove their loyalty, 17,000 Hawaiian Nisei and some from the mainland fought against the Germans in Italy, turning in one of the war's best unit records for bravery. Others acted as interpretors in the Pacific theater.

Treatment of conscientious objectors and the few individuals who opposed the war on political grounds was exemplary in comparison with the treatment of Japanese-Americans. Never did government action ap-

This girl was one of thousands of Japanese-Americans who were forced into concentration camps in 1942 without trial or evidence of their danger to national security.

SABOTEURS

The Germans attempted to put several teams of saboteurs in the United States from submarines, and there may have been some successful attempts at sabotage at defense plants. However, of 19,649 reported cases, the F.B.I. was unable to trace a single one to enemy action. Between 1938 and 1945, the F.B.I. arrested about 4,000 people, mostly German aliens, who were accused of espionage activities. Only 94 were convicted.

proach the ugliness of the First World War period. While some 1,700 known Nazis and Fascists were arrested, German-Americans and Italian-Americans were not persecuted as a people. In retrospect, this might appear to be surprising since the war against Japan was essentially a war for economic domination of Asia, whereas Nazi Germany was palpably a criminal state that—it was clear by 1943—was practicing genocide against Europe's Jews.

But the Japanese were of a different race from most Americans and had a vastly different cultural attitude toward war. Americans found it easier to hate the enemy in Asia and to shrug off or support mistreatment of their distant cousins in the United States.

DEFEATING GERMANY FIRST

Even before the Japanese were stopped at the Battle of Midway, President Roosevelt and his advisers had concluded that they must defeat Germany first, directing the preponderance of American power to the European theater. Their reason was sound. Japan did not threaten the Western Hemisphere, but Germany did. The Nazis had ideological bedmates in power in several South American republics and there were large German populations in Brazil, Uruguay, and Argentina.

More important, American strategists understood that, in time, Japan must inevitably buckle under superior American power; there was no need to rush in the Pacific. By way of contrast, if either Russia or England collapsed, or if Hitler were allowed too much time to entrench his regime on the continent of Europe, it might be impossible to defeat him. Already in 1942, the Germans were so firmly entrenched in western Europe that Allied leaders could not agree on how best to challenge them. "Notwithstanding the entry of Japan into the war," General George Marshall wrote at the end of 1941, "our view is that Germany is still the prime enemy and her defeat is the key to victory. Once Germany is defeated, the collapse of Italy and the defeat of Japan must follow.

Friction Among the Allies

Roosevelt and British Prime Minister Winston Churchill sometimes disagreed, but the two men were bound together by sincere mutual admiration and trust. Their relations with Soviet Premier Stalin, by way of contrast, was marred by suspicion that, on Stalin's part, bordered on paranoia. Churchill had been a staunch anti-Communist before the war and made no bones about the fact that the Russian alliance was a marriage of convenience.

Roosevelt actually had a soft spot for Stalin personally and believed he could allay the Russian's suspicions that he and Churchill wanted to sit the ground war out while Germany and the Soviet Union bled each other to exhaustion.

To weaken the German onslaught in Russia, the United States Army Air Corps (later the independent Air Force) joined the British in nearly constant day and night bombing raids over Germany. Eventually, 2.7 million tons of bombs would level German cities. Roosevelt also dispatched massive shipments of arms and other supplies to Russia and, on an impulse, told Stalin that, before 1942 was out, the British and Americans would open a second front on the ground in Europe, easing the horrendous pressure on the Soviets.

But a second front was out of the question in 1942. American industry was only in the process of converting to wartime production. The best the two Western Allies could muster was an attack on German and Italian forces in North Africa.

The African Campaign and Stalingrad

The British and Anzacs (Australians and New Zealanders) had fought a see-saw stalemate in Libya and Egypt with Italian troops and German Field Marshal Erwin Rommel's *Afrika Korps* since the beginning of the war. In mid-1942, the Germans and some Italian desert forces held the forward line not far from Alexandria, threatening the Suez Canal, Britain's link with India. In October, under the command of British General Bernard Montgomery, their arsenal beefed up by Sherman tanks from the United States, the British launched a counterattack at El Alamein. Montgomery sent the Germans reeling and, in November 1942, as he advanced from the east, Americans commanded by General Dwight D. Eisenhower landed far to the west in French North Africa.

Making a deal with French forces, which had been under the thumb of the Germans, Eisenhower moved eastward and, at Kasserine Pass in February 1943, American tank forces fought the first major American battle in the European theater. The German lines held when Hitler recalled Rommel, "the desert fox," to Germany. Without him at the helm, and overwhelmed by Allied numerical superiority, the *Afrika Korps* collapsed.

Almost simultaneously, deep within the Soviet Union, the Russians won a far more important victory, surrounding and capturing 250,000 seasoned German soldiers at Stalingrad. There seemed little doubt in any Allied capital that the course of the war had been turned against the Germans. Roosevelt told Churchill that "Uncle Joe," as he called Stalin, "is killing more Germans and destroying more equipment than you and I put together."

General Dwight D. Eisenhower briefs a group of paratroopers about to leave for the coast of France where they would be among one million Allied troops who began liberating that country from Nazi control, June 6, 1944.

The Invasion of Italy

In July 1943, an American, British, and Anzac force opened what they believed would be a second front by invading Sicily. They conquered the island in six weeks and Americans got a colorful hero to crow about: the eccentric General George Patton, who rallied his troops in coarse "blood and guts" language and was a personally brave, even reckless commander of tanks, a cavalry officer from out of the past. (In fact, Patton believed in reincarnation and thought he had lived as any number of fabled soldiers in past lives.)

Under General Mark Clark, Allied troops promptly moved into mainland Italy and knocked the Italian army out of the war. Already beset by guerrilla action behind the lines by Italian partisans, mostly Socialists and Communists, Mussolini was ousted by the conservative Field Marshal Pietro Badoglio who believed, quite correctly, that his country had become Hitler's pawn.

Nevertheless, the victories in Italy soon soured. Hitler rescued Mussolini from his captors and established him

as the puppet head of the "Republic of Salo" in northern Italy. To take the place of the Italian troops who had gone over to the Allies, he withdrew German units to easily defended strongholds south of Rome. It was ruggedly mountainous country, and only after eight months of bloody, almost constant battle did the Americans reach the capital.

Then, once again, the Germans held. Despite massive bombardment that plunged Italian cities into famine, Hitler was able to establish a defensive line across the Italian boot with relatively few troops. Germany itself would fall to the Allies before they made much headway against the *Wehrmacht*'s positions in the South.

Ike

Churchill wanted to send an invasion force into the Balkans, which he called "the soft underbelly of Europe." Roosevelt and his advisors disagreed, believing that the mountains of Greece and Yugoslavia would provide the Germans with the same protections they found in Italy.

Moreover, they regarded the problem of supplying an army in the Eastern Mediterranean as unnecessarily difficult. Their plan, slated for 1944, was to attack Hitler's Fortress Europe from Britain, across the English Channel into France.

"Operation Overlord" was to be the largest amphibious invasion in history. To direct it, Roosevelt made a choice of commander that was surprising to many. Along with Chief of Staff George C. Marshall, the president selected General Dwight D. Eisenhower, known universally as "Ike." Eisenhower had had a respectable career in the peacetime army. He had been able enough a field commander in North Africa but by no means an outstanding one. He was not a colorful figure like MacArthur, nor particularly popular with the troops like his friend, Omar Bradley. Eisenhower was a desk general, an executive, but such a man, an organizer, was precisely what was called for by an enterprise of the scale of Operation Overlord.

Eisenhower had another indispensable talent. He was a natural diplomat. He had a temper; close aides were terrified by his tirades in private. But when the doors opened and colleagues entered, he was supremely affable, smiling, conciliatory, willing to bend on non-essentials, pleasantly firm in pushing through plans on which his superiors had agreed. Eisenhower had a genius for smoothing over differences among headstrong associates, with whom he was surrounded. Churchill was a great man and aware of it. Field Marshall Montgomery was hideously vain and peevish, the very opposite of Eisenhower. The leader of the Free French in England, Charles DeGaulle, would not accept the fact that he was a principal in making plans more out of courtesy than because of the forces at his disposal.

D-Day

Most important, Eisenhower was cautious and thorough, knowing that if the invasion of France failed, the war in Europe might well be lost. His task was immense beyond

imagining. He had to find and mobilize 4,000 vessels, 11,000 aircraft, tens of thousands of motor vehicles and weapons of various sorts, as well as billeting and training more than 2 million soldiers. Such a massive operation could not go unnoticed by the Germans, of course, but the British and Americans successfully kept secret the date of "D-Day" and, rather more remarkably, the place of the invasion.

The date was June 6, 1944, and the place was Normandy in northwestern France. Eisenhower's caution and meticulous planning of every detail paid off. The Allied troops—1 million men—marched across France and into Paris on August 25. Immediately thereafter they entered Belgium. By September, they were across the German border, farther than the Allies had penetrated by the end of the First World War.

Politics and Strategy

The British and Americans disagreed about how to finish off Germany. Montgomery wanted to concentrate all Allied forces into one narrow thrust into the heart of Germany, a traditional strategy that had much to recommend it. Tactfully, Eisenhower overruled him. In part his decision was military, reflecting his innate cautiousness and perhaps his study of the American Civil War, in which such concentrated assaults were repeatedly stymied. Eisenhower feared that creating too long and weak a flank, not to mention a single extended supply line, would tempt the Germans into a massive counterattack that might lead to disaster, a much longer war, even the necessity of negotiating a peace. He preferred to exploit the overwhelming Allied superiority in arms and men by advancing slowly on a broad front that extended from the North Sea to the border of Switzerland.

Diplomatic and political considerations entered into Eisenhower's decision too. Still absorbing tremendous casualties as they slowly pushed the Germans westward, the Russians remained suspicious of American and British motives. Stalin jumped at every rumor that his allies were considering a separate peace. Some American diplomats feared that too rapid an American and British thrust would only arouse Stalin's suspicions that, when Germany was finished off, the Allies would turn on Russia. On an earthier level, Eisenhower worried about spontaneous trouble between his soldiers and the Red Army if an orderly rendezvous were not arranged in advance. Finally, the risky single-thrust strategy was Montgomery's; he would command it. Eisenhower did not share his British colleague's supreme confidence in his own abilities and worried how the American public would take to a British General managing the European war.

IKE'S CONTINGENCY PLAN

Knowing that he would be busy on D-Day, General Eisenhower scribbled out the following note to be dispatched to Washington in the event that the invasion of Europe was a failure:

Our landings in the Cherbourg-Havre area have failed to gain a satisfactory foothold and I have withdrawn the troops. My decision to attack at this time and place was based upon the best information available. The troops, the air corps and the navy did all that bravery and devotion to duty could do. If any blame or fault attaches to the attempt it is mine alone.

The Bulge and the End

For a while in 1944, it appeared that Eisenhower's strategy of advancing slowly was a mistake. In the summer, V-2 rockets from sanctuaries inside Germany began to rain down on London, killing 8,000 people. The V-2's were not decisive weapons from a military point of view, but with the end of the war apparently in sight, their psychological effect was disheartening to civilians. There was no warning from a V-2, as there was in conventional aerial attack—only a whine high in the air, a few seconds of silence, and an explosion.

Much more demoralizing was a German military counteroffensive in Belgium in the bitter cold and snowy December of 1944. In the Battle of the Bulge, German troops pushed the Americans and British back, creating a "bulge" in the lines and threatening to split the Allied forces in two. But a division under General Anthony McAuliffe that was isolated at Bastogne refused to surrender ("Nuts!" McAuliffe replied to the German commander), weakening the German offensive as the Belgians had done at Liège in 1914. Then, a break in the weather allowed the Allies to exploit their air superiority and, after two weeks, they advanced again. One by one, German defenses collapsed.

Along with his oldest and closest Nazi party associates, a Hitler close to breakdown withdrew to a bunker under the streets of Berlin where he presided over the prema-

Winston Churchill, Franklin D. Roosevelt, and Joseph Stalin pose for photographers at Yalta,
February 1945.

ture disintegration of his "Thousand-Year Empire." To the end, he thought in terms of the perverted romanticism of his ideology. It was *Götterdämmerung*, the mythical final battle of the Norse gods. On April 30, 1945, Hitler committed suicide after having named Admiral Karl Doenitz his successor as *Führer*. A few days later, Doenitz surrendered.

Wartime Diplomacy

Eisenhower's sensitivity to Russian suspicions reflected President Roosevelt's policy. At a personal meeting with Stalin at Teheran in Iran late in 1943, and again at Yalta in the Crimea in February 1945, F.D.R. did his best to assuage the Russian's fears by acquiescing or, at least, by not strenuously resisting Stalin's proposals for the organization of postwar Europe.

In after years, when the Soviet Union was the Cold War enemy and Americans had come to lament Russian domination of Eastern Europe, Yalta became a byword

for diplomatic blunder and even, to a few extremists, for treasonous "sellout" to Communism. It was at Yalta that Roosevelt and Churchill tacitly consented to Stalin's insistence that the Soviet Union had "special interests" in Eastern Europe, that is, governments friendly to the Soviet Union.

Right-wing extremists were later to say that F.D.R. betrayed the Poles, Czechs, Hungarians, Romanians, and Bulgarians because he was himself sympathetic to Communism. Other less hysterical analysts suspected that the president's weariness and illness, obvious in the haggard face and sagging jaw of the official photographs, caused him to reason poorly in dealing with the calculating Stalin.

Whatever effect Roosevelt's failing health had on his mental processes, there was nothing irrational about his concessions to Russia. Roosevelt and Churchill did not give Stalin anything that he did not already have. In February 1945, the Red Army was racing over and occupying the very countries that Stalin envisioned as buffer states against renewed German aggression or other threats from the West. No doubt Churchill and F.D.R. expected the postwar states of Eastern Europe to have greater independence than Stalin was willing to allow. Historians disagree as to whether Stalin intended to enforce an iron grip on the region in 1945 or altered his policy later, when the Cold War was underway.

THE TWILIGHT OF JAPAN, THE NUCLEAR DAWN

Also influencing Roosevelt at Yalta was his desire to enlist the Soviet Union in the war against Japan in order to save American lives in the final battles. While agreeing that the Red Army would attack Japanese forces in China, Stalin insisted on delaying action until the Soviet Union felt secure in Europe.

Pacific Strategy

After Midway in June 1942, American strategy in the war against Japan involved three distinct campaigns. First, just as the United States pumped material into Russia, supplies were flown into China from India, "over the hump" of the Himalayas, in order to keep the Chinese in the war. Unfortunately, Chiang Kai-shek was no Stalin, and his Kuomintang troops were no Red Army.

Chiang hated and feared his Chinese Communist allies as much as he hated the Japanese. He diverted hundreds of thousands of troops to battling them, and never forced the kind of battle on the Japanese that the Americans needed in order to weaken Japanese defenses in the Pacific. Inefficiency and corruption in Chiang's government resulted in gross misuse of American supplies.

General Joseph W. "Vinegar Joe" Stilwell, the gritty American commander in China, despised Chiang. He poured out an avalanche of warnings to Washington about the incompetence of "the monkey," as he called the Generalissimo, and the corruption of his political allies. But when Stilwell tried to get command of the Chinese army for himself, Roosevelt recalled him. Somewhat to Churchill's amazement, Roosevelt was convinced that Chiang was a valuable ally.

The second and third prongs of the attack on Japan were more successful, but extremely bloody. After driving the Japanese out of the Solomons in order to ensure Australia's security, one force under MacArthur began to push toward the Japanese homeland via New Guinea and the Philippines. Another, commanded by Admiral Chester W. Nimitz, struck through the central Pacific, capturing islands from which aircraft could reach and bomb Japan.

Island Warfare

To soldiers slogging through the mud and frigid cold of Italy and France, the troops in the Pacific were on a picnic, basking in a lovely climate and only periodically meeting the enemy in battle. Ernie Pyle, considered the best newspaper correspondent of the war, made this comparison in his celebration of the American fighting man in Europe. (Ironically, Pyle survived Europe and was killed by Japanese machine-gun fire on Ie Shima in the closing months of the war.)

Life behind the lines in the Pacific could be pleasant, although novelist James Michener wrote that the men "rotted" between battles, "sweated twenty pounds away . . . and waited. And pretty soon you hated the man next to you, and you dreaded the look of a coconut tree." Capturing islands that were specks on the map meant battles more vicious than those in Europe. The Japanese soldier was a formidable fighter. He was indoctrinated with a fanatical sense of duty and taught that it was a betrayal of national and personal honor to surrender, even when his army was obviously defeated. Japanese soldiers were sworn to fight to the death, taking down as many of the enemy as they could.

To an astonishing degree, this was how they fought. It took the Americans six months to win control of microscopic Guadalcanal in the Solomons beginning in August 1942, even though the defenders had not had time to complete their fortifications.

In New Guinea and along the route through the Gilbert, Marshall, and Marianas islands that Nimitz was to follow, the concrete bunkers and gun emplacements were stronger than in the Solomons, and the resistance of the Japanese was chillingly effective. Marines discovered at places like Tarawa in the Gilberts in November 1943 that when a battle was over, they had few prisoners. They had to kill almost every Japanese on the island at high cost to themselves.

As MacArthur and Nimitz moved closer to Japan, the fighting grew tougher. Attacking the Marianas and the Philippines in 1944, both American forces were hit hard. But MacArthur's dramatic return to Luzon boosted morale, and Nimitz's capture of the Marianas enabled larger land-based American planes to bomb the Japanese homeland at will. The wooden cities of Japan went up like tinder when hit by incendiary devices. A single raid on Tokyo on March 9, 1945, killed 85,000 people and destroyed 250,000 buildings.

By no means were all the Japanese-occupied islands retaken. Both MacArthur and Nimitz advocated "island hopping," leaving less-important Japanese holdings

Battles in the Pacific were generally brief, but hideously bloody.

alone, to wither as they were cut off from supplies. When the war finally ended, there were still some Japanese units operating in New Guinea, the point of farthest Japanese advance.

Fighting to the Last Man

By the spring of 1945, Japan's situation was hopeless. Germany was defeated, thus freeing hundreds of thousands of battle-hardened soldiers for combat in the Pacific. Japan's leaders correctly calculated that the Soviet Union was on the verge of declaring war on them. After the huge Battle of Leyte Gulf in October 1944, the Japanese navy ceased to exist as a fighting force, while the Americans cruised the seas with 4,000 ships, shelling the Japanese coast at will. United States submarines destroyed half of the island nation's vital merchant fleet within a few months.

Some Japanese leaders put out peace feelers via the Russians, with whom Japan was not yet at war. But the high command was divided. Fanatics high in the government prevented an open appeal for peace. They were themselves victims of the extreme nationalistic fervor they instilled in their men, and they had 5 million soldiers in uniform. There were 2 million in Japan itself,

and about the same number in China, where Chiang's half-hearted warmaking had been just enough to forge them into first-rate soldiers without inflicting heavy casualties.

With so many soldiers fighting to the death, the taking of islands close to Japan resulted in hundreds of thousands of casualties. Iwo Jima, a desolate tiny volcano needed for a landing strip, cost 4,000 American lives. Saipan was even bloodier and the invasion of Okinawa,

WORLD WAR II CASUALTIES			
	Total mobilized	Killed or died	Wounded
United States	16,113,000	407,000	672,000
China	17,251,000	1,325,000	1,762,000
Germany	20,000,000	3,250,000	7,250,000
Italy	3,100,000	136,000	225,000
Japan	9,700,000	1,270,000	140,000
U.S.S.R.	—	6,115,000	14,012,000
United Kingdom	5,896,000	357,000	369,000
TOTAL	72,060,000	12,860,000	24,430,000

HOW THEY LIVED

STUDYING A NEW KIND OF WAR

"Tarawa was not a very big battle, as battles go," wrote G. D. Lillibridge, the historian who was a second lieutenant there in November 1943, "and it was all over in seventy-two hours." The casualties totaled only 3,300 U.S. Marines, about the same number of elite Japanese Special Naval Landing Forces, and 2,000 Japanese and Korean laborers who doubled as soldiers. A few months earlier, by comparison, half a world away in the Stalingrad campaign, the German *Wehrmacht* lost 500,000 men.

And yet, like Stalingrad, "Bloody Tarawa" was a landmark, even a turning point, of the Second World War. If the numbers were trivial, the incidence of the casualties was appalling, especially for a nation whose wartime leaders, since Lincoln and Grant, have thought of minimizing losses in battle as a major determinant of strategy. Lillibridge's 39-man platoon lost 26; 323 of 500 drivers of landing craft died; overall, more than one-third of the American attackers were killed or wounded. The figures stunned the admirals who planned the battle and the people at home who read about it.

So did the fanaticism of the Japanese defenders. Americans had heard that the Japanese fighting man considered surrender under any circumstances to be shameful. That was in the abstract. Few were prepared to learn that only 17 of 5,000 Japanese on the tiny atoll of Betio were captured, most of them because they were too seriously wounded to commit suicide.

This willingness to die for nothing but a code of honor incomprehensible to Americans was not something that could be taught in a training film. It was bred into Japan's young men from infancy. In his reflections on the battle, something of an attempt to exorcise demons that had haunted him for 25 years, Lillibridge remembered a Japanese man his platoon had trapped during the mopping-up operation. Another Japanese Marine was moaning in agony from his wounds. The defender would reassure his dying friend, then hurl challenges and insults at Lillibridge's platoon,

his voice raised against us in the raging pitch that comes from fear and anger and then lowered to a soothing tone as he sought to comfort his mortally wounded companion. . . . Doomed and knowing he was doomed, he never lost control of himself and remained in command of the situation until the end.

Betio, only two miles long and 800 yards wide—half the size of New York's Central Park—was the largest of the 25 islands of the Tarawa atoll, a coral formation in the sprawling Gilbert Islands. The Japanese airstrip there was the chief strategic objective of the American assault. Japanese planes based in Tarawa could worry American supply lines between Hawaii and Australia. In a way, by November 1943, Tarawa represented the final fragment of Japanese offensive capability.

It was a tiny fragment. Just as important as the airstrip to Admirals Chester W. Nimitz and Raymond Spruance was to use Tarawa to test their theories of amphibious assault before what was anticipated to be far more difficult fighting in the Marshall Islands early in 1944 and, after that, an island by island advance toward Japan.

"There had to be a Tarawa, a first assault on a strongly defended coral atoll," an American officer explained. An amphibious assault against an entrenched, waiting enemy was a new kind of war for the American military, or at least an untried technique. Ironically, the Americans thought that Tarawa would be easy, more training-exercise than battle. They had no illusions about the fierceness of Japanese troops. However, Betio was small; the Japanese had been digging in there a comparatively short time; the American assault force was huge, covering eight square miles of Pacific; and officers awed by the destructiveness of naval bombardment were sure they would "obliterate the defenses on Betio." Taking his cue from his superiors, Lieutenant Lillibridge told his platoon that "there was no need to worry, no necessity for anyone to get killed, although possibly someone might get slightly wounded."

In fact, the pre-dawn bombardment did destroy Rear Admiral Keiji Shibasaki's communications with most of his troops. However, the network of concrete blockhouses, coconut-log pillboxes, and underwater barricades he had built in just a few months, what one analyst called a "complete defensive system," was substantially untouched by the big guns and aerial bombs. The willingness of the Japanese marines and even common laborers to die more than compensated for their isolation from Shibasaki's bunker.

Nature more than compensated for the massiveness of the American attack. The tide was lower than hoped and the larger American landing crafts could not clear the reef that fringed Betio. This meant that all but the first wave of marines had to wade, breast deep, 800 yards to shore.

This was the element of amphibious attack in the Pacific that was really tested at Tarawa. Could men with no more armor than "a khaki shirt," no way to defend themselves, and in effect no support while they were slogging half a mile in water, even get to the beach, let alone establish enough of a base from which to displace enemies who, during this same critical time, were free to wreak havoc with them?

Getting to the beach was the first horror that would haunt the survivors of Tarawa and subsequent Pacific landings for the rest of their lives. Men remembered it as a "nightmarish turtle race," run in slow-motion. It was "like being completely suspended, like being under a strong anesthetic." "I could have sworn that I could have reached out and touched a hundred bullets." "The water never seemed clear of tiny men."

It was their tininess, perhaps, that enabled the Americans to reach the beach through a storm of machine-gun and cannon fire. They had to push through the floating corpses of their comrades, hundreds of thousands of fish killed by the bombardment, stepping on other dead marines. The lagoon was literally red with blood for hours.

The second nightmare waited on the beach. Shibasaki had constructed a sea wall of coconut logs, three to five feet high. At first it seemed to be a shelter. The exhausted marines threw themselves under it. In fact, Japanese mortars had been meticulously registered to batter the long thin line, while to peek above the palisade meant to draw the fire of 200 perfectly positioned Japanese machine guns. More than one marine remembered that he was capable of moving beyond the sea wall only because to remain there meant certain death. About half the American casualties were suffered in the water, most of the rest on the beach. The carnage was condensed in such a way as to leave lifelong psychological scars.

One by one, almost always at close quarters, the blockhouses and pillboxes were wiped out. Betio was taken in three days, only one more than called-for by commanders who thought it would be a "walkover." The aftermath was as morally devastating as the battle. Like at the Wilderness and the Marne, the vegetation that had covered the island was literally destroyed. Hundreds of bodies floating in the surf and festering in the blockhouses bloated and rotted in the tropical heat. The triumphant marines looked like anything but victors. They sat staring, exhausted, just beginning to comprehend what they had been through, as if they had been captured by their enemies. "I passed boys who . . . looked older than their fathers," General Holland Smith said, "it had chilled

their souls. They found it hard to believe they were actually alive."

Smith and the other commanders learned a great deal from the "training exercise" at Tarawa, not the least of which lessons was not to gamble on tides over coral reefs. Not until the last months of the Pacific War, when the close approach to the Japanese homeland made larger forces of Japanese defenders even fiercer in their resistance, would the extremity of Tarawa's terror be repeated.

The Pacific commanders also learned that while the vast American superiority of armament and firepower was essential and telling, taking the Pacific island was much more personal and human an effort than twentieth century military men had come to assume. With a grace rare in a modern officer, General Julian Smith frankly asserted,

There was one thing that won this battle . . . and that was the supreme courage of the Marines. The prisoners tell us that what broke their morale was not the bombing, not the naval gunfire, but the sight of Marines who kept coming ashore.

Soldiers in the European theater, Americans at home, and more than a few troops in the Pacific Campaign, looked on the Pacific war as a picnic. G. D. Lillibridge and others remembered the idyllic holiday quality, however involuntary the vacation was, of the long months between battles spent in Hawaii, Australia, or New Zealand. Correspondent Robert Sherrod, who lived through Tarawa, wrote of "the brilliant sunlight, the far-reaching, incredibly blue Pacific, the soft breezes at evening and the Southern Cross in the sky." The idyll became a part of American popular culture with the publication of James Michener's *Tales of the South Pacific,* and the musical comedy, *South Pacific,* that was based on it. Hawaii enjoyed a second great tourist boom (the first followed annexation) as a result of the Americans' rediscovery of the islands during the war.

But if life between battles was idyllic—and the whole Pacific war a pleasure to noncombat troops—the ferocity of battle was, as Lillibridge writes in another place, perhaps the greatest in the conflict.

THE
PACIFIC
THEATER

SCALE

| 0 | 500 | 1000 | 1500 | 2000 Miles |

| 0 | 1000 | 2000 | 3000 Kilometers |

⟵ ALLIED OFFENSIVES, 1942-1945

▬▬ EXTENT OF JAPANESE CONTROL, AUGUST 1942

considered part of Japan, killed or wounded 80,000 Americans. In the same fighting, more than 100,000 Japanese died, and only 8,000 surrendered. Planners guessed that the invasion of Japan itself, scheduled for November 1, 1945, would cost 1 million casualties, as many as the United States had suffered in over three years of fighting in both Europe and the Pacific.

A Birth and a Death

This chilling prediction helped to make the atomic bomb so appealing to policy-makers. The Manhattan Project, code name of the group that built the bomb, dated from 1939, when the German-born physicist Albert Einstein wrote to President Roosevelt that it was

possible to unleash inconceivable amounts of energy by nuclear fission, splitting an atom. Einstein was a pacifist, but as a Jew he was also a refugee from Nazism who believed that German science was capable of producing a nuclear bomb. Such a device in Hitler's hands was an appalling prospect.

Einstein was too prestigious to ignore, and the government secretly allotted $2 billion to the Manhattan Project. Under the direction of J. Robert Oppenheimer, scientists working on Long Island, underneath a football stadium in Chicago, and at isolated Los Alamos in New Mexico progressed steadily and, by April 1945, told Washington that they were four months away from testing a bomb.

The decision whether or not to use it did not fall to

A view of Hiroshima and of two victims after it was flattened by an atomic bomb, August 6, 1945.

President Roosevelt. Reelected to a fourth term in 1944 over Thomas E. Dewey, the governor of New York, Roosevelt died of a massive stroke on April 12, 1945. He was at Warm Springs, Georgia, sitting for a portrait painter when he said, "I have a terrific headache," slumped in his chair, and died.

The outpouring of grief that swept the nation at the loss of the man who had been in office longer than any other president was real and profound. Silent crowds lined the tracks to watch the train that brought F.D.R. back to Washington for the last time. People wept in the streets of every city. But in Washington, the sorrow was overshadowed by apprehensions that his successor, Harry S Truman, was not up to being president.

Truman, Little Boy, and Fat Man

Truman was an honest politico who had risen as a dependable and hard worker for the Kansas City machine of Boss Thomas J. Pendergast. He proved his abilities as chairman of an important Senate committee during the war, but impressed few as the caliber of person to head a nation. Unprepossessing in appearance and manner, bespectacled, something of a dandy (he once operated a

THE COSTS OF WAR

The Second World War was the most expensive war that the United States ever fought:

Revolutionary War	$149	million
War of 1812	124	million
Mexican War	107	million
Civil War (Union only)	8	billion
Spanish-American War	2.5	billion
First World War	66	billion
Second World War	560	billion
Korean War	70	billion
Vietnam War	121.5	billion

It took the personal intervention of Emperor Hirohito to persuade the Japanese military to surrender to the United States. The official surrender took place aboard the battleship Missouri *on September 2, 1945.*

haberdashery), and given to salty language, Truman had been nominated as vice-president in 1944 as a compromise candidate. Democratic conservatives wanted the left-liberal vice-president elected in 1940, Henry A. Wallace out of the number-two spot, but they could not force conservative James J. Byrnes on the liberals. The two wings of the party settled on Truman.

Truman was as shocked by his accession as anyone else. "I don't know whether you fellows ever had a load of hay or a bull fall on you," he told reporters on his first full day in office, "but last night the moon, the stars, and all the planets fell on me." If he joined others in being unsure of his abilities, Truman knew how to make difficult decisions and never doubted his responsibility to lead. A plaque on his desk read "The Buck Stops Here"; as the president of the United States, he could not "pass the buck" to anyone else.

Truman met with Churchill and Stalin at Potsdam in July 1945, but to Stalin only alluded to the bomb. When some—not all—of his advisors informed him that the alternative to using it was a conventional invasion of Japan and horrendously high American casualties, he opted as Roosevelt always had, to avoid massive carnage. On August 6, an atomic bomb nicknamed "Little Boy" was dropped on Hiroshima, killing 100,000 people in an instant and dooming another 100,000 to death from injury and radiation poisoning. Two days later, "Fat Man" was exploded over Nagasaki.

Incredibly, the Japanese high command still wanted to fight on. Had they known that the Americans had no more atomic bombs in their arsenal, they might have carried the debate. But Emperor Hirohito stepped in and agreed to surrender on August 15, 1945, if he were allowed to keep his throne. Because the Americans valued him as a symbol of social stability in Japan, they agreed. The war ended officially on the decks of the battleship *Missouri* on September 2.

Was the Bomb Necessary?

At first there was only wonder at a weapon that could destroy a whole city, and joy that the war was over. Within a few years, however, many Americans began to debate the wisdom and morality of having used the atomic bomb. When novelist John Hersey's *Hiroshima* detailed the destruction of that ancient city in vivid, human terms, some of Truman's critics stated that he was guilty of a war crime worse than any the Japanese had perpetrated, and exceeded only by the Nazi murder of 6 million European Jews. Truman and his defenders replied that the nuclear assaults on Hiroshima and Nagasaki were humane acts since millions of Japanese as well as Americans would have been killed had Japan been invaded.

When other critics said that the Japanese surrender could have been forced by a demonstration of the bomb on an uninhabited island, as Secretary of War Stimson had suggested, defenders pointed out that no one was positive that the device would actually work. An announced demonstration that fizzled would have encouraged the Japanese die-hards to fight all the harder.

Much later, a group of historians known as "revisionists" suggested that Little Boy and Fat Man were dropped not so much to end the war with Japan but to inaugurate the Cold War with the Soviet Union. In bombing Japan, the revisionist argument went, Truman was showing the Russians that the United States held the trump card in any postwar dispute. Because history is not a science capable of absolute proof, the debate over the use of the bomb will continue indefinitely. Only two things are certain: the atomic bomb ended the Second World War decisively and ahead of schedule, and it ushered in a new and dangerous epoch in world affairs, the nuclear age.

For Further Reading

The standard history of America's Great War is Albert R. Buchanan, *The United States and World War II* (1962). More comprehensive studies include Martha Hoyle, *A World in Flames: A History of World War II* (1970) and Fletcher Pratt, *War for the World* (1950) but, of course, the literature is exhaustive, with a great number of excellent popular histories. Although hardly a study in objectivity, Winston Churchill, *The Second World War* (1948–53) will be rewarding to every student.

On diplomatic and political issues, see Robert Beitzell, *The Uneasy Alliance: America, Britain, and Russia, 1941–1943* (1972); John M. Blum, *V Was for Victory: Politics and American Culture During World War II* (1976); Robert Dallek, *Franklin D. Roosevelt and American Foreign Policy, 1932–1945* (1979); Robert A. Divine, *Roosevelt and World War II* (1969); Norman A. Graebner, *The Age of Global Power: The United States Since 1938* (1979); Gabriel Kolko, *The Politics of War: The World and United States Foreign Policy, 1943–1945* (1968); Joseph P. Lash, *Roosevelt and Churchill* (1976); and Gaddis Smith, *American Diplomacy During the Second World War, 1940–1945* (1965).

Military history is the major focus of Stephen Ambrose, *The Supreme Commander: The War Years of General Dwight D. Eisenhower* (1970); William Manchester, *American Caesar: Douglas MacArthur, 1880–1960* (1978); Charles B. McDonald, *The Mighty Endeavor: American Armed Forces in the European Theater in World War II* (1969); Samuel Eliot Morison, *The Two-Ocean War: A Short History of the United States Navy in the Second World War* (1963); Cornelius Ryan, *The Longest Day* (1959); John Toland, *The Last Hundred Days* (1966) and *The Rising Sun: The Decline and Fall of the Japanese Empire* (1970); Russell F. Weigley, *The American Way of War: A History of United States Military Strategy and Policy* (1973).

Books on the home front include Roger Daniels, *Concentration Camps USA* (1971); some chapters of Carl M. Degler, *At Odds: Women and the Family in America from the Revolution to the Present* (1980); Jack Goodman, *While You Were Gone: A Report on Wartime Life in the United States* (1946); Richard Lingeman, *Don't You Know There's a War On* (1970); Richard Polenberg, *War and Society: The United States, 1941–1945* (1972); Michi Weglyn, *Years of Infamy: The Untold Story of America's Concentration Camps* (1976).

The reasons for the dropping of the atomic bomb on Japan in 1945 are hotly argued in Gar Alperovitz, *Atomic Diplomacy: Hiroshima and Potsdam* (1965); Herbert Feis, *The Atomic Bomb and World War II* (1966); and Greg Herken, *The Winning Weapon* (1980).

A radioactive mushroom cloud covers Bikini Atoll following a test of the atomic bomb, July 25, 1946.

A TIME OF ANXIETIES

THE UNITED STATES IN THE EARLY NUCLEAR AGE 1946 - 1952

Few wars have ended so abruptly as the Pacific theater of the Second World War. Divided and deliberating one week, shattered by the news of the atomic bomb the next, the Japanese government collapsed overnight.

Never had a new historical era been so unmistakably proclaimed as by the fireballs over Hiroshima and Nagasaki. Slowly during the final months of 1945, it dawned on Americans and other peoples that the world had undergone a major passage, that old rules and guidelines would not necessarily help them to negotiate the future.

THE SHADOW OF COLD WAR

But they had not left the past behind. History is legacy. The consequences of past actions live on whether or not people choose to recognize them. Three great legacies of the Second World War were so profound that they fostered anxieties that loom menacingly over the United States and the world to this day.

Legacies

The first legacy of the Second World War was, of course, the powerful weapon that ended it. Nuclear bombs meant that it was technologically possible for humanity to destroy civilization, perhaps even the natural world as we have known it. Such a circumstance was, to say the least, novel in history.

A second legacy of the war was the realization that human beings were morally quite capable of using such a technology in monstrous ways. It was not so much President Truman's decision to use the atomic bomb. However justified or cynical that decision may have been, neither Truman nor his advisors quite understood how horrible a weapon nuclear fission was. Few predicted the thousands of maimings and lingering deaths from radiation poisoning in Hiroshima and Nagasaki.

Further, in the spring of 1945, Allied troops discovered that reports of genocide in Nazi Europe had not been exaggerated. The Nazis had systematically exterminated 6 million Jews and probably 1 million other people, many of them in "camps" that were specifically designed for killing people and disposing of their bodies on a mass scale. The photographs and films of the walking skeletons of Dachau, Belsen, Auschwitz, and Buchenwald; the "shower baths" where the victims were gassed; the cremation ovens; the human garbage dumps, arms and legs protruding obscenely from heaps of corpses like discarded furniture: these shocking spectacles mocked human pretensions to enlightenment and decency such as not even the slaughter of the First World War had done. That, at least, had been mindless. Nazi genocide was deliberate, calculated, and methodical. Never again would it be possible to assume, as most of Western civilization had assumed for more than a century, that reason, science, technology, and efficiency were moving the human race toward an ever better future.

The third legacy of the war was that only two nations emerged from it as genuine victors—the United States and the Soviet Union—and that, once the Nazis were defeated, they had little in common. For about two years after the war, Russian and American leaders tried to preserve the wartime alliance or, at least, to maintain the pretense of friendship. By 1947, however, the two great powers were in a state of "cold war," belligerence without violent confrontation.

At first, Americans were more annoyed than frightened by what they believed was Soviet ingratitude and treachery. Their nation held the trump card, the atomic bomb. Then, in September 1949, the Soviets successfully tested a nuclear device. The holocaust of which the race had proved itself nimbly capable seemed likely to be ignited sooner or later.

Roots of Soviet-American Animosity

The origins of the Russo-American Cold War lay in irreconcilable values and thirty years of history. The American commitment to democratic government, maximum liberty for individuals, and a capitalist economy was incompatible with the conviction of the Bolsheviks of 1917 that they could overcome the "sluggishness of history" and achieve their revolution by the creation, at least temporarily, of a dictatorial, repressive, and ruthless state power.

Obnoxious as Soviet tyranny was to Americans, however, it cannot in itself explain American hostility to the Soviets. (The United States had often found it convenient to come to terms with non-Communist dictators.) Also important was the American commitment to maintaining an "open door" for trade and investment everywhere in the world. This principle was incompatible with Soviet determination to prevent capitalist economic penetration in those parts of the world they controlled, and the fitful Soviet determination to export Communist revolution and expand the U.S.S.R.'s political sway.

With such contradictory values and goals, the Soviet Union and the United States could marry only when there was a shotgun at their backs, which Nazi Germany provided between 1941 and 1945. Even then, despite cordial personal relations between Roosevelt and Stalin, neither American nor Russian policy-makers deluded themselves that the conflict of interests had disappeared. People high in the American government, such as James Byrnes and Harry S Truman continued to find Russian Communism intolerably noxious. The Russians, Stalin foremost among them, remained suspicious of the intentions of the United States and Great Britain. For a decade and more after 1917, the Western nations had isolated and threatened to destroy the revolution that the Bolsheviks had made. Stalin fidgeted and seethed when Roosevelt and Churchill were slow to establish a second front in Europe. The Americans and the British worried that, after the war, Communist Russia would be a great

Prisoners in a Nazi concentration camp await their release in this 1945 photo by Margaret Bourke-White.

power for the first time, in a position to dominate its neighbors.

An Insoluble Problem

Roosevelt apparently believed that he could handle Stalin's repeatedly expressed insistence that the nations bordering Russia be "friendly," while ensuring that they were not Soviet satellites. Although it is difficult to imagine what specifics he had in mind, Roosevelt apparently thought that he could ensure that Poland, Czechoslovakia, and the Balkan countries would be democratic, open to American cooperation and trade while posing no threat to Soviet security.

At best, this was naïve. Political democracy, as it was defined in Roosevelt's and Churchill's Atlantic Charter, was alien to Eastern European history and culture. Moreover, some Eastern European countries, particularly Poland, were historically blood enemies of Russia. If the

Western Allies had suppressed the memory that the Soviet Union had joined Nazi Germany in invading Poland in 1939, the Poles did not. Indeed, Polish hatred for the Russians was given new life in 1943, when the Germans released persuasive evidence that the Red Army had secretly massacred 5,000 captured Polish officers at Katyn in 1940.

Then, late in the war, with Russian troops advancing rapidly toward Warsaw, the Polish government-in-exile in London called for an uprising behind the German lines. At this point, Stalin abruptly halted the Russian advance, and the relieved Germans were able to butcher the poorly armed Polish partisans. Red Army soldiers were as brutal toward Polish civilians as they were toward Germans. A democratic Poland could not be subordinate to Russia in the sense that Stalin demanded Poland be. A Poland friendly to Russia could not be democratically governed.

Roosevelt's confidence that he could iron out these wrinkles on the basis of his personal cordiality toward Stalin also required that he defy his own mortality, to which he should have been very sensitive in early 1945; his health had been rapidly, visibly deteriorating for several years. Nevertheless, he continued to treat diplomacy as a personal monopoly. When he died before the war was over, he left an inexperienced and uninformed Harry S Truman to make a settlement with Stalin.

Truman Draws a Line

Truman was not the sly manipulator Roosevelt had been. His virtues as a man and as president were his frankness, bluntness, and willingness to make and stick by a decision. On the subject of the Soviet Union he had made a decision decades earlier. Like most Americans he did not like the Russians. Even before he first met Stalin at Potsdam, he summoned Soviet Ambassador V. M. Molotov to the White House and scolded him so harshly for several apparent Russian policy turns that Molotov exclaimed, "I have never been talked to like that in my life!"

By 1946, it was obvious that the Russians were not going to permit free elections in Poland. While Truman remained cautious in his official pronouncements on the subject, he gave full approval to Winston Churchill's speech in Fulton, Missouri, in March 1946. An "iron curtain" had descended across Europe, the former prime minister said, and it was time for the Western democracies to call a halt to the expansion of atheistic Communism.

In September 1946, Truman again signaled the confrontational turn of his Soviet policy. He fired Secretary of Commerce (and former vice president) Henry A. Wallace, the one member of his cabinet who called openly for accommodating the anxieties of the Soviet Union.

Containment and the Truman Doctrine

By 1947, Truman had a policy that went beyond merely "getting tough with the Russians." First in a series of confidential memoranda, and then in an article signed by "Mister X" in the influential journal *Foreign Affairs*, a Soviet expert in the State Department, George F. Kennan, argued that because of the ancient Russian compulsion to expand to the west and the virtually pathological Soviet fear of the Western nations, it would be impossible to come to a quick, amicable settlement with Stalin. American policy must therefore be to contain Russian expansionism by drawing clear limits as to where the United States would tolerate Russian domination,

namely, those parts of Europe that already were under Russian control, and no more.

In Kennan's view, the Soviets would test American resolve but, Russian history seemed to show, very carefully. While the Soviets wanted to extend their sway to the west as far as possible, they did not want war any more than did the United States. If American policymakers made it unmistakeably clear that they would tolerate no more Russian gains, the Soviets would stop. Kennan envisioned a long period of tense, suspicious relations. In time, however, when the Russians felt secure, it would become possible to deal diplomatically with them and establish a genuine peace. In the meantime, Cold War was preferable to bloodletting and the possibility of world destruction.

At the same time "containment policy" was being "leaked" to the public, Truman was presented with an opportunity to put it into practice. In early 1947, the Soviets seemed to be stepping up their support of Communist guerrillas in Greece and Communist parties in Italy and France. On March 12, Truman asked Congress to appropriate $400 million in military assistance to the pro-Western governments of Greece and Turkey. This principle of decisively supporting anti-Communist regimes with massive aid came to be known as the Truman Doctrine.

The Marshall Plan

On June 5, 1947, Secretary of State George C. Marshall proposed a much more ambitious program, which came to be called the Marshall Plan. The United States would invest vast sums of money in the economic reconstruction of Europe. Not only would the former Western

---

AN UNSORDID ACT

Winston Churchill called the Marshall Plan "the most unsordid act in history." In a speech at Harvard University in 1947, George Marshall explained his intentions:

The truth of the matter is that Europe's requirements for the next three or four years of foreign food and other essential products—principally from America—are so much greater than her present ability to pay that she must have substantial additional help, or face economic, social, and political deterioration of a very grave character.

The remedy lies in breaking the vicious circle and restoring the confidence of the European people in the economic future of their own countries and of Europe as a whole. The manufacturer and the farmer throughout wide areas must be able and willing to exchange their products for currencies the continuing value of which is not open to question.

A plane carrying supplies flies into West Berlin following a move by Joseph Stalin in June 1948 to block overland routes to that city from West Germany.

European Allies be invited to apply for American assistance, but defeated Germany (then divided into British, French, American, and Soviet zones of occupation) would receive aid. Indeed, Marshall invited the Soviet Union and the nations behind Churchill's Iron Curtain to participate.

Marshall and Truman calculated that Russia and its satellite states would reject the offer. By late 1947, Stalin's troops were firmly in control of the countries of Eastern Europe, including the one nation there with a democratic tradition of some strength, Czechoslovakia. Already in June 1946, Stalin had made it clear that he would brook no Western interference in these countries. He turned down a proposal by elder statesman Bernard Baruch to outlaw nuclear weapons because the plan involved enforcement on the scene by the United Nations, which had been formed in 1945 under a charter that had evolved from the agreements of the various wartime Allied conferences.

The Americans had calculated correctly: the Soviets condemned the Marshall Plan. Massive American aid was pumped only into those countries where a political purpose could be served by overcoming the economic and social chaos in which Communism flourished.

Freezing the Lines

Containment policy worked. Neither Greece nor Turkey fell to pro-Russian guerrillas nor Italy and France to Communist parties. The policy received its most severe test in June 1948, when Stalin blockaded West Berlin, deep within Communist East Germany. Unable to provision the city of 2 million by overland routes, the United States could have given up Berlin or invaded East Germany. Instead, a massive airlift was organized. For a year, huge C-47s and C-54s flew in the necessities and a few of the luxuries that the West Berliners needed in order to hold out. By this action, the Truman administration made it clear that the United States did not want war, but neither would it tolerate further Soviet expansion.

The Soviets responded quite as George Kennan had predicted. Instead of invading West Berlin or shooting down the airlift planes, they watched. In May 1949, having determined that the United States would not give in, the Soviets lifted the blockade.

By that time, the Cold War had entered a new phase. In April 1949, along with Canada and nine European nations, the United States signed a treaty that established the North Atlantic Treaty Organization

(NATO), the first peacetime military alliance in American history. The NATO countries promised to consider an attack against any of them as grounds for going to war together.

The Soviets then wrote the Warsaw Pact, an alliance of the nations of Eastern Europe. In September 1949, the Soviet Union exploded its first atomic bomb, and soon thereafter the United States perfected the hydrogen bomb, a much more destructive weapon. The nuclear-arms race was under way.

DOMESTIC POLITICS UNDER TRUMAN

All the while Harry S Truman was effecting a decisive and articulate foreign policy, he was struggling to cope with postwar domestic problems. These were considerable: rapid inflation, a serious shortage of housing, and a series of bitter industrial disputes. At first Truman seemed to flounder. Professional politicians and ordinary voters alike began to suspect his competence. In his predecessor's regal shadow, Truman cut a second-rate figure. Compared with dynamic Eleanor Roosevelt, who was even more active in liberal causes after her husband's death, Bess Truman was a plain, frumpy homebody. The deadly serious nuclear age seemed to have caught the United States without a leader up to its challenges.

The Republican Comeback of 1946

Capitalizing on anxieties of this sort, the Republicans ran their congressional election campaign of 1946 on a simple but effective two-word slogan, "Had Enough?" Apparently the voters had. They elected Republican majorities in both houses of Congress for the first time since 1930. One freshman Democratic senator who bucked the landslide, J. William Fulbright of Arkansas, suggested that Truman resign in favor of a Republican president. The Republicans did not take this proposal seriously, but, positive that they would elect their nominee in 1948, they set out to prepare that undesignated candidate's way by dismantling as many New Deal reforms as they could.

One of their most striking successes was the Taft-Hartley Labor-Management Relations Act of 1947. This law, enacted over Truman's veto, reversed the New Deal's active support of the union movement that had been enshrined in the Wagner Act of 1935. Taft-Hartley emphasized the rights of workers not to join labor organizations, most notably by abolishing the closed-shop. That is, under the New Deal, employees of a company

that recognized a union as the workers' bargaining agent—the body that negotiated wages and hours with the company—were required to belong to that union as a condition of employment; employment was closed to all but union members. Taft-Hartley guaranteed the right of individuals not to join a union.

The Taft-Hartley Act was not a "slave labor" law, as Truman called it in his veto message; nor did it cripple the union movement. Indeed, its chief effect was to arouse organized labor, now more than 10 million strong, to rally behind Truman. This unexpected support (for Truman had not been considered especially friendly to organized labor) showed the president a way to fight the Republican Eightieth Congress. He vetoed 80 of its anti-New Deal enactments, thus converting himself into a crusading liberal. When Republican critics mocked his homey manners and common appearance, he turned the tables on them by becoming the common man, denouncing his enemies in Congress as stooges of the rich and privileged. Coining his own slogan, the Fair Deal, he sent to Capitol Hill proposal after proposal that expanded social services. Among his programs was a national health-insurance plan such as most European nations had adopted.

Civil Rights

The Truman health plan failed to pass, as did the president's demand that Congress act to mitigate discrimination against blacks. In 1947, the Presidential Committee on Civil Rights reported to Truman on racial discrimination in the United States, particularly as it related to employment practices and the continued condoning of the lynching of blacks in the South. Truman sent its far-reaching recommendations to Congress, where an alliance of complacent Republicans and Southern Democrats killed them. Truman responded with an executive order that banned racial discrimination in the army and navy, in the civil service, and in companies that did business with the federal government.

Truman's civil-rights program was quite moderate. He

THE 52-20 CLUB

Members of the 52-20 Club of 1945 and 1946 were demobilized soldiers and sailors who were allowed $20 a week for 52 weeks or until such time as they found a job. Although many were accused of avoiding work because of this payment, the average length of membership in the club was only three months.

Learning from Past Mistakes

In a number of ways, F.D.R. and Harry S Truman pointedly departed from American policy toward Europe after the First World War. In sponsoring the United Nations, the United States departed radically from the American boycott of the League of Nations. Unlike Woodrow Wilson, who named no prominent Republican to his peace commission at Versailles, thus contributing to American opposition to the League, Roosevelt made Republican Senator Arthur H. Vandenberg, a former isolationist, a member of the American delegation that wrote the Charter of the United Nations.

With the Marshall Plan, President Truman recognized the folly of the Coolidge administration of the 1920s in refusing to help Europe economically by arranging for a significant modfication of the flow of reparations from Germany and debt payments by Britain and France.

did not attempt to touch "Jim Crow," the system of strict social segregation that provided for separate public facilities for the white and black races in the Southern and border states, including Truman's home state of Missouri. But he went further than Roosevelt had dared, and his program was politically very shrewd. Hundreds of thousands of blacks had moved out of the South, where they were politically powerless, into big cities in Northern and Midwestern states with large electoral votes. For a Democratic president to continue to support segregation was to risk throwing these big states to the Republicans, especially because the leading contenders for the Republican presidential nomination, Robert Taft and New York governor Thomas E. Dewey, had been friendly to black aspirations.

Margaret's Dad

Harry Truman believed that politicians, and presidents most of all, should be thick-skinned when it came to criticism. "If you can't stand the heat," he said, "get out of the kitchen." However, he did not think this principle applied to concert singers, particularly when the singer was his daughter, Margaret. When her recital was panned by the music critic of the *Washington Post* ("She is flat a good deal of the time."), Truman wrote to the critic: "You sound like a frustrated old man who never made a success, an eight-ulcer man on a four-ulcer job, and all four ulcers working. I never met you, but if I do you'll need a new nose and a supporter below."

Planning Ahead

So confident were the Republicans that they were going to win the election of 1948 that the Republican Congress made a record appropriation for the inauguration festivities on January 20. The benefactor of the lavish parade, of course, was the Democratic president whom the Republicans despised, Harry S Truman.

Four Candidates

By the spring of 1948, Truman's popularity was on the upswing. Americans were getting accustomed to, even fond of, the president's hard-hitting style. Nevertheless, no political expert gave Truman a chance to survive the presidential election in November. The Democrats had been in power 16 years, longer than any party since the Virginia Dynasty of Jefferson, Madison, and Monroe. The inefficiency of many New Deal bureaucracies was undeniable, and rumors of corruption were persistent.

Then, to turn worse into impossible, the party split three ways. Henry A. Wallace led left-wing liberals into the newly formed Progressive party. He claimed to be the true heir of New Deal liberalism and insisted that there was no reason to abandon the nation's wartime friendship with the Soviet Union. Democrats from the Deep South, angry at Truman's civil-rights reforms, and a strong plank condemning racial discrimination in the party platform written by the young liberal mayor of Minneapolis, Hubert H. Humphrey, formed the States' Rights, or "Dixiecrat," party. They named Strom Thurmond of South Carolina as their candidate.

Thurmond had fewer illusions of winning the election than did Wallace, who had a mystical streak. Thurmond's purpose was to take credit for denying Truman the election, thus impressing on Northern liberal Democrats the necessity of sticking with their traditional support of Southern segregationists.

Presented with what looked like a gift victory, the Republicans passed over their leading conservative, Senator Robert A. Taft of Ohio, the son of President William Howard Taft. Robert Taft had led the onslaught on the New Deal and Truman, but he was rather too nasty and peevish, driven as much by hate as principle, to be likeable. Republican moderates calculated that if any candidate would send voters who had "had enough" back to the Democrats for more, it was Taft. Instead, they chose the safe Thomas E. Dewey, their candidate in 1944, to take on Truman.

Give 'Em Hell, Harry

Dewey adopted an election strategy that was tried and true. Every poll showed him winning with ease. There-

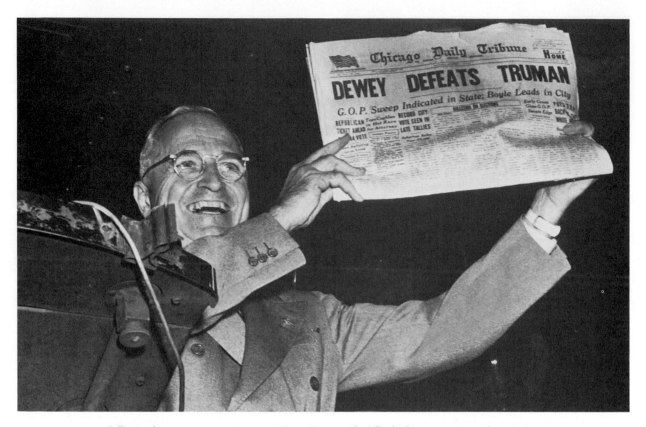

Following his narrow victory in 1948, Harry Truman gleefully displays a newspaper that relied on early returns to predict his defeat by Republican presidential candidate Thomas Dewey.

fore, just as F.D.R. had done when a sure victor in 1932, he ran a low key, noncommittal campaign. He would not jeopardize his lead by saying anything that might alienate any group of voters.

Truman, faced with certain defeat, had nothing to lose by speaking out. "Give 'em hell, Harry," a supporter shouted at a rally, and Truman did. During the summer of 1948, he called Congress into special session and a corps of assistants led by Clark Clifford sent bill after bill to the Republican Congress. As the Republicans voted down his proposals, Truman toured the country, blaming the nation's problems on the "no-good, do-nothing Eightieth Congress." Did Americans want four more years of that sort of thing under a lackluster Thomas E. Dewey?

On election night, the editors of the Republican Chicago *Tribune* glanced at the early returns, which favored Dewey, and decided to scoop the competition by publishing an edition declaring the New Yorker to be the new president. The next day, Harry Truman took great pleasure in posing for photographs while pointing to the *Tribune*'s headline, for Dewey had not won. Truman narrowly squeaked out victories in almost all the large

industrial states and the majority of farm states. His popular vote was under 50 percent, and he lost a few Gulf states to Thurmond. But he was president and by a whopping 303 to 189 electoral vote margin.

CONTAINMENT IN CHINA

The Fair Deal did not fare so well as its author did. Like many presidents who had other things in mind, Truman found himself preoccupied with such serious problems abroad that domestic reforms seemed insignificant by comparison. Also like other presidents who had to become diplomats, Truman discovered that he was not chief executive in world affairs, but only one player in a game in which the rules defied the power at his disposal and even his own understanding of them.

In Asia, only the Philippines and Japan were firm American allies. Given independence in 1946, the Philippines remained beholden to American financial aid and responded with friendship. In Japan, a capitalist democracy was slowly emerging as a consequence of massive Marshall Plan-type assistance and the enlightened military occupation of the country under Douglas MacArthur. Understanding Japanese traditions better than he understood American, MacArthur established himself as a shogun, or a dictator who ruled while the emperor reigned. The shogun was a familiar figure in Japanese history, and the Japanese were comfortable with a new one.

Rejected Option

In China, however, the Truman administration failed because the president ignored the advice of his best advisers and tried to adapt to the Asian mainland the policy of containment that was working in Europe. The trouble was that the Soviet expansionism responsible for the Cold War in Europe did not lie at the bottom of Communist successes in China. Nor were the Chinese Communists, at least until after the Second World War, necessarily opposed to an understanding with the United States. Kennan understood the difference between Europe and China and tried to point it out. Truman, the State Department, and the American public did not listen.

During and after the Second World War, two governments claimed to represent the will of the Chinese people: the Kuomintang, or Nationalist, regime of Chiang Kai-shek, and the powerful Communist party and military force behind Mao Zedong. Some Americans who were familiar with China urged Washington not to oppose Mao but to come to terms with him during the war. General Joseph W. Stilwell repeatedly warned Roosevelt that the people around Chiang were hopelessly corrupt and unpopular, while Mao commanded the loyalty of China's largest social class, the peasantry.

After the war, acting as a special envoy to China, George C. Marshall suggested that the Chinese Communists were not necessarily tools of the Soviets but could be encouraged to chart an independent course through cooperation and friendship. Mao was bent on revolutionary change at home, particularly in regard to land, which was in the hands of an elite allied to Chiang. Marshall, like many others who were familiar with the Nationalists, did not find Mao's program unattractive since the Kuomintang party included butchers of peasants and thieves who misappropriated American material aid for their own profit.

The China Lobby

But Chiang had his American backers, an active, articulate, and well-connected "China Lobby," organized and headed by his brilliant wife, Madame Chiang, who spent much of her time in the United States. This group drew support from conservative congressmen; influential church leaders such as the Catholic archbishop of New York, Francis Cardinal Spellman; and much of the press, most importantly Henry L. Luce, the publisher of *Time* magazine, and Clare Boothe Luce, a Republican congresswoman and eloquent speaker.

Through 1949, the China Lobby bombarded Americans with false information: most Chinese supported Chiang; Chiang was defeating Mao's forces on the battlefield; Mao was a Soviet stooge like the puppet leaders of Eastern Europe. So effective was the campaign that Americans were shocked at the end of 1949 when Chiang suddenly fled the mainland for the island province of Taiwan (then better known by its name as a Japanese colony—Formosa). They thought that Chiang had been winning the war. Instead of admitting that they had been wrong, at least in regard to the power of the Nationalists, the China Lobby insisted that Chiang had not been repudiated but merely betrayed by inadequate American support. They urged that aid be increased and that Chiang be "unleashed" for an assault on the mainland.

Truman and his new Secretary of State, Dean Acheson, knew better than to "unleash" Chiang Kai-shek. To have done so would have meant either humiliation when he was defeated or involvement in a war on the mainland of Asia, which every military strategist, from Douglas MacArthur on down, warned against. Whether Truman and Acheson ever rued the fact that they had ignored the advice of Stilwell, Marshall, and others to come to terms with Mao Zedong's Communists is not clear. Whether American friendship would have significantly changed the course of Chinese history under Mao is also beyond certain knowledge. What is known is that China as a foe was dangerous and unpredictable precisely because China was not, as Americans continued to believe, a Soviet satellite.

Containment Policy Falters

Truman and Acheson were applying the principle of containment to East Asia when events left them behind. No one, including themselves, was quite certain about where the United States would accept Communist control and where the line of containment was to be drawn. Japan was off limits, of course, but what of Quemoy and Matsu, tiny islands off the coast of China that, like Taiwan, were occupied by Chiang's Nationalists? And what of the Republic of Korea, set up by the United States in the southern half of the former Japanese colony of Chosen? Was the little country, bordered on the north by the thirty-eighth parallel (38° north latitude), to be protected like the nations of Western Europe?

Feeling the sting of the China Lobby's attacks, Tru-

"Police action" in Korea: U.S. Infantry troops return from the front, June 1951.

man's last Secretary of State, Dean Acheson, was vague, and the president was indecisive. In a similar situation in 1914, the mischievousness of two weak countries started a war, and that was what happened in 1950. The Communist government of North Korea and the pro-American government of Syngman Rhee in South Korea exchanged ever more serious threats. In June, ostensibly responding to South Korean troop movements, the North Korean army swept across the thirty-eighth parallel and quickly drove Rhee's R.O.K. (Republic of Korea) troops, and the American Eighth Army, to the toe of the peninsula.

The Korean Conflict

Truman already had stationed an American fleet in Korean waters, and he responded immediately and forcibly.

Thanks to the absence of the Soviet delegation to the United Nations, he was able to win the vote necessary to make the U.N. the sponsor of a "police action" on the peninsula. With the United States providing almost all the "police," General MacArthur took command of the expedition.

In a daring maneuver that might have served as the capstone of a brilliant military career, MacArthur engineered an amphibious landing at Inchon, deep behind North Korean lines, cutting off and capturing 100,000 enemy troops. The Americans and R.O.K.s then surged rapidly northward, crossing the thirty-eighth parallel in September 1950. By October 26, they had occupied virtually the whole peninsula. At one point, American soldiers stood on the banks of the Yalu River, which divides Korea from Chinese Manchuria.

The headiness of winning so quickly prevented Tru-

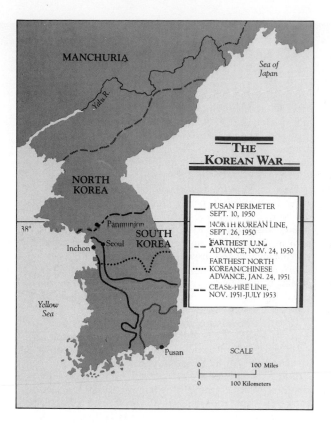

THE
KOREAN WAR

— PUSAN PERIMETER
SEPT. 10, 1950

— NORTH KOREAN LINE,
SEPT. 26, 1950

--- FARTHEST U.N.
ADVANCE, NOV. 24, 1950

···· FARTHEST NORTH
KOREAN/CHINESE
ADVANCE, JAN. 24, 1951

-- CEASE-FIRE LINE,
NOV. 1951-JULY 1953

SCALE

0   100 Miles

0   100 Kilometers

on both sides, neither side knew quite what to do. Some days at Panmunjom, the negotiators simply sat at the table facing one another and saying nothing.

MacArthur's Debacle

With good reason, the American people were frustrated. Not five years after the Second World War, the Korean Conflict put 5.7 million young men in uniform, killed 54,000 of them, and wounded 100,000. Defense expenditures soared from $40 billion in 1950 to $71 billion in 1952. Truman and Acheson had said that the goal was containment, but having "contained," they were unable to conclude hostilities. What was wrong?

In the spring of 1951, General MacArthur offered an answer. Forgetting his own warning against a war with the Chinese on the Asian mainland, and perhaps bruised in the ego by the stalemate, he complained to reporters that the only reason he had not won the war was that Truman would not permit him to bomb the enemy's supply depots in Manchuria. In March, MacArthur went further; he sent a letter to Republican congressman Joseph W. Martin in which he wrote that "there is no substitute for victory" and directly assailed the commander-in-chief for accepting a stalemate. In April, Martin went public with the letter.

This attack on civilian command of the armed forces, a constitutional principle, appalled Truman's military advisers, and on April 11, with their support, the president fired MacArthur. The American people, remembering the general's accomplishments in the Second World War and reckoning that he knew how to fight better than Truman did, cheered the old warrior upon his return to the United States. He was feted with ticker-tape parades in every city he visited, and addressed Congress in a broadcast speech that was listened to by more people than had tuned in to Truman's inaugural address in 1949.

MacArthur concluded his congressional appearance by quoting a line from an old barracks song, "old soldiers never die; they just fade away," but he had no intention of fading anywhere. Establishing residence and a kind of command headquarters at New York's Waldorf-Astoria Hotel, he continued to issue political proclamations. He wanted the Republican nomination for the presidency in 1952; then he would battle Truman's containment policy with his promises of victory in the Cold War.

But the good general was a poor politician. He had spent half his life outside the country, and he was handicapped by a messianic vision of himself: the people would come to him. They did not. As the very clever politician Harry S Truman had calculated when he had dismissed the general, enthusiasm for MacArthur faded

man and the U.N. from reflecting on MacArthur's assurances that the Chinese would not intervene in the war. He was wrong. With its coal and iron deposits, Manchuria was vital to Mao's plans to industrialize China. Furthermore, the northeastern province had, twice before, been the avenue through which the Middle Kingdom had been invaded. Mao threw 200,000 Chinese "volunteers" at the Americans. By the end of 1950, these veterans, still hardened by the wars with Chiang, drove MacArthur back to a line that zigzagged across the thirty-eighth parallel.

There, whether because the Chinese were willing to settle for a "draw" or because American troops found their footing and dug in, stalemate ensued. For two years, the Americans, R.O.K.s, and token delegations of troops from other United Nations countries fought the North Koreans and Chinese over forlorn hills and ridges that they had to number because they had never been named. Even after armistice talks began, first at Kaesong and then in a truce zone at Panmunjom, the war dragged on. The Chinese had won their goal, which was to protect their borders, and the Americans had ensured the independence of the Republic of Korea. In the days when the objects of war were clear and concrete, that was the point at which wars were ended. But in the Cold War, with ideological rivalry taking on a religious significance

---

HOW THEY LIVED

AWAKE!

During the Truman years, millions of Americans were introduced to the Jehovah's Witnesses for the first time. Rather than preaching from street-corner soapboxes, as the sects they seemed to resemble did, the Witnesses showed up on the thresholds of grand homes, middle-class tract houses, and declining urban apartments and row houses alike. Always neatly dressed, always in pairs, often racially mixed, they clutched briefcases or handbags stuffed with their books, tracts, and copies of two monthly magazines, *The Watchtower* and *Awake!* The Witnesses were never jolly nor backslapping in one well-known American evangelical tradition. Their manner was solemn, grim, thin-lipped. Their ice-breaking question was blunt and cheerless: did the householder (usually a housewife during the daytime hours) think that all was well with the world?

The Second World War left in its wake the lingering smell of the extermination camps and Hiroshima, the shock of the lowering of the Iron Curtain and the Communist triumph in China, news of cold war spies and the cries of subversion in Washington. In the vague but general sense that the war had created a more threatening world than it destroyed, the Jehovah's Witnesses won many invitations to come in and talk. The sect that was 70 years old in 1949, but still tiny, began to grow, and the numbers of its fulltime walkers of streets and ringers of doorbells (24,000 in 1984) became more conspicuous. In 1978, the Witnesses numbered more than 600,000 in the United States, two million worldwide. Their Watchtower Tract Society was one of the largest publishing houses in the world. *Awake!* alone had a circulation of eight million in 34 languages.

The Witnesses took shape during the 1870s in Alle-

gheny City, Pennsylvania, in the midst of the iron and steel belt that epitomized industrial progress to some, a hell of soot, smoke, sparkling flame, and social insecurity to others. The founder, Charles Taze Russell, was a Presbyterian who, like many troubled believers before him, found grievous flaws in the traditional faiths, and styled himself "God's Mouthpiece."

At first, the Witnesses seemed like just another variant on the fundamentalist, millennarian, catastrophe-minded groups that have sprung up in times of trying social ferment. They taught that the Bible was "inspired and historically accurate," a single, reassuring absolute in a world of whirling flux and instability. In the 1980s, the American Witnesses' street ministers were probably nimbler in finding the apt Biblical citation for an occasion than the deans and doyennes of America's most prestigious divinity schools.

Like the Millerites of the 1840s, the Witnesses said that "the end of the world" was nigh. In 1876, Russell predicted that Armageddon—the final battle between good and evil—would occur in 1914. When the First World War, with its unprecedented horrors, erupted in that year, Witness membership jumped. Russell's successor named 1918, the end of the Great War. Others have set the date at 1925, 1941, 1975, and 1984. In times of anxiety like the late 1940s and early 1950s, the perception that the state of the world incontrovertibly precludes an indefinite future is a common historical response, particularly by those whom society has rejected, despised, or merely left behind. Like other fundamentalist groups, the Witnesses were most successful among the poor, downtrodden, and ignorant.

However, the Witnesses were unique fundamentalists

---

within a few months. MacArthur was left to spend his final years in obscurity. In the meantime, the Korean War dragged on, chewing up lives like a machine.

YEARS OF TENSION

Periodically in American history, during times of great political or social stress, many people have turned to "conspiracy theories" to account for their anxieties. The era of the Korean War was just such a time. Substantial numbers of Americans came to believe that the failure to achieve a sense of security after the glorious total victory in the Second World War must be the result of sinister forces working quietly but effectively within the United States.

"Twenty Years of Treason"

The view that at Yalta, President Roosevelt had sold out Eastern Europe to Stalin was an early expression of this "paranoid streak," belief in a sinister conspiracy at work to destroy America from within. Then, in March 1947, President Truman inadvertently fueled anxieties by ordering all government employees to sign loyalty oaths, statements that they did not belong to the Communist party or to other groups suspected of disloyalty. Eventually, 30 states followed this example, requiring an oath even of people who waxed the floors of state university basketball courts.

Truman also promoted the belief that there was treason in government by allowing his supporters to "red bait" Henry Wallace in the 1948 presidential campaign. Wallace was an eccentric, and he may well have been mistaken in his analysis of Soviet intentions in 1948.

and millennarians in several ways. Hardly inclined to be "right-wingers" preaching anti-Semitism and antiblack racism, the Witnesses totally rejected racial discrimination of any kind. As a consequence, they have been immensely successful proselytizers among African Americans.

Hardly uncritical super-patriots, the Witnesses considered all governments—America's included—as evil. Their meeting houses, called "Kingdom Halls," indicate that they consider themselves subjects of God's (Jehovah's) realm. They merely submit to those powers of the state that do not conflict with Jehovah's law. They do not participate in government or politics.

As a result of their refusal to serve in the armed forces, thousands of Witnesses were imprisoned during World War II. They puzzled authorities by their passivity and self-enforced order in prison, and also by their disdain for other political and conscientious objectors to military service. In fact, the Witnesses considered their fellow prisoners as misguided "instruments of satan," too. The Witnesses were not pacifists in any but the functional sense of the word. They looked forward with zest to Armageddon when they will themselves take up arms for Jehovah and exterminate those who have rejected their message and witness.

The Jehovah's Witnesses are also peculiar in that they do not believe in hell. When Jehovah's reign begins, the "instruments of satan" will simply cease to exist. A material universe will be ruled by 144,000 Witnesses who alone, with Jesus, will reside in heaven.

In their vision of the post-Armageddon earth, the importance of the Truman years in the development of the organization can be seen in a most curious way. Pictorial depictions of Jehovah's kingdom in *Awake!* and *Watchtower* show lions lying down with lambs (the ancient biblical image), but the restored Eden is a broad, weedless lawn mowed as closely as a golfing green surrounding a sprawling "ranch-type" house such as was the beau-ideal, the "good life," for millions of Americans in the late 1940s and early 1950s. Smiling, loving, neatly and conventionally dressed and barbered suburbanites (no wings and halos), albeit of all races, populate this paradise. Often, guests are arriving for a backyard barbecue.

The Witnesses' paradise bears a close resemblance to the consumer paradise that advertisers of automobiles, television sets, furniture, and carpets pictured during the postwar years; even the style of the artwork is similar. Such aspirations in a time of increasing affluence allowed most Americans to cope with the anxieties of the Truman era. To the Witnesses, such things represented the post-millennial universe.

In the 1990s, when much of society has questioned the suburban ideal of the 1950s, the Witnesses are still loyal to it, perhaps because so few of them have achieved it. The organization also shows signs of evolving into a large, wealthy, well-established, and increasingly bureaucratized body headquartered in Brooklyn, New York. Its chief official, William Van De Wall, said in 1984 that "we do not know the day or the hour, but we do feel that we are in the time of the end. We are living in the general time period." It was such an accommodation—a dodging of specific predictions that lead to crises—that in the nineteenth century transformed disreputable Millerites into acceptable Seventh Day Adventists.

But he was no Communist party stooge. In calling him one, as many Democratic speech-makers did, they created a political tactic that, in the end, could only work against them. If there were traitors in high places, the Democratic party was responsible, because, as of 1952, they had been running the country for twenty years.

Long before 1952, frustrated right-wing Republicans such as John Bricker of Ohio, William F. Knowland of California, and Karl Mundt of North Dakota raised the specter of "twenty years of treason." The two chief beneficiaries of the scare were Richard M. Nixon, a young first-term congressman from southern California, and Joseph McCarthy, the junior senator from Wisconsin.

Alger Hiss and Richard Nixon

Richard M. Nixon built the beginnings of his career on the ashes of the less illustrious but still distinguished career of a former New Dealer named Alger Hiss. A bright young Ivy Leaguer during the 1930s when he had gone to Washington to work in the Agriculture Department, Hiss had risen to be a middle level aide to Roosevelt at the time of the Yalta Conference. He was aloof and fastidious in his manner, a bit of a snob, and he was a militant liberal.

In 1948, a journalist named Whittaker Chambers, who confessed to having been a Communist during the 1930s, accused Hiss of having helped him funnel classified American documents to the Soviets. At first his testimony aroused little fuss. Chambers had a reputation for erratic behavior and, indeed, making things up. From a legal point of view, there seemed scant reason to pursue the matter; all the acts of which Hiss was accused had transpired too long in the past to be prosecuted, and he was no longer in government service in 1948. It was Hiss who forced the issue to a reckoning. He indignantly

FLYING SAUCER SCARE

In 1947, a commercial pilot over the state of Washington sighted a cluster of "saucer-like things" and reported them to the federal government. By 1950, six-hundred Americans a year were seeing flying saucers. No one ever proved if the sightings were frauds, the fruit of mass hysteria, evidence of visitors from outer space, or of some new top-secret air force plane. The movie industry, looking for a kind of film with which to combat television, had no trouble making a choice. The early 1950s were years of dozens of movies about extraterrestrial creatures—usually, but not always, bent on destruction—who visited Earth.

swore under oath that everything Chambers said was false. Indeed, Hiss insisted, he did not even know Chambers.

To liberals, the well-spoken Hiss, with his exemplary record in public service, was obviously telling the truth. The seedy Chambers, with his background in Henry L. Luce's *Time* magazine, was a liar. But many ordinary Americans, especially working-class ethnics and citizens of Western farming states, were not so sure. With his nasal aristocratic accent and expensive tailored clothing, Hiss represented the Eastern Establishment, traditionally an object of suspicion, and the long-entrenched New Deal bureaucracy, of which they had grown weary.

Congressman Nixon shared these feelings and, following a hunch, pursued the Hiss case when other Republicans lost interest. Nixon persuaded Chambers to produce microfilms that seemed to show that Hiss had indeed retyped classified documents for some reason. In cross-examination at congressional hearings, he poked hole after hole in Hiss's defense.

Largely because of Nixon's efforts, Hiss was convicted of perjury. Additional thousands of Americans wondered how many other bright New Dealers were spies. More than one Republican pointed out that Hiss had been a friend of none other than the "no-win" Secretary of State Dean Acheson and that the men resembled each other in their manners and appearance. Indeed, Acheson's style grated even more harshly than Hiss's. He favored London-made tweeds and sported a bristling waxed moustache. Richard Nixon, whose social awkwardness and furtiveness at work might otherwise have obscured him for life, looked good by comparison.

Senator Joe McCarthy

Senator Joseph McCarthy of Wisconsin was another unlikely character to play a major role in the government

of a nation. Not only awkward and furtive, he was a crude, bullying man who seems to have been less cruel than uncomprehending of what cruelty was. He was also facing an election in 1952 in which he seemed sure to be defeated, so lackluster had been his record in the Senate. Groping for an issue, he rejected friends' suggestions that he focus on the advantages the proposed St. Lawrence Seaway would bestow on Wisconsin, a Great Lakes state, and instead, almost by accident, discovered that anxiety about Communist subversion was his ticket to a kind of political stardom.

In 1950, McCarthy told a Republican audience in Wheeling, West Virginia, that he possessed a list of 205 Communists who were working in the State Department with the full knowledge of Secretary of State Acheson. In other words, Acheson himself, as well as other high-ranking government officials, actively abetted Communist subversion.

McCarthy had no such list, of course. Only two days later, he could not remember if he had said the names totaled 205 or 57. He never released a single name and never fingered a single Communist in government. Because he was so reckless, interested in nothing but publicity, McCarthy probably was headed for a fall from the moment he stepped into the limelight. But the tumultuous response that met his use of the "big lie"—making a complete falsehood so fabulous and retelling it so often that people believed that "it must be true"—was an alarming symptom of just how anxious American society had become.

When a few senators publicly denounced his irresponsibility, McCarthy showed just how sensitive was the nerve he had touched. Senator Millard Tydings of Maryland was a conservative whose family name gave him practically a proprietary interest in a Senate seat in his state. In 1950, McCarthy threw his support behind Tydings's unknown opponent, fabricated a photograph showing Tydings shaking hands with American Communist party leader Earl Browder, and the senator went down to defeat.

McCarthyism

Following Tydings's defeat, civil libertarians outside politics worried because senators who opposed McCarthy's smear tactics were afraid to speak up lest they suffer the same fate. By 1952, McCarthy was so powerful that Republican presidential candidate Dwight D. Eisenhower, whose military career had been sponsored by George C. Marshall, and who detested the vulgar McCarthy, refrained from praising Marshall in Wisconsin because the former Secretary of State was one of McCarthy's "traitors."

In the meantime, liberal Democrats in Congress

rushed to prove their loyalty by voting for dubious laws such as the McCarran Internal Security Act, which effectively outlawed the Communist party, by defining dozens of liberal lobby groups as "Communist fronts," and even by providing for the establishment of concentration camps in the event of a national emergency. In 1951, the Supreme Court fell into line with its decision in *Dennis et al. v. United States*. By a vote of 6 to 2, the Court agreed that it was a crime to advocate the forcible overthrow of the government, a position that Communists were defined as holding by virtue of their membership in the party.

At the peak of McCarthy's power, only a very few opinion makers outside politics, such as cartoonist Herbert Block and television commentator Edward R. Murrow, and a few universities, including the University of Wisconsin in McCarthy's home state, refused to be intimidated by the senator's bullying. Not until 1954, however, did McCarthy's career come to an end. Failing to get preferential treatment for an intimate draftee friend of his chief aide, Roy Cohn, McCarthy accused the United States Army of being infiltrated by Communists. This recklessness emboldened the Senate to move against him. He was censured in December 1954 by a vote of 72 to 22. It was only the third time in American history that the nation's most exclusive club had turned on one of its own members.

The Making of a Politician

Nixon and McCarthy built their careers on exploiting and aggravating anxieties. The leader of the conservative wing of the Republican party, Senator Robert A. Taft of Ohio, did the same. Although personally less than electrifying and cultivating an image of rectitude, Taft encouraged his party's least responsible hell-raisers as a way of chipping at the Democrats.

But the American people turned to no mover and shaker to guide them through the 1950s. Instead, they chose a man with no background in politics, whose strength was a warm personality and whose talent was a knack for smoothing over conflict.

After World War II, General Dwight David Eisenhower wrote his memoirs of the war, *Crusade in Europe*, and early in 1948 he accepted the presidency of Columbia University. Leaders of both parties approached him in his uptown New York office with offers to nominate him as president. Truman himself told Ike that if he would accept the Democratic nomination, Truman would gladly step aside.

Eisenhower was not interested. He was a career military man who, unlike MacArthur, believed that soldiers should stay out of politics. It is not certain that Eisenhower ever bothered to vote before 1948, and he identified with neither party. But he did not identify with university life either. Ike's intellectual interests ran to pulp western novels and, after a lifetime accustomed to military order and expecting instructions to be carried out, he found the chaos of shepherding anarchic academics intolerable.

As one of New York's most eminent citizens, however, Eisenhower drifted into close professional and personal association with the wealthy Eastern businessmen who dominated the moderate wing of the Republican party. They showered him with gifts such as had turned General Grant's head, and financial advice that, uncannily, was inevitably sound. As an administrator himself, something of a businessman in uniform, Eisenhower found it easy to assimilate their politics.

In 1950, Ike took a leave of absence from Columbia to take command of NATO troops in Europe. There, with the Korean Conflict dragging on to no conceivable end, MacArthur's insubordination (which shocked him), and the rise of demagogues like McCarthy, he grew increasingly receptive to the pleas of his moderate Republican friends that he run for president. Like them, Eisenhower felt no obsession to return the United States to the pre–New Deal free-enterprise idyll that Taft fantasized. He and they had come to terms with the basic reforms of the Roosevelt era. What disturbed Ike and the moderates was corruption in the Truman administration, excessive government expenditures, and bureaucratic waste. Gradually, Eisenhower came to concede that he could defeat any Democrat by virtue of his tremendous personal popularity while, with Senator Taft as the party's nominee, the Republicans might well go down to defeat.

The Campaign of 1952

Indeed, many conservative Republicans who admired Taft also wanted Eisenhower to run. They were more interested in victory at the polls than in honoring their veteran leader. They agreed with the Eisenhower moderates that Taft's uncompromising conservative stands would alienate voters who had benefited from the New Deal, but who were otherwise weary of the long Democratic era. Eisenhower's lack of a political record was a positive advantage. Eisenhower did not excite people; he reassured them. But that was precisely what, the majority of the Republican party guessed, the nation craved in 1952.

Eisenhower's Democratic opponent was the governor of Illinois, Adlai E. Stevenson. He was a New Deal liberal, but he had taken no part in the increasingly unpopular Truman administration. Stevenson was also a superb campaigner, personable, witty, and as attractively modest in manner as Eisenhower. For a few weeks late in the summer of 1952, it appeared as though Stevenson were catching up. He enchanted reporters covering the election with his eloquence while Eisenhower, who functioned best in small groups, seemed to bumble on the podium.

But Stevenson labored under too many handicaps, and Eisenhower's shrewd campaign managers made the most of them. They actually turned Stevenson's intelligence and glibness on the rostrum against him, pointing out that "eggheads" (intellectuals) were responsible for "the mess in Washington." In October, Eisenhower administered the *coup de grâce*. While Stevenson defended the policy on which the limited war in Korea was based, Eisenhower promised that, if he were elected, he would "go to Korea" and end the aimless war. Nothing could have better reminded voters that Eisenhower had been the director of the successful war in Europe.

Landslide

Stevenson won nine southern states. Although a supporter of civil rights for blacks, he brought the Dixiecrats

back into the Democratic party by naming as his running mate a Southern moderate who supported segregation quietly, John Sparkman of Alabama. Otherwise, Eisenhower swept the nation, winning 55 percent of the popular vote and 442 electoral votes to Stevenson's 89.

In December, before he was inaugurated, Eisenhower kept his promise to go to Korea. He donned military gear and was filmed talking and sipping coffee with soldiers on the front lines. He had long recognized that an all-out conventional offensive was foolish. Now, by threatening to use the atomic bomb to end the stalemate—probably a bluff he had no intention of following through on—he dragooned the Chinese and North Koreans to agree to an end to hostilities in July 1953.

It was an auspicious beginning. Indeed, in March 1953, the *bête noire* of postwar American frustrations, Soviet dictator Joseph Stalin, had died. The first summer of the Eisenhower presidency was scarcely underway when Americans could feel with reason that they were embarked on a new age of normalcy.

For Further Reading

There are a surprising number of good general histories treating the immediate postwar era. The most recent are William L. O'Neill, *American High: The Years of Confidence, 1945–1960* (1987) and James Gilbert, *Another Chance* (1984), but see also Eric Goldman, *The Crucial Decade and After* (1961); Godfrey Hodgson, *America in Our Time: From World War II to Nixon* (1976); and William E. Leuchtenburg, *A Troubled Feast: American Society Since 1945* (1979). Also consult the introductory sections of C.C. Alexander, *Holding the Line: The Eisenhower Era, 1952–1961* (1975).

On Truman and his administration, see that articulate president's own *Memoirs* (1955–1956), and a remembrance by his daughter, Margaret Truman, *Harry S Truman* (1973); William C. Berman, *The Politics of Civil Rights in the Truman Administration* (1970); Bert Cochran, *Truman and the Crisis Presidency* (1973); Susan Hartmann, *Truman and the Eightieth Congress* (1971); R. F. Haynes, *The Awesome Power: Harry S Truman as Commander in Chief* (1973); James T. Paterson, *Mr. Republican: A Biography of Robert A. Taft* (1975); and Allen Yarnell, *Democrats and Progressives: The 1948 Election as a Test of Postwar Liberalism* (1974).

The trying diplomatic problems of the times are

treated in Herbert Feis, *Between War and Peace: The Potsdam Conference* (1960) and the same author's *From Trust to Terror: The Onset of the Cold War, 1945–1950* (1970); John L. Gaddis, *The United States and the Origins of the Cold War, 1941–1947* (1972); Norman A. Graebner, *The Age of Global Power: The United States Since 1938* (1979); Gabriel Kolko, *The Limits of Power: The World and United States Foreign Policy, 1945–1954* (1972); Walter LaFeber, *America, Russia, and the Cold War, 1945–1980* (1981); Thomas G. Paterson, *Cold War Critics: Alternatives to American Foreign Policy in the Truman Years* (1972); J.L. Snell, *Illusion and Necessity: The Diplomacy of Global War* (1963); and again William Appleman Williams, *The Tragedy of American Diplomacy* (1962).

On Korea: Carl Berger, *The Korea Knot: A Military–Political History* (1957); R. F. Haynes, *The Awesome Power: Harry S Truman as Commander in Chief* (1973); William Manchester, *American Caesar: Douglas MacArthur* (1978); G. D. Paige, *The Korean Decision* (1968); David Rees, *Korea: The Limited War* (1964); and John W. Spanier, *The Truman–MacArthur Controversy* (1965). McCarthyism and other manifestations of the Red scare of the early 1950s are treated in David Caute,

The Great Fear: The Anti-Communist Purge Under Truman and Eisenhower (1978); Stanley Kutler, *The American Inquisition* (1982); Norman D. Markowitz, *Rise and Fall of the People's Century: Henry A. Wallace and American Liberalism, 1941–1948* (1974); Victor Navasky, *Naming Names* (1980); William L. O'Neill, *A Better World* (1982); Thomas C. Reeves, *The Life and Times of Joe McCarthy* (1982); Walter and Miriam Schneir, *Invitation to an Inquest* (1972); Allen Weinstein, *Perjury! The Hiss-Chambers Conflict* (1978).

The suburban communities that sprung up across the United States during the 1950s were characterized by rows of nearly identical single-family houses.

EISENHOWER COUNTRY

AMERICAN LIFE IN THE 1950's

The voters of 1952 wanted no upheaval. They wanted a change of pace. A large majority of Americans accepted the inevitability of the ongoing Cold War with Communism, but they wanted an end to the stalemate in Korea. Most Americans approved of the basic reforms that the Roosevelt and Truman administrations had carried out; they did not want to return to the days of Coolidge and Hoover. But after a generation of government by the Democratic party, they were ready for new faces in Washington.

Most of all, Americans wanted to cool off. They were weary of crusades, the intense moral demands of reform and war. There was a sense of 1920 about the election of 1952, voters opting for a calmer, reassuring America in which they could savor the rewards of living in the world's richest nation.

LEADERSHIP

Reassurance is what Dwight D. Eisenhower gave them. The grinning, amiable Ike was a perfect regent. He kept the peace through two full terms in office. He replaced the jaded political pros, earnest intellectuals, and liberal reformers of the Roosevelt–Truman era with cool-headed administrators like himself, and with the wealthy businessmen who had become his friends.

They were neither colorful nor exciting. "Eight millionaires and a plumber," a scornful Democrat sniffed about Eisenhower's cabinet, and Secretary of Labor Martin Durkin, the leader of the A.F.L. plumbers union, resigned within a year of his appointment to be replaced by another rich businessman. When Congress created the cabinet-level Department of Health, Education, and Welfare, Eisenhower's choice to head it was not a social worker with a cause to serve, but Oveta Culp Hobby. She had been the no-nonsense head of the Women's Army Corps during the Second World War; she was a military bureaucrat like Ike himself.

Ike's Style and Its Critics

Eisenhower's style was calculated to soothe. Rather than leaping into political cat fights with claws flashing, which had been Truman's way, Ike sidled away from disputes and left the shouting to subordinates. His special assistant, Sherman Adams of New Hampshire, screened every person who applied to see the president. Adams turned away anyone who might involve Ike in a controversy, or trick him into making an embarrassing statement, to which Eisenhower seemed sometimes prone. Adams also studied every document that was to cross the president's desk, weeding out those he thought trivial and summarizing the rest. Eisenhower disliked reading more than a page or so on any subject, a "brief" such as he had dealt with in the army.

Critics claimed that Adams was more powerful than an appointed official should be. They said that he made many presidential-level decisions himself, and he probably did. But there was never any doubt that the flinty, abrupt New Englander had Eisenhower's complete confidence. In 1958, when it was learned that Adams had

Dwight D. Eisenhower, "Ike," personified America in the 1950s.

rigged some government decisions to favor a long-time friend, businessman Bernard Goldfine, and had accepted at least an expensive coat from Goldfine in return, he was forced to resign his post. Eisenhower let him go, but he bitterly resented the loss of an aide who had served his purposes so well.

The president delegated considerable power to the members of his cabinet. They were expected to study the details of issues, report to him, and, if they disagreed among themselves, to debate the question. Ike, the commander with ultimate responsibility, listened and handed down the decision. Whenever possible, he preferred compromise to backing one adviser against another. That was how he had worked during the Second World War.

Liberal Democrats and intellectuals, outsiders in Washington during the 1950s, poked fun at Eisenhower's losing battle with the English language at press conferences. Not a reflective man and never happy before large audiences, Eisenhower could lapse into gobbledygook. He spoke in disjointed phrases or his sentences meandered endlessly, finally trailing off in a scratch of the head without quite touching on the question he had been asked. Some of Eisenhower's aides suggested that

Ike knew exactly what he was doing at all times: "confusing" his interrogators when it did not suit him to answer them.

Eisenhower's apparent lethargy also aroused critics. The nation was drifting, they said, while Ike relaxed on his gentleman's farm on the battlefield at Gettysburg, and took too many vacations in climes where the golf courses were always green and the clubhouses air-conditioned.

We're in the Money

But the critics never got through to the majority of Americans. They did not object to a president who took it easy. In 1956, when Ike ran for reelection against Adlai Stevenson, a year after suffering a serious heart attack and just a few months after undergoing major abdominal surgery, the voters reelected him by an even larger margin than in 1952. Better easy-going Ike in questionable health than a healthy Stevenson forever calling on them to roll up their sleeves again, right wrongs, and finish up the New Deal.

For a majority of Americans, the 1950s were good times, an age of unprecedented prosperity. There had not been a shift in the distribution of wealth. The poor remained about as numerous as they had been for decades. The lowest-paid 20 percent of the population earned the same 3 to 4 percent of the national income that they had earned during the 1920s. The very rich held on to their big slice of the economic pie: The wealthiest 20 percent of the population continued to enjoy 44 to 45 percent of the national income. Proportionately, therefore, the middle 60 percent of the population were no better off than before.

What made the difference in the 1950s was the size of the pie from which all were taking their slices. America was vastly richer as a result of the extraordinary economic growth of the Second World War decade. Thanks to New Deal tax reforms and the powerful labor unions that protected one worker in three, indirectly helping another third, Americans in the middle found themselves with a great deal of "discretionary income," money that was not needed to provide the immediate necessities of life. In 1950, discretionary income totaled $100 billion compared with $40 billion in 1940. This sum increased steadily throughout the decade.

Traditional values of thrift and frugality dictated that such extra money be saved or invested. However, with a generation of daily denial behind them—the hard times of the Great Depression and the sacrifices demanded by the Second World War—newly affluent Americans itched to spend their riches on goods and services that made life more comfortable, varied, and stimulating. A host of new consumer-oriented industries cropped up to urge them on.

Enjoy Yourself

"Enjoy yourself," a popular song went. "It's later than you think." Americans did. They lavished their extra money on a cornucopia of goods and services—some trivial, some momentous in their cultural consequences, and most designed to amuse and entertain economically secure people in their spare time. The middle classes upgraded their diets, eating more meat and vegetables and fewer of the bulky, starchy bread and potatoes that had sustained their parents. Mass-produced convenience foods such as frozen vegetables became staples of middle-class diet. Frozen vegetables could be cooked in five or ten minutes, freeing people to enjoy additional leisure time.

Fashion in dress, buying clothes in order to be "in style," became a diversion in which tens of millions of middle-class citizens, rather than just a handful of very rich people, could indulge. Mass-producers of clothing imitated the creations of Paris couturiers with affordable department store versions of "the latest." The designers encouraged the impulse to be a step ahead of neighbors by changing styles annually. In 1953, more people could identify and more or less explain the significance of Christian Dior (a French clothing designer) than could identify the plumber in Eisenhower's cabinet.

Faddism

The 1950s were a good time for fads, frivolous behavior in which people participated for no better reason than they could afford to do so and others already were. In late 1954, a Walt Disney television program about the nineteenth-century frontiersman and politician Davy Crockett inspired a mania for coonskin caps (usually made from rabbit or synthetic fur), lunch boxes decorated with pictures of Davy shooting bears, and plastic "long rifles" and bowie knives reasonably safe for use in backyard Alamos. Virtually any homely object with the magic name of Crockett printed on it became a bestseller. Within six months, Americans spent more than $100 million in memory of the Tennessee adventurer and Whig who never quite made it big himself.

In 1958, a toy manufacturer brought out a plastic version of an Australian exercise device, a hoop that was twirled about the hips by means of hula-like gyrations. Almost overnight, 30 million "hula hoops" were sold for $1.98 (and, after the fad declined, for as little as 50 cents).

To some extent, the numerous manias of the 1950s were instigated and promoted by the advertising industry. For example, a chemical compound, chlorophyll, became the rage of the early 1950s when manufacturers of more than 90 products, ranging from chewing gum through dog food, said that the green stuff improved the odor of the breath and body of those who ate it, chewed it, shampooed or bathed with it, or rubbed it into the armpits. Americans responded by spending $135 million on chlorophyll products. The boom may have busted when the American Medical Association pointed out that goats, notoriously hard on the nose, consumed chlorophyll all day, every day. More likely, like all fads, chlorophyll simply ran its course.

Other fads profited no one but the newspapers and magazines that reported them. College students competed to see how many of them could squeeze into a telephone booth or a minuscule Volkswagen automobile, challenging others to top their record. Such behavior worried social critics. They concluded that inane faddism revealed the emptiness of lives based on material consumption: people defined themselves in terms of what they could buy. Others were distressed by the conformism of which fads were only the most bizarre example. The American people, it seemed, would do anything and think anything that they were told to do and think, or that others were doing and thinking. But they were afraid of the eccentric, the unpopular, and the adventurous.

The Boob Tube

The most significant new consumer bauble of the 1950s, to become a major force for conformism, was the home television receiver. Developed in workable form as early as 1927, "radio with a picture" had remained a toy of electronics hobbyists and the very wealthy until after the Second World War. In 1946, there were only 8,000 privately owned "TV sets" in the United States, about one for every 18,000 people.

Then, gambling that Americans were ready to spend their extra money on a new kind of entertainment, the radio networks plunged into television, making more extensive programming available. By 1950, almost 4 mil-

Children born in the 1940s and 1950s were the first generation of Americans to grow up with television.

lion sets had been sold, one for every 32 people in the country. By 1960, the skeletons of obsolete small-screen receivers were conspicuous in dumps even in rural states. By 1970, more American households were equipped with a television set than had refrigerators, bathtubs, or indoor toilets. Never in history did a whole society fall so suddenly and hopelessly in love with a device.

At first, high-minded network executives and retooled radio reporters such as Edward R. Murrow hoped that television would be an agent of education and uplift. Corporations making consumer products agreed, and sponsored programs bringing serious plays, both classics and dramas written especially for television, to the small screen. Playwrights such as Paddy Chayefsky and Rod Serling got their start writing for shows such as *Playhouse Ninety* and *Studio One*.

But American television, like American radio, was a private enterprise that depended on advertisers for its profits, and advertisers soon learned that a mass audience wanted light entertainment. Americans made a multi-millionaire of "Mr. Television," Milton Berle, who had been but a fair to middling burlesque comic. Rather more remarkable, a New York gossip columnist utterly lacking in a stage personality, Ed Sullivan, became a national celebrity by hosting a variety show that surrounded one celebrity singer or comedian with trained dog acts, trained bird acts, trained seal acts, and ventriloquists.

Cowboys and Quiz Shows

Beginning in 1955, Americans watched westerns. The networks launched about 40 different dramas set in an imaginary Wild West and, by 1957, one-third of television "prime time," the evening hours between supper-

"MAD MAN" MUNTZ

Just as has happened when other completely new consumer goods attracted the fancy of Americans—automobiles, radio receivers, miniaturized calculators, computers—the early television industry was a competitive free-for-all, with dozens of manufacturers hoping to establish themselves as giants of the industry. One of the most intriguing companies was Muntz TV, which promoted its inexpensive sets as if the item were a dubious gadget being hawked at a county fair. "Mad Man" Muntz said that he got his name—he said it on TV as well as on billboards and in magazine advertisements—because he wanted to give his sets away but his wife wouldn't let him. "She says I'm crazy." Also, as in the cases of radios, calculators, computers, the era of all-out competition passed. After the "shakeout," a comparatively few TV set manufacturers remained, mostly old, large electronics makers. In their turn they were displaced by Japanese imports in the 1970s.

time and bedtime, was devoted to horses, sheriffs, bad-men, and saloon girls with hearts of gold. In New York City, with seven channels, it was possible to watch 51 western shows a week; in Los Angeles 64 hours of westerns aired each week.

One of the first, "Gunsmoke," ran through 635 half-hour episodes; it was estimated that one-quarter of the world's population saw at least one program in which Marshall Matt Dillon made Dodge City, Kansas, safe for decent law-abiding citizens. A somewhat less popular show, "Death Valley Days," revived the career of an on-again, off-again actor, Ronald Reagan, and set him off on a trail that would lead to the White House.

Late in the decade, quiz shows offering huge prizes—$64,000 and up—caught the popular imagination. Millions watched avidly as intense intellectuals and idiot-savants rattled off the names of opera characters and kings of Poland. Then, in 1959, it was revealed that Charles Van Doren, a Columbia University professor and scion of a distinguished academic family, had been fed the correct answers before the show. What was worse, he agonized like a soap opera heroine on camera as he pretended to retrieve some obscure morsel of knowledge from deep within his brain. Intellectuals said they were shocked by Van Doren's betrayal of academic integrity. The quiz shows went off the air. Ordinary folks just changed the channel. "Gunsmoke" was still going strong, although its writers admitted some strain in coming up with plots. "We've used up De Maupassant," said one, "and we're halfway through Maugham."

Social and Cultural Consequences

The social and cultural consequences of America's marriage to "the tube" are still not fully appreciated. In the short run, television seemed to kill off other kinds of popular entertainment such as the movies, social dancing, and radio. Hollywood studios that specialized in churning out low-budget films went bankrupt when empty neighborhood theaters closed their doors. However, prestigious movie companies such as Metro–Goldwyn–Mayer, Columbia Pictures, and Warner Brothers survived and prospered by concentrating on expensive, grandiose epics that could not be duplicated on the small black-and-white home screen; by experimenting with themes that were thought unsuitable for showing in homes; and, in the 1960s, by producing shows for home television.

The "big bands" that had toured the country playing for local dances since the 1930s broke up when deserted dance halls closed. But the recorded music industry survived in the age of television by emphasizing individual ballad singers, such as Perry Como, Jo Stafford, Patti Page, and Frankie Laine, who promoted sales of their

TELEVISION AND THE MOVIES

In 1946, 82 million Americans went to the movies each week. Ten years later, only about half that many did. The others were at home watching television.

recordings on television. Radio stations adapted to the big change by scrapping the dramatic and comedy shows that television could do with pictures, and offering instead a format of music, news, and weather aimed at people who were driving their cars or working and could not, during those hours, watch television.

Curiously, the "one-eyed monster" did not much change the reading habits of older Americans. Even though Americans were soon staring into the flickering blue light for three hours a day, the time they devoted to magazines and newspapers declined very little. Purchases of books, particularly cheap paperback editions, rose 53 percent over what they had been during the 1940s.

What older Americans cut out in order to watch TV was socializing with one another. Instead of chatting with neighbors or with other members of their families, instead of meeting at dances, clubs, even on the street outside the neighborhood movie theater, Americans barricaded themselves in their homes, hushing up or resenting all interruptions. The frozen food industry invented the "TV dinner," a complete meal that could be put in and taken out of the oven during commercials or station breaks and eaten in silence in front of the set on a "TV table," a metal tray on folding legs, one for each member of the nuclear family, perhaps an extra one or two for when grandparents, equally agog before the tube, paid a visit.

Fears for the Future

Rather more worrisome was the passive enthusiasm with which children born in the television age were enslaved by the tube. Networks and local stations filled late-afternoon hours and much of Saturday and Sunday mornings with programs that were aimed at children and avidly sponsored by toy makers and manufacturers of breakfast cereals and sweets. If adults who had grown up before the advent of television continued to read, children did not. In 1955, a book by Rudolf Fleisch called *Why Johnny Can't Read* presented Americans with disturbing evidence that they were raising a generation of functional illiterates.

Nevertheless, and regardless of class, race, occupation, or region, Americans took television to their hearts. For good or ill, they were exposed at the same moment to the same entertainment, commercials, and even speech patterns. National businesses discovered that they could compete with local merchants thanks to the hypnotic influence of television advertising.

Because the network and even local news programs preferred announcers who spoke "standard American English," regional variations in speech declined. City people and country people, who had been sharply divided by hostile world views in the previous generation, came to look, speak, and think alike. However, neither country folk nor city folk set the cultural tone of the age of Eisenhower. The people who did were pioneers of a new kind of American community, the middle-class automobile suburb.

SUBURBIA AND ITS VALUES

The essence of the good life, to Americans of the 1950s, was to escape from the cities (and the country) and set up housekeeping in single-home dwellings in the suburbs. In part, this massive movement of population in the late 1940s and 1950s was an expression of an anti-urban bias that dates back to the nation's rural beginnings. As a people, Americans never have been quite at ease with city life.

Flight from the Cities

In part, young couples of the postwar period had little choice as to where they would live. The Second World War had forced millions of them to delay marrying and starting a family for up to four years. In 1945 and 1946, they rushed into marriage, childbearing, and searching for a place to live. But because of the stagnation of the domestic construction industry during the depression and the war, when young couples looked for housing in the cities, they found impossibly high rents and real-estate prices.

To demolish old neighborhoods as the first step of new construction meant temporarily worsening an already

TELEVISION IN AMERICA

	Number of TV Households	Percentage of American Homes with TV
1945	5,000	—
1950	3,880,000	9.0
1955	30,700,000	64.5
1960	45,750,000	87.1
1970	59,550,000	95.2
1978	72,900,000	98.0

critical housing shortage. The solution was the rapid development of entirely new "tracts" or "subdivisions" on the outskirts of cities, far enough from the centers that the price of land was cheap, but close enough that breadwinners could get to their jobs. Of the 1 million housing starts in 1946 and the 2 million in 1950 (compared with 142,000 in 1944), the vast majority was in the suburbs.

The first of the great suburban developments was Levittown, New York, the brainchild of a family company that adapted the assembly line to home building. In order to keep selling prices low, the Levitt brothers used cheap materials and only a few different blue prints. The houses of suburbia were identical, constructed all at once and very quickly. Armies of workers swarmed over the tract, grading thousands of acres at a sweep, and laying out miles of gently curving streets within a few days. Practically before they were done, battalions of men laid down water, gas, sewer, and electrical lines, while teams of carpenters erected hundreds of simple, identical shells.

Then came waves of roofers, plumbers, electricians, carpet layers, painters, decorators, and other craftsmen, each finishing their specialized task on a given house within hours or even minutes. Buyers were so anxious to move in that they were happy to take care of the cleaning up and landscaping themselves. Within four years, Levittown, New York, was transformed from a potato farm into a city of 17,000 homes. On the outskirts of most large cities, developers who imitated the Levitts worked similar miracles. The population of suburbs, never more than a small fraction of the whole, soared. By 1960, as many Americans lived in suburbs as in large cities.

Conformists . . . ?

No sooner did suburbia take shape than it attracted social and cultural criticism. Novelists and sociologists pointed out that the population of the new communities was distressingly homogeneous: 95 percent white, young (20 to 35 years old), married couples with infant children, all of whom made roughly the same income from similar skilled and white-collar jobs.

Not only did the flight from the center cities leave urban centers to the elderly, the poor, and the racial minorities—an implausible tax base—but it segregated the suburbanites too, cutting them off from interaction with other ages, classes, and races of people. Homogeneous communities were narrow-minded communities, critics said; suburbia's values were timid, bland, and superficial.

In politics, people whose comforts and security were made possible by New Deal reforms were afraid to experiment. The suburbanites were staunch supporters of the Eisenhower equilibrium. They swelled the member-

ship lists of churches and synagogues, but insisted on easy, undisturbing beliefs. Rabbi Joshua Liebman, Catholic Bishop Fulton J. Sheen, and the Reverend Norman Vincent Peale told the people of the three major faiths that the purpose of religion was to make them feel good: they, in effect, were at the center of the universe. The Reverend Billy Graham established himself as the country's leading revivalist by shunning the fire and brimstone of earlier evangelists and promoting his transparent blue eyes, wavy hair, and beautiful smile. A survey of Christians showed that while 80 percent believed that the Bible was the revealed word of God, only 35 percent could name the authors of the four gospels and 50 percent could not name one. Among Jews, highly secular and social Reform Judaism grew more quickly than Conservative Judaism. Outside of the insular urban communities of Jews who clung to Polish and Russian pasts, Orthodox synagogues were hard to find.

Suburban life was isolated and fragmented, in part because of television, in part because the new communities were built with little thought for social services—schools, shops, parks, professional offices. When such traditional social centers were constructed, they were miles from residences; thus suburbanites had to drive some distance even to buy a quart of milk. As a result, the suburban single-family dwelling became a kind of fortress that residents left only to hop into a car and drive somewhere else and back again. Supermarkets encouraged weekly rather than daily shopping expeditions, thus eliminating another traditional occasion of social life.

. . . Or Social Pioneers?

Such criticisms made little impression on the people at whom they were aimed. Suburbanites wanted homes they could afford, and they found the physical roominess of life outside the cities well worth the social isolation and cultural blandness. If the houses were cheaply constructed and identical, they were far better than no houses.

Moreover, the new suburbanites, thrown into brand new towns with no roots and traditions, were great creators of institutions. Lacking established social services and governments, they formed an intricate network of voluntary associations that were entirely supported by private funds and energies. There were the churches and synagogues built from scratch, thousands of new chapters of political parties, garden clubs, literary societies, and bowling leagues. Most important of all were programs that revolved around their children: dancing schools, Cub Scouts and Brownies, Little Leagues, and community swimming pools.

Since everyone was a stranger in town, the informal cocktail party became an efficient means by which to

ELEVATOR MUSIC

"Elevator music," deliberately bland background music played at low volume in restaurants, hotels, offices, shops—and elevators—is heard by 80 million Americans a day. It was originally called "furniture music" by its creator, a composer named Eric Satie, who said in 1920 that it would "fill the same role as light and heat—as *comfort*." Satie urged Americans, "Don't enter a house which does not have furniture music," but the concept caught on only after 1934, when the name "Muzak" was coined.

Muzak is played in the Pentagon and in the White House. President Lyndon Johnson pumped Muzak all over his ranch in Texas by mounting speakers on trees.

introduce people to one another. Because guests milled around the stand-up parties at will, it was not awkward to invite the most casual supermarket or Little League grandstand acquaintances to come on over. Alcohol lubricated easy conversation among strangers, and statisticians noticed a change in American drinking habits toward the consumption of neutral spirits such as gin and vodka, which could be disguised in sweet soda pop or fruit juices. The conclusion was that people who did not particularly like to drink were drinking to make themselves more comfortable and because it was the thing to do.

Insolent Chariots

The suburb could not have developed without the readily available family automobile. In turn, the growth of suburbia made the automobile king, a necessity of life and in some ways a tyrant. Each family needed a car because suburbanites worked some distance from their homes and public transportation to many of the new communities did not exist. Because it was necessary for a suburban housewife and mother to cover considerable distances each day, the two-car family became a common phenomenon: one suburban family in five owned two vehicles.

Sales of new cars rose from none during the Second World War to 6.7 million in 1950, and continued to maintain high levels throughout the 1950s. In 1945, there were 25.8 million automobiles registered in the United States. By 1960, with the population increased by 35 percent, car ownership more than doubled, to 61.7 million vehicles.

The automobile was the most important means by which people displayed their status. Unlike the size of paychecks and bank accounts, the family car showed—it sat in the driveway for all to see. Automobile manufacturers devised and encouraged finely honed images

for their chariots. The family that was "moving up" was expected to "trade up" from a low-priced Ford, Plymouth, or "Chevy" to a Dodge, Pontiac, or Mercury, and aspire to eventual ownership of a Chrysler, Lincoln, or Cadillac. Indeed, the easy availability of credit made it possible for people to "keep up with the Joneses" by buying beyond their means, going deeply into debt for the sake of appearances. From 1946 through 1970, short-term loans—money borrowed in order to buy consumer goods—increased from $8 billion to $127 billion!

The Automobile Economy

Virtually universal car ownership among the middle classes fueled the growth of businesses that were devoted to cars or dependent on them. Service stations (gasoline consumption doubled during the 1950s), parts stores, car washes, motels, drive-in restaurants, and drive-in movie theaters blossomed on the outskirts of residential suburbs. The suburban shopping mall rivaled city and town centers as the middle-class American marketplace. In 1945, there were eight automobile-oriented shopping centers in the United States. In 1960, there were almost 4,000.

Automobiles demanded roads. In 1956, Washington responded with the Interstate Highway Act, under which the government began pumping a total of $1 billion a year into road construction. (By 1960, this expenditure rose to $2.9 billion a year.) Over 41,000 miles of new roads ran crosscountry, but 5,000 miles of freeway were urban, connecting suburbs to big cities.

Not only did this road network encourage further urban sprawl, but it made the cities less livable. Already sapped of their middle classes, once lively urban neighborhoods were carved into isolated residential islands that were walled off from one another by the massive concrete abutments of the freeways. Suburbanite cars roared in on them daily, clogging the streets, raising noise to unprecedented levels, and fouling the air for those who could not afford to move out. Progressively poorer without a middle-class tax base, cities deteriorated physically and suffered from neglected schools and hospitals and rising crime rates. During the 1960s, faced with these problems, the center-city department stores and light industries joined the suburban movement, relocating in shopping centers or on empty tracts near the residential suburbs. When they left, they took not only their tax contributions, but jobs previously available to city dwellers.

Baby Boom

During and immediately after the Second World War, the number of births in the United States took a gigantic leap. While about 2.5 million babies were born in each year of the 1930s, 3.4 million saw the light of day in 1946 and 3.8 million in 1947. Population experts expected this. The depression and war had forced young couples to put off starting families. After a few years of catching up, demographers said, the low birth rate typical of the first half of the century would reassert itself.

They were wrong. The annual number of births continued to increase until 1961 (4.2 million) and did not drop to low levels until the 1970s. The same young couples who were buying unprecedented numbers of new homes and automobiles were having larger families than their parents.

Although all social groups participated in the "baby boom," children were most noticeable in suburbia, where, because most adults were young, children were proportionately more important. Beginning about 1952, when the first boom babies started school, massive efforts were required to provide educational and recreational facilities for them. Businesses oriented toward children, from toy makers to diaper services, sprouted and bloomed.

As the boom babies matured, they attracted attention to the needs and demands of each age group they swelled. By the end of the 1950s, economists observed that middle-class teenagers were a significant consumer group in their own right. They had $10 billion of their own to spend each year. All of it was discretionary! Their necessities were provided by their doting parents.

Magazines that appealed to young people prospered, including *Seventeen* (clothing and cosmetics for girls) and *Hot Rod* (automobiles for boys). Film studios made movies about adolescents and their problems. Beginning in the early 1950s, a new kind of popular music swept the country. Rock-'n'-roll was based on the rhythms of black music as it had evolved in the mid-twentieth century, but was usually performed by whites, often teenagers themselves. On the one hand, it was rebellious. Elvis Presley, a truck driver from Memphis, scandalized the country with an act that included suggestive hip movements which he said (probably truthfully) he was helpless to control. On the other hand, it was juvenile. Whereas popular songs had previously dealt with themes that were more or less adult, the new music's subjects were high school senior proms, double-dating, teenage lovers lost tragically while racing to beat the Twentieth Century Limited to the crossing. A new kind of record, the compact and nearly unbreakable 45-rpm disk that sold for only 89 cents, became the medium of competition for teenage dollars.

What worried social critics was that older people, seemingly outnumbered by the young, often adopted adolescent ideals and role models. By the end of the decade, one of television's most popular programs was "American Bandstand," an afternoon show on which

Hip-swinging, guitar-strumming Elvis Presley popularized rock-n-roll during the 1950s.

teenagers rock-'n'-rolled to recorded music and discussed adolescent problems. Adolescents watched it, of course, but so did housewives at their irons and kitchen sinks. Adults discussed the relative merits of their favorite pubescent dancers. Never before had adult society taken much notice of teenage culture. The baby-boom generation seemed to be proclaiming the society's cultural standards.

A New Role For Women

Middle-class America's twin obsessions with enjoying life and catering to its children caused a significant, if temporary, shift in the status of women. Since the beginning of the century, women of all social classes had been moving into occupations and professions that previously had been considered masculine monopolies. Throughout the 1940s, increasing numbers of women finished high school, attended college, studied medicine, the law, and other professions, and took jobs that would have been unthinkable for women before 1900. The Second World War seemed to hasten this blurring of

HOW THEY LIVED

FASHION AND THE FIFTIES

In 1840, the British consul in Boston noted with distaste that Americans did not observe social propriety in the way they dressed. Instead of wearing clothes that were appropriate to their station in life, as an English gentleman thought should be done, Americans dressed more or less the same, and the democracy of dress did not mean a drabbest common denominator. On the contrary, servant girls were "strongly infected with the national bad taste for being over-dressed; they are, when walking the streets, scarcely to be distinguished from their employers." In other words, they were *fashionable*.

By the twentieth century, the democratization of fashion in the United States was complete. The wealthy had a monopoly of the latest from Paris for only as long as it took the American garment industry to copy designs and mass-produce cheap versions of expensive "originals." Indeed, the insistence of American women of almost every social class on their right to dress as the arbiters of fashion pleased accelerated the natural life cycle of a style. The only way the wealthy woman could conspicuously display her capability to spend freely was to move rapidly from one new look to another, always one frantic step ahead of the power shears and sewing machines of the New York garment district.

In 1940, very soon after the Great Depression, the American clothing industry was doing $3 billion in business annually. By the end of the 1950s, it was by some criteria the third largest industry in the United States. Also during those two decades, American dress designers established partial independence from Paris, the capital of fashion, but not from the social preoccupations and values that were neatly reflected in the garments they produced.

The fashions of the years of the Second World War were a product of four forces: the effective shutdown of the design business in occupied Paris; the rationing of materials; the unprecedented prominence of the military in daily life; and the entry of women into the professions and jobs previously held by men.

Because they had been so dependent on Paris for ideas, American fashion designers were disoriented by the fall of France and able on their own to come up with only a variant on 1930s styles. One of the factors that forced some change was the government's restrictions on the amount of fabric that might go into clothing. Skirts could be no larger than 72 inches around. Belts more than two inches wide, more than one patch pocket on blouses, and generous hems were forbidden, as were frills, fringes, and flounces. The result was a severe look in women's dress, accentuated by the fact that with so many uniforms on the streets, civilian clothing took on a military look. It also took on a "masculine look," according to fashion historians; the silhouette of women's clothing was straight and angular, with padded shoulders that emulated the male physique.

In 1947, Christian Dior, a Paris designer, reestablished French primacy in the fashion world. His "New Look" celebrated the end of wartime shortages with long, full, and flowing skirts. More interesting, Dior proclaimed a new femininity in fashion. "Your bosoms, your shoulders and hips are round, your waist is tiny, your skirt's bulk suggests fragile feminine legs," an American fashion editor wrote. Dior blouses were left unbuttoned at the top, and more formal bodices were cut in a deep V or cut low to expose shoulders.

The Frenchman either was very lucky or was a very shrewd psychologist. In the United States, the chief market for fashion in the postwar years, women were opting in droves for the home over the office, factory, and public life. As Betty Friedan would later explain, the new domesticity of the 1950s led to a halt and even a drop in the numbers of women entering the professions and other spheres that were traditionally the preserve of men.

But the domesticity of the 1950s was not the domesticity of a hundred years earlier. Thanks to labor-saving home appliances and the money to buy them, a yen for recreation after the austere years of rationing, and the steady relaxation of moral codes, the 1950s housewife was able to be "fashionable" to a degree previously open only to the doyennes of high society.

Another consequence of the new domesticity of the postwar years was the great baby boom, which in turn affected women's fashion. Just as the numerical dominance of young people led to the prominence of juvenile themes in films and popular music, the two-thirds of the female population that was under 30 years of age affected the way women dressed. "For the first time in fashion," wrote Jane Dormer, the British student of the subject, "clothes that had originally been intended for children climbed up the ladder into the adult wardrobe." While Dior and the Parisian couturiers continued to decree what was worn on formal occasions, American teenagers set the standards for casual wear, not only for themselves but for women of all but advanced age. The most conspicuous of these styles was that of the ingénue: "childlike circular skirts," crinolines, hoop skirts, frilled petticoats that were seen not only at junior high school dances but at cocktail parties on mothers of five. Girls and women began to wear their hair loose and flowing or in ponytails, both styles then closely associated with juveniles.

Hollywood both responded to and fed this kind of fashion by coming up with actresses such as Audrey Hepburn, Debbie Reynolds, and Sandra Dee, who specialized in innocent, naïve, little-girlish parts. Well into their thirties, these women clung to what clothing historian Anne Fogarty has called the "paper doll look." Not until the 1960s, when women adopted new values, would this fashion, like all fashions to a later age, look ridiculous.

the lines between what the two sexes could do as women took the place of men in heavy and dirty industrial jobs.

When the war ended, however, most women willingly left those jobs and enthusiastically embraced the traditional roles of wife, homemaker, and mother. By the 1950s, middle America once more assumed that woman's place was in the home. However, the new woman was not the shrinking violet of the nineteenth century. If she was not employed, the woman of the 1950s was constantly out and about, the backbone of an active social whirl. Because the moral code that had required that women be sequestered had long since withered, the modern American girl, wife, and mother were expected to be active and attractive.

Wives were considered partners in furthering their husbands' careers as sociable hostesses and companions. Women's magazines such as *Cosmopolitan* and *Redbook* first hinted, then shouted that wives should be "sexy."

Sexiness also got a boost from two books published by University of Indiana Professor Alfred Kinsey, *Sexual Behavior in the Human Male* (1948) and *Sexual Behavior in the Human Female* (1953). Although Kinsey studiously versed the conclusions of some 18,000 interviews in scientific language, his revelation that premarital and extramarital sexual intercourse, unorthodox sexual practices, and even homosexual episodes were rather common made for sensational reading and discussion.

Kinsey was condemned as a promoter of immoral and unnatural practices and unspeakable acts, which of course he was not, and even of encouraging communism, a ubiquitous accusation during the 1950s. His methods also came under attack from fellow researchers, and the fact that he described as "human" behavior findings based on a rather narrow segment of humanity: white, generally middle-class America. But that was humanity in suburbia, and white middle-class Americans were the people who bought and read books and, no doubt, were often inspired by them.

AGAINST THE GRAIN

There would be no significant challenge to the new sexy domesticity until 1963, when Betty Friedan published *The Feminine Mystique*. In this bestseller, Friedan pointed out that American women had lost ground in their fight for emancipation since 1945. She defined the home as a prison, woman as sex object as demeaned, and said that women should move out into the world of jobs, politics, and other realms that she defined as productive. Criticism of other aspects of the culture of the 1950s, however, was widespread even during the age of Eisenhower.

Dissenters

As early as 1942, Philip Wylie's *Generation of Vipers* told the country that indulgence of children, particularly by their mothers ("Momism"), was creating tyrannical monsters. When juvenile-delinquency rates soared during the 1950s, even in the well-to-do suburbs, other writers elaborated on Wylie. John Keats attacked the sterility of suburban life, especially the social irresponsibility of the developers that left new developments without vital social centers. Later, in *Insolent Chariots*, he turned his attention to the automobile as an economic tyrant and a socially destructive force.

In *The Organization Man* (1956), William H. Whyte, Jr. fastened on the work place, arguing that jobs in the huge corporations and government bureaucracies that dominated the American economy placed the highest premium on anonymity, lack of imagination and enterprise, and generally just fitting in. Sociologist David Riesman suggested in *The Lonely Crowd* (1950) that Americans were becoming "other-directed." They no longer took their values from their heritage or their parents, least of all from within themselves, but thought and acted according to what was acceptable to those around them.

Sloan Wilson fictionalized the conformism and cultural aridity of suburban life in *The Man in the Gray Flannel Suit* (1955), a novel about a suburban commuter who works in the advertising industry. In *The Hidden Persuaders* (1957), Vance Packard reinforced the assault on advertising by pointing out that all Americans were manipulated by advertisements that played not on the virtues of the product for sale but on people's feelings and insecurities.

Beatniks and Squares

The beat generation, or "beatniks" as people called its exemplars, offered a less articulate critique of Eisenhower tranquility. Originally a literary school centered around novelist Jack Kerouac and poet Allen Ginsberg, "beat" evolved into a bohemian lifestyle with capitals in New York's Greenwich Village, San Francisco's North Beach, and Venice, California, near Los Angeles.

Beatniks rebelled against what they considered to be the intellectually and socially stultifying aspects of 1950s America. They shunned regular employment. They took no interest in politics and public life. They mocked the American enchantment with consumer goods by dressing in T-shirts and rumpled khaki trousers, the women innocent of cosmetics and the intricate hairstyles of suburbia. They made a great deal of the lack of furniture in their cheap walk-up apartments, calling their homes "pads" after the mattress on the floor.

The beatniks were highly intellectual. Or, at least,

they prided themselves on discovering and discussing obscure writers and philosophers, particularly exponents of an abstruse form of Buddhism called Zen. They rejected the ostensibly strict sexual morality of the "squares" and lived together without benefit of marriage; a few were homosexual or dabbled in homosexual practices. Their music was jazz as played by blacks, whom they regarded as free of the corruptions of white America.

Beatniks simultaneously repelled, amused, and fascinated conventional American society. Traditional moralists demanded that police raid beatnik coffee houses in search of marijuana (which beatniks introduced to white America) and amateur poets reading sexually explicit verse. Preachers in the traditional churches inveighed against the moral decay that the beatniks represented.

But sexual mores were changing in suburbia, too. To be divorced was no longer to be shunned as a moral pariah. The courts approved the publication of books formerly banned as obscene, with celebrated cases revolving around D. H. Lawrence's *Lady Chatterley's Lover* and Henry Miller's *Tropic of Cancer*. The furor over Ginsberg's long poem *Howl* (1955), which included a few racy lines, made it a bestseller. Suburbanites, the favorite targets of beat mockery, flocked to Greenwich Village and North Beach on weekends to dabble in beat-

nik fashions. Like most cultural rebels, the beatniks did not really challenge society's basic assumptions. They merely provided another form of entertainment.

The Awakening of Black America

The protest against racial discrimination was an altogether different matter. Rather than sniping at trivialities such as lifestyle, America's blacks during the 1950s demonstrated to whites that the mansion they had built included a cellar in which civil rights were systematically denied to 15 million people.

For more than half a century, black leaders such as W.E.B. Du Bois, Mary McLeod Bethune, A. Philip Randolph, and Bayard Rustin had fought a frustrating battle against racial prejudice. Their most important organization, the National Association for the Advancement of Colored People, had won some significant victories in the courts. Lynching, once a weekly occurrence in the South and rarely punished, had almost disappeared in the 1950s. Under Truman, the armed forces were desegregated (African American recruits were no longer placed in all-black units), and the Supreme Court ordered several Southern states to admit blacks to state-supported professional schools because the segregated medical and legal training they offered blacks was not equal in quality to that provided for whites.

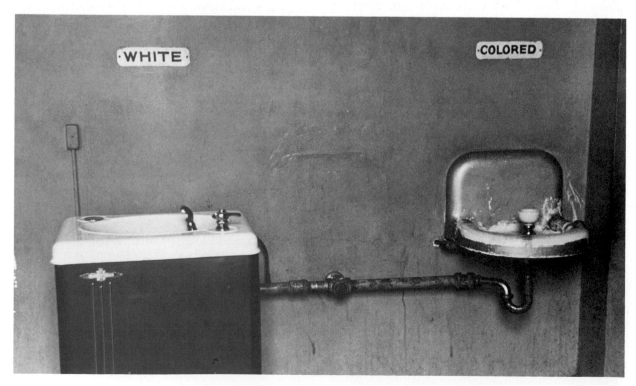

Throughout much of the United States, and particularly in the South, racial discrimination was evident in the segregation of schools, neighborhoods, bathroom facilities, and drinking fountains.

Nevertheless, when Eisenhower moved into the White House, all the former slave states plus Oklahoma retained laws on the books that segregated parks, movie theaters, waiting rooms, trains, buses, and schools. Four more states legally permitted one form or another of racial segregation. (Fifteen states explicitly prohibited it.)

In the Deep South, public drinking fountains were labeled "white" and "colored," and some states actually provided different Bibles in court for the swearing in of witnesses. This strict color line had had federal sanction since 1896, when, in the case of *Plessy v. Ferguson*, the Supreme Court had declared that racially separate public facilities were constitutional as long as they were equal in quality.

The Brown Case

In 1954, Thurgood Marshall, the N.A.A.C.P.'s legal strategist, argued before the Supreme Court that racially separate educational facilities were intrinsically unequal because segregation burdened blacks with a constant reminder of their inequality. In *Brown v. Board of Education of Topeka* (1954), the Court unanimously agreed.

In some parts of the South, school administrators complied quickly and without incident. However, in Little Rock, Arkansas, in September 1957, an angry mob of white adults greeted the first African-American pupils to enroll in Central High School with shouts, curses, and rocks. Claiming that he was protecting the peace, but actually currying the favor of white racists, Governor Orval Faubus called out the Arkansas National Guard to prevent the black children from enrolling.

Eisenhower blamed the turmoil on both Earl Warren, the new chief justice, and Orval Faubus. Sharing the belief of many Americans that there was no great harm done by segregation, Eisenhower regarded the Brown decision as a mistake. If nothing else, by arousing black Americans to protest, it disturbed the tranquility that Ike treasured, and he did not believe that laws could change people's feelings. He later said that his appointment of Earl Warren to the Supreme Court was the worst decision that he had ever made.

Nevertheless, the Supreme Court had spoken and Ike was a constitutionalist. To him, the Court's ruling had the force of federal law, and Faubus was defying it. Eisenhower superseded the governor's command of the National Guard and ordered the troops to enforce the integration of Central High. Overnight, the mission of the Arkansas National Guard was reversed.

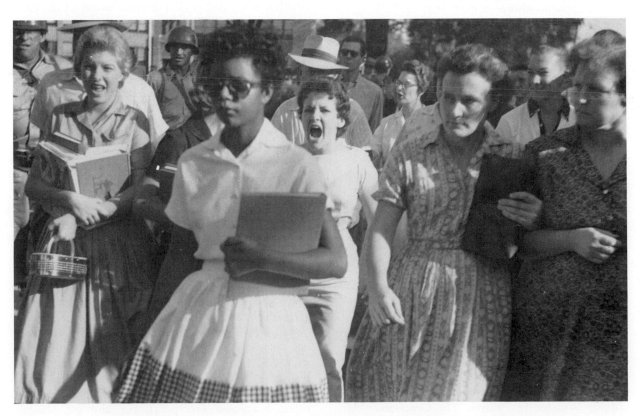

Black students, escorted and protected by the National Guard, enter the all-white Central High School in Little Rock, Arkansas, in 1957.

From the Courts to the Streets

The battle to integrate the schools continued for a decade. Beginning in 1955, however, the civil-rights movement ceased to be a protest of lawyers and lawsuits and became a peaceful revolution by hundreds of thousands of black Americans who were no longer willing to be second-class citizens.

The leader of the upheaval was Martin Luther King, Jr., a young preacher in Montgomery, Alabama. In December 1955, Rosa Parks, a black seamstress, refused to give up her seat on a bus to a white man, as city law required, and King became the spokesman for a black boycott of the Montgomery buses. When the city tried to defend the color line, the dispute attracted journalists and television reporters from all over the country.

King's house was bombed, and he explained his strategy for ending racial discrimination from the wreckage of his front porch. Nonviolent civil disobedience, King said, meant refusing to obey morally reprehensible laws such as those that sustained segregation, but without violence. When arrested, protestors should not resist. Not only was this the moral course of action—King hated violence of all kinds—but it was politically effective. When decent people were confronted with the sight of Southern police officers brutalizing peaceful blacks and their white supporters simply because they demanded their rights as citizens, they would, King believed, force politicians to support civil rights.

Although it led to considerable suffering by demonstrators and to several deaths, King's strategy worked. A few important labor leaders such as Walter Reuther of the United Automobile Workers marched with the young minister and helped finance the Southern Christian Leadership Conference (S.C.L.C.), which King founded to spearhead the fight for equality. After 1960, when S.C.L.C.'s youth organization, the Student Nonviolent Coordinating Committee (S.N.C.C.), peacefully violated laws that prohibited blacks from eating at lunch counters in the South, white university students in the North picketed branches of the offending chain stores in their hometowns. When white mobs burned a bus on which white and black "freedom riders" were defying segregation, the federal government sent marshals south to investigate and prosecute violent white racists.

Although King fell out of favor with some younger blacks in the late 1960s, he loomed over his era as only President Eisenhower did, and with far greater historical consequence. After his assassination in 1968, under circumstances that remain somewhat mysterious, several states made his birthday a holiday, and in 1986 it became an official federal holiday. But King and black Americans only began their fight for equality during the age of Eisenhower. It was the next decade, the troubled 1960s, which saw the end of civil discrimination on the basis of race.

For Further Reading

See these solid general histories: C. C. Alexander, *Holding the Line: The Eisenhower Era, 1952–1961* (1975); James Gilbert, *Another Chance: America Since 1945* (1984); Eric Goldman, *The Crucial Decade and After* (1961); Godfrey Hodgson, *America in Our Time: From World War II to Nixon* (1976); William E. Leuchtenburg, *A Troubled Feast: American Society Since 1945* (1979); and William L. O'Neill, *American High: The Years of Confidence, 1945–1960* (1987).

In addition to O'Neill, the following books are good on American society in the 1950s: Daniel Boorstin, *The Image* (1962); John Kenneth Galbraith, *The Affluent Society* (1958); Paul Goodman, *Growing Up Absurd* (1960); E. Larrabee, *The Self-Conscious Society* (1960); David Riesman, *The Lonely Crowd: A Study of the Changing American Character* (1950); the appropriate chapters of Sheila M. Rothman, *Woman's Proper Place: A History of Changing Ideas and Practices, 1870 to the Present* (1978); C. Taeuber, *The Changing Population of the United States* (1958); William H. Whyte, *The Organization Man* (1956); Robert C. Woods, *Suburbia* (1959). The bohe-

mian dissenters of the era are treated in Bruce Cook, *The Beat Generation* (1971).

Racial segregation and its crumbling have been extensively studied. See James Baldwin, *The Fire Next Time* (1963) and Martin Luther King, Jr., *Stride Toward Freedom* (1958) for profound insight into black resentments and aspirations. Also see Archibald Cox, *The Warren Court: Constitutional Decision as an Instrument of Reform* (1968); Richard Kluger, *Simple Justice: The History of Brown v. Board of Education and Black America's Struggle for Equality* (1975); Philip B. Kurland, *Politics, the Constitution, and the Warren Court* (1970); Louis E. Lomax, *The Negro Revolt* (1963); Benjamin Muse, *Ten Years of Prelude: The Story of Integration Since the Supreme Court's 1954 Decision* (1964); C. E. Silberman, *Crisis in Black and White* (1964).

President Eisenhower's reputation among historians has generally risen in recent years, although it is still hotly argued. The standard biography is Stephen Ambrose, *Eisenhower* (1983–84), but also see Marquis Childs, *Eisenhower: Captive Hero* (1958); Dwight D. Eisenhower, *The White House Years* (1965); Peter Lyon, *Eisenhower: Portrait of a Hero* (1974); and F. M. Shattuck, *The 1956 Presidential Election* (1956). Biographical studies of other notables of the 1950s include Townshend Hoopes, *The Devil and John Foster Dulles* (1973); John Bartlow Martin, *The Life of Adlai E. Stevenson* (1976–77); Stephen B. Oates, *Let the Trumpet Sound: The Life of Martin Luther King, Jr.* (1982); James T. Paterson, *Mr. Republican: A Biography of Robert A. Taft* (1975); Thomas C. Reeves, *The Life and Times of Joe McCarthy* (1982); John D. Weaver, *Warren* (1967); G. Edward White, *Earl Warren: A Public Life* (1982).

John F. and Jacqueline Kennedy at his Inauguration Ball, 1961.

CONSENSUS AND CAMELOT

POLICIES OF THE EISENHOWER AND KENNEDY ADMINISTRATIONS 1953 - 1963

Four decades have elapsed since Dwight D. Eisenhower became president in 1953. The leaders of that

era are dead. Many of the issues over which they quarreled, sometimes bitterly, have long since been

resolved. Others have been adjudged trivial. The times seem remote to a people who were, over-

whelmingly, only children during the 1950s and early 1960s, or not yet born. With our sophisticated

electronic means of recording and communicating, the preservation of the events of the 1950s and

1960s in grainy black-and-white film enhances the sense that this is the stuff of "ancient history."

In fact, the age of Eisenhower and Kennedy is recent, almost contemporary history, "only yesterday." Its affairs still register vividly in the memories of the elderly and the middle-aged. The historian who tries to sift out the meaning of a time on which the perspective of remoteness is lacking must be content with a sieve of dubious quality—and be aware of the fact. The many strands of continuity between those times and our own preclude detachment and make objectivity difficult. What was important? What was not? Who can say for sure? Here and there, a few fools can.

One characteristic of the decade of Dwight D. Eisenhower and John F. Kennedy does stand out in high relief. Both presidents enjoyed something like a consensus in optimism, a general accord that almost all was well in the American corner of the world. There were dissidents and malcontents; but most Americans of the 1950s and early 1960s felt that however serious a national problem was, they were in the hands of leaders who were both capable and well-intentioned.

IKE'S DOMESTIC COMPROMISE

I n his heart and soul, Dwight D. Eisenhower was an old-fashioned conservative. As a career soldier, he had been isolated from the mainstream of political development. He thought of government in terms of his small-town childhood in Kansas and Texas at the turn of the century, and the gruff platitudes about free enterprise he swapped with the rich businessmen who befriended him after the Second World War.

The tremendous expansion of federal power during the New Deal and the Second World War disturbed him. Perhaps because the peacetime army in which he served was so stingily financed, he shuddered at the size of the government's budget and at the very notion of annual deficits piling up into a mountain of national debt. He believed that businessmen in the private sector were better qualified to manage the economy than were the bureaucratic agencies that had been created under Roosevelt and Truman. He criticized the Tennessee Valley Authority, the liberal model of regional economic and social planning, as "creeping socialism" and suggested that its facilities be sold off to private power companies.

The Best Laid Schemes o' Mice and Men . . .

Some of Ike's advisers, such as Secretary of Agriculture Ezra Taft Benson of Utah, were downright reactionary in their hostility to government regulation, social-welfare programs, and the big bureaucracies that implemented them. Given his own way, Benson would have rampaged through the office buildings of Washington like an avenging angel.

Secretary of Defense Charles Wilson sounded like a ghost of the Coolidge era when he gave his opinion of the role that corporations should play in framing national policy. In what was only in part a slip of the tongue, Wilson told a Senate committee that "what was good for the country was good for General Motors and vice versa." (Wilson came to government from the General Motors board of directors.)

When Dr. Jonas Salk perfected a vaccine that promised to wipe out polio, then a scourge of children, Secretary of Health, Education, and Welfare Oveta Culp Hobby warned that even though an immunization program might well eradicate the disease, a government-sponsored program would be socialistic.

. . . Gang Aft Agley

That was how Ike's advisers spoke. When it came time to take action, however, the president was moderate, pragmatic, and realistic. He was able to face up to the fact that the America of his Kansas boyhood was gone forever and that the federal government had to take some responsibility for economic and social welfare in the complicated world of the mid-twentieth century. His administration did sponsor a polio immunization program.

Eisenhower also discovered the risks of trusting his businessmen friends too closely when he supported a private company, Dixon-Yates, in a dispute with the T.V.A. over which of them would construct a new generating facility for the Atomic Energy Commission. Rather than the contest between "free enterprise" and "creeping socialism" that had been described to him, Ike discovered that Dixon-Yates executives were mired deeply in collusion with friendly A.E.C. officials in what amounted to a raid on the Treasury—"socialism for the rich." He withdrew his support of Dixon-Yates and accepted a face-saving compromise in which the city of Memphis, in the public sector but not federal, built the plant.

Even Ezra T. Benson had to swallow his distaste for the agricultural-subsidy programs that he wanted to abolish. The 1950s were years of distress in the farm belt, and the application of free-market principles would have transformed them into years of catastrophe. As agricultural productivity continued to increase but neither domestic consumption nor foreign demand kept pace, grain piled up in volcano-shaped cones in the streets of farm towns throughout the Midwest. Farm income dipped, and farm families left the land for city and town jobs in

THE COLD WAR CONTINUES 769

numbers not seen since the 1920s. Food production never lagged; big agri-business corporations gobbled up and consolidated family farms, operating them like any other industry. One reason they were able to profit where farm families could not was that the Eisenhower administration quietly expanded the subsidy programs against which Benson had railed.

The Soil Bank Act of 1956 authorized the payment of money to landowners for every acre they took out of cultivation in order to reduce production. Within ten years, $1 of every $6 that farmers and agricultural corporations pocketed at harvest time came not from sales but from the federal government—for crops that were never planted. Eisenhower also adopted New Deal-like policies when he introduced programs under which the federal government purchased surplus crops for school lunches and foreign-aid programs.

Dynamic Conservatism

The clearest indication that "dynamic conservatism" (as Eisenhower called his political compromise) included taking responsibility for the health of the economy came when the sharp reduction of military expenditures after the Korean War threatened to push the country into a depression. Eisenhower responded by asking Congress to lower taxes, and he persuaded the Federal Reserve Board to loosen credit restrictions so as to put more money into the hands of consumers, that is, to make it easier for them to borrow and spend.

In 1957 and 1958, a somewhat worse recession threw 7 percent of the work force out of jobs. Ike responded with several large public-works projects like the New Deal programs that he earlier had condemned. In the area of social welfare, over 10 million names were added to the lists of people who received Social Security payments during Eisenhower's presidency.

THE COLD WAR CONTINUES

The Cold War continued under Eisenhower. Indeed, every president after Harry S Truman had to design foreign policy around the overwhelming fact that the United States was locked into a competition with the Soviet Union that left very little room for maneuver.

The Nature of the Beast

Because the United States and the U.S.S.R. were nuclear superpowers, the contest between them could not rationally be resolved by the timeless test of decisive war. Already by the age of Eisenhower, it was obvious that armed conflict between the United States and the Soviet Union would lead to vast physical devastation in both countries and the death of tens of millions of people. By 1961, when Ike retired, nuclear technology was advanced to the point that world war could readily lead to the destruction of civilization and, conceivably, the earth's capacity to support human life. Every president from Ike to Jimmy Carter understood and clearly stated that there would be no winners in a nuclear war.

Therefore, until the United States and the Soviet Union trusted each other enough to agree on disarmament, policy-makers had to live with the balance of terror and compete with their rivals under the threat of it. The history of American foreign relations between the 1950s and the 1990s is the story of how a succession of presidents and Secretaries of State coped with these restraints.

More Bang for a Buck

Although Dwight D. Eisenhower spent much of his life in an army uniform, he wanted to be remembered as a man of peace. "I have seen enough war," he said, and as president he acted with moderation in crisis situations. By the time he left office, Eisenhower appeared to distrust the motives of his generals and the business leaders who supported him. In his farewell address of 1961, Ike told Americans to beware of the "military-industrial complex," the intimate and self-serving alliance of the Pentagon (the Defense Department), and the big corporations that made their money by selling weapons to the government. Along with like-minded intellectuals in the universities and "think tanks," with their ivory-tower theories of how to fight the Cold War, Ike said, the military establishment and arms industry were apt to be reckless in the use of armed force.

Eisenhower's fiscal conservatism also played a role in his defense policy. If he were to balance the federal budget—to spend no more money in a year than the Treasury collected in taxes—he had to cut military expenditures, the biggest single item in the budget. Because complete disarmament was out of the question, Eisenhower adopted a comparatively inexpensive plan for maintaining national security, the "more bang for a buck" policy. Encouraged by penny-pinching Secretary of the Treasury George Humphrey, the president cut spending on the conventional army and navy and concentrated on building up America's nuclear deterrent: atomic and hydrogen bombs and the sophisticated ships, planes, and missiles capable of delivering them to Soviet targets. This purely defensive policy threatened no one, Ike told the world. The United States would never start a nuclear war, but the Soviet Union, unless it were deterred by the threat of "massive retaliation," might very well do so.

Critics claimed that the policy meant all or nothing.

The United States could destroy the world, but could the nation respond in proportion to minor Soviet provocations? Secretary Humphrey was not impressed. With the frustrations of the limited war in Korea fresh in his mind, he growled that the United States had "no business getting into little wars . . . . Let's intervene decisively with all we have got or stay out."

Other Eisenhower supporters said that the reduced army and navy were more than adequate to act in minor crises. In 1958, when Eisenhower suspected that Communists intended to take over Lebanon, he was able to send marines into the Middle Eastern nation to stabilize a government friendly to the United States. It was only a long, expensive, and demoralizing conventional war like Korea for which he did not choose to prepare.

Peaceful Coexistence

The United States was directly involved in no wars of note during Eisenhower's eight years in office. In part this may have been due to a significant change in Soviet leadership. Joseph Stalin, suspicious to the point of mental imbalance late in life, died in 1953. After a few years of figurehead leaders and murky maneuvering in the Kremlin, he was succeeded by an altogether different kind of strong man, a rotund, homely, and very clever Ukrainian named Nikita Khrushchev.

Khrushchev bewildered American "Kremlinologists," as Soviet experts came to call themselves. And that may have been one of his purposes. At times he seemed to be a coarse buffoon who habitually drank too much vodka and showed it. Visiting the United Nations, he stunned the assembly of dignitaries by taking off his shoe and banging it on the desk in front of him to protest a speaker of whom he disapproved. At other times Khrushchev was witty and charming, almost slick.

The new premier could issue frightening warlike challenges to the United States. But he was also the man who denounced Stalinist totalitarianism at home in 1956 and called for peaceful coexistence with American capitalism. Khrushchev claimed that the Cold War would be resolved by historical forces rather than by armed conflict. "We will bury you," he told American capitalists; the world would peacefully choose the Soviet way of life.

Kitchen Debates

A comparison of American and Soviet societies in the 1950s and 1960s mocked Khrushchev's boast, and helped to explain his interest in slowing down the arms race. Despite his reforms, Soviet citizens remained under tight political controls; the secret police was not dissolved. The Soviet economy was sluggish. Because a country inestimably poorer than the United States had to match American spending on armaments, daily life in Russia was drab. Long lines of people at shops waiting not only for the most modest of luxuries but for basic foodstuffs was hardly preferable to the American consumer cornucopia.

Vice President Richard M. Nixon understood the impact of the contrast on both Americans and people in other countries when he visited Moscow in 1959. He engaged Khrushchev in a debate in front of a mock-up of an appliance-filled American kitchen, pointing out that there was nothing like it in Russia.

Khrushchev was annoyed at being sandbagged by Nixon on his own ground—American photographers were carefully placed for the "kitchen debate"—but the yawning gulf between daily life in the two superpowers was a major reason he wanted some sort of rapprochement with the United States. Only by cutting the cost of the arms race could Soviet agriculture and consumer industries be built up.

Khrushchev had one edge in the salesmanship contest with American spokesmen. He was flexible and opportunistic, even cynical, while the chief foreign representative of the United States under Eisenhower, Secretary of State John Foster Dulles, was a man of antique principle, petrified mind, and the charm of the bullfrog he resembled.

Dull, Duller, Dulles

On the basis of his credentials, Dulles should have been a grand success. He was related to two previous secretaries of state, and he had begun his diplomatic career half a century earlier. During the years he was out of government, Dulles practiced international law with a

---

AMERICA UNDERGROUND

For a time in the 1950s, fear of Soviet nuclear attack spawned a minor building boom in "fallout shelters," covered pits in backyards to which, upon hearing the sirens, families would repair and thus survive the atomic bomb. Although magazines such as *Popular Science* and *Popular Mechanics* suggested fairly cheap do-it-yourself models, a professionally built shelter, carpeted and painted beige, cost $3,000, the price of a decent house. Even if her family never used their shelter, a suburban Los Angeles woman said, it "will make a wonderful place for the children to play in." Other people pointed out that shelters were useful storage areas. In the theological journals, ministers and priests argued about a person's moral justification in shooting neighbors and relatives who had not been so prudent in building their own shelters and, in the moment of crisis, were trying to horn in.

Vice President Richard Nixon debates with Russian premier Nikita Khrushchev in front of a mock-up of a typical American kitchen in Moscow, 1959.

firm that was considered the best in the business. At the top of that business in 1953 when Eisenhower named him Secretary of State, Dulles turned out to be handicapped by an impossible personality for a diplomat and a simplistic view of the world. He was a pious Presbyterian of a discredited old school, as self-righteous, intolerant, and humorless as any Puritan of old New England. "Dull, Duller, Dulles," the Democrats intoned.

He believed that Communists were evil incarnate, veritable agents of Satan. He was unable to respond when Khrushchev hinted that he wanted to ease tensions, and he found it difficult to deal with neutral nations that maintained friendly relations with the Soviets. Photographs of Dulles with neutral national leaders like Jawaharlal Nehru of India reveal a man who fears he will be defiled if he sits too closely.

Such undiplomatic manners made him unpopular not only in the Third World (countries aligned with neither the United States nor the Soviet Union), but among the diplomats who represented America's allies. To make matters worse, Dulles insisted on representing his policies in person. He flew 500,000 miles on the job, demoralizing American ambassadors by converting them into mere ceremonial figures who greeted his plane and then disappeared.

In his conception of the emerging nations of the Third World and of revolutionary movements in the republics of Latin America, Dulles's limitations were even more damaging. The old colonial empires of the European nations were falling apart during the 1950s as new Asian and African countries were founded almost annually. Often committed at least in word to radical social reform, including socialist institutions, the leaders of these countries were rarely pro-Soviet. They needed American friendship and, most of all, American financial aid. In many parts of Latin America, revolutionaries determined to oust reactionary and repressive dictatorships had by necessity and principle to reduce American eco-

John Foster Dulles, secretary of state under Eisenhower, was a staunch supporter of the Cold War.

nomic power in their countries. But all except the infantile ideologues among them recognized the advantage of having good relations with the nation that had sponsored the Marshall Plan.

Picking the Wrong Friends

Instead of exploiting the widespread good will toward the United States or, at least, the cordiality of necessity, Dulles divided the world into "us" and "them," with "us" defined as those nations that lined up behind the United States in every particular. He wrote off all independently-minded national leaders and all revolutionary movements as Communist inspired. Along with his brother, Allen Dulles, who headed the semi-secret Central Intelligence Agency (C.I.A.), he threw American influence behind reactionary regimes, including repressive and often brutal dictatorships in Portugal, Nicaragua, the Dominican Republic, and Cuba, simply because they were pro-American, "us."

Dulles wasted no time in implementing his simplistic views. In 1953, the United States helped the unpopular Shah of Iran overthrow a reform-minded prime minister, Mohammed Mossadegh, despite the fact that, with its border on the Soviet Union and long fear of Russian domination, Iran could not afford to cozy up to Russia no matter who was in power. In 1954, the C.I.A. took the lead in overthrowing a democratically chosen prime minister in Guatemala, Jacobo Arbenz, because he expropriated American-owned banana plantations.

Also in 1954, Dulles refused to sign the Geneva Accords, which ended a long and tragic war in Vietnam between France and a Communist-led independence movement that, because of the historical Vietnamese hostility toward China, may have been open to cooperation with the United States.

Dulles's actions in Iran, Latin America, and Southeast Asia were to redound in setbacks to American foreign policy for four decades. Dulles said, in effect, that the United States opposed social progress in those parts of the world where change was most sorely needed. His blindness provided Khrushchev with the opportunity to play the friend of anticolonialism, freedom, and reform. The pretense ill-suited the imperialist, dictatorial, and ideologically hidebound Soviet Union, but Khrushchev and Dulles worked together to make it look plausible.

Brinkmanship and Massive Retaliation

Eisenhower, by conviction or default, backed up Dulles's policies in the Third World. He balked, however, at the Secretary's advocacy of "brinkmanship" and "massive retaliation" in relations with the Soviet Union and, because the Chinese Communists were defined as Soviet flunkeys, the People's Republic of China.

Dulles rejected containment as immoral because George Kennan and the Truman administration had called for merely holding the line against the spread of Communism in the hopes that, in the future, the Soviets would prove amenable to a settlement based on trust and good will. Dulles could not imagine accepting Communist states as part of the world community and said that it was not necessary that the United States do so. America would win the Cold War by going to the brink of hot war, threatening "massive retaliation," nuclear attack, in disputes with the Soviets.

Indeed, Dulles meant to provoke disputes that would enable him to put brinkmanship into action. In 1953, the Korean War just concluded, Dulles hinted that he would support Chiang Kai-shek if the exiled Nationalist Chinese leader invaded the People's Republic. In the same year, with the Soviet leadership in a state of flux following Stalin's death, Dulles led the peoples of the satellite states of Eastern Europe to believe that Americans would come to their aid if they rebelled against Russian domination.

Moderation in Practice

However, when the Chinese Communists began to shell two tiny islands controlled by Chiang, Quemoy and

Matsu, Ike backed off, forcing Dulles to do the same. Eisenhower stated clearly for the first time that it was only Taiwan the United States would defend. The artillery exchanges between the two Chinas soon developed into a ritual worthy of the Mandarins, a far more "limited war" than Korea. At one point, the Communists insisted only on the right to shell Quemoy and Matsu on alternate days of the month.

In Hungary in 1956, Dulles's talk of rolling back the iron curtain contributed to a more tragic event. Anti-Soviet Hungarians rebelled and took control of Budapest. The Soviets hesitated, as though waiting to see what the Americans would do. They regarded Hungary as vital to their security, but feared all-out war on the issue. When Eisenhower did nothing, Soviet tanks and infantry rolled into Budapest, easily quashing the revolution. The net effect of the episode was to undercut confidence in Dulles's bold words throughout the world.

Also in 1956, Eisenhower and Dulles angered three important allies by first appearing to encourage them to take action against increasingly pro-Soviet Egypt, and then refusing to back them. Britain, France, and Israel invaded Egypt to prevent the government of President Gamal Abdel Nasser from taking control of the Suez Canal. When Khrushchev threatened to send Russian "volunteers" to Egypt's aid, Eisenhower announced his opposition to the allied assault. Humiliated, the British, French, and Israelis withdrew. They could not carry on without American support.

Summitry and the U-2

When Dulles resigned a month before he died of cancer in 1959, Eisenhower took personal charge of foreign policy. Oddly, having allowed so much rein to Dulles for six years, he was rather well-equipped to administer foreign relations. Of all American presidents, only Hoover and John Quincy Adams had spent more of their lives abroad than he. Eisenhower had lived for long periods in France, England, the Philippines, Panama, and Al-

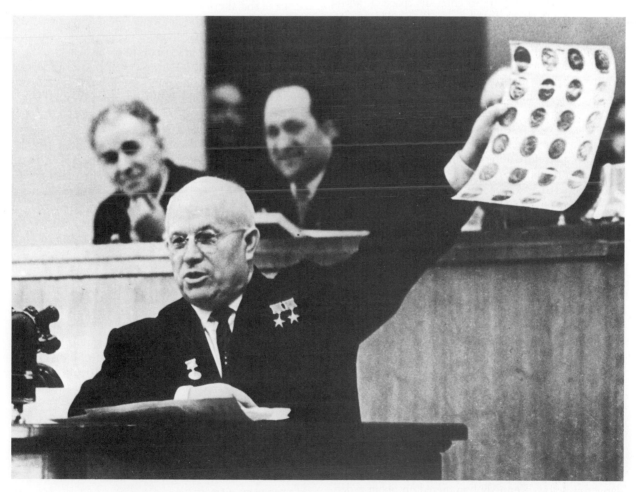

Khrushchev holds up evidence of spying found in an American U-2 plane shot down by the Russians on May 1, 1960.

geria. His experience in dealing with American allies during World War II had demanded the utmost in diplomatic tact.

For a time, Ike seemed to be easing Soviet-American tensions. With Dulles out of the way, he and Khrushchev outdid one another with statements of good will, and they agreed to exchange friendly visits. Khrushchev made his tour of the United States in 1959 and scored a rousing personal success. In the flesh and on his best behavior, he captivated many Americans with his unpretentious manner and interest in everyday things. Khrushchev even drew laughter when, having been refused admission to Disneyland for security reasons, he explained that the real reason was that the amusement park was a disguise for rocket installations.

Eisenhower's visit to Russia was scheduled for May 1960. Because Eisenhower had been a hero in the Soviet Union during the Second World War, there was every reason to expect another amicable tour. Then, on May 5, Khrushchev announced that the Russians had shot down an American plane in their air space. It was a U-2, a top-secret high-altitude craft designed for spying. Assuming that the pilot had been killed in the crash (or had committed suicide, as U-2 pilots were provided the means to do), Eisenhower said that it was a weather-monitoring plane that had flown off course.

Khrushchev pounced. He revealed that the U-2 pilot, Francis Gary Powers, was alive and had confessed to being a spy. Possibly because he hoped to salvage Eisenhower's forthcoming trip to Russia, Khrushchev hinted in the wording of his announcement that Ike should lay the blame on subordinates.

Ike refused to do so. Smarting under Democratic party attacks that he had never been in charge of foreign policy, he acknowledged his personal approval of all U-2 flights. Khrushchev attacked Eisenhower as a warmonger and canceled his invitation to tour Russia. The Cold War was suddenly chillier than at any time since the truce in Korea.

1960: A CHANGING OF THE GUARD

The chill in Soviet-American relations perfectly suited the strategy of the Democratic presidential nominee in 1960, John Fitzgerald Kennedy. A 42-year-old senator from Massachusetts, Kennedy's chief criticism of the Eisenhower administration was his contention that Ike had, with his stingy spending policies, let American defenses and the power to deter Soviet aggression slip dangerously low. Kennedy hammered on about a dangerous "missile gap," a gross disparity between the rock-

ets the Soviets had available to assault the United States, and those in the American arsenal. This was colossal nonsense but, such matters as numbers of missiles being secret, neither Eisenhower nor the Republican candidate for president, Richard M. Nixon, could convincingly respond.

Times Change

Eisenhower was still very popular in 1960. Had the Twenty-second Amendment to the Constitution, adopted by Republicans in 1951 as a posthumous slap at F.D.R., not forbidden a third term, the 70-year-old president would likely have been reelected. Americans still liked Ike.

And yet the country was a little tired of the 1950s. The American population was younger than at any time in the twentieth century and restless under the cautious style of the dead decade. As prosperous as the age of Eisenhower was, it was a stale and boring time in the opinion of an increasing number of Americans. The books of social critics such as Whyte and Packard had been bestsellers. Although they were out of power, the Democratic liberals had loudly and relentlessly criticized Eisenhower lethargy in journals like *The Nation* and the *New Republic*. Liberal university professors were effective propagandists, spreading their views among young people. Although it was not a liberal majority, the Democrats had controlled both houses of Congress for six of Eisenhower's eight years in office.

As 1960 approached, the feeling that it was time "to get the country moving again" was in the air. In 1959, *Life*, the favorite magazine of the middle classes, published a series of articles by prominent Americans ranging from Adlai Stevenson to Billy Graham on the subject of "the national purpose." Almost all the contributors expressed an uneasiness that a sense of purpose was just not there.

THE KENNEDY WIT

When we got into office, the thing that surprised me most was to find that things were just as bad as we'd been saying they were.

Washington is a city of Southern efficiency and Northern charm.

It has recently been observed that whether I serve one or two terms in the presidency, I will find myself at the end of that period at what might be called an awkward age—too old to begin a new career and too young to write my memoirs.

John F. Kennedy

Kennedy was a politician who knew how to exploit this apprehension of drift. As Eisenhower was tailor-made for the 1950s, Kennedy seemed to fit the spirit of the emerging new decade. He was rich and attractive, breezy and witty. He had distinguished himself for bravery (although not the best of sense) during the Second World War; he had an attractive young wife, and he was ambitious.

Kennedy had weaknesses that would have destroyed a political career twenty years later. He was a satyr, ever on the search for women, boasting to friends of the number of his one-night conquests, and maintaining longer relationships with several mistresses, including actress Marilyn Monroe and one Judith Flexner, who had personal connections with organized crime.

But he was discreet and journalists were more restrained in the 1960s, regarding such matters as sexual habits a man's or woman's own business. Kennedy was unbeatable in Massachusetts politics. He had won election to the House and the Senate in years that had not been kind to Democrats, and in 1956, he had made a bid for the Democratic party's vice-presidential nomination. He lost, but that turned out to be a blessing. Kennedy had not shared in the humiliation of the party's defeat that year, but by putting up an exciting fight on national television (the only contest in a dull political year), he had made his name known in every corner of the country.

The avalanche of publicity in 1956 had done another favor for Kennedy by initiating discussion of his religion. The senator was a Roman Catholic, and it was thought that too many people would vote against any Catholic for a member of that church to be elected to national office. The longer the question was examined, however, the less attractive the anti-Catholic position looked. When Martin Luther King, Jr.'s, father (a Baptist minister) expressed his old-fashioned prejudices on the score, the civil-rights leader so hastily dissociated himself from them that he became, in the process, virtually committed to the Democratic nominee.

Kennedy and his team of advisers, which he started to assemble in 1957, understood the importance of manipulating the mass media, especially television, in creating a favorable image of their candidate. The campaign that he launched was calculated to convince younger Americans that he was more flexible, more open to change, than any of his rivals.

The Democratic Campaign

Kennedy's competition for the nomination included Adlai Stevenson, badly shopworn in an age that craved novelty, but still hoping to be drafted; Lyndon B. John-son of Texas, the efficient leader of the Senate Democrats; Hubert H. Humphrey of Minnesota, a leading liberal; and several minor candidates who prayed for a deadlocked convention.

Humphrey was the only one to challenge Kennedy head-on in the primary elections, and he was quickly eliminated. By edging him in Wisconsin, which neighbors Minnesota, Kennedy established himself as a national figure. Kennedy then won in West Virginia, a heavily Protestant "Bible belt" state where, experts said, anti-Catholic feeling would wipe Kennedy out. Humphrey dropped out, and Kennedy's forces talked old-time political bosses like Governor Mike Di Salle of Ohio and Mayor Richard E. Daley of Chicago, who had been sitting the fence as bosses do, into supporting him as the most likely to win in November. By the time of the convention, Lyndon Johnson had been outraced, and Kennedy won on the first ballot.

Kennedy then chose Johnson as his vice-presidential running-mate. He expected and wanted to be turned down, but knew he needed Johnson's good will to win votes in the South. When Johnson shocked him by accepting, Kennedy's good manners turned out to be the shrewdest move of a brilliantly played game. Although Johnson's syrupy Texas drawl occasioned ridicule in the Northeast, he was popular in the Southern states where Kennedy was weak. Single-handedly, Johnson won Texas for the Democrats, a key to a close election. In the North, Kennedy's religion actually helped him by winning back many upwardly mobile Catholics who had been drifting toward the Republicans as the party of respectability.

A Modern Election

The Republican standard-bearer was Vice President Richard M. Nixon, who easily fought off a challenge by New York governor Nelson Rockefeller. Nixon had a difficult assignment. In order to keep the Republican organization behind him, he had to defend Eisenhower's policies. But he also had to appeal to the new spirit of youth and change.

Nixon handled this juggling act remarkably well, but not without cost. Emphasizing his experience in the executive branch, he created an image of the responsible diplomat that did not mesh with his past reputation for free-swinging smears and dirty tricks. Reporters revived the nickname "Tricky Dicky" and the line, "Would you buy a used car from this man?" Kennedy wisecracked that Nixon played so many parts that no one knew who the real Nixon was, including the vice president himself.

Mistrust would dog Richard Nixon to the end of his career. Nevertheless, in 1960 he almost won the elec-

John Kennedy and Richard Nixon grimly face each other in a television studio during the presidential campaign debates of 1960.

tion. The totals gave Kennedy a wafer-thin margin of 118,574 votes out of the almost 70 million cast. His 303 to 219 electoral vote margin, apparently more comfortable, concealed narrow scrapes in several large states. Many analysts believed that Illinois went Democratic only because of fraudulent vote counts in Richard E. Daley's Chicago.

Other commentators said that Kennedy won because his wife was more glamorous than Pat Nixon, who abhorred public life, or because the Massachusetts senator looked better in the first of four nationally televised debates with Nixon. Kennedy was tan, healthy, confident, and assertive, while Nixon was visibly nervous, and an inept make-up job failed to cover his five-o'clock shadow.

It is impossible to know how much the appearances of the candidates affected the decisions of 70 million people. After 1960, however, many politicians and political scientists came to believe that in the age of tele-vision a candidate's image, rather than issues, was the key to winning elections. By 1990, no major politician would dream of running a campaign without the advice—even the control—of a high-priced advertising firm.

CAMELOT

As president, Kennedy remained a master at projecting an attractive image. Although no more an intellectual than Eisenhower (his favorite writer was Ian Fleming, creator of the British superspy James Bond), the new president won the hearts and talents of the intelligentsia, who had attacked Ike, to his cause with friendly gestures. He invited the venerable poet Robert Frost to read his verses at the inauguration, and cellist Pablo Casals to perform at the White House. Genuinely athletic and competitive, Kennedy appealed to young suburbanites by releasing photographs of his large family playing rough-and-tumble touch football at their Cape Cod vacation home.

There were plenty of Kennedy haters, but the vigor of his administration (*vigor* was a favorite Kennedy word) and his undeniable charm, wit, and self-deprecating humor captivated a good many Americans. Inspired by the blockbuster musical of the early 1960s, *Camelot*, they spoke of the Kennedy White House as though it were an idyll, like King Arthur's reign in the mythical past.

Like Eisenhower, Kennedy seemed to be assembling a consensus that excluded only groups of the lunatic fringe and, much to Kennedy's dismay, Southern segregationist Democrats. But just as in the Arthurian legend, the Kennedy Camelot was short-lived. One Mordred outside the house of the Round Table was quite enough to bring him down.

The New Frontier

Historically, John F. Kennedy is more important as an inspiration for the reforms (and tragedies) of the 1960s than for what he actually accomplished. His inaugural address was eloquent and moving. "The torch has been passed to a new generation of Americans," he warned the world, and to Americans he said, "Ask not what your country can do for you; ask what you can do for your country." He sent Congress a pile of legislation that was more innovative than any presidential program between the time of F.D.R.'s Hundred Days and Ronald Reagan's conservative agenda of 1981.

The New Frontier, as Kennedy called his program, included federal aid to education (both directly to institutions and in the form of low-interest student loans), assistance to chronically depressed Appalachia and the

Aided by a handsome family that included photogenic toddler John-John, Kennedy increased his popularity among the public as his term in office progressed.

nation's decaying center cities, and help for the poor, the ill, and the aged. In 1962, Kennedy proposed a massive space research and development program, setting the goal of overtaking the Soviet Union, which beat the United States in orbiting the first artificial satellite in 1957 and the first human space traveler in 1961. Kennedy meant to send an American to the moon by 1970.

In Congress, however, despite comfortable Democratic majorities, the president was frustrated. Not only did most Republicans oppose the New Frontier, but Kennedy was unable to swing the powerful bloc of Southern Democrats behind his program. The Southerners traditionally opposed big government spending on anything but defense and public-works projects located in the South, and they were angered when the president and his brother, Attorney General Robert F. Kennedy, made friendly overtures to the growing civil-rights movement.

Consequently, Kennedy was able to push through only a few of his proposals, such as the Peace Corps (volunteers working in underdeveloped countries in Latin America, Asia, and Africa) and the space program (which brought money to the South).

We Shall Overcome

Kennedy wanted Southern congressmen on his side and was willing to go slow in accommodating the growing civil rights movement. But African-Americans and increasing numbers of white allies would not be put off for the sake of Kennedy's legislative program. Martin Luther King, Jr.'s Southern Christian Leadership Conference, its offshoot, the Student Non-violent Coordinating Committee (S.N.C.C.), and other older groups like the Congress of Racial Equality (C.O.R.E.) were energized by the election of 1960. They struck out at racial discrimination on a dozen fronts, sponsoring demonstrations, protests, and nonviolent civil disobedience throughout the South.

White mobs pummeled black and white demonstrators and law officers turned high-pressure fire hoses on them, unleashed vicious attack dogs, and tortured demonstrators with electric cattle prods. Black churches, the typical meeting place of civil-rights workers, were fire-bombed, and several children were killed. A bus carrying C.O.R.E. "freedom riders" was burned to the ground. In April 1963, Medgar Evers, the moderate leader of the

HOW THEY LIVED

SUBURBAN LANDSCAPE

Until the 1950s, most American cities were densely populated and quite compact. Crowded urban neighborhoods of tenements and row homes abutted directly on farmland or other open country. Indeed, as late as 1940, there were 10,000 acres of cultivated land *within* the city limits of Philadelphia.

There were suburbs, but they did not much resemble the classic American suburban community of today. Before the Second World War, suburbs radiated out from city centers in ribbons, along the commuter train lines that made them possible. Prewar suburbs were themselves rather compact villages of two- and three-storey homes and even apartment blocks of five and six storeys. Suburbanites may have fled the dirt, noise, traffic, and crowding of city life, but they had no choice but to live near the railway station that was the lifeline of their community. The typical breadwinner's work remained in the city, and all but the wealthiest commuters had to walk from their homes to the train. Shops, markets, banks, public buildings, movie theaters, and other commercial services clustered conveniently near "the station."

This suburban landscape was reshaped beyond recognition during the late 1940s and 1950s. The architect of the change was the automobile in the possession of millions of modestly fixed people who formerly had only dreamed of owning one. In the age of mass automobile ownership, getting to work and just getting around the suburbs no longer depended on a combination of shoeleather and the commuter railway. Instead of radiating out from cities in ribbons of population, postwar suburbs sprawled over what had been farmland or wasteland without reference to traditional transportation networks.

Even the least pretentious of the new communities, such as the several Levittowns, were spacious tracts, with modest blue-collar homes built on lots of a quarter-acre.

To young couples accustomed to three-room apartments or a bedroom in the home of a parent, they were veritable greenswards. To celebrate their liberation from urban congestion, many of the new suburbanites demanded a kind of domestic architecture they had learned from Hollywood films to associate with the wide open spaces of the Far West and the glamor of southern California.

The ranch house was the brainchild of architect Clifford May of San Diego. A designer of grand homes for well-to-do clients during the 1930s, May was inspired by the traditional single-storey dwellings of the Hispanic Southwest, where the weather was mild (or hot), where acreage had always been plentiful, and where adobe construction discouraged building walls too high. During the Depression, May designed some 50 homes in southern California that were, in his words, "about sunshine and informal outdoor living." His ranch houses featured courtyards and rooms that opened wide to the clement outdoors.

Such a lifestyle was impossible in the Northeast and Midwest, where winters were long and cold. However, single-storey construction came to be a status symbol by the end of the Second World War. May himself built tracts of "Yankee Version" ranch houses with board and batten or clapboard siding instead of stucco, and a roof of shingles instead of tile. There were no courtyards in ranch houses built "back East," but picture windows let the sight of the outdoors in without its weather. Much of Levittown, Pennsylvania, was built in ranch houses costing between $9,900 and $15,500.

Such suburbs had no focal point like the prewar suburb's railroad station. However, new landmarks of the good life, once exotic curiosities like the ranch house, became commonplace in postwar suburbia. The supermarket, a huge self-service grocery store providing just about

---

N.A.A.C.P. in Mississippi, was shot to death in the driveway of his home.

Kennedy and his brother, Attorney General Robert F. Kennedy, could not ignore such violence. However, they were forced to take decisive and dramatic federal action only when two Southern governors, Ross Barnett of Mississippi and George Wallace of Alabama, said that they would personally prevent the integration of their state universities and tacitly encouraged mobs to riot. Unable to reason with the governors by phone, the Kennedys sent 400 marshals, 300 soldiers, and spent $4 million to ensure that one black man, James Meredith, be admitted to the University of Mississippi. George Wallace of Alabama, after making a show to appeal to segregationists in his state, stepped aside without violence.

The March on Washington

What wedded the Kennedys to the Civil Rights Movement, however, was a massive demonstration, the March on Washington of August 1963, which was organized and led by Martin Luther King, Jr. Believing that the time had come for decisive federal action, King led 200,000 supporters to the Lincoln Memorial in Washington, where he delivered the greatest sermon of his life:

I have a dream today that one day... little black boys and black girls will be able to join hands with little white boys and white girls and walk together as sisters and brothers.... When we let freedom ring, when we let it ring from every village and every hamlet, from every state and every city, we will be able to speed up that day when all of God's children, black men and white men, Jews and Gentiles, Protestants and Catholics, will be able everything needed to keep a house, dated from 1930 when Michael Cullen opened a "warehouse grocery" on Long Island, New York. Cullen patented a shopping cart that could hold a week's worth of groceries and touted himself "The World's Greatest Price Wrecker." He kept costs down by locating his supermarkets in factories and warehouses that had been closed by the Depression. Landlords were delighted to sign long leases with him at minimal rents. Cullen lured shoppers to his stores by offering about 300 of the 1,000 items he stocked at his own cost.

Still, in order to exploit the supermarket's bargains, a shopper needed a car. Although more costly, the long-established and conveniently located "Mom and Pop" grocery, to which marketers could walk daily, remained the norm of food retailing in suburb as well as in the cities during the 1930s. By 1940, there were only 6,000 super-markets in the United States, about one for every 22,000 people.

By 1950, however, with automobile suburbs sprawling on the outskirts of every large city, there were 14,000 super-markets nationwide, one for each 11,000 people. Throughout 1951, new ones opened at the rate of three each day. By 1960, the supermarket was by far the chief source of the American family's daily bread—purchased weekly. In 33,000 markets (one per 5,400 people, just about the saturation point), Americans purchased 70 per-cent of the foods they consumed at home. Car-owning suburbanites had transformed the American means of food distribution as well as the very landscape through which they drove daily.

The first drive-in theater opened on June 6, 1933, in Camden, New Jersey, on a busy highway leading from Philadelphia to the seashore. Richard Hollingshead had had the idea while showing home movies in his backyard during hot summer evenings. He laid out a tract of waste-land into 50-foot-wide aisles, built ramps so that viewers could see over the cars in front of them, sunk the projec-tion pit, and charged 25 cents a person, a maximum of $1 per car, to watch old movies (the only ones distributors would rent to him or other drive-in operators). Origi-nally, Hollingshead used a few huge speakers to bring the soundtrack to his customers. However, this system meant he had to shut down during cold weather, when custom-ers could not be expected to leave their car windows open. In the 1940s, operators of drive-ins solved the prob-lem of seasonal closings by developing the individual in-car speaker.

The drive-in theater was ready-made for the suburbs. It could be profitable only where land was cheap, and the population of the postwar suburbs was comprised largely of young couples with small children, for whom going to a traditional movie theater was inconvenient. Early drive-ins were advertised as family centers where people bored with the film could chat, kids could frolic safely in play-grounds built directly under the towering screens, and "inveterate smokers could smoke without offending others." There were only 10 drive-in theaters in the United States in 1939. Between 1945 and 1950, as the suburbs mushroomed, 5,000 were built.

The drive-in soon lost its image as a family center. In-deed, a writer for *Motion Picture Daily* commented when Hollingshead opened the first, "the Romeos who lost out in the back seats of picture houses when West Point ush-ers . . . came into deluxe houses are waking up in a new world." As the "passion pit," however, the drive-in thea-ter continued to prosper in suburbia, for the tots in the playground in the 1940s became the lusty teenagers of the 1950s.

---

to join hands and sing, in the words of that old Negro spiritual, "Free at last! Free at last! Thank God Almighty, we are free at last!

Concluding that he had no choice but to choose be-tween segregationist Democrats in the South (who were not supporting him on much of anything) and the large black vote in the North, which was strategically located in the cities of the states with the most electoral votes, Kennedy announced his support of a sweeping civil-rights bill to be debated in Congress in 1964.

KENNEDY'S FOREIGN POLICY

Kennedy was committed to fighting the Cold War with the Soviet Union and he could sound like a young John Foster Dulles in saying so: "Freedom and communism are in deadly embrace; the world cannot exist half slave and half free." Acting on his campaign claim that a missile gap between the Soviet Union and the United States threatened American security, he lavished money on research programs designed to improve the rockets with which, in case of war with Russia, nuclear weapons would be delivered.

Flexible Response

However, Kennedy's foreign policy advisors—mostly in-tellectuals from universities and "think tanks"—such as Walt W. Rostow and McGeorge Bundy were critics of Dulles "brinkmanship," threatening massive retaliation with nuclear weapons at every Soviet provocation. In-

Peace Corps volunteer in Venezuela.

stead, updating containment policy to apply to a world theater, they advocated a policy of "flexible response." The United States would respond to Soviet actions in proportion to their seriousness.

For example—what was to prove a fatal example—if the Soviets were suspected of funding or actively aiding guerrilla movements against regimes that were friendly to the United States or that sought American aid, the United States would fund the military forces of those regimes and offer expert advisors to help them. If the Soviets were suspected of subverting elections in the Third World, the United States would launch its own covert operations to manipulate events on disputed turf.

PREJUDICE

Marian Anderson (black operatic soprano): "Sometimes, it's like a hair across your cheek. You can't see it, you can't find it with your fingers, but you keep brushing at it because the feel of it is irritating."

James Baldwin: "It is a great shock at the age of five or six to find that in a world of Gary Coopers you are the Indian."

Toward these ends, Kennedy sponsored the development of elite anti-guerrilla units in the army, most notably the Special Forces or Green Berets, and he increased funding of the spy network maintained by the Central Intelligence Agency.

Into the Third World

Unlike Eisenhower, who thought in traditional terms that wealthy Europe and Japan were the areas that counted in the Cold War competition, Kennedy stated that "the great battleground for the defense and expansion of freedom today is the whole southern half of the globe—Asia, Latin America, Africa, and the Middle East—-the lands of the rising peoples."

He preferred to back democratic reform movements in the developing countries. Kennedy took the lead in organizing the Alliance for Progress in the Western Hemisphere, a program that offered economic aid to friendly Latin American nations in the hope that they would adopt free institutions.

However, the choice in the volatile Third World was rarely between liberal-minded reform movements and pro-Communist dictatorships. Envy of American riches, the common perception that the United States reflexively supported exploitative dictators, the flexibility and

Police dogs attack a civil rights demonstrator in Birmingham, Alabama, 1963.

opportunism of the Soviets, and the romantic zaniness common in revolutionary movements meant that most "liberation movements" were at best suspicious of American intentions and willing to overlook the Russian record because of Soviet revolutionary rhetoric. Consequently, Kennedy and his successors often found their only friends among reactionaries hostile to reform.

The Bay of Pigs

Cuba was the first Third World battleground to come to Kennedy's attention, and his "flexible response" proved to be a disaster. Since 1959, Cuba had been under the control of a revolutionary regime headed by Fidel Castro. Constantly baiting the United States in interminable but impassioned speeches, Castro began, during 1960, to expropriate American property before negotiating compensation. He had riled Eisenhower, who approved

a C.I.A. project to arm and train 2,000 anti-Castro Cubans in Florida and Central America.

They were ready to invade Cuba when Kennedy took over and, despite misgivings, Kennedy decided to go ahead. The Central Intelligence Agency assured him that Castro was unpopular with the Cuban people. At the sound of the first shot, anti-Castro rebellions would break out all over the island.

On April 17, 1961, the anti-Castro forces waded ashore at the Bahía de Cochinos, (the Bay of Pigs) on Cuba's southern coast. The invasion was a disaster from the start. There was no uprising. Castro's troops, seasoned by three years of revolution, made short work of the battle and Castro's popularity soared at home for having resisted what he called imperialist aggression.

Kennedy, instead of ousting an anti-American but still flexible revolutionary leader, pushed Castro into the arms of the Soviets for fear of another assault. Indeed, Kennedy was denounced all over Latin America, and, on national television, he assumed full responsibility for the fiasco.

The Vienna Summit

The Bay of Pigs disaster heartened the Soviet leader Nikita Khrushchev to take a harder line toward the United States than he had through most of the 1950s. Perhaps he sensed that the youth and inexperience of the new president provided rare opportunities for easy limited victories in the game of maneuver at which Khrushchev was so deft.

At a summit meeting in Vienna in June, Kennedy found himself outwitted and upstaged by Khrushchev. The Russian tongue-tied him in private and, when they were before reporters, treated him like a nice boy who only needed teaching. A man of perhaps too much self-confidence, Kennedy returned home seething with anger, and Khrushchev was encouraged to act more recklessly. The Soviets resumed nuclear testing in the atmosphere and ordered the sealing of the border between East and West Berlin.

The Berlin Wall

The Communist regime of East Germany had been plagued by the defection of their citizens, particularly highly trained technologists who could double and triple their incomes in West Germany's booming economy. This "brain drain" threatened to cripple East German industry, and the Communists winced at each defection as a Western propaganda victory, people "voting with their feet." To put an end to it, Khrushchev built a wall through the city that was as ugly in reality as it was symbolically.

Kennedy allowed the Berlin Wall to stand, and he was immediately attacked by critics who said that he could have bulldozed it without interference from the Russians. The proposition was arguable but Kennedy was no brinkman—until October 1962.

The Big Crunch

In October 1962, a U-2 flight over Cuba revealed that the Soviets were constructing installations for nuclear missiles aimed at the United States. Such a threat based but a hundred miles from the United States was, Kennedy knew, something the American people would not tolerate. Before revealing his discovery, he met with a committee specially constituted to analyze the crisis.

Quickly, Kennedy rejected a proposal by Dean Acheson and others that bombers be dispatched to destroy the missile sites. He also rejected a proposal for an American invasion of the island. Although the president did not know it at the time, this was a wise decision. While the C.I.A. had reported (blundering again) that there was only a handful of Soviets on the island, in fact there were 40,000 Russian troops. The C.I.A. also grossly underestimated the size of the Cuban Army, which numbered 270,000 men and women.

Instead, President Kennedy adopted his brother's more moderate and flexible approach. Announcing the discovery of the missiles to the American people, he simultaneously proclaimed a naval blockade of Cuba and demanded that the sites be dismantled and any nuclear weapons on the island be removed.

Castro panicked (it was learned in 1989), fleeing to a bunker beneath the Soviet Embassy and demanding a Russian nuclear strike on the United States. No doubt, the Cuban's rashness gave Khrushchev pause but, for four days, he refused to budge. Work on the sites continued, and Soviet ships loaded with 20 missiles continued on their way to Cuba to be added to the 20 already there (fully a third of the Russian arsenal!). Americans gathered solemnly around their television sets, apprehensive that the nuclear holocaust would begin any hour. Secretary of State Dean Rusk revealed that the White House was nervous too. "We're eyeball to eyeball," he said.

Rusk added, "I think the other fellow just blinked." The Cuba-bound freighters first stopped in mid-ocean and then turned around. On October 26, Khrushchev sent a long conciliatory letter to Kennedy in which he agreed to remove the missiles if the United States pledged never to invade Cuba. The next day, a second letter said that the Soviets would withdraw their nuclear weapons if the United States would remove its missiles from Turkey, which bordered the Soviet Union.

Before the Cuban Missile Crisis began, Kennedy had been considering dismantling the Turkish missile sites as a gesture of friendship. Calculating that the difference in the two Soviet offers indicated indecision in the Kremlin, he saw a chance for a prestigious victory. Kennedy ignored Khruschev's second note and accepted the terms of the first. On October 28, Khrushchev accepted.

Relations Improve

The president thought that the Cuban Missile Crisis was the turning point of his presidency. He made commemorative gifts to everyone who had advised or merely stood by him during that tense October. In fact, both Kennedy and the Soviets were shaken by their flirtation with catastrophe and acted more responsibly after 1962. A "hot line" was installed in both the White House and the Kremlin so that, in future crises, Russian and American leaders could communicate instantly with one another. Then, following a Kennedy speech, the Soviet Union joined the United States and the United Kingdom in signing a treaty that banned nuclear testing in the atmosphere. (France and China, the only other nuclear powers, did not sign.)

Assassination

By the fall of 1963, Kennedy had regained the confidence he exuded in the campaign of 1960. He had scored a major diplomatic victory in the Cuban Missile Crisis and was no longer so uncomfortable about his decision to embrace the Civil Rights Movement and write off Southern white extremists. He believed that the Civil Rights Act he proposed for 1964 would ensure the electoral votes of the populous Northeastern states in the presidential election that year, and began to make plans to convince Southern moderates that they should accept the civil rights revolution.

Toward this end, he agreed to accompany Vice President Johnson on a major political tour in Texas. It began with cheering crowds, and Kennedy was reassured. Then, as the long motorcade passed through Dealey Plaza in downtown Dallas, the president's head was literally blown to bits by rifle fire. Within a short time, Dallas police arrested Lee Harvey Oswald, a ne'er-do-well ex-marine, and worker in a textbook clearing house that overlooked the plaza, for the crime.

Kennedy's murder unleashed a storm of pent-up anxieties and conspiracy theories. Because Dallas, where Kennedy was killed, was a hotbed of often paranoiac right-wing political organizations, including the John Birch Society, which believed that Dwight D. Eisenhower was a conscious agent of international Communism, liberals were inclined to blame Kennedy's loss on such unhealthy extremism. Stories circulated of Dallas schoolchildren cheering when they heard the news.

But Oswald's own political associations seemed to have been entirely with left-wing organizations. Indeed, he had lived for a time in the Soviet Union and tried to renounce his American citizenship. Right-wingers were confirmed in their theories that Communist agents were everywhere. Others posited a "Mafia Connection"; yet others attributed the murder to the Central Intelligence Agency.

Lee Harvey Oswald was not able to clear (or further muddy) things up. Two days after the assassination, he was murdered in the basement of the Dallas police headquarters by a night-club operator named Jack Ruby, who claimed to have been distracted by the death of a president he idolized.

A blue-ribbon investigating commission headed by Chief Justice Earl Warren found that Oswald had acted alone; he was not assisted in his act. Simply put, he was a misfit. However, sloppy evidence gathering and soft spots in one or another of the Warren Commission's conclusions continued to serve as grist for literally hundreds of articles and books that espoused theories about how the murder had taken place. In 1988, on the 25th

As a grief-stricken America watched on television, Lyndon B. Johnson, his wife to his right and Jacqueline Kennedy to his left, takes the oath of office aboard Air Force I, *November 22, 1963.*

anniversary of the Kennedy assassination, a large majority of Americans stated that they did not accept the official account of the murder as the true story. In 1991, a dramatic film about the assassination that, seriously or not, implicated numerous government agencies in the killing was a huge commercial success.

Beginning of an Era

John F. Kennedy was not a great president. He accomplished little at home, and his policy of intervening directly in what was, in 1961, a minor war in Southeast Asia was to poison American life and squander the international good will the United States had banked in World War II and its aftermath.

But his assassination was a great tragedy, far more momentous in its consequences than even the murder of Abraham Lincoln nearly a hundred years earlier. For Lincoln's work was largely done when he died. Kennedy, if not particularly successful in pushing through the legislation his administration sponsored during the "Thousand Days" of his presidency, had just begun. He was building a basis of political support such as had allowed Dwight D. Eisenhower to govern with authority, and doing so by appealing to the better instincts of the American people. His untimely death not only created a climate in which conspiracy theories about it flourished, but also left a void of idealism, confidence, and good will that has not yet been filled.

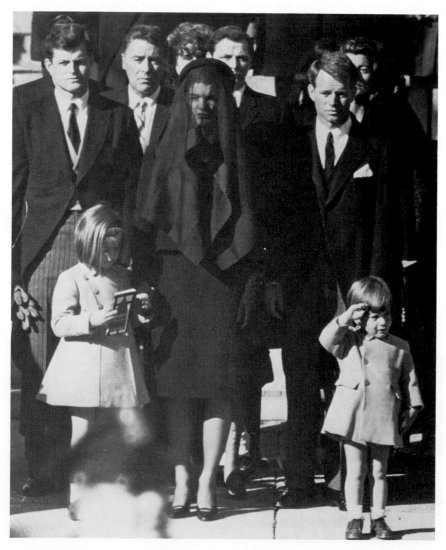

John Kennedy, Jr., salutes his father's coffin on November 25, 1963. Behind him is his uncle, Robert Kennedy, who was assassinated during his own presidential campaign in 1968.

For Further Reading

Overviews of the 1950s and 1960s include James Gilbert, *Another Chance: America Since 1945* (1984); Eric Goldman, *The Crucial Decade and After* (1961); Godfrey Hodgson, *America in Our Time: From World War II to Nixon* (1976); William E. Leuchtenburg, *A Troubled Feast: American Society Since 1945* (1979); and James L. Sundquist, *Politics and Policy: The Eisenhower, Kennedy, and Johnson Years* (1968).

On the Eisenhower years, see C. C. Alexander, *Holding the Line: The Eisenhower Era, 1952–1961* (1975); see also Eisenhower's own *The White House Years* (1965); P. A. Carter, *Another Part of the Fifties* (1983); B. W. Cook, *The Declassified Eisenhower* (1981); Robert A. Divine, *Eisenhower and the Cold War* (1981); T. Hoopes, *The Devil and John Foster Dulles* (1973); Peter Lyon, *Eisenhower: Portrait of a Hero* (1974); Richard M. Nixon, *Six Crises* (1962); William L. O'Neill, *American High: The Years of Confidence, 1945–1960* (1987); and H. G. Vatter, *The U.S. Economy in the 1950s* (1963).

The era of John F. Kennedy's brief presidency has been, if anything, studied more intensively than Eisenhower's. See Ronald Berman, *America in the Sixties* (1968); Bruce Miroff, *Pragmatic Illusions: The Presidential Politics of John F. Kennedy* (1976); William L. O'Neill, *Coming Apart: An Informal History of the 1960s* (1971); L. G. Paper, *The Promise and the Performance: The Leadership of John F. Kennedy* (1975); Herbert Parmet, *Jack: The Struggle of John Fitzgerald Kennedy* (1980) and *JFK: The Presidency of John Fitzgerald Kennedy* (1983); and Arthur M. Schlesinger, Jr., *A Thousand Days* (1965). On Kennedy's election, see the first in a series of such studies by Theodore H. White, *The Making of the President 1960* (1961). The president's assassination has been the subject of so many books—some crackbrained, many insightful—that it is impossible to be representative and name but a few. Perhaps the one with which to begin a study of that tragic event is William Manchester, *Death of a President* (1967).

The decisions of Chief Justice Earl Warren's Supreme Court were as important in shaping the American politics of the future as presidential and congressional policies. See Archibald Cox, *The Warren Court: Constitutional Decision as an Instrument of Reform* (1968) and Philip B. Kurland, *Politics, the Constitution, and the Warren Court* (1970).

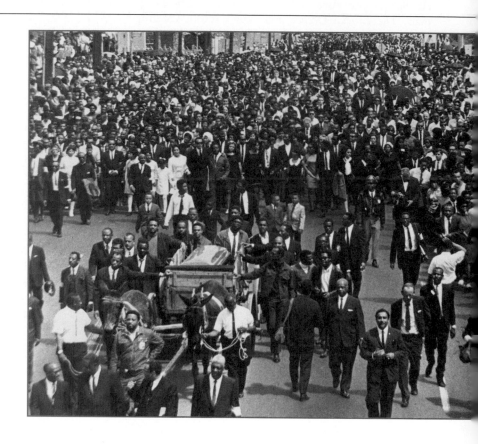

Martin Luther King, Jr.'s funeral cortege.

YEARS OF TURBULENCE

CONFLICT AT HOME AND ABROAD 1961 - 1968

In classical drama, the tragic hero overcomes great obstacles to rise to lofty heights, not always by the most delicate of means. Then, at the pinnacle of attainment and glory, he is destroyed, not so much by enemies (although they are glad to be present to pick up the pieces) as by flaws in the hero's own character.

Lyndon Baines Johnson and Richard M. Nixon were tragic figures in this mold. Both rose (from ordinary beginnings) to win the presidency of the United States. Both savored the exercise of power.

Both were successful in the spheres in which they preferred to labor: Johnson as a domestic reformer in the footsteps of his idol, Franklin D. Roosevelt; Nixon as a diplomat, an arranger of affairs among nations, which he regarded as the principal job of the twentieth-century president.

And both were cast down in disgrace, Johnson because he clung stubbornly to a cause both lost and discredited, and Nixon because of behavior that was not only unworthy of a president, but explicable only as a reflection of a flawed character. Johnson's undoing came about in foreign policy, which had never particularly interested him, and Nixon's on the domestic front, which he believed could take care of itself.

LYNDON BAINES JOHNSON

L yndon Johnson—L.B.J.—came out of what people call "the sticks," the Pedernales river country of rural Texas. His family's means were middling, and Johnson's father either uninspiring or simply not much interested in his son. Although the distinguished University of Texas was nearby, Johnson was able to attend only a teacher's college. He taught school for a year, but the life seemed dull compared to the hubbub, machinations, and possibilities of Texas politics. In 1931, he went to Washington as a congressman's aide, became a devotee of the New Deal, and returned to Texas to win a special election to Congress in 1937.

In 1948, Johnson won the Democratic nomination to the Senate in a controversial primary. Because his margin was a handful of somewhat dubious votes, Texans called him "Landslide Lyndon." But in the Lone Star State in the 1940s, the Democratic nomination was tantamount to election and the voters did their duty. Back in Washington as a Senator in 1949, Johnson's rise was meteoric. Taken in tow by Sam Rayburn, a legendary Speaker of the House, Johnson was named party whip in 1951 and majority leader of the Senate in 1955.

The Wheeler-Dealer

Johnson owed Rayburn for his speedy rise to power, but he held fast to it because he was very good at what he did. He was the master assembler of Senate majorities, by turns administering large doses of folksy charm, bargaining with senators who were pursuing pet projects, arm-twisting, and, so it was said, a little blackmail. Rumor was that Johnson "had something" on every Dem-

ocrat and most of the Republicans in the Senate; he was not a man to be crossed when he was after something.

These political skills and dealings enabled President Lyndon B. Johnson to push through Kennedy's New Frontier and much more, a comprehensive program of national reform that he called the Great Society. Oddly, except in political terms, this very expensive program began with a tax cut. By reducing Kennedy's budget for 1964 by a mere $3.6 billion, Johnson was able to win congressional support for a $10 billion tax cut, always a crowd pleaser. After so popular a start, Johnson moved on to what was to be the greatest of his monuments, a veritable revolution in the civil status of African Americans and the beginnings of a social revolution in relations between the races. In the Civil Rights Act of 1964, Johnson put to work the Fourteenth Amendment to the Constitution, which had been in abeyance for a century.

A Southerner Ends Segregation

Between 1955 and 1965, when civil-rights activists were fighting to end racial segregation in the South, a few faint voices suggested that when the Jim Crow laws were gone, as they must go, white and black Southerners would enjoy better, more human relations than black and white Northerners would. Such observers reasoned that while legal segregation was a Southern institution, interaction between blacks and whites in the South was personal and even intimate. In the North, by way of contrast, while blacks suffered few legal disabilities, comprehensive residential segregation in the big cities isolated the two races as if they were two nations.

With some Southern police forces routinely brutalizing African-American protesters during those years, and some high-ranking Southern white politicians huffing and puffing that they would fight to the death to save white supremacy, it was difficult to take such notions seriously.

But it was a Southerner, himself a nominal exponent of segregation as late as 1960, who wrote an end to Jim Crow. In fact, Johnson had long found segregation distasteful and reactionary while, for the sake of election, he accepted it in Texas. "I'll tell you what's at the bottom of it," he said to an aide in 1960. "If you can convince the lowest white man he's better than the best colored man, he won't notice you're picking his pocket. Hell, give him somebody to look down on, and he'll empty his pockets for you."

By 1964, like the Kennedys, Johnson was convinced that the days of Jim Crow were gone and that the future of the Democratic party might depend on black votes in large Northern cities—and in the South. By means of shrewd bargaining and "the Johnson treatment," he pushed through the Civil Rights Act of 1964, effectively outlawing school segregation and the "white" and "colored" signs on public accommodations that had marked everyday life in the South for half a century. The Act also created a Fair Employment Practices Commission to work toward ending a yawning "unemployment gap" between the white and black work forces.

Nor was Johnson done. When Mississippi extremists took irregular and violent action against a civil rights campaign in that state in 1964—the Mississippi Freedom Summer—Johnson responded with another civil rights bill that ensured the right of African Americans to vote.

The Mississippi Freedom Summer

Rural white Mississippians may well have been the most stubborn of segregationists. The symbol of the Mississippi Democratic party was a white cock and the words "white supremacy." Because the state was perceived as the sturdiest redoubt of Jim Crow, the Student Nonviolent Coordinating Committee, an alliance of black and white university students, chose Mississippi as the focus of a campaign in the summer of 1964 to register blacks to vote. If Mississippi could be cracked, they reasoned, racial discrimination would crumble all over the South.

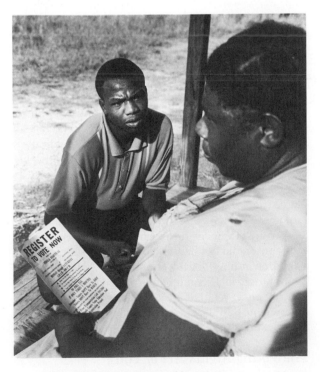

A young black man urges an elder to register to vote in Edwards, Mississippi.

The Freedom Summer was a disillusioning experience to many of the idealistic young white liberals who descended on Mississippi from Northern states. Instead of finding a black population as idealistic and militant as their African-American colleagues back home, they found a people as wary of outsiders as "the rednecks" around them were, and cautious to the marrow after more than a half century of witnessing unpunished lynchings and suffering daily humiliation. Poor Mississippi blacks resented their oppression, but they knew that when the bright-faced Northern white students went back to school in September, the newspaper reporters with them, they would still be there, vulnerable to economic manipulation and violence. Many blacks did register to vote—or tried to do so; others sat on the porches of their shacks rocking, gave the S.N.C.C. militants a glass of ice water, and sent them on their way.

Indeed, the presence of Northern civil rights workers and dozens of reporters did not stay violence even during the summer of 1964. S.N.C.C. workers were harassed as a matter of daily routine, tailed by cars full of men wherever they drove, and regularly terrorized. The most celebrated case of violence occurred near Philadelphia, Mississippi, when one black S.N.C.C. worker and two whites were kidnapped and murdered, almost certainly with the connivance of law enforcement officials.

Amidst these atrocities and fear, some Mississippi blacks and a few white allies, led by the forceful Fannie Lou Hamer, organized the Mississippi Freedom Democratic party and sent a delegation to the 1964 Democratic party convention in Atlantic City, New Jersey. The Freedom Democrats, supported by most Northern state delegates, demanded that they, and not the segregationist regular Democrats, be recognized by the national party.

Working through longtime liberal Hubert Humphrey, whom he had selected to be his vice-presidential running mate, Johnson tried to work out a compromise, dividing Mississippi's convention votes between the rival groups. The Freedom Democrats were not happy with "half a loaf," but the segregationists were furious and walked out of the convention, announcing that they would vote Republican in November.

THE GREAT SOCIETY

The Atlantic City convention was a turning point for the Democratic party. It marked the party's transformation into an unequivocally liberal party and, briefly, a triumphant one. Johnson and the Democratic leadership had no choice but to let the die-hard Southern

"Ten, nine, eight, seven . . .

six, five, four, three . . .

two, one . . .

These are the stakes. To make a world in which all of God's children can live . . .

or to go into the dark. We must either love each other or we must die . . .

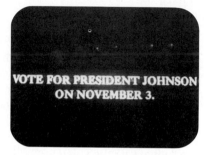

The stakes are too high for you to stay home."

One of the most powerful political messages ever seen on television, this commercial for Lyndon Johnson intimated that, if elected, Barry Goldwater would plunge the nation into nuclear war.

segregationists go. In shedding them, they not only lost the faction of the party that had stood in the way of wooing African-American voters, they discarded Southern Democrats who had traditionally opposed liberal legislation of all kinds.

The Election of 1964

The election of 1964 seemed to prove the "black strategy" wise. The president's Republican challenger, Senator Barry Goldwater of Arizona, was personally a tolerant man, but racists and other extremists of the far right had made him their hero. Their fanaticism helped transform his conservatism into a carping, vindictive negativism based on hatred, fear, and frighteningly simple solutions to problems that seemed to threaten democracy and the rights of the weak.

Republican moderates cringed when Goldwater, accepting the party's nomination, said that "extremism in the pursuit of liberty is no vice." Worst of all, in an age of a nuclear balance of terror, the grandson of a guntoting frontier merchant sounded like a lover of war when he spoke on foreign policy. He seemed to say that the Cold War with the Soviet Union was a matter of which country was "tougher." Democratic strategists

were able to depict Goldwater as a man who would rush for the red button in times of crisis. One Democratic television commercial depicted a little girl playing in a field of wildflowers and dissolved into a film of a nuclear blast.

The Democrats won in a landslide. Johnson won 61 percent of the popular vote and majorities in all but six states, five states of the Deep South plus Goldwater's native Arizona. As important as the prestige the big victory meant, Johnson's coattails pulled in seventy first-term Democratic congressmen from normally Republican districts. The party's edge in the House was 295 to 140, in the Senate 68 to 32. The congressional log-jam that stymied Kennedy had been blown into toothpicks, and Johnson did not hesitate to move. He sent waves of legislation rolling down Pennsylvania Avenue to the Capitol, not only rounding out the civil rights revolution, but enacting his "Great Society," the creation of a government that assumed responsibility for social welfare on a massive scale.

The Voting Rights Act of 1965

The Voting Rights Act of 1965 put the federal power of law enforcement behind the rights of African-Americans to vote. Secure in this right for the first time in almost a century, black Southerners rushed to register. Only ten years after Martin Luther King, Jr. had led his boycott against segregation on buses in Montgomery, the legal obstacles to black equality fell. Before long, Southern white politicians who had built their careers on race baiting were showing up at black gatherings, beaming, shaking hands, kissing babies, and talking about unfortunate misunderstandings.

A former S.N.C.C. worker named Julian Bond was elected to the Georgia state assembly. He was amused that businessmen who once called him a dangerous radical now wanted to take him out to lunch. By the early 1970s, all Southern Democrats were courting black votes, however awkward it was for some. In Alabama's gubernatorial election of 1982, George Wallace, the Southern symbol of resistance to integration in the early 1960s, not only courted black votes, but owed his election to them; African-Americans in Alabama found his Republican opponent by far a worse choice.

Even Southern Republicans stopped expressing the sentiments that had originally taken them into the G.O.P. Strom Thurmond of South Carolina, a deft practitioner of the "nigger-baiting" school of Southern politics who became a Republican in part because of liberal Democratic policies on race, was addressing black audiences by 1982.

The Voting Rights Act of 1965 also prompted an increase in black voting in the Northern and Western states. Not only Atlanta and New Orleans, but Newark, Gary, and Detroit elected black mayors during the 1970s. By 1984, the nation's second and third largest cities, Chicago and Los Angeles, plus Philadelphia, had black mayors. Tom Bradley of Los Angeles, a former policeman, just missed winning the governorship of California in 1982.

The Great Society

If L.B.J.'s sponsorship of full civil rights for blacks was partly forced on him by political realities, his concern for the poor and disadvantaged of all races was sincere and deeply felt. He had had to struggle himself and, in Texas politics, had been regarded as a friend of Mexican-Americans, most of whom were poor and treated scarcely better than blacks. Johnson worshipped Franklin D. Roosevelt and wanted to be remembered in history as the president who completed what the New Deal had started. He envisioned an America:

. . .where no child will go unfed and no youngster will go unschooled; where every child has a good teacher and every teacher has good pay, and both have good classrooms; where every human being has dignity and every worker has a job;

where education is blind to color and employment is unaware of race: where decency appeals and courage abounds.

Johnson's "War on Poverty," which was directed by the new Office of Economic Opportunity, funded a Job Corps that retrained unemployed people for the new kinds of jobs available in high-technology industries. The O.E.O. recruited boys and girls from impoverished families for catch-up education in special Head Start schools and young men and women for placement in universities. Other programs provided financial help and tutoring in order to compensate for the economic and cultural handicaps of growing up in poverty. Volunteers in Service to America (VISTA) was a domestic Peace Corps, sending social workers and teachers into decaying inner cities and poor rural areas. Medicare provided government-funded health insurance for the elderly, chronically ill, and very poor.

Nor did the Great Society neglect the middle and working classes. Generous funding of schools, colleges, and universities and extremely cheap student loans made it possible for hundreds of thousands of young people to secure an education otherwise closed to them.

Some of these acts were legislated before the lopsided election of 1964. But it was after his great victory, thanks to the hordes of freshman Democratic congressmen beholden entirely to Johnson's landslide for their seats, that the program was completed.

VIETNAM! VIETNAM!

"Were there no outside world," the political journalist Theodore H. White wrote in 1969, just five years after Lyndon Johnson's great electoral triumph, "Lyndon Johnson might conceivably have gone down as the greatest of twentieth-century presidents." Obviously, White had written off the possibility of such an honor.

So had all but a few of the president's devotees. By 1969—by 1967!—virtually no one was saying as, just a few years earlier, L.B.J.'s aide Jack Valenti did without embarrassment, "I sleep each night a little better, a little more confidently because Lyndon Johnson is my president." More typical in 1967 was the statement of Senator Eugene McCarthy, a member of Johnson's own party: "We've got a wild man in the White House, and we are going to have to treat him as such."

What happened? A war happened. The builder of the Great Society at home mired the United States in a war in a Southeast Asian country of which, before 1964, many Americans had never heard. Johnson inherited

A VISTA volunteer, one of thousands of recruits in the War on Poverty, talks to a child in Alabama.

the American presence in Vietnam from Kennedy—and from Eisenhower and Dulles. But it was he who made the decisions that transformed a minor foreign policy problem, and apparently one that could have been easily resolved, into an insidious cancer that spread into every organ of the American body politic.

A Long Way from the Pedernales

During the nineteenth century, the French had established firm imperial control over most of Indochina, the peninsula that pendles from the Asian mainland east of India and includes the present-day nations of Vietnam, Laos, and Cambodia. As elsewhere in their empire, the French fostered the growth of a native elite dedicated to French culture and the Roman Catholic religion. This Indochinese elite prospered and was favored by the French both economically and with a share in governing the colony.

However, the majority of Vietnamese, Cambodians, and Laotians remained peasants or menial laborers, perhaps treated worse because their rulers were foreign, perhaps not, but in any case resenting the French presence and wanting them out. One such nationalist was Ho Chih Minh, who went to Paris as a seaman and, in 1920, was a founding member of the French Communist Party. Ho lived in Russia and China until World War II when he returned to Vietnam to organize a guerrilla movement, the Viet Minh, to fight the Japanese who had occupied the country after the defeat of France in Europe.

Partly because of Ho Chih Minh's contribution to the war effort in harassing the Japanese, President Roosevelt favored setting up an independent Vietnam after the war. Ho, with support from many non-Communists, proclaimed the republic of Vietnam in 1945. Later, when French forces returned, he agreed to keep Vietnam

Ho Chi Minh founded the Viet Minh to fight for an independent Vietnam.

within the French imperial community as long as the nation was a self-governing commonwealth.

The French, their pride wounded by their ignominious collapse during World War II, refused to cooperate with Ho. Instead, they set up a puppet regime and the Viet Minh took once again to the jungles and rice paddies where they launched a guerrilla war that lasted eight years. In 1950, the United States began to funnel aid to the French but, after a decisive defeat in the battle of Dien Bien Phu in 1954, the French gave up and left. According to the Geneva Accord signed that same year, Vietnam was to be temporarily divided at the 17th parallel into two zones. Ho's Viet Minh would govern the northern half of the country from Hanoi; a non-Communist government would administer the southern part of the country from Saigon. After two years, when the bitterness and tumult of the long war had moderated, democratic elections would be held to determine the nation's future.

It was all a long way from the Pedernales River. What did the United States have to do with a war between Indochinese demanding independence and a weak and divided France trying to salvage an obsolete empire?

The Beginnings of American Involvement

The Cold War and John Foster Dulles's obsessive crusade against Communism involved the United States in Vietnamese affairs. As he was elsewhere in the world, Dulles was blind to the fact that, although a Communist, Ho Chih Minh had initially been cordial to the United States. Ho was aware that F.D.R. had favored an independent Vietnam and patterned Vietnam's Declaration of Independence on the American document of 1776. Although it is impossible to know Ho's long-term intentions during the long war with the French, his Viet Minh included substantial non-Communist elements. Some evidence hints that Ho counted on American economic aid to build up the Vietnamese nation.

Instead of feeling Ho out, Dulles pumped millions of dollars into the French war effort and even considered using nuclear weapons to lift the Viet Minh's siege of the French at Dien Bien Phu. Eisenhower vetoed that proposal, as he usually did when Dulles began to tremble with fervor, and the United States attended the Geneva conference that ended French rule. Dulles refused to sign the Geneva Accord, but the United States announced that it would do nothing to interfere with its provisions, including the election to be held in 1956.

Events and propaganda by the Chinese Lobby altered American policy. About a million anti-Communist North Vietnamese fled to below the seventeenth parallel between 1954 and 1956, and there were several instances of mistreatment of Roman Catholics in the North. A Vietnamese nationalist who had lived in exile in the United States, Ngo Dinh Diem, returned to the South and was portrayed in the United States as his nation's George Washington. The Eisenhower administration gave Diem $320 million in aid in 1955 and supported his refusal to hold elections in 1956. Instead, he proclaimed the Republic of Vietnam in the South.

For several years, Diem appeared to succeed. Then, in 1960, opposition groups, including South Vietnamese Communists, formed the National Liberation Front and launched, yet again, a guerrilla war aimed at unifying the country. The N.L.F. attacked isolated patrols of Diem's soldiers, killed village officials loyal to the regime, terrorized ordinary villagers, and actually set up local governments in many parts of South Vietnam, collecting taxes and administering justice.

Diem described his enemies as "Viet Cong," Vietnamese Communists, although many non-Communists belonged to the N.L.F. during this era. He claimed that the guerrilla movement was inspired, aided, and abetted by North Vietnam, which was quite true, but obscured the fact that virtually all of the Viet Cong's 15,000 soldiers in 1960 were South Vietnamese peasants. Both the Eisenhower and Kennedy administrations pumped millions into his regime.

Buddhist monk Quang Duc immolates himself to protest the anti-Buddhist policies of South Vietnamese president Ngo Dinh Diem. The photo was taken by Malcolm Brown and was among the most shocking to come out of the Vietnam War.

Kennedy's Uncertainty

Kennedy's military advisors urged him to send 10,000 American troops to help Diem, telling him that "the essence of the problem in Vietnam is military." Kennedy was unconvinced. He had just been stung by C.I.A. advice at the Bay of Pigs and wondered why Diem's A.R.V.N. (Army of the Republic of Vietnam), which numbered 250,000, could not handle a much smaller body of part-time guerrillas. He compromised by sending 3,000 "Green Berets," U.S. Army Special Forces expert in counterinsurgency, fighting guerrillas, to advise the A.R.V.N. Slowly, the American presence increased. By the end of 1962, there were 11,000 American military advisors in South Vietnam.

By mid-1963, however, Kennedy had soured on Diem. Isolated from the people of the country as he shambled around the presidential palace day and night, surrounded and dominated by corrupt relatives, Diem approved of repressive policies, high taxes, and favoritism toward Roman Catholic Vietnamese. In a few short years, the George Washington of Vietnam had become a peevish, unpopular dictator. Buddhist monks led protests in Saigon, Hue, and other cities, some setting themselves aflame in intersections. Capitalizing on the unrest, the N.L.F. stepped up its campaign in the countryside. During the day, Diem's regime more or less governed South Vietnam. Once the sun had set, the Saigon government controlled little more than the capital, other major towns, and part of the fertile rice-growing Mekong River delta. Elsewhere, N.L.F. guerrillas moved freely.

Kennedy may have given up on the possibility of military victory. At least, he planned to reduce the American contingent in the country, 16,000 strong by the fall of 1963. When some advisers protested, insisting that another increase in American manpower would win the war, he replied that to get involved more deeply was like "taking a drink. The effect wears off, and you have to take another."

Perhaps hoping to arrange a political settlement—like much recent history, the story is muddled and hotly contested—Kennedy agreed to tolerate a *coup d'état* by high-ranking A.R.V.N. officers that would remove Diem from the scene. An American plane was reserved to take Diem and his family out of the country but, in November 1963, when the A.R.V.N. struck, Diem was assassinated. A month later, Kennedy was dead. While the United States was undergoing a period of mourning and transition, South Vietnam was plunged into comic-opera political instability as one general toppled another and the N.L.F. increased its power in the countryside.

MR. JOHNSON'S WAR

President Johnson ordered modest increases in the number of American military "advisors" in early 1964. But he, like Kennedy, seemed at first to want out of the war. Through intermediaries, he offered economic aid to North Vietnam in return for peace talks. The North Vietnamese replied that they could not speak for the N.L.F. The N.L.F., to which Johnson also referred as the Viet Cong, refused to negotiate until all American soldiers were withdrawn from the country.

The President's Vision

This Johnson refused to do. Although he was no John Foster Dulles, L.B.J.'s view of the Cold War had been shaped in the 1950s by the belief that Communism was monolithic, an international movement directed ultimately from the Kremlin. Just enough men and supplies reached the N.L.F. from the North to convince him that the war in Vietnam was not civil, but a war of subversion dependent on outside interference. He vowed that he was "not going to be the President who saw Southeast Asia go the way China went."

Johnson subscribed to the "domino theory" of Communist expansion propounded none too gracefully by President Eisenhower several years earlier: "You knock over the first one, and what will happen to the last one is the certainty that it will go over very quickly." When Johnson looked at Southeast Asia, he saw a line of fallen dominos stretching from Russia through China to North Vietnam, and a line of standing dominos beginning in South Vietnam, Laos, and Cambodia and extending to the Philippines and even Japan. As early as 1961, he had said, "We must decide whether to help these countries to the best of our ability or throw in the towel in the area and pull back our defenses to San Francisco."

The Tonkin Gulf Resolution

As late as October 1964 (shortly before Johnson faced the saber-rattling Goldwater in the presidential election), the president assured Americans that "we are not about to send American boys nine or ten thousand miles away from home to do what Asian boys ought to be doing for themselves." In reality, he was thinking about widening the war by means of a massive American military effort as early as the summer of 1964. In August, he was informed that North Vietnamese patrol boats had attacked American destroyers in the Gulf of Tonkin. He then asked Congress for authority "to take all necessary measures to repel any armed attack against the forces of the United States and to prevent future aggression."

Only two Senators voted against the Gulf of Tonkin Resolution. One of them, Ernest Gruening of Alaska, said that he would not vote for "a predated declaration of war." In fact, whatever Johnson's motives at the time, he was to use the Gulf of Tonkin Resolution to turn the Vietnam conflict into a major war. By the end of 1964, the American military contingent in South Vietnam had been increased to 23,000, all, however, still described as advisors.

Escalation

Then, in February 1965, the Viet Cong attacked an American military base near Pleiku. Citing the Tonkin Gulf Resolution, Johnson sent in 3,500 Marines, the first official combat troops, to South Vietnam. In April, 20,000 more troops arrived. By the end of 1965 there were 200,000 American troops in South Vietnam. This number doubled by the end of 1966 and reached 500,000 by the end of 1967.

Between 1965 and 1968, the U.S. Air Force carried out heavy bombing of North Vietnam. To deprive the Viet Cong of shelter in the South Vietnam jungle, planes sprayed defoliants over tens of thousands of acres, killing trees, underbrush, and crops. American soldiers then moved in on "search and destroy" missions.

Johnson's policy of step by step increases in the intensity of the war was known as "escalation." His object was to prove to the enemy that fighting the American military machine was a hopeless cause. Briefly in 1965 and 1967, he stopped bombing and offered peace terms to North Vietnam.

Both proposals were rejected. Instead, North Vietnam matched each American escalation with an escalation of its own. Beginning in 1964 and escalating in 1966, North Vietnam sent its own soldiers into the war to replace dead Viet Cong. Within two years, 100,000 North Vietnamese were in the South. Step by step, a civil war between two groups of South Vietnamese became very largely a war between Americans and North Vietnamese.

China and the Soviet Union also escalated their contribution to the war. Both countries supplied North Vietnam with ground-to-air missiles and other sophisticated weapons as well as economic aid.

seemed as distant as ever. In just a few weeks after the Tet Offensive, public approval of Johnson's handling of the war dropped from 40 percent to 26 percent. L.B.J. was badly shaken. Years later, two top aides reported they were so worried about his judgment that they secretly consulted psychiatrists.

TROUBLED YEARS

Johnson craved consensus, a word he used as often as Kennedy had called for vigor. In making his plea for civil-rights legislation, he adopted the slogan of the movement, "We Shall Overcome." He meant that all Americans would rise above the blight of racial hatred and discrimination. Another favorite presidential saying was a quotation from the biblical book of Isaiah: "Let us come together." The old manipulator of votes was not, as president, content with a majority, not even so large a one as he won in 1964. He wanted a unity of Americans behind him and his vision of a Great Society. The practical politician was a dreamer.

What L.B.J. got was a people divided more bitterly, perhaps, than at any time since the Civil War. The major cause of the social divisions of the 1960s was the war in Vietnam.

The Tet Offensive

Nevertheless, at the beginning of 1968, the American commander, General William Westmoreland, told L.B.J. that victory was within reach. His words had scarcely been reported in the newspapers when, in the midst of the celebrations of Tet, Vietnam's traditional lunar New Year, 70,000 Viet Cong and North Vietnamese launched attacks on 30 South Vietnamese cities. For several days they controled much of the city of Hue. In Saigon, enemy commandos attacked the American embassy itself. The Viet Cong took back jungle areas the "search and destroy" missions had cleared.

The Americans regrouped and, when the Tet Offensive was over, the Viet Cong and North Vietnamese had suffered horrendous casualties. In May, they agreed to begin peace talks in Paris. However, the American people's confidence in the war had also been severely shaken. The number of American boys dead, reported each evening on television, had soared from an average 26 a week in 1965 to 96 a week in 1966 and 180 a week in 1967. In 1968, more than 280 Americans were killed in Vietnam each week. The cost of the war had risen to $25 billion a year, nearly $70 million a day!

Despite this tremendous effort and loss of life, victory

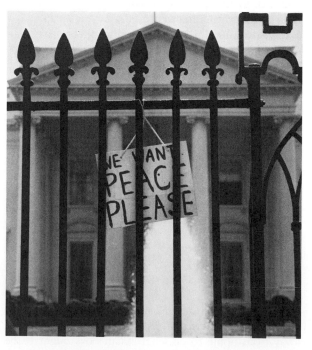

A war protestor's sign hangs on the White House fence.

Hawks and Doves

Until 1965, the chief criticism of Johnson's Vietnam policy came from conservative Republicans like Barry Goldwater, some retired military men, and extremists like members of the John Birch Society. They said that in moving so cautiously, Johnson was making the same mistake President Truman had made in Korea. He was fighting for a limited purpose, a negotiated peace, rather than for total victory. Known as "Hawks," these critics wanted to use American military might to crush the Viet Cong and North Vietnamese. Former Air Force Chief of Staff Curtis LeMay called for bombing North Vietnam "into the Stone Age."

After L.B.J. escalated the war, becoming a Hawk himself, his chief critics were the "Doves," people who called for an end to the fighting or, at least, more serious efforts to negotiate a peace. As the war dragged on and the casualty lists mounted, this antiwar movement grew in size and militance.

Most Doves were liberal Democrats, members of L.B.J.'s own party. Doves included members of Congress, university professors and school teachers, ministers, priests and nuns, some working people, many middle-class professionals, and even several retired generals. College students, although they were deferred from the draft that sent young men to Vietnam, were attracted to the antiwar movement in great numbers.

Mass demonstrations made for good television news features and put the antiwar movement at the center of public attention. In October 1965, 100,000 people attended demonstrations in ninety cities. In April 1967, about 300,000 Americans marched in opposition to the war in New York and San Francisco. Some young men burned their draft cards and went to jail rather than into the army. Some 40,000 went into exile, especially in Canada and Sweden. More than 500,000 soldiers deserted during the Vietnam years and there were some

250,000 "bad discharges." Draft dodgers with influential social and political connections could join the National Guard in order to avoid combat service.

Antiwar Arguments

Doves opposed the war for many different reasons, some contradictory. A few were members of radical groups such as the Progressive Labor Party, which admired Mao Zedong. They openly hoped that Ho Chih Minh would defeat the "imperialist capitalist" United States. Many youthful romantics, who knew little about Communism, were enchanted by the spectacle of the outnumbered, poorly-equipped Viet Cong resisting American power.

Other Doves like the famous pediatrician, Dr. Benjamin Spock, were anti-Communists. However, they believed that the United States was fighting against the wishes of a majority of Vietnamese and, therefore, was in the wrong. They disapproved of the fact that their powerful nation was showering terrible destruction on a small, poor country.

Religious pacifists like the Quakers opposed the war because they opposed all wars. Other morally concerned people, who agreed that some wars were justified, felt that the war in Vietnam was not one of them. They objected to the fact that, with no clear battle lines, American troops were making war on civilians as well as on enemy soldiers.

Bombs and defoliants took many innocent lives. In addition, a few American soldiers were guilty of deliberate atrocities. The worst occured at the village of My Lai in March 1968 when American troops killed 347 unarmed men, women, and children. The Viet Cong were guilty of similar crimes but that, Doves said, did not justify Americans in stooping to the same level.

Some critics of the war emphasized politics and diplomacy. They pointed out that the United States was exhausting itself fighting in a small, unimportant country while the power of China and the Soviet Union was untouched. Diplomat George Kennan and Senator William Fulbright of Arkansas argued that the United States was neglecting its commitments elsewhere in the world. Senators Gaylord Nelson of Wisconsin and Wayne Morse of Oregon pointed out that the American war effort was alienating other Third World nations and even America's most trusted allies.

Black Separatism

The antiwar movement was not the only expression of discontent in the Great Society. What is most remarkable about the troubles of the 1960s is that anti-Johnson protest was noisiest among the very groups that most benefited from L.B.J.'s reforms.

DEMONSTRATION DECADE

Between 1963 and 1968, according to the National Commission on the Causes and Prevention of Violence, there were

369 civil-rights demonstrations
239 black riots and disturbances
213 white terrorist attacks against civil-rights workers
104 antiwar demonstrations
91 student protests on campus
54 segregationist clashes with counter-demonstrators
24 anti-integration demonstrations

A demonstration in support of the Vietnam War.

Some of the fiercest anti-Johnson rhetoric came from young African Americans, for whom the president believed he did so much. While the majority of black people supported the Great Society, many younger militants, particularly in the North, attacked the president's integrationist policies in the name of the "black-power" movement.

Black power meant many things. To civil rights campaigner Jesse Jackson, and to some intellectuals such as sociologist Charles Hamilton, it meant pressure politics in the time-honored tradition of American ethnic groups: blacks demanding concessions for people of their race on the basis of the votes they could either deliver to or withhold from a political candidate. To a tiny group of black nationalists, it meant demanding a part of the United States for the formation of a separate nation for African Americans only. To the great majority of advocates of black power, the slogan reduced to little more than fad and fashion, dressing up in dashikis, wearing hair styles called "Afros," and cutting off friendships and casual social relationships with whites. It was an odd affirmation of the social segregation that was a pillar of the old Jim Crow laws.

Black power was not a political program, but a cry of anguish and anger against the discrimination of the past and the discovery that civil equality of itself did little to remedy the social and psychological burdens from which African Americans suffered: poverty, high unemployment, inferior educational opportunities, severe health problems unknown to whites, high crime rates in black neighborhoods, a sense of inadequacy bred over three centuries of oppression.

Malcolm X and Violence

The most formidable spokesman for black separatism was Malcolm Little, a Detroiter and ex-petty criminal who styled himself Malcolm X, stating that a slave owner had stolen his real African name. An adherent of a religious sect known as the Nation of Islam, or Black Muslims (for Christianity was said to be a "white man's religion"), Malcolm was a spellbinding preacher. He said that black people should reject Martin Luther King, Jr.'s, call to integrate into American society and, instead, separate from whites and glory in their blackness. Many young blacks, particularly in the North, were captivated by this message of defiance. One convert was a West Indian immigrant, Stokely Carmichael, who expelled all whites from S.N.C.C. in 1966, effectively taking that group out of the Civil Rights Movement.

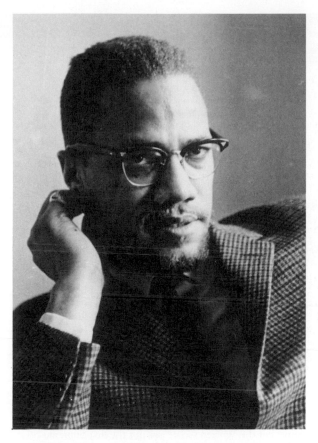

Malcolm X was a founder of the black power movement of the 1960s.

A mule-drawn cart carries the body of civil rights leader Martin Luther King, Jr., at his funeral in Atlanta, Georgia.

Malcolm X's admonition to meet white racist violence with black violence appealed to former civil-rights workers who had been beaten by police and to African-American teenagers in the urban ghettos. Carmichael's successor as the head of S.N.C.C., Hubert Geroid "H. Rap" Brown, proclaimed as his motto, "Burn, Baby, Burn." In Oakland, California, two college students, Huey P. Newton and Bobby Seale, formed the Black Panther Party for Self-Defense. They were immediately involved in violent confrontations with police because of their insistence that they be allowed to patrol black neighborhoods with firearms.

Violence haunted black America during the 1960s. Malcolm X fell out of favor with the Black Muslims and was gunned down by assassins in 1965. Also in 1965, a riot in the Watts district of Los Angeles resulted in 34 deaths and $35 million in property damages. In 1966 and 1967, black riots raged in the ghettos of many cities. When Martin Luther King, Jr., was killed by a white racist, James Earl Ray, in 1968, the smoke from buildings set afire by rioters in Washington wafted into the White House itself.

The Student Movement

Just as troubling was discontent among another group that was favored by Johnson's Great Society reforms, university students. By 1963, it already was clear that the baby-boom generation was not so passive in its politics as the youth of the 1950s had been. Students dem-

BLACK POWER

The most conspicuous individual in the emergence of the black-power movement was West-Indian-born Stokely Carmichael. In 1966, he explained what he meant by black power: "If we are to proceed toward true liberation, we must cut ourselves off from white people. We must form our own institutions, credit unions, co-ops, political parties, write our own histories. . . ."

NOTABLE PEOPLE

EARL WARREN (1891–1974)

For sixteen years, Earl Warren of California was Chief Justice of the Supreme Court. Appointed by Eisenhower in 1953, he served long enough to inaugurate another Republican Californian, whom he did not much like, Richard Nixon. In the meantime, he led a Court that was more active in making decisions that shaped American historical development than any since the Marshall Court of the early nineteenth century, and Warren was the most controversial Chief Justice since Roger B. Taney and his divisive Dred Scott decision of 1857.

Earl Warren was born in Los Angeles in 1891, attended the University of California at Berkeley, and, when he graduated from law school, remained in northern California. After service in the army during the First World War, he made his home in Oakland and, in 1925, was elected district attorney of Alameda County.

He appeared to be satisfied with a career in county politics, remaining district attorney for fourteen years and virtually unknown elsewhere. However, a tough policy toward organized rackets brought him to the attention of the state's Republican bosses, and Warren was nominated for and elected California attorney general in 1939. The post traditionally was a stepping stone to the governorship in that state, and Warren's career took off. Fighting organized crime at the state level enabled him to win the Republican nomination for governor in 1942 and, quite easily, the election. Warren was so popular that, in 1946, because statewide nominations were made in a popular primary, he won both the Republican and Democratic nominations for governor and received 92 percent of the popular vote. This victory caught the eye of the national leadership of the Republican party, and in 1948, Warren was tapped to run for vice president with Thomas E. Dewey of New York. The Republicans believed that they were winners in 1948, so Warren, just fifty-seven years old, seemed to be headed for the White House. Of course, Dewey was defeated in one of the great presidential upsets. Nevertheless, Warren was easily reelected to the California governorship in 1950.

As governor, Warren was aligned with neither the conservative nor the liberal wing of the Republican party. In fact, while clearly less shrill than William Knowland, the right-wing senator from California, Warren had been responsible for orders during the Second World War that allowed the seizure of property from Japanese-Americans who had been interned by the federal government. There was little in his career to anticipate what he would do after President Eisenhower named him Chief Justice in 1953.

What he did was to assume immediately the leadership of the Court liberals—most of the justices had been appointed by Franklin D. Roosevelt—and spearhead a rush of decisions that overturned long-entrenched policies and practices in racial segregation, apportionment of legislative districts, and police procedure.

He is best remembered for having written the unanimous decision that forbade racial segregation in the schools, *Brown* v. *Board of Education of Topeka* (1953). A series of similar decisions regarding segregation by race paved the way for congressional approval of the Civil Rights Acts of 1964 and 1965. They also made Warren the target of critics not only among segregationists but also among judicial conservatives who believed that the Warren Court had made its decision in the *Brown* case not on legal but on sociological grounds. (They had a point, but the Warren Court was not the first Supreme Court to do so.)

Warren won enemies among professional politicians as a result of a series of decisions on the issue of representation in elections to the House of Representatives and to state legislatures. It was common in states that were both urban and rural for rural voters to be "overrepresented"; because district lines had been drawn before cities had grown to house so many people, farm areas got to elect more legislators and congressmen than did city voters. In Virginia, for example, eighty-four rural voters had the same representation as one hundred city voters. In 1946, the Supreme Court had refused to intervene in this practice on the grounds that it was a political matter, which

onstrated against capital punishment, protested against the violations of civil liberties by groups like the House Un-American Activities Committee, and worked in the Civil Rights Movement. In 1963, a new national youth organization, Students for a Democratic Society (S.D.S.), issued the "Port Huron statement," a comprehensive critique of American society written by a graduate of the University of Michigan, Tom Hayden. The S.D.S. called for young people to take the lead in drafting

a program by which the United States could be made genuinely democratic and a force for peace and justice.

Like the advocates of black power, the New Left, as S.D.S. and other organizations came to be called, was not so much a political movement as an explosion of anger and frustration. Hayden and a few other youth leaders tried to channel student energies into concrete concerns like civil rights for African Americans, the problems of the poor, and the power of large corporations indeed it was: rural state assemblymen refused to give up their privileged position.

In *Baker* v. *Carr* (1962), however, the Warren Court ordered that states redraw the lines of congressional districts on the basis of "one man, one vote," all districts to contain approximately the same population. In *Westberry* v. *Sanders* (1964) and *Reynolds* v. *Sims* (1964), the Court went further. The justices ruled that "one man, one vote" also applied to state legislatures, and to *both houses*. Because the upper houses of most state legislatures were patterned on the United States Senate, with each member representing a county, these decisions revolutionized state government. Warren and a five to four majority of the Court said that whereas the Constitution provided for unequal representation in the Senate, state legislatures did not have the same mandate. In a sense, these decisions made the upper houses of state legislatures superfluous: they, like the lower houses, would be based on population.

The most controversial area in which the Warren court "legislated," as critics averred, was in police procedure. Three cases mark the development of what many people of the 1960s and 1970s regarded as Court insistence on coddling criminals. In *Mapp* v. *Ohio* (1961), the Court ruled that police could not use as a basis for criminal prosecution evidence that had been seized without a warrant. In the abstract, the decision was unexceptional, but in specific cases, it seemed to protect violators of the law. Mapp, for instance, was a woman whose house had been raided on suspicion that she dealt in drugs. No evidence to that effect was discovered, but police did discover obscene materials, which were used in court against her. The Court's decision in the matter seemed to rule out prosecution in any cases when the evidence used was not the specific object of a warranted search.

In *Escobedo* v. *Illinois* (1964), the Court overturned a conviction. While the defendant, Danny Escobedo, was obviously guilty of the crime of which he had been convicted, he had been refused the right to see his lawyer when police were questioning him. Much more offensive

to the growing anti-Warren forces who called for "law and order" was *Miranda* v. *Arizona* (1968), in which Warren himself wrote that a suspect in a crime must be informed immediately of his rights (particularly under the Fifth Amendment, which protects against self-incrimination), or any conviction secured could be in jeopardy. To many police officers and some civilians, the necessity of repeating a legally foolproof litany of constitutional rights in heated arrest situations was making the war against crime impossible and putting the rights of suspected criminals above those of victims. An "Impeach Earl Warren" movement sprang up during the 1960s, but never grew large enough to threaten the Chief Justice's job.

Immediately after President Kennedy's assassination in 1963, a reluctant Warren gave in to Lyndon Johnson's insistence that he head a commission to investigate the murder. He may have had a premonition that no possible findings would go unattacked. He was right. Despite the voluminous report (26 volumes of testimony from 552 witnesses, with an 888-page summation of evidence and conclusions), the Warren Commission was criticized for slipshod work and even of a "cover-up" in its conclusions that Lee Harvey Oswald was the sole killer and that the murder of Oswald by Jack Ruby was also unconnected to any conspiracy. Nevertheless, no conclusive evidence to the contrary has since been presented.

Warren tried to resign his post when Johnson was still president so that his successor would also be a liberal. However, when Johnson tried to give the Chief Justiceship to an old friend, Associate Justice Abe Fortas, enemies in the Senate dug up some irregularities in Fortas's record and prevented the appointment. Warren remained in office until 1969, when Richard Nixon replaced him with Warren Burger, a more conservative jurist whose revisions of the Warren Court decisions did not turn them around as much as many of Warren critics had hoped. Warren died in 1974.

in American society. But most of the campus riots of the late 1960s were unfocused, aimed at local grievances such as student participation in setting university rules, or directed against the war in Vietnam, a matter beyond the competence of university presidents and local merchants (major targets of student rebellion) to solve.

Massive protest on campuses began at the University of California at Berkeley with the founding of the Free Speech Movement in 1964. By 1968, protest took a

violent turn with students at Columbia University seizing several buildings and refusing to budge until they were forcibly removed by police.

The Counterculture

By 1966, many young people, high school as well as college students, were dropping out of politics to pursue a personal rebellion. In the Haight-Ashbury district of

San Francisco and in the East Village of New York, thousands of teenagers gathered to establish what they called a "counterculture," a new way of living based on promiscuous sex, drugs (particularly marijuana and a synthetic hallucinogen, LSD), and extravagant colorful clothing. They called themselves "flower children," free of the pressures and preoccupations of American materialism. Other Americans called them "hippies" and were alternately amused by them, or condemned them as lazy, immoral "long-haired kids." In both New York and San Francisco, tour buses took curiosity seekers through hippie neighborhoods as though they were exotic foreign countries. When tourists from small towns snapped shots of counterculture fauna, some hippies whipped out cameras and took pictures of them.

When commercialization seemed to be destroying the vitality of the counterculture, numerous flower children retreated to communes in the California mountains and New Mexico desert. But because the self-fulfillment of individuals was the principal goal of the phenomenon, and because drugs played a large part in the culture, the communes were doomed from the start. The most fundamental matters of procuring the necessities of health and sanitation were neglected.

THE ELECTION OF 1968

No president can survive a serious economic depression in a year that he must stand for reelection. Lyndon Johnson, able to shout gleefully while striding through an airplane in 1964, "I am the king! I am the king!," discovered in 1968 that a reigning monarch cannot survive a serious social, cultural, and moral depression. He did not even try. Early in 1968, the Great Society in tatters, he announced that he would not run for reelection.

Eugene McCarthy, Regicide

In 1967, Eugene McCarthy was in his second term as senator from Minnesota. He was a tall man with a gray solemnity about him that bordered on glumness. His record as a liberal workhorse was solid, but no one thought of him as a mover and shaker. Minnesota already had its walking earthquake of energy and exuberance in Vice President Hubert Humphrey. McCarthy seemed just right to stay at home, anchoring Minnesota's long liberal tradition in Midwestern bedrock.

But McCarthy was anguished by the issue that the vice president had to dodge, the war in Vietnam. Late in 1967, he announced that he would stand as a candi-

date for the Democratic presidential nomination, challenging Lyndon B. Johnson on that issue.

Political pundits admired McCarthy's principle and pluck. A few were enchanted by his diffidence: with plenty of mediocrities lusting unashamedly after public office, he seemed genuinely to believe that a public servant should serve a cause. But the experts gave him little chance. McCarthy's only base of support was within the largely middle-class antiwar movement. The labor unions, vital to Democratic party success at the polls, begrudged him several votes against their legislative programs; he struck no chord among either black or ethnic minorities (despite his somewhat mystical Roman Catholic religion); and he positively disdained big city mayors like Chicago's Richard E. Daley. A portion of the educated, cultured, affluent liberal middle class was not, the professionals said, a foundation on which to build an electoral majority.

Johnson Retires

Time was to prove them right. But in 1968, antiwar activists were so aroused that, like Barry Goldwater's right-wing shock troops in the Republican party in 1964, they were able to turn the Democratic party upside down. At McCarthy's call, thousands of university students dropped their studies and rushed to New Hamp-

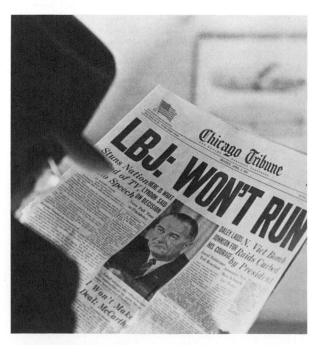

After Eugene McCarthy's moral victory in the New Hampshire primary in March 1968, President Johnson announced his retirement.

shire, scene of the first presidential primary. They agreed to get "clean for Gene," shearing their long "hippie" hair, shaving their beards, and donning neckties, brassieres, and proper dresses so as not to alienate the people of the conservative state from the issue at hand—the war. Sleeping on the floors of McCarthy storefront headquarters, they rang door bells, handed out pamphlets at supermarkets, and stuffed envelopes.

President Johnson knew enough of the country's anxiety over the war to be concerned. He kept his name off the ballot. Instead, the governor of New Hampshire ran as his proxy. The vote was evenly split, but such a rebuke of an incumbent president in a traditionally cautious and conservative state promised bigger McCarthy victories elsewhere. Johnson knew it. On national television, he announced that he would retire when his term expired.

The Democrats: Who Will End the War?

Johnson's announcement caught everyone by surprise. Vice President Humphrey, in Mexico on a good-will tour, rushed back to Washington to throw his hat into the ring. He had an immediate edge on McCarthy because of long-standing ties with labor, blacks, big-city Democratic machines, the party's professionals, and contributors generous with a dollar.

The McCarthy backers expected Humphrey to run and welcomed the contest. What they could not foresee was that in the wake of Johnson's withdrawal, Robert F. Kennedy also rushed to enter the race. Kennedy was a real threat to both McCarthy and Humphrey. Johnson had eased him out of his cabinet as soon after John Kennedy's death as it was seemly to do so. L.B.J. did not like "Bobby," whose presence kept him in the Kennedy shadow. In fact, R.F.K. looked on Johnson almost as a usurper of a Kennedy birthright. After methodical public opinion polls typical of the Kennedy clan showed that he could win a Senate seat in New York despite his lack of association with the state, Robert Kennedy ran, won, and became a critic of the war and a leading liberal spokesman.

His connections with minorities were as strong as Humphrey's. He was a close personal friend of Cesar Chavez, leader of the mostly Hispanic farmworkers' union in California and the Southwest. Even with blacks, on whose behalf Humphrey had labored since the 1940s, Kennedy was popular. When Martin Luther King, Jr., was assassinated on April 4, 1968, Bobby's response seemed more sincere and was better received than the respects of any other Democrat. He had maintained his connections with the old-line party professionals and the labor movement. Indeed, within the Democratic party, his political realism and opportunism

Minutes before he was assassinated, Senator Robert Kennedy celebrates his victory in the California Democratic primary.

made him anathema only to the group that continued to support McCarthy. They attacked him as avidly as they attacked Johnson and Humphrey as an exemplar of the "old politics."

Kennedy ran strong although not without setbacks. For example, McCarthy won the next-to-last primary, in Oregon. Then, on the very night he won the last of the primaries, in California, Robert Kennedy was assassinated, shot point-blank in the head by Sirhan B. Sirhan, a Jordanian who disliked Kennedy's support for the Jewish state of Israel.

The tragedy demoralized the antiwar Democrats and undoubtedly contributed to the week-long riots in Chicago that made a mockery of the Democratic national convention. Many Kennedy supporters found it impossible to swing behind McCarthy and backed Senator George McGovern of South Dakota instead. With a divided opposition, Humphrey was able to win the Democratic nomination on the first ballot. As a gesture toward blue-collar ethnics whose aspirations had been aroused by John F. Kennedy, and who seemed to be supporting Bobby, Humphrey chose a Roman Catholic running mate, Senator Edmund B. Muskie of Maine.

Nixon and Wallace

Richard M. Nixon easily won the Republican nomination at a placid convention in Miami Beach. Although the former vice president had retired from politics in 1962, after failing in an attempt to become governor of California, he had doggedly rebuilt his position in the G.O.P. He firmed up his support among Eastern moderate Republicans and won over Republican conservatives by working hard for Goldwater in 1964. After 1964, Nixon attended every local Republican function to which he was invited, no matter how small the town, insignificant the occasion, or tawdry the candidate he was to endorse. By making himself so available to the party's grass-roots workers, the far from charismatic Nixon built up energetic, active cadres of supporters.

The Democrats were badly split. Many in the antiwar wing of the party announced that they would vote for the pacifist pediatrician Benjamin Spock. Humphrey tried to woo them back by hinting that he would end the war but, as Johnson's vice president, he could not repudiate L.B.J.'s policy. The Democratic split and Humphrey's ambiguity enabled Nixon to waffle on the war issue. He espoused a hawkish military policy at the same time that he reminded voters that a Republican president, Dwight D. Eisenhower, had ended the war in Korea.

The chief threat to a Nixon victory seemed to come from the American Independent party, founded by Governor George Wallace when he calculated that he had no chance to win the Democratic nomination. A diminutive, combative man—reporters called him a bantam fighting cock—Wallace barnstormed the country and attempted to forge an odd alliance of Republican right-wing extremists and blue-collar working people who felt that the Democratic party had forgotten them in its anxiety to appeal to the blacks. This "white backlash" vote appeared to grow after Robert Kennedy was killed. Already indifferent to the aloof McCarthy, many blue-collar white ethnics who had liked Kennedy personally found Wallace much more to their taste than civil-rights pioneer Hubert Humphrey.

A Close Call

It was obvious that Wallace could not win the election. His purpose was to take just enough electoral votes from both Humphrey and Nixon to throw the election into the House of Representatives. Because each state casts one vote when a president is selected in the House, anti-integration Southern congressmen under Wallace's leadership, so Wallace imagined, could make a deal with Nixon: a reversal of Democratic party civil rights policies in return for their support.

Fearing this possibility, Humphrey called on Nixon to pledge with him that neither of them would deal with Wallace and his thinly veiled racism. Instead, Humphrey proposed, he and Nixon should pledge that in the case that neither won in the electoral college, each would direct his supporters in the House to vote for whomever of the two finished with the most votes.

Nixon evaded the challenge, and in the end it did not matter. Although Wallace did better than any third-party candidate since 1924, winning 13.5 percent of the popular vote and 46 electoral votes, Nixon eked out a plurality of 500,000 votes and an absolute majority in the electoral college. It was close. A rush of blue-collar workers back to Humphrey during the final week of the campaign indicated to some pollsters that he would have won had the election been held a week or two later. Some Democratic strategists quietly blamed the loss of Johnson who, peevish even towards this loyal vice president at the end, did little to help Humphrey. Or the explanation of Nixon's victory may well have been those antiwar Democrats who could not bring themselves to vote for Humphrey. In time, their "New Age" politics would transform the great political alliance forged by Franklin D. Roosevelt into a party for whom the presidency was a nearly unattainable prize.

For Further Reading

Consult the bibliographies for Chapters 47 and 48 for overviews of the 1960s. In addition, see Ronald Berman, *America in the Sixties* (1968); Robert Caro, *The Years of Lyndon Johnson* (1982); Theodore Draper, *Abuse of Power* (1967); Jim F. Heath, *Decade of Disillusion: The Kennedy-Johnson Years* (1975); Doris Kearns, *Lyndon Johnson and the American Dream* (1976); Merle Miller, *Lyndon: An Oral Biography* (1980); William L. O'Neill, *Coming Apart: An Informal History of the 1960s* (1971); Richard Walton, *The Foreign Policy of John F. Kennedy*

(1972); Theodore H. White, *The Making of the President, 1964* (1965) and *The Making of the President, 1968* (1969).

There is a huge literature dealing with the Vietnam War, its causes and consequences. Among the most useful books are Frances Fitzgerald, *Fire in the Lake* (1972); David Halberstam, *The Making of a Quagmire* (1956); G. C. Herring, *America's Longest War* (1986); G. M. Kahn, *Intervention: How America Became Involved in Vietnam* (1986); Gabriel Kolko, *Anatomy of a War*

(1985); Marcus G. Raskin and Bernard Fall, *The Vietnam Reader* (1965); and Arthur M. Schlesinger, Jr., *Bitter Heritage: Vietnam and American Democracy* (1967).

On the antiwar and related agitations of what was called "the Movement," see Joseph R. Conlin, *The Troubles: A Jaundiced Glance Back at the Movement of the 1960s* (1982); Morris Dickstein, *Gates of Eden: American Culture in the Sixties* (1977); Todd Gitlin, *The Whole World is Watching* (1981); Kenneth Keniston, *Young Radicals* (1968); Theodore Roszak, *The Making of a Counter-Culture* (1969); Kirkpatrick Sale, *SDS* (1973); and Irwin Unger, *The Movement* (1974).

On the rather more significant Civil Rights Movement, see D. Garrow, *Bearing of the Cross* (1986); Alex Haley, *The Autobiography of Malcolm X* (1965); Sam A. Levitan *et al.*, *Still a Dream: The Changing Status of Blacks Since 1960* (1975); Anthony Lewis, *Portait of a Decade* (1964); David Lewis, *King: A Critical Biography* (1970); Stephen B. Oates, *Let the Trumpet Sound* (1982); James T. Patterson, *America's Struggle Against Poverty, 1900–1980* (1981); H. Sitkoff, *The Struggle for Black Equality* (1981); and Harold Zinn, *SNCC* (1965).

The shelves were still bare as Gerald Ford began work during his first days as President.

THE PRESIDENCY IN CRISIS

POLICIES OF THE NIXON, FORD, AND CARTER ADMINISTRATIONS 1968 - 1980

The heroes of Greek myth were constantly pursuing Proteus, the herdsman of the seas, for he could foresee the future and, once captured, he was obligated to reveal what he knew. But Proteus was rarely caught—he also possessed the curious power to assume the shape of any creature or thing, easily wriggling out of a captor's grasp.

Richard Milhous Nixon, so his critics said, was never captured because he was never in his own shape. John F. Kennedy, who ran against him for the presidency in 1960, said that Dick Nixon had assumed so many shapes that he had forgotten who he was and what he stood for. Liberals called him "Tricky Dicky." At several turns in his career, his Republican partisans felt constrained to assure Americans that the "Old Nixon" was no more; it was a "New Nixon" who needed their votes.

But the "Real Nixon," like the real Proteus, remained elusive and enigmatic to the end. Senator Barry Goldwater said that Richard M. Nixon was "the most complete loner I've ever known."

THE NIXON PRESIDENCY

Nixon will always be a compelling figure. He lacked the personal qualities the pundits said were keys to success in late-twentieth-century politics: physical attractiveness, grace, wit, a camera presence, the aura of "a nice guy." Nixon was shy and furtive in manner. His discomfort and defensiveness in front of a crowd often came off as insincerity.

The liberals' hatred for him had the intensity of a diabolical possession, but those who hated the liberals did not love Nixon. Dwight D. Eisenhower came within a hair of dumping him as vice-presidential nominee in 1952 and considered doing so again in 1956. In 1960, Ike humiliated Nixon by saying he was unable to recall a single instance in which Nixon contributed to a presidential decision. The right-wing Republicans whom Nixon served well for more than two decades accepted him without quite trusting him.

Richard Nixon clawed his way from a lower-middle-class background in southern California to the top of the heap through hard work and the tenacious bite of a bulldog. Although he overstated it in his autobiographical *Six Crises*, he overcame tremendous obstacles and repeated humiliation. If the self-made Horatio Alger boy is an American hero, Nixon should be ensconced in a pantheon for, unlike the Alger heroes, Nixon was all pluck and little luck. Whatever else may be said of Richard Nixon, it must be noted that he earned everything he ever got.

Political Savvy

As president, Nixon took little interest in domestic matters, believing that "the country could run itself domestically without a president." He left important decisions and directives to two young White House aides, H. R. Haldeman and John Ehrlichman. Brassy where their boss was secretive, Haldeman and Erlichman insulated Nixon from Congress and even his own cabinet

as effectively as Sherman Adams had done for Ike. But they were themselves arrogant, unpopular with almost everyone. They did nothing to shore up political support for the Nixon administration. They would have few friends when the tides of fortune turned against them.

Nixon left politicking to Vice-President Spiro T. Agnew, a former governor of Maryland who had been named to the ticket to attract blue-collar and white ethnic voters who were drawn to George Wallace. Agnew was an energetic campaigner and, once elected, cheerleader. He delighted conservatives by flailing student antiwar protestors, permissive educators who tolerated their disruptive activities, liberal Supreme Court justices, and the national news media. Agnew was fond of tongue-twisting alliteration, and his partisan audiences loved it. His masterpiece was "nattering nabobs of negativism," that is, journalists.

Agnew's liberal-baiting provided Nixon with a superb smokescreen for, despite his many denunciations of big-spending liberal government, the president was not interested in dismantling the New Deal or even the Great Society. His only major modification of the liberal welfare state he inherited was "the New Federalism," a policy of turning federal tax monies over to the states to spend on social programs.

On other fronts, Nixon might have been a middle-of-the-road Democrat. He sponsored a scheme for welfare reform, the Family Assistance Plan, that was to provide a flat annual payment to poor families in return for the agreement by heads of household to register with employment agencies. (It failed in Congress.) When, in 1971, inflation threatened his reelection campaign, Nixon slapped on wage and price controls, a Republican anathema for half a century.

And yet, the conservative yelping was muted. Quite shrewdly, Nixon understood that the grass-roots conservatives he called the "Silent Majority" had been repelled far less by liberal economic policy than by the myriad non-economic causes that liberals had come to emphasize by the 1970s: what many whites perceived as kid-gloves treatment of blacks, the often gamey demands of feminists and advocates of "gay rights," the antiwar movement's shrill antipatriotism, and the decisions of the Warren Court that emphasized the rights of accused criminals and seemed to hobble police in enforcing the law.

Reshaping the Supreme Court

Thanks to a mistake by Lyndon Johnson in the waning days of his administration, Nixon was able to move immediately to reshape the Supreme Court. Elderly Chief Justice Earl Warren (an old Nixon nemesis) had offered to retire while Johnson was still president so that L.B.J.

Richard Nixon in the Oval office with aides Robert Haldeman (left) and John Erlichman (center, seated).

could name another liberal activist in his place. Johnson picked an old Texas crony already on the Court, Abe Fortas, who was immediately revealed to have accepted payments for public appearances that were, at best, of dubious propriety. Johnson had to back down and Warren retired only after Nixon was sworn in.

Nixon's choice to replace him was Warren Burger of Minnesota. Burger was conservative but, as an advocate of judicial restraint rather than antiliberal activism, he was somewhat disappointing to the right-wing of the Republican party. When Fortas himself left the Court in 1970, Nixon tried to mollify the right-wingers by naming Clement Haynsworth of South Carolina to the Court. However, Haynsworth had several pro-segregation decisions in his portfolio, and Senate Democrats rejected him.

An angry Nixon then blundered badly. Insisting that the South must have a seat on the Court, he hurriedly named a mediocrity from Florida whose mere knowledge of the law was problematical. When he too was rejected by the Senate, the president had to return to a friend of Burger from Minnesota, Harry A. Blackmun. Nixon's two additional appointments, Lewis F. Powell and William H. Rehnquist (later Chief Justice) were more conservative in the eyes of the "Silent Majority."

Just as Nixon left the basic outlines of the welfare state intact, the Burger Court merely moderated Warren Court rulings. On the domestic front, Nixon seemed to achieve just what he wanted, an equilibrium enabling him to concentrate on what he believed to be the modern president's chief responsibility and his own ticket into the history books: foreign relations.

NIXON'S VIETNAM

No foreign problem was so pressing as the ongoing war in Vietnam. Nixon knew well that Lyndon Johnson's political career had been prematurely snuffed out by the agonizing, endless conflict. "The damned fool" Johnson had, in the words of a protest song of the era, mired himself "hip deep in the Big Muddy," and been helpless to do anything but to tell the nation to "push on." Nixon wanted out of the war. But how to turn the trick?

Vietnamization

Nixon had been vice president when Eisenhower freed the nation from another quagmire in Korea. But Ike's course of action in 1953 was not available in 1969. Eisenhower had threatened the Chinese and North Ko-

Children hit by napalm flee in agony in Trangbang, South Vietnam, June 8, 1972.

reans with nuclear weapons; that was not an option in the era of the nuclear balance of terror. Ike had settled the Korean Conflict on the basis of an independent South Korea with American troops on the scene to ensure security. In 1969, the Viet Cong and North Vietnamese insisted that they would not conclude hostilities as long as there were American troops in South Vietnam. Finally, Eisenhower had not had to deal with a militant antiwar movement at home.

Nixon's scheme was of necessity more subtle. First, to neutralize the antiwar movement, Nixon set out to reduce the sickening casualty lists that weekly provided the protesters with new recruits. In July 1969, he promulgated the Nixon Doctrine, stating that while the United States would "participate in the defense and development of allies and friends," Americans would no longer "undertake all the defense of the free nations of the world."

In Vietnam, the Nixon Doctrine translated as the "Vietnamization" of the war. The large but unreliable A.R.V.N. was thoroughly retrained to replace American boys on the bloody front lines. As South Vietnamese units were deemed ready for combat, American troops came home. At about the same speed that L.B.J. had

escalated the American presence, Nixon de-escalated it. From a high of 541,000 American soldiers in South Vietnam when Nixon took office, the American force declined to 335,000 in 1970 and 24,000 in 1972.

Nixon had returned the American ground war to where it had been in 1964 and, so it seemed at first, he had reduced the militant antiwar movement to a hard core of pacifists and New Left "anti-imperialists" whom Agnew denounced as traitors and Nixon as "bums." Democrats in Congress who had defended Johnson's war demanded that Nixon make more serious efforts to negotiate an end to it. But the president replied, not implausibly, that a truculent North Vietnam, and not he, was the major obstacle to peace.

Expanding the War

Politically, Nixon could not afford simply to pull out of Vietnam. He was beholden for his election to his own hard core of "Hawks" who believed that Johnson had failed in Vietnam because he had not been "tough" enough. Nixon reassured such supporters: "We will not be humiliated. We will not be defeated." Much as he and his chief foreign policy advisor, Henry A. Kissinger,

The Vietnam War Memorial in Washington, D.C., was erected in November 1982, seven years after the conclusion of the war.

wanted the war ended, they had to salvage the independence of South Vietnam in order to save face.

Consequently, all the while he reduced the American presence in Vietnam, Nixon attempted to bludgeon the enemy into meaningful negotiations by expanding the scope of the war. In the spring of 1969, Nixon sent Air Force bombers over neutral Cambodia to destroy sanctuaries where about 50,000 North Vietnamese troops rested up after battles. For a year, the American people knew nothing of these attacks. Then, in 1970, Nixon sent ground forces into Cambodia, an attack that could not be concealed.

The result was a thunderous uproar. Critics condemned the president for attacking a neutral nation. Several hundred university presidents closed their campuses for fear of student violence, and events at two colleges proved their wisdom in doing so. At Kent State University in Ohio, members of the National Guard, many of whom had joined to avoid being drafted and sent to Southeast Asia, opened fire on demonstrators. Four persons were killed and eleven wounded. Ten days later, two students at Jackson State College in Mississippi were killed by police.

Congress reacted to the widening of the war by repealing the Tonkin Gulf Resolution which gave the president authority to fight it. Nixon responded that the repeal was immaterial. As Commander-in-chief, he said, he had the right to take whatever military action he believed necessary. Nonetheless, when the war was further expanded into Laos in February 1971, A.R.V.N. troops carried the burden of the fighting.

Falling Dominos

Vietnamization did not work. Without American troops by their side, the A.R.V.N. was humiliated in Laos. The Communist Pathet Lao grew in strength until 1975 when it seized control of the country. Tens of thousands of refugees who feared Communist rule fled.

In Cambodia, the consequences of expanding the war were far worse. Many young Cambodians were so angered by American bombing that they flocked to join the Khmer Rouge, once scarcely large enough to stage a soccer game. The Khmer Rouge increased in size from a mere 3,000 in 1970 to 30,000 in just a few years. In 1976, the head of the force, Pol Pot, came to power and created one of the most criminal regimes the world has ever known. In three years, his fanatical followers murdered as many as 3 million of their own people out of a population of 7.2 million! If Hitler's campaign of genocide against the Jews of Nazi-occupied Europe was proportional to Pol Pot's, the toll in the Nazi death camps would not have been 6 million, but something on the order of 150 million.

Eisenhower's Asian "dominos" had fallen, but not because the United States had been weak in the face of a military threat. They toppled because the United States had escalated and expanded a war that, in 1963, had been little more than a brawl. In the process, Southeast Asian moderates and neutrals like Cambodia's Prince Sihanouk were undercut. By the mid-1970s, North Vietnam was dominated by militarists and Cambodia by a monster. Laos was in the hands of a once tiny Communist movement.

Finis

In South Vietnam, the fighting dragged on until the fall of 1972 when, after suffering twelve days of earth-shaking bombing, the North Vietnamese finally faced up to the fact that the war was a stalemate. Foreign Minister Le Duc Tho met with Kissinger and arranged a cease-fire. The Paris Accords they signed went into effect in January 1973. The treaty required the United States to withdraw all its troops from Vietnam within 60 days while the North Vietnamese released all prisoners of war. Until free elections were held, North Vietnamese troops could remain in the country.

South Vietnamese president Nguyen Van Thieu regarded the settlement as a sell-out. It enabled Nixon to save face while Thieu was faced with a massive enemy force within South Vietnamese borders. For two years, the country simmered. Then, in April 1975, the A.R.V.N. collapsed and the North Vietnamese army attacked a virtually undefended Saigon. A short time later, North and South Vietnam were united and Saigon was rather unattractively renamed Ho Chi Minh City.

Ironically, Cambodia's nightmare was brought to an end only when the North Vietnamese invaded the country and overthrew Pol Pot. Rather more remarkable, as late as 1990 the United States insisted that Pol Pot was the legitimate ruler of Cambodia and, in 1991, engineered a settlement in which the Khmer Rouge shared in the government of the nation.

Bottom Line

The long war ravaged a once prosperous corner of the world. Once an exporter of rice, Vietnam remained short of food through the 1980s. About a million A.R.V.N. soldiers lost their lives, the Viet Cong and North Vietnamese about the same number. Estimates of civilian dead ran as high as 3.5 million. About 5.2 million acres of jungle and farmland were ruined by defoliation. American bombing also devastated hundreds of cities, towns, bridges, and highways. The Air Force dropped more bombs on Vietnam than in all of Europe during World War II.

The vengefulness of the victors caused a massive flight of refugees. About 10 percent of the people of Southeast Asia fled their homelands after the war. Some spent everything they owned to bribe venal North Vietnamese officials to let them go. Others piled into leaky boats and cast off into open waters, untold numbers to die. To the credit of the United States, some 600,000 Vietnamese, Laotians, Cambodians, and ethnic minorities (whom every government in Southeast Asia bullied) were admitted as immigrants.

The war cost the United States something like $150 billion, more than any other American war except World War II. Some 2.7 million American men and women served in the conflict; 57,000 of them were killed and 300,000 were wounded. Many men were disabled for life. Some lost limbs; others were poisoned by Agent Orange, the toxic defoliant the army used to clear jungle. Yet others were addicted to drugs or alcohol. Mental disturbances and violent crime were alarmingly common among Vietnam veterans.

And yet, for ten years, Vietnam veterans were ignored, shunned, even discriminated against. Politicians, not only liberals who had opposed the war but the superpatriotic Hawks who had wanted the troops to fight on indefinitely, neglected to vote money for government programs to help them. Only in 1982, almost a decade after the war ended, was a monument to the soldiers erected in Washington, D.C. Not until 1991, after the stunning success of the American military in Iraq, did the then president George Bush feel that the "Vietnam Syndrome" had been put to rest.

NIXON–KISSINGER FOREIGN POLICY

Nixon called the Vietnam war a "sideshow." Henry A. Kissinger said that it was a mere "footnote" to history. Both men wanted to bring the conflict to an end so that they could bring about what, quite rightly, they regarded as a revolution in world diplomacy, a complete reordering of relations among the world's great powers.

The Long Crusade

It is impossible to say just how much of the Nixon-Kissinger foreign policy was Nixon's and how much was Kissinger's, and apportioning credit is not very important. The fact was that both men envisioned a new relationship among the great powers that flew in the face of American assumptions since the dawn of the Cold War.

That is, for more than twenty years before the Nixon presidency, virtually all American policy-makers and shapers of public opinion had described the world as divided into two inevitably hostile camps: the United States and its allies, most importantly Western Europe and Japan; and the Soviet Union and its client states, particularly the gigantic People's Republic of China. Few so eagerly looked forward to a showdown between the two camps as John Foster Dulles had done, but diplomats and politicians who favored *détente*—a relaxation of tensions—had to phrase their views very carefully or have their courage and patriotism questioned.

The pre-presidential Richard M. Nixon had consistently played on the theme of inevitable superpower hostility and the disloyalty of those who were "soft on

---

KISSINGER ON THE COLD WAR

"The superpowers often behave like two heavily armed blind men feeling their way around a room, each believing himself in mortal peril from the other whom he assumes to have perfect vision. . . . Each tends to ascribe to the other side a consistency, foresight and coherence that its own experience belies. Of course, over time even two blind men can do enormous damage to each other, not to speak of the room."

Henry A. Kissinger,
The White House Years (1979)

Communism." But at some point during Nixon's eight years as a private citizen, he ceased to believe in this rhetoric. Privately, Nixon came to two important conclusions quite at odds with the great anti-Communist crusade.

Premises of Détente

First, Nixon concluded that the nuclear balance of power made a superpower showdown unthinkable. Therefore, to continue to incite high tension between the Soviets and Americans was to waste resources while indefinitely running the risk of accidental world war.

Second, Nixon recognized that the old bipolar view of geopolitics on which the Cold War was predicated was nonsense. Japan, once a docile American client, was now one of the world's economic powers. The nations of Western Europe, groping toward unity, were openly trying to define an independent economic, political, and military role for themselves. The People's Republic of China, if ever subservient to the Soviet Union, was no longer so. Reports reached the West of Sino-Soviet battles on their 2,000-mile-long border.

Nixon thought of himself as a hard-headed realist. He meant to win his place in history by effecting a diplomatic revolution in which the great powers dealt with one another not as Hatfields and McCoys, but as "interested parties" rationally making deals for the benefit of each, and to ensure peace. In 1971, he said, "it will be a safer world and a better world, if we have a strong and healthy United States, Europe, Soviet Union, China, Japan—each balancing the other, not playing one against the other, an even balance."

Nixon's views were influenced and reinforced by Henry Kissinger. A witty, urbane, brilliant, and cheerfully conceited refugee from Naziism, Kissinger never quite lost his German accent nor his taste for *Realpolitik*, the amoral, opportunistic approach to diplomacy of one of his historical idols, Count Otto von Bismarck. Kissinger believed that the leaders of the Soviet Union and China were as little concerned with ideology and crusades as he and Nixon were, and only needed encouragement to launch a new era. His calculation was dramatically confirmed in 1971 at a time when the Vietnam War was raging and, officially, the ripest of denunciations were flying among Chinese, Russians, and Americans.

Lifelong Cold War warrior Richard Nixon meets lifelong revolutionary, Mao Zedong.

Rapprochement with China

In 1971, an American table-tennis team on a tour of Japan was startled to receive an invitation from the People's Republic of China to play a series of exhibition games there before they returned home. Sports writers noted wryly that the Chinese had picked a game in which they would trounce the Americans (they did), but diplomats recognized the implications of the apparently trivial event. For more than 20 years, the United States and China had had no open contact with one another, the leaders of both nations ritually denouncing the other as mortal enemies.

Kissinger virtually commanded the ping-pong players to go to China and shortly thereafter opened talks with Chinese diplomats. He flew secretly to Beijing where he arranged for a good-will tour by Nixon himself in February 1972. Only then was the amazing news announced: the lifelong scourge of Red China would tour the Forbidden City and Great Wall and sit down with chopsticks at a Mandarin banquet with Mao Zedong and Zhou Enlai, drinking toasts to eternal Sino-American amity with fiery Chinese spirits.

Nixon's meeting with Mao was ceremonial; the Chairman was senile and fading. However, discussions with Zhou, who had long advocated better relations with the West and his proteges, Hua Guofeng (who was to succeed Mao in 1976) and Deng Xiaoping, who had done time in prison for advocating "capitalistic" reforms of China's moribund economy, reassured Nixon that he had calculated correctly.

Almost overnight, Sino-American relations warmed. The United States dropped its opposition to China's demand for a seat in the United Nations and established a legation in Beijing. (In 1979, the two countries established full diplomatic relations.)

Chinese students were invited to study in American universities and China opened its doors to American tourists, who came by the tens of thousands. American industrialists involved in everything from oil exploration to the bottling of soft drinks flew to China, anxious to sell American technology and consumer goods in the market that had long symbolized the traveling salesman's ultimate "territory."

Détente with the Soviet Union

China did not turn out to be much of a customer. The Chinese population was huge, but the country was poor and in economic chaos; there was neither money nor goods with which to pay for the expensive high-technology exports in which alone, by the 1970s, American industry was still supreme. Nor were the new leaders of China interested in resuming the status of a colonial market or in embracing wide-open political institutions. Their principal motive in courting American friendship was diplomatic, to win some edge of security in their conflict with the Soviet Union. They were "playing the America card."

That was all right with the realistic Nixon and Kissinger. They were "playing the China card," putting the fear of a closer Sino-American relationship into the Soviets, who represented a genuine threat to American security. Their gambit worked. In June 1972, just months after his China trip, Nixon flew to the Soviet Union and signed a preliminary agreement in the opening series of Strategic Arms Limitation Talks (SALT), the first significant step toward a slowdown of the arms race since the Kennedy administration.

At home, the photos of Nixon clinking champagne glasses with Mao and hugging Brezhnev bewildered his conservative supporters and flummoxed his liberal critics. In fact, as Nixon knew, undoubtedly savoring it, only a Republican with an impeccable Cold-Warrior past could have accomplished what he did. Had a liberal Democratic president shared a Peking duck with Mao Zedong, Nixon himself would have held the noose at the demonstrations outside the White House.

Shuttle Diplomacy

Nixon was grateful to Kissinger and, in 1973, named him Secretary of State. Well into 1974, Kissinger's diplomatic successes piled up. His greatest triumph came in the Middle East after the Yom Kippur War of 1973, in which Egypt and Syria attacked Israel and, for the first time in the long Arab–Israeli conflict, inflicted terrible casualties and fought the Israelis to a draw.

Knowing that the Israelis were not inclined to accept less than victory and fearing what a prolonged war in the oil-rich Middle East would mean for the United States, Kissinger shuttled seemingly without sleep among Damascus, Cairo, and Tel Aviv, carrying proposal and counterproposal for a settlement. Unlike Dulles, who also had represented American interests on the fly, Kissinger was a brilliant diplomat. He ended the war, and the terms he prevailed on all the warring powers to accept actually increased American influence in the region. He won the gratitude and friendship of Egyptian President Anwar Sadat, while not alienating Israel.

After 1974, however, Kissinger lost his magic touch, in part because of revived world tensions that were not his fault. Soviet Premier Leonid Brezhnev may have wanted to reduce the chance of direct conflict between Russia and the United States. However, he continued to aid guerrilla movements in Africa and Latin America. Cuba's Fidel Castro, with a large army to keep in trim, exported advisors and combat troops to several countries, most notably to Angola in southwestern Africa.

But Nixon and Kissinger were also willing, even anxious to fight the Cold War by proxy in the Third World, competing with the Soviets for spheres of influence. While right-wing Republicans opposed to *détente* stepped up their attacks on Kissinger, he was actually pursuing their kind of confrontational policies in strife-torn countries like Angola.

The most damaging mark on Kissinger's record as the diplomat-in-chief of a democratic country came in 1974. It was revealed that, the previous year, he had been aware of and may have instigated and aided militarists in Chile who overthrew and murdered the president, Salvador Allende. Allende had been a bungler but he was Chile's democratically elected head and his American-backed successor, Agostín Pinochet, instituted a barbaric and brutal regime marked by torture and murder of opponents.

WATERGATE AND GERALD FORD

By 1974, when news of the Pinochet connection broke in the United States, Kissinger was no longer serving Richard Nixon. The crisis of the presidency that had begun when Lyndon Johnson was repudiated took on a new dimension of gravity when Nixon was forced to resign in disgrace. The debacle had its beginnings in the election campaign of 1972 in which, thanks to a transformation of the Democratic party, victory was in Nixon's hip pocket from the start.

Redefining Liberalism

Between 1968 and 1972, activist middle-class liberals won control of several key Democratic party committees and remade party machinery according to their ideals. They enacted new procedures and standards for selecting convention delegates that penalized old party stalwarts: the labor unions, the big city machines, those Southern "good old boys" who had not already gone Republican, and other political pros. The McGovern reforms (named for the liberal, antiwar Senator from South Dakota) guaranteed representation of women and minority groups at party conventions largely on the basis of their sex and ethnic origins.

The Election of 1972

As an immediate result of the reforms, the Democratic delegates who gathered in Miami in the summer of 1972 formed the youngest convention in political history, counted more women and members of minorities among the delegates than any other, and was strongly antiwar. They nominated Senator McGovern to head their ticket and adopted a platform calling for a negotiated end to the Southeast Asian war (then Vietnamized but still raging), and supporting the demands of some women's organizations that the decision as to whether or not a fetus should be aborted belonged to the pregnant woman herself, and no other person or institution.

A sincere and decent man who was deeply grieved by the war, McGovern tried to distance himself from some extremes of his party, particularly "gay rights" advocates who, McGovern understood, were not likely to win the affection of working-class people who traditionally voted Democratic. He emphasized peace in Vietnam and tax reform that would benefit middle- and lower-income people, and his integrity compared well with Nixon's longstanding reputation for deviousness.

But virtually no labor unions supported him and many political pros sat on their hands. The Republicans, by way of contrast, ran an effective campaign. They depicted McGovern as a bumbling and indecisive radical. When McGovern first defended his running mate, Senator Thomas Eagleton, who had undergone psychiatric treatment several years earlier, and then forced Eagleton to drop out, his race was doomed.

Nixon won 60.8 percent of the popular vote and carried every state but Massachusetts and the District of Columbia. In only eight years, he had reversed the Republican humiliation of 1964. He had had a lot of help from the Democrats but his achievement was nonetheless remarkable. However, Nixon's days of glorious triumph were, like Lyndon Johnson's in 1964, to be few.

Covering up a Burglary

On June 17, 1972, early in the presidential campaign, Washington police had arrested five men who were trying to plant electronic eavesdropping devices in Democratic party headquarters in a Washington apartment and office complex called the Watergate. Three of the suspects were on the payroll of the Committee to Reelect the President (an unwisely chosen name inasmuch as it abbreviated as CREEP), and McGovern tried to exploit the incident as part of his integrity campaign. But the ploy fizzled when Nixon and his campaign manager, Attorney General John Mitchell, denied any knowledge of the incident and denounced the burglars as common criminals.

In fact, Nixon knew nothing about the break-in in advance, but he soon learned that the burglars had acted on orders from his own aides. He never considered reporting or disciplining his men. Instead, almost nonchalantly, he instructed his staff to find money to hush up the men in jail. However, two of them, James E. McCord and Howard Hunt refused to take the fall and informed Judge John Sirica that they had taken orders from highly-placed Nixon administration officials.

Rumors began to fly. Two reporters for the *Washington Post*, Robert Woodward and Carl Bernstein, made contact with an anonymous informant who fed them information. A special Senate investigating committee

---

HOW THEY LIVED

The Typical American of the 1980s: A Statistical Portrait

The statistical American of the year 1980 was a Caucasian female, a little more than 30 years old, married to her first husband, with one child and about to have another. She was a shade over 5 feet 4 inches tall and weighed 134 pounds. Statisticians are not sure of the color of her hair and eyes, but they were probably on the brownish side. Statisticians are sure that she had tried marijuana when she was younger, but no longer used it in the 1980s (although some of her friends still did). She did not smoke cigarettes, but at least had tried them in the past; she still drank, just this side of moderately.

The statistical American adult female of the 1980s considered herself middle class, and had attended college but had not necessarily graduated. She was likely to work outside the home, but economic conditions during the first half of the decade made her opportunities uncertain. Her household income was about $20,000 a year; she and her husband were watching their budget closely, which they were not accustomed to doing. It is a toss-up whether or not she voted in 1984 (or at all during the 1970s). She was decreasingly interested in feminism as the 1980s progressed and the failure of the ERA faded into memory. She was marginally more likely to be registered as a Democrat than as a Republican, but she was more likely to have voted for Ronald Reagan in 1984 than in 1980.

More than half of the statistical American's female friends were married. Most of her friends who have been divorced have married again within three years. The statistical American of the 1980s attached no stigma to divorce, and experienced only a slight sense of unease with people who lived with members of the opposite sex without benefit of marriage. But she found it difficult to agree that homosexuality is nothing more than an "alternate lifestyle" on a moral parity with heterosexuality. She was both amused and repelled by the culture of the "gay" communities about which she read, but by 1985 was not so indulgent as she had been because of the quantum leap in the spread of deadly AIDS.

She almost certainly had sex with her husband before they married, and almost as likely with at least one other man. There is a fair chance that she had a brief fling since marriage, probably during a "trial separation."

The statistical American was more likely to be Protestant than Catholic. However, she was more likely to be Catholic than a member of any other *individual* denomination. If a Catholic, she practiced birth control, most likely using the pill, in defiance of Church directives. Moreover, Catholic or Protestant, she attended church services far less frequently than had her mother.

The statistical American was in excellent health; she saw a dentist and a doctor more than once a year, and paid a little less than half of the cost of health care (state and federal government picked up about the same, private industry and philanthropy the rest). She had a life expectancy of almost 78 years, and would outlive her husband by eight years, with the prospects that her dotage would be economically trying.

The statistical American lived in a state with a population of about 3 million people—Colorado, Iowa, Oklahoma, Connecticut—and in a city of about 100,000 people—Roanoke, Virginia; Reno, Nevada; Durham, North Carolina.

Or perhaps, she lived at the population center of the United States, which in 1980 was west of the Mississippi River for the first time in American history. It was located "one mile west of the De Soto City Hall, Jefferson County, Missouri." An equal number of people in the continental United States lived east of that point as west, as many north of it as south.

As the question about her state and city of residence indicates, the statistical American is a somewhat absurd contrivance, distilled out of the majorities, means, and medians of the United States Census Bureau; the responses to surveys taken by a number of public-opinion experts; and, simply, the probabilities of the educated guess.

The virtue of the United States remains rooted in its diversity of people as well as of resources and in the survival of those people's right to change their minds as many times as they wish. And, as far as matters of public policy are concerned, to form majorities and effect their wishes. For a nation that has reached its third century, that is not so bad an accomplishment. In the star-crossed history of the human race, it has not been done in many other places.

---

headed by Sam Ervin of North Carolina picked away at the tangle from yet another direction, slowly tracing not only the Watergate break-in and cover-up but other illegal acts to the White House itself.

The Imperial Presidency

Each month that passed, dramatic insights into the inner workings of the Nixon presidency were revealed. On

Nixon's own orders, an "enemies list" had been compiled. On it were journalists, politicians, intellectuals, and even movie stars who had made statements criticizing Nixon. One Donald Segretti was put in charge of a "dirty tricks" campaign, planting half-truths, rumors, and lies to discredit critics of the administration. G. Gordon Liddy, who was involved in the Watergate break-in, had proposed fantastic schemes involving yachts and prostitutes to entrap "enemies." The "dirty tricks" campaign grew so foul that not even J. Edgar Hoover, the none too squeamish head of the F.B.I., would touch it.

Watergate, it turned out, had been just one of several "surreptitious entries" sponsored by the administration. Nixon's aides also engineered the burglary of a Los Angeles psychiatrist's office to secure information about a Defense Department employee who had published confidential information about the prosecution of the war in Vietnam.

Observers spoke of an "Imperial Presidency." Nixon and his advisors had become so arrogant in their possession of power that they believed they were above the law. Indeed, several years later, Nixon himself was to tell an interviewer on television, "When the president does it, that means it is not illegal."

If imperial in their pretensions, however, "all the president's men" were singularly lacking in a sense of nobility. One by one, Nixon aides abandoned ship, each convinced that he was being set up as the sole fall-guy for his colleagues. Each deserter named others and described their roles in the cover-up and dirty-tricks campaign. A snarl of half-truths and lies descended on the president himself.

In the midst of the scandal, Vice President Spiro Agnew pleaded no-contest to income-tax evasion and charges that he had accepted bribes when he was governor of Maryland. Agnew was forced to resign from the vice-presidency in October 1973. He was replaced under the terms of the Twenty-Fifth Amendment by Congressman Gerald Ford of Michigan.

Resignation

Then came Nixon's turn. He had kept tape recordings of conversations in his Oval Office that clearly implicated him in the Watergate cover-up (and revealed him as having a rather foul mouth: the transcripts of the tapes were peppered with "expletive deleted"). After long fights in the courts, the president was ordered to surrender the tapes to investigators.

Why Nixon did not destroy the incriminating recordings early in the Watergate crisis remains a mystery. It was suggested that greed—the money that the electronic documents would bring after he left the presidency—accounts for his fatal blunder. Others saw the preservation of the tapes as another manifestation of Nixon's imperial megalomania. He could not conceive of the fact that a court could order the president of the United States to abide by laws that applied to mere citizens.

After the House of Representatives Judiciary Committee recommended impeaching Nixon, he threw in the towel. On August 9, 1974, on national television, he resigned the presidency and flew to his home in San Clemente, California.

Richard Nixon forces a smile as he departs Washington after his resignation.

A Ford, Not a Lincoln

Gerald Ford's career had not been distinguished. Holding a safe seat in the House from Michigan, he had risen to be minority leader on the basis of seniority and dutifully toeing the Republican party line. His sole ambition when events made him first vice president and then president, was to be Speaker of the House, but the Republicans never came close to winning a majority of Representatives.

Ford was not a particularly intelligent man. Lyndon Johnson once told reporters that Gerry Ford's trouble was that he had played center on the University of Michigan football team without a helmet. Others quipped that he could not walk and chew gum at the same time. Newspaper photographers fairly laid in wait to ridicule him by snapping shots of him bumping his head on door frames, tumbling down the slopes of the Rockies on everything but his skis, slicing golf balls into crowds of spectators.

And yet his simplicity and forthrightness were a relief after Nixon's squirming and deception. He told the American people that fate had given them "a Ford, not a Lincoln," and he had no pretensions. Democrats howled "deal" when Ford pardoned Nixon of all crimes he may have committed, but Ford's explanation, that the American people needed to put Watergate behind them, was plausible and in character. Two very nearly

Gerald Ford appointed Nelson Rockefeller as his vice president.

successful attempts to assassinate him by deranged women in California helped to win sympathy for the first president who had not been elected to any national office.

Despite his unusual route to the White House, Gerald Ford had no intention of being a caretaker president. But it was Ford's misfortune, as it had been Tyler's, to face serious problems without the confidence and support of an important segment of his party. The Republican party's right-wing, led by former California governor, Ronald Reagan, did not like *détente* nor Nixon's, now Ford's refusal to launch a frontal attack on government regulation and the liberal welfare state.

Running on Half-Empty

The most serious of the woes that faced Ford struck at a reflexive assumption of twentieth-century American life: that cheap energy was available in unlimited quantities to fuel the economy and support the freewheeling lifestyle of the middle class.

By the mid-1970s, 90 percent of the American economy was generated by the burning of fossil fuels: coal, natural gas, and petroleum. Fossil fuels are nonrenewable sources of energy. Unlike food crops, lumber, and water—or, for that matter, a horse and a pair of sturdy legs—they cannot be called on again once they have been used. The supply of them is finite. While experts disagreed about the extent of the world's reserves of coal, gas, and oil, no one challenged the obvious fact that one day they would be no more.

The United States was by far the biggest user of non-renewable sources of energy. In 1973, while comprising about 6 percent of the world's population, Americans consumed fully 33 percent of the world's annual production of oil. Much of it was burned to less than basic ends. Americans overheated and overcooled their offices and houses. They pumped gasoline into a dizzying variety of purely recreational vehicles, some of which brought the roar of the freeway to the wilderness and devastated fragile land. Their worship of the wasteful private automobile meant that few taxes were spent on public mass transit systems. They packaged their consumer goods in throw-away containers of glass, metal, paper, and petroleum-based plastics; supermarkets wrapped lemons individually in transparent plastic and fast-food cheeseburgers were cradled in plastic foam caskets that were discarded within seconds of being handed over the counter. The bill of indictment went on but, resisting criticism and satire alike, American consumption increased.

OPEC and the Energy Crisis

About 61 percent of the oil that Americans consumed in the 1970s was produced at home, and large reserves remained under native ground. But the nation also imported huge quantities of crude, and in October 1973, Americans discovered just how little control they had over the 39 percent of their oil that came from abroad.

In that month, the Organization of Petroleum Exporting Countries (OPEC) temporarily halted oil shipments and announced the first of a series of big jumps in the price of their product. One of their justifications was that the irresponsible consumption habits of the ad-

---

CONSTITUTIONAL CONTRADICTION?

Gerald Ford was appointed to the vice presidency under the provisions of the Twenty-fifth Amendment, ratified in 1967, which stipulates that "whenever there is a vacancy in the office of the Vice President, the President shall nominate a Vice President. . . ." When he succeeded to the presidency, he appointed Nelson A. Rockefeller to the vice presidency. Neither the president nor the vice president held office by virtue of election. However, as some constitutional experts were quick to point out, Article II, Section 1 of the Constitution provides that the president and vice president are to "be elected."

In fact, the contradiction was always there, if never put to the test. The U.S. Constitution and laws hold that the Secretary of State and the Speaker of the House were next in line to the presidency after the vice president. A case could be made that the Speaker was elected, but not the Secretary of State.

The lines at a Los Angeles gas station stretched for blocks during the gasoline shortage in 1979.

vanced Western nations, particularly the United States, jeopardized their future.

OPEC leaders reasoned that if the oil-exporting nations continued to supply oil cheaply, consuming nations would continue to burn it profligately, thus hastening the day the wells ran dry. On that day, if the oil-exporting nations had not laid the basis for another kind of economy, they would be destitute. Particularly in the oil-rich Middle East, there were few alternative resources to support fast-growing populations. Therefore, by raising prices, the OPEC nations would earn capital with which to build for a future without oil, while simultaneously encouraging the consuming nations to conserve, thus lengthening the era when oil would be available.

From a geopolitical perspective, there was much to be said for the argument, but ordinary Americans (and the people of other consumer nations) rarely thought geopolitically. They were stunned when they had to wait in long lines in order to pay unprecedented prices for gasoline. In some big cities and Hawaii, gasoline for private cars was not to be had for weeks.

The price of gasoline never climbed to Japanese or European levels, but it was shock enough for people who were accustomed to buying "two dollars' worth" to discover that $2 bought a little more than enough to drive

home. Moreover, the prices of goods that required oil in their production climbed too. Inflation, already a problem under Nixon, worsened from 9 percent a year when Ford became president to 12 percent.

Whip Inflation Now!

Opposed to wage and price controls such as Nixon had employed, Ford launched a campaign called WIN!, for "Whip Inflation Now!" He urged Americans to slow down inflation by refusing to buy exorbitantly priced goods and by ceasing to demand higher wages from their employers. The campaign was ridiculed from the start, and within a few weeks Ford quietly retired the WIN! button that he had been wearing on his lapel. He had seen few others in his travels about the country and began to feel like a man in a funny hat.

Instead, Ford tightened the money supply in order to slow down the economy, which resulted in the most serious recession since 1937, with unemployment climbing to 9 percent. Ford was stymied by the same vicious circle that caught up his predecessor and successor: slowing inflation meant throwing people out of work; fighting unemployment meant inflation; trying to steer a middle course meant "stagflation," mild recession plus inflation.

Image Problems

As a congressman, Ford had been a hawk on Vietnam. When the North Vietnamese launched their attack on Saigon early in 1975, his first impulse was to intervene with American troops. Congress refused to respond and Henry Kissinger, who had stayed on as Secretary of State, talked him out of presidential action. Ford tried to display his determination to exercise American armed might in May 1975, when Cambodian Communists seized an American ship, the *Mayaguez*. Ford ordered in the marines, who successfully rescued the captives. But in order to have 39 seamen returned to their homes, 38 marines died.

Kissinger savored the reports that the president hung breathlessly on his every word, but such stories only further enraged the Kissinger-hating right-wing of the Republican party and made it easier for the Democrats to mock Ford as being not bright enough to handle his job.

Early in 1976, polls showed Ford losing to most of the likely Democratic candidates. Capitalizing on them, Ronald Reagan, the sweetheart of the right-wing Republicans, launched a well-financed campaign to replace him as the party's candidate. Using his control of party organization, Ford beat Reagan at the convention but the travails of his two years in office took their toll. He could not overcome the image that he was the most accidental of presidents, never elected to national office. His full pardon of Nixon came back to haunt him and, in November, he lost narrowly to a most unlikely Democratic candidate, James Earl Carter of Georgia, who called himself Jimmy. The Democrats were back, but the decline in the prestige of the presidency continued.

QUIET CRISIS

Since Eisenhower, every president had been identified closely with Congress, the arena of national politics. The day of the governor candidate seemed to be in the past. Then Jimmy Carter came out of nowhere to win the Democratic nomination in 1976. His political career consisted of one term in the Georgia assembly and one term as governor.

Indeed, it was Carter's lack of association with the federal government that helped him win the nomination and, by a slim margin, the presidency. Without a real animus for Gerald Ford, many Americans were attracted to the idea of an "outsider," which is how Carter presented himself. "Hello, my name is Jimmy Carter and I'm running for president," he told thousands of people face to face in his softly musical Georgia accent. Once he started winning primaries, the media did the rest.

CLEANUP

In 1912 the Chicago Sanitation Department cleared the streets of the carcasses of 10,000 dead horses. In 1968 the Chicago Police Department cleared the streets of 24,500 carcasses of dead automobiles.

When television commentators said that there was a bandwagon rolling, voters dutifully responded by jumping on it.

Inauguration Day, when Carter and his wife, Rosalyn, walked the length of Pennsylvania Avenue, was very nearly the last entirely satisfactory day of the Carter presidency. Whether the perspective of time will attribute his failure as chief executive to his unsuitability to the office or the massiveness of the problems he faced, it is difficult to imagine future historians looking at the Carter era any differently than it is now remembered, dolefully.

The Panama Treaty

Carter had his successes, especially in foreign relations. Among his achievements was defusing an explosive situation in Central America where Panamanians and others had long protested American sovereignty over the Panama Canal Zone. The narrow strip of U.S. territory bisected the small republic and seemed to be an intolerable insult in an age when nationalist sensibilities in small countries were as touchy as boils.

American diplomats saw no need to hold on to the Canal Zone in the face of Panamanian protests. The United States would be able to occupy the Canal within hours in the case of an international crisis. After several false starts at working out a treaty under Johnson and Nixon, in 1978 the Senate narrowly ratified an agreement with Panama to guarantee the permanent neutrality of the canal itself while gradually transferring sovereignty over it to Panama, culminating on December 31, 1999.

JIMMY CARTER AND THE SEGREGATIONISTS

Future president Jimmy Carter had an unusual record for a white Southerner of his age on the segregation issue. In the 1950s, as a successful businessman in Plains, Georgia, he had been asked to join the anti-black White Citizens' Councils, whose membership fee was only $5. Carter replied, "I've got $5 but I'd flush it down the toilet before I'd give it to you."

By signing the treaty, Carter muted Latin American denunciations of "*yanqui imperialismo.*" Nevertheless, right-wing politicians, led by Ronald Reagan, who had begun to campaign for the presidency as soon as Carter was inaugurated, denounced the treaty. In the tradition of Joseph McCarthy, Reagan called it yet another retreat from national pride and greatness by a weak president.

Peacemaking

Carter's greatest achievement was to save the rapprochement between Israel and Egypt that began to take shape in November 1977, when Egyptian President Anwar Sadat, risking the enmity of the entire Arab world, addressed the Israeli Knesset, or parliament, calling for a permanent peace in the Middle East. Rather than cooperate with Sadat, Israeli prime minister Menachem Begin, a former terrorist, seemed to sabotage Sadat's peacemaking efforts by refusing to make concessions commensurate with the Egyptian president's high-stakes gamble.

In 1978, Carter brought Sadat and Begin to Camp David, the presidential retreat in the Maryland woods outside Washington. There, Sadat grew so angry with Begin's refusal to compromise that he actually packed his suitcases. Although Carter was unable to persuade Begin to agree that the West Bank of the Jordan River, which Israel had occupied in 1967, must eventually be returned to Arab rule, he did bring the two men together. In March 1979, Israel and Egypt signed a treaty.

In the United States, the political effect of this dramatic diplomatic turn was to swing American sympathies in the dispute in the direction of Sadat. Begin was unpopular even among American Jews, who traditionally were staunch supporters of Israel. Jewish contributions to Israeli causes dropped sharply. Carter himself betrayed impatience and annoyance with the Begin government and sympathy for the Palestinian refugees. Carter deserved the Nobel Peace Prize for pulling off the Camp David Accords.

The End of Détente

The Nobel Committee may have snubbed him because, while Carter advanced the cause of peace in the Middle East, he abandoned the policy of *détente* that Nixon, Kissinger, and Ford had nurtured. Like Nixon, Carter virtually ignored his first Secretary of State, a professional diplomat, Cyrus Vance, and depended on a White House advisor, Zbigniew Brzezinski, for advice.

Unlike the flexible and opportunistic Kissinger, Brzezinski was an anti-Soviet ideologue. Himself a Polish refugee from Communism, Brzezinski's distrust of the Soviet Union blinded him to opportunities to improve

---

MINORITY PRESIDENTS

When Jimmy Carter won the forty-eighth presidential election by just a hair under 50 percent of the popular vote, it was the sixteenth time the victor had the support of less than half the voters:

President	Year	Percent
John Quincy Adams	1824	30.5
James K. Polk	1844	49.6
Zachary Taylor	1848	47.4
James Buchanan	1856	45.3
Abraham Lincoln	1860	39.8
Rutherford B. Hayes	1876	48.0
James A. Garfield	1880	48.5
Grover Cleveland	1884	48.5
Benjamin Harrison	1888	47.9
Grover Cleveland	1892	46.1
Woodrow Wilson	1912	41.9
Woodrow Wilson	1916	49.4
Harry S Truman	1948	49.5
John F. Kennedy	1960	49.9
Richard M. Nixon	1968	43.4
Jimmy Carter	1976	50.0

Lincoln would surely not have won the election of 1864 by an absolute majority (or at all) had the Southern states not been in rebellion. Three victorious candidates had fewer popular votes than their defeated opponents: John Quincy Adams in 1824, Rutherford B. Hayes in 1876, and Benjamin Harrison in 1888. In the three-way race in 1992, Arkansas Governor Bill Clinton won a substantial electoral vote victory with only 43 percent of the popular vote.

---

relations between the nuclear superpowers, or even prompted him to sabotage Soviet overtures. Moreover, whereas Kissinger had been a charmer, Brzezinski was tactless and crude in a world in which protocol and manners can be as important as substance. The foreign ministers of several of America's allies discreetly informed the State Department that they would not deal with him under any circumstances.

But Carter was as obsessively hostile to the Soviet Union as Brzezinski and pre-Nixon policy-makers. He denounced the Soviet Union for trampling on human rights while neglecting to mention the far more brutal policies of American allies such as Iran, Chile, and several Central American states.

In March 1977, Carter interrupted and set back the Strategic Arms Limitation Talks with completely new proposals. Eventually, a new SALT-II treaty was negotiated and signed, but Carter withdrew it from Senate consideration in December 1979 when the Soviet Union invaded Afghanistan to prop up a client government in December 1979. By the end of Carter's term of office, *détente* was dead.

*Anwar Sadat, Jimmy Carter, and Menachem Begin shake hands following the signing of the
Camp David Accords in 1978.*

. . . Plus c'est la même chose

Inflation reached new heights under Carter, almost 20 percent during 1980. By the end of the year, $1 was worth only 15 cents in 1940 values. That is, on the average, it took $1 in 1980 to purchase what in 1940 cost 15 cents. The dollar had suffered fully half of this loss during the 1970s.

Carter could not be faulted for the energy crisis. After the crunch of 1974, Americans had become energy conscious, replacing their big "gas guzzlers" with more efficient smaller cars. Even this sensible turn contributed to the nation's economic malaise, however. American automobile manufacturers had repeatedly refused to develop small energy-efficient cars. For a while in the 1960s, after the success of the Germans' Volkswagen "Beetle," Ford, General Motors, and Chrysler had made compact cars. But within a few years, "compacts" had miraculously grown to be nearly as large as the tradi-

tional "full-sized car." Now, in the crunch of the 1970s, American auto makers had nothing with which to compete with a flood of Japanese imports: Toyotas, Datsuns, Hondas, and myriad others. The automobile buyer's dollars sailed abroad across the Pacific.

Even then, by 1979, oil consumption was higher than ever, and an even higher proportion of it was being imported than in 1976. American oil refiners actually cut back on domestic production, which led many people to wonder if the crisis was genuine or was just a cover while the industry reaped windfall profits—which it did. As prices soared, all the refiners reported dividends of unprecedented size.

The price of electricity also rose, by 200 percent and more, because so much of it was generated by burning fossil fuels. The utility companies called for the construction of more nuclear power plants in anticipation of even higher rate increases. But Americans had become apprehensive about nuclear energy as an alternative to fossil fuels following an accident and near catastrophe at the Three Mile Island nuclear plant near Harrisburg, Pennsylvania; the release, at about the same time, of *The China Syndrome*, a film that portrayed a similar accident; the discovery that a California reactor that was about to open was crisscrossed with flaws, and built astride a major earthquake fault; and the tremendous costs needed to build safe nuclear power plants.

Embarrassment and Drift

Carter was repeatedly embarrassed by his aides and family, and himself had a talent for foolery. Genuinely suspicious of the Washington Establishment, he surrounded himself with cronies from Georgia who did not quite understand the etiquettes and rituals of the capital. Banker Bert Lance, whom Carter wanted as Budget Director, was identified with petty but unacceptable loan scams. Carter's ambassador to the United Nations, former civil rights activist, Andrew Young, met secretly with leaders of the Palestine Liberation Organization (P.L.O.), an anti-Israel terrorist organization that the United States did not recognize. Carter had to fire him.

The national press, stimulated by its role in uncovering the Watergate scandal to constant muckraking, leaped on every trivial incident—a Carter aide tipsy in a cocktail lounge; the president's "down-home" brother Billy's outrageous opinions—to embarrass the president.

The deeply religious Carter himself frankly but disingenuously told an interviewer for *Playboy* magazine, "I've looked on a lot of women with lust. I've committed adultery in my heart many times," and tittering journalists did not allow him to forget it. In 1980, when Carter's career was on the line, his mother told a reporter, "Sometimes when I look at all my children, I say to myself, 'Lillian, you should have stayed a virgin.'"

A much more serious handicap was the Carter administration's lack of direction. "Carter believes fifty things," one of his advisers said, "but no one thing. He holds explicit, thorough positions on every issue under the sun, but he has no large view of relations between them." In this, Carter was not unlike most Americans. He had the "engineer" mentality that is often described as the American way of thinking: as it arises, face each specific problem and work out a specific solution.

Such pragmatism had worked for Franklin D. Roosevelt. It did not work for Jimmy Carter. With him at the helm, pragmatic government resembled a ship without a rudder, drifting aimlessly. Carter was sensitive to what he called a "national malaise" but only embarrassed himself when he tried to address the amorphous problem. He called 130 prominent men and women from every sector of American life to Washington and, having heard from them, was able to announce only that there was "a crisis of the American spirit"—right back where he started from.

For Further Reading

James Gilbert, *Another Chance: America Since 1945* (1984) provides a general overview of this period; Godfrey Hodgson, *America in Our Time* (1976) deals with the first part of it. However, we are too close to the 1970s to expect too dependable a narrative history of the decade. Many contemporary historians were themselves participants and partisans during these years. Many of the major players are still around trying to shape their posterity.

Many have written memoirs, perhaps as much for monstrous advances from publishers as for self-justification. These accounts can, nevertheless, be useful and are, in any case, valuable sources. See *The Memoirs of Richard Nixon* (1978); George McGovern, *Grassroots* (1977); *A Time to Heal: The Autobiography of Gerald Ford* (1979); Henry A. Kissinger, *White House Years* (1979) and *Years of Upheaval* (1982); Jimmy Carter, *Keeping Faith* (1982); and Rosalynn Carter, *First Lady from Plains* (1984). A fascinating study of Nixon written before his fall is Garry Wills, *Nixon Agonistes* (1970). On Kissinger, see Robert Morris, *Uncertain Greatness: Henry Kissinger and American Foreign Policy* (1977).

Carl Bernstein and Robert Woodward, *All the President's Men* (1974) is by the two reporters for the *Washington Post* that doggedly investigated the Watergate affair and helped bring about Nixon's fall. Perhaps the most insightful analysis of what happened is Arthur M. Schlesinger Jr., *The Imperial Presidency* (1973). See also T. H. White, *Breach of Faith* (1975); Leon Jaworski, *The Right and the Power* (1976); and Sam Ervin, *The Whole Truth: The Watergate Conspiracy* (1980).

On national politics and policy during the 1970s, see David Broder, *The Party's Over* (1972); Samuel Lubell, *The Hidden Crisis in American Politics* (1970); A. J. Reichley, *Conservatives in an Age of Change: The Nixon and Ford Administrations* (1981); Theodore H. White, *The Making of a President 1972* (1973). See Henry Kissinger's memoirs above for foreign policy, and on specific issues: R. L. Garthoff, *Detente and Confrontation* (1985); A. E. Goodman, *The Lost Peace: America's Search for a Negotiated Settlement of the Vietnam War* (1978); on Central America, R. A. Pastor, *Condemned to Repetition* (1987); W. B. Quandt, *Decade of Decision: American Foreign Policy Toward the Arab-Israeli Conflict* (1978); and G. Sick, *All Fall Down: America's Tragic Encounter with Iran* (1985).

*Five presidents—Bush, Reagan, Carter, Ford, and Nixon—
gather to dedicate the Ronald Reagan Library in California.
Carter remarked, "At least all of you have met a Democratic
president. I haven't had that honor." In January 1993,
he would have that chance.*

MORNING IN AMERICA
The United States at Century's End

As some observers saw it, Americans went on a tear of self-indulgence after the disillusioning experiences of Vietnam and Watergate. Writer Tom Wolfe called the 1970s the "Me Decade." Historian Christopher Lasch wrote of a culture of narcissism. President Jimmy Carter anguished about what was called a malaise of the American spirit.

In the 1980s, with Ronald Reagan in the White House, the malaise lifted, but by no means the widespread obsession with self. The 1980s seemed to be characterized by greed and social irresponsibility. National wealth amassed over a century was squandered in consumption and non-productive financial manipulations. The federal debt grew so large as to threaten the standard of living for generations to come. Someone remarked that the Americans of century's end were the first generation in the nation's history to value the short-term killing more highly than their children's future.

THE TEMPER OF AN ERA

But did the nation's mood really shift radically in the 1970s? Were the young people of the preceding decade so selfless and socially conscious by definition, preoccupied by racial injustice, poverty, and war, whereas in the 1970s Americans turned inward to their personal pleasure and individual potential? Or was this mood swing due to nothing more than the meanderings of Father Time?

Us

"The Movement" of the 1960s had a motto, "You can't trust anyone over thirty." In the 1970s, the people who had invoked those words celebrated their thirtieth birthdays. The baby-boomers were still the "do your own thing" generation and, thanks to their numbers, they were still dictating much about the national style. But their "thing" had changed with age. They grew bored with political action and moral outrage as means of self-gratification and looked elsewhere.

In the 1970s, baby-boomer self-indulgence simply took on commercial shape. One raging consumer fad followed another, with some of the biggest profits made by companies selling products that combined fun and physical exercise. Americans spent billions of dollars on ski equipment, tennis paraphernalia, ten-speed bicycles, hang-gliders, backpacking gear, and a shopping mall stuffed full of other sporting gear. Jogging became a national mania, claiming as its devotées by 1980 one adult

ANCESTORS

In 1982, the Census Bureau reported that 51.6 million Americans traced their ancestry to Germany compared with 43.7 million who claimed an Irish background and 40 million who had English forebears. But if Scots-Americans and Welsh-Americans were added to the English as being of British origin, that would have been the largest group. About 16 million claimed African ancestors; and 2.8 million, Asian.

DISPOSABLE AMERICA

Each year, Americans throw out of their homes (not their places of work) some 160 to 180 million tons of what they variously call trash, garbage, or rubbish. This amounts to a half ton per person per year.

Much of the total is made up of products designed to be disposable. Every day, on average, each American discards almost five pounds of "disposables." On a given day, Americans throw away 123 million paper and plastic cups, 44 million paper and plastic diapers, 5.5 million razor blades and disposable razors, 4.4 million disposable pens, and nearly a million disposable cigarette lighters.

in five. The most primitive form of exercise was the basis of a multimillion dollar business!

The Natural History of Swinging

A revolution in sexual morality that was long in the making reached its climax in the 1970s when, in the mainsrtream, casual sexual encounters were effectively legitimized. This development owed first of all to the widespread use of "the pill," a reliable birth-control device, which allayed women's fear of pregnancy. Antibiotic control of venereal disease eliminated another dread that had inhibited previous generations. A third source of loosened sexual attitudes may have been a ruling by the Supreme Court that graphic depictions of sexual acts were protected by the constitutional right of free speech. While standards of enforcement varied from state to state and city to city, sexually explicit books and films—"porn"—became freely available.

"Singles bars," places to meet a sexual partner for a "one night stand," were fixtures in every big city and many towns. Managers of "adult motels" suspended mirrors on ceilings and pumped pornographic movies to TV sets in scented rooms. Landlords converted apartment complexes to accommodate "swinging singles" with party rooms, saunas, and hot tubs. Marriage practices could hardly have been unaffected. The divorce rate soared from 2.5 divorces per 1000 population in 1965 to 5.3 per 1000 in 1979. The illegitimate birth rate tripled during the 1960s and 1970s, and abortions increased at an equal rate. Homosexuals, previously quietly tolerated in cities such as New York, San Francisco, and New Orleans, "came out of the closet," renamed themselves "gays," and demanded that their "sexual preference" be recognized as an "alternate lifestyle."

Flies in the Ointment

Just as medical control of venereal disease helped to ignite the sexual revolution, disease played a key role in cooling it down after 1980. A penicillin-resistant strain

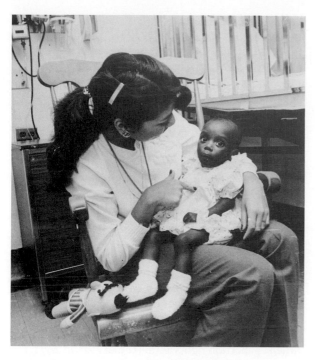

By the 1990s, AIDS was spreading rapidly among non-homosexuals and non-needle users such as this abandoned infant.

hallucinogenic celebrated by the hippies in the 1960s, lost popularity, but marijuana remained a staple of home life across a broad social spectrum. Cocaine enjoyed a reign as a high-status euphoric because it was expensive and thought to be harmless when "snorted" (absorbed through the mucous membranes of the nose).

When cocaine was found to be highly addictive, it lost some luster among educated Americans. However, a cheap form of the drug that was smoked or injected, "crack," flooded American cities, to be sold openly on street corners and in parks. Crack had plenty of middle-class buyers, but its chief victims were the urban poor. Not only was crack use heavy among the poor, pestilential "crack houses" and reckless shootings by rival dealers turned poor neighborhoods into war zones. Drug-related violence was so out of hand in some big cities that it affected the actuarial tables. By 1990, violent death was the chief cause of death among black males 15 to 34 years of age.

Women's Lib

In the 1970s, only one social movement of note achieved a large following—the new feminism. In 1966, after her

of gonorrhea made the rounds among "swingers," and herpes, an old and minor venereal infection, reached epidemic proportions. Rather more serious was an entirely new affliction, Acquired Immune Deficiency Syndrome—AIDS—which slowly and agonizingly killed its victims.

The H.I.V. virus (thought to be the cause of AIDS) is transmitted by the introduction into a person's bloodstream of infected blood, semen, or some other bodily fluids. In impoverished nations such as Uganda and Haiti, plagued by filthy living conditions and chronic health problems resulting in open sores, AIDS threatens the general population. In the United States and other developed countries, about 90 percent of AIDS victims were homosexuals and intravenous drug users. The remaining 10 percent were hemophiliacs, others receiving transfusions of infected blood, Haitians or Africans in the United States, people having sexual intercourse with members of the high-risk groups, and people who untruthfully denied homosexuality or needle use. By the 1990s, however, with an estimated 1.5 million Americans carrying the H.I.V. virus, the disease was spreading rapidly among heterosexuals who used no hypodermic needles.

Drugs

In the 1970s, use of recreational drugs spread both in the middle class and among the urban poor. LSD, the

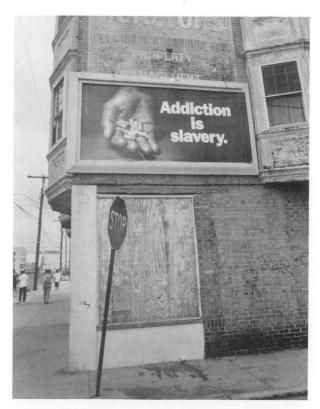

The ravages of drug use and the violent crime associated with it were worst among the urban poor.

book *The Feminine Mystique* (1963) received a rousing response, Betty Friedan organized the National Organization for Women (N.O.W.), a pressure group designed to secure legal and social sexual equality. At first, "women's lib" was widely ridiculed because of the antics of fringe elements such as S.C.U.M., the Society for Cutting Up Men. But the essence of the new feminism was too serious to be ignored and the influence of N.O.W. too great to sidestep.

N.O.W.'s early victories were deceptively easy. Archaic state laws preventing married women from borrowing money or having bank accounts without the approval of their husbands were quickly repealed. Divorce laws were changed to provide for equal division of property between the alienated spouses. Legal action or social pressure forced many corporations to pay men and women equally for equal work, and women won entrance to jobs that had previously been restricted to men, particularly in manual and dangerous work such as construction and firefighting.

The women's movement also counted among its successes the virtual extirpation of "gender-specific" words like fireman, postman, and chairman. Almost instantaneously, business and government took to speaking of "mailcarriers" and "chairpersons." On little more than the demand of Gloria Steinem, the editor of Ms. magazine, women were addressed by that new title, a neutral hybrid of "Miss" and "Mrs." To the new feminists, because the ancient titles identified a woman's marital status, they were demeaning. By the 1990s, even grammar was affected. Rather than continue to use the pronoun *he* collectively (to refer to both men and women), Americans virtually abolished agreement in number. For example, "After *a student* reads this book, *they* ought to know something of American history" became the norm, not an error.

Professional schools and employers adopted affirmative action programs by which they were obligated to admit or to hire women (and members of designated minority groups) in preference to white males if applicants were equally qualified. In practice, apparently less qualified women, blacks, Hispanics, and others were often given preferential treatment, resulting in quota systems such as liberals had fought against when they had been used to discriminate against minorities.

Beginning with the Bakke case of 1978, the Supreme Court dealt several major blows to such programs. In 1989, the Court threw out programs in several cities by which a percentage of municipal contracts were reserved for "minority firms" that did not have to bid against firms owned by white males. By the 1990s, the reaction against affirmative action was so intense as to allow a former Ku Kluxer, David Duke, to twice win a majority of white votes in statewide elections in Louisiana, largely by condemning the policy.

Feminist Issues

N.O.W.'s biggest setback was the failure of the Equal Rights Amendment, which forbade all legal and social discrimination on the basis of sex. Congress sent the E.R.A. to the states for ratification in 1972 and, within a few years, it was approved by all but a handful of the 38 states needed to make it a part of the Constitution.

Then, seemingly from nowhere, rose a groundswell of opposition led by a longtime right-wing Republican writer, Phyllis Schlafly. She cautioned that the E.R.A. would lead to the loss of certain privileges that women enjoyed, such as exemption from military conscription. Her boldness encouraged hundreds of state legislators to fight the women's movement. When the 1979 deadline for ratification was reached, the E.R.A. was still three states short of approval. Congress then extended the deadline to 1982 but the net result was that three states rescinded their earlier votes in favor of ratification. Whether or not this action was constitutional, the E.R.A. won ratification in no additional states, and died.

With that death, N.O.W. and other women's groups turned to abortion rights as their chief goal. In 1973, the Supreme Court had declared in *Roe v. Wade* that, in effect, state governments could not prevent a pregnant woman from having an abortion. By the end of the decade, spearheaded by fundamentalist Protestants, Mormons, and Roman Catholics, the political right made the "Right to Life," prohibition of most or all abortions, into a sacred cause. The women's movement and most liberals responded with the cry of "Choice," defending the *Roe* decision. In 1992, a Supreme Court that was extremely conservative on most other issues, narrowly upheld the basic principles of *Roe*.

By the nineties, the issue of sexual harassment vied with abortion rights as the chief concern of the feminist movement. Strictly defined, sexual harassment meant the proposition, by a person in power, to guarantee job security, promotion (or, in universities, a good grade) in return for sexual favors. In practice, mere flirtation or a sexual proposition in the work place without visible strings attached could be defined as harassment. In 1991, Clarence Thomas, a nominee to the Supreme Court, was the center of a sensational inquest when a young attorney who had worked under him a decade earlier, Anita Hill, accused him of repeatedly using vulgar language and discussing pornographic movies in her presence.

Changing Times

The failure of the E.R.A. anticipated the collapse of Democratic party liberalism in the 1980s. Like other liberal causes of the 1970s, E.R.A. appealed almost exclusively to educated, affluent middle-class liberals. It never sparked much interest among working-class

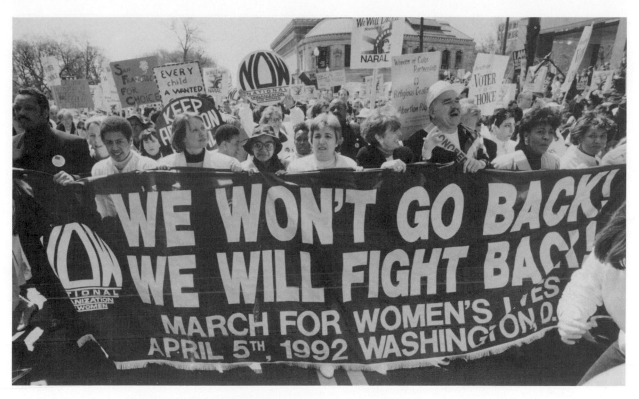

"Choice"—the right of a woman to an abortion on demand—was the paramount cause of American feminists in the early 1990s.

women (or men), nor among ethnic minorities, which had been bastions of the Democratic party vote. Nor did other tenets of "New Age" liberalism (a term coined by a conservative critic)—support for a woman's right to an abortion on demand; acceptance of gay and lesbian lifestyles as moral and proper; zealous defense of the rights of accused criminals; apparent blanket criticism of American mores; reflexive support for nearly every foreign critic of the United States. These left ordinary Americans cold. As late as March 1992, a nationwide poll showed a substantial majority of American women stating that they were not feminists.

The New Age liberals were articulate and politically active. The McGovern reforms of the Democratic party gave them a voice in making party policy out of all proportion to their numbers. However, with their success within the party, they alienated important constituents of the Democratic coalition that had governed the country for half a century.

To capitalize on the unease among traditionally Democratic groups—Southern whites, Northern blue-collar workers who clung to traditional morality, the labor unions, intensely patriotic white ethnics—conservative Republican strategists played down their economic agenda, which favored the well-to-do. Instead, they emphasized morality, traditional values, law and order, and

the flag. The Democratic party as a whole was tarred as the source of the perceived decadence in American society. Because of Watergate and the accidental presidency of Gerald Ford, the strategy of the Republican right-wingers did not bear fruit until 1980. But when it did, the vintage was sweet to those who drank of it.

A CHANGING OF THE GUARD

Republican conservatives grew more sanguine about their election prospects in 1980 with each month of the Carter presidency. Carter had won the White House very narrowly in 1976, and "stagflation" steadily eroded his popularity. The Camp David Accords had been a triumph but, in other areas of foreign policy, such as the Panama Canal treaty, the president's actions were not especially popular. Then came the disaster.

The Iranian Tragedy

Carter believed that Reza Pahlavi, the pro-Western shah of Iran, was a popular ruler at home. He described Iran as an "island of stability" in the Middle East.

This was a delusion. The shah had alienated just about everyone in Iran except the westernized middle and up-

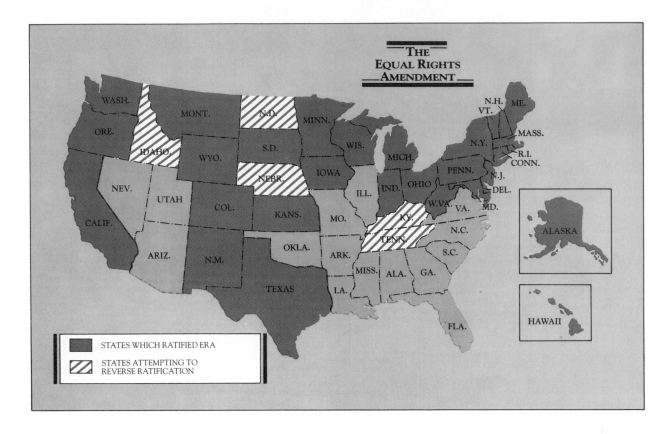

THE EQUAL RIGHTS AMENDMENT

STATES WHICH RATIFIED ERA

STATES ATTEMPTING TO REVERSE RATIFICATION

per classes. Liberal and leftist Iranians suffered at the hands of SAVAK, the shah's brutal secret police. The deeply religious peasantry, the largest single social group in the country, was mesmerized by reactionary Muslim mullahs who taught that the shah's westernized regime was blasphemous.

In January 1979, the shah fled Iran and Muslim fundamentalists, led by the fanatical Ayatollah Ruhollah Khomeini, seized power. In October, when Carter admitted the shah to the United States for treatment of a terminal cancer, Iranian students seized the United States embassy compound in Teheran and took 50 Americans hostage. For more than a year, they languished in confinement. Not until January 20, 1981, the day Jimmy Carter left the White House, were they to be released.

Political Consequences

Sympathy for the Ayatollah's revolution was short-lived in the United States. His regime executed political opponents and "moral offenders" on a scale that made the shah look like Good King Wenceslaus. Khomeini prolonged an eight-year war with Iraq that killed 200,000 Iranians, including children sent on suicide attacks. In 1989, he promised salvation and a large cash bounty to any Muslim who killed Salmon Rushdie, author of The

Satanic Verses, a book he found blasphemous. Khomeini was an embarassment to many pious Muslims, but his power in Iran was immense. In holding the embassy hostages, he wrote an end to the political career of James Earl Carter.

The tide of public opinion turned decisively against Carter after he beat back a challenge for the Democratic party nomination by Massachusetts Senator Edward Kennedy. The Republican nominee who benefited from his debacle was the darling of the party's conservatives, Ronald Reagan. In the primary elections, he easily defeated middle-of-the-roaders George Bush and John Anderson, a congressman from Illinois. Then, when Anderson left the Republican party to run as an independent, Reagan shrewdly placated Republican moderates by naming Bush to be his vice-presidential nominee.

The Reagan Campaign

Reagan did not attack Carter's handling of the hostage crisis directly. To have done so might well have revived sympathy for the luckless president. Instead, he blasted Carter's foreign policy in general. He blamed the president for America's low prestige abroad, saying it was due to softness with the Soviets and weakness in backing up foreign friends. Toughness and a massive military buildup, Reagan said, was needed to stop the slide of American influence, prestige, and pride.

Domestically, Reagan focused on the state of the economy. He promised to reduce regulation of business which, he said, destroyed initiative; to stop inflation, increase employment, cut government spending, and balance the federal budget by 1984.

Reagan's patriotic tub-thumping appealed to many blue-collar workers and white Southerners who had traditionally voted Democratic. At the same time, his strategists ensured the loyalty of the right-wing Republicans who had won the nomination for him. Fundamentalist preachers such as the Reverend Jerry Falwell organized independent Political Action Committees (P.A.C.s) that rallied voters who believed that Democratic party liberalism was responsible for what they saw as a decline in morality. Falwell's "Moral Majority" blamed the Democrats for everything from the high divorce rate to violent crime in big cities.

The Mandate

Most political pundits predicted a close election. Several said the winner would be decided by the outcome in California, the last big state to report its returns. In fact, the election of 1980 was over two hours before the polls closed on the West Coast. Reagan won an electoral college landslide, 489 votes to just 49 for Carter. His popular vote edge was 43.9 million to Carter's 35.5 million with 5.7 million votes going to John Anderson.

The old Democratic coalition lay in tatters. The Irish-American and Italian-American vote, always dependably Democratic, went for Reagan. In all but three states, Slavic-Americans voted for him. Jews, who had once been 80 to 90 percent Democratic, split about evenly, as did labor union members. Reagan won 60 percent of the elderly vote. Young people, whom the New Age liberals had lionized as their vanguard, cast 60 percent of their vote for the Republican candidate.

The right-wing P.A.C.s also defeated half a dozen liberal Democratic Senators, including 1972 presidential nominee, George McGovern. For the first time in

---

URBAN DECAY

In New York City every day between 1977 and 1980, 600 to 2,100 subway cars were out of service because of age, mistreatment, and vandalism. Between 80 and 300 trains had to be canceled each day. There were 2,200 to 5,000 fires in the New York subway system each year. In 1980, it took 40 minutes to take a trip on the subway that took 10 minutes in 1910.

PRIORITIES IN THE 1980s

In 1983, the United States spent 57 cents *per capita* on public broadcasting, as compared to $10 *per capita* in Japan, $18 in Great Britain, and $22 in Canada. In the private sector, the cost of making one episode of the television program *Miami Vice* was $1.5 million. The annual budget of the vice squad in the city of Miami, Florida, a major clearing house for imported drugs, was just $1.1 million.

---

nearly 30 years, the Republicans had a majority in the Senate. The Democrats still held the House of Representatives. However, enough conservative Democrats, startled by the results, announced they would support the president so that Reagan had a working majority in both houses. A new era had begun.

THE REAGAN REVOLUTION

The election of 1980 changed the nature of American government more than any election since 1932. Ronald Reagan and the people surrounding him were at odds with general principles that, since the 1930s, most Democratic and Republican party leaders had accepted as the rules of the game. Reagan was 78 when he left the White House in 1989, the oldest person ever to hold the post. And yet, he stamped his personality and values on the 1980s as indelibly as Franklin D. Roosevelt stamped his on the 1930s.

Man of the Decade

"He has no dark side," one of Reagan's aides said of him, "What you see is what you get." The American people had seen a good deal of Ronald Reagan for more than forty years. He was a successful film actor in the 1940s and the host of a popular television show in the 1950s. During the 1960s, he campaigned tirelessly for conservative causes. Reagan was governor of California between 1967 and 1975 and a serious contender for the Republican nomination for president in 1976.

Few people who knew Reagan personally disliked him. He was a cheerful, even-tempered raconteur, a walking *People* magazine with his wealth of show-business stories. He won the affection of the remoter public when, shortly after his inauguration, he was shot by an emotionally disturbed young man. Reagan cracked a joke on the operating table, and snapped back from a serious wound as quickly as if he were a teenager. Reagan was called "the Great Communicator" for his ability to sell himself.

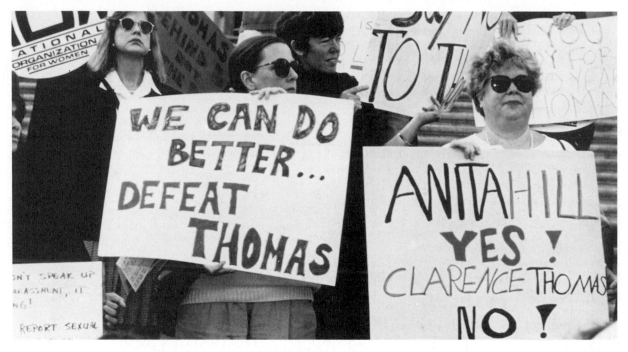

Feminists and most liberals opposed the appointment of Clarence Thomas to the Supreme Court because of accusations he had harassed a young woman with sexual language.

He was also known as "the Teflon president." He was so well liked that nothing messy stuck to him personally, neither his own bad decisions, an administration that brimmed with scandal, nor when former aides ridiculed him.

The Teflon President

The criticisms that did not stick to Reagan were legion. Former aides said that Reagan was interested only in the gratification of being president, that he understood few of the complexities of government, and saw no point in studying them. Others were shocked by his habit of sleeping long hours each day. It was said that he dozed off at cabinet meetings and came to life only while watching old movies. Senator John Glenn of Ohio quipped in 1984: "We've got the president worried now. He's had some sleepless afternoons."

Other critics charged that Reagan was still an actor reading lines written by others. Eloquent in his prepared speeches, he often stumbled when asked questions off the cuff. In 1985, television showed his wife, Nancy, whispering that he should say "We're working on that" when a question was asked. But nothing could alienate the majority of Americans. After the Vietnam tragedy, Watergate scandal, and foundering Carter years, Ronald Reagan's breezy cheerfulness and optimism restored confidence in the presidency.

Social Policies

Like other conservatives, Reagan held the Supreme Court, dominated by liberals for fifty years, responsible for many of the social ills he saw around him. During his eight years in office, a series of vacancies allowed him to continue the transformation of the Court into a conservative body that had begun under Nixon. Reagan's first appointee was Sandra Day O'Connor of Arizona, a protégé of Nixon's most conservative appointee, William Rehnquist. By naming her, the first woman on the Court, Reagan simultaneously pleased feminists while adding a generally conservative vote.

In 1986, Reagan made the forceful Rehnquist Chief Justice and added Antonin Scalia, a witty and persuasive arch-conservative, to the high court. Only in 1988, at

TIME FLIES

A study by a scientific management firm in the late 1980s revealed that the average American living to his or her life expectancy will spend seven years in the bathroom, six years eating, five years waiting in lines, four years cleaning house, three years in meetings, one year "looking for things," eight months opening junk mail, and six months waiting at red lights.

*The figure of Ronald Reagan loomed over the 1980s as Franklin D. Roosevelt's loomed over the
1930s.*

the end of his term, did Reagan run into trouble getting his nominees confirmed. The Senate found one too political in his judgments and a second proved to have been a marijuana-smoker as a young man.

This episode was especially embarrassing to Reagan because he had called for an international War on Drugs. Nancy Reagan headed a campaign to fight the use of drugs among American teenagers. Stung by criticism that she cared for little but expensive evening gowns, Mrs. Reagan devoted long hours to an anti-drug crusade known as "Just Say No!"

"Reaganomics" in Theory

Reagan's immense popularity owed in part to extraordinarily good luck. Some of the problems that had harried Ford and wiped Carter out resolved themselves spontaneously during his presidency. The Iran–Iraq war prevented the Ayatollah from vexing Americans during the 1980s. In the Soviet Union, the death of Leonid Brezhnev in November 1982, and three years of interim leadership by doddering old Bolsheviks meant that the Cold War adversary was almost without direction until 1985.

The OPEC nations broke ranks and oil prices col-

lapsed. Indeed, the keystone of Reagan's popularity was the fact that, after two difficult years, his presidency was a time of general prosperity for middle and upper-class Americans. This prosperity, Reagan believed, was due to his economic policy, which critics mocked as "Reaganomics."

During the campaign of 1980, Reagan promised to restore prosperity by ending inflation and unemployment, reducing government regulation of business, and balancing the budget. Part of his program was based on "supply-side economics," a theory that emphasized increasing the nation's supply of goods and services while

---

CITIZEN CONSUMERS

Immigrants sworn in as United States citizens in Santa Fe in April 1985 received a gift packet including the Preamble to the Constitution, a pamphlet describing etiquette toward the American flag, directories to the Safeway supermarket and Motel 6 chains, discount coupons from local businesses, and membership in the Radio Shack "battery club."

HOW THEY LIVED

HOW THEY CELEBRATED

"Break out the flag, strike up the band, light up the sky!" In disarming old-fashioned band concert language, President Gerald Ford proclaimed the bicentennial of the United States on July 4, 1976. The highlight of the year-long celebration was the visit to New York harbor of sailing vessels from all over the world.

On July 4, 1986, Americans held another big party, this time to celebrate the hundredth birthday of the Statue of Liberty. Again the "tall ships" came and the night sky over New York harbor was illuminated with a fireworks display said to be the biggest in history.

For those who looked for symbols in the celebrations, there were plenty. Whereas, in 1876, the centerpiece of the centennial exposition had been the giant Corliss steam engine, a symbol of the future, the sailing ships were a nostalgic look backward, as if Americans saw little advantage in looking ahead. A mammoth exposition had to be called off because the people who lived near the selected site in northeast Philadelphia did not want millions of their countrymen as guests, nor the increased congestion and crime such a crowd would mean. Have the party somewhere else—anywhere else—they said; but no one else wanted it either. (NIMBY, "Not In My Back Yard," was a common cry of the era.) The promoters, mourning the profits they would not pocket, gave up.

Money seemed to be the motive force behind the Statue of Liberty celebration too. Exclusive rights to televise a national patriotic observance were auctioned to the highest bidder, as if the event were the hot dog and beer contract at a prizefight. The fireworks display was splendid and, yet, also an extraordinary expenditure for a few moments of glitter—an encapsulation of the era of Ronald Reagan.

In 1992, it was time for another anniversary, the quincentennial of the discovery of America by Christopher Columbus, and another controversy. Indeed, the festival went awry almost from the start when the Commission created by Congress in 1984 to plan the commemoration was surrounded by rumors of maladministration and even the outright corruption that characterized so much about the 1980s. By early 1991, the Commission was broke; its first chairman resigned in something like disgrace.

By that time, the quincentennial was also battered by demands that the Columbian discovery was no cause for celebration. Susan Shown Harjo, head of the Morningstar Foundation, an organization dedicated to the promotion of Native American arts, reshaped herself into a political militant, writing and speechifying that, for Indians, the arrival of Columbus was the start of 500 years of oppression and domination. Delivering much the same message, Russell Means, head of the American Indian Movement, enjoyed a revival of the fame he had won as an agitator in the 1960s.

While a majority of Indians and the general population took little interest in "Columbus-bashing," the protests against the celebration were well-publicized because it had the support of much of the intelligentsia, university professors, journalists, and activists in liberal church groups who were articulate and assertive by definition. And they were uncompromising, some literally condemning an event that was as inevitable in the late fifteenth century as day following night.

A San Francisco anthropologist wrote that she mourned "this Quincentennial of genocide, ecocide, and colonialism." A writer in *Conscience* magazine called Columbus "one of history's most influential, enduring mass murderers" who had "a voracious appetite for enslaving, raping, torturing, and murdering native women." Writer Kirkpatrick Sale published *The Conquest of Eden*, which contrasted a pre-Columbian America that was an idyll with a western civilization that was unalloyed evil.

God, gold, and glory, then, were the stuff of this man's dreams, as they were the motivations for the millions who would follow him. What does that say, ultimately, about a man, about the culture whose product he was.

Nor did Sale have a good word for Christopher Columbus, even refusing to concede that he was a superb sailor.

Despite the astonishing absoluteness of Sale's book, he was invited to address numerous conferences on Columbus, including one sponsored by no less eminent a product of western civilization than the Smithsonian Institution. Indeed, the most remarkable aspect of the attacks on the Quincentennial celebration was the support given it by groups in the mainstream of the culture. By New Year's Day 1992, virtually no one, the officers of the Quincentennial Commission included, dared to use the word *discovery* in connection with Columbus. An institute at Lutheran Augsburg College in Minneapolis called for "understanding 1492 not as an occasion to be celebrated but as marking one of the bloodiest turning points in human history." With numerous educational and religious organizations echoing these words, millions of schoolchildren must have been taught to feel badly about Columbus Day—seven days a week: For the National Council of Churches proclaimed 1992 as a year of mourning, apology, and atonement.

The United States at century's end was a nation with deep divisions, suspicions, and hostilities to overcome and an intelligentsia so out of touch with mainstream society as to appear to be from a different planet.

allowing the distribution of wealth—each person's share of the consequent prosperity—to take care of itself.

Thus, Reagan called for cutting the taxes of upper- and middle-income Americans. Unlike the poor, who would spend tax savings on consumer goods, supply-siders argued, the affluent already had a comfortable life. Therefore, they would invest tax savings, supplying capital to the economy. Economic growth would create jobs for the unemployed and, therefore, more people paying taxes. Expensive social welfare programs could be cut back, reducing government expenditures. The budget would be balanced and inflation halted. Democrats pointed out that the plan resembled the "trickle-down" economics of Calvin Coolidge during the 1920s, policies that had contributed to the Great Depression of the 1930s. Reagan was not impressed.

Prosperity in Practice

At the president's behest, Congress reduced taxes by 25 percent over three years. The drop, for those with good incomes, was considerable. A family making $75,000 a year had paid federal income taxes of 52.9 percent during the 1950s and 39.3 percent during the 1970s. By 1985, after the Reagan tax cut, it paid only 29.6 percent.

With the tax cut, government income dropped $131 billion, which Reagan said he would make up by slashing expenditures on social programs. He cut 37,000 jobs from the federal payroll and reduced expenditures on education, medical research, food stamps, and other programs instituted during the 1960s to aid the poor. Federal spending on low-income housing dropped from $32 billion in 1980 to $7 billion in 1988.

The Deficit Mushrooms

However, the Reagan prosperity had little to do with supply-side economics. Too much of the tax savings of upper- and middle-class people went not into investment but into consumption of luxury goods. By 1986, investment in manufacturing was only one percent higher than it had been in the recession year of 1982. By way of contrast, sales of high-priced homes boomed. Expensive imports such as Jaguar and Mercedes-Benz automobiles soared.

The money that fed the Reagan consumption binge came from abroad. West German and Japanese investors pumped money into the United States, buying real estate, corporations, banks, stocks, and U.S. Treasury bonds in huge numbers. Then they made their money back as Americans spent it on imported consumer goods. From being the world's largest creditor nation when Reagan became president, the United States became the world's greatest debtor nation. In 1981, foreigners owed Americans $2,500 for each American family of four. By 1989, Americans owed foreigners $7,000 for each family of four.

The federal deficit—the government's debt—was worse than private debt. The costs of Social Security, pensions, and Reagan's military buildup were immense. Moreover, all the while he called for a constitutional amendment mandating a balanced budget, Reagan spent and borrowed at levels that smashed all records. In 1981, the federal government owed $738 billion, about 26 cents on each dollar produced and earned in the United States that year. In 1989, the debt was $2.1 trillion, about 43 cents on each dollar produced and earned. The president who criticized Jimmy Carter for borrowing borrowed more money in eight years than 39 previous presidents had borrowed in nearly 200 years!

Deregulation

Since the New Deal, the federal government had closely regulated many aspects of economic life. This regulation, Reagan said, discouraged the spirit of enterprise. As president, he weakened the regulatory agencies by cutting their budgets or by abolishing or relaxing restrictions. Some of Reagan's appointees to the agencies simply neglected to do their jobs. Airlines, trucking companies, banks, and brokers selling stocks and bonds found there was no longer a federal watchdog outside their doors.

Profits increased and so did abuses. Airlines closed down routes that did not make enough money and raised fares on well-traveled air lanes. In 1981, a person could fly from San Francisco to Los Angeles on an unrestricted ticket for $36. In 1989, the same ticket cost $148. Consumer advocates claimed that the deregulated airlines sent unsafe planes and unqualified pilots aloft. Similar criticisms were made of the condition of trucks and the qualifications of many truck drivers.

The Environment

Reagan was largely indifferent to environmental protection. But his major appointees were not; they had no sympathy for "tree huggers." The head of the Environmental Protection Agency, Ann Burford, had to resign in 1983 when it was revealed she had actively interfered with the enforcement of agency regulations. The president vetoed a Clean Water Act aimed at stopping the dumping of toxic industrial wastes. His first Secretary of the Interior, James Watt of Colorado, tried to open scenic coastline to off-shore oil drillers.

Watt was a spokesman for the "sagebrush rebels," Western businessmen who wanted the federal government to turn all public lands over to the states which would then open them to private mining, logging, and grazing companies for exploitation. He was forced to resign only after making a statement offensive to blacks,

Jews, and the physically handicapped. In the meantime, Watt's cynicism and tactlessness resulted in the runaway growth of environmental groups. The Wilderness Society claimed 48,000 members in 1981, 240,000 in 1989. The Natural Resources Defense Council increased its membership from 85,000 to 170,000 during the 1980s. The World Wildlife Fund had 60,000 members in 1982, a million in 1990. The Sierra Club and Audubon Society made similar gains.

Financial Fraud

The deregulation of financial institutions led to irresponsible and corrupt practices in banks and savings and loan associations (sometimes called thrift societies). In 1988 alone, 135 thrifts had to be bailed out or closed by the Federal Savings and Loan Insurance Corporation.

This agency, like the Federal Deposit Insurance Corporation for banks, guaranteed savings accounts. Before the Reagan deregulation, however, the F.S.L.I.C. and F.D.I.C. had also enforced high management standards on the people who ran the thrifts and banks. During the Reagan years, supervision was virtually nil and corruption abounded. The son of Vice-President George Bush was involved in dubious decisions that cost the nation dearly. The champion thief was Michael Millken, who saddled Savings and Loans with billions of dollars in "junk bonds," loans that promised to pay high interest precisely because no investor both sensible and honest would touch them.

Millken, who in one year made $550 million in commissions, eventually went to jail. So did several prominent figures on Wall Street, the nation's financial center. Freed of close supervision by the Federal Securities and Exchange Commission, respected stockbrokers turned to fraud. By paying bribes to executives in large corporations, they learned before the general public of important decisions that affected the price of stocks. Using this "insider information," they bought and sold shares at immense profit.

The most celebrated case involved Ivan Boesky. His frauds were so grand that, in order to reduce his term in prison, he agreed in November 1987 to pay a fine of $100 million and pay back the money he had illegally earned.

Through it all, the Reagan administration continued to approve corporate mergers and takeovers that did little but enrich a few individuals. In 1970, there had been 10 corporate reshufflings paying fees of $1 million or more to those who arranged them. In 1980, there were 94, in 1986, 346. In 1988, the government approved a deal between tobacco giant R. J. Reynolds and the Nabisco company despite the fact that, even the principals admitted, the only consequences would be higher prices for consumers, fewer jobs in the two companies, and personal profits of $10 million and more for a handful of shareholders.

The Election of 1984

In 1984, Walter Mondale of Minnesota, vice president under Jimmy Carter, won the Democratic party nomination by beating back challenges from Senator Gary Hart of Colorado and the Reverend Jesse Jackson, a civil rights activist and the first African-American to be a serious contender for a major party presidential nomination. Jackson was a hypnotic orator in the tradition of the black churches from which he had emerged. Hart was the New Age liberal candidate.

Mondale hoped that what he called the "sleaze factor," the widespread corruption in the Reagan administration, would be enough to help him overcome the president's personal popularity. But he was unable to bring back the traditionally Democratic voters who had gone for Reagan in 1980. Mondale was perceived as a pork-barrel candidate, promising something to every constituent group. Moreover, some of Mondale's gestures made little political sense. For example, he named a woman, Geraldine Ferraro, as his running mate despite the fact that feminists were not apt to vote Republican under any circumstances.

And then, Reagan's popularity was at its peak in 1984. He won a massive landslide, carrying every state except Minnesota and the District of Columbia. Almost 59 percent of the voters chose him. He announced that the theme of his second term was "Morning in America."

FOREIGN POLICY IN THE 1980s

Reagan was a Cold Warrior. He had criticized his predecessors for trusting the Soviet Union in any way. In

---

REAGANISM

Garry Wills, one of the leading political commentators of the 1980s, wrote during the waning months of the Reagan presidency,

Ronald Reagan did not build a structure; he cast a spell. There was no Reagan revolution, just a Reagan bedazzlement. The magic is going off almost as mysteriously as the spell was woven in the first place. There is no edifice of policies solid enough to tumble, piece by piece, its props being knocked out singly or in groups. The whole thing is not falling down; it was never weighty enough for that. It is simply evanescing.

1982, he called Russia an "evil empire . . . the focus of evil in the world." As late as 1985, he promulgated the Reagan Doctrine, that the United States would support any anti-Communist struggle anywhere in the world.

By the time he left office in 1989, however, Reagan scored a major breakthrough in nuclear arms reduction and set the stage for a historic rapprochement between the United States and the Cold War enemy. His policies towards other parts of the world also proved unpredictable.

South Africa and the Middle East

The Reagan doctrine led the president to support a number of unpopular regimes and movements. While he criticized South Africa's policy of *apartheid* (strict segregation of races), he resisted calls for economic sanctions designed to force the South African regime to change. Reagan also supported rebels in Angola who were fighting a government backed by the Soviet Union and Cuba.

Reagan continued Jimmy Carter's policy of aiding anti-Russian rebels in Afghanistan despite the fact that they were Muslim fundamentalists of the sort who kept Khomeini in power in Iran. In 1983, he sent Marines to Lebanon, which was torn by a multi-sided war involving religion and foreign intervention. When a suicide bomber driving an explosive-laden truck killed 241 sleeping Marines, he withdrew the force. His Teflon worked as ever. Reagan was not widely criticized either for sending the Marines in or for withdrawing them in failure.

In 1986, Reagan won applause by bombing Libya. The Libyan leader, Muammar Qadaffi, had long been suspected of financing terrorists. When American intelligence claimed to have evidence of a direct link between Qadaffi and terrorists in West Germany, American bombers raided several Libyan cities. Public opinion approved the expedition.

Reagan also took action in the long bloody war between Iran and Iraq. In May 1987, to ensure that oil tankers moved safely in the Persian Gulf, he sent American warships to protect the seaways. Although designed to prevent Iranian attacks, the fleet's only serious loss came when an Iraqi plane attacked the *U.S.S. Stark*, killing 37 servicemen. In 1988, an American naval vessel was inadvertently responsible for a tragedy when an Iranian civilian airliner was shot down by accident.

Central America

The president also applied the Reagan Doctrine in the Caribbean and Central America. In October 1983, he ordered a surprise attack on Grenada, a tiny island nation of only 110,000 people. The island was in chaos after the assassination of a Marxist leader. Although critics feared that one such invasion would lead to others, the president's action was popular.

Much more controversial was his policy in Central America. Many liberal critics opposed United States support of a repressive government in El Salvador and U.S. opposition to the revolutionary Sandinista government of Nicaragua. When, in 1983, El Salvador elected a moderate over an extreme rightist as president, criticism of Reagan's policy in that country faded.

However, many members of Congress continued to oppose American support of the Nicaraguan Contras, guerrillas fighting the leftist Sandinista government of the country. Some said that the United States was causing turmoil and misery in an already wretched and misgoverned country by keeping it at war. Others said that the Contras were reactionary and anti-democratic. Yet others feared that the United States would become involved in another Vietnam quagmire. Between 1984 and 1986, a worried Congress attached the Boland Amendments to a number of bills providing money for foreign aid. They prohibited the government from directly aiding military actions in Nicaragua.

The Iran-Contra Affair

Rather than accept this policy, Reagan told a top aide "to figure out a way to take action." Top Reagan aides then embarked on a bizarre adventure that made a mockery of the president's view of world politics as a competition between good and evil. Two National Security Advisors, Robert McFarlane and John Poindexter, and a Marine Colonel, Oliver North, secretly sold arms to the Ayatollah Khomeini's Iran. Some of the huge profits from the deal simply disappeared into someone's pocket. The balance was given to the Contras.

This illegal action was taken without the knowledge of either Secretary of Defense Casper Weinberger or Secretary of State George Schultz. The role of the president in it was never clearly defined as Reagan changed

Oliver North was accused of violating federal law in the Iran–Contra affair.

his story several times. It was clear that he had either supported a violation of the law or that he did not know what was going on in his own administration. And liberals screamed bloody murder. But Ronald Reagan was no ordinary political target. Times were good; stocks and real estate values were rising; the American public seemed not to notice.

Changing Policies

Even before the Iran-Contra crisis broke, Reagan's foreign policy underwent significant change. Despite the Reagan Doctrine, when protests in Haiti in 1986 against the anti-Communist Jean-Claude Duvalier turned into full-scale revolt, rather than backing Duvalier, American agents played an important role in persuading him to go into exile.

The United States played a central role in the ouster of the strongly pro-American but corrupt president of the Philippines, Ferdinand Marcos. When Marcos declared himself the victor in a disputed election, riots broke out throughout the country. Fearing a civil war, the United States supported his opponent, Corazon Aquino. Marcos was given asylum in Hawaii so as to get him out of the Philippines.

Weapons Buildup

The most important of Reagan's foreign policy shifts was in his view of the Soviet Union. During his first years in office, he destroyed the spirit of *détente* that had begun under Richard Nixon. Calling the SALT-II treaty a "one way street" with Americans making all the concessions to the Soviets, he refused to submit it to the Senate for ratification. In 1986, Reagan announced that the United States would no longer be bound by SALT-I.

In the meantime, the president sponsored the greatest peacetime military buildup in history, spending $2 trillion improving old systems and developing new ones. Battleships were taken out of mothballs and put to sea, and the MX missile, which Reagan renamed the Peacekeeper, was revived. When it was announced that the Peacekeepers were to be installed in old Minuteman missile silos, critics said that Reagan was planning a "first strike" against the Soviets. It was well-known, they said, that the Russians had the Minuteman sites targeted. Therefore, they were useless unless the missiles in them were to be fired to begin a war.

In 1983, Pershing II missiles were installed in West Germany, from where they could hit Soviet targets in five minutes. The Russians responded by increasing their striking capacity. A new arms race seemed to be underway. By 1985, the two superpowers had more than 50,000 nuclear warheads between them.

The most controversial of Reagan's weapons proposals was S.D.I., the Strategic Defense Initiative, known as "Star Wars" after a popular movie. Just a theory, S.D.I. was a system by which satellites orbiting the earth would be equipped with lasers fired at missiles by computer. Reagan claimed that the system would create an umbrella preventing a missile attack on the United States.

Criticism of Star Wars took several forms. Some scientists said that S.D.I. simply would not work. Military experts pointed out that low-flying missiles and planes would not be affected by lasers in space. Financial experts worried that the astronomical costs of the project would bankrupt the United States. Antiwar groups said that S.D.I. was actually an offensive, not a defensive weapon. By making the United States safer from nuclear attack, it would encourage a reckless president to attack the Soviet Union. Yet others said that the Soviets would simply develop countermeasures, which had always been the case in military technology.

Turning Toward Disarmament

Still, it was not criticism that led President Reagan to reverse direction on nuclear buildup. During his second term, the hawkish Casper Weinberger resigned as Secretary of Defense because of the illness of his wife, and the more statesmanlike Secretary of State, George Schultz, the "dove" in the administration, won greater influence over the president.

White House insiders said that Nancy Reagan played a big part in persuading the president to turn toward disarmament. Deeply devoted to her husband, she was concerned about his place in history, and she knew that presidents who worked for peace had higher historical reputations than those who seemed to be war-mongers.

The concerns of allies in Europe also influenced the president. Antinuclear protesters swarmed around American bases in Germany, Britain, and Spain. Chancellor Helmut Kohl of West Germany, President François Mitterrand of France, and Prime Minister Margaret Thatcher remained loyal to the NATO alliance. However, all made it clear that they were unnerved by some of Reagan's more reckless speeches. Most important, the Soviet Union underwent profound changes during the 1980s.

Mikhail Gorbachev

In 1985, after five years of uncertain leadership in the Soviet Union, Mikhail Gorbachev emerged as head of both the Soviet government and Communist party. At home, Gorbachev tried to institute far-reaching economic and political reforms. The policy of *perestroika* (restructuring) was designed to revive the moribund Soviet economy. *Glasnost* (opening) promised political and intellectual freedoms unheard of in the Soviet Union.

Gorbachev knew that the success of his reforms depended on his ability to divert Soviet resources from the military to the domestic economy. Personable and articulate, with a wife as fashionable as Nancy Reagan, the Premier soon won confidence and even affection in the West, including the United States. At first, Reagan resisted Gorbachev's proposals.

Then, in Washington in December 1987, the two men, all smiles and cordiality, signed a treaty eliminating many short-range and medium-range missiles. The Soviets destroyed 1,752 missiles and the Americans 867. These represented only 4 percent of the nuclear missiles in existence. Nevertheless, nuclear power 32,000 times the force of the Hiroshima bomb was wiped out.

ENTER GEORGE HERBERT BUSH

The Democrats approached the presidential campaign of 1988 with high hopes. They believed that the Reagan era had been an aberration, the personal triumph of a fabulously popular individual, not the first chapter of Republican ascendancy. The Democrats had regained control of the Senate in 1986. They enjoyed a comfortable grip on the House, and held a majority of the nation's governorships. Why should the Democrats not hold the presidency too?

The Seven Dwarfs

As always when election victory seems likely, the Democrats were swamped with would-be nominees. The front-runner in the early going was Gary Hart, the boyish former Senator from Colorado who had given Mondale a tough race in the 1976 primaries. But, in a bizarre sequence of events, including publication of a photo showing the married Hart with a young model on his lap aboard a yacht called the *Monkey Business*, political analysts suggested that the candidate's judgment was, perhaps, a little less than called for by the presidency.

When a humiliated Hart withdrew from the race, the remaining candidates were ridiculed as "the seven dwarfs" for their own deficiency—of presidential stature. In fact, several of the dwarfs were able men, and Jesse Jackson remained, as he had been in 1976, one of the nation's most exciting orators. Because he was black, however, with controversial episodes of his own in both his public and personal life, Jackson was considered unelectable by most party professionals.

They openly hoped that Senator Sam Nunn of Georgia, a thoughtful and respected expert on national defense, would jump into the 35 primary election races for the nomination; or Governor Mario Cuomo of New York, a peerless orator whose thoughtful humanism was tempered by hard-headed political realism.

But neither did, and the nomination went to Governor Michael Dukakis of Massachusetts. The son of Greek immigrants, Dukakis had been a successful governor, balancing budgets while the Reagan administration spent and borrowed. During his administration, a state with serious economic difficulties became a prosperous center of finance and high-tech industry. For vice president, Dukakis chose the courtly Senator Lloyd Bentsen of Texas, reminding voters of the Massachusetts–Texas combination that had won the election of 1960.

Bush for the Republicans

The Republican nominee was George Bush, who handily defeated Senator Robert Dole of Kansas in the primaries. Bush was a wealthy oilman who had held a number of appointive positions in government before becoming vice president under Reagan. A critic of Reagan's "voodoo economics" in 1980, Bush became the administration's chief cheerleader after that election. He drew ridicule for his enthusiasm, but it enabled him to establish ties with the conservative wing of the Republican party that had earlier looked at him with jaundiced eyes.

During the primary campaign, Dole hinted that Bush was a "wimp," that he had led so sheltered a life as to lack the toughness required of a president. Bush had indeed enjoyed the privileges of the very rich since birth, and it showed. But he was not lacking in personal courage. He had flown 58 missions as a bomber pilot during World War II. Rather more troubling was his reputation as a bumbler. (He had crashed his planes on five of those missions.) Indeed, after defeating Dole in the primary elections, he made what seemed a fatal political blunder.

As his running mate, Bush chose Senator Danforth Quayle of Indiana, all of whose achievements since first tying his shoes seemed to owe to his father's wealth and influence. Quayle admitted he had "majored in golf" at university. There was also reason to believe that he had dodged military service during the Vietnam War when his father's friends created a place for him in the National Guard. His admission to law school was irregular. Quayle's political career had been built on his movie-star good looks and careful programming by political handlers. During the campaign of 1988, they made sure that he spoke mostly to screened groups of party faithful or to high school and elementary school pupils.

The Campaign

Dukakis attacked Bush's judgment in picking Quayle and tried to contrast his proven competence with Bush's missteps. But Dukakis's public persona was cold, mechanical, and dull. Pundits joked of "Zorba the Clerk." By way of contrast, winning the Republican nomination, his first election victory since 1968, seemed to liberate Bush. As Dukakis grew drabber, Bush exuded confidence and authority, promising both to continue the policies of the "Reagan-Bush Administration" and to usher in "a kinder, gentler America."

While Bush took the high road, Republican strategists smeared Dukakis because a murderer paroled during his tenure in Massachusetts killed again. They hammered on the fact that Dukakis was a member of the American Civil Liberties Union, which had become a citadel of New Age liberalism, piously defending even the rights of pupils to wear t-shirts emblazoned with obscene messages to school. Dukakis was put on the defensive, forced to point out that he was not responsible for Massachusetts parole policies and that he disagreed with many preachments of the A.C.L.U. He improved on Mondale's and Carter's losing efforts in 1984 and 1980. Statisticians observed that a change of half a million votes in eleven states would have given him the election. But Bush won 54 percent of the popular vote and 426 electoral votes to 112 for Dukakis.

Dubious Legacy

A few months before Bush's election, Ronald Reagan told a joke to an audience of Republicans. "Two fellows," he said,

were out hiking in the woods and suddenly looked up and saw a grizzly bear coming over the hill toward them. One of them

President George Herbert Walker Bush

immediately reached into his pack, pulled out a pair of sneakers, started removing his boots and putting on the sneakers. And the other one, standing there, said, "You don't think you can outrun that grizzly, do you?" And the first one said, "I don't have to. I just have to be able to outrun you."

Reagan was able to outrun Bush. When he retired to his ranch near Santa Barbara, California in January 1989, it still appeared to be morning in America. In fact, he bequeathed to George Bush a host of problems that soon threatened to blow up into serious crises.

The federal government was drowning in debt. The population as a whole was in hock to foreigners. The deficit and balance of trade grew a bit worse with most passing months. Reaganomics had skewed the distribution of wealth sharply in favor of the rich. While the average annual income of the richest one percent of the population increased from $280,000 to $550,000 on Reagan's watch, the average income of working families dropped by as much as $2,000. While there were few if any billionaires in the United States in 1980, there were more than 50 in 1988. The very rich enjoyed tax savings of 25 percent under Reagan. The median middle-class family paid $400 more per year in 1989 than it had in 1980.

The poor were far more deprived than they had been before Reagan. In 1989, there were 2.5 million fewer

Dubious legacy of the age of Reagan: one of the growing swarm of homeless people in New York City.

low-income housing units in the United States than in 1980. One child in five had no health insurance and immunizations declined annually. Whooping cough and tuberculosis, diseases thought conquered, made a comeback among the urban poor. The numbers of homeless people reached at least 600,000 by 1991. Crime, especially violent crime, was up dramatically.

Dozens of respected economists warned of impending disaster, but President Bush seemed to think that the "voodoo economics" he had once ridiculed would continue to work for him. He was lucky for a time. In 1989 and 1990, extraordinary events in the Communist world distracted the nation's attention from domestic issues. Then, early in 1991, the United States fought a war of startling brevity and astonishing success. At one point, Bush's "approval" rating in the polls topped 90 percent.

The Collapse of Communism

On May 15, 1989, Mikhail Gorbachev arrived in Beijing to mend fences with the Chinese government. Among those who greeted him were thousands of demonstrators in Tiananmen Square, the huge plaza at the center of the Chinese capital. With university students in the vanguard, the protesters demanded reforms along the lines of Gorbachev's *glasnost*. Within two days, there were a million people in the square.

The whole drama was played out "live" on American television, for two news bureaus were in Beijing with reporters and equipment to cover the Gorbachev visit. Americans even caught some glimpses of the brutal suppression of the rebellion in June, which resulted in at least 500 deaths and, according to some sources, 7,000.

Chinese Communist hard-liners succeeded in holding on to power. In Eastern Europe, however, the countries that had been satellites of the Soviet Union since World War II took advantage of Gorbachev's relaxation of controls to oust their Communist rulers. Poland elected a non-Communist government in mid-1989. By the end of the year, Czechoslovakia followed suit. In October, Erich Honecker, the Communist chief of East Germany resigned and, the next month, a festive crowd breached the Berlin Wall. In December, the much-hated dictator of Rumania, Nicolae Ceausescu, "the genius of the Carpathians," was killed by anti-party revolutionaries. In April 1990, Hungary elected an anti-Communist government. In a few astonishing months, a European order almost half a century old had been liquidated.

Indeed, Communist party control of the Soviet Union—and Gorbachev's position along with it—dissipated in a remarkably short time. *Glasnost* had successfully opened up Soviet society, but *perestroika* had not succeeded in bringing vitality to the Soviet economy. Food shortages in cities led to increasing protests. On May Day, 1990, the holiday of Communism, Gorbachev and his colleagues were roundly jeered as they reviewed the traditional parade. A few days later, Boris Yeltsin, a former ally of Gorbachev become obdurate critic, was elected president of the Russian Republic, the

---

LAND OF VIOLENCE

On March 12, 1991, the Senate Judiciary Committee called the United States "the most violent and self-destructive nation on earth." There were reasons to say so. In 1945, New York City reported 292 homicides; in 1990 there were 2,200. In 1945, there were 1,417 armed robberies in New York, in 1990, there were 100,000—one every five minutes.

Nor was violence out of proportion in the city that was everyone's favorite whipping boy. The murder rate in Washington, D.C. was two and a half times as bad as New York's at 472 in 1990. (Frankfurt, Germany, about the same size as Washington, had 20 to 30 murders a year.) Nationwide, there were three homicides an hour in the United States (23,300 in 1990). This was nine times the murder rate in England, 11 times the rate in Japan. The American incidence of rape was 23 times that of Italy, 26 times that of Japan.

The unsuccessful revolution of Chinese students in Tianamen Square was played out live on American television.

largest constituent of the Soviet Union. For the next year and a half, Yeltsin increased his following at Gorbachev's expense by calling for a free market economy and supporting claims to independence in many of the other 14 republics. At the end of 1991, the Soviet Union was formally dissolved. Gorbachev, the man who had begun it all, remained as popular as ever in Europe and the United States. But he was retired from politics in Russia with little ceremony and audible regret. By the summer of 1991, Yeltsin was offering to sell Russian assets to foreigners in return for cancelling Russian debt.

Successes in Latin America

George Bush could and did crow that the Cold War was over and that Republican policies had won it. The Republican "get tough" stance and the fabulously expensive arms race had laid bare the fatal weaknesses of the Communist states. Rather more important, with the leaders of the Soviet Union preoccupied by the specter of chaos at home, Bush and his able Secretary of State, James Baker, were able to win a series of victories both in the corridors of diplomacy and on the battlefield.

In December 1989, Bush succeeded in doing what Reagan had failed to do, toppling Manuel Noriega from power in Panama. After several provocations, including the shooting of an American military officer, Bush sent 12,000 troops into Panama in a surprise attack, where they joined another 12,000 already stationed at the Panama Canal. Within a few days, with little loss in American lives, Noriega was out of power and a client government installed.

In February 1990, as Soviet and Cuban aid to Nicaragua dried up, the Sandinistas were voted out of power by a political alliance strongly backed by the United States. A less desirable right-wing party took control of El Salvador but, thanks to American prodding, moderated its policies and signed an armistice and agreement with leftist rebels, ending the long war in that country. World affairs were going well for the president.

Crisis in the Middle East

Indeed, Bush's greatest success abroad was in the Middle East. It was precipitated in August 1990 by the invasion of Kuwait, a tiny oil-rich sheikdom on the Persian Gulf,

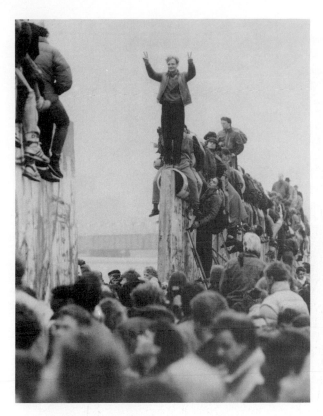

More than any other single event, the fall of the Berlin Wall symbolized the collapse of communism in Europe.

attack. Just one day after the deadline passed, the allies launched a withering air attack that, in little more than a week, totaled 12,000 sorties. With an American television reporter in Iraq, the world was presented with the phenomenon of watching a war from both sides.

In the face of this onslaught, Saddam sent most of his air force to neighboring Iran, leaving the skies to American planes. Probably, like some Americans, he believed that his huge army, dug in behind formidable defenses, would turn back any ground assault. He was wrong. His army was large, but most Iraqi soldiers were poorly trained, and even mistreated by their officers. The air war was chillingly effective, not only devastating Iraqi communications and the transportation system, but terrifying front-line Iraqi troops so that, when the ground attack came, most surrendered without resistance.

Just as important, an indefatigable James Baker and a technological success story succeeded in foiling Saddam's ploy to bring Israel into the war, thus rallying the Arab world to his side. While Baker cajoled both Israelis and Arabs, American Patriot ground-to-air missiles—defensive weapons—destroyed most SCUD missiles Saddam aimed at Israel and Saudi Arabia.

The allied ground attack came on February 23, 1992. In just a few days, the Iraqi army was routed by a daring flanking action designed by commanding general Norman Schwarzkopf. However, for the sake of a slogan and because he did not want to destabilize Iraq completely, Bush ordered a halt to the ground war when it was 100 hours old.

Mixed Results

This was a mistake. Saddam was not ousted by Iraqi rebels as Bush believed he would be. Before the war was a year in the past, with Saddam rebuilding his military force and Kuwait's reactionary ruling family making few changes in that country, many Americans wondered if the war had indeed been won. Bush's triumph was further marred by revelations that his administration had actively and generously encouraged Iraq up to the very eve of Saddam Hussein's adventure.

Still, the Gulf War had its salutory consequences. A decision by the United Nations against an errant member was carried out with dispatch. Never was the international organization's prestige higher. Dictators of small countries were put on warning that mischief-making which might lead to a general war would not be tolerated. Hostages held for years by anti-western Islamic organizations were released in 1991.

For George Bush, the war seemed to be a political bonanza. He announced that Americans had put the "Vietnam Syndrome"—a demoralized army and defeatism at home—behind them. The president's ratings in public opinion polls soared in early 1991. In the excite-

by armed forces from Iraq. Fearing that Saddam Hussein would next invade Saudi Arabia, Bush and Baker quickly secured a unanimous vote in the United Nations Security Council calling for a boycott of all foreign trade with Iraq. Although rich in oil, Iraq needed to import virtually all the rest of the materials needed to support a modern economy.

Many Americans, representing the breadth of the political spectrum, believed that economic sanctions alone would be enough to force Saddam out of Kuwait. They urged the administration to hunker down and wait. Bush and Baker disagreed. They feared, with plenty of precedents on their side, that as time went on, the boycott would disintegrate. That fear, and apprehensions for the security of Saudi Arabia, prompted Bush to send a token American military force to Saudi Arabia on August 7. When, far from buckling, Saddam grew more defiant, annexing Kuwait, Bush sent more than 400,000 troops to Saudi Arabia. Other nations, especially Britain, France, and Egypt also sent large contingents.

The Hundred Hours War

On November 29, the Security Council voted to give Saddam until January 15, 1991, to evacuate Kuwait. If he did not, the American-led force was authorized to

General Norman Schwarzkopf, commander of Operation Desert Storm, wanted to completely destroy Iraq's military rather than end the war when it was 100 hours old.

ment of watching a miraculously successful war on television, Americans seemed to forget their serious economic problems at home. But it was only for a season. By the time the presidential election campaign began in earnest early in 1992, a recession that would not abate had virtually driven the Hundred Hour War into the realm of ancient history.

DOUBLESPEAK

Aided and abetted by journalists, spokesmen for the armed forces during the Gulf War purveyed a jargon that, had the situation not been so grave, would have been ludicrous.

Armed Situation	=	Battle
To visit a site	=	To bomb
Hard targets	=	Buildings
Soft targets	=	People
What bombs do to hard targets and soft targets	=	Service the target, degrade, attrit, neutralize, eliminate, cleanse, sanitize, impact

Primary Elections 1992

President Bush found himself challenged in the Republican primary elections by a right-wing television commentator, Patrick Buchanan, who had vociferously opposed the Gulf War. Buchanan won no primaries, but by taking almost 40 percent of the Republican votes in some states, he signalled that Bush was in trouble in his own party. Sensitive to this, Bush made what may have been a fatal mistake: He and chief campaign advisor James Baker allowed Buchanan and other right-wing Republicans to address the party's national convention. True or not, Democrats argued that, as in 1964, the Republican party had been taken over by its extremists.

The Democratic party's primary campaign began uncertainly with a substantial number of would-be nominees winning the convention delegates of at least one state. Senator Thomas Harkin of Iowa, a liberal with a populist manner, won his own state. Paul Tsongas of Massachusetts won New Hampshire and Maryland. Senator Robert Kerrey of Nebraska won South Dakota. Former California Governor Jerry Brown, despite a nagging reputation for bizarre beliefs—he was sometimes called "Governor Moonbeam"—won Vermont and most of the delegates from Colorado.

Billionaire Ross Perot quit the presidential campaign of 1992 when it appeared that he would have to spend the $100 million he pledged to his supporters.

But the year belonged to Governor William Clinton of Arkansas, who rode out accusations of adultery and criticisms that he was too "slick" to be trusted and sewed up the convention before it met. Clinton's strategy was to stand for liberal "life-style" issues (he was pro-choice on abortion and called for an end to discrimination against homosexuals) with an economic policy that emphasized growth.

The Perot Phenomenon

When the Democrats met in convention in New York City in July, they believed they could defeat Bush because of a split in the Reagan coalition. Some conservative Republicans who had never liked the president and former Democrats who had voted for Reagan swarmed wholesale to support the independent candidacy of H. Ross Perot, a self-made Texas billionaire. On a television interview show earlier in the year, Perot had said that he would consider running for president if grassroots volunteers got his name on the ballot in all 50 states.

Although he offered little in the way of a program, hundreds of thousands of obviously discontented Americans formed local "Perot for President" organizations. In June, polls showed him leading both Clinton and Bush. By mid-July, he was on the ballot in 24 states, with a dozen more on the verge of approving him.

Then, on the day Governor Clinton was to accept the Democratic nomination, Perot quit the race. His showing in the polls had declined and a top aide had resigned, complaining that Perot would take little advice.

Many of Perot's supporters condemned him, some bitterly. But others, still on Perot's payroll, continued to gather signatures on petitions to put him on state ballots. Then, with no warning, Perot jumped back into the race, claiming (without any evidence) the he had quit earlier when he learned that a Republican "dirty tricks" squad planned to disrupt his daughter's wedding unless he dropped out.

The Election of 1992

Perot never won back many of his followers. Nevertheless, in drawing 19 percent of the popular vote, he did better than any third party presidential candidate since Theodore Roosevelt in 1912.

Perot's candidacy almost certainly helped Bill Clinton to carry several mountain states that had not gone Democratic since 1964. Clinton also won California, a Republican stronghold for decades, thanks to the severity of the recession there. In electoral votes, the entire Northeast and several southern states also went Democratic.

George Bush won the big states of Florida and Texas, plus Indiana, Virginia, the Carolinas, and much of the West. But the perception that his inaction had contributed to the recession, made him a one-term president. With only 43 percent of the popular vote, Clinton won 370 electoral votes to 168 for George Bush.

Congress was also Democratic—and more feminine: Two women were elected to the Senate from California; an African American woman won a Senate seat in Illinois. So hopes were high in the wake of the contest that the "gridlock" of the Bush years—unresolvable conflict between president and Congress—was at an end.

For Further Reading

Chapter 51 is about our yesterday, and most historians concede that all attempts to write the history of very recent times are destined to be seriously flawed. Perhaps some of the books listed here will become classics, to be read indefinitely into the future because of their extraordinary insights or—in the estimation of the future—their veracity. It is impossible to say of which of these books that will be so, and which will moulder on library shelves, untouched even by vandals.

Surely the most likely candidate as shrewd observer of

his times is Garry Wills, whose *Reagan's America: Innocent at Home* (1987) is as provocative as his contemporary study of Nixon. Also useful in understanding the symbol of the 1980s is the man's own *Where's the Rest of Me?* (1965), an account of his conversion from youthful liberalism to the conservative politics for which he will be remembered. Also on this subject, see A. Edwards, *Early Reagan: The Rise to Power* (1987). Two of the many books by principals in the Reagan administration are Donald Regan, *For the Record* (1988) and Larry Speakes, *Speaking Out* (1988). See also P. Steinfels, *The Neoconservatives* (1979) and S. Blumenthal, *The Rise of the Counter-Establishment* (1986).

On foreign policy during the 1980s: R. L. Garthoff, *Détente and Confrontation: American–Soviet Relations from Nixon to Reagan* (1985) which does not, however, deal with Reagan's turn toward accommodation with the Soviets late in his term. On covert operations, see G. F. Treverton, *Covert Action* (1987) and B. Woodward, *Veil: The Secret Wars of the C.I.A., 1981–1987* (1987). P. Kennedy, in *The Rise and Fall of the Great Powers* (1987), may offer an explanation of why contemporary Americans find their nation's place in the world so perplexing.

Appendixes

Appendixes

Appendixes

The Declaration of Independence*

The Unamimous Declaration of the Thirteen United States of America,

When in the Course of human events it becomes necessary for one people to dissolve the political bands which have connected them with another, and to assume among the Powers of the earth, the separate and equal station to which the Laws of Nature and of Nature's God entitle them, a decent respect to the opinions of mankind requires that they should declare the causes which impel them to the separation.

We hold these truths to be self-evident, that all men are created equal, that they are endowed by their Creator with certain unalienable Rights, that among these are Life, Liberty and the pursuit of Happiness. That to secure these rights, Governments are instituted among Men, deriving their just Powers from the consent of the governed. That whenever any Form of Government becomes destructive of these ends, it is the Right of the People to alter or to abolish it, and to institute new Government, laying its foundaton on such principles and organizing its Powers in such form, as to them shall seem most likely to effect their Safety and Happiness. Prudence, indeed, will dictate that Governments long established should not be changed for light and transient causes; and accordingly all experience hath shewn, that mankind are more disposed to suffer, while evils are sufferable, than to right themselves by abolishing the forms to which they are accustomed. But when a long train of abuses and usurpations, pursuing invariably the same Object evinces a design to reduce them under absolute Despotism, it is their right, it is their duty to throw off such Government, and to provide new Guards for their future security. Such has been the patient sufferance of these Colonies; and such is now the necessity which constrains them to alter their former Systems of Government. The history of the present King of Great Britain is a history of repeated injuries and usurpations, all having in direct object the establishment of an absolute Tyranny over these States. To prove this, let Facts be submitted to a candid world.

He has refused his Assent to Laws, the most wholesome and necessary for the public good.

He has forbidden his Governors to pass Laws of immediate and pressing importance, unless suspended in their operation till his Assent should be obtained; and when so suspended, he has utterly neglected to attend to them.

He has refused to pass other Laws for the accommodation of large districts of people, unless those people would relinquish the right of Representation in the Legislature, a right inestimable to them and formidable to tyrants only.

He has called together legislative bodies at places unusual, uncomfortable, and distant from the depository of their Public Records, for the sole Purpose of fatiguing them into compliance with his measures.

He has dissolved Representative Houses repeatedly, for opposing with manly firmness his invasions on the rights of the People.

He has refused for a long time, after such dissolutions, to cause others to be elected; whereby the Legislative Powers, incapable of Annihilation, have returned to the People at large for their exercise; the State remaining in the mean time exposed to all the dangers of invasion from without, and convulsions within.

He has endeavoured to prevent the Population of these States; for that purpose obstructing the Laws for Naturalization of Foreigners; refusing to pass others to encourage their migrations hither, and raising the conditions of new Appropriations of Lands.

He has obstructed the Administration of Justice, by refusing his Assent to Laws for establishing Judiciary Powers.

He has made Judges dependent on his Will alone, for the tenure of their offices, and the amount and payment of their salaries.

He has erected a multitude of New Offices, and sent hither swarms of Officers to harass our People, and eat out their substance.

He has kept among us, in times of peace, Standing Armies without the consent of our legislatures.

He has affected to render the Military independent of and superior to the Civil Power.

He has combined with others to subject us to a jurisdiction foreign to our constitution, and unacknowledged by our laws;

---

*Reprinted from the facsimile of the engrossed copy in the National Archives. The original spelling, capitalization, and punctuation have been retained. Paragraphing has been added.

giving his Assent to their Acts of pretended Legislation:

For Quartering large bodies of armed troops among us:

For protecting them, by a mock Trial, from Punishment for any Murders which they should commit on the Inhabitants of these States:

For cutting off our Trade with all parts of the world:

For imposing Taxes on us without our Consent:

For depriving us in many cases, of the benefits of Trial by Jury:

For transporting us beyond Seas to be tried for pretended offences:

For abolishing the free System of English Laws in a neighbouring Province, establishing therein an Arbitrary government, and enlarging its Boundaries so as to render it at once an example and fit instrument for introducing the same absolute rule into these Colonies:

For taking away our Charters, abolishing our most valuable Laws, and altering fundamentally the Forms of our Governments:

For suspending our own Legislatures, and declaring themselves invested with Power to legislate for us in all cases whatsoever.

He has abdicated Government here, by declaring us out of his Protection, and waging War against us.

He has plundered our seas, ravaged our Coasts, burnt our towns, and destroyed the lives of our people.

He is at this time transporting large Armies of foreign Mercenaries to compleat the works of death, desolation and tyranny, already begun with circumstances of Cruelty and perfidy scarcely paralleled in the most barbarous ages, and totally unworthy the Head of a civilized nation.

He has constrained our fellow Citizens taken Captive on the high Seas to bear Arms against their Country, to become the executioners of their friends and Brethren, or to fall themselves by their Hands.

He has excited domestic insurrections amongst us, and has endeavoured to bring on the inhabitants of our frontiers, the merciless Indian Savages, whose known rule of warfare, is an undistinguished destruction of all ages, sexes and conditions.

In every stage of these Oppressions We have Petitioned for Redress in the most humble terms: Our repeated Petitions have been answered only by repeated injury. A Prince, whose character is thus marked by every act which may define a Tyrant, is unfit to be the ruler of a free People.

Nor have We been wanting in attentions to our British brethren. We have warned them from time to time of attempts by their legislature to extend an unwarrantable jurisdiction over us. We hae reminded them of the circumstances of our emigration and settlement here. We have appealed to their native justice and magnanimity, and we have conjured them by the ties of our common kindred to disavow these usurpations, which, would inevitably interrupt our connections and correspondence. They too have been deaf to the voice of justice and of consanguinity. We must, therefore, acquiesce in the necessity, which denounces our Separation, and hold them, as we hold the rest of mankind, Enemies in War, in Peace Friends.

We, therefore, the Representatives of the United States of America, in General Congress, Assembled, appealing to the Supreme Judge of the world for the rectitude of our intentions, do, in the Name, and by Authority of the good People of these Colonies, solemnly publish and declare, That these United Colonies are, and of Right ought to be FREE AND INDEPENDENT STATES; that they are Absolved from all Allegiance to the British Crown, and that all political connection between them and the State of Great Britain, is and ought to be totally dissolved; and that, as Free and Independent States, they have full Power to levy War, conclude Peace, contract Alliances, establish Commerce, and to do all other Acts and Things which Independent States may of right do. And for the support of this Declaration, with a firm reliance on the protection of divine Providence, we mutually pledge to each other our Lives, our Fortunes and our sacred Honor.

The Constitution of the United States of America*

We the People of the United States, in Order to form a more perfect Union, establish Justice, insure domestic Tranquility, provide for the common defence, promote the general Welfare, and secure the Blessings of Liberty to ourselves and our Posterity, do ordain and establish this Constitution for the United States of America.

Article. I.

Section. 1. All legislative Powers herein granted shall be vested in a Congress of the United States, which shall consist of a Senate and House of Representatives.

Section. 2. The House of Representatives shall be composed of Members chosen every second Year by the People of the several States, and the Electors in each State shall have the Qualifications requisite for Electors of the most numerous Branch of the State Legislature.

No Person shall be a Representative who shall not have attained to the Age of twenty five Years, and been seven Years a Citizen of the United Staes, and who shall not, when elected, be an Inhabitant of that State in which he shall be chosen.

Representatives and direct Taxes† shall be apportioned among the several States which may be included within this Union, according to their respective Numbers, which shall be determined by adding to the whole Number of free Persons, including those bound to Service for a Term of Years, and excluding Indians not taxed, three fifths of all other Persons.‡ The actual Enumeration shall be made within three Years after the first Meeting of the Congress of the United States, and within every subsequent Term of ten Years, in such Manner as they shall by Law direct. The Number of Representatives shall not exceed one for every thirty Thousand, but each State shall have at least one Representative; and until such enumeration shall be made, the State of New Hampshire shall be entitled to chuse three; Massachusetts eight; Rhode Island and Providence Plantations one; Connecticut five; New York six; New Jersey four; Pennsylvania eight; Delaware one; Maryland six; Virginia ten; North Carolina five; South Carolina five; and Georgia three.

When vacancies happen in the Representation from any State, the Executive Authority thereof shall issue Writs of Election to fill such Vacancies.

The House of Representatives shall chuse their Speaker and other Officers; and shall have the sole Power of Impeachment.

Section. 3. The Senate of the United States shall be composed of two senators from each State, chosen by the Legislature thereof, for six Years; and each Senator shall have one Vote.*

Immediately after they shall be assembled in Consequence of the first Election, they shall be divided as equally as may be into three Classes. The Seats of the Senators of the first Class shall be vacated at the Expiration of the second Year, of the second Class at the Expiration of the fourth Year, and of the third Class at the Expiration of the sixth Year, so that one third may be chosen every second Year; and if Vacancies happen by Resignation, or otherwise, during the Recess of the Legislature of any State, the Executive thereof may make temporary Appointments until the next Meeting of the Legislature, which shall then fill such Vacancies.†

No Person shall be a Senator who shall not have attained to the Age of thirty Years, and been nine Years a Citizen of the United States, and who shall not, when elected, be an Inhabitant of that State for which he shall be chosen.

The Vice President of the United States shall be President of the Senate, but shall have no Vote, unless they be equally divided.

The Senate shall chuse their other Officers, and also a President pro tempore, in the Absence of the Vice President, or when he shall exercise the Office of President of the United States.

The Senate shall have the sole Power to try all Impeachments. When sitting for that Purpose, they shall be on Oath or Affirmation. When the President of the United States is tried, the Chief Justice shall preside: And no Person shall be convicted without the Concurrence of two thirds of the Members present.

Judgment in Cases of Impeachment shall not extend further than to removal from Office, and disqualification to hold and

---

*From the engrossed copy in the National Archives. Original spelling, capitalization, and punctuation have been retained.
†Modified by the Sixteenth Amendment.
‡Replaced by the Fourteenth Amendment.

*Superseded by the Seventeenth Amendment.
†Modified by the Seventeenth Amendment.

enjoy any Office of honor, Trust of Profit under the United States: but the Party convicted shall nevertheless be liable and subject to Indictment, Trial, Judgment and Punishment, according to Law.

Section. 4. The Times, Places and Manner of holding Elections for Senators and Representatives, shall be prescribed in each State by the Legislature thereof, but the Congress may at any time by Law make or alter such Regulation, except as to the Places of chusing Senators.

The Congress shall assemble at least once in every Year, and such Meeting shall be on the first Monday in December, unless they shall by Law appoint a different Day.*

Section. 5. Each House shall be the Judge of the Elections, Returns and Qualifications of its own Members, and a Majority of each shall constitute a Quorum to do Business; but a smaller Number may adjourn from day to day, and may be authorized to compel the Attendance of absent members, in such manner, and under such Penalties as each House may provide.

Each House may determine the Rules of its Proceedings, punish its Members for disorderly Behaviour, and, with the Concurrence of two thirds, expel a Member.

Each House shall keep a Journal of its Proceedings, and from time to time publish the same, excepting such Parts as may in their Judgment require Secrecy; and the Yeas and Nays of the Members of either House on any question shall, at the Desire of one fifth of those Present, be entered on the Journal.

Neither House, during the Session of Congress, shall, without the Consent of the other, adjourn for more than three days, nor to any other Place than that in which the two Houses shall be sitting.

Secton. 6. The Senators and Representatives shall receive a Compensation for their Services, to be ascertained by Law, and paid out of the Treasury of the United States. They shall in all Cases, except Treason, Felony and Breach of the Peace, be privileged from Arrest during their Attendance at the Session of their respective Houses, and in going to and returning from the same; and for any Speech or Debate in either House, they shall not be questioned in any other Place.

No Senator or Representative shall, during the Time for which he was elected, be appointed to any civil Office under the Authority of the United States, which shall have been created, or the Emoluments whereof shall have been encreased during such time; and no Person holding any Office under the United States, shall be a Member of either House during his Continuance in Office.

Section. 7. All Bills for raising Revenue shall originate in the House of Representatives; but the Senate may propose or concur with Amendments as on other bills.

Every Bill which shall have passed the House of Representatives and the Senate shall, before it become a Law, be pre-

sented to the President of the United States; If he approve he shall sign it, but if not he shall return it, with his Objections to that House in which it shall have originated, who shall enter the Objections at large on their Journal, and proceed to reconsider it. If after such Reconsideration two thirds of that House shall agree to pass the Bill, it shall be sent, together with the Objections, to the other House, by which it shall likewise be reconsidered, and if approved by two thirds of that House, it shall become a Law. But in all such Cases the Votes of both Houses shall be determined by yeas and Nays, and the Names of the Persons voting for and against the Bill shall be entered on the Journal of each House respectively. If any Bill shall not be returned by the President within ten Days (Sundays excepted) after it shall have been presented to him, the Same shall be a Law, in Manner as if he had signed it, unless the Congress by their Adjournment prevent its Return, in which Case it shall not be a Law.

Every Order, Resolution, or Vote to which the Concurrence of the Senate and House of Representatives may be necessary (except on a question of Adjournment) shall be presented to the President of the United States; and before the Same shall take Effect, shall be approved by him, or being disapproved by him shall be repassed by two thirds of the Senate and House of Representatives, according to the rules and Limitations prescribed in the Case of a Bill.

Section. 8. The Congress shall have Power To lay and collect Taxes, Duties, Imposts and Excises, to pay the Debts and provide for the common Defence and general Welfare of the United States; but all Duties, Imposts and Excises shall be uniform throughout the United States;

To borrow Money on the credit of the United States;

To regulate Commerce with foreign Nations, and among the several States, and with the Indian Tribes;

To establish an uniform Rule of Naturalization, and uniform Laws on the subject of Bankruptcies throughout the United States;

To coin Money, regulate the Value thereof, and of foreign Coin, and fix the Standard of Weights and Measures;

To provide for the Punishment of counterfeiting the Securities and current Coin of the United States;

To establish Post Office and post Roads;

To promote the Progress of Science and useful Arts, by securing for limited Times to Authors and Inventors the exclusive Right to their respective Writings and Discoveries;

To constitute Tribunals inferior to the supreme Court;

To define and punish Piracies and Felonies committed on the high Seas, and Offences against the Law of Nations;

To declare War, grant Letters of Marque and Reprisal, and make Rules concerning Captures on Land and Water;

To raise and support Armies, but no Appropriation of Money to that Use shall be for a longer Term than two Years;

To provide and maintain a Navy;

*Superseded by the Twentieth Amendment.

To make Rules for the government and Regulation of the land and naval Forces;

To provide for calling forth the Militia to execute the Laws of the Union, suppress Insurrections and repel Invasions;

To provide for organizing, arming, and disciplining, the Militia, and for governing such Part of them as may be employed in the Service of the United States, reserving to the States respectively, the Appointment of the Officers, and the Authority of training the Militia according to the discipline prescribed by Congress;

To exercise exclusive Legislation in all Cases whatsoever, over such District (not exceeding ten Miles square) as may, by Cession of particular States, and the Acceptance of Congress, become the Seat of the Government of the United States, and to exercise like Authority over all Places purchased by the consent of the Legislature of the State in which the Same shall be, for the Erection of Forts, Magazines, Arsenals, dock-Yards, and other needful Buildings;—And

To make all Laws which shall be necessary and proper for carrying into Execution the foregoing Powers, and all other Powers vested by this Constitution in the Government of the United States, or in any Department or Officer thereof.

Section. 9. The Migration or Importation of such Persons as any of the States now existing shall think proper to admit, shall not be prohibited by the Congress prior to the Year one thousand eight hundred and eight, but a Tax or Duty may be imposed on such Importation, not exceeding ten dollars for each Person.

The Privilege of the Writ of Habeas Corpus shall not be suspended, unless when in Cases of Rebellion or Invasion the public Safety may require it.

No Bill of Attainder or ex post facto Law shall be passed.

No Capitation, or other direct, Tax shall be laid, unless in Proportion to the Census or Enumeration herein before directed to be taken.

No Tax or Duty shall be laid on Articles exported from any State.

No Preference shall be given by any Regulation of Commerce or Revenue to the Ports of one State over those of another: nor shall Vessels bound to, or from, one State, be obliged to enter, clear, or pay Duties in another.

No Money shall be drawn from the Treasury, but in Consequence of Appropriations made by Law, and a regular Statement and Account of the Receipts and Expenditures of all public Money shall be published from time to time.

No Title of Nobility shall be granted by the United States: And no Person holding any Office or Profit or Trust under them, shall, without the Consent of the Congress, accept of any present, Emolument, Office, or Title, of any kind whatever, from any King, Prince, or foreign State.

Section. 10. No State shall enter into any Treaty, Alliance, or Confederation; grant Letters of Marque and Reprisal; coin Money; emit bills of Credit; make any Thing but gold and silver Coin a Tender in Payment of Debts; pass any Bill of Attainder, ex post facto Law, or Law impairing the Obligation of Contracts, or grant any Title of Nobility.

No state shall, without the Consent of the Congress, lay any Imposts or Duties on Imports or Exports, except what may be absolutely necessary for executing its inspection Laws: and the net Produce of all Duties and Imposts, laid by any State on Imports or Exports, shall be for the Use of the Treasury of the United States; and all such Laws shall be subject to the Revision and Controul of the Congress.

No State shall, without the Consent of Congress, lay any Duty of Tonnage, keep Troops or Ships of War in time of peace, enter into any Agreement or Compact with another Stae, or with a foreign Power, or engage in War, unless actually invaded, or in such imminent Danger as will not admit of delay.

Article. II.

Section. 1. The executive Power shall be vested in a President of the United States of America. He shall hold his Office during the Term of four Years, and, together with the Vice President, chosen for the same Term, be elected, as follows:

Each State shall appoint, in such Manner as the Legislature thereof may direct, a Number of Electors, equal to the whole Number of Senators and Representatives to which the State may be entitled in the Congress: but no Senator or Representative, or Person holding an Office of Trust or Profit under the United States, shall be appointed an Elector.

The Electors shall meet in their respective States, and vote by Ballot for two Persons, of whom one at least shall not be an Inhabitant of the same State with themselves. And they shall make a List of all the Persons voted for, and of the Number of Votes for each; which List they shall sign and certify, and transmit sealed to the Seat of the Government of the United States, directed to the President of the Senate. The President of the Senate shall, in the Presence of the Senate and House of Representatives, open all the Certificates, and the Votes shall then be counted. The Person having the greatest Number of Votes shall be the President, if such Number be a Majority of the whole Number of Electors appointed; and if there be more than one who have such Majority, and have an equal Number of Votes, then the House of Representatives shall immediately chuse by Ballot one of them for President; and if no Person have a Majority, then from the five highest on the List the said House shall in like Manner chuse the President. But in chusing the President, the Votes shall be taken by States, the Representation from each State having one Vote; A quorum for this Purpose shall consist of a Member or Members from two thirds of the States, and a Majority of all the States shall be necessary to a Choice. In every Case, after the Choice of the President, the Person having the greatest Number of

Votes of the Electors shall be the Vice President. But if there should remain two or more who have equal Votes, the Senate shall chuse from them by Ballot the Vice President.*

The Congress may determine the Time of chusing the Electors, and the Day on which they shall give their Votes; which Day shall be the same througout the United States.

No Person except a natural born Citizen, or a Citizen of the United States, at the time of the Adoption of this Constitution, shall be eligible to the Office of President, neither shall any Person be eligible to that Office who shall not have attained to the Age of thirty five Years, and been fourteen Years a Resident within the United States.

In Case of the Removal of the President from Office, or of his Death, Resignation, or Inability to discharge the Powers and Duties of the said Office, the Same shall devolve on the Vice President, and the Congress may by Law provide for the Case of Removal, Death, Resignation or Inability, both of the President and Vice President, declaring what Officer shall then act as President, and such Officer shall act accordingly, until the Disability be removed, or a President shall be elected.†

The President shall, at stated Times, receive for his Services, a Compensation, which shall neither be encreased nor diminished during the Period for which he shall have been elected, and he shall not receive within that Period any other Emolument from the United States, or any of them.

Before he enter on the Execution of his Office, he shall take the following Oath or Affirmation:—I do solemnly swear (or affirm) that I will faithfully execute the Office of President of the United States, and will to the best of my Ability, preserve, protect and defend the Constitution of the United States."
Section. 2. The President shall be Commander in Chief of the Army and Navy of the United States, and of the Militia of the several States, when called into the actual Service of the United States; he may require the Opinion, in writing, of the principal Officer in each of the executive Departments, upon any Subject relating to the Duties of their respective Offices, and he shall have Power to grant Reprieves and Pardons for Offences against the United States, except in cases of Impeachment.

He shall have Power, by and with the Advice and Consent of the Senate, to make Treaties, provided two thirds of the Senators present concur; and he shall nominate, and by and with the Advice and Consent of the Senate, shall appoint Ambassadors, other public Ministers and Consuls, Judges of the supreme Court, and all other Officers of the United States, whose Appointments are not herein otherwise provided for, and which shall be established by Law; but the Congress may by Law vest the Appointment of such inferior Officers, as they

think proper, in the President alone, in the Courts of Law, or in the Heads of Departments.

The President shall have Power to fill up all Vacancies that may happen during the Recess of the Senate, by granting Commissions which shall expire at the End of their next Session.
Section. 3. He shall from time to time give to the Congress Information of the State of the Union, and recommend to their Consideration such Measures as he shall judge necessary and expedient; he may, on extraordinary Occasions, convene both Houses, or either of them, and in Case of Disagreement between them, with respect to the Time of Adjournment, he may adjourn them to such Time as he shall think proper; he shall receive Ambassadors and other public Ministers; he shall take Care that the Laws be faithfully executed, and shall Commission all the Officers of the United States.
Section. 4. the President, Vice President and all civil Officers of the United States, shall be removed from Office on Impeachment for, and Conviction of, Treason, Bribery, or other high Crimes and Misdemeanors.

Article. III.

Section. 1. The judicial Power of the United States, shall be vested in one supreme Court, and in such inferior Courts as the Congress may from time to time ordain and establish. The Judges, both of the supreme and inferior Courts, shall hold their Offices during good Behaviour, and shall, at stated Times, receive for their Services, a Compensation, which shall not be diminished during their Continuance in Office.
Section. 2. The judicial Power shall extend to all Cases, in Law and Equity, arising under this Constitution, the Laws of the United States, and Treaties made, or which shall be made, under their Authority;—to all Cases affecting Ambassadors, other public Ministers and Consuls;—to all Cases of admiralty and maritime Jurisdiction;—to Controversies to which the United States shall be a Party;—to Controversies between two or more States;—between a State and Citizens of another State;*—between Citizens of different States,—between Citizens of the same State claiming Lands under Grants of different States, and between a State, or the Citizens thereof, and foreign States, Citizens or Subjects.

In all Cases affecting Ambassadors, other public Ministers and Consuls, and those in which a State shall be Party, the supreme Court shall have original Jurisdiction. In all the other Cases before mentioned, the supreme Court shall have appellate Jurisdiction, both as to Law and Fact, with such Exceptions, and under such Regulations as the Congress shall make.

The Trial of all Crimes, except in Cases of Impeachment, shall be by Jury; and such Trial shall be held in the State where the said Crimes shall have been committed; but when not

---

*Superseded by the Twelfth Amendment.
†Modified by the Twenty-fifth Amendment.

*Modified by the Eleventh Amendment.

committed within any State, the trial shall be at such Place or Places as the Congress may by Law have directed.

Section. 3. Treason against the United States, shall consist only in levying War against them, or in adhering to their Enemies, giving them Aid and Comfort. No Person shall be convicted of Treason unless on the Testimony of two Witnesses to the same overt Act, or on Confession in open Court.

The Congress shall have Power to declare the Punishment of Treason, but no Attainder of Treason shall work Corruption of Blood, or Forfeiture except during the Life of the Person attainted.

Article. IV.

Section. 1. Full Faith and Credit shall be given in each State to the public Acts, Records, and judicial Proceedings of every other State. And the Congress may by general Laws prescribe the Manner in which such Acts, Records and Proceedings shall be proved, and the Effect thereof.

Section. 2. The Citizens of each State shall be entitled to all Privileges and Immunities of Citizens in the several States.

A Person charged in any State with Treason, Felony, or other Crime, who shall flee from Justice, and be found in another State, shall on Demand of the executive Authority of the State from which he fled, be delivered up, to be removed to the State having Jurisdiction of the Crime.

No Person held to Service or Labour in one State, under the Laws thereof, escaping into another, shall, in Consequence of any Law or Regulation therein, be discharged from such Service or Labour, but shall be delivered up on Claim of the Party to whom such Service or Labour may be due.

Section. 3. New States may be admitted by the Congress into this Union; but no new State shall be formed or erected within the Jursidiction of any other State, nor any State be formed by the Junction of two or more States, or Parts of States, without the Consent of the Legislatures of the States concerned as well as of the Congress.

The Congress shall have Power to dispose of and make all needful Rules and Regulations respecting the Territory or other Property belonging to the United States; and nothing in this Constitution shall be so construed as to Prejudice any Claims of the United States, or of any particular State.

Section. 4. The United States shall guarantee to every State in this Union a Republican Form of Government, and shall protect each of them against Invasion; and on Application of the Legislature, or of the Executive (when the Legislature cannot be convened) against domestic Violence.

Article. V.

The Congress, whenever two thirds of both Houses shall deem it necessary, shall propose Amendments to this Constitution, or, on the Application of the Legislatures of two thirds of the several States, shall call a Convention for proposing Amendments, which, in either Case, shall be valid to all Intents and Purposes, as Part of this Constitution, when ratified by the Legislatures of three fourths of the several States, or by Conventions in three fourths thereof, as the one or the other Mode of Ratification may be proposed by the Congress; Provided that no Amendment which may be made prior to the Year One thousand eight hundred and eight shall in any Manner affect the first and fourth Clauses in the Ninth Section of the first Article; and that no State, without its Consent, shall be deprived of its equal Suffrage in the Senate.

Article. VI.

All Debts contracted and Engagements entered into, before the Adoption of this Constitution, shall be as valid against the United States under this Constitution, as under the Confederation.

This Constitution, and the Laws of the United States which shall be made in Pursuance thereof; and all Treaties made, or which shall be made, under the Authority of the United States, shall be the supreme Law of the Land; and the Judges in every State shall be bound thereby, any Thing in the Constitution or Laws of any State to the Contrary notwithstanding.

The Senators and Representatives before mentioned, and the Members of the several State Legislatures, and all executive and judicial Officers, both of the United States and of the several States, shall be bound by Oath or Affirmation, to support this Constitution; but no religious Test shall ever be required as a Qualification to any Office or public Trust under the United States.

Article. VII.

The Ratification of the Conventions of nine States, shall be sufficient for the Establishment of this Constitution between the States so ratifying the Same.

done in Convention by the Unanimous Consent of the States present the Seventeenth Day of September in the Year of our Lord one thousand seven hundred and Eighty seven and of the Independence of the United States of America the twelfth. *In witness* whereof We have hereunto subscribed our Names,

Articles in Addition to, and Amendment of, the Constitution of the United States of America, Proposed by Congress, and Ratified by the Legislatures of the Several States, Pursuant to the Fifth Article of the Original Constitution.

Amendment I*

Congress shall make no law respecting an establishment of religion, or prohibiting the free exercise thereof; or abridging

---

*The first ten amendments were passed by Congress September 25, 1789. They were ratified by three-fourths of the states December 15, 1791.

the freedom of speech, or of the press; or the right of the people peaceably to assemble, and to petition the Government for a redress of grievances.

Amendment II

A well regulated Militia, being necessary to the security of a free State, the right of the people to keep and bear Arms shall not be infringed.

Amendment III

No Soldier shall, in time of peace, be quartered in any house, without the consent of the Owner, nor in time of war, but in a manner to be prescribed by law.

Amendment IV

The right of the people to be secure in their persons, houses, papers, and effects, against unreasonable searches and seizures, shall not be violated, and no Warrants shall issue, but upon probable cause, supported by Oath or affirmation, and particularly describing the place to be searched, and the persons or things to be seized.

Amendment V

No person shall be held to answer for a capital or otherwise infamous crime, unless on a presentment or indictment of a Grand Jury, except in cases arising in the land or naval forces, or in the Militia, when in actual service in time of War or public danger; nor shall any person be subject for the same offence to be twice put in jeopardy of life or limb; nor shall be compelled in any criminal case to be a witness against himself, nor be deprived of life, liberty, or property, without due process of law; nor shall private property be taken for public use, without just compensation.

Amendment VI

In all criminal prosecutions, the accused shall enjoy the right to a speedy and public trial, by an impartial jury of the State and district wherein the crime shall have been committed, which district shall have been previously ascertained by law, and to be informed of the nature and cause of the accusation; to be confronted with the witnesses against him; to have compulsory process for obtaining witnesses in his favor, and to have the Assistance of Counsel for his defence.

Amendment VII

In suits at common law, where the value in controversy shall exceed twenty dollars, the right of trial by jury shall be preserved, and no fact tried by a jury, shall be otherwise reexamined in any Court of the United States, than according to the rules of the common law.

Amendment VIII

Excessive bail shall not be required, nor excessive fines imposed, nor cruel and unusual punishments inflicted.

Amendment IX

The enumeration in the Constitution, of certain rights, shall not be construed to deny or disparage others retained by the people.

Amendment X

The powers not delegated to the United States by the Constitution; nor prohibited by it to the States, are reserved to the States respectively, or to the people.

Amendment XI*

The Judicial power of the United States shall not be construed to extend to any suit in law or equity, commenced or prosecuted against one of the United States by Citizens of another State, or by Citizens or Subjects of any Foreign State.

Amendment XII†

The Electors shall meet in their respective States and vote by ballot for President and Vice-President, one of whom, at least, shall not be an inhabitant of the same State with themselves; they shall name in their ballots the person voted for as President, and in distinct ballots the person voted for as Vice-President, and they shall make distinct lists of all persons voted for as President, and of all persons voted for as Vice-President, and of the number of votes for each, which lists they shall sign and certify, and transmit sealed to the seat of the government of the United States, directed to the President of the Senate;— The President of the Senate shall, in the presence of the Senate and House of Representatives, open all the certificates and the votes shall then be counted;—The person having the greatest number of votes for President, shall be the President, if such number be a majority of the whole number of Electors appointed; and if no person have such majority, then from the persons having the highest numbers not exceeding three on the list of those voted for as President, the House of Representatives shall choose immediately, by ballot, the President. But in choosing the President, the votes shall be taken by states, the representation from each state having one vote; a quorum for this purpose shall consist of a member or members from two-thirds of the states, and a majority of all the states shall be necessary to a choice. And if the House of Representatives shall not choose a President whenever the right of choice shall devolve upon them, before the fourth day of March next following, then the Vice-President shall act as President, as in the case of the death or other constitutional disability of the

*Passed March 4, 1794. Ratified January 23, 1795.
†Passed December 9, 1803. Ratified June 15, 1804.

President.—The person having the greatest number of votes as Vice-President, shall be the Vice-President, if such number be a majority of the whole number of Electors appointed, and if no person have a majority, then from the two highest numbers on the list, the Senate shall choose the Vice-President; a quorum for the purpose shall consist of two-thirds of the whole number of Senators, and a majority of the whole number shall be necessary to a choice. But no person constitutionally ineligible to the office of President shall be eligible to that of Vice-President of the United States.

Amendment XIII*

Section. 1. Neither slavery nor involuntary servitude, except as a punishment for crime whereof the party shall have been duly convicted, shall exist within the United States, or any place subject to their jurisdiction.
Section. 2. Congress shall have power to enforce this article by appropriate legislation.

Amendment XIV†

Section. 1. All persons born or naturalized in the United States, and subject to the jurisdiction thereof, are citizens of the United States and of the State wherein they reside. No State shall make or enforce any law which shall abridge the privileges or immunities of citizens of the United States; nor shall any State deprive any person of life, liberty, or property, without due process of law; nor deny to any person within its jursidiction the equal protection of the laws.
Section. 2. Representatives shall be apportioned among the several States according to their respective numbers, counting the whole number of persons in each State, excluding Indians not taxed. But when the right to vote at any election for the choice of electors for President and Vice-President of the United States, Representatives in Congress, the Executive and Judicial officers of a State, or the members of the Legislature thereof, is denied to any of the male inhabitants of such State, being twenty-one years of age, and citizens of the United States, or in any way abridged, except for participation in rebellion, or other crime, the basis of representation therein shall be reduced in the proportion which the number of such male citizens shall bear to the whole number of male citizens twenty-one years of age in such State.
Section. 3. No person shall be a Senator or Representative in Congress, or elector of President and Vice-President, or hold any office, civil or military, under the United States, or under any State, who, having previously taken an oath, as a member of Congress, or as an officer of the United States, or as a member of any State legislature, or as an executive or judicial officer of any State, to support the Constitution of the United States, shall have engaged in insurrection or rebellion against the same, or given aid or comfort to the enemies thereof. But Congress may by a vote of two-thirds of each House, remove such disability.
Section. 4. The validity of the public debt of the United States, authorized by law, including debts incurred for payment of pensions and bounties for services in suppressing insurrection or rebellion, shall not be questioned. But neither the United States nor any State shall assume or pay any debt or obligation incurred in aid of insurrection or rebellion against the United States, or any claim for the loss or emancipation of any slave; but all such debts, obligations, and claims shall be held illegal and void.
Section. 5. The Congress shall have the power to enforce, by appropriate legislation, the provisions of this article.

Amendment XV*

Section. 1. The right of citizens of the United States to vote shall not be denied or abridged by the United States or by any State on account of race, color, or previous condition of servitude—
Section. 2. The Congress shall have power to enforce this article by appropriate legislation.

Amendment XVI†

The Congress shall have power to lay and collect taxes on incomes, from whatever source derived, without apportionment among the several States, and without regard to any census or enumeration.

Amendment XVII‡

The Senate of the United States shall be composed of two Senators from each State, elected by the people thereof, for six years; and each Senator shall have one vote. The electors in each State shall have the qualifications requisite for electors of the most numerous branch of the State legislatures.

When vacancies happen in the representation of any State in the Senate, the executive authority of such State shall issue writs of election to fill such vacancies: *Provided,* That the legislature of any State may empower the executive thereof to make temporary appointments until the people fill the vacancies by election as the legislature may direct.

This amendment shall not be so construed as to affect the election or term of any Senator chosen before it becomes valid as part of the Constitution.

*Passed January 31, 1865. Ratified December 6, 1865.
†Passed June 13, 1866. Ratified July 9, 1868.

*Passed February 26, 1869. Ratified February 2, 1870.
†Passed July 12, 1909. Ratified February 3, 1913.
‡Passed May 13, 1912. Ratified April 8, 1913.

Amendment XVIII*

Section. 1. After one year from the ratification of this article the manufacture, sale, or transportation of intoxicating liquors within, the importation thereof into, or the exportation thereof from the United States and all territory subject to the jurisdiction thereof for beverage purposes is hereby prohibited.
Section. 2. The Congress and the several States shall have concurrent power to enforce this article by appropriate legislation.
Section. 3. This article shall be inoperative unless it shall have been ratified as an amendment to the Constitution by the legislatures of the several States, as provided in the Constitution, within seven years from the date of the submission hereof to the States by the Congress.

Amendment XIX†

The right of citizens of the United States to vote shall not be denied or abridged by the United States or by any State on account of sex.

Congress shall have power to enforce this article by appropriate legislation.

Amendment XX‡

Section. 1. The terms of the President and Vice-President shall end at noon on the 20th day of January, and the terms of Senators and Representatives at noon on the 3d day of January, of the years in which such terms would have ended if this article had not been ratified; and the terms of their successors shall then begin.
Section. 2. The Congress shall assemble at least once in every year, and such meeting shall begin at noon the 3d day of January, unless they shall by law appoint a different day.
Section. 3. If, at the time fixed for the beginning of the term of the President, the President elect shall have died, the Vice-President elect shall become President. If a President shall not have been chosen before the time fixed for the beginning of his term, or if the President elect shall have failed to qualify, then the Vice-President elect shall act as President until a President shall have qualified; and the Congress may by law provide for the case wherein neither a President elect nor a Vice-President elect shall have qualified, declaring who shall then act as President, or the manner in which one who is to act shall be selected, and such person shall act accordingly until a President or Vice-President shall have qualified.
Section. 4. The Congress may by law provide for the case of the death of any of the persons from whom the House of Representatives may choose a President whenever the right of

choice shall have devolved upon them, and for the case of the death of any of the persons from whom the Senate may choose a Vice-President whenever the right of choice shall have devolved upon them.
Section. 5. Sections 1 and 2 shall take effect on the 15th day of October following the ratification of this article.
Section. 6. This article shall be inoperative unless it shall have been ratified as an amendment to the Constitution by the legislatures of three-fourths of the several States within seven years from the date of its submission.

Amendment XXI*

Section. 1. The eighteenth article of amendment to the Constitution of the United States is hereby repealed.
Section. 2. The transportation or importation into any State, Territory, or possession of the United States for delivery or use therein of intoxicating liquors, in violation of the laws thereof, is hereby prohibited.
Section. 3. This article shall be inoperative unless it shall have been ratified as an amendment of the Constitution by conventions in the several States, as provided in the Constitution, within seven years from the date of the submission hereof to the States by the Congress.

Amendment XXII†

No person shall be elected to the office of the President more than twice, and no person who has held the office of President, or acted as President, for more than two years of a term to which some other person was elected President shall be elected to the office of the President more than once.

But this Article shall not apply to any person holding the office of President when this Article was proposed by the Congress, and shall not prevent any person who may be holding the office of President, or acting as President, during the term within this Article becomes operative from holding the office of President or acting as President during the remainder of such term.

Amendment XXIII‡

Section. 1. The district constituting the seat of Government of the United States shall appoint in such manner as the Congress may direct:

A number of electors of President and Vice President equal to the whole number of Senators and Representatives in Congress to which the District would be entitled if it were a State, but in no event more than the least populous State; they shall be in addition to those appointed by the States, but they shall

*Passed December 18, 1917. Ratified January 16, 1919.
†Passed June 4, 1919. Ratified August 18, 1920.
‡Passed March 2, 1932. Ratified January 23, 1933.

*Passed February 20, 1933. Ratified December 5, 1933.
†Passed March 12, 1947. Ratified March 1, 1951.
‡Passed June 16, 1960. Ratified April 3, 1961.

be considered, for the purposes of the election of President and Vice President, to be electors appointed by the State; and they shall meet in the District and perform such duties as provided by the twelfth article of amendment.

Section. 2. The Congress shall have power to enforce this article by appropriate legislation.

Amendment XXIV*

Section. 1. The right of citizens of the United States to vote in any primary or other election for President or Vice President, or for Senator or Representative in Congress, shall not be denied or abridged by the United States or any State by reason of failure to pay any poll tax or other tax.

Section. 2. The Congress shall have power to enforce this article by appropriate legislation.

Amendment XXV†

Section. 1. In case of the removal of the President from office or of his death or resignation, the Vice President shall become President.

Section. 2. Whenever there is a vacancy in the office of the Vice President, the President shall nominate a Vice President who shall take office upon confirmation by a majority vote of both Houses of Congress.

Section. 3. Whenever the President transmits to the President pro tempore of the Senate and the Speaker of the House of Representatives his written declaration that he is unable to discharge the powers and duties of his office, and until he transmits to them a written declaration to the contrary, such powers and duties shall be discharged by the Vice President as Acting President.

Section. 4. Whenever the Vice President and a majority of either the principal officers of the executive department or of such other body as Congress may by law provide, transmit to the President pro tempore of the Senate and the Speaker of the House of Representatives their written declaration that the President is unable to discharge the powers and duties of his office, the Vice President shall immediately assume the powers and duties of the office of Acting President.

Section. 4. Whenever the Vice President and a majority of either the principal officers of the executive department or of such other body as Congress may by law provide, transmit to the President pro tempore of the Senate and the Speaker of the House of Representative their written declaration that the President is unable to discharge the powers and duties of his office, the Vice President shall immediately assume the powers and duties of the office of Acting President.

Thereafter, when the President transmits to the President pro tempore of the Senate and the Speaker of the House of Representatives his written declaration that no inability exists, he shall resume the powers and duties of his office unless the Vice President and a majority of either the principal officers of the executive department or of such other body as Congress may by law provide, transmit within four days to the President pro tempore of the Senate and the Speaker of the House of Representatives their written declaration that the President is unable to discharge the powers and duties of his office. Thereupon Congress shall decide the issue, assembling within forty-eight hours for that purpose if not in session. If the Congress, within twenty-one days after receipt of the latter written declaration, or, if Congress is not in session, within twenty-one days after Congress is required to assemble, determines by two-thirds vote of both Houses that the President is unable to discharge the powers and duties of his office, the Vice President shall continue to discharge the same as Acting President; otherwise, the President shall resume the powers and duties of his office.

Amendment XXVI*

Section. 1. The right of citizens of the United States, who are eighteen years of age or older, to vote shall not be denied or abridged by the United States or by any State on account of age.

Section. 2. The Congress shall have power to enforce this article by appropriate legislation.

*Passed August 27, 1962. Ratified January 23, 1964.
†Passed July 6, 1965. Ratified February 11, 1967.

*Passed March 23, 1971. Ratified July 5, 1971.

Admission of States

Order of Admission	State	Date of Admission	Order of Admission	State	Date of Admission
1	Delaware	December 7, 1787	26	Michigan	January 26, 1837
2	Pennsylvania	December 12, 1787	27	Florida	March 3, 1845
3	New Jersey	December 18, 1787	28	Texas	December 29, 1845
4	Georgia	January 2, 1788	29	Iowa	December 28, 1846
5	Connecticut	January 9, 1788	30	Wisconsin	May 29, 1848
6	Massachusetts	February 6, 1788	31	California	September 9, 1850
7	Maryland	April 28, 1788	32	Minnesota	May 11, 1858
8	South Carolina	May 23, 1788	33	Oregon	February 14, 1859
9	New Hampshire	June 21, 1788	34	Kansas	January 29, 1861
10	Virginia	June 25, 1788	35	West Virginia	June 20, 1863
11	New York	July 26, 1788	36	Nevada	October 31, 1864
12	North Carolina	November 21, 1789	37	Nebraska	March 1, 1867
13	Rhode Island	May 29, 1790	38	Colorado	August 1, 1876
14	Vermont	March 4, 1791	39	North Dakota	November 2, 1889
15	Kentucky	June 1, 1792	40	South Dakota	November 2, 1889
16	Tennessee	June 1, 1796	41	Montana	November 8, 1889
17	Ohio	March 1, 1803	42	Washington	November 11, 1889
18	Louisiana	April 30, 1812	43	Idaho	July 3, 1890
19	Indiana	December 11, 1816	44	Wyoming	July 10, 1890
20	Mississippi	December 10, 1817	45	Utah	January 4, 1896
21	Illinois	December 3, 1818	46	Oklahoma	November 16, 1907
22	Alabama	December 14, 1819	47	New Mexico	January 6, 1912
23	Maine	March 15, 1820	48	Arizona	February 14, 1912
24	Missouri	August 10, 1821	49	Alaska	January 3, 1959
25	Arkansas	June 15, 1836	50	Hawaii	August 21, 1959

Growth of U.S. Population and Area

Census	Population of United States	Increase over Preceding Census		Land Area (Sq. Mi.)·	Pop. per Sq. Mi.
		Number	Percent		
1790	3,929,214			867,980	4.5
1800	5,308,483	1,379,269	35.1	867,980	6.1
1810	7,239,881	1,931,398	36.4	1,685,865	4.3
1820	9,638,453	2,398,572	33.1	1,753,588	5.5
1830	12,866,020	3,227,567	33.5	1,753,588	7.3
1840	17,069,453	4,203,433	32.7	1,753,588	9.7
1850	23,191,876	6,122,423	35.9	2,944,337	7.9
1860	31,433,321	8,251,445	35.6	2,973,965	10.6
1870	39,818,449	8,375,128	26.6	2,973,965	13.4
1880	50,155,783	10,337,334	26.0	2,973,965	16.9
1890	62,947,714	12,791,931	25.5	2,973,965	21.2
1900	75,994,575	13,046,861	20.7	2,974,159	25.6
1910	91,972,266	15,997,691	21.0	2,973,890	30.9
1920	105,710,620	13,738,354	14.9	2,973,776	35.5
1930	122,775,046	17,064,426	16.1	2,977,128	41.2
1940	131,669,275	8,894,229	7.2	2,977,128	44.2
1950	150,697,361	19,028,086	14.5	2,974,726*	50.7
1960 †	179,323,175	28,625,814	19.0	3,540,911	50.6
1970	203,235,298	23,912,123	13.3	3,536,855	57.5
1980	226,504,825	23,269,527	11.4	3,536,855	64.0
1990	250,122,000	23,617,175	9.4	3,536,855	70.6

*As measured in 1940; shrinkage offset by increase in water area.
†First year for which figures include Alaska and Hawaii.

Political Party Affiliations in Congress and the Presidency, 1789–1993*

Congress	Year	House* Majority Party	House* Principal Minority Party	House* Other (except Vacancies)	Senate* Majority Party	Senate* Principal Minority Party	Senate* Other (except Vacancies)	President and Party
1st	1789–1791	Ad-38	Op-26	—	Ad-17	Op-9	—	F (Washington)
2nd	1791–1793	F-37	DR-33	—	F-16	DR-13	—	F (Washington)
3rd	1793–1795	DR-57	F-48	—	F-17	DR-13	—	F (Washington)
4th	1795–1797	F-54	DR-52	—	F-19	DR-13	—	F (Washington)
5th	1797–1799	F-58	DR-48	—	F-20	DR-12	—	F (John Adams)
6th	1799–1801	F-64	DR-42	—	F-19	DR-13	—	F (John Adams)
7th	1801–1803	DR-69	F-36	—	DR-18	F-13	—	DR (Jefferson)
8th	1803–1805	DR-102	F-39	—	DR-25	F-9	—	DR (Jefferson)
9th	1805–1807	DR-116	F-25	—	DR-27	F-7	—	DR (Jefferson)
10th	1807–1809	DR-118	F-24	—	DR-28	F-6	—	DR (Jefferson)
11th	1809–1811	DR-94	F-48	—	DR-28	F-6	—	DR (Madison)
12th	1811–1813	DR-108	F-36	—	DR-30	F-6	—	DR (Madison)
13th	1813–1815	DR-112	F-68	—	DR-27	F-9	—	DR (Madison)
14th	1815–1817	DR-117	F-65	—	DR-25	F-11	—	DR (Madison)
15th	1817–1819	DR-141	F-42	—	DR-34	F-10	—	DR (Monroe)
16th	1819–1821	DR-156	F-27	—	DR-35	F-7	—	DR (Monroe)
17th	1821–1823	DR-158	F-25	—	DR-44	F-4	—	DR (Monroe)
18th	1823–1825	DR-187	F-26	—	DR-44	F-4	—	DR (Monroe)
19th	1825–1827	Ad-105	J-97	—	Ad-26	J-20	—	C (J. Q. Adams)
20th	1827–1829	J-119	Ad-94	—	J-28	Ad-20	—	C (J. Q. Adams)
21st	1829–1831	D-139	NR-74	—	D-26	NR-22	—	D (Jackson)
22nd	1831–1833	D-141	NR-58	14	D-25	NR-21	2	D (Jackson)
23rd	1833–1835	D-147	AM-53	60	D-20	NR-20	8	D (Jackson)
24th	1835–1837	D-145	W-98	—	D-27	W-25	—	D (Jackson)
25th	1837–1839	D-108	W-107	24	D-30	W-18	4	D (Van Buren)
26th	1839–1841	D-124	W-118	—	D-28	W-22	—	D (Van Buren)
27th	1841–1843	W-133	D-102	6	W-28	D-22	2	W (Harrison) / W (Tyler)
28th	1843–1845	D-142	W-79	1	W-28	D-25	1	W (Tyler)
29th	1845–1847	D-143	W-77	6	D-31	W-25	—	D (Polk)
30th	1847–1849	W-115	D-108	4	D-36	W-21	1	D (Polk)
31st	1849–1851	D-112	W-109	9	D-35	W-25	2	W (Taylor) / W (Fillmore)
32nd	1851–1853	D-140	W-88	5	D-35	W-24	3	W (Fillmore)
33rd	1853–1855	D-159	W-71	4	D-38	W-22	2	D (Pierce)
34th	1855–1857	R-108	D-83	43	D-40	R-15	5	D (Pierce)
35th	1857–1859	D-118	R-92	26	D-36	R-20	8	D (Buchanan)
36th	1859–1861	R-114	D-92	31	D-36	R-26	4	D (Buchanan)
37th	1861–1863	R-105	D-43	30	R-31	D-10	8	R (Lincoln)
38th	1863–1865	R-102	D-75	9	R-36	D-9	5	R (Lincoln)
39th	1865–1867	U-149	D-42	—	U-42	D-10	—	R (Lincoln) / R (Johnson)
40th	1867–1869	R-143	D-49	—	R-42	D-11	—	R (Johnson)
41st	1869–1871	R-149	D-63	—	R-56	D-11	—	R (Grant)
42nd	1871–1873	R-134	D-104	5	R-52	D-17	5	R (Grant)
43rd	1873–1875	R-194	D-92	14	R-49	D-19	5	R (Grant)
44th	1875–1877	D-169	R-109	14	R-45	D-29	2	R (Grant)
45th	1877–1879	D-153	R-140	—	R-39	D-36	1	R (Hayes)
46th	1879–1881	D-149	R-130	14	D-42	R-33	1	R (Hayes)
47th	1881–1883	R-147	D-135	11	R-37	D-37	1	R (Garfield) / R (Arthur)

*Letter symbols for political parties. Ad—Administration; AM—Anti-Masonic; C—Coalition; D—Democratic; DR—Democratic-Republican; F—Federalist; J—Jacksonian; NR—National-Republican; Op—Opposition; R—Republican; U—Unionist; W—Whig.

Source: *Historical Statistics of the United States: Colonial Times to the Present*, Various eds. Washington, D.C.: GOP.

Political Party Affiliations in Congress and the Presidency, 1789–1993 *(continued)*

		House*			Senate*			
Congress	Year	Majority Party	Principal Minority Party	Other (except Vacancies)	Majority Party	Principal Minority Party	Other (except Vacancies)	President and Party
48th	1883–1885	D-197	R-118	10	R-38	D-36	2	R (Arthur)
49th	1885–1887	D-193	R-140	2	R-43	D-34	—	D (Cleveland)
50th	1887–1889	D-169	R-152	4	R-39	D-37	—	D (Cleveland)
51st	1889–1891	R-166	R-88	—	R-39	D-37	—	R (B. Harrison)
52nd	1891–1893	D-235	R-127	9	R-47	D-39	2	R (B. Harrison)
53rd	1893–1895	D-218	D-105	11	D-44	R-38	3	D (Cleveland)
54th	1895–1897	R-244	D-113	7	R-43	D-39	6	D (Cleveland)
55th	1887–1899	R-204	D-163	40	R-47	D-34	7	R (McKinley)
56th	1899–1901	R-185	D-151	9	R-53	D-26	8	R (McKinley)
57th	1901–1903	R-197		9	R-55	D-31	4	R (McKinley) R (T. Roosevelt)
58th	1903–1905	R-208	D-178	—	R-57	D-33	—	R (T. Roosevelt)
59th	1905–1907	R-250	D-136	—	R-57	D-33	—	R (T. Roosevelt)
60th	1907–1909	R-222	D-164	—	R-61	D-31	—	R (T. Roosevelt)
61st	1909–1911	R-219	D-172	—	R-61	D-32	—	R (Taft)
62nd	1911–1913	D-228	R-161	1	R-51	D-41	—	R (Taft)
63rd	1913–1915	D-291	R-127	17	D-51	R-44	1	D (Wilson)
64th	1915–1917	D-230	R-196	9	D-56	R-40	—	D (Wilson)
65th	1917–1919	D-216	R-210	6	D-53	R-42	—	D (Wilson)
66th	1919–1921	R-240	D-190	3	R-49	D-47	—	D (Wilson)
67th	1921–1923	R-301	D-131	1	R-59	D-37	—	R (Harding)
68th	1923–1925	R-225	D-205	5	R-51	D-43	2	R (Coolidge)
70th	1925–1927	R-247	D-183	4	R-56	D-39	1	R (Coolidge)
71st	1927–1929	R-237	D-195	3	R-49	D-46	1	R (Coolidge)
72nd	1929–1931	R-267	D-167	1	R-56	D-39	1	R (Hoover)
73rd	1931–1933	D-220	R-214	1	R-48	D-47	1	R (Hoover)
74th	1933–1935	D-310	R-117	5	D-60	R-35	1	D (F. Roosevelt)
75th	1935–1937	D-319	R-103	10	D-69	R-25	2	D (F. Roosevelt)
76th	1937–1939	D-331	R-89	13	D-76	R-16	4	D (F. Roosevelt)
77th	1939–1941	D-261	R-164	4	D-69	R-23	4	D (F. Roosevelt)
78th	1941–1943	D-268	R-162	5	D-66	R-28	2	D (F. Roosevelt)
79th	1943–1945	D-218	R-208	4	D-58	R-37	1	D (F. Roosevelt)
80th	1945–1947	D-242	R-190	2	D-56	R-38	1	D (Truman)
81st	1947–1949	R-245	R-188	1	R-51	D-45	—	D (Truman)
82nd	1949–1951	D-263	R-171	1	D-54	R-42	—	D (Truman)
83rd	1951–1953	D-243	R-199	1	D-49	R-47	—	D (Truman)
84th	1953–1955	R-221	D-211	1	R-48	D-47	1	R (Eisenhower)
85th	1955–1957	D-232	R-203	—	D-48	R-47	1	R (Eisenhower)
86th	1957–1959	D-233	R-200	—	D-49	R-47	—	R (Eisenhower)
87th	1959–1961	D-283	R-153	—	D-64	R-34	—	R (Eisenhower)
88th	1961–1963	D-263	R-174	—	D-65	R-35	—	D (Kennedy)
	1963–1965	D-258	R-177	—	D-67	R-33	—	D (Kennedy) D (Johnson)
89th	1965–1967	D-295	R-140	—	D-68	R-32	—	D (Johnson)
90th	1967–1969	D-247	R-187	1	D-64	R-36	—	D (Johnson)
91st	1969–1971	D-243	R-192	—	D-58	R-42	—	R (Nixon)
92nd	1971–1973	D-255	R-180	—	D-54	R-44	2	R (Nixon)
93rd	1973–1975	D-242	R-192	1	D-56	R-42	2	R (Nixon, Ford)
94th	1975–1977	D-291	R-144	—	D-61	R-37	2	R (Ford)
95th	1977–1979	D-292	R-143	—	D-61	R-38	1	D (Carter)
96th	1979–1981	D-277	R-158	—	D-58	R-41	1	D (Carter)
97th	1981–1983	D-242	R-192	—	R-54	D-45	1	R (Reagan)
98th	1983–1985	D-266	R-167	2	R-55	D-45	—	R (Reagan)
99th	1985–1987	D-252	R-183	—	R-53	D-47	—	R (Reagan)
100th	1987–1989	D-258	R-177	—	D-55	R-45	—	R (Reagan)
101st	1989–1991	D-262	R-173	—	D-57	R-43	—	R (Bush)
102nd	1991–1993	D-267	R-167	1	D-57	R-43	—	R (Bush)

Presidential Elections, 1789–1992*

Year	Voter Participation (Percent)	Candidates	Parties	Popular Vote	Electoral Vote†	Percent of Popular Vote
1789		GEORGE WASHINGTON	No party designations		69	
		John Adams			34	
		Minor Candidates			35	
1792		GEORGE WASHINGTON	No party designations		132	
		John Adams			77	
		George Clinton			50	
		Minor Candidates			5	
1796		JOHN ADAMS	Federalist		71	
		Thomas Jefferson	Democratic-Republican		68	
		Thomas Pinckney	Federalist		59	
		Aaron Burr	Democratic-Republican		30	
		Minor Candidates			48	
1800		THOMASA JEFFERSON	Democratic-Republican		73	
		Aaron Burr	Democratic-Republican		73	
		John Adams	Federalist		65	
		Charles C. Pinckney	Federalist		64	
		John Jay	Federalist		1	
1804		THOMAS JEFFERSON	Democratic-Republican		162	
		Charles C. Pinckney	Federalist		14	
1808		JAMES MADISON	Democratic-Republican		122	
		Charles C. Pinckney	Federalist		47	
		George Clinton	Democratic-Republican		6	
1812		JAMES MADISON	Democratic Republican		128	
		DeWitt Clinton	Federalist		89	
1816		JAMES MONROE	Democratic-Republican		183	
		Rufus King	Federalist		34	
1820		JAMES MONROE	Democratic-Republican		231	
		John Quincy Adams	Independent Republican		1	
1824	26.9	JOHN QUINCY ADAMS	Democratic-Republican	108,740	84	30.5
		Andrew Jackson	Democratic-Republican	153,544	99	43.1
		William H. Crawford	Democratic-Republican	46,618	41	13.1
		Henry Clay	Democratic-Republican	47,136	37	13.2
1828	57.6	ANDREW JACKSON	Democratic	647,286	178	56.0
		John Quincy Adams	National Republican	508,064	83	44.0
1832	55.4	ANDREW JACKSON	Democratic	687,502	219	55.0
		Henry Clay	National Republican	530,189	49	42.4
		William Wirt	Anti-Masonic		7	
		John Floyd	National Republican	33,108	11	2.6
1836	57.8	MARTIN VAN BUREN	Democratic	765,483	170	50.9
		William H. Harrison	Whig		73	
		Hugh L. White	Whig	739,795	26	49.1
		Daniel Webster	Whig		14	
		W. P. Mangum	Whig		11	
1840	80.2	WILLIAM H. HARRISON	Whig	1,274,624	234	53.1
		Martin Van Buren	Democratic	1,127,781	60	46.9
1844	78.9	JAMES K. POLK	Democratic	1,338,464	170	49.6
		Henry Clay	Whig	1,300,097	105	48.1
		James G. Birney	Liberty	62,300		2.3
1848	72.7	ZACHARY TAYLOR	Whig	1,360,967	163	47.4
		Lewis Cass	Democratic	1,222,342	127	42.5
		Martin Van Buren	Free Soil	291,263		10.1
1852	69.6	FRANKLIN PIERCE	Democratic	1,601,117	254	50.9
		Winfield Scott	Whig	1,385,453	42	44.1
		John P. Hale	Free Soil	155,825		5.0

*Candidates receiving less than 1 percent of the popular vote have been omitted. For that reason the percentage of popular vote given for any election year may not total 100 percent.

†Before the passage of the Twelfth Amendment in 1804, the Electoral College voted for two presidential candidates; the runner-up became Vice President.

Figures are from *Historical Statistics of the United States, Colonial Times to 1957* (1961), pp. 682–83; the U. S. Department of Justice.

Presidential Elections, 1789–1992 (continued)

Year	Voter Participation (Percent)	Candidates	Parties	Popular Vote	Electoral Vote†	Percent of Popular Vote
1856	78.9	JAMES BUCHANAN	Democratic	1,832,955	174	45.3
		John C. Frémont	Republican	1,339,932	114	33.1
		Millard Fillmore	American	871,731	8	21.6
1860	81.2	ABRAHAM LINCOLN	Republican	1,865,593	180	39.8
		Stephen A. Douglas	Democratic	1,382,713	12	29.5
		John C. Breckinridge	Democratic	848,356	72	18.1
		John Bell	Constitutional Union	592,906	39	12.6
1864	73.8	ABRAHAM LINCOLN	Republican	2,206,938	212	55.0
		George B. McClellan	Democratic	1,803,787	21	45.0
1868	78.1	ULYSSES S. GRANT	Republican	3,013,421	214	52.7
		Horatio Seymour	Democratic	2,706,829	80	47.3
1872	71.3	ULYSSES S. GRANT	Republican	3,596,745	286	55.6
		Horace Greeley*	Democratic	2,843,446		43.9
1876	81.8	RUTHERFORD B. HAYES	Republican	4,036,572	185	48.0
		Samuel J. Tilden	Democratic	4,284,020	184	51.0
1880	79.4	JAMES A. GARFIELD	Republican	4,453,295	214	48.5
		Winfield S. Hancock	Democratic	4,414,082	155	48.1
		James B. Weaver	Greenback-Labor	308,578		3.4
1884	77.5	GROVER CLEVELAND	Democratic	4,879,507	219	48.5
		James G. Blaine	Republican	4,850,293	182	48.2
		Benjamin F. Butler	Greenback-Labor	175,370		1.8
		John P. St. John	Prohibition	150,369		1.5
1888	79.3	BENJAMIN HARRISON	Republican	5,477,129	233	47.9
		Grover Cleveland	Democratic	5,537,857	168	48.6
		Clinton B. Fisk	Prohibition	249,506		2.2
		Anson J. Streeter	Union Labor	146,935		1.3
1892	74.7	GROVER CLEVELAND	Democratic	5,555,426	277	46.1
		Benjamin Harrison	Republican	5,182,690	145	43.0
		James B. Weaver	People's	1,029,846	22	8.5
		John Bidwell	Prohibition	264,133		2.2
1896	79.3	WILLIAM McKINLEY	Republican	7,102,246	271	51.1
		William J. Bryan	Democratic	6,492,559	176	47.7
1900	73,2	WILLIAM McKINLEY	Republican	7,218,491	292	51.7
		William J. Bryan	Democratic; Populist	6,356,734	155	45.5
		John C. Wooley	Prohibition	208,914		1.5
1904	65.2	THEODORE ROOSEVELT	Republican	7,628,461	336	57.4
		Alton B. Parker	Democratic	5,084,223	140	37.6
		Eugene V. Debs	Socialist	402,283		3.0
		Silas C. Swallow	Prohibition	258,536		1.9
1908	65.4	WILLIAM H. TAFT	Republican	7,675,320	321	51.6
		William J. Bryan	Democratic	6,412,294	162	43.1
		Eugene V. Debs	Socialist	420,793		2.8
		Eugene W. Chafin	Prohibition	253,840		1.7
1912	58.8	WOODROW WILSON	Democratic	6,296,547	435	41.9
		Theodore Roosevelt	Progressive	4,118,571	88	27.4
		William H. Taft	Republican	3,486,720	8	23.2
		Eugene V. Debs	Socialist	900,672		6.0
		Eugene W. Chafin	Prohibition	206,275		1.4

*Greeley died shortly after the election; the electors supporting him then divided their votes among minor candidates.

Presidential Elections, 1789–1992 (continued)

Year	Voter Participation (Percent)	Candidates	Parties	Popular Vote	Electoral Vote†	Percent of Popular Vote
1916	61.6	WOODROW WILSON	Democratic	9,127,695	277	49.4
		Charles E. Hughes	Republican	8,533,507	254	46.2
		A. L. Benson	Socialist	585,113		3.2
		J. Frank Hanly	Prohibition	220,506		1.2
1920	49.2	WARREN G. HARDING	Republican	16,143,407	404	60.4
		James N. Cox	Democratic	9,130,328	127	34.2
		Eugene V. Debs	Socialist	919,799		3.4
		P. P. Christensen	Farmer-Labor	265,411		1.0
1924	48.9	CALVIN COOLIDGE	Republican	15,718,211	382	54.0
		John W. Davis	Democratic	8,385,283	136	28.8
		Robert M. La Follette	Progressive	4,831,289	13	16.6
1928	56.9	HERBERT C. HOOVER	Republican	21,391,993	444	58.2
		Alfred E. Smith	Democratic	15,016,169	87	40.9
1932	56.9	FRANKLIN D. ROOSEVELT	Democratic	22,809,638	472	57.4
		Herbert C. Hoover	Republican	15,758,901	59	39.7
		Norman Thomas	Socialist	881,951		2.2
1936	61.0	FRANKLIN D. ROOSEVELT	Democratic	27,752,869	523	60.8
		Alfred M. Landon	Republican	16,674,665	8	36.5
		William Lemke	Union	882,479		1.9
1940	62.5	FRANKLIN D. ROOSEVELT	Democratic	27,307,819	449	54.8
		Wendell L. Willkie	Republican	22,321,018	82	44.8
1944	55.9	FRANKLIN D. ROOSEVELT	Democratic	25,606,585	432	53.5
		Thomas E. Dewey	Republican	22,014,745	99	46.0
1948	53.0	HARRY S. TRUMAN	Democratic	24,105,812	303	49.5
		Thomas E. Dewey	Republican	21,970,065	189	45.1
		J. Strom Thurmond	States' Rights	1,169,063	39	2.4
		Henry A. Wallace	Progressive	1,157,172		2.4
1952	63.3	DWIGHT D. EISENHOWER	Republican	33,936,234	442	55.1
		Adlai E. Stevenson	Democratic	27,314,992	89	44.4
1956	60.6	DWIGHT D. EISENHOWER	Republican	35,590,472	457	57.6
		Adlai E. Stevenson	Democratic	26,022,752	73	42.1
1960	64.0	JOHN F. KENNEDY	Democratic	34,227,096	303	49.9
		Richard M. Nixon	Republican	34,108,546	219	49.6
1964	61.7	LYNDON B. JOHNSON	Democratic	43,126,506	486	61.1
		Barry M. Goldwater	Republican	27,176,799	52	38.5
1968	60.6	RICHARD M. NIXON	Republican	31,785,480	301	43.4
		Hubert H. Humphrey	Democratic	31,275,165	191	42.7
		George C. Wallace	American Independent	9,906,473	46	13.5
1972	55.5	RICHARD M. NIXON	Republican	47,169,911	520	60.7
		George S. McGovern	Democratic	29,170,383	17	37.5
1976	54.3	JIMMY CARTER	Democratic	40,827,394	297	50.0
		Gerald R. Ford	Republican	39,145,977	240	47.9
1980	53.2	RONALD W. REAGAN	Republican	43,899,248	489	50.8
		Jimmy Carter	Democratic	35,481,435	49	41.0
		John B. Anderson	Independent	5,719,437		6.6
		Ed Clark	Libertarian	920,859		1.0
1984	53.3	RONALD W. REAGAN	Republican	54,281,858	525	59.0
		Walter Mondale	Democratic	37,457,215	13	41.0
1988	50.2	GEORGE H. BUSH	Republican	48,138,478	426	53.4
		Michael Dukakis	Democrat	41,114,068	112	45.6
1992	55.2	BILL CLINTON	Democrat	44,908,232	370	43.0
		George Bush	Republican	38,167,000	168	37.7

PHOTO CREDITS

(Page numbers are in boldface type. l = left; r = right; t = top; b = bottom.)

Chapter 1
2: Courtesy of The Huntington Library, San Marino, California. 4: Courtesy of the Trustees of the British Museum. 10: Courtesy of The New-York Historical Society, New York. 12: The Bettmann Archive. 16: Biblioteque National, Paris. 17: The American Museum of Natural History.

Chapter 2
20: The Folger Shakespeare Library. 24(t): Library of Congress. 24(b): SIR WALTER RALEIGH by Zuccaro, National Portrait Gallery, London. 31: Courtesy of the John Carter Brown Library at Brown University. 32: The Jamestown Foundation.

Chapter 3
34: HBJ Picture Collection. 38: Courtesy of Essex Institute, Salem, MA. 40: © 1992 The New Haven Colony Historical Society. 41: HBJ Picture Collection. 42: Library of Congress. 45: The Bettmann Archive. 46: The Historical Society of Pennsylvania.

Chapter 4
50: Courtesy of the John Carter Brown Library at Brown University. 53: Courtesy of The New-York Historical Society, New York. 57: Metropolitan Museum of Art. 58: Colonial Williamsburg Foundation. 61(t): Culver Pictures. 61(b): Courtesy of Essex Institute, Salem, MA.

Chapter 5
64: Courtesy, Winterthur Museum. 68(t): Library of Congress. 68(b): BURNING FALLEN TREES IN A GIRDLED CLEARING by W. J. Bennett. Courtesy of Mabel Brady Graven Collection. Yale University Art Gallery. 72: Edward E. Ayer Collection of The Newberry Library, Chicago. 77: Courtesy, American Antiquarian Society. 78: Library of Congress.

Chapter 6
82: Library of Congress. 84: Library of Congress. 86: New York Public Library. 91: New York Public Library, Rare Book Room. 93: New York Public Library, Rare Book Room. 96: GEORGE WASHINGTON by Charles Wilson Peale, 1772 (detail). Historical Society of Pennsylvania.

Chapter 7
98: Library of Congress. 103: HBJ Picture Collection. 105(l): Library of Congress. 105(r): Culver Pictures. 107: Historical Picture Service. 109: New York Public Library. 110: Courtesy of Essex Institute, Salem, MA.

Chapter 8
112: Library of Congress. 115: Photographed by Art Kiely, The Connecticut Historical Society, Hartford, CT; The Connecticut Historical Society, Hartford, CT. 117: Library of Congress. 118: The Bettmann Archive. 120: Anne S. K. Brown Military Collection, Brown University Library. 125: Library of Congress. 127: DECLARATION OF INDEPENDENCE (detail) by John Trumbull (American 1756-1843) © Yale University Art Gallery.

Chapter 9
128: The Continental Insurance Companies. 131: Library of Congress. 132: Library of Congress. 134: Historical Society of Pennsylvania. 135: WASHINGTON AT VERPLANK'S POINT by John Trumbull, 1790. (Detail. Oil on canvas 30″ × 20 1/8″, rectangular) courtesy Henry Francis DuPont Winterthur Museum. 136: Valley Forge National Historic Park, National Park Service, U.S. Department of the Interior. 141: Anne S. K. Brown Military Collection, Brown University Library.

Chapter 10
142: Eastern National Park and Monument Association. 153: New York Public Library, Rare Book Room. 154: National Archives C-5915. 156: ALEXANDER HAMILTON by John Trumbull © Yale University Art Gallery. 158: Library of Congress.

Chapter 11
160: Library of Congress. 162: Metropolitan Museum of Art. 170: Brown Brothers. 171: JOHN ADAMS Charles Wilson Peale, Independence National Historical Park Collection. 174: Courtesy of the Lilly Library, Indiana University, Bloomington, Indiana.

Chapter 12
178: Monticello; Thomas Jefferson Memorial Foundation. 180: Portrait by Rembrandt Peale, Independence National Historical Park Collection. 182: Maryland Historical Society. 186: Montana Historical Society, Gift of the artist. 189: Rhode Island Historical Society. 192: (L) New York Public Library; (R) Courtesy of The New-York Historical Society. 193: Courtesy of the Field Museum of Natural History. 195: Courtesy of The New-York Historical Society.

Chapter 13
196: Hulton Picture Library. 199: North Carolina Department of Archives and History. 200–201: Smithsonian Institution. 205: All rights reserved. The Metropolitan Museum of Art, gift of I. N. Phelps Stokes, Edward S. Hawes, Alice Mary Hawes, Marion Hawes, 1937. 206: Bureau of Public Roads, Department of the Interior. 210: Courtesy of The New-York Historical Society. 211: Library of Congress.

Chapter 14
214: The Metropolitan Museum of Art, Joseph Pulitzer Bequest, 1942. 219: The Metropolitan Museum of Art, gift of Mrs. J. Insley Blair, 1948. 220: WINTER SCENE BROOKLYN by Francis Guy, 1817–1820. Oil on canvas, 58 3/4″ × 75″, The Brooklyn Institute of Arts and Sciences. 221: The Rhode Island Historical Society. 226: Courtesy, The Massachusetts Historical Society.

Chapter 15
230: THE PRESIDENT'S LEVEE or ALL CREATION GOING TO THE WHITE HOUSE by Robert Cruikshank, lithograph. White House Collection. 234(t): University of Hartford, J.

Doyle DeWitt Collection. **234(b):** Daguerreotype by Southworth and Hawes. All rights reserved, Metropolitan Museum of Art gift of I. N. Phelps Stokes, Edward Hawes, Alice Mary Hawes, Marion Augusta Hawes, 1937. **238:** Courtesy of The New-York Historical Society. **239:** ANDREW JACKSON by Thomas Sully. In the collection of the Corcoran Gallery of Art, gift of William Wilson Corcoran. **243:** Courtesy of the Edward E. Ayer Collection, Newberry Library, Chicago.

Chapter 16

246: Library of Congress. **248:** Photo by Matthew Brady. Library of Congress. **251:** Courtesy of The New-York Historical Society. **252:** Photo by Matthew Brady. Library of Congress. **255:** Chicago Historical Society. **258(t):** Courtesy of The New-York Historical Society. **258(b):** Library of Congress.

Chapter 17

262: Library of Congress. **265:** Private Collection, Courtesy of Childs Gallery, Boston and New York. **270:** Utah State Historical Society. **271:** Courtesy of The New-York Historical Society. **272:** The Bettmann Archive. **273:** Daguerreotype by J. J. Hawes. International Museum of Photography at George Eastman House. **274:** Library of Congress. **275:** The Bettmann Archive.

Chapter 18

276: Museum of the City of New York. **279:** The Bettmann Archive. **281:** Photo by Robert L. Perry. **283:** Library of Congress. **284:** The Bettmann Archive. **286:** Sophia Smith Collection (Women's History Archive), Smith College, Northampton, MA.

Chapter 19

288: PLANTATION ON THE MISSISSIPPI, (detail) Currier and Ives. Yale University Art Gallery, the Mabel Brady Gavan Collection. **293(t):** United States Army Military History Institute. **293(b):** Sophia Smith Collection (Women's History Archive), Smith College, Northampton, MA. **296:** Library of Congress. **297:** From the Penn School Collection. Permission granted by Penn Center, Inc., St. Helena Island, South Carolina. **298:** Old Court House Museum, Vicksburg, MS. **300:** National Archives.

Chapter 20

302: A RIDE FOR LIBERTY-THE FUGITIVE SLAVES circa 1862 by Eastman Johnson 1824-1906, oil on board 55.8 × 66.6 (22 × 26 1/4) The Brooklyn Museum, 40.59A. Gift of Miss Gwendolyn O. L. Conkling. **304:** Courtesy of The New-York Historical Society. **305:** National Portrait Gallery, Smithsonian Institution. **306:** Courtesy of The New York Historical Society. **307:** Library of Congress. **310:** U. S. Army Military History Institute. **311:** U. S. Army Military History Institute. **312:** Photo by Timothy O'Sullivan, Library of Congress.

Chapter 21

316: The Harry T. Peters Collection. Museum of the City of New York. **321:** Library of Congress. **324:** Association of American Railroads. **327:** Western Americana Collection, Beinecke Rare Book and Manuscript Library, Yale University. **328:** All rights reserved. The Metropolitan Museum of Art, gift of I. N. Phelps Stokes, and the Hawes Family, 1937.

Chapter 22

332: Library of Congress. **336:** Kansas State Historical Society. **337:** Seaver Center for Western History Research, Los Angeles County Museum of Natural History. **341:** Library of Congress. **344:** Library of Congress.

Chapter 23

346: Library of Congress. **349:** Library of Congress. **350:** Courtesy of The New-York Historical Society. **352:** Sophia Smith Collection (Women's History Archive), Smith College, North-

ampton, MA. **356:** Photo by Matthew Brady, February 2, 1860. The Bettmann Archive. **358:** Library of Congress. **359:** The Bettmann Archive. **360:** Library of Congress. **361:** Meserve Collection, Library of Congress. **364:** Courtesy of The New-York Historical Society.

Chapter 24

366: Library of Congress. **369:** Photo by Timothy O'Sullivan, National Archives. **371:** U. S. Army Military History Institute. **372:** Photo by Matthew Brady, Library of Congress. **373:** PANIC ON THE ROAD BETWEEN BULL RUN AND CENTERVILLE, probably July 21, 1861. Pencil sketch, Anonymous. Museum of Fine Arts, Boston. M. and M. Karolik Collection. **379:** Library of Congress. **380:** The Bettmann Archive.

Chapter 25

382: National Archives. **385:** Photo by Matthew Brady, Library of Congress. **386:** Library of Congress. **389:** Photo by Timothy O'Sullivan, U. S. Army Military History Institute. **393(t):** Library of Congress. **393(b):** Library of Congress. **394:** Courtesy of The New-York Historical Society. **395:** Photo by Alexander Gardner, Library of Congress.

Chapter 26

398: Library of Congress. **401:** All rights reserved Metropolitan Museum of Art. **402:** Photo by Matthew Brady, 1865. Brady-Handy Collection. Library of Congress. **403:** The Valentine Museum, Richmond, VA. **406:** Culver Pictures. **407:** Library of Congress. **410:** Library of Congress. **411:** Ralph Becker Collection of Political Americana, Smithsonian Institution.

Chapter 27

414: HBJ Picture Collection. **418:** Smithsonian Institution. **419:** University of Hartford Collection. **421:** Keystone-Mast Collection. California Museum of Photography, University of California, Riverside. **425:** Library of Congress. **428:** Brown Brothers.

Chapter 28

432: Library of Congress. **435:** Special collection, University of Oregon. **437:** U. S. Department of the Interior, National Park Service, Edison National Historic Site. **441:** Southern Pacific Transportation Company. **445(t):** Great Northern Railway. **445(b):** Brown Brothers. **447(t):** Library of Congress. **447(b):** Culver Pictures.

Chapter 29

450: Photograph by Byron, The Byron Collection. Museum of the City of New York. **453:** Library of Congress. **454:** Culver Pictures. **455:** Courtesy of The New-York Historical Society. **459:** Photo by Jacob Riis, Riis Collection. Museum of the City of New York. **461:** Keystone-Mast Collection. California Museum of Photography, University of California, Riverside. **462:** Photo by Byron, March 28, 1903, Byron Collection. Museum of the City of New York. **463:** The Preservation Society of Newport County Photo. **464:** Culver Pictures. **465:** Photo by Gertrude Kasebeir, ca. 1903. International Museum of Photography at George Eastman House.

Chapter 30

466: Library of Congress. **468:** Photo by Lewis W. Hine, 1910. Library of Congress. **469:** Photo by Lewis W. Hine. Library of Congress. **471:** Photograph by Lewis W. Hine, The Jacob A. Riis Collection #EE. Museum of the City of New York. **473:** Library of Congress. **476:** Keystone-Mast Collection. California Museum of Photography, University of California, Riverside. **480:** Mrs. J. R. Cade. Copy from the University of Texas Institute of Texan Cultures at San Antonio.

Index